COMPLETE SOLUTIONS MANUAL

Alicia Paterno Parsi
Duquesne University

Arash Parsi
Duquesne University

Tomislav Pintauer
Duquesne University

Lucio Gelmini
Grant MacEwan College

Robert W. Hilts
Grant MacEwan College

General Chemistry
Principles and Modern Applications
Eleventh Edition

Ralph H. Petrucci
California State University, San Bernardino

F. Geoffrey Herring
University of British Columbia

Jeffry D. Madura
Duquesne University

Carey Bissonnette
University of Waterloo

PEARSON

Toronto

ISBN-13: 978-0-13-292504-4

Executive Acquisitions Editor: Cathleen Sullivan
Developmental Editor: Joanne Sutherland
Project Manager: Sarah Gallagher

Printed and bound in the United States of America.

PEARSON

ISBN-13: 978-0-13-292504-4

Contents

Preface

The *Complete Solutions Manual* to accompany the 11th edition of *General Chemistry* contains full solutions to all of the in-chapter exercises and end-of-chapter exercises and problems, namely,

- Practice Examples (A and B)
- Integrative Examples
- Exercises
- Integrative and Advanced Exercises
- Feature Problems
- Self-Assessment Exercises

Each solution is preceded by its level of difficulty, set in parentheses (E = easy, M = moderate, and D = difficult). Solutions with the question number underlined indicate that these are solutions for the red questions in the textbook. Solutions for all of the red textbook questions are included in the *Selected Solutions Manual* (978-0-13-338790-2).

Stepwise Approach and Conversion Pathway Approach

Solutions to selected questions are provided in both the Stepwise Approach and Conversion Pathway Approach. These two methods of problem solving are modeled after the text, and their purpose is to help you set up problems as you begin your problem-solving journey in the solutions.

Molecular Formulas of Organic Compounds

For brevity, the molecular formulas of organic compounds in the *Complete Solutions Manual* are often written as CxHyOz rather than as the condensed structural formulas found in the textbook. For example, the formula of glycerol, $HOCH_2CH(OH)CH_2OH$, is written as $C_3H_8O_3$.

CHAPTER 1
MATTER—ITS PROPERTIES AND MEASUREMENT
PRACTICE EXAMPLES

1A (E) Convert the Fahrenheit temperature to Celsius and compare.
$$^\circ C = \left(^\circ F - 32\,^\circ F\right)\tfrac{5\,^\circ C}{9\,^\circ F} = \left(350\,^\circ F - 32\,^\circ F\right)\tfrac{5\,^\circ C}{9\,^\circ F} = 177\,^\circ C.$$

1B (E) We convert the Fahrenheit temperature to
Celsius. $^\circ C = \left(^\circ F - 32\,^\circ F\right)\tfrac{5\,^\circ C}{9\,^\circ F} = \left(-15\,^\circ F - 32\,^\circ F\right)\tfrac{5\,^\circ C}{9\,^\circ F} = -26\,^\circ C.$ The antifreeze only protects to
$-22\,^\circ C$ and thus it will not offer protection to temperatures as low as $-15\,^\circ F = -26.1\,^\circ C.$

2A (E) The mass is the difference between the mass of the full and empty flask.
$$\text{density} = \frac{291.4\text{ g} - 108.6\text{ g}}{125\text{ mL}} = 1.46\text{ g/mL}$$

2B (E) First determine the volume required. $V = (1.000 \times 10^3\text{ g}) \div (8.96\text{ g cm}^{-3}) = 111.\underline{6}\text{ cm}^3.$
Next determine the radius using the relationship between volume of a sphere and radius.
$$V = \frac{4}{3}\pi r^3 = 111.\underline{6}\text{ cm}^3 = \frac{4}{3}(3.1416)r^3 \qquad r = \sqrt[3]{\frac{111.6 \times 3}{4(3.1416)}} = 2.987\text{ cm}$$

3A (E) The volume of the stone is the difference between the level in the graduated cylinder with the stone present and with it absent.
$$\text{density} = \frac{\text{mass}}{\text{volume}} = \frac{28.4\text{ g rock}}{44.1\text{ mL rock \& water} - 33.8\text{ mL water}} = 2.76\text{ g/mL} = 2.76\text{ g/cm}^3$$

3B (E) The water level will remain unchanged. The mass of the ice cube displaces the same mass of liquid water. A 10.0 g ice cube will displace 10.0 g of water. When the ice cube melts, it simply replaces the displaced water, leaving the liquid level unchanged.

4A (E) The mass of ethanol can be found using dimensional analysis.
$$\text{ethanol mass} = 25\text{ L gasohol} \times \frac{1000\text{ mL}}{1\text{ L}} \times \frac{0.71\text{ g gasohol}}{1\text{ mL gasohol}} \times \frac{10\text{ g ethanol}}{100\text{ g gasohol}} \times \frac{1\text{ kg ethanol}}{1000\text{ g ethanol}}$$
$$= 1.8\text{ kg ethanol}$$

4B (E) We use the mass percent to determine the mass of the 25.0 mL sample.
$$\text{rubbing alcohol mass} = 15.0\text{ g (isopropyl alcohol)} \times \frac{100.0\text{ g rubbing alcohol}}{70.0\text{ g (isopropyl alcohol)}}$$
$$= 21.4\underline{3}\text{ g rubbing alcohol}$$
$$\text{rubbing alcohol density} = \frac{21.4\text{ g}}{25.0\text{ mL}} = 0.857\text{ g/mL}$$

5A (M) For this calculation, the value 0.000456 has the least precision (three significant figures), thus the final answer must also be quoted to three significant figures.

$$\frac{62.356}{0.000456 \times 6.422 \times 10^3} = 21.3$$

5B (M) For this calculation, the value 1.3×10^{-3} has the least precision (two significant figures), thus the final answer must also be quoted to two significant figures.

$$\frac{8.21 \times 10^4 \times 1.3 \times 10^{-3}}{0.00236 \times 4.071 \times 10^{-2}} = 1.1 \times 10^6$$

6A (M) The number in the calculation that has the least precision is 102.1 (± 0.1), thus the final answer must be quoted to just one decimal place. $0.236 + 128.55 - 102.1 = 26.7$

6B (M) This is easier to visualize if the numbers are not in exponential notation.

$$\frac{\left(1.302 \times 10^3\right) + 952.7}{\left(1.57 \times 10^2\right) - 12.22} = \frac{1302 + 952.7}{157 - 12.22} = \frac{2255}{145} = 15.6$$

INTEGRATIVE EXAMPLE

A (D) *Stepwise Approach:* First, determine the density of the alloy by the oil displacement.
Mass of oil displaced = mass of alloy in air – mass of alloy in oil
$$= 211.5 \text{ g} - 135.3 \text{ g} = 76.2 \text{ g}$$

$V_{Oil} = m / d = 76.2 \text{ g} / 0.926 \text{ g/mL} = 82.3 \text{ mL} = V_{Mg-Al}$

$d_{Mg-Al} = 211.5 \text{ g} / 82.3 \text{ mL} = 2.57 \text{ g/cm}^3$

Now, since the density is a linear function of the composition,

$d_{Mg-Al} = mx + b$, where x is the mass fraction of Mg, and b is the y-intercept.

Substituting 0 for x (no Al in the alloy), everything is Mg and the equation becomes:

$1.74 = m \, 0 + b$. Therefore, $b = 1.74$

Assuming 1 for x (100% by weight Al):

$2.70 = (m \times 1) + 1.74$, therefore, $m = 0.96$

Therefore, for an alloy:

$2.57 = 0.96x + 1.74$

$x = 0.86 =$ mass % of Al

Mass % of Mg $= 1 - 0.86 = 0.14$, 14%

B (M) *Stepwise approach:*

Mass of seawater = $d \cdot V$ = 1.027 g/mL × 1500 mL = 1540.5 g

$$1540.5 \text{ g seawater} \times \frac{2.67 \text{ g NaCl}}{100 \text{ g seawater}} \times \frac{39.34 \text{ g Na}}{100 \text{ g NaCl}} = 16.18 \text{ g Na}$$

Then, convert mass of Na to atoms of Na

$$16.18 \text{ g Na} \times \frac{1 \text{ kg Na}}{1000 \text{ g Na}} \times \frac{1 \text{ Na atom}}{3.817 \times 10^{-26} \text{ kg Na}} = 4.239 \times 10^{23} \text{ Na atoms}$$

Conversion Pathway:

$$1540.5 \text{ g seawater} \times \frac{2.67 \text{ g NaCl}}{100 \text{ g seawater}} \times \frac{39.34 \text{ g Na}}{100 \text{ g NaCl}} \times \frac{1 \text{ kg Na}}{1000 \text{ g Na}} \times \frac{1 \text{ Na atom}}{3.8175 \times 10^{-26} \text{ kg Na}}$$

EXERCISES

The Scientific Method

1. **(E)** One theory is preferred over another if it can correctly predict a wider range of phenomena and if it has fewer assumptions.

2. **(E)** No. The greater the number of experiments that conform to the predictions of the law, the more confidence we have in the law. There is no point at which the law is ever verified with absolute certainty.

3. **(E)** For a given set of conditions, a cause, is expected to produce a certain result or effect. Although these cause-and-effect relationships may be difficult to unravel at times ("God is subtle"), they nevertheless do exist ("He is not malicious").

4. **(E)** As opposed to scientific laws, legislative laws are voted on by people and thus are subject to the whims and desires of the electorate. Legislative laws can be revoked by a grassroots majority, whereas scientific laws can only be modified if they do not account for experimental observations. As well, legislative laws are imposed on people, who are expected to modify their behaviors, whereas, scientific laws cannot be imposed on nature, nor will nature change to suit a particular scientific law that is proposed.

5. **(E)** The experiment should be carefully set up so as to create a controlled situation in which one can make careful observations after altering the experimental parameters, preferably one at a time. The results must be reproducible (to within experimental error) and, as more and more experiments are conducted, a pattern should begin to emerge, from which a comparison to the current theory can be made.

6. **(E)** For a theory to be considered plausible, it must, first and foremost, agree with and/or predict the results from controlled experiments. It should also involve the fewest number of assumptions. The best theories predict new phenomena that are subsequently observed after the appropriate experiments have been performed.

Properties and Classification of Matter

7. **(E)** When an object displays a physical property it retains its basic chemical identity. By contrast, the display of a chemical property is accompanied by a change in composition.

    (a) Physical: The iron nail is not changed in any significant way when it is attracted to a magnet. Its basic chemical identity is unchanged.

    (b) Chemical: The paper is converted to ash, $CO_2(g)$, and $H_2O(g)$ along with the evolution of considerable energy.

    (c) Chemical: The green patina is the result of the combination of water, oxygen, and carbon dioxide with the copper in the bronze to produce basic copper carbonate.

    (d) Physical: Neither the block of wood nor the water has changed its identity.

8. **(E)** When an object displays a physical property it retains its basic chemical identity. By contrast, the display of a chemical property is accompanied by a change in composition.

    (a) Chemical: The change in the color of the apple indicates that a new substance (oxidized apple) has formed by reaction with air.

    (b) Physical: The marble slab is not changed into another substance by feeling it.

    (c) Physical: The sapphire retains its identity as it displays its color.

    (d) Chemical: After firing, the properties of the clay have changed from soft and pliable to rigid and brittle. New substances have formed. (Many of the changes involve driving off water and slightly melting the silicates that remain. These molten substances cool and harden when removed from the kiln.)

9. **(E) (a)** Homogeneous mixture: Air is a mixture of nitrogen, oxygen, argon, and traces of other gases. By "fresh," we mean no particles of smoke, pollen, etc., are present. Such species would produce a heterogeneous mixture.

    (b) Heterogeneous mixture: A silver-plated spoon has a surface coating of the element silver and an underlying baser metal (typically iron). This would make the coated spoon a heterogeneous mixture.

    (c) Heterogeneous mixture: Garlic salt is simply garlic powder mixed with table salt. Pieces of garlic can be distinguished from those of salt by careful examination.

    (d) Substance: Ice is simply solid water (assuming no air bubbles).

10. **(E) (a)** Heterogeneous mixture: We can clearly see air pockets within the solid matrix. On close examination, we can distinguish different kinds of solids by their colors.

   (b) Homogeneous mixture: Modern inks are solutions of dyes in water. Older inks often were heterogeneous mixtures: suspensions of particles of carbon black (soot) in water.

   (c) Substance: This is assuming that no gases or organic chemicals are dissolved in the water.

   (d) Heterogeneous mixture: The pieces of orange pulp can be seen through a microscope. Most "cloudy" liquids are heterogeneous mixtures; the small particles impede the transmission of light.

11. **(E) (a)** If a magnet is drawn through the mixture, the iron filings will be attracted to the magnet and the wood will be left behind.

   (b) When the glass-sucrose mixture is mixed with water, the sucrose will dissolve, whereas the glass will not. The water can then be boiled off to produce pure sucrose.

   (c) Olive oil will float to the top of a container and can be separated from water, which is more dense. It would be best to use something with a narrow opening that has the ability to drain off the water layer at the bottom (i.e., buret).

   (d) The gold flakes will settle to the bottom if the mixture is left undisturbed. The water then can be decanted (i.e., carefully poured off).

12. **(E) (a)** Physical: This is simply a mixture of sand and sugar (i.e., not chemically bonded).

   (b) Chemical: Oxygen needs to be removed from the iron oxide.

   (c) Physical: Seawater is a solution of various substances dissolved in water.

   (d) Physical: The water-sand slurry is simply a heterogeneous mixture.

Exponential Arithmetic

13. **(E) (a)** $8950. = 8.950 \times 10^3$ (4 sig. fig.)

   (b) $10,700. = 1.0700 \times 10^4$ (5 sig. fig.)   **(c)** $0.0240 = 2.40 \times 10^{-2}$

   (d) $0.0047 = 4.7 \times 10^{-3}$ **(e)** $938.3 = 9.383 \times 10^2$ **(f)** $275,482 = 2.75482 \times 10^5$

14. **(E) (a)** $5.12 \times 10^{-3} = 0.00512$ **(b)** $8.05 \times 10^{-5} = 0.0000805$

   (c) $291.1 \times 10^{-4} = 0.02911$ **(d)** $72.1 \times 10^{-2} = 0.721$

15. **(E) (a)** 34,000 centimeters / second $= 3.4 \times 10^4$ cm/s

   (b) 6378 km $= 6.378 \times 10^3$ km

   (c) (trillionth $= 1 \times 10^{-12}$) hence, 74×10^{-12} m or 7.4×10^{-11} m

   (d) $\dfrac{(2.2 \times 10^3) + (4.7 \times 10^2)}{5.8 \times 10^{-3}} = \dfrac{2.7 \times 10^3}{5.8 \times 10^{-3}} = 4.6 \times 10^5$

16. **(E) (a)** 173 thousand trillion watts $= 173,000,000,000,000,000$ W $= 1.73 \times 10^{17}$ W

   (b) one ten-millionth of a meter $= 1 \div 10,000,000$ m $= 1 \times 10^{-7}$ m

   (c) (trillionth $= 1 \times 10^{-12}$) hence, 142×10^{-12} m or 1.42×10^{-10} m

   (d) $\dfrac{(5.07 \times 10^4) \times (1.8 \times 10^{-3})^2}{0.065 + (3.3 \times 10^{-2})} = \dfrac{0.16}{0.098} = 1.6$

Significant Figures

17. **(E) (a)** An exact number—500 sheets in a ream of paper.

   (b) Pouring the milk into the bottle is a process that is subject to error; there can be slightly more or slightly less than one liter of milk in the bottle. This is a measured quantity.

   (c) Measured quantity: The distance between any pair of planetary bodies can only be determined through certain astronomical measurements, which are subject to error.

   (d) Measured quantity: The internuclear separation quoted for O_2 is an estimated value derived from experimental data, which contains some inherent error.

18. **(E) (a)** The number of pages in the text is determined by counting; the result is an exact number.

   (b) An exact number: Although the number of days can vary from one month to another (say, from January to February), the month of January always has 31 days.

   (c) Measured quantity: The area is determined by calculations based on measurements. These measurements are subject to error.

   (d) Measured quantity: Average internuclear distance for adjacent atoms in a gold medal is an estimated value derived from X-ray diffraction data, which contain some inherent error.

19. **(E)** Each of the following is expressed to four significant figures.

   (a) $3984.6 \approx 3985$ **(b)** $422.04 \approx 422.0$ **(c)** $186,000 = 1.860 \times 10^5$

   (d) $33,900 \approx 3.390 \times 10^4$ **(e)** 6.321×10^4 is correct   **(f)** $5.0472 \times 10^{-4} \approx 5.047 \times 10^{-4}$

20. **(E) (a)** 450 has two or three significant figures; trailing zeros left of the decimal are indeterminate, if no decimal point is present.

   (b) 98.6 has three significant figures; non-zero digits are significant.

   (c) 0.0033 has two significant digits; leading zeros are not significant.

   (d) 902.10 has five significant digits; trailing zeros to the right of the decimal point are significant, as are zeros flanked by non-zero digits.

   (e) 0.02173 has four significant digits; leading zeros are not significant.

(f) 7000 can have anywhere from one to four significant figures; trailing zeros left of the decimal are indeterminate, if no decimal point is shown.

(g) 7.02 has three significant figures; zeros flanked by non-zero digits are significant.

(h) 67,000,000 can have anywhere from two to eight significant figures; there is no way to determine which, if any, of the zeros are significant, without the presence of a decimal point.

21. **(E) (a)** $0.406 \times 0.0023 = 9.3 \times 10^{-4}$ **(b)** $0.1357 \times 16.80 \times 0.096 = 2.2 \times 10^{-1}$

(c) $0.458 + 0.12 - 0.037 = 5.4 \times 10^{-1}$ **(d)** $32.18 + 0.055 - 1.652 = 3.058 \times 10^{1}$

22. **(M) (a)** $\dfrac{320 \times 24.9}{0.080} = \dfrac{3.2 \times 10^{2} \times 2.49 \times 10^{1}}{8.0 \times 10^{-2}} = 1.0 \times 10^{5}$

(b) $\dfrac{432.7 \times 6.5 \times 0.002300}{62 \times 0.103} = \dfrac{4.327 \times 10^{2} \times 6.5 \times 2.300 \times 10^{-3}}{6.2 \times 10^{1} \times 1.03 \times 10^{-1}} = 1.0$

(c) $\dfrac{32.44 + 4.9 - 0.304}{82.94} = \dfrac{3.244 \times 10^{1} + 4.9 - 3.04 \times 10^{-1}}{8.294 \times 10^{1}} = 4.47 \times 10^{-1}$

(d) $\dfrac{8.002 + 0.3040}{13.4 - 0.066 + 1.02} = \dfrac{8.002 + 3.040 \times 10^{-1}}{1.34 \times 10^{1} - 6.6 \times 10^{-2} + 1.02} = 5.79 \times 10^{-1}$

23. **(M) (a)** 2.44×10^{4} **(b)** 1.5×10^{3} **(c)** 40.0

(d) 2.131×10^{3} **(e)** 4.8×10^{-3}

24. **(M) (a)** 7.5×10^{1} **(b)** 6.3×10^{12} **(c)** 4.6×10^{3}

(d) 1.058×10^{-1} **(e)** 4.2×10^{-3}

25. **(M) (a)** The average speed is obtained by dividing the distance traveled (in miles) by the elapsed time (in hours). First, we need to obtain the elapsed time, in hours.

$$9 \text{ days} \times \frac{24 \text{ h}}{1 \text{ d}} = 216.000 \text{ h} \quad 3 \text{ min} \times \frac{1 \text{ h}}{60 \text{ min}} = 0.050 \text{ h} \quad 44 \text{ s} \times \frac{1 \text{ h}}{3600 \text{ s}} = 0.012 \text{ h}$$

total time $= 216.000 \text{ h} + 0.050 \text{ h} + 0.012 \text{ h} = 216.062 \text{ h}$

average speed $= \dfrac{25,012 \text{ mi}}{216.062 \text{ h}} \times \dfrac{1.609344 \text{ km}}{1 \text{ mi}} = 186.30 \text{ km/h}$

(b) First compute the mass of fuel remaining

$$\text{mass} = 14 \text{ gal} \times \frac{4 \text{ qt}}{1 \text{ gal}} \times \frac{0.9464 \text{ L}}{1 \text{ qt}} \times \frac{1000 \text{ mL}}{1 \text{ L}} \times \frac{0.70 \text{ g}}{1 \text{ mL}} \times \frac{1 \text{ lb}}{453.6 \text{ g}} = 82 \text{ lb}$$

Next determine the mass of fuel used, and then finally, the fuel consumption. Notice that the initial quantity of fuel is not known precisely, perhaps at best to the nearest 10 lb, certainly ("nearly 9000 lb") is not to the nearest pound.

$$\text{mass of fuel used} = (9000 \text{ lb} - 82 \text{ lb}) \times \frac{0.4536 \text{ kg}}{1 \text{ lb}} \cong 4045 \text{ kg}$$

$$\text{fuel consumption} = \frac{25,012 \text{ mi}}{4045 \text{ kg}} \times \frac{1.609344 \text{ km}}{1 \text{ mi}} = 9.95 \text{ km/kg or} \sim 10 \text{ km/kg}$$

26. **(M)** If the proved reserve truly was an estimate, rather than an actual measurement, it would have been difficult to estimate it to the nearest trillion cubic feet. A statement such as 2,911,000 trillion cubic feet (or even 3×10^{18} ft^3) would have more realistically reflected the precision with which the proved reserve was known.

Units of Measurement

27. **(E) (a)** $0.127 \text{ L} \times \frac{1000 \text{ mL}}{1 \text{ L}} = 127 \text{ mL}$ **(b)** $15.8 \text{ mL} \times \frac{1 \text{ L}}{1000 \text{ mL}} = 0.0158 \text{ L}$

 (c) $981 \text{ cm}^3 \times \frac{1 \text{ L}}{1000 \text{ cm}^3} = 0.981 \text{ L}$ **(d)** $2.65 \text{ m}^3 \times \left(\frac{100 \text{ cm}}{1 \text{ m}}\right)^3 = 2.65 \times 10^6 \text{ cm}^3$

28. **(E) (a)** $2.35 \text{ kg} \times \frac{1000 \text{ g}}{1 \text{ kg}} = 2.35 \times 10^3 \text{ g}$ **(b)** $792 \text{ g} \times \frac{1 \text{ kg}}{1000 \text{ g}} = 0.792 \text{ kg}$

 (c) $3869 \text{ mm} \times \frac{1 \text{ cm}}{10 \text{ mm}} = 386.9 \text{ cm}$ **(d)** $0.043 \text{ cm} \times \frac{10 \text{ mm}}{1 \text{ cm}} = 0.43 \text{ mm}$

29. **(E) (a)** $68.4 \text{ in.} \times \frac{2.54 \text{ cm}}{1 \text{ in.}} = 174 \text{ cm}$ **(b)** $94 \text{ ft} \times \frac{12 \text{ in.}}{1 \text{ ft}} \times \frac{2.54 \text{ cm}}{1 \text{ in.}} \times \frac{1 \text{ m}}{100 \text{ cm}} = 29 \text{ m}$

 (c) $1.42 \text{ lb} \times \frac{453.6 \text{ g}}{1 \text{ lb}} = 644 \text{ g}$ **(d)** $248 \text{ lb} \times \frac{0.4536 \text{ kg}}{1 \text{ lb}} = 112 \text{ kg}$

 (e) $1.85 \text{ gal} \times \frac{4 \text{ qt}}{1 \text{ gal}} \times \frac{0.9464 \text{ dm}^3}{1 \text{ qt}} = 7.00 \text{ dm}^3$

 (f) $3.72 \text{ qt} \times \frac{0.9464 \text{ L}}{1 \text{ qt}} \times \frac{1000 \text{ mL}}{1 \text{ L}} = 3.52 \times 10^3 \text{ mL}$

30. **(M) (a)** $1.00 \text{ km}^2 \times \left(\dfrac{1000 \text{ m}}{1 \text{ km}} \right)^2 = 1.00 \times 10^6 \text{ m}^2$

(b) $1.00 \text{ m}^3 \times \left(\dfrac{100 \text{ cm}}{1 \text{ m}} \right)^3 = 1.00 \times 10^6 \text{ cm}^3$

(c) $1.00 \text{ mi}^2 \times \left(\dfrac{5280 \text{ ft}}{1 \text{ mi}} \times \dfrac{12 \text{ in.}}{1 \text{ ft}} \times \dfrac{2.54 \text{ cm}}{1 \text{ in.}} \times \dfrac{1 \text{ m}}{100 \text{ cm}} \right)^2 = 2.59 \times 10^6 \text{ m}^2$

31. **(E)** Express both masses in the same units for comparison.

$3245 \mu g \times \left(\dfrac{1 \text{ g}}{10^6 \mu g} \right) \times \left(\dfrac{10^3 \text{ mg}}{1 \text{ g}} \right) = 3.245 \text{ mg},$ which is larger than 0.00515 mg.

32. **(E)** Express both masses in the same units for comparison. $0.000475 \text{ kg} \times \dfrac{1000 \text{ g}}{1 \text{ kg}} = 0.475 \text{ g},$

which is smaller than $3257 \text{ mg} \times \dfrac{1 \text{ g}}{10^3 \text{ mg}} = 3.257 \text{ g}.$

33. **(E)** *Conversion pathway approach:*

$\text{height} = 15 \text{ hands} \times \dfrac{4 \text{ in.}}{1 \text{ hand}} \times \dfrac{2.54 \text{ cm}}{1 \text{ in.}} \times \dfrac{1 \text{ m}}{100 \text{ cm}} = 1.5 \text{ m}$

Stepwise approach:

$15 \text{ hands} \times \dfrac{4 \text{ in.}}{1 \text{ hand}} = 60 \text{ in.}$

$60 \text{ in.} \times \dfrac{2.54 \text{ cm}}{1 \text{ in.}} = 152.4 \text{ cm}$

$152.4 \text{ cm} \times \dfrac{1 \text{ m}}{100 \text{ cm}} = 1.524 \text{ m} = 1.5 \text{ m}$

34. **(M)** A mile is defined as being 5280 ft in length. We must use this conversion factor to find the length of a link in inches.

$1.00 \text{ link} \times \dfrac{1 \text{ chain}}{100 \text{ links}} \times \dfrac{1 \text{ furlong}}{10 \text{ chains}} \times \dfrac{1 \text{ mi}}{8 \text{ furlongs}} \times \dfrac{5280 \text{ ft}}{1 \text{ mi}} \times \dfrac{12 \text{ in.}}{1 \text{ ft}} \times \dfrac{2.54 \text{ cm}}{1 \text{ in.}} = 20.1 \text{ cm}$

35. **(M) (a)** We use the speed as a conversion factor, but need to convert yards into meters.

$\text{time} = 100.0 \text{ m} \times \dfrac{9.3 \text{ s}}{100 \text{ yd}} \times \dfrac{1 \text{ yd}}{36 \text{ in.}} \times \dfrac{39.37 \text{ in.}}{1 \text{ m}} = 10. \text{ s}$

The final answer can only be quoted to a maximum of two significant figures.

(b) We need to convert yards to meters.

$$\text{speed} = \frac{100 \text{ yd}}{9.3 \text{ s}} \times \frac{36 \text{ in.}}{1 \text{ yd}} \times \frac{2.54 \text{ cm}}{1 \text{ in.}} \times \frac{1 \text{ m}}{100 \text{ cm}} = 9.8\underline{3} \text{ m/s}$$

(c) The speed is used as a conversion factor.

$$\text{time} = 1.45 \text{ km} \times \frac{1000 \text{ m}}{1 \text{ km}} \times \frac{1 \text{ s}}{9.8\underline{3} \text{ m}} \times \frac{1 \text{ min}}{60 \text{ s}} = 2.5 \text{ min}$$

36. **(M) (a)** $\text{mass (mg)} = 2 \text{ tablets} \times \dfrac{5.0 \text{ gr}}{1 \text{ tablet}} \times \dfrac{1.0 \text{ g}}{15 \text{ gr}} \times \dfrac{1000 \text{ mg}}{1 \text{ g}} = 6.7 \times 10^2 \text{ mg}$

(b) $\text{dosage rate} = \dfrac{6.7 \times 10^2 \text{ mg}}{161 \text{ lb}} \times \dfrac{1 \text{ lb}}{453.6 \text{ g}} \times \dfrac{1000 \text{ g}}{1 \text{ kg}} = 9.2 \text{ mg aspirin/kg body weight}$

(c) $\text{time} = 1.0 \text{ kg} \times \dfrac{1000 \text{ g}}{1 \text{ kg}} \times \dfrac{2 \text{ tablets}}{0.67 \text{ g}} \times \dfrac{1 \text{ day}}{2 \text{ tablets}} = 1.5 \times 10^3 \text{ days}$

37. **(D)** $1 \text{ hectare} = 1 \text{ hm}^2 \times \left(\dfrac{100 \text{ m}}{1 \text{ hm}} \times \dfrac{100 \text{ cm}}{1 \text{ m}} \times \dfrac{1 \text{ in.}}{2.54 \text{ cm}} \times \dfrac{1 \text{ ft}}{12 \text{ in.}} \times \dfrac{1 \text{ mi}}{5280 \text{ ft}} \right)^2 \times \dfrac{640 \text{ acres}}{1 \text{ mi}^2}$

$1 \text{ hectare} = 2.47 \text{ acres}$

38. **(D)** Here we must convert pounds per cubic inch into grams per cubic centimeter:

$$\text{density for metallic iron} = \frac{0.284 \text{ lb}}{1 \text{ in.}^3} \times \frac{454 \text{ g}}{1 \text{ lb}} \times \frac{(1 \text{ in.})^3}{(2.54 \text{ cm})^3} = 7.87 \frac{\text{g}}{\text{cm}^3}$$

39. **(D)** $\text{pressure} = \dfrac{32 \text{ lb}}{1 \text{ in.}^2} \times \dfrac{453.6 \text{ g}}{1 \text{ lb}} \times \left(\dfrac{1 \text{ in.}}{2.54 \text{ cm}} \right)^2 = 2.2 \times 10^3 \text{ g/cm}^2$

$\text{pressure} = \dfrac{2.2 \times 10^3 \text{ g}}{1 \text{ cm}^2} \times \dfrac{1 \text{ kg}}{1000 \text{ g}} \times \left(\dfrac{100 \text{ cm}}{1 \text{ m}} \right)^2 = 2.2 \times 10^4 \text{ kg/m}^2$

40. **(D)** First we will calculate the radius for a typical red blood cell using the equation for the volume of a sphere. $V = 4/3 \pi r^3 = 90.0 \times 10^{-12} \text{ cm}^3$
$r^3 = 2.15 \times 10^{-11} \text{ cm}^3$ and $r = 2.78 \times 10^{-4} \text{ cm}$

Thus, the diameter is $2 \times r = 2 \times 2.78 \times 10^{-4} \text{ cm} \times \dfrac{10 \text{ mm}}{1 \text{ cm}} = 5.56 \times 10^{-3} \text{ mm}$

Temperature Scales

41. **(E)**   low: $t(°F) = \frac{9\,°F}{5\,°C}t(°C) + 32\,°F = \frac{9\,°F}{5\,°C}(-10\,°C) + 32\,°F = 14\,°F$

           high: $t(°F) = \frac{9\,°F}{5\,°C}t(°C) + 32\,°F = \frac{9\,°F}{5\,°C}(50\,°C) + 32\,°F = 122\,°F$

42. **(E)**   high: $t(°C) = (t(°F) - 32\,°F)\frac{5\,°C}{9\,°F} = (118\,°F - 32\,°F)\frac{5\,°C}{9\,°F} = 47.8\,°C \approx 48\,°C$

           low: $t(°C) = (t(°F) - 32\,°F)\frac{5\,°C}{9\,°F} = (17\,°F - 32\,°F)\frac{5\,°C}{9\,°F} = -8.3\,°C$

43. **(M)**   Let us determine the Fahrenheit equivalent of absolute zero.

$$t(°F) = \frac{9\,°F}{5\,°C}t(°C) + 32\,°F = \frac{9\,°F}{5\,°C}(-273.15\,°C) + 32\,°F = -459.7\,°F$$

A temperature of $-465\,°F$ cannot be achieved because it is below absolute zero.

44. **(M)** Determine the Celsius temperature that corresponds to the highest Fahrenheit temperature, $240\,°F$. $t(°C) = (t(°F) - 32\,°F)\frac{5\,°C}{9\,°F} = (240\,°F - 32\,°F)\frac{5\,°C}{9\,°F} = 116\,°C$

Because $116\,°C$ is above the range of the thermometer, this thermometer cannot be used in this candy-making assignment.

45. **(D) (a)**   From the data provided we can write down the following relationship:
$-38.9\,°C = 0\,°M$ and $356.9\,°C = 100\,°M$. To find the mathematical relationship between these two scales, we can treat each relationship as a point on a two-dimensional Cartesian graph:

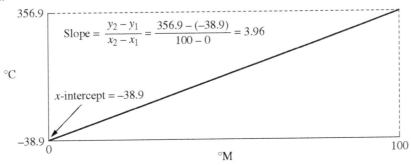

Therefore, the equation for the line is $y = 3.96x - 38.9$. The algebraic relationship between the two temperature scales is

$$t(°C) = 3.96(°M) - 38.9 \text{ or rearranging, } t(°M) = \frac{t(°C) + 38.9}{3.96}$$

Alternatively, note that the change in temperature in $°C$ corresponding to a change of $100\,°M$ is $[356.9 - (-38.9)] = 395.8\,°C$, hence, $(100\,°M/395.8\,°C) = 1\,°M/3.96\,°C$. This factor must be multiplied by the number of degrees Celsius above zero on the M scale. This number of degrees is $t(°C) + 38.9$, which leads to the general equation $t(°M) = [t(°C) + 38.9]/3.96$.

The boiling point of water is $100\,°C$, corresponding to $t(°M) = \dfrac{100 + 38.9}{3.96} = 35.1\,°M$

(b) $t(°M) = \dfrac{-273.15 + 38.9}{3.96} = -59.2\,°M$ would be the absolute zero on this scale.

46. **(D) (a)** From the data provided we can write down the following relationship: $-77.75 = 0 \,°A$ and $-33.35 \,°C = 100 \,°A$. To find the mathematical relationship between these two scales, we can treat each relationship as a point on a two-dimensional Cartesian graph.

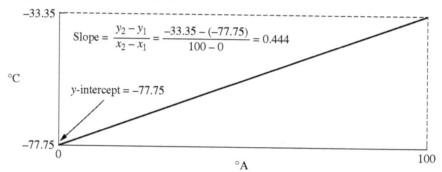

Therefore, the equation for the line is $y = 0.444x - 77.75$
The algebraic relationship between the two temperature scales is

$t(°C) = 0.444(°A) - 77.75$ or rearranging $t(°A) = \dfrac{t(°C) + 77.75}{0.444}$

The boiling point of water (100 °C) corresponds to $t(°A) = \dfrac{100 + 77.75}{0.444} = 400 \,°A$

(b) $t(°A) = \dfrac{-273.15 + 77.75}{0.444} = -440 \,°A$

Density

47. **(E)** butyric acid density $= \dfrac{mass}{volume} = \dfrac{2088 \text{ g}}{2.18 \text{ L}} \times \dfrac{1 \text{ L}}{1000 \text{ mL}} = 0.958 \text{ g/mL}$

48. **(E)** chloroform density $= \dfrac{mass}{volume} = \dfrac{22.54 \text{ kg}}{15.2 \text{ L}} \times \dfrac{1 \text{ L}}{1000 \text{ mL}} \times \dfrac{1000 \text{ g}}{1 \text{ kg}} = 1.48 \text{ g/mL}$

49. **(M)** The mass of acetone is the difference in masses between empty and filled masses.

Conversion pathway approach:

$$\text{density} = \dfrac{437.5 \text{ lb} - 75.0 \text{ lb}}{55.0 \text{ gal}} \times \dfrac{453.6 \text{ g}}{1 \text{ lb}} \times \dfrac{1 \text{ gal}}{3.785 \text{ L}} \times \dfrac{1 \text{ L}}{1000 \text{ mL}} = 0.790 \text{ g/mL}$$

Stepwise approach:

$$437.5 \text{ lb} - 75.0 \text{ lb} = 362.5 \text{ lb}$$

$$362.5 \text{ lb} \times \dfrac{453.6 \text{ g}}{1 \text{ lb}} = 1.644 \times 10^5 \text{ g}$$

$$55.0 \text{ gal} \times \frac{3.785 \text{ L}}{1 \text{ gal}} = 208 \text{ L}$$

$$208 \text{ L} \times \frac{1000 \text{ mL}}{1 \text{ L}} = 2.08 \times 10^5 \text{mL}$$

$$\frac{1.644 \times 10^5 \text{g}}{2.08 \times 10^5 \text{mL}} = 0.790 \text{ g/mL}$$

50. **(M)** Density is a conversion factor.

$$\text{volume} = (283.2 \text{ g filled} - 121.3 \text{ g empty}) \times \frac{1 \text{ mL}}{1.59 \text{ g}} = 102 \text{ mL}$$

51. **(M)** acetone mass $= 7.50 \text{ L antifreeze} \times \dfrac{1000 \text{ mL}}{1 \text{ L}} \times \dfrac{0.9867 \text{ g antifreeze}}{1 \text{ mL antifreeze}} \times \dfrac{8.50 \text{ g acetone}}{100.0 \text{ g antifreeze}}$

$$\times \frac{1 \text{ kg}}{1000 \text{ g}} = 0.629 \text{ kg acetone}$$

52. **(M)**

$$\text{solution mass} = 1.00 \text{ kg sucrose} \times \frac{1000 \text{ g sucrose}}{1 \text{ kg sucrose}} \times \frac{100.00 \text{ g solution}}{10.05 \text{ g sucrose}} = 9.95 \times 10^3 \text{ g solution}$$

53. **(M)** fertilizer mass $= 225 \text{ g nitrogen} \times \dfrac{1 \text{ kg N}}{1000 \text{ g N}} \times \dfrac{100 \text{ kg fertilizer}}{21 \text{ kg N}} = 1.0\underline{7} \text{ kg fertilizer}$

54. **(M)**

$$m_{\text{acetic acid}} = 1.00 \text{ L vinegar} \times \frac{1000 \text{ mL vinegar}}{1 \text{ L}} \times \frac{1.006 \text{ g vinegar}}{1 \text{ mL vinegar}} \times \frac{5.4 \text{ g acetic acid}}{100 \text{ g vinegar}}$$

$$m_{\text{acetic acid}} = 54.\underline{3} \text{ g acetic acid}$$

55. **(M)** The calculated volume of the iron block is converted to its mass by using the provided density.

$$\text{mass} = 52.8 \text{ cm} \times 6.74 \text{ cm} \times 3.73 \text{ cm} \times 7.86 \frac{\text{g}}{\text{cm}^3} = 1.04 \times 10^4 \text{ g iron}$$

56. **(D)** The calculated volume of the steel cylinder is converted to its mass by using the provided density.

$$\text{mass} = V(\text{density}) = \pi r^2 h(d) = 3.14159 (1.88 \text{ cm})^2 \, 18.35 \text{ cm} \times 7.75 \frac{\text{g}}{\text{cm}^3} = 1.58 \times 10^3 \text{ g steel}$$

57. **(M)** We start by determining the mass of each item.

(1) mass of iron bar $= (81.5 \text{ cm} \times 2.1 \text{ cm} \times 1.6 \text{ cm}) \times 7.86 \text{ g/cm}^3 = 2.2 \times 10^3 \text{ g iron}$

(2)   mass of Al foil $= \left(12.12 \text{ m} \times 3.62 \text{ m} \times 0.003 \times 10^{-2} \text{m}\right) \times \left(\dfrac{100 \text{ cm}}{1 \text{ m}}\right)^3 \times 2.70 \text{ g Al/cm}^3$

$= 4 \times 10^3 \text{ g Al}$

(3)   mass of water $= 4.051 \text{ L} \times \dfrac{1000 \text{ cm}^3}{1 \text{ L}} \times 0.998 \text{ g / cm}^3 = 4.04 \times 10^3 \text{ g water}$

In order of increasing mass, the items are: iron bar < aluminum foil < water. Strictly speaking, the rules for significant figures do not allow us to distinguish between the masses of aluminum and water.

58.   (M) Total volume of 125 pieces of shot

$V = 8.9 \text{ mL} - 8.4 \text{ mL} = 0.5 \text{ mL}; \qquad \dfrac{\text{mass}}{\text{shot}} = \dfrac{0.5 \text{ mL}}{125 \text{ shot}} \times \dfrac{1 \text{ cm}^3}{1 \text{ mL}} \times \dfrac{8.92 \text{ g}}{1 \text{ cm}^3} = 0.04 \text{ g/shot}$

<u>**59.**</u>   **(D)** First determine the volume of the aluminum foil, then its area, and finally its thickness.

volume $= 2.568 \text{ g} \times \dfrac{1 \text{ cm}^3}{2.70 \text{ g}} = 0.951 \text{ cm}^3; \qquad$ area $= \left(22.86 \text{ cm}\right)^2 = 522.6 \text{ cm}^2$

thickness $= \dfrac{\text{volume}}{\text{area}} = \dfrac{0.951 \text{ cm}^3}{522.6 \text{ cm}^2} \times \dfrac{10 \text{ mm}}{1 \text{ cm}} = 1.82 \times 10^{-2} \text{ mm}$

60.   (D) The vertical piece of steel has a volume $= 12.78 \text{ cm} \times 1.35 \text{ cm} \times 2.75 \text{ cm} = 47.4 \text{ cm}^3$
The horizontal piece of steel has a volume $= 10.26 \text{ cm} \times 1.35 \text{ cm} \times 2.75 \text{ cm} = 38.1 \text{ cm}^3$
$V_{\text{total}} = 47.4 \text{ cm}^3 + 38.1 \text{ cm}^3 = 85.5 \text{ cm}^3.$ mass $= 85.5 \text{ cm}^3 \times 7.78 \text{ g/cm}^3 = 665 \text{ g of steel}$

<u>**61.**</u>   **(D)** Here we are asked to calculate the number of liters of whole blood that must be collected in order to end up with 0.5 kg of red blood cells. Each red blood cell has a mass of $90.0 \times 10^{-12} \text{ cm}^3 \times 1.096 \text{ g cm}^{-3} = 9.864 \times 10^{-11} \text{ g}$

red blood cells (mass per mL) $= \dfrac{9.864 \times 10^{-11} \text{ g}}{1 \text{ cell}} \times \dfrac{5.4 \times 10^9 \text{ cells}}{1 \text{ mL}} = \dfrac{0.533 \text{ g red blood cells}}{1 \text{ mL of blood}}$

For 0.5 kg or 5×10^2 g of red blood cells, we require

$= 5 \times 10^2 \text{ g red blood cells} \times \dfrac{1 \text{ mL of blood}}{0.533 \text{ g red blood cells}} = 9 \times 10^2 \text{ mL of blood or 0.9 L blood}$

62.   (D) The mass of the liquid mixture can be found by subtracting the mass of the full bottle from the mass of the empty bottle $= 15.4448 \text{ g} - 12.4631 \text{ g} = 2.9817 \text{ g liquid}$. Similarly, the total mass of the water that can be accommodated in the bottle is $13.5441 \text{ g} - 12.4631 \text{ g} = 1.0810 \text{ g H}_2\text{O}$. The volume of the water and hence the internal volume for the bottle is equal to

$1.0810 \text{ g H}_2\text{O} \times \dfrac{1 \text{ mL H}_2\text{O}}{0.9970 \text{ g H}_2\text{O}} = 1.084 \text{ mL H}_2\text{O} (25 \text{ °C})$

Thus, the density of the liquid mixture $= \dfrac{2.9817 \text{ g liquid}}{1.084 \text{ mL}} = 2.751 \text{ g mL}^{-1}$

Since the calcite just floats in this mixture of liquids, it must have the same density as the mixture. Consequently, the solid calcite sample must have a density of 2.751 g mL^{-1} as well.

Percent Composition

63. **(E)** The percent of students with each grade is obtained by dividing the number of students with that grade by the total number of students. $\%A = \dfrac{7 \text{ A's}}{76 \text{ students}} \times 100\% = 9.2\% \text{ A}$

$\%B = \dfrac{22 \text{ B's}}{76 \text{ students}} \times 100\% = 28.9\% \text{ B}$ $\%C = \dfrac{37 \text{ C's}}{76 \text{ students}} \times 100\% = 48.7\% \text{ C}$

$\%D = \dfrac{8 \text{ D's}}{76 \text{ students}} \times 100\% = 11\% \text{ D}$ $\%F = \dfrac{2 \text{ F's}}{76 \text{ students}} \times 100\% = 3\% \text{ F}$

Note that the percentages add to 101% due to rounding effects.

64. **(E)** The number of students with a certain grade is determined by multiplying the total number of students by the fraction of students who earned that grade.

no. of A's $= 84 \text{ students} \times \dfrac{18 \text{ A's}}{100 \text{ students}} = 15 \text{ A's}$

no. of B's $= 84 \text{ students} \times \dfrac{25 \text{ B's}}{100 \text{ students}} = 21 \text{ B's}$ no. of C's $= 84 \text{ students} \times \dfrac{32 \text{ C's}}{100 \text{ students}} = 27 \text{ C's}$

no. of D's $= 84 \text{ students} \times \dfrac{13 \text{ D's}}{100 \text{ students}} = 11 \text{ D's}$ no. of F's $= 84 \text{ students} \times \dfrac{12 \text{ F's}}{100 \text{ students}} = 10 \text{ F's}$

65. **(M)** Use the percent composition as a conversion factor.

Conversion pathway approach:

mass of sucrose $= 3.50 \text{ L} \times \dfrac{1000 \text{ mL}}{1 \text{ L}} \times \dfrac{1.118 \text{ g soln}}{1 \text{ mL}} \times \dfrac{28.0 \text{ g sucrose}}{100 \text{ g soln}} = 1.10 \times 10^3 \text{ g sucrose}$

Stepwise approach:

$3.50 \text{ L} \times \dfrac{1000 \text{ mL}}{1 \text{ L}} = 3.50 \times 10^3 \text{ mL}$

$3.50 \times 10^3 \text{ mL} \times \dfrac{1.118 \text{ g soln}}{1 \text{ mL}} = 3.91 \times 10^3 \text{ g soln}$

$3.91 \times 10^3 \text{ g soln} \times \dfrac{28.0 \text{ g sucrose}}{100 \text{ g soln}} = 1.10 \times 10^3 \text{ g sucrose}$

66. **(D)** Again, percent composition is used as a conversion factor. We are careful to label both the numerator and denominator for each factor.

$$V_{solution} = 2.75 \text{ kg sodium hydroxide} \times \frac{1000 \text{ g}}{1 \text{ kg}} \times \frac{100.0 \text{ g soln}}{12.0 \text{ g sodium hydroxide}} \times \frac{1 \text{ mL}}{1.131 \text{ g soln}}$$

$$= 2.03 \times 10^4 \text{ mL}$$

$$V_{solution} = 2.03 \times 10^4 \text{ mL soln} \times \frac{1 \text{ L}}{1000 \text{ mL}} = 20.3 \text{ L soln}$$

INTEGRATIVE AND ADVANCED EXERCISES

67. **(M)** 99.9 is known to 0.1 part in 99.9, or 0.1%. 1.008 is known to 0.001 part in 1.008, or 0.1%. The product 100.7 also is known to 0.1 part in 100.7, or 0.1%, which is the same precision as the two factors. On the other hand, the three-significant-figure product, 101, is known to 1 part in 101 or 1%, which is ten times less precise than either of the two factors. Thus, the result is properly expressed to four significant figures.

68. **(M)**

$$1.543 = 1.5794 - 1.836 \times 10^{-3}(t - 15) \quad 1.543 - 1.5794 = -1.836 \times 10^{-3}(t - 15) = 0.036\underline{4}$$

$$(t - 15) = \frac{-0.036\underline{4}}{-1.836 \times 10^{-3}} = 19.\underline{8} \, °C \quad t = 19.\underline{8} + 15 = 34.\underline{8} \, °C$$

69. **(D)** volume needed $= 18,000 \text{ gal} \times \frac{4 \text{ qt}}{1 \text{ gal}} \times \frac{0.9464 \text{ L}}{1 \text{ qt}} \times \frac{1000 \text{ mL}}{1 \text{ L}} \times \frac{1.00 \text{ g}}{1 \text{ mL}} \times \frac{1 \text{ g Cl}}{10^6 \text{ g water}}$

$$\times \frac{100 \text{ g soln}}{7 \text{ g Cl}} \times \frac{1 \text{ mL soln}}{1.10 \text{ g soln}} \times \frac{1 \text{ L soln}}{1000 \text{ mL soln}} = 0.9 \text{ L soln}$$

70. **(D)** We first determine the volume of steel needed. This volume, divided by the cross-sectional area of the bar of steel, gives the length of the steel bar needed.

$$V = 1.000 \text{ kg steel} \times \frac{1000 \text{ g steel}}{1 \text{ kg steel}} \times \frac{1 \text{ cm}^3 \text{ steel}}{7.70 \text{ g steel}} = 129.\underline{87} \text{ cm}^3 \text{ of steel}$$

For an equilateral triangle of length s, area $= \frac{s^2 \sqrt{3}}{4} = \frac{(2.50 \text{ in.})^2 \sqrt{3}}{4} = 2.70\underline{6} \text{ in.}^2$

$$\text{length} = \frac{\text{volume}}{\text{area}} = \frac{129.\underline{87} \text{ cm}^3}{2.70\underline{6} \text{ in.}^2} \times \left(\frac{1 \text{ in.}}{2.54 \text{ cm}}\right)^2 \times \frac{1 \text{ in.}}{2.54 \text{ cm}} = 2.93 \text{ in.}$$

71. **(D)** *Conversion pathway approach:*

$$\text{NaCl mass} = 330,000,000 \text{ mi}^3 \times \left(\frac{5280 \text{ ft}}{1 \text{ mi}} \times \frac{12 \text{ in.}}{1 \text{ ft}} \times \frac{2.54 \text{ cm}}{1 \text{ in.}}\right)^3 \times \frac{1 \text{ mL}}{1 \text{ cm}^3} \times \frac{1.03 \text{ g}}{1 \text{ mL}}$$

$$\times \frac{3.5 \text{ g sodium chloride}}{100.0 \text{ g seawater}} \times \frac{1 \text{ lb}}{453.6 \text{ g}} \times \frac{1 \text{ ton}}{2000 \text{ lb}} = 5.5 \times 10^{16} \text{ tons}$$

Stepwise approach:

$$330{,}000{,}000 \text{ mi}^3 \times \left(\frac{5280 \text{ ft}}{1 \text{ mi}}\right)^3 = 4.9\times10^{19} \text{ ft}^3$$

$$4.9\times10^{19} \text{ ft}^3 \times \left(\frac{12 \text{ in.}}{1 \text{ ft}}\right)^3 = 8.4\times10^{22} \text{ in.}^3$$

$$8.4\times10^{22} \text{ in.}^3 \times \left(\frac{2.54 \text{ cm}}{1 \text{ in.}}\right)^3 = 1.4\times10^{24} \text{ cm}^3$$

$$1.4\times10^{24} \text{ cm}^3 \times \frac{1 \text{ mL}}{1 \text{ cm}^3} \times \frac{1.03 \text{ g}}{1 \text{ mL}} = 1.4\times10^{24} \text{ g}$$

$$1.4\times10^{24}\text{g} \times \frac{3.5 \text{ g sodium chloride}}{100.0 \text{ g seawater}} = 4.9\times10^{22} \text{ g NaCl}$$

$$4.9\times10^{22} \text{ g NaCl} \times \frac{1 \text{ lb}}{453.6 \text{ g}} = 1.1\times10^{20} \text{ lb}$$

$$1.1\times10^{20} \text{ lb} \times \frac{1 \text{ ton}}{2000 \text{ lb}} = 5.4\times10^{16} \text{ tons}$$

The answers for the stepwise and conversion pathway approaches differ slightly due to a cumulative rounding error that is present in the stepwise approach.

72. **(D)** First, we find the volume of the wire, then its cross-sectional area, and finally its length. We carry an additional significant figure through the early stages of the calculation to help avoid rounding errors.

$$V = 1 \text{ lb} \times \frac{453.6 \text{ g}}{1 \text{ lb}} \times \frac{1 \text{ cm}^3}{8.92 \text{ g}} = 50.8\underline{5}\,\text{cm}^3 \qquad \text{Note: area} = \pi r^2$$

$$\text{area} = 3.1416 \times \left(\frac{0.05082 \text{ in.}}{2} \times \frac{2.54 \text{ cm}}{1 \text{ in.}}\right)^2 = 0.01309\,\text{cm}^2$$

$$\text{length} = \frac{\text{volume}}{\text{area}} = \frac{50.8\underline{5} \text{ cm}^3}{0.01309 \text{ cm}^2} \times \frac{1 \text{ m}}{100 \text{ cm}} = 38.8 \text{ m}$$

73. **(M)** $V_{\text{seawater}} = 1.50\times10^5 \text{ ton Mg} \times \dfrac{2000 \text{ lb Mg}}{1 \text{ ton Mg}} \times \dfrac{453.6 \text{ g Mg}}{1 \text{ lb Mg}} \times \dfrac{1000 \text{ g seawater}}{1.4 \text{ g Mg}} \times$

$$\frac{0.001 \text{ L}}{1.025 \text{ g seawater}} \times \frac{1 \text{ m}^3}{1000 \text{ L}} = 9.5\times10^7 \text{ m}^3 \text{ seawater}$$

74. **(D) (a)** $\quad \text{dustfall} = \dfrac{10 \text{ ton}}{1 \text{ mi}^2 \cdot 1 \text{ mo}} \times \left(\dfrac{1 \text{ mi}}{5280 \text{ ft}} \times \dfrac{1 \text{ ft}}{12 \text{ in.}} \times \dfrac{39.37 \text{ in.}}{1 \text{ m}}\right)^2 \times \dfrac{2000 \text{ lb}}{1 \text{ ton}} \times \dfrac{454 \text{ g}}{1 \text{ lb}} \times \dfrac{1000 \text{ mg}}{1 \text{ g}}$

$$= \frac{3.5\times10^3 \text{ mg}}{1 \text{ m}^2 \cdot 1 \text{ mo}} \times \frac{1 \text{ month}}{30 \text{ d}} \times \frac{1 \text{ d}}{24 \text{ h}} = \frac{5 \text{ mg}}{1 \text{ m}^2 \cdot 1\text{h}}$$

(b) This problem is solved by the conversion factor method, starting with the volume that deposits on each square meter, 1 mm deep.

$$\frac{(1.0 \text{ mm} \times 1 \text{ m}^2)}{1 \text{ m}^2} \times \frac{1 \text{ cm}}{10 \text{ mm}} \times \left(\frac{100 \text{ cm}}{1 \text{ m}}\right)^2 \times \frac{2 \text{ g}}{1 \text{ cm}^3} \times \frac{1000 \text{ mg}}{1 \text{ g}} \times \frac{1 \text{ m}^2 \cdot \text{h}}{4.9 \text{ mg}} = 4.1 \times 10^5 \text{ h} = 5 \times 10^1 \text{ y}$$

It would take about half a century to accumulate a depth of 1 mm.

75. **(D) (a)** $\text{volume} = 3.54 \times 10^6$ acre-feet $\times \dfrac{1 \text{ mi}^2}{640 \text{ acre}} \times \left(\dfrac{5280 \text{ ft}}{1 \text{ mi}}\right)^2 = 1.54 \times 10^{11} \text{ ft}^3$

    (b) $\text{volume} = 1.54 \times 10^{11} \text{ ft}^3 \times \left(\dfrac{12 \text{ in.}}{1 \text{ ft}} \times \dfrac{2.54 \text{ cm}}{1 \text{ in.}} \times \dfrac{1 \text{ m}}{100 \text{ cm}}\right)^3 = 4.36 \times 10^9 \text{ m}^3$

    (c) $\text{volume} = 4.36 \times 10^9 \text{ m}^3 \times \dfrac{1000 \text{ L}}{1 \text{ m}^3} \times \dfrac{1 \text{ gal}}{3.785 \text{ L}} = 1.15 \times 10^{12}$ gal

76. **(M)** Let F be the Fahrenheit temperature and C be the Celsius temperature. $C = (F - 32)\frac{5}{9}$

    (a) $F = C - 49$ $C = (C - 49 - 32)\frac{5}{9} = \frac{5}{9}(C - 81)$ $C = \frac{5}{9}C - \frac{5}{9}(81)$ $C = \frac{5}{9}C - 45$

        $\frac{4}{9}C = -45$ Hence: $C = -101.\underline{25}$

        When it is ~ -101 °C, the temperature in Fahrenheit is -150 °F (49°lower).

    (b) $F = 2C$ $C = (2C - 32)\frac{5}{9} = \frac{10}{9}C - 17.8$ $17.8 = \frac{10}{9}C - C = \frac{1}{9}C$

        $C = 9 \times 17.8 = 160.$ °C $F = \frac{9}{5}C + 32 = \frac{9}{5}(160.) + 32 = 320.$ °F

    (c) $F = \frac{1}{8}C$ $C = (\frac{1}{8}C - 32)\frac{5}{9} = \frac{5}{72}C - 17.8$ $17.8 = \frac{5}{72}C - C = -\frac{67}{72}C$

        $C = -\dfrac{72 \times 17.8}{67} = -19.1$ °C $F = \frac{9}{5}C + 32 = \frac{9}{5}(-19.1) + 32 = -2.4$ °F

    (d) $F = C + 300$ $C = (C + 300 - 32)\frac{5}{9} = \frac{5}{9}C + 148.9$ $148.9 = \frac{4}{9}C$

        $C = \dfrac{9 \times 148.9}{4} = 335$ °C $F = \frac{9}{5}C + 32 = \frac{9}{5}(335) + 32 = 635$ °F

77. **(M)** We will use the density of diatomaceous earth, and its mass in the cylinder, to find the volume occupied by the diatomaceous earth.

    $\text{diatomaceous earth volume} = 8.0 \text{ g} \times \dfrac{1 \text{ cm}^3}{2.2 \text{ g}} = 3.6 \text{ cm}^3$

The added water volume will occupy the remaining volume in the graduated cylinder.
water volume $= 100.0 \text{ mL} - 3.6 \text{ mL} = 96.4 \text{ mL}$

78. **(M)** We will use the density of water, and its mass in the pycnometer, to find the volume of liquid held by the pycnometer.

$$\text{pycnometer volume} = (35.552\,g - 25.601\,g) \times \frac{1\,mL}{0.99821\,g} = 9.969\,mL$$

The mass of the methanol and the pyncnometer's volume determine liquid density.

$$\text{density of methanol} = \frac{33.490\,g - 25.601\,g}{9.969\,mL} = 0.7914\,g/mL$$

79. **(D)** We use the density of water, and its mass in the pycnometer, to find the volume of liquid held by the pycnometer.

$$\text{pycnometer volume} = (35.552\,g - 25.601\,g) \times \frac{1\,mL}{0.99821\,g} = 9.969\,mL$$

The mass of the ethanol and the pyncnometer's volume determine liquid density.

$$\text{density of ethanol} = \frac{33.470\,g - 25.601\,g}{9.969\,mL} = 0.7893\,g/mL$$

The difference in the density of pure methanol and pure ethanol is 0.0020 g/mL. If the density of the solution is a linear function of the volume-percent composition, we would see that the maximum change in density (0.0020 g/mL) corresponds to a change of 100% in the volume percent. This means that the absolute best accuracy that one can obtain is a differentiation of 0.0001 g/mL between the two solutions. This represents a change in the volume % of ~ 5%. Given this apparatus, if the volume percent does not change by at least 5%, we would not be able to differentiate based on density (probably more like a 10 % difference would be required, given that our error when measuring two solutions is more likely $\pm$ 0.0002 g/mL).

80. **(D)** We first determine the pycnometer's volume.

$$\text{pycnometer volume} = (35.55\,g - 25.60\,g) \times \frac{1\,mL}{0.9982\,g} = 9.97\,mL$$

Then we determine the volume of water present with the lead.

$$\text{volume of water} = (44.83\,g - 10.20\,g - 25.60\,g) \times \frac{1\,mL}{0.9982\,g} = 9.05\,mL$$

Difference between the two volumes is the volume of lead, which leads to the density of lead.

$$\text{density} = \frac{10.20\,g}{(9.97\,mL - 9.05\,mL)} = 11\,g/mL$$

Note that the difference in the denominator has just two significant digits.

81. **(M)** $\text{Water used (in kg/week)} = 1.8 \times 10^{6}\,\text{people} \times \left(\frac{750\,L}{1\,day}\right) \times \left(\frac{7\,day}{1\,week}\right) \times \frac{1\,kg}{1\,L}$

$$= 9.45 \times 10^{9}\,\text{kg water/week}$$

Given: Sodium hypochlorite is NaClO

$$\text{mass of NaClO} = 9.45 \times 10^9 \text{ kg water} \left(\frac{1 \text{ kg chlorine}}{1 \times 10^6 \text{ kg water}} \right) \times \left(\frac{100 \text{ kg NaClO}}{47.62 \text{ kg chlorine}} \right)$$

$$= 1.98 \times 10^4 \text{ kg sodium hypochlorite}$$

82. **(M)** $\dfrac{1.77 \text{ lb}}{1 \text{ L}} \times \dfrac{1 \text{ kg}}{2.2046 \text{ lb}} = 0.803 \text{ kg L}^{-1}$

22,300 kg of fuel are required, hence:

$$22,300 \text{ kg fuel} \times \frac{1 \text{ L}}{0.803 \text{ kg}} = 2.78 \times 10^4 \text{ L of fuel}$$

(Note, the plane had 7682 L of fuel left in the tank.)
Hence, the volume of fuel that should have been added $= 2.78 \times 10^4 \text{ L} - 0.7682 \text{ L}$
$= 2.01 \times 10^4 \text{ L}$

83. **(D) (a)** Density of water at 10. °C:

$$\text{density} = \frac{0.99984 + (1.6945 \times 10^{-2}(10.) - (7.987 \times 10^{-6}(10.)^2)}{1 + (1.6880 \times 10^{-2}(10.))} = 0.9997 \text{ g cm}^{-3} \text{ (4 sig fig)}$$

(b) Set $a = 0.99984$, $b = 1.6945 \times 10^2$, $c = 7.987 \times 10^{-6}$, $d = 1.6880 \times 10^{-2}$ (for simplicity)

$$0.99860 = \frac{0.99984 + (1.6945 \times 10^{-2}(t) - (7.987 \times 10^{-6}(t)^2)}{1 + (1.6880 \times 10^{-2}t)} = \frac{a + bt - ct^2}{1 + dt}$$

Multiply both sides by $(1 + dt)$: $0.99860(1 + dt)$
$= 0.99860 + 0.99860dt = a + bt - ct^2$
Bring all terms to the left hand side: $0 = a + bt - ct^2 - 0.99860 - 0.99860dt$
Collect terms $0 = a - 0.99860 + bt - 0.99860dt - ct^2$
Substitute in for a, b, c and d:
$0 = 0.99984 - 0.99860 + 1.6945 \times 10^{-2}t - 0.99860(1.6880 \times 10^{-2})t - 7.987 \times 10^{-6}t^2$
Simplify: $0 = 0.00124 + 0.000088623t - 7.987 \times 10^{-6}t^2$
Solve the quadratic equation: $t = 19.188$ °C

(c) **i)** Maximum density by estimation:
Determine density every 5 °C then narrow down the range to the degree.
First set of data suggests ~5 °C, the second set of data suggests ~4 °C
and the final set of data suggests about 4.1 °C (+/–0.1 °C)

1st data set		2nd data set		3rd data set	
0 °C	0.999840	3 °C	0.999965	3.6 °C	0.999972
5 °C	0.999968	4 °C	0.999974	3.8 °C	0.999973
10 °C	0.999736	5 °C	0.999968	4.0 °C	0.999974
15 °C	0.999216	6 °C	0.999948	4.2 °C	0.999974
20 °C	0.998464	7 °C	0.999914	4.4 °C	0.999973

ii) Graphical method shown below:

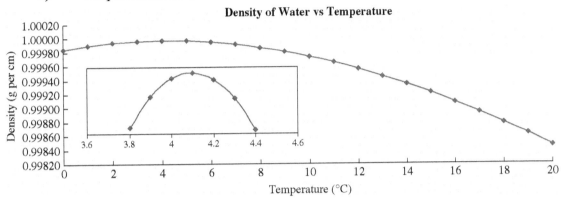

Density of Water vs Temperature

iii) Method based on differential calculus: set the first derivative equal to zero

Set $a = 0.99984$, $b = 1.6945 \times 10^2$, $c = 7.987 \times 10^{-6}$, $d = 1.6880 \times 10^{-2}$ (simplicity)

$$f(t) = \frac{a + bt - ct^2}{1 + dt} \quad f'(t) = \frac{(b - 2ct)(1 + dt) - (a + bt - ct^2)d}{(1 + dt)^2} \quad \text{(quotient rule)}$$

$$f'(t) = \frac{b + bdt - 2ct - 2cdt^2 - ad - bdt + cdt^2}{(1 + dt)^2} = \frac{b - 2ct - cdt^2 - ad}{(1 + dt)^2} = 0 \text{ (max)}$$

We need to set the first derivative = 0, hence consider the numerator = 0

Basically we need to solve a quadratic: $0 = -cdt^2 - 2ct + b - ad$

$$t = \frac{2c \pm \sqrt{(2c)^2 - 4(-cd)(b - ad)}}{-2cd} \quad \text{only the positive solution is acceptable.}$$

Plug in $a = 0.99984$, $b = 1.6945 \times 10^2$, $c = 7.987 \times 10^{-6}$, $d = 1.6880 \times 10^{-2}$

By solving the quadratic equation, one finds that a temperature of 4.09655 °C has the highest density (0.999974 g cm^{-3}). Hence, ~ 4.1 °C is the temperature where water has its maximum density.

84. **(D)** First, calculate the volume of the piece of Styrofoam:

$V = 36.0 \text{ cm} \times 24.0 \text{ cm} \times 5.0 \text{ cm} = 4.32 \times 10^3 \text{ cm}^3$

Calculate the volume of water displaced (using dimensions in the figure):

$V = 36.0 \text{ cm} \times 24.0 \text{ cm} \times 3.0 \text{ cm} = 2.592 \times 10^3 \text{ cm}^3$

The mass of displaced water is given as: $m = d \times V = 1.00 \text{ g/cm}^3 \times 2.592 \times 10^3 \text{ cm}^3$

$= 2.592 \times 10^3 \text{ g}$

Since the object floats, it means that the water is exerting a force equivalent to the mass of Styrofoam/book times the acceleration due to gravity (g). We can factor out g, and are left with masses of Styrofoam and water:

mass of book + mass of Styrofoam = mass of water

$1.5 \times 10^3 \text{ g} + d \times 4.32 \times 10^3 \text{ cm}^3 = 2.592 \times 10^3 \text{ g}$

Solving for d, we obtain:

$d = 0.25 \text{ g/cm}^3$

85. (M) (a) When the mixture is pure benzene, $\%N = 0$, $d = 1/1.153 = 0.867$ g/cm^3
(b) When mixture is pure naphthalene, $\%N = 100$, $d = 1.02$ g/cm^3
(c) $\%N = 1.15$, $d = 0.869$ g/cm^3
(d) Using $d = 0.952$ g/cm^3 and the quadratic formula to solve for $\%N$. $\%N = 58.4$

86. (M) First, calculate the total mass of ice in the Antarctic, which yields the total mass of water which is obtained if all the ice melts:

$$3.01\times10^7 \text{ km}^3 \text{ ice} \times \frac{(1\times10^5 \text{ cm})^3}{1 \text{ km}^3} \times \frac{0.92 \text{ g ice}}{1 \text{ cm}^3 \text{ ice}} = 2.769\times10^{22} \text{ g ice}$$

all of which converts to water. The volume of this extra water is then calculated.

$$2.769\times10^{22} \text{ g H}_2\text{O} \times \frac{1 \text{ cm}^3 \text{ H}_2\text{O}}{1 \text{ g H}_2\text{O}} \times \frac{1 \text{ km}^3 \text{ H}_2\text{O}}{(1\times10^5 \text{ cm})^3 \text{ H}_2\text{O}} = 2.769\times10^7 \text{ km}^3 \text{ H}_2\text{O}$$

Assuming that V (H$_2$O on Earth) $= A \times h = 3.62\times10^8$ km$^2 \times h$, the total increase in the height of sea levels with the addition of the melted continental ice will be:

$$h = 2.769\times10^7 \text{ km}^3 / 3.62\times10^8 \text{ km}^2 = 0.0765 \text{ km} = 76.4 \text{ m.}$$

87. (M) First, calculate the mass of wine: 4.72 kg – 1.70 kg = 3.02 kg
Then, calculate the mass of ethyl alcohol (ethanol) in the bottle:

$$3.02 \text{ kg wine} \times \frac{1000 \text{ g wine}}{1 \text{ kg wine}} \times \frac{11.5 \text{ g ethanol}}{100 \text{ g wine}} = 347.3 \text{ g ethanol}$$

Then, use the above amount to determine how much ethanol is in 250 mL of wine:

$$250.0 \text{ mL ethanol} \times \frac{1 \text{ L ethanol}}{1000 \text{ mL ethanol}} \times \frac{347.3 \text{ g ethanol}}{3.00 \text{ L bottle}} = 28.9 \text{ g ethanol}$$

88. (M) First, determine the total volume of tungsten:

$$\text{vol W} = m/d = \frac{0.0429 \text{ g W}}{19.3 \text{ g/cm}^3} \times \frac{(10 \text{ mm})^3}{1 \text{ cm}^3} = 2.22 \text{ mm}^3 \text{ W}$$

The wire can be viewed as a cylinder. Therefore:
vol cylinder $= A \times h = \pi(d/2)^2 \times h = \pi(d/2)^2 \times (0.200 \text{ m} \times 1000 \text{ mm}/1 \text{ m}) = 2.22 \text{ mm}^3$
Solving for d, we obtain: $d = 0.119$ mm

89. (M) First, determine the amount of ethyl alcohol (ethanol) that will cause a BAC of 0.10%:

$$\text{mass of ethanol} = \frac{0.100 \text{ g ethanol}}{100 \text{ mL of blood}} \times 5400 \text{ mL blood} = 5.4 \text{ g ethanol}$$

This person's body metabolizes alcohol at a rate of 10.0 g/h. Therefore, in 3 hours, this person metabolizes 30.0 g of alcohol. For this individual to have a BAC of 0.10% after 3 hours, he must consume 30.0 + 5.4 = 35.4 g of ethanol.

Now, calculate how many glasses of wine are needed for a total intake of 35.4 g of ethanol:

$$35.4 \text{ g ethanol} \times \frac{100 \text{ g wine}}{11.5 \text{ g eth.}} \times \frac{1 \text{ mL wine}}{1.01 \text{ g wine}} \times \frac{1 \text{ glass wine}}{145 \text{ mL wine}} = 2.1 \text{ glasses of wine}$$

FEATURE PROBLEMS

90. **(M)** All of the pennies minted before 1982 weigh more than 3.00 g, while all of those minted after 1982 weigh less than 2.60 g. It would not be unreasonable to infer that the composition of a penny changed in 1982. In fact, pennies minted prior to 1982 are composed of almost pure copper (about 96% pure). Those minted after 1982 are composed of zinc with a thin copper cladding. Both types of pennies were minted in 1982.

91. **(E)** After sitting in a bathtub that was nearly full and observing the water splashing over the side, Archimedes realized that the crown—when submerged in water—would displace a volume of water equal to its volume. Once Archimedes determined the volume in this way and determined the mass of the crown with a balance, he was able to calculate the crown's density. Since the gold-silver alloy has a different density (it is lower) than pure gold, Archimedes could tell that the crown was not pure gold.

92. **(M)** Notice that the liquid does not fill each of the floating glass balls. The quantity of liquid in each glass ball is sufficient to give each ball a slightly different density. Note that the density of the glass ball is determined by the density of the liquid, the density of the glass (greater than the liquid's density), and the density of the air. Since the density of the liquid in the cylinder varies slightly with temperature—the liquid's volume increases as temperature goes up, but its mass does not change, ergo, different balls will be buoyant at different temperatures.

93. **(M)** The density of the canoe is determined by the density of the concrete and the density of the hollow space inside the canoe, where the passengers sit. It is the hollow space, (filled with air), that makes the density of the canoe less than that of water (1.0 g/cm^3). If the concrete canoe fills with water, it will sink to the bottom, unlike a wooden canoe.

94. **(D)** In sketch (a), the mass of the plastic block appears to be 50.0 g.
In sketch (b), the plastic block is clearly visible on the bottom of a beaker filled with ethanol, showing that it is both insoluble in and more dense than ethanol (i.e., > 0.789 g/cm^3).
In sketch (c), because the plastic block floats on bromoform, the density of the plastic must be less than that for bromoform (i.e., < 2.890 g/cm^3). Moreover, because the block is ~ 40% submerged, the volume of bromoform having the same 50.0 g mass as the block is only about 40% of the volume of the block. Thus, using the expression $V = m/d$, we can write
volume of displaced bromoform ~ $0.40 \times V_{block}$

$$\frac{\text{mass of bromoform}}{\text{density of bromoform}} = \frac{0.40 \times \text{mass of block}}{\text{density of plastic}} = \frac{50.0 \text{ g of bromoform}}{2.890 \frac{\text{g bromoform}}{\text{cm}^3}} = 0.40 \times \frac{50.0 \text{ g of plastic}}{\text{density of plastic}}$$

$$\text{density of plastic} \approx \frac{2.890 \frac{\text{g bromoform}}{\text{cm}^3}}{50.0 \text{ g of bromoform}} \times 0.40 \times 50.0 \text{ g of plastic} \approx 1.16 \frac{\text{g}}{\text{cm}^3}$$

The information provided in sketch (d) provides us with an alternative method for estimating the density of the plastic (use the fact that the density of water is 0.99821 g/cm^3 at 20 °C).

mass of water displaced = 50.0 g – 5.6 g = 44.4 g

$$\text{volume of water displaced} = 44.4 \text{ g} \times \frac{1 \text{ cm}^3}{0.99821 \text{ g}} = 44.5 \text{ cm}^3$$

$$\text{Therefore the density of the plastic} = \frac{mass}{volume} = \frac{50.0 \text{ g}}{44.5 \text{ cm}^3} = 1.12 \frac{\text{g}}{\text{cm}^3}$$

This is reasonably close to the estimate based on the information in sketch (c).

95. **(M)** One needs to convert (lb of force) into (Newtons) 1 lb of force = 1 slug × 1 ft s^{-2}

(1 slug = 14.59 kg). Therefore, 1 lb of force = $\dfrac{14.59 \text{ kg} \cdot 1 \text{ ft}}{1 \text{ s}^2}$

$$= \left(\frac{14.59 \text{ kg} \times 1 \text{ ft}}{1 \text{ s}^2} \right) \left(\frac{12 \text{ in.}}{1 \text{ ft}} \right) \left(\frac{2.54 \text{ cm}}{1 \text{ in.}} \right) \left(\frac{1 \text{ m}}{100 \text{ cm}} \right) = \frac{4.45 \text{ kg} \cdot \text{m}}{1 \text{ s}^2} = 4.45 \text{ Newtons}$$

From this result it is clear that 1 lb of force = 4.45 Newtons.

SELF-ASSESSMENT EXERCISES

96. **(E)** (a) mL: milliliters, is 1/1000 of a liter or the volume of 1 g of H_2O at 25 °C. (b) % by mass: number of grams of a substance in 100 g of a mixture or compound. (c) °C: degrees Celsius, 1/100 of the temperature difference between the freezing and boiling points of water at sea level. (d) density: an intrinsic property of matter expressed as the ratio between a mass of a substance and the volume it occupies. (e) element: matter composed of a single type of atom.

97. **(E)** (a) SI (*le Système International d'Unités*) base units are seven decimal-based measurement systems used to quantify length, mass, time, electric current, temperature, luminous intensity and amount of a substance. (b) Significant figures are an indication of the capability of the measuring device and how precise can the measurement can possibly be. (c) Natural law is the reduction of observed data into a simple mathematical or verbal expression. (d) Exponential notation is a method of expressing numbers as multiples of powers of 10.

98. **(E)** (a) Mass is an intrinsic property of matter, and is determined by the total number of atoms making up the substance. Weight is the acceleration due to gravity imparted on the material, and can change depending on the gravitational field exerted on the material. (b) An intensive property does not depend on the amount of material present (such as density), while an extensive property depends on the amount of material present (such as volume of the sample). (c) Substance in simple terms is any matter with a definite chemical composition, whereas a mixture contains more than one substance. (d) Systematic error is a consistent error inherent to the measurement (such as the scale with an offset), whereas random errors are not consistent and are most likely the result of the observer making mistakes during measurement. (e) A hypothesis is a tentative explanation of a natural law. A theory is a hypothesis that has been supported by experimentation and data.

99. **(E)** (c) an experiment

100. **(E)** The answer is (e), a natural law.

101. **(E)** (c) an element. Mixtures (both homogeneous and heterogeneous) can be separated by physical means. A compound can be decomposed into its elements by chemical means. A pure substance can be an element or a compound, and therefore some pure substances can be decomposed by chemical means.

102. **(E)** The answer is (a), because the gas is fully dissolved in the liquid and remains there until the cap is removed. (b) and (c) are pure substances and therefore not mixtures, and material in a kitchen blender is heterogeneous in appearance.

103. **(E)** The answer is (c), the same. Mass is an intrinsic property of matter, and does not change with varying gravitational fields. Weight, which is acceleration due to gravity, does change.

104. **(E)** (d) $(1.172 - 0.4963)(4.193) = 2.83$ has the correct number of significant figures in the answer. (a) should have 3 significant figures and the answer shows 4. (b) should have 3 significant figures and the answer shows 2. (c) should have 2 significant figures and the answer shows 3.

105. **(E)** (d) and (f).

106. **(E)** The answer is (d). To compare, all values are converted to Kelvins.
Converting (c) 217 °F to K: $T (\text{K}) = ((217 - 32) \times 5/9) + 273 = 376$ K.
Converting (d) 105 °C to K: $105 + 273 = 378$ K.

107. **(M)** The answer is (b). The results are listed as follows: (a) 752 mL H_2O × 1 g/mL = 752 g.
(b) 1050 mL ethanol × 0.789 g/mL = 828 g. (c) 750 g as stated.
(d) (19.20 cm × 19.20 cm × 19.20 cm) balsa wood × 0.11 g/mL = 779 g.

108. **(E)** (a) $475 \text{ g} \left(\dfrac{1 \text{ mL}}{10.5 \text{ g}} \right) = 45.2 \text{ mL}$

109. **(E)** The problem can be solved using dimensional analysis:

(a) g/L: $0.9982 \dfrac{\text{g}}{\text{cm}^3} \times \dfrac{1000 \text{ cm}^3}{1 \text{ L}} = 998.2 \dfrac{\text{g}}{\text{L}}$

(b) kg/m^3: $0.9982 \dfrac{\text{g}}{\text{cm}^3} \times \dfrac{1 \text{ kg}}{1000 \text{ g}} \times \dfrac{(100 \text{ cm})^3}{1 \text{ m}^3} = 998.2 \dfrac{\text{kg}}{\text{m}^3}$

(c) kg/m^3: $0.9982 \dfrac{\text{g}}{\text{cm}^3} \times \dfrac{1 \text{ kg}}{1000 \text{ g}} \times \dfrac{(100 \text{ cm})^3}{1 \text{ m}^3} \times \dfrac{(1000 \text{ m})^3}{1 \text{ km}^3} = 9.982 \times 10^{11} \dfrac{\text{kg}}{\text{km}^3}$

110. **(E)** Student A is more accurate, Student B more precise.

111. (E) The answer is (b). Simply determining the volume from the dimensions (36 cm × 20.2 cm × 0.9 cm, noting that 9 mm = 0.9 cm) gives a volume of 654.48 cm^3. Since one of the dimensions only has one significant figure, the volume is 7×10^2 cm^3.

112. (E) (e), (a), (c), (b), (d), listed in order of increasing significant figures, which indicates an increasing precision in the measurement.

113. (E) The answer is (d). A 10.0 L solution with a density of 1.295 g/mL has a mass of 12,950 g, 30 mass% of which is an iron compound. Since the iron compound is 34.4% by mass iron, the total Fe content is 12950 × 0.300 × 0.344 = Having an iron content of 34.4 % Fe means that the mass is 1336 g or ~1340 g.

114. (M) First, you must determine the volume of copper. To do this, the mass of water displaced by the copper is determined, and the density used to calculate the volume of copper as shown below:

$\Delta m = 25.305 - 22.486 = 2.819$ g, mass of displaced water
Vol. of displaced $H_2O = m/d = 2.819$ g $/ 0.9982$ g·mL$^{-1} = 2.824$ mL or cm^3 = Vol. of Cu

Vol of Cu = 2.824 cm^3 = surf. Area × thickness = 248 cm^2 × x
Solving for x, the value of thickness is therefore 0.0114 cm or 0.114 mm.

115. (E) In short, no, because a pure substance by definition is homogeneous. However, if there are other phases of the same pure substance present (such as pure ice in pure water), we have a heterogeneous mixture from a physical standpoint.

116. (E) (a) Physical change: no change of identity, only of physical state. *Air* is a mixture that later is separated physically. *Pressure* is not a form of matter.
(b) Physical change: separation of a mixture. *Temperature* is not a form of matter. *Liquid air* is a mixture that later is separated physically. *Liquid nitrogen* is an element.
(c) Chemical change: two new substances are produced. *Natural gas* is possibly a mixture, more likely a compound, since it is later used in a reaction. *Steam* and *carbon dioxide* are compounds. *Hydrogen* is an element.
(d) Chemical change: a compound is produced from elements. *Ammonia gas* is a compound.
(e) Physical change: separation of a mixture

117. (M) To construct a concept map, one must first start with the most general concepts. These concepts are defined by or in terms of other more specific concepts discussed in those sections. In this chapter, these concepts are very well categorized by the sections. Looking at sections 1-1 through 1-4, the following general concepts are being discussed: The Scientific Method (1-1), Properties of Matter (1-2) and Measurement of Matter (1-4). The next stage is to consider more specific concepts that derive from the general ones. Classification of Matter (1-3) is a subset of Properties of Matter, because properties are needed to classify matter. Density and Percent Composition (1-5) and Uncertainties in Scientific Measurements (1-6) are both subsets of Measurement of Matter. The subject of Buoyancy would be a subset of (1-5). Significant Figures (1-7) would be a subset of (1-6). Afterwards, link the general and more specific concepts with one or two simple words. Take a look at the subsection headings and problems for more refining of the general and specific concepts.

CHAPTER 2
ATOMS AND THE ATOMIC THEORY
PRACTICE EXAMPLES

1A **(E)** The total mass must be the same before and after reaction.
mass before reaction = 0.382 g magnesium + 2.652 g nitrogen = 3.034 g
mass after reaction = magnesium nitride mass + 2.505 g nitrogen = 3.034 g
magnesium nitride mass = 3.034 g − 2.505 g = 0.529 g magnesium nitride

1B **(E)** Again, the total mass is the same before and after the reaction.
mass before reaction = 7.12 g magnesium + 1.80 g bromine = 8.92 g
mass after reaction = 2.07 g magnesium bromide + magnesium mass = 8.92 g
magnesium mass = 8.92 g − 2.07 g = 6.85 g magnesium

2A **(M)** In Example 2-2 we are told that 0.500 g MgO contains 0.301 g of Mg. With this information, we can determine the mass of magnesium needed to form 2.000 g of magnesium oxide.

$$\text{mass of Mg} = 2.000 \text{ g MgO} \times \frac{0.301 \text{ g Mg}}{0.500 \text{ g MgO}} = 1.20 \text{ g Mg}$$

The remainder of the 2.00 g of magnesium oxide is the mass of oxygen.
mass of oxygen = 2.00 g magnesium oxide − 1.20 g magnesium = 0.80 g oxygen

2B **(M)** In Example 2-2, we see that a 0.500 g sample of MgO has 0.301 g Mg, hence, it must have 0.199 g O_2. From this we see that if we have equal masses of Mg and O_2, the oxygen is in excess. First we find out how many grams of oxygen reacts with 10.00 g of Mg.

$$\text{mass}_{\text{oxygen}} = 10.00 \text{ g Mg} \times \frac{0.199 \text{ g O}_2}{0.301 \text{ g Mg}} = 6.61 \text{ g O}_2 \text{ (used up)}$$

Hence, 10.00 g − 6.61 g = 3.39 g O_2 unreacted. Mg is the limiting reactant.
MgO(s) mass = mass Mg + Mass O_2 = 10.00 g + 6.61 g = 16.61 g MgO.
There are only two substances present, 16.61 g of MgO (product) and 3.39 g of unreacted O_2

3A **(E)** Silver has 47 protons. If the isotope in question has 62 neutrons, then it has a mass number of 109. This can be represented as $^{109}_{47}\text{Ag}$.

3B **(E)** Tin has 50 electrons and 50 protons when neutral, while a neutral cadmium atom has 48 electrons. This means that we are dealing with Sn^{2+}. We do not know how many neutrons tin has. so there can be more than one answer. For instance, $^{116}_{50}\text{Sn}^{2+}$, $^{117}_{50}\text{Sn}^{2+}$, $^{118}_{50}\text{Sn}^{2+}$, $^{119}_{50}\text{Sn}^{2+}$, and $^{120}_{50}\text{Sn}^{2+}$ are all possible answers.

4A **(E)** The ratio of the masses of ^{202}Hg and ^{12}C is: $\dfrac{^{202}\text{Hg}}{^{12}\text{C}} = \dfrac{201.97062 \text{ u}}{12 \text{ u}} = 16.830885$

4B **(E)** Atomic mass is 12 u × 13.16034 = 157.9241 u. The isotope is $^{158}_{64}$Gd. Using an atomic mass of 15.9949 u for ^{16}O, the mass of $^{158}_{64}$Gd relative to ^{16}O is

$$\text{relative mass to oxygen-16} = \frac{157.9241 \text{ u}}{15.9949 \text{ u}} = 9.87340$$

5A **(E)** The atomic mass of boron is 10.81, which is closer to 11.0093054 than to 10.0129370. Thus, boron-11 is the isotope that is present in greater abundance.

5B **(E)** The average atomic mass of indium is 114.82, and one isotope is known to be ^{113}In. Since the weighted-average atomic mass is almost 115, the second isotope must be larger than both In-113 and In-114. Clearly, then, the second isotope must be In-115 (^{115}In). Since the average atomic mass of indium is closest to the mass of the second isotope, In-115, then ^{115}In is the more abundant isotope.

6A **(M)** Weighted-average atomic mass of Si =

$$(27.9769265325 \text{ u} \times 0.9223) \rightarrow 25.8\underline{0} \text{ u}$$
$$(28.976494700 \text{ u} \times 0.04685) \rightarrow 1.35\underline{8} \text{ u}$$
$$\underline{(29.973377017 \text{ u} \times 0.03092) \rightarrow 0.9268 \text{ u}}$$
$$28.08\underline{48} \text{ u}$$

We should report the weighted-average atomic mass of Si as 28.08 u.

6B **(M)** We let x be the fractional abundance of lithium-6.

$$6.941 \text{ u} = [x \times 6.01512 \text{ u}] + [(1-x) \times 7.01600 \text{ u}] = x \times 6.01512 \text{ u} + 7.01600 \text{ u} - x \times 7.01600 \text{ u}$$

$$6.941 \text{ u} - 7.01600 \text{ u} = x \times 6.01512 \text{ u} - x \times 7.01600 \text{ u} = -x \times 1.00088 \text{ u}$$

$$x = \frac{6.941 \text{ u} - 7.01600 \text{ u}}{-1.00088 \text{ u}} = 0.075 \text{ Percent isotopic abundances}: 7.5\% \text{ lithium-6}, \ 92.5\% \text{ lithium-7}$$

7A **(M)** We assume that atoms lose or gain relatively few electrons to become ions. Thus, elements that will form cations will be on the left-hand side of the periodic table, while elements that will form anions will be on the right-hand side. The number of electrons "lost" when a cation forms is usually equal to the last digit of the periodic group number; the number of electrons added when an anion forms is typically eight minus the last digit of the group number.

Li is in group 1(1A); it should form a cation by losing one electron: Li^+.
S is in group 6(6A); it should form an anion by adding two electrons: S^{2-}.
Ra is in group 2(2A); it should form a cation by losing two electrons: Ra^{2+}.
F and I are both group 17(7A); they should form anions by gaining an electron: F^- and I^-.
Al is in group 13(3A); it should form a cation by losing three electrons: Al^{3+}.

7B **(M)** Main-group elements are in the "A" families, while transition elements are in the "B" families. Metals, nonmetals, metalloids, and noble gases are color coded in the periodic table inside the front cover of the textbook.

Na is a main-group metal in group 1(1A).	Re is a transition metal in group 7(7B).
S is a main-group nonmetal in group 16(6A).	I is a main-group nonmetal in group 17(7A).
Kr is a nonmetal in group 18(8A).	Mg is a main-group metal in group 2(2A).
U is an inner transition metal, an actinide.	Si is a main-group metalloid in group 14(4A).
B is a metalloid in group 13(3A).	Al is a main-group metal in group 13(3A).
As is a main-group metalloid in group 15(5A).	H is a main-group nonmetal in group 1(1A). (H is believed to be a metal at extremely high pressures.)

8A **(E)** This is similar to Practice Examples 2-8A and 2-8B.

$$\text{Cu mass} = 2.35 \times 10^{24} \text{ Cu atoms} \times \frac{1 \text{ mol Cu}}{6.022 \times 10^{23} \text{ atoms}} \times \frac{63.546 \text{ g Cu}}{1 \text{ mol Cu}} = 248 \text{ g Cu}$$

8B **(M)** Of all lead atoms, 24.1% are lead-206, or 241 ^{206}Pb atoms in every 1000 lead atoms. First we need to convert a 22.6 gram sample of lead into moles of lead (below) and then, by using Avogadro's constant, and the percent isotopic abundance, we can determine the number of ^{206}Pb atoms.

$$n_{Pb} = 22.6 \text{ g Pb} \times \frac{1 \text{ mol Pb}}{207.2 \text{ g Pb}} = 0.109 \text{ mol Pb}$$

$$^{206}\text{Pb atoms} = 0.109 \text{ mol Pb} \times \frac{6.022 \times 10^{23} \text{ Pb atoms}}{1 \text{ mol Pb}} \times \frac{241 \ ^{206}\text{Pb atoms}}{1000 \text{ Pb atoms}} = 1.58 \times 10^{22} \ ^{206}\text{Pb atoms}$$

9A **(M)** Both the density and the molar mass of Pb serve as conversion factors.

$$\text{atoms of Pb} = 0.105 \text{ cm}^3 \text{ Pb} \times \frac{11.34 \text{ g}}{1 \text{ cm}^3} \times \frac{1 \text{ mol Pb}}{207.2 \text{ g}} \times \frac{6.022 \times 10^{23} \text{ Pb atoms}}{1 \text{ mol Pb}} = 3.46 \times 10^{21} \text{ Pb atoms}$$

9B **(M)** First we find the number of rhenium atoms in 0.100 mg of the element.

$$0.100 \text{ mg} \times \frac{1 \text{ g}}{1000 \text{ mg}} \times \frac{1 \text{ mol Re}}{186.21 \text{ g Re}} \times \frac{6.022 \times 10^{23} \text{ Re atoms}}{1 \text{ mol Re}} = 3.23 \times 10^{17} \text{ Re atoms}$$

$$\% \text{ abundance } ^{187}\text{Re} = \frac{2.02 \times 10^{17} \text{ atoms } ^{187}\text{Re}}{3.23 \times 10^{17} \text{ Re atoms}} \times 100\% = 62.5\%$$

INTEGRATIVE EXAMPLE

A. **(M)**

Stepwise approach:

First, determine the total number of Cu atoms in the crystal by determining the volume of the crystal and calculating the mass of Cu from density. Then we can determine the amount of ^{63}Cu by noting its relative abundance

$$\text{Volume of crystal} = (25 \text{ nm})^3 \times \frac{1 \text{ cm}^3}{(1 \times 10^7 \text{ nm})^3} = 1.5625 \times 10^{-17} \text{ cm}^3$$

$$\text{Mass of Cu in crystal} = d \cdot V = 8.92 \text{ g/cm}^3 \times 1.5625 \times 10^{-17} = 1.3938 \times 10^{-16} \text{ g}$$

\# of Cu atoms =

$$1.3938 \times 10^{-16} \text{ g Cu} \times \frac{1 \text{ mol Cu}}{63.546 \text{ g Cu}} \times \frac{6.022 \times 10^{23} \text{ Cu atoms}}{1 \text{ mol Cu}} = 1.3208 \times 10^6 \text{ Cu atoms}$$

Therefore, the number of ^{63}Cu atoms, assuming 69.17% abundance, is 9.14×10^5 atoms.

Conversion pathway approach:

$$\frac{8.92 \text{ g Cu}}{1 \text{ cm}^3} \times \frac{1 \text{ cm}^3}{(1 \times 10^7 \text{ nm})^3} \times \frac{(25 \text{ nm})^3}{\text{crystal}} \times \frac{1 \text{ mol Cu}}{63.546 \text{ g Cu}} \times \frac{6.022 \times 10^{23} \text{ Cu atoms}}{1 \text{ mol Cu}}$$

$$\times \frac{69.17 \text{ atoms of } ^{63}\text{Cu}}{100 \text{ Cu atoms}} = 9.14 \times 10^5 \text{ atoms of } ^{63}\text{Cu}$$

B. **(M)**

Stepwise approach:

Calculate the mass of Fe in a serving of cereal, determine mass of ^{58}Fe in that amount of cereal, and determine how many servings of cereal are needed to reach 58 g of ^{58}Fe.

Amount of Fe in a serving of cereal = 18 mg × 0.45 = 8.1 mg Fe per serving

First calculate the amount of Fe

$$0.0081 \text{ g Fe} \times \frac{1 \text{ mol Fe}}{55.845 \text{ g Fe}} = 1.45 \times 10^{-4} \text{ mol Fe}$$

Then calculate ^{58}Fe amount:

$$1.45 \times 10^{-4} \text{ mol Fe} \times \frac{0.282 \text{ mol } ^{58}\text{Fe}}{100 \text{ mol Fe}} = 4.090 \times 10^{-7} \text{ mol } ^{58}\text{Fe}$$

Converting mol of ^{58}F to # of servings:

$$\frac{4.090 \times 10^{-7}\, mol\; ^{58}Fe}{1\, serving} \times \frac{57.9333\, g\; ^{58}Fe}{1\, mol\; ^{58}Fe} = 2.37 \times 10^{-5}\, g\; ^{58}Fe\; per\; serving$$

Total # of servings = 58 g total / 2.37×10^{-5} per serving = 2.4477×10^{6} servings

Conversion Pathway Approach:

The number of servings of dry cereal to ingest 58 g of ^{58}Fe =

$$58.0\, g\; ^{58}Fe \times \frac{1\, mol\; ^{58}Fe}{57.9333\, g\; ^{58}Fe} \times \frac{100\, mol\; Fe}{0.282\, mol\; ^{58}Fe} \times \frac{58.845\, g\; Fe}{1\, mol\; Fe} \times \frac{1\, cereal\; serving}{0.018\, g\; Fe \times 0.45}$$

$$= 2.4477 \times 10^{6}\, servings$$

$$2.44477 \times 10^{6}\, servings \times \frac{1\, year}{365\, servings} = 6706\, years$$

EXERCISES

Law of Conservation of Mass

1. **(E)** The observations cited do not necessarily violate the law of conservation of mass. The oxide formed when iron rusts is a solid and remains with the solid iron, increasing the mass of the solid by an amount equal to the mass of the oxygen that has combined. The oxide formed when a match burns is a gas and will not remain with the solid product (the ash); the mass of the ash thus is less than that of the match. We would have to collect all reactants and all products and weigh them to determine if the law of conservation of mass is obeyed or violated.

2. **(E)** The magnesium that is burned in air combines with some of the oxygen in the air and this oxygen (which, of course, was not weighed when the magnesium metal was weighed) adds its mass to the mass of the magnesium, making the magnesium oxide product weigh more than did the original magnesium. When this same reaction is carried out in a flashbulb, the oxygen (in fact, some excess oxygen) that will combine with the magnesium is already present in the bulb before the reaction. Consequently, the product contains no unweighed oxygen.

3. **(E)** By the law of conservation of mass, all of the magnesium initially present and all of the oxygen that reacted are present in the product. Thus, the mass of oxygen that has reacted is obtained by difference. mass of oxygen = 0.674 g MgO − 0.406 g Mg = 0.268 g oxygen

4. **(E)** Reaction: $2\, K(s) + Cl_2(g) \rightarrow 2\, KCl(s)$
Mass of Cl_2 reacted = 8.178 g − 6.867 g = 1.311 g $Cl_2(g)$

$$m_{KCl} = 1.311\, g\; Cl_2 \times \frac{1\, mol\; Cl_2}{70.90\, g\; Cl_2} \times \frac{2\, mol\; KCl}{1\, mol\; Cl_2} \times \frac{74.55\, g\; KCl}{1\, mol\; KCl} = 2.757\, g\; KCl$$

5. **(M)** We need to compare the mass before reaction (initial) with that after reaction (final) to answer this question.

initial mass = 10.500 g calcium hydroxide + 11.125 g ammonium chloride = 21.625 g

final mass = 14.336 g solid residue + (69.605 – 62.316) g of gases = 21.625 g

These data support the law of conservation of mass. Note that the gain in the mass of water is equal to the mass of gas absorbed by the water.

6. **(M)** We compute the mass of the reactants and compare that with the mass of the products to answer this question.

reactant mass = mass of calcium carbonate + mass of hydrochloric acid solution

$$= 10.00 \text{ g calcium carbonate} + 100.0 \text{ mL soln} \times \frac{1.148 \text{ g}}{1 \text{ mL soln}}$$

$$= 10.00 \text{ g calcium carbonate} + 114.8 \text{ g solution} \ = 124.8 \text{ g reactants}$$

product mass = mass of solution + mass of carbon dioxide

$$= 120.40 \text{ g soln} + 2.22 \text{ L gas} \times \frac{1.9769 \text{ g}}{1 \text{ L gas}}$$

$$= 120.40 \text{ g soln} + 4.39 \text{ g carbon dioxide}$$

$$= 124.79 \text{ g products} \left(\begin{array}{l} \text{The same mass within experimental error,} \\ \text{thus, the law of conservation of mass obeyed.} \end{array} \right)$$

Law of Constant Composition

7. **(E)**

(a) Ratio of O: MgO by mass $= \dfrac{(0.755 - 0.455) \text{ g}}{0.755 \text{ g}} = 0.397$

(b) Ratio of O: Mg in MgO by mass $= \dfrac{0.300 \text{ g}}{0.455 \text{ g}} = 0.659$

(c) Percent magnesium by mass $= \dfrac{0.455 \text{ g Mg}}{0.755 \text{ g MgO}} \times 100\% = 60.3\%$

8. **(M)**

(a) We can determine that carbon dioxide has a fixed composition by finding the % C in each sample. (In the calculations below, the abbreviation "cmpd" is short for compound.)

$$\%C = \frac{3.62 \text{ g C}}{13.26 \text{ g cmpd}} \times 100\% = 27.3\% \text{ C} \qquad \%C = \frac{5.91 \text{ g C}}{21.66 \text{ g cmpd}} \times 100\% = 27.3\% \text{ C}$$

$$\%C = \frac{7.07 \text{ g C}}{25.91 \text{ g cmpd}} \times 100\% = 27.3\% \text{ C}$$

Since all three samples have the same percent of carbon, these data do establish that carbon dioxide has a fixed composition.

(b) Carbon dioxide contains only carbon and oxygen. As determined in (a), carbon dioxide is 27.3% C by mass. The percent of oxygen in carbon dioxide is obtained by difference. %O = 100.0 % – (27.3 %C) = 72.7 %O

9. **(M)** In the first experiment, 2.18 g of sodium produces 5.54 g of sodium chloride. In the second experiment, 2.10 g of chlorine produces 3.46 g of sodium chloride. The amount of sodium contained in this second sample of sodium chloride is given by

mass of sodium = 3.46 g sodium chloride − 2.10 g chlorine = 1.36 g sodium.

We now have sufficient information to determine the % Na in each of the samples of sodium chloride.

$$\%Na = \frac{2.18\,g\,Na}{5.54\,g\,cmpd} \times 100\% = 39.4\%\,Na \qquad \%Na = \frac{1.36\,g\,Na}{3.46\,g\,cmpd} \times 100\% = 39.3\%\,Na$$

Thus, the two samples of sodium chloride have the same composition. Recognize that, based on significant figures, each percent has an uncertainty of ±0.1%.

10. **(E)** If the two samples of water have the same % H, the law of constant composition is demonstrated. Notice that, in the second experiment, the mass of the compound is equal to the sum of the masses of the elements produced from it.

$$\%H = \frac{3.06\ g\ H}{27.35\,g\,H_2O} \times 100\% = 11.2\%\,H \qquad \%H = \frac{1.45\ g\ H}{(1.45+11.51)\,g\,H_2O} \times 100\% = 11.2\%\,H$$

Thus, the results are consistent with the law of constant composition.

11. **(E)** The mass of sulfur (0.312 g) needed to produce 0.623 g sulfur dioxide provides the information required for the conversion factor.

$$sulfur\ mass = 0.842\,g\ sulfur\ dioxide \times \frac{0.312\,g\ sulfur}{0.623\,g\ sulfur\ dioxide} = 0.422\,g\ sulfur$$

12. **(M)**
(a) From the first experiment we see that 1.16 g of compound is produced per gram of Hg. These masses enable us to determine the mass of compound produced from 1.50 g Hg.

$$mass\ of\ cmpd = 1.50\,g\ Hg \times \frac{1.16\,g\ cmpd}{1.00\,g\ Hg} = 1.74\,g\ cmpd$$

(b) Since the compound weighs 0.24 g more than the mass of mercury (1.50 g) that was used, 0.24 g of sulfur must have reacted. Thus, the unreacted sulfur has a mass of 0.76 g (= 1.00 g initially present − 0.24 g reacted).

Law of Multiple Proportions

13. **(M)** By dividing the mass of the oxygen per gram of sulfur in the second sulfur-oxygen compound (compound 2) by the mass of oxygen per gram of sulfur in the first sulfur-oxygen compound (compound 1), we obtain the ratio (shown to the right):

$$\dfrac{\dfrac{1.497 \text{ g of O}}{1.000 \text{ g of S}} \ (\text{cmpd 2})}{\dfrac{0.998 \text{ g of O}}{1.000 \text{ g of S}} \ (\text{cmpd 1})} = \dfrac{1.500}{1}$$

To get the simplest whole number ratio we need to multiply both the numerator and the denominator by 2. This gives the simple whole number ratio 3/2. In other words, for a given mass of sulfur, the mass of oxygen in the second compound (SO_3) relative to the mass of oxygen in the first compound (SO_2) is in a ratio of 3:2. These results are entirely consistent with the Law of Multiple Proportions because the same two elements, sulfur and oxygen in this case, have reacted together to give <u>two</u> different compounds that have masses of oxygen that are in the ratio of small positive integers for a fixed amount of sulfur.

14. **(M)** This question is similar to question 13 in that two elements, phosphorus and chlorine in this case, have combined to give <u>two</u> different compounds. This time, however, different masses have been used for <u>both</u> of the elements in the second compound. To see if the Law of Multiple Proportions is being followed, the mass of one of the two elements must be set to the same value in both compounds. This can be achieved by dividing the masses of both phosphorus and chlorine in reaction 2 by 2.500:

"normalized" mass of phosphorus = $\dfrac{2.500 \text{ g phosphorus}}{2.500} = 1.000$ g of phosphorus

"normalized" mass of chlorine = $\dfrac{14.308 \text{ g chlorine}}{2.500} = 5.723$ g of chlorine

Now the mass of phosphorus for both reactions is <u>fixed</u> at 1.000 g. Next, we will divide each amount of chlorine by the fixed mass of phosphorus with which they are combined. This gives

$$\dfrac{\dfrac{3.433 \text{ g of Cl}}{1.000 \text{ g P}} \ (\text{cmpd 1})}{\dfrac{5.723 \text{ g of Cl}}{1.000 \text{ g P}} \ (\text{cmpd 2})} = 0.600 = 6:10 \text{ or } 3:5$$

15. **(M)**

(a) First of all we need to fix the mass of nitrogen in all three compounds to some common value, for example, 1.000 g. This can be accomplished by multiplying the masses of hydrogen and nitrogen in compound A by 2 and the amount of hydrogen and nitrogen in compound C by 4/3 (1.333):

Cmpd A "normalized" mass of nitrogen $= 0.500 \text{ g N} \times 2 = 1.000 \text{ g N}$
           "normalized" mass of hydrogen $= 0.108 \text{ g H} \times 2 = 0.216 \text{ g H}$

Cmpd C "normalized" mass of nitrogen $= 0.750 \text{ g N} \times 1.333 = 1.000 \text{ g N}$
           "normalized" mass of hydrogen $= 0.108 \text{ g H} \times 1.333 = 0.144 \text{ g H}$

Next, we divide the mass of hydrogen in each compound by the smallest mass of hydrogen, namely, 0.0720 g. This gives 3.000 for compound A, 1.000 for compound B, and 2.000 for compound C. The ratio of the amounts of hydrogen in the three compounds is 3 (cmpd A) : 1 (cmpd B) : 2 (cmpd C)

These results are consistent with the Law of Multiple Proportions because the masses of hydrogen in the three compounds end up in a ratio of small whole numbers when the mass of nitrogen in all three compounds is normalized to a simple value (1.000 g here).

(b) The text states that compound B is N_2H_2. This means that, based on the relative amounts of hydrogen calculated in part (a), compound A might be N_2H_6 and compound C, N_2H_4. Actually, compound A is NH_3, but we have no way of knowing this from the data. Note that the H:N ratios in NH_3 and N_2H_6 are the same, 3H:1N.

16. (M)

(a) As with the previous problem, one of the two elements must have the same mass in all of the compounds. This can be most readily achieved by setting the mass of iodine in all four compounds to 1.000 g. With this approach we only need to manipulate the data for compounds B and C. To normalize the amount of iodine in compound B to 1.000 g, we need to multiply the masses of both iodine and fluorine by 2. To accomplish the analogous normalization of compound C, we must multiply by 4/3 (1.333).

Cmpd B: "normalized" mass of iodine   = 0. 500 g I   × 2   = 1.000 g I
        "normalized" mass of fluorine = 0.2246 g F × 2   = 0.4492 g F

Cmpd C: "normalized" mass of iodine   = 0.750 g I   × 1.333 = 1.000 g I
        "normalized" mass of fluorine = 0.5614 g F × 1.333 = 0.7485 g F

Next we divide the mass of fluorine in each compound by the smallest mass of fluorine, namely, 0.1497 g. This gives 1.000 for compound A, 3.001 for compound B, 5.000 for compound C, and 7.001 for compound D. The ratios of the amounts of fluorine in the four compounds A : B : C : D is 1 : 3 : 5 : 7. These results are consistent with the law of multiple proportions because for a fixed amount of iodine (1.000 g), the masses of fluorine in the four compounds are in the ratio of small whole numbers.

(b) As with the preceding problem, we can figure out the empirical formulas for the four iodine-fluorine containing compounds from the ratios of the amounts of fluorine that were determined in 16(a): Cmpd A: IF   Cmpd B: IF_3 Cmpd C: IF_5 Cmpd D: IF_7

17. **(M)** One oxide of copper has about 20% oxygen by mass. If we assume a 100 gram sample, then ~ 20 grams of the sample is oxygen (~1.25 moles) and 80 grams is copper (~1.26 moles). This would give an empirical formula of CuO (copper(II) oxide). The second oxide has less oxygen by mass, hence the empirical formula must have less oxygen or more copper (Cu:O ratio greater than 1). If we keep whole number ratios of atoms, a plausible formula would be Cu_2O (copper(I) oxide), where the mass percent oxygen is $\approx 11\%$.

18. **(M)** Assuming the intermediate is "half-way" between CO (oxygen-carbon mass ratio = 16:12 or 1.333) and CO_2 (oxygen-carbon mass ratio = 32:12 or 2.6667), then the oxygen- carbon ratio would be 2:1, or O:C = 24:12. This mass ratio gives a mole ratio of O:C = 1.5:1. Empirical formulas are simple whole number ratios of elements; hence, a formula of C_3O_2 must be the correct empirical formula for this carbon oxide. (Note: C_3O_2 is called tricarbon dioxide or carbon suboxide).

Fundamental Charges and Mass-to-Charge Ratios

19. **(M)** We can calculate the charge on each drop, express each in terms of 10^{-19} C, and finally express each in terms of $e = 1.6 \times 10^{-19}$ C.

drop 1: $\quad 1.28 \times 10^{-18}$ $\qquad\qquad\qquad = 12.8 \times 10^{-19}\,C \quad = 8e$

drops 2 & 3: $1.28 \times 10^{-18} \div 2 = 0.640 \times 10^{-18}\,C = 6.40 \times 10^{-19}\,C \quad = 4e$

drop 4: $\quad 1.28 \times 10^{-18} \div 8 = 0.160 \times 10^{-18}\,C = 1.60 \times 10^{-19}\,C \quad = 1e$

drop 5: $\quad 1.28 \times 10^{-18} \times 4 = 5.12 \times 10^{-18}\,C \quad = 51.2 \times 10^{-19}\,C \quad = 32e$

We see that these values are consistent with the charge that Millikan found for that of the electron, and he could have inferred the correct charge from these data, since they are all multiples of e.

20. **(M)** We calculate each drop's charge, express each in terms of 10^{-19} C, and then, express each in terms of $e = 1.6 \times 10^{-19}$ C.

drop 1: $6.41 \times 10^{-19}\,C \qquad = 6.41 \times 10^{-19}\,C \qquad\qquad\qquad\quad = 4e$

drop 2: $6.41 \times 10^{-19} \div 2 \quad = 3.21 \times 10^{-19}\,C \quad = 3.21 \times 10^{-19}\,C \quad = 2e$

drop 3: $6.41 \times 10^{-19} \times 2 \quad = 1.28 \times 10^{-18}\,C \quad = 12.8 \times 10^{-19}\,C \quad = 8e$

drop 4: $1.44 \times 10^{-18} \qquad\quad = 14.4 \times 10^{-19}\,C \qquad\qquad\qquad = 9e$

drop 5: $1.44 \times 10^{-18} \div 3 \quad = 4.8 \times 10^{-19}\,C \quad = 4.8 \times 10^{-19}\,C \quad = 3e$

We see that these values are consistent with the charge that Millikan found for that of the electron. He could have inferred the correct charge from these values, since they are all multiples of e, and have no other common factor.

21. **(M)**
    (a) Determine the ratio of the mass of a hydrogen atom to that of an electron. We use the mass of a proton plus that of an electron for the mass of a hydrogen atom.

$$\frac{\text{mass of proton} + \text{mass of electron}}{\text{mass of electron}} = \frac{1.0073\,u + 0.00055\,u}{0.00055\,u} = 1.8 \times 10^3$$

$$or \qquad \frac{\text{mass of electron}}{\text{mass of proton} + \text{mass of electron}} = \frac{1}{1.8 \times 10^3} = 5.6 \times 10^{-4}$$

(b) The only two mass-to-charge ratios that we can determine from the data in Table 2-1 are those for the proton (a hydrogen ion, H^+) and the electron.

For the proton : $\dfrac{\text{mass}}{\text{charge}} = \dfrac{1.673 \times 10^{-24}\,\text{g}}{1.602 \times 10^{-19}\,\text{C}} = 1.044 \times 10^{-5}\,\text{g/C}$

For the electron : $\dfrac{\text{mass}}{\text{charge}} = \dfrac{9.109 \times 10^{-28}\,\text{g}}{1.602 \times 10^{-19}\,\text{C}} = 5.686 \times 10^{-9}\,\text{g/C}$

The hydrogen ion is the lightest positive ion available. We see that the mass-to-charge ratio for a positive particle is considerably larger than that for an electron.

22. **(M)** We do not have the precise isotopic masses for the two ions. The values of the mass-to-charge ratios are only approximate. This is because some of the mass is converted to energy (binding energy), that holds all of the positively charged protons in the nucleus together. Consequently, we have used a three-significant-figure mass for a nucleon, rather than the more precisely known proton and neutron masses. (Recall that the term "nucleon" refers to a nuclear particle— either a proton or a neutron.)

$^{127}I^-$ $\dfrac{m}{e} = \dfrac{127\text{ nucleons}}{1\text{ electron}} \times \dfrac{1\text{ electron}}{1.602 \times 10^{-19}\,\text{C}} \times \dfrac{1.67 \times 10^{-24}\,\text{g}}{1\text{ nucleon}} = 1.32 \times 10^{-3}\,\text{g/C}$ $(7.55 \times 10^2\,\text{C/g})$

$^{32}S^{2-}$ $\dfrac{m}{e} = \dfrac{32\text{ nucleons}}{2\text{ electrons}} \times \dfrac{1\text{ electron}}{1.602 \times 10^{-19}\,\text{C}} \times \dfrac{1.67 \times 10^{-24}\,\text{g}}{1\text{ nucleon}} = 1.67 \times 10^{-4}\,\text{g/C}$ $(6.00 \times 10^3\,\text{C/g})$

Atomic Number, Mass Number, and Isotopes

23. **(E) (a)** cobalt-60 $^{60}_{27}\text{Co}$ **(b)** phosphorus-32 $^{32}_{15}\text{P}$ **(c)** iron-59 $^{59}_{26}\text{Fe}$ **(d)** radium-226 $^{226}_{88}\text{Ra}$

24. **(E)** The nucleus of $^{202}_{80}\text{Hg}$ contains 80 protons and $(202 - 80) = 122$ neutrons. Thus, the percent of nucleons that are neutrons is given by

$\%\text{ neutrons} = \dfrac{122\text{ neutrons}}{202\text{ nucleons}} \times 100 = 60.4\%\text{ neutrons}$

25.

Name	Symbol	Number of Protons	Number of Electrons	Number of Neutrons	Mass Number
(E) Sodium	$^{23}_{11}\text{Na}$	11	11	12	23
Silicon	$^{28}_{14}\text{Si}$	14	14[a]	14	28
Rubidium	$^{85}_{37}\text{Rb}$	37	37[a]	48	85
Potassium	$^{40}_{19}\text{K}$	19	19	21	40
Arsenic[a]	$^{75}_{33}\text{As}$	33[a]	33	42	75
Neon	$^{20}_{10}\text{Ne}^{2+}$	10	8	10	20
Bromine[b]	$^{80}_{35}\text{Br}$	35	35	45	80
Lead[b]	$^{208}_{82}\text{Pb}$	82	82	126	208

^{a} This result assumes that a neutral atom is involved.

^{b} Insufficient data. Does not characterize a specific nuclide; several possibilities exist. The minimum information needed is the atomic number (or some way to obtain it, such as from the name or the symbol of the element involved), the number of electrons (or some way to obtain it, such as the charge on the species), and the mass number (or the number of neutrons).

26. (E)

   (a) Since all of these species are neutral atoms, the numbers of electrons are the atomic numbers, the subscript numbers. The symbols must be arranged in order of increasing value of these subscripts. $^{40}_{18}Ar < ^{39}_{19}K < ^{58}_{27}Co < ^{59}_{29}Cu < ^{120}_{48}Cd < ^{112}_{50}Sn < ^{122}_{52}Te$

   (b) The number of neutrons is given by the difference between the mass number and the atomic number, $A-Z$. This is the difference between superscripted and subscripted values and is provided (in parentheses) after each element in the following list.
$^{39}_{19}K(20) < ^{40}_{18}Ar(22) < ^{59}_{29}Cu(30) < ^{58}_{27}Co(31) < ^{112}_{50}Sn(62) < ^{122}_{52}Te(70) < ^{120}_{48}Cd(72)$

   (c) Here the nuclides are arranged by increasing mass number, given by the superscripts.
$^{39}_{19}K < ^{40}_{18}Ar < ^{58}_{27}Co < ^{59}_{29}Cu < ^{112}_{50}Sn < ^{120}_{48}Cd < ^{122}_{52}Te$

27. (E)

   (a) A ^{108}Pd atom has 46 protons and 46 electrons. The atom described is neutral, hence, the number of electrons must equal the number of protons.

      Since there are 108 nucleons in the nucleus, the number of neutrons is 62 ($=108$ nucleons -46 protons).

   (b) The ratio of the two masses is determined as follows: $\dfrac{^{108}Pd}{^{12}C} = \dfrac{107.90389\,u}{12\,u} = 8.9919908$

28. (E)

   (a) The atomic number of Ra is 88 and equals the number of protons in the nucleus. The ion's charge is +2 and, thus, there are two more protons than electrons: no. protons = no. electrons $+ 2 = 88$; no. electrons $= 88 - 2 = 86$. The mass number (228) is the sum of the atomic number and the number of neutrons: $228 = 88 +$ no. neutrons; Hence, the number of neutrons $= 228 - 88 = 140$ neutrons.

   (b) The mass of ^{16}O is 15.9949 u.   ratio $= \dfrac{\text{mass of isotope}}{\text{mass of }^{16}O} = \dfrac{228.030\,u}{15.9949\,u} = 14.2564$

29. (E) The mass of ^{16}O is 15.9949 u.   isotopic mass $= 15.9949\,u \times 6.68374 = 106.936\,u$

30. **(E)** The mass of ^{16}O is 15.9949 u.

mass of heavier isotope $= 15.9949\,u \times 7.1838 = 114.90\underline{4}\,u = $ mass of ^{115}In

mass of lighter isotope $= \dfrac{114.90\underline{4}\,u}{1.0177} = 112.91\,u = $ mass of ^{113}In

31. **(E)** Each isotopic mass must be divided by the isotopic mass of ^{12}C, 12 u, an exact number.

(a) $^{35}Cl \div {}^{12}C = 34.96885\,u \div 12\,u = 2.914071$

(b) $^{26}Mg \div {}^{12}C = 25.98259\,u \div 12\,u = 2.165216$

(c) $^{222}Rn \div {}^{12}C = 222.0175\,u \div 12\,u = 18.50146$

32. **(M)** We need to work through the mass ratios in sequence to determine the mass of ^{81}Br.

mass of $^{19}F = $ mass of $^{12}C \times 1.5832 = 12\,u \times 1.5832 = 18.998\,u$

mass of $^{35}Cl = $ mass of $^{19}F \times 1.8406 = 18.998\,u \times 1.8406 = 34.968\,u$

mass of $^{81}Br = $ mass of $^{35}Cl \times 2.3140 = 34.968\,u \times 2.3140 = 80.916\,u$

33. **(E)** First, we determine the number of protons, neutrons, and electrons in each species.

species:	$^{24}_{12}Mg^{2+}$	$^{47}_{24}Cr$	$^{60}_{27}Co^{3+}$	$^{35}_{17}Cl^{-}$	$^{124}_{50}Sn^{2+}$	$^{226}_{90}Th$	$^{90}_{38}Sr$
protons:	12	24	27	17	50	90	38
neutrons:	12	23	33	18	74	136	52
electrons:	10	24	24	18	48	90	38

(a) The numbers of neutrons and electrons are equal for $^{35}_{17}Cl^{-}$.

(b) $^{60}_{27}Co^{3+}$ has protons (27), neutrons (33), and electrons (24) in the ratio 9:11:8.

(c) The species $^{124}_{50}Sn^{2+}$ has a number of neutrons (74) equal to its number of protons (50) plus one-half its number of electrons $(48 \div 2 = 24)$.

34. **(a)** Atoms with equal numbers of protons and neutrons will have mass numbers that are approximately twice the size of their atomic numbers. The following species are approximately suitable (with numbers of protons and neutrons in parentheses).

$^{24}_{12}Mg^{2+}$ (12 p$^+$, 12 n), $^{47}_{24}Cr$ (24 p$^+$, 23 n), $^{60}_{27}Co^{3+}$ (27 p$^+$, 33 n), and $^{35}_{17}Cl^{-}$ (17 p$^+$, 18 n). Of these four nuclides, only $^{24}_{12}Mg^{2+}$ has equal numbers of protons and neutrons.

(b) A species in which protons have more than 50% of the mass must have a mass number smaller than twice the atomic number. Of these species, only in $^{47}_{24}Cr$ is more than 50% of the mass contributed by the protons.

(c) A species with about 50% more neutrons than protons will have a mass number that is at least 2.5 times greater than the atomic number. Only $^{226}_{90}Th$ has >50% more neutrons than protons (number of neutrons $= 226 - 90 = 136$; number of protons $= 90$; $90 \times 1.5 = 135$, less than the total number of neutrons). ^{124}Sn is close, having 74 neutrons, and 50 protons, so $50 \times 1.5 = 75$, slightly less than 50%.

35. **(E)**

If we let n represent the number of neutrons and p represent the number of protons, then $p + 4 = n$. The mass number is the sum of the number of protons and the number of neutrons: $p + n = 44$. Substitution of $n = p + 4$ yields $p + p + 4 = 44$. From this relation, we see $p = 20$. Reference to the periodic table indicates that 20 is the atomic number of the element calcium.

36. **(M)** We will use the same type of strategy and the same notation as we used previously in Equation 35 to come up with the answer.

$n = p + 1$ There is one more neutron than the number of protons.

$n + p = 9 \times 3 = 27$ The mass number equals nine times the ion's charge of 3+.

Substitute the first relationship into the second, and solve for p.

$27 = (p + 1) + p = 2p + 1$

$p = \dfrac{27 - 1}{2} = 13$

Thus this is the 3+ action of the isotope Al-27 $\rightarrow {}^{27}_{13}\text{Al}^{3+}$.

37. **(M)** The number of protons is the same as the atomic number for iodine, which is 53. There is one more electron than the number of protons because there is a negative charge on the ion. Therefore the number of electrons is 54. The number of neutrons is equal to 70, mass number minus atomic number.

38. **(E)** For iodine, $Z = 53$, and so it has 53 protons. Because the overall charge on the ion is 1−, there are 54 electrons in a single ion of iodine-131. The number of neutrons is $131 - 53 = 78$.

39. **(E)** For americium, $Z = 95$. There are 95 protons, 95 electrons, and $241 - 95 = 146$ neutrons in a single atom of americium-241.

40. **(E)** For cobalt, $Z = 27$. There are 27 protons, 27 electrons, and $60 - 27 = 33$ neutrons in a single atom of cobalt-60.

Atomic Mass Units, Atomic Masses

41. **(E)** There are no chlorine atoms that have a mass of 35.45 u. The masses of individual chlorine atoms are close to integers and this mass is about midway between two integers. It is an average atomic mass, the result of averaging two (or more) isotopic masses, each weighted by its isotopic abundance.

42. **(E)** It is exceedingly unlikely that another nuclide would have an exact integral mass. The mass of carbon-12 is *defined* as precisely 12 u. Each nuclidic mass is close to integral, but none that we have encountered in this chapter are precisely integral. The reason is that each nuclide is composed of protons, neutrons, and electrons, none of which have integral masses, and there is a small quantity of the mass of each nucleon (nuclear particle) lost in the binding energy holding the nuclides together. It would be highly unlikely that all of these contributions would add up to a precisely integral mass.

43. **(E)** To determine the weighted-average atomic mass, we use the following expression:

$$\text{average atomic mass} = \sum (\text{isotopic mass} \times \text{fractional isotopic abundance})$$

Each of the three percents given is converted to a fractional abundance by dividing it by 100.

$$\text{Mg atomic mass} = (23.985042\,\text{u} \times 0.7899) + (24.985837\,\text{u} \times 0.1000) + (25.982593\,\text{u} \times 0.1101)$$

$$= 18.95\,\text{u} + 2.499\,\text{u} + 2.861\,\text{u} = 24.31\,\text{u}$$

44. **(E)** To determine the average atomic mass, we use the following expression:

$$\text{average atomic mass} = \sum (\text{isotopic mass} \times \text{fractional isotopic abundance})$$

Each of the three percents given is converted to a fractional abundance by dividing it by 100.

$$\text{Cr atomic mass} = (49.9461 \times 0.0435) + (51.9405 \times 0.8379) + (52.9407 \times 0.0950) + (53.9389 \times 0.0236)$$

$$= 2.17\,\text{u} + 43.52\,\text{u} + 5.03\,\text{u} + 1.27\,\text{u} = 51.99\,\text{u}$$

If all digits are carried and then the answer is rounded at the end, the answer is 52.00 u.

45. **(E)** We will use the expression to determine the weighted-average atomic mass.

$$107.868\,\text{u} = (106.905092\,\text{u} \times 0.5184) + (^{109}\text{Ag} \times 0.4816) = 55.42\,\text{u} + 0.4816\,^{109}\text{Ag}$$

$$107.868\,\text{u} - 55.42\,\text{u} = 0.4816\,^{109}\text{Ag} = 52.45\,\text{u} \qquad ^{109}\text{Ag} = \frac{52.45\,\text{u}}{0.4816} = 108.9\,\text{u}$$

46. **(M)** The percent abundance of the two isotopes must add to 100.00%, since there are only two naturally occurring isotopes of gallium. Thus, we can determine the percent abundance of the second isotope by using difference:

$$\text{second isotope} = 100.00\% - 60.11\% = 39.89\%$$

From the periodic table, we see that the atomic mass of gallium is 69.723 u. We use this value in the expression to determine the weighted-average atomic mass, along with the isotopic mass of ^{69}Ga and the fractional abundances of the two isotopes (the percent abundances divided by 100).

$$69.723\,\text{u} = (0.6011 \times 68.925581\,\text{u}) + (0.3989 \times \text{other isotope}) = 41.43\,\text{u} + (0.3989 \times \text{other isotope})$$

$$\text{other isotope} = \frac{69.723 - 41.43\,\text{u}}{0.3989} = 70.92\,\text{u} = \text{mass of } ^{71}\text{Ga, the other isotope}$$

47. **(M)** Since the three percent abundances total 100%, the percent abundance of ^{40}K is found by difference. % $^{40}K = 100.0000\% - 93.2581\% - 6.7302\% = 0.0117\%$

Then the expression for the weighted-average atomic mass is used, with the percent abundances converted to fractional abundances by dividing by 100. Note that the average atomic mass of potassium is 39.0983 u.

$$39.0983\,u = (0.932581 \times 38.963707\,u) + (0.000117 \times 39.963999\,u) + (0.067302 \times \text{mass of}\,^{41}K)$$

$$= 36.3368\,u + 0.00468\,u + (0.067302 \times \text{mass of}\,^{41}K)$$

$$\text{mass of}\,^{41}K = \frac{39.0983\,u - (36.3368\,u + 0.00468\,u)}{0.067302} = 40.962\,u$$

48. **(M)** We use the expression for determining the weighted-average atomic mass, where x represents the fractional abundance of ^{10}B and $(1-x)$ the fractional abundance of ^{11}B

$$10.81\,u = (10.012937\,u \times x) + [11.009305 \times (1-x)] = 10.012937x + 11.009305 - 11.009305x$$

$$10.81 - 11.009305 = -0.20 = 10.012937x - 11.009305x = -0.996368x$$

$$x = \frac{0.20}{0.996368} = 0.20$$

$$\therefore 20\%\,^{10}B \quad \text{and} \quad (100.0 - 20) = 80\%\,^{11}B$$

Mass Spectrometry

49. **(M)**
(a)

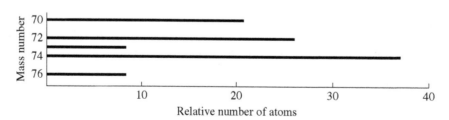

(b) As before, we multiply each isotopic mass by its fractional abundance, after which, we sum these products to obtain the (average) atomic mass for the element.

$$(0.205 \times 70) + (0.274 \times 72) + (0.078 \times 73) + (0.365 \times 74) + (0.078 \times 76)$$

$$= 14 + 20. + 5.7 + 27 + 5.9 = 72.6 = \text{average atomic mass of germanium}$$

The result is only approximately correct because the isotopic masses are given to only two significant figures. Thus, only a two-significant-figure result can be quoted.

50. (M)

(a) Six unique HCl molecules are possible (called isotopomers):

$^1H^{35}Cl,\ ^2H^{35}Cl,\ ^3H^{35}Cl,\ ^1H^{37}Cl,\ ^2H^{37}Cl,\ and\ ^3H^{37}Cl$

The mass numbers of the six different possible types of molecules are obtained by summing the mass numbers of the two atoms in each molecule:

$^1H^{35}Cl$ has $A = 36$ $^2H^{35}Cl$ has $A = 37$ $^3H^{35}Cl$ has $A = 38$

$^1H^{37}Cl$ has $A = 38$ $^2H^{37}Cl$ has $A = 39$ $^3H^{37}Cl$ has $A = 40$

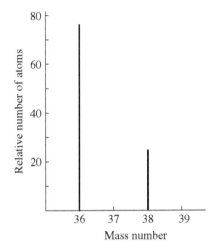

(b) The most abundant molecule contains the isotope for each element that is most abundant. It is $^1H^{35}Cl$. The second most abundant molecule is $^1H^{37}Cl$. The relative abundance of each type of molecule is determined by multiplying together the fractional abundances of the two isotopes present. Relative abundances of the molecules are as follows.

$^1H^{35}Cl: 75.76\%$ $^1H^{37}Cl: 24.23\%$

$^2H^{35}Cl: 0.011\%$ $^2H^{37}Cl: 0.0036\%$

$^3H^{35}Cl: < 0.0008\%$ $^3H^{37}Cl: < 0.0002\%$

The Periodic Table

51. (E)

(a) Ge is in group 14 and in the fourth period.

(b) Other elements in group 16(6A) are similar to S: O, Se, and Te. Most of the elements in the periodic table are unlike S, but particularly metals such as Na, K, and Rb.

(c) The alkali metal (group 1), in the fifth period is Rb.

(d) The halogen (group 17) in the sixth period is At.

52. (E)

(a) Au is in group 11 and in the sixth period.

(b) Ar, $Z = 18$, is a noble gas. Xe is a noble gas with atomic number (54) greater than 50.

(c) If an element forms a stable anion with charge 2–, it is in group 16.

(d) If an element forms a stable cation with charge 3+, it is in group 13.

53. (E) If the seventh period of the periodic table is 32 members long, it will be the same length as the sixth period. Elements in the same family (vertical group), will have atomic numbers 32 units higher. The noble gas following radon will have atomic number $= 86 + 32 = 118$. The alkali metal following francium will have atomic number $= 87 + 32 = 119$.

54. (M) There are several interchanges: Ar/K, Co/Ni, Te/I, Th/Pa, U/Np, Pu/Am, Sg/Bh
The reverse order is necessary because the periodic table lists elements in order of increasing atomic number (protons in the nucleus) and not in order of increasing atomic masses.

The Avogadro Constant and the Mole

55. (E)

(a) atoms of Fe $= 15.8 \text{ mol Fe} \times \dfrac{6.022 \times 10^{23} \text{ atoms Fe}}{1 \text{ mol Fe}} = 9.51 \times 10^{24}$ atoms Fe

(b) atoms of Ag $= 0.000467 \text{ mol Ag} \times \dfrac{6.022 \times 10^{23} \text{ atoms Ag}}{1 \text{ mol Ag}} = 2.81 \times 10^{20}$ atoms Ag

(c) atoms of Na $= 8.5 \times 10^{-11} \text{ mol Na} \times \dfrac{6.022 \times 10^{23} \text{ atoms Na}}{1 \text{ mol Na}} = 5.1 \times 10^{13}$ atoms Na

56. (E) Since the molar mass of nitrogen is 14.0 g/mol, 25.0 g N is almost two moles (1.79 mol N), while 6.022×10^{23} Ni atoms is about one mole, and 52.0 g Cr (52.00 g/mol Cr) is also almost one mole. Finally, 10.0 cm³ Fe (55.85 g/mol Fe) has a mass of about 79 g, and contains about 1.4 moles of atoms. Thus, 25.0 g N contains the greatest number of atoms.
Note: Even if you take nitrogen as N₂, the answer is the same.

57. (E)

(a) moles of Zn $= 415.0 \text{ g Zn} \times \dfrac{1 \text{ mol Zn}}{65.38 \text{ g Zn}} = 6.347$ mol Zn

(b) # of Cr atoms $= 147,400 \text{ g Cr} \times \dfrac{1 \text{ mol Cr}}{51.996 \text{ g Cr}} \times \dfrac{6.022 \times 10^{23} \text{ atoms Cr}}{1 \text{ mol Cr}}$

$\qquad = 1.707 \times 10^{27}$ atoms Cr

(c) mass Au $= 1.0 \times 10^{12} \text{atoms Au} \times \dfrac{1 \text{ mol Au}}{6.022 \times 10^{23} \text{ atoms Au}} \times \dfrac{196.97 \text{ g Au}}{1 \text{ mol Au}} = 3.3 \times 10^{-10}$ g Au

(d) mass of F atom $= 1 \text{ atom F} \times \dfrac{1 \text{ mol F}}{6.022 \times 10^{23} \text{atoms F}} \times \dfrac{18.998 \text{ g F}}{1 \text{ mol F}} = 3.1547 \times 10^{-23}$ g F

For exactly 1 F atom, the number of sig figs in the answer is determined by the least precise number in the calculation, namely the mass of fluorine.

58. (E)

(a) number Kr atoms = 5.25 mg Kr $\times \dfrac{1 \text{ g Kr}}{1000 \text{ mg Kr}} \times \dfrac{1 \text{ mol Kr}}{83.80 \text{ g Kr}} \times \dfrac{6.022 \times 10^{23} \text{ atoms Kr}}{1 \text{ mol Kr}}$

$= 3.77 \times 10^{19}$ atoms Kr

(b) Molar mass is defined as the mass per mole of substance. mass = 2.09 g.
This calculation requires that the number of moles be determined.

moles = 2.80×10^{22} atoms $\times \dfrac{1 \text{ mol}}{6.022 \times 10^{23} \text{ atoms}} = 0.0465$ mol

molar mass = $\dfrac{\text{mass}}{\text{moles}} = \dfrac{2.09 \text{ g}}{0.0465 \text{ mol}} = 44.9$ g/mol   The element is Sc, scandium.

(c) mass P = 44.75 g Mg $\times \dfrac{1 \text{ mol Mg}}{24.305 \text{ g Mg}} \times \dfrac{1 \text{ mol P}}{1 \text{ mol Mg}} \times \dfrac{30.9738 \text{ g P}}{1 \text{ mol P}} = 57.03$ g P

Note: The same answer is obtained if you assume phosphorus is P$_4$ instead of P.

59. (E) Determine the mass of Cu in the jewelry, then convert to moles and finally to the number of atoms. If sterling silver is 92.5% by mass Ag, it is 100 – 92.5 = 7.5% by mass Cu.

Conversion pathway approach:

number of Cu atoms = 33.24 g sterling $\times \dfrac{7.5 \text{ g Cu}}{100.0 \text{ g sterling}} \times \dfrac{1 \text{ mol Cu}}{63.546 \text{ g Cu}} \times \dfrac{6.022 \times 10^{23} \text{ atoms Cu}}{1 \text{ mol Cu}}$

$= 2.4 \times 10^{22}$ Cu atoms

Stepwise approach:

33.24 g sterling $\times \dfrac{7.5 \text{ g Cu}}{100.0 \text{ g sterling}} = 2.493$ g Cu

2.493 g Cu $\times \dfrac{1 \text{ mol Cu}}{63.546 \text{ g Cu}} = 0.03923$ mol Cu

0.03923 mol Cu $\times \dfrac{6.022 \times 10^{23} \text{ atoms Cu}}{1 \text{ mol Cu}} = 2.4 \times 10^{22}$ Cu atoms

60. (E) We first need to determine the amount in moles of each metal.

amount of Pb = 50.0 cm^3 solder $\times \dfrac{9.4 \text{ g solder}}{1 \text{ cm}^3} \times \dfrac{67 \text{ g Pb}}{100 \text{ g solder}} \times \dfrac{1 \text{ mol Pb}}{207.2 \text{ g Pb}} = 1.5$ mol Pb

amount of Sn = 50.0 cm^3 solder $\times \dfrac{9.4 \text{ g solder}}{1 \text{ cm}^3} \times \dfrac{33 \text{ g Sn}}{100 \text{ g solder}} \times \dfrac{1 \text{ mol Sn}}{118.7 \text{ g Sn}} = 1.3$ mol Sn

total atoms = $(1.5 \text{ mol Pb} + 1.3 \text{ mol Sn}) \times \dfrac{6.022 \times 10^{23} \text{ atoms}}{1 \text{ mol}} = 1.7 \times 10^{24}$ atoms

61. **(E)** We first need to determine the number of Pb atoms of all types in 215 mg of Pb, and then use the percent isotopic abundance to determine the number of ^{204}Pb atoms present.

$$^{204}\text{Pb atoms} = 215 \text{ mg Pb} \times \frac{1 \text{ g}}{1000 \text{ mg}} \times \frac{1 \text{ mol Pb}}{207.2 \text{ g Pb}} \times \frac{6.022 \times 10^{23} \text{atoms}}{1 \text{ mol Pb}} \times \frac{14 \ ^{204}\text{Pb atoms}}{1000 \text{ Pb atoms}}$$

$$= 8.7 \times 10^{18} \text{ atoms } ^{204}\text{Pb}$$

62. **(E)**

$$\text{mass of alloy} = 7.25 \times 10^{23} \text{ Cd atoms} \times \frac{1 \text{ mol Cd}}{6.022 \times 10^{23} \text{ Cd atoms}} \times \frac{112.4 \text{ g Cd}}{1 \text{ mol Cd}} \times \frac{100.0 \text{ g alloy}}{8.0 \text{ g Cd}}$$

$$= 1.7 \times 10^3 \text{ g alloy}$$

63. **(E)** We will use the average atomic mass of lead, 207.2 g/mol, to answer this question.

(a) $\dfrac{30 \ \mu\text{g Pb}}{1 \text{ dL}} \times \dfrac{1 \text{ dL}}{0.1 \text{ L}} \times \dfrac{1 \text{ g Pb}}{10^6 \ \mu\text{g Pb}} \times \dfrac{1 \text{ mol Pb}}{207.2 \text{ g}} = 1.4\underline{5} \times 10^{-6} \text{ mol Pb / L}$

(b) $\dfrac{1.4\underline{5} \times 10^{-6} \text{ mol Pb}}{\text{L}} \times \dfrac{1 \text{ L}}{1000 \text{ mL}} \times \dfrac{6.022 \times 10^{23} \text{ atoms}}{1 \text{ mol}} = 8.7 \times 10^{14} \text{ Pb atoms / mL}$

64. **(M)** The concentration of Pb in air provides the principal conversion factor. Other conversion factors are needed to convert to and from its units, beginning with the 0.500 L volume, and ending with the number of atoms.

$$\text{no. Pb atoms} = 0.500 \text{ L} \times \frac{1 \text{ m}^3}{1000 \text{ L}} \times \frac{3.11 \ \mu\text{g Pb}}{1 \text{ m}^3} \times \frac{1 \text{ g Pb}}{10^6 \ \mu\text{g Pb}} \times \frac{1 \text{ mol Pb}}{207.2 \text{ g Pb}} \times \frac{6.022 \times 10^{23} \text{ Pb atoms}}{1 \text{ mol Pb}}$$

$$= 4.52 \times 10^{12} \text{ Pb atoms}$$

65. **(M)** To answer this question, we simply need to calculate the ratio of the mass (in grams) of each sample to its molar mass. Whichever elemental sample gives the largest ratio will be the one that has the greatest number of atoms.

(a) Iron sample: $10 \text{ cm} \times 10 \text{ cm} \times 10 \text{ cm} \times 7.86 \text{ g cm}^{-3} = 7860 \text{ g Fe}$

$$7860 \text{ g Fe} \times \frac{1 \text{ mol Fe}}{55.845 \text{ g Fe}} = 141 \text{ mol of Fe atoms}$$

(b) Hydrogen sample: $\dfrac{1.00 \times 10^3 \text{g H}_2}{2 \times (1.008 \text{ g H})} \times 1 \text{ mol H} = 496 \text{ mol of H}_2 \text{ molecules} =$

$$992 \text{ mol of H atoms}$$

(c) Sulfur sample: $\dfrac{2.00 \times 10^4 \text{ g S}}{32.06 \text{ g S}} \times 1 \text{ mol S} = 624 \text{ mol of S atoms}$

(d) Mercury sample: $76 \text{ lb Hg} \times \dfrac{454 \text{ g Hg}}{1 \text{ lb Hg}} \times \dfrac{1 \text{ mol Hg}}{200.6 \text{ g Hg}} = 172 \text{ mol of Hg atoms}$

Clearly, then, it is the 1.00 kg sample of hydrogen that contains the greatest number of atoms.

66. (M)

(a) 23 g Na = 1 mol with a density ~ 1 g/cm^3. 1 mole = 23 g, so volume of 25.5 mol ~ 600 cm^3.

(b) Liquid bromine occupies 725 mL or 725 cm^3 (given).

(c) 1.25×10^{25} atoms Cr is ~20 moles. At ~50 g/mol, this represents approximately 1000 g. Given the density of 9.4 g/cm^3, this represents about 100 cm^3 of volume.

(d) 2150 g solder at 9.4 g/cm^3 represents approximately 200 cm^3.

From this we can see that the liquid bromine would occupy the largest volume.

INTEGRATIVE AND ADVANCED EXERCISES

67. (M)

(a) $\text{total mass(40 °C)} = 2.50 \text{ g} + 100.0 \text{ mL} \times \dfrac{0.9922 \text{ g}}{1 \text{ mL}} = 2.50 \text{ g} + 99.22 \text{ g} = 101.72 \text{ g}$

$\text{mass of solution (20 °C)} = 100 \text{ mL} \times \dfrac{1.0085 \text{ g}}{1 \text{ mL}} = 100.85 \text{ g}$

$\text{solid crystallized} = \text{total mass(40 °C)} - \text{solution mass(20°C)}$
$= 101.72 \text{ g} - 100.85 \text{ g} = 0.87 \text{ g}$

(b) The answer cannot be more precise because both the initial mass and the subtraction only allows the reporting of masses to ± 0.01 g. For a more precise answer, more significant figures would be required for the initial mass (2.50 g) and the densities of the water and solution.

68. (M) We now recognize that the values of 24.3 u and 35.3 u for the masses of Mg and Cl represent a weighted-average that considers the mass and abundance of each isotope. The experimental mass of each isotope is very close to the natural number and therefore very close to an integer multiple of the mass of ^{1}H, thus supporting Prout's hypothesis.

69. (M) Each atom of ^{19}F contains 9 protons (1.0073 u each), 10 neutrons (1.0087 u each), and 9 electrons (0.0005486 u each). The mass of each atom should be the sum of the masses of these particles.

$\text{Total mass} = \left(9 \text{ protons} \times \dfrac{1.0073 \text{ u}}{1 \text{ proton}}\right) + \left(10 \text{ neutrons} \times \dfrac{1.0087 \text{ u}}{1 \text{ neutron}}\right) + \left(9 \text{ electrons} \times \dfrac{0.0005486 \text{ u}}{1 \text{ electron}}\right)$
$= 9.0657 \text{ u} + 10.087 \text{ u} + 0.004937 \text{ u} = 19.158 \text{ u}$

This compares with a mass of 18.9984 u given in the periodic table. The difference, 0.160 u per atom, is called the mass defect and represents the energy that holds the nucleus together, the nuclear binding energy. This binding energy is released when 9 protons and 9 neutrons fuse to give a fluorine-19 nucleus.

70. (M)

$\text{volume of nucleus(single proton)} = \dfrac{4}{3}\pi r^3 = 1.3333 \times 3.14159 \times (0.5 \times 10^{-13} \text{ cm})^3 = 5 \times 10^{-40} \text{ cm}^3$

$\text{density} = \dfrac{1.673 \times 10^{-24} \text{ g}}{5 \times 10^{-40} \text{ cm}^3} = 3 \times 10^{15} \text{ g/cm}^3$

71. (M) This method of establishing the Avogadro constant uses fundamental constants.

$$1.000 \text{ g } ^{12}\text{C} \times \frac{1 \text{ mol } ^{12}\text{C}}{12 \text{ g } ^{12}\text{C}} \times \frac{6.022 \times 10^{23} \text{ } ^{12}\text{C atoms}}{1 \text{ mol } ^{12}\text{C}} \times \frac{12 \text{ u}}{1 \text{ } ^{12}\text{C atom}} = 6.022 \times 10^{23} \text{ u}$$

72. (M) Let Z = # of protons, N = # of neutrons, E = # of electrons, and A = # of nucleons = $Z + N$.

(a) $Z + N = 234$ The mass number is 234 and the species is an atom.
   $N = 1.600 \, Z$ The atom has 60.0% more neutrons than protons.
   Next we will substitute the second expression into the first and solve for Z.
   $Z + N = 234 = Z + 1.600 \, Z = 2.600 \, Z$

   $$Z = \frac{234}{2.600} = 90 \text{ protons}$$

   Thus this is an atom of the isotope ^{234}Th.

(b) $Z = E + 2$ The ion has a charge of +2. $Z = 1.100 \, E$
   There are 10.0% more protons than electrons. By equating these two expressions and solving for E, we can find the number of electrons. $E + 2 = 1.100 \, E$

   $2 = 1.100 \, E - E = 0.100 \, E$ $E = \dfrac{2}{0.100} = 20 \text{ electrons}$ $Z = 20 + 2 = 22$, (titanium).

   The ion is Ti^{2+}. There is not enough information to determine the mass number.

(c) $Z + N = 110$ The mass number is 110.
   $Z = E + 2$ The species is a cation with a charge of +2.
   $N = 1.25 \, E$ Thus, there are 25.0% more neutrons than electrons. By substituting the second and third expressions into the first, we can solve for E, the number of electrons.

   $(E + 2) + 1.25 \, E = 110 = 2.25 \, E + 2$ $108 = 2.25 \, E$ $E = \dfrac{108}{2.25} = 48$

   Then $Z = 48 + 2 = 50$, (the element is Sn) $N = 1.25 \times 48 = 60$ Thus, it is $^{110}\text{Sn}^{2+}$.

73. (E) Because the net ionic charge (+2) is one-tenth of its the nuclear charge, the nuclear charge is $+20$. This is also the atomic number of the nuclide, which means the element is calcium. The number of electrons is 20 for a neutral calcium atom, but only 18 for a calcium ion with a net 2+ charge. Four more than 18 is 22 neutrons. The ion described is $^{42}_{20}\text{Ca}^{2+}$.

74. (M) $A = Z + N = 2.50 \, Z$ The mass number is 2.50 times the atomic number.
The neutron number of selenium-82 equals $82 - 34 = 48$, since $Z = 34$ for Se. The neutron number of isotope Y also equals 48, which equals 1.33 times the atomic number of isotope Y.

Thus $48 = 1.33 \times Z_\text{Y}$ $Z_\text{Y} = \dfrac{48}{1.33} = 36$

The mass number of isotope Y = $48 + 36 = 84$ = the atomic number of E, and thus, the element is Po. Thus, from the relationship in the first line, the mass number of
$E = 2.50 \, Z = 2.50 \times 84 = 210$ The isotope E is ^{210}Po.

75. As a result of the redefinition, all masses will decrease by a factor of $35.00000/35.453 = 0.98722$.

(a) atomic mass of He $4.00260 \times 0.98722 = 3.9515$
atomic mass of Na $22.9898 \times 0.98722 = 22.696$
atomic mass of I $126.905 \times 0.98722 = 125.28$

(b) These three elements have nearly integral atomic masses based on C-12 because these three elements and C-12 all consist mainly of one stable isotope, rather than a mixture of two or more stable isotopes, with each being present in significant amounts (10% or more), as is the case with chlorine.

76. **(M)** To solve this question, represent the fractional abundance of ^{14}N by x and that of ^{14}N by $(1-x)$. Then use the expression for determining average atomic mass.
$14.0067 = 14.0031x + 15.0001(1-x)$
$14.0067 - 15.0001 = 14.0031x - 15.0001x$ OR $-0.9934 = -0.9970x$

$x = \dfrac{0.9934}{0.9970} \times 100\% = 99.64\% =$ percent isotopic abundance of ^{14}N.

Thus, $0.36\% =$ percent isotopic abundance of ^{15}N.

77. **(D)** In this case, we will use the expression for determining average atomic mass—the sum of products of nuclidic mass times fractional abundances (from Figure 2-14)—to answer the question.

^{196}Hg: $195.9658 \text{ u} \times 0.00146 = 0.286 \text{ u}$

^{198}Hg: $197.9668 \text{ u} \times 0.1002 = 19.84 \text{ u}$ ^{199}Hg: $198.9683 \text{ u} \times 0.1684 = 33.51 \text{ u}$

^{200}Hg: $199.9683 \text{ u} \times 0.2313 = 46.25 \text{ u}$ ^{201}Hg: $200.9703 \text{ u} \times 0.1322 = 26.57 \text{ u}$

^{202}Hg: $201.9706 \text{ u} \times 0.2980 = 60.19 \text{ u}$ ^{204}Hg: $203.9735 \text{ u} \times 0.0685 = 14.0 \text{ u}$

Atomic weight $= 0.286 \text{ u} + 19.84 \text{ u} + 33.51 \text{ u} + 46.25 \text{ u} + 26.57 \text{ u} + 60.19 \text{ u} + 14.0 \text{ u} = 200.6 \text{ u}$

78. **(D)** The sum of the percent abundances of the two minor isotopes equals $100.00\% - 84.68\% = 15.32\%$. Thus, we denote the fractional abundance of ^{73}Ge as x, and the other as $(0.1532 - x)$. These fractions are then used in the expression for average atomic mass.

atomic mass $= 72.64 \text{ u} = (69.92425 \text{ u} \times 0.2085) + (71.92208 \text{ u} \times 0.2754) + (73.92118 \text{ u} \times 0.3629)$
$+ (72.92346 \text{ u} \times x) + [75.92140 \text{ u} \times (0.1532 - x)]$

$72.64 \text{ u} = (14.5792 \text{ u}) + (19.8073 \text{ u}) + (26.8260 \text{ u}) + (72.92346 \text{ u} x) + [11.6312 \text{ u} - 75.92140 \text{ u} x)]$

$-0.2037 = -2.99794x$ Hence: $x = 0.068$.

^{73}Ge has 6.8% isotopic abundance and ^{76}Ge has 8.5% isotopic abundance.

From the calculations, we can see that the number of significant figures drops from four in the percent isotopic abundances supplied to only two significant figures owing to the imprecision in the supplied values of the percent isotopic abundance.

79. **(D)** First, it must be understood that because we don't know the exact percent abundance of ^{84}Kr, all the percent abundances for the other isotopes will also be approximate. From the question, we may initially infer the following:

- Assume percent abundance of ^{84}Kr ~ 55% as a start (somewhat more than 50)
- Let percent abundance of ^{82}Kr = x%; percent abundance ^{83}Kr ~ ^{82}Kr = x%
- ^{86}Kr = 1.50(percent abundance of ^{82}Kr) = 1.50(x%)
- ^{80}Kr = 0.196(percent abundance of ^{82}Kr) = 0.196(x%)
- ^{78}Kr = 0.030(percent abundance of ^{82}Kr) = 0.030(x%)

$$100\% = \%^{78}Kr + \%^{80}Kr + \%^{82}Kr + \%^{83}Kr + \%^{84}Kr + \%^{86}Kr$$
$$100\% = 0.030(x\%) + 0.196(x\%) + x\% + x\% + \%^{84}Kr + 1.50(x\%)$$
$$100\% = 3.726(x\%) + \%^{84}Kr$$

Assuming percent abundance of ^{84}Kr is 55%, solving for x gives a value of 12.1% for percent abundance of ^{82}Kr, from which the remaining abundances can be calculated based on the above relationships, as shown below:

^{78}Kr: 0.03 × 12.1 = 0.363%; ^{80}Kr: 0.196 × 12.1 = 2.37%; ^{83}Kr: same as ^{82}Kr; ^{86}Kr: 1.5 × 12.1 = 18.15%.

The weighted-average isotopic mass calculated from the above abundances is as follows:
Weighted-average isotopic mass = 0.030(12.1%)(77.9204 u) + 0.196(12.1%)(79.9164 u) + 12.1%(81.9135 u) + 12.1%(82.9141 u) + 55%(83.9115 u) + 1.50(12.1%)(85.9106 u) = 83.8064 u

As stated above, the problem here is the inaccuracy of the percent abundance for ^{84}Kr, which is crudely estimated to be ~ 55%. If we vary this percentage, we vary the relative abundance of all other isotopes accordingly. Since we know the weighted-average atomic mass of Kr is 83.80, we can try different values for ^{84}Kr abundance and figure out which gives us the closest value to the given weighted-average isotopic mass:

Percent Abundance ^{84}Kr	Weighted-Average Isotopic Mass
50%	83.793
51%	83.796
52%	83.799
53%	83.801
54%	83.803
55%	83.806

From this table, we can see that the answer is somewhere between 52% and 53%.

80. **(D)** Four molecules are possible, given below with their calculated molecular masses.

^{35}Cl ^{79}Br mass = 34.9689 u + 78.9183 u = 113.8872 u

^{35}Cl ^{81}Br mass = 34.9689 u + 80.9163 u = 115.8852 u

^{37}Cl ^{79}Br mass = 36.9658 u + 78.9183 u = 115.8841 u

^{37}Cl ^{81}Br mass = 36.9658 u + 80.9163 u = 117.8821 u

Each molecule has a different intensity pattern (relative number of molecules), based on the isotopic abundance of the isotopes making up each molecule. If we divide all of the values by the lowest ratio, we can get a better idea of the relative ratio of each molecule.

^{35}Cl ^{79}Br Intensity = (0.7577) × (0.5069) = 0.3841 ÷ 0.1195 = 3.214

^{35}Cl ^{81}Br Intensity = (0.7577) × (0.4931) = 0.3736 ÷ 0.1195 = 3.127

^{37}Cl ^{79}Br Intensity = (0.2423) × (0.5069) = 0.1228 ÷ 0.1195 = 1.028

^{37}Cl ^{81}Br Intensity = (0.2423) × (0.4931) = 0.1195 ÷ 0.1195 = 1.000

A plot of intensity versus molecular mass reveals the following pattern under ideal circumstances (high resolution mass spectrometry).

81. **(M)** Let's begin by finding the volume of copper metal.

$$\text{wire diameter (cm)} = 0.03196 \text{ in.} \times \frac{2.54 \text{ cm}}{1 \text{ in.}} = 0.08118 \text{ cm}$$

The radius is 0.08118 cm × 1/2 = 0.04059 cm

The volume of $Cu(cm^3) = \pi r^2 h = 3.1416 \times (0.04059 \text{ cm})^2 \times 150 \text{ cm} = 0.7764 \text{ cm}^3$

So, the mass of $Cu = 0 \text{ cm}^3 \times \dfrac{8.92 \text{ g Cu}}{1 \text{ cm}^3} = 6.93 \text{ g Cu}$

The number of moles of $Cu = 6.93 \text{ g Cu} \times \dfrac{1 \text{ mol Cu}}{63.546 \text{ g Cu}} = 0.109 \text{ mol Cu}$

Cu atoms in the wire = $0.109 \text{ mol Cu} \times \dfrac{6.022 \times 10^{23} \text{ atoms Cu}}{1 \text{ mol Cu}} = 6.56 \times 10^{22} \text{ atoms}$

82. (D) volume $= l \times w \times h - \pi r^2 h$

$$= (15.0 \text{ cm} \times 12.5 \text{ cm} \times 0.300 \text{ cm}) - (3.1416) \times \left(\frac{2.50 \text{ cm}}{2}\right)^2 \times (0.300 \text{ cm})$$

$$= (56.2\underline{5} \text{ cm} - 1.47 \text{ cm}) = 54.8 \text{ cm}^3$$

mass of object $= 54.8 \text{ cm}^3 \times \dfrac{8.80 \text{ g}}{1 \text{ cm}^3} = 482 \text{ g Monel metal}$

Then determine the number of silicon atoms in this quantity of alloy.

$$482 \text{ g Monel metal} \times \frac{2.2 \times 10^{-4} \text{ g Si}}{1.000 \text{ g metal}} \times \frac{1 \text{ mol Si}}{28.05 \text{ g Si}} \times \frac{6.022 \times 10^{23} \text{ Si atoms}}{1 \text{ mol Si}} = 2.3 \times 10^{21} \text{ Si atoms}$$

Finally, determine the number of ^{30}Si atoms in this quantity of silicon.

$$\text{number of } ^{30}\text{Si atoms} = (2.3 \times 10^{21} \text{ Si atoms}) \times \left(\frac{3.10 \quad ^{30}\text{Si atoms}}{100 \quad \text{Si atoms}}\right) = 7.1 \times 10^{19} \quad ^{30}\text{Si}$$

83. (M) The percent isotopic abundance of deuterium of 0.015% means that, in a sample of 100,000 H atoms, only 15 ^{2}H are present.

$$\text{mass H}_2 = 2.50 \times 10^{21} \text{ atoms } ^2\text{H} \times \frac{100,000 \text{ H atoms}}{15 \text{ atoms } ^2\text{H}} \times \frac{1 \text{ mol H}}{6.022 \times 10^{23} \text{H atoms}} \times \frac{1 \text{ mol H}_2}{2 \text{ mol H}} \times \frac{2.016 \text{ g H}_2}{1 \text{ mol H}_2}$$

mass H$_2$ = 27.9 g H$_2$ is required such that we have 2.50×10^{21} atoms ^{2}H.

84. (M) The numbers sum to 21 ($= 10 + 6 + 5$). Thus, in one mole of the alloy there is $^{10}/_{21}$ mol Bi, $^6/_{21}$ mol Pb, and $^5/_{21}$ mol Sn. The mass of this mole of material is figured in a similar fashion to computing a weighted-average atomic mass from isotopic masses.

$$\text{mass of alloy} = \left(\frac{10}{21} \text{ mol Bi} \times \frac{209.0 \text{ g}}{1 \text{ mol Bi}}\right) + \left(\frac{6}{21} \text{ mol Pb} \times \frac{207.2 \text{ g}}{1 \text{ mol Pb}}\right) + \left(\frac{5}{21} \text{ mol Sn} \times \frac{118.7}{1 \text{ mol Sn}}\right)$$

$$= 99.52 \text{ g Bi} + 59.20 \text{ g Pb} + 28.26 \text{ g Sn} = 186.98 \text{ g alloy}$$

85. (M) The atom ratios are of course, the same as the mole ratios. We first determine the mass of alloy that contains 5.00 mol Ag, 4.00 mol Cu, and 1.00 mol Zn.

$$\text{mass} = 5.00 \text{ mol Ag} \times \frac{107.87 \text{ g Ag}}{1 \text{ mol Ag}} + 4.00 \text{ mol Cu} \times \frac{63.546 \text{ g Cu}}{1 \text{ mol Cu}} + 1.00 \text{ mol Zn} \times \frac{65.38 \text{ g Zn}}{1 \text{ mol Zn}}$$

$$= 539.\underline{4} \text{ g Ag} + 254.\underline{2} \text{ g Cu} + 65.38 \text{ g Zn} = 859 \text{ g alloy}$$

Then, for 1.00 kg of the alloy, (1000 g), we need 1000/859 moles. (859 g is the alloy's "molar mass.")

$$\text{mass of Ag} = 1000 \text{ g alloy} \times \frac{539 \text{ g Ag}}{859 \text{ g alloy}} = 627 \text{ g Ag}$$

$$\text{mass of Cu} = 1000 \text{ g alloy} \times \frac{254 \text{ g Cu}}{859 \text{ g alloy}} = 296 \text{ g Cu}$$

$$\text{mass of Zn} = 1000 \text{ g alloy} \times \frac{65.4 \text{ g Zn}}{859 \text{ g alloy}} = 76.1 \text{ g Zn}$$

86. **(M)** The relative masses of Sn and Pb are 207.2 g Pb (assume one mole of Pb) to $(2.73 \times 118.71 \text{ g/mol Sn} =)$ 324 g Sn. Then the mass of cadmium, on the same scale, is 207.2/1.78 = 116 g Cd.

$$\% \text{ Sn} = \frac{324 \text{ g Sn}}{207.2 + 324 + 116 \text{ g alloy}} \times 100\% = \frac{324 \text{ g Sn}}{647 \text{ g alloy}} \times 100\% = 50.1\% \text{ Sn}$$

$$\% \text{ Pb} = \frac{207.2 \text{ g Pb}}{647 \text{ g alloy}} \times 100\% = 32.0\% \text{ Pb} \qquad \% \text{ Cd} = \frac{116 \text{ g Cd}}{647 \text{ g alloy}} \times 100\% = 17.9\% \text{ Cd}$$

87. **(M)** We need to apply the law of conservation of mass and convert volumes to masses:

Calculate the mass of zinc: $125 \text{ cm}^3 \times 7.13 \text{ g/cm}^3 = 891 \text{ g}$

Calculate the mass of iodine: $125 \text{ cm}^3 \times 4.93 \text{ g/cm}^3 = 616 \text{ g}$

Calculate the mass of zinc iodide: $164 \text{ cm}^3 \times 4.74 \text{ g/cm}^3 = 777 \text{ g}$

Calculate the mass of zinc unreacted: $(891 + 616 - 777) \text{ g} = 730 \text{ g}$

Calculate the volume of zinc unreacted: $730 \text{ g} \times 1 \text{ cm}^3 / 7.13 \text{ g} = 102 \text{ cm}^3$

88. (D) First, calculate the total number of Ag atoms in a 1 cm³ crystal:.

$$10.5 \text{ g Ag} \times \frac{1 \text{ mol Ag}}{107.87 \text{ g Ag}} \times \frac{6.02 \times 10^{23} \text{ Ag atoms}}{1 \text{ mol Ag}} = 5.86 \times 10^{22} \text{ atoms of Ag}$$

The actual volume taken up by the Ag atoms (considering that there is 26% empty space in the crystal) is: $1 \text{ cm}^3 \times 0.74 = 0.74 \text{ cm}^3$

Therefore, the volume of each atom is: $\dfrac{0.74 \text{ cm}^3}{5.86 \times 10^{22} \text{ atoms}} = 1.263 \times 10^{-23} \text{ cm}^3$

Volume of a sphere is expressed as $V = 1.263 \times 10^{-23} \text{ cm}^3 = (4/3) \pi r^3$
Solving for r, we get 1.44×10^{-8} cm or 144 pm.

FEATURE PROBLEMS

89. **(M)** The product mass differs from that of the reactants by $(5.62 - 2.50 =)$ 3.12 grains. In order to determine the percent gain in mass, we need to convert the reactant mass to grains.

$$13 \text{ onces} \times \frac{8 \text{ gros}}{1 \text{ once}} = 104 \text{ gros} \times (104 + 2) \text{ gros} \times \frac{72 \text{ grains}}{1 \text{ gros}} = 7632 \text{ grains}$$

$$\% \text{ mass increase} = \frac{3.12 \text{ grains increase}}{(7632 + 2.50) \text{ grains original}} \times 100\% = 0.0409\% \text{ mass increase}$$

The sensitivity of Lavoisier's balance can be as little as 0.01 grain, which seems to be the limit of the readability of the balance; alternatively, it can be as large as 3.12 grains, which assumes that all of the error in the experiment is due to the (in)sensitivity of the balance. Let us convert 0.01 grains to a mass in grams.

$$\text{minimum error} = 0.01 \text{ gr} \times \frac{1 \text{ gros}}{72 \text{ gr}} \times \frac{1 \text{ once}}{8 \text{ gros}} \times \frac{1 \text{ livre}}{16 \text{ once}} \times \frac{30.59 \text{ g}}{1 \text{ livre}} = 3 \times 10^{-5} \text{g} = 0.03 \text{ mg}$$

$$\text{maximum error} = 3.12 \text{ gr} \times \frac{3 \times 10^{-5} \text{ g}}{0.01 \text{ gr}} = 9 \times 10^{-3} \text{ g} = 9 \text{ mg}$$

The maximum error is close to that of a common modern laboratory balance, which has a sensitivity of 1 mg. The minimum error is approximated by a good quality analytical balance. Thus we conclude that Lavoisier's results conform closely to the law of conservation of mass.

90. **(D)** One way to determine the common factor of which all 13 numbers are multiples is to first divide all of them by the smallest number in the set. The ratios thus obtained may be either integers or rational numbers whose decimal equivalents are easy to recognize.

Obs.	1	2	3	4	5	6	7	8	9	10	11	12	13
Quan.	19.6	24.60	29.62	34.47	39.38	44.42	49.41	53.91	59.12	63.68	68.65	78.34	83.22
Ratio	1.00	1.251	1.507	1.753	2.003	2.259	2.513	2.742	3.007	3.239	3.492	3.984	4.233
Mult.	4.00	5.005	6.026	7.013	8.012	9.038	10.05	10.97	12.03	12.96	13.97	15.94	16.93
Int.	4	5	6	7	8	9	10	11	12	13	14	16	17

The row labeled "Mult." is obtained by multiplying the row "Ratio" by 4.000. In the row labeled "Int." we give the integer closest to each of these multipliers. It is obvious that each of the 13 measurements is exceedingly close to a common quantity multiplied by an integer.

91. **(M)** In a 60-year-old chemistry textbook, the atomic mass for oxygen would be exactly 16 u because chemists assigned precisely 16 u as the atomic mass of the naturally occurring mixture of oxygen isotopes. This value is slightly higher than the value of 15.9994 in modern chemistry textbooks. Thus, we would expect all other atomic masses to be slightly higher as well in the older textbooks.

92. **(D)** We begin with the amount of reparations and obtain the volume in cubic kilometers with a series of conversion factors.

Conversion pathway approach:

$$V = \$28.8 \times 10^9 \times \frac{1\,\text{troy oz Au}}{\$21.25} \times \frac{31.103\,\text{g Au}}{1\,\text{troy oz Au}} \times \frac{1\,\text{mol Au}}{196.97\,\text{g Au}} \times \frac{6.022 \times 10^{23}\,\text{atoms Au}}{1\,\text{mol Au}}$$

$$\times \frac{1\,\text{ton seawater}}{4.67 \times 10^{17}\,\text{Au atoms}} \times \frac{2000\,\text{lb seawater}}{1\,\text{ton seawater}} \times \frac{453.6\ \text{g seawater}}{1\,\text{lb seawater}} \times \frac{1\,\text{cm}^3\ \text{seawater}}{1.03\,\text{g seawater}}$$

$$\times \left(\frac{1\,\text{m}}{100\,\text{cm}} \times \frac{1\,\text{km}}{1000\,\text{m}}\right)^3 = 2.43 \times 10^5\,\text{km}^3$$

Stepwise approach:

$$\$28.8 \times 10^9 \times \frac{1\,\text{troy oz Au}}{\$21.25} \times \frac{31.103\,\text{g Au}}{1\,\text{troy oz Au}} = 4.22 \times 10^{10}\text{g Au}$$

$$4.22 \times 10^{10}\text{g Au} \times \frac{1\,\text{mol Au}}{196.97\,\text{g Au}} \times \frac{6.022 \times 10^{23}\,\text{atoms Au}}{1\,\text{mol Au}} = 1.29 \times 10^{32}\,\text{atoms Au}$$

$$1.29 \times 10^{32}\,\text{atoms Au} \times \frac{1\,\text{ton seawater}}{4.67 \times 10^{17}\,\text{Au atoms}} \times \frac{2000\,\text{lb seawater}}{1\,\text{ton seawater}} = 5.52 \times 10^{17}\text{lb seawater}$$

$$5.52 \times 10^{17}\text{lb seawater} \times \frac{453.6\ \text{g seawater}}{1\,\text{lb seawater}} \times \frac{1\,\text{cm}^3\ \text{seawater}}{1.03\,\text{g seawater}} = 2.43 \times 10^{20}\text{cm}^3\ \text{seawater}$$

$$2.43 \times 10^{20}\text{cm}^3\ \text{seawater} \times \left(\frac{1\,\text{m}}{100\,\text{cm}} \times \frac{1\,\text{km}}{1000\,\text{m}}\right)^3 = 2.43 \times 10^5\,\text{km}^3$$

93. **(D)** We start by using the percent isotopic abundances for ^{87}Rb and ^{85}Rb along with the data in the "spiked" mass spectrum to find the total mass of Rb in the sample. Then, we calculate the Rb content in the rock sample in ppm by mass by dividing the mass of Rb by the total mass of the rock sample, and then multiplying the result by 10^6 to convert to ppm.

^{87}Rb = 27.83% isotopic abundance ^{85}Rb = 72.17% isotopic abundance

Therefore, $\dfrac{^{87}\text{Rb(isotopic)}}{^{85}\text{Rb(isotopic)}} = \dfrac{27.83\%}{72.17\%} = 0.3856$

For the ^{87}Rb(spiked) sample, the ^{87}Rb peak in the mass spectrum is 1.12 times as tall as the ^{85}Rb peak. Thus, for this sample $\dfrac{^{87}\text{Rb(isotopic)} + {}^{87}\text{Rb(spiked)}}{^{85}\text{Rb(isotopic)}} = 1.12$

Using this relationship, we can now find the masses of both ^{85}Rb and ^{87}Rb in the sample.

So, $\dfrac{^{87}Rb(isotopic)}{^{85}Rb(isotopic)} = 0.3856;$ $\qquad ^{85}Rb(isotopic) = \dfrac{^{87}Rb(isotopic)}{0.3856}$

$^{87}Rb(isotopic) + {}^{87}Rb(spiked) = \dfrac{1.12 \times {}^{87}Rb\ (isotopic)}{0.3856} = 2.905\ {}^{87}Rb(isotopic)$

$^{87}Rb(spiked) = 1.905\ {}^{87}Rb(isotopic)$

and $\dfrac{^{87}Rb(isotopic) + {}^{87}Rb(spiked)}{^{85}Rb(isotopic)} = \dfrac{^{87}Rb(isotopic) + {}^{87}Rb(spiked)}{\dfrac{^{87}Rb(isotopic)}{0.3856}} = 1.12$

Since the mass of ^{87}Rb(spiked) is equal to 29.45 μg, the mass of ^{87}Rb(isotopic) must be

$\dfrac{29.45\ \mu g}{1.905} = 15.46\ \mu g$ of ^{87}Rb(isotopic)

So, the mass of ^{85}Rb(isotopic) $= \dfrac{15.46\ \mu g\ of\ {}^{87}Rb(isotopic)}{0.3856} = 40.09\ \mu g$ of ^{85}Rb(isotopic)

Therefore, the total mass of Rb in the sample = 15.46 μg of ^{87}Rb(isotopic) + 40.09 μg of ^{85}Rb(isotopic) = 55.55 μg of Rb. Convert to grams:

$= 55.55\ \mu g$ of Rb $\times \dfrac{1\ g\ Rb}{1 \times 10^6\ \mu g\ Rb} = 5.555 \times 10^{-5}\ g\ Rb$

Rb content (ppm) $= \dfrac{5.555 \times 10^{-5}\ g\ Rb}{0.350\ g\ of\ rock} \times 10^6 = 159\ ppm\ Rb$

SELF-ASSESSMENT EXERCISES

94. **(E)**

(a) $_{Z}^{A}E$: The element "E" with the atomic number of Z (i.e., Z protons in the nucleus) and atomic mass of A (i.e., total of protons and neutrons equals A).

(b) β particle: An electron produced as a result of the decay of a neutron

(c) Isotope: Nuclei that share the same atomic number but have different atomic masses

(d) ^{16}O: An oxygen nucleus containing 8 neutrons

(e) Molar mass: Mass of one mole of a substance

95. (E)

(a) The total mass of substances present after the chemical reaction is the same as the total mass of substances before the chemical reaction. More universally, mass is neither created nor destroyed, but converts from one form to another.

(b) Rutherford's model of the atom postulates the existence of positively charged fundamental particles at the nucleus of the atom.

(c) An average value used to express the atomic mass of an element by taking into account the atomic masses and relative abundances of all the naturally occurring isotopes of the element.

(d) A spectrum showing the mass/charge ratio of various atoms in a matrix

96. (E)

(a) Cathode rays are beams of electrons being generated from a negatively charged surface (cathode) moving to a positively charged surface (anode). X-rays are high energy photons, which are typically generated when the high energy beam of electrons impinges on the anode.

(b) Protons and neutrons are both fundamental particles that make up an atom's nucleus. Protons are positively charged and neutrons have no charge.

(c) Nuclear charge is determined by the numbers of protons in the nucleus. Ionic charge is determined by the difference between the number of protons and electrons in the atom.

(d) Periods are horizontal rows in the periodic table, while groups are vertical columns.

(e) Metals are generally characterized by their malleability, ductility, and ability to conduct electricity and heat well. Nonmetals are generally brittle and nonconductive.

(f) The Avogadro constant is the number of elementary entities (atoms, molecules, etc.) in one mole of a substance. A mole is the amount of a substance that contains the same number of elementary entities as there are atoms in exactly 12 g of pure carbon-12.

97. **(E)** $\left(\dfrac{1}{5} \times 10.013 \text{ u}\right) + \left(\dfrac{4}{5} \times 11.009 \text{ u}\right) = 10.810 \text{ u}$. Therefore, the element is boron.

98. **(E)** The answer is (b). If all of the zinc reacts and the total amount of the product (zinc sulfide) is 14.9 g, then 4.9 g of S must have reacted with zinc. Therefore, 3.1 g of S remain.

99. **(E)** The answer is (d). It should be remembered that atoms combine in ratios of whole numbers. Therefore:

(a) 16 g O × (1 mol O/16 g O) = 1 mol O, and 85.5 g Rb × (1 mol Rb/85.5 g Rb) = 1 mol Rb Therefore, the O: Rb ratio is 1:1.

(b) Same calculations as above give an O: Rb ratio of 0.5:0.5, or 1:1.

(c) Same type calculation gives an O: Rb ratio of 2:1.

Because all of the above combine in O and Rb in whole number ratios, they are all at least theoretically possible.

100. (E) If the compound contains 46.7% X, then the percent of oxygen would be 100.0% − 46.7 = 53.3%. Assuming the sample is 100.0 g, there would be 53.3 g of oxygen present.

$$53.3 \text{ g O} \left(\frac{1 \text{ mol O}}{16.00 \text{ g O}} \right) = 3.331 \text{ mol O}$$

The formula of the compound is XO; therefore, X and O are in a 1:1 mole ratio.

$$\frac{46.7 \text{ g X}}{3.331 \text{ mol X}} = 14.0 \text{ g/mol X}$$

101. (E) The answer is (c). Cathode rays are beams of electrons, and as such have identical properties to β particles, although they may not have the same energy.

102. (E) The answer is (a), that the greatest portion of the mass of an atom is concentrated in a small but positively charged nucleus.

103. (E) The answer is (d). A hydrogen atom has one proton and one electron, so its charge is zero. A neutron has the same charge as a proton, but is neutral. Since most of the mass of the atom is at the nucleus, a neutron has nearly the same mass as a hydrogen atom.

104. (E) All the choices in this question are fundamental particles (e).

105. (E) Dalton (d) is correct.

106. (E) There are no particles that have the same mass as the hydrogen atom and a negative charge. The correct answer is (e).

107. (E) $^{35}_{17}\text{Cl}^+$

108. (E) The answer is (d), calcium, because they are in the same group.

109. (E) (a) Group 18, (b) Group 17, (c) Group 13 and Group 1 (d) Group 18

110. (E) (d) and (f)

111. (E) (c), because it is not close to being a whole number

112. (M) The answer is (d). Even with the mass scale being redefined based on ^{84}Xe, the mass ratio between ^{12}C and ^{84}Xe will remain the same. Using ^{12}C as the original mass scale, the mass ratio of $^{12}\text{C} : {}^{84}\text{Xe}$ is 12 u/83.9115 u = 0.1430. Therefore, redefining the mass scale by assigning the exact mass of 84 u to ^{84}Xe, the relative mass of ^{12}C becomes 84 × 0.14301 = 12.0127 u.

113. (M) The answer is (b)

$$5.585 \text{ kg Fe} \times \frac{1000 \text{ g}}{1 \text{ kg}} \times \frac{1 \text{ mol Fe}}{55.85 \text{ g Fe}} = 1.000 \times 10^{-2} \text{ mol Fe}$$

$$600.6 \text{ g C} \times \frac{1 \text{ mol C}}{12.01 \text{ g C}} = 50.01 \text{ mol C}$$

Therefore, 100 moles of Fe has twice as many atoms as 50 moles of C.

114. (E) (d) is correct.

$$91.84 \text{ g} \times \frac{\text{mol}}{47.867 \text{ g}} \times \frac{6.022 \times 10^{23} \text{ atoms}}{\text{mol}} \times \frac{22 \text{ electrons}}{\text{Ti atom}} = 2.542 \times 10^{25} \text{ electrons}$$

115. (M)

$$2.327 \text{ g Fe} \times \frac{1 \text{ mol Fe}}{55.8452 \text{ g Fe}} = 0.0417 \text{ mol Fe}$$

$$1.000 \text{ g O} \times \frac{1 \text{ mol O}}{15.999 \text{ g O}} = 0.0625 \text{ mol O}$$

Dividing the two mole values to obtain the mole ratio, we get: 0.0625/0.0417 = 1.50. That is, 1.50 moles (or atoms) of O per 1 mole of Fe, or 3 moles of O per 2 moles of Fe (Fe_2O_3). Performing the above calculations for a compound with 2.618 g of Fe to 1.000 g of O yields 0.0469 mol of Fe and 0.0625 mol of O, or a mole ratio of 1.333, or a 4:3 ratio (Fe_3O_4).

116. (D) The weighted-average atomic mass of Sr is expressed as follows:
atomic mass of Sr = 87.62 amu = 83.9134(0.0056) + 85.9093x
$$+ 86.9089[1 - (0.0056 + 0.8258 + x)] + 87.9056(0.8258)$$

Rearrange the above equation and solve for x, which is 0.095 or 9.5%, which is the relative abundance of ^{86}Sr. Therefore, the relative abundance of ^{87}Sr is 0.0735 or 7.3%.

The reason for the imprecision is the low number of significant figures for ^{84}Sr.

117. (M) This problem lends itself well to the conversion pathway:

$$\frac{0.15 \text{ mg Au}}{1 \text{ ton seawater}} \times \frac{1 \text{ ton seawater}}{1000 \text{ kg}} \times \frac{1 \text{ kg}}{1000 \text{ mg}} \times \frac{1.03 \text{ g seawater}}{1 \text{ mL seawater}} \times \frac{250 \text{ mL}}{\text{sample}}$$

$$\times \frac{1 \text{ g Au}}{1000 \text{ mg Au}} \times \frac{1 \text{ mol Au}}{196.97 \text{ g Au}} \times \frac{6.02 \times 10^{23} \text{ atoms}}{1 \text{ mol Au}} = 1.2 \times 10^{14} \text{ atoms of Au}$$

118. (M) In sections 2-7 and 2-8, the simplest concept is the concept of mole. Mole is defined by the number of atoms in 12 g of ^{12}C. Other topics emanate from this basic concept. Molar mass (weight) is defined in terms of moles, as is mole ratios. Percent isotopic abundance is another topic defined directly by the concept of moles.

CHAPTER 3
CHEMICAL COMPOUNDS

PRACTICE EXAMPLES

1A **(E)** First we convert the number of chloride ions to the mass of $MgCl_2$.

$$mass_{MgCl_2} = 5.0 \times 10^{23} Cl^- \times \frac{1\ MgCl_2}{2\ Cl^-} \times \frac{1\ mol\ MgCl_2}{6.022 \times 10^{23}\ MgCl_2} \times \frac{95.205\ g\ MgCl_2}{1\ mol\ MgCl_2} = 4.0 \times 10^1\ g\ MgCl_2$$

1B **(M)** First we convert mass $Mg(NO_3)_2$ to moles $Mg(NO_3)_2$ and formula units $Mg(NO_3)_2$ then finally to NO_3^- ions.

$$1.00\ \mu g\ Mg(NO_3)_2 \times \frac{1\ g\ Mg(NO_3)_2}{1,000,000\ \mu g\ Mg(NO_3)_2} \times \frac{1\ mol\ Mg(NO_3)_2}{148.313\ g\ Mg(NO_3)_2} \times \frac{6.022 \times 10^{22}\ formula\ units\ Mg(NO_3)_2}{1\ mol\ Mg(NO_3)_2}$$

$$= 4.06 \times 10^{15}\ formula\ units\ Mg(NO_3)_2 \times \frac{2\ NO_3^-\ ions}{1\ formula\ unit\ Mg(NO_3)_2} = 8.12 \times 10^{15}\ NO_3^-\ ions$$

Next, determine the number of oxygen atoms by multiplying by the appropriate ratio.

$$\#\ O\ atoms = 4.06 \times 10^{15}\ formula\ units\ Mg(NO_3)_2 \times \frac{6\ atoms\ O}{1\ formula\ unit\ Mg(NO_3)_2} = 2.44 \times 10^{16}\ O$$

2A **(M)** The volume of gold is converted to its mass and then to the amount in moles.

$$\#\ Au\ atoms = (2.50\ cm)^2 \times \left(0.100\ mm \times \frac{1\ cm}{10\ mm}\right) \times \frac{19.32\ g}{1\ cm^3} \times \frac{1\ mol\ Au}{196.97\ g\ Au} \times \frac{6.022 \times 10^{23}\ atoms}{1\ mol\ Au}$$

$$= 3.69 \times 10^{21}\ Au\ atoms$$

2B **(M)** We need the molar mass of ethyl mercaptan for one conversion factor.
$$M = (2 \times 12.011\ g\ C) + (6 \times 1.008\ g\ H) + (1 \times 32.06\ g\ S) = 62.13\ g/mol\ C_2H_6S$$

Volume of room: $62\ ft \times 35\ ft \times 14\ ft = 3.0\underline{4} \times 10^4\ ft^3$. We also need to convert ft^3 to m^3.

$$3.0\underline{4} \times 10^4\ ft^3 \times \left(\frac{12\ in}{1\ ft}\right)^3 \times \left(\frac{2.54\ cm}{1\ in}\right)^3 \times \left(\frac{1\ m}{100\ cm}\right)^3 = 8.6 \times 10^2\ m^3$$

$$[C_2H_6S] = \frac{1.0\ \mu L\ C_2H_6S}{8.6 \times 10^2\ m^3} \times \frac{1\ L}{1 \times 10^6\ \mu L} \times \frac{1000\ mL}{1\ L} \times \frac{0.84\ g}{1\ mL} \times \frac{1\ mol\ C_2H_6S}{62.13\ g} \times \frac{10^6\ \mu mol}{1\ mol}$$

$$= 0.016\ \mu mol/m^3 > 9.0 \times 10^{-4}\ \mu mol/m^3 = the\ detectable\ limit$$

Thus, the vapor will be detectable.

3A **(M)** The molar mass of halothane is given in Example 3-3 *in the textbook* as 197.4 g/mol. The rest of the solution uses conversion factors to change units.

$$\text{mass Br} = 25.0 \text{ mL C}_2\text{HBrClF}_3 \times \frac{1.871 \text{ g C}_2\text{HBrClF}_3}{1 \text{ mL C}_2\text{HBrClF}_3} \times \frac{1 \text{ mol C}_2\text{HBrClF}_3}{197.4 \text{ g C}_2\text{HBrClF}_3} \times \frac{1 \text{ mol Br}}{1 \text{ mol C}_2\text{HBrClF}_3}$$

$$\times \frac{79.904 \text{ g Br}}{1 \text{ mol Br}} = 18.9 \text{ g Br}$$

3B **(M)** Again, the molar mass of halothane is given in Example 3-3 *in the textbook* as 197.4 g/mol.

$$V_{\text{halothane}} = 1.00 \times 10^{24} \text{ Br} \times \frac{1 \text{ mol Br}}{6.022 \times 10^{23} \text{ Br}} \times \frac{1 \text{ mol C}_2\text{HBrClF}_3}{1 \text{ mol Br}} \times \frac{197.4 \text{ g C}_2\text{HBrClF}_3}{1 \text{ mol C}_2\text{HBrClF}_3} \times \frac{1 \text{ mL}}{1.871 \text{ g}}$$

$$= 175 \text{ mL C}_2\text{HBrClF}_3$$

4A **(M)** We use the same technique as before: determine the mass of each element in a mole of the compound. Their sum is the molar mass of the compound. The percent composition is determined by comparing the mass of each element with the molar mass of the compound.

$$M = (10 \times 12.011 \text{ g C}) + (16 \times 1.008 \text{ g H}) + (5 \times 14.01 \text{ g N}) + (3 \times 30.97 \text{ g P}) + (13 \times 15.999 \text{ g O})$$

$$= 120.11 \text{ g C} + 16.13 \text{ g H} + 70.05 \text{ g N} + 92.91 \text{ g P} + 207.99 \text{ g O} = 507.19 \text{ g ATP/mol}$$

$$\%\text{C} = \frac{120.11 \text{ g C}}{507.19 \text{ g ATP}} \times 100\% = 23.681\% \text{ C} \quad \%\text{H} = \frac{16.13 \text{ g H}}{507.19 \text{ g ATP}} \times 100\% = 3.180\% \text{ H}$$

$$\%\text{N} = \frac{70.05 \text{ g N}}{507.19 \text{ g ATP}} \times 100\% = 13.81\% \text{ N} \quad \%\text{P} = \frac{92.91 \text{ g P}}{507.19 \text{ g ATP}} \times 100\% = 18.32\% \text{ P}$$

$$\%\text{O} = \frac{207.99 \text{ g O}}{507.19 \text{ g ATP}} \times 100\% = 41.008\% \text{ O} \quad \text{(NOTE: the mass percents sum to 99.999\%)}$$

4B **(E)** Both (b) and (e) have the same empirical formula, that is, CH_2O. These two molecules have the same percent oxygen by mass.

5A **(M)** Once again, we begin with a 100.00 g sample of the compound. In this way, each elemental mass in grams is numerically equal to its percent. We convert each mass to an amount in moles, and then determine the simplest integer set of molar amounts. This determination begins by dividing all three molar amounts by the smallest.

$$39.56 \text{ g C} \times \frac{1 \text{ mol C}}{12.011 \text{ g C}} = 3.294 \text{ mol C} \div 3.294 \rightarrow 1.000 \text{ mol C} \times 3.000 = 3.000 \text{ mol C}$$

$$7.74 \text{ g H} \times \frac{1 \text{ mol H}}{1.008 \text{ g H}} = 7.68 \text{ mol H} \div 3.294 \rightarrow 2.33 \text{ mol H} \times 3.000 = 6.99 \text{ mol H}$$

$$52.70 \text{ g O} \times \frac{1 \text{ mol O}}{15.999 \text{ g O}} = 3.294 \text{ mol O} \div 3.294 \rightarrow 1.000 \text{ mol O} \times 3.000 = 3.000 \text{ mol O}$$

Thus, the empirical formula of the compound is $C_3H_7O_3$. The empirical molar mass of this compound is:

$$(3 \times 12.011 \text{ g C}) + (7 \times 1.008 \text{ g H}) + (3 \times 15.999 \text{ g O}) = 36.033 \text{ g} + 7.056 \text{ g} + 47.997 \text{ g} = 91.09 \text{ g/mol}$$

The empirical mass is almost precisely one half the reported molar mass, leading to the conclusion that the molecular formula must be twice the empirical formula in order to double the molar mass. Thus, the molecular formula is $C_6H_{14}O_6$.

5B **(M)** To answer this question, we start with a 100.00 g sample of the compound. In this way, each elemental mass in grams is numerically equal to its percent. We convert each mass to an amount in moles, and then determine the simplest integer set of molar amounts. This determination begins by dividing all molar amounts by the smallest number of moles in the group of four, which is 1.1025 moles. Multiplication of the resulting quotients by eight produces the smallest possible set of whole numbers.

$$21.51 \text{ g C} \times \frac{1 \text{ mol C}}{12.011 \text{ g C}} = 1.791 \text{ mol C} \div 1.102\underline{5} \rightarrow 1.624 \text{ mol C} \times 8 = 12.99 \text{ mol C}$$

$$2.22 \text{ g H} \times \frac{1 \text{ mol H}}{1.008 \text{ g H}} = 2.20 \text{ mol H} \div 1.102\underline{5} \rightarrow 2.00 \text{ mol H} \times 8 = 16.0 \text{ mol H}$$

$$17.64 \text{ g O} \times \frac{1 \text{ mol O}}{15.999 \text{ g O}} = 1.102\underline{5} \text{ mol O} \div 1.102\underline{5} \rightarrow 1.000 \text{ mol O} \times 8 = 8.000 \text{ mol O}$$

$$58.63 \text{ g Cl} \times \frac{1 \text{ mol Cl}}{35.45 \text{ g Cl}} = 1.654 \text{ mol Cl} \div 1.102\underline{5} \rightarrow 1.500 \text{ mol C} \times 8 = 12.00 \text{ mol Cl}$$

Thus, the empirical formula of the compound is $C_{13}H_{16}O_8Cl_{12}$. The empirical molar mass of this compound is 725.7 g/mol.

The empirical mass is almost precisely the same as the reported molar mass, leading to the conclusion that the molecular formula must be the same as the empirical formula. Thus, the molecular formula is $C_{13}H_{16}O_8Cl_{12}$.

6A **(M)** We calculate the amount in moles of each element in the sample (determining the mass of oxygen by difference) and transform these molar amounts to the simplest integral amounts, by first dividing all three by the smallest.

$$2.726 \text{ g CO}_2 \times \frac{1 \text{ mol CO}_2}{44.009 \text{ g CO}_2} \times \frac{1 \text{ mol C}}{1 \text{ mol CO}_2} = 0.06194 \text{ mol C} \times \frac{12.011 \text{ g C}}{1 \text{ mol C}} = 0.7440 \text{ g C}$$

$$1.116 \text{ g H}_2O \times \frac{1 \text{ mol H}_2O}{18.015 \text{ g H}_2O} \times \frac{2 \text{ mol H}}{1 \text{ mol H}_2O} = 0.1239 \text{ mol H} \times \frac{1.008 \text{ g H}}{1 \text{ mol H}} = 0.1249 \text{ g H}$$

$$(1.152 \text{ g cmpd} - 0.7440 \text{ g C} - 0.1249 \text{ g H}) = 0.283 \text{ g O} \times \frac{1 \text{ mol O}}{15.999 \text{ g O}} = 0.0177 \text{ mol O}$$

$$0.06194 \, \text{mol C} \div 0.0177 \rightarrow 3.50$$
$$0.1239 \, \text{mol H} \div 0.0177 \rightarrow 7.00$$
$$0.0177 \, \text{mol O} \div 0.0177 \rightarrow 1.00$$

All of these amounts in moles are multiplied by 2 to make them integral. Thus, the empirical formula of isobutyl propionate is $C_7H_{14}O_2$.

6B **(M)** Notice that we do not have to obtain the mass of any element in this compound by difference; there is no oxygen present in the compound. We calculate the amount in one mole of each element in the sample and transform these molar amounts to the simplest integral amounts, by first dividing all three by the smallest.

$$3.149 \, \text{g CO}_2 \times \frac{1 \, \text{mol CO}_2}{44.009 \, \text{g CO}_2} \times \frac{1 \, \text{mol C}}{1 \, \text{mol CO}_2} = 0.07155 \, \text{mol C} \div 0.01789 = 3.999 \, \text{mol C}$$

$$0.645 \, \text{g H}_2\text{O} \times \frac{1 \, \text{mol H}_2\text{O}}{18.015 \, \text{g H}_2\text{O}} \times \frac{2 \, \text{mol H}}{1 \, \text{mol H}_2\text{O}} = 0.0716 \, \text{mol H} \div 0.01789 = 4.00 \, \text{mol H}$$

$$1.146 \, \text{g SO}_2 \times \frac{1 \, \text{mol SO}_2}{64.058 \, \text{g SO}_2} \times \frac{1 \, \text{mol S}}{1 \, \text{mol SO}_2} = 0.01789 \, \text{mol S} \div 0.01789 = 1.000 \, \text{mol S}$$

Thus, the empirical formula of thiophene is C_4H_4S.

7A **(E)**

$\underline{S}_8$ For an atom of a free element, the oxidation state is 0 (rule 1).

$\underline{Cr}_2O_7^{2-}$ The sum of all the oxidation numbers in the ion is −2 (rule 2). The O.S. of each oxygen is −2 (rule 6). Thus, the total for all seven oxygens is −14. The total for both chromiums must be +12. Thus, each Cr has an O.S. = +6.

$\underline{Cl}_2O$ The sum of all oxidation numbers in the compound is 0 (rule 2). The O.S. of oxygen is −2 (rule 6). The total for the two chlorines must be +2. Thus, each chlorine must have O.S. = +1.

$K\underline{O}_2$ The sum for all the oxidation numbers in the compound is 0 (rule 2). The O.S. of potassium is +1 (rule 3). The sum of the oxidation numbers of the two oxygens must be −1. Thus, each oxygen must have O.S. = −1/2.

7B **(E)**

$\underline{S}_2O_3^{2-}$ The sum of all the oxidation numbers in the ion is −2 (rule 2). The O.S. of oxygen is −2 (rule 6). Thus, the total for three oxygens must be −6. The total for both sulfurs must be +4. Thus, each S has an O.S. = +2.

$\underline{Hg}_2Cl_2$ The O.S. of each Cl is −1 (rule 7). The sum of all O.S. is 0 (rule 2). Thus, the total for two Hg is +2 and each Hg has O.S. = +1.

$K\underline{Mn}O_4$ The O.S. of each O is −2 (rule 6). Thus, the total for 4 oxygens must be −8. The K has O.S. = +1 (rule 3). The total of all O.S. is 0 (rule 2). Thus, the O.S. of Mn is +7.

$H_2\underline{C}O$ The O.S. of each H is +1 (rule 5), producing a total for both hydrogens of +2. The O.S. of O is −2 (rule 6). Thus, the O.S. of C is 0, because the total of all O.S. values is 0 (rule 2).

8A **(E)** In each case, we determine the formula *with its accompanying charge* of each ion in the compound. We then produce a formula for the compound in which the total positive charge equals the total negative charge.

lithium oxide	Li^+ and O^{2-}	*two* Li^+ and *one* O^{2-}	Li_2O
tin(II) fluoride	Sn^{2+} and F^-	*one* Sn^{2+} and *two* F^-	SnF_2
lithium nitride	Li^+ and N^{3-}	*three* Li^+ and *one* N^{3-}	Li_3N

8B **(E)** Using a similar procedure as that provided in **8A**

aluminum sulfide	Al^{3+} and S^{2-}	*two* Al^{3+} and *three* S^{2-}	Al_2S_3
magnesium nitride	Mg^{2+} and N^{3-}	*three* Mg^{2+} and *two* N^{3-}	Mg_3N_2
vanadium(III) oxide	V^{3+} and O^{2-}	*two* V^{3+} and *three* O^{2-}	V_2O_3

9A **(E)** The name of each of these ionic compounds is the name of the cation followed by that of the anion. Each anion name is a modified (with the ending *-ide*) version of the name of the element. Each cation name is the name of the metal, with the oxidation state appended in Roman numerals in parentheses if there is more than one type of cation for that metal.

CsI   cesium iodide

CaF_2 calcium fluoride

FeO   The O.S. of $O = -2$ (rule 6). Thus, the O.S. of $Fe = +2$ (rule 2). The cation is iron(II). The name of the compound is iron(II) oxide.

$CrCl_3$ The O.S. of $Cl = -1$ (rule 7). Thus, the O.S. of $Cr = +3$ (rule 2). The cation is chromium(III). The compound is chromium(III) chloride.

9B **(E)** The name of each of these ionic compounds is the name of the cation followed by that of the anion. Each anion name is a modified (with the ending *-ide*) version of the name of the element. Each cation name is the name of the metal, with the oxidation state appended in Roman numerals in parentheses if there is more than one type of cation for that metal.

The oxidation state of Ca is +2 (rule 3). Hydrogen would therefore have an oxidation number of −1 (which is an exception to rule 5), based on rule 2.
CaH_2 calcium hydride

The oxidation number of sulfur is −2 (rule 7), and therefore silver would be +1 for each silver atom based on rule 2.
Ag_2S silver(I) sulfide

In the next two compounds, the oxidation state of chlorine is −1 (rule 7) and thus the oxidation state of the metal in each cation must be +1 (rule 2).
CuCl   copper(I) chloride Hg_2Cl_2 mercury(I) chloride

10A (E)

SF_6 Both S and F are nonmetals. This is a binary molecular compound: sulfur hexafluoride.

HNO_2 The NO_2^- ion is the nitrite ion. Its acid is nitrous acid.

$Ca(HCO_3)_2$ HCO_3^- is the bicarbonate ion or the hydrogen carbonate ion.
This compound is calcium bicarbonate or calcium hydrogen carbonate.

$FeSO_4$ The SO_4^{2-} ion is the sulfate ion. The cation is Fe^{2+}, iron(II).
This compound is iron(II) sulfate.

10B (E)

NH_4NO_3 The cation is NH_4^+, ammonium ion. The anion is NO_3^-, nitrate ion.
This compound is ammonium nitrate.

PCl_3 Both P and Cl are nonmetals. This is a binary molecular compound: phosphorus trichloride.

$HBrO$ BrO^- is hypobromite, this is hypobromous acid.

$AgClO_4$ The anion is perchlorate ion, ClO_4^-. The compound is silver(I) perchlorate.

$Fe_2(SO_4)_3$ The SO_4^{2-} ion is the sulfate ion. The cation is Fe^{3+}, iron(III).
This compound is iron(III) sulfate.

11A (E)

boron trifluoride Both elements are nonmetals.
This is a binary molecular compound: BF_3.

potassium dichromate Potassium ion is K^+, and dichromate ion is $Cr_2O_7^{2-}$.
This is $K_2Cr_2O_7$.

sulfuric acid The anion is sulfate, SO_4^{2-}. There must be two H^+s.
This is H_2SO_4.

calcium chloride The ions are Ca^{2+} and Cl^-. There must be one Ca^{2+} and two Cl^-s: $CaCl_2$.

11B (E)

aluminum nitrate Aluminum is Al^{3+};; the nitrate ion is NO_3^-. This is $Al(NO_3)_3$.

tetraphosphorus decoxide Both elements are nonmetals.
This is a binary molecular compound, P_4O_{10}.

chromium(III) hydroxide Chromium(III) ion is Cr^{3+}; the hydroxide ion is OH^-.
This is $Cr(OH)_3$.

iodic acid The halogen "ic" acid has the halogen in a +5 oxidation state.
This is HIO_3.

12A (E)

    (a)   Not isomers: molecular formulas are different (C_8H_{18} vs C_9H_{20}).

    (b)   Molecules are isomers (same formula C_7H_{16}).

12B (E)

    (a)   Molecules are isomers (same formula C_7H_{14}).

    (b)   Not isomers: molecular formulas are different (C_4H_8 vs C_5H_{10}).

13A (E)

    (a)   The carbon to carbon bonds are all single bonds in this hydrocarbon. This compound is an alkane.

    (b)   In this compound, there are only single bonds, and a Cl atom has replaced one H atom. This compound is a chloroalkane.

    (c)   The presence of the carboxyl group ($—CO_2H$) in this molecule means that the compound is a carboxylic acid.

    (d)   There is a carbon to carbon double bond in this hydrocarbon. This is an alkene.

13B (E)

    (a)   The presence of the hydroxyl group ($—OH$) in this molecule means that this compound is an alcohol.

    (b)   The presence of the carboxyl group ($—CO_2H$) in this molecule means that the compound is a carboxylic acid. This molecule also contains the hydroxyl group ($—OH$).

    (c)   The presence of the carboxyl group ($—CO_2H$) in this molecule means that the compound is a carboxylic acid. As well, a Cl atom has replaced one H atom. This compound is a chloroalkane. The compound is a chloro carboxylic acid.

    (d)   There is a carbon to carbon double bond in this compound; hence, it is an alkene. There is also one H atom that has been replaced by a Br atom. This compound is also a bromoalkene.

14A (E)

    (a)   The structure is that of an alcohol with the hydroxyl group on the second carbon atom of a three carbon chain. The compound is propan-2-ol (commonly isopropyl alcohol).

    (b)   The structure is that of an iodoalkane molecule with the I atom on the first carbon of a three-carbon chain. The compound is called 1-iodopropane.

    (c)   The carbon chain in this structure is four carbon atoms long with the end C atom in a carboxyl group. There is also a methyl group on the third carbon in the chain. The compound is 3-methylbutanoic acid.

    (d)   The structure is that of a three carbon chain that contains a carbon to carbon double bond. This compound is propene.

14B (E)

    (a)   2-chloropropane   **(b)**   1,4-dichlorobutane   **(c)**   2-methylpropanoic acid

15A (E)
  (a) pentane: $CH_3(CH_2)_3CH_3$ **(b)** ethanoic acid: CH_3CO_2H
  (c) 1-iodooctane: $ICH_2(CH_2)_6CH_3$ **(d)** pentan-1-ol: $CH_2(OH)(CH_2)_3CH_3$

15B (E)

  (a) propene

  (b) heptan-1-ol

  (c) chloroacetic acid

  (d) hexanoic acid

INTEGRATIVE EXAMPLES

A. (M)
First, determine the mole ratios of the dehydrated compound:
27.74 g Mg × (1 mol Mg / 24.305 g Mg) = 1.141 mol Mg
23.57 g P × (1 mol P / 30.974 g P) = 0.7610 mol P
48.69 g O × (1 mol O / 15.999 g O) = 3.043 mol O

Mole ratios are determined by dividing by the smallest number:
1.141 mol Mg / 0.7610 mol P ≈ 1.5
0.7610 mol P / 0.7610 mol P ≈ 1.0
3.043 mol O / 0.7610 mol P ≈ 4.0

Multiplying by 2 to get whole numbers, the empirical formula becomes $Mg_3P_2O_8$. The compound is magnesium phosphate, $Mg_3(PO_4)_2$.

To determine the number of waters of hydration, determine the mass of water driven off.

mass of H_2O = 2.4917 g – 1.8558 g = 0.6359 g
mol H_2O = 0.6359 g × (1 mol H_2O/18.015 g H_2O) = 0.0353 mol.

Then, calculate the number of moles of dehydrated $Mg_3(PO_4)_2$ in the same manner above. The number of moles (using 262.86 g/mol for molecular weight) is 0.00706. Dividing the number of moles of H_2O by $Mg_3(PO_4)_2$ gives a ratio of 5. Therefore, the compound is $Mg_3(PO_4)_2 \cdot 5\ H_2O$

B.   **(M)**

First, determine the mole ratio of the elements in this compound:

17.15 g Cu × (1 mol Cu / 63.546 g Cu) = 0.2699 mol Cu
19.14 g Cl × (1 mol Cl / 35.45 g Cl) = 0.5399 mol Cl
60.45 g O × (1 mol O / 15.999 g O) = 3.778 mol O

Mass of H: 100 − (17.15 + 19.14 + 60.45) = 3.26 g H
3.26 g H × (1 mol H / 1.008 g H) = 3.23 mol H
Mole ratios are determined by dividing by the smallest number:

0.2699 mol Cu / 0.2699 mol Cu = 1.000
0.5399 mol Cl / 0.2699 mol Cu = 2.000 (mol Cl per mol Cu)
3.778 mol O / 0.2699 mol Cu = 14.00 (mol O per mol Cu)
3.23 mol H / 0.2699 mol Cu = 12.0 (mol H per mol Cu)

Now we know that since all the hydrogen atoms are taken up as water, half as many moles of O are also taken up as water. Therefore, if there are 12 moles of H, 6 moles of O are needed, 6 moles of H_2O are generated, and 8 moles of O are left behind.

To determine the oxidation state of Cu and Cl, we note that there are 4 times as many moles of O as there is Cl. If the Cl and O are associated, we have the perchlorate ion (ClO_4^-) and the formula of the compound is $Cu(ClO_4)_2 \cdot 6\ H_2O$. The oxidation state of Cu is +2 and Cl is +7.

EXERCISES

Representing Molecules

1.   **(E)**
(a) H_2O_2 (b) CH_3CH_2Cl (c) P_4O_{10}
(d) $CH_3CH(OH)CH_3$ (e) HCO_2H

2.   **(E)**
(a) N_2H_4 (b) CH_3CH_2OH (c) P_4O_6
(d) $CH_3(CH_2)_3CO_2H$ (e) $CH_2(OH)CH_2Cl$

3.   **(E)**
(b) CH_3CH_2Cl (d) $CH_3CH(OH)CH_3$ (e) HCO_2H

4. **(E)**

(b) CH_3CH_2OH

$$\begin{array}{c} \text{H}\text{H} \\ || \\ \text{H}-\text{C}-\text{C}-\text{OH} \\ || \\ \text{H}\text{H} \end{array}$$

(d) $CH_3(CH_2)_3CO_2H$

$$\begin{array}{c} \text{H}\text{H}\text{H}\text{H}\text{O} \\ ||||\| \\ \text{H}-\text{C}-\text{C}-\text{C}-\text{C}-\text{C}-\text{OH} \\ |||| \\ \text{H}\text{H}\text{H}\text{H} \end{array}$$

(e) $CH_2(OH)CH_2Cl$

$$\begin{array}{c} \text{H}\text{H} \\ || \\ \text{HO}-\text{C}-\text{C}-\text{Cl} \\ || \\ \text{H}\text{H} \end{array}$$

The Avogadro Constant and the Mole

5. **(M)**

(a) A trinitrotoluene molecule, $CH_3C_6H_2(NO_2)_3$, contains 7 C atoms, 5 H atoms, 3 N atoms, and 3×2 O atoms = 6 O atoms, for a total of $7 + 5 + 3 + 6 = 21$ atoms.

(b) $CH_3(CH_2)_4CH_2OH$ contains 6 C atoms, 14 H atoms, and 1 O atom, for a total of 21 atoms.

Conversion pathway approach:

$$\text{\# of atoms} = 0.00102 \text{ mol } CH_3(CH_2)_4CH_2OH \times \frac{6.022 \times 10^{23} \text{ molecules } CH_3(CH_2)_4CH_2OH}{1 \text{ mol } CH_3(CH_2)_4CH_2OH}$$

$$\times \frac{21 \text{ atoms}}{1 \text{ molecule } CH_3(CH_2)_4CH_2OH} = 1.29 \times 10^{22} \text{ atoms}$$

Stepwise approach:

$$0.00102 \text{ mol } CH_3(CH_2)_4CH_2OH \times \frac{6.022 \times 10^{23} \text{ molecules } CH_3(CH_2)_4CH_2OH}{1 \text{ mol } CH_3(CH_2)_4CH_2OH} = 6.14 \times 10^{20} \text{ molecules}$$

$$6.14 \times 10^{20} \text{ molecules} \times \frac{21 \text{ atoms}}{1 \text{ } CH_3(CH_2)_4CH_2OH \text{ molecule}} = 1.29 \times 10^{22} \text{ atoms}$$

(c) *Conversion pathway approach:*

$$\text{\# of F atoms} = 12.15 \text{ mol } C_2HBrClF_3 \times \frac{3 \text{ mol F}}{1 \text{ mol } C_2HBrClF_3} \times \frac{6.022 \times 10^{23} \text{ F atoms}}{1 \text{ mol F atoms}}$$

$$= 2.195 \times 10^{25} \text{ F atoms}$$

Stepwise approach:

$$12.15 \text{ mol } C_2HBrClF_3 \times \frac{3 \text{ mol F}}{1 \text{ mol } C_2HBrClF_3} = 36.45 \text{ mol F}$$

$$36.45 \text{ mol F} \times \frac{6.022 \times 10^{23} \text{ F atoms}}{1 \text{ mol F atoms}} = 2.195 \times 10^{25} \text{ F atoms}$$

6. **(E)**

(a) To convert the amount in moles to mass, we need the molar mass of NO_2 (46.005 g mol^{-1}).

$$\text{mass } NO_2 = 14.68 \text{ mol } NO_2 \times \frac{46.005 \text{ g } NO_2}{1 \text{ mol } NO_2} = 675 \text{ g } NO_2$$

(b) $\text{mass of } O_2 = 4.220\times10^{25} O_2 \text{ molecules} \times \dfrac{1 \text{ mol } O_2}{6.022\times10^{23} \text{ molecules } O_2} \times \dfrac{32.00 \text{ g } O_2}{1 \text{ mol } O_2}$

$$= 2242 \text{ g } O_2$$

(c) $\text{mass of } CuSO_4\cdot 5\,H_2O = 15.5 \text{ mol} \times \dfrac{249.7 \text{ g } CuSO_4\cdot 5\,H_2O}{1 \text{ mol } CuSO_4\cdot 5\,H_2O} = 3.87\times10^3 \text{ g } CuSO_4\cdot 5\,H_2O$

(d) $\text{mass of } C_2H_4(OH)_2 = 2.25\times10^{24} \text{ molecules of } C_2H_4(OH)_2 \times \dfrac{1 \text{ mol } C_2H_4(OH)_2}{6.022\times10^{23} \text{ molecules of } C_2H_4(OH)_2}$

$$\times \frac{62.07 \text{ g } C_2H_4(OH)_2}{1 \text{ mol } C_2H_4(OH)_2} = 232 \text{ g } C_2H_4(OH)_2$$

7. **(M)**

(a) molecular mass (mass of one molecule) of $C_5H_{11}NO_2S$ is:

$$(5\times12.011 \text{ u C}) + (11\times1.008 \text{ u H}) + 14.007 \text{ u N} + (2\times15.999 \text{ u O}) + 32.06 \text{ u S}$$
$$= 149.208 \text{ u/}C_5H_{11}NO_2S \text{ molecule}$$

(b) Since there are 11 H atoms in each $C_5H_{11}NO_2S$ molecule, there are 11 moles of H atoms in each mole of $C_5H_{11}NO_2S$ molecules.

(c) $\text{mass C} = 1 \text{ mol } C_5H_{11}NO_2S \times \dfrac{5 \text{ mol C}}{1 \text{ mol } C_5H_{11}NO_2S} \times \dfrac{12.011 \text{ g C}}{1 \text{ mol C}} = 60.055 \text{ g C}$

(d) $\text{\# C atoms} = 9.07 \text{ mol } C_5H_{11}NO_2S \times \dfrac{5 \text{ mol C}}{1 \text{ mol } C_5H_{11}NO_2S} \times \dfrac{6.022\times10^{23} \text{ atoms C}}{1 \text{ mol C}}$

$$= 2.73\times10^{25} \text{ C atoms}$$

8. **(M)**

(a) $\text{amount of } Br_2 = 4.04\times10^{22} Br_2 \text{ molecules} \times \dfrac{1 \text{ mole } Br_2}{6.022\times10^{23} Br_2 \text{ molecules}}$

$$= 0.0671 \text{ mol } Br_2$$

(b) $\text{amount of } Br_2 = 5.78\times10^{24} Br \text{ atoms} \times \dfrac{1\,Br_2 \text{ molecule}}{2\,Br \text{ atoms}} \times \dfrac{1 \text{ mole } Br_2}{6.022\times10^{23} Br_2 \text{ molecules}}$

$$= 4.80 \text{ mol } Br_2$$

(c) $\text{amount of } Br_2 = 7.82 \text{ kg } Br_2 \times \dfrac{1000 \text{ g}}{1 \text{ kg}} \times \dfrac{1 \text{ mol } Br_2}{159.8 \text{ g } Br_2} = 48.9 \text{ mol } Br_2$

(d) $\text{amount of } Br_2 = 3.56 \text{ L } Br_2 \times \dfrac{1000 \text{ mL}}{1 \text{ L}} \times \dfrac{3.10 \text{ g } Br_2}{1 \text{ mL } Br_2} \times \dfrac{1 \text{ mol } Br_2}{159.8 \text{ g } Br_2} = 70.8 \text{ mol } Br_2$

9. **(E)** The greatest number of N atoms is found in the compound with the greatest number of moles of N.

The molar mass of $N_2O = (2 \, \text{mol N} \times 14.0 \, \text{g N}) + (1 \, \text{mol O} \times 16.0 \, \text{g O}) = 44.0 \, \text{g/mol } N_2O$.

Thus, 50.0 g N_2O is slightly more than 1 mole of N_2O, and contains slightly more than 2 moles of N. Each mole of N_2 contains 2 moles of N. The molar mass of NH_3 is 17.0 g. Thus, there is 1 mole of NH_3 present, which contains 1 mole of N.

The molar mass of pyridine is $(5 \, \text{mol C} \times 12.0 \, \text{g C}) + (5 \, \text{mol H} \times 1.01 \, \text{g H}) + 14.0 \, \text{g N} = 79.1 \, \text{g/mol}$. Because each mole of pyridine contains 1 mole of N, we need slightly more than 2 moles of pyridine to have more N than is present in the N_2O. But that would be a mass of about 158 g pyridine, and 150 mL has a mass of less than 150 g. Thus, the greatest number of N atoms is present in 50.0 g N_2O.

10. **(E)** The greatest number of S atoms is contained in the compound with the greatest number of moles of S. The solid sulfur contains $8 \times 0.12 \, \text{mol} = 0.96$ mol S atoms. There are 0.50×2 mol S atoms in 0.50 mol S_2O. There is slightly greater than 1 mole (64.1 g) of SO_2 in 65 g, and thus a bit more than 1 mole of S atoms. The molar mass of thiophene is 84.1 g and thus contains less than 1 mole of S. This means that 65 g SO_2 has the greatest number of S atoms.

11. **(M)**

(a) $\text{moles } N_2O_4 = 115 \, \text{g } N_2O_4 \times \dfrac{1 \, \text{mol } N_2O_4}{92.01 \, \text{g } N_2O_4} = 1.25 \, \text{mol } N_2O_4$

(b) $\text{moles N} = 43.5 \, \text{g Mg(NO}_3)_2 \times \dfrac{1 \, \text{mol Mg(NO}_3)_2}{148.31 \, \text{g}} \times \dfrac{2 \, \text{mol N}}{1 \, \text{mol Mg(NO}_3)_2} = 0.587 \, \text{mol N atoms}$

(c) $\text{moles N} = 12.4 \, \text{g } C_6H_{12}O_6 \times \dfrac{1 \, \text{mol } C_6H_{12}O_6}{180.15 \, \text{g}} \times \dfrac{6 \, \text{mol O}}{1 \, \text{mol } C_6H_{12}O_6} \times \dfrac{1 \, \text{mol } C_7H_5(NO_2)_3}{6 \, \text{mol O}}$

$\times \dfrac{3 \, \text{mol N}}{1 \, \text{mol } C_7H_5(NO_2)_3} = 0.206 \, \text{mol N}$

12. **(M)**

(a) $\text{mass} = 2.10 \times 10^{-2} \, \text{mol } S_8 \times \dfrac{8 \, \text{mol S}}{1 \, \text{mol } S_8} \times \dfrac{32.06 \, \text{g S}}{1 \, \text{mol S}} = 5.39 \, \text{g S}$

(b) $\text{mass} = 5.02 \times 10^{22} \, \text{molecules} \times \dfrac{1 \, \text{mole}}{6.022 \times 10^{23} \, \text{molecules}} \times \dfrac{256.43 \, \text{g } C_{16}H_{32}O_2}{1 \, \text{mole } C_{16}H_{32}O_2}$

$= 21.4 \, \text{g } C_{16}H_{32}O_2 \, \text{(palmitic acid)}.$

(c) $\text{mass} = 2.95 \, \text{mol N} \times \dfrac{1 \, \text{mol } C_6H_9N_3O_2}{3 \, \text{mol N}} \times \dfrac{155.157 \, \text{g } C_6H_9N_3O_2}{1 \, \text{mol } C_6H_9N_3O_2} = 152.6 \, \text{g } C_6H_9N_3O_2$

13. **(M)** The number of Fe atoms in 6 L of blood can be found using the following conversion pathway.

$$= 6\,\text{L blood} \times \frac{1000\,\text{mL}}{1\,\text{L}} \times \frac{15.5\,\text{g Hb}}{100\,\text{mL blood}} \times \frac{1\,\text{mol Hb}}{64,500\,\text{g Hb}} \times \frac{4\,\text{mol Fe}}{1\,\text{mol Hb}} \times \frac{6.022 \times 10^{23}\,\text{atoms Fe}}{1\,\text{mol Fe}}$$

$$= 3 \times 10^{22}\,\text{Fe atoms}$$

14. **(M)**

   (a) $\text{volume} = \pi r^2 \times h = 3.1416 \times \left(\dfrac{1.22\,\text{cm}}{2}\right)^2 \times 6.50\,\text{cm} = 7.60\,\text{cm}^3$

$$\text{mol } P_4 = 7.60\,\text{cm}^3 \times \frac{1.823\,\text{g } P_4}{1\,\text{cm}^3} \times \frac{1\,\text{mol } P_4}{123.896\,\text{g } P_4} = 0.112\,\text{mol } P_4$$

   (b) $\text{\# P atoms} = 0.112\,\text{mol } P_4 \times \dfrac{4\,\text{mol P}}{1\,\text{mol } P_4} \times \dfrac{6.022 \times 10^{23}\,\text{P}}{1\,\text{mol P}} = 2.70 \times 10^{23}\,\text{P atoms}$

Chemical Formulas

15. **(E)** For glucose (blood sugar), $C_6H_{12}O_6$,

   (a) FALSE The percentages by mass of C and O are *different* than in CO. For one thing, CO contains no hydrogen.

   (b) TRUE   In dihydroxyacetone, $(CH_2OH)_2$ CO or $C_3H_6O_3$, the ratio of C:H:O $= 3:6:3$ or 1:2:1. In glucose, this ratio is C:H:O $= 6:12:6 = 1:2:1$. Thus, the ratios are the same.

   (c) FALSE The proportions, by number of atoms, of C and O are the same in glucose. Since, however, C and O have different molar masses, their proportions by mass must be *different*.

   (d) FALSE Each mole of glucose contains $(12 \times 1.008 =)12.1$ g H. But each mole also contains 72.1 g C and 96.0 g O. Thus, the highest percentage, by mass, is that of O. The highest percentage, by number of atoms, is that of H.

16. **(E)** For sorbic acid, $C_6H_8O_2$,

   (a) FALSE The C:H:O mole ratio is 3:4:1, but the mass ratio differs because moles of different elements have different molar masses.

   (b) TRUE   Since the two compounds have the same empirical formula, they have the same mass percent composition.

   (c) TRUE   Aspidinol, $C_{12}H_{16}O_4$, and sorbic acid have the same empirical formula, C_3H_4O.

   (d) TRUE   The ratio of H atoms to O atoms is $8:2 = 4:1$. Thus, the mass ratio is
$$(4\,\text{mol H} \times 1\text{g H}):(1\,\text{mol O} \times 16.0\,\text{g O}) = 4\,\text{g H}:16\,\text{g O} = 1\,\text{g H}:4\,\text{g O}.$$

17. **(M)**

   (a) $Cu(UO_2)_2(PO_4)_2 \cdot 8\,H_2O$ has 1 Cu, 2 U, 2 P, 20 O, and 16 H, or a total of 41 atoms.

   (b) By number, $Cu(UO_2)_2(PO_4)_2 \cdot 8\,H_2O$ has a H to O ratio of 16:20 or 4:5 or 0.800 H atoms/O atom.

(c) By number, $Cu(UO_2)_2(PO_4)_2 \cdot 8\,H_2O$ has a Cu to P ratio of 1:2.

The mass ratio of Cu:P is $\dfrac{1\,mol\,Cu \times \dfrac{63.546\,g\,Cu}{1\,mol\,Cu}}{2\,mol\,P \times \dfrac{30.974\,g\,P}{1\,mol\,P}} = 1.026$.

(d) With a mass percent slightly greater than 50%, U has the largest mass percent, with oxygen coming in at ~34%.

$$mass\,\%\,U = \frac{mass\,U\,in\,Cu(UO_2)_2(PO_4)_2 \cdot 8\,H_2O}{total\,mass\,of\,Cu(UO_2)_2(PO_4)_2 \cdot 8\,H_2O} \times 100\%$$

$$= \frac{2 \times 238.03\,g/mol}{937.660\,g/mol} \times 100\%$$

$$= 50.77\%$$

$$mass\,\%\,O = \frac{mass\,O\,in\,Cu(UO_2)_2(PO_4)_2 \cdot 8H_2O}{total\,mass\,of\,Cu(UO_2)_2(PO_4)_2 \cdot 8H_2O} \times 100\%$$

$$= \frac{20 \times 15.999\,g/mol}{937.660\,g/mol} \times 100\%$$

$$= 34.13\%$$

(e) $1.00\,g\,P \times \dfrac{1\,mol\,P}{30.974\,g\,P} \times \dfrac{1\,mol\,Cu(UO_2)_2(PO_4)_2 \cdot 8\,H_2O}{2\,mol\,P} \times$

$\dfrac{937.666\,g\,Cu(UO_2)_2(PO_4)_2 \cdot 8\,H_2O}{1\,mol\,Cu(UO_2)_2(PO_4)_2 \cdot 8\,H_2O}$

$= 15.1\,g\,of\,Cu(UO_2)_2(PO_4)_2 \cdot 8\,H_2O$

18. (M)

(a) A formula unit of $Ge\left[S(CH_2)_4 CH_3\right]_4$ contains:

1 Ge atom   4 S atoms $4(4+1) = 20$ C atoms $4\left[4(2)+3\right] = 44$ H atoms

For a total of $1+4+20+44 = 69$ atoms per formula unit

(b) $\dfrac{\#\,of\,C\,atoms}{\#\,of\,H\,atoms} = \dfrac{20\,C\,atoms}{44\,H\,atoms} = \dfrac{5\,C\,atoms}{11\,H\,atoms} = 0.455\,C\,atom/H\,atom$

(c) $\dfrac{mass\,Ge}{mass\,S} = \dfrac{1\,mol\,Ge \times \dfrac{72.630\,g\,Ge}{1\,mol\,Ge}}{4\,mol\,S \times \dfrac{32.06\,g\,S}{1\,mol\,S}} = \dfrac{72.630\,g\,Ge}{128.24\,g\,S} = 0.566\,g\,Ge/g\,S$

(d) $mass\,of\,S = 1\,mol\,Ge\left[S(CH_2)_4 CH_3\right]_4 \times \dfrac{4\,mol\,S}{1\,mol\,Ge\left[S(CH_2)_4 CH_3\right]_4} \times \dfrac{32.06\,g\,S}{1\,mol\,S} = 128.264\,g\,S$

(e) $\#\,of\,C\,atoms = 33.10\,g\,cmpd \times \dfrac{1\,mol\,cmpd}{485.44\,g\,cmpd} \times \dfrac{20\,mol\,C}{1\,mol\,cmpd} \times \dfrac{6.0221 \times 10^{23}\,C\,atoms}{1\,mol\,C}$

$= 8.212 \times 10^{23}\,C\,atoms$

Percent Composition of Compounds

19. **(E)** The information obtained in the course of calculating the molar mass is used to determine the mass percent of H in decane.

$$\text{molar mass } C_{10}H_{22} = \left(\frac{10 \text{ mol C}}{1 \text{ mol } C_{10}H_{22}} \times \frac{12.011 \text{ g C}}{1 \text{ mol C}} \right) + \left(\frac{22 \text{ mol H}}{1 \text{ mol } C_{10}H_{22}} \times \frac{1.008 \text{ g H}}{1 \text{ mol H}} \right)$$

$$= \frac{120.11 \text{ g C}}{1 \text{ mol } C_{10}H_{22}} + \frac{22.176 \text{ g H}}{1 \text{ mol } C_{10}H_{22}} = \frac{142.29 \text{ g}}{1 \text{ mol } C_{10}H_{22}}$$

$$\%H = \frac{22.176 \text{ g H/mol decane}}{142.29 \text{ g } C_{10}H_{22}/\text{mol decane}} \times 100\% = 15.369\% \text{ H}$$

20. **(E)** Determine the mass of O in one mole of $Cu_2(OH)_2CO_3$ and the molar mass of $Cu_2(OH)_2CO_3$.

$$\text{mass O/mol } Cu_2(OH)_2CO_3 = \frac{5 \text{ mol O}}{1 \text{ mol } Cu_2(OH)_2CO_3} \times \frac{15.999 \text{ g O}}{1 \text{ mol O}} = 80.00 \text{ g O/mol } Cu_2(OH)_2CO_3$$

$$\text{molar mass } Cu_2(OH)_2CO_3 = (2 \times 63.546 \text{ g Cu}) + (5 \times 15.999 \text{ g O}) + (2 \times 1.008 \text{ g H}) + 12.011 \text{ g C}$$

$$= 221.114 \text{ g/mol } Cu_2(OH)_2CO_3$$

$$\text{percent oxygen in sample} = \frac{79.995 \text{ g}}{221.114 \text{ g}} \times 100\% = 36.18\% \text{ O}$$

21. **(E)** $C(CH_3)_3CH_2CH(CH_3)_2$ has a molar mass of 114.231 g/mol and one mole contains 18.143 g of H.

$$\text{percent hydrogen in sample} = \frac{18.143 \text{ g}}{114.231 \text{ g}} \times 100\% = 15.88\% \text{ H}$$

22. **(E)** Determine the mass of a mole of $Cr(NO_3)_3 \cdot 9 H_2O$, and then the mass of water in a mole.

$$\text{molar mass } Cr(NO_3)_3 \cdot 9 H_2O = 51.996 \text{ g Cr} + (3 \times 14.007 \text{ g N}) + (18 \times 15.999 \text{ g O})$$

$$+ (18 \times 1.008 \text{ g H}) = 400.148 \text{ g/mol } Cr(NO_3)_3 \cdot 9 H_2O$$

$$\text{mass } H_2O = \frac{9 \text{ mol } H_2O}{1 \text{ mol } Cr(NO_3)_3 \cdot 9 H_2O} \times \frac{18.015 \text{ g } H_2O}{1 \text{ mol } H_2O} = 162.14 \text{ g } H_2O/\text{mol } Cr(NO_3)_3 \cdot 9 H_2O$$

$$\frac{162.14 \text{ g } H_2O/\text{mol } Cr(NO_3)_3 \cdot 9 H_2O}{400.148 \text{ g/mol } Cr(NO_3)_3 \cdot 9 H_2O} \times 100\% = 40.5\% \text{ H}_2O$$

23. **(E)** molar mass $= (20 \text{ mol C} \times 12.011 \text{ g C}) + (24 \text{ mol H} \times 1.008 \text{ g H}) + (2 \text{ mol N} \times 14.007 \text{ g N})$

$$+ (2 \text{ mol O} \times 15.999 \text{ g O}) = 324.42 \text{ g/mol}$$

$$\%C = \frac{240.22}{324.42} \times 100\% = 74.046 \%C \qquad \%H = \frac{24.192}{324.42} \times 100\% = 7.4570 \%H$$

$$\%N = \frac{28.014}{324.42} \times 100\% = 8.6351 \%N \qquad \%O = \frac{31.998}{324.42} \times 100\% = 9.8631 \%O$$

24. **(E)** The molar mass of $Cu(C_{18}H_{33}O_2)_2$ is 626.466 g/mol. One mole contains 66 H (66.528 g H), 36 C (432.396 g C), 4 O (63.996 g O) and 1 Cu (63.546 g Cu).

$$\%C = \frac{432.396 \text{ g}}{626.466 \text{ g}} \times 100\% = 69.0215 \%C \qquad \%H = \frac{66.528 \text{ g}}{626.466 \text{ g}} \times 100\% = 10.619 \%H$$

$$\%Cu = \frac{63.546 \text{ g}}{626.466 \text{ g}} \times 100\% = 10.144 \%Cu \qquad \%O = \frac{63.996 \text{ g}}{626.466 \text{ g}} \times 100\% = 10.216 \%O$$

25. **(E)** In each case, we first determine the molar mass of the compound, and then the mass of the indicated element in one mole of the compound. Finally, we determine the percent by mass of the indicated element to four significant figures.

(a) molar mass $Pb(C_2H_5)_4 = 207.2 \text{ g Pb} + (8 \times 12.011 \text{ g C}) + (20 \times 1.008 \text{ g H})$

$$= 323.448 \text{ g/mol } Pb(C_2H_5)_4$$

$$\text{mass Pb/mol } Pb(C_2H_5)_4 = \frac{1 \text{ mol Pb}}{1 \text{ mol } Pb(C_2H_5)_4} \times \frac{207.2 \text{ g Pb}}{1 \text{ mol Pb}} = 207.2 \text{ g Pb/mol } Pb(C_2H_5)_4$$

$$\% Pb = \frac{207.2 \text{ g Pb}}{323.448 \text{ g } Pb(C_2H_5)_4} \times 100\% = 64.06\% \text{ Pb}$$

(b) molar mass $Fe_4[Fe(CN)_6]_3 = (7 \times 55.845 \text{ g Fe}) + (18 \times 12.011 \text{ g C}) + (18 \times 14.007 \text{ g N})$

$$= 859.253 \text{ g/mol } Fe_4[Fe(CN)_6]_3$$

$$\frac{\text{mass Fe}}{\text{mol } Fe_4[Fe(CN)_6]_3} = \frac{7 \text{ mol Fe}}{1 \text{ mol } Fe_4[Fe(CN)_6]_3} \times \frac{55.845 \text{ g Fe}}{1 \text{ mol Fe}} = 390.915 \text{ g Fe/mol } Fe_4[Fe(CN)_6]_3$$

$$\%Fe = \frac{390.915 \text{ g Fe}}{859.253 \text{ g } Fe_4[Fe(CN)_6]_3} \times 100\% = 45.495\% \text{ Fe}$$

(c) molar mass $C_{55}H_{72}MgN_4O_5$

$$= (55 \times 12.011\,g\,C) + (72 \times 1.008\,g\,H) + (1 \times 24.305\,g\,Mg) + (4 \times 14.007\,g\,N) + (5 \times 15.999\,g\,O)$$

$$= 893.509\,g/mol\,C_{55}H_{72}MgN_4O_5$$

$$\frac{mass\,Mg}{mol\,C_{55}H_{72}MgN_4O_5} = \frac{1\,mol\,Mg}{1\,mol\,C_{55}H_{72}MgN_4O_5} \times \frac{24.305\,g\,Mg}{1\,mol\,Mg} = \frac{24.305\,g\,Mg}{mol\,C_{55}H_{72}MgN_4O_5}$$

$$\%Mg = \frac{24.305\,g\,Mg}{893.509g\,C_{55}H_{72}MgN_4O_5} \times 100\% = 2.7202\%\,Mg$$

26. **(E)**

(a) $\%Zr = \frac{1\,mol\,Zr}{1\,mol\,ZrSiO_4} \times \frac{1\,mol\,ZrSiO_4}{183.31g\,ZrSiO_4} \times \frac{91.224\,g\,Zr}{1\,mol\,Zr} \times 100\% = 49.765\%\,Zr$

(b) $\%Be = \frac{3\,mol\,Fe}{1\,mol\,Be_3Al_2Si_6O_{18}} \times \frac{1\,mol\,Be_3Al_2Si_6O_{18}}{537.502\,g\,Be_3Al_2Si_6O_{18}} \times \frac{9.01218\,g\,Be}{1\,mol\,Be} \times 100\%$

$\%\,Be = 5.03004\%\,Be$

(c) $\%Fe = \frac{3\,mol\,Fe}{1\,mol\,Fe_3Al_2Si_3O_{12}} \times \frac{1\,mol\,Fe_3Al_2Si_3O_{12}}{497.753\,g\,Fe_3Al_2Si_3O_{12}} \times \frac{55.845\,g\,Fe}{1\,mol\,Fe} \times 100\%$

$\%Fe = 33.658\%\,Fe$

(d) $\%S = \frac{1\,mol\,S}{1\,mol\,Na_4SSi_3Al_3O_{12}} \times \frac{1\,mol\,Na_4SSi_3Al_3O_{12}}{481.219\,g\,Na_4SSi_3Al_3O_{12}} \times \frac{32.06\,g\,S}{1\,mol\,S} \times 100\%$

$\%S = 6.6622\%\,S$

27. **(M)** Oxide with the largest %Cr will have the largest number of moles of Cr per mole of oxygen.

CrO: $\frac{1\,mol\,Cr}{1\,mol\,O} = 1\,mol\,Cr/mol\,O$ $\quad$ Cr_2O_3: $\frac{2\,mol\,Cr}{3\,mol\,O} = 0.667\,mol\,Cr/mol\,O$

CrO_2: $\frac{1\,mol\,Cr}{2\,mol\,O} = 0.500\,mol\,Cr/mol\,O$ $\quad$ CrO_3: $\frac{1\,mol\,Cr}{3\,mol\,O} = 0.333\,mol\,Cr/mol\,O$

Arranged in order of increasing %Cr: $CrO_3 < CrO_2 < Cr_2O_3 < CrO$

28. **(M)** For SO_2 and Na_2S, a mole of each contains a mole of S and two moles of another element; in the case of SO_2, the other element (oxygen) has a smaller atomic mass than the other element in Na_2S (Na), causing SO_2 to have a higher mass percent sulfur. For S_2Cl_2 and $Na_2S_2O_3$, a mole of each contains two moles of S; for S_2Cl_2, the rest of the mole has a mass of 71.0 g; while for $Na_2S_2O_3$, it would be $(2 \times 23) + (3 \times 16) = 94$ g. Sulfur makes up the greater proportion of the mass in S_2Cl_2, giving it the larger percent of S. Now we compare

SO_2 and S_2Cl_2: SO_2 contains one mole of S (32.1 g) and S_2Cl_2 contains two moles of S (64.2 g). In S_2Cl_2 the remainder of a mole has a mass of 71.0 g, while in SO_2 the remainder of a mole would be $2 \times 16.0 = 32.0$ g. Thus, SO_2 has the highest percent of S so far. For CH_3CH_2SH compared to SO_2, we see that both compounds have one S atom, SO_2 has two O atoms (each with a molar mass of ~16 g mol^{-1}), and CH_3CH_2SH effectively has two CH_3 groups (each CH_3 group with a mass of ~15 g mol^{-1}). Thus, CH_3CH_2SH has the highest percentage sulfur by mass of the compounds listed.

Chemical Formulas from Percent Composition

29. **(M)** SO_3 (40.05% S) and S_2O (80.0% S) (2 O atoms $\approx$ 1 S atom in terms of atomic masses) Note the molar masses are quite close (within 0.05 g/mol).

30. **(M)** The element chromium has an atomic mass of 52.0 u. Thus, there can only be one chromium atom per formula unit of the compound. (Two atoms of chromium have a mass of 104 u, more than the formula mass of the compound.) Three of the four remaining atoms in the formula unit must be oxygen. Thus, the oxide is CrO_3, chromium(VI) oxide.

31. **(M)** Determine the % oxygen by difference.
$\%\,O = 100.00\% - 45.27\%\,C - 9.50\%\,H = 45.23\%\,O$
The following calculations are based on a 100.00 g sample.

$$\text{mol O} = 45.23\,g \times \frac{1\,\text{mol O}}{15.999\,g\,O} = 2.827\,\text{mol O} \quad \div 2.827 \to 1.000\,\text{mol O}$$

$$\text{mol C} = 45.27\,g\,C \times \frac{1\,\text{mol C}}{12.011\,g\,C} = 3.769\,\text{mol C} \quad \div 2.827 \to 1.333\,\text{mol C}$$

$$\text{mol H} = 9.50\,g\,H \times \frac{1\,\text{mol H}}{1.008\,g\,H} = 9.42\,\text{mol H} \quad \div 2.827 \to 3.33\,\text{mol H}$$

Multiply all amounts by 3 to obtain integers. Empirical formula is $C_4H_{10}O_3$.

32. **(M)** We base our calculation on 100.0 g of monosodium glutamate.

$$13.6\,g\,Na \times \frac{1\,\text{mol Na}}{22.99\,g\,Na} = 0.592\,\text{mol Na} \quad \div 0.592 \to 1.00\,\text{mol Na}$$

$$35.5\,g\,C \times \frac{1\,\text{mol C}}{12.01\,g\,C} = 2.96\,\text{mol C} \quad \div 0.592 \to 5.00\,\text{mol C}$$

$$4.8\,g\,H \times \frac{1\,\text{mol H}}{1.01\,g\,H} = 4.8\,\text{mol H} \quad \div 0.592 \to 8.1\,\text{mol H}$$

$$8.3\,g\,N \times \frac{1\,\text{mol N}}{14.0\,g\,N} = 0.59\,\text{mol N} \quad \div 0.592 \to 1.0\,\text{mol N}$$

$$37.8\,g\,O \times \frac{1\,\text{mol O}}{16.00\,g\,O} = 2.36\,\text{mol O} \quad \div 0.592 \to 3.99\,\text{mol O}$$

Empirical formula : $NaC_5H_8NO_4$

33. **(M)**

(a)

$$74.01 \text{g C} \times \frac{1 \text{mol C}}{12.011 \text{ g C}} = 6.162 \text{ mol C} \qquad \div 1.298 \rightarrow 4.747 \text{ mol C}$$

$$5.23 \text{ g H} \times \frac{1 \text{mol H}}{1.008 \text{ g H}} = 5.19 \text{ mol H} \qquad \div 1.298 \rightarrow 4.00 \text{ mol H}$$

$$20.76 \text{ g O} \times \frac{1 \text{mol O}}{15.999 \text{ g O}} = 1.298 \text{ mol O} \qquad \div 1.298 \rightarrow 1.000 \text{ mol O}$$

Multiply each of the mole numbers by 4 to obtain an empirical formula of $C_{19}H_{16}O_4$.

(b)

$$39.98 \text{g C} \times \frac{1 \text{mol C}}{12.011 \text{g C}} = 3.3286 \text{ mol C} \quad \div 0.7399 \rightarrow 4.499 \text{ mol C}$$

$$3.73 \text{g H} \times \frac{1 \text{mol H}}{1.008 \text{ g H}} = 3.70 \text{ mol H} \qquad \div 0.7399 \rightarrow 5.00 \text{ mol H}$$

$$20.73 \text{g N} \times \frac{1 \text{mol N}}{14.007 \text{ g N}} = 1.480 \text{ mol N} \quad \div 0.7399 \rightarrow 2.000 \text{ mol N}$$

$$11.84 \text{g O} \times \frac{1 \text{mol O}}{15.999 \text{ g O}} = 0.7400 \text{ mol O} \div 0.7399 \rightarrow 1.000 \text{ mol O}$$

$$23.72 \text{g S} \times \frac{1 \text{mol S}}{32.06 \text{ g S}} = 0.7399 \text{ mol S} \quad \div 0.7399 \rightarrow 1.000 \text{ mol S}$$

Multiply by 2 to obtain the empirical formula

$C_9H_{10}N_4O_2S_2$

34. **(M)**

(a)

$$95.21 \text{ g C} \times \frac{1 \text{mol C}}{12.011 \text{ g C}} = 7.927 \text{ mol C} \div 4.74 \rightarrow 1.67 \text{ mol C}$$

$$4.79 \text{ g H} \times \frac{1 \text{mol H}}{1.008 \text{ g H}} = 4.75 \text{ mol H} \div 4.75 \rightarrow 1.00 \text{ mol H}$$

Multiply each of the mole numbers by 3 to obtain an empirical formula of C_5H_3.

(b) Each percent is numerically equal to the mass of that element present in 100.00 g of the compound. These masses then are converted to amounts of the elements, in moles.

$$\text{amount C} = 38.37 \text{g C} \times \frac{1 \text{mol C}}{12.011 \text{g C}} = 3.195 \text{ mol C} \qquad \div 0.491 \rightarrow 6.51 \text{ mol C}$$

$$\text{amount H} = 1.49 \text{g H} \times \frac{1 \text{mol H}}{1.008 \text{g H}} = 1.48 \text{ mol H} \qquad \div 0.491 \rightarrow 3.01 \text{ mol H}$$

$$\text{amount Cl} = 52.28 \text{g Cl} \times \frac{1 \text{mol Cl}}{35.45 \text{g Cl}} = 1.475 \text{ mol Cl} \div 0.491 \rightarrow 3.004 \text{ mol Cl}$$

$$\text{amount O} = 7.86 \text{g O} \times \frac{1 \text{mol O}}{16.00 \text{ g O}} = 0.491 \text{ mol O} \qquad \div 0.491 \rightarrow 1.00 \text{ mol O}$$

Multiply each number of moles by 2 to obtain the empirical formula: $C_{13}H_6Cl_6O_2$.

35. Convert each percentage into the mass in 100.00 g, and then to the moles of that element.

$$94.34 \text{ g C} \times \frac{1 \text{ mol C}}{12.011 \text{ g C}} = 7.854 \text{ mol C} \qquad \div 5.62 = 1.40 \text{ mol C} \times 5 = 7.00$$

$$5.66 \text{ g H} \times \frac{1 \text{ mol H}}{1.008 \text{ g H}} = 5.62 \text{ mol H} \qquad \div 5.62 = 1.00 \text{ mol H} \times 5 = 5.00$$

Multiply by 5 to achieve whole number ratios. The empirical formula is C_5H_7, and the formula mass $[(7 \times 12.011 \text{ g C}) + (5 \times 1.008 \text{ g H})] = 89.117$ u. Since this empirical molar mass is one-half of the 178 u, the correct molecular mass, the molecular formula must be twice the empirical formula. Molecular formula: $C_{14}H_{10}$

36. **(M)** The percent of selenium in each oxide is found by difference.

First oxide: $\% \text{Se} = 100.0\% - 28.8\% \qquad \text{O} = 71.2\% \text{ Se}$

A 100.0 gram sample would contain 28.8 g O and 71.2 g Se

$$28.8 \text{ g O} \times \frac{1 \text{ mol O}}{16.00 \text{ g O}} = 1.80 \text{ mol O} \qquad \div 0.902 \quad \rightarrow 2.00 \text{ mol O}$$

$$71.2 \text{ g Se} \times \frac{1 \text{ mol Se}}{78.96 \text{ g Se}} = 0.902 \text{ mol Se} \quad \div 0.902 \quad \rightarrow 1.00 \text{ mol Se}$$

The empirical formula is SeO_2. An appropriate name is selenium dioxide.

Second oxide: $\% \text{Se} = 100.0\% - 37.8\% \, \text{O} = 62.2\% \text{ Se}$

A 100.0 gram sample would contain 37.8 g O and 62.2 g Se

$$37.8 \text{ g O} \times \frac{1 \text{ mol O}}{16.00 \text{ g O}} = 2.36 \text{ mol O} \qquad \div 0.788 \quad \rightarrow 2.99 \text{ mol O}$$

$$62.2 \text{ g Se} \times \frac{1 \text{ mol Se}}{78.96 \text{ g Se}} = 0.788 \text{ mol Se} \quad \div 0.788 \quad \rightarrow 1.00 \text{ mol Se}$$

The empirical formula is SeO_3. An appropriate name is selenium trioxide.

37. **(M)** Determine the mass of oxygen by difference. Then convert all masses to amounts in moles. oxygen mass $= 100.00 \text{ g} - 73.27 \text{ g C} - 3.84 \text{ g H} - 10.68 \text{ g N} = 12.21 \text{ g O}$

$$\text{amount C} = 73.27 \text{ g C} \times \frac{1 \text{ mol C}}{12.011 \text{ g C}} = 6.100 \text{ mol C} \qquad \div 0.7625 \quad \rightarrow 8.000 \text{ mol C}$$

$$\text{amount H} = 3.84 \text{ g H} \times \frac{1 \text{ mol H}}{1.008 \text{ g H}} = 3.81 \text{ mol H} \qquad \div 0.7625 \quad \rightarrow 5.00 \text{ mol H}$$

$$\text{amount N} = 10.68 \text{ g N} \times \frac{1 \text{ mol N}}{14.007 \text{ g N}} = 0.7625 \text{ mol N} \qquad \div 0.7625 \quad \rightarrow 1.000 \text{ mol N}$$

$$\text{amount O} = 12.21 \text{ g O} \times \frac{1 \text{ mol O}}{15.999 \text{ g O}} = 0.7632 \text{ mol O} \qquad \div 0.7625 \quad \rightarrow 1.001 \text{ mol O}$$

The empirical formula is C_8H_5NO, which has an empirical mass of 131 u. This is almost exactly half the molecular mass of 262.3 u. Thus, the molecular formula is twice the empirical formula and is $C_{16}H_{10}N_2O_2$.

38. **(M)** Convert each percentage into the mass in 100.00 g, and then to the moles of that element.

$$\text{amount C} = 44.45\ \text{g C} \times \frac{1\,\text{mol C}}{12.011\,\text{g C}} = 3.701\,\text{mol C} \quad \div\ 3.70 \quad \rightarrow 1.00\ \text{mol C}$$

$$\text{amount H} = 3.73\,\text{g H} \times \frac{1\,\text{mol H}}{1.008\,\text{g H}} = 3.70\,\text{mol H} \quad \div\ 3.70 \quad \rightarrow 1.00\ \text{mol H}$$

$$\text{amount N} = 51.82\ \text{g N} \times \frac{1\,\text{mol N}}{14.007\,\text{g N}} = 3.700\,\text{mol N} \quad \div\ 3.70 \quad \rightarrow 1.00\ \text{mol N}$$

The empirical formula is CHN, which has an empirical mass of 27.026 u. This is one fifth the molecular mass of 135.14 u. Thus, the molecular formula is five times greater than the empirical formula and is $C_5H_5N_5$.

39. **(M)** The molar mass of element X has the units of grams per mole. We can determine the amount, in moles of Cl, and convert that to the amount of X, equivalent to 25.0 g of X.

$$\text{molar mass} = \frac{25.0\,\text{g X}}{75.0\,\text{g Cl}} \times \frac{35.45\,\text{g Cl}}{1\,\text{mol Cl}} \times \frac{4\,\text{mol Cl}}{1\,\text{mol X}} = \frac{47.3\,\text{g X}}{1\,\text{mol X}}$$

The atomic mass is 47.3 u. This atomic mass is close to that of the element titanium, which therefore is identified as element X.

40. **(M)** The molar mass of element X has the units of grams per mole. We can determine the amount, relative to the mass percent Cl. Assume 1 mole of compound. This contains 15.9994 g O and 70.905 g Cl. The following relation must hold true.

$$\text{mass percent Cl} = 59.6\% = 0.596 = \frac{\text{mass Cl in one mole}}{\text{mass of one mole of XOCl}_2} = \frac{70.90\ \text{g}}{(X+15.999+70.90)\ \text{g}}$$

$$0.596 = \frac{70.90}{(X+86.89)} \quad \text{or} \quad 0.596X + 51.79 = 70.90 \quad 0.596X = 19.11$$

$$\text{Hence, } X = \frac{19.11}{0.596} = 32.0\underline{6} \quad \text{The atomic mass of } X = 32.1\ \text{g mol}^{-1} \quad X \text{ is the element sulfur}$$

41. **(M)** Consider 100 g of chlorophyll, which contains 2.72 g of Mg. To answer this problem, we must take note of the fact that 1 mole of chlorophyll contains 1 mole of Mg.

$$\frac{100\,\text{g chlorophyll}}{2.72\,\text{g Mg}} \times \frac{24.305\,\text{g Mg}}{1\,\text{mol Mg}} \times \frac{1\,\text{mol Mg}}{1\,\text{mol chlorophyll}} = 894\ \text{g mol}^{-1}$$

Therefore, the molecular mass of chlorophyll is 894 u.

42. **(D)** Compound I has a molecular mass of 137 u. We are told that chlorine constitutes 77.5% of the mass, so the mass of chlorine in each molecule is $137\ \text{u} \times \dfrac{77.5}{100} = 106\ \text{u}$.

This corresponds to three chlorine atoms (106 u ÷ 35.45 u/Cl atom = 2.99 or 3 Cl atoms). The remaining 31 u, (137 u – 106 u), is the mass for element X in one molecule of Compound I. Compound II has 85.1% chlorine by mass, so the mass of chlorine in each molecule of Compound II is $208\ \text{u} \times \dfrac{85.1}{100} = 177\ \text{u}$.

This corresponds to five Cl atoms (177 u ÷ 35.45 u/Cl atom = 4.99 ~5 chlorine atoms). The remaining mass is 31 u (208 u – 177 u), which is very close to the mass of X found in each molecule of Compound I. Thus, we have two compounds: X_nCl_3, which has a molecular mass of 137 u, and X_nCl_5, which has a molecular mass of 208 u.

(We also know that the mass of X in both molecular species is ~31 u). If we assume that $n = 1$ in the formulas above, then element X must be phosphorus (30.974 u) and the formulas for the compounds are PCl_3 (Compound I) and PCl_5 (Compound II).

Combustion Analysis

43. **(M)**

(a) First we determine the mass of carbon and of hydrogen present in the sample. Remember that a hydrocarbon contains only hydrogen and carbon.

$$0.6260 \text{ g CO}_2 \times \frac{1 \text{ mol CO}_2}{44.009 \text{ g CO}_2} \times \frac{1 \text{ mol C}}{1 \text{ mol CO}_2} = 0.01422 \text{ mol C} \times \frac{12.011 \text{ g C}}{1 \text{ mol C}} = 0.1708 \text{ g C}$$

$$0.1602 \text{ g H}_2\text{O} \times \frac{1 \text{ mol H}_2\text{O}}{18.015 \text{ g H}_2\text{O}} \times \frac{2 \text{ mol H}}{1 \text{ mol H}_2\text{O}} = 0.01779 \text{ mol H} \times \frac{1.008 \text{ g H}}{1 \text{ mol H}} = 0.01793 \text{ g H}$$

Then the % C and % H are found.

$$\%\text{C} = \frac{0.1708}{0.1888 \text{ g cmpd}} \times 100\% = 90.47\% \text{ C} \quad \%\text{H} = \frac{0.01793 \text{ g H}}{0.1888 \text{ g cmpd}} \times 100\% = 9.497\% \text{ H}$$

(b) Use the moles of C and H from part (a), and divide both by the smallest value, namely 0.01422 mol. Thus   0.01422 mol C ÷ 0.01422 mol = 1.000 mol H;
                    0.01779 mol H ÷ 0.01422 mol = 1.250 mol H.
The empirical formula is obtained by multiplying these mole numbers by 4. It is C_4H_5.

(c) The molar mass of the empirical formula C_4H_5 is [4 × 12.011 + 5 × 1.008] = 53.084 g/mol. This value is 1/2 of the actual molar mass. The molecular formula is twice the empirical formula. ∴ Molecular formula: C_8H_{10}.

44. **(M)** Determine the mass of carbon and of hydrogen present in the sample.

$$1.1518 \text{ g CO}_2 \times \frac{1 \text{ mol CO}_2}{44.090 \text{ g CO}_2} \times \frac{1 \text{ mol C}}{1 \text{ mol CO}_2} = 0.026172 \text{ mol C} \times \frac{12.011 \text{ g C}}{1 \text{ mol C}} = 0.3144 \text{ g C}$$

$$0.2694 \text{ g H}_2\text{O} \times \frac{1 \text{ mol H}_2\text{O}}{18.015 \text{ g H}_2\text{O}} \times \frac{2 \text{ mol H}}{1 \text{ mol H}_2\text{O}} = 0.029908 \text{ mol H} \times \frac{1.008 \text{ g H}}{1 \text{ mol H}} = 0.03015 \text{ g H}$$

(a) The percent composition can be determined using the masses of C and H.

$$\%\text{C} = \frac{0.3144 \text{ g C}}{0.4039 \text{ g cmpd}} \times 100\% = 77.83\% \text{ C} \quad \%\text{H} = \frac{0.030148 \text{ g H}}{0.4039 \text{ g cmpd}} \times 100\% = 7.4641\% \text{ H}$$

% O = 100% – 77.84% – 7.4641% = 14.71%
These percents can be used in determining the empirical formula if one wishes.

(b) To find the empirical formula, determine the mass of oxygen by difference, and its amount in moles. Mass O = 0.04039 g – 0.3144 g – 0.0302 g = 0.0593 g

$$0.0593 \text{ g O} \times \frac{1 \text{ mol O}}{16.00 \text{ g O}} = 0.00371 \text{ mol O} \div 0.00371 \rightarrow 1.00 \text{ mol O}$$

$$0.026172 \text{ mol C} \div 0.00371 \rightarrow 7.05 \text{ mol C}$$

$$0.029908 \text{ mol H} \div 0.00371 \rightarrow 8.06 \text{ mol H}$$

Empirical formula is C_7H_8O.

(c) The molecular formula is found by realizing that a mole of empirical units has a mass of $(7 \times 12.0 \text{ g C} + 8 \times 1.0 \text{ g H} + 16.0 \text{ g O}) = 108.0$ g. Since this agrees with the molecular mass, the molecular formula is the same as the empirical formula: C_7H_8O.

45. **(M)** First, determine the mass of carbon and hydrogen present in the sample.

$$0.458 \text{ g CO}_2 \times \frac{1 \text{ mol CO}_2}{44.01 \text{ g CO}_2} \times \frac{1 \text{ mol C}}{1 \text{ mol CO}_2} = 0.0104 \text{ mol C} \times \frac{12.011 \text{ g C}}{1 \text{ mol C}} = 0.125 \text{ g C}$$

$$0.374 \text{ g H}_2\text{O} \times \frac{1 \text{ mol H}_2\text{O}}{18.015 \text{ g H}_2\text{O}} \times \frac{2 \text{ mol H}}{1 \text{ mol H}_2\text{O}} = 0.0415 \text{ mol H} \times \frac{1.008 \text{ g H}}{1 \text{ mol H}} = 0.0418 \text{ g H}$$

Then, the mass of N that this sample would have produced is determined. (Note that this is also the mass of N_2 produced in the reaction.)

$$0.226 \text{ g N}_2 \times \frac{0.312 \text{ g 1st sample}}{0.486 \text{ g 2nd sample}} = 0.145 \text{ g N}_2$$

From which we can calculate the mass of N in the sample.

$$0.145 \text{ g N}_2 \times \frac{1 \text{ mol N}_2}{28.014 \text{ g N}_2} \times \frac{2 \text{ mol N}}{1 \text{ mol N}_2} \times \frac{14.007 \text{ g N}}{1 \text{ mol N}} = 0.145 \text{ g N}$$

We may alternatively determine the mass of N by difference:
0.312 g – 0.125 g C – 0.0418 g H = 0.145 g N

Then, we can calculate the relative number of moles of each element.

$$0.145 \text{ g N} \times \frac{1 \text{ mol N}}{14.007 \text{ g N}} = 0.0104 \text{ mol N} \div 0.0104 \rightarrow 1.00 \text{ mol N}$$

$$0.0104 \text{ mol C} \div 0.0104 \rightarrow 1.00 \text{ mol C}$$

$$0.0415 \text{ mol H} \div 0.0104 \rightarrow 4.01 \text{ mol H}$$

Thus, the empirical formula is CH_4N

46. **(M)** Thiophene contains only carbon, hydrogen, and sulfur, so there is no need to determine the mass of oxygen by difference. We simply determine the amount of each element from the mass of its combustion product.

$$2.7224 \text{ g CO}_2 \times \frac{1 \text{ mol CO}_2}{44.009 \text{ g CO}_2} \times \frac{1 \text{ mol C}}{1 \text{ mol CO}_2} = 0.061859 \text{ mol C} \div 0.01548 \rightarrow 3.996 \text{ mol C}$$

$$0.5575 \text{ g H}_2\text{O} \times \frac{1 \text{ mol H}_2\text{O}}{18.015 \text{ g H}_2\text{O}} \times \frac{2 \text{ mol H}}{1 \text{ mol H}_2\text{O}} = 0.06189 \text{ mol H} \div 0.01548 \rightarrow 3.999 \text{ mol H}$$

$$0.9915 \text{ g SO}_2 \times \frac{1 \text{ mol SO}_2}{64.058 \text{ g SO}_2} \times \frac{1 \text{ mol S}}{1 \text{ mol SO}_2} = 0.01548 \text{ mol S} \div 0.01548 \rightarrow 1.00 \text{ mol S}$$

The empirical formula of thiophene is C_4H_4S.

47. **(M)** Each mole of CO_2 is produced from a mole of C. Therefore, the compound with the largest number of moles of C per mole of the compound will produce the largest amount of CO_2 and, thus, also the largest mass of CO_2. Of the compounds listed, namely CH_4, C_2H_5OH, $C_{10}H_8$, and C_6H_5OH, $C_{10}H_8$ has the largest number of moles of C per mole of the compound and will produce the greatest mass of CO_2 per mole on complete combustion.

48. **(M)** The compound that produces the largest mass of water per gram of the compound will have the largest amount of hydrogen per gram of the compound. Thus, we need to compare the ratios of amount of hydrogen per mole to the molar mass for each compound. Note that C_2H_5OH has as much H per mole as does C_6H_5OH, but C_6H_5OH has a higher molar mass. Thus, C_2H_5OH produces more H_2O per gram than does C_6H_5OH. Notice also that CH_4 has 4 H's per C, while $C_{10}H_8$ has 8 H's per 10 C's or 0.8 H per C. Thus CH_4 will produce more H_2O than will $C_{10}H_8$. Thus, we are left with comparing CH_4 to C_2H_5OH. The O in the second compound has about the same mass (16 u) as does C (12 u). Thus, in CH_4 there are 4 H's per C, while in C_2H_5OH there are about 2 H's per C. Thus CH_4 will produce the most water per gram on combustion, of all four compounds.

49. **(M)** The molecular formula for $CH_3CH(OH)CH_2CH_3$ is $C_4H_{10}O$. Here we will use the fact that $C_4H_{10}O$ has a molar mass of 74.123 g/mol to calculate the masses of CO_2 and H_2O:

Mass of CO_2:
Conversion pathway approach:

$$1.562 \text{ g C}_4\text{H}_{10}\text{O} \times \frac{1 \text{ mol C}_4\text{H}_{10}\text{O}}{74.123 \text{ g C}_4\text{H}_{10}\text{O}} \times \frac{4 \text{ mol C}}{1 \text{ mol C}_4\text{H}_{10}\text{O}} \times \frac{1 \text{ mol CO}_2}{1 \text{ mol C}} \times \frac{44.009 \text{ g CO}_2}{1 \text{ mol CO}_2} = 3.710 \text{ g CO}_2$$

Stepwise approach:

$$1.562 \text{ g } C_4H_{10}O \times \frac{1 \text{ mol } C_4H_{10}O}{74.123 \text{ g } C_4H_{10}O} = 0.02107 \text{ mol } C_4H_{10}O \times \frac{4 \text{ mol C}}{1 \text{ mol } C_4H_{10}O} = 0.08429 \text{ mol C}$$

$$0.08429 \text{ mol C} \times \frac{1 \text{ mol } CO_2}{1 \text{ mol C}} = 0.08429 \text{ mol } CO_2 \times \frac{44.009 \text{ g } CO_2}{1 \text{ mol } CO_2} = 3.710 \text{ g } CO_2$$

Mass of H_2O:
Conversion pathway approach:

$$1.562 \text{ g } C_4H_{10}O \times \frac{1 \text{ mol } C_4H_{10}O}{74.123 \text{ g } C_4H_{10}O} \times \frac{10 \text{ mol H}}{1 \text{ mol } C_4H_{10}O} \times \frac{1 \text{ mol } H_2O}{2 \text{ mol H}} \times \frac{18.015 \text{ g } H_2O}{1 \text{ mol } H_2O} = 1.898 \text{ g } H_2O$$

Stepwise approach:

$$1.562 \text{ g } C_4H_{10}O \times \frac{1 \text{ mol } C_4H_{10}O}{74.123 \text{ g } C_4H_{10}O} = 0.02107 \text{ mol } C_4H_{10}O$$

$$0.02107 \text{ mol } C_4H_{10}O \times \frac{10 \text{ mol H}}{1 \text{ mol } C_4H_{10}O} = 0.2107 \text{ mol H}$$

$$0.2107 \text{ mol H} \times \frac{1 \text{ mol } H_2O}{2 \text{ mol H}} = 0.1054 \text{ mol } H_2O \times \frac{18.015 \text{ g } H_2O}{1 \text{ mol } H_2O} = 1.898 \text{ g } H_2O$$

50. **(D)** moles of $C_2H_6S = 3.15 \text{ mL} \times \frac{0.84 \text{ g } C_2H_6S}{1 \text{ mL } C_2H_6S} \times \frac{1 \text{ mol } C_2H_6S}{62.13 \text{ g } C_2H_6S} = 0.042\underline{6} \text{ mol } C_2H_6S$

Thus, the mass of CO_2 expected is

$$= 0.042\underline{6} \text{ mol } C_2H_6S \times \frac{2 \text{ mol } CO_2}{1 \text{ mol } C_2H_6S} \times \frac{44.009 \text{ g } CO_2}{1 \text{ mol } CO_2} = 3.7\underline{5} \text{ g of } CO_2(g)$$

The mass of $SO_2(g)$ expected from the complete combustion is

$$= 0.042\underline{6} \text{ mol } C_2H_6S \times \frac{1 \text{ mol } SO_2}{1 \text{ mol } C_2H_6S} \times \frac{64.058 \text{ g } SO_2}{1 \text{ mol } H_2O} = 2.7\underline{3} \text{ g of } SO_2(g)$$

The mass of $H_2O(l)$ expected from the complete combustion is

$$= 0.042\underline{6} \text{ mol } C_2H_6S \times \frac{6 \text{ mol H}}{1 \text{ mol } C_2H_6S} \times \frac{1 \text{ mol } H_2O}{2 \text{ mol H}} \times \frac{18.015 \text{ g } H_2O}{1 \text{ mol } H_2O} = 2.3 \text{ g of } H_2O(l)$$

Oxidation States

51. **(E)** The oxidation state (O.S.) is given first, followed by the explanation for its assignment.

(a) $C = -4$ in CH_4 — H has an oxidation state of $+1$ in its nonmetal compounds. (Remember that the sum of the oxidation states in a neutral compound equals 0.)

(b) $S = +4$ in SF_4 — F has O.S. $= -1$ in its compounds.

(c) $O = -1$ in Na_2O_2 — Na has O.S. $= +1$ in its compounds.

(d) $C = 0$ in $C_2H_3O_2^-$ — H has O.S. $= +1$ in its nonmetal compounds; that of $O = -2$ (usually). (Remember that the sum of the oxidation states in a polyatomic ion equals the charge on that ion.)

(e) $Fe = +6$ in FeO_4^{2-} — O has O.S. $= -2$ in most of its compounds (especially metal containing compounds).

52. **(E)** The oxidation state of sulfur in each species is determined below. Remember that the oxidation state of O is -2 in its compounds. And the sum of the oxidation states in an ion equals the charge on that ion.

(a) $S = +4$ in SO_3^{2-} **(b)** $S = +2$ in $S_2O_3^{2-}$ **(c)** $S = +7$ in $S_2O_8^{2-}$

(d) $S = +6$ in HSO_4^- **(e)** $S = +2.5$ in $S_4O_6^{2-}$

53. **(E)** Remember that the oxidation state of oxygen is usually -2 in its compounds. Cr^{3+} and O^{2-} form Cr_2O_3, chromium(III) oxide. Cr^{4+} and O^{2-} form CrO_2, chromium(IV) oxide. Cr^{6+} and O^{2-} form CrO_3, chromium(VI) oxide.

54. **(E)** Remember that oxygen usually has an oxidation state of -2 in its compounds.

$N = +1$ in N_2O, dinitrogen monoxide $N = +2$ in NO, nitric oxide or nitrogen monoxide

$N = +3$ in N_2O_3, dinitrogen trioxide $N = +4$ in NO_2, nitrogen dioxide

$N = +5$ in N_2O_5, dinitrogen pentoxide

55. **(E)**

(a) $O = +2$ in OF_2 — F has an oxidation state of -1 in its compounds.

(b) $O = +1$ in O_2F_2 — F has O.S. $= -1$ in its compounds.

(c) $O = \dfrac{-1}{2}$ in CsO_2 — Cs has O.S. $= +1$ in its compounds.

(d) $O = -1$ in BaO_2 — Ba has O.S. $= +2$ in its compounds.

56. **(E)**

(a)	MgH_2	Mg = +2	H = –1	
(b)	CsO_3	Cs = +1	O = –1/3	
(c)	HOF	H = +1	F = –1	O = 0
(d)	$NaAlH_4$	Na = +1	H = –1[*]	Al = +3

[*]Note: in metal hydrides, H has an oxidation number of –1.

Nomenclature

57. **(E)**

(a)	SrO	strontium oxide	**(b)**	ZnS	zinc sulfide
(c)	K_2CrO_4	potassium chromate	**(d)**	Cs_2SO_4	cesium sulfate
(e)	Cr_2O_3	chromium(III) oxide	**(f)**	$Fe_2(SO_4)_3$	iron(III) sulfate
(g)	$Mg(HCO_3)_2$	magnesium hydrogen carbonate or magnesium bicarbonate	**(h)**	$(NH_4)_2HPO_4$	ammonium hydrogen phosphate
(i)	$Ca(HSO_3)_2$	calcium hydrogen sulfite	**(j)**	$Cu(OH)_2$	copper(II) hydroxide
(k)	HNO_3	nitric acid	**(l)**	$KClO_4$	potassium perchlorate
(m)	$HBrO_3$	bromic acid	**(n)**	H_3PO_3	phosphorous acid

58. **(E)**

(a)	$Ba(NO_3)_2$	barium nitrate	**(b)**	HNO_2	nitrous acid
(c)	CrO_2	chromium(IV) oxide	**(d)**	KIO_3	potassium iodate
(e)	LiCN	lithium cyanide	**(f)**	KIO	potassium hypoiodite
(g)	$Fe(OH)_2$	iron(II) hydroxide	**(h)**	$Ca(H_2PO_4)_2$	calcium dihydrogen phosphate
(i)	H_3PO_4	phosphoric acid	**(j)**	$NaHSO_4$	sodium hydrogen sulfate
(k)	$Na_2Cr_2O_7$	sodium dichromate	**(l)**	$NH_4C_2H_3O_2$	ammonium acetate
(m)	MgC_2O_4	magnesium oxalate	**(n)**	$Na_2C_2O_4$	sodium oxalate

59. **(E)**

(a)	CS_2	carbon disulfide	**(b)**	SiF_4	silicon tetrafluoride
(c)	ClF_5	chlorine pentafluoride	**(d)**	N_2O_5	dinitrogen pentoxide
(e)	SF_6	sulfur hexafluoride	**(f)**	I_2Cl_6	diiodine hexachloride

60. (E)
(a) ICl iodine monochloride   **(b)** ClF_3 chlorine trifluoride
(c) SiF_4 silicon tetrafluoride   **(d)** PF_5 phosphorus pentafluoride
(e) NO_2 nitrogen dioxide   **(f)** S_4N_4 tetrasulfur tetranitride

61. (E)
(a) $Al_2(SO_4)_3$ aluminum sulfate   **(b)** $(NH_4)_2Cr_2O_7$ ammonium dichromate
(c) SiF_4 silicon tetrafluoride   **(d)** Fe_2O_3 iron(III) oxide
(e) C_3S_2 tricarbon disulfide   **(f)** $Co(NO_3)_2$ cobalt(II) nitrate
(g) $Sr(NO_2)_2$ strontium nitrite   **(h)** $HBr(aq)$ hydrobromic acid
(i) HIO_3 iodic acid   **(j)** PCl_2F_3 phosphorus dichloride trifluoride

62. (E)
(a) $Mg(ClO_4)_2$ magnesium perchlorate   **(b)** $Pb(C_2H_3O_2)_2$ lead(II) acetate
(c) SnO_2 tin(IV) oxide   **(d)** $HI(aq)$ hydroiodic acid
(e) $HClO_2$ chlorous acid   **(f)** $NaHSO_3$ sodium hydrogen sulfite
(g) $Ca(H_2PO_4)_2$ calcium dihydrogen phosphate   **(h)** $AlPO_4$ aluminum phosphate
(i) N_2O_4 dinitrogen tetroxide   **(j)** S_2Cl_2 disulfur dichloride

63. (E)
(a) Ti^{4+} and Cl^- produce $TiCl_4$ **(b)** Fe^{3+} and SO_4^{2-} produce $Fe_2(SO_4)_3$
(c) Cl^{7+} and O^{2-} produce Cl_2O_7 **(d)** S^{7+} and O^{2-} produce $S_2O_8^{2-}$

64. (E)
(a) N^{5+} and O^{2-} produce N_2O_5 **(b)** N^{3+}, O^{2-} and H^+ produce HNO_2
(c) $C^{+4/3}$ and O^{2-} produce C_3O_2 **(d)** $S^{+2.5}$ and O^{2-} produce $S_4O_6^{2-}$

65. (E)
(a) $HClO_2$ chlorous acid   **(b)** H_2SO_3 sulfurous acid
(c) H_2Se hydroselenic acid   **(d)** HNO_2 nitrous acid

66. (E)
(a) $HF(aq)$ hydrofluoric acid   **(b)** HNO_3 nitric acid
(c) H_3PO_3 phosphorous acid   **(d)** H_2SO_4 sulfuric acid

67. **(E)**

(a) OF_2 oxygen difluoride   **(b)** XeF_2 xenon difluoride

(c) $CuSO_3$ copper(II) sulfite   **(d)** $(NH_4)_2HPO_4$ ammonium hydrogen phosphate

Both (c) and (d) are ionic compounds.

68. (E)

(a) KNO_2 potassium nitrite   **(b)** BrF_3 bromine trifluoride

(c) S_2Cl_2 disulfur dichloride   **(d)** $Mg(ClO)_2$ magnesium hypochlorite

(e) Cl_2O dichlorine monoxide

Both (a) and (d) are ionic compounds.

Hydrates

69. **(E)** The hydrate with the greatest mass percent H_2O is the one that gives the largest result for the number of moles of water in the hydrate's empirical formula, divided by the mass of one mole of the anhydrous salt for the hydrate.

$$\frac{5\,H_2O}{CuSO_4} = \frac{5\,mol\,H_2O}{159.6\,g} = 0.03133 \qquad \frac{6\,H_2O}{MgCl_2} = \frac{6\,mol\,H_2O}{95.2\,g} = 0.0630$$

$$\frac{18\,H_2O}{Cr_2(SO_4)_3} = \frac{18\,mol\,H_2O}{392.3\,g} = 0.04588 \qquad \frac{2\,H_2O}{LiC_2H_3O_2} = \frac{2\,mol\,H_2O}{66.0\,g} = 0.0303$$

The hydrate with the greatest % H_2O therefore is $MgCl_2 \cdot 6\,H_2O$

70. **(E)** A mole of this hydrate will contain about the same mass of H_2O and of Na_2SO_3.

molar mass $Na_2SO_3 = (2 \times 23.0\,g\,Na) + 32.1\,g\,S + (3 \times 16.0\,g\,O) = 126.1\,g/mol$

number of mol $H_2O = 126.1\,g \times \dfrac{1\,mol\,H_2O}{18.0\,g\,H_2O} = 7.01\,mol\,H_2O$

Thus, the formula of the hydrate is $Na_2SO_3 \cdot 7\,H_2O$.

71. **(M)**

molar mass $CuSO_4 = 63.546\,g\,Cu + 32.066\,g\,S + (4 \times 15.9994\,g\,O) = 159.61\,g\,CuSO_4/mol$.

Note that each $CuSO_4$ will pick up 5 equivalents of H_2O to give $CuSO_4 \cdot 5H_2O$.

Conversion pathway approach:

mass of required $CuSO_4 = 12.6\,g\,H_2O \times \dfrac{1\,mol\,H_2O}{18.015\,g\,H_2O} \times \dfrac{1\,mol\,CuSO_4}{5\,mol\,H_2O} \times \dfrac{159.61\,g\,CuSO_4}{1\,mol\,CuSO_4}$

$= 22.3\,g\,CuSO_4$ is the minimum amount required to remove all the water

Stepwise approach:

$$12.6 \text{ g H}_2\text{O} \times \frac{1 \text{ mol H}_2\text{O}}{18.0153 \text{ g H}_2\text{O}} = 0.699 \text{ mol H}_2\text{O} \times \frac{1 \text{ mol CuSO}_4}{5 \text{ mol H}_2\text{O}} = 0.140 \text{ mol CuSO}_4$$

$$0.140 \text{ mol CuSO}_4 \times \frac{159.60 \text{ g CuSO}_4}{1 \text{ mol CuSO}_4} = 22.3 \text{ g CuSO}_4$$

= is the minimum amount required to remove all the water

72. **(M)** The increase in mass of the solid is the result of each mole of the solid absorbing 10 moles of water.

$$\text{increase in mass} = 36.15 \text{ g Na}_2\text{SO}_4 \times \frac{1 \text{ mol Na}_2\text{SO}_4}{142.036 \text{ g Na}_2\text{SO}_4} \times \frac{10 \text{ mol H}_2\text{O added}}{1 \text{ mol Na}_2\text{SO}_4} \times \frac{18.0153 \text{ g H}_2\text{O}}{1 \text{ mol H}_2\text{O}}$$

$$= 45.85 \text{ g H}_2\text{O added}$$

73. **(M)** We start by converting to molar amounts for each element based on 100.0 g:

$$20.3 \text{ g Cu} \times \frac{1 \text{ mol Cu}}{63.546 \text{ g Cu}} = 0.319 \text{ mol Cu} \quad \div 0.319 \rightarrow 1.00 \text{ mol Cu}$$

$$8.95 \text{ g Si} \times \frac{1 \text{ mol Si}}{28.085 \text{ g Si}} = 0.319 \text{ mol Si} \quad \div 0.319 \rightarrow 1.00 \text{ mol Si}$$

$$36.3 \text{ g F} \times \frac{1 \text{ mol F}}{18.998 \text{ g F}} = 1.91 \text{ mol F} \quad \div 0.319 \rightarrow 5.99 \text{ mol F}$$

$$34.5 \text{ g H}_2\text{O} \times \frac{1 \text{ mol H}_2\text{O}}{18.015 \text{ g}} = 1.91\underline{5} \text{ mol H}_2\text{O} \div 0.319 \rightarrow 6.00 \text{ mol H}_2\text{O}$$

Thus the empirical formula for the hydrate is $CuSiF_6 \cdot 6 \text{ H}_2\text{O}$.

74. **(M)** Let's start by looking at the data provided.

mass of anhydrous compound = 3.967 g

mass of water = 8.129 g − 3.967 g = 4.162 g

$$\text{moles of anhydrous compound} = 3.967 \text{ g MgSO}_4 \times \frac{1 \text{ mol MgSO}_4}{120.37 \text{ g}} = 0.03296 \text{ mol}$$

$$\text{moles of H}_2\text{O} = 4.162 \text{ g} \times \frac{1 \text{ mol H}_2\text{O}}{18.015 \text{ g H}_2\text{O}} = 0.2310 \text{ mol H}_2\text{O}$$

$$\text{setting up proportions} \quad \frac{0.2310 \text{ mol H}_2\text{O}}{0.03296 \text{ mol anhydrous compound}} = \frac{x \text{ mol H}_2\text{O}}{1.00 \text{ mol anhydrous compound}}$$

$x = 7.009$ Thus, the formula of the hydrate is $MgSO_4 \cdot 7H_2O$.

Organic Compounds and Organic Nomenclature

75. **(E)** Answer is (b), butan-2-ol is the most appropriate name for this molecule. It has a four carbon atom chain with a hydroxyl group on the carbon second from the end.

76. **(E)** Answer (c), butanoic acid is the most appropriate name for this molecule. It has a four carbon atom chain with an acid group on the first carbon (terminal carbon atom)

<u>77.</u> **(E)** Molecules (a), (b), (c), and (d) are structural isomers. They share a common formula, namely $C_5H_{12}O$, but have different molecular structures. Molecule (e) has a different chemical formula ($C_6H_{14}O$) and hence cannot be classified as an isomer. It should be pointed out that molecules (a) and (c) are identical as well as being isomers of (b).

78. **(E)** Molecules (a), (b), and (c) are structural isomers. They share a common formula, namely $C_5H_{11}Cl$, but have different molecular structures. Molecule (d) has a different chemical formula ($C_6H_{13}Cl$) and hence cannot be classified as an isomer.

<u>79.</u> **(E)**
(a)	$CH_3(CH_2)_5CH_3$	**(b)**	$CH_3CH_2CO_2H$
(c)	$CH_3CH_2CH_2CH(CH_3)CH_2OH$	**(d)**	CH_3CH_2F

80. **(E)**
(a)	$CH_3(CH_2)_6CH_3$	**(b)**	$CH_3(CH_2)_5CO_2H$
(c)	$CH_3(CH_2)_2CH(OH)CH_2CH_3$	**(d)**	$CH_3CHClCH_2CH_3$

<u>81.</u> **(M)**
(a)	methanol; CH_3OH	Molecular mass = 32.04 u
(b)	2-chlorohexane; $CH_3(CH_2)_3CHClCH_3$	Molecular mass = 120.6 u
(c)	pentanoic acid; $CH_3(CH_2)_3CO_2H$	Molecular mass = 102.1 u
(d)	2-methylprooan-1-ol $CH_3CH(CH_3)CH_2OH$	Molecular mass = 74.12 u

82. **(M)**
(a)	pentan-2-ol; $CH_3CH_2CH_2CH(OH)CH_3$	Molecular mass = 88.15 u
(b)	propanoic acid; $CH_3CH_2CO_2H$	Molecular mass = 74.08 u
(c)	1-bromobutane; $CH_3(CH_2)_2CH_2Br$	Molecular mass = 137.0 u
(d)	3-chlorobutanoic acid; $CH_3CHClCH_2CO_2H$	Molecular mass = 122.6 u

INTEGRATIVE AND ADVANCED EXERCISES

83. (M)

molar mass $= (1 \times 6.94 \text{ g Li}) + (1 \times 26.982 \text{ g Al}) + (2 \times 28.05 \text{ g Si}) + (6 \times 15.999 \text{ g O}) = 186.02 \text{ g/mol}$

Conversion pathway approch:

$$\text{number of Li}-6 \text{ atoms} = 518 \text{ g spodumene} \times \frac{1 \text{ mol spodumene}}{186.02 \text{ g spodumene}} \times \frac{1 \text{ mol Li}}{1 \text{ mol spodumene}} \times \frac{7.40 \text{ mol Li-6}}{100.00 \text{ mol total Li}}$$

$$\times \frac{6.022 \times 10^{23} \text{ Li-6 atoms}}{1 \text{ mol Li-6}} = 1.24 \times 10^{23} \text{ Li-6 atoms}$$

Stepwise approch:

$$518 \text{ g spodumene} \times \frac{1 \text{ mol spodumene}}{186.02 \text{ g spodumene}} = 2.78 \text{ mol spodumene}$$

$$2.78 \text{ mol spodumene} \times \frac{1 \text{ mol Li}}{1 \text{ mol spodumene}} = 2.78 \text{ mol Li}$$

$$2.78 \text{ mol Li} \times \frac{7.40 \text{ mol Li-6}}{100.00 \text{ mol total Li}} = 0.206 \text{ mol Li-6}$$

$$0.206 \text{ mol Li-6} \times \frac{6.022 \times 10^{23} \text{ Li-6 atoms}}{1 \text{ mol Li-6}} = 1.24 \times 10^{23} \text{ Li-6 atoms}$$

84. (M) Determine the mass of each element in the sample.

$$\text{mass Sn} = 0.245 \text{ g SnO}_2 \times \frac{1 \text{ mol SnO}_2}{150.71 \text{ g SnO}_2} \times \frac{1 \text{ mol Sn}}{1 \text{ mol SnO}_2} \times \frac{118.71 \text{ g Sn}}{1 \text{ mol Sn}} = 0.193 \text{ g Sn}$$

$$\text{mass Pb} = 0.115 \text{ g PbSO}_4 \times \frac{1 \text{ mol PbSO}_4}{303.26 \text{ g PbSO}_4} \times \frac{1 \text{ mol Pb}}{1 \text{ mol PbSO}_4} \times \frac{207.2 \text{ g Pb}}{1 \text{ mol Pb}} = 0.0786 \text{ g Pb}$$

$$\text{mass Zn} = 0.246 \text{ g Zn}_2\text{P}_2\text{O}_7 \times \frac{1 \text{ mol Zn}_2\text{P}_2\text{O}_7}{304.72 \text{ g Zn}_2\text{P}_2\text{O}_7} \times \frac{2 \text{ mol Zn}}{1 \text{ mol Zn}_2\text{P}_2\text{O}_7} \times \frac{65.38 \text{ g Zn}}{1 \text{ mol Zn}} = 0.106 \text{ g Zn}$$

Then determine the % of each element in the sample.

$$\% \text{ Sn} = \frac{0.193 \text{ g Sn}}{1.1713 \text{ g brass}} \times 100\% = 16.5\% \text{ Sn} \qquad \% \text{ Pb} = \frac{0.0786 \text{ g Pb}}{1.1713 \text{ g brass}} \times 100\% = 6.71\% \text{ Pb}$$

$$\% \text{ Zn} = \frac{0.106 \text{ g Zn}}{1.1713 \text{ g brass}} \times 100\% = 9.05\% \text{ Zn}$$

The % Cu is found by difference.

$$\%\text{Cu} = 100\% - 16.5\% \text{ Sn} - 6.71\% \text{ Pb} - 9.05\% \text{ Zn} = 67.7\% \text{ Cu}$$

85. (M) $1 \text{ lb} = 16 \text{ oz} = 453.59237 \text{ g}$ or $1 \text{ oz} = 28.35 \text{ g}$

$$3.50 \text{ oz meat} \times \frac{28.35 \text{ g meat}}{1 \text{ oz meat}} \times \frac{0.12 \text{ g } C_6H_5COONa}{100 \text{ g meat}} \times \frac{22.990 \text{ g Na}}{144.105 \text{ g } C_6H_5COONa} \times \frac{1000 \text{ mg Na}}{1 \text{ g Na}}$$

$$= 19.0 \text{ mg Na}$$

86. (M) First, we determine the amount of each mineral necessary to obtain 1 kg or 1000 g of boron.

$$1000 \text{ g B} \times \frac{1 \text{ mol B}}{10.81 \text{ g B}} \times \frac{1 \text{ mol } Na_2B_4O_7 \cdot 4 H_2O}{4 \text{ mol B}} \times \frac{273.28 \text{ g } Na_2B_4O_7 \cdot 4 H_2O}{1 \text{ mol } Na_2B_4O_7 \cdot 4 H_2O}$$

$$= 6,319.\underline{5} \text{ g } Na_2B_4O_7 \cdot 4 H_2O$$

$$1000 \text{ g B} \times \frac{1 \text{ mol B}}{10.81 \text{ g B}} \times \frac{1 \text{ mol } Na_2B_4O_7 \cdot 4 H_2O}{4 \text{ mol B}} \times \frac{381.372 \text{ g } Na_2B_4O_7 \cdot 10 H_2O}{1 \text{ mol } Na_2B_4O_7 \cdot 4 H_2O}$$

$$= 8,819.\underline{1} \text{ g } Na_2B_4O_7 \cdot 10 H_2O$$

The difference between these two masses is the required additional mass. Hence, $8819.\underline{1} \text{ g} - 6319.\underline{5} \text{ g} = 2499.\underline{6} \text{ g}$. Thus, an additional 2.500 kg mass is required.

87. (M) $N_A = \dfrac{9.64853415 \times 10^4 \text{ C}}{1 \text{ mol Ag}} \times \dfrac{1 \text{ mol Ag}}{1 \text{ mol e}^-} \times \dfrac{1 \text{ e}^-}{1.602176462 \times 10^{-19} \text{C}} = \dfrac{6.0221422 \times 10^{23} \text{ e}^-}{\text{mole e}^-}$

88. (M) First, determine the formula of the compound. The compound is 26.58% K, 35.45% Cr and 37.97% O. Assuming 100 g of compound, 26.58 g are potassium, 35.45 g are chromium, and 37.97 g are oxygen.

$$26.58 \text{ g K} \times \frac{1 \text{ mol K}}{39.10 \text{ g K}} = 0.6798 \text{ mol K} \quad \div 0.6798 \text{ mol} \rightarrow 1.000 \text{ mol K}$$

$$35.45 \text{ g Cr} \times \frac{1 \text{ mol Cr}}{52.00 \text{ g Cr}} = 0.6818 \text{ mol Cr} \quad \div 0.6798 \text{ mol} \rightarrow 1.000 \text{ mol Cr}$$

$$37.97 \text{ g O} \times \frac{1 \text{ mol O}}{16.00 \text{ g O}} = 2.373 \text{ mol O} \quad \div 0.6798 \text{ mol} \rightarrow 3.491 \text{ mol O}$$

$2 \times KCrO_{3.5} = K_2Cr_2O_7$ which is the formula of the compound

The oxidation state of Cr is +6 and the compound $K_2Cr_2O_7$ is named potassium dichromate.

89. (M) It is not possible to have less than 1 molecule of S_8. In order to determine whether it is possible to have 1.00×10^{-23} g of S_8, determine how many molecules that number is equivalent to.

$$1.00 \times 10^{-23} \text{ g } S_8 \times \frac{1 \text{ mol } S_8}{256.48 \text{ g } S_8} \times \frac{6.022 \times 10^{23} \text{ molecules } S_8}{1 \text{ mol } S_8} = 1.0235 \text{ molecules } S_8$$

Therefore it is **not** possible to have 1.00×10^{-23} g of S_8.

$$1 \text{ molecule } S_8 \times \frac{1 \text{ mol } S_8}{6.022 \times 10^{23} \text{ molecules } S_8} \times \frac{256.48 \text{ g } S}{1 \text{ mol } S_8} = 4.26 \times 10^{-22} \text{ g } S$$

$$4.26 \times 10^{-22} \text{ g } S \times \frac{1 \text{ yg } S}{10^{-24} \text{ g } S} = 426 \text{ yoctograms } S$$

90. (E) A hydrocarbon with a double bond has the molecular formula C_nH_{2n}.

While the moles of H_2O will be greater than the moles of CO_2 as with any other hydrocarbon, the mass of H_2O will never exceed that of CO_2. To prove this, we consider the fact that a hydrocarbon with the greatest ratio of the amount of hydrogen to the amount of carbon will produce the greatest mass of H_2O per gram of CO_2. This hydrocarbon is CH_4, and it produces 2 mol H_2O for every mole of CO_2. From this information, we can determine the maximum ratio of mass H_2O/mass CO_2.

$$\frac{\text{mass } H_2O}{\text{mass } CO_2} = \frac{2 \text{ mol } H_2O}{1 \text{ mol } CO_2} \times \frac{18.02 \text{ g } H_2O}{1 \text{ mol } H_2O} \times \frac{1 \text{ mol } CO_2}{44.01 \text{ g } CO_2} = 0.8189 \text{ g } H_2O/\text{g } CO_2$$

Thus no hydrocarbon exists that yields a greater mass of H_2O than of CO_2.

91. (M) We determine the masses of CO_2 and H_2O produced by burning the C_3H_8.

$$\text{mass}_{CO_2} = 6.00 \text{ g } C_3H_8 \times \frac{1 \text{ mol } C_3H_8}{44.097 \text{ g } C_3H_8} \times \frac{3 \text{ mol } C}{1 \text{ mol } C_3H_8} \times \frac{1 \text{ mol } CO_2}{1 \text{ mol } C} \times \frac{44.01 \text{ g } CO_2}{1 \text{ mol } CO_2}$$

$$= 17.9\underline{6} \text{ g } CO_2$$

$$\text{mass}_{H_2O} = 6.00 \text{ g } C_3H_8 \times \frac{1 \text{ mol } C_3H_8}{44.097 \text{ g } C_3H_8} \times \frac{8 \text{ mol } H}{1 \text{ mol } C_3H_8} \times \frac{1 \text{ mol } H_2O}{2 \text{ mol } H} \times \frac{18.015 \text{ g } H_2O}{1 \text{ mol } H_2O}$$

$$= 9.80\underline{5} \text{ g } H_2O$$

Then, from the masses of CO_2 and H_2O in the unknown compound, we determine the amounts of C and H in that compound and finally its empirical formula.

$$\text{amount C} = (29.0 - 17.9\underline{6}) \text{ g } CO_2 \times \frac{1 \text{ mol } CO_2}{44.01 \text{ g } CO_2} \times \frac{1 \text{ mol } C}{1 \text{ mol } CO_2} = 0.251 \text{ mol C}$$

$$\text{amount H} = (18.8 - 9.80\underline{5}) \text{ g } H_2O \times \frac{1 \text{ mol } H_2O}{18.015 \text{ g } H_2O} \times \frac{2 \text{ mol } H}{1 \text{ mol } H_2O} = 0.998\underline{6} \text{ mol H}$$

The empirical formula of the unknown compound is CH_4. The C:H ratio is $0.9986/0.251 = 3.98$. The molecular formula can be calculated by knowing that we have 0.251 moles, which accounts for the 4.00 g of hydrocarbon (40% of 10.0 g). This gives a molar mass of $4.00 \div 0.251 = 15.9$ g/mol. This is nearly the same as the molar mass of the empirical formula CH_4 (16.04 g/mol).

92. **(M)**

(a) We determine the mass of CO_2 produced from the mixture, with x representing the mass of CH_4, and then solve for x.

$$n_{carbon} = x \text{ g } CH_4 \times \frac{1 \text{ mol } CH_4}{16.043 \text{ g } CH_4} \times \frac{1 \text{ mol C}}{1 \text{ mol } CH_4} + (0.732 - x)\text{g } C_2H_6 \times \frac{1 \text{ mol } C_2H_6}{30.070 \text{ g } C_2H_6} \times \frac{2 \text{ mol C}}{1 \text{ mol } C_2H_6}$$

$$2.064 \text{ } CO_2 = \left(\frac{x}{16.043} + \frac{2(0.732 - x)}{30.070}\right) \text{mol C} \times \frac{1 \text{mol } CO_2}{1 \text{ mol C}} \times \frac{44.009 \text{ g } CO_2}{1 \text{ mol } CO_2}$$

$$2.064 \text{ } CO_2 = 2.7433x + 2.142 - 2.9272x = -0.1839x + 2.142$$

$$x = \frac{2.142 - 2.064}{0.1839} = 0.4\underline{2} \text{ g } CH_4$$

$$\%CH_4 = \frac{0.42 \text{ g } CH_4}{0.732 \text{ g mixture}} \times 100\% = 57\% \text{ } CH_4 \approx 60\% \text{ } CH_4 \text{ and } 4\underline{3}\% \text{ } C_2H_6 \sim 40\% \text{ } C_2H_6$$

(b) In 100 g of mixture there are the following amounts.

$$\text{amount } CH_4 = 5\underline{7} \text{ g } CH_4 \times \frac{1 \text{ mol } CH_4}{16.043 \text{ g } CH_4} = 3.\underline{6} \text{ mol } CH_4$$

$$\text{amount } C_2H_6 = 4\underline{3} \text{ g } C_2H_6 \times \frac{1 \text{ mol } C_2H_6}{30.070 \text{ g } C_2H_6} = 1.\underline{4} \text{ mol } C_2H_6$$

$$\text{mol } \% \text{ } CH_4 = \frac{3\underline{6} \text{ mol } CH_4}{5\underline{0} \text{ mol total}} \times 100\% = 7\underline{2} \text{ mol\% } CH_4 \text{ and } 2\underline{8} \text{ mol\% } C_2H_6$$

93. **(M)** Since the compound is composed of H_2SO_4 and H_2O, we will need to determine the percent composition of both H_2SO_4 and water.

$$\% \text{ } H_2SO_4 = \frac{\# \text{ grams } H_2SO_4}{\text{total mass in grams}} \times 100\%$$

$$\# \text{ g } H_2SO_4 = 65.2 \text{ g } (NH_4)_2SO_4 \times \frac{1 \text{ mol } (NH_4)_2SO_4}{132.15 \text{ g } (NH_4)_2SO_4} \times \frac{1 \text{ mol } H_2SO_4}{1 \text{ mol } (NH_4)_2SO_4} \times \frac{98.08 \text{ g } H_2SO_4}{1 \text{ mol } H_2SO_4} = 48.4 \text{ g}$$

$$\text{total mass} = 32.0 \text{ mL mixture} \times \frac{1.78 \text{ g mixture}}{1 \text{ mL mixture}} = 57.0 \text{ g mixture}$$

$$\% \text{ } H_2SO_4 = \frac{48.4 \text{ g}}{57.0 \text{ g}} \times 100\% = 85.0\%$$

$$\% \text{ } H_2O = 100.0 - 85.0 = 15.0\%$$

94. (E) $\% \text{ Ag} = \dfrac{\text{mass Ag}}{\text{mass sample}} \times 100\%$

Using 35.446 g/mol as the molar mass of Cl and 107.87 g/mol as the molar mass of Ag, we find that the molar mass of AgCl is $(107.87 + 35.446)$ g/mol = 143.316 g/mol = 143.32 g/mol. (The number of decimal places in this result is determined by the number of decimal places in the molar mass of Ag.) Using 143.32 g/mol for the molar mass of AgCl, we have

$$31.56 \text{ g AgCl} \times \frac{1 \text{ mol AgCl}}{143.32 \text{ g AgCl}} \times \frac{1 \text{ mol Ag}}{1 \text{ mol AgCl}} \times \frac{107.87 \text{ g Ag}}{1 \text{ mol Ag}} = 23.75 \text{ g Ag}$$

$$\% \text{ Ag} = \frac{23.75 \text{ g}}{26.39 \text{ g}} \times 100\% = 90.00\%$$

Now, using 35.457 g/mol as the molar mass of Cl, we find that the molar mass of AgCl is $(107.87 + 35.457)$ g/mol = 143.327 g/mol = 143.33 g/mol and

$$31.56 \text{ g AgCl} \times \frac{1 \text{ mol AgCl}}{143.33 \text{ g AgCl}} \times \frac{1 \text{ mol Ag}}{1 \text{ mol AgCl}} \times \frac{107.87 \text{ g Ag}}{1 \text{ mol Ag}} = 23.75 \text{ g Ag}$$

We see from this calculation that the mass of Ag obtained is the same (to four significant figures). Therefore, the corresponding value for the % Ag will also be 90.00%.

In this case, the fact that the atomic mass of Cl is given as an interval has little effect on the calculated final result.

95. (D)

$$9.0 \times 10^{-4} \frac{\mu \text{ mol C}_2\text{H}_6\text{S}}{\text{m}^3 \text{ air}} \times \frac{1 \times 10^{-6} \text{ mol C}_2\text{H}_6\text{S}}{1 \mu \text{ mol C}_2\text{H}_6\text{S}} \times \frac{62.13 \text{ g C}_2\text{H}_6\text{S}}{1 \text{ mol C}_2\text{H}_6\text{S}} \times \frac{1 \text{ m}^3}{(100)^3 \text{ cm}^3} \times$$

$$\frac{1 \text{ cm}^3}{1 \text{ mL}} \times \frac{1000 \text{ mL}}{1 \text{ L}} \times \frac{1 \text{ L air}}{1.2 \text{ g air}} = 4.7 \times 10^{-11} \frac{\text{g C}_2\text{H}_6\text{S}}{\text{g air}}$$

$$4.7 \times 10^{-11} \frac{\text{g C}_2\text{H}_6\text{S}}{\text{g air}} \times \frac{1 \times 10^9 \text{ g}}{1 \text{ billion grams}} = 0.0466 \text{ ppb} = 0.05 \text{ ppb}$$

96. (D)

(a) If we have one mole of entities, then we must have 0.7808 mol N_2, 0.2095 mol O_2, 0.0093 mol Ar, and 0.0004 mol CO_2.

$$0.7808 \text{ mol N}_2 \times \frac{28.02 \text{ g N}_2}{1 \text{ mol N}_2} = 21.88 \text{ g N}_2$$

$$0.2095 \text{ mol O}_2 \times \frac{32.00 \text{ g O}_2}{1 \text{ mol O}_2} = 6.704 \text{ g O}_2$$

$$0.0004 \text{ mol CO}_2 \times \frac{44.01 \text{ g CO}_2}{1 \text{ mol CO}_2} = 0.0176 \text{ g CO}_2$$

$$0.0093 \text{ mol Ar} \times \frac{39.948 \text{ g Ar}}{1 \text{ mol Ar}} = 0.3715 \text{ g Ar}$$

mass of air sample $= 21.88$g $N_2 +$ 6.704 g $O_2 + 0.0176$ g $CO_2 + 0.3715$ g $Ar = 28.97$ g

(b) $1\ m^3 \times \dfrac{(100)^3\ cm^3}{1\ m^3} \times \dfrac{1\ mL}{1\ cm^3} \times \dfrac{1\ L}{1000\ mL} \times \dfrac{1.2\ g}{1\ L} = 1200$ g dry air

$1200\ g \times \dfrac{1\ mol\ entities}{28.97\ g} \times \dfrac{1.14 \times 10^{-4}}{100} = 4.72 \times 10^{-5}$ mol Kr

4.72×10^{-5} mol Kr $\times \dfrac{83.80\ g}{1\ mol} = 3.96 \times 10^{-3}$ g Kr $= 4.0$ mg Kr

97. (M)
(a) Make the assumption that $1\ mL\ H_2O = 1\ g\ H_2O$.

$350\ g\ H_2O \times \dfrac{0.8\ g\ CHCl_3}{1,000,000,000\ g\ H_2O} \times \dfrac{1\ mol\ CHCl_3}{119.377\ g\ CHCl_3} \times \dfrac{6.022 \times 10^{23}\ CHCl_3}{1\ mol\ CHCl_3} = 1.41 \times 10^{15}\ CHCl_3$

(b) $1.14 \times 10^{15}\ CHCl_3 \times \dfrac{1\ mol\ CHCl_3}{6.022 \times 10^{23}\ CHCl_3} \times \dfrac{119.377\ g\ CHCl_3}{1\ mol\ CHCl_3} = 2.25 \times 10^{-7}$ g $CHCl_3$

Alternatively, $350\ g\ H_2O \times \dfrac{1\ g\ CHCl_3}{1,000,000,000\ g\ H_2O} = 3.50 \times 10^{-7}$ g $CHCl_3$

This amount would not be detected with an ordinary analytical balance. You would require something that was at least 300 times more sensitive.

98. (M). We can determine both the number of moles of M and the mass of M in 0.1131 g MSO_4. Their quotient is the atomic mass of M.

mol $M^{2+} = 0.2193$ g $BaSO_4 \times \dfrac{1\ mol\ BaSO_4}{233.39\ g\ BaSO_4} \times \dfrac{1\ mol\ SO_4^{2-}}{1\ mol\ BaSO_4} \times \dfrac{1\ mol\ M^{2+}}{1\ mol\ SO_4^{2-}} = 0.0009396$ mol M^{2+}

mass $SO_4^{2-} = 0.0009396$ mol $M^{2+} \times \dfrac{1\ mol\ SO_4^{2-}}{1\ mol\ M^{2+}} \times \dfrac{96.064\ g\ SO_4^{2-}}{1\ mol\ SO_4^{2-}} = 0.09026$ g SO_4^{2-}

mass M $=$ mass $MSO_4 -$ mass $SO_4^{2-} = 0.1131$ g $MSO_4 - 0.09026$ g $SO_4^{2-} = 0.0228$ g M

atomic mass M $= \dfrac{mass\ M}{moles\ M} = \dfrac{0.0228\ g\ M}{0.0009396\ mol\ M} = 24.3$ g M/mol

M is the element magnesium.

99. (M) mass $SO_4^{2-} = 1.511$ g $BaSO_4 \times \dfrac{1\ mol\ BaSO_4}{233.39\ g\ BaSO_4} \times \dfrac{1\ mol\ SO_4^{2-}}{1\ mol\ BaSO_4} = 0.006474$ mol SO_4^{2-}

0.006474 mol $SO_4^{2-} \times \dfrac{96.064\ g\ SO_4^{2-}}{1\ mol\ SO_4^{2-}} = 0.6219$ g SO_4^{2-}

amount M $= 0.006474$ mol $SO_4^{2-} \times \dfrac{2\ mol\ M^{3+}}{3\ mol\ SO_4^{2-}} = 0.004316$ mol M^{3+}

mass M $= 0.738$ g $M_2(SO_4)_3 - 0.6219$ g $SO_4^{2-} = 0.116$ g M

atomic mass of M $= \dfrac{0.116\ g\ M}{0.004316\ mol\ M} = 26.9$ g M/mol $\qquad$ M is the element aluminum.

100. (D) Set up an equation in the usual conversion-factor format, to determine what mass of MS can be obtained from the given mass of M_2O_3. Of course, the mass of MS is not unknown; it is 0.685 g. What is unknown is the atomic mass of the element M; let's call this x and solve for x.

$$0.685 \text{ g MS} = 0.622 \text{ g } M_2O_3 \times \frac{1 \text{ mol } M_2O_3}{[2x + (3 \times 16.0)] \text{ g } M_2O_3} \times \frac{2 \text{ mol M}}{1 \text{ mol } M_2O_3} \times \frac{1 \text{ mol MS}}{1 \text{ mol M}} \times \frac{(x + 32.1) \text{ g MS}}{1 \text{ mol MS}}$$

$$0.685 \text{ g MS} = \frac{0.622 \times 2 \times (x + 32.1)}{2x + 48.0} \qquad 1.24\underline{4}x + 39.9 = 1.37x + 32.9 \quad 0.126x = 7.0$$

$x = 56$ is the atomic mass of M $\qquad$ M is element 56, iron (Fe)

101. (D) Let x = mol $MgCl_2$ in the sample, and y = mol NaCl. Set up two equations.

$$0.6110 = \frac{2x \times 35.45 \text{ g Cl} + 35.45y \text{ g Cl}}{0.5200 \text{ g sample}} \qquad 0.5200 \text{ g} = 95.205x \text{ g } MgCl_2 + 58.44 \, y \text{ g NaCl}$$

We then solve these two equations for x.

$$0.6110 \times 0.5200 = 0.3177 = 70.9x + 35.45y \qquad \frac{0.3177}{35.45} = 0.008962 = 2x + y$$

$$y = 0.008962 - 2x$$

$$0.5200 = 95.205x + 58.44(0.008962 - 2x)$$

$$= 95.205x + 0.5237 - 116.88x$$

$$0.5200 - 0.5237 = -0.0037 = (95.205 - 116.88)x = -21.675x$$

$$-0.0037 = -21.675x$$

$$x = \frac{0.0037}{21.675}$$

$$x = 1.7 \times 10^{-4} \text{ mol } MgCl_2$$

Then determine the value of y.
$$y = 0.008962 - 2x = 0.008962 - 2 \times 0.00017 = 0.00862 \text{ mol NaCl}$$

$$\text{mass } MgCl_2 = 1.7 \times 10^{-4} \text{ mol } MgCl_2 \times \frac{95.21 \text{ g } MgCl_2}{1 \text{ mol } MgCl_2} = 0.016 \text{ g } MgCl_2$$

$$\text{mass NaCl} = 0.00862 \text{ mol NaCl} \times \frac{58.44 \text{ g NaCl}}{1 \text{ mol NaCl}} = 0.504 \text{ g NaCl}$$

$$\%MgCl_2 = \frac{0.016 \text{ g } MgCl_2}{0.5200 \text{ g sample}} \times 100\% = 3.1\% \, MgCl_2 \quad \% \text{ NaCl} = \frac{0.504 \text{ g NaCl}}{0.5200 \text{ g sample}} \times 100\% = 96.9\% \text{ NaCl}$$

The precision of the calculation is poor because there is only a small % $MgCl_2$ in the mixture. When calculating the number of moles of $MgCl_2$, 0.5237 is subtracted from 0.5200 as shown above. The number of significant figures is reduced by this subtraction, which has the effect of reducing the precision in subsequent calculations.

102. (M) First, we determine the mass of Pb in 2.750 g Pb_3O_4.

$$\text{mass Pb} = 2.750 \text{ g } Pb_3O_4 \times \frac{1 \text{ mol } Pb_3O_4}{685.596 \text{ g } Pb_3O_4} \times \frac{3 \text{ mol Pb}}{1 \text{ mol } Pb_3O_4} \times \frac{207.2 \text{ g Pb}}{1 \text{ mol Pb}}$$

$$= 2.493 \text{ g Pb}$$

Then, we determine the amounts of O and Pb in the second oxide. From these, we determine the empirical formula of the second oxide.

$$\text{amount O} = (2.686 \text{ g} - 2.493 \text{ g}) \text{ O} \times \frac{1 \text{ mol O}}{16.00 \text{ g O}} = 0.0121 \text{ mol O}$$

$$\text{amount Pb} = 2.493 \text{ g Pb} \times \frac{1 \text{ mol Pb}}{207.2 \text{ g Pb}} = 0.0120 \text{ mol Pb}$$

Thus, the empirical formula of the second oxide is PbO.

103. (M) If we determine the mass of anhydrous $ZnSO_4$ in the hydrate, we then can determine the mass of water, and the formula of the hydrate.

$$\text{mass } ZnSO_4 = 0.8223 \text{ g } BaSO_4 \times \frac{1 \text{ mol } BaSO_4}{233.386 \text{ g}} \times \frac{1 \text{ mol } ZnSO_4}{1 \text{ mol } BaSO_4} \times \frac{161.454 \text{ g } ZnSO_4}{1 \text{ mol } ZnSO_4}$$

$$= 0.5688 \text{ g } ZnSO_4$$

The water present in the hydrate is obtained by difference.

mass H_2O = 1.013 g hydrate $-$ 0.5688 g $ZnSO_4$ = 0.444 g H_2O

The hydrate's formula is determined by a method similar to that for obtaining an empirical formula.

$$\text{amt. } ZnSO_4 = 0.5688 \text{ g} \times \frac{1 \text{ mol } ZnSO_4}{161.436 \text{ mol } ZnSO_4} = 0.003523 \text{ mol } ZnSO_4 \div 0.003523 \longrightarrow 1.00 \text{ mol } ZnSO_4$$

$$\text{amt. } H_2O = 0.444 \text{ g} \times \frac{1 \text{ mol } H_2O}{18.015 \text{ g } H_2O} = 0.02465 \text{ mol } H_2O \div 0.003523 \longrightarrow 7.00 \text{ mol } H_2O$$

Thus, the formula of the hydrate is $ZnSO_4 \cdot 7 H_2O$.

104. (M) $\dfrac{1.552 \text{ g MI}}{1.186 \text{ g I}} \times \dfrac{126.904 \text{ g I}}{1 \text{ mol I}} \times \dfrac{1 \text{ mol I}}{1 \text{ mol MI}} = \dfrac{166.1 \text{ g MI}}{1 \text{ mol MI}}$ (This is the molar mass of MI.)

Subtract the mass of 1 mol of I to obtain the molar mass of M.

molar mass M = $(166.1 - 126.904)$ g mol^{-1} = 39.2 g mol^{-1}

The cation is probably K (39.098 g mol^{-1}).

Alternatively, find mass of M in sample: 1.552 g MI $-$ 1.186 g I = 0.366 g M

$$\frac{0.366 \text{ g M}}{1.186 \text{ g I}} \times \frac{126.90 \text{ g I}}{1 \text{ mol I}} \times \frac{1 \text{ mol I}}{1 \text{ mol M}} = 39.2 \text{ g mol}^{-1}$$

105. (M)

$$13 \text{ atoms} \times \frac{15.38 \text{ atoms E}}{100 \text{ atoms in formula unit}} = \frac{1.999 \text{ atoms E}}{\text{formula unit}} \quad \therefore H_x E_2 O_z \quad (\text{Note: } x + z = 11)$$

34.80% E by mass, hence, 65.20% H and O by mass

178 u × 0.3480 E = 61.944 u for 2 atoms of E, $\therefore$ E = 30.972 u Probably P (30.974 u)

H and O in formula unit = 178 u – 30.972 u = 116 u

$x + z = 11$ or $x = 11 - z$ and $x(1.008 \text{ u}) + z(15.999 \text{ u}) = 116$ u

Substitute and solve for z: $(11 - z)(1.008 \text{ u}) + z(15.999 \text{ u}) = 116$ u

$11.08734 \text{ u} - 1.008 \text{ u}(z) + 15.999 \text{ u}(z) = 116$ u   Divide through by u and collect terms

$105 = 14.9915(z)$ or $z = 7$ and $x = 11 - z = 11 - 7 = 4$.

Therefore, the formula is $H_4P_2O_7$ (as a check, 13 atoms and 177.975 u ~ 178 u).

106. (M) First find the mass of carbon, hydrogen, chlorine, and oxygen. From the molar ratios, we determine the molecular formula.

$$2.094 \text{ g CO}_2 \times \frac{1 \text{ mol CO}_2}{44.009 \text{ g CO}_2} \times \frac{1 \text{ mol C}}{1 \text{ mol CO}_2} = 0.04759 \text{ mol C} \times \frac{12.011 \text{ g C}}{1 \text{ mol C}} = 0.5716 \text{ g C}$$

$$0.286 \text{ g H}_2O \times \frac{1 \text{ mol H}_2O}{18.015 \text{ g H}_2O} \times \frac{2 \text{ mol H}}{1 \text{ mol H}_2O} = 0.03175 \text{ mol H} \times \frac{1.008 \text{ g H}}{1 \text{ mol H}} = 0.0320 \text{ g H}$$

$$\text{moles of chlorine} = \frac{\text{mol C}}{2} = \frac{0.04759}{2} = 0.02380 \text{ mol Cl}$$

$$\text{mass of Cl} = 0.02380 \text{ mol Cl} \times \frac{35.45 \text{ g Cl}}{1 \text{ mol Cl}} = 0.8436 \text{ g Cl}$$

mass of oxygen obtained by difference: 1.510 g – 0.8436 g – 0.5716 g – 0.0320 g = 0.063 g O

$$\text{moles of oxygen} = 0.063 \text{ g O} \times \frac{1 \text{ mol O}}{15.999 \text{ g O}} = 0.00394 \text{ mol O}$$

Divide the number of moles of each element by 0.00394 to give an empirical formula of $C_{12.1}H_{8.06}Cl_{6.04}O_{1.00}$ owing to the fact that the oxygen mass is obtained by difference, and it has only two significant digits and thus a higher degree of uncertainty.

The empirical formula is $C_{12}H_8Cl_6O$, which with a molecular mass of 381 u has the same molecular mass as the molecular formula. Hence, this empirical formula is also the molecular formula.

107. (M) 1.271 g Na_2SO_4 absorbs 0.387 g H_2O

$$mass_{Na_2SO_4 \cdot 10 H_2O} = 0.387 \text{ g } H_2O \times \frac{1 \text{ mol } H_2O}{18.015 \text{ g } H_2O} \times \frac{1 \text{ mol } Na_2SO_4 \cdot 10 H_2O}{10 \text{ mol } H_2O} \times \frac{322.186 \text{ g } Na_2SO_4 \cdot 10 H_2O}{1 \text{ mol } Na_2SO_4 \cdot 10 H_2O}$$

$$= 0.692 \text{ g } Na_2SO_4 \cdot 10 H_2O$$

$$\text{mass percent } Na_2SO_4 \cdot 10 H_2O = \frac{0.692 \text{ g}}{(1.271 \text{g} + 0.387 \text{g})} \times 100\% = 41.7\%$$

108. (D) Let X = molar mass of Bi and Y = moles of Bi_2O_3

molar mass of $Bi(C_6H_5)_3$ = X + (18 × 12.011 g mol^{-1} + 15 × 1.008 g mol^{-1})
  = X + 231.318 g mol^{-1}

molar mass of Bi_2O_3 = 2X + (3 × 15.999 g mol^{-1} = 2X + 47.997 g mol^{-1}

Consider the reaction: 2 $Bi(C_6H_5)_3 \rightarrow Bi_2O_3$

If Y = moles of Bi_2O_3, then 2Y = moles of $Bi(C_6H_5)_3$.

For both the reactant and the product, mass = MM × moles. Therefore,

5.610 g = 2Y(X + 231.318 g mol^{-1}) = 2XY + (2Y) 231.318 g mol^{-1}, and
2.969 g = Y(2X + 47.997 g mol^{-1}) = 2XY + (Y) 47.997 g mol^{-1}

Rearrange 5.610 g = 2XY + (Y) 231.318 g mol^{-1} to 2XY
  = 5.610 g – (2Y) 231.318 g mol^{-1}

Substitute for 2XY in 2.969 = 2XY + (Y)47.997 g mol^{-1}
2.969 g = 5.610 g – (2Y) 231.318 g mol^{-1} + (Y) 47.997 g mol^{-1}
  = 5.610 g – (Y) 414.639 g mol^{-1}

Collect terms and solve for Y.

5.610 g –2.969 g = (Y) 414.639 g mol^{-1} = 2.641 g
Y = 2.641 g ÷ 414.639 g mol^{-1} = 0.0063694 mol

Substitute Y in 2.969g = 2XY + (Y) 47.997 g mol^{-1} and solve for X, the molar mass of Bi
2.969g = 2X(0.0063694 mol) + (0.0063694 mol) 47.997 g mol^{-1}

$$X = \frac{2.969 \text{g} - (0.0063694 \text{ mol}) 47.997 \text{ g mol}^{-1}}{(2)0.0063694 \text{ mol}} = 209.1 \text{g mol}^{-1} \text{ (Actually it is 208.98 g mol}^{-1}\text{)}$$

109. (D)

volume of Au = 0.25 mm × 15 mm × 15 mm = 56.25 mm^3

$$56.25 \text{ mm}^3 \times \frac{1 \text{ cm}^3}{(10)^3 \text{ mm}^3} \times \frac{19.3 \text{ g Au}}{\text{cm}^3} = 1.086 \text{ g Au}$$

$$1.086 \text{ g Au} \times \frac{1 \text{ mol Au}}{196.97 \text{ g Au}} = 5.51 \times 10^{-3} \text{ mol Au}$$

$$1.400 \text{ g} - 1.086 \text{ g} = 0.314 \text{ g F} \times \frac{1 \text{ mol F}}{18.998 \text{ g F}} = 0.0165 \text{ mol F}$$

$$\frac{5.51 \times 10^{-3}}{5.51 \times 10^{-3}} = 1 \text{ mol Au}$$

$$\frac{0.0165}{5.51 \times 10^{-3}} = 3 \text{ mol F}$$

The formula is therefore AuF_3, which is gold(III) fluoride.

110. (M)

Calculate the mass of chlorine: $0.244 \text{ L} \times 2.898 \text{ g/L} = 0.707 \text{ g chlorine}$

Calculate the mass of iodine: $1.553 \text{ g} - 0.707 \text{ g} = 0.846 \text{ g iodine}$

Calculate the moles of chlorine: $0.707 \text{ g}/35.45 \text{ g/mol} = 0.0199 \text{ mol chlorine}$

Calculate the moles of iodine: $0.846 \text{ g}/126.90 \text{ g/mol} = 0.00667 \text{ mol iodine}$

Calculate the mole ratio: $0.0199:0.00667 = 1:2.98 \approx 1:3$

Calculate the empirical molar mass: $(126.90 + 3 \times 35.45) \text{ g/mol} = 233.25 \text{ g/mol}$

Because $467/233.25 \approx 2$, the molecular formula is I_2Cl_6.

111. (M)

The coating is a compound of copper and iodine. The mass of iodine reacting with the copper strip is $0.733 \text{ g} - 0.725 \text{ g} = 0.008 \text{ g}$.

The mass of the copper reacted is $0.725 \text{ g} - 0.721 \text{ g} = 0.004 \text{ g}$.

The masses of copper and iodine that reacted are known with very low precision (only one significant figure). Therefore, in the following calculations, we are justified in rounding the molar masses of I and Cu (126.90 and 63.546 g/mol, respectively) to two significant figures and the final result to one significant figure.

The amount of iodine is $0.008 \text{ g} \times \dfrac{1}{130 \text{ g mol}^{-1}} = 6 \times 10^{-5} \text{ mol}$

The amount of copper is $0.004 \text{ g} \times \dfrac{1}{64 \text{ g mol}^{-1}} = 6 \times 10^{-5} \text{ mol}$

The compound contains equal amounts (moles) of Cu and I. Therefore, the empirical formula is CuI.

FEATURE PROBLEMS

112. (D)

    (a) "5-10-5" fertilizer contains 5.00 g N (that is, 5.00% N), 10.00 g P_2O_5, and 5.00 g K_2O in 100.00 g fertilizer. We convert the last two numbers into masses of the two elements.

        (1) $\% P = 10.00\% \text{ } P_2O_5 \times \dfrac{1 \text{ mol } P_2O_5}{141.9 \text{ g } P_2O_5} \times \dfrac{2 \text{ mol P}}{1 \text{ mol } P_2O_5} \times \dfrac{30.97 \text{ g P}}{1 \text{ mol P}} = 4.37\% \text{ P}$

        (2) $\% K = 5.00\% \text{ } K_2O \times \dfrac{1 \text{ mol } K_2O}{94.20 \text{ g } K_2O} \times \dfrac{2 \text{ mol K}}{1 \text{ mol } K_2O} \times \dfrac{39.10 \text{ g K}}{1 \text{ mol K}} = 4.15\% \text{ K}$

(b) First, we determine %P and then convert it to $\% P_2O_5$, given that 10.0% P_2O_5 is equivalent to 4.37% P.

(1) $\% P_2O_5 = \dfrac{2\,\text{mol P}}{1\,\text{mol Ca}(H_2PO_4)_2} \times \dfrac{30.97\,\text{g P}}{1\,\text{mol P}} \times \dfrac{1\,\text{mol Ca}(H_2PO_4)_2}{234.05\,\text{g Ca}(H_2PO_4)_2} \times 100\%$

$\times \dfrac{10.0\% P_2O_5}{4.37\% P} = 60.6\% \ P_2O_5$

(2) $\% P_2O_5 = \dfrac{1\,\text{mol P}}{1\,\text{mol}(NH_4)_2 HPO_4} \times \dfrac{30.97\,\text{g P}}{1\,\text{mol P}} \times \dfrac{1\,\text{mol}(NH_4)_2 HPO_4}{132.06\,\text{g}(NH_4)_2 HPO_4} \times 100\%$

$\times \dfrac{10.0\% P_2O_5}{4.37\% P} = 53.7\% \ P_2O_5$

(c) If the mass ratio of $(NH_4)_2HPO_4$ to KCl is set at $5.00:1.00$, then for every 5.00 g of $(NH_4)_2HPO_4$ in the mixture there must be 1.00 g of KCl. Let's start by finding the %N, %P, and %K for the fertilizer mixture.

$\%N\,(\text{by mass}) = \dfrac{2\,\text{mol N}}{1\,\text{mol}(NH_4)_2 HPO_4} \times \dfrac{1\,\text{mol}(NH_4)_2 HPO_4}{132.06\,\text{g}(NH_4)_2 PO_4} \times \dfrac{14.007\,\text{g N}}{1\,\text{mol N}} \times \dfrac{5.00\,\text{g}(NH_4)_2 HPO_4}{6.00\,\text{g mixture}} \times 100\%$

$= 17.7\% \ N$

$\%P\,(\text{by mass}) = \dfrac{1\,\text{mol P}}{1\,\text{mol}(NH_4)_2 HPO_4} \times \dfrac{1\,\text{mol}(NH_4)_2 HPO_4}{132.06\,\text{g}(NH_4)_2 HPO_4} \times \dfrac{30.9738\,\text{g P}}{1\,\text{mol P}} \times \dfrac{5.00\,\text{g}(NH_4)_2 HPO_4}{6.00\,\text{g of mixture}} \times 100\%$

$= 19.5\% \ P$

$\%K\,(\text{by mass}) = \dfrac{1\,\text{mol K}}{1\,\text{mol KCl}} \times \dfrac{1\,\text{mol KCl}}{74.55\,\text{g KCl}} \times \dfrac{39.0983\,\text{g K}}{1\,\text{mol K}} \times \dfrac{1.00\,\text{g KCl}}{6.00\,\text{g mixture}} \times 100\%$

$= 8.74\% \ K$

Next, we convert %P to $\% P_2O_5$ and %K to $\% K_2O$.

$\% P_2O_5 = 19.5\% \ P \times \dfrac{10.0\% P_2O_5}{4.37\% P} = 44.\underline{6}\% \ P_2O_5$

$\% K_2O = 8.\underline{74}\% \ K \times \dfrac{5.00\% K_2O}{4.15\% K} = 1\underline{0}.5\% \ K_2O$

Thus, the combination of 5.00 g $(NH_4)_2HPO_4$ with 1.00 g KCl affords a "17.7-44.6-10.5" fertilizer, that is, 17.7% N, a percentage of phosphorus expressed as 44.6% P_2O_5, and a percentage of potassium expressed as 10.5% K_2O.

(d) A "5-10-5" fertilizer must possess the mass ratio 5.00 g N: 4.37 g P: 4.15 g K per 100 g of fertilizer. Thus a "5-10-5" fertilizer requires an N:P relative mass ratio of 5.00 g N:4.37 g P = 1.00 g N:0.874 g P. Note specifically that the fertilizer has a somewhat *greater* mass of N than of P.

If all of the N and P in the fertilizer comes solely from $(NH_4)_2HPO_4$, then the atom ratio of N relative to P will remain fixed at 2 N:1 P. Whether or not an inert non-fertilizing filler is present in the mix is immaterial. The relative N:P mass ratio is (2×14.01) g N:30.97 g P, that is, 0.905 g N:1.00 g P. Note specifically that $(NH_4)_2HPO_4$ has a somewhat *lesser* mass of N than of P. Clearly, it is impossible to make a "5-10-5" fertilizer if the only fertilizing components are $(NH_4)_2HPO_4$ and KCl.

113. (D)

(a) First, calculate the mass of water that was present in the hydrate prior to heating.

mass of H_2O = 2.574 g $CuSO_4 \cdot x\ H_2O$ − 1.647 g $CuSO_4$ = 0.927 g H_2O

Next, we need to find the number of moles of anhydrous copper(II) sulfate and water that were initially present together in the original hydrate sample.

moles of $CuSO_4$ = 1.647 g $CuSO_4 \times \dfrac{1\ \text{mol}\ CuSO_4}{159.6\ \text{g}\ CuSO_4}$ = 0.01032 moles $CuSO_4$

moles of H_2O = 0.927 g $H_2O \times \dfrac{1\ \text{mol}\ H_2O}{18.015\ \text{g}\ H_2O}$ = 0.05146 moles of water

The empirical formula is obtained by dividing the number of moles of water by the number of moles of $CuSO_4$ (x = ratio of moles of water to moles of $CuSO_4$)

$x = \dfrac{0.05146\ \text{moles}\ H_2O}{0.01032\ \text{moles}\ CuSO_4}$ = 4.99 ~ 5 The empirical formula is $CuSO_4 \cdot 5\ H_2O$.

(b) mass of water present in hydrate = 2.574 g − 1.833 g = 0.741 g H_2O

moles of water = 0.741 g $H_2O \times \dfrac{1\ \text{mol}\ H_2O}{18.015\ \text{g}\ H_2O}$ = 0.0411 moles of water

mass of $CuSO_4$ present in hydrate = 1.833 g $CuSO_4$

moles of $CuSO_4$ = 1.833 g $CuSO_4 \times \dfrac{1\ \text{mol}\ CuSO_4}{159.602\ \text{g}\ CuSO_4}$ = 0.0115 mol $CuSO_4$

The empirical formula is obtained by dividing the number of moles of water by the number of moles of $CuSO_4$ (x = ratio of moles of water to moles of $CuSO_4$).

$x = \dfrac{0.0411\ \text{moles}\ H_2O}{0.0115\ \text{moles}\ CuSO_4}$ = 3.58 ~ 4.

Since the hydrate has not been completely dehydrated, there is no problem with obtaining non-integer "garbage" values.

So, the empirical formula is $CuSO_4 \cdot 4\ H_2O$.

(c) When copper(II) sulfate is strongly heated, it decomposes to give $SO_3(g)$ and $CuO(s)$. The black residue formed at 1000°C in this experiment is probably CuO. The empirical formula for copper(II) oxide is CuO. Let's calculate the percentages of Cu and O by mass for CuO:

mass percent copper = $\dfrac{63.546\ \text{g}\ Cu}{79.545\ \text{g}\ CuO} \times 100\%$ = 79.89% by mass Cu

mass percent oxygen = $\dfrac{15.999\ \text{g}\ O}{79.545\ \text{g}\ CuO} \times 100\%$ = 20.11% by mass O

The number of moles of CuO formed (by reheating to 1000 °C)

$$= 0.812 \text{ g CuO} \times \frac{1 \text{ mol CuO}}{79.545 \text{ g CuO}} = 0.0102 \text{ moles of CuO}$$

This is very close to the number of moles of anhydrous $CuSO_4$ formed at 400. °C. Thus, it would appear that upon heating to 1000 °C, the sample of $CuSO_4$ was essentially completely converted to CuO.

114. (D)

(a) The formula for stearic acid, obtained from the molecular model, is $CH_3(CH_2)_{16}CO_2H$. The number of moles of stearic acid in 10.0 grams is

$$= 10.0 \text{ g stearic acid} \times \frac{1 \text{ mol stearic acid}}{284.48 \text{ g stearic acid}} = 3.51\underline{5} \times 10^{-2} \text{ mol of stearic acid.}$$

The layer of stearic acid is one molecule thick. According to the figure provided with the question, each stearic acid molecule has a cross-sectional area of ~0.22 nm^2. In order to find the stearic acid coverage in square meters, we must multiply the total number of stearic acid molecules by the cross-sectional area for an individual stearic acid molecule. The number of stearic acid molecules is:

$$= 3.51\underline{5} \times 10^{-2} \text{ mol of stearic acid} \times \frac{6.022 \times 10^{23} \text{ molecules}}{1 \text{ mol of stearic acid}} = 2.11\underline{7} \times 10^{22} \text{ molecules}$$

$$\text{area in m}^2 = 2.11\underline{7} \times 10^{22} \text{ molecules of stearic acid} \times \frac{0.22 \text{ nm}^2}{\text{molecule}} \times \frac{(1 \text{ m})^2}{(1 \times 10^9 \text{ nm})^2}$$

The area in m^2 = 4657 m^2 or 4.7×10^3 m^2 (with correct number of sig. fig.)

(b) The density for stearic acid is 0.85 g cm^{-3}. Thus, 0.85 grams of stearic acid occupies 1 cm^3. Find the number of moles of stearic acid in 0.85 g of stearic acid

$$= 0.85 \text{ grams of stearic acid} \times \frac{1 \text{ mol stearic acid}}{284.48 \text{ g stearic acid}} = 3.0 \times 10^{-3} \text{ mol of stearic}$$

acid. This number of moles of acid occupies 1 cm^3 of space. So, the number of stearic acid molecules in 1 cm^3

$$= 3.0 \times 10^{-3} \text{ mol of stearic acid} \times \frac{6.022 \times 10^{23} \text{ molecules}}{1 \text{ mol of stearic acid}}$$

$$= 1.8 \times 10^{21} \text{ stearic acid molecules.}$$

Thus, the volume for a single stearic acid molecule in nm^3

$$= 1 \text{ cm}^3 \times \frac{1}{1.8 \times 10^{21} \text{ molecules stearic acid}} \times \frac{(1.0 \times 10^7 \text{ nm})^3}{(1 \text{ cm})^3} = 0.55\underline{6} \text{ nm}^3$$

The volume of a rectangular column is simply the area of its base multiplied by its height (i.e., V = area of base (in nm^2) × height (in nm)).

So, the average height of a stearic acid molecule $= \dfrac{0.556 \text{ nm}^3}{0.22 \text{ nm}^2} = 2.5 \text{ nm}$

(c) The density for oleic acid = 0.895 g mL^{-1}. So, the concentration for oleic acid is

$$= \frac{0.895 \text{ g acid}}{10.00 \text{ mL}} = 0.0895 \text{ g mL}^{-1} \text{ (solution 1)}$$

This solution is then divided by 10, three more times, to give a final concentration of $8.9\underline{5} \times 10^{-5}$ g mL^{-1}. A 0.10 mL sample of this solution contains:

$$= \frac{8.95 \times 10^{-5} \text{ g acid}}{1.00 \text{ mL}} \times 0.10 \text{ mL} = 8.9\underline{5} \times 10^{-6} \text{ g of acid.}$$

The number of acid molecules $= 85 \text{ cm}^2 \times \dfrac{1}{4.6 \times 10^{-15} \text{cm}^2 \text{ per molecule}}$

$$= 1.8\underline{5} \times 10^{16} \text{ oleic acid molecules.}$$

So, 8.95×10^{-6} g of oleic acid corresponds to 1.85×10^{16} oleic acid molecules.

The molar mass for oleic acid, $C_{18}H_{34}O_2$, is 282.47 g mol^{-1}.

The number of moles of oleic acid is

$$= 8.9\underline{5} \times 10^{-6} \text{ g} \times \frac{1 \text{ mol oleic acid}}{282.47 \text{ g}} = 3.1\underline{7} \times 10^{-8} \text{ mol}$$

So, Avogadro's number here would be equal to:

$$= \frac{1.8\underline{5} \times 10^{16} \text{ oleic acid molecules}}{3.1\underline{7} \times 10^{-8} \text{ oleic acid moles}} = 5.8 \times 10^{23} \text{ molecules per mole of oleic acid.}$$

SELF-ASSESSMENT EXERCISES

115. (E)
    (a) Formula unit: The smallest reducible ratio of atoms in a molecule or ionic compound
    (b) P_4: An allotrope of the element phosphorus
    (c) Molecular compound: A compound where bonds are formed by sharing of electrons between atoms
    (d) Binary compound: A compound formed between two elements
    (e) Hydrate: A molecular or ionic compound that is accompanied with a fixed number of water molecules as an adduct.

116. (E)
    (a) Mole of compound: An amount of compound that contains 6.02×10^{23} molecules of that compound (or, a mass of compound equal to its molecular weight).
    (b) Structural formula: The formula that shows in what order the various atoms in the molecule are connected to each other and what is the mode of their bonding
    (c) Oxidation state: The apparent number of electrons from a particular atom which are involved in bonding with other atoms (either being lost, gained, or shared)
    (d) C–H–O determination: A process by which C and H and O weight% in a compound are determined by careful combustion and measuring the amounts of the evolved products specific to combustion of C, H, and O.

117. (E)
    (a) Molecular mass is the mass of one molecule of a compound, while molar mass is the mass of one mole of that compound (or the molecular mass multiplied by 6.02×10^{23}).
    (b) Empirical formula is the simplest formula for the compound, and shows the types of atoms and their ratios, whereas a molecular formula lists the types and actual number of atoms in the formula (a molecular formula is the empirical formula times an integer).
    (c) Systematic name is the name of a compound that follows established guidelines where the number and possibly oxidation state of each element is provided in the name, whereas a trivial name is a common name given to a compound that usually tells us nothing about its composition (like water or ammonia or red rust).
    (d) Hydroxyl functional group is –OH, where the covalent bond to the rest of the molecule is made through the oxygen. Carboxyl functional group is –C(=O)O, where the covalent bond to the rest of the molecule is made through the carbon, and a proton can attach to one of the oxygens.

118. (E)
    (a) Mass of one atom of nitrogen (in amu).
    (b) Mass of one molecule of dinitrogen gas, N_2 (in amu)
    (c) Mass of one mole of dinitrogen N_2 (in g/mol).

119. **(E)** The answer is (c), because 12.01 g of H_2O = 0.667 mol H_2O, which equates to 0.667×3 = 2.00 moles of atoms. One mole of Br_2 also has 2.00 moles of atoms.

120. **(E)** The answer is (b). N_2H_4 can be reduced further to an empirical formula of NH_2.

121. **(E)** The answer is (d), because total atomic mass is 14 for N and 7 for H.

122. **(E)** Answer is (a).
   (a) 50.0 g N_2O × (1 mol N_2O/44.0 g N_2O) × (2 mol N/1 mol N_2O) = 2.27 mol
   (b) 17.0 g NH_3 × (1 mol NH_3/17.0 g NH_3) × (1 mol N/1 mol NH_3) = 1.00 mol
   (c) 150 mL C_5H_5N × (0.983 g/1 mL) × (1 mol Pyr/79.0 g Pyr) × (1 mol N/1 mol Pyr) = 1.87 mol
   (d) 1 mol N_2 × (2 mol N/1 mol N_2) = 2.0

123. **(M)**

$$\frac{2.9 \text{ g Fe}}{\text{total blood}} \times \frac{\text{total blood}}{2.6 \times 10^{13} \text{ red blood cells}} \times \frac{1 \text{ mol Fe}}{55.8 \text{ g Fe}} \times \frac{6.02 \times 10^{23} \text{ Fe atoms}}{\text{mol Fe}}$$

$$= 1.2 \times 10^9 \frac{\text{Fe atoms}}{\text{red blood cell}}$$

124. **(E)** Answer is (c).
Mass % of F = (19×3)/(X + 19×3) = 0.65
Solving for X, we get X = 30.7 or 31 u

125. **(E)** Answer is (c). Total formal charge on H: +4. Total charge on O: –12, and the ion has a negative charge. Therefore, oxidation state of I = –12 + 4 + 1 = 7.

126. **(E)** The correct answer is +6 (choice c). Magnesium has a +2 oxidation state, and oxygen is –2. Manganese would need to be +6 for the charge on the molecule to sum to zero.

127. **(M)** Choice (a) is hydrogen periodate and is therefore the correct answer. Na_2SO_3 is sodium sulfite, $KClO_2$ is potassium chlorite, HFO is hydrogen hypofluorite, and NO_2 is nitrogen dioxide.

128. **(E)** $Sr(HCO_3)_2$ is strontium bicarbonate (choice d).

129. **(E)** The answer is (b). Ca is a +2 ion and ClO_2^- is –1 anion.

130. **(E)** Li_3P has a molar mass of 51.79 g mol^{-1} (choice d).

131. **(E)** The answer is (d). Multiplying O atomic mass by 4 (64 u) is nearly the same as the atomic mass of Cu (63.55).

132. (E) The answer is (d). Answer (a) isn't correct. While having the correct number of atoms, it is not an isomer because it is only a molecular formula and gives no information on atom bonding. Answer (b) isn't correct, because it's the exact same molecule as stated in the question. Answer (c) isn't correct because it doesn't have enough atoms. Therefore, the answer is (d), because it has the correct number of atoms in a different configuration.

133. (M) First, find out the mass of Na_2SO_3, which is 126.0 g/mol. Then:
Mass H_2O $(x) = 0.5$ $(x + $ Mass $Na_2SO_3)$.
$x = 0.5x + 63$.
Solving for x, we obtain $x = 126$ g (mass of H_2O)
Since we have 126 g of water, the number of moles of H_2O is 126 g/18.0 g $mol^{-1} = 7$
Therefore, the formula is $Na_2SO_3 \cdot 7 H_2O$.

134. (M)
(a) Based on this composition, molar mass of malachite is calculated to be 221.18 g/mol. Since there are two moles of Cu per mole of malachite, the %mass of Cu is:

$$1000 \text{ g malachite} \times \frac{1 \text{ mol mal.}}{221.18 \text{ g mal.}} \times \frac{2 \text{ mol Cu}}{1 \text{ mol mal.}} \times \frac{63.546 \text{ g Cu}}{1 \text{ mol Cu}} = 574.61 \text{ g Cu}$$

$$\% \text{ Cu} = \frac{574.61 \text{ g}}{1000 \text{ g}} \times 100 = 57.46\%$$

(b) The formula for copper(II) oxide is CuO. Therefore, for one mole of malachite, there are two moles of CuO. Therefore,

$$1000 \text{ g malachite} \times \frac{1 \text{ mol mal.}}{221.18 \text{ g mal.}} \times \frac{2 \text{ mol CuO}}{1 \text{ mol mal.}} \times \frac{79.545 \text{ g CuO}}{1 \text{ mol CuO}}$$

mass CuO = 719.5 g

135. (D) Molar mass of acetaminophen is 151.2 u, or 151.2 g/mol. To determine the molecular formula, calculate the moles of various constituting elements, as shown below:

mol C = 63.56 g C × (1 mol C/12.011 g C) = 5.292 mol C
mol H = 6.00 g H × (1 mol H/1.008 g H) = 5.95 mol H
mol N = 9.27 g N × (1 mol N/14.01 g N) = 0.662 mol N
mol O = 21.17 g O × (1 mol O/15.999 g O) = 1.323 mol O

Then, divide all values by the smallest to determine mole ratios:
5.92 mol C / 0.662 mol N → 7.99 mol C
5.95 mol H / 0.662 mol N → 8.99 mol H
0.662 mol N / 0.662 mol N → 1.00 mol N
1.323 mol O / 0.662 mol N → 2.00 mol C

The C:H:N:O ratio is 8:9:1:2. The empirical formula is therefore $C_8H_9NO_2$. The molar mass of this formula unit is 151.1, which is the same as the molar mass of acetaminophen. Therefore, the empirical formula obtained is also the same as the molecular formula.

136. (D) The first step is to determine the mass of C, H, and O.

$$\text{mol C} = 6.029 \text{ g CO}_2 \times \frac{1 \text{ mol CO}_2}{44.009 \text{ g CO}_2} \times \frac{1 \text{ mol C}}{1 \text{ mol CO}_2} = 0.1370 \text{ mol}$$

mass of C $= 0.1370$ mol C$\times(12.011$ g C$/1$ mol C$) = 1.646$ g C

$$\text{mol H} = 1.709 \text{ g H}_2\text{O} \times \frac{1 \text{ mol H}_2\text{O}}{18.015 \text{ g H}_2\text{O}} \times \frac{2 \text{ mol H}}{1 \text{ mol H}_2\text{O}} = 0.1897 \text{ mol}$$

mass of H $= 0.1897$ mol H$\times(1.008$ g H$/1$ mol H$) = 0.1912$ g H

Mass of oxygen is obtained by difference: mass of O $= 2.174$ g $- (1.646 + 0.1912) = 0.337$ g

$$\text{mol O} = 0.337 \text{ g O} \times \frac{1 \text{ mol O}}{16.00 \text{ g O}} = 0.0211 \text{ mol}$$

(a) % Composition:
   1.646 g C / 2.174 g Ibo = 75.71% C
   0.191 g H / 2.174 g Ibo = 8.79% H
   0.337 g O / 2.174 g Ibo = 15.5% O

(b) To determine the empirical formula, divide all mole values by the lowest one:
   0.1370 mol C / 0.0211 mol O $\rightarrow$ 6.49 mol C
   0.1897 mol H / 0.0211 mol O $\rightarrow$ 8.99 mol H
   0.0211 mol O / 0.0211 mol O $\rightarrow$ 1.00 mol O

   The empirical formula is obtained by multiplying the above ratios by 2. The formula is $C_{13}H_{18}O_2$.

137. (M) To construct a concept map, one must first start with the most general concepts. These concepts contain or are defined by more specific terms and concepts discussed in those sections. In this chapter, the main themes are types of chemical compounds (3-1), the mole concept (3-2), the composition of chemical compounds (3-3), oxidation state (3-4), and naming compounds (3-5). Naming of inorganic compounds (3-6) and organic compounds (3-7) are sub-topics of section 3-6. Take a look at the subsection headings and problems for more refining of the general and specific concepts.

CHAPTER 4
CHEMICAL REACTIONS

PRACTICE EXAMPLES

1A **(E)**

Unbalanced reaction:	$HgS(s) + CaO(s)$	$\rightarrow CaS(s) + CaSO_4(s) + Hg(l)$
Balance O atoms:	$HgS(s) + 4\,CaO(s)$	$\rightarrow CaS(s) + CaSO_4(s) + Hg(l)$
Balance Ca atoms:	$HgS(s) + 4\,CaO(s)$	$\rightarrow 3\,CaS(s) + CaSO_4(s) + Hg(l)$
Balance S atoms:	$4\,HgS(s) + 4\,CaO(s)$	$\rightarrow 3\,CaS(s) + CaSO_4(s) + Hg(l)$
Balance Hg atoms:	$4\,HgS(s) + 4\,CaO(s)$	$\rightarrow 3\,CaS(s) + CaSO_4(s) + 4\,Hg(l)$
Self Check:	$4\,Hg + 4\,S + 4\,O + 4\,Ca \rightarrow 4\,Hg + 4\,S + 4\,O + 4\,Ca$	

1B **(E)**

Unbalanced reaction:	$C_7H_6O_2S(l) + O_2(g)$	$\rightarrow CO_2(g) + H_2O(l) + SO_2(g)$
Balance C atoms:	$C_7H_6O_2S(l) + O_2(g)$	$\rightarrow 7\,CO_2(g) + H_2O(l) + SO_2(g)$
Balance S atoms:	$C_7H_6O_2S(l) + O_2(g)$	$\rightarrow 7\,CO_2(g) + H_2O(l) + SO_2(g)$
Balance H atoms:	$C_7H_6O_2S(l) + O_2(g)$	$\rightarrow 7\,CO_2(g) + 3\,H_2O(l) + SO_2(g)$
Balance O atoms:	$C_7H_6O_2S(l) + 8.5\,O_2(g)$	$\rightarrow 7\,CO_2(g) + 3\,H_2O(l) + SO_2(g)$
Multiply by 2 (whole #):	$2\,C_7H_6O_2S(l) + 17\,O_2(g) \rightarrow 14\,CO_2(g) + 6\,H_2O(l) + 2\,SO_2(g)$	
Self Check:	$14\,C + 12\,H + 2\,S + 38\,O \rightarrow 14\,C + 12\,H + 2\,S + 38\,O$	

2A **(E)** The balanced chemical equation provides the factor needed to convert from moles $KClO_3$ to moles O_2. Amount $O_2 = 1.76\,mol\,KClO_3 \times \dfrac{3\,mol\,O_2}{2\,mol\,KClO_3} = 2.64\,mol\,O_2$

2B **(E)** First, find the molar mass of Ag_2O.

$(2\,mol\,Ag \times 107.87\,g/mol\,Ag) + 16.00\,g\,O = 231.74\,g\,Ag_2O\,/\,mol$

amount $Ag = 1.00\,kg\,Ag_2O \times \dfrac{1000\,g}{1.00\,kg} \times \dfrac{1\,mol\,Ag_2O}{231.74\,g\,Ag_2O} \times \dfrac{2\,mol\,Ag}{1\,mol\,Ag_2O} = 8.63\,mol\,Ag$

3A **(E)** The balanced chemical equation provides the factor to convert from amount of Mg to amount of Mg_3N_2. First we must determine the molar mass of Mg_3N_2.

molar mass $= (3\,mol\,Mg \times 24.305\,g/mol\,Mg) + (2\,mol\,N \times 14.007\,g/mol\,N) = 100.93\,g\,Mg_3N_2$

mass $Mg_3N_2 = 3.82\,g\,Mg \times \dfrac{1\,mol\,Mg}{24.31\,g\,Mg} \times \dfrac{1\,mol\,Mg_3N_2}{3\,mol\,Mg} \times \dfrac{100.93\,g\,Mg_3N_2}{1\,mol\,Mg_3N_2} = 5.29\,g\,Mg_3N_2$

3B **(E)** The pivotal conversion is from $H_2(g)$ to $CH_3OH(l)$. For this we use the balanced equation, which requires that we use the amounts in moles of both substances. The solution involves converting to and from amounts, using molar masses.

mass $H_2(g) = 1.00\,kg\,CH_3OH(l) \times \dfrac{1000\,g}{1\,kg} \times \dfrac{1\,mol\,CH_3OH}{32.04\,g\,CH_3OH} \times \dfrac{2\,mol\,H_2}{1\,mol\,CH_3OH} \times \dfrac{2.016\,g\,H_2}{1\,mol\,H_2}$

mass $H_2(g) = 126\,g\,H_2$

4A **(M)** The equation for the cited reaction is: $2\,NH_3\,(g) + 1.5\,O_2\,(g) \longrightarrow N_2\,(g) + 3\,H_2O\,(l)$

The pivotal conversion is from one substance to another, in moles, with the balanced chemical equation providing the conversion factor.

$$\text{mass } NH_3\,(g) = 1.00\,g\,O_2\,(g) \times \frac{1\,mol\,O_2}{32.00\,g\,O_2} \times \frac{2\,mol\,NH_3}{1.5\,mol\,O_2} \times \frac{17.031\,g\,NH_3}{1\,mol\,H_2} = 0.710\,g\;NH_3$$

4B **(M)** The equation for the combustion reaction is:

$$C_8H_{18}\,(l) + \frac{25}{2}\,O_2\,(g) \rightarrow 8\,CO_2\,(g) + 9\,H_2O\,(l)$$

$$\text{mass } O_2 = 1.00\,g\,C_8H_{18} \times \frac{1\,mol\,C_8H_{18}}{114.23\,g\,C_8H_{18}} \times \frac{12.5\,mol\,O_2}{1\,mol\,C_8H_{18}} \times \frac{32.00\,g\,O_2}{1\,mol\,O_2} = 3.50\,g\,O_2\,(g)$$

5A **(M)** We must convert mass $H_2 \rightarrow$ amount of $H_2 \rightarrow$ amount of $Al \rightarrow$ mass of $Al \rightarrow$ mass of alloy $\rightarrow$ volume of alloy. The calculation is performed as follows: each arrow in the preceding sentence requires a conversion factor.

$$V_{alloy} = 1.000\,g\,H_2 \times \frac{1\,mol\,H_2}{2.016\,g\,H_2} \times \frac{2\,mol\,Al}{3\,mol\,H_2} \times \frac{26.98\,g\,Al}{1\,mol\,Al} \times \frac{100.0\,g\,alloy}{93.7\,g\,Al} \times \frac{1\,cm^3\,alloy}{2.85\,g\,alloy}$$

$$= 3.34\,cm^3\,alloy$$

5B **(M)** In the example, $0.207\,g\,H_2$ is collected from 1.97 g alloy; the alloy is 6.3% Cu by mass. This information provides the conversion factors we need.

$$\text{mass } Cu = 1.31\,g\,H_2 \times \frac{1.97\,g\,alloy}{0.207\,g\,H_2} \times \frac{6.3\,g\,Cu}{100.0\,g\,alloy} = 0.79\,g\,Cu$$

Notice that we do not have to consider each step separately. We can simply use values produced in the course of the calculation as conversion factors.

6A **(M)** The cited reaction is $2\,Al\,(s) + 6\,HCl\,(aq) \rightarrow 2\,AlCl_3\,(aq) + 3\,H_2\,(g)$. The HCl(aq) solution has a density of 1.14 g/mL and contains 28.0% HCl. We need to convert between the substances HCl and H_2; the important conversion factor comes from the balanced chemical equation. The sequence of conversions is: volume of HCl(aq) $\rightarrow$ mass of HCl(aq) $\rightarrow$ mass of pure HCl $\rightarrow$ amount of HCl $\rightarrow$ amount of $H_2 \rightarrow$ mass of H_2.

In the calculation below, each arrow in the sequence is replaced by a conversion factor.

$$\text{mass } H_2 = 0.05\,mL\,HCl\,(aq) \times \frac{1.14\,g\,soln}{1\,mL\,soln} \times \frac{28.0\,g\,HCl}{100.0\,g\,soln} \times \frac{1\,mol\,HCl}{36.46\,g\,HCl} \times \frac{3\,mol\,H_2}{6\,mol\,HCl} \times \frac{2.016\,g\,H_2}{1\,mol\,H_2}$$

$$= 4 \times 10^{-4}\,g\,H_2\,(g) = 0.4\,mg\,H_2\,(g)$$

6B **(M)** Density is necessary to determine the mass of the vinegar, and then the mass of acetic acid.

$$\text{mass } CO_2\,(g) = 5.00\,mL\,vinegar \times \frac{1.01\,g}{1\,mL} \times \frac{0.040\,g\,acid}{1\,g\,vinegar} \times \frac{1\,mol\,CH_3COOH}{60.05\,g\,CH_3COOH} \times \frac{1\,mol\,CO_2}{1\,mol\,CH_3COOH} \times \frac{44.01\,g\,CO_2}{1\,mol\,CO_2}$$

$$= 0.15\,g\,CO_2$$

wrong answer

7A **(M)** Determine the amount in moles of acetone and the volume in liters of the solution.

$$\text{molarity of acetone} = \frac{22.3\,\text{g}\,(CH_3)_2\,CO \times \dfrac{1\,\text{mol}\,(CH_3)_2\,CO}{58.08\,\text{g}\,(CH_3)_2\,CO}}{1.25\,\text{L soln}} = 0.307\,\text{M}$$

7B **(M)** The molar mass of acetic acid, CH_3COOH, is 60.05 g/mol. We begin with the quantity of acetic acid in the numerator and that of the solution in the denominator, and transform to the appropriate units for each.

$$\text{molarity} = \frac{15.0\,\text{mL}\,CH_3COOH}{500.0\,\text{mL soln}} \times \frac{1000\,\text{mL}}{1\,\text{L soln}} \times \frac{1.048\,\text{g}\,CH_3COOH}{1\,\text{mL}\,CH_3COOH} \times \frac{1\,\text{mol}\,CH_3COOH}{60.05\,\text{g}\,CH_3COOH} = 0.524\,\text{M}$$

8A **(E)** The molar mass of $NaNO_3$ is 84.99 g/mol. We recall that "M" stands for "mol/L soln."

$$\text{mass}\,NaNO_3 = 125\,\text{mL soln} \times \frac{1\,\text{L}}{1000\,\text{mL}} \times \frac{10.8\,\text{mol}\,NaNO_3}{1\,\text{L soln}} \times \frac{84.99\,\text{g}\,NaNO_3}{1\,\text{mol}\,NaNO_3} = 115\,\text{g}\,NaNO_3$$

8B **(E)** We begin by determining the molar mass of $Na_2SO_4 \cdot 10\,H_2O$. The amount of solute needed is computed from the concentration and volume of the solution.

$$\text{mass}\,Na_2SO_4 \cdot 10\,H_2O = 355\,\text{mL soln} \times \frac{1\,\text{L}}{1000\,\text{mL}} \times \frac{0.445\,\text{mol}\,Na_2SO_4}{1\,\text{L soln}} \times \frac{1\,\text{mol}\,Na_2SO_4 \cdot 10\,H_2O}{1\,\text{mol}\,Na_2SO_4}$$

$$\times \frac{322.21\,\text{g}\,Na_2SO_4 \cdot 10\,H_2O}{1\,\text{mol}\,Na_2SO_4 \cdot 10\,H_2O} = 50.9\,\text{g}\,Na_2SO_4 \cdot 10\,H_2O$$

9A **(E)** The amount of solute in the concentrated solution doesn't change when the solution is diluted. We take advantage of an alternative definition of molarity to answer the question: millimoles of solute/milliliter of solution.

$$\text{amount}\,K_2CrO_4 = 15.00\,\text{mL} \times \frac{0.450\,\text{mmol}\,K_2CrO_4}{1\,\text{mL soln}} = 6.75\,\text{mmol}\,K_2CrO_4$$

$$K_2CrO_4\,\text{molarity, dilute solution} = \frac{6.75\,\text{mmol}\,K_2CrO_4}{100.00\,\text{mL soln}} = 0.0675\,\text{M}$$

9B **(E)** We know the initial concentration (0.105 M) and volume (275 mL) of the solution, along with its final volume (237 mL). The final concentration equals the initial concentration times a ratio of the two volumes.

$$c_f = c_i \times \frac{V_i}{V_f} = 0.105\,\text{M} \times \frac{275\,\text{mL}}{237\,\text{mL}} = 0.122\,\text{M}$$

10A **(M)** The balanced equation is $K_2CrO_4 (aq) + 2\,AgNO_3 (aq) \rightarrow Ag_2CrO_4 (s) + 2\,KNO_3 (aq)$.

The molar mass of Ag_2CrO_4 is 331.73 g/mol. The conversions needed are mass

$Ag_2CrO_4 \rightarrow$ amount Ag_2CrO_4 (moles) $\rightarrow$ amount K_2CrO_4 (moles) $\rightarrow$ volume K_2CrO_4 (aq).

$$V_{K_2CrO_4} = 1.50\,g\,Ag_2CrO_4 \times \frac{1\,mol\,Ag_2CrO_4}{331.73\,g\,Ag_2CrO_4} \times \frac{1\,mol\,K_2CrO_4}{1\,mol\,Ag_2CrO_4} \times \frac{1\,L\,soln}{0.250\,mol\,K_2CrO_4}$$

$$\times \frac{1000\,mL\,solution}{1\,L\,solution} = 18.1\,mL$$

10B **(M)** Balanced reaction: $2\,AgNO_3(aq) + K_2CrO_4(aq) \rightarrow Ag_2CrO_4(s) + 2\,KNO_3(aq)$

moles of $K_2CrO_4 = c \times V = 0.0855\,M \times 0.175\,L\,sol = 0.0149\underline{6}\,mol\,K_2CrO_4$

moles of $AgNO_3 = 0.0149\underline{6}\,mol\,K_2CrO_4 \times \dfrac{2\,mol\,AgNO_3}{1\,mol\,K_2CrO_4} = 0.0299\,mol\,AgNO_3$

$$V_{AgNO_3} = \frac{n}{c} = \frac{0.0299\,mol\,AgNO_3}{0.150\,\dfrac{mol\,L^{-1}}{L}\,AgNO_3} = 0.199\underline{5}\,L\;or\;2.00 \times 10^2\,mL\;(0.200\,L)\;of\;AgNO_3$$

Mass of Ag_2CrO_4 formed $= 0.0149\underline{6}\,mol\,K_2CrO_4 \times \dfrac{1\,mol\,Ag_2CrO_4}{1\,mol\,K_2CrO_4} \times \dfrac{331.73\,g\,Ag_2CrO_4}{1\,mol\,Ag_2CrO_4}$

Mass of Ag_2CrO_4 formed $= 4.96\,g\,Ag_2CrO_4$

11A **(M)** Reaction: $P_4 (s) + 6\,Cl_2 (g) \rightarrow 4\,PCl_3 (l)$. We must determine the mass of PCl_3 formed by each reactant.

mass PCl_3 from $P_4 = 215\,g\,P_4 \times \dfrac{1\,mol\,P_4}{123.89\,g\,P_4} \times \dfrac{4\,mol\,PCl_3}{1\,mol\,P_4} \times \dfrac{137.32\,g\,PCl_3}{1\,mol\,PCl_3} = 953\,g\,PCl_3$

mass PCl_3 from $Cl_2 = 725\,g\,Cl_2 \times \dfrac{1\,mol\,Cl_2}{70.91\,g\,Cl_2} \times \dfrac{4\,mol\,PCl_3}{6\,mol\,Cl_2} \times \dfrac{137.32\,g\,PCl_3}{1\,mol\,PCl_3} = 936\,g\,PCl_3$

Thus, a maximum of $936\,g\,PCl_3$ can be produced; there is not enough Cl_2 to produce any more.

11B **(M)** Since data are supplied and the answer is requested in kilograms (thousands of grams), we can use kilomoles (thousands of moles) to solve the problem. We calculate the amount in kilomoles of $POCl_3$ that would be produced if each of the reactants were completely converted to product. The smallest of these amounts is the one that is actually produced (this is a limiting reactant question).

amount $POCl_3$ from $PCl_3 = 1.00\,kg\,PCl_3 \times \dfrac{1\,kmol\,PCl_3}{137.32\,kg\,PCl_3} \times \dfrac{10\,kmol\,POCl_3}{6\,kmol\,PCl_3} = 0.0121\,kmol\,POCl_3$

amount $POCl_3$ from $Cl_2 = 1.00\,kg\,Cl_2 \times \dfrac{1\,kmol\,Cl_2}{70.90\,kg\,Cl_2} \times \dfrac{10\,kmol\,POCl_3}{6\,kmol\,Cl_2} = 0.0235\,kmol\,POCl_3$

amount $POCl_3$ from $P_4H_{10} = 1.00\,kg\,P_4O_{10} \times \dfrac{1\,kmol\,P_4O_{10}}{283.89\,kg\,P_4O_{10}} \times \dfrac{10\,kmol\,POCl_3}{1\,kmol\,P_4O_{10}} = 0.0352\,kmol\,POCl_3$

Thus, a maximum of $0.0121\,kmol\,POCl_3$ can be produced.

We next determine the mass of the product.

$$\text{mass POCl}_3 = 0.0121 \, \text{kmol POCl}_3 \times \frac{153.33 \, \text{kg POCl}_3}{1 \, \text{kmol POCl}_3} = 1.86 \, \text{kg POCl}_3$$

12A **(M)** The 725 g Cl_2 limits the mass of product formed. The $P_4(s)$ therefore is the reactant in excess. From the quantity of excess reactant we can find the amount of product formed: 953 g PCl_3 − 936 g PCl_3 = 17 g PCl_3. We calculate how much P_4 this is, both in the traditional way and by using the initial $(215 \, \text{g} \, P_4)$ and final $(953 \, \text{g} \, PCl_3)$ values of the previous calculation.

$$\text{mass } P_4 = 17 \, \text{g PCl}_3 \times \frac{1 \, \text{mol PCl}_3}{137.33 \, \text{g PCl}_3} \times \frac{1 \, \text{mol } P_4}{4 \, \text{mol PCl}_3} \times \frac{123.89 \, \text{g } P_4}{1 \, \text{mol } P_4} = 3.8 \, \text{g } P_4$$

12B **(M)** Find the amount of $H_2O(l)$ formed by each reactant, to determine the limiting reactant.

$$\text{amount } H_2O \text{ from } H_2 = 12.2 \, \text{g } H_2 \times \frac{1 \, \text{mol } H_2}{2.016 \, \text{g } H_2} \times \frac{2 \, \text{mol } H_2O}{2 \, \text{mol } H_2} = 6.05 \, \text{mol } H_2O$$

$$\text{amount } H_2O \text{ from } O_2 = 154 \, \text{g } O_2 \times \frac{1 \, \text{mol } O_2}{32.00 \, \text{g } O_2} \times \frac{2 \, \text{mol } H_2O}{1 \, \text{mol } O_2} = 9.63 \, \text{mol } H_2O$$

Since H_2 is limiting, we must compute the mass of O_2 needed to react with all of the H_2

$$\text{mass } O_2 \text{ reacting} = 6.05 \, \text{mol } H_2O \text{ produced} \times \frac{1 \, \text{mol } O_2}{2 \, \text{mol } H_2O} \times \frac{32.00 \, \text{g } O_2}{1 \, \text{mol } O_2} = 96.8 \, \text{g } O_2 \text{ reacting}$$

$$\text{mass } O_2 \text{ remaining} = 154 \, \text{g originally present} - 96.8 \, \text{g } O_2 \text{ reacting} = 57 \, \text{g } O_2 \text{ remaining}$$

13A **(M)**

(a) The theoretical yield is the calculated maximum mass of product expected if we were to assume that the reaction has no losses (100% reaction).

$$\text{mass } CH_2O(g) = 1.00 \, \text{mol } CH_3OH \times \frac{1 \, \text{mol } CH_2O}{1 \, \text{mol } CH_3OH} \times \frac{30.03 \, \text{g } CH_2O}{1 \, \text{mol } CH_2O} = 30.0 \, \text{g } CH_2O$$

(b) The actual yield is what is obtained experimentally: 25.7 g CH_2O (g).

(c) The percent yield is the ratio of actual yield to theoretical yield, multiplied by 100%:

$$\% \text{ yield} = \frac{25.7 \, \text{g CH}_2\text{O produced}}{30.0 \, \text{g CH}_2\text{O calculated}} \times 100\% = 85.6\% \text{ yield}$$

13B **(M)** First determine the mass of product formed by each reactant.

$$\text{mass PCl}_3 \text{ from } P_4 = 25.0 \, \text{g } P_4 \times \frac{1 \, \text{mol } P_4}{123.89 \, \text{g } P_4} \times \frac{4 \, \text{mol PCl}_3}{1 \, \text{mol } P_4} \times \frac{137.32 \, \text{g PCl}_3}{1 \, \text{mol PCl}_3} = 111 \, \text{g PCl}_3$$

$$\text{mass PCl}_3 \text{ from } Cl_2 = 91.5 \, \text{g } Cl_2 \times \frac{1 \, \text{mol } Cl_2}{70.91 \, \text{g } Cl_2} \times \frac{4 \, \text{mol PCl}_3}{6 \, \text{mol } Cl_2} \times \frac{137.32 \, \text{g PCl}_3}{1 \, \text{mol PCl}_3} = 118 \, \text{g PCl}_3$$

Thus, the limiting reactant is P_4, and 111 g PCl_3 should be produced. This is the theoretical maximum yield. The actual yield is 104 g PCl_3. Thus, the percent yield of the reaction is

$$\frac{104 \, \text{g PCl}_3 \text{ produced}}{111 \, \text{g PCl}_3 \text{ calculated}} \times 100\% = 93.7\% \text{ yield.}$$

14A **(M)** The reaction is $2\,NH_3\,(g) + CO_2\,(g) \rightarrow CO\,(NH_2)_2\,(s) + H_2O\,(l)$. We need to distinguish between mass of urea produced (actual yield) and mass of urea predicted (theoretical yield).

$$\text{mass } CO_2 = 50.0\,g\,CO(NH_2)_2 \text{ produced} \times \frac{100.0\,g\text{ predicted}}{87.5\,g\text{ produced}} \times \frac{1\,mol\,CO(NH_2)_2}{60.1\,g\,CO(NH_2)_2} \times \frac{1\,mol\,CO_2}{1\,mol\,CO(NH_2)_2}$$

$$\times \frac{44.01\,g\,CO_2}{1\,mol\,CO_2} = 41.8\,g\,CO_2 \text{ needed}$$

14B **(M)** Care must be taken to use the proper units/labels in each conversion factor. Note, you cannot calculate the molar mass of an impure material or mixture.

$$\text{mass } C_6H_{11}OH = 45.0\,g\,C_6H_{10} \text{ produced} \times \frac{100.0\,g\,C_6H_{10}\text{ cal'd}}{86.2\,g\,C_6H_{10}\text{ produc'd}} \times \frac{1\,mol\,C_6H_{10}}{82.1\,g\,C_6H_{10}} \times \frac{1\,mol\,C_6H_{11}OH}{1\,mol\,C_6H_{10}}$$

$$\times \frac{100.2\,g\text{ pure }C_6H_{11}OH}{1\,mol\,C_6H_{11}OH} \times \frac{100.0\text{ g impure }C_6H_{11}OH}{92.3\text{ g pure }C_6H_{11}OH} = 69.0\text{ g impure }C_6H_{11}OH$$

15A **(M)** We can trace the nitrogen through the sequence of reactions. We notice that 4 moles of N (as 4 mol NH_3) are consumed in the first reaction, and 4 moles of N (as 4 mol NO) are produced. In the second reaction, 2 moles of N (as 2 mol NO) are consumed and 2 moles of N (as 2 mol NO_2) are produced. In the last reaction, 3 moles of N (as 3 mol NO_2) are consumed and just 2 moles of N (as 2 mol HNO_3) are produced.

$$\text{mass } HNO_3 = 1.00\,kg\,NH_3 \times \frac{1000\,g\,NH_3}{1\,kg\,NH_3} \times \frac{1\,mol\,NH_3}{17.03\,g\,NH_3} \times \frac{4\,mol\,NO}{4\,mol\,NH_3} \times \frac{2\,mol\,NO_2}{2\,mol\,NO}$$

$$\times \frac{2\,mol\,HNO_3}{3\,mol\,NO_2} \times \frac{63.01\,g\,HNO_3}{1\,mol\,HNO_3} = 2.47 \times 10^3\,g\,HNO_3$$

15B **(M)**

$$\text{mass } KNO_3 = 95\,g\,NaN_3 \times \frac{1\,mol\,NaN_3}{65.03\,g\,NaN_3} \times \frac{2\,mol\,Na}{2\,mol\,NaN_3} \times \frac{2\,mol\,KNO_3}{10\,mol\,Na} \times \frac{102\,g\,KNO_3}{1\,mol\,KNO_3}$$

$$= 29.80 \approx 30\text{ g }KNO_3$$

$$\text{mass } SiO_2\,(1) = 1.461\,mol\,NaN_3 \times \frac{2\,mol\,Na}{2\,mol\,NaN_3} \times \frac{1\,mol\,K_2O}{10\,mol\,Na} \times \frac{1\,mol\,SiO_2}{1\,mol\,K_2O} \times \frac{64.06\,g\,SiO_2}{1\,mol\,SiO_2}$$

$$= 9.36\text{ g} \approx 9.4\text{ g }SiO_2$$

$$\text{mass } SiO_2\,(2) = 1.461\,mol\,NaN_3 \times \frac{2\,mol\,Na}{2\,mol\,NaN_3} \times \frac{5\,mol\,Na_2O}{10\,mol\,Na} \times \frac{1\,mol\,SiO_2}{1\,mol\,Na_2O} \times \frac{64.06\,g\,SiO_2}{1\,mol\,SiO_2}$$

$$= 46.80\text{ g} \approx 47\text{ g }SiO_2$$

Therefore, the total mass of SiO_2 is the sum of the above two results. Approximately 56 g of SiO_2 and 30 g of KNO_3 are needed.

16A **(D)** Let the mass of Al be m g. Then the mass of Mg will be $(1.00 - m)$ g. We can now write expressions for the mass of H_2 that can be obtained from m g Al and $(1.00 - m)$ g Mg.

$$\text{mass of } H_2 \text{ from Al} = (m) \text{ g Al} \times \frac{1 \text{ mol Al}}{26.98 \text{ g Al}} \times \frac{3 \text{ mol } H_2}{2 \text{ mol Al}} \times \frac{2.016 \text{ g } H_2}{1 \text{ mol } H_2} = (m)\, 0.1121 \text{ g } H_2$$

$$\text{mass of } H_2 \text{ from Mg} = (1.00 - m) \text{ g Al} \times \frac{1 \text{ mol Mg}}{24.305 \text{ g Mg}} \times \frac{1 \text{ mol } H_2}{1 \text{ mol Mg}} \times \frac{2.016 \text{ g } H_2}{1 \text{ mol } H_2}$$

$$= (1.00 - m)\, 0.0829 \text{ g } H_2$$

Now, we note that the total mass of H_2 generated is 0.107 g. Therefore,

Mass $H_2 = (m)(0.1121) + (1.00 - m)(0.0829) = 0.107$
Solving for m gives a value of 0.82 g.

Therefore, mass of Al = 0.83 g. Since the sample is 1.00 g, Mg is 17 wt%.
mass of Mg = $1.00 - 0.83 = 0.17$ g, or 17 wt%.

16B **(D)** Mass of CuO and Cu_2O is done in identical fashion to the above problem:

$$\text{mass of Cu from CuO} = (1.500 - x) \text{ g CuO} \times \frac{1 \text{ mol CuO}}{79.545 \text{ g CuO}} \times \frac{1 \text{ mol Cu}}{1 \text{ mol CuO}} \times \frac{63.546 \text{ g Cu}}{1 \text{ mol Cu}}$$

$$= (1.500 - x)\, 0.7989 \text{ g Cu}$$

$$\text{mass of Cu from } Cu_2O = (x) \text{ g } Cu_2O \times \frac{1 \text{ mol } Cu_2O}{143.091 \text{ g } Cu_2O} \times \frac{2 \text{ mol Cu}}{1 \text{ mol } Cu_2O} \times \frac{63.546 \text{ g Cu}}{1 \text{ mol Cu}}$$

$$= (x)\, 0.8882 \text{ g Cu}$$

Now, we note that the total mass of pure Cu is 1.2244 g. Therefore,

Mass Cu = $(1.500 - x)(0.7989) + (x)(0.8882) = 1.2244$
Solving for x gives a value of 0.292 g.

Therefore, mass of Cu_2O = 0.292 g
mass % of Cu_2O = 0.292 g/1.500 × 100 = 19.47

17A **(E)** In the balanced equation, 3 moles of Fe is required to react with 4 moles of H_2O. With 0.500 moles of each available, H_2O is the limiting reactant. Therefore, the maximum possible value for the extent of this reaction if all of the H_2O reacts is

$$\Delta n_{H_2O} = v_{H_2O} \cdot \xi \text{ with } v_{H_2O} = -4$$

$$\Delta n_{H_2O} = n_{H_2O, \text{ final}} - n_{H_2O, \text{ initial}} = 0 \text{ mol} - 0.500 \text{ mol} = -0.500 \text{ mol}$$

$$\xi = \Delta n_{H_2O} / v_{H_2O} = -0.500 \text{ mol} / (-4) = 0.125 \text{ mol}$$

17B **(M)** The amount of NOCl generated can be used to determine the extent of the reaction:

$$\Delta n_{\text{NOCl}} = v_{\text{NOCl}} \cdot \xi \text{ with } v_{\text{NOCl}} = +4$$

The amount of NOCl generated is

$$1.17 \text{ g NOCl} \times \frac{1 \text{ mol NOCl}}{65.459 \text{ g NOCl}} = 0.0179 \text{ mol NOCl}$$

$$\Delta n_{\text{NOCl}} = n_{\text{NOCl, final}} - n_{\text{NOCl, initial}} = 0.0179 \text{ mol} - 0 \text{ mol} = 0.0179 \text{ mol}$$

$$\xi = \Delta n_{\text{NOCl}} / v_{\text{NOCl}} = 0.0179 \text{ mol}/4 = 0.00447 \text{ mol}$$

With the extent, ξ, determined, the amount of N_2 that reacted can now be calculated.

$$\Delta n_{N_2} = v_{N_2} \xi = -2(0.00447 \text{ mol}) = -0.00894 \text{ mol}$$

Since the reaction started with 1.00 g N_2, the initial amount of N_2 is

$$1.00 \text{ g N}_2 \times \frac{1 \text{ mol N}_2}{28.02 \text{ g N}_2} = 0.0357 \text{ mol N}_2$$

The percentage of N_2 that reacted is (0.00894 mol N_2 / 0.0357 mol N_2) × 100% = 25.0%.

INTEGRATIVE EXAMPLE

A. (D)

Balancing the equation gives the following:

$$C_6H_{10}O_4(l) + 2 NH_3(g) + 4 H_2(g) \rightarrow C_6H_{16}N_2(l) + 4 H_2O(l)$$

Stepwise approach:

The first step is to calculate the number of moles of each reactant from the masses given.

$$\text{mol } C_6H_{10}O_4 = 4.15 \text{ kg} \times \frac{1000 \text{ g}}{1 \text{ kg}} \times \frac{1 \text{ mol}}{146.14 \text{ g}} = 28.30 \text{ mol}$$

$$\text{mol } NH_3 = 0.547 \text{ kg} \times \frac{1000 \text{ g}}{1 \text{ kg}} \times \frac{1 \text{ mol}}{17.03 \text{ g}} = 32.12 \text{ mol}$$

$$\text{mol } H_2 = 0.172 \text{ kg} \times \frac{1000 \text{ g}}{1 \text{ kg}} \times \frac{1 \text{ mol}}{2.016 \text{ g}} = 85.32 \text{ mol}$$

To determine the limiting reactant, calculate the number of moles of product that can be obtained from each of the reactants. The reactant yielding the least amount of product is the limiting reactant.

$$\text{mol of } C_6H_{16}N_2 \text{ from } C_6H_{10}O_4 = 28.30 \text{ mol} \times \frac{1 \text{ mol } C_6H_{16}N_2}{1 \text{ mol } C_6H_{10}O_4} = 28.30 \text{ mol}$$

$$\text{mol of } C_6H_{16}N_2 \text{ from } NH_3 = 32.12 \text{ mol} \times \frac{1 \text{ mol } C_6H_{16}N_2}{2 \text{ mol } NH_3} = 16.06 \text{ mol}$$

$$\text{mol of } C_6H_{16}N_2 \text{ from } H_2 = 85.32 \text{ mol} \times \frac{1 \text{ mol } C_6H_{16}N_2}{4 \text{ mol } H_2} = 21.33 \text{ mol}$$

NH_3 yields the fewest moles of product, and is the limiting reactant.

To calculate the % yield, the theoretical yield must first be calculated using the limiting reactant:

$$\text{Theoretical yield} = 16.06 \text{ mol } C_6H_{16}N_2 \times \frac{116.21 \text{ g } C_6H_{16}N_2}{1 \text{ mol } C_6H_{16}N_2} \times \frac{1 \text{ kg}}{1000 \text{ g}} = 1.866 \text{ kg}$$

$$\text{% yield} = \frac{1.46 \text{ kg}}{1.866 \text{ kg}} \times 100 = 78.2 \text{ yield}$$

Conversion pathway approach:

$$\text{mol of } C_6H_{16}N_2 \text{ from } C_6H_{10}O_4 = 4.15 \text{ kg } C_6H_{10}O_4 \times \frac{1000 \text{ g}}{1 \text{ kg}} \times \frac{1 \text{ mol}}{146.16 \text{ g}} \times \frac{1 \text{ mol } C_6H_{16}N_2}{1 \text{ mol } C_6H_{10}O_4} = 28.4 \text{ mol}$$

$$\text{mol of } C_6H_{16}N_2 \text{ from } NH_3 = 0.547 \text{ kg } NH_3 \times \frac{1000 \text{ g}}{1 \text{ kg}} \times \frac{1 \text{ mol}}{17.03 \text{ g}} \times \frac{1 \text{ mol } C_6H_{16}N_2}{2 \text{ mol } NH_3} = 16.05 \text{ mol}$$

$$\text{mol of } C_6H_{16}N_2 \text{ from } H_2 = 0.172 \text{ kg } H_2 \times \frac{1000 \text{ g}}{1 \text{ kg}} \times \frac{1 \text{ mol}}{2.016 \text{ g}} \times \frac{1 \text{ mol } C_6H_{16}N_2}{4 \text{ mol } H_2} = 21.3 \text{ mol}$$

NH_3 yields the fewest moles of product and is therefore the limiting reactant. The % yield is determined exactly as above.

B. (M)

Balancing the equation gives the following:

$$Zn(s) + 2HCl(aq) \rightarrow ZnCl_2(aq) + H_2(g)$$

Stepwise approach:

To determine the amount of zinc in sample, the amount of HCl reacted has to be calculated first:

$$\text{Before reaction: } 0.0179 \text{ M HCl} \times 750.0 \text{ mL} \times \frac{1 \text{ L}}{1000 \text{ mL}} = 0.0134 \text{ mol HCl}$$

After reaction: $0.0043 \text{ M HCl} \times 750.0 \text{ mL} \times \dfrac{1 \text{ L}}{1000 \text{ mL}} = 0.00323 \text{ mol HCl}$

moles of HCl consumed $= 0.0134 - 0.00323 = 0.0102 \text{ mol}$

Based on the number of moles of HCl consumed, the number of moles of Zn reacted can be determined:

$0.0102 \text{ mol HCl} \times \dfrac{1 \text{ mol Zn}}{2 \text{ mol HCl}} \times \dfrac{65.38 \text{ g Zn}}{1 \text{ mol Zn}} = 0.3334 \text{ g Zn}$

Purity of Zn $= \dfrac{0.3334 \text{ g Zn reacted}}{0.4000 \text{ g Zn in sample}} \times 100\% = 83.3\% \text{ pure}$

Conversion pathway approach:

$\left(0.0179 - 0.0043 \text{ M HCl}\right) \times 750.0 \text{ mL} \times \dfrac{1 \text{ L}}{1000 \text{ mL}}$

$\qquad = 0.0102 \text{ mol HCl}$

Note that we can only subtract concentrations in the above example because the volume has not changed. Had there been a volume change, we would have to individually convert each concentration to moles first.

$\left(0.0102 \text{ mol HCl} \times \dfrac{1 \text{ mol Zn}}{2 \text{ mol HCl}} \times \dfrac{65.38 \text{ g Zn}}{1 \text{ mol Zn}}\right) / 0.4000 \text{ g} \times 100\% = 83.4\% \text{ Zn}$

EXERCISES

Writing and Balancing Chemical Equations

1. **(E)** **(a)** $2 \text{ SO}_3 \longrightarrow 2 \text{ SO}_2 + \text{O}_2$

  (b) $\text{Cl}_2\text{O}_7 + \text{H}_2\text{O} \longrightarrow 2 \text{ HClO}_4$

  (c) $3 \text{ NO}_2 + \text{H}_2\text{O} \longrightarrow 2 \text{ HNO}_3 + \text{NO}$

  (d) $\text{PCl}_3 + 3 \text{ H}_2\text{O} \longrightarrow \text{H}_3\text{PO}_3 + 3 \text{ HCl}$

2. **(E)** **(a)** $3 \text{ P}_2\text{H}_4 \longrightarrow 4 \text{ PH}_3 + \frac{1}{2}\text{P}_4$ or $6 \text{ P}_2\text{H}_4 \longrightarrow 8 \text{ PH}_3 + \text{P}_4$

  (b) $\text{P}_4 + 6 \text{ Cl}_2 \longrightarrow 4 \text{ PCl}_3$

  (c) $2 \text{ FeCl}_3 + 3 \text{ H}_2\text{S} \longrightarrow \text{Fe}_2\text{S}_3 + 6 \text{ HCl}$

  (d) $\text{Mg}_3\text{N}_2 + 6 \text{ H}_2\text{O} \longrightarrow 3 \text{ Mg(OH)}_2 + 2 \text{ NH}_3$

3. **(E)** **(a)** $3\,PbO + 2\,NH_3 \longrightarrow 3\,Pb + N_2 + 3\,H_2O$

(b) $2\,FeSO_4 \longrightarrow Fe_2O_3 + 2\,SO_2 + \frac{1}{2}O_2$ or $4\,FeSO_4 \longrightarrow 2\,Fe_2O_3 + 4\,SO_2 + O_2$

(c) $6\,S_2Cl_2 + 16\,NH_3 \longrightarrow N_4S_4 + 12\,NH_4Cl + S_8$

(d) $C_3H_7CH(OH)CH(C_2H_5)CH_2OH + \frac{23}{2}O_2 \longrightarrow 8\,CO_2 + 9\,H_2O$

or $2\,C_3H_7CH(OH)CH(C_2H_5)CH_2OH + 23\,O_2 \longrightarrow 16\,CO_2 + 18\,H_2O$

4. **(E)** **(a)** $SO_2Cl_2 + 8\,HI \rightarrow H_2S + 2\,H_2O + 2\,HCl + 4\,I_2$

(b) $FeTiO_3 + 2\,H_2SO_4 + 5\,H_2O \longrightarrow FeSO_4 \cdot 7\,H_2O + TiOSO_4$

(c) $2\,Fe_3O_4 + 12\,HCl + 3\,Cl_2 \longrightarrow 6\,FeCl_3 + 6\,H_2O + O_2$

(d) $C_6H_5CH_2SSCH_2C_6H_5 + \frac{39}{2}O_2 \longrightarrow 14\,CO_2 + 2\,SO_2 + 7\,H_2O$

or $2\,C_6H_5CH_2SSCH_2C_6H_5 + 39\,O_2 \longrightarrow 28\,CO_2 + 4\,SO_2 + 14\,H_2O$

5. **(E)** **(a)** $2\,Mg(s) + O_2(g) \rightarrow 2\,MgO(s)$

(b) $2\,NO(g) + O_2(g) \rightarrow 2\,NO_2(g)$

(c) $2\,C_2H_6(g) + 7\,O_2(g) \rightarrow 4\,CO_2(g) + 6\,H_2O(l)$

(d) $Ag_2SO_4(aq) + BaI_2(aq) \rightarrow BaSO_4(s) + 2\,AgI(s)$

6. **(E)** **(a)** $3\,Mg(s) + N_2(g) \rightarrow Mg_3N_2(s)$

(b) $KClO_3(s) \longrightarrow KCl(s) + \frac{3}{2}O_2(g)$ *or* $2\,KClO_3(s) \longrightarrow 2\,KCl(s) + 3\,O_2(g)$

(c) $NaOH(s) + NH_4Cl(s) \longrightarrow NaCl(s) + NH_3(g) + H_2O(g)$

(d) $2\,Na(s) + 2\,H_2O(l) \longrightarrow 2\,NaOH(aq) + H_2(g)$

7. **(E)** **(a)** $2\,C_4H_{10}(g) + 13\,O_2(g) \rightarrow 8\,CO_2(g) + 10\,H_2O(l)$

(b) $2\,CH_3CH(OH)CH_3(l) + 9\,O_2(g) \rightarrow 6\,CO_2(g) + 8\,H_2O(l)$

(c) $CH_3CH(OH)COOH(s) + 3\,O_2(g) \rightarrow 3\,CO_2(g) + 3\,H_2O(l)$

8. **(E)** **(a)** $2\,C_3H_6(g) + 9\,O_2(g) \rightarrow 6\,CO_2(g) + 6\,H_2O(l)$

(b) $C_6H_5COSH(l) + 9\,O_2(g) \rightarrow 7\,CO_2(g) + 3\,H_2O(l) + SO_2(g)$

(c) $2\,CH_2(OH)CH(OH)CH_2OH(l) + 7\,O_2(g) \rightarrow 6\,CO_2(g) + 8\,H_2O(l)$

9. **(E)** **(a)** $NH_4NO_3(s) \xrightarrow{\Delta} N_2O(g) + 2\,H_2O(g)$

(b) $Na_2CO_3(aq) + 2\,HCl(aq) \rightarrow 2\,NaCl(aq) + H_2O(l) + CO_2(g)$

(c) $2\,CH_4(g) + 2\,NH_3(g) + 3\,O_2(g) \rightarrow 2\,HCN(g) + 6\,H_2O(g)$

10. **(E)** **(a)** $2\,SO_2(g) + O_2(g) \rightarrow 2\,SO_3(g)$

(b) $CaCO_3(s) + H_2O(l) + CO_2(aq) \rightarrow Ca(HCO_3)_2(aq)$

(c) $4\,NH_3(g) + 6\,NO(g) \rightarrow 5\,N_2(g) + 6\,H_2O(g)$

11. **(E)**

Unbalanced reaction:	$N_2H_4(g) + N_2O_4(g)$	$\rightarrow H_2O(g) + N_2(g)$
Balance H atoms:	$N_2H_4(g) + N_2O_4(g)$	$\rightarrow 2\ H_2O(g) + N_2(g)$
Balance O atoms:	$N_2H_4(g) + 1/2\ N_2O_4(g)$	$\rightarrow 2\ H_2O(g) + N_2(g)$
Balance N atoms:	$N_2H_4(g) + 1/2\ N_2O_4(g)$	$\rightarrow 2\ H_2O(g) + 3/2\ N_2(g)$
Multiply by 2 (whole #)	$2\ N_2H_4(g) + N_2O_4(g)$	$\rightarrow 4\ H_2O(g) + 3\ N_2(g)$
Self Check:	$6\ N + 8\ H + 4\ O$	$\rightarrow 6\ N + 8\ H + 4\ O$

12. **(E)**

Unbalanced reaction:	$NH_3(g) + O_2(g)$	$\rightarrow H_2O(g) + NO(g)$
Balance H atoms:	$2\ NH_3(g) + O_2(g)$	$\rightarrow 3\ H_2O(g) + NO(g)$
Balance N atoms:	$2\ NH_3(g) + O_2(g)$	$\rightarrow 3\ H_2O(g) + 2\ NO(g)$
Balance O atoms:	$2\ NH_3(g) + 5/2\ O_2(g)$	$\rightarrow 3\ H_2O(g) + 2\ NO(g)$
Multiply by 2 (whole #)	$4\ NH_3(g) + 5\ O_2(g)$	$\rightarrow 6\ H_2O(g) + 4\ NO(g)$
Self Check:	$4\ N + 12\ H + 10\ O$	$\rightarrow 4\ N + 12\ H + 10\ O$

Stoichiometry of Chemical Reactions

13. **(E)** In order to write the balanced chemical equation for the reaction, we will need to determine the formula of the chromium oxide product.
First determine the number of moles of chromium and oxygen, and then calculate the mole ratio.

$$\text{\# mol Cr} = 0.689\ \text{g Cr} \times \frac{1\ \text{mol Cr}}{52.00\ \text{g Cr}} = 0.01325\ \text{mol Cr}$$

$$\text{\# mol O} = 0.636\ \text{g O}_2 \times \frac{1\ \text{mol O}_2}{32.00\ \text{g O}_2} \times \frac{2\ \text{mol O}}{1\ \text{mol O}_2} = 0.03975\ \text{mol O}$$

$$\frac{0.03975\ \text{mol O}}{0.01325\ \text{mol Cr}} = \frac{3\ \text{mol O}}{1\ \text{mol Cr}}$$ Therefore, the formula for the product is CrO_3.

Balanced equation = $\qquad 2\ Cr(s) + 3\ O_2(g) \rightarrow 2\ CrO_3(s)$

14. **(E)** In order to write the balanced chemical equation for the reaction, we will need to determine the formula of the manganese oxide product.
First determine the number of moles of manganese and oxygen, and then calculate the mole ratio.

$$\text{\# mol O} = 1.142\ \text{g O} \times \frac{1\ \text{mol O}}{16.00\ \text{g O}} = 0.071375\ \text{mol O}$$

$$\text{\# g Mn} = 3.104\ \text{g oxide} - 1.142\ \text{g O} = 1.962\ \text{g Mn}$$

$$\text{\# mol Mn} = 1.962\ \text{g Mn} \times \frac{1\ \text{mol Mn}}{54.94\ \text{g Mn}} = 0.03571\ \text{mol Mn}$$

$$\frac{0.071375\ \text{mol O}}{0.03571\ \text{mol Mn}} = \frac{2\ \text{mol O}}{1\ \text{mol Mn}}$$ Therefore, the formula of the product is MnO_2.

Balanced equation = $\qquad Mn(s) + O_2(g) \rightarrow MnO_2(s)$

15. **(E)** The conversion factor is obtained from the balanced chemical equation.

$$515 \text{ g Cl}_2 \times \frac{1 \text{ mol Cl}_2}{70.90 \text{ g Cl}_2} = 7.26 \text{ mol Cl}_2$$

$$\text{moles FeCl}_3 = 7.26 \text{ mol Cl}_2 \times \frac{2 \text{ mol FeCl}_3}{3 \text{ mol Cl}_2} = 4.84 \text{ mol FeCl}_3$$

16. **(E)** Each calculation uses the stoichiometric coefficients from the balanced chemical equation and the molar mass of the reactant.

$$\text{Moles PCl}_3 = 75.8 \text{g} \times \frac{1 \text{ mol PCl}_3}{137.32 \text{ g PCl}_3} = 0.552 \text{ mol PCl}_3$$

$$\text{mass Cl}_2 = 0.552 \text{ mol PCl}_3 \times \frac{6 \text{ mol Cl}_2}{4 \text{ mol PCl}_3} \times \frac{70.90 \text{ g Cl}_2}{1 \text{ mol Cl}_2} = 58.7 \text{ g Cl}_2$$

$$\text{mass P}_4 = 0.552 \text{ mol PCl}_3 \times \frac{1 \text{ mol P}_4}{4 \text{ mol PCl}_3} \times \frac{123.9 \text{ g P}_4}{1 \text{ mol P}_4} = 17.1 \text{ g P}_4$$

17. **(E)**

(a) *Conversion pathway approach:*

$$32.8 \text{ g KClO}_3 \times \frac{1 \text{ mol KClO}_3}{122.6 \text{ g KClO}_3} \times \frac{3 \text{ mol O}_2}{2 \text{ mol KClO}_3} = 0.401 \text{ mol O}_2$$

Stepwise approach:

$$32.8 \text{ g KClO}_3 \times \frac{1 \text{ mol KClO}_3}{122.6 \text{ g KClO}_3} = 0.268 \text{ mol KClO}_3$$

$$0.268 \text{ mol KClO}_3 \times \frac{3 \text{ mol O}_2}{2 \text{ mol KClO}_3} = 0.402 \text{ mol O}_2$$

(b) *Conversion pathway approach:*

$$\text{mass KClO}_3 = 50.0 \text{ g O}_2 \times \frac{1 \text{ mol O}_2}{32.00 \text{ g O}_2} \times \frac{2 \text{ mol KClO}_3}{3 \text{ mol O}_2} \times \frac{122.6 \text{ g KClO}_3}{1 \text{ mol KClO}_3} = 128 \text{ g KClO}_3$$

Stepwise approach:

$$50.0 \text{ g O}_2 \times \frac{1 \text{ mol O}_2}{32.00 \text{ g O}_2} = 1.56 \text{ mol O}_2$$

$$1.56 \text{ mol O}_2 \times \frac{2 \text{ mol KClO}_3}{3 \text{ mol O}_2} = 1.04 \text{ mol KClO}_3$$

$$1.04 \text{ mol KClO}_3 \times \frac{122.6 \text{ g KClO}_3}{1 \text{ mol KClO}_3} = 128 \text{ g KClO}_3$$

(c) *Conversion pathway approach:*

$$\text{mass KCl} = 28.3 \text{ g O}_2 \times \frac{1 \text{ mol O}_2}{32.00 \text{ g O}_2} \times \frac{2 \text{ mol KCl}}{3 \text{ mol O}_2} \times \frac{74.55 \text{ g KCl}}{1 \text{ mol KCl}} = 43.9 \text{ g KCl}$$

Stepwise approach:

$$28.3\,\text{g O}_2 \times \frac{1\,\text{mol O}_2}{32.00\,\text{g O}_2} = 0.884\,\text{mol O}_2$$

$$0.884\,\text{mol O}_2 \times \frac{2\,\text{mol KCl}}{3\,\text{mol O}_2} = 0.589\,\text{mol KCl}$$

$$0.589\,\text{mol KCl} \times \frac{74.55\,\text{g KCl}}{1\,\text{mol KCl}} = 43.9\,\text{g KCl}$$

18. **(M)** **(a)** $\text{mass H}_2 = 87.2\,\text{g Fe} \times \dfrac{1\,\text{mol Fe}}{55.85\,\text{g Fe}} \times \dfrac{4\,\text{mol H}_2}{3\,\text{mol Fe}} \times \dfrac{2.016\,\text{g H}_2}{1\,\text{mol H}_2} = 4.20\,\text{g H}_2$

    (b) $\text{mass H}_2\text{O} = 25.0\,\text{g Fe} \times \dfrac{1\,\text{mol Fe}}{55.85\,\text{g Fe}} \times \dfrac{4\,\text{mol H}_2\text{O}}{3\,\text{mol Fe}} \times \dfrac{18.02\,\text{g H}_2\text{O}}{1\,\text{mol H}_2\text{O}} = 10.75\,\text{g H}_2\text{O}$

    (c) $\text{mass Fe}_3\text{O}_4 = 29.2\,\text{g H}_2 \times \dfrac{1\,\text{mol H}_2}{2.016\,\text{g H}_2} \times \dfrac{1\,\text{mol Fe}_3\text{O}_4}{4\,\text{mol H}_2} \times \dfrac{231.54\,\text{g Fe}_3\text{O}_4}{1\,\text{mol Fe}_3\text{O}_4}$

        $= 838\,\text{g Fe}_3\text{O}_4$

19. **(M)** Balance the given equation, and then solve the problem.

$$2\,\text{Ag}_2\text{CO}_3\,(s) \xrightarrow{\ \Delta\ } 4\,\text{Ag}\,(s) + 2\,\text{CO}_2\,(g) + \text{O}_2\,(g)$$

$$\text{mass Ag}_2\text{CO}_3 = 75.1\,\text{g Ag} \times \frac{1\,\text{mol Ag}}{107.87\,\text{g Ag}} \times \frac{2\,\text{mol Ag}_2\text{CO}_3}{4\,\text{mol Ag}} \times \frac{275.75\,\text{g Ag}_2\text{CO}_3}{1\,\text{mol Ag}_2\text{CO}_3} = 96.0\,\text{g Ag}_2\text{CO}_3$$

20. **(E)** The balanced equation is

$$\text{Ca}_3(\text{PO}_4)_2(s) + 4\,\text{HNO}_3(aq) \rightarrow \text{Ca}(\text{H}_2\text{PO}_4)_2(s) + 2\,\text{Ca}(\text{NO}_3)_2(aq)$$

$$\text{mass HNO}_3 = 125\,\text{kg Ca}(\text{H}_2\text{PO}_4)_2 \times \frac{1\,\text{kmol Ca}(\text{H}_2\text{PO}_4)_2}{234.05\,\text{kg Ca}(\text{H}_2\text{PO}_4)_2} \times \frac{4\,\text{kmol HNO}_3}{1\,\text{kmol Ca}(\text{H}_2\text{PO}_4)_2} \times \frac{63.01\,\text{kg HNO}_3}{1\,\text{kmol HNO}_3}$$

$$= 135\,\text{kg HNO}_3$$

21. **(M)** The balanced equation is $\text{CaH}_2(s) + 2\,\text{H}_2\text{O}(l) \rightarrow \text{Ca}(\text{OH})_2(s) + 2\,\text{H}_2(g)$

    (a) $\text{mass H}_2 = 127\,\text{g CaH}_2 \times \dfrac{1\,\text{mol CaH}_2}{42.094\,\text{g CaH}_2} \times \dfrac{2\,\text{mol H}_2}{1\,\text{mol CaH}_2} \times \dfrac{2.016\,\text{g H}_2}{1\,\text{mol H}_2} = 12.2\,\text{g H}_2$

    (b) $\text{mass H}_2\text{O} = 56.2\,\text{g CaH}_2 \times \dfrac{1\,\text{mol CaH}_2}{42.094\,\text{g CaH}_2} \times \dfrac{2\,\text{mol H}_2\text{O}}{1\,\text{mol CaH}_2} \times \dfrac{18.015\,\text{g H}_2\text{O}}{1\,\text{mol H}_2\text{O}} = 48.1\,\text{g H}_2\text{O}$

    (c) $\text{mass CaH}_2 = 8.12 \times 10^{24}\,\text{molecules H}_2 \times \dfrac{1\,\text{mol H}_2}{6.022 \times 10^{23}\,\text{molecules H}_2} \times \dfrac{1\,\text{mol CaH}_2}{2\,\text{mol H}_2} \times \dfrac{42.094\,\text{g CaH}_2}{1\,\text{mol CaH}_2}$

        $= 284\,\text{g CaH}_2$

22. (E)

(a) $\text{amount O}_2 = 88.0\,\text{g CO}_2 \times \dfrac{1\,\text{mol CO}_2}{44.01\,\text{g CO}_2} \times \dfrac{3\,\text{mol O}_2}{2\,\text{mol CO}_2} = 3.00\,\text{mol O}_2$

(b) $\text{mass KO}_2 = 1.000\times10^3\,\text{g CO}_2 \times \dfrac{1\,\text{mol CO}_2}{44.01\,\text{g CO}_2} \times \dfrac{4\,\text{mol KO}_2}{2\,\text{mol CO}_2} \times \dfrac{71.10\,\text{g KO}_2}{1\,\text{mol KO}_2} = 3231\,\text{g KO}_2$

(c) $\text{mol of K}_2\text{CO}_3 = 1.00\,\text{mg KO}_2 \times \dfrac{1\,\text{g KO}_2}{1000\,\text{mg}} \times \dfrac{1\,\text{mol KO}_2}{71.10\,\text{g KO}_2} \times \dfrac{2\,\text{mol K}_2\text{CO}_3}{4\,\text{mol KO}_2}$

$= 7.03\times10^{-6}\,\text{mol K}_2\text{CO}_3$

23. (M) The balanced equation is $\text{Fe}_2\text{O}_3(s) + 3\,\text{C}(s) \xrightarrow{\Delta} 2\,\text{Fe}(l) + 3\,\text{CO}(g)$

$\text{mass Fe}_2\text{O}_3 = 523\,\text{kg Fe} \times \dfrac{1\,\text{kmol Fe}}{55.85\,\text{kg Fe}} \times \dfrac{1\,\text{kmol Fe}_2\text{O}_3}{2\,\text{kmol Fe}} \times \dfrac{159.7\,\text{kg Fe}_2\text{O}_3}{1\,\text{kmol Fe}_2\text{O}_3} = 748\,\text{kg Fe}_2\text{O}_3$

$\%\,\text{Fe}_2\text{O}_3 \text{ in ore} = \dfrac{748\,\text{kg Fe}_2\text{O}_3}{938\,\text{kg ore}} \times 100\% = 79.7\%\ \text{Fe}_2\text{O}_3$

24. (M) The following reaction occurs: $2\,\text{Ag}_2\text{O}(s) \xrightarrow{\text{heat}} 4\,\text{Ag}(s) + \text{O}_2(g)$

$\text{mass Ag}_2\text{O} = 0.187\,\text{g O}_2 \times \dfrac{1\,\text{mol O}_2}{32.0\,\text{g O}_2} \times \dfrac{2\,\text{mol Ag}_2\text{O}}{1\,\text{mol O}_2} \times \dfrac{231.7\,\text{g Ag}_2\text{O}}{1\,\text{mol Ag}_2\text{O}} = 2.71\,\text{g Ag}_2\text{O}$

$\%\,\text{Ag}_2\text{O} = \dfrac{2.71\,\text{g Ag}_2\text{O}}{3.13\,\text{g sample}} \times 100\% = 86.6\%\ \text{Ag}_2\text{O}$

25. (M) $\text{B}_{10}\text{H}_{14} + 11\,\text{O}_2 \rightarrow 5\,\text{B}_2\text{O}_3 + 7\,\text{H}_2\text{O}$

$\%\text{ by mass B}_{10}\text{H}_{14} = \dfrac{\#\,\text{g B}_{10}\text{H}_{14}}{\#\,\text{g B}_{10}\text{H}_{14} + \#\,\text{g O}_2} \times 100$

1 mol $\text{B}_{10}\text{H}_{14}$ reacts with 11 mol O_2 (exactly)

$\text{mass B}_{10}\text{H}_{14} = 1\,\text{mol B}_{10}\text{H}_{14} \times \dfrac{122.21\,\text{g B}_{10}\text{H}_{14}}{1\,\text{mol B}_{10}\text{H}_{14}} = 122.22\,\text{g B}_{10}\text{H}_{14}$

$\text{mass O}_2 = 11\,\text{mol O}_2 \times \dfrac{32.00\,\text{g O}_2}{1\,\text{mol O}_2} = 352.00\,\text{g O}_2$

$\%\text{ by mass B}_{10}\text{H}_{14} = \dfrac{122.21\,\text{g B}_{10}\text{H}_{14}}{122.22\,\text{g B}_{10}\text{H}_{14} + 352.00\,\text{g O}_2} \times 100\% = 25.8$

26. **(M)** $10 \, \text{Al(s)} + 6 \, \text{NH}_4\text{ClO}_4\text{(s)} \rightarrow 4 \, \text{Al}_2\text{O}_3\text{(s)} + 2 \, \text{AlCl}_3\text{(s)} + 12 \, \text{H}_2\text{O(l)} + 3 \, \text{N}_2\text{(g)}$

$$1 \, \text{kg Al} \times \frac{1000 \, \text{g Al}}{1 \, \text{kg Al}} \times \frac{1 \, \text{mol Al}}{26.98 \, \text{g Al}} \times \frac{6 \, \text{mol NH}_4\text{ClO}_4}{10 \, \text{mol Al}} \times \frac{117.49 \, \text{g NH}_4\text{ClO}_4}{1 \, \text{mol NH}_4\text{ClO}_4} = 2.61 \times 10^3 \, \text{g NH}_4\text{ClO}_4$$

27. **(E)** $2 \, \text{Al(s)} + 6 \, \text{HCl(aq)} \rightarrow 2 \, \text{AlCl}_3\text{(aq)} + 3 \, \text{H}_2\text{(g)}$. First determine the mass of Al in the foil.

$$\text{mass Al} = \left(10.25 \, \text{cm} \times 5.50 \, \text{cm} \times 0.601 \, \text{mm}\right) \times \frac{1 \, \text{cm}}{10 \, \text{mm}} \times \frac{2.70 \, \text{g Al}}{1 \, \text{cm}^3} = 9.15 \, \text{g Al}$$

$$\text{mass H}_2 = 9.15 \, \text{g Al} \times \frac{1 \, \text{mol Al}}{26.98 \, \text{g Al}} \times \frac{3 \, \text{mol H}_2}{2 \, \text{mol Al}} \times \frac{2.016 \, \text{g H}_2}{1 \, \text{mol H}_2} = 1.03 \, \text{g H}_2$$

28. **(E)** $2 \, \text{Al(s)} + 6 \, \text{HCl(aq)} \rightarrow 2 \, \text{AlCl}_3\text{(aq)} + 3 \, \text{H}_2\text{(g)}$

$$\text{mass H}_2 = 225 \, \text{mL soln} \times \frac{1.088 \, \text{g}}{1 \, \text{mL}} \times \frac{18.0 \, \text{g HCl}}{100.0 \, \text{g soln}} \times \frac{1 \, \text{mol HCl}}{36.46 \, \text{g HCl}} \times \frac{3 \, \text{mol H}_2}{6 \, \text{mol HCl}} \times \frac{2.016 \, \text{g H}_2}{1 \, \text{mol H}_2}$$
$$= 1.22 \, \text{g H}_2$$

29. **(E)** First write the balanced chemical equation for each reaction.

$$2 \, \text{Na(s)} + 2 \, \text{HCl(aq)} \rightarrow 2 \, \text{NaCl(aq)} + \text{H}_2\text{(g)} \qquad \text{Mg(s)} + 2 \, \text{HCl(aq)} \rightarrow \text{MgCl}_2\text{(aq)} + \text{H}_2\text{(g)}$$
$$2 \, \text{Al(s)} + 6 \, \text{HCl(aq)} \rightarrow 2 \, \text{AlCl}_3\text{(aq)} + 3 \, \text{H}_2\text{(g)} \qquad \text{Zn(s)} + 2 \, \text{HCl(aq)} \rightarrow \text{ZnCl}_2\text{(aq)} + \text{H}_2\text{(g)}$$

Three of the reactions—those of Na, Mg, and Zn—produce 1 mole of $\text{H}_2\text{(g)}$. The one of these three that produces the most hydrogen per gram of metal is the one for which the metal's atomic mass is the smallest, remembering to compare twice the atomic mass for Na. The atomic masses are: 2×23 u for Na, 24.3 u for Mg, and 65.4 u for Zn. Thus, among these three, Mg produces the most H_2 per gram of metal, specifically 1 mol H_2 per 24.3 g Mg. In the case of Al, 3 moles of H_2 are produced by 2 moles of the metal, or 54 g Al. This reduces as follows: 3 mol $\text{H}_2 / 54 \, \text{g Al} = 1 \, \text{mol H}_2 / 18$ g Al. Thus, Al produces the largest amount of H_2 per gram of metal.

30. **(E)** In order for a substance to yield the same mass of $\text{CO}_2\text{(g)}$ per gram of compound as does ethanol when combusted in excess oxygen, the substance must have the same empirical formula. Compound (d), CH_3OCH_3, is the only compound that fits the description. In fact, compound (d) has the same formula as ethanol, $\text{CH}_3\text{CH}_2\text{OH}$, as they are structural isomers, and they should give the same amount of $\text{CO}_2\text{(g)}$ when combusted in excess O_2.

Molarity

31. **(M)**

(a) $\text{CH}_3\text{OH molarity } (c) = \dfrac{2.92 \text{ mol CH}_3\text{OH}}{7.16 \text{ L}} = 0.408 \text{ M}$

(b) $\text{CH}_3\text{CH}_2\text{OH molarity } (c) = \dfrac{7.69 \text{ mmol CH}_3\text{CH}_2\text{OH}}{50.00 \text{ mL}} = 0.154 \text{ M}$

(c) $\text{CO}(\text{NH}_2)_2 \text{ molarity } (c) = \dfrac{25.2 \text{ g CO}(\text{NH}_2)_2}{275 \text{ mL}} \times \dfrac{1 \text{ mol CO}(\text{NH}_2)_2}{60.06 \text{ g CO}(\text{NH}_2)_2} \times \dfrac{1000 \text{ mL}}{1 \text{ L}} = 1.53 \text{ M}$

32. **(E)**

(a) $\text{CH}_3\text{CH}_2\text{OH molarity } (c) = \dfrac{2.25 \times 10^{-4} \text{ mol CH}_3\text{CH}_2\text{OH}}{125 \text{ mL}} \times \dfrac{1000 \text{ mL}}{1 \text{ L}} = 0.00180 \text{ M}$

(b) $(\text{CH}_3)_2\text{CO molarity } (c) = \dfrac{57.5 \text{ g }(\text{CH}_3)_2\text{CO}}{525 \text{ mL}} \times \dfrac{1 \text{ mol }(\text{CH}_3)_2\text{CO}}{58.08 \text{ g }(\text{CH}_3)_2\text{CO}} \times \dfrac{1000 \text{ mL}}{1 \text{ L}} = 1.88\underline{6} \text{ M}$

(c) $\text{C}_3\text{H}_5(\text{OH})_3 \text{ molarity } (c) = \dfrac{18.5 \text{ mL C}_3\text{H}_5(\text{OH})_3}{375 \text{ mL soln}} \times \dfrac{1.26 \text{ g}}{1 \text{ mL}} \times \dfrac{1 \text{ mol C}_3\text{H}_5(\text{OH})_3}{92.09 \text{ g C}_3\text{H}_5(\text{OH})_3} \times \dfrac{1000 \text{ mL}}{1 \text{ L}} = 0.675 \text{ M}$

33. **(E)**

(a) *Conversion pathway approach:*

$[\text{C}_{12}\text{H}_{22}\text{O}_{11}] = \dfrac{150.0 \text{ g C}_{12}\text{H}_{22}\text{O}_{11}}{250.0 \text{ mL soln}} \times \dfrac{1000 \text{ mL}}{1 \text{ L}} \times \dfrac{1 \text{ mol C}_{12}\text{H}_{22}\text{O}_{11}}{342.3 \text{ g C}_{12}\text{H}_{22}\text{O}_{11}} = 1.753 \text{ M}$

Stepwise approach:

$150.0 \text{ g C}_{12}\text{H}_{22}\text{O}_{11} \times \dfrac{1 \text{ mol C}_{12}\text{H}_{22}\text{O}_{11}}{342.3 \text{ g C}_{12}\text{H}_{22}\text{O}_{11}} = 0.4382 \text{ mol C}_{12}\text{H}_{22}\text{O}_{11}$

$250.0 \text{ mL soln} \times \dfrac{1 \text{ L}}{1000 \text{ mL}} = 0.2500 \text{ L}$

$[\text{C}_{12}\text{H}_{22}\text{O}_{11}] = \dfrac{0.4382 \text{ mol C}_{12}\text{H}_{22}\text{O}_{11}}{0.2500 \text{ L}} = 1.753 \text{ M}$

(b) *Conversion pathway approach:*

$[\text{CO}(\text{NH}_2)_2] = \dfrac{98.3 \text{ mg solid}}{5.00 \text{ mL soln}} \times \dfrac{97.9 \text{ mg CO}(\text{NH}_2)_2}{100 \text{ mg solid}} \times \dfrac{1 \text{ mmol CO}(\text{NH}_2)_2}{60.06 \text{ mg CO}(\text{NH}_2)_2}$

$= 0.320 \text{ M CO}(\text{NH}_2)_2$

Stepwise approach:

$$98.3 \text{ mg solid} \times \frac{97.9 \text{ mg CO(NH}_2)_2}{100 \text{ mg solid}} = 96.2 \text{ mg CO(NH}_2)_2$$

$$96.2 \text{ mg CO(NH}_2)_2 \times \frac{1 \text{ g CO(NH}_2)_2}{1000 \text{ mg CO(NH}_2)_2} = 0.0962 \text{ g CO(NH}_2)_2$$

$$0.0962 \text{ g CO(NH}_2)_2 \times \frac{1 \text{ mol CO(NH}_2)_2}{60.06 \text{ g CO(NH}_2)_2} = 1.60 \times 10^{-3} \text{ mol CO(NH}_2)_2$$

$$5.00 \text{ mL soln} \times \frac{1 \text{ L}}{1000 \text{ mL}} = 0.00500 \text{ L}$$

$$[\text{CO(NH}_2)_2] = \frac{1.60 \times 10^{-3} \text{ mol CO(NH}_2)_2}{0.00500 \text{ L}} = 0.320 \text{ M}$$

(c) *Conversion pathway approach:*

$$[\text{CH}_3\text{OH}] = \frac{125.0 \text{ mL CH}_3\text{OH}}{15.0 \text{ L soln}} \times \frac{0.792 \text{ g}}{1 \text{ mL}} \times \frac{1 \text{ mol CH}_3\text{OH}}{32.04 \text{ g CH}_3\text{OH}} = 0.206 \text{ M}$$

Stepwise approach:

$$[\text{CH}_3\text{OH}] = \frac{125.0 \text{ mL CH}_3\text{OH}}{15.0 \text{ L soln}} \times \frac{0.792 \text{ g}}{1 \text{ mL}} \times \frac{1 \text{ mol CH}_3\text{OH}}{32.04 \text{ g CH}_3\text{OH}} = 0.206 \text{ M}$$

$$125.0 \text{ mL CH}_3\text{OH} \times \frac{0.792 \text{ g}}{1 \text{ mL}} = 99.0 \text{ g CH}_3\text{OH}$$

$$99.0 \text{ g CH}_3\text{OH} \times \frac{1 \text{ mol CH}_3\text{OH}}{32.04 \text{ g CH}_3\text{OH}} = 3.09 \text{ mol CH}_3\text{OH}$$

$$[\text{CH}_3\text{OH}] = \frac{3.09 \text{ mol CH}_3\text{OH}}{15.0 \text{ L soln}} = 0.206 \text{ M}$$

34. (E)

(a) $[\text{H}_2\text{C}_4\text{H}_5\text{NO}_4] = \dfrac{0.405 \text{ g H}_2\text{C}_4\text{H}_5\text{NO}_4}{100.0 \text{ mL}} \times \dfrac{1000 \text{ mL}}{1 \text{ L}} \times \dfrac{1 \text{ mol H}_2\text{C}_4\text{H}_5\text{NO}_4}{133.10 \text{ g H}_2\text{C}_4\text{H}_5\text{NO}_4} = 0.0304 \text{ M}$

(b) $[\text{C}_3\text{H}_6\text{O}] = \dfrac{35.0 \text{ mL C}_3\text{H}_6\text{O}}{425 \text{ mL soln}} \times \dfrac{1000 \text{ mL}}{1 \text{ L}} \times \dfrac{0.790 \text{ g C}_3\text{H}_6\text{O}}{1 \text{ mL}} \times \dfrac{1 \text{ mol}}{58.08 \text{ g C}_3\text{H}_6\text{O}} = 1.12 \text{ M}$

(c) $[(\text{C}_2\text{H}_5)_2\text{O}] = \dfrac{8.8 \text{ mg}(\text{C}_2\text{H}_5)_2\text{O}}{3.00 \text{ L soln}} \times \dfrac{1 \text{ g}}{1000 \text{ mg}} \times \dfrac{1 \text{ mol}(\text{C}_2\text{H}_5)_2\text{O}}{74.12 \text{ g}(\text{C}_2\text{H}_5)_2\text{O}} = 4.0 \times 10^{-5} \text{ M}$

35. (E)

(a) $\text{mass C}_6\text{H}_{12}\text{O}_6 = 75.0 \text{ mL soln} \times \dfrac{1 \text{ L}}{1000 \text{ mL}} \times \dfrac{0.350 \text{ mol C}_6\text{H}_{12}\text{O}_6}{1 \text{ L soln}} \times \dfrac{180.16 \text{ g C}_6\text{H}_{12}\text{O}_6}{1 \text{ mol C}_6\text{H}_{12}\text{O}_6} = 4.73 \text{ g}$

(b) $V_{\text{CH}_3\text{OH}} = 2.25 \text{ L soln} \times \dfrac{0.485 \text{ mol}}{1 \text{ L}} \times \dfrac{32.04 \text{ g CH}_3\text{OH}}{1 \text{ mol CH}_3\text{OH}} \times \dfrac{1 \text{ mL}}{0.792 \text{ g}} = 44.1 \text{ mL CH}_3\text{OH}$

36. **(E)**

(a) $V_{CH_3CH_2OH} = 200.0\,L\;soln \times \dfrac{1.65\,mol\;CH_3CH_2OH}{1\,L} \times \dfrac{46.07\,g\;CH_3CH_2OH}{1\,mol\;CH_3CH_2OH} \times \dfrac{1\,mL}{0.789\,g}$

$\times \dfrac{1\,L}{1000\,mL} = 19.3\,L$

(b) $V_{HCl} = 12.0\,L \times \dfrac{0.234\,mol\;HCl}{1\,L} \times \dfrac{36.46\,g\;HCl}{1\,mol\;HCl} \times \dfrac{100\,g\;soln}{36.0\,g\;HCl} \times \dfrac{1\,mL\;soln}{1.18\,g} = 241\,mL$

37. **(M)**

(a) $\dfrac{85\,mg\;C_6H_{12}O_6}{1\,dL\;blood} \times \dfrac{1\,g}{1000\,mg} \times \dfrac{10\,dL}{1\,L} \times \dfrac{1\,mol\;C_6H_{12}O_6}{180.16\,g\;C_6H_{12}O_6} \times \dfrac{1\,mmol\;C_6H_{12}O_6}{1 \times 10^{-3}\,mol\;C_6H_{12}O_6}$

$= 4.7\,\dfrac{mmol\;C_6H_{12}O_6}{L}$

(b) Molarity $= 4.7 \times 10^{-3}\,\dfrac{mol\;C_6H_{12}O_6}{L}$

38. **(M)**

(a) Molarity $= \dfrac{1.2\,mg\;F^-}{1\,L} \times \dfrac{1\,g}{1000\,mg} \times \dfrac{1\,mol\;F^-}{19.00\,g\;F^-} = 6.3 \times 10^{-5}\,\dfrac{mol\;F^-}{L}$

(b) # g KF $= \dfrac{6.3 \times 10^{-5}\,mol\;F^-}{1\,L\;water} \times 1.6 \times 10^8\,L\;water \times \dfrac{1\,mol\;KF}{1\,mol\;F^-} \times \dfrac{58.1\,g\;KF}{1\,mol\;KF} = 5.9 \times 10^5\,g\;KF$

39. **(E)** First we determine each concentration in moles per liter and find the 0.500 M solution.

(a) $[KCl] = \dfrac{0.500\,g\;KCl}{1\,mL} \times \dfrac{1\,mol\;KCl}{74.548\,g\;KCl} \times \dfrac{1000\,mL}{1\,L} = 6.71\,M\;KCl$

(b) $[KCl] = \dfrac{36.0\,g\;KCl}{1\,L} \times \dfrac{1\,mol\;KCl}{74.548\,g\;KCl} = 0.483\,M\;KCl$

(c) $[KCl] = \dfrac{7.46\,mg\;KCl}{1\,mL} \times \dfrac{1\,g\;KCl}{1000\,mg\;KCl} \times \dfrac{1\,mol\;KCl}{74.548\,g\;KCl} \times \dfrac{1000\,mL}{1\,L} = 0.100\,M\;KCl$

(d) $[KCl] = \dfrac{373\,g\;KCl}{10.00\,L} \times \dfrac{1\,mol\;KCl}{74.548\,g\;KCl} = 0.500\,M\;KCl$

Solution (d) is a 0.500 M KCl solution.

40. **(E)** By inspection, we see that (b) and (c) are the only two that are not per volume of solution. These two solutions need not be considered. A close inspection of the remaining choices reveals that the units for (a) are equivalent to those for (d), that is g NaCl per liter of solution is equivalent to mg NaCl per mL of solution (the mass:volume ratio is the same).

41. **(E)** We determine the molar concentration for the 46% by mass sucrose solution.

$$[C_{12}H_{22}O_{11}] = \frac{46\ g\ C_{12}H_{22}O_{11} \times \dfrac{1\ mol\ C_{12}H_{22}O_{11}}{342.3\ g\ C_{12}H_{22}O_{11}}}{100\ g\ soln \times \dfrac{1\ mL}{1.21\ g\ soln} \times \dfrac{1\ L}{1000\ mL}} = 1.6\ M$$

The 46% by mass sucrose solution is the more concentrated.

42. **(E)** Here we must calculate the $[CH_3CH_2OH]$ in the white wine and compare it with 1.71 M CH_3CH_2OH, the concentration of the solution described in Example 4-8.

$$[CH_3CH_2OH] = \frac{11\ g\ CH_3CH_2OH}{100.0\ g\ soln} \times \frac{0.95\ g\ soln}{1\ mL} \times \frac{1000\ mL}{1\ L} \times \frac{1\ mol\ CH_3CH_2OH}{46.1\ g\ CH_3CH_2OH}$$

$$= 2.3\ M\ CH_3CH_2OH$$

Thus, the white wine has a greater ethyl alcohol content.

43. **(E)** $[KNO_3] = \dfrac{0.01000\ L\ conc'd\ soln \times \dfrac{2.05\ mol\ KNO_3}{1L}}{0.250\ L\ diluted\ solution} = 0.0820\ M$

44. **(E)**

Volume of concentrated $AgNO_3$ solution

$$V_{AgNO_3} = 500.0\ mL\ dilute\ soln \times \frac{0.350\ mmol\ AgNO_3}{1\ mL\ dilute\ soln} \times \frac{1\ mL\ conc.\ soln.}{2.00\ mmol\ AgNO_3} = 87.5\ mL\ conc.\ soln$$

45. **(E)** Both the diluted and concentrated solutions contain the same number of moles of K_2SO_4. This number is given in the numerator of the following expression.

$$K_2SO_4\ molarity = \frac{0.125\ L \times \dfrac{0.198\ mol\ K_2SO_4}{1L}}{0.105\ L} = 0.236\ M\ K_2SO_4$$

46. **(E)** $[HCl] = \dfrac{0.500\ L\ dilute\ sol'n \times \dfrac{0.085\ mol\ HCl}{1\ L\ soln}}{0.0250\ L} = 1.7\ M$

47. **(E)** Let us compute how many mL of dilute ($_{dil}$) solution we obtain from each mL of concentrated ($_{conc}$) solution. $c_{dil}V_{dil} = c_{conc}V_{conc}$ becomes $x\ mL \times 0.0125\ M = 1.00\ mL \times 0.250 M$ and $x = 20$ Thus, the ratio of the volume of the volumetric flask to that of the pipet would be 20:1. We could use a 100.0 mL flask and a 5.00 mL pipet, a 1000.0 mL flask and a 50.00 mL pipet, or a 500.0 mL flask and a 25.00 mL pipet. There are many combinations that could be used.

48. **(E)** First we must determine the amount of solute in the final solution and then the volume of the initial, more concentrated, solution that must be used.

$$\text{volume conc'd soln} = 250.0\,\text{mL} \times \frac{0.175\,\text{mmol KCl}}{1\,\text{mL dil soln}} \times \frac{1\,\text{mL conc'd soln}}{0.496\,\text{mmol KCl}} = 88.2\ \text{mL}$$

Thus the instructions are as follows: Place 88.2 mL of 0.496 M KCl in a 250 mL volumetric flask. Dilute to the mark with distilled water, stopping to mix thoroughly several times during the addition of water.

Chemical Reactions in Solutions

49. **(M)**

(a) $\text{mass Na}_2\text{S} = 27.8\,\text{mL} \times \dfrac{1\,\text{L}}{1000\,\text{mL}} \times \dfrac{0.163\,\text{mol AgNO}_3}{1\,\text{L soln}} \times \dfrac{1\,\text{mol Na}_2\text{S}}{2\,\text{mol AgNO}_3}$

$\times \dfrac{78.05\,\text{g Na}_2\text{S}}{1\,\text{mol Na}_2\text{S}} = 0.177\,\text{g Na}_2\text{S}$

(b) $\text{mass Ag}_2\text{S} = 0.177\,\text{g Na}_2\text{S} \times \dfrac{1\,\text{mol Na}_2\text{S}}{78.04\,\text{g Na}_2\text{S}} \times \dfrac{1\,\text{mol Ag}_2\text{S}}{1\,\text{mol Na}_2\text{S}} \times \dfrac{247.80\,\text{g Ag}_2\text{S}}{1\,\text{mol Ag}_2\text{S}} = 0.562\,\text{g Ag}_2\text{S}$

50. **(M)** The balanced chemical equation provides us with the conversion factor between the two compounds.

(a) $\text{mass NaHCO}_3 = 525\,\text{mL solution} \times \dfrac{1\,\text{L solution}}{1000\,\text{mL solution}} \times \dfrac{0.220\,\text{mol Cu(NO}_3)_2}{1\,\text{L solution}} \times \dfrac{2\,\text{mol NaHCO}_3}{1\,\text{mol Cu(NO}_3)_2}$

$\times \dfrac{84.0058\ \text{g NaHCO}_3}{1\ \text{mol NaHCO}_3} = 19.4\ \text{g NaHCO}_3$

(b) $\text{mass CuCO}_3 = 525\,\text{mL solution} \times \dfrac{1\,\text{L solution}}{1000\,\text{mL solution}} \times \dfrac{0.220\,\text{mol Cu(NO}_3)_2}{1\,\text{L}} \times \dfrac{1\,\text{mol CuCO}_3}{1\,\text{mol Cu(NO}_3)_2}$

$\times \dfrac{123.6\ \text{g CuCO}_3}{1\,\text{mol CuCO}_3} = 14.3\ \text{g CuCO}_3$

51. **(M)** The molarity can be expressed as millimoles of solute per milliliter of solution.

$$V_{\text{K}_2\text{CrO}_4} = 415\,\text{mL} \times \frac{0.186\,\text{mmol AgNO}_3}{1\,\text{mL soln}} \times \frac{1\,\text{mmol K}_2\text{CrO}_4}{2\,\text{mmol AgNO}_3} \times \frac{1\,\text{mL K}_2\text{CrO}_4\,(\text{aq})}{0.650\,\text{mmol K}_2\text{CrO}_4}$$

$$= 59.4\ \text{mL K}_2\text{CrO}_4$$

52. **(D)** **(a)** $\text{mass Ca(OH)}_2 = 415\,\text{mL} \times \dfrac{1\,\text{L}}{1000\,\text{mL}} \times \dfrac{0.477\,\text{mol HCl}}{1\,\text{L soln}} \times \dfrac{1\,\text{mol Ca(OH)}_2}{2\,\text{mol HCl}}$

$\times \dfrac{74.1\,\text{g Ca(OH)}_2}{1\,\text{mol Ca(OH)}_2} = 7.33\,\text{g Ca(OH)}_2$

(b) $\text{mass Ca(OH)}_2 = 324\,\text{L} \times \dfrac{1.12\,\text{kg}}{1\,\text{L}} \times \dfrac{24.28\,\text{kg HCl}}{100.00\,\text{kg soln}} \times \dfrac{1\,\text{kmol HCl}}{36.46\,\text{kg HCl}}$

$\times \dfrac{1\,\text{kmol Ca(OH)}_2}{2\,\text{kmol HCl}} \times \dfrac{74.10\,\text{kg Ca(OH)}_2}{1\,\text{kmol Ca(OH)}_2} = 89.5\,\text{kg Ca(OH)}_2$

53. **(D)** The balanced chemical equation for the reaction is:

$2\ \text{HNO}_3(\text{aq}) + \text{Ca(OH)}_2(\text{aq}) \rightarrow \text{Ca(NO}_3)_2(\text{aq}) + 2\ \text{H}_2\text{O(l)}$

$\#\ \text{mol HNO}_3 = 0.02978\,\text{L soln} \times \dfrac{0.0142\,\text{mol Ca(OH)}_2}{1\,\text{L soln}} \times \dfrac{2\,\text{mol HNO}_3}{1\,\text{mol Ca(OH)}_2} = 8.46 \times 10^{-4}\,\text{mol HNO}_3$

All of the HNO_3 that reacts was contained in the initial, undiluted 1.00 mL sample. Since the moles of HNO_3 are the same in the diluted and undiluted solutions, one can divide the moles of HNO_3 by the volume of the undiluted solution to obtain the molarity.

$\text{Molarity} = \dfrac{8.46 \times 10^{-4}\,\text{mol HNO}_3}{0.00100\,\text{L}} = 8.46 \times 10^{-3}\ \dfrac{\text{mol HNO}_3}{\text{L}}$

54. **(M)** The balanced chemical equation for the reaction is:

$\text{H}_3\text{PO}_4(\text{aq}) + 2\ \text{NaOH(aq)} \rightarrow \text{Na}_2\text{HPO}_4(\text{aq}) + 2\ \text{H}_2\text{O(l)}$

$0.0491\,\text{L soln} \times \dfrac{0.217\,\text{mol NaOH}}{1\,\text{L soln}} \times \dfrac{1\,\text{mol HPO}_4^{2-}}{2\,\text{mol NaOH}} \times \dfrac{1}{0.005\,\text{L}} = 1.06\,\text{M HPO}_4^{2-}$

55. **(M)**

(a) We know that the Al forms the AlCl_3.

$\text{mol AlCl}_3 = 1.87\,\text{g Al} \times \dfrac{1\,\text{mol Al}}{26.98\,\text{g Al}} \times \dfrac{1\,\text{mol AlCl}_3}{1\,\text{mol Al}} = 0.0693\,\text{mol AlCl}_3$

(b) $[\text{AlCl}_3] = \dfrac{0.0693\,\text{mol AlCl}_3}{23.8\,\text{mL}} \times \dfrac{1000\,\text{mL}}{1\,\text{L}} = 2.91\,\text{M AlCl}_3$

56. **(M)** The balanced chemical reaction indicates that 4 mol NaNO_2 are formed from 2 mol Na_2CO_3.

$[\text{NaNO}_2] = \dfrac{138\,\text{g Na}_2\text{CO}_3}{1.42\,\text{L soln}} \times \dfrac{1\,\text{mol Na}_2\text{CO}_3}{106.0\,\text{g Na}_2\text{CO}_3} \times \dfrac{4\,\text{mol NaNO}_2}{2\,\text{mol Na}_2\text{CO}_3} = 1.83\,\text{M NaNO}_2$

57. **(M)** The volume of solution determines the amount of product.

$\text{mass Ag}_2\text{CrO}_4 = 415\,\text{mL} \times \dfrac{1\,\text{L}}{1000\,\text{mL}} \times \dfrac{0.186\,\text{mol AgNO}_3}{1\,\text{L soln}} \times \dfrac{1\,\text{mol Ag}_2\text{CrO}_4}{2\,\text{mol AgNO}_3} \times \dfrac{331.73\,\text{g Ag}_2\text{CrO}_4}{1\,\text{mol Ag}_2\text{CrO}_4}$

$\text{mass Ag}_2\text{CrO}_4 = 12.8\,\text{g Ag}_2\text{CrO}_4$

58. **(M)** $V_{KMnO_4} = 12.5 \text{ g KI} \times \dfrac{1 \text{ mol KI}}{166.0023 \text{ g KI}} \times \dfrac{2 \text{ mol KMnO}_4}{10 \text{ mol KI}} \times \dfrac{1 \text{ L KMnO}_4}{0.0665 \text{ mol KMnO}_4}$

$= 0.226 \text{ L KMnO}_4$

59. **(M)** mass Na $= 155 \text{ mL soln} \times \dfrac{1 \text{ L}}{1000 \text{ mL}} \times \dfrac{0.175 \text{ mol NaOH}}{1 \text{ L soln}} \times \dfrac{2 \text{ mol Na}}{2 \text{ mol NaOH}} \times \dfrac{22.99 \text{ g Na}}{1 \text{ mol Na}}$

$= 0.624 \text{ g Na}$

60. **(M)** We determine the amount of HCl present initially, and the amount desired.

amount HCl present $= 250.0 \text{ mL} \times \dfrac{1.023 \text{ mmol HCl}}{1 \text{ mL soln}} = 255.8 \text{ mmol HCl}$

amount HCl desired $= 250.0 \text{ mL} \times \dfrac{1.000 \text{ mmol HCl}}{1 \text{ mL soln}} = 250.0 \text{ mmol HCl}$

mass Mg $= (255.8 - 250.0) \text{ mmol HCl} \times \dfrac{1 \text{ mmol Mg}}{2 \text{ mmol HCl}} \times \dfrac{24.3 \text{ mg Mg}}{1 \text{ mmol Mg}} = 70. \text{ mg Mg}$

61. **(M)** The mass of oxalic acid enables us to determine the amount of NaOH in the solution.

$[\text{NaOH}] = \dfrac{0.3126 \text{ g H}_2\text{C}_2\text{O}_4}{26.21 \text{ mL soln}} \times \dfrac{1000 \text{ mL}}{1 \text{ L soln}} \times \dfrac{1 \text{ mol H}_2\text{C}_2\text{O}_4}{90.04 \text{ g H}_2\text{C}_2\text{O}_4} \times \dfrac{2 \text{ mol NaOH}}{1 \text{ mol H}_2\text{C}_2\text{O}_4} = 0.2649 \text{ M}$

62. **(D)** The total amount of HCl present is the amount that reacted with the $CaCO_3$ plus the amount that reacted with the $Ba(OH)_2$ (aq).

$\begin{aligned}\text{moles HCl from} \\ \text{CaCO}_3 \text{ reaction}\end{aligned} = 0.1000 \text{ g CaCO}_3 \times \dfrac{1 \text{ mol CaCO}_3}{100.09 \text{ g CaCO}_3} \times \dfrac{2 \text{ mol HCl}}{1 \text{ mol CaCO}_3} \times \dfrac{1000 \text{ mmol}}{1 \text{ mol}}$

$= 1.998 \text{ mmol HCl}$

$\begin{aligned}\text{moles HCl from} \\ \text{Ba(OH)}_2 \text{ reaction}\end{aligned} = 43.82 \text{ mL} \times \dfrac{0.01185 \text{ mmol Ba(OH)}_2}{1 \text{ mL soln}} \times \dfrac{2 \text{ mmol HCl}}{1 \text{ mmol Ba(OH)}_2}$

$= 1.039 \text{ mmol HCl}$

The HCl molarity is this total mmol of HCl divided by the total volume of 25.00 mL.

$[\text{HCl}] = \dfrac{(1.998 + 1.039) \text{ mmol HCl}}{25.00 \text{ mL}} = 0.1215 \text{ M}$

Determining the Limiting Reactant

63. **(E)** The limiting reactant is NH_3. For every mole of $NH_3(g)$ that reacts, a mole of NO(g) forms. Since 3.00 moles of $NH_3(g)$ reacts, 3.00 moles of NO(g) forms (1:1 mole ratio).

64. **(E)** The reaction of interest is: $CaH_2(s) + 2 H_2O(l) \rightarrow Ca(OH)_2(s) + 2 H_2(g)$
The limiting reactant is $H_2O(l)$. The mole ratio between water and hydrogen gas is 1:1. Hence, if 1.54 moles of $H_2O(l)$ reacts, 1.54 moles of $H_2(g)$ forms (1:1 mole ratio).

65. (M) First we must determine the number of moles of NO produced by each reactant. The one producing the smaller amount of NO is the limiting reactant.

$$\text{mol NO} = 0.696\,\text{mol Cu} \times \frac{2\,\text{mol NO}}{3\,\text{mol Cu}} = 0.464\,\text{mol NO}$$

Conversion pathway approach:

$$\text{mol NO} = 136\,\text{mL HNO}_3\,(\text{aq}) \times \frac{1\,\text{L}}{1000\,\text{mL}} \times \frac{6.0\,\text{mol HNO}_3}{1\,\text{L}} \times \frac{2\,\text{mol NO}}{8\,\text{mol HNO}_3} = 0.204\,\text{mol NO}$$

Stepwise approach:

$$136\,\text{mL HNO}_3\,(\text{aq}) \times \frac{1\,\text{L}}{1000\,\text{mL}} = 0.136\,\text{L HNO}_3$$

$$0.136\,\text{L} \times \frac{6.0\,\text{mol HNO}_3}{1\,\text{L}} = 0.816\,\text{mol HNO}_3$$

$$0.816\,\text{mol HNO}_3 \times \frac{2\,\text{mol NO}}{8\,\text{mol HNO}_3} = 0.204\,\text{mol NO}$$

Since $HNO_3(aq)$ is the limiting reactant, it will be completely consumed, leaving some Cu unreacted.

66. (M) First determine the mass of H_2 produced from each of the reactants. The smaller mass is that produced by the limiting reactant, which is the mass that should be produced.

$$\text{mass H}_2\,(\text{Al}) = 1.84\,\text{g Al} \times \frac{1\,\text{mol Al}}{26.98\,\text{g Al}} \times \frac{3\,\text{mol H}_2}{2\,\text{mol Al}} \times \frac{2.016\,\text{g H}_2}{1\,\text{mol H}_2} = 0.206\,\text{g H}_2$$

$$\text{mass H}_2\,(\text{HCl}) = 75.0\,\text{mL} \times \frac{1\,\text{L}}{1000\,\text{mL}} \times \frac{2.95\,\text{mol HCl}}{1\,\text{L}} \times \frac{3\,\text{mol H}_2}{6\,\text{mol HCl}} \times \frac{2.016\,\text{g H}_2}{1\,\text{mol H}_2} = 0.223\,\text{g H}_2$$

Thus, $0.206\,\text{g}$ H_2 should be produced.

67. (M) First we need to determine the amount of Na_2CS_3 produced from each of the reactants.

$$n_{\text{Na}_2\text{CS}_3\,(\text{from CS}_2)} = 92.5\,\text{mL CS}_2 \times \frac{1.26\,\text{g}}{1\,\text{mL}} \times \frac{1\,\text{mol CS}_2}{76.13\,\text{g CS}_2} \times \frac{2\,\text{mol Na}_2\text{CS}_3}{3\,\text{mol CS}_2} = 1.02\,\text{mol Na}_2\text{CS}_3$$

$$n_{\text{Na}_2\text{CS}_3\,(\text{from NaOH})} = 2.78\,\text{mol NaOH} \times \frac{2\,\text{mol Na}_2\text{CS}_3}{6\,\text{mol NaOH}} = 0.927\,\text{mol Na}_2\text{CS}_3$$

Thus, the mass produced is $0.927\,\text{mol Na}_2\text{CS}_3 \times \dfrac{154.2\,\text{g Na}_2\text{CS}_3}{1\,\text{mol Na}_2\text{CS}_3} = 143\,\text{g Na}_2\text{CS}_3$

68. (D) Since the two reactants combine in an equimolar basis, the one present with the fewer number of moles is the limiting reactant and determines the mass of the products.

$$n_{\text{ZnSO}_4} = 315\,\text{mL} \times \frac{1\,\text{L}}{1000\,\text{mL}} \times \frac{0.275\,\text{mol ZnSO}_4}{1\,\text{L soln}} = 0.0866\,\text{mol ZnSO}_4$$

$$n_{\text{BaS}} = 285\,\text{mL} \times \frac{1\,\text{L}}{1000\,\text{mL}} \times \frac{0.315\,\text{mol BaS}}{1\,\text{L soln}} = 0.0898\,\text{mol BaS}$$

Thus, $ZnSO_4$ is the limiting reactant and 0.0866 mol of each of the products will be produced.

$$\text{mass products} = \left(0.0866\,\text{mol BaSO}_4 \times \frac{233.4\,\text{g BaSO}_4}{1\,\text{mol BaSO}_4}\right) + \left(0.0866\,\text{mol ZnS} \times \frac{97.46\,\text{g ZnS}}{1\,\text{mol ZnS}}\right)$$

$$= 28.7\,\text{g product mixture (lithopone)}$$

69. **(D)**

$$Ca(OH)_2(s) + 2\,NH_4Cl(s) \rightarrow CaCl_2(aq) + 2\,H_2O(l) + 2\,NH_3(g)$$

First compute the amount of NH_3 formed from each reactant in this limiting reactant problem.

$$n_{NH_3\,(\text{from NH}_4\text{Cl})} = 33.0\,\text{g NH}_4\text{Cl} \times \frac{1\,\text{mol NH}_4\text{Cl}}{53.49\,\text{g NH}_4\text{Cl}} \times \frac{2\,\text{mol NH}_3}{2\,\text{mol NH}_4\text{Cl}} = 0.617\,\text{mol NH}_3$$

$$n_{NH_3\,(\text{from Ca(OH)}_2)} = 33.0\,\text{g Ca(OH)}_2 \times \frac{1\,\text{mol Ca(OH)}_2}{74.09\,\text{g Ca(OH)}_2} \times \frac{2\,\text{mol NH}_3}{1\,\text{mol Ca(OH)}_2} = 0.891\,\text{mol NH}_3$$

Thus, 0.617 mol NH_3 should be produced as NH_4Cl is the limiting reactant.

$$\text{mass NH}_3 = 0.617\,\text{mol NH}_3 \times \frac{17.03\,\text{g NH}_3}{1\,\text{mol NH}_3} = 10.5\,\text{g NH}_3$$

Now we will determine the mass of reactant in excess, $Ca(OH)_2$.

$$Ca(OH)_2\,\text{used} = 0.617\,\text{mol NH}_3 \times \frac{1\,\text{mol Ca(OH)}_2}{2\,\text{mol NH}_3} \times \frac{74.09\,\text{g Ca(OH)}_2}{1\,\text{mol Ca(OH)}_2} = 22.9\,\text{g Ca(OH)}_2$$

$$\text{excess mass Ca(OH)}_2 = 33.0\,\text{g Ca(OH)}_2 - 22.9\,\text{g Ca(OH)}_2 = 10.1\,\text{g excess Ca(OH)}_2$$

70. **(D)** The balanced chemical equation is:

$$Ca(OCl)_2(s) + 4\,HCl(aq) \rightarrow CaCl_2(aq) + 2\,H_2O(l) + 2\,Cl_2(g)$$

$$n_{Cl_2\,(\text{from Ca(OCl)}_2)} = 50.0\,\text{g Ca(OCl)}_2 \times \frac{1\,\text{mol Ca(OCl)}_2}{142.98\,\text{g Ca(OCl)}_2} \times \frac{2\,\text{mol Cl}_2}{1\,\text{mol Ca(OCl)}_2} = 0.699\,\text{mol Cl}_2$$

$$n_{Cl_2\,(\text{from HCl})} = 275\,\text{mL} \times \frac{1\,\text{L}}{1000\,\text{mL}} \times \frac{6.00\,\text{mol HCl}}{1\,\text{L soln}} \times \frac{2\,\text{mol Cl}_2}{4\,\text{mol HCl}} = 0.825\,\text{mol Cl}_2$$

Thus, mass Cl_2 expected $= 0.699\,\text{mol Cl}_2 \times \dfrac{70.91\,\text{g Cl}_2}{1\,\text{mol Cl}_2} = 49.6\,\text{g Cl}_2$

The excess reactant is the one that produces the most Cl_2, namely HCl(aq). The quantity of excess HCl(aq) is determined from the amount of excess $Cl_2(g)$ it theoretically could produce (if it were the limiting reactant).

$$V_{\text{excess HCl}} = (0.825 - 0.699)\,\text{mol Cl}_2 \times \frac{4\,\text{mol HCl}}{2\,\text{mol Cl}_2} \times \frac{1000\,\text{mL}}{6.00\,\text{mol HCl}}$$

$$= 42.0\,\text{mL excess 6.00 M HCl(aq)}$$

$$\text{mass excess HCl} = (0.825 - 0.699)\,\text{mol Cl}_2 \times \frac{4\,\text{mol HCl}}{2\,\text{mol Cl}_2} \times \frac{36.46\,\text{g HCl}}{1\,\text{mol HCl}} = 9.19\,\text{g excess HCl}$$

71. **(M)** The number of grams of $CrSO_4$ that can be made from the reaction mixture is determined by finding the limiting reactant, and using the limiting reactant to calculate the mass of product that can be formed. The limiting reactant can determined by calculating the amount of product formed from each of the reactants. Whichever reactant produces the smallest amount of product is the limiting reactant.

$$3.2 \text{ mol Zn} \times \frac{2 \text{ mol } CrSO_4}{4 \text{ mol Zn}} \times \frac{148.06 \text{ g } CrSO_4}{1 \text{ mol } CrSO_4} = 236.90 \text{ g } CrSO_4$$

$$1.7 \text{ mol } K_2Cr_2O_7 \times \frac{2 \text{ mol } CrSO_4}{1 \text{ mol } K_2Cr_2O_7} \times \frac{148.06 \text{ g } CrSO_4}{1 \text{ mol } CrSO_4} = 503.40 \text{ g } CrSO_4$$

$$5.0 \text{ mol } H_2SO_4 \times \frac{2 \text{ mol } CrSO_4}{7 \text{ mol } H_2SO_4} \times \frac{148.06 \text{ g } CrSO_4}{1 \text{ mol } CrSO_4} = 211.51 \text{ g } CrSO_4$$

H_2SO_4 is the limiting reactant since it produces the least amount of $CrSO_4$. Therefore, the maximum number of grams of $CrSO_4$ that can be made is 211.51 g.

72. **(M)** The number of grams of $TiCl_4$ that can be made from the reaction mixture is determined by finding the limiting reactant, and using the limiting reactant to calculate the mass of product that can be formed. The limiting reactant can determined by calculating the amount of product formed from each of the reactants. Whichever reactant produces the smallest amount of product is the limiting reactant.

$$35 \text{ g } TiO_2 \times \frac{1 \text{ mol } TiO_2}{79.88 \text{ g } TiO_2} \times \frac{3 \text{ mol } TiCl_4}{3 \text{ mol } TiO_2} \times \frac{189.67 \text{ g } TiCl_4}{1 \text{ mol } TiCl_4} = 83.1 \text{ g } TiCl_4$$

$$45 \text{ g } Cl_2 \times \frac{1 \text{ mol } Cl_2}{70.90 \text{ g } Cl_2} \times \frac{3 \text{ mol } TiCl_4}{6 \text{ mol } Cl_2} \times \frac{189.67 \text{ g } TiCl_4}{1 \text{ mol } TiCl_4} = 60.2 \text{ g } TiCl_4$$

$$11 \text{ g C} \times \frac{1 \text{ mol } Cl_2}{12.01 \text{ g C}} \times \frac{3 \text{ mol } TiCl_4}{4 \text{ mol C}} \times \frac{189.67 \text{ g } TiCl_4}{1 \text{ mol } TiCl_4} = 130 \text{ g } TiCl_4$$

Cl_2 is the limiting reactant. Therefore, 6.0×10^1 g $TiCl_4$ is expected.

Theoretical, Actual, and Percent Yields

73. **(M)**

(a) $$277 \text{ g } CCl_4 \times \frac{1 \text{ mol } CCl_4}{153.81 \text{ g } CCl_4} = 1.80 \text{ mol } CCl_4$$

Since the stoichiometry indicates that 1 mole CCl_2F_2 is produced per mole CCl_4, the use of 1.80 mole CCl_4 should produce 1.80 mole CCl_2F_2. This is the theoretical yield of the reaction.

(b) $187 \text{g CCl}_2\text{F}_2 \times \dfrac{1 \text{mol CCl}_2\text{F}_2}{120.91 \text{g CCl}_2\text{F}_2} = 1.55 \text{ mol CCl}_2\text{F}_2$

The actual yield of the reaction is the amount actually produced, $1.55 \text{ mol CCl}_2\text{F}_2$.

(c) $\% \text{ yield} = \dfrac{1.55 \text{mol CCl}_2\text{F}_2 \text{ obtained}}{1.80 \text{mol CCl}_2\text{F}_2 \text{ calculated}} \times 100\% = 86.1\% \text{ yield}$

74. (M) (a) $\text{mass C}_6\text{H}_{10} = 100.0 \text{g C}_6\text{H}_{11}\text{OH} \times \dfrac{1 \text{mol C}_6\text{H}_{11}\text{OH}}{100.16 \text{g C}_6\text{H}_{11}\text{OH}} \times \dfrac{1 \text{mol C}_6\text{H}_{10}}{1 \text{mol C}_6\text{H}_{11}\text{OH}}$

$\times \dfrac{82.146 \text{g C}_6\text{H}_{10}}{1 \text{mol C}_6\text{H}_{10}} = 82.01 \text{g C}_6\text{H}_{10} = \text{theoretical yield}$

(b) $\text{percent yield} = \dfrac{64.0 \text{g C}_6\text{H}_{10} \text{ produced}}{82.01 \text{g C}_6\text{H}_{10} \text{ calculated}} \times 100\% = 78.0\% \text{ yield}$

(c) $\text{mass C}_6\text{H}_{11}\text{OH} = 100.0 \text{g C}_6\text{H}_{10} \text{ produced} \times \dfrac{1.000 \text{g calculated}}{0.780 \text{g produced}} \times \dfrac{1 \text{mol C}_6\text{H}_{10}}{82.15 \text{g C}_6\text{H}_{10}}$

$\times \dfrac{1 \text{mol C}_6\text{H}_{11}\text{OH}}{1 \text{mol C}_6\text{H}_{10}} \times \dfrac{100.2 \text{g C}_6\text{H}_{11}\text{OH}}{1 \text{mol C}_6\text{H}_{11}\text{OH}} = 156 \text{g C}_6\text{H}_{11}\text{OH are needed}$

75. (D) $\% \text{ yield} = \dfrac{\text{actual yield}}{\text{theoretical yield}} \times 100\%$

The actual yield is given in the problem and is equal to 28.2 g.
In order to determine the theoretical yield, we must find the limiting reactant and do stoichiometry.

Conversion pathway approach:

$7.81 \text{ g Al}_2\text{O}_3 \times \dfrac{1 \text{ mol Al}_2\text{O}_3}{101.96 \text{ g Al}_2\text{O}_3} \times \dfrac{2 \text{ mol Na}_3\text{AlF}_6}{1 \text{ mol Al}_2\text{O}_3} \times \dfrac{209.94 \text{ g Na}_3\text{AlF}_6}{1 \text{ mol Na}_3\text{AlF}_6} = 32.2 \text{ g Na}_3\text{AlF}_6$

$3.50 \text{ L} \times \dfrac{0.141 \text{ mol}}{1 \text{ L}} \times \dfrac{2 \text{ mol Na}_3\text{AlF}_6}{6 \text{ mol NaOH}} \times \dfrac{209.94 \text{ g Na}_3\text{AlF}_6}{1 \text{ mol Na}_3\text{AlF}_6} = 34.5 \text{ g Na}_3\text{AlF}_6$

Stepwise approach:

Amount of Na₃AlF₆ produced from Al₂O₃ if all Al₂O₃ reacts

$7.81 \text{ g Al}_2\text{O}_3 \times \dfrac{1 \text{ mol Al}_2\text{O}_3}{101.96 \text{ g Al}_2\text{O}_3} = 0.0766 \text{ mol Al}_2\text{O}_3$

$0.0766 \text{ mol Al}_2\text{O}_3 \times \dfrac{2 \text{ mol Na}_3\text{AlF}_6}{1 \text{ mol Al}_2\text{O}_3} = 0.153 \text{ mol Na}_3\text{AlF}_6$

$0.153 \text{ mol Na}_3\text{AlF}_6 \times \dfrac{209.94 \text{ g Na}_3\text{AlF}_6}{1 \text{ mol Na}_3\text{AlF}_6} = 32.1 \text{g Na}_3\text{AlF}_6$

Amount of Na₃AlF₆ produced from NaOH if all NaOH reacts

$$3.50 \text{ L} \times \frac{0.141 \text{ mol NaOH}}{1 \text{ L}} = 0.494 \text{ mol NaOH}$$

$$0.494 \text{ mol NaOH} \times \frac{2 \text{ mol Na}_3\text{AlF}_6}{6 \text{ mol NaOH}} = 0.165 \text{ mol Na}_3\text{AlF}_6$$

$$0.165 \text{ mol Na}_3\text{AlF}_6 \times \frac{209.94 \text{ g Na}_3\text{AlF}_6}{1 \text{ mol Na}_3\text{AlF}_6} = 34.5 \text{ g Na}_3\text{AlF}_6$$

Al_2O_3 is the limiting reactant. $\qquad$ % yield $= \dfrac{28.2 \text{ g}}{32.2 \text{ g}} \times 100\% = 87.6\%$

76. **(D)** The balanced equation is $2 \text{ NH}_3(g) + 3 \text{ CuO}(s) \rightarrow \text{N}_2(g) + 3 \text{ Cu}(s) + 3 \text{ H}_2\text{O}(g)$

$$\% \text{ yield} = \frac{6.63 \text{ g}}{\text{theoretical yield}} \times 100\%$$

$$18.1 \text{ g NH}_3 \times \frac{1 \text{ mol NH}_3}{17.03 \text{ g NH}_3} \times \frac{1 \text{ mol N}_2}{2 \text{ mol NH}_3} \times \frac{28.01 \text{ g N}_2}{1 \text{ mol N}_2} = 14.9 \text{ g N}_2$$

$$90.4 \text{ g CuO} \times \frac{1 \text{ mol CuO}}{79.55 \text{ g CuO}} \times \frac{1 \text{ mol N}_2}{3 \text{ mol CuO}} \times \frac{28.01 \text{ g N}_2}{1 \text{ mol N}_2} = 10.6 \text{ g N}_2$$

CuO is the limiting reactant. The theoretical yield of N_2 is 10.6 g.

$$\% \text{ yield} = \frac{6.63 \text{ g}}{10.6 \text{ g}} \times 100\% = 62.5\%$$

77. **(M) (a)** We first need to solve the limiting reactant problem involved here.

$$n_{\text{C}_4\text{H}_9\text{Br (from C}_4\text{H}_9\text{OH})} = 15.0 \text{ g C}_4\text{H}_9\text{OH} \times \frac{1 \text{ mol C}_4\text{H}_9\text{OH}}{74.12 \text{ g C}_4\text{H}_9\text{OH}} \times \frac{1 \text{ mol C}_4\text{H}_9\text{Br}}{1 \text{ mol C}_4\text{H}_9\text{OH}} = 0.202 \text{ mol C}_4\text{H}_9\text{Br}$$

$$n_{\text{C}_4\text{H}_9\text{Br (from NaBr)}} = 22.4 \text{ g NaBr} \times \frac{1 \text{ mol NaBr}}{102.9 \text{ g NaBr}} \times \frac{1 \text{ mol C}_4\text{H}_9\text{Br}}{1 \text{ mol NaBr}} = 0.218 \text{ mol C}_4\text{H}_9\text{Br}$$

$$n_{\text{C}_4\text{H}_9\text{Br (from H}_2\text{SO}_4)} = 32.7 \text{ g H}_2\text{SO}_4 \times \frac{1 \text{ mol H}_2\text{SO}_4}{98.1 \text{ g H}_2\text{SO}_4} \times \frac{1 \text{ mol C}_4\text{H}_9\text{Br}}{1 \text{ mol H}_2\text{SO}_4} = 0.333 \text{ mol C}_4\text{H}_9\text{Br}$$

Thus the theoretical yield of $\text{C}_4\text{H}_9\text{Br} = 0.202 \text{ mol C}_4\text{H}_9\text{Br} \times \dfrac{137.0 \text{ g C}_4\text{H}_9\text{Br}}{1 \text{ mol C}_4\text{H}_9\text{Br}} = 27.7 \text{ g C}_4\text{H}_9\text{Br}$

(b) The actual yield is the mass obtained, 17.1 g $\text{C}_4\text{H}_9\text{Br}$.

(c) Then, % yield $= \dfrac{17.1 \text{ g C}_4\text{H}_9\text{Br produced}}{27.7 \text{ g C}_4\text{H}_9\text{Br expected}} \times 100\% = 61.7\%$ yield

78. (M) (a) Again, we solve the limiting reactant problem first.

$$n_{(C_6H_5N)_2} \text{ (from } C_6H_5NO_2) = 0.10\,L\ C_6H_5NO_2 \times \frac{1000\,mL}{1\,L} \times \frac{1.20\,g}{1\,mL} \times \frac{1\,mol\ C_6H_5NO_2}{123.1\,g\ C_6H_5NO_2}$$

$$\times \frac{1\,mol\,(C_6H_5N)_2}{2\,mol\ C_6H_5NO_2} = 0.49\,mol\,(C_6H_5N)_2$$

$$n_{(C_6H_5N)_2} \text{ (from } C_6H_{14}O_4) = 0.30\,L\ C_6H_{14}O_4 \times \frac{1000\,mL}{1\,L} \times \frac{1.12\,g}{1\,mL} \times \frac{1\,mol\ C_6H_{14}O_4}{150.2\ g\ C_6H_{14}O_4}$$

$$\times \frac{1\,mol\,(C_6H_5N)_2}{4\,mol\ C_6H_{14}O_4} = 0.56\,mol\,(C_6H_5N)_2$$

Thus the theoretical yield for $(C_6H_5N)_2 = 0.49\,mol\,(C_6H_5N)_2 \times \dfrac{182.2\,g\,(C_6H_5N)_2}{1\,mol\,(C_6H_5N)_2} = 89\,g\,(C_6H_5N)_2$

(b) actual yield $= 55\,g\,(C_6H_5N)_2$ produced

(c) percent yield $= \dfrac{55\,g\,(C_6H_5N)_2 \text{ produced}}{89\,g\,(C_6H_5N)_2 \text{ expected}} \times 100\% = 62\%$ yield

79. (M) Balanced equation: $3\,CH_3COOH + PCl_3 \rightarrow 3\,CH_3COCl + H_3PO_3$

$$\text{mass acid} = 75\,g\ CH_3COCl \times \frac{100.0\,g\ \text{calculated}}{78.2\,g\ \text{produced}} \times \frac{1\,mol\ CH_3COCl}{78.5\,g\ CH_3COCl} \times \frac{3\,mol\ CH_3COOH}{3\,mol\ CH_3COCl}$$

$$\times \frac{60.1\,g\ \text{pure}\ CH_3COOH}{1\,mol\ CH_3COOH} \times \frac{100\,g\ \text{commercial}}{97\,g\ \text{pure}\ CH_3COOH} = 76\ \text{g commercial}\ CH_3COOH$$

80. (M) $\text{mass}\ CH_2Cl_2 = 112\,g\ CH_4 \times \dfrac{1\,mol\ CH_4}{16.04\,g\ CH_4} \times \dfrac{1\,mol\ CH_3Cl}{1\,mol\ CH_4} \times \dfrac{0.92\,mol\ CH_3Cl \text{ produced}}{1.00\,mol\ CH_3Cl \text{ expected}}$

$$\times \frac{1\,mol\ CH_2Cl_2}{1\,mol\ CH_3Cl} \times \frac{84.93\,g\ CH_2Cl_2}{1\,mol\ CH_2Cl_2} \times \frac{0.92\,g\ CH_2Cl_2 \text{ produced}}{1.00\,g\ CH_2Cl_2 \text{ calculated}} = 5.0 \times 10^2\,g\ CH_2Cl_2$$

81. (E) A less-than-100% yield of desired product in synthesis reactions is always the case. This is because of side reactions that yield products other than those desired and because of the loss of material on the glassware, on filter paper, etc. during the various steps of the procedure. A main criterion for choosing a synthesis reaction is how economically it can be run. In the analysis of a compound, on the other hand, it is essential that all of the material present be detected. Therefore, a 100% yield is required; none of the material present in the sample can be lost during the analysis. Therefore analysis reactions are carefully chosen to meet this 100 % yield criterion; they need not be economical to run.

82. (M) The theoretical yield is 2.07 g Ag_2CrO_4. If the mass actually obtained is less than this, it is likely that some of the pure material was not recovered, perhaps stuck to the walls of the flask in which the reaction occurred, or left suspended in the solution. Thus while it is almost a certainty that less than 2.07 g will be obtained, the absolute maximum mass of Ag_2CrO_4 expected is 2.07 g. If the precipitate weighs more than 2.07 g, the extra mass must be impurities (e.g., the precipitate was not thoroughly dried).

Consecutive Reactions, Simultaneous Reactions

83. **(D)** We must determine the amount of HCl needed to react with each component of the mixture.

$$Mg(OH)_2(s) + 2\,HCl(aq) \longrightarrow MgCl_2(aq) + 2\,H_2O(l)$$

$$MgCO_3(s) + 2\,HCl(aq) \longrightarrow MgCl_2(aq) + H_2O(l) + CO_2(g)$$

$$n_{HCl\,(consumed\,by\,MgCO_3)} = 425\,g\,mixt. \times \frac{35.2\,g\,MgCO_3}{100.0\,g\,mixt.} \times \frac{1\,mol\,MgCO_3}{84.3\,g\,MgCO_3} \times \frac{2\,mol\,HCl}{1\,mol\,MgCO_3} = 3.55\,mol\,HCl$$

$$n_{HCl\,(consumed\,by\,Mg(OH)_2)} = 425\,g\,mixt. \times \frac{64.8\,g\,Mg(OH)_2}{100.0\,g\,mixt.} \times \frac{1\,mol\,Mg(OH)_2}{58.3\,g\,Mg(OH)_2} \times \frac{2\,mol\,HCl}{1\,mol\,MgCO_3} = 9.45\,mol\,HCl$$

$$mass\,HCl = (3.55 + 9.45)\,mol\,HCl \times \frac{36.46\,g\,HCl}{1\,mol\,HCl} = 474\,g\,HCl$$

84. **(D)** Here we need to determine the amount of CO_2 produced from each reactant.

$$C_3H_8(g) + 5\,O_2(g) \longrightarrow 3\,CO_2(g) + 4\,H_2O(l)$$

$$2\,C_4H_{10}(g) + 13\,O_2(g) \longrightarrow 8\,CO_2(g) + 10\,H_2O(l)$$

$$n_{CO_2\,(from\,C_3H_8)} = 406\,g\,mixt. \times \frac{72.7\,g\,C_3H_8}{100.0\,g\,mixt.} \times \frac{1\,mol\,C_3H_8}{44.10\,g\,C_3H_8} \times \frac{3\,mol\,CO_2}{1\,mol\,C_3H_8} = 20.1\,mol\,CO_2$$

$$n_{CO_2\,(from\,C_4H_{10})} = 406\,g\,mixt. \times \frac{27.3\,g\,C_4H_{10}}{100.0\,g\,mixt} \times \frac{1\,mol\,C_4H_{10}}{58.12\,g\,C_4H_{10}} \times \frac{8\,mol\,CO_2}{2\,mol\,C_4H_{10}} = 7.63\,mol\,CO_2$$

$$mass\,CO_2 = (20.1 + 7.63)\,mol\,CO_2 \times \frac{44.01\,g\,CO_2}{1\,mol\,CO_2} = 1.22 \times 10^3\,g\,CO_2$$

85. **(M)** The molar ratios given by the stoichiometric coefficients in the balanced chemical equations are used in the solution, namely

$$CH_4(g) + 4\,Cl_2(g) \rightarrow CCl_4(g) + 4\,HCl(g)$$

$$CCl_4(g) + 2\,HF(g) \rightarrow CCl_2F_2(g) + 2\,HCl(g)$$

$$amount\,Cl_2 = 2.25 \times 10^3\,g\,CCl_2F_2 \times \frac{1\,mol\,CCl_2F_2}{120.91\,g\,CCl_2F_2} \times \frac{1\,mol\,CCl_4}{1\,mol\,CCl_2F_2} \times \frac{4\,mol\,Cl_2}{1\,mol\,CCl_4} = 74.4\,mol\,Cl_2$$

86. **(M)** Balanced Equations:

$$C_2H_6(g) + \tfrac{7}{2}\,O_2(g) \rightarrow 2\,CO_2(g) + 3\,H_2O(l)$$

$$CO_2(g) + Ba(OH)_2(aq) \rightarrow BaCO_3(s) + H_2O(l)$$

Conversion pathway approach:

$$mass_{C_2H_6} = 0.506\,g\,BaCO_3 \times \frac{1\,mol\,BaCO_3}{197.3\,g\,BaCO_3} \times \frac{1\,mol\,CO_2}{1\,mol\,BaCO_3} \times \frac{2\,mol\,C_2H_6}{4\,mol\,CO_2} \times \frac{30.07\,g\,C_2H_6}{1\,mol\,C_2H_6} = 0.0386\,g\,C_2H_6$$

Stepwise approach:

$$0.506 \text{ g BaCO}_3 \times \frac{1 \text{ mol BaCO}_3}{197.3 \text{ g BaCO}_3} = 2.56 \times 10^{-3} \text{ mol BaCO}_3$$

$$2.56 \times 10^{-3} \text{ mol BaCO}_3 \times \frac{1 \text{ mol CO}_2}{1 \text{ mol BaCO}_3} = 2.56 \times 10^{-3} \text{ mol CO}_2$$

$$2.56 \times 10^{-3} \text{ mol CO}_2 \times \frac{2 \text{ mol C}_2\text{H}_6}{4 \text{ mol CO}_2} = 1.28 \times 10^{-3} \text{ mol C}_2\text{H}_6$$

$$1.28 \times 10^{-3} \text{ mol C}_2\text{H}_6 \times \frac{30.07 \text{ g C}_2\text{H}_6}{1 \text{ mol C}_2\text{H}_6} = 0.0386 \text{ g C}_2\text{H}_6$$

87. **(D)** $\text{NaI(aq)} + \text{AgNO}_3\text{(aq)} \rightarrow \text{AgI(s)} + \text{NaNO}_3\text{(aq)}$ (multiply by 4)

       $2 \text{ AgI(s)} + \text{Fe(s)} \rightarrow \text{FeI}_2\text{(aq)} + 2 \text{ Ag(s)}$ (multiply by 2)

       $\underline{2 \text{ FeI}_2\text{(aq)} + 3 \text{ Cl}_2\text{(g)} \rightarrow 2 \text{ FeCl}_3\text{(aq)} + 2 \text{ I}_2\text{(s)}}$ (unchanged)

$4\text{NaI(aq)} + 4\text{AgNO}_3\text{(aq)} + 2\text{Fe(s)} + 3\text{Cl}_2\text{(g)} \rightarrow 4\text{NaNO}_3\text{(aq)} + 4\text{Ag(s)} + 2\text{FeCl}_3\text{(aq)} + 2\text{I}_2\text{(s)}$

For every 4 moles of AgNO_3, 2 moles of $\text{I}_2\text{(s)}$ are produced. The mass of AgNO_3 required

$$= 1.00 \text{ kg I}_2\text{(s)} \times \frac{1000 \text{ g I}_2\text{(s)}}{1 \text{ kg I}_2\text{(s)}} \times \frac{1 \text{ mol I}_2\text{(s)}}{253.809 \text{ g I}_2\text{(s)}} \times \frac{4 \text{ mol AgNO}_3\text{(s)}}{2 \text{ mol I}_2\text{(s)}} \times \frac{169.873 \text{ g AgNO}_3\text{(s)}}{1 \text{ mol AgNO}_3\text{(s)}}$$

$= 133\underline{8.59} \text{ g AgNO}_3$ per kg of I_2 produced or 1.34 kg AgNO_3 per kg of I_2 produced

88. **(D)** $\text{Fe} + \text{Br}_2 \rightarrow \text{FeBr}_2$ (multiply by 3)

$3 \text{ FeBr}_2 + \text{Br}_2 \rightarrow \text{Fe}_3\text{Br}_8$

$\underline{\text{Fe}_3\text{Br}_8 + 4 \text{ Na}_2\text{CO}_3 \rightarrow 8 \text{ NaBr} + 4 \text{ CO}_2 + \text{Fe}_3\text{O}_4}$

$3 \text{ Fe} + 4 \text{ Br}_2 + 4 \text{ Na}_2\text{CO}_3 \rightarrow 8 \text{ NaBr} + 4 \text{ CO}_2 + \text{Fe}_3\text{O}_4$

Hence, 3 moles Fe(s) forms 8 mol NaBr

$$\text{Mass}_{\text{Fe consumed}} = 2.50 \times 10^3 \text{ kg NaBr} \times \frac{1000 \text{ g NaBr}}{1 \text{ kg NaBr}} \times \frac{1 \text{ mol NaBr}}{102.894 \text{ g NaBr}} \times \frac{3 \text{ mol Fe}}{8 \text{ mol NaBr}} \times \frac{55.845 \text{ g Fe}}{1 \text{ mol Fe}}$$

$$= 509 \times 10^3 \text{ g Fe} \times \frac{1 \text{ kg Fe}}{1000 \text{ g Fe}} = 509 \text{ kg Fe required to produce } 2.5 \times 10^3 \text{ kg KBr}$$

89. **(M)**

(a)

$\text{SiO}_2\text{(s)} + 2 \text{ C(s)} \xrightarrow{\Delta} \text{Si(s)} + 2 \text{ CO(g)}$

$\text{Si(s)} + 2 \text{ Cl}_2\text{(g)} \rightarrow \text{SiCl}_4\text{(l)}$

$\text{SiCl}_4\text{(l)} + 2 \text{ H}_2\text{(g)} \rightarrow \text{Si(s, ultrapure)} + 4 \text{ HCl(g)}$

(b) $1 \text{ kg Si (ultrapure, s)} \times \dfrac{1000 \text{ g}}{1 \text{kg}} \times \dfrac{1 \text{ mol Si}}{28.09 \text{ g}} \times \dfrac{1 \text{ mol SiCl}_4}{1 \text{ mol Si ultrapure}} \times \dfrac{1 \text{ mol Si}}{1 \text{ mol SiCl}_4}$

$\times \dfrac{2 \text{ mol C}}{1 \text{ mol Si}} \times \dfrac{12.01 \text{ g C}}{1 \text{ mol C}} = 885 \text{ g C}$

$$1 \text{ kg Si (ultrapure, s)} \times \frac{1000 \text{ g}}{1 \text{kg}} \times \frac{1 \text{ mol Si}}{28.09 \text{ g}} \times \frac{1 \text{ mol SiCl}_4}{1 \text{ mol Si ultrapure}} \times \frac{2 \text{ mol Cl}_2}{1 \text{ mol SiCl}_4}$$

$$\times \frac{70.91 \text{ g Cl}_2}{1 \text{ mol Cl}_2} = 5.05 \times 10^3 \text{ g Cl}_2$$

$$1 \text{ kg Si (ultrapure, s)} \times \frac{1000 \text{ g}}{1 \text{kg}} \times \frac{1 \text{ mol Si}}{28.09 \text{ g}} \times \frac{2 \text{ mol H}_2}{1 \text{ mol Si ultrapure}} \times \frac{2.016 \text{ g H}_2}{1 \text{ mol H}_2} = 144 \text{ g H}_2$$

90. (D)

$$1 \text{ kg HNO}_3 \times \frac{1000 \text{ g}}{1 \text{ kg}} \times \frac{1 \text{ mol HNO}_3}{63.02 \text{ g HNO}_3} \times \frac{3 \text{ mol NO}_2}{2 \text{ mol HNO}_3} \times \frac{2 \text{ mol NO}}{2 \text{ mol NO}_2} \times$$

$$\frac{4 \text{ mol NH}_3}{4 \text{ mol NO}} \times \frac{3 \text{ mol H}_2}{2 \text{ mol NH}_3} \times \frac{2.016 \text{ g H}_2}{1 \text{mol H}_2} = 71.98 \text{ g H}_2$$

$$1 \text{ kg HNO}_3 \times \frac{1000 \text{ g}}{1 \text{ kg}} \times \frac{1 \text{ mol HNO}_3}{63.02 \text{ g HNO}_3} \times \frac{3 \text{ mol NO}_2}{2 \text{ mol HNO}_3} \times \frac{2 \text{ mol NO}}{2 \text{ mol NO}_2} \times$$

$$\frac{4 \text{ mol NH}_3}{4 \text{ mol NO}} \times \frac{1 \text{ mol N}_2}{2 \text{ mol NH}_3} \times \frac{28.02 \text{ g N}_2}{1 \text{mol N}_2} = 333.5 \text{ g N}_2$$

In order to determine the mole ratio between O_2 and HNO_3, it is helpful to sum the individual steps and write the overall reaction, since O_2 is listed as a reactant in two different steps. The four reactions cannot simply be added together. Rather, we must figure out how to add all four steps so that N_2, H_2 an O_2 are the only reactants, and NO is not an intermediate but is one of the final products.

First, multiply step 1 by a factor of two and add it to step 2:
$$2 \times [\ N_2(g) + 3\ H_2(g) \rightarrow 2\ NH_3(g)\ ]$$
$$4\ NH_3(g) + 5\ O_2(g) \rightarrow 4\ NO(g) + 6\ H_2O(g)$$

The resulting reaction is: $\quad 2N_2 + 6H_2 + 5O_2 \rightarrow 6\ H_2O + 4\ NO$
Which can be summed with step 3 multiplied by a factor of two:
$$2 \times [2\ NO + O_2 \rightarrow 2NO_2]$$

The resulting reaction is: $2\ N_2 + 6\ H_2 + 7\ O_2 \rightarrow 6\ H_2O + 4\ NO_2$
Multiply the resulting reaction by a factor of three:
$$3 \times [2\ N_2 + 6\ H_2 + 7\ O_2 \rightarrow 6\ H_2O + 4\ NO_2\ ]$$
Sum the above reaction with step 4 multiplied by a factor of four:
$$4 \times [3\ NO_2 + H_2O \rightarrow 2\ HNO_3 + NO]$$

The overall reaction is therefore:
$$6\ N_2 + 18\ H_2 + 21\ O_2 \rightarrow \quad 8\ HNO_3 + 4\ NO + 14\ H_2O$$

$$1 \text{ kg HNO}_3 \times \frac{1000 \text{ g}}{1 \text{ kg}} \times \frac{1 \text{ mol HNO}_3}{63.02 \text{ g HNO}_3} \times \frac{21 \text{ mol O}_2}{8 \text{ mol HNO}_3} \times \frac{31.998 \text{ g O}_2}{1 \text{mol O}_2} = 1333 \text{ g O}_2$$

Alternatively, another method of solving for the number of grams of O_2 is:

$$\text{number of mol HNO}_3 = 1000 \text{ g} / 63.02 \text{ g mol}^{-1} = 15.87 \text{ mol}$$

$$15.87 \text{ mol HNO}_3 \times \frac{3 \text{ mol NO}_2}{2 \text{ mol HNO}_3} \times \frac{2 \text{ mol NO}}{2 \text{ mol NO}_2} \times \left[\frac{1 \text{ mol O}_2}{2 \text{ mol NO}} + \frac{5 \text{ mol O}_2}{4 \text{ mol NO}} \right] \times \frac{32.00 \text{ g O}_2}{1 \text{ mol O}_2}$$

$$= 1.33 \times 10^3 \text{ g O}_2$$

91. (D) The reactions are as follows.
$$MgCO_3(s) \rightarrow MgO(s) + CO_2(g)$$
$$CaCO_3(s) \rightarrow CaO(s) + CO_2(g)$$

$$\% \text{ by mass of MgCO}_3 = \frac{\text{g MgCO}_3}{\text{g MgCO}_3 + \text{g CaCO}_3} \times 100\%$$

Let m = mass, in grams, of $MgCO_3$ in the mixture and
let $24.00 - m$ = mass in grams of $CaCO_3$ in the mixture.

Convert from g $MgCO_3$ to g CO_2 to obtain an expression for the mass of CO_2 produced by the first reaction.

$$\text{g CO}_2 \text{ from MgCO}_3 = m \text{ g MgCO}_3 \times \frac{1 \text{ mol MgCO}_3}{84.32 \text{ g MgCO}_3} \times \frac{1 \text{ mol CO}_2}{1 \text{ mol MgCO}_3} \times \frac{44.01 \text{ g CO}_2}{1 \text{ mol CO}_2}$$

Convert from g $CaCO_3$ to g CO_2 to obtain an expression for the mass of CO_2 produced by the second reaction.

$$\text{g CO}_2 \text{ from CaCO}_3 = (24.00 - m) \text{ g CaCO}_3 \times \frac{1 \text{ mol CaCO}_3}{100.09 \text{ g CaCO}_3} \times \frac{1 \text{ mol CO}_2}{1 \text{ mol CaCO}_3} \times \frac{44.01 \text{ g CO}_2}{1 \text{ mol CO}_2}$$

The sum of these two expressions is equal to 12.00 g CO_2. Thus:
$$\left[m \times \frac{44.01}{84.32} \right] + \left[(24.00 - m) \times \frac{44.01}{100.09} \right] = 12.00$$

Solve for m: $m = 17.60$ g

$$\% \text{ by mass of MgCO}_3 = \frac{17.60 \text{ g}}{24.00 \text{ g}} \times 100\% = 73.33\%$$

92. (D) Assuming the mass of the sample is 100.0 g, the sample contains 72.0 g Fe.

$$\% \text{ by mass of Fe}_2O_3 = \frac{\text{g Fe}_2O_3}{\text{g Fe}_2O_3 + \text{g FeO}} \times 100\%$$

Total mass of Fe in sample = mass of Fe from Fe_2O_3 + mass of Fe from FeO

Let m be the mass, in grams, of Fe_2O_3 in the mixture.

$$\text{g Fe from } Fe_2O_3 = m \text{ g } Fe_2O_3 \times \frac{1 \text{ mol } Fe_2O_3}{159.7 \text{ g } Fe_2O_3} \times \frac{2 \text{ mol Fe}}{1 \text{ mol } Fe_2O_3} \times \frac{55.85 \text{ g Fe}}{1 \text{ mol Fe}}$$

The mass of FeO is $(100 - m)$ grams.

$$\text{g Fe from FeO} = (100 - m) \text{ g FeO} \times \frac{1 \text{ mol FeO}}{71.85 \text{ g FeO}} \times \frac{1 \text{ mol Fe}}{1 \text{ mol FeO}} \times \frac{55.85 \text{ g Fe}}{1 \text{ mol Fe}}$$

The sum of these two expressions is equal to 72.0 g Fe. Thus:

$$72.0 = \left[m \times 2 \times \frac{55.85}{159.7} \right] + \left[(100.0 - m) \times \frac{55.85}{71.85} \right]$$

Solve for m: $m = 73.6$ g

$$\% \text{ by mass of } Fe_2O_3 = \frac{73.6 \text{ g}}{100.0 \text{ g}} \times 100\% = 73.6\%$$

INTEGRATIVE AND ADVANCED EXERCISES

93. (E)

(a) $CaCO_3(s) \xrightarrow{\Delta} CaO(s) + CO_2(g)$

(b) $2\,ZnS(s) + 3\,O_2(g) \xrightarrow{\Delta} 2\,ZnO(s) + 2\,SO_2(g)$

(c) $C_3H_8(g) + 3\,H_2O(g) \longrightarrow 3\,CO(g) + 7\,H_2(g)$

(d) $4\,SO_2(g) + 2\,Na_2S(aq) + Na_2CO_3(aq) \longrightarrow CO_2(g) + 3\,Na_2S_2O_3(aq)$

94. (E)

(a) $4\,Ca_3(PO_4)_2 + 12\,SiO_2(s) + 20\,C(s) \xrightarrow{\Delta} 12\,CaSiO_3(s) + 2\,P_4(g) + 20\,CO(g)$

$P_4(s) + 6\,Cl_2(g) \longrightarrow 4\,PCl_3(g)$

$PCl_3(g) + 3\,H_2O(l) \longrightarrow H_3PO_3(aq) + 3\,HCl(aq)$

(b) $2\,Cu(s) + O_2(g) + CO_2(g) + H_2O(g) \longrightarrow Cu_2(OH)_2CO_3(s)$

(c) $P_4(s) + 5\,O_2(g) \longrightarrow P_4O_{10}(s) \xrightarrow{6\,H_2O} 4\,H_3PO_4(aq)$

(d) $3\,Ca(H_2PO_4)_2(aq) + 8\,NaHCO_3(aq) \longrightarrow Ca_3(PO_4)_2(aq) + 4\,Na_2HPO_4(aq) + 8\,CO_2(g) + 8\,H_2O(l)$

95. (M) The balanced equation is as follows:

$2\,LiOH(s) + CO_2(g) \rightarrow Li_2CO_3(s) + H_2O(l)$

Conversion pathway approach:

$$\text{g LiOH} = \frac{1.00 \times 10^3 \text{ g } CO_2}{\text{astronaut day}} \times \frac{1 \text{ mol } CO_2}{44.01 \text{ g } CO_2} \times 3 \text{ astronauts} \times 6 \text{ days} \times \frac{2 \text{ mol LiOH}}{1 \text{ mol } CO_2} \times \frac{23.95 \text{ g LiOH}}{1 \text{ mol LiOH}}$$

$$= 1.96 \times 10^4 \text{ g LiOH}$$

Stepwise approach:

$$\frac{1.00 \times 10^3 \text{ g CO}_2}{\text{astronaut day}} \times \frac{1 \text{ mol CO}_2}{44.01 \text{ g CO}_2} = 22.7 \frac{\text{mol CO}_2}{\text{astronaut day}}$$

$$22.7 \frac{\text{mol CO}_2}{\text{astronaut day}} \times 3 \text{ astronauts} = 68.2 \frac{\text{mol CO}_2}{\text{day}}$$

$$68.2 \frac{\text{mol CO}_2}{\text{day}} \times 6 \text{ days} = 409 \text{ mol CO}_2$$

$$409 \text{ mol CO}_2 \times \frac{2 \text{ mol LiOH}}{1 \text{ mol CO}_2} = 818 \text{ mol LiOH}$$

$$818 \text{ mol LiOH} \times \frac{23.95 \text{ g LiOH}}{1 \text{ mol LiOH}} = 1.96 \times 10^4 \text{ g LiOH}$$

96. **(M)** mass $CaCO_3 = 0.981 \text{ g CO}_2 \times \dfrac{1 \text{ mol CO}_2}{44.01 \text{ g CO}_2} \times \dfrac{1 \text{ mol CaCO}_3}{1 \text{ mol CO}_2} \times \dfrac{100.1 \text{ g CaCO}_3}{1 \text{ mol CaCO}_3} = 2.23 \text{ g CaCO}_3$

$\% \text{ CaCO}_3 = \dfrac{2.23 \text{ g CaCO}_3}{3.28 \text{ g sample}} \times 100\% = 68.0\% \text{ CaCO}_3$ (by mass)

97. **(D)** We determine the empirical formula, basing our calculation on 100.0 g of the compound.

amount Fe $= 72.3 \text{ g Fe} \times \dfrac{1 \text{ mol Fe}}{55.85 \text{ g Fe}} = 1.29 \text{ mol Fe} \qquad \div 1.29 \longrightarrow 1.00 \text{ mol Fe}$

amount O $= 27.7 \text{ g O} \times \dfrac{1 \text{ mol O}}{16.00 \text{ g O}} = 1.73 \text{ mol O} \qquad \div 1.29 \longrightarrow 1.34 \text{ mol O}$

The empirical formula is Fe_3O_4 and the balanced equation is as follows.

$$3 Fe_2O_3(s) + H_2(g) \longrightarrow 2 Fe_3O_4(s) + H_2O(g)$$

98. **(D)** Assume 100.0 g of the compound Fe_xS_y, then:
Number of moles of S atoms = 36.5g/32.066 g S/mol = 1.13$\underline{8}$ mol
Number of moles of Fe atoms = 63.5g/ 55.847g Fe/mol = 1.137 mol
So the empirical formula for the iron-containing reactant is FeS
Assume 100 g of the compound Fe_xO_y, then:
Number of moles of O atoms = 27.6g/16.0 g O/mol = 1.725 mol
Number of moles of Fe atoms = 72.4g/ 55.847g Fe/mol = 1.296 mol
So the empirical formula for the iron-containing product is Fe_3O_4
Balanced equation: $3 FeS + 5 O_2 \rightarrow Fe_3O_4 + 3 SO_2$

99. **(M)**

$$\text{M CH}_3\text{CH}_2\text{OH} = \frac{\text{mol CH}_3\text{CH}_2\text{OH}}{\text{volume of solution}}$$

$$\text{mol CH}_3\text{CH}_2\text{OH} = 50.0 \text{ mL} \times 0.7893 \frac{\text{g CH}_3\text{CH}_2\text{OH}}{\text{mL}} \times \frac{1 \text{ mol CH}_3\text{CH}_2\text{OH}}{46.07 \text{ g CH}_3\text{CH}_2\text{OH}} = 0.857 \text{ mol}$$

$$\text{Molarity} = \frac{0.857 \text{ mol CH}_3\text{CH}_2\text{OH}}{0.0965 \text{ L solution}} = 8.88 \text{ M CH}_3\text{CH}_2\text{OH}$$

100. **(M)**

(a) H_2O volume = 72.061 g × 1 mL / 0.99705 g = 72.274 mL
CH_3OH volume = 192.25 g × 1 mL / 0.78706 g = 244.26 mL
The volume sum of the two pure liquids is 316.53 mL

Masses are always additive.
Mass of solution = 72.061 g + 192.25 g = 264.31 g
Volume of solution = 264.31 g × 1 mL / 0.86070 g = 307.09 mL

The volume of the solution is 9.44 mL less than the sum of the pure liquid volumes. The volumes are <u>not</u> additive.

(b) $$\text{Molarity} = \frac{192.25 \text{ g CH}_3\text{OH} \times \dfrac{1 \text{ mol CH}_3\text{OH}}{32.042 \text{ g CH}_3\text{OH}}}{0.30709 \text{ L}} = 19.538 \frac{\text{mol CH}_3\text{OH}}{\text{L}}$$

101. **(D)** Let V be the volume of 0.149 M HCl(aq) that is required.

moles of HCl in solution C = moles HCl in solution A + moles HCl in solution B
$(V + 0.100) \times 0.205 \text{ M} = \qquad (V \times 0.149 \text{ M}) + \qquad (0.100 \times 0.285 \text{ M})$

Solve for V: $\qquad V = 0.143 \text{ L} = 143 \text{ mL}$

102. (D) Let V be the volume of 0.0175 M CH_3OH(aq) that is required.

moles CH_3OH in solution C = moles CH_3OH in solution A + moles CH_3OH in solution B
$(V + 0.0500) \times 0.0200 \text{ M} \quad = \quad (V \times 0.0175 \text{ M}) \quad + \quad (0.050 \times 0.0248 \text{ M})$

Solve for V: $V = 0.0960 \text{ L} = 96.0 \text{ mL}$

103. (M) $\dfrac{1.52 \text{ g Na}}{1 \times 10^6 \text{ g soln}} \times \dfrac{1 \text{ g soln}}{1 \text{ mL soln}} \times \dfrac{1000 \text{ mL}}{1 \text{ L}} \times \dfrac{1 \text{ mol Na}}{22.99 \text{ g Na}} \times \dfrac{1 \text{ mol NaCl}}{1 \text{ mol Na}} \times \dfrac{58.44 \text{ g NaCl}}{1 \text{ mol NaCl}}$

$= 0.003864 \text{ M NaCl}$

104. (D)

$$\text{mass Ca(NO}_3)_2 = 50.0\,\text{L soln} \times \frac{1000\,\text{mL}}{1\,\text{L}} \times \frac{1.00\,\text{g soln}}{1\,\text{mL soln}} \times \frac{2.35\,\text{g Ca}}{10^6\,\text{g soln}} \times \frac{1\,\text{mol Ca}}{40.08\,\text{g Ca}}$$

$$\times \frac{1\,\text{mol Ca(NO}_3)_2}{1\,\text{mol Ca}} \times \frac{164.09\,\text{g Ca(NO}_3)_2}{1\,\text{mol Ca(NO}_3)_2} \times \frac{1000\,\text{mg}}{1\,\text{g}} = 481\,\text{mg Ca(NO}_3)_2$$

105. (D) We can compute the volume of Al that reacts with the given quantity of HCl.

$$V_{\text{Al}} = 0.05\,\text{mL} \times \frac{1\,\text{L}}{1000\,\text{mL}} \times \frac{12.0\,\text{mol HCl}}{1\,\text{L}} \times \frac{2\,\text{mol Al}}{6\,\text{mol HCl}} \times \frac{27.0\,\text{g Al}}{1\,\text{mol Al}} \times \frac{1\,\text{cm}^3}{2.70\,\text{g Al}} = 0.002\,\text{cm}^3$$

$$\text{area} = \frac{\text{volume}}{\text{thickness}} = \frac{0.002\,\text{cm}^3}{0.10\,\text{mm}} \times \frac{10\,\text{mm}}{1\,\text{cm}} = 0.2\,\text{cm}^2$$

106. (D) Here we need to determine the amount of HCl before and after reaction; the difference is the amount of HCl that reacted.

$$\text{initial amount HCl} = 0.05000\,\text{L} \times \frac{1.035\,\text{mol HCl}}{1\,\text{L}} = 0.05175\,\text{mol HCl}$$

$$\text{final amount HCl} = 0.05000\,\text{L} \times \frac{0.812\,\text{mol HCl}}{1\,\text{L}} = 0.0406\,\text{mol HCl}$$

$$\text{mass Zn} = (0.05175 - 0.0406)\,\text{mol HCl} \times \frac{1\,\text{mol Zn}}{2\,\text{mol HCl}} \times \frac{65.38\,\text{g Zn}}{1\,\text{mol Zn}} = 0.365\,\text{g Zn}$$

107. (M) Let us first determine the moles of NH_4NO_3 in the dilute solution.

$$\text{mass}_{\text{NH}_4\text{NO}_3} = 1000\,\text{mL} \times \frac{2.37 \times 10^{-3}\,\text{g N}}{1\,\text{mL}} \times \frac{1\,\text{mol N}}{14.007\,\text{g N}} \times \frac{1\,\text{mol NH}_4\text{NO}_3}{2\,\text{mol N}} = 0.0846\,\text{mol NH}_4\text{NO}_3$$

$$\text{volume of solution} = 0.0846\,\text{mol NH}_4\text{NO}_3 \times \frac{1\,\text{L soln}}{0.715\,\text{mol NH}_4\text{NO}_3} \times \frac{1000\,\text{mL}}{1\,\text{L}} = 118\,\text{mL soln}$$

108. (D) First we determine the molarity of seawater.

$$\text{concentration} = \frac{2.8\,\text{g NaCl}}{100.0\,\text{g soln}} \times \frac{1.03\,\text{g}}{1\,\text{mL soln}} \times \frac{1000\,\text{mL}}{1\,\text{L soln}} \times \frac{1\,\text{mol NaCl}}{58.44\,\text{g NaCl}} = 0.49\,\text{M NaCl}$$

Then the volume of the final solution: $c_1V_1 = c_2V_2$ $V_2 = \dfrac{0.49\,\text{M} \times 1.00 \times 10^6\,\text{L}}{5.45\,\text{M}} = 9.0 \times 10^4\,\text{L}$

Volume to be evaporated $= 1.00 \times 10^6\,\text{L} - 9.0 \times 10^4\,\text{L} = 9.1 \times 10^5\,\text{L}$ of water to be evaporated

109. (D) Here we must determine the amount of PbI_2 produced from each solute in this limiting reactant problem.

$$n_{PbI_2 \text{ (from KI)}} = 99.8\,\text{mL} \times \frac{1.093\,\text{g}}{1\,\text{mL soln}} \times \frac{0.120\,\text{g KI}}{1\,\text{g soln}} \times \frac{1\,\text{mol KI}}{166.00\,\text{g KI}} \times \frac{1\,\text{mol PbI}_2}{2\,\text{mol KI}} = 0.0394\,\text{mol PbI}_2$$

$$n_{PbI_2 \text{ (from Pb(NO}_3)_2)} = 96.7\,\text{mL} \times \frac{1.134\,\text{g}}{1\,\text{mL soln}} \times \frac{0.140\,\text{g Pb(NO}_3)_2}{1\,\text{g soln}} \times \frac{1\,\text{mol Pb(NO}_3)_2}{331.2\,\text{g Pb(NO}_3)_2} \times \frac{1\,\text{mol PbI}_2}{1\,\text{mol Pb(NO}_3)_2}$$

$$= 0.0464\,\text{mol PbI}_2$$

Then the mass of PbI_2 is computed from the smaller amount produced.

$$\text{mass PbI}_2 = 0.0394\,\text{mol PbI}_2 \times \frac{461.0\,\text{g PbI}_2}{1\,\text{mol PbI}_2} = 18.2\,\text{g PbI}_2$$

110. (D) $CaCO_3(s) + 2\,HCl(aq) \longrightarrow CaCl_2(aq) + H_2O(l) + CO_2(g)$

$$\text{Amount of HCl reacted} = 45.0\ \text{g CaCO}_3 \times \frac{1\,\text{mol CaCO}_3}{100.09\,\text{g CaCO}_3} \times \frac{2\,\text{mol HCl}}{1\,\text{mol CaCO}_3} = 0.899\,\text{mol HCl}$$

$$\text{Init. amt. of HCl} = 1.25\,\text{L soln} \times \frac{1000\,\text{mL}}{1\text{L}} \times \frac{1.13\,\text{g}}{1\,\text{mL}} \times \frac{0.257\text{g HCl}}{1\,\text{g soln}} \times \frac{1\,\text{mol HCl}}{36.46\,\text{g HCl}} = 9.96\,\text{mol HCl}$$

$$\text{Final HCl concentration} = \frac{9.96\ \text{mol HCl} - 0.899\,\text{mol HCl}}{1.25\,\text{L soln}} = 7.25\,\text{M HCl}$$

111. (D) We allow the mass of Al in the alloy to be represented by x. We then set up an expression for determining the mass of H_2 and solve this expression for x.

$$0.105\,\text{g H}_2 = \left((2.05 - x)\ \text{g Fe} \times \frac{1\ \text{mol Fe}}{55.85\ \text{g Fe}} \times \frac{1\ \text{mol H}_2}{1\ \text{mol Fe}} \times \frac{2.02\ \text{g H}_2}{1\ \text{mol H}_2} \right)$$

$$+ \left(x\,\text{g Al} \times \frac{1\ \text{mol Al}}{27.0\ \text{g Al}} \times \frac{3\ \text{mol H}_2}{2\ \text{mol Al}} \times \frac{2.02\ \text{g H}_2}{1\ \text{mol H}_2} \right)$$

$$0.105 = (2.05 - x)0.0362 + 0.112x = 0.0742 + (0.112 - 0.0362)x = 0.0742 + 0.076x$$

$$0.076\,x = 0.105 - 0.0742 = 0.031 \qquad x = \frac{0.031}{0.076} = 0.41\,\text{g Al}$$

$$\%\text{Al} = \frac{0.41\ \text{g Al}}{2.05\,\text{g alloy}} = 20.\%\,\text{Al (by mass) and the alloy is also 80\% Fe (by mass).}$$

112. (D) $Mg(s) + 2 HCl(aq) \longrightarrow MgCl_2(aq) + H_2(g)$

$2 Al(s) + 6 HCl(aq) \longrightarrow 2 AlCl_3(aq) + 3 H_2(g)$

Let x represent the mass of Mg.

$$0.0163 \text{ g H}_2 \times \frac{1 \text{ mol H}_2}{2.016 \text{ g H}_2} = x \text{ g Mg} \times \frac{1 \text{ mol Mg}}{24.305 \text{ g Mg}} \times \frac{1 \text{ mol H}_2}{1 \text{ mol Mg}} + (0.155 - x)\text{g Al} \times \frac{1 \text{ mol Al}}{26.982 \text{ g Al}} \times \frac{3 \text{ mol H}_2}{2 \text{ mol Al}}$$

$$0.00809 = 0.041144x + 0.00862 - 0.055593x \qquad x = \frac{0.00862 - 0.00809}{0.055593 - 0.041144} = 0.0367 \text{ g Mg}$$

$$\% \text{ Mg} = \frac{0.0367 \text{ g Mg}}{0.155 \text{ g alloy}} \times 100\% = 23.7\% \text{ Mg or } \sim 24\% \text{ Mg (by mass)}.$$

113. (M)

(a) To determine the extent of the reaction for Cu, the initial and final amounts of Cu need to be calculated.

$$n_{\text{Cu,initial}} = 3.177 \text{ g Cu} \times \frac{1 \text{ mol Cu}}{63.546 \text{ g Cu}} = 0.05000 \text{ mol}$$

$$n_{\text{Cu,final}} = 0.0739 \text{ g Cu} \times \frac{1 \text{ mol Cu}}{63.546 \text{ g Cu}} = 0.00116 \text{ mol}$$

$$n_{\text{HNO}_3,\text{initial}} = (0.500 \text{ mol L}^{-1})(0.8000 \text{ L}) = 0.400 \text{ mol}$$

The following summary helps us to better visualize the relationships among the initial and final amounts of reactants and products. All the values are in moles.

	3 Cu	+	8 HNO₃	→	3 Cu(NO₃)₂	+	2 NO	+	4 H₂O
initial:	0.05000		0.400		0		0		0
change:	-3ξ		-8ξ		$+3\xi$		$+2\xi$		$+4\xi$
final:	0.00116		0.400-8ξ		3ξ		2ξ		4ξ

The change in the amount of Cu is

$$\Delta n_{\text{Cu}} = n_{\text{Cu, final}} - n_{\text{Cu, initial}} = 0.00116 \text{ mol} - 0.05000 \text{ mol} = -0.04884 \text{ mol}$$

Since $\Delta n_{\text{Cu}} = v_{\text{Cu}}\xi$ with $v_{\text{Cu}} = -3$, we calculate

$$\xi = \Delta n_{\text{Cu}} / v_{\text{Cu}} = (-0.04884 \text{ mol}) / (-3) = 0.01628$$

(b) The tabular summary in (a) shows that the amount of NO produced is 2ξ and the amount of HNO₃ remaining is $0.400 \text{ mol} - 8\xi$. Since $\xi = 0.01628$ mol, we have:

$$n_{\text{NO, final}} = 2\xi = 0.03256 \text{ mol}$$

$$n_{\text{HNO}_3,\text{final}} = 0.400 \text{ mol} - 8\,\xi = (0.400 - 8 \times 0.01628) \text{ mol} = 0.270 \text{ mol}$$

114. (M) Let's calculate the initial amount of H_2O_2 and the final amount of O_2.

$$n_{H_2O_2,\,initial} = 8.67\,g \times \frac{1\,mol}{34.01\,g} = 0.255\,mol$$

$$n_{O_2,\,final} = 3.74\,g \times \frac{1\,mol}{32.00\,g} = 0.117\,mol$$

The following summary helps us visualize the relationships among the initial and final amounts of reactants and products. All amounts are in moles.

	$2\,H_2O_2$	$\rightarrow$	$2\,H_2O_2$	$+$	O_2
initial:	0.255		0		0
change:	$-2\,\xi$		$+2\,\xi$		$+\xi$
final:	$0.255 - 2\,\xi$		$2\,\xi$		$\xi = 0.117$

The summary shows that the change in the amount of O_2 is $+\xi$ and, therefore, the extent of reaction is $\xi = 0.117$ mol. We obtain the same result by using the relationship $\Delta n_{O_2} = v_{O_2}\,\xi$, with $v_{O_2} = +1$ and $\Delta n_{O_2} = n_{O_2,\,final} - n_{O_2,\,initial} = 0.117\,mol - 0\,mol = 0.117\,mol$.

The amount of H_2O_2 that reacted is $2\xi = 2(0.117\,mol) = 0.234\,mol$. Therefore, the percentage of H_2O_2 that is reacted is $(0.234\,mol/0.255\,mol) \times 100 = 91.8\%$.

115. (D) One way to solve this problem would be to calculate the mass of CO_2 produced from a 0.220 g sample of each alcohol. The results are 0.303 g CO_2 from 0.220 g CH_3OH and 0.421 g CO_2 from 0.220 g CH_3CH_2OH. Obviously a mixture has been burned. But we have sufficient information to determine the composition of the mixture. First we need the balanced equations for the combustion reactions. Then, we represent the mass of CH_3OH by x.

$$2\,CH_3OH(l) + 3\,O_2(g) \rightarrow 2\,CO_2(g) + 4\,H_2O(l) \quad CH_3CH_2OH(l) + 3\,O_2(g) \rightarrow 2\,CO_2(g) + 3\,H_2O(l)$$

$$mass\,CO_2 = 0.352\,g\,CO_2 = \left(x\,g\,CH_3OH \times \frac{1\,mol\,CH_3OH}{32.04\,g\,CH_3OH} \times \frac{2\,mol\,CO_2}{2\,mol\,CH_3OH} \times \frac{44.01\,g\,CO_2}{1\,mol\,CO_2} \right)$$

$$+ \left((0.220 - x)\,g\,CH_3CH_2OH \times \frac{1\,mol\,CH_3CH_2OH}{46.07\,g\,CH_3CH_2OH} \times \frac{2\,mol\,CO_2}{1\,mol\,C_2H_5OH} \times \frac{44.01\,g\,CO_2}{1\,mol\,CO_2} \right)$$

$$= 1.374x + (0.220 - x)1.911 = 0.421 - 0.537x$$

$$-0.537x = 0.352 - 0.420 = -0.068 \quad or \quad x = \frac{-0.068}{-0.537} = 0.127\,g\,CH_3OH$$

By difference, the mass of CH_3CH_2OH is $0.220\,g - 0.127\,g = 0.093\,g\,CH_3OH$

116. (D) $CH_3CH_2OH(l) + 3\,O_2(g) \longrightarrow 2\,CO_2(g) + 3\,H_2O(l)$

$(CH_3CH_2)_2O(l) + 6\,O_2(g) \longrightarrow 4\,CO_2(g) + 5\,H_2O(l)$

Since this is classic mixture problem, we can use the systems of equations method to find the mass percents. First we let x be the mass of $(C_2H_5)_2O$ and y be the mass of CH3CH2OH. Thus,

$x + y = 1.005$ g or $y = 1.005$ g $- x$

We then construct a second equation involving x that relates the mass of carbon dioxide formed to the masses of ethanol and diethyl ether.

$$1.963 \text{ g } CO_2 \times \frac{1 \text{ mol } CO_2}{44.010 \text{ g } CO_2} = x \text{ g } (C_2H_5)_2O \times \frac{1 \text{ mol } (C_2H_5)_2O}{74.123 \text{ g } (C_2H_5)_2O} \times \frac{4 \text{ mol } CO_2}{1 \text{ mol } (C_2H_5)_2O}$$

$$+ (1.005 - x) \text{ g } CH_3CH_2OH \times \frac{1 \text{ mol } CH_3CH_2OH}{46.07 \text{ g } CH_3CH_2OH} \times \frac{2 \text{ mol } CO_2}{1 \text{ mol } CH_3CH_2OH}$$

$$0.04460 = 0.05396x + 0.04363 - 0.04341x \qquad x = \frac{0.04460 - 0.04363}{0.05396 - 0.04341} = 0.092 \text{ g } (C_2H_5)_2O$$

$$\% \ (CH_3CH_2)_2O \text{ (by mass)} = \frac{0.092 \text{ g } (C_2H_5)_2O}{1.005 \text{ g mixture}} \times 100\% = 9.2\% \ (C_2H_5)_2O$$

$$\% \ CH_3CH_2OH \text{ (by mass)} = 100.0\% - 9.2\% \ (C_2H_5)_2O = 90.8\% \ CH_3CH_2OH$$

117. (D) $\% \ Cu \text{ (by mass)} = \dfrac{\# \text{ g } Cu}{0.7391 \text{ g mixture}} \times 100$

Let x = the mass, in grams, of $CuCl_2$ in the mixture.

Let $0.7391 - x$ = mass in grams of $FeCl_3$.

Total moles $AgNO_3$ = mol $AgNO_3$ react with $CuCl_2$ + mol $AgNO_3$ react with $FeCl_3$

Total moles $AgNO_3 = 0.8691 \text{ L} \times \dfrac{0.1463 \text{ mol}}{1 \text{ L}} = 0.01271$ mol $AgNO_3$

To obtain an expression for the amount of $AgNO_3$ consumed by the first reaction, convert from grams of $CuCl_2$ to moles of AgCl:

$$\text{mol } AgNO_3 \text{ that reacts with } CuCl_2 = x \text{ g } CuCl_2 \times \frac{1 \text{ mol } CuCl_2}{134.45 \text{ g } CuCl_2} \times \frac{2 \text{ mol } AgNO_3}{1 \text{ mol } CuCl_2}$$

$$\text{mol } AgNO_3 \text{ that reacts with } CuCl_2 = \frac{2x}{134.45} = 0.014875x$$

To obtain an expression for the amount of $AgNO_3$ consumed by the second reaction, convert from grams of $FeCl_3$ to moles of $AgNO_3$:

$$\text{mol } AgNO_3 \text{ that reacts with } FeCl_3 = (0.7391 - x) \text{ g } FeCl_3 \times \frac{1 \text{ mol } FeCl_3}{162.21 \text{ g } FeCl_3} \times \frac{3 \text{ mol } AgNO_3}{1 \text{ mol } FeCl_3}$$

$$\text{mol } AgNO_3 \text{ that reacts with } FeCl_3 = (0.7391 - x) \times 0.018496 = 0.013668 - 0.018496x$$

The sum of these two expressions is equal to the total number of moles of $AgNO_3$:

Total moles $AgNO_3 = 0.014875x + 0.013668 - 0.018496x = 0.01271$
$$x = 0.2646 \text{ g CuCl}_2$$

This is the mass of $CuCl_2$ in the mixture. We must now convert this to the mass of Cu in the mixture.

$$\# \text{ g Cu} = 0.2646 \text{ g CuCl}_2 \times \frac{1 \text{ mol CuCl}_2}{134.45 \text{ g CuCl}_2} \times \frac{1 \text{ mol Cu}}{1 \text{ mol CuCl}_2} \times \frac{63.546 \text{ g Cu}}{1 \text{ mol Cu}} = 0.1253 \text{ g Cu}$$

$$\% \text{ Cu} = \frac{0.1253 \text{ g Cu}}{0.7391 \text{ g}} \times 100\% = 16.95\%$$

118. (D)

(a) $\quad \text{mol Cu}^{2+} = 48.7 \text{ g Cu}^{2+} \times \frac{1 \text{ mol Cu}^{2+}}{63.55 \text{ g Cu}^{2+}} = 0.766 \text{ mol Cu}^{2+} \div 0.307 \longrightarrow 2.50 \text{ mol Cu}^{2+}$

$\text{mol CrO}_4^{2-} = 35.6 \text{ g CrO}_4^{2-} \times \frac{1 \text{ mol CrO}_4^{2-}}{115.99 \text{ g CrO}_4^{2-}} = 0.307 \text{ mol CrO}_4^{2-} \div 0.307 \longrightarrow 1.00 \text{ mol CrO}_4^{2-}$

$\text{mol OH}^- = 15.7 \text{ g OH}^- \times \frac{1 \text{ mol OH}^-}{17.01 \text{ g OH}^-} = 0.923 \text{ mol OH}^- \div 0.307 \longrightarrow 3.01 \text{ mol OH}^-$

Empirical formula: $Cu_5(CrO_4)_2(OH)_6$

(b) $\quad 5 \text{ CuSO}_4(aq) + 2 \text{ K}_2\text{CrO}_4(aq) + 6 \text{ H}_2\text{O}(l)$

$$\downarrow$$

$$Cu_5(CrO_4)_2(OH)_6(s) + 2 \text{ K}_2\text{SO}_4(aq) + 3 \text{ H}_2\text{SO}_4(aq)$$

119. (D) We first need to compute the empirical formula of malonic acid.

$34.62 \text{ g C} \times \frac{1 \text{ mol C}}{12.01 \text{ g C}} = 2.883 \text{ mol C} \qquad \div 2.883 \longrightarrow 1.000 \text{ mol C}$

$3.88 \text{ g H} \times \frac{1 \text{ mol H}}{1.01 \text{ g H}} = 3.84 \text{ mol H} \qquad \div 2.883 \longrightarrow 1.33 \text{ mol H}$

$61.50 \text{ g O} \times \frac{1 \text{ mol O}}{16.00 \text{ g O}} = 3.844 \text{ mol O} \qquad \div 2.883 \longrightarrow 1.333 \text{ mol O}$

Multiply each of these mole numbers by 3 to obtain the empirical formula $C_3H_4O_4$.
Combustion reaction: $C_3H_4O_4(l) + 2 \text{ O}_2(g) \longrightarrow 3 \text{ CO}_2(g) + 2 \text{ H}_2\text{O}(l)$

120. (D)

$2 \text{ Al}(s) + \text{Fe}_2\text{O}_3(s) \rightarrow \text{Al}_2\text{O}_3(s) + 2 \text{ Fe}(s)$

$\text{mass of Fe}_2\text{O}_3 = 2.5 \text{ g Al} \times \frac{1 \text{ mol Al}}{26.982 \text{ g Al}} \times \frac{1 \text{ mol Fe}_2\text{O}_3}{2 \text{ mol Al}} \times \frac{159.69 \text{ g Fe}_2\text{O}_3}{2 \text{ mol Fe}_2\text{O}_3} = 7.4 \text{ g Fe}_2\text{O}_3 \text{ needed}$

Using 2.5 g Al_2O_3, only 7.4 g of Fe_2O_3 needed, but there are 9.5 g available. Therefore, Al is the limiting reactant.

(a) Mass of Fe = 2.5 g Al $\times \dfrac{1 \text{ mol Al}}{26.982 \text{ g Al}} \times \dfrac{2 \text{ mol Fe}}{2 \text{ mol Al}} \times \dfrac{55.85 \text{ g Fe}}{1 \text{ mol Fe}} = 5.2$ g Fe

(b) Mass of excess Fe_2O_3 = 9.5 g − 7.4 g = 2.1 g

121. **(M)** Compute the amount of $AgNO_3$ in the solution on hand and the amount of $AgNO_3$ in the desired solution. the difference is the amount of $AgNO_3$ that must be added; simply convert this amount to a mass.

amount $AgNO_3$ present = 50.00 mL $\times \dfrac{0.0500 \text{ mmol } AgNO_3}{1 \text{ mL soln}} = 2.50$ mmol $AgNO_3$

amount $AgNO_3$ desired = 100.0 mL $\times \dfrac{0.0750 \text{ mmol } AgNO_3}{1 \text{ mL soln}} = 7.50$ mmol $AgNO_3$

mass $AgNO_3 = (7.50 - 2.50)$ mmol $AgNO_3 \times \dfrac{1 \text{ mol } AgNO_3}{1000 \text{ mmol } AgNO_3} \times \dfrac{169.9 \text{ g Ag } NO_3}{1 \text{ mol } AgNO_3}$

$= 0.850$ g $AgNO_3$

122. **(E)** The balanced equation for the reaction is: $S_8(s) + 4 \ Cl_2(g) \rightarrow 4 \ S_2Cl_2(l)$
Both "a" and "b" are consistent with the stoichiometry of this equation. Neither bottom row box is valid. Box (c) does not account for all the S_8, since we started out with 3 molecules, but end up with 1 S_8 molecule and 4 S_2Cl_2 molecules. Box (d) shows a yield of 2 S_8 molecules and 8 S_2Cl_2 molecules so we ended up with more sulfur atoms than we started with. This, of course, violates the Law of Conservation of Mass.

123. **(D)** The pertinent equations are as follows:

$$C_3N_3(OH)_3(s) \xrightarrow{\Delta} 3 \ HNCO(g)$$

$$8 \ HNCO(g) + 6 \ NO_2(g) \xrightarrow{\Delta} 7 \ N_2(g) + 8 \ CO_2(g) + 4 \ H_2O(l)$$

The above mole ratios are used to calculate moles of $C_3N_3(OH)_3$ assuming 1.00 g of NO_2.

mass $C_3N_3(OH)_3 = 1.00$ g $NO_2 \times \dfrac{1 \text{ mol } NO_2}{46.00 \text{ g } NO_2} \times \dfrac{8 \text{ mol HNCO}}{6 \text{ mol } NO_2} \times \dfrac{1 \text{ mol } C_3N_3(OH)_3}{3 \text{ mol HNCO}}$

$\times \dfrac{129.1 \text{ g mol } C_3N_3(OH)_3}{1 \text{ mol } C_3N_3(OH)_3} = 1.25$ g $C_3N_3(OH)_3$

124. **(D)** The reactant is $(NH_4)_2Cr_2O_7$ and two of the products are Cr_2O_3 and H_2O. Since the third product contains only one type of atom, the third product must be N_2. The balanced equation for the reaction is:

$(NH_4)_2Cr_2O_7(s) \longrightarrow Cr_2O_3(s) + 4 \ H_2O(l) + N_2(g)$

1000 g $(NH_4)_2Cr_2O_7 \times \dfrac{1 \text{ mol } (NH_4)_2Cr_2O_7}{252.065 \text{ g } (NH_4)_2Cr_2O_7} \times \dfrac{1 \text{ mol } N_2}{1 \text{ mol } (NH_4)_2Cr_2O_7} \times \dfrac{28.014 \text{ g } N_2}{1 \text{ mol } N_2}$

$= 111.1$ g N_2

125. **(D)** There are many ways one can go about answering this question. We must use all of the most concentrated solution and dilute this solution down using the next most concentrated solution. Hence, start with 345 mL of 1.29 M then add x L of the 0.775 M solution. The value of x is obtained by solving the following equation.

$$1.25 \text{ M} = \frac{(1.29 \text{ M} \times 0.345 \text{ L}) + (0.775 \text{ M} \times x)}{(0.345 + x) \text{ L}}$$

$$1.25 \text{ M} \times (0.345 + x) \text{ L} = (1.29 \text{ M} \times 0.345 \text{ L}) + (0.775 \text{ M} \times x)$$

$$0.43125 + 1.25x = 0.44505 + 0.775x \quad \text{Thus, } 0.0138 = 0.475x$$

$x = 0.029$ L or 29 mL
A total of (29 mL + 345 mL) = 374 mL may be prepared this way.

126. **(M)**

balanced equation: $FeTiO_3 + 2H_2SO_4 + 4H_2O \longrightarrow TiOSO_4 + FeSO_4 \cdot 7H_2O$

$$1.00 \times 10^3 \text{ kg FeTiO}_3 \times \frac{1 \text{ kmol FeTiO}_3}{151.725 \text{ kg FeTiO}_3} \times \frac{1 \text{ kmol FeSO}_4 \cdot 7 \text{ H}_2\text{O}}{1 \text{ kmol FeTiO}_3} \times \frac{278.01 \text{ kg FeSO}_4 \cdot 7 \text{ H}_2\text{O}}{1 \text{ kmol FeSO}_4 \cdot 7 \text{ H}_2\text{O}}$$

$$= 1.83 \times 10^3 \text{ kg FeSO}_4 \cdot 7 \text{ H}_2\text{O}$$

127. **(M)** mass of $Fe_2O_3 = 1.00 \times 10^3$ kg $FeSO_4 \cdot 7 H_2O \times \dfrac{1 \text{ kmol FeSO}_4 \cdot 7 \text{ H}_2\text{O}}{278.01 \text{ kg FeSO}_4 \cdot 7 \text{ H}_2\text{O}}$

$$\times \frac{1 \text{ kmol Fe}_2\text{O}_3}{2 \text{ kmol FeSO}_4 \cdot 7 \text{ H}_2\text{O}}$$

$$\times \frac{159.69 \text{ kg Fe}_2\text{O}_3}{1 \text{ kmol Fe}_2\text{O}_3} = 287 \text{ kg Fe}_2\text{O}_3$$

128. **(D)**

(a) $6 \text{ CO(NH}_2)_2(\text{l}) \rightarrow 6 \text{ HNCO(l)} + 6 \text{ NH}_3(\text{g}) \rightarrow \text{C}_3\text{N}_3(\text{NH}_2)_3(\text{l}) + 3 \text{ CO}_2(\text{g})$

(b) mass $C_3N_3(NH_2)_3 = 100.0$ kg $CO(NH_2)_2 \times \dfrac{1 \text{ kmol CO(NH}_2)_2}{60.06 \text{ kg CO(NH}_2)_2} \times \dfrac{1 \text{ kmol C}_3\text{N}_3(\text{NH}_2)_3}{6 \text{ kmol CO(NH}_2)_2}$

$$\times \frac{126.12 \text{ kg C}_3\text{N}_3(\text{NH}_2)_3}{1 \text{ kmol C}_3\text{N}_3(\text{NH}_2)_3} \times \frac{84 \text{ g actual yield}}{100 \text{ g theoretical yield}} = 29.\underline{4} \text{ kg C}_3\text{N}_3(\text{NH}_2)_3$$

129. **(M)**

(a) $2 \text{ C}_3\text{H}_6(\text{g}) + 2 \text{ NH}_3(\text{g}) + 3 \text{ O}_2(\text{g}) \rightarrow 2 \text{ C}_3\text{H}_3\text{N(l)} + 6 \text{ H}_2\text{O(l)}$

(b) For every kilogram of propylene we get 0.73 kilogram of acrylonitrile; we can also say that for every gram of propylene we get 0.73 gram of acrylonitrile. One gram of propylene is 0.023$\underline{8}$ mol of propylene. The corresponding quantity of NH_3 is 0.023$\underline{8}$ mol or 0.40$\underline{5}$ g; then because NH_3 and C_3H_6 are required in the same molar amount (2:2) for the reaction, 0.40$\underline{5}$ of a kg of NH_3 will be required for every 0.73 of a kg of acrylonitrile. To get 1000 kg of acrylonitrile we need, by simple proportion, $1000 \times (0.40\underline{5})/0.73 = 555$ kg.

130. **(D)** It is helpful to first calculate the molar masses of all reactants used and the desired product. The molar masses, in g/mol, are as follows.

Desired product: $C_6H_5NH_2$, 93.129
Reaction #1: C_6H_6, 78.114 $(CH_3)_3SiN_3$, 115.211 F_3CSO_3H, 150.07   NaOH, 39.997
Reaction #2: HNO_3, 63.012 H_2, 2.016

We now focus on making 1 mole of $C_6H_5NH_2$ (or 93.129 g $C_6H_5NH_2$) by each reaction. For reaction #1, we need 1 mole (or 78.114 g) of C_6H_6, 1 mole (or 115.221 g) of $(CH_3)_3SiN_3$, 2 moles (or 2 × 150.07 g) of F_3CSO_3H, and 1 mole (or 39.997 g) of NaOH. Therefore,

$$\% \text{ atom economy} = \frac{93.129\,g}{78.114\,g + 115.221\,g + 2\times150.07\,g + 39.997\,g}\times100 = 17$$

For reaction #2, we need 1 mole (or 78.114 g) of C_6H_6, 1 mole (or 63.012 g) of HNO_3, and 3 moles (or 3 × 2.016 g) of H_2.

$$\% \text{ atom economy} = \frac{93.129\,g}{78.114\,g + 63.012\,g + 3\times2.016\,g}\times100 = 63$$

131. **(M)** The reaction is:
$$2\,NaOH(aq) + Cl_2(g) + 2\,NH_3(aq) \rightarrow N_2H_4(aq) + 2\,NaCl(aq) + 2\,H_2O(l)$$

(a) $\% \text{ AE} = \dfrac{32.046 \text{ g per mole reaction}}{184.956 \text{ g per mole reaction}}\times100\% = 17\%$

(b) $2\,H_2 + N_2 \rightarrow N_2H_4$ has an AE of 100%.

132. **(E)** If the sample that was caught is representative of all fish in the lake, there are five marked fish for every 18 fish. Thus, the total number of fish in the lake is determined.
$$\text{total fish} = 100 \text{ marked fish}\times\frac{18\,\text{fish}}{5\,\text{marked fish}} = 360 \text{ fish} \approx 4\times10^2 \text{ fish}$$

FEATURE PROBLEMS

133. **(D)**

(a)   The graph obtained is one of two straight lines, meeting at a peak of about 2.50 g $Pb(NO_3)_2$, corresponding to about 3.5 g PbI_2. Maximum mass of PbI_2 (calculated)
$$= 2.503\,g\,KI\times\frac{1\,mol\,KI}{166.0\,g\,KI}\times\frac{1\,mol\,PbI_2}{2\,mol\,KI}\times\frac{461.02\,g\,PbI_2}{1\,mol\,PbI_2} = 3.476\,g\,PbI_2$$

(b)   The total quantity of reactant is limited to 5.000 g. If either reactant is in excess, the amount in excess will be "wasted," because it cannot be used to form product. Thus, we obtain the maximum amount of product when neither reactant is in excess (i.e., when there is a stoichiometric amount of each present). The balanced chemical equation for this reaction, $2\,KI + Pb(NO_3)_2 \rightarrow 2\,KNO_3 + PbI_2$, shows that stoichiometric quantities are two moles of KI (166.00 g/mol) for each mole of

$Pb(NO_3)_2$ (331.21 g/mol). If we have 5.000 g total, we can let the mass of KI equal x g, so that the mass of

$$Pb(NO_3)_2 = (5.000 - x) \text{ g. and the amount } KI = x \text{ g KI} \times \frac{1 \text{ mol KI}}{166.00 \text{ g KI}} = \frac{x}{166.00}$$

$$\text{amount } Pb(NO_3)_2 = (5.000 - x) \text{ g } Pb(NO_3)_2 \times \frac{1 \text{ mol } Pb(NO_3)_2}{331.21 \text{ g } Pb(NO_3)_2} = \frac{5.000 - x}{331.21}$$

At the point of stoichiometric balance, amount $KI = 2 \times$ amount $Pb(NO_3)_2$

$$\frac{x}{166.00} = 2 \times \frac{5.000 - x}{331.21} \quad OR \quad 331.21 x = 10.00 \times 166.00 - 332.00 x$$

$$x = \frac{1660.0}{331.21 + 332.00} = 2.503 \text{ g KI} \times \frac{1 \text{ mol KI}}{166.00 \text{ g KI}} = 0.01508 \text{ mol KI}$$

$$5.000 - x = 2.497 \text{ g } Pb(NO_3)_2 \times \frac{1 \text{ mol } Pb(NO_3)_2}{331.21 \text{ g } Pb(NO_3)_2} = 0.007539 \text{ mol } Pb(NO_3)_2$$

As a mass ratio we have: $\dfrac{2.503 \text{ g KI}}{2.497 \text{ g } Pb(NO_3)_2} = \dfrac{1.002 \text{ g KI}}{1 \text{ g } Pb(NO_3)_2}$

As a molar ratio we have: $\dfrac{0.01508 \text{ mol KI}}{0.007539 \text{ mol } Pb(NO_3)_2} = \dfrac{2 \text{ mol KI}}{1 \text{ mol } Pb(NO_3)_2}$

(c) The molar ratio just determined in part (b) is the same as the ratio of the coefficients for KI and $Pb(NO_3)_2$ in the balanced chemical equation. To determine the proportions precisely, we simply use the balanced chemical equation.

134. (M) The more HCl used, the more impure the sample (compared to $NaHCO_3$, twice as much HCl is needed to neutralize Na_2CO_3).
Sample from trona: 6.93 g sample forms 11.89 g AgCl or 1.72 g AgCl per gram sample.
Sample derived from manufactured sodium bicarbonate: 6.78 g sample forms 11.77 g AgCl or 1.74 g AgCl per gram sample.
Thus the trona sample is purer (i.e., it has the greater mass percent $NaHCO_3$).

SELF-ASSESSMENT EXERCISES

135. (E)

(a) $\overset{\Delta}{\rightarrow}$: A reaction proceeds when heated, that is, heat is playing the role of one of the reactants.

(b) (aq): The species is fully soluble in water and the reaction has water present to make the dissociation happen

(c) stoichiometric coefficient: number of moles of a species that reacts or forms for an ideal balanced equation

(d) overall equation: the combination of several related reaction equations to give one reaction

136. **(E)**

    (a) Balancing a chemical equations: making the total number of each type of atoms on both sides of the reaction be equal

    (b) Making a solution by dilution: making a solution of known concentration by taking a known volume of a more concentrated solution and diluting it to a known volume

    (c) Determining the limiting reactant: establishing which reactant is completely consumed in a reaction. A quick way to determine the limiting reactant is to establish which reactant that has the smallest value of ($n/coeff$).

137. **(E)**

    (a) *Chemical formula* is the number and kind of each atom constituting a molecule or formula unit, whereas a *chemical equation* is the relative number of moles of various reactants and the products they yield

    (b) *Stoichiometric factor* is the mole ratio of reactants reacting with each other while *stoichiometric coefficient* is the number of moles of reactants and products needed to balance a chemical equation

    (c) *Solute* is a substance that dissolves in a solvent. A *solvent* is the component of the solution which determines the solution's phase (i.e. solid, liquid or gas)

    (d) *Actual yield* is the mass of product collected after a reaction, and *percent yield* is the ratio between actual and theoretical yields multiplied by 100.

    (e) *Consecutive* reactions are reactions that occur one after the other in a specific order, *simultaneous* reactions occur at the same time

138. **(E)** The answer is (d). Start balancing in the following order: N, O, H and Cu

$$3\ Cu(s) + 8\ HNO_3(aq) \rightarrow 3\ Cu(NO_3)_2(aq) + 4\ H_2O(l) + 2\ NO(g)$$

139. **(E)** The answer is (d). To determine the number of moles of NH_3, used the balanced equation:

$$\#\ moles\ NH_3 = 1\ mol\ H_2O \times \frac{2\ mol\ NH_3}{3\ mol\ H_2O} = 0.666\ mol\ NH_3$$

140. **(M)** The answer is (a). To determine the number of moles of NH_3, use the balanced equation:

$$2\ KMnO_4 + 10\ KI + 8\ H_2SO_4 \rightarrow 6\ K_2SO_4 + 2\ MnSO_4 + 5\ I_2 + 8\ H_2O$$

$$5\ mol\ KMnO_4 \times \frac{6\ mol\ K_2SO_4}{2\ mol\ KMnO_4} = 15\ mol\ K_2SO_4$$

$$5\ mol\ KI \times \frac{6\ mol\ K_2SO_4}{10\ mol\ KI} = 3\ mol\ K_2SO_4$$

$$5\ mol\ H_2SO_4 \times \frac{6\ mol\ K_2SO_4}{8\ mol\ H_2SO_4} = 3.75\ mol\ K_2SO_4$$

141. **(E)** The answer is (a). To determine the answer, used the balanced equation:

$2\ Ag_2(CO_3)\ (s) \rightarrow 4\ Ag(s) + 2\ CO_2(g) + O_2(g)$

The ratio between O_2 and CO_2 is 1:2.

142. **(E)** The answer is (c). To solve this, calculate the number of moles of $NaNO_3$.

mol $NaNO_3 = 1.00\ M \times 1.00\ L = 1.00\ mol$

$$1.00\ mol\ NaNO_3 \times \frac{85.0\ g\ NaNO_3}{1\ mol\ NaNO_3} = 85.0\ g\ NaNO_3$$

Concentration = 85.0 g $NaNO_3$/L. While (b) also technically gives you the correct value at 25 °C, it is not the definition of molarity.

143. **(D)** The amount of K+ present in 200.0 mL of 0.240 M K_2SO_4 is

$$0.2000\ L \times \frac{0.240\ mol\ K_2SO_4}{1\ L} \times \frac{2\ mol\ K^+}{1\ mol\ K_2SO_4} = 0.096\ mol\ K^+$$

Let V be the volume of KNO_3 solution added in L.

$$0.400\ M = \frac{0.096\ mol\ K^+ + (0.160\ M \times V)}{V + 0.200\ L}$$

$$V = 0.0667\ L = 66.7\ mL$$

144. **(E)** The answer is (d). There is no need for calculation, because a starting solution of 0.4 M is needed to make a 0.50 M solution, and the only way to make a more concentrated solution is to evaporate off some of the water.

145. **(M)** The answer is (b). To determine the molarity, number of moles of LiBr need to be determined first. Therefore, weight % concentration needs to be converted to number of moles with the aid of the density:

Conc. = 5.30% by mass = 5.30 g LiBr/100 g solution

Volume of solution = mass / Density = $100\ g\ sol'n \times \dfrac{1\ mL}{1.040\ g} = 96.15\ mL$

$$mol\ LiBr = 5.30\ g\ LiBr \times \frac{1\ mol\ LiBr}{86.84\ g\ LiBr} = 0.0610\ mol$$

$$Molarity = \frac{0.0610\ mol}{96.15\ mL} \times \frac{1000\ mL}{1\ L} = 0.635\ M$$

146. **(M)** The answer is (d). To determine % yield, calculate the theoretical mole yield:

$$mol\ CCl_2F = 2.00\ mol\ CCl_4 \times \frac{1\ mol\ CCl_2F}{1\ mol\ CCl_4} = 2.00\ mol\ CCl_2F$$

$$\%\ yield = \frac{1.70\ mol}{2.00\ mol} \times 100 = 85.0\%$$

147. (M)

$$18.0 \text{ g Fe}_2\text{O}_3 \times \frac{1 \text{ mol Fe}_2\text{O}_3}{159.7 \text{ g Fe}_2\text{O}_3} \times \frac{4 \text{ mol Fe}}{2 \text{ mol Fe}_2\text{O}_3} \times \frac{55.845 \text{ g Fe}}{1 \text{ mol Fe}} = 12.6 \text{ g Fe}$$

(assuming all the Fe_2O_3 reacts)

$$2.5 \text{ g C} \times \frac{1 \text{ mol C}}{12.011 \text{ g C}} \times \frac{4 \text{ mol Fe}}{3 \text{ mol C}} \times \frac{55.845 \text{ g Fe}}{1 \text{ mol Fe}} = 15.5 \text{ g Fe}$$ (assuming all the C reacts)

Fe_2O_3 is the limiting reactant and 12.6 g of Fe are produced by this reaction.

148. (D) We have 26.4 g mixture × 0.40 g CaO/g mixture = 10.6 g CaO

$$10.5 \text{ g CaO} \times \frac{1 \text{ mol CaO}}{56.08 \text{ g CaO}} \times \frac{1 \text{ mol CaCl}_2}{1 \text{ mol CaO}} \times \frac{110.98 \text{ g CaCl}_2}{1 \text{ mol CaCl}_2} = 20.\underline{78} \text{ g CaCl}_2$$

26.4 g mixture − 10.6 g CaO = 15.8 g NaOH

$$15.8 \text{ g NaOH} \times \frac{1 \text{ mol NaOH}}{40.00 \text{ g NaOH}} \times \frac{1 \text{ mol NaCl}}{1 \text{ mol NaOH}} \times \frac{58.44 \text{ g NaCl}}{1 \text{ mol NaCl}} = 23.\underline{08} \text{ g NaCl}$$

Total mass of solid = mass of $CaCl_2$ + mass of NaCl = 20.8 g + 23.1 g = 43.9 g

149. (D) To balance the below equations, balance C first, then O and finally H.

(a) $2 \text{ C}_8\text{H}_{18} + 25 \text{ O}_2 \rightarrow 16 \text{ CO}_2 + 18 \text{ H}_2\text{O}$

(b) For this part, we note that 25% of the available carbon atoms in C_8H_{18} form CO and the remainder for CO_2. Therefore,
$2 \text{ C}_8\text{H}_{18} + 25 \text{ O}_2 \rightarrow 12 \text{ CO}_2 + 4 \text{ CO} + 18 \text{ H}_2\text{O}$

150. (D) To determine the compound, the number of moles of each compound needs to be determined, which then helps determine number of moles of emitted CO_2:

$$\text{mass CO}_2 = 1.000 \text{ g CaCO}_3 \times \frac{1 \text{ mol CaCO}_3}{100.08 \text{ g CaCO}_3} \times \frac{1 \text{ mol CO}_2}{1 \text{ mol CaCO}_3} \times \frac{44.0 \text{ g CO}_2}{1 \text{ mol CO}_2}$$

$$= 0.4396 \text{ g CO}_2$$

$$\text{mass CO}_2 = 1.000 \text{ g MgCO}_3 \times \frac{1 \text{ mol MgCO}_3}{84.30 \text{ g MgCO}_3} \times \frac{1 \text{ mol CO}_2}{1 \text{ mol CaCO}_3} \times \frac{44.0 \text{ g CO}_2}{1 \text{ mol CO}_2}$$

$$= 0.5219 \text{ g CO}_2$$

$$\text{mass CO}_2 = 1.000 \text{ g CaCO}_3 \cdot \text{MgCO}_3 \times \frac{1 \text{ mol dolomite}}{184.38 \text{ g dolomite}} \times \frac{2 \text{ mol CO}_2}{1 \text{ mol dolomite}}$$

$$\times \frac{44.0 \text{ g CO}_2}{1 \text{ mol CO}_2} = 0.4773 \text{ g CO}_2$$

Therefore, dolomite is the compound.

151. **(D)** The answer is (b). First, the total amount of carbon in our mixture of CH_4 and C_2H_6 must be determined by using the amount of CO_2

$$\text{mass of C} = 2.776 \text{ g CO}_2 \times \frac{1 \text{ mol CO}_2}{44.01 \text{ g CO}_2} \times \frac{1 \text{ mol C}}{1 \text{ mol CO}_2} \times \frac{12.01 \text{ g C}}{1 \text{ mol C}} = 0.758 \text{ g C}$$

Let the mass of CH_4 in the mixture be x g. Then the mass of C_2H_6 will be $(1.000 - x)$ g. Then, the amounts of CH_4 and C_2H_6 can be determined by making sure that the moles of carbon for both add up to 0.0631:

$$x \text{ g CH}_4 \times \left(\frac{1 \text{ mol CH}_4}{16.05 \text{ g CH}_4} \times \frac{1 \text{ mol C}}{1 \text{ mol CH}_4} \times \frac{12.01 \text{ g C}}{1 \text{ mol C}} \right)$$

$$+ (1.000 - x) \times \left(\frac{1 \text{ mol C}_2\text{H}_6}{30.08 \text{ g C}_2\text{H}_6} \times \frac{2 \text{ mol C}}{1 \text{ mol C}_2\text{H}_6} \times \frac{12.01 \text{ g C}}{1 \text{ mol C}} \right) = 0.757 \text{ g C (from CO}_2)$$

$$0.748 \, x + (1 - x)(0.798) = 0.757$$

$$x = \text{mass of CH}_4 = 0.82 \text{ g, or 82\% of a 1.00 g sample}$$

152. **(D)** The answer is (c). To do this, perform a stepwise conversion of moles of reactants to moles of products, as shown below:

$$4.00 \text{ mol NH}_3 \times \frac{4 \text{ mol NO}}{4 \text{ mol NH}_3} \times \frac{2 \text{ mol NO}_2}{2 \text{ mol NO}} \times \frac{2 \text{ mol HNO}_3}{3 \text{ mol NO}_2} = 2.67 \text{ mol HNO}_3$$

153. **(E)** All the following reactions incorporate all the reactant atoms into the desired product. Consequently, they all have a percent AE of 100%.

    (a) $Rb + \frac{1}{2} Br_2 + 2 O_2 \longrightarrow RbBrO_4$

    (b) $S + H_2 + 2 O_2 \longrightarrow H_2SO_4$

    (c) $Mg + Cl_2 + 3 O_2 \longrightarrow Mg(ClO_3)_2$

    (d) $Na + \frac{1}{2} N_2 + O_2 \longrightarrow NaNO_2$

154. **(M)** To construct a concept map, one must first start with the most general concepts. These concepts contain other more specific concepts discussed in those sections. Looking at sections 4-3, 4-4, and 4-5, it is apparent that the concepts of solution concentration and reaction stoichiometry are the most general ones being discussed. The next stage is to consider more specific concepts that derive from the general ones. In the case of solution concentration, the concept of molarity is a more specific case, and solution dilution yet another. For reaction stoichiometry, the most obvious more specific concept is limiting reactants. Afterwards, link the general and more specific concepts with one or two simple words. For example, molarity is an "expression of" concentration. Take a look at the subsection headings and problems for more refining of the general and specific concepts.

CHAPTER 5

INTRODUCTION TO REACTIONS
IN AQUEOUS SOLUTIONS

PRACTICE EXAMPLES

1A. **(E)** To calculate the total concentration of Cl^- in seawater, let's focus on a 1.0 L sample.

$$n_{Cl^-}(\text{total}) = n_{Cl^-}(\text{from NaCl}) + n_{Cl^-}(\text{from MgCl}_2)$$

$$= 1 \text{ L soln} \times \frac{0.438 \text{ mol NaCl}}{1 \text{ L soln}} \times \frac{1 \text{ mol Cl}^-}{1 \text{ mol NaCl}} + 1 \text{ L soln} \times \frac{0.0512 \text{ mol MgCl}_2}{1 \text{ L soln}} \times \frac{2 \text{ mol Cl}^-}{1 \text{ mol MgCl}_2}$$

$$= 0.438 \text{ mol Cl}^- + 0.102 \text{ mol Cl}^-$$

$$= 0.540 \text{ mol Cl}^-$$

Because there are 0.540 mol Cl^- in a 1.0 L sample, $[Cl^-] = 0.540$ M.

<u>1B</u> **(E)**

(a) $\dfrac{1.5 \text{ mg F}^-}{1 \text{ L}} \times \dfrac{1 \text{ g F}^-}{1000 \text{ mg F}^-} \times \dfrac{1 \text{ mol F}^-}{18.998 \text{ F}^-} = 7.9 \times 10^{-5} \text{ M F}^-$

(b) $1.00 \times 10^6 \text{ L} \times \dfrac{7.9 \times 10^{-5} \text{ mol F}^-}{1 \text{ L}} \times \dfrac{1 \text{ mol CaF}_2}{2 \text{ mol F}^-} \times \dfrac{78.074 \text{ g CaF}_2}{1 \text{ mol CaF}_2} \times \dfrac{1 \text{ kg}}{1000 \text{ g}} = 3.1 \text{ kg CaF}_2$

<u>2A</u> **(E)** In each case, we use the solubility rules to determine whether either product is insoluble. The ions in each product compound are determined by simply "switching the partners" of the reactant compounds. The designation "(aq)" on each reactant indicates that it is soluble.

(a) Possible products are potassium chloride, KCl, which is soluble, and aluminum hydroxide, $Al(OH)_3$, which is not. Net ionic equation:

$$Al^{3+}(aq) + 3 OH^-(aq) \rightarrow Al(OH)_3(s)$$

(b) Possible products are iron(III) sulfate, $Fe_2(SO_4)_3$, and potassium bromide, KBr, both of which are soluble. No reaction occurs.

(c) Possible products are calcium nitrate, $Ca(NO_3)_2$, which is soluble, and lead(II) iodide, PbI_2, which is insoluble. Net ionic equation: $Pb^{2+}(aq) + 2 I^-(aq) \rightarrow PbI_2(s)$

2B **(E)**

(a) Possible products are sodium chloride, NaCl, which is soluble, and aluminum phosphate, $AlPO_4$, which is insoluble. Net ionic equation:

$$Al^{3+}(aq) + PO_4^{3-}(aq) \rightarrow AlPO_4(s)$$

(b) Possible products are aluminum chloride, $AlCl_3$, which is soluble, and barium sulfate, $BaSO_4$, which is insoluble. Net ionic equation: $Ba^{2+}(aq) + SO_4^{2-}(aq) \rightarrow BaSO_4(s)$

(c) Possible products are ammonium nitrate, NH_4NO_3, which is soluble, and lead(II) carbonate, $PbCO_3$, which is insoluble. Net ionic equation:

$$Pb^{2+}(aq) + CO_3^{2-}(aq) \rightarrow PbCO_3(s)$$

3A **(E)** Propionic acid is a weak acid, not dissociated completely in aqueous solution. Ammonia similarly is a weak base. The acid and base react to form a salt solution of ammonium propionate.

$$NH_3(aq) + CH_3CH_2COOH(aq) \rightarrow NH_4^+(aq) + CH_3CH_2COO^-(aq)$$

3B **(E)** Since acetic acid is a weak acid, it is not dissociated completely in aqueous solution (except at infinite dilution); it is misleading to write it in ionic form. The products of this reaction are the gas carbon dioxide, the molecular compound water, and the ionic solute calcium acetate. Only the latter exists as ions in aqueous solution.

$$CaCO_3(s) + 2\ CH_3COOH(aq) \rightarrow CO_2(g) + H_2O(l) + Ca^{2+}(aq) + 2\ CH_3COO^-(aq)$$

4A **(M)**

(a) Elements do not change oxidation states during this reaction. It is not an oxidation–reduction reaction.

(b) The presence of $O_2(g)$ as a product indicates that this is an oxidation–reduction reaction. Oxygen is oxidized from O.S. = –2 in NO_3^- to O.S. = 0 in $O_2(g)$. Nitrogen is reduced from O.S. = +5 in NO_3^- to O.S. = +4 in NO_2.

4B **(M)** Vanadium is oxidized from O.S. = +4 in VO^{2+} to an O.S. = +5 in VO_2^+ while manganese is reduced from O.S. = +7 in MnO_4^- to O.S. = +2 in Mn^{2+}.

5A **(M)** Aluminum is oxidized (from an O.S. of 0 to an O.S. of +3), while hydrogen is reduced (from an O.S. of +1 to an O.S. of 0).

$$Al + HCl \rightarrow AlCl_3 + H_2$$

$$Al + H^+ \rightarrow Al^{3+} + H_2$$

Oxidation: $\{Al(s) \rightarrow Al^{3+}(aq) + 3\ e^-\} \times 2$

Reduction: $\{2\ H^+(aq) + 2\ e^- \rightarrow H_2(g)\} \times 3$

Overall: $2\ Al(s) + 6\ H^+(aq) \rightarrow 2\ Al^{3+}(aq) + 3\ H_2(g)$

5B **(M)** Bromide is oxidized (from -1 to 0), while chlorine is reduced (from 0 to -1).

$Cl_2 + NaBr \rightarrow Br_2 + NaCl$

$Cl_2 + Br^- \rightarrow Br_2 + Cl^-$

Oxidation: $2\,Br^-(aq) \rightarrow Br_2(l) + 2\,e^-$

Reduction: $Cl_2(g) + 2\,e^- \rightarrow 2\,Cl^-(aq)$

Overall: $2\,Br^-(aq) + Cl_2(g) \rightarrow Br_2(l) + 2\,Cl^-(aq)$

6A **(D)**

Step 1: Write the two skeleton half-equations.

$Fe^{2+}(aq) \rightarrow Fe^{3+}(aq)$ *and* $MnO_4^-(aq) \rightarrow Mn^{2+}(aq)$

Step 2: Balance each skeleton half-equation for O (with H_2O) and for H atoms (with H^+).

$Fe^{2+}(aq) \rightarrow Fe^{3+}(aq)$ *and* $MnO_4^-(aq) + 8\,H^+(aq) \rightarrow Mn^{2+}(aq) + 4\,H_2O(l)$

Step 3: Balance electric charge by adding electrons.

$Fe^{2+}(aq) \rightarrow Fe^{3+}(aq) + e^-$ *and* $MnO_4^-(aq) + 8\,H^+(aq) + 5\,e^- \rightarrow Mn^{2+}(aq) + 4\,H_2O(l)$

Step 4: Combine the two half-equations

Oxidation: $\{Fe^{2+}(aq) \rightarrow Fe^{3+}(aq) + e^-\} \times 5$

Reduction: $MnO_4^-(aq) + 8\,H^+(aq) + 5\,e^- \rightarrow Mn^{2+}(aq) + 4\,H_2O(l)$

Overall: $MnO_4^-(aq) + 8\,H^+(aq) + 5\,Fe^{2+}(aq) \rightarrow Mn^{2+}(aq) + 4\,H_2O(l) + 5\,Fe^{3+}(aq)$

6B **(D)**

Step 1: Uranium is oxidized and chromium is reduced in this reaction. The "skeleton" half-equations are: $UO^{2+}(aq) \rightarrow UO_2^{2+}(aq)$ *and* $Cr_2O_7^{2-}(aq) \rightarrow Cr^{3+}(aq)$

Step 2: First, balance the chromium skeleton half-equation for chromium atoms:

$Cr_2O_7^{2-}(aq) \rightarrow 2\,Cr^{3+}(aq)$

Next, balance oxygen atoms with water molecules in each half-equation:

$UO^{2+}(aq) + H_2O(l) \rightarrow UO_2^{2+}(aq)$ *and* $Cr_2O_7^{2-}(aq) \rightarrow 2\,Cr^{3+}(aq) + 7\,H_2O(l)$

Then, balance hydrogen atoms with hydrogen ions in each half-equation:

$UO^{2+}(aq) + H_2O(l) \rightarrow UO_2^{2+}(aq) + 2\,H^+(aq)$

$Cr_2O_7^{2-}(aq) + 14\,H^+(aq) \rightarrow 2\,Cr^{3+}(aq) + 7\,H_2O(l)$

Step 3: Balance the charge of each half-equation with electrons.

$UO^{2+}(aq) + H_2O(l) \rightarrow UO_2^{2+}(aq) + 2\,H^+(aq) + 2\,e^-$

$Cr_2O_7^{2-}(aq) + 14\,H^+(aq) + 6\,e^- \rightarrow 2\,Cr^{3+}(aq) + 7\,H_2O(l)$

Step 4: Multiply the uranium half-equation by 3 and add the chromium half-equation to it.

Oxidation: $\{UO^{2+}(aq) + H_2O(l) \rightarrow UO_2^{2+}(aq) + 2\,H^+(aq) + 2\,e^-\} \times 3$

Reduction: $Cr_2O_7^{2-}(aq) + 14\,H^+(aq) + 6\,e^- \rightarrow 2\,Cr^{3+}(aq) + 7\,H_2O(l)$

$3\,UO^{2+}(aq) + Cr_2O_7^{2-}(aq) + 14\,H^+(aq) + 3\,H_2O(l) \rightarrow 3\,UO_2^{2+}(aq) + 2\,Cr^{3+}(aq) + 7\,H_2O(l) + 6\,H^+(aq)$

Step 5:   Simplify. Subtract 3 $H_2O(l)$ and 6 H^+ (aq) from each side of the equation.

Overall: $3\ UO^{2+}(aq) +\ Cr_2O_7^{2-}(aq) + 8\ H^+(aq) \rightarrow 3\ UO_2^{2+}(aq) + 2\ Cr^{3+}(aq) + 4\ H_2O(l)$

7A   (D)

Step 1:   Write the two skeleton half-equations.

$S(s) \rightarrow SO_3^{2-}(aq)\ \ and\ \ OCl^-(aq) \rightarrow Cl^-(aq)$

Step 2:   Balance each skeleton half-equation for O (with H_2O) and for H atoms (with H^+).

$3\ H_2O(l) +\ S(s) \rightarrow SO_3^{2-}(aq) + 6\ H^+$

$OCl^-(aq) + 2\ H^+ \rightarrow Cl^-(aq) + H_2O(l)$

Step 3:   Balance electric charge by adding electrons.

$3\ H_2O(l) + S(s) \rightarrow SO_3^{2-}(aq) + 6\ H^+(aq) + 4\ e^-$

$OCl^-(aq) + 2\ H^+(aq) + 2\ e^- \rightarrow Cl^-(aq) + H_2O(l)$

Step 4:   Change from an acidic medium to a basic one by adding OH^- to eliminate H^+.

$3H_2O(l) +\ S(s) + 6\ OH^-(aq) \rightarrow SO_3^{2-}(aq) + 6\ H^+(aq) + 6\ OH^-(aq) + 4\ e^-$

$OCl^-(aq) + 2\ H^+(aq) + 2\ OH^-(aq) + 2\ e^- \rightarrow Cl^-(aq) + H_2O(l) + 2\ OH^-(aq)$

Step 5:   Simplify by removing the items present on both sides of each half-equation, and combine the half-equations to obtain the net redox equation.

Oxidation: $S(s) + 6\ OH^-(aq) \rightarrow SO_3^{2-}(aq) + 3\ H_2O(l) + 4\ e^-$

Reduction: $\{OCl^-(aq) +\ H_2O(l) + 2\ e^- \rightarrow\ Cl^-(aq) + 2\ OH^-(aq)\} \times 2$

Overall: $S(s) +\ 6\ OH^-(aq) + 2\ OCl^-(aq) + 2H_2O(l) \rightarrow SO_3^{2-}(aq) + 3\ H_2O(l) + 2\ Cl^-(aq) + 4\ OH^-$

Simplify by removing the species present on both sides.

Net ionic equation: $S(s) + 2\ OH^-(aq) + 2\ OCl^-(aq) \rightarrow SO_3^{2-}(aq) +\ H_2O(l) + 2\ Cl^-(aq)$

7B   (D)

Step 1:   Write the two skeleton half-equations.

$MnO_4^-(aq) \rightarrow\ MnO_2(s)\ and\ SO_3^{2-}(aq) \rightarrow SO_4^{2-}(aq)$

Step 2:   Balance each skeleton half-equation for O (with H_2O) and for H atoms (with H^+).

$MnO_4^-(aq) + 4\ H^+(aq) \rightarrow\ MnO_2(s) + 2\ H_2O(l)$

$SO_3^{2-}(aq) + H_2O(l) \rightarrow SO_4^{2-}(aq) + 2H^+(aq)$

Step 3:   Balance electric charge by adding electrons.

$MnO_4^-(aq) + 4\ H^+(aq) + 3\ e^- \rightarrow\ MnO_2(s) + 2\ H_2O(l)$

$SO_3^{2-}(aq) +\ H_2O(l) \rightarrow SO_4^{2-}(aq) + 2\ H^+(aq) + 2\ e^-$

Step 4:   Change from an acidic medium to a basic one by adding OH^- to eliminate H^+.

$MnO_4^-(aq) + 4\ H^+(aq) + 4\ OH^-(aq) + 3\ e^- \rightarrow\ MnO_2(s) + H_2O(l) + 4\ OH^-(aq)$

$SO_3^{2-}(aq) + H_2O(l) + 2\ OH^-(aq) \rightarrow SO_4^{2-}(aq) + 2\ H^+(aq) +\ 2OH^-(aq) + 2\ e^-$

Step 5: Simplify by removing species present on both sides of each half-equation, and combine the half-equations to obtain the net redox equation.

Oxidation: $\{MnO_4^- (aq) + 2\,H_2O(l) + 3\,e^- \rightarrow MnO_2(s) + 4\,OH^-(aq)\} \times 2$

Reduction: $\{SO_3^{2-}(aq) + 2\,OH^-(aq) \rightarrow SO_4^{2-}(aq) + H_2O(l) + 2\,e^-\} \times 3$

$2\,MnO_4^-(aq) + 3\,SO_3^{2-}(aq) + 6\,OH^-(aq) + 4\,H_2O(l) \rightarrow$
$$2\,MnO_2(s) + 3\,SO_4^{2-}(aq) + 3\,H_2O(l) + 8\,OH^-(aq)$$

Simplify by removing species present on both sides.

Overall: $2\,MnO_4^-(aq) + 3\,SO_3^{2-}(aq) + H_2O(l) \rightarrow 2\,MnO_2(s) + 3\,SO_4^{2-}(aq) + 2\,OH^-(aq)$

8A **(M)** Since the oxidation state of H is 0 in H_2 (g) and is +1 in both $NH_3(g)$ and $H_2O(g)$, hydrogen is oxidized. A substance that is oxidized is called a reducing agent. In addition, the oxidation state of N in NO_2 (g) is +4, while it is −3 in NH_3; the oxidation state of the element N decreases during this reaction, meaning that NO_2 (g) is reduced. The substance that is reduced is called the oxidizing agent.

8B **(M)** In $\left[Au(CN)_2\right]^-$ (aq), gold has an oxidation state of +1; Au has been oxidized and, thus, Au(s) (oxidization state = 0), is the reducing agent. In OH^- (aq), oxygen has an oxidation state of −2; O has been reduced and thus, $O_2(g)$ (oxidation state = 0) is the oxidizing agent.

9A **(M)** We first determine the amount of NaOH that reacts with 0.500 g $KHC_8H_4O_4$ (or KHP, for short).

$$n_{NaOH} = 0.5000 \text{ g KHP} \times \frac{1 \text{ mol KHP}}{204.22 \text{ g KHP}} \times \frac{1 \text{ mol OH}^-}{1 \text{ mol KHP}} \times \frac{1 \text{ mol NaOH}}{1 \text{ mol OH}^-} = 0.002448 \text{ mol NaOH}$$

$$\text{molarity of NaOH} = \frac{0.002448 \text{ mol NaOH}}{24.03 \text{ mL soln}} \times \frac{1000 \text{ mL}}{1 \text{ L}} = 0.1019 \text{ M}$$

9B **(M)** The net ionic equation when solid hydroxides react with a strong acid is $OH^- + H^+ \rightarrow H_2O$. There are two sources of OH^-: NaOH and $Ca(OH)_2$. We compute the amount of OH^- from each source and add the results.

$$\text{moles of OH}^- \text{ from NaOH}: = 0.235 \text{ g sample} \times \frac{92.5 \text{ g NaOH}}{100.0 \text{ g sample}} \times \frac{1 \text{ mol NaOH}}{39.997 \text{ g NaOH}} \times$$

$$\frac{1 \text{ mol OH}^-}{1 \text{ mol NaOH}} = 0.00543 \text{ mol OH}^-$$

$$\text{moles of OH}^- \text{ from } Ca(OH)_2: = 0.235 \text{ g sample} \times \frac{7.5 \text{ g } Ca(OH)_2}{100.0 \text{ g sample}} \times$$

$$\frac{1 \text{ mol } Ca(OH)_2}{74.092 \text{ g } Ca(OH)_2} \times \frac{2 \text{ mol OH}^-}{1 \text{ mol } Ca(OH)_2} = 0.00048 \text{ mol OH}^-$$

total amount $OH^- = 0.00543$ mol from NaOH $+ 0.00048$ mol from $Ca(OH)_2$
$$= 0.00591 \text{ mol OH}^-$$

$$\text{molarity of HCl} = \frac{0.00591 \text{ mol OH}^-}{45.6 \text{ mL HCl soln}} \times \frac{1 \text{ mol H}^+}{1 \text{ mol OH}^-} \times \frac{1 \text{ mol HCl}}{1 \text{ mol H}^+} \times \frac{1000 \text{ mL soln}}{1 \text{ L soln}}$$
$$= 0.130 \text{ M}$$

10A **(M)** First, determine the mass of iron that has reacted as Fe^{2+} with the titrant. The balanced chemical equation provides the essential conversion factor to answer this question.

Namely: $5\,Fe^{2+}(aq) + MnO_4^-(aq) + 8\,H^+(aq) \longrightarrow 5\,Fe^{3+}(aq) + Mn^{2+}(aq) + 4\,H_2O(l)$

$$\text{mass Fe} = 0.04125 \text{ L titrant} \times \frac{0.02140 \text{ mol } MnO_4^-}{1 \text{ L titrant}} \times \frac{5 \text{ mol } Fe^{2+}}{1 \text{ mol } MnO_4^-} \times \frac{55.845 \text{ g Fe}}{1 \text{ mol } Fe^{2+}}$$

$$= 0.246 \text{ g Fe}$$

Then determine the % Fe in the ore. $\% \text{ Fe} = \dfrac{0.246 \text{ g Fe}}{0.376 \text{ g ore}} \times 100\% = 65.4\% \text{ Fe}$

10B **(M)** The balanced equation provides us with the essential conversion factor to answer this question. See the solution to Exercise 111(b) for detail concerning the balancing of this equation.

Namely: $5\,C_2O_4^{2-}(aq) + 2\,MnO_4^-(aq) + 16\,H^+(aq) \longrightarrow 10\,CO_2(g) + 2\,Mn^{2+}(aq) + 8\,H_2O(l)$

$$\text{amount } MnO_4^- = 0.2482 \text{ g } Na_2C_2O_4 \times \frac{1 \text{ mol } Na_2C_2O_4}{134.00 \text{ g } Na_2C_2O_4} \times \frac{1 \text{ mol } C_2O_4^{2-}}{1 \text{ mol } Na_2C_2O_4} \times \frac{2 \text{ mol } MnO_4^-}{5 \text{ mol } C_2O_4^{2-}}$$

$$= 0.0007409 \text{ mol } MnO_4^-$$

$$\text{molarity of } KMnO_4 = \frac{0.0007409 \text{ mol } MnO_4^-}{23.68 \text{ mL soln}} \times \frac{1000 \text{ mL}}{1 \text{ L}} \times \frac{1 \text{ mol } KMnO_4}{1 \text{ mol } MnO_4^-} = 0.03129 \text{ M}$$

INTEGRATIVE EXAMPLE

A. **(M)** First, balance the equation. Break down the reaction of chlorate and ferrous ion as follows:

$$ClO_3^- + 6\,H^+ + 6\,e^- \rightarrow Cl^- + 3\,H_2O$$

$$6\left(Fe^{2+} \rightarrow Fe^{3+} + e^-\right)$$

Net reaction: $ClO_3^- + 6\,Fe^{2+} + 6\,H^+ \rightarrow Cl^- + 6\,Fe^{3+} + 3\,H_2O$

The reaction between Fe^{2+} and Ce^{4+} is already balanced. To calculate the moles of Fe^{2+} that remains after the reaction with ClO_3^-, determine the moles of Ce^{4+} that react with Fe^{2+}:

$\text{mol } Ce^{4+} = 0.01259 \text{ L} \times 0.08362 \text{ M} = 1.0527 \times 10^{-3} \text{ mol} = \text{mol of excess } Fe^{2+}$

$\text{total mol of } Fe^{2+} = 0.0500 \text{ L} \times 0.09101 = 4.551 \times 10^{-3} \text{ mol}$

Therefore, the moles of Fe^{2+} reacted $= 4.551 \times 10^{-3} - 1.0527 \times 10^{-3} = 3.498 \times 10^{-3} \text{ mol}$. To determine the mass of $KClO_3$, use the mole ratios in the balanced equation in conjunction with the molar mass of $KClO_3$.

$$3.498 \times 10^{-3} \text{ mol } Fe^{2+} \times \frac{1 \text{ mol } ClO_3^-}{6 \text{ mol } Fe^{2+}} \times \frac{1 \text{ mol } KClO_3}{1 \text{ mol } ClO_3^-} \times \frac{122.54 \text{ g } KClO_3}{1 \text{ mol } KClO_3}$$

$$= 0.07144 \text{ g } KClO_3$$

$$\% KClO_3 = \frac{0.07144 \text{ g}}{0.1432 \text{ g}} \times 100\% = 49.89\%$$

B. **(M)** First, balance the equation. Break down the reaction of arsenous acid and permanganate as follows:

Oxidation: $\{H_3AsO_3 + H_2O \rightarrow H_3AsO_4 + 2\ e^- + 2H^+\} \times 5$

Reduction: $\{MnO_4^- + 83\ H^+ 5e^- \rightarrow Mn^{2+} + 4\ H_2O\} \times 2$

Overall: $5\ H_3AsO_3 + 2\ MnO_4^- + 6\ H^+ \rightarrow 5\ H_3AsO_4 + 2\ Mn^{2+} + 3\ H_2O$

moles of $MnO_4^- = 0.02377\ L \times 0.02144\ M = 5.0963 \times 10^{-4}\ mol$

To calculate the mass of As, use the mole ratios in the balanced equation in conjunction with the molar mass of As:

$$5.0963 \times 10^{-4} mol\ MnO_4^- \times \frac{5\ mol\ H_3AsO_3}{2\ mol\ MnO_4^-} \times \frac{1\ mol\ As}{1\ mol\ H_3AsO_3} \times \frac{74.922\ g\ As}{1\ mol\ As}$$

$= 0.095456\ g\ As$

$$mass\%\ As = \frac{0.095456\ g}{7.25\ g} \times 100\% = 1.32\%$$

EXERCISES

Strong Electrolytes, Weak Electrolytes, and Nonelectrolytes

1. **(E)**
   (a) Because its formula begins with hydrogen, HC_6H_5O is an acid. It is not listed in Table 5-1, so it is a weak acid. A weak acid is a *weak electrolyte*.
   (b) Li_2SO_4 is an ionic compound, that is, a salt. A salt is a *strong electrolyte*.
   (c) MgI_2 also is a salt, a *strong electrolyte*.
   (d) $(CH_3CH_2)_2O$ is a molecular compound whose formula does not begin with H. Thus, it is neither an acid nor a salt. It also is not built around nitrogen, and thus it does not behave as a weak base. This is a *nonelectrolyte*.
   (e) $Sr(OH)_2$ is a *strong electrolyte*, one of the strong bases listed in Table 5-2.

2. **(E)**
   (a) The best electrical conductor is the solution of the strong electrolyte: 0.10 M NaCl. In each liter of this solution, there are 0.10 mol Na^+ ions and 0.10 mol Cl^- ions.
   (b) The poorest electrical conductor is the solution of the nonelectrolyte: 0.10 M CH_3CH_2OH. In this solution, the concentration of ions is negligible.

3. **(E)** HCl is practically 100% ionized in water. The apparatus should light up brightly. A solution of both HCl and CH_3COOH will yield similar results. In strongly acidic solutions, the weak acid CH_3COOH does not contribute to the conductivity of the solution. However, the strong acid HCl is always 100% ionized in water and is unaffected by the presence of the weak acid CH_3COOH. The apparatus should light up brightly.

4. **(E)** NH_3 (aq) is a weak base; CH_3COOH (aq) is a weak acid. The reaction produces a solution of ammonium acetate, $NH_4CH_3COO(aq)$, a salt and a strong electrolyte.

$$NH_3(aq) + CH_3COOH(aq) \rightarrow NH_4^+(aq) + CH_3COO(aq)$$

5. **(E)**
(a) Barium bromide: strong electrolyte
(b) Propionic acid: weak electrolyte
(c) Ammonia: weak electrolyte

6. **(E)**

Sodium chloride (strong electrolyte)

Na^+ Cl^- Na^+ Cl^-

Cl^- Na^+ Cl^- Na^+

Hypochlorous acid (weak electrolyte)

$H-O-Cl$
$H-O-Cl[O-Cl]^-$
$H-O-ClH_3O^+H-O-Cl$

Ammonium chloride (strong electrolyte)

$\left[\begin{matrix}H\\|\\H\text{-}N\text{-}H\\|\\H\end{matrix}\right]^+ Cl^- \left[\begin{matrix}H\\|\\H\text{-}N\text{-}H\\|\\H\end{matrix}\right]^+ Cl^- \left[\begin{matrix}H\\|\\H\text{-}N\text{-}H\\|\\H\end{matrix}\right]^+ Cl^-$

Methanol (nonelectrolyte)

$H-O-CH_3H-O-CH_3$
$H-O-CH_3$
$H-O-CH_3H-O-CH_3$

Ion Concentrations

7. **(E)**

(a) $\left[K^+\right] = \dfrac{0.238 \text{ mol } KNO_3}{1 \text{ L soln}} \times \dfrac{1 \text{ mol } K^+}{1 \text{ mol } KNO_3} = 0.238 \text{ M}$

(b) $\left[NO_3^-\right] = \dfrac{0.167 \text{ mol } Ca(NO_3)_2}{1 \text{ L soln}} \times \dfrac{2 \text{ mol } NO_3^-}{1 \text{ mol } Ca(NO_3)_2} = 0.334 \text{ M}$

(c) $\left[Al^{3+}\right] = \dfrac{0.083 \text{ mol } Al_2(SO_4)_3}{1 \text{ L soln}} \times \dfrac{2 \text{ mol } Al^{3+}}{1 \text{ mol } Al_2(SO_4)_3} = 0.166 \text{ M}$

(d) $\left[Na^+\right] = \dfrac{0.209 \text{ mol } Na_3PO_4}{1 \text{ L soln}} \times \dfrac{3 \text{ mol } Na^+}{1 \text{ mol } Na_3PO_4} = 0.627 \text{ M}$

8. **(E)** Choice (d) is the solution with the greatest concentration of sulfate ions.

(a) If we assume for the moment that H_2SO_4 ionizes completely to $2\ H^+$ and SO_4^{2-} (it does not), then

$$\frac{0.075\ \text{mol}\ H_2SO_4}{\text{L soln}} \times \frac{1\ \text{mol}\ SO_4^{2-}}{1\ \text{mol}\ H_2SO_4} = \frac{0.075\ \text{mol}\ SO_4^{2-}}{\text{L soln}}$$

However, H_2SO_4 does not ionize completely to $2\ H^+$ and SO_4^{2-}. (H_2SO_4 ionizes completely to H^+ and HSO_4^{2-}. Only some of the HSO_4^- produced by the ionization of H_2SO_4 ionizes further to SO_4^{2-}. Therefore, in 0.075 M H_2SO_4, the concentration of SO_4^{2-} is less than 0.075 mol/L.

(b) $\dfrac{0.22\ \text{mol}\ MgSO_4}{\text{L soln}} \times \dfrac{1\ \text{mol}\ SO_4^{2-}}{1\ \text{mol}\ H_2SO_4} = \dfrac{0.22\ \text{mol}\ SO_4^{2-}}{\text{L soln}}$

(c) $\dfrac{0.15\ \text{mol}\ Na_2SO_4}{\text{L soln}} \times \dfrac{1\ \text{mol}\ SO_4^{2-}}{1\ \text{mol}\ Na_2SO_4} = \dfrac{0.15\ \text{mol}\ SO_4^{2-}}{\text{L soln}}$

(d) $\dfrac{0.080\ \text{mol}\ Al_2(SO_4)_3}{\text{L soln}} \times \dfrac{3\ \text{mol}\ SO_4^{2-}}{1\ \text{mol}\ Al_2(SO_4)_3} = \dfrac{0.24\ \text{mol}\ SO_4^{2-}}{\text{L soln}}$

(e) $\dfrac{0.20\ \text{mol}\ CuSO_4}{\text{L soln}} \times \dfrac{1\ \text{mol}\ SO_4^{2-}}{1\ \text{mol}\ CuSO_4} = \dfrac{0.20\ \text{mol}\ SO_4^{2-}}{\text{L soln}}$

9. **(E)**

Conversion pathway approach:

$$[OH^-] = \frac{0.132\ \text{g}\ Ba(OH)_2 \cdot 8\ H_2O}{275\ \text{mL soln}} \times \frac{1000\ \text{mL}}{1\ \text{L}} \times \frac{1\ \text{mol}\ Ba(OH)_2 \cdot 8\ H_2O}{315.5\ \text{g}\ Ba(OH)_2 \cdot 8\ H_2O} \times \frac{2\ \text{mol}\ OH^-}{1\ \text{mol}\ Ba(OH)_2 \cdot 8\ H_2O}$$

$$= 3.04 \times 10^{-3}\ M$$

Stepwise approach:

$$\frac{0.132\ \text{g}\ Ba(OH)_2 \cdot 8\ H_2O}{275\ \text{mL soln}} \times \frac{1000\ \text{mL}}{1\ \text{L}} = 0.480\ \text{g/L}$$

$$\frac{0.480\ \text{g}}{1\ \text{L}} \times \frac{1\ \text{mol}\ Ba(OH)_2 \cdot 8\ H_2O}{315.5\ \text{g}\ Ba(OH)_2 \cdot 8\ H_2O} = \frac{0.00152\ \text{mol}\ Ba(OH)_2 \times 8\ H_2O}{\text{L}}$$

$$\frac{0.00152\ \text{mol}\ Ba(OH)_2 \times 8\ H_2O}{1\ \text{L}} \times \frac{2\ \text{mol}\ OH^-}{1\ \text{mol}\ Ba(OH)_2 \cdot 8\ H_2O} = \frac{3.04 \times 10^{-3}\ \text{mol}\ OH^-}{\text{L}}$$

10. **(E)** $\left[K^+\right] = \dfrac{0.126 \ \text{mol KCl}}{1 \ \text{L soln}} \times \dfrac{1 \ \text{mol K}^+}{1 \ \text{mol KCl}} = 0.126 \ \text{M}$

$\left[Mg^{2+}\right] = \dfrac{0.148 \ \text{mol MgCl}_2}{1 \ \text{L soln}} \times \dfrac{1 \ \text{mol Mg}^{2+}}{1 \ \text{mol MgCl}_2} = 0.148 \ \text{M}$

Now determine the amount of Cl^- in 1.00 L of the solution.

$\text{mol Cl}^- = \left(\dfrac{0.126 \ \text{mol KCl}}{1 \ \text{L soln}} \times \dfrac{1 \ \text{mol Cl}^-}{1 \ \text{mol KCl}} \right) + \left(\dfrac{0.148 \ \text{mol MgCl}_2}{1 \ \text{L soln}} \times \dfrac{2 \ \text{mol Cl}^-}{1 \ \text{mol MgCl}_2} \right)$

$= 0.126 \ \text{mol Cl}^- + 0.296 \ \text{mol Cl}^- = 0.422 \ \text{mol Cl}^-$

$\left[Cl^-\right] = \dfrac{0.422 \ \text{mol Cl}^-}{1 \ \text{L soln}} = 0.422 \ \text{M}$

11. **(E)**

(a) $[Ca^{2+}] = \dfrac{14.2 \ \text{mg Ca}^{2+}}{1 \ \text{L solution}} \times \dfrac{1 \ \text{g Ca}^{2+}}{1000 \ \text{mg Ca}^{2+}} \times \dfrac{1 \ \text{mol Ca}^{2+}}{40.078 \ \text{g Ca}^{2+}} = 3.54 \times 10^{-4} \ \text{M}$

(b) $[K^+] = \dfrac{32.8 \ \text{mg K}^+}{100 \ \text{mL solution}} \times \dfrac{1 \ \text{g K}^+}{1000 \ \text{mg K}^+} \times \dfrac{1000 \ \text{mL solution}}{1 \ \text{L solution}} \times \dfrac{1 \ \text{mol K}^+}{39.0983 \ \text{g K}^+} = 8.39 \times 10^{-3} \ \text{M}$

(c) $[Zn^{2+}] = \dfrac{225 \ \mu\text{g Zn}^{2+}}{1 \ \text{mL solution}} \times \dfrac{1 \ \text{g Zn}^{2+}}{1 \times 10^6 \ \mu\text{g Zn}^{2+}} \times \dfrac{1000 \ \text{mL solution}}{1 \ \text{L solution}} \times \dfrac{1 \ \text{mol Zn}^{2+}}{65.39 \ \text{g Zn}^{2+}} = 3.44 \times 10^{-3} \ \text{M}$

12. **(E)** $\text{molarity of NaF} = \dfrac{0.9 \ \text{mg F}^-}{1 \ \text{L}} \times \dfrac{1 \ \text{g}}{1000 \ \text{mg}} \times \dfrac{1 \ \text{mol F}^-}{18.998 \ \text{g F}^-} \times \dfrac{1 \ \text{mol NaF}}{1 \ \text{mol F}^-}$

$= 4.7 \times 10^{-5} \ \text{M} = 5 \times 10^{-5} \ \text{M}$

13. **(E)** In order to determine the solution with the largest concentration of K^+, we begin by converting each concentration to a common concentration unit, namely, molarity of K^+.

$\dfrac{0.0850 \ \text{mol K}_2\text{SO}_4}{1 \ \text{L solution}} \times \dfrac{2 \ \text{mol K}^+}{1 \ \text{mol K}_2\text{SO}_4} = 0.17 \ \text{M}$

$\dfrac{1.25 \ \text{g KBr}}{100 \ \text{mL solution}} \times \dfrac{1000 \ \text{mL solution}}{1 \ \text{L solution}} \times \dfrac{1 \ \text{mol KBr}}{119.0 \ \text{g KBr}} \times \dfrac{1 \ \text{mol K}^+}{1 \ \text{mol KBr}} = 0.105 \ \text{M}$

$\dfrac{8.1 \ \text{mg K}^+}{1 \ \text{mL solution}} \times \dfrac{1000 \ \text{mL solution}}{1 \ \text{L solution}} \times \dfrac{1 \ \text{g K}^+}{1000 \ \text{mg K}^+} \times \dfrac{1 \ \text{mol K}^+}{39.10 \ \text{g K}^+} = 0.207 \ \text{M}$

Clearly, the solution containing 8.1 mg K^+ per mL gives the largest K^+ of the three solutions.

14. **(E)**

(c) NH_3 is a weak base and would have an exceedingly low $[H^+]$; the answer is not 1.00 M NH_3. CH_3COOH is a weak acid; 0.011 M CH_3COOH would have a low $[H^+]$. H_2SO_4 has two ionizable protons per mole while HCl has but one. Thus, H_2SO_4 would have the highest $[H^+]$ in a 0.010 M aqueous solution.

15. **(M)** Determine the amount of I^- in the solution as it now exists, and the amount of I^- in the solution of the desired concentration. The difference in these two amounts is the amount of I^- that must be added. Convert this amount to a mass of MgI_2 in grams.

$$\text{moles of } I^- \text{ in final solution} = 250.0 \text{ mL} \times \frac{1 \text{ L}}{1000 \text{ mL}} \times \frac{0.1000 \text{ mol } I^-}{1 \text{ L soln}} = 0.02500 \text{ mol } I^-$$

$$\text{moles of } I^- \text{ in KI solution} = 250.0 \text{ mL} \times \frac{1 \text{ L}}{1000 \text{ mL}} \times \frac{0.0876 \text{ mol KI}}{1 \text{ L soln}} \times \frac{1 \text{ mol } I^-}{1 \text{ mol KI}} = 0.0219 \text{ mol } I^-$$

$$\text{mass } MgI_2 \text{ required} = (0.02500 - 0.0219) \text{ mol } I^- \times \frac{1 \text{ mol } MgI_2}{2 \text{ mol } I^-} \times \frac{278.11 \text{ g } MgI_2}{1 \text{ mol } MgI_2} \times \frac{1000 \text{ mg}}{1 \text{ g}}$$

$$= 4.3 \times 10^2 \text{ mg } MgI_2$$

16. **(M)** The final volume is 982 mL. We can use the conversion pathway approach to obtain the $[K^+]$.

$$[K^+] = \frac{\dfrac{15.5 \text{ mg } K_2SO_4}{1 \text{ mL}} \times 1000 \text{ mL}}{0.982 \text{ L solution}} \times \frac{1 \text{ g } K_2SO_4}{1000 \text{ mg } K_2SO_4} \times \frac{1 \text{ mol } K_2SO_4}{174.25 \text{ g } K_2SO_4} \times \frac{2 \text{ mol } K^+}{1 \text{ mol } K_2SO_4}$$

$$= 0.181 \text{ M}$$

17. **(M)** moles of chloride ion

$$= \left(0.225 \text{ L} \times \frac{0.625 \text{ mol KCl}}{1 \text{ L}} \times \frac{1 \text{ mol } Cl^-}{1 \text{ mol KCl}} \right) + \left(0.615 \text{ L} \times \frac{0.385 \text{ mol } MgCl_2}{1 \text{ L}} \times \frac{2 \text{ mol } Cl^-}{1 \text{ mol } MgCl_2} \right)$$

$$= 0.141 \text{ mol } Cl^- + 0.474 \text{ mol } Cl^- = 0.615 \text{ mol } Cl^- \quad [Cl^-] = \frac{0.615 \text{ mol } Cl^-}{0.225 \text{ L} + 0.615 \text{ L}} = 0.732 \text{ M}$$

18. **(M)** amount of NO_3^- ion =

$$\left(0.275 \text{ L} \times \frac{0.283 \text{ mol } KNO_3}{1 \text{ L}} \times \frac{1 \text{ mol } NO_3^-}{1 \text{ mol } KNO_3} \right) +$$

$$\left(0.328 \text{ L} \times \frac{0.421 \text{ mol } Mg(NO_3)_2}{1 \text{ L}} \times \frac{2 \text{ mol } NO_3^-}{1 \text{ mol } Mg(NO_3)_2} \right)$$

$$= 0.0778 \text{ mol } NO_3^- + 0.276 \text{ mol } NO_3^- = 0.354 \text{ mol } NO_3^-$$

$$[NO_3^-] = \frac{0.354 \text{ mol } NO_3^-}{0.275 \text{ L} + 0.328 \text{ L} + 0.784 \text{ L}} = 0.255 \text{ M}$$

Predicting Precipitation Reactions

19. **(E)** In each case, each available cation is paired with the available anions, one at a time, to determine if a compound is produced that is insoluble, based on the solubility rules of Chapter 5. Then a net ionic equation is written to summarize this information.

(a) $Pb^{2+}(aq) + 2\,Br^-(aq) \rightarrow PbBr_2(s)$

(b) No reaction occurs (all are spectator ions).

(c) $Fe^{3+}(aq) + 3\,OH^-(aq) \rightarrow Fe(OH)_3(s)$

20. **(E)**

(a) $Ca^{2+}(aq) + CO_3^{2-}(aq) \rightarrow CaCO_3(s)$

(b) $Ba^{2+}(aq) + SO_4^{2-}(aq) \rightarrow BaSO_4(s)$

(c) No precipitate forms (all ions stay in solution).

21. **(E)**

Mixture	Result (Net Ionic Equation)
(a) $HI(aq) + Zn(NO_3)_2(aq)$:	No reaction occurs.
(b) $CuSO_4(aq) + Na_2CO_3(aq)$:	$Cu^{2+}(aq) + CO_3^{2-}(aq) \rightarrow CuCO_3(s)$
(c) $Cu(NO_3)_2(aq) + Na_3PO_4(aq)$:	$3\,Cu^{2+}(aq) + 2\,PO_4^{3-}(aq) \rightarrow Cu_3(PO_4)_2(s)$

22. **(E)**

Mixture	Result (Net Ionic Equation)
(a) $AgNO_3(aq) + CuCl_2(aq)$:	$Ag^+(aq) + Cl^-(aq) \rightarrow AgCl(s)$
(b) $Na_2S(aq) + FeCl_2(aq)$:	$S^{2-}(aq) + Fe^{2+}(aq) \rightarrow FeS(s)$
(c) $Na_2CO_3(aq) + AgNO_3(aq)$:	$CO_3^{2-}(aq) + 2\,Ag^+(aq) \rightarrow Ag_2CO_3(s)$

23. **(E)**

(a) Add $K_2SO_4(aq)$; $BaSO_4(s)$ will form and $MgSO_4$ will not precipitate.

$$BaCl_2(s) + K_2SO_4(aq) \rightarrow BaSO_4(s) + 2\,KCl(aq)$$

(b) Add $H_2O(l)$; $Na_2CO_3(s)$ dissolves, but $MgCO_3$ (s) will not dissolve (appreciably).

$$Na_2CO_3(s) \xrightarrow{\text{water}} 2\,Na^+(aq) + CO_3^{2-}(aq)$$

(c) Add $KCl(aq)$; $AgCl(s)$ will form, while $Cu(NO_3)_2$ (s) will dissolve.

$$AgNO_3(s) + KCl(aq) \rightarrow AgCl(s) + KNO_3(aq)$$

24. (M)

(a) Add H_2O. $Cu(NO_3)_2(s)$ will dissolve, while $PbSO_4(s)$ will not dissolve (appreciably).

$$Cu(NO_3)_2(s) \xrightarrow{\text{water}} Cu^{2+}(aq) + 2\,NO_3^-(aq)$$

(b) Add $HCl(aq)$. $Mg(OH)_2(s)$ will dissolve, but $BaSO_4(s)$ will not dissolve (appreciably).

$$Mg(OH)_2(s) + 2\,HCl(aq) \rightarrow MgCl_2(aq) + 2\,H_2O(l)$$

(c) Add $HCl(aq)$. Both carbonates dissolve, but $PbCl_2(s)$ will precipitate while $CaCl_2(aq)$ remains dissolved.

$$PbCO_3(s) + 2\,HCl(aq) \rightarrow PbCl_2(s) + H_2O(l) + CO_2(g)$$

$$CaCO_3(s) + 2\,HCl(aq) \rightarrow CaCl_2(aq) + H_2O(l) + CO_2(g)$$

25. (M)

Mixture	Net Ionic Equation
(a) $Sr(NO_3)_2(aq) + K_2SO_4(aq)$:	$Sr^{2+}(aq) + SO_4^{2-}(aq) \rightarrow SrSO_4(s)$
(b) $Mg(NO_3)_2(aq) + NaOH(aq)$:	$Mg^{2+}(aq) + 2\,OH^-(aq) \rightarrow Mg(OH)_2(s)$
(c) $BaCl_2(aq) + K_2SO_4(aq)$:	$Ba^{2+}(aq) + SO_4^{2-}(aq) \rightarrow BaSO_4(s)$
	(upon filtering, KCl (aq) is obtained)

26. (M)

Mixture	Net Ionic Equation
(a) $BaCl_2(aq) + K_2SO_4(aq)$:	$Ba^{2+}(aq) + SO_4^{2-}(aq) \rightarrow BaSO_4(s)$
(b) $NaCl(aq) + AgNO_3(aq)$:	$AgCl(s) + Na^+(aq) + NO_3^-(aq)$
alternatively	
$BaCl_2(aq) + AgNO_3(aq)$:	$AgCl(s) + Ba^{2+}(aq) + SO_4^{2-}(aq)$
(c) $Sr(NO_3)_2(aq) + K_2SO_4(aq)$:	$Sr^{2+}(aq) + SO_4^{2-}(aq) \rightarrow SrSO_4(s)$
	(upon filtering, KNO₃ (aq) is obtained)

Acid–Base Reactions

27. (E) The type of reaction is given first, followed by the net ionic equation.

(a) Neutralization: $OH^-(aq) + CH_3COOH(aq) \rightarrow H_2O(l) + C_2H_3O_2^-(aq)$

(b) No reaction occurs. This is the physical mixing of two acids.

(c) Gas evolution: $FeS(s) + 2\,H^+(aq) \rightarrow H_2S(g) + Fe^{2+}(aq)$

(d) Gas evolution: $HCO_3^-(aq) + H^+(aq) \rightarrow H_2O(l) + CO_2(g)$

(e) Redox: $Mg(s) + 2\,H^+(aq) \rightarrow Mg^{2+}(aq) + H_2(g)$

28. **(E)**

(a) $NaHCO_3(s) + H^+(aq) \longrightarrow Na^+(aq) + H_2O(l) + CO_2(g)$

(b) $CaCO_3(s) + 2 H^+(aq) \longrightarrow Ca^{2+}(aq) + H_2O(l) + CO_2(g)$

(c) $Mg(OH)_2(s) + 2 H^+(aq) \longrightarrow Mg^{2+}(aq) + 2 H_2O(l)$

(d) $Mg(OH)_2(s) + 2 H^+(aq) \longrightarrow Mg^{2+}(aq) + 2 H_2O(l)$
$Al(OH)_3(s) + 3 H^+(aq) \longrightarrow Al^{3+}(aq) + 3 H_2O(l)$

(e) $NaAl(OH)_2 CO_3(s) + 4 H^+(aq) \longrightarrow Al^{3+}(aq) + Na^+(aq) + 3 H_2O(l) + CO_2(g)$

29. **(M)**

As a salt: $NaHSO_4(aq) \rightarrow Na^+(aq) + HSO_4^-(aq)$

As an acid: $HSO_4^-(aq) + OH^-(aq) \rightarrow H_2O(l) + SO_4^{2-}(aq)$

30. **(M)** Because all three compounds contain an ammonium cation, all are formed by the reaction of an acid with aqueous ammonia. The identity of the anion determines which acid present.

(a) $2 NH_3(aq) + H_3PO_4(aq) \longrightarrow (NH_4)_2 HPO_4(aq)$

(b) $NH_3(aq) + HNO_3(aq) \rightarrow NH_4NO_3(aq)$

(c) $2 NH_3(aq) + H_2SO_4(aq) \longrightarrow (NH_4)_2 SO_4(aq)$

31. **(M)** Use (b) NH_3 (aq): NH_3 affords the OH^- ions necessary to form $Mg(OH)_2(s)$.

Applicable reactions: $\{NH_3(aq) + H_2O(l) \rightarrow NH_4^+(aq) + OH^-(aq)\} \times 2$
$MgCl_2(aq) \rightarrow Mg^{2+}(aq) + 2 Cl^-(aq)$
$Mg^{2+}(aq) + 2 OH^-(aq) \rightarrow Mg(OH)_2(s)$

32. **(E)** HCl(aq) reacts with $KHSO_3$(aq) to give SO_2(g) via the thermodynamically unstable intermediate sulfurous acid (H_2SO_3).

(b) $KHSO_3$ reacts with HCl(aq) to form a gas according the net ionic equation below.
Net ionic equation: $H^+(aq) + HSO_3^-(aq) \rightarrow H_2O(l) + SO_2(g)$

(a), (c), and (d) do not form gaseous products.

(a) $H^+(aq) + SO_4^{2-}(aq) \longrightarrow HSO_4^-(aq)$

(c) $OH^-(aq) + H^+(aq) \longrightarrow H_2O(l)$

(d) $CaCl_2(aq) + HCl(aq) \longrightarrow$ no reaction

Oxidation–Reduction (Redox) Equations

__33.__ **(E)**

(a) The O.S. of H is $+1$, that of O is -2, that of C is $+4$, and that of Mg is $+2$ on each side of this equation. This is not a redox equation.

(b) The O.S. of Cl is 0 on the left and -1 on the right side of this equation. The O.S. of Br is -1 on the left and 0 on the right side of this equation. This is a redox reaction.

(c) The O.S. of Ag is 0 on the left and $+1$ on the right side of this equation. The O.S. of N is $+5$ on the left and $+4$ on the right side of this equation. This is a redox reaction.

(d) On both sides of the equation the O.S. of O is -2, that of Ag is $+1$, and that of Cr is $+6$. Thus, this is not a redox equation.

__34.__ **(E)**

(a) In this reaction, iron is reduced from Fe^{3+} (aq) to Fe^{2+} (aq) *and* manganese is reduced from a $+7$ O.S. in MnO_4^-(aq) to a $+2$ O.S. in Mn^{2+} (aq). Thus, there are two reductions and no oxidation, which is impossible.

(b) In this reaction, chlorine is oxidized from an O.S. of 0 in Cl_2 (aq) to an O.S. of $+1$ in ClO^- (aq) *and* oxygen is oxidized from an O.S. of -1 in H_2O_2 (aq) to an O.S. of 0 in O_2 (g). Consequently there are two oxidation reactions and no reduction reactions, which is impossible.

__35.__ **(E)**

(a) Reduction: $\quad 2\,SO_3^{\,2-}(aq)+6\ H^+(aq)+4\ e^- \rightarrow\ S_2O_3^{\,2-}(aq)+3\ H_2O(l)$

(b) Reduction: $\quad 2\,NO_3^-(aq)+10\ H^+(aq)+8\ e^- \rightarrow\ N_2O(g)+5\ H_2O(l)$

(c) Oxidation: $\quad Al(s)+4\ OH^-(aq) \rightarrow Al(OH)_4^-(aq)+3\ e^-$

__36.__ **(E)**

(a) $H_2C_2O_4 \xrightarrow{\text{acidic}} 2\,CO_2 + 2\,H^+ + 2e^- \qquad\qquad$ Oxidation

(b) $6\,e^- + 14\,H^+ + Cr_2O_7^{2-} \xrightarrow{\text{acidic}} 2\,Cr^{3+} + 7\,H_2O \qquad$ Reduction

(c) $2\,H_2O + 3\,e^- + MnO_4^- \xrightarrow{\text{basic}} MnO_2 + 4\,OH^- \qquad$ Reduction

__37.__ **(M)**

(a) Oxidation: $\{2\ I^-(aq) \rightarrow\ I_2(s)+2\ e^-\ \}\times 5$

Reduction: $\{MnO_4^-(aq)+8\ H^+(aq)+5\ e^- \rightarrow\ Mn^{2+}(aq)+4\ H_2O(l)\ \}\times 2$

Overall: $10\ I^-(aq)+2\ MnO_4^-(aq)+16\ H^+(aq) \rightarrow 5\ I_2(s)+2\ Mn^{2+}(aq)+8\ H_2O(l)$

(b) Oxidation: $\{ N_2H_4(l) \rightarrow N_2(g) + 4\ H^+(aq) + 4\ e^- \} \times 3$

Reduction: $\{ BrO_3^-(aq) + 6\ H^+(aq) + 6\ e^- \rightarrow Br^-(aq) + 3\ H_2O(l) \} \times 2$

Overall: $3\ N_2H_4(l) + 2\ BrO_3^-(aq) \rightarrow 3\ N_2(g) + 2\ Br^-(aq) + 6\ H_2O(l)$

(c) Oxidation: $Fe^{2+}(aq) \rightarrow Fe^{3+}(aq) + e^-$

Reduction: $VO_4^{3-}(aq) + 6\ H^+(aq) + e^- \rightarrow VO^{2+}(aq) + 3\ H_2O(l)$

Overall: $Fe^{2+}(aq) + VO_4^{3-}(aq) + 6\ H^+(aq) \rightarrow Fe^{3+}(aq) + VO^{2+}(aq) + 3\ H_2O(l)$

(d) Oxidation: $\{ UO^{2+}(aq) + H_2O(l) \rightarrow UO_2^{2+}(aq) + 2\ H^+(aq) + 2\ e^- \} \times 3$

Reduction: $\{ NO_3^-(aq) + 4\ H^+(aq) + 3\ e^- \rightarrow NO(g) + 2\ H_2O(l) \} \times 2$

Overall: $3\ UO^{2+}(aq) + 2\ NO_3^-(aq) + 2\ H^+(aq) \rightarrow 3\ UO_2^{2+}(aq) + 2\ NO(g) + H_2O(l)$

38. **(M)**

(a) Oxidation: $\{ P_4(s) + 16\ H_2O(l) \rightarrow 4\ H_2PO_4^-(aq) + 24\ H^+(aq) + 20\ e^- \} \times 3$

Reduction: $\{ NO_3^-(aq) + 4\ H^+(aq) + 3\ e^- \rightarrow NO(g) + 2\ H_2O(l) \} \times 20$

Overall: $3\ P_4(s) + 20\ NO_3^-(aq) + 8\ H_2O + 8\ H^+(aq) \rightarrow 12\ H_2PO_4^-(aq) + 20\ NO(g)$

(b) Oxidation: $\{ S_2O_3^{2-}(aq) + 5\ H_2O(l) \rightarrow 2\ SO_4^{2-}(aq) + 10\ H^+(aq) + 8\ e^- \} \times 5$

Reduction: $\{ MnO_4^-(aq) + 8\ H^+(aq) + 5\ e^- \rightarrow Mn^{2+}(aq) + 4\ H_2O(l) \} \times 8$

Overall: $5\ S_2O_3^{2-}(aq) + 8\ MnO_4^-(aq) + 14\ H^+(aq) \rightarrow 10\ SO_4^{2-}(aq) + 8\ Mn^{2+}(aq) + 7\ H_2O(l)$

(c) Oxidation: $2\ HS^-(aq) + 3\ H_2O(l) \rightarrow S_2O_3^{2-}(aq) + 8\ H^+(aq) + 8\ e^-$

Reduction: $\{ 2\ HSO_3^-(aq) + 4\ H^+(aq) + 4\ e^- \rightarrow S_2O_3^{2-}(aq) + 3\ H_2O(l) \} \times 2$

Overall: $2\ HS^-(aq) + 4\ HSO_3^-(aq) \rightarrow 3\ S_2O_3^{2-}(aq) + 3\ H_2O(l)$

(d) Oxidation: $2\ NH_3OH^+(aq) \rightarrow N_2O(g) + H_2O(l) + 6\ H^+(aq) + 4\ e^-$

Reduction: $\{ Fe^{3+}(aq) + e^- \rightarrow Fe^{2+}(aq) \} \times 4$

Overall: $4\ Fe^{3+}(aq) + 2\ NH_3OH^+(aq) \rightarrow 4\ Fe^{2+}(aq) + N_2O(g) + H_2O(l) + 6\ H^+(aq)$

39. (M)

(a) Oxidation: $\{ MnO_2(s) + 4\ OH^-(aq) \rightarrow MnO_4^-(aq) + 2\ H_2O(l) + 3\ e^- \} \times 2$

Reduction: $ClO_3^-(aq) + 3\ H_2O(l) + 6\ e^- \rightarrow Cl^-(aq) + 6\ OH^-(aq)$

Overall: $2\ MnO_2(s) + ClO_3^-(aq) + 2\ OH^-(aq) \rightarrow 2\ MnO_4^-(aq) + Cl^-(aq) + H_2O(l)$

(b) Oxidation: $\{ Fe(OH)_3(s) + 5\ OH^-(aq) \rightarrow FeO_4^{2-}(aq) + 4\ H_2O(l) + 3\ e^- \} \times 2$

Reduction: $\{ OCl^-(aq) + H_2O(l) + 2\ e^- \rightarrow Cl^-(aq) + 2OH^-(aq) \} \times 3$

Overall: $2\ Fe(OH)_3(s) + 3\ OCl^-(aq) + 4\ OH^-(aq) \rightarrow 2\ FeO_4^{2-}(aq) + 3\ Cl^-(aq) + 5\ H_2O(l)$

(c) Oxidation: $\{ ClO_2(aq) + 2\ OH^-(aq) \rightarrow ClO_3^-(aq) + H_2O(l) + e^- \} \times 5$

Reduction: $ClO_2(aq) + 2\ H_2O(l) + 5\ e^- \rightarrow Cl^-(aq) + 4\ OH^-(aq)$

Overall: $6\ ClO_2(aq) + 6\ OH^-(aq) \rightarrow 5\ ClO_3^-(aq) + Cl^-(aq) + 3\ H_2O(l)$

(d) Oxidation: $\{ Ag(s) \rightarrow Ag^+(aq) + 1\ e^- \} \times 3$

Reduction: $4\ H_2O(l) + CrO_4^{2-} + 3\ e^- \rightarrow Cr(OH)_3(s) + 5\ OH^-$

Overall: $3\ Ag(s) + CrO_4^{2-} + 4\ H_2O(l) \rightarrow 3\ Ag^+(aq) + Cr(OH)_3(s) + 5\ OH^-$

40. (M)

(a) Oxidation: $\{ S_2O_4^{2-} + 4\ OH^- \rightarrow 2\ SO_3^{2-} + 2\ H_2O + 2\ e^- \} \times 3$

Reduction: $\{ CrO_4^{2-} + 4\ H_2O + 3\ e^- \rightarrow Cr(OH)_3 + 5\ OH^- \} \times 2$

Overall: $3\ S_2O_4^{2-} + 2\ CrO_4^{2-} + 2\ H_2O + 2\ OH^- \rightarrow 6\ SO_3^{2-} + 2\ Cr(OH)_3$

(b) Oxidation: $N_2H_4(l) + 4\ OH^-(aq) \rightarrow N_2(g) + 4\ H_2O(l) + 4\ e^-$

Reduction: $\{ [Fe(CN)_6]^{3-}(aq) + e^- \rightarrow [Fe(CN)_6]^{4-}(aq) \} \times 4$

Overall: $4[Fe(CN)_6]^{3-}(aq) + N_2H_4(l) + 4\ OH^-(aq) \rightarrow 4[Fe(CN)_6]^{4-}(aq) + N_2(g) + 4\ H_2O(l)$

(c) Oxidation: $\{ Fe(OH)_2(s) + OH^-(aq) \rightarrow Fe(OH)_3(s) + e^- \} \times 4$

Reduction: $O_2(g) + 2\ H_2O(l) + 4\ e^- \rightarrow 4\ OH^-(aq)$

Overall: $4\ Fe(OH)_2(s) + O_2(g) + 2\ H_2O(l) \rightarrow 4\ Fe(OH)_3(s)$

(d) Oxidation: $\{ C_2H_5OH(aq) + 5\ OH^-(aq) \rightarrow C_2H_3O_2^-(aq) + 4\ H_2O(l) + 4\ e^- \} \times 3$

Reduction: $\{ MnO_4^-(aq) + 2\ H_2O(l) + 3\ e^- \rightarrow MnO_2(s) + 4\ OH^-(aq) \} \times 4$

Overall: $3\ C_2H_5OH(aq) + 4\ MnO_4^-(aq) \rightarrow 3\ C_2H_3O_2^-(aq) + 4\ MnO_2(s) + OH^-(aq) + 4\ H_2O(l)$

41. **(M)**

(a) Oxidation: $Cl_2(g) + 12 \ OH^-(aq) \rightarrow 2 \ ClO_3^-(aq) + 6 \ H_2O(l) + 10 \ e^-$

Reduction: $\{ Cl_2(g) + 2 \ e^- \rightarrow 2 \ Cl^-(aq) \} \times 5$

Overall: $6 \ Cl_2(g) + 12 \ OH^-(aq) \rightarrow 10 \ Cl^-(aq) + 2 \ ClO_3^-(aq) + 6 \ H_2O(l)$

Or: $3 \ Cl_2(g) + 6 \ OH^-(aq) \rightarrow 5 \ Cl^-(aq) + ClO_3^-(aq) + 3 \ H_2O(l)$

(b) Oxidation: $S_2O_4^{2-}(aq) + 2 \ H_2O(l) \rightarrow 2 \ HSO_3^-(aq) + 2 \ H^+(aq) + 2 \ e^-$

Reduction: $S_2O_4^{2-}(aq) + 2 \ H^+(aq) + 2 \ e^- \rightarrow S_2O_3^{2-}(aq) + H_2O(l)$

Overall: $2 \ S_2O_4^{2-}(aq) + H_2O(l) \rightarrow 2 \ HSO_3^-(aq) + S_2O_3^{2-}(aq)$

42. **(M)**

(a) Oxidation: $\{ MnO_4^{2-}(aq) \rightarrow MnO_4^-(aq) + e^- \} \times 2$

Reduction: $MnO_4^{2-}(aq) + 2 \ H_2O(l) + 2 \ e^- \rightarrow MnO_2(s) + 4 \ OH^-(aq)$

Overall: $3 \ MnO_4^{2-}(aq) + 2 \ H_2O(l) \rightarrow 2 \ MnO_4^-(aq) + MnO_2(s) + 4 \ OH^-(aq)$

(b) Oxidation: $\{ P_4(s) + 8 \ OH^-(aq) \rightarrow 4 \ H_2PO_2^-(aq) + 4 \ e^- \} \times 3$

Reduction: $P_4(s) + 12 \ H_2O(l) + 12 \ e^- \rightarrow 4 \ PH_3(g) + 12 \ OH^-(aq)$

Overall: $4 \ P_4(s) + 12 \ OH^-(aq) + 12 \ H_2O(l) \rightarrow 12 \ H_2PO_2^-(aq) + 4 \ PH_3(g)$

(c) Oxidation: $S_8(s) + 24 \ OH^-(aq) \rightarrow 4 \ S_2O_3^{2-}(aq) + 12 \ H_2O(l) + 16 \ e^-$

Reduction: $S_8(s) + 16 \ e^- \rightarrow 8 \ S^{2-}(aq)$

Overall: $2 \ S_8(s) + 24 \ OH^-(aq) \rightarrow 8 \ S^{2-}(aq) + 4 \ S_2O_3^{2-}(aq) + 12 \ H_2O(l)$

(d) Oxidation: $As_2S_3(s) + 40 \ OH^-(aq) \rightarrow 2 \ AsO_4^{3-}(aq) + 3 \ SO_4^{2-}(aq) + 20 \ H_2O + 28 \ e^-$

Reduction: $\{ H_2O_2(aq) + 2 \ e^- \rightarrow 2 \ OH^-(aq) \} \times 14$

Overall: $As_2S_3(s) + 12 \ OH^-(aq) + 14 \ H_2O_2(aq) \rightarrow 2 \ AsO_4^{3-}(aq) + 3 \ SO_4^{2-}(aq) + 20 \ H_2O(l)$

43. **(M)**

(a) Oxidation: $\{ NO_2^-(aq) + H_2O(l) \rightarrow NO_3^-(aq) + 2 \ H^+(aq) + 2 \ e^- \} \times 5$

Reduction: $\{ MnO_4^-(aq) + 8 \ H^+(aq) + 5 \ e^- \rightarrow Mn^{2+}(aq) + 4 \ H_2O(l) \} \times 2$

Overall: $5 \ NO_2^-(aq) + 2 \ MnO_4^-(aq) + 6 \ H^+(aq) \rightarrow 5 \ NO_3^-(aq) + 2 \ Mn^{2+}(aq) + 3 \ H_2O(l)$

(b) Oxidation: $\{ Mn^{2+} (aq) + 4\, OH^- (aq) \rightarrow MnO_2 (s) + 2\, H_2O (l) + 2\, e^- \} \times 3$

Reduction: $\underline{\{ MnO_4^- (aq) + 2\, H_2O (l) + 3\, e^- \rightarrow MnO_2 (s) + 4\, OH^- (aq)\} \times 2}$

Overall: $3\, Mn^{2+} (aq) + 2\, MnO_4^- (aq) + 4\, OH^- (aq) \rightarrow 5\, MnO_2 (s) + 2\, H_2O (l)$

(c) Oxidation: $\{ C_2H_5OH \rightarrow CH_3CHO + 2\, H^+ (aq) + 2\, e^- \} \times 3$

Reduction: $\underline{Cr_2O_7^{2-} (aq) + 14\, H^+ (aq) + 6\, e^- \rightarrow 2\, Cr^{3+} (aq) + 7\, H_2O(l)}$

Overall: $Cr_2O_7^{2-} (aq) + 8\, H^+ (aq) + 3\, C_2H_5OH \rightarrow 2\, Cr^{3+} (aq) + 7\, H_2O(l) + 3\, CH_3CHO$

44. (M)

(a) Oxidation: $\{ Al(s) \rightarrow Al^{3+} (aq) + 3\, e^- \} \times 2$

Reduction: $\underline{\{ 2\, HI(aq) + 2\, e^- \rightarrow 2\, I^- (aq) + H_2 (g) \} \times 3}$

Overall: $2\, Al(s) + 6\, HI(aq) \rightarrow 2\, AlI_3(aq) + 3\, H_2(g)$

(b) Oxidation: $Zn(s) \rightarrow Zn^{2+} (aq) + 2\, e^-$

Reduction: $\underline{\{ VO^{2+} (aq) + 2\, H^+ (aq) + e^- \rightarrow V^{3+} (aq) + H_2O(l) \} \times 2}$

Overall: $Zn(s) + 2\, VO^{2+} (aq) + 4\, H^+ (aq) \rightarrow Zn^{2+}(aq) + 2\, V^{3+}(aq) + 2\, H_2O(l)$

(c) Oxidation: $H_2O + CH_3OH \rightarrow CO_2 + 6\, H^+ + 6\, e^-$

Reduction: $\underline{\{ ClO_3^- (aq) + 2\, H^+ (aq) + e^- \rightarrow ClO_2 (aq) + H_2O(l) \} \times 6}$

Overall: $CH_3OH + 6\, ClO_3^- (aq) + 6\, H^+ \rightarrow 6\, ClO_2 (aq) + 5\, H_2O(l) + CO_2$

45. **(D)** For the purpose of balancing its redox equation, each of the reactions is treated as if it takes place in acidic aqueous solution.

(a) $2\, H_2O(g) + CH_4(g) \rightarrow CO_2(g) + 8\, H^+(g) + 8\, e^-$

$\underline{\{ 2\, e^- + 2\, H^+(g) + NO(g) \rightarrow \tfrac{1}{2}\, N_2(g) + H_2O(g) \} \times 4}$

$CH_4(g) + 4\, NO(g) \rightarrow 2\, N_2(g) + CO_2(g) + 2\, H_2O(g)$

(b) $\{ H_2S(g) \rightarrow 1/8\, S_8(s) + 2\, H^+(g) + 2\, e^- \} \times 2$

$\underline{4\, e^- + 4\, H^+(g) + SO_2(g) \rightarrow 1/8\, S_8(s) + 2\, H_2O(g)}$

$2\, H_2S(g) + SO_2(g) \rightarrow 3/8\, S_8(s) + 2\, H_2O(g)$ or

$16\, H_2S(g) + 8\, SO_2(g) \rightarrow 3\, S_8(s) + 16\, H_2O(g)$

(c) $\{ Cl_2O(g) + 2\, NH_4^+(aq) + 2\, H^+(aq) + 4\, e^- \rightarrow 2\, NH_4Cl(s) + H_2O(l)\} \times 3$

$\{ 2\, NH_3(g) \rightarrow N_2(g) + 6\, e^- + 6\, H^+(aq)\} \times 2$

$\underline{6\, NH_3(g) + 6\, H^+(aq) \rightarrow 6\, NH_4^+(aq)}$

$10\, NH_3(g) + 3\, Cl_2O(g) \rightarrow 6\, NH_4Cl(s) + 2\, N_2(g) + 3\, H_2O(l)$

46. **(D)** For the purpose of balancing its redox equation, each of the reactions is treated as if it takes place in acidic aqueous solution.

(a) $CH_4(g) + NH_3(g) \rightarrow HCN(g) + 6\,e^- + 6\,H^+$

$\underline{\{2\,e^- + 2\,H^+(g) + \frac{1}{2}\,O_2(g) \rightarrow H_2O(g)\} \times 3}$

$CH_4(g) + NH_3(g) + 3/2\,O_2(g) \rightarrow HCN(g) + 3\,H_2O(g)$

(b) $\{H_2(g) \rightarrow 2\,H^+(aq) + 2\,e^-\} \times 5$

$\underline{2\,NO(g) + 10\,H^+(aq) + 10\,e^- \rightarrow 2\,NH_3(g) + 2\,H_2O(l)}$

$5\,H_2(g) + 2\,NO(g) \rightarrow 2\,NH_3(g) + 2\,H_2O(g)$

(c) $\{Fe(s) \rightarrow Fe^{3+}(aq) + 3\,e^-\} \times 4$

$\underline{\{4\,e^- + 2\,H_2O(l) + O_2(g) \rightarrow 4\,OH^-(aq)\} \times 3}$

$4\,Fe(s) + 6\,H_2O(l) + 3\,O_2(g) \rightarrow 4\,Fe(OH)_3(s)$

Oxidizing and Reducing Agents

47. **(E)** The oxidizing agents experience a decrease in the oxidation state of one of their elements, while the reducing agents experience an increase in the oxidation state of one of their elements.

(a) $SO_3^{2-}(aq)$ is the reducing agent; the O.S. of $S = +4$ in SO_3^{2-} and $= +6$ in SO_4^{2-}.

$MnO_4^-(aq)$ is the oxidizing agent; the O.S. of $Mn = +7$ in MnO_4^- and $+2$ in Mn^{2+}.

(b) $H_2(g)$ is the reducing agent; the O.S. of $H = 0$ in $H_2(g)$ and $= +1$ in $H_2O(g)$.

$NO_2(g)$ is the oxidizing agent; the O.S. of $N = +4$ in $NO_2(g)$ and -3 in $NH_3(g)$.

(c) $\left[Fe(CN)_6\right]^{4-}(aq)$ is the reducing agent; the O.S. of $Fe = +2$ in $\left[Fe(CN)_6\right]^{4-}$

and $= +3$ in $\left[Fe(CN)_6\right]^{3-}$. $H_2O_2(aq)$ is the oxidizing agent; the O.S. of $O = -1$

in H_2O_2 and $= -2$ in H_2O.

48. **(E)**

(a) $2\,S_2O_3^{2-}(aq) + I_2(s) \rightarrow S_4O_6^{2-}(aq) + 2\,I^-(aq)$

(b) $S_2O_3^{2-}(aq) + 4\,Cl_2(g) + 5\,H_2O(l) \rightarrow 2\,HSO_4^-(aq) + 8\,Cl^-(aq) + 8\,H^+(aq)$

(c) $S_2O_3^{2-}(aq) + 4\,OCl^-(aq) + 2\,OH^-(aq) \rightarrow 2\,SO_4^{2-}(aq) + 4\,Cl^-(aq) + H_2O(l)$

Neutralization and Acid–Base Titrations

49. (E) The problem is most easily solved with amounts in millimoles.

$$V_{NaOH} = 10.00 \ \text{mL HCl(aq)} \times \frac{0.128 \ \text{mmol HCl}}{1 \ \text{mL HCl(aq)}} \times \frac{1 \ \text{mmol H}^+}{1 \ \text{mmol HCl}} \times \frac{1 \ \text{mmol OH}^-}{1 \ \text{mmol H}^+}$$

$$\times \frac{1 \ \text{mmol NaOH}}{1 \ \text{mmol OH}^-} \times \frac{1 \ \text{mL NaOH(aq)}}{0.0962 \ \text{mmol NaOH}} = 13.3 \ \text{mL NaOH(aq) soln}$$

50. (M)

$$\text{molarity of NaOH} = \frac{10.00 \ \text{mL acid} \times \dfrac{0.1012 \ \text{mmol H}_2\text{SO}_4}{1 \ \text{mL acid}} \times \dfrac{2 \ \text{mmol NaOH}}{1 \ \text{mmol H}_2\text{SO}_4}}{23.31 \ \text{mL base}} = 0.08683 \ \text{M}$$

51. (E) The net reaction is $OH^-(aq) + CH_3CH_2COOH(aq) \rightarrow H_2O(l) + CH_3CH_2COO^-(aq)$.

Conversion pathway approach:

$$V_{base} = 25.00 \ \text{mL acid} \times \frac{0.3057 \ \text{mmol CH}_3\text{CH}_2\text{COOH}}{1 \ \text{mL acid}} \times$$

$$\frac{1 \ \text{mmol KOH}}{1 \ \text{mmol CH}_3\text{CH}_2\text{COOH}} \times \frac{1 \ \text{mL base}}{2.155 \ \text{mmol KOH}}$$

$$= 3.546 \ \text{mL KOH solution}$$

Stepwise approach:

$$25.00 \ \text{mL acid} \times \frac{0.3057 \ \text{mmol CH}_3\text{CH}_2\text{COOH}}{1 \ \text{mL acid}} = 7.643 \ \text{mmol CH}_3\text{CH}_2\text{COOH}$$

$$7.643 \ \text{mmol CH}_3\text{CH}_2\text{COOH} \times \frac{1 \ \text{mmol KOH}}{1 \ \text{mmol CH}_3\text{CH}_2\text{COOH}} = 7.643 \ \text{mmol KOH}$$

$$7.643 \ \text{mmol KOH} \times \frac{1 \ \text{mL base}}{2.155 \ \text{mmol KOH}} = 3.546 \ \text{mL KOH solution}$$

52. (E) Titration reaction: $Ba(OH)_2(aq) + 2 \ HNO_3(aq) \rightarrow Ba(NO_3)_2(aq) + 2 \ H_2O(l)$

$$V_{base} = 200.0 \ \text{mL acid} \times \frac{0.0165 \ \text{mol HNO}_3}{1 \ \text{mL acid}} \times \frac{1 \ \text{mmol Ba(OH)}_2}{2 \ \text{mmol HNO}_3} \times \frac{1 \ \text{mL base}}{0.0750 \ \text{mmol Ba(OH)}_2}$$

$$= 22.0 \ \text{mL Ba(OH)}_2 \ \text{solution}$$

53. (E) $NaOH(aq) + HCl(aq) \rightarrow NaCl(aq) + H_2O(l)$ is the titration reaction.

$$\text{molarity of NaOH} = \frac{0.02834 \ \text{L} \times \dfrac{0.1085 \ \text{mol HCl}}{1 \ \text{L soln}} \times \dfrac{1 \ \text{mol NaOH}}{1 \ \text{mol HCl}}}{0.02500 \ \text{L sample}} = 0.1230 \ \text{M}$$

54. (E)

$$[NH_3] = \frac{28.72\,mL\,acid \times \dfrac{1.021\,mmol\,HCl}{1\,mL\,acid} \times \dfrac{1\,mmol\,H^+}{1\,mmol\,HCl} \times \dfrac{1\,mmol\,NH_3}{1\,mmol\,H^+}}{5.00\ \ mL\ sample} = 5.86\ \ M$$

55. (M) The mass of acetylsalicylic acid is converted to the amount of NaOH, in millimoles, that will react with it.

$$molarity\ of\ NaOH = \frac{0.32\ g\ HC_9H_7O_4}{23\ mL\ NaOH\,(aq)} \times \frac{1\ mol\ HC_9H_7O_4}{180.2\ g\ HC_9H_7O_4}$$

$$\times \frac{1\ mol\ NaOH}{1\ mol\ HC_9H_7O_4} \times \frac{1000\ mmol\ NaOH}{1\ mol\ NaOH}$$

$$= 0.077\ M$$

56. (M)

(a)

$$vol\ conc.\ acid = 20.0\ \ L \times \frac{0.10\ mol\ HCl}{1\ L\ soln} \times \frac{36.5\ g\ HCl}{1\ \ mol\ HCl} \times \frac{100\ g\ conc\ soln}{38\ g\ HCl} \times \frac{1\ mL}{1.19\ g\ conc\ soln}$$

$$= 1.6 \times 10^2\ \ mL\ conc.\ acid$$

(b) The titration reaction is $HCl\,(aq) +\ NaOH\,(aq) \rightarrow\ NaCl\,(aq) +\ H_2O\,(l)$

$$molarity\ of\ HCl = \frac{20.93\,mL\,base \times \dfrac{0.1186\,mmol\,NaOH}{1\,mL\,base} \times \dfrac{1\,mmol\,HCl}{1\,mmol\,NaOH}}{25.00\ mL\ acid} = 0.09929\ M$$

(c) First of all, the volume of the dilute solution (20 L) is known at best to a precision of two significant figures. Secondly, HCl is somewhat volatile (we can smell its odor above the solution) and some will likely be lost during the process of preparing the solution.

57. (M) The equation for the reaction is $HNO_3\,(aq) +\ KOH\,(aq) \rightarrow\ KNO_3\,(aq) +\ H_2O\,(l)$.

This equation shows that equal numbers of moles are needed for a complete reaction. We compute the amount of each reactant.

$$mmol\ HNO_3 = 25.00\ \ mL\ acid \times \frac{0.132\ \ mmol\ HNO_3}{1\ \ mL\ acid} = 3.30\ \ mmol\ HNO_3$$

$$mmol\ KOH = 10.00\ mL\ base \times \frac{0.318\ \ mmol\ KOH}{1\ \ mL\ base} = 3.18\ mmol\ KOH$$

There is more acid present than base. Thus, the resulting solution is acidic.

58. (M) Here we compute the amount of acetic acid in the vinegar and the amount of acetic acid needed to react with the sodium carbonate. If there is more than enough acid to react with the solid, the solution will remain acidic.

$$acetic\ acid\ in\ vinegar = 125\ mL \times \frac{0.762\ mmol\ CH_3COOH}{1\ mL\ vinegar} = 95.3\ \ mmol\ CH_3COOH$$

$$Na_2CO_3\,(s) + 2\ CH_3COOH\,(aq) \rightarrow 2\ NaCH_3COO\,(aq) +\ H_2O\,(l) +\ CO_2\,(g)$$

acetic acid required for solid:

$$= 7.55 \ \text{g Na}_2\text{CO}_3 \times \frac{1000 \ \text{mmol Na}_2\text{CO}_3}{106.0 \ \text{g Na}_2\text{CO}_3} \times \frac{2 \ \text{mmol CH}_3\text{COOH}}{1 \ \text{mmol Na}_2\text{CO}_3} = 143 \ \text{mmol CH}_3\text{COOH}$$

Clearly there is not enough acetic acid present to react with all of the sodium carbonate. The resulting solution will not be acidic. In fact, the solution will contain only a trace amount of acetic acid (CH_3COOH).

59. **(M)** $V_{\text{base}} = 5.00 \ \text{mL vinegar} \times \dfrac{1.01 \ \text{g vinegar}}{1 \ \text{mL}} \times \dfrac{4.0 \ \text{g CH}_3\text{COOH}}{100.0 \ \text{g vinegar}} \times \dfrac{1 \ \text{mol CH}_3\text{COOH}}{60.0 \ \text{g CH}_3\text{COOH}}$

$$\times \frac{1 \ \text{mol NaOH}}{1 \ \text{mol CH}_3\text{COOH}} \times \frac{1 \ \text{L base}}{0.1000 \ \text{mol NaOH}} \times \frac{1000 \ \text{mL}}{1 \ \text{L}} = 34 \ \text{mL base}$$

60. **(M)** The titration reaction is $2 \ \text{NaOH}(aq) + \text{H}_2\text{SO}_4(aq) \rightarrow \text{Na}_2\text{SO}_4(aq) + 2 \ \text{H}_2\text{O}(l)$

It is most convenient to consider molarity as millimoles per milliliter when solving this problem.

$$\text{molarity of H}_2\text{SO}_4 = \frac{49.74 \ \text{mL base} \times \dfrac{0.935 \ \text{mmol NaOH}}{1 \ \text{mL base}} \times \dfrac{1 \ \text{mmol H}_2\text{SO}_4}{2 \ \text{mmol NaOH}}}{5.00 \ \text{mL battery acid}} = 4.65 \ \text{M}$$

Thus, the battery acid is *not* sufficiently concentrated.

61. **(E)** Answer is (d): 120% of necessary titrant added in titration of NH_3

$$\left.\begin{array}{l} 5 \ \text{NH}_3 \\ + \\ 5 \ \text{HCl} \\ + \end{array}\right\} \begin{array}{l} \text{required for} \\ \text{equivalence} \\ \text{point} \end{array} \qquad \longrightarrow \qquad \begin{array}{l} 5 \ \text{NH}_4^+ + 6 \ \text{Cl}^- + \text{H}_3\text{O}^+ \\ \text{(depicted in question's drawing)} \end{array}$$

$$1 \ \text{HCl}\} \quad 20\% \ \text{excess}$$

62. **(E)**

(a) $\text{H}_2\text{O}(l) + \text{K}^+(aq) + \text{Cl}^-(aq)$

(b) $\text{CH}_3\text{COOH}(aq) + \text{CH}_3\text{COO}^-(aq) + \text{H}_2\text{O}(l) + \text{Na}^+(aq)$

Stoichiometry of Oxidation–Reduction Reactions

63. **(M)**

Conversion pathway approach

$$[MnO_4^-] = \frac{0.1078 \text{ g As}_2O_3 \times \dfrac{1 \text{ mol As}_2O_3}{197.84 \text{ g As}_2O_3} \times \dfrac{4 \text{ mol MnO}_4^-}{5 \text{ mol As}_2O_3} \times \dfrac{1 \text{ mol KMnO}_4}{1 \text{ mol MnO}_4^-}}{22.15 \text{ mL} \times \dfrac{1 \text{ L}}{1000 \text{ mL}}} = 0.01968 \text{ M}$$

Stepwise approach:

$$0.1078 \text{ g As}_2O_3 \times \frac{1 \text{ mol As}_2O_3}{197.84 \text{ g As}_2O_3} = 5.449 \times 10^{-4} \text{ mol As}_2O_3$$

$$5.449 \times 10^{-4} \text{ mol As}_2O_3 \times \frac{4 \text{ mol MnO}^{-4}}{5 \text{ mol As}_2O_3} = 4.359 \times 10^{-4} \text{ mol MnO}_4^-$$

$$4.359 \times 10^{-4} \text{ mol MnO}_4^- \times \frac{1 \text{ mol KMnO}_4}{1 \text{ mol MnO}_4^-} = 4.359 \times 10^{-4} \text{ mol KMnO}_4$$

$$22.15 \text{ mL} \times \frac{1 \text{ L}}{1000 \text{ mL}} = 0.02215 \text{ L solution}$$

$$\text{molarity of KMnO}_4 = \frac{4.359 \times 10^{-4} \text{ mol KMnO}_4}{0.02215 \text{ L solution}} = 1.968 \times 10^{-2} \text{ M}$$

64. **(E)** The balanced equation for the titration is:

$$5 \text{ SO}_3^{2-}(aq) + 2 \text{ MnO}_4^-(aq) + 6 \text{ H}^+(aq) \rightarrow 5 \text{ SO}_4^{2-}(aq) + 2 \text{ Mn}^{2+}(aq) + 3 \text{ H}_2O(l)$$

$$[SO_3^{2-}] = \frac{31.46 \text{ mL} \times \dfrac{0.02237 \text{ mmol KMnO}_4}{1 \text{ mL}} \times \dfrac{1 \text{ mmol MnO}_4^-}{1 \text{ mmol KMnO}_4} \times \dfrac{5 \text{ mmol SO}_3^{2-}}{2 \text{ mmol MnO}_4^-}}{25.00 \text{ mL}} = 0.07038 \text{ M}$$

65. **(M)** First, we will determine the mass of Fe, then the percentage of iron in the ore.

$$\text{mass Fe} = 28.72 \text{ mL} \times \frac{1 \text{ L}}{1000 \text{ mL}} \times \frac{0.05051 \text{ mol Cr}_2O_7^{2-}}{1 \text{ L soln}} \times \frac{6 \text{ mol Fe}^{2+}}{1 \text{ mol Cr}_2O_7^{2-}} \times \frac{55.85 \text{ g Fe}}{1 \text{ mol Fe}^{2+}}$$

$$\text{mass Fe} = 0.4861 \text{ g Fe} \qquad \% \text{Fe} = \frac{0.4861 \text{ g Fe}}{0.9132 \text{ g ore}} \times 100\% = 53.23\% \text{ Fe}$$

66. **(M)** First, balance the titration equation.

Oxidation: $\{ \text{Mn}^{2+}(aq) + 4 \text{ OH}^-(aq) \rightarrow \text{MnO}_2(s) + 2 \text{ H}_2O(l) + 2 \text{ e}^- \} \times 3$

Reduction: $\{ \text{MnO}_4^-(aq) + 2 \text{ H}_2O(l) + 3 \text{ e}^- \rightarrow \text{MnO}_2(s) + 4 \text{ OH}^-(aq) \} \times 2$

Overall: $\quad 3 \text{ Mn}^{2+}(aq) + 2 \text{ MnO}_4^-(aq) + 4 \text{ OH}^-(aq) \rightarrow 5 \text{ MnO}_2(s) + 2 \text{ H}_2O(l)$

$$[Mn^{2+}] = \frac{78.42 \text{ mL titrant} \times \dfrac{0.04997 \text{ mmol MnO}_4^-}{1 \text{ mL titrant}} \times \dfrac{3 \text{ mmol Mn}^{2+}}{2 \text{ mmol MnO}_4^-}}{50.00 \text{ mL soln}} = 0.1176 \text{ M Mn}^{2+}$$

67. **(M)** First, balance the titration equation:

Oxidation: $\{ C_2O_4^{2-}(aq) \rightarrow 2\ CO_2(g) + 2\ e^- \} \times 5$

Reduction: $\{ MnO_4^-(aq) + 8\ H^+(aq) + 5\ e^- \rightarrow Mn^{2+}(aq) + 4\ H_2O(l) \} \times 2$

Overall: $5\ C_2O_4^{2-}(aq) + 2\ MnO_4^-(aq) + 16\ H^+(aq) \rightarrow 10\ CO_2(g) + 2\ Mn^{2+}(aq) + 8\ H_2O(l)$

$mass_{Na_2C_2O_4} = 1.00\ \text{L satd soln Na}_2\text{C}_2\text{O}_4 \times \dfrac{1000\ \text{mL}}{1\ \text{L}} \times \dfrac{25.8\ \text{mL satd soln KMnO}_4}{5.00\ \text{mL satd soln Na}_2\text{C}_2\text{O}_4} \times \dfrac{0.02140\ \text{mol KMnO}_4}{1000\ \text{mL KMnO}_4}$

$\times \dfrac{1\ \text{mol MnO}_4^-}{1\ \text{mol KMnO}_4} \times \dfrac{5\ \text{mol C}_2\text{O}_4^{2-}}{2\ \text{mol MnO}_4^-} \times \dfrac{1\ \text{mol Na}_2\text{C}_2\text{O}_4}{1\ \text{mol C}_2\text{O}_4^{2-}} \times \dfrac{134.0\ \text{g Na}_2\text{C}_2\text{O}_4}{1\ \text{mol Na}_2\text{C}_2\text{O}_4}$

$mass_{Na_2C_2O_4} = 37.0\ \text{g Na}_2\text{C}_2\text{O}_4$

68. **(M)** Balanced equation:

$3\ S_2O_4^{2-}(aq) + 2\ CrO_4^{2-}(aq) + 4\ H_2O(l) \rightarrow 6\ SO_3^{2-}(aq) + 2\ Cr(OH)_3(s) + 2\ H^+(aq)$

(a) $mass\ Cr(OH)_3 = 100.\ \text{L soln} \times \dfrac{0.0126\ \text{mol CrO}_4^{2-}}{1\ \text{L soln}} \times \dfrac{2\ \text{mol Cr(OH)}_3}{2\ \text{mol CrO}_4^{2-}} \times \dfrac{103.0\ \text{g Cr(OH)}_3}{1\ \text{mol Cr(OH)}_3}$

$= 130\ \text{g Cr(OH)}_3$

(b) $mass\ Na_2S_2O_4 = 100.\ \text{L soln} \times \dfrac{0.0126\ \text{mol CrO}_4^{2-}}{1\ \text{L soln}} \times \dfrac{3\ \text{mol S}_2\text{O}_4^{2-}}{2\ \text{mol CrO}_4^{2-}} \times \dfrac{1\ \text{mol Na}_2\text{S}_2\text{O}_4}{1\ \text{mol S}_2\text{O}_4^{2-}}$

$\times \dfrac{174.1\ \text{g Na}_2\text{S}_2\text{O}_4}{1\ \text{mol Na}_2\text{S}_2\text{O}_4} = 329\ \text{g Na}_2\text{S}_2\text{O}_4$

INTEGRATIVE AND ADVANCED EXERCISES

69. (M)

(a) $2\ Na(s) + 2\ H_2O(l) \longrightarrow 2\ NaOH(aq) + H_2(g)$

(b) $Fe^{3+}(aq) + 3\ OH^-(aq) \longrightarrow Fe(OH)_3(s)$

(c) $Fe(OH)_3(s) + 3\ H_3O^+(aq) \longrightarrow Fe^{3+}(aq) + 6\ H_2O(l)$

or $Fe(OH)_3(s) + 3\ H^+(aq) \longrightarrow Fe^{3+}(aq) + 3\ H_2O(l)$

70. (M)

(a) $2\ HCl(aq) + FeS(s) \longrightarrow FeCl_2(aq) + H_2S(g)$

(b) Oxidation: $\qquad 2\ Cl^-(aq) \longrightarrow Cl_2(aq) + 2\ e^-$

Reduction: $\qquad MnO_2(s) + 4\ H^+(aq) + 2\ e^- \longrightarrow Mn^{2+}(aq) + 2\ H_2O\ (l)$

Overall: $\qquad\qquad 2\ Cl^-(aq) + MnO_2(s) + 4\ H^+(aq) \longrightarrow Cl_2(g) + Mn^{2+}(aq) + 2\ H_2O(l)$

+ Spectator Ions: $\quad 4\ HCl(aq) + MnO_2(s) \longrightarrow Cl_2(g) + MnCl_2(aq) + 2\ H_2O(l)$

(c) Because $NH_3(aq)$ is a weak base, the reaction takes place in alkaline solution.

Oxidation: $\quad 2\,NH_3(aq) \longrightarrow N_2(g) + 6\,H^+ + 6\,e^-$

Reduction: $\quad \{Br_2 + 2\,e^- \longrightarrow 2\,Br^-(aq)\} \qquad\qquad \times 3$

Overall: $\quad 2\,NH_3(aq) + 3\,Br_2 \longrightarrow N_2(g) + 6\,H^+ + 6\,Br^-(aq)$

The spectator ion is $NH_4^+(aq)$; first, add 6 $NH_3(aq)$ on each side, to "neutralize" H^+.

$$2\,NH_3(aq) + 3\,Br_2 + 6\,NH_3(aq) \longrightarrow N_2(g) + 6\,H^+ + 6\,Br^-(aq) + 6\,NH_3(aq)$$

Then, recognize that $NH_3(aq) + H^+(aq) \longrightarrow NH_4^+(aq)$, and $NH_4Br(aq)$ is really $NH_4^+(aq) + Br^-(aq)$.

$$8\,NH_3(aq) + 3\,Br_2 \longrightarrow N_2(g) + 6\,NH_4Br(aq)$$

(d) $Ba(ClO_2)_2(s) + H_2SO_4(aq) \longrightarrow 2\,HClO_2(aq) + BaSO_4(s)$

71. **(M)** A possible product, based on solubility rules, is $Ca_3(PO_4)_2$. We determine the % Ca in this compound.

$$\begin{aligned}
\text{molar mass} \quad &= 3 \times 40.078\text{ g Ca} + 2 \times 30.974\text{ g P} + 8 \times 15.999\text{ g O} \\
&= 120.23\text{ g Ca} + 61.948\text{ g P} + 127.99\text{ g O} = 310.17\text{ g}
\end{aligned}$$

$$\%\text{ Ca} = \frac{120.23\text{ g Ca}}{310.17\text{ g Ca}_3(\text{PO}_4)_2} \times 100\% = 38.763\%$$

Thus, $Ca_3(PO_4)_2$ is the predicted product. The net ionic equation follows.

$$3\,Ca^{2+}(aq) + 2\,HPO_4^{2-}(aq) \longrightarrow Ca_3(PO_4)_2(s) + 2\,H^+(aq)$$

72. **(M)** We can calculate the initial concentration of OH⁻.

$$[OH^-] = \frac{0.0250\text{ mol Ba(OH)}_2}{1\text{ L soln}} \times \frac{2\text{ mol OH}^-}{1\text{ L soln}} = 0.0500\text{ M}$$

We can determine the ratio of the dilute (volumetric flask) to the concentrated (pipet) solutions.

$$V_{conc} \times c_{conc} = V_{dil} \times c_{dil} = V_{conc} \times 0.0500\text{ M} = V_{dil} \times 0.0100\text{ M} \qquad \frac{V_{dil}}{V_{conc}} = \frac{0.0500\text{ M}}{0.0100\text{ M}} = 5.00$$

If we pipet 0.0250 M $Ba(OH)_2$ with a 50.00 mL pipet into a 250.0 mL flask, and fill this flask, with mixing, to the mark with distilled water, the resulting solution will be 0.0100 M OH^-.

73. (M)

(a) A small amount of $Na_2CO_3(s)$ mixed in with $NaOH(s)$ will have a very small effect on the pH of the final solution which for most practical cases negligile. Let's assume that the contamination is ~0.2% by mass relative to NaOH, and 1 L of a 0.1000 M solution is made.

To make a 0.1000 M NaOH solution, the amount of NaOH needed is as follows:

$$0.1000 \text{ mol NaOH} \times \frac{39.998 \text{ g NaOH}}{1 \text{ mol NaOH}} = 3.998 \text{ g NaOH}$$

Since 0.2% of this by weight is Na_2CO_3, the total mass of Na_2CO_3 is 0.007996 g. HCl reacts with NaOH and Na_2CO_3 as follows:

$$NaOH(s) + HCl(aq) \longrightarrow NaCl(aq) + H_2O \text{ (l)} \text{ AND}$$

$$Na_2CO_3(s) + 2 HCl(aq) \longrightarrow 2 NaCl(aq) + CO_2(g) + H_2O(l)$$

The amount of HCl reacted with each is therefore:

$$3.990 \text{ g NaOH} \times \frac{1 \text{ mol NaOH}}{39.998 \text{ g NaOH}} \times \frac{1 \text{ mol HCl}}{1 \text{ mol NaOH}} = 0.09980 \text{ mol HCl reacted}$$

$$0.007996 \text{ g Na}_2\text{CO}_3 \times \frac{1 \text{ mol Na}_2\text{CO}_3}{105.99 \text{ g Na}_2\text{CO}_3} \times \frac{2 \text{ mol HCl}}{1 \text{ mol Na}_2\text{CO}_3} = 1.509 \times 10^{-4} \text{ mol HCl reacted}$$

The amount of HCl needed to react with 0.2% of Na_2CO_3 is 0.15% of the total HCl reacted, which is a very small amount except very precise measurements.

(b) As the proportion of $Na_2CO_3(s)$ grows, the error it introduces becomes more significant and makes an unstandardized solution unusable for precise work. For example, trying to make the same 0.1000 M NaOH, having a 2% contamination affects the results as follows:

3.998 g NaOH × 0.02 = 0.07996 g Na_2CO_3, making the actual NaOH mass 3.918 g.

$$3.918 \text{ g NaOH} \times \frac{1 \text{ mol NaOH}}{39.998 \text{ g NaOH}} \times \frac{1 \text{ mol HCl}}{1 \text{ mol Na}_2\text{CO}_3} = 0.09800 \text{ mol HCl reacted}$$

$$0.07996 \text{ g Na}_2\text{CO}_3 \times \frac{1 \text{ mol Na}_2\text{CO}_3}{105.99 \text{ g Na}_2\text{CO}_3} \times \frac{2 \text{ mol HCl}}{1 \text{ mol Na}_2\text{CO}_3} = 1.509 \times 10^{-3} \text{ mol HCl reacted}$$

The amount of HCl needed to react with 2% of Na_2CO_3 contamination is 1.5% of the total HCl reacted, which is significant enough to make a standardized solution not trustworthy.

74. (D) Let us first determine the mass of Mg in the sample analyzed.

Conversion pathway approach:

$$\text{mass Mg} = 0.0549 \text{ g Mg}_2\text{P}_2\text{O}_7 \times \frac{1 \text{ mol Mg}_2\text{P}_2\text{O}_7}{222.55 \text{ g Mg}_2\text{P}_2\text{O}_7} \times \frac{2 \text{ mol Mg}}{1 \text{ mol Mg}_2\text{P}_2\text{O}_7} \times \frac{24.305 \text{ g}}{1 \text{ mol Mg}} = 0.0120 \text{ g Mg}$$

$$\text{ppm Mg} = 10^6 \text{ g sample} \times \frac{0.0120 \text{ g Mg}}{110.520 \text{ g sample}} = 108 \text{ ppm Mg}$$

Stepwise approach:

$$0.0549 \text{ g Mg}_2\text{P}_2\text{O}_7 \times \frac{1 \text{ mol Mg}_2\text{P}_2\text{O}_7}{222.55 \text{ g Mg}_2\text{P}_2\text{O}_7} = 2.47 \times 10^{-4} \text{mol Mg}_2\text{P}_2\text{O}_7$$

$$2.47 \times 10^{-4} \text{mol Mg}_2\text{P}_2\text{O}_7 \times \frac{2 \text{ mol Mg}}{1 \text{ mol Mg}_2\text{P}_2\text{O}_7} = 4.93 \times 10^{-4} \text{mol Mg}$$

$$4.93 \times 10^{-4} \text{mol Mg} \times \frac{24.305 \text{ g}}{1 \text{ mol Mg}} = 0.0120 \text{ g Mg}$$

$$\text{ppm Mg} = 10^6 \text{ g sample} \times \frac{0.0120 \text{ g Mg}}{110.520 \text{ g sample}} = 108 \text{ ppm Mg}$$

75. (M) Let V represent the volume of 0.248 M $CaCl_2$ that must be added.

We know that $[Cl^-]$ = 0.250 M, but also,

$$[Cl^-] = \frac{0.335 \text{ L} \dfrac{0.186 \text{ mol KCl}}{1 \text{ L soln}} \times \dfrac{1 \text{ mol Cl}^-}{1 \text{ mol KCl}} + V \times \dfrac{0.248 \text{ mol CaCl}_2}{1 \text{ L soln}} \times \dfrac{2 \text{ mol Cl}^-}{1 \text{ mol CaCl}_2}}{0.335 \text{ L} + V}$$

$$0.250(0.335 + V) = 0.0838 + 0.250 \, V = 0.0623 + 0.496 \, V \qquad V = \frac{0.0838 - 0.0623}{0.496 - 0.250} = 0.0874 \text{ L}$$

76. (D)

(a) Cu^{2+} would produce a colored solid, while for NH_4^+/Na^+, no solids are expected (these cations form very soluble salts). Therefore, Cu^{2+}, NH_4^+, and Na^+ are not present. Thus the possible cations are Ba^{2+} and Mg^{2+} (both give colorless solutions).

(b) Gas evolution when the solid reacts with HCl(aq) suggests the presence of carbonate (CO_3^{2-}).

$$2 \text{ H}^+(aq) + CO_3^{2-}(aq) \rightarrow \text{``H}_2\text{CO}_3(aq)\text{''} \rightarrow H_2O(l) + CO_2(g)$$

If the solid is indeed a mixture of carbonates, the net ionic equation for the reaction of the solid with HCl(aq) would be:

$$BaCO_3(s) + MgCO_3(s) + 4 \text{ H}^+(aq) \rightarrow Ba^{2+}(aq) + Mg^{2+}(aq) + 2 \text{ H}_2O(l) + 2 \text{ CO}_2(g)$$

The solution above contains $Ba^{2+} + Mg^{2+}$ ions, so the addition of $(NH_4)_2SO_4(aq)$ should result in the formation of the insoluble sulfates of these two metal ions. This is consistent with the observations.

Net ionic equation: $Ba^{2+}(aq) + Mg^{2+}(aq) + 2\ SO_4^{2-} \rightarrow BaSO_4(s) + MgSO_4(s)$.

If the solution above the solid should contain small quantities of all of the ions present in the solid, then it should contain $Ba^{2+}(aq)$, $Mg^{2+}(aq)$, and CO_3^{2-} (aq). Addition of KOH should result in the formation of the hydroxide of the two metal ions and potassium carbonate.

Note: K_2CO_3 and $Ba(OH)_2$ are both relatively soluble species, hence, neither of these species should precipitate out of solution. However, $Mg(OH)_2$, is relatively insoluble. A precipitate ($Mg(OH)_2(s)$ which is white) is expected to form. This is consistent with the observations provided. We can conclude that the solid is likely a mixture of $BaCO_3(s)$ and $MgCO_3(s)$. Without additional data, this conclusion would indeed explain all of the observations provided.

77. (M)

(a) Oxidation: $\{IBr(aq) + 3\ H_2O(l) \longrightarrow IO_3^-(aq) + Br^-(aq) + 6\ H^+(aq) + 4\ e^-\}$ $\times 3$

Reduction: $\{BrO_3^- + 6\ H^+(aq) + 6\ e^- \longrightarrow Br^-(aq) + 3\ H_2O\}$ $\times 2$

Overall: $3\ IBr(aq) + 3\ H_2O(l) + 2\ BrO_3^-(aq) \longrightarrow 3\ IO_3^-(aq) + 5\ Br^-(aq) + 6\ H^+(aq)$

(b) Oxidation: $\{Sn(s) \longrightarrow Sn^{2+}(aq) + 2\ e^-\}$ $\times 3$

Reduction: $C_2H_5NO_3(aq) + 6\ H^+(aq) + 6\ e^- \longrightarrow C_2H_5OH(aq) + NH_2OH(aq) + H_2O(l)$

Overall: $3\ Sn(s) + C_2H_5NO_3(aq) + 6\ H^+(aq) \longrightarrow 3\ Sn^{2+}(aq) + C_2H_5OH(aq) + NH_2OH(aq) + H_2O(l)$

(c) Oxidation: $\{As_2S_3(s) + 8\ H_2O(l) \longrightarrow 2\ H_3AsO_4(aq) + 3\ S(s) + 10\ H^+(aq) + 10\ e^-\}$ $\times 3$

Reduction: $\{NO_3^-(aq) + 4\ H^+(aq) + 3\ e^- \longrightarrow NO(g) + 2\ H_2O\}$ $\times 10$

Overall: $3\ As_2S_3(s) + 4\ H_2O(l) + 10\ NO_3^-(aq) + 10\ H^+(aq) \longrightarrow 6\ H_3AsO_4(aq) + 9\ S(s) + 10\ NO(g)$

(d) Oxidation: $I_2(aq) + 6\ H_2O(l) \longrightarrow 2\ IO_3^-(aq) + 12\ H^+(aq) + 10\ e^-$

Reduction: $\{H_5IO_6(aq) + H^+(aq) + 2\ e^- \longrightarrow IO_3^-(aq) + 3\ H_2O\}$ $\times 5$

Overall: $I_2(aq) + 5\ H_5IO_6(aq) \longrightarrow 7\ IO_3^-(aq) + 9\ H_2O(l) + 7\ H^+(aq)$

(e) Oxidation: $\{2\ S_2F_2(g) + 6\ H_2O(l) \longrightarrow H_2S_4O_6(aq) + 4\ HF(aq) + 6\ H^+(aq) + 6\ e^-\}$ $\times 4$

Reduction: $\{4\ S_2F_2(g) + 8\ H^+(aq) + 8\ e^- \longrightarrow S_8(s) + 8\ HF(aq)\}$ $\times 3$

Overall: $20\ S_2F_2(g) + 24\ H_2O(l) \longrightarrow 4\ H_2S_4O_6(aq) + 3\ S_8(s) + 40\ HF(aq)$

78. (M)

(a) Oxidation: $\{Fe_2S_3(s) + 6\ OH^-(aq) \longrightarrow 2\ Fe(OH)_3(s) + 3\ S(s)\ +\ 6\ e^-\} \times 2$

Reduction: $\{O_2(g) + 2\ H_2O(l) + 4\ e^- \longrightarrow 4\ OH^-(aq)\} \times 3$

Overall: $2\ Fe_2S_3(s) + 3\ O_2(g) + 6\ H_2O(l) \longrightarrow 4\ Fe(OH)_3(s) + 6\ S(s)$

(b) Oxidation: $\{4\ OH^-(aq) \longrightarrow O_2(g) + 2\ H_2O(l) +\ 4\ e^-\} \times 3$

Reduction: $\{O_2^-(aq) + 2\ H_2O(l) +\ 3\ e^- \longrightarrow 4\ OH^-(aq)\ \} \times 4$

Overall: $4\ O_2^-(aq) + 2\ H_2O(l) \longrightarrow 3\ O_2(g) + 4\ OH^-(aq)$

(c) Oxidation: $\{CrI_3(s) + 32\ OH^-(aq) \longrightarrow CrO_4^{2-}(aq) + 3\ IO_4^-(aq) + 16\ H_2O + 27\ e^-\ \} \times 2$

Reduction: $\{H_2O_2(aq) + 2\ e^- \longrightarrow 2\ OH^-(aq)\} \times 27$

Overall: $2\ CrI_3(s) + 10\ OH^-(aq) + 27\ H_2O_2(aq) \longrightarrow 2\ CrO_4^{2-}(aq) + 6\ IO_4^-(aq) + 32\ H_2O$

(d) Oxidation: $\{Ag(s)\ +\ 2\ CN^-(aq) \longrightarrow [Ag(CN)_2]^-(aq) + e^-\} \times 4$

Reduction: $2H_2O(l) + O_2(g) + 4\ e^- \longrightarrow 4\ OH^-(aq)$

Overall: $4\ Ag(s) + 8\ CN^-(aq) + 2\ H_2O + O_2(g) \longrightarrow 4[Ag(CN)_2]^-(aq) + 4\ OH^-(aq)$

(e) Oxidation: $B_2Cl_4(aq) + 8\ OH^-(aq) \longrightarrow 2\ BO_2^-(aq) +\ 4\ Cl^-(aq) +\ 4\ H_2O + 2\ e^-$

Reduction: $2\ H_2O(l) + 2\ e^- \longrightarrow H_2(g) + 2\ OH^-(aq)$

Overall: $B_2Cl_4(aq) + 6\ OH^-(aq) \longrightarrow 2\ BO_2^-(aq) + 4\ Cl^-(aq) + 2\ H_2O(l) + H_2(g)$

79. (M)

Oxidation: $\{P_4(s) +\ 16\ H_2O(l) \longrightarrow 4\ H_3PO_4(aq) +\ 20\ H^+(aq) + 20\ e^-\} \times 3$

Reduction: $\{P_4(s) + 12\ H^+(aq) + 12\ e^- \longrightarrow 4\ PH_3(g)\} \times 5$

Overall: $8\ P_4(s) +\ 48\ H_2O(l) \longrightarrow 12\ H_3PO_4(aq) + 20\ PH_3(g)$

Or: $2\ P_4(s) +\ 12\ H_2O(l) \longrightarrow 3\ H_3PO_4(aq) +\ 5\ PH_3(g)$

80. (D)

(a) Oxidation: $\{FeS_2 + 8\ H_2O \rightarrow Fe^{3+} + 2\ SO_4^{2-} + 16\ OH^+ + 15\ e^-\} \times 4$

Reduction: $\{O_2 + 4\ H^+ + 4\ e^- \rightarrow 2\ H_2O\} \times 15$

Overall: $4\ FeS_2(s) + 15\ O_2(g) + 2\ H_2O(l) \rightarrow 4\ Fe^{3+}(aq) + 8\ SO_4^{2-}(aq) + 4\ H^+(aq)$

(b) One kilogram of tailings contains 0.03 kg (30 g) of S. We have

$$\text{moles of FeS}_2 = 30 \text{ g S} \times \frac{1 \text{ mol S}}{32.06 \text{ g S}} \times \frac{1 \text{ mol FeS}_2}{2 \text{ mol S}} = 0.468 \text{ mol FeS}_2$$

$$\text{moles of H}^+ = 0.468 \text{ mol FeS}_2 \times \frac{4 \text{ mol H}^+}{4 \text{ mol FeS}_2} = 0.467 \text{ mol H}^+$$

$$\text{moles of CaCO}_3 = 0.467 \text{ mol H}^+ \times \frac{1 \text{ mol CaCO}_3}{2 \text{ mol H}^+} = 0.234 \text{ mol CaCO}_3$$

$$\text{mass of CaCO}_3 = 0.234 \text{ mol CaCO}_3 \times \frac{100.09 \text{ g CaCO}_3}{1 \text{ mol CaCO}_3} = 23.4 \text{ g CaCO}_3$$

81. (D) The neutralization reaction is $H_2SO_4(aq) + Ba(OH)_2(aq) \longrightarrow BaSO_4(s) + 2H_2O(l)$.

First, we determine the molarity of H_2SO_4 in the 10.00 mL of diluted acid.

$$\text{molarity of H}_2SO_4 = \frac{32.12 \text{ mL base} \times \dfrac{0.00498 \text{ mmol Ba(OH)}_2}{1 \text{ mL base}} \times \dfrac{1 \text{ mmol H}_2SO_4}{1 \text{ mmol Ba(OH)}_2}}{10.00 \text{ mL acid}} = 0.0170 \text{ M H}_2SO_4$$

Next, we determine the molarity of H_2SO_4 in the concentrated solution, using $V_{\text{conc}} \times c_{\text{conc}} = V_{\text{dil}} \times c_{\text{dil}}$.

$$1.00 \text{ mL} \times c_{\text{conc}} = 250.0 \text{ mL} \times 0.0162 \text{ M} \qquad c_{\text{conc}} = \frac{250.0 \text{ mL} \times 0.0162 \text{ M}}{1.00 \text{ mL}} = 4.25 \text{ M H}_2SO_4$$

$$\%H_2SO_4 = \frac{4.05 \text{ mol H}_2SO_4}{1 \text{ L soln}} \times \frac{98.07 \text{ g H}_2SO_4}{1 \text{ mol H}_2SO_4} \times \frac{1 \text{ L}}{1000 \text{ mL}} \times \frac{1 \text{ mL}}{1.303 \text{ g}} \times 100\% = 32.0\% \text{ H}_2SO_4$$

82. (D) The titration reaction is: $CaCO_3(s) + 2H^+(aq) \longrightarrow Ca^{2+}(aq) + H_2O(l) + CO_2(g)$.

Now we calculate the mass of the marble, through several steps, as follows.

$$\text{initial moles HCl} = 2.00 \text{ L} \times \frac{2.52 \text{ mol HCl}}{1 \text{ L soln}} = 5.04 \text{ mol HCl}$$

$NaOH(aq) + HCl(aq) \longrightarrow NaCl(aq) + H_2O$ is the titration reaction.

$$\text{final molarity of HCl} = \frac{0.02487 \text{ L} \times \dfrac{0.9987 \text{ mol NaOH}}{1 \text{ L}} \times \dfrac{1 \text{ mol HCl}}{1 \text{ mol NaOH}}}{0.01000 \text{ L}} = 2.484 \text{ M}$$

$$\text{final amount HCl} = 2.00 \text{ L} \times \frac{2.484 \text{ mol HCl}}{1 \text{ L soln}} = 4.968 \text{ mol HCl}$$

$$\text{mass CaCO}_3 = (5.04 - 4.968) \text{ mol HCl} \times \frac{1 \text{ mol CaCO}_3}{2 \text{ mol HCl}} \times \frac{100.1 \text{ g CaCO}_3}{1 \text{ mol CaCO}_3}$$

$$= 3.6 \text{ g CaCO}_3 \sim 4 \text{ g CaCO}_3$$

There are two reasons why the final result can be determined to about one significant figure. The first is the limited precision of the data given, as in the three-significant-figure limitation of the initial concentration and the total volume of the solution. The second is that the initial solution is quite concentrated for the job it must do. If it were one-tenth as concentrated, the final result could be determined more precisely because the concentration of the solution would have decreased to a greater extent.

83. (M)

Oxidation: $\{2\ Cl^-(aq) \longrightarrow Cl_2(g) + 2\ e^-\}$ ×3

Reduction: $Cr_2O_7^{2-}(aq) + 14\ H^+(aq) + 6\ e^- \longrightarrow 2\ Cr^{3+}(aq) + 7\ H_2O$

Overall: $6\ Cl^-(aq) + Cr_2O_7^{2-}(aq) + 14\ H^+(aq) \longrightarrow 2\ Cr^{3+}(aq) + 7\ H_2O + 3\ Cl_2(g)$

We need to determine the amount of $Cl_2(g)$ produced from each of the reactants. The limiting reactant is the one that produces the lesser amount of Cl_2.

$$\text{amount Cl}_2 = 325\ mL \times \frac{1.15\ g}{1\ mL} \times \frac{30.1\ g\ HCl}{100.\ g\ soln} \times \frac{1\ mol\ HCl}{36.46\ g\ HCl} \times \frac{1\ mol\ Cl^-}{1\ mol\ HCl} \times \frac{3\ mol\ Cl_2}{6\ mol\ Cl^-}$$

$$= 1.54\ mol\ Cl_2$$

$$\text{amount Cl}_2 = 62.6\ g \times \frac{98.5\ g\ K_2Cr_2O_7}{100.\ g\ sample} \times \frac{1\ mol\ K_2Cr_2O_7}{294.2\ g\ K_2Cr_2O_7} \times \frac{1\ mol\ Cr_2O_7^{2-}}{1\ mol\ K_2Cr_2O_7} \times \frac{3\ mol\ Cl_2}{1\ mol\ Cr_2O_7^{2-}}$$

$$= 0.629\ mol\ Cl_2, \text{ the amount produced from the limiting reactant}$$

Then we determine the mass of $Cl_2(g)$ produced. $= 0.629\ mol\ Cl_2 \times \dfrac{70.90\ g\ Cl_2}{1\ mol\ Cl_2} = 44.6\ g\ Cl_2$

84. (M)

Oxidation: $\{As_2O_3(s) + 5\ H_2O(l) \longrightarrow 2H_3AsO_4(aq) + 4\ H^+(aq) + 4\ e^-\}$ ×5

Reduction: $\{MnO_4^-(aq) + 8\ H^+(aq) + 5\ e^- \longrightarrow Mn^{2+}(aq) + 4\ H_2O(l)\}$ ×4

Overall: $5\ As_2O_3(s) + 9\ H_2O(l) + 4\ MnO_4^-(aq) + 12\ H^+(aq) \longrightarrow 10\ H_3AsO_4(aq) + 4\ Mn^{2+}(aq)$

molarity of $KMnO_4 = 0.02140$ M, as in Example 5-10.

$$\text{soln. volume} = 0.1304\ g \times \frac{99.96\ g\ As_2O_3}{100.00\ g\ sample} \times \frac{1\ mol\ As_2O_3}{197.84\ g\ As_2O_3} \times \frac{4\ mol\ MnO_4^-}{5\ mol\ As_2O_3} \times \frac{1\ mol\ KMnO_4}{1\ mol\ MnO_4^-}$$

$$\times \frac{1\ L\ soln}{0.02140\ mol\ KMnO_4} \times \frac{1000\ mL}{1\ L} = 24.63\ mL\ soln$$

85. (M)

$$Cl_2(g) + NaClO_2(aq) \longrightarrow NaCl(aq) + ClO_2(g) \quad \text{(not balanced)}$$

$$Cl_2(g) + 2\,NaClO_2(aq) \longrightarrow 2\,NaCl(aq) + 2\,ClO_2(g)$$

$$\text{amount } ClO_2 = 1\,\text{gal} \times \frac{3.785\,\text{L}}{1\,\text{gal}} \times \frac{2.0\,\text{mol } NaClO_2}{1\,\text{L soln}} \times \frac{2\,\text{mol } ClO_2}{2\,\text{mol } NaClO_2} \times \frac{67.45\,\text{g } ClO_2}{1\,\text{mol } ClO_2}$$

$$\times \frac{97\,\text{g } ClO_2 \text{ produced}}{100\,\text{g } ClO_2 \text{ calculated}} = 5.0 \times 10^2\,\text{g } ClO_2(g)$$

86. (M) $CaCO_3(s) + 2\,HCl(aq) \rightarrow CaCl_2(aq) + H_2O(l) + CO_2(g)$

$HCl(aq) + NaOH(aq) \rightarrow H_2O(l) + NaCl(aq)$

$n_{HCl(initial)} = 0.06500\,\text{L} \times 0.4984\,\text{M} = 0.3240\,\text{mol HCl}$

$n_{OH^-} = 0.03845\,\text{L} \times 0.2257\,\text{M} = 0.008678\,\text{mol OH}^-$

$$n_{HCl(excess)} = 0.008678\,\text{mol OH}^- \times \frac{1\,\text{mol HCl}}{1\,\text{mol OH}^-} = 0.008678\,\text{mol HCl}$$

$n_{HCl(reacted)} = n_{HCl(initial)} - n_{HCl(excess)} = 0.03240\,\text{mol HCl} - 0.008678\,\text{mol HCl} = 0.2372\,\text{mol HCl}$

$$\text{mass } Ca^{2+} = 0.02372\,\text{mol HCl} \times \frac{1\,\text{mol } CaCO_3}{2\,\text{mol HCl}} \times \frac{1\,\text{mol } Ca^{2+}}{1\,\text{mol } CaCO_3} \times \frac{40.078\,\text{g } Ca^{2+}}{1\,\text{mol } Ca^{2+}} \times \frac{1000\,\text{mg } Ca^{2+}}{1\,\text{g } Ca^{2+}}$$

$$= 475.3\,\text{mg } Ca^{2+}$$

87. (M) Let X_{KOH} = mass of KOH in grams and X_{LiOH} be the mass of LiOH in grams.

(Note: Molar masses: KOH = 56.105 g mol^{-1} and LiOH = 23.95 g mol^{-1})

moles of HCl = $c \times V = 0.3520\,\text{M} \times 0.02828\,\text{L} = 0.009956\,\text{mol HCl}$

We can set up two equations for the two unknowns:

$X_{KOH} + X_{LiOH} = 0.4324$ g and since moles of HCl = moles of OH$^-$ (Stoichiometry is 1:1)

$$0.009956\,\text{mol OH}^- = \frac{X_{KOH}}{56.105} + \frac{X_{LiOH}}{23.95}$$

Make the substitution that $X_{KOH} = 0.4324\,\text{g} - X_{LiOH}$

$$0.009956\,\text{mol OH}^- = \frac{(0.4324 - X_{LiOH})}{56.105} + \frac{X_{LiOH}}{23.95} = \frac{0.4324}{56.105} - \frac{X_{LiOH}}{56.105} + \frac{X_{LiOH}}{23.95}$$

Collect terms: $0.009956\,\text{mol OH}^- = 0.007707\,\text{mol OH}^- + 0.02393 X_{LiOH}\,\text{mol OH}^-$

$0.009956\,\text{mol OH}^- - 0.007707\,\text{mol OH}^- = 0.02393 X_{LiOH}\,\text{mol OH}^- = 0.002249\,\text{mol OH}^-$

$X_{LiOH} = 0.09397\,\text{g LiOH}$ hence, $X_{KOH} = 0.4324\,\text{g} - 0.09397\,\text{g} = 0.3384\,\text{g}$

$$\text{Mass \% LiOH} = \frac{0.09397\,\text{g}}{0.4324\,\text{g}} \times 100 = 21.73 \qquad \text{Mass \% KOH} = \frac{0.3384\,\text{g}}{0.4324\,\text{g}} \times 100 = 78.26$$

88. (D)

(a) First, balance the redox equations needed for the calculation.

Oxidation: $\{HSO_3^- (aq) + H_2O(l) \rightarrow SO_4^{2-} (aq) + 3\,H^+ (aq) + 2\,e^-\} \times 3$

Reduction: $\underline{IO_3^- (aq) + 6\,H^+ (aq) + 6\,e^- \rightarrow I^- (aq) + 3\,H_2O(l)}$

Overall: $3\,HSO_3^- (aq) + IO_3^- (aq) \rightarrow 3\,SO_4^{2-} (aq) + 3\,H^+ (aq) + I^- (aq)$

The solution volume of 5.00 L contains 29.0 g $NaIO_3$. This represents
29.0 g/197.9 g/mol $NaIO_3$ = 0.147 mol $NaIO_3$.

(b) From the above equation, we need 3 times that molar amount of $NaHSO_3$, which is
3(0.147 mol) = 0.441 mol $NaHSO_3$; the molar mass of $NaHSO_3$ is 104.06 g/mol.

The required mass then is 0.441(104.06) = 45.9 g.

For the second process:

Oxidation: $\{2\,I^- (aq) \rightarrow I_2(aq) + 2\,e^-\} \times 5$

Reduction: $\underline{2\,IO_3^- (aq) + 12\,H^+ (aq) + 10\,e^- \rightarrow I_2(aq) + 6\,H_2O(l)}$

Overall: $5\,I^- (aq) + IO_3^- (aq) + 6\,H^+ (aq) \rightarrow 3\,I_2(aq) + 3\,H_2O(l)$

In Step 1, we produced 1 mol of I^- for every mole of IO_3^- reactant; therefore we had
0.147 mol I^-.

In step 2, we require 1/5 mol IO_3^- for every mol of I^-.

We require only 1.00 L of the solution in the question instead of the 5.00 L in the first
step.

89. (D)

$Mg(OH)_2(aq) + 2\,HCl(aq) \rightarrow MgCl_2(aq) + 2\,H_2O(l)$ (1)

$Al(OH)_3(aq) + 3\,HCl(aq) \rightarrow AlCl_3(aq) + 3\,H_2O(l)$ (2)

$HCl(aq) + NaOH(aq) \rightarrow NaCl(aq) + H_2O(l)$ (3)

initial moles of HCl = $0.0500 \text{ L} \times \dfrac{0.500 \text{ mol}}{1 \text{ L}} = 0.0250$ mol

moles of HCl that reacted with NaOH = moles of HCl left over from reaction with active
ingredients

$= 0.0165 \text{ L} \times \dfrac{0.377 \text{ mol NaOH}}{1 \text{ L}} \times \dfrac{1 \text{ mol HCl}}{1 \text{ mol NaOH}} = 6.22 \times 10^{-3}$ mol

moles of HCl that react with active ingredients = $0.0250 \text{ mol} - 6.22 \times 10^{-3} \text{ mol} = 0.0188$ mol

$\begin{bmatrix} \text{\# moles HCl that} \\ \text{react with Mg(OH)}_2 \end{bmatrix} + \begin{bmatrix} \text{\# moles HCl that} \\ \text{react with Al(OH)}_3 \end{bmatrix} = \text{total moles of HCl reacted/used}$

Let the mass of $Mg(OH)_2$ in the sample be X grams.

moles HCl that react with $Mg(OH)_2$ =

$$\left[X \text{ g } Mg(OH)_2 \times \frac{1 \text{ mol } Mg(OH)_2}{58.32 \text{ g } Mg(OH)_2} \times \frac{2 \text{ mol HCl}}{1 \text{ mol } Mg(OH)_2} \right]$$

moles HCl that react with $Al(OH)_3$ =

$$\left[(0.500 - X) \text{ g } Al(OH)_3 \times \frac{1 \text{ mol } Al(OH)_3}{78.00 \text{ g } Al(OH)_3} \times \frac{3 \text{ mol HCl}}{1 \text{ mol } Al(OH)_3} \right]$$

$$\frac{2X}{58.32} + \frac{3(0.500 - X)}{78.00} = 0.0188$$

X = 0.108, therefore the mass of $Mg(OH)_2$ in the sample is 0.108 grams.

% $Mg(OH)_2$ = (0.108/0.500) × 100 = 21.6   %Al = 100 − %$Mg(OH)_2$ = 78.4

90. (D) The first step is to balance the chemical equation. Using the method outlined in the text, we obtain the following result:

$$8 \text{ H}^+(aq) + MnO_4^-(aq) + 5 \text{ Fe}^{2+}(aq) \rightarrow Mn^{2+}(aq) + 5 \text{ Fe}^{3+}(aq) + 4 \text{ H}_2O(l)$$

$$0.04217 \text{ L} \times \frac{0.01621 \text{ mol } KMnO_4}{1 \text{ L}} \times \frac{1 \text{ mol } MnO_4^-}{1 \text{ mol } KMnO_4} \times \frac{5 \text{ mol } Fe^{2+}}{1 \text{ mol } MnO_4^-} = 0.003418 \text{ mol } Fe^{2+}$$

$$0.003418 \text{ mol Fe in sample} \times \frac{55.845 \text{ g}}{1 \text{ mol}} = 0.1909 \text{ g Fe}$$

0.2729 g sample − 0.1909 g Fe = 0.0820 g O

$$0.0820 \text{ g O} \times \frac{1 \text{ mol}}{16.00 \text{ g}} = 0.005125 \text{ mol O} \xrightarrow{+0.003418} = 1.499$$

$$0.003418 \text{ mol Fe} \xrightarrow{+0.003418} = 1.000$$

The empirical formula is $FeO_{1.5}$, or Fe_2O_3.

91. (M)

$$0.1386 \text{ g AgI} \times \frac{1 \text{ mol AgI}}{234.77 \text{ g AgI}} \times \frac{1 \text{ mol } CHI_3}{3 \text{ mol AgI}} \times \frac{1 \text{ mol } C_{19}H_{16}O_4}{1 \text{ mol } CHI_3} \times \frac{308.33 \text{ g } C_{19}H_{16}O_4}{1 \text{ mol } C_{19}H_{16}O_4}$$

$$= 0.06068 \text{ g } C_{19}H_{16}O_4$$

$$\% \ C_{19}H_{16}O_4 = \frac{0.06068 \text{ g}}{13.96 \text{ g}} \times 100 = 0.4346$$

92. (M) The first step is to balance the chemical equation. By using the method described in the text, we obtain the following result:

$$3\ CuS(s) + 8\ NO_3^-(aq) + 11\ H^+(aq) \rightarrow 3\ Cu^{2+}(aq) + 8\ NO(g) + 3\ HSO_4^-(aq) + 4\ H_2O(l)$$

The next step is to calculate the volume of solution required:

$$1\ kg\ CuS \times \frac{1000\ g}{1\ kg} \times \frac{1\ mol\ CuS}{95.61\ g\ CuS} \times \frac{8\ mol\ HNO_3}{3\ mol\ CuS} \times \frac{63.01\ g\ HNO_3}{1\ mol\ HNO_3} = 1757.7\ g\ HNO_3$$

$$1757.7\ g\ HNO_3 \times \frac{100\ g\ soln}{70\ g\ HNO_3} \times \frac{1\ mL\ soln}{1.40\ g\ soln} = 1793.6\ mL = 2000\ mL\ (\text{to 1 sig fig})$$

93. (M) (a)

$$CaO(s) + H_2O(l) \rightarrow Ca^{2+}(aq) + 2\ OH^-(aq)$$

$$H_2PO_4^-(aq) + 2\ OH^-(aq) \rightarrow PO_4^{3-}(aq) + 2\ H_2O(l)$$

$$HPO_4^-(aq) + OH^-(aq) \rightarrow PO_4^{3-}(aq) + H_2O(l)$$

$$5\ Ca^{2+}(aq) + 3\ PO_4^{3-}(aq) + OH^-(aq) \rightarrow Ca_5(PO_4)_3OH(s)$$

(b) $1.00 \times 10^4\ L \times \dfrac{10.0 \times 10^{-3}\ g\ P}{L} \times \dfrac{1\ mol\ P}{30.97\ g\ P} \times \dfrac{1\ mol\ PO_4^{3-}}{1\ mol\ P} \times \dfrac{5\ mol\ Ca^{2+}}{3\ mol\ PO_4^{3-}}$

$$\times \frac{1\ mol\ CaO}{1\ mol\ Ca^{2+}} \times \frac{56.08\ g\ CaO}{1\ mol\ CaO} = 301.80\ g\ CaO = 302\ g = 0.302\ kg$$

FEATURE PROBLEMS

94. (D) From the volume of titrant, we can calculate both the amount in moles of NaC_5H_5 and (through its molar mass of 88.08 g/mol) the mass of NaC_5H_5 in a sample. The remaining mass in a sample is that of C_4H_8O (72.11 g/mol), whose amount in moles we calculate. The ratio of the molar amount of C_4H_8O in the sample to the molar amount of NaC_5H_5 is the value of x.
Conversion pathway approach:

$$\text{moles of } NaC_5H_5 = 0.01492\ L \times \frac{0.1001\ mol\ HCl}{1\ L\ soln} \times \frac{1\ mol\ NaOH}{1\ mol\ HCl} \times \frac{1\ mol\ NaC_5H_5}{1\ mol\ NaOH}$$

$$= 0.001493\ mol\ NaC_5H_5$$

$$\text{mass of } C_4H_8O = 0.242\ g\ sample - \left(0.001493\ mol\ NaC_5H_5 \times \frac{88.09\ g\ NaC_5H_5}{1\ mol\ NaC_5H_5} \right)$$

$$= 0.111\ g\ C_4H_8O$$

$$x = \frac{0.110\ g\ C_4H_8O \times \dfrac{1\ mol\ C_4H_8O}{72.11\ g\ C_4H_8O}}{0.001493\ mol\ NaC_5H_5} = 1.03$$

Stepwise approach:

$$0.01492 \ L \times \frac{0.1001 \ mol \ HCl}{1 \ L \ soln} = 1.493 \times 10^{-3} \ mol \ HCl$$

$$1.493 \times 10^{-3} \ mol \ HCl \times \frac{1 \ mol \ NaOH}{1 \ mol \ HCl} = 1.493 \times 10^{-3} \ mol \ NaOH$$

$$1.493 \times 10^{-3} \ mol \ NaOH \times \frac{1 \ mol \ NaC_5H_5}{1 \ mol \ NaOH} = 1.493 \times 10^{-3} \ mol \ NaC_5H_5$$

$$1.493 \times 10^{-3} \ mol \ NaC_5H_5 \times \frac{88.09 \ g \ NaC_5H_5}{1 \ mol \ NaC_5H_5} = 0.1315 \ g \ NaC_5H_5$$

mass of $C_4H_8O = 0.242$ g sample $- \ 0.1315$ g $NaC_5H_5 = 0.111$ g C_4H_8O

$$0.111 g \ C_4H_8O \times \frac{1 mol \ C_4H_8O}{72.11 g \ C_4H_8O} = 1.54 \times 10^{-3} \ mol \ C_4H_8O$$

$$\frac{1.54 \times 10^{-3} \ mol \ C_4H_8O}{0.001493 \ mol \ NaC_5H_5} = 1.03$$

For the second sample, parallel calculations give 0.001200 mol NaC_5H_5, 0.093 g C_4H_8, $x = 1.1$. There is rounding error in this second calculation because it is limited to two significant figures. The best answer is from the first run $x \sim 1.03$ or 1. The formula is $NaC_5H_5(THF)_1$.

95. **(D)** First, we balance the two equations.

Oxidation: $H_2C_2O_4(aq) \rightarrow 2 \ CO_2(g) + 2 \ H^+(aq) + 2 \ e^-$

Reduction: $MnO_2(s) + 4 \ H^+(aq) + 2 \ e^- \rightarrow Mn^{2+}(aq) + 2 \ H_2O(l)$

Overall: $H_2C_2O_4(aq) + MnO_2(s) + 2 \ H^+(aq) \rightarrow 2 \ CO_2(g) + Mn^{2+}(aq) + 2 \ H_2O(l)$

Oxidation: $\{ H_2C_2O_4(aq) \rightarrow 2 \ CO_2(g) + 2 \ H^+(aq) + 2 \ e^- \} \times 5$

Reduction: $\{ MnO_4^-(aq) + 8 \ H^+(aq) + 5 \ e^- \rightarrow Mn^{2+}(aq) + 4 \ H_2O(l) \} \times 2$

Overall: $5 \ H_2C_2O_4(aq) + 2 \ MnO_4^-(aq) + 6 \ H^+(aq) \rightarrow 10 \ CO_2(g) + 2 \ Mn^{2+}(aq) + 8 \ H_2O(l)$

Next, we determine the mass of the excess oxalic acid.

$$\text{mass } H_2C_2O_4 \cdot 2 \ H_2O = 0.03006 \ L \times \frac{0.1000 \ mol \ KMnO_4}{1 L} \times \frac{1 \ mol \ MnO_4^-}{1 \ mol \ KMnO_4} \times \frac{5 \ mol \ H_2C_2O_4}{2 \ mol \ MnO_4^-}$$

$$\times \frac{1 \ mol \ H_2C_2O_4 \cdot 2 \ H_2O}{1 \ mol \ H_2C_2O_4} \times \frac{126.06 \ g \ H_2C_2O_4 \cdot 2 \ H_2O}{1 \ mol \ H_2C_2O_4 \cdot 2 \ H_2O} = 0.9474 \ g \ H_2C_2O_4 \cdot 2 \ H_2O$$

The mass of $H_2C_2O_4 \cdot 2H_2O$ that reacted with $MnO_2 = 1.651$ g $- 0.9474$ g $= 0.704$ g $H_2C_2O_4 \cdot 2 \ H_2O$

$$\text{mass } MnO_2 = 0.704 \ g \ H_2C_2O_4 \cdot 2 \ H_2O \times \frac{1 \ mol \ H_2C_2O_4}{126.06 \ g \ H_2C_2O_4 \cdot 2 \ H_2O} \times \frac{1 \ mol \ MnO_2}{1 \ mol \ H_2C_2O_4} \times \frac{86.9 \ g \ MnO_2}{1 \ mol \ MnO_2}$$

$$= 0.485 \ g \ MnO_2$$

$$\% \ MnO_2 = \frac{0.485 \ g \ MnO_2}{0.533 \ g \ sample} \times 100\% = 91.0\% \ MnO_2$$

96. **(D)** Reactions: $2\ NH_3 + H_2SO_4 \rightarrow (NH_4)_2SO_4$ and $\quad H_2SO_4 + 2\ NaOH \rightarrow 2\ H_2O + Na_2SO_4$

n_{OH^-} (used to find moles H_2SO_4 in excess) $= 0.03224\ L \times 0.4498\ M = 0.01450\ mol\ OH^-$

$n_{H_2SO_4}$ (in excess) $= 0.01450\ mol\ OH^- \times \dfrac{1\ mol\ H_2SO_4}{2\ mol\ OH^-} = 0.00725\underline{108}\ mol\ H_2SO_4$

n_{OH^-} (used to find moles H_2SO_4 in separate unreacted sample) $= 0.02224\ L \times 0.4498\ M$

$= 0.0100\underline{035}\ mol\ OH^-$

$n_{H_2SO_4}$ (initial) $= 0.0100\underline{035}\ mol\ OH^- \times \dfrac{1\ mol\ H_2SO_4}{2\ mol\ OH^-} = 0.005002\ mol\ H_2SO_4$

NOTE: this was in a 25.00 mL sample: we need to scale up to 50.00 mL.

Hence, $n_{H_2SO_4}$ (initial) $= 2 \times 0.005002\ mol\ H_2SO_4 = 0.0100\underline{035}\ mol\ H_2SO_4$

$n_{H_2SO_4}$ (reacted) $= n_{H_2SO_4}$ (initial) $- n_{H_2SO_4}$ (excess)

$= 0.0100\underline{035}\ mol\ H_2SO_4 - 0.00725\underline{108}\ mol\ H_2SO_4 = 0.00275\ mol\ H_2SO_4$

$n_{NH_3} = 0.00275\ mol\ H_2SO_4 \times \dfrac{2\ mol\ NH_3}{1\ mol\ H_2SO_4} = 0.00550\underline{5}\ mol\ NH_3$

$mass_{NH_3} = 0.00550\underline{5}\ mol\ NH_3 \times \dfrac{1\ mol\ N}{1\ mol\ NH_3} \times \dfrac{14.007\ g\ N}{1\ mol\ N} = 0.0771\ g\ N\ in\ sample$

mass protein in sample $= 0.0771\ g\ N\ in\ sample \times \dfrac{100\ g\ protein}{16\ g\ N} = 0.48\underline{2}\ g\ protein\ in\ sample$

percent protein in sample $= \dfrac{0.48\underline{2}\ g\ protein\ in\ sample}{1.250\ g\ sample} \times 100\% = 38.\underline{6}\%\ protein$

<u>**97.**</u> **(D)**

The molecular formula for CH_3CH_2OH is C_2H_6O and for CH_3COOH is $C_2H_4O_2$.

The first step is to balance the oxidation–reduction reaction.

Oxidation: $\{C_2H_6O + H_2O \rightarrow C_2H_4O_2 + 4\ H^+ + 4\ e^-\} \times 3$

Reduction: $\{Cr_2O_7^{2-} + 14\ H^+ + 6\ e^- \rightarrow 2\ Cr^{3+} + 7\ H_2O\} \times 2$

Overall: $3\ C_2H_6O + 2\ Cr_2O_7^{2-} + 16\ H^+ \rightarrow 3\ C_2H_4O_2 + 4\ Cr^{3+} + 11\ H_2O$

Before the breath test:

$\dfrac{0.75\ mg\ K_2Cr_2O_7}{3\ mL} \times \dfrac{1\ g}{1000\ mg} \times \dfrac{1\ mol}{294.18\ g} \times \dfrac{1000\ mL}{1\ L} = 8.498 \times 10^{-4}\ M$

$= 8 \times 10^{-4}\ M\ (\text{to 1 sig fig})$

For the breath sample:

$BrAC = \dfrac{0.05\ g\ C_2H_6O}{100\ mL\ blood} \times \dfrac{1\ mL\ blood}{2100\ mL\ breath} = \dfrac{2.38 \times 10^{-7}\ g\ C_2H_6O}{mL\ breath}$

mass $C_2H_6O = \dfrac{2.38 \times 10^{-7}\ g\ C_2H_6O}{mL\ breath} \times 500.\ mL\ breath = 1.19 \times 10^{-4}\ g\ C_2H_6O$

Calculate the amount of $K_2Cr_2O_7$ that reacts:

$$1.19 \times 10^{-4}\,\text{g C}_2\text{H}_6\text{O} \times \frac{1\,\text{mol C}_2\text{H}_6\text{O}}{46.069\,\text{g C}_2\text{H}_6\text{O}} \times \frac{2\,\text{mol Cr}_2\text{O}_7^{2-}}{3\,\text{mol C}_2\text{H}_6\text{O}} \times \frac{1\,\text{mol K}_2\text{Cr}_2\text{O}_7}{1\,\text{mol Cr}_2\text{O}_7^{2-}}$$

$$= 1.72 \times 10^{-6}\,\text{mol K}_2\text{Cr}_2\text{O}_7$$

mol $K_2Cr_2O_7$ remaining = moles $K_2Cr_2O_7$ before – moles $K_2Cr_2O_7$ that reacts

moles $K_2Cr_2O_7$ before $= 0.75\,\text{mg K}_2\text{Cr}_2\text{O}_7 \times \dfrac{1\,\text{g}}{1000\,\text{mg}} \times \dfrac{1\,\text{mol}}{294.18\,\text{g}} = 2.5 \times 10^{-6}\,\text{mol}$

mol $K_2Cr_2O_7$ remaining $= 2.5 \times 10^{-6}\,\text{mol} - 1.72 \times 10^{-6}\,\text{mol} = 0.78 \times 10^{-6}\,\text{mol}$

concentration of $K_2Cr_2O_7$ after the breath test $= 0.78 \times 10^{-6}\,\text{mol}/0.003\,\text{L} = 2.6 \times 10^{-4}\,\text{mol/L} = 3 \times 10^{-4}\,\text{mol/L}$ (to 1 sig fig)

98. (D)

(a) *Step 1: Assign oxidation states to each element in the reaction and identify the species being oxidized and reduced.*

The oxidation state of Cr is +6 in $Cr_2O_7^{2-}$ and +3 in Cr^{3+}. The oxidation state of Cl is -1 in Cl^- and 0 in Cl_2. Each Cr gains three electrons and each Cl loses one electron.

Step 2: Write separate, unbalanced half-equations for the oxidation and reduction half-reactions.

Oxidation: $Cl^- \rightarrow Cl_2$

Reduction: $Cr_2O_7^{2-} \rightarrow Cr^{3+}$

Step 3: Balance the separate half-equations, in this order:

First, with respect to the element being oxidized or reduced

Oxidation: $2\,Cl^- \rightarrow Cl_2$

Reduction: $Cr_2O_7^{2-} \rightarrow 2\,Cr^{3+}$

Then, by adding electrons to one side or the other to account for the number of electrons produced (oxidation) or consumed (reduction)

Keep in mind that *each* Cl loses one electron and *each* Cr gains three electrons.

Oxidation: $2\,Cl^- \rightarrow Cl_2 + 2\,e^-$

Reduction: $Cr_2O_7^{2-} + 6\,e^- \rightarrow 2\,Cr^{3+}$

Step 4: Combine the half-equations algebraically so that the total number of electrons cancels out.

Oxidation: $\{2\,Cl^- \rightarrow Cl_2 + 2\,e^-\} \times 3$

Reduction: $\underline{\{Cr_2O_7^{2-} + 6\,e^- \rightarrow 2\,Cr^{3+}\}}$

Overall: $6\,Cl^- + Cr_2O_7^{2-} \rightarrow 3\,Cl_2 + 2\,Cr^{3+}$

Step 5: Balance the net charge by adding either H^+ (for acidic solutions) or OH^- (for basic solutions).

The reaction occurs in acidic solution, so we use H^+ to balance charge. The total charge on the left side of the overall equation is $6(-1) + (-2) = -8$. The total charge on the right side is $3(0) + 2(+3) = +6$. To balance charge, add 14 H^+ to the left side:

$$6\,Cl^- + Cr_2O_7^{2-} + 14\,H^+ \rightarrow 3\,Cl_2 + 2\,Cr^{3+}$$

Step 6: Balance H and O by adding H_2O.

Add 7 H_2O to the right side to balance hydrogen. This also balances oxygen. The balanced equation is given below:

$$6\,Cl^- + Cr_2O_7^{2-} + 14\,H^+ \rightarrow 3\,Cl_2 + 2\,Cr^{3+} + 7\,H_2O$$

(b) *Step 1: Assign oxidation states to each element in the reaction and identify the species being oxidized and reduced.*

The oxidation state of C is +3 in $C_2O_4^{2-}$ (treating the C's as equivalent) and +4 in CO_3^{2-}. The oxidation state of Mn is +7 in MnO_4^- and +4 in MnO_2. Each Mn gains three electrons and each C loses one electron.

Step 2: Write separate, unbalanced half-equations for the oxidation and reduction half-reactions.

Oxidation: $C_2O_4^{2-} \rightarrow CO_3^{2-}$

Reduction: $MnO_4^- \rightarrow MnO_2$

Step 3: Balance the separate half-equations, in this order:

First with respect to the element being oxidized or reduced

Oxidation: $C_2O_4^{2-} \rightarrow 2\,CO_3^{2-}$

Reduction: $MnO_4^- \rightarrow MnO_2$

Then, by adding electrons to one side or the other to account for the number of electrons produced (oxidation) or consumed (reduction)

Keep in mind that *each* C loses one electron and *each* Mn gains three electrons.

Oxidation: $C_2O_4^{2-} \rightarrow 2\,CO_3^{2-} + 2\,e^-$

Reduction: $MnO_4^- + 3\,e^- \rightarrow MnO_2$

Step 4: Combine the half-equations algebraically so that the total number of electrons cancels out.

Oxidation: $\{C_2O_4^{2-} \rightarrow 2\,CO_3^{2-} + 2\,e^-\} \times 3$

Reduction: $\underline{\{MnO_4^- + 3\,e^- \rightarrow MnO_2\} \times 2}$

Overall: $3\,C_2O_4^{2-} + 2\,MnO_4^- \rightarrow 6\,CO_3^{2-} + 2\,MnO_2$

Step 5: Balance the net charge by adding either H^+ (for acidic solutions) or OH^- (for basic solutions).

The reaction occurs in basic solution, so we use OH^- to balance charge. The total charge on the left side of the overall equation is $3(-2) + 2(-1) = -8$. The total charge on the right side is $6(-2) + 2(0) = -12$. To balance charge, we must add 4 OH^- to the left side:

$$3\ C_2O_4^{2-} + 2\ MnO_4^- + 4\ OH^- \rightarrow 6\ CO_3^{2-} + 2\ MnO_2$$

Step 6: Balance H and O by adding H_2O.

Add 2 H_2O to the right-hand side to balance hydrogen. This also balances oxygen. The balanced equation is given below:

$$3\ C_2O_4^{2-} + 2\ MnO_4^- + 4\ OH^- \rightarrow 6\ CO_3^{2-} + 2\ MnO_2 + 2\ H_2O$$

SELF-ASSESSMENT EXERCISES

99. (E)

   (a) $\rightleftharpoons$: The process/reaction is reversible

   (b) [ ] : A shorthand notation to indicate molar concentration

   (c) A spectator ion does not participate in a reaction and remains unchanged.

   (d) A weak acid is one that does not fully ionize in water. A solution of that acid contains a large amount of the acid in its in molecular form.

100. (E)

   (a) Half-equation method of balancing redox reactions: A method of balancing equations in which the major oxidation and reduction half-reactions are balanced separately

   (b) Disproportionation reaction: A reaction in which a substance is both oxidized and reduced

   (c) Titration: A method of determining the concentration of an unknown by reacting it with a reactant of known volume and concentration

   (d) Standardization of a solution: The process of determining the exact concentration of a solution

101. (E)

   (a) Strong electrolyte vs. strong acid: A strong electrolyte ionizes fully in water to its constituent ions. A strong acid ionizes fully in water to give a proton and an anion. A strong acid is always a strong electrolyte, but a strong electrolyte need not be an acid

   (b) Oxidizing vs. reducing agent: An oxidizing agent removes electrons from a reactant (it gets reduced itself), while a reducing agent gives electrons to a reactant (it gets oxidized itself).

   (c) Precipitation vs. neutralization reaction: In a precipitation reaction, an insoluble product is formed and is removed from the solution phase. In a neutralization reaction, an acid and a base react with each other to form a salt and perhaps also water.

   (d) Half-reaction vs. overall reaction: A half-reaction represents either the oxidation or reduction portion of a reaction. The overall reaction is the summation of the oxidation and reduction half-reactions.

102. **(E)** The answer is (b).

Conversion pathway approach:

$$0.300 \text{ L} \times \frac{0.0050 \text{ mol Ba(OH)}_2}{1 \text{ L}} \times \frac{2 \text{ mol OH}^-}{1 \text{ mol Ba(OH)}_2} = 0.0030 \text{ mol}$$

Stepwise approach:

$$0.300 \text{ L} \times \frac{0.0050 \text{ mol Ba(OH)}_2}{1 \text{ L}} = 1.5 \times 10^{-3} \text{ mol Ba(OH)}_2$$

$$1.5 \times 10^{-3} \text{ mol Ba(OH)}_2 \times \frac{2 \text{ mol OH}^-}{1 \text{ mol Ba(OH)}_2} = 0.0030 \text{ mol}$$

103. **(E)** The answer is (d). A 0.10 M solution of H_2SO_4 will have $[H^+]$ somewhere between 0.10 M and 0.20 M, which is greater than $[H^+]$ for any of the other solutions. As pointed out in Table 5.2, H_2SO_4 is a strong acid only in its first ionization step. So the first ionization step will provide 0.10 mol/L of H^+ and the second ionization will make an additional contribution that is less than 0.10 mol/L.

104. **(E)** The answer is (c). Based on the solubility guidelines in Table 5-1, carbonates (CO_3^{2-}) are insoluble.

105. **(M)** The answer is (a). Reaction with ZnO gives $ZnCl_2$ (soluble) and H_2O. There is no reaction with NaBr and Na_2SO_4, since all species are aqueous. By the process of elimination, (a) is the answer.

106. **(D)** The solid compound dissolves readily to yield a solution that conducts electricity. Therefore, the unknown compound is either a soluble ionic compound or a strong acid or base. The pungent odor produced by treatment with NaOH(aq) indicates the presence of NH_4^+ ions in the solid compound, which react with OH^- as follows: $NH_4^+ + OH^- \rightarrow NH_3 + H_2O$. The presence of NH_4^+ ions in the compound is consistent with the observation that the compound is soluble. Treatment of the solid with $Cu(NO_3)_2$ does not produce a precipitate, an observation that indicates the anion of the unknown solid combines with Cu^{2+} to produce a soluble copper compound. Focusing on information provided in Table 5.1, the anion could be NO_3^-, CH_3COO^-, ClO_4^-, Cl^-, Br^-, I^-, or SO_4^{2-}. However, treatment of the unknown solid with Ba^{2+}(aq) yields a precipitate, an observation that eliminates all these anions except for sulfate. The unknown might be $(NH_4)_2SO_4$.

107. **(E)**

Balanced equation: $2 \text{ KI} + Pb(NO_3)_2 \rightarrow 2 \text{ KNO}_3 + PbI_2$

Net ionic equation: $2 \text{ I}^- + Pb^{2+} \rightarrow PbI_2 \text{ (s)}$

108. **(E)**

Balanced equation: $Na_2CO_3 + 2 \text{ HCl} \rightarrow 2 \text{ NaCl} + H_2O + CO_2$

Net ionic equation: $CO_3^{2-} + 2 \text{ H}^+ \rightarrow H_2O \text{ (l)} + CO_2 \text{(g)}$

109. (M)

(a) Balanced equation: $2\,Na_3PO_4 + 3\,Zn(NO_3)_2 \rightarrow 6\,NaNO_3 + Zn_3(PO_4)_2$

Net ionic equation: $3\,Zn^{2+} + PO_4^{3-} \rightarrow Zn_3(PO_4)_2\,(s)$

(b) Balanced equation: $2\,NaOH + Cu(NO_3)_2 \rightarrow Cu(OH)_2 + 2\,NaNO_3$

Net ionic equation: $Cu^{2+} + 2\,OH^- \rightarrow Cu(OH)_2\,(s)$

(c) Balanced equation: $NiCl_2 + Na_2CO_3 \rightarrow NiCO_3 + 2\,NaCl$

Net ionic equation: $Ni^{2+} + CO_3^{2-} \rightarrow NiCO_3\,(s)$

110. (M)

(a) Species oxidized: N in NO

(b) Species reduced: O_2

(c) Oxidizing agent: O_2

(d) Reducing agent: NO

(e) Gains electrons: O_2

(f) Loses electrons: NO

111. (M)

(a)

Oxidation:	$Cl_2(aq) + 4\,OH^-(aq)$	$\rightarrow$	$2\,ClO^-(aq) + 2\,H_2O(l) + 2e^-$
Reduction:	$Cl_2(aq) + 2e^-$	$\rightarrow$	$2\,Cl^-(aq)$
Overall:	$2\,Cl_2(aq) + 4\,OH^-(aq)$	$\rightarrow$	$2\,ClO^-(aq) + 2\,Cl^-(aq) + 2\,H_2O(l)$
or:	$Cl_2(aq) + 2\,OH^-(aq)$	$\rightarrow$	$ClO^-(aq) + Cl^-(aq) + H_2O(l)$

(b)

Oxidation: $\{\,C_2O_4^{2-}(aq) \rightarrow 2\,CO_2(g) + 2e^-\,\} \times 5$

Reduction: $\{\,MnO_4^-(aq) + 8\,H^+(aq) + 5e^- \rightarrow Mn^{2+}(aq) + 4\,H_2O(l)\,\} \times 2$

Overall: $5\,C_2O_4^{2-}(aq) + 2\,MnO_4^-(aq) + 16\,H^+(aq) \rightarrow 10\,CO_2(g) + 2\,Mn^{2+}(aq) + 8\,H_2O(l)$

112. (M) The answer is (b). The charges need to be balanced on both sides. Using a coefficient of 4, the charges on both sides of the reaction becomes +12.

113. (D) The answer is (d), $5\,ClO^-$ to $1\,I_2$. The work to balance the half-equations is shown below:

Reduction: $5\,ClO^- + 2\,H^+ + 2\,e^- \rightarrow Cl^- + H_2O$

Oxidation: $I_2 + 6\,H_2O \rightarrow 2\,IO_3^- + 10\,e^- + 12\,H^+$

To combine the above reactions, the oxidation reaction should be multiplied by 5. The combined equation is:

Combined: $5\,ClO^- + I_2 + H_2O \rightarrow 5\,Cl^- + 2\,IO_3^- + 2\,H^+$

114. (M) The answer is (a). The balanced half-equation is as follows:

$NpO_2^+ + 4\,H^+ + e^- \rightarrow Np^{4+} + 2\,H_2O$

115. (E) The answer is (c). SO_2 is a gas and a nonelectrolyte, HF is a weak acid and therefore a weak electrolyte, and $FeSO_4$ fully dissociates in water and therefore is a strong electrolyte.

116. **(E)** The answer is (b). HNO_2 is a weak acid, NH_3 is a weak base, and NH_4NO_2 is the salt formed by their reaction.

117. **(E)** The answer is (d). $Pb(ClO_4)_2$ and $Ca(NO_3)_2$ are soluble in water. Hg_2SO_4 is insoluble.

118. **(M)**
   (a) False. Based on solubility rules, $BaCl_2$ dissolves well in water. Therefore, it is a strong electrolyte.
   (b) True. Since H^- is a base, H_2O is by necessity an acid. It also reduces H^- (–1) to H_2 (0).
   (c) False. The product of such a reaction would be NaCl and H_2CO_3, neither of which precipitates out.
   (d) False. HF is among the strongest of weak acids. It is not a strong acid, because it doesn't completely ionize in water.
   (e) True. For every mole of $Mg(NO_3)_2$, there are 3 moles of ions, in contrast to 2 moles of ions for $NaNO_3$.

119. **(M)**
   (a) No. Oxidation states of C, H or O do not change throughout the reaction.
   (b) Yes. Li is oxidized to Li^+ and H in H_2O is reduced from +1 to 0 in H_2.
   (c) Yes. Ag is oxidized and Pt is reduced.
   (d) No. Oxidation states of Cl, Ca, H, and O remain unchanged.

120. **(E)** The dissociation of acetic acid in water can be expressed as follows:
$HAc + H_2O \rightarrow Ac^- + H_3O^+$
If HAc dissociates by 5% and assuming an initial value of 100 HAc molecules, 5 molecules of HAc dissociate to give 5 H^+ and 5 Ac^- ions, while 95 HAc molecules remain. In other words, for every 19 HAc molecules, there is one H^+ and one Ac^-.

121. **(M)** To construct a concept map, one must first start with the most general concepts. These concepts are defined by or in terms of other simpler concepts discussed in those sections. In this case, the overarching concept is oxidation-reduction reactions. This concept can be further explained by defining electron transfer. Oxidation involves the loss of electrons, reduction the gain. Subtopics that fall under the rubric of oxidation-reduction reactions are oxidizing agents (which get reduced) and reducing agents. The concept of half-reactions is another subtopic, and balancing half-reaction falls under half-reactions. Balancing the overall reaction falls under the subtopic of balancing half reactions. Take a look at the subsection headings and problems for more refining of the general and specific concepts.

CHAPTER 6
GASES

PRACTICE EXAMPLES

1A (E) The pressure measured by each liquid must be the same. They are related through $P = g\,h\,d$ Thus, we have the following: $g\,h_{DEG}\,d_{DEG} = g\,h_{Hg}\,d_{Hg}$. The g's cancel; we substitute known values:

$9.25\ m_{DEG} \times 1.118\ g/cm^3\,_{DEG} = h_{Hg} \times 13.6\ g/cm^3$

$h_{Hg} = 9.25\,m \times \dfrac{1.118\,g/cm^3}{13.6\,g/cm^3} = 0.760\ m\ Hg,\ \ P = 0.760\ mHg = 760\ mmHg$

1B (E) The solution is found through the expression relating density and height: $h_{TEG}d_{TEG} = h_{Hg}d_{Hg}$

We substitute known values and solve for triethylene glycol's density:
$9.14\ m_{TEG} \times d_{TEG} = 757\ mmHg \times 13.6\ g/cm^3$. Using unit conversions, we get

$d_{TEG} = \dfrac{0.757\ m}{9.14\ m} \times 13.6\ g/cm^3 = 1.13\ g/cm^3$

2A (E) We know that $P_{gas} = P_{bar.} + \Delta P$ with $P_{bar.} = 748.2$ mmHg. We are told that $\Delta P = 7.8$ mmHg. Thus, $P_{gas} = 748.2$ mmHg + 7.8 mmHg = 756.0 mmHg.

2B (M) The difference in pressure between the two levels must be the same, just expressed in different units. Hence, this problem is almost a repetition of Practice Example 6-1.
$h_{Hg} = 748.2$ mmHg – 739.6 mmHg = 8.6 mmHg. Again we have $g\,h_g\,d_g = g\,h_{Hg}\,d_{Hg}$. This becomes $h_g \times 1.26\ g/cm^3 = 8.6\ mmHg \times 13.6\ g/cm^3$

$h_g = 8.6\,mmHg \times \dfrac{13.6\,g/cm^3}{1.26\,g/cm^3} = 93\,mm\ glycerol$

3A (M) $A = \pi r^2$ (here $r = \frac{1}{2}(2.60\ cm \times \dfrac{1\ m}{100\ cm}) = 0.0130\ m$)

$A = \pi(0.0130\ m)^2 = 5.31 \times 10^{-4}\ m^2$
$F = m \times g = (1.000\ kg)(9.81\ m\ s^{-2}) = 9.81\ kg\ m\ s^{-2} = 9.81\ N$
$P = \dfrac{F}{A} = \dfrac{9.81\ N}{5.31 \times 10^{-4}\ m^2} = 18{,}475\ N\ m^{-2}\ or\ 1.85 \times 10^4\ Pa$
$P\ (Torr) = 1.85 \times 10^4\ Pa \times = 139\ Torr$

3B **(M)** Final pressure = 100 mbar. $100 \text{ mbar} \times \dfrac{101,325 \text{ Pa}}{1013.25 \text{ mbar}} = 1.000 \times 10^4 \text{ Pa}$

The area of the cylinder is unchanged from that in Example 6-3, $(1.32 \times 10^{-3} \text{ m}^2)$.

$P = \dfrac{F}{A} = 1.000 \times 10^4 \text{ Pa} = \dfrac{F}{1.32 \times 10^{-3} \text{ m}^2}$

Solving for F, we find $F = 13.2$ (Pa)m^2 = 13.2 (N m^{-2})m^2 = 13.2 N

$F = m \times g = 13.2 \text{ kg m s}^{-2} = m \times 9.81 \text{ m s}^{-2}$

total mass = mass of cylinder + mass added weight = $m = \dfrac{F}{g} = \dfrac{13.2 \text{ kg m s}^{-2}}{9.81 \text{ m s}^{-2}} = 1.35 \text{ kg}$

An additional 350 grams must be added to the top of the 1.000 kg (1000 g) red cylinder to increase the pressure to 100 mbar. It is not necessary to add a mass with the same cross-sectional area. The pressure will only be exerted over the area that is the base of the cylinder on the surface beneath it.

4A **(M)** The ideal gas equation is solved for volume. Conversions are made within the equation.

$V = \dfrac{nRT}{P} = \dfrac{\left(20.2 \text{ g NH}_3 \times \dfrac{1 \text{ mol NH}_3}{17.03 \text{ g NH}_3}\right) \times \dfrac{0.08206 \text{ L} \cdot \text{atm}}{\text{mol} \cdot \text{K}} \times (-25 + 273) \text{ K}}{752 \text{ mmHg} \times \dfrac{1 \text{ atm}}{760 \text{ mmHg}}} = 24.4 \text{ L NH}_3$

4B **(E)** The amount of $Cl_2(g)$ is 0.193 mol Cl_2 and the pressure is 0.993 bar. This information is substituted into the ideal gas equation after it has been solved for temperature.

$T = \dfrac{PV}{nR} = \dfrac{0.993 \text{ bar} \times 7.50 \text{ L}}{0.193 \text{ mol} \times 0.08314 \text{ bar L mol}^{-1} \text{ K}^{-1}} = 464 \text{ K}$

5A **(E)** The ideal gas equation is solved for amount and the quantities are substituted.

$n = \dfrac{PV}{RT} = \dfrac{10.5 \text{ atm} \times 5.00 \text{ L}}{\dfrac{0.08206 \text{ atm L}}{\text{mol K}} \times (30.0 + 273.15) \text{ K}} = 2.11 \text{ mol}$

5B **(M)**

$n = \dfrac{PV}{RT} = \dfrac{\left(6.67 \times 10^{-7} \text{ Pa}\right)\left(3.45 \text{ m}^3\right)}{(8.3145 \text{ Pa m}^3 \text{ L mol}^{-1} \text{ K}^{-1})(25 + 273.15)\text{K}} = 9.28 \times 10^{-10} \text{ mol N}_2$

molecules of N_2 = 9.28×10^{-10} mol $N_2 \times \dfrac{6.022 \times 10^{23} \text{ molecules N}_2}{1 \text{ mol N}_2}$

$= 5.59 \times 10^{14}$ molecules N_2

6A **(E)** The general gas equation is solved for volume, after the constant amount in moles is cancelled. Temperatures are converted to kelvin.

$$V_2 = \frac{V_1 P_1 T_2}{P_2 T_1} = \frac{1.00\,\text{mL} \times 2.14\,\text{atm} \times (37.8 + 273.2)\,\text{K}}{1.02\,\text{atm} \times (36.2 + 273.2)\,\text{K}} = 2.11\,\text{mL}$$

6B **(M)** The flask has a volume of 1.00 L and initially contains $O_2(g)$ at STP. The mass of $O_2(g)$ that must be released is obtained from the difference in the amount of $O_2(g)$ at the two temperatures, 273 K and 373 K. We also could compute the masses separately and subtract them.

$$\text{mass released} = \left(n_{\text{STP}} - n_{100\,°\text{C}}\right) \times M_{O_2} = \left(\frac{PV}{R \times 273\,\text{K}} - \frac{PV}{R \times 373\,\text{K}}\right) \times M_{O_2} = \frac{PV}{R}\left(\frac{1}{273\,\text{K}} - \frac{1}{373\,\text{K}}\right) \times M_{O_2}$$

$$= \frac{1.00\,\text{bar} \times 1.00\,\text{L}}{0.08314\,\text{bar L mol}^{-1}\,\text{K}^{-1}}\left(\frac{1}{273\,\text{K}} - \frac{1}{373\,\text{K}}\right) \times \frac{32.00\,\text{g}}{1\,\text{mol O}_2} = 0.378\,\text{g O}_2$$

7A **(M)** The volume of the vessel is 0.09841 L. The mass of the O_2 sample is $(40.4868 - 40.1305)\,\text{g} = 0.3563\,\text{g}$. We substitute other values into the expression for molar mass.

$$M = \frac{mRT}{PV} = \frac{(0.3563\,\text{g}) \times \dfrac{0.08206\,\text{atm L}}{\text{mol} \cdot \text{K}} \times (22.4 + 273.2)\,\text{K}}{\left(772\,\text{mmHg} \times \dfrac{1\,\text{atm}}{760\,\text{mmHg}}\right) \times 0.09841\,\text{L}} = 86.5\,\text{g/mol}$$

7B **(M)** The gas's molar mass is the mass of the sample (1.27 g) divided by the amount of the gas in moles. The amount can be determined from the ideal gas equation.

$$n = \frac{PV}{RT} = \frac{0.982\,\text{bar} \times 1.07\,\text{L}}{\dfrac{0.08314\,\text{bar L}}{\text{mol K}} \times (25 + 273)\,\text{K}} = 0.0424\,\text{mol gas}$$

$$M = \frac{1.27\,\text{g}}{0.0424\,\text{mol}} = 30.0\,\text{g/mol}$$

This answer is in good agreement with the molar mass of NO, 30.006 g/mol.

8A **(M)** The molar mass of He is 4.003 g/mol. This is substituted into the expression for density.

$$d = \frac{MP}{RT} = \frac{4.003\,\text{g mol}^{-1} \times 0.987\,\text{bar}}{0.08314\,\text{bar L mol}^{-1}\,\text{K}^{-1} \times 298\,\text{K}} = 0.159\,\text{g/L}$$

When compared to the density of air under the same conditions (1.16 g/L, based on the "average molar mass of air" = 28.8 g/mol) the density of He is only about one seventh as much. Thus, helium is less dense ("lighter") than air.

8B **(M)** The suggested solution is a simple one; we merely need to solve for mass of gas from density and its moles from the ideal gas equation.

$$m(\text{gas}) = d \times V = (1.00 \text{ g/L})(1.00 \text{ L}) = 1.00 \text{ g}$$

$$n = \frac{PV}{RT} = \frac{\left(745 \text{ mmHg} \times \dfrac{1 \text{ atm}}{760 \text{ mmHg}}\right)(1.00 \text{ L})}{0.08206 \text{ L atm mol}^{-1} \text{ K}^{-1} \times 382 \text{ K}} = 0.0312 \text{ mol}$$

Therefore, the molar mass of the gas is as follows:

$$M = \frac{m}{n} = \frac{1.00 \text{ g}}{0.0312 \text{ mol}} = 32.0 \text{ g/mol}$$

The molecular weight suggests that the gas is O_2.

9A **(M)** The balanced equation is $2 \text{ NaN}_3(s) \xrightarrow{\Delta} 2 \text{ Na}(l) + 3 \text{ N}_2(g)$

$$\text{moles N}_2 = \frac{PV}{RT} = \frac{\left(776 \text{ mmHg} \times \dfrac{1 \text{ atm}}{760 \text{ mmHg}}\right) \times 20.0 \text{ L}}{\dfrac{0.08206 \text{ atm L}}{\text{mol K}} \times (30.0 + 273.2) \text{ K}} = 0.821 \text{ mol N}_2$$

Now, solve the stoichiometry problem.

$$\text{mass NaN}_3 = 0.821 \text{ mol N}_2 \times \frac{2 \text{ mol NaN}_3}{3 \text{ mol N}_2} \times \frac{65.01 \text{ g NaN}_3}{1 \text{ mol NaN}_3} = 35.6 \text{ g NaN}_3$$

9B **(M)** Here we are not dealing with gaseous reactants; the law of combining volumes cannot be used. From the ideal gas equation we determine the amount of $N_2(g)$ per liter under the specified conditions. Then we determine the amount of $Na(l)$ produced simultaneously, and finally the mass of that $Na(l)$.

$$\text{mass of Na}(l) = \frac{1.00 \text{ bar} \times 1.000 \text{ L}}{\dfrac{0.08314 \text{ bar L}}{\text{mol K}} \times (25 + 273) \text{ K}} \times \frac{2 \text{ mol Na}}{3 \text{ mol N}_2} \times \frac{22.99 \text{ g Na}}{1 \text{ mol Na}} = 0.619 \text{ g Na}(l)$$

10A **(E)** The law of combining volumes permits us to use stoichiometric coefficients for volume ratios.

$$O_2 \text{ volume} = 1.00 \text{ L NO}(g) \times \frac{5 \text{ L O}_2}{4 \text{ L NO}} = 1.25 \text{ L O}_2(g)$$

10B **(E)** The first task is to balance the chemical equation. There must be three moles of hydrogen for every mole of nitrogen in both products (because of the formula of NH_3) and reactants: $N_2(g) + 3 H_2(g) \rightarrow 2 NH_3(g)$. The volumes of gaseous reactants and products are related by their stoichiometric coefficients, as long as all gases are at the same temperature and pressure.

$$\text{volume NH}_3(g) = 225 \text{ L H}_2(g) \times \frac{2 \text{ L NH}_3(g)}{3 \text{ L H}_2(g)} = 150. \text{ L NH}_3$$

11A **(M)** We can work easily with the ideal gas equation, with a the new temperature of $T = (55+273)$ K $= 328$ K. The amount of Ne added is readily computed.

$$n_{Ne} = 12.5 \text{ g Ne} \times \frac{1 \text{ mol Ne}}{20.18 \text{ g Ne}} = 0.619 \text{ mol Ne}$$

$$P = \frac{n_{tot}RT}{V} = \frac{(1.75+0.619) \text{mol} \times \dfrac{0.08314 \text{ bar L}}{\text{mol K}} \times 328 \text{ K}}{5.0 \text{ L}} = 13 \text{ bar}$$

11B **(E)** The total volume initially is 2.0 L $+ 8.0$ L $= 10.0$ L. These two mixed ideal gases then obey the general gas equation as if they were one gas.

$$P_2 = \frac{P_1 V_1 T_2}{V_2 T_1} = \frac{1.00 \text{ atm} \times 10.0 \text{ L} \times 298 \text{ K}}{2.0 \text{ L} \times 273 \text{ K}} = 5.5 \text{ atm}$$

12A **(M)** The partial pressures are proportional to the mole fractions.

$$P_{H_2O} = \frac{n_{H_2O}}{n_{tot}} \times P_{tot} = \frac{0.00278 \text{ mol}}{0.197 \text{ mol} + 0.00278 \text{ mol}} \times 2.50 \text{ atm} = 0.0348 \text{ atm}$$

$$P_{CO_2} = P_{tot} - P_{H_2O} = 2.50 \text{ atm} - 0.0348 \text{ atm} = 2.47 \text{ atm}$$

12B **(M)** Expression (6.17) indicates that, in a mixture of gases, the mole percent equals the volume percent, which in turn equals the pressure percent. Thus, we can apply these volume percents—converted to fractions by dividing by 100—directly to the total pressure.

N_2 pressure $= 0.7808 \times 748$ mmHg $= 584$ mmHg,

O_2 pressure $= 0.2095 \times 748$ mmHg $= 157$ mmHg,

Ar pressure $= 0.0093 \times 748$ mmHg $= 7.0$ mmHg,

CO_2 pressure $= 0.00036 \times 748$ mmHg $= 0.27$ mmHg

13A **(M)** First compute the moles of $H_2(g)$, then use stoichiometry to convert to moles of HCl.

$$\text{amount HCl} = \frac{\left((755-25.2) \text{ mmHg} \times \dfrac{1 \text{ atm}}{760 \text{ mmHg}}\right) \times 0.0355 \text{ L}}{\dfrac{0.08206 \text{ atm L}}{\text{mol K}} \times (26+273) \text{ K}} \times \frac{6 \text{ mol HCl}}{3 \text{ mol H}_2} = 0.00278 \text{ mol HCl}$$

13B **(M)** The volume occupied by the $O_2(g)$ at its partial pressure is the same as the volume occupied by the mixed gases: water vapor and $O_2(g)$. The partial pressure of $O_2(g)$ is found by difference.

$$P_{O_2} = P_{bar.} - P_{H_2O} = 749.2 \text{ mmHg} - 23.8 \text{ mmHg} = 725.4 \text{ mmHg}$$

$$\text{mol } O_2 = \frac{PV}{RT} = \frac{\left(725.4 \text{ mmHg} \times \dfrac{1 \text{ atm}}{760 \text{ mmHg}}\right)(0.395 \text{ L})}{\left(0.08206 \text{ atm L mol}^{-1}\text{K}^{-1}\right)(298 \text{ K})} = 0.0154 \text{ mol } O_2$$

$$\text{mass Ag}_2\text{O} = 0.0154 \text{ mol O}_2 \times \frac{2 \text{ mol Ag}_2\text{O}}{1 \text{ mol O}_2} \times \frac{231.74 \text{ g Ag}_2\text{O}}{1 \text{ mol Ag}_2\text{O}} = 7.14 \text{ g Ag}_2\text{O}$$

$$\text{Mass\% Ag}_2\text{O} = 7.14 \text{ g}/8.07 \text{ g} \times 100 = 88.4$$

14A **(M)** The gas with the smaller molar mass, NH_3 at 17.0 g/mol, has the greater root-mean-square speed.

$$u_{rms} = \sqrt{\frac{3RT}{M}} = \sqrt{\frac{3 \times 8.3145 \text{ kg m}^2 \text{ s}^{-2} \text{mol}^{-1} \text{ K}^{-1} \times 298 \text{ K}}{0.0170 \text{ kg mol}^{-1}}} = 661 \text{ m/s}$$

14B **(D)**

$$\text{bullet speed} = \frac{2180 \text{ mi}}{1\text{h}} \times \frac{1\text{h}}{3600\text{s}} \times \frac{5280 \text{ ft}}{1 \text{ mi}} \times \frac{12 \text{ in.}}{1 \text{ ft}} \times \frac{2.54 \text{ cm}}{1 \text{ in.}} \times \frac{1 \text{ m}}{100 \text{ cm}} = 974.5 \text{ m/s}$$

Solve the rms-speed equation (6.20) for temperature by first squaring both sides.

$$\left(u_{rms}\right)^2 = \frac{3RT}{M} \qquad T = \frac{\left(u_{rms}\right)^2 M}{3R} = \frac{\left(\frac{974.5 \text{ m}}{1\text{s}}\right)^2 \times \frac{2.016 \times 10^{-3} \text{kg}}{1 \text{ mol H}_2}}{3 \times \frac{8.3145 \text{ kg m}^2}{\text{s}^2 \text{ mol K}}} = 76.75 \text{ K}$$

We expected the temperature to be lower than 298 K. Note that the speed of the bullet is about half the speed of a H_2 molecule at 298 K. To halve the speed of a molecule, its temperature must be divided by four.

15A **(M)** The only difference is the gas's molar mass. 2.2×10^{-4} mol N_2 effuses through the orifice in 105 s.

$$\frac{? \text{ mol O}_2}{2.2 \times 10^{-4} \text{ mol N}_2} = \sqrt{\frac{M_{N_2}}{M_{O_2}}} = \sqrt{\frac{28.014 \text{ g/mol}}{31.998 \text{ g/mol}}} = 0.9357$$

$$\text{moles O}_2 = 0.9357 \times \left(2.2 \times 10^{-4}\right) = 2.1 \times 10^{-4} \text{ mol O}_2$$

15B **(M)** Rates of effusion are related by the square root of the ratio of the molar masses of the two gases. H_2, effuses faster (by virtue of being lighter), and thus requires a shorter time for the same amount of gas to effuse.

$$\text{time}_{H_2} = \text{time}_{N_2} \times \sqrt{\frac{M_{H_2}}{M_{N_2}}} = 105 \text{ s} \times \sqrt{\frac{2.016 \text{ g/mol}}{28.014 \text{ g/mol}}} = 28.2 \text{ s}$$

16A **(M)** Effusion times are related as the square root of the molar mass. It requires 87.3 s for Kr to effuse.

$$\frac{\text{unknown time}}{\text{Kr time}} = \sqrt{\frac{M_{unk}}{M_{Kr}}} \qquad \text{substitute in values} \qquad \frac{131.3 \text{ s}}{87.3 \text{ s}} = \sqrt{\frac{M_{unk}}{83.80 \text{ g/mol}}} = 1.50$$

$$M_{unk} = \left(1.504\right)^2 \times 83.80 \text{ g/mol} = 1.90 \times 10^2 \text{ g/mol}$$

16B **(M)** This problem is solved in virtually the same manner as Practice Example 18B. The lighter gas is ethane, with a molar mass of 30.07 g/mol.

$$C_2H_6 \text{ time} = Kr \text{ time} \times \sqrt{\frac{M_{C_2H_6}}{M_{Kr}}} = 87.3 \text{ s} \times \sqrt{\frac{30.07 \text{ g/mol}}{83.80 \text{ g/mol}}} = 52.3 \text{ s}$$

17A **(D)** Because one mole of gas is being considered, the value of an^2 is numerically the same as the value of a, and the value of nb is numerically the same as the value of b.

$$P = \frac{nRT}{V - nb} - \frac{an^2}{V^2} = \frac{1.00 \text{ mol} \times \dfrac{0.083145 \text{ bar L}}{\text{mol K}} \times 273 \text{ K}}{(2.00 - 0.0429) \text{ L}} - \frac{3.66 \text{ L}^2 \text{ bar mol}^{-2}}{(2.00 \text{ L})^2} = 11.6 \text{ bar} - 0.915 \text{ bar}$$

$$= 10.7 \text{ bar } CO_2(g) \quad \text{compared with 10.1 bar for } Cl_2(g)$$

$$P_{ideal} = \frac{nRT}{V} = \frac{1.00 \text{ mol} \times \dfrac{0.083145 \text{ bar L}}{\text{mol K}} \times 273 \text{ K}}{2.00 \text{ L}} = 11.35 \sim 11.4 \text{ bar}$$

$Cl_2(g)$ shows a greater deviation from ideal gas behavior than does $CO_2(g)$.

17B **(M)** Because one mole of gas is being considered, the value of an^2 is numerically the same as the value of a, and the value of nb is numerically the same as the value of b.

$$P = \frac{nRT}{V - nb} - \frac{an^2}{V^2} = \frac{1.00 \text{ mol} \times \dfrac{0.083145 \text{ bar L}}{\text{mol K}} \times 273 \text{ K}}{(2.00 - 0.0395) \text{ L}} - \frac{1.47 \text{ L}^2 \text{ bar}}{(2.00 \text{ L})^2} = 11.6 \text{ bar} - 0.368 \text{ bar}$$

$$= 11.2 \text{ bar } CO(g)$$

compared to 10.1 bar for $Cl_2(g)$, 11.2 bar for CO, and 10.7 bar for $CO_2(g)$.

Thus, $Cl_2(g)$ displays the greatest deviation from ideality, 11.4 bar.

INTEGRATIVE EXERCISE

A. **(M)** Let's assume that we have a 1 L sample of this gas, and determine how many moles of gas are present:

$$n = \frac{PV}{RT} = \frac{(101.3 \text{ kPa})(1.00 \text{ L})}{(8.3145 \text{ kPa L} \cdot \text{K}^{-1}\text{mol}^{-1})(298 \text{ K})} = 0.0409 \text{ mol}$$

Knowing the density of the gas (1.637 g/L) and its volume (1 L) gives us the mass of 1 L of gas, or 1.637 g. Therefore, the molar mass of this gas is:

(1.637 g / 0.0409 mol) = 40.03 g/mol

Now, determine the number of moles of C and H to ascertain the empirical formula:

$$\text{mol C: } 1.687 \text{ g CO}_2 \times \frac{1 \text{ mol CO}_2}{44.01 \text{ g CO}_2} \times \frac{1 \text{ mol C}}{1 \text{ mol CO}_2} = 0.0383 \text{ mol}$$

$$\text{mol H: } 0.4605 \text{ g H}_2\text{O} \times \frac{1 \text{ mol H}_2\text{O}}{18.02 \text{ g H}_2\text{O}} \times \frac{2 \text{ mol H}}{1 \text{ mol H}_2\text{O}} = 0.05111 \text{ mol}$$

Dividing by the smallest value (0.0383 mol C), we get a H:C ratio of 1.33:1, or 4:3. Therefore, the empirical formula is C_3H_4, which has a molar mass of 40.07, which is essentially the same as the molar mass calculated. Therefore, the actual formula is also C_3H_4. Below are three possible Lewis structures:

B. **(D)** First, let us determine the amount of each element in the compound:

$$\text{mol C: } 151.2 \times 10^{-3} \text{ g CO}_2 \times \frac{1 \text{ mol CO}_2}{44.01 \text{ g CO}_2} \times \frac{1 \text{ mol C}}{1 \text{ mol CO}_2} = 0.003435 \text{ mol C}$$

$$\text{g C: } 0.003435 \text{ mol C} \times \frac{12.01 \text{ g C}}{1 \text{ mol C}} = 0.04126 \text{ g C}$$

$$\text{mol H: } 69.62 \times 10^{-3} \text{ g H}_2\text{O} \times \frac{1 \text{ mol H}_2\text{O}}{18.02 \text{ g H}_2\text{O}} \times \frac{2 \text{ mol H}}{1 \text{ mol H}_2\text{O}} = 0.007727 \text{ mol H}$$

$$\text{g H: } 0.007727 \text{ mol H} \times \frac{1.008 \text{ g H}}{1 \text{ mol H}} = 0.007789 \text{ g H}$$

$$\text{mol N: } \frac{PV}{RT} = \frac{1 \text{ atm} \cdot 9.62 \times 10^{-3} \text{ L}}{\left(0.08206 \text{ atm L mol}^{-1} \text{ K}^{-1}\right)(273 \text{ K})} \times \frac{2 \text{ mol N}}{1 \text{ mol N}_2} = 0.0008589 \text{ mol N}$$

$$\text{g N: } 0.0008589 \text{ mol N} \times \frac{14.01 \text{ g N}}{1 \text{ mol N}} = 0.01203 \text{ g N}$$

Therefore, the mass of O is determined by subtracting the sum of the above masses from the mass of the compound:

$$\text{g O: } 0.1023 - (0.04126 + 0.007804 + 0.01203) = 0.04121 \text{ g O}$$

$$\text{mol O: } 0.04121 \text{ g O} \times \frac{1 \text{ mol O}}{16.00 \text{ g O}} = 0.002576 \text{ mol O}$$

To determine the empirical formula, all of the calculated moles above should be divided by the smallest value. Doing so will give the following ratios:
C: 0.003435/0.0008589 = 4
H: 0.007727/0.0008589 = 9
N: 1
O: 0.002576/0.0008589 = 3

The empirical formula is $C_4H_9NO_3$, and has a molar mass of 119.14 g/mol.

To determine the actual formula, we have to calculate its molecular mass. We know the density at a given volume and therefore we need to find out the number of moles. Before that, we should convert the experimental conditions to more convenient units. $T = 127\ °C + 273 = 400$ K, and $P = 748$ mmHg/760 mmHg = 0.9842 atm.

$$n = \frac{PV}{RT} = \frac{(0.9842\ \text{atm})1\ \text{L}}{\left(0.08206\ \text{atm L mol}^{-1}\ \text{K}^{-1}\right)(400\ \text{K})} = 0.02999\ \text{mol}$$

$$M = \text{g/mol} = 3.57\ \text{g}/0.02999\ \text{mol} = 119\ \text{g/mol}$$

Therefore, the empirical and molecular formulas are the same, being $C_4H_9NO_3$.

EXERCISES

Pressure and Its Measurement

1. (E)

(a) $P = 736\ \text{mmHg} \times \dfrac{1\ \text{atm}}{760\ \text{mmHg}} = 0.968\ \text{atm}$

(b) $P = 0.776\ \text{bar} \times \dfrac{1\ \text{atm}}{1.01325\ \text{bar}} = 0.766\ \text{atm}$

(c) $P = 892\ \text{torr} \times \dfrac{1\ \text{atm}}{760\ \text{Torr}} = 1.17\ \text{atm}$

(d) $P = 225\ \text{kPa} \times \dfrac{1000\ \text{Pa}}{1\ \text{kPa}} \times \dfrac{1\ \text{atm}}{101,325\ \text{Pa}} = 2.22\ \text{atm}$

2. (E)

(a) $h = 0.984\ \text{atm} \times \dfrac{760\ \text{mmHg}}{1\ \text{atm}} = 748\ \text{mmHg}$

(b) $h = 928\ \text{Torr} = 928\ \text{mmHg}$

(c) $h = 142\ \text{ft H}_2\text{O} \times \dfrac{12\ \text{in.}}{1\ \text{ft}} \times \dfrac{2.54\ \text{cm}}{1\ \text{in.}} \times \dfrac{10\ \text{mmH}_2\text{O}}{1\ \text{cm H}_2\text{O}} \times \dfrac{1\ \text{mmHg}}{13.6\ \text{mmH}_2\text{O}} \times \dfrac{1\ \text{mHg}}{1000\ \text{mmHg}} = 3.18\ \text{mHg}$

3. (E) We use: $h_{\text{bnz}} d_{\text{bnz}} = h_{\text{Hg}} d_{\text{Hg}}$

$$h_{\text{bnz}} = 0.970\ \text{atm} \times \frac{0.760\ \text{mHg}}{1\ \text{atm}} \times \frac{13.6\ \text{g/cm}^3\ \text{Hg}}{0.879\ \text{g/cm}^3\ \text{benzene}} = 11.4\ \text{m benzene}$$

4. (E) We use: $h_{\text{gly}} d_{\text{gly}} = h_{\text{CCl}_4} d_{\text{CCl}_4}$

$$h_{\text{gly}} = 3.02\ \text{m CCl}_4 \times \frac{1.59\ \text{g/cm}^3\ \text{CCl}_4}{1.26\ \text{g/cm}^3\ \text{glycerol}} = 3.81\ \text{m glycerol}$$

5. (E) $P = P_{\text{bar}} - h_1 = 740\ \text{mmHg} - 30\ \text{mm}\ (h_1) = 710\ \text{mmHg}$

6. **(E)** $P = P_{bar} + h_1 = 740$ mmHg $+ 30$ mm $(h_1) = 770$ mmHg

7. $F = m \times g$ and 1 atm $= 101{,}325$ Pa $= 101{,}325$ kg m^{-1} s$^{-2} = P = \dfrac{F}{A} = \dfrac{m \times 9.81\text{ m s}^{-2}}{1\text{ m}^2}$

   $$\text{mass (per m}^2) = \frac{101{,}325\text{ kg m}^{-1}\text{s}^{-2} \times 1\text{ m}^2}{9.81\text{ m s}^{-2}} = 10{,}329\text{ kg}$$

   (Note: 1 m$^2 = (100$ cm$)^2 = 10{,}000$ cm^2)

   $$P\text{ (kg cm}^{-2}) = \frac{m}{A} = \frac{10{,}329\text{ kg}}{10{,}000\text{ cm}^2} = 1.03\text{ kg cm}^{-2}$$

8. **(E)** Start by noting that 1 atm is defined as 101,325 Pa. Pascals is the unit name used to describe SI units of force (F) per unit area, and is expressed as N/m^2. Since $F = ma$, the MKS units for pressure are kg·m·s^{-2}·m^{-2}, or kg·m^{-1}·s^{-2}. The Imperial unit of measuring force is pounds-force, or lbf. Considering acceleration due to gravity, an object weighing 1 N has a mass of $(1/9.8$ m/s$^2)$ 0.102 kg. We now can convert the MKS units to psi as follows:

   $$101{,}325\,\frac{\text{N}}{\text{m}^2} \times \frac{0.102\text{ kg}}{1\text{ N}} \times \frac{1\text{ lb}}{0.453\text{ kg}} \times \frac{1\text{ m}^2}{(100\text{ cm})^2} \times \frac{(2.54\text{ cm})^2}{1\text{ in.}^2} = 14.7\text{ psi}$$

The Simple Gas Laws

9. **(E)**

   (a) $V = 26.7\text{ L} \times \dfrac{762\text{ Torr}}{385\text{ Torr}} = 52.8\text{ L}$

   (b) $V = 26.7\text{ L} \times \dfrac{762\text{ Torr}}{3.68\text{ atm} \times \dfrac{760\text{ Torr}}{1\text{ atm}}} = 7.27\text{ L}$

10. **(E)** Apply Charles's law: $V = kT$. $\qquad T_i = 26 + 273 = 299$ K

    (a) $T = 98 + 273 = 371$ K $\qquad V = 886\text{ mL} \times \dfrac{371\text{ K}}{299\text{ K}} = 1.10 \times 10^3\text{ mL}$

    (b) $T = (-20 + 273)\text{ K} = 253$ K $\qquad V = 886\text{ mL} \times \dfrac{253\text{ K}}{299\text{ K}} = 7.50 \times 10^2\text{ mL}$

11. **(E)** Charles's law states that $V_1/T_1 = V_2/T_2$. Since $V_1 = 3.0$ L, $T_1 = (177 + 273)$, K $= 450$ K, and $V_2 = 1.50$ L, then:

    $$\frac{3.0\text{ L}}{450\text{ K}} = \frac{1.50\text{ L}}{T_2}, \text{ and } T_2 = 225\text{ K}$$

12. **(E)** $P_f = P_i \times \dfrac{V_i}{V_f} = \left(105\text{ kPa} \times \dfrac{0.725\text{ L}}{2.25\text{ L}}\right) = 33.8\text{ kPa}$

13. **(E)** $P_i = P_f \times \dfrac{V_f}{V_i} = \left(721\text{ mmHg} \times \dfrac{35.8\text{ L} + 1875\text{ L}}{35.8\text{ L}}\right) \times \dfrac{1\text{ atm}}{760\text{ mmHg}} = 50.6\text{ atm}$

14. **(E)** We let P represent barometric pressure, and solve the Boyle's law expression below for P.

$$P \times 42.0 \text{ mL} = (P + 85 \text{ mmHg}) \times 37.7 \text{ mL} \qquad 42.0P = 37.7P + 3.2 \times 10^3$$

$$P = \frac{3.2 \times 10^3}{42.0 - 37.7} = 7.4 \times 10^2 \text{ mmHg}$$

15. **(E)** Combining Boyle's and Charles's law, we get the following expression: $\dfrac{P_1 V_1}{T_1} = \dfrac{P_2 V_2}{T_2}$

Therefore,

$$T_2 = \frac{P_2 V_2 T_1}{P_1 V_1} = \frac{(0.340 \text{ atm})(5.00 \times 10^3 \text{ m}^3)(300 \text{ K})}{(1.000 \text{ atm})(2.00 \times 10^3 \text{ m}^3)} = 255 \text{ K}$$

16. **(E)** First, convert temperatures from Celsius to the Kelvin scale.

$22 \text{ °C} + 273.15 = 295.15 \text{ K} \qquad -22 \text{ °C} = (-22 + 273.15) = 251.15 \text{ K}$

Volume decrease is proportional to the ratio of the temperatures in Kelvin.

$$\text{volume contraction} = \frac{251.15 \text{ K}}{295.15 \text{ K}} = 0.851 \text{ (volume will be about 85\% of its original volume).}$$

17. **(E)** STP: $P = 1$ bar and $T = 273.15$ K

$$\text{mass}_{\text{Ar}} = \frac{1.00 \text{ bar} \times 0.0750 \text{ L}}{0.08314 \dfrac{\text{bar L}}{\text{K mol}} \times 273.15 \text{ K}} \times \frac{39.948 \text{ g Ar}}{1 \text{ mol Ar}} = 0.132 \text{ g Ar}$$

18. **(M)** STP: $P = 1$ bar and $T = 273.15$ K (note: one mole of gas at STP occupies 22.711 L).

$$V = \frac{nRT}{P} = \frac{\left(250.0 \text{ g Cl}_2 \times \dfrac{1 \text{ mol Cl}_2}{70.90 \text{ g}}\right)\left(0.08314 \dfrac{\text{bar L}}{\text{K mol}}\right) 273.15 \text{ K}}{1.000 \text{ bar}} = 80.08 \text{ L Cl}_2$$

Alternatively $V = n \times V_m = \left(250.0 \text{ g Cl}_2 \times \dfrac{1 \text{ mol Cl}_2}{70.90 \text{ g}}\right) \times \dfrac{22.711 \text{ L at STP}}{1 \text{ mol}} = 80.08 \text{ L Cl}_2$

19. **(M)** In the following calculations, we use the fact that 1 mol of gas occupies 22.711 L at STP (1 bar and 273.15 K). See equation (6.10).

(a) *Conversion pathway approach:*

$$\text{mass} = 27.6 \text{ mL} \times \frac{1 \text{ L}}{1000 \text{ mL}} \times \frac{1 \text{ mol PH}_3}{22.711 \text{ L (at STP)}} \times \frac{34.0 \text{ g PH}_3}{1 \text{ mol PH}_3} \times \frac{1000 \text{ mg PH}_3}{1 \text{ g}}$$

$$= 41.3 \text{ mg PH}_3$$

Stepwise approach:

$$27.6 \text{ mL} \times \frac{1 \text{ L}}{1000 \text{ mL}} = 0.0276 \text{ L}$$

$$0.0276 \text{ L} \times \frac{1 \text{ mol PH}_3}{22.711 \text{ L (at STP)}} = 1.215 \times 10^{-3} \text{ mol PH}_3$$

$$1.215 \times 10^{-3} \text{ mol PH}_3 \times \frac{34.00 \text{ g PH}_3}{1 \text{ mol PH}_3} = 0.0413 \text{ g PH}_3$$

$$0.0413 \text{ g PH}_3 \times \frac{1000 \text{ mg PH}_3}{1 \text{ g}} = 41.3 \text{ mg PH}_3$$

(b) number of molecules of $PH_3 = 1.215 \times 10^{-3} \text{ mol PH}_3 \times \dfrac{6.022 \times 10^{23} \text{ molecules}}{1 \text{ mol PH}_3}$

$$= 7.32 \times 10^{20} \text{ molecules}$$

20. (E)

(a) $\text{mass} = 5.0 \times 10^{17} \text{ atoms} \times \dfrac{1 \text{ mol Rn}}{6.022 \times 10^{23} \text{ atoms}} = 8.30 \times 10^{-7} \text{ mol} \times \dfrac{222 \text{ g Rn}}{1 \text{ mol Rn}} \times \dfrac{10^6 \, \mu g}{1 \text{ g}}$

$$= 1.8 \times 10^2 \, \mu g \text{ Rn}$$

(b) $\text{volume} = 8.30 \times 10^{-7} \text{ mol} \times \dfrac{22.711 \text{ L (at STP)}}{1 \text{ mol}} \times \dfrac{10^6 \, \mu L}{1 \text{ L}} = 19 \mu L \text{ (at STP)}$

21. **(M)** At the higher elevation of the mountains, the atmospheric pressure is lower than at the beach. However, the bag is virtually leak proof; no gas escapes. Thus, the gas inside the bag expands in the lower pressure until the bag is filled to near bursting. (It would have been difficult to predict this result. The temperature in the mountains is usually lower than at the beach. The lower temperature would *decrease* the pressure of the gas.)

22. **(M)** Based on densities, 1 mHg = 13.6 mH$_2$O. For 30 m of water,

$$30 \text{ mH}_2\text{O} \times \frac{1 \text{ mHg}}{13.6 \text{ mH}_2\text{O}} = 2.2 \text{ mHg} \quad P_{\text{water}} = 2.2 \text{ mHg} \times \frac{1000 \text{ mm}}{1 \text{ m}} \times \frac{1 \text{ atm}}{760 \text{ mmHg}} = 2.9 \text{ atm}$$

To this we add the pressure of the atmosphere above the water:
$P_{\text{total}} = 2.9 \text{ atm} + 1.0 \text{ atm} = 3.9 \text{ atm}.$

When the diver rises to the surface, she rises to a pressure of 1.0 atm. Since the pressure is about one fourth of the pressure below the surface, the gas in her lungs attempts to expand to four times the volume of her lungs. It is quite likely that her lungs would burst.

General Gas Equation

23. **(E)** Because the number of moles of gas does not change, $\dfrac{P_i V_i}{T_i} = nR = \dfrac{P_f V_f}{T_f}$ is

obtained from the ideal gas equation. This expression can be rearranged as follows.

$$V_f = \frac{V_i \, P_i \, T_f}{P_f \, T_i} = \frac{4.25 \text{ L} \times 748 \text{ mmHg} \times (26.8 + 273.2)\text{K}}{742 \text{ mmHg} \times (25.6 + 273.2)\text{K}} = 4.30 \text{ L}$$

24. **(E)** We first compute the pressure at $25\,^\circ\mathrm{C}$ as a result of the additional gas. Of course, the gas pressure increases proportionally to the increase in the mass of gas, because the mass is proportional to the number of moles of gas.

$$P = \frac{12.5\ \mathrm{g}}{10.0\ \mathrm{g}} \times 102\ \mathrm{kPa} = 127.5\ \mathrm{kPa}$$

Now we compute the pressure resulting from increasing the temperature.

$$P = \frac{(62+273)\ \mathrm{K}}{(25+273)\ \mathrm{K}} \times 127.5\ \mathrm{kPa} = 143\ \mathrm{kPa}$$

25. **(E)** Volume and pressure are constant. Hence $n_i T_i = \dfrac{PV}{R} = n_f T_f$

$$\frac{n_f}{n_i} = \frac{T_i}{T_f} = \frac{(21+273)\ \mathrm{K}}{(210+273)\ \mathrm{K}} = 0.609\ (60.9\%\ \text{of the gas remains})$$

Hence, 39.1% of the gas must be released. Mass of gas released $= 12.5\ \mathrm{g} \times \dfrac{39.1}{100} = 4.89\ \mathrm{g}$

26. **(M)** First determine the mass of O_2 in the cylinder under the final conditions.

$$\text{mass } O_2 = n \times M = \frac{PV}{RT}M = \frac{1.15\ \mathrm{atm} \times 34.0\ \mathrm{L} \times 32.0\ \mathrm{g/mol}}{0.08206\ \dfrac{\mathrm{atm\ L}}{\mathrm{mol\ K}}(22+273)\mathrm{K}} = 51.7\ \mathrm{g\ } O_2$$

mass of O_2 to be released $= 305\ \mathrm{g} - 51.7\ \mathrm{g} = 253\ \mathrm{g\ } O_2$

Ideal Gas Equation

27. **(M)** Assume that the $CO_2(g)$ behaves ideally and use the ideal gas equation: $PV = nRT$

$$V = \frac{nRT}{P} = \frac{\left(89.2\ \mathrm{g} \times \dfrac{1\ \mathrm{mol\ } CO_2}{44.01\ \mathrm{g}}\right) 8.314\ \dfrac{\mathrm{kPa\ L}}{\mathrm{mol\ K}}(37+273.2)\ \mathrm{K}}{98.3\ \mathrm{kPa}} = 53.2\ \mathrm{L}$$

28. **(M)** $P = \dfrac{nRT}{V} = \dfrac{\left(35.8\ \mathrm{g\ } O_2 \times \dfrac{1\ \mathrm{mol\ } O_2}{32.00\ \mathrm{g\ } O_2}\right) \times \dfrac{8.314\ \mathrm{kPa\ L}}{\mathrm{mol\ K}} \times (46+273)\ \mathrm{K}}{12.8\ \mathrm{L}} = 232\ \mathrm{kPa}$

29. **(E)** mass $= n \times M = \dfrac{PV}{RT}$ $\qquad M = \dfrac{11.2\ \mathrm{atm} \times 18.5\ \mathrm{L} \times 83.80\ \mathrm{g/mol}}{0.08206\ \dfrac{\mathrm{atm\ L}}{\mathrm{mol\ K}}(28.2+273.2)\,\mathrm{K}} = 702\ \mathrm{g\ Kr}$

30. **(M)**

mol He $= 7.41\ \mathrm{g\ He} \times (1\ \mathrm{mol\ He}/4.003\ \mathrm{g\ He}) = 1.85\ \mathrm{mol}$

$$T = \frac{PV}{nR} = \frac{3.50\ \mathrm{atm} \times 72.8\ \mathrm{L}}{1.85\ \mathrm{mol} \times 0.08206\ \dfrac{\mathrm{atm\ L}}{\mathrm{mol\ K}}} = 1.68 \times 10^3\ \mathrm{K}$$

$t(^\circ\mathrm{C}) = (1.68 \times 10^3 - 273) = 1.41 \times 10^3\ ^\circ\mathrm{C}$

31. (M) $n_{gas} = 5.0 \times 10^9$ molecules gas $\times \dfrac{1 \text{ mol gas}}{6.022 \times 10^{23} \text{ molecules gas}} = 8.3 \times 10^{-15}$ mol gas

We next determine the pressure that the gas exerts at 25 °C in a cubic meter

$$P = \dfrac{8.3 \times 10^{-15} \text{ mol gas} \times 8.314 \dfrac{\text{kPa L}}{\text{mol K}} \times 273 \text{ K}}{1 \text{ m}^3 \times \left(\dfrac{10 \text{ dm}}{1 \text{ m}}\right)^3 \times \left(\dfrac{1 \text{ L}}{1 \text{ dm}^3}\right)} \times \dfrac{1000 \text{ Pa}}{1 \text{ kPa}} = 2.1 \times 10^{-11} \text{ Pa}$$

32. (M)

$$n_{CO_2} = 1242 \text{ g CO}_2 \times \dfrac{1 \text{ mol CO}_2}{44.009 \text{ g CO}_2} = 28.22 \text{ mol CO}_2 \qquad T = (-25 + 273)\text{K} = 248 \text{ K}$$

$$V_{CO_2} = \pi r^2 h = 3.1416 \times \left(\dfrac{0.250 \text{ m}}{2}\right)^2 1.75 \text{ m} \times \dfrac{1000 \text{ L}}{1 \text{ m}^3} = 85.9 \text{ L}$$

$$P = \dfrac{28.22 \text{ mol CO}_2 \times 8.314 \dfrac{\text{kPa L}}{\text{mol K}} \times 248 \text{ K} \times \dfrac{1000 \text{ Pa}}{1 \text{ kPa}}}{85.9 \text{ L}} = 6.77 \times 10^5 \text{ Pa}$$

33. (E) The basic ideal law relationship applies here. Molar volume is the amount of volume that one mole of a gas occupies. If $PV = nRT$, then molar volume is V/n, and the relationship rearranges to:

$$\dfrac{V}{n} = V_m = \dfrac{RT}{P}$$

(a) $V_m = (298 \text{ K} \cdot 0.08206 \text{ atm L mol}^{-1} \text{ K}^{-1})/1.00 \text{ atm} = 24.4 \text{ L mol}^{-1}$

(b) $P_{atm} = 748 \text{ mmHg} / 760 \text{ mmHg} = 0.978 \text{ atm}$
$V_m = (373 \text{ K} \cdot 0.08206 \text{ atm L mol}^{-1} \text{ K}^{-1})/0.978 \text{ atm} = 31.3 \text{ L mol}^{-1}$

34. (E) The molar volume formula given above can be rearranged to solve for T.
$T = (P/R) \cdot V_m = (2.5 \text{ atm}/0.08205 \text{ atm L mol}^{-1} \text{ K}^{-1}) \times 22.4 \text{ L mol}^{-1} = 682 \text{ K}$

Determining Molar Mass

35. (M) Use the ideal gas equation to determine the amount in moles of the given quantity of gas.

$$M = \dfrac{mRT}{PV} = \dfrac{0.418 \text{ g} \times 8.314 \dfrac{\text{kPa L}}{\text{mol K}} \times 339.5 \text{ K}}{99.0 \text{ kPa} \times 0.115 \text{ L}} = 104 \text{ g mol}^{-1}$$

Alternatively

$$n = \dfrac{PV}{RT} = \dfrac{99.0 \text{ kPa} \left(115 \text{ mL} \times \dfrac{1 \text{ L}}{1000 \text{ mL}}\right)}{8.314 \dfrac{\text{kPa L}}{\text{mol K}}(66.3 + 273.2) \text{ K}} = 0.00403 \text{ mol} \qquad M = \dfrac{0.418 \text{ g}}{0.00403 \text{ mol}} = 104 \text{ g/mol}$$

36. **(M)** Use the ideal gas equation to determine the amount in moles in 1 L of gas.

$$n = \frac{PV}{RT} = \frac{96.7 \text{ kPa} \times 1 \text{ L}}{8.314 \dfrac{\text{kPa L}}{\text{mol K}} \times 415 \text{ K}} = 0.02802 \text{ mol} \qquad M = \frac{\text{mass}}{\text{moles}} = \frac{0.841 \text{ g}}{0.02802 \text{ mol}} = 30.0 \text{ g mol}^{-1}$$

37. **(M)** First we determine the empirical formula for the sulfur fluoride. Assume a 100 g sample of S_xF_y.

$$\text{moles S} = 29.6 \text{ g S} \times \frac{1 \text{ mol S}}{32.06 \text{ g S}} = 0.923 \text{ mol S} \quad \text{moles F} = 70.4 \text{ g F} \times \frac{1 \text{ mol F}}{18.998 \text{ g F}} = 3.706 \text{ mol F}$$

Dividing the number of moles of each element by 0.923 moles gives the empirical formula SF_4.

To find the molar mass we use the relationship:

$$\text{Molar mass} = \frac{dRT}{P} = \frac{4.5 \text{ g L}^{-1} \times 0.08206 \text{ atm L mol}^{-1} \text{ K}^{-1} \times 293 \text{ K}}{1.0 \text{ atm}} = 10\underline{8} \text{ g mol}^{-1}$$

$$\text{Thus, molecular formula} = \left(\text{empirical formula}\right) \times \left(\frac{\text{molecular formula mass}}{\text{empirical formula mass}}\right)$$

$$= \frac{10\underline{8} \text{ g mol}^{-1}}{108.06 \text{ g mol}^{-1}} \times SF_4 = SF_4$$

38. **(M)** We first determine the molar mass of the gas.

$$T = 24.3 + 273.2 = 297.5 \text{ K} \qquad\qquad P = 742 \text{ mmHg} \times \frac{1 \text{ atm}}{760 \text{ mmHg}} = 0.976 \text{ atm}$$

$$M = \frac{mRT}{PV} = \frac{2.650 \text{ g} \times 0.08206 \text{ atm L mol}^{-1}\text{K}^{-1} \times 297.5 \text{ K}}{0.976 \text{ atm} \times \left(428 \text{ mL} \times \dfrac{1 \text{ L}}{1000 \text{ mL}}\right)} = 155 \text{ g/mol}$$

Then we determine the empirical formula of the gas, based on a 100.0 g sample.

$$\text{mol C} = 15.5 \text{ g C} \times \frac{1 \text{ mol C}}{12.01 \text{ g C}} = 1.29 \text{ mol C} \div 0.649 \rightarrow 1.99 \text{ mol C}$$

$$\text{mol Cl} = 23.0 \text{ g Cl} \times \frac{1 \text{ mol Cl}}{35.45 \text{ g Cl}} = 0.649 \text{ mol Cl} \div 0.649 \rightarrow 1.00 \text{ mol Cl}$$

$$\text{mol F} = 61.5 \text{ g F} \times \frac{1 \text{ mol F}}{19.00 \text{ g F}} = 3.24 \text{ mol F} \div 0.649 \rightarrow 4.99 \text{ mol F}$$

Thus, the empirical formula is C_2ClF_5, which has a molar mass of 154.5 g/mol. This is the same as the experimentally determined molar mass. Hence, the molecular formula is C_2ClF_5.

39. **(M)**

$$M = \frac{mRT}{PV} = \frac{0.231 \text{ g} \times 0.08206 \dfrac{\text{atm L}}{\text{mol K}} \times (23 + 273) \text{ K}}{\left(749 \text{ mmHg} \times \dfrac{1 \text{ atm}}{760 \text{ mmHg}}\right) \times \left(102 \text{ mL} \times \dfrac{1 \text{ L}}{1000 \text{ mL}}\right)} = 55.8 \text{ g/mol}$$

Chapter 6: Gases

The formula contains 4 atoms of carbon. (5 atoms of carbon gives a molar mass of at least 60—too high—and 3 C atoms gives a molar mass of 36—too low to be made up by adding H's.) To produce a molar mass of 56 with 4 carbons requires the inclusion of 8 atoms of H in the formula of the compound. Thus the formula is C_4H_8.

40. **(M)** First, we obtain the mass of acetylene, and then acetylene's molar mass.
mass of acetylene $= 56.2445 \text{ g} - 56.1035 \text{ g} = 0.1410 \text{ g}$ acetylene

$$M = \frac{mRT}{PV} = \frac{0.1410 \text{ g} \times 0.08206 \, \frac{\text{atm L}}{\text{mol K}} \times (20.02 + 273.15) \text{ K}}{\left(749.3 \text{ mmHg} \times \frac{1 \text{ atm}}{760 \text{ mmHg}}\right) \times \left(132.10 \text{ mL} \times \frac{1 \text{ L}}{1000 \text{ mL}}\right)} = 26.04 \text{ g/mol}$$

The formula contains 2 atoms of carbon (3 atoms of carbon gives a molar mass of at least 36—too high—and 1 C atom gives a molar mass of 12—too low to be made up by adding H's.) To produce a molar mass of 26 with 2 carbons requires the inclusion of 2 atoms of H in the formula. Thus the formula is C_2H_2.

Gas Densities

41. **(E)** $d = \frac{MP}{RT} \rightarrow P = \frac{dRT}{M} = \frac{1.80 \text{ g/L} \times 0.08206 \, \frac{\text{L atm}}{\text{mol K}} \times (32 + 273) \text{ K}}{28.0 \text{ g/mol}} \times \frac{760 \text{ mmHg}}{1 \text{ atm}}$

$P = 1.21 \times 10^3 \text{ mmHg}$

Molar volume $= \frac{1 \text{ L}}{1.8 \text{ g}} \, N_2 \times \frac{28.0 \text{ g } N_2}{1 \text{ mol } N_2} = 15.6 \text{ L/mol}$

42. **(E)** $M = \frac{dRT}{M} = \frac{2.56 \text{ g/L} \times 8.314 \text{ kPa L K}^{-1} \text{ mol}^{-1} \times (22.8 + 273.2) \text{ K}}{101 \text{ kPa}} = 62.4 \text{ g/mol}$

Molar volume $= \frac{62.4 \text{ g}}{1 \text{ mol}} \times \frac{1 \text{ L}}{2.56 \text{ g}} = 24.4 \text{ L/mol}$

43. **(M)**

   (a) $d = \frac{MP}{RT} = \frac{28.96 \text{ g/mol} \times 1.00 \text{ atm}}{0.08206 \frac{\text{atm L}}{\text{mol K}} \times (25 + 273) \text{K}} = 1.18 \text{ g/L air}$

   (b) $d = \frac{MP}{RT} = \frac{44.0 \text{ g/mol CO}_2 \times 1.00 \text{ atm}}{0.08206 \frac{\text{atm L}}{\text{mol K}} \times (25 + 273) \text{K}} = 1.80 \text{ g/L CO}_2$

   Since this density is greater than that of air, the balloon will not rise in air when filled with CO_2 at 25 °C; instead, it will sink!

44. **(E)** $d = \frac{MP}{RT}$ becomes $T = \frac{MP}{Rd} = \frac{44.0 \text{ g/mol} \times 1.00 \text{ atm}}{0.08206 \frac{\text{atm L}}{\text{mol K}} \times 1.18 \text{ g/L}} = 454 \text{ K} = 181 \, ^\circ\text{C}$

45. **(E)** $d = \dfrac{MP}{RT}$ becomes $M = \dfrac{dRT}{P} = \dfrac{2.64 \text{ g/L} \times 0.08314 \dfrac{\text{bar L}}{\text{mol K}} \times (310 + 273)\text{K}}{1.03 \text{ bar}} = 124 \text{ g/mol}$

Since the atomic mass of phosphorus is 31.0, the formula of phosphorus molecules in the vapor must be P_4. $(4 \text{ atoms}/\text{molecule} \times 31.0 = 124)$

46. **(M)** We first determine the molar mass of the gas, then its empirical formula. These two pieces of information are combined to obtain the molecular formula of the gas.

$$M = \dfrac{dRT}{P} = \dfrac{2.33 \text{ g/L} \times 0.08206 \dfrac{\text{atm L}}{\text{mol K}} \times 296 \text{ K}}{746 \text{ mmHg} \times \dfrac{1 \text{ atm}}{760 \text{ mmHg}}} = 57.7 \text{ g/mol}$$

$$\text{mol C} = 82.7 \text{ g C} \times \dfrac{1 \text{ mol C}}{12.0 \text{ g C}} = 6.89 \text{ mol C} \div 6.89 \rightarrow 1.00 \text{ mol C}$$

$$\text{mol H} = 17.3 \text{ g H} \times \dfrac{1 \text{ mol H}}{1.01 \text{ g H}} = 17.1 \text{ mol H} \div 6.89 \rightarrow 2.48 \text{ mol H}$$

Multiply both of these mole numbers by 2 to obtain the empirical formula, C_2H_5, which has an empirical molar mass of 29.0 g/mol. Since the molar mass (calculated as 57.7 g/mol above) is twice the empirical molar mass, twice the empirical formula is the molecular formula, namely, C_4H_{10}.

Gases in Chemical Reactions

47. **(E)** Balanced equation: $C_3H_8(g) + 5 \text{ O}_2(g) \rightarrow 3 \text{ CO}_2(g) + 4 \text{ H}_2O(l)$

Use the law of combining volumes. O_2 volume $= 75.6 \text{ L C}_3\text{H}_8 \times \dfrac{5 \text{ L O}_2}{1 \text{ L C}_3\text{H}_8} = 378 \text{ L O}_2$

48. **(E)** Each mole of gas occupies 22.711 L at STP.

H_2 STP volume $= 1.000 \text{ g Al} \times \dfrac{1 \text{ mol Al}}{26.98 \text{ g Al}} \times \dfrac{3 \text{ mol H}_2(g)}{2 \text{ mol Al(s)}} \times \dfrac{22.711 \text{ L H}_2(g) \text{ at STP}}{1 \text{ mol H}_2}$

$= 1.262 \text{ L H}_2(g)$

49. **(M)** Determine the moles of $SO_2(g)$ produced and then use the ideal gas equation.

Conversion pathway approach:

$\text{mol SO}_2 = \left(1.2 \times 10^6 \text{ kg coal} \times \dfrac{3.28 \text{ kg S}}{100.00 \text{ kg coal}} \times \dfrac{1000 \text{ g S}}{1 \text{ kg S}} \times \dfrac{1 \text{ mol S}}{32.1 \text{ g S}} \times \dfrac{1 \text{ mol SO}_2}{1 \text{ mol S}} \right)$

$= 1.23 \times 10^6 \text{ mol SO}_2$

$V = \dfrac{nRT}{P}$

$V = \dfrac{1.23 \times 10^6 \text{ mol SO}_2 \times 0.08206 \dfrac{\text{atm L}}{\text{mol K}} \times 296 \text{ K}}{738 \text{ mmHg} \times \dfrac{1 \text{ atm}}{760 \text{ mmHg}}} = 3.1 \times 10^7 \text{ L SO}_2$

Stepwise approach:

$$1.2 \times 10^6 \text{ kg coal} \times \frac{3.28 \text{ kg S}}{100.00 \text{ kg coal}} = 3.94 \times 10^4 \text{ kg S}$$

$$3.94 \times 10^4 \text{ kg S} \times \frac{1000 \text{ g S}}{1 \text{ kg S}} = 3.94 \times 10^7 \text{ g S}$$

$$3.94 \times 10^7 \text{ g S} \times \frac{1 \text{ mol S}}{32.1 \text{ g S}} = 1.23 \times 10^6 \text{ mol S}$$

$$1.23 \times 10^6 \text{ mol S} \times \frac{1 \text{ mol SO}_2}{1 \text{ mol S}} = 1.23 \times 10^6 \text{ mol SO}_2$$

$$V = \frac{nRT}{P} = \frac{1.23 \times 10^6 \text{ mol SO}_2 \times 0.08206 \dfrac{\text{atm L}}{\text{mol K}} \times 296 \text{ K}}{738 \text{ mmHg} \times \dfrac{1 \text{ atm}}{760 \text{ mmHg}}} = 3.1 \times 10^7 \text{ L SO}_2$$

50. **(M)** Determine first the amount of $CO_2(g)$ that can be removed. Then use the ideal gas equation.

$$1.00 \text{ kg LiOH} \times \frac{1000 \text{ g}}{1 \text{ kg}} \times \frac{1 \text{ mol LiOH}}{23.95 \text{ g LiOH}} \times \frac{1 \text{ mol CO}_2}{2 \text{ mol LiOH}} = 20.9 \text{ mol CO}_2$$

$$V = \frac{nRT}{P} = \frac{20.9 \text{ mol} \times 0.8314 \text{ bar L mol}^{-1} \text{ K}^{-1} \times (25.9 + 273.2) \text{ K}}{1.00 \text{ bar}} = 5.20 \times 10^2 \text{ L}$$

51. **(M)** Determine the moles of O_2, and then the mass of $KClO_3$ that produced this amount of O_2.

$$n_{O_2} = \frac{98.3 \text{ kPa} \times \left(119 \text{ mL} \times \dfrac{1 \text{ L}}{1000 \text{ mL}}\right)}{8.314 \text{ kPa L K}^{-1} \text{ mol}^{-1} \times (22.4 + 273.2) \text{ K}} = 0.00476 \text{ mol}$$

$$\text{mass KClO}_3 = 0.00476 \text{ mol O}_2 \times \frac{2 \text{ mol KClO}_3}{3 \text{ mol O}_2} \times \frac{122.5 \text{ g KClO}_3}{1 \text{ mol KClO}_3} = 0.389 \text{ g KClO}_3$$

$$\% \text{ KClO}_3 = \frac{0.389 \text{ g KClO}_3}{3.57 \text{ g sample}} \times 100\% = 10.9\% \text{ KClO}_3$$

52. **(M)** Determine the moles and volume of O_2 liberated. $2 \text{ H}_2\text{O}_2(aq) \rightarrow 2 \text{ H}_2\text{O}(l) + \text{O}_2(g)$

$$n_{O_2} = 10.0 \text{ mL soln} \times \frac{1.01 \text{ g}}{1 \text{ mL}} \times \frac{3.00 \text{ g H}_2\text{O}_2}{100 \text{ g soln}} \times \frac{1 \text{ mol H}_2\text{O}_2}{34.01 \text{ g H}_2\text{O}_2} \times \frac{1 \text{ mol O}_2}{2 \text{ mol H}_2\text{O}_2}$$

$$= 0.00446 \text{ mol O}_2$$

$$V_{O_2} = \frac{0.00446 \text{ mol} \times 0.08314 \text{ bar L mol}^{-1} \text{ K}^{-1} \times (22 + 273) \text{ K}}{1.00 \text{ bar}} \times \frac{1000 \text{ mL}}{1 \text{ L}} = 109 \text{ mL}$$

53. **(M)** First we need to find the number of moles of CO(g)

Reaction is $3\ CO(g) + 7\ H_2(g) \longrightarrow C_3H_8(g) + 3\ H_2O(l)$

$$n_{CO} = \frac{PV}{RT} = \frac{28.5\ L \times 760\ Torr \times \dfrac{1\ atm}{760\ Torr}}{0.08206\ \dfrac{L\ atm}{K\ mol} \times 273.15\ K} = 1.27\ mol$$

$$V_{H_2\ (required)} = \frac{n_{H_2} RT}{P} = \frac{1.27\ mol\ CO \times \dfrac{7\ mol\ H_2}{3\ mol\ CO} \times 0.08206\ \dfrac{atm\ L}{mol\ K} \times 299\ K}{751\ mmHg \times \dfrac{1\ atm}{760\ mmHg}} = 73.7\ L\ H_2$$

54. **(M)**

(a) In this case, H_2 is the limiting reactant.

$$Volume\ NH_3 = 313\ L\ H_2 \times \frac{2\ L\ NH_3}{3\ L\ H_2} = 209\ L\ NH_3$$

(b) Moles of NH_3 (at 315 °C and 5.25 atm) $= \dfrac{5.25\ atm \times 313\ L}{0.08206\ \dfrac{atm\ L}{mol\ K} \times (315 + 273)K}$

$$= 3.41 \times 10^1\ mol\ H_2 \times \frac{2\ mol\ NH_3}{3\ mol\ H_2} = 2.27 \times 10^1\ mol\ NH_3$$

$$V\ (at\ 25\ °C,\ 727\ mmHg) = \frac{2.27 \times 10^1\ mol\ NH_3 \times 0.08206\ \dfrac{atm\ L}{mol\ K} \times 298\ K}{727\ mmHg \times \dfrac{1\ atm}{760\ mmHg}}$$

$$= 5.80 \times 10^2\ L\ NH_3$$

Mixtures of Gases

55. **(M)** Determine the total amount of gas; then use the ideal gas equation, assuming that the gases behave ideally.

$$n_{total} = n_{Ne} + n_{Ar} = 15.2\ g \times \frac{1\ mol}{20.18\ g} + 34.8\ g \times \frac{1\ mol}{39.95\ g} = 0.753\ mol + 0.871\ mol = 1.624\ mol$$

$$V_{total} = \frac{1.624\ mol \times 0.08314\ bar\ L\ mol^{-1}\ K^{-1} \times (273.2 + 26.7)\ K}{7.24\ bar} = 5.59\ L$$

56. **(M)** $2.24\ L\ H_2(g)$ at 0.0 °C and 1.00 atm is $0.100\ mol\ H_2(g)$. After 0.10 mol He is added, the container holds 0.20 mol gas.

$$V = \frac{nRT}{P} = \frac{0.20\ mol \times 0.08206\ \dfrac{atm\ L}{mol\ K} (273 + 100)K}{1.00\ atm} = 6.1\ L$$

57. **(M)** The two pressures are related, as are the number of moles of $N_2(g)$ to the total number of moles of gas.

$$\text{moles } N_2 = \frac{PV}{RT} = \frac{28.2 \text{ atm} \times 53.7 \text{ L}}{0.08206 \dfrac{\text{atm L}}{\text{mol K}} \times (26 + 273) \text{K}} = 61.7 \text{ mol } N_2$$

$$\text{total moles of gas} = 61.7 \text{ mol } N_2 \times \frac{75.0 \text{ atm}}{28.2 \text{ atm}} = 164 \text{ mol gas}$$

$$\text{mass Ne} = (164 \text{ mol total} - 61.7 \text{ mol } N_2) \times \frac{20.18 \text{ g Ne}}{1 \text{ mol Ne}} = 2.06 \times 10^3 \text{ g Ne}$$

58. **(M)** For each gas, use $P_i V_i = P_f V_f$ to calculate the final pressure, and add the resulting partial pressures.

$$P_{H_2} = 762 \text{ mmHg} \times \frac{2.35 \text{ L}}{5.52 \text{ L}} = 324 \text{ mmHg} \qquad P_{He} = 728 \text{ mmHg} \times \frac{3.17 \text{ L}}{5.52 \text{ L}} = 418 \text{ mmHg}$$

$$P_{total} = P_{H_2} + P_{He} = 324 \text{ mmHg} + 418 \text{ mmHg} = 742 \text{ mmHg}$$

59. **(M)** Initial pressure of the cylinder

$$P = \frac{nRT}{V} = \frac{\left(1.60 \text{ g } O_2 \times \dfrac{1 \text{ mol } O_2}{31.998 \text{ g } O_2}\right)(0.08206 \text{ atm L mol}^{-1} \text{ K}^{-1})(273.15 \text{ K})}{2.24 \text{ L}} = 0.500 \text{ atm}$$

We need to quadruple the pressure from 0.500 atm to 2.00 atm.

The mass of O_2 needs to quadruple as well from $1.60 \text{ g} \rightarrow 6.40 \text{ g}$ or add 4.80 g O_2

(this answer eliminates answer (a) and (b) as being correct).

One could also increase the pressure by adding the same number of another gas (e.g. He)

mass of He $= n_{He} \times M_{He}$

(Note: moles of O_2 needed $= 4.80 \text{ g} \times \dfrac{1 \text{ mol } O_2}{31.998 \text{ g } O_2} = 0.150 \text{ mol } O_2 = 0.150 \text{ mol He}$)

$$\text{mass of He} = 0.150 \text{ mol He} \times \frac{4.0026 \text{ g He}}{1 \text{ mol He}} = 0.600 \text{ g He} \quad ((d) \text{ is correct, add } 0.600 \text{ g He})$$

60. **(M)**

(a) First determine the moles of each gas, then the total moles, and finally the total pressure.

$$4.0 \text{ g } H_2 \times \frac{1 \text{ mol } H_2}{2.02 \text{ g } H_2} = 2.0 \text{ mol } H_2 \qquad 10.0 \text{ g He} \times \frac{1 \text{ mol He}}{4.00 \text{ g He}} = 2.50 \text{ mol He}$$

$$P = \frac{nRT}{V} = \frac{(2.0 + 2.50) \text{ mol} \times 0.08206 \dfrac{\text{atm L}}{\text{mol K}} \times 273 \text{ K}}{5.2 \text{ L}} = 19 \text{ atm}$$

(b) $\quad P_{H_2} = 19 \text{ atm} \times \dfrac{2.0 \text{ mol } H_2}{4.5 \text{ mol total}} = 8.4 \text{ atm} \qquad\qquad P_{He} = 19 \text{ atm} - 8.4 \text{ atm} = 11 \text{ atm}$

61. **(M)**

(a) $P_{benzene} = \dfrac{nRT}{V} = \dfrac{\left(0.728 \text{ g} \times \dfrac{1 \text{ mol } C_6H_6}{78.11 \text{ g } C_6H_6}\right) \times 0.08206 \dfrac{\text{atm L}}{\text{mol K}} \times (35+273) \text{ K}}{2.00 \text{ L}} \times \dfrac{760 \text{ mmHg}}{1 \text{ atm}}$

$= 89.5 \text{ mmHg}$

$P_{total} = 89.5 \text{ mmHg } C_6H_6(g) + 752 \text{ mmHg Ar}(g) = 842 \text{ mmHg}$

(b) $P_{Ar} = 752 \text{ mmHg}$ $\qquad\qquad\qquad$ $P_{benzene} = 89.5 \text{ mmHg}$

62. **(D)**

(a) The $\%CO_2$ in ordinary air is 0.036%, while from the data of this problem, the $\%CO_2$ in expired air is 3.8%.

$\dfrac{P(CO_2 \text{ expired air})}{P(CO_2 \text{ ordinary air})} = \dfrac{3.8\% \ CO_2}{0.036\% \ CO_2} = 1.1 \times 10^2 \ CO_2 \text{ (expired air to ordinary air)}$

(b/c) Density should be related to average molar mass. We expect the average molar mass of air to be between the molar masses of its two principal constituents, N_2 (28.0 g/mol) and O_2 (32.0 g/mol). The average molar mass of normal air is approximately 28.9 g/mol. Expired air would be made more dense by the presence of more CO_2 (44.0 g/mol) and less dense by the presence of more H_2O (18.0 g/mol). The change might be minimal. In fact, it is, as the following calculation shows.

$M_{exp.air} = \left(0.742 \text{ mol } N_2 \times \dfrac{28.014 \text{ g } N_2}{1 \text{ mol } N_2}\right) + \left(0.152 \text{ mol } O_2 \times \dfrac{31.998 \text{ g } O_2}{1 \text{ mol } O_2}\right)$

$+ \left(0.038 \text{ mol } CO_2 \times \dfrac{44.01 \text{ g } CO_2}{1 \text{ mol } CO_2}\right) + \left(0.059 \text{ mol } H_2O \times \dfrac{18.02 \text{ g } H_2O}{1 \text{ mol } H_2O}\right)$

$+ \left(0.009 \text{ mol Ar} \times \dfrac{39.9 \text{ g Ar}}{1 \text{ mol Ar}}\right) = 28.7 \text{ g/mol of expired air}$

Since the average molar mass of expired air is less than the average molar mass of ordinary air, expired air is less dense than ordinary air. Calculating the densities:

$d(\text{expired air}) = \dfrac{(28.7 \text{ g/mol})(1.00 \text{ atm})}{(0.08206 \text{ atm L mol}^{-1} \text{ K}^{-1})(37+273 \text{ K})} = 1.13 \text{ g/L}$

$d(\text{ordinary air}) = 1.14 \text{ g/L}$

63. **(E)** 1.00 g $H_2 \approx 0.50$ mol H_2 $\quad$ 1.00 g He ≈ 0.25 mol He

Adding 1.00 g of He to a vessel that only contains 1.00 g of H_2 results in the number of moles of gas being increased by 50%. Situation (b) best represents the resulting mixture, as the volume has increased by 50%.

64. **(E)** The answer is (b), because the volume at 275 K with 1.5 times as many atoms is roughly 4/3 larger than the drawing.

65. **(M)** For each gas, use $P_iV_i = P_fV_f$ to calculate the final partial pressure and then add the resulting partial pressures to obtain the total pressure.

For O_2: $\qquad P_f = \dfrac{V_i}{V_f} \times P_i = \dfrac{4.0\ \text{L}}{2.0\ \text{L}} \times 1.0\ \text{bar} = 2.0\ \text{bar}$

For N_2: $\qquad P_f = \dfrac{V_i}{V_f} \times P_i = \dfrac{2.0\ \text{L}}{2.0\ \text{L}} \times 2.0\ \text{bar} = 2.0\ \text{bar}$

Total pressure = 2.0 bar + 2.0 bar = 4.0 bar

66. **(M)** For each gas, use $P_iV_i = P_fV_f$ to obtain an expression for the final partial pressure, and then add the resulting expressions to obtain an expression for the total pressure.

For He: $\qquad P_f = \dfrac{V_i}{V_f} \times P_i = \dfrac{1.0\ \text{L}}{V_f} \times 0.75\ \text{atm}$

For Xe: $\qquad P_f = \dfrac{V_i}{V_f} \times P_i = \dfrac{2.5\ \text{L}}{V_f} \times 0.45\ \text{atm}$

For Ar: $\qquad P_f = \dfrac{V_i}{V_f} \times P_i = \dfrac{1.0\ \text{L}}{V_f} \times 1.20\ \text{atm}$

$$P_{\text{total}} = \dfrac{1.0\ \text{L}}{V_f} \times 0.75\ \text{atm} + \dfrac{2.5\ \text{L}}{V_f} \times 0.45\ \text{atm} + \dfrac{1.0\ \text{L}}{V_f} \times 1.20\ \text{atm}$$

$$= \dfrac{(1.0 \times 0.75 + 2.5 \times 0.45 + 1.0 \times 1.20)\ \text{atm L}}{V_f} = \dfrac{3.075\ \text{atm L}}{V_f}$$

But $P_{\text{total}} = 0.675$ atm, and the final volume is

$V_f = 1.0\ \text{L} + 2.5\ \text{L} + 1.0\ \text{L} + V_{\text{tube}} = 4.5\ \text{L} + V_{\text{tube}}$

Therefore, we can write

$$\dfrac{3.075\ \text{atm L}}{4.5\ \text{L} + V_{\text{tube}}} = 0.675\ \text{atm}$$

from which we get

$$V_{\text{tube}} = \left(\dfrac{3.075}{0.675} - 4.5 \right)\ \text{L} = (4.56 - 4.5)\ \text{L} = 0.06\ \text{L} = 0.1\ \text{L}$$

Collecting Gases over Liquids

67. **(M)** The pressure of the liberated $H_2(g)$ is 744 mmHg $- 23.8$ mmHg $= 720.$ mmHg

$$V = \frac{nRT}{P} = \frac{\left(1.65 \text{ g Al} \times \dfrac{1 \text{ mol Al}}{26.98 \text{ g Al}} \times \dfrac{3 \text{ mol H}_2}{2 \text{ mol Al}}\right) 0.08206 \dfrac{\text{atm L}}{\text{mol K}} (25+273)\text{K}}{720. \text{ mmHg} \times \dfrac{1 \text{ atm}}{760 \text{ mmHg}}} = 2.37 \text{ L H}_2(g)$$

This is the total volume of both gases, each with a different partial pressure.

68. **(D)**

(a) The total pressure is the sum of the partial pressures of $O_2(g)$ and the vapor pressure of water.

$$P_{\text{total}} = P_{O_2} + P_{H_2O} = 756 \text{ mmHg} = P_{O_2} + 19 \text{ mmHg}$$

$$P_{O_2} = (756-19) \text{ mmHg} = 737 \text{ mmHg}$$

(b) The volume percent is equal to the pressure percent.

$$\%O_2(g) \text{ by volume} = \frac{V_{O_2}}{V_{\text{total}}} \times 100\% = \frac{P_{O_2}}{P_{\text{total}}} \times 100\% = \frac{737 \text{ mmHg of O}_2}{756 \text{ mm Hg total}} \times 100\% = 97.5\%$$

(c) Determine the mass of $O_2(g)$ collected by multiplying the amount of O_2 collected, in moles, by the molar mass of $O_2(g)$.

$$\text{mass}_{O_2} = \frac{PV}{RT} = \frac{\left(737 \text{ mmHg} \times \dfrac{1 \text{ atm}}{760 \text{ mmHg}}\right)\left(89.3 \text{ mL} \times \dfrac{1 \text{ L}}{1000 \text{ mL}}\right)}{0.08206 \dfrac{\text{atm L}}{\text{mol K}} (21.3+273.2)\text{K}} \times \frac{32.00 \text{ g O}_2}{1 \text{ mol O}_2} = 0.115 \text{ g O}_2$$

69. **(M)** We first determine the pressure of the gas collected. This would be its "dry gas" pressure and, when added to 22.4 mmHg, gives the barometric pressure.

$$P = \frac{nRT}{V} = \frac{\left(1.46 \text{ g} \times \dfrac{1 \text{ mol O}_2}{32.0 \text{ g O}_2}\right) 0.08206 \dfrac{\text{atm L}}{\text{mol K}} \times 297 \text{ K}}{1.16 \text{ L}} \times \frac{760 \text{ mmHg}}{1 \text{ atm}} = 729 \text{ mmHg}$$

$$P_{\text{bar.}} = 729 \text{ mm Hg} + 22.4 \text{ mmHg} = 751 \text{ mmHg}$$

70. **(M)** We first determine the "dry gas" pressure of helium. This pressure, subtracted from the barometric pressure of 738.6 mmHg, gives the vapor pressure of hexane at $25 \,^\circ\text{C}$.

$$P = \frac{nRT}{V} = \frac{\left(1.072 \text{ g} \times \dfrac{1 \text{ mol He}}{4.003 \text{ g He}}\right) 0.08206 \dfrac{\text{atm L}}{\text{mol K}} \times 298.2 \text{ K}}{8.446 \text{ L}} \times \frac{760 \text{ mmHg}}{1 \text{ atm}} = 589.7 \text{ mmHg}$$

vapor pressure of hexane $= 738.6$ mmHg $- 589.7$ mmHg $= 148.9$ mmHg

71. **(M)** The first step is to balance the equation:

$$2\,NaClO_3 \xrightarrow{\Delta} 2\,NaCl + 3\,O_2$$

The pressure of O_2 is determined by subtracting the known vapor pressure of water at the given temperature from the measured total pressure.

$P_{O_2} = P_{tot} - P_{H_2O} = 734\ \text{Torr} - 21.07\ \text{Torr} = 713\ \text{Torr}$

$P_{atm} = 713\ \text{mmHg} \times 1\ \text{atm} / 760\ \text{Torr} = 0.938\ \text{atm}$

$$\text{mol } O_2 = \frac{PV}{RT} = \frac{(0.938\ \text{atm})(0.0572\ \text{L})}{(0.08206\ \text{atm L mol}^{-1}\,\text{K}^{-1})(296\ \text{K})} = 0.00221\ \text{mol}$$

Mass of $NaClO_3$ is then determined as follows:

$$0.00221\ \text{mol } O_2 \times \frac{2\ \text{mol } NaClO_3}{3\ \text{mol } O_2} \times \frac{106.44\ \text{g}}{1\ \text{mol } NaClO_3} = 0.1568\ \text{g } NaClO_3$$

$$\%NaClO_3 = \frac{0.157\ \text{g}}{0.8765\ \text{g}} \times 100 = 17.9$$

72. **(M)** The work for this problem is nearly identical to the above problem.

$$2\,KClO_3 \xrightarrow{\Delta} 2\,KCl + 3\,O_2$$

The pressure of O_2 is determined by subtracting the known vapor pressure of water at the given temperature from the measured total pressure.

$P_{O_2} = P_{tot} - P_{H_2O} = 323\ \text{Torr} - 25.22\ \text{Torr} = 298\ \text{Torr}$

$P_{atm} = 298\ \text{mmHg} \times 1\ \text{atm} / 760\ \text{mmHg} = 0.392\ \text{atm}$

$$\text{mol } O_2 = \frac{PV}{RT} = \frac{(0.392\ \text{atm})(0.229\ \text{L})}{(0.08206\ \text{atm L mol}^{-1}\,\text{K}^{-1})(299\ \text{K})} = 0.00366\ \text{mol}$$

Mass of $KClO_3$ is then determined as follows:

$$0.00366\ \text{mol } O_2 \times \frac{2\ \text{mol } KClO_3}{3\ \text{mol } O_2} \times \frac{122.54\ \text{g}}{1\ \text{mol } KClO_3} = 0.299\ \text{g } KClO_3$$

$$\%KClO_3 = \frac{0.299\ \text{g}}{0.415\ \text{g}} \times 100 = 72.0$$

Kinetic-Molecular Theory

73. **(M)** Recall that $1\ \mathrm{J} = \mathrm{kg\ m^2\ s^{-2}}$

$$u_{rms} = \sqrt{\frac{3RT}{M}} = \sqrt{\frac{3 \times 8.3145 \dfrac{\mathrm{J}}{\mathrm{mol\ K}} \times \dfrac{1\ \mathrm{kg\ m^2\ s^{-2}}}{1\ \mathrm{J}} \times 303\ \mathrm{K}}{\dfrac{70.91 \times 10^{-3}\ \mathrm{kg\ Cl_2}}{1\ \mathrm{mol\ Cl_2}}}} = 326\ \mathrm{m/s}$$

74. **(M)**

$$2 = \frac{\sqrt{\dfrac{3RT_1}{M}}}{\sqrt{\dfrac{3RT_2}{M}}} = \sqrt{\frac{T_1}{T_2}} = \sqrt{\frac{T_1}{273\ \mathrm{K}}} \quad \text{Square both sides and solve for } T_1. \quad T_1 = 4 \times 273\ \mathrm{K} = 1092\ \mathrm{K}$$

Alternatively, recall that $1\ \mathrm{J} = \mathrm{kg\ m^2\ s^{-2}}$

$$u_{rms} = \sqrt{\frac{3RT}{M}} = 1.84 \times 10^3\ \mathrm{m/s} \quad \text{Solve this equation for temperature with } u_{rms} \text{ doubled.}$$

$$T = \frac{M u_{rms}^2}{3R} = \frac{2.016 \times 10^{-3}\ \mathrm{kg/mol}\ (2 \times 1.84 \times 10^3\ \mathrm{m/s})^2}{3 \times 8.3145 \dfrac{\mathrm{J}}{\mathrm{mol\ K}} \times \dfrac{1\ \mathrm{kg\ m^2\ s^{-2}}}{1\ \mathrm{J}}} = 1.09 \times 10^3\ \mathrm{K}$$

75. **(M)** $M = \dfrac{3RT}{(u_{rms})^2} =$

$$\frac{3 \times 8.3145\ \dfrac{\mathrm{J}}{\mathrm{mol\ K}} \times 298\ \mathrm{K}}{\left(2180 \dfrac{\mathrm{mi}}{\mathrm{hr}} \times \dfrac{1\ \mathrm{hr}}{3600\ \mathrm{sec}} \times \dfrac{5280\ \mathrm{ft}}{1\ \mathrm{mi}} \times \dfrac{12\ \mathrm{in.}}{1\ \mathrm{ft}} \times \dfrac{1\ \mathrm{m}}{39.37\ \mathrm{in.}}\right)^2} = 0.00783\ \mathrm{kg/mol}$$

$$= 7.83\ \mathrm{g/mol\ or\ } 7.83\ u$$

76. **(E)** A noble gas with molecules having u_{rms} at 25 °C greater than that of a rifle bullet will have a molar mass less than 7.8 g/mol. Helium is the only possibility. A noble gas with a slower u_{rms} will have a molar mass greater than 7.8 g/mol; any one of the other noble gases will have a slower u_{rms}.

77. **(E)** We equate the two expressions for root mean square speed, cancel the common factors, and solve for the temperature of Ne. Note that the units of molar masses do not have to be in kg/mol in this calculation; they simply must be expressed in the same units.

$$\sqrt{\frac{3RT}{M}} = \sqrt{\frac{3R \times 300\ \mathrm{K}}{4.003}} = \sqrt{\frac{3R \times T_{Ne}}{20.18}} \quad \text{Square both sides: } \frac{300\ \mathrm{K}}{4.003} = \frac{T_{Ne}}{20.18}$$

Solve for T_{Ne}: $\quad T_{Ne} = 300\ \mathrm{K} \times \dfrac{20.18}{4.003} = 1.51 \times 10^3\ \mathrm{K}$

78. **(E)** u_m, the modal speed, is the speed that occurs most often, 55 mi/h

$$\text{average speed} = \frac{38+44+45+48+50+55+55+57+58+60}{10} = 51.0 \text{ mi/h} = \bar{u}$$

$$u_{rms} = \sqrt{\frac{38^2+44^2+45^2+48^2+50^2+55^2+55^2+57^2+58^2+60^2}{10}} = \sqrt{\frac{26472}{10}} = 51.5 \text{ mi/h}$$

79. **(D)** The greatest pitfall of this type of problem is using improper units. Therefore, convert everything to SI units.

$M_{O_2} = 32.0 \text{ g/mol} = 32.0 \times 10^{-3} \text{ kg/mol}$

Mass of O_2 molecule: $\frac{32.0 \times 10^{-3} \text{ kg}}{\text{mol}} \times \frac{1 \text{ mol}}{6.022 \times 10^{23} \text{ molecule}} = 5.314 \times 10^{-26} \text{ kg}$

$R = 8.3145 \text{ J mol}^{-1} \text{K}^{-1}$, or kg m^2/(s^2 mol K)

Now, we must determine the u_{rms} first to determine kinetic energy:

$$\overline{u_{rms}} = \sqrt{\frac{3\,RT}{M}} = \sqrt{\frac{3 \times 8.3145 \times 298}{32.0 \times 10^{-3}}} = 482 \text{ m/s}$$

Kinetic energy of an O_2 molecule is as follows:

$$\bar{e}_k = \frac{1}{2} m \overline{u_{rms}^2} = \frac{1}{2}(5.314 \times 10^{-26} \text{ kg})(482 \text{ m/s})^2 = 6.17 \times 10^{-21} \text{ J}$$

80. **(D)** To calculate the total kinetic energy for a certain quantity of gas molecules, we must first calculate the (average) kinetic energy for one molecule and then apply it to the bulk.

$M\,N_2 = 28.0 \text{ g/mol} = 28.0 \times 10^{-3} \text{ kg/mol}$

Mass of N_2 molecule: $\frac{28.0 \times 10^{-3} \text{ kg}}{1 \text{ mol}} \times \frac{1 \text{ mol}}{6.022 \times 10^{23} \text{ molecule}} = 4.650 \times 10^{-26} \text{ kg}$

$R = 8.3145 \text{ J mol}^{-1} \text{K}^{-1}$, or kg m^2/(s^2 mol K)

Now determine the u_{rms} first to determine kinetic energy:

$$\overline{u_{rms}} = \sqrt{\frac{3RT}{M}} = \sqrt{\frac{3 \times 8.3145 \times 298}{28.0 \times 10^{-3}}} = 515 \text{ m/s}$$

Kinetic energy of an N_2 molecule is calculated as follows:

$$\bar{e}_k = \frac{1}{2} m \overline{u_{rms}^2} = \frac{1}{2}(4.650 \times 10^{-26} \text{ kg})(515 \text{ m/s})^2 = 6.17 \times 10^{-21} \text{ J}$$

Therefore, the kinetic energy of 155 g of N_2 is:

$$\bar{e}_k: \ 155 \text{ g N}_2 \times \frac{1 \text{ mol N}_2}{14.0 \text{ g N}_2} \times \frac{6.022 \times 10^{23} \text{ molecule}}{1 \text{ mol N}_2} \times \frac{6.17 \times 10^{-21} \text{ J}}{1 \text{ molecule}} = 4.11 \times 10^4 \text{ J}$$

Diffusion and Effusion of Gases

81. **(M)**

$$\frac{\text{rate (NO}_2)}{\text{rate (N}_2\text{O})} = \sqrt{\frac{M \text{ (N}_2\text{O})}{M(\text{NO}_2)}} = \sqrt{\frac{44.02 \text{ g/mol}}{46.01 \text{ g/mol}}} = 0.9781 = \frac{x \text{ mol NO}_2/t}{0.00484 \text{ mol N}_2\text{O}/t}$$

$$\text{mol NO}_2 = 0.00484 \text{ mol} \times 0.9781 = 0.00473 \text{ mol NO}_2$$

82. **(M)**

$$\frac{\text{rate } (N_2)}{\text{rate (unknown)}} = \frac{\text{mol } (N_2)/38 \text{ s}}{\text{mol (unknown)}/64 \text{ s}} = \frac{64 \text{ s}}{38 \text{ s}} = 1.68 = \sqrt{\frac{M(\text{unknown})}{M(N_2)}}$$

$$M(\text{unknown}) = (1.68)^2 M(N_2) = (1.68)^2 (28.01 \text{ g/mol}) = 79 \text{ g/mol}$$

83. **(M)**

(a) $\dfrac{\text{rate (N}_2)}{\text{rate (O}_2)} = \sqrt{\dfrac{M \text{ (O}_2)}{M(\text{N}_2)}} = \sqrt{\dfrac{32.00 \text{ g/mol}}{28.01 \text{ g/mol}}} = 1.07$

(b) $\dfrac{\text{rate (H}_2\text{O})}{\text{rate (D}_2\text{O})} = \sqrt{\dfrac{M \text{ (D}_2\text{O})}{M(\text{H}_2\text{O})}} = \sqrt{\dfrac{20.0 \text{ g/mol}}{18.02 \text{ g/mol}}} = 1.05$

(c) $\dfrac{\text{rate (}^{14}\text{CO}_2)}{\text{rate (}^{12}\text{CO}_2)} = \sqrt{\dfrac{M \text{ (}^{12}\text{CO}_2)}{M(^{14}\text{CO}_2)}} = \sqrt{\dfrac{44.0 \text{ g/mol}}{46.0 \text{ g/mol}}} = 0.978$

(d) $\dfrac{\text{rate (}^{235}\text{UF}_6)}{\text{rate (}^{238}\text{UF}_6)} = \sqrt{\dfrac{M \text{ (}^{238}\text{UF}_6)}{M(^{235}\text{UF}_6)}} = \sqrt{\dfrac{352 \text{ g/mol}}{349 \text{ g/mol}}} = 1.004$

84. **(M)**

$$\frac{\text{rate of effusion O}_2}{\text{rate of effusion SO}_2} = \sqrt{\frac{M(\text{SO}_2)}{M(\text{O}_2)}} = \sqrt{\frac{64 \text{ g/mol}}{32 \text{ g/mol}}} = \sqrt{2} = 1.4$$

O_2 will effuse at 1.4 times the rate of effusion of SO_2. The situation depicted in (c) best represents the distribution of the molecules. If 5 molecules of SO_2 effuse, we would expect that 1.4 times as many O_2 molecules effuse over the same period of time.

$(1.4 \times 5 = 7 \text{ molecules of O}_2)$. This is depicted in situation (c).

85. **(M)** For ideal gases, the effusion rate is inversely proportional to their molecular mass. As such, the rate of effusion of a known gas can be determined if the rate of effusion for another gas is known:

$$\frac{\text{rate of effusion of Ne}}{\text{rate of effusion of He}} = \sqrt{\frac{M_{\text{He}}}{M_{\text{Ne}}}}$$

Since effusion is loosely defined as movement of a fixed number of atoms per unit time, and since in this problem we are looking at the time it takes for the same number of moles of both Ne and He to effuse, the above equation can be rearranged as follows:

$$\frac{mol_{Ne}}{time_{Ne}} \Big/ \frac{mol_{He}}{time_{He}} = \frac{time_{He}}{time_{Ne}} = \sqrt{\frac{M_{He}}{M_{Ne}}}$$

$$\frac{x}{22 \text{ h}} = \sqrt{\frac{4.00 \text{ g/mol}}{20.18 \text{ g/mol}}}$$

Solving for x,
$$x = 22 \times \sqrt{4.00/20.18} = 9.80 \text{ h}$$

86. **(M)** The same reasoning discussed above works in this problem:

$$\frac{mol_{Rn}}{time_{Rn}} \Big/ \frac{mol_{Hg}}{time_{Hg}} = \frac{time_{Hg}}{time_{Rn}} = \sqrt{\frac{M_{Hg}}{M_{Rn}}}$$

$$\frac{1}{1.082} = \sqrt{\frac{200.59}{M_{Rn}}}$$

Solving for M_{Rn} gives a value of 235 g/mol.

Nonideal Gases

87. **(M)** To facilitate calculations at several temperatures, substitute the given quantities into the ideal gas and van der Waals equations, and simplify the resulting expressions.

$$P_{ideal} = \frac{1.00 \text{ mol} \times 0.08314 \text{ bar L mol}^{-1} \text{ K}^{-1} \times T}{2.00 \text{ L}} = 0.0415\underline{7} \text{ bar K}^{-1} \times T$$

$$P_{vdw} = \frac{1.00 \text{ mol} \times 0.08314 \text{ bar L mol}^{-1} \text{ K}^{-1} \times T}{2.00 \text{ L} - 1.00 \text{ mol} \times 0.0542 \text{ L mol}^{-1}} - \frac{(1.00 \text{ mol})^2 \times 6.34 \text{ bar L}^2 \text{ mol}^{-2}}{(2.00 \text{ L})^2}$$

$$= 0.0427\underline{3} \text{ bar K}^{-1} \times T - 1.58\underline{5} \text{ bar}$$

(a) For $T = (100 + 273) \text{ K} = 373 \text{ K}$:

$$P_{ideal} = 0.0415\underline{7} \text{ bar K}^{-1} \times 373 \text{ K} = 15.5 \text{ bar}$$

$$P_{vdw} = 0.0427\underline{3} \text{ bar K}^{-1} \times 373 \text{ K} - 1.58\underline{5} \text{ bar} = 14.4 \text{ bar}$$

(b) For $T = (200 + 273) \text{ K} = 473 \text{ K}$:

$$P_{ideal} = 0.0415\underline{7} \text{ bar K}^{-1} \times 473 \text{ K} = 19.7 \text{ bar}$$

$$P_{vdw} = 0.0427\underline{3} \text{ bar K}^{-1} \times 473 \text{ K} - 1.58\underline{5} \text{ bar} = 18.6 \text{ bar}$$

(c) For $T = (400 + 273) \text{ K} = 673 \text{ K}$:

$$P_{ideal} = 0.0415\underline{7} \text{ bar K}^{-1} \times 673 \text{ K} = 28.0 \text{ bar}$$

$$P_{vdw} = 0.0427\underline{3} \text{ bar K}^{-1} \times 673 \text{ K} - 1.58\underline{5} \text{ bar} = 27.1 \text{ bar}$$

These results, along with those of Example 6-17, are summarized below. The percent difference is calculated as $100\% \times (P_{\text{ideal}} - P_{\text{vdw}})/P_{\text{vdw}}$. These results support the observation that a gas tends to behave more like an ideal gas as temperature increases.

t, °C	P_{ideal}, bar	P_{vdw}, bar	$P_{\text{ideal}} - P_{\text{vdw}}$	Percent difference
0	11.3	10.1	1.2 bar	12%
100	15.5	14.4	1.1 bar	7.6%
200	19.7	18.6	1.1 bar	5.9%
400	28.0	27.1	0.9 bar	3.3%

88. (M)

(a) $V = 100.0$ L,

$$P_{\text{vdw}} = \frac{nRT}{V-nb} - \frac{n^2a}{V^2} = \frac{1.50 \text{ mol} \times \dfrac{0.083145 \text{ L bar}}{\text{mol K}} \times 298 \text{ K}}{(100.0 - 1.50 \times 0.0879)\text{L}} - \frac{1.50^2 \times 7.857 \text{ L}^2 \text{ bar}}{(100.0 \text{ L})^2}$$

$$= 0.3721 - 0.0018 \text{ bar SO}_2\,(g) = 0.3704 \text{ atm}$$

$$P_{\text{ideal}} = \frac{1.50 \text{ mol} \times \dfrac{0.083145 \text{ L bar}}{\text{mol K}} \times 298 \text{ K}}{100.0 \text{ L}} = 0.372 \text{ bar}$$

The two pressures are almost equal.

(b) $V = 50.0$ L, $P_{\text{vdw}} = 0.739$ bar; $P_{\text{ideal}} = 0.744$ bar.
Here the two pressures agree within a few percent.

(c) $V = 20.0$ L, $P_{\text{vdw}} = 1.82$ bar; $P_{\text{ideal}} = 1.86$ bar

(d) $V = 10.0$ L, $P_{\text{vdw}} = 3.60$ bar; $P_{\text{ideal}} = 3.72$ bar

89. (E) The van der Waals parameter b is defined as the excluded volume per mole, or the volume that is taken up by 1 mole of gas once converted to a liquid.

From Table 6-5, $b_{\text{He}} = 0.0238$ L/mol. Therefore, the volume of a single He atom is:

Conversion pathway approach:

$$\frac{0.0238 \text{ L}}{1 \text{ mol He}} \times \frac{1 \text{ mol He}}{6.022 \times 10^{23} \text{ atoms}} \times \frac{1 \text{ m}^3}{1000 \text{ L}} \times \frac{(1 \times 10^{12} \text{ pm})^3}{1 \text{ m}^3} = 3.95 \times 10^7 \text{ pm}^3/\text{He atom}$$

Step-wise approach:

$$\frac{0.0238\,\text{L}}{\text{mol He}} \times \frac{1\,\text{mol He}}{6.022\times10^{23}\,\text{atoms}} = 3.95\times10^{-26}\,\text{L/atom}$$

$$3.95\times10^{-26}\,\text{L/atom} \times \frac{1\,\text{m}^3}{1000\,\text{L}} = 3.95\times10^{-29}\,\text{m}^3/\text{atom}$$

$$3.95\times10^{-29}\,\text{m}^3/\text{atom} \times \frac{\left(1\times10^{12}\,\text{pm}\right)^3}{1\,\text{m}^3} = 3.95\times10^{7}\,\text{pm}^3 / \text{He atom}$$

$V = (4/3)\,\pi\,r^3$. Rearranging to solve for r gives $r = \sqrt[3]{(3V)/(4\pi)}$. Solving for r gives an atomic radius of 211.3 pm.

90. **(M)**
(a) The process is very similar to the above example. From Table 6-5, $b_{CH4} = 0.0431$ L/mol. Therefore, the volume of a single CH_4 molecule is:

$$\frac{0.0431\,\text{L}}{\text{mol CH}_4} \times \frac{1\,\text{mol CH}_4}{6.022\times10^{23}\,\text{molecule}} \times \frac{1\,\text{m}^3}{1000\,\text{L}} \times \frac{\left(1\times10^{-12}\,\text{pm}\right)^3}{1\,\text{m}^3} = 7.16\times10^{7}\,\text{pm}^3/\text{CH}_4\,\text{molecule}$$

$V = (4/3)\,\pi\,r^3$. Solving for r gives a molecular radius of 258 pm. This value is greater than $r = 228$ pm, because our calculated value is based on b, which is the volume taken up by a mole of gas that has been condensed into a liquid.

(b) Compression ratio is given as follows:

$$V_m = \frac{1\,\text{mL}}{66.02\,\text{g}} \times \frac{1\,\text{L}}{1000\,\text{mL}} \times \frac{16.043\,\text{g}}{1\,\text{mol}} = 2.43\times10^{-3}\,\text{L mol}^{-1}$$

$$Z = \frac{PV_m}{RT} = \frac{(100\,\text{bar})(2.43\times10^{-3}\,\text{L mol}^{-1})}{\left(0.083145\,\text{bar}\cdot\text{L}\cdot\text{mol}^{-1}\cdot\text{K}^{-1}\right)(325\,\text{K})} = 9.0\times10^{-3}$$

INTEGRATIVE AND ADVANCED EXERCISES

91. **(E)** A millimeter of mercury is 1/760 of an atmosphere of pressure at sea level. The density of mercury (13.5951 g/cm^3) needs to be included in this definition and, because the density of mercury, like that of other liquids, varies somewhat with temperature, the pressure will vary if the density varies. The acceleration due to gravity (9.80665 m/s^2) needs to be included because pressure is a *force* per unit area, not just a mass per unit area, and this force depends on the acceleration applied to the given mass, i.e., force = mass × acceleration.

92. **(E)** Of course, we express the temperatures in Kelvin:

$0\,°C = 273\,\text{K}, -100\,°C = 173\,\text{K}, -200\,°C = \text{K}, -250\,°C = \text{K}$, and $-270\,°C = 3\,\text{K}$.

(A) $\dfrac{V}{T} = k = \dfrac{10.0\text{ cm}^3}{400\text{ K}} = 0.0250\text{ cm}^3\text{ K}^{-1}$

$V = 0.0250\text{ cm}^3\text{K}^{-1} \times 273\text{ K} = 6.83\text{ cm}^3$

$V = 0.0250\text{ cm}^3\text{ K}^{-1} \times 173\text{ K} = 4.33\text{ cm}^3$ $\qquad V = 0.0250\text{ cm}^3\text{ K}^{-1} \times 73\text{ K} = 1.8\text{ cm}^3$

$V = 0.0250\text{ cm}^3\text{ K}^{-1} \times 23\text{ K} = 0.58\text{ cm}^3$ $\qquad V = 0.0250\text{ cm}^3\text{ K}^{-1} \times 3\text{ K} = 0.08\text{ cm}^3$

(B) $\dfrac{V}{T} = k = \dfrac{20.0\text{ cm}^3}{400\text{ K}} = 0.0500\text{ cm}^3\text{ K}^{-1}$ $\quad V = 0.0500\text{ cm}^3\text{ K}^{-1} \times 273\text{ K} = 13.7\text{ cm}^3$

$V = 0.0500\text{ cm}^3\text{ K}^{-1} \times 173\text{ K} = 8.65\text{ cm}^3$ $\qquad V = 0.0500\text{ cm}^3\text{ K}^{-1} \times 73\text{ K} = 3.7\text{ cm}^3$

$V = 0.0500\text{ cm}^3\text{ K}^{-1} \times 23\text{ K} = 1.2\text{ cm}^3$ $\qquad V = 0.0500\text{ cm}^3\text{ K}^{-1} \times 3\text{ K} = 0.2\text{ cm}^3$

(C) $\dfrac{V}{T} = k = \dfrac{40.0\text{ cm}^3}{400\text{ K}} = 0.100\text{ cm}^3\text{ K}^{-1}$ $\qquad V = 0.100\text{ cm}^3\text{ K}^{-1} \times 273\text{ K} = 27.3\text{ cm}^3$

$V = 0.100\text{ cm}^3\text{ K}^{-1} \times 173\text{ K} = 17.3\text{ cm}^3$ $\qquad V = 0.100\text{ cm}^3\text{ K}^{-1} \times 73\text{ K} = 7.3\text{ cm}^3$

$V = 0.100\text{ cm}^3\text{ K}^{-1} \times 23\text{ K} = 2.3\text{ cm}^3$ $\qquad V = 0.100\text{ cm}^3\text{ K}^{-1} \times 3\text{ K} = 0.3\text{ cm}^3$

As expected, in all three cases the volume of each gas goes to zero at 0 K.

93. (M) Initial sketch shows 1 mole of gas at STP with a volume of ~22.4 L.

Velocity of particles = v_i. Note that velocity increases as $\sqrt{T}$ (i.e., quadrupling temperature results in a doubling of the velocity of the particles).

(a) Pressure drops to 1/3 of its original value (1 atm $\rightarrow$ 0.333 atm). The number of moles and temperature are constant. Volume of the gas should increase from 22.4 L $\rightarrow \approx 67$ L while the velocity remains unchanged at v_i.

(b) Pressure stays constant at its original value (1.00 atm). The number of moles is unchanged, while the temperature drops to half of its value (273 K $\rightarrow$ 137 K). Volume of the gas should decrease from 22.4 L $\rightarrow \approx 11.2$ L while the velocity drops to about 71% to $0.71v_i$ ($\sqrt{T} \rightarrow \sqrt{0.5 \times T}$).

(c) Pressure drops to 1/2 of its original value (1 atm $\rightarrow$ 0.5 atm). The number of moles remains constant, while the temperature is increased to twice it original value (273 K $\rightarrow$ 546 K). Volume of the gas should quadruple, increasing the volume from 22.4 L $\rightarrow \approx 90$ L. Velocity of the molecules increases by 41% to $1.41v_i$ ($\sqrt{T} \rightarrow \sqrt{2 \times T}$).

(d) Pressure increases to 2.25 times its original value (2.25 atm) owing to a temperature increase of 50% (273 K $\rightarrow \approx 410$ K) and a 50% increase in the number of particles (1 mol to 1.5 mol). The volume of the gas should remain unchanged at 22.4 L, while the velocity increases by 22% to $1.22v_i$ ($\sqrt{T} \rightarrow \sqrt{1.5 \times T}$).

$n = 1$ mol $P = 1$ atm $V = 22.4$ L $T = 273$ K $v = v_i$	**(initial)**
$n = 1$ mol $P = 0.333$ atm $V = 11.2$ L $T = 273$ K $v = v_i$	**(a)**
$n = 1$ mol $P = 1$ atm $V = 11.2$ L $T = 137$ K $v = 0.71\, v_i$	**(b)**
$n = 1$ mol $P = 0.500$ atm $V = 11.2$ L $T = 273$ K $v = v_i$	**(c)**
$n = 1$ mol $P = 2.25$ atm $V = 22.4$ L $T = 273$ K $v = v_i$	**(d)**

94. **(M)** We know that the sum of the moles of gas in the two bulbs is 1.00 mol, and that both bulbs have the same volume, and are at the same pressure because they are connected. Therefore,

$$n_1 T_1 = n_2 T_2$$

$$\frac{n_1}{n_2} = \frac{T_2}{T_1} = \frac{350 \text{ K}}{225 \text{ K}} = 1.556$$

$$n_1 = 1.556\, n_2$$

Therefore,
$n_2(1.556) + n_2 = 1.00$. Solving the equation gives (Flask 2) $n_2 = 0.391$, and (Flask 1) $n_1 = 0.609$.

95. **(M)** First, calculate the number of moles of gas:

$$n = \frac{PV}{RT} = \frac{(1.00 \text{ atm})(6.30 \text{ L})}{\left(0.08206 \text{ atm L mol}^{-1} \text{ K}^{-1}\right)(323 \text{ K})} = 0.2377 \text{ mol}$$

Molecular mass (M) then can be calculated:
$M = (10.0 \text{ g})/(0.2377 \text{ mol}) = 42.07$ g/mol
Now we must determine the mole ratio of C to H:
85.6 g C $\times$ (1 mol C/12.01 g C) = 7.13 mol
14.4 g H $\times$ (1 mol H/1.01 g H) = 14.3 mol

Now, divide both by the smallest number:
C:C mole ratio = 1
H:C mole ratio = 2

Therefore, the empirical formula is CH_2, with a formula unit molar mass of ~14.03 g/mol. To determine molecular formula, divide MM by formula unit MM: 42.07/14.03 = 3.00. Therefore, the molecular formula is C_3H_6.

96. **(M)** First we determine the molar mass of the hydrocarbon.

$$M = \frac{mRT}{PV} = \frac{0.7178\,g \times 8.314\,\frac{kPa\,L}{mol\,K}(65.0 + 273.2)\,K}{99.2\,kPa \times 0.3907\,L} = 52.0 \text{ g/mol}$$

Now determine the empirical formula. A hydrocarbon contains just hydrogen and carbon.

$$\text{amount C} = 2.4267\,g\,CO_2 \times \frac{1\,mol\,CO_2}{44.01\,g\,CO_2} \times \frac{1\,mol\,C}{1\,mol\,CO_2} = 0.05514\,mol\,C \div 0.05514 \rightarrow 1.000\,mol\,C$$

$$\text{amount H} = 0.4967\,g\,H_2O \times \frac{1\,mol\,H_2O}{18.02\,g\,H_2O} \times \frac{2\,mol\,H}{1\,mol\,H_2O} = 0.05513\,mol\,H \div 0.05514 \rightarrow 1.000\,mol\,H$$

The empirical formula is CH. This gives an empirical molar mass of 13 g/mol, almost precisely one-fourth of the experimental molar mass. The molecular formula is therefore C_4H_4.

97. **(M)**

Stepwise approach:
Note that three moles of gas are produced for each mole of NH_4NO_3 that decomposes.

$$\text{amount of gas} = 3.05\,g\,NH_4NO_3 \times \frac{1\,mol\,NH_4NO_3}{80.04\,g\,NH_4NO_3} \times \frac{3\,mol\,gas}{1\,mol\,NH_4NO_3} = 0.114\,mol\,gas$$

$$T = 250 + 273 = 523\,K$$

$$P = \frac{nRT}{V} = \frac{0.114\,mol \times 0.08206\,L\,atm\,mol^{-1}\,K^{-1} \times 523\,K}{2.18\,L} = 2.25\,atm$$

Conversion pathway:

$$P = \frac{nRT}{V}$$

$$P = \frac{3.05\,g\,NH_4NO_3 \times \frac{1\,mol\,NH_4NO_3}{80.04\,g\,NH_4NO_3} \times \frac{3\,mol\,gas}{1\,mol\,NH_4NO_3} \times 0.08206\,atm\,L\,mol^{-1}\,K^{-1} \times 523\,K}{2.18\,L}$$

$$= 2.25\,atm$$

98. **(M)** First, let's convert the given units to those easier used:

$P = 101 \text{ kPa} \times (1 \text{ bar}/101 \text{ kPa}) \times (1 \text{ atm}/1.01 \text{ bar}) = 0.9901 \text{ atm}$

$T = (819 + 273) \text{ K} = 1092 \text{ K}$

$$\text{mol NH}_4\text{NO}_2 = 128 \text{ g NH}_4\text{NO}_2 \times \frac{1 \text{ mol NH}_4\text{NO}_2}{64.052 \text{ g NH}_4\text{NO}_2} = 1.998 \text{ mol}$$

$$\text{mol gas} = 1.998 \text{ mol NH}_4\text{NO}_2 \times \frac{3 \text{ mol gas}}{1 \text{ mol NH}_4\text{NO}_2} = 5.994$$

$$V = \frac{nRT}{P} = \frac{(5.994 \text{ mol})(0.08206 \text{ atm L mol}^{-1}\text{ K}^{-1})(1092 \text{ K})}{0.9901 \text{ atm}} = 542 \text{ L}$$

99. **(M)**

(a) $n_{H_2} = 1.00 \text{ g}/2.02 \text{ g/mol} = 0.495 \text{ mol H}_2$; $n_{O_2} = 8.60 \text{ g}/32.0 \text{ g/mol} = 0.269 \text{ mol O}_2$

The limiting reactant in the production of water is H_2 (0.495 mol) with O_2 (0.269 mol) in excess.

	2 H$_2$(g)	+	O$_2$(g)	→	2 H$_2$O(l)
(initial)	0.495 mol		0.269 mol		0
after reaction	~0		0.022 mol		0.495 mol

so $P_{\text{total}} = P_{O_2} + P_{H_2O}$

$$P_{O_2} = \frac{n_{O_2}RT}{V} = \frac{0.022 \text{ mol} \times 0.08206 \text{ atm L mol}^{-1}\text{ K}^{-1} \times 298 \text{ K}}{1.50 \text{ L}} = 0.359 \text{ atm}$$

$$P_{\text{total}} = 0.359 \text{ atm} + \frac{23.8 \text{ mmHg}}{760 \text{ mmHg/atm}} = 0.39 \text{ atm}$$

100. **(M)**

(a) $$\text{mL O}_2/\text{min} = \frac{4.0 \text{ L air}}{1 \text{ min}} \times \frac{1000 \text{ mL}}{1 \text{ L}} \times \frac{3.8 \text{ mL CO}_2}{100 \text{ mL air}} \times \frac{1 \text{ mL O}_2}{2 \text{ mL CO}_2} = 76 \text{ mL O}_2/\text{min}$$

(b) We first determine the amount of O$_2$ produced per minute, then the rate of consumption of Na$_2$O$_2$.

$$P = 735 \text{ mmHg} \times \frac{1 \text{ atm}}{760 \text{ mmHg}} = 0.967 \text{ atm} \qquad T = 25 + 273 = 298 \text{ K}$$

$$n = \frac{PV}{RT} = \frac{0.967 \text{ atm} \times 0.076 \text{ L}}{0.08206 \text{ atm L mol}^{-1}\text{ K}^{-1} \times 298 \text{ K}} = 0.0030 \text{ mol O}_2$$

$$\text{rate} = \frac{0.0030 \text{ mol O}_2}{1 \text{ min}} \times \frac{2 \text{ mol Na}_2\text{O}_2}{1 \text{ mol O}_2} \times \frac{77.98 \text{ g Na}_2\text{O}_2}{1 \text{ mol Na}_2\text{O}_2} \times \frac{60 \text{ min}}{1 \text{ h}} = 28 \text{ g Na}_2\text{O}_2/\text{h}$$

101. (E) Determine relative numbers of moles, and the mole fractions of the 3 gases in the 100.0 g gaseous mixture.

amount $N_2 = 46.5$ g $N_2 \times \dfrac{1 \text{ mol } N_2}{28.01 \text{ g } N_2} = 1.66$ mol N_2 $\div 2.86$ mol $\longrightarrow 0.580$

amount $Ne = 12.7$ g $Ne \times \dfrac{1 \text{ mol } Ne}{20.18 \text{ g } Ne} = 0.629$ mol Ne $\div 2.86$ mol $\longrightarrow 0.220$

amount $Cl_2 = 40.8$ g $Cl_2 \times \dfrac{1 \text{ mol } Cl_2}{70.9 \text{ g } Cl_2} = 0.575$ mol Cl_2 $\div 2.86$ mol $\longrightarrow 0.201$

total amount $= 1.66$ mol $N_2 + 0.629$ mol $Ne + 0.575$ mol $Cl_2 = 2.86$ mol

Since the total pressure of the mixture is 1 atm, the partial pressure of each gas is numerically very close to its mole fraction. Thus, the partial pressure of Cl_2 is 0.201 atm or 153 mmHg.

102. (M) Let us first determine the molar mass of this mixture.

$$M = \frac{dRT}{P} = \frac{0.518 \text{ g L}^{-1} \times 0.08206 \text{ atm L mol}^{-1} \text{ K}^{-1} \times 298 \text{ K}}{721 \text{ mmHg} \times \dfrac{1 \text{ atm}}{760 \text{ mmHg}}} = 13.4 \text{ g/mol}$$

Then we let x be the mole fraction of He in the mixture.

$$13.4 \text{ g/mol} = x \times 4.003 \text{ g/mol} + (1.000 - x) \times 32.00 \text{ g/mol} = 4.003x + 32.00 - 32.00x$$

$$x = \frac{32.00 - 13.4}{32.00 - 4.003} = 0.664$$

Thus, one mole of the mixture contains 0.664 mol He. We determine the mass of that He and then the % He by mass in the mixture.

mass He $= 0.664$ mol He $\times \dfrac{4.003 \text{ g He}}{1 \text{ mol He}} = 2.66$ g He $\qquad$ % He $= \dfrac{2.66 \text{ g He}}{13.4 \text{ g mixture}} \times 100\% = 19.9\%$ He

103. (M) The volume percents in a mixture of gases also equal mole percents, which can be converted to mole fractions by dividing by 100.

$$M_{air} = \left(0.7808 \text{ mol } N_2 \times \frac{28.014 \text{ g } N_2}{1 \text{ mol } N_2} \right) + \left(0.2095 \text{ mol } O_2 \times \frac{31.998 \text{ g } O_2}{1 \text{ mol } O_2} \right)$$

$$+ \left(0.00036 \text{ mol } CO_2 \times \frac{44.009 \text{ g } CO_2}{1 \text{ mol } CO_2} \right) + \left(0.0093 \text{ mol } Ar \times \frac{39.948 \text{ g } Ar}{1 \text{ mol } Ar} \right) = 28.96 \text{ g/mol}$$

104. (M)

(a) $P_{tot} = P_{O_2} + P_{N_2O} = 154 \text{ Torr} + 612 \text{ Torr} = 766 \text{ Torr}$

We know that $P_{O_2} = X_{O_2} P_{tot}$. Therefore, $X_{O_2} = 154/766 = 0.20$

To determine the wt% of O_2 and N_2O, we have to use the mole fractions and determine the mass of each species:

mass O_2: $0.20 \text{ mol } O_2 \times \dfrac{32.0 \text{ g } O_2}{1 \text{ mol } O_2} = 6.432 \text{ g}$

mass N_2O: $0.80 \text{ mol } N_2O \times \dfrac{44.0 \text{ g } N_2O}{1 \text{ mol } N_2O} = 35.20 \text{ g}$

wt% $O_2 = \dfrac{6.432}{6.432 + 35.20} \times 100 = 15.4\%$

wt% $N_2O = 100 - 15.4 = 84.6\%$

(b) Apparent molar mass of the mixture:

$(32.00 \text{ g/mol})(154 \text{ Torr}/766 \text{ Torr}) + (44.02 \text{ g/mol})(612 \text{ Torr}/766 \text{ Torr}) = 41.6 \text{ g/mol}$

105. (M) The amount of $N_2(g)$ plus the amount of $He(g)$ equals the total amount of gas. We use this equality, and substitute with the ideal gas equation, letting V symbolize the volume of cylinder B.

$n_{N_2} + n_{He} = n_{total}$ becomes $P_{N_2} \times V_{N_2} + P_{He} \times V_{He} = P_{total} \times V_{total}$

since all temperatures are equal.

Substitution gives $(8.35 \text{ atm} \times 48.2 \text{ L}) + (9.50 \text{ atm} \times V) = 8.71 \text{ atm} (48.2 \text{ L} + V)$

$402 \text{ atm L} + 9.50\,V = 420 \text{ atm L} + 8.71\,V \qquad V = \dfrac{420 - 402}{9.50 - 8.71} = 23 \text{ L}$

106. (M) To construct a closed-end manometer, fill the tube with mercury, making sure to remove any air bubbles. Inverting the tube results in a column of mercury with a vacuum in the space directly above the column.

When the container is evacuated, the heights of both mercury columns are equal. As the gas pressure in the container increases, the heights of the mercury columns will change. Because the system is closed, P_{bar} is not needed. One drawback of this system is that gas pressure much larger than one atmosphere cannot easily be handled unless a very long column is used. (> 1 meter). Otherwise, the column of mercury would be pushed up to the closed end of the manometer at a critical pressure, and remain unchanged with increasing pressure.

An open-ended manometer, would be better suited to measuring higher pressure than lower pressure. A gas pressure of one atmosphere results in the columns of mercury being equal. A sidearm of 760 mm pressure would allow one to measure pressures up to 2 atmospheres.

107. (D)

(a) $M_{av} = \dfrac{8.0}{100}\left(44.01\dfrac{g}{mol}\right) + \dfrac{23.2}{100}\left(28.01\dfrac{g}{mol}\right) + \dfrac{17.7}{100}\left(2.016\dfrac{g}{mol}\right)$
$+ \dfrac{1.1}{100}\left(16.043\dfrac{g}{mol}\right) + \dfrac{50.5}{100}\left(28.01\dfrac{g}{mol}\right)$

$M_{av} = 24.5\underline{6}$ g/mol $\quad$ density $= \dfrac{PM}{RT} = \dfrac{\left(763\ mmHg \times \dfrac{1\ atm}{760\ mmHg}\right)24.56\dfrac{g}{mol}}{\left(0.08206\dfrac{atm\ L}{mol\ K}\right)296\ K} = 1.015\dfrac{g}{L}$

(b) $P_{CO} = P_{total} \times \dfrac{V\%}{100\%} = 763\ mmHg \times \dfrac{23.2\%}{100\%} = 177\ mmHg$ or 0.233 atm

(c) $CO(g) + \frac{1}{2} O_2(g) \rightarrow CO_2(g)$
$H_2(g) + \frac{1}{2} O_2(g) \rightarrow H_2O(g)$
$CH_4(g) + 2 O_2(g) \rightarrow CO_2(g) + 2 H_2O(g)$
Use the fact that volume is directly proportional to moles when the pressure and temperature are constant. 1000 L of producer gas contains:
232 L CO which requires $\qquad$ 116 L O_2
177 L H_2 which requires $\qquad$ 88.5 L O_2
11 L CH_4 which requires $\qquad$ 22 L O_2
$\qquad\qquad\qquad\qquad\qquad\qquad\quad$ 226.$\underline{5}$ L O_2 (Note: air is 20.95% O_2 by volume)

Thus, the reaction requires $\dfrac{226.5\ L}{0.2095} = 1.08 \times 10^3$ L.

108. (M) First, balance the equation:
$2\ C_8H_{18} + 25\ O_2 \rightarrow 16\ CO_2 + 18\ H_2O$

mol O_2 needed: $2000\ g\ C_8H_{18} \times \dfrac{1\ mol\ C_8H_{18}}{114.23\ g\ C_8H_{18}} \times \dfrac{25\ mol\ O_2}{2\ mol\ C_8H_{18}}$

$= 218.86$ mol O_2

Using the ideal gas equation, we can determine the volume of 177.33 mol of O_2:

vol $O_2 = \dfrac{nRT}{P} = \dfrac{(218.86\ mol)(8.314\ kPa\ L\ mol^{-1}\ K^{-1})(298\ K)}{101\ kPa} = 5369$ L

To determine the volume of air needed, we note that O_2 represents 20.9% of air by volume: $V_{air} \times 0.209 = 5369$ L. Solving for V_{air} gives 2.57×10^4 L.

109. (M) First recognize that 3 moles of gas are produced from every 2 moles of water, and compute the number of moles of gas produced. Then determine the partial pressure these gases would exert.

$$\text{amount of gas} = 1.32 \text{ g } H_2O \times \frac{1 \text{ mol } H_2O}{18.02 \text{ g } H_2O} \times \frac{3 \text{ mol gas}}{2 \text{ mol } H_2O} = 0.110 \text{ mol gas}$$

$$P = \frac{nRT}{V} = \frac{0.110 \text{ mol} \times 0.08206 \text{ atm L mol}^{-1} \text{ K}^{-1} \times 303 \text{ K}}{2.90 \text{ L}} \times \frac{760 \text{ mmHg}}{1 \text{ atm}} = 717 \text{ mmHg}$$

Then the vapor pressure (partial pressure) of water is determined by difference.

$$P_{water} = 748 \text{ mmHg} - 717 \text{ mmHg} = 31 \text{ mmHg}$$

110. (D) First, balance the equations:

$Fe + 2 HCl \rightarrow 2 FeCl_2 + H_2$

$2 Al + 6 HCl \rightarrow 2 AlCl_3 + 3 H_2$

Then, we calculate the partial pressure of O_2:

$$P_{O_2} = P_{tot} - P_{H_2O} = 841 - 16.5 = 824.5 \text{ Torr}$$

$$P_{O_2} = 824.5 \text{ Torr} \times (1 \text{ atm}/760 \text{ Torr}) = 1.085 \text{ atm}$$

$$\text{mol } H_2 = \frac{(1.085 \text{ atm})(0.159 \text{ L})}{(0.08206 \text{ atm L mol}^{-1} \text{ K}^{-1})(19.0 + 273.2 \text{ K})} = 0.00720 \text{ mol}$$

Now, we will try to relate the total moles of H_2 to the mass of Fe in the original sample. Let the mass of Fe in the original sample be m g. The mass of Al in the original sample will be $(0.1924 - m)$ g. We can write:

$$n_{H_2,tot} = n_{H_2} \text{ (from reaction of Fe)} + n_{H_2} \text{ (from reaction of Al)}$$

$$0.00720 \text{ mol } H_2 = m \text{ g Fe} \times \frac{1 \text{ mol Fe}}{55.85 \text{ g Fe}} \times \frac{1 \text{ mol } H_2}{1 \text{ mol Fe}} + (0.1924 - m) \text{ g Al} \times \frac{1 \text{ mol Al}}{26.98 \text{ g Al}} \times \frac{3 \text{ mol } H_2}{2 \text{ mol Al}}$$

$$0.00720 = \frac{m}{55.85} + \frac{(0.1924 - m)}{26.98} \times \frac{3}{2}$$

Solving the expression above gives $m = 0.0928$. Therefore:

$$\%Fe = \frac{0.0928 \text{ g}}{0.1924 \text{ g}} \times 100 = 48.2$$

111. (M) The total pressure of the mixture of O_2 and H_2O is 737 mmHg, and the partial pressure of H_2O is 25.2 mmHg.

(a) The percent of water vapor by volume equals its percent pressure.

$$\%H_2O = \frac{25.2 \text{ mmHg}}{737 \text{ mmHg}} \times 100\% = 3.42\% \text{ } H_2O \text{ by volume}$$

(b) The % water vapor by number of molecules equals its percent pressure, 3.42% by number.

(c) One mole of the combined gases contains 0.0342 mol H_2O and 0.9658 mol O_2.

$$\text{molar mass} = 0.0342 \text{ mol } H_2O \times \frac{18.02 \text{ g } H_2O}{1 \text{ mol } H_2O} + 0.9658 \text{ mol } O_2 \times \frac{31.999 \text{ g } O_2}{1 \text{ mol } O_2}$$

$$= 0.616 \text{ g } H_2O + 30.90 \text{ g } O_2 = 31.52 \text{ g}$$

$$\% \, H_2O = \frac{0.616 \text{ g } H_2O}{31.52 \text{ g}} \times 100\% = 1.95\% \, H_2O \text{ by mass}$$

112. (D)

(a) 1 mol of the mixture at 0 °C and 1 atm occupies a volume of 22.414 L. It contains 0.79 mol He and 0.21 mol O_2.

$$\text{density} = \frac{\text{mass}}{\text{volume}} = \frac{0.79 \text{ mol He} \times \dfrac{4.003 \text{ g He}}{1 \text{ mol He}} + 0.21 \text{ mol } O_2 \times \dfrac{32.00 \text{ g } O_2}{1 \text{ mol } O_2}}{22.414 \text{ L}} = 0.44 \text{ g/L}$$

Let's focus on a 1.00 L sample (which weighs 0.44 g), and calculate the final volume when the temperature is increased from 0 °C to 25 °C.

$$V_{\text{final}} = 1.00 \text{ L} \times \frac{(25 + 273.2) \text{ K}}{273.2 \text{ K}} = 1.09 \text{ L} \qquad d_{\text{final}} = \frac{0.44 \text{ g}}{1.09 \text{ L}} = 0.40 \text{ g/L}$$

We determine the apparent molar masses of each mixture by multiplying the mole fraction (numerically equal to the volume fraction) of each gas by its molar mass, and then summing these products for all gases in the mixture.

$$M_{\text{air}} = \left(0.7808 \times \frac{28.01 \text{ g } N_2}{1 \text{ mol } N_2} \right) + \left(0.2095 \times \frac{32.00 \text{ g } O_2}{1 \text{ mol } O_2} \right) + \left(0.0093 \times \frac{39.95 \text{ g Ar}}{1 \text{ mol Ar}} \right) + \left(0.00036 \times \frac{44.01 \text{ g } CO_2}{1 \text{ mol } CO_2} \right)$$

$$= 21.87 \text{ g } N_2 + 6.704 \text{ g } O_2 + 0.374 \text{ g Ar} + 0.016 \text{ g } CO_2 = 28.96 \text{ g/mol air}$$

$$M_{\text{mix}} = \left(0.79 \times \frac{4.003 \text{ g He}}{1 \text{ mol He}} \right) + \left(0.21 \times \frac{32.00 \text{ g } O_2}{1 \text{ mol } O_2} \right) = 3.2 \text{ g He} + 6.7 \text{ g } O_2 = \frac{9.9 \text{ g mixture}}{\text{mol}}$$

(b) In order to prepare two gases with the same density, the volume of the gas of smaller molar mass must be smaller by a factor equal to the ratio of the molar masses. According to Boyle's law, this means that the pressure on the less dense gas must be larger by a factor equal to a ratio of molar masses.

$$P_{\text{mix}} = \frac{28.95}{9.9} \times 1.00 \text{ atm} = 2.9 \text{ atm}$$

113. (M) First, determine the moles of Cl_2 and NaClO. Then, determine the limiting reactant

$$\text{mol } Cl_2 = \frac{(4.66 \text{ atm})(1.0 \text{ L})}{(0.08206 \text{ atm L mol}^{-1} \text{ K}^{-1})(283 \text{ K})} = 0.201 \text{ mol}$$

$$\text{mol NaClO} = (0.750 \text{ L})(2.00 \text{ M}) = 1.50 \text{ mol}$$

$$0.201 \text{ mol } Cl_2 \times \frac{4 \text{ mol NaClO}}{1 \text{ mol } Cl_2} = 0.804 \text{ mol NaClO needed}$$

Therefore, NaClO is the excess reactant.

Now, we must calculate the theoretical yield of ClO_2:

$$0.201 \, mol \, Cl_2 \times \frac{2 \, mol \, ClO_2}{1 \, mol \, Cl_2} \times \frac{67.45 \, g \, ClO_2}{1 \, mol \, ClO_2} = 27.1 \, g \, ClO_2$$

$$\% \, yield = \frac{25.9 \, g}{27.1 \, g} \times 100 = 95.6\%$$

114. **(M)** First, determine the moles of $Na_2S_2O_3$, then use the chemical equations given to determine the moles of O_3 in the mixture:

$$mol \, Na_2S_2O_3 = 0.0262 \, L \times 0.1359 \, M = 0.003561 \, mol$$

$$mol \, O_3: \, 0.003561 \, mol \, Na_2S_2O_3 \times \frac{1 \, mol \, I_3^-}{2 \, mol \, Na_2S_2O_3} \times \frac{1 \, mol \, O_3}{1 \, mol \, I_3^-} = 0.001780 \, mol \, O_3$$

Using the ideal gas equation, we can determine the moles of gas:

$$moles \, of \, gas = \frac{(0.993 \, atm)(53.2 \, L)}{(0.08206 \, atm \, L \, mol^{-1} \, K^{-1})(291 \, K)} = 2.21 \, mol$$

$$X_{O_3} = \frac{0.001780 \, mol}{2.21 \, mol \, total} = 8.05 \times 10^{-4}$$

115. **(D)** First compute the pressure of the water vapor at 30.1°C.

$$P_{H_2O} = \frac{\left(0.1052 \, g \times \dfrac{1 \, mol \, H_2O}{18.015 \, g \, H_2O} \right) \times \dfrac{0.08206 \, atm \, L}{mol \, K} \times (30.1 + 273.2) \, K}{8.050 \, L} \times \frac{760 \, mmHg}{1 \, atm} = 13.72 \, mmHg$$

The water vapor is kept in the 8.050-L container, which means that its pressure is proportional to the absolute temperature in the container. Thus, for each of the six temperatures, we need to calculate two numbers: (1) the pressure due to this water (because gas pressure varies with temperature), and (2) 80% of the vapor pressure. The temperature we are seeking is where the two numbers agree.

$$P_{water}(T) = 13.72 \, mmHg \times \frac{(T + 273.2) \, K}{(30.1 + 273.2) \, K}$$

For example, $P(20 \, °C) = 13.72 \, mmHg \times \dfrac{(20. + 273.2) \, K}{(30.1 + 273.2) \, K} = 13.3 \, mmHg$

T	20. °C	19. °C	18. °C	17. °C	16. °C	15. °C
P_{water}, mmHg	13.3	13.2	13.2	13.1	13.1	13.0
80.0% v.p., mmHg	14.0	13.2	12.4	11.6	10.9	10.2

At approximately 19 °C, the relative humidity of the air will be 80.0%.

116. (D)

P_{gas} (mmHg)	$1/A \propto 1/V$ (cm^{-1})
810.8	0.0358
739.8	0.0328
896.8	0.0394
996.8	0.0437
1123	0.0493
1278	0.0562
1494	0.0658
1796	0.0787
2216	0.0980
2986	0.1316

Factors that would affect the slope of this straight line are related to deviations real gases exhibit from ideality. At higher pressures, real gases tend to interact more, exerting forces of attraction and repulsion that Boyle's law does not take into account.

117. (D)

(a) $T = (10 + 273)\text{ K} = 283\text{ K}$ $M = 28.96\text{ g mol}^{-1}$ (from question 99) or $0.02896\text{ kg mol}^{-1}$

$$R = 8.314472 \frac{\text{kg m}}{\text{s}^2\text{ K mol}} \quad g = 9.80665 \frac{\text{m}}{\text{s}^2} \quad h = 14494\text{ ft} \times \frac{12\text{ in.}}{1\text{ ft}} \times \frac{2.54\text{ cm}}{1\text{ in.}} \times \frac{1\text{ m}}{100\text{ cm}} = 4417.8\text{ m}$$

$$P = P_0 \times 10^{\frac{-Mgh}{2.303\,RT}} = 760\text{ mmHg} \times 10^{\left(\frac{-\left(0.02896\frac{\text{kg}}{\text{mol}}\right)\left(9.80665\frac{\text{m}}{\text{s}^2}\right)4417.8\text{ m}}{2.303\left(8.314472\frac{\text{kg m}}{\text{s}^2\text{ mol K}}\right)283\text{ K}}\right)}$$

$$= 760 \times 10^{-0.2314} = 446\text{ mmHg}$$

(b) $h = 900\text{ ft} \times \frac{12\text{ in.}}{1\text{ ft}} \times \frac{2.54\text{ cm}}{1\text{ in.}} \times \frac{1\text{ m}}{100\text{ cm}} = 274.3\text{ m}$

$$P = P_0 \times 10^{\left(\frac{-\left(0.02896\frac{\text{kg}}{\text{mol}}\right)\left(9.80665\frac{\text{m}}{\text{s}^2}\right)274.3\text{ m}}{2.303\left(8.314472\frac{\text{kg m}}{\text{s}^2\text{ mol K}}\right)283\text{ K}}\right)} = 0.967455\,P_0 = \frac{29}{30}P_0$$

or $\frac{1}{30}$ smaller

<u>118.</u> (M)

(a) $\overline{u}_{rms}$ is determined as follows:

$$\overline{u}_{rms} = \sqrt{\frac{3RT}{M}} = \sqrt{\frac{3\left(8.3145\text{ J}\cdot\text{mol}^{-1}\cdot\text{K}^{-1}\right)(298\text{ K})}{32.00 \times 10^{-3}\text{ kg}}} = 482\text{ m/s}$$

(b) $\quad F_u = 4\pi\left(\dfrac{M}{2\pi RT}\right)^{3/2} u^2 \exp\left(-Mu^2/2RT\right)$

$$F_u = 4\pi\left(\dfrac{32.00\times10^{-3}}{2\pi(8.3145)(298)}\right)^{3/2}(498)^2 \exp\left(-\dfrac{(32.00\times10^{-3})(498)^2}{2(8.3145)(298)}\right) = 1.92\times10^{-3}$$

<u>**119.**</u> **(D)** Potential energy (E_p) of an object is highest when the kinetic energy (E_k) of the object is zero and the object has attained its maximum height. Therefore, we must determine the kinetic energy. But first, we have to determine the velocity of the N_2 molecule.

$$\overline{u}_{rms} = \sqrt{\dfrac{3RT}{M}} \doteq \sqrt{\dfrac{3\left(8.3145\ \text{J}\cdot\text{mol}^{-1}\cdot\text{K}^{-1}\right)\left(300\ \text{K}\right)}{28.00\times10^{-3}\ kg}} = 517\ \text{m/s}$$

$$\overline{E_k} = \dfrac{1}{2}\,\overline{mu_{rms}^2} = \dfrac{1}{2}\left(28.00\times10^{-3}\ kg\right)(517\ \text{m/s})^2 = 3742\ \text{J}$$

$$\overline{E_k} = \overline{E_p} \Rightarrow m\cdot g\cdot h = \left(28.00\times10^{-3}\ \text{kg}\right)\left(9.8\ \text{m/s}^2\right)\cdot h = 3742\ \text{J}$$

Solving for h, the altitude reached by an N_2 molecule is 13637 m or 13.6 km.

120. (D)

$$u = \begin{pmatrix} 0 \\ 500 \\ 100 \\ 1500 \\ 2000 \\ 2500 \\ 3500 \end{pmatrix}\ \text{m/s} \qquad f = \begin{pmatrix} 0 \\ 1.493\times10^{-4} \\ 4.281\times10^{-4} \\ 5.531\times10^{-4} \\ 4.522\times10^{-4} \\ 2.603\times10^{-4} \\ 3.558\times10^{-5} \end{pmatrix}$$

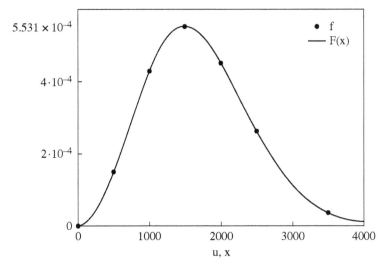

121. (D) (a) First multiply out the left-hand side of the equation.

$$\left(P + \frac{an^2}{V^2}\right)(V - nb) = nRT = PV - Pnb + \frac{an^2}{V} - \frac{abn^3}{V^2}$$

Now multiply the entire equation through by V^2, and collect all terms on the right-hand side.

$$0 = -nRTV^2 + PV^3 - PnbV^2 + an^2V - abn^3$$

Finally, divide the entire equation by P and collect terms with the same power of V, to obtain:

$$0 = V^3 - n\left(\frac{RT + bP}{P}\right)V^2 + \left(\frac{n^2a}{P}\right)V - \frac{n^3ab}{P} = 0$$

(b)

$$n = 185 \text{ g } CO_2 \times \frac{1 \text{ mol } CO_2}{44.0 \text{ g } CO_2} = 4.20 \text{ mol } CO_2$$

$$0 = V^3 - 4.20 \text{ mol}\left(\frac{(0.08206 \text{ atm L mol}^{-1} \text{ K}^{-1} \times 286 \text{ K}) + (0.0429 \text{ L mol}^{-1} \times 12.5 \text{ atm})}{12.5 \text{ atm}}\right)V^2$$

$$+ \left(\frac{(4.20 \text{ mol})^2 \, 3.61 \text{ L}^2 \text{ atm mol}^{-2}}{12.5 \text{ atm}}\right)V - \frac{(4.20 \text{ mol})^3 \, 3.61 \text{ L}^2 \text{ atm mol}^{-2} \times 0.0429 \text{ L mol}^{-1}}{12.5 \text{ atm}}$$

$$= V^3 - 8.07 \, V^2 + 5.09 \, V - 0.918$$

We can solve this equation by the method of successive approximations. As a first value, we use the volume obtained from the ideal gas equation:

$$V = \frac{nRT}{P} = \frac{4.20 \text{ mol} \times 0.08206 \text{ atm L mol}^{-1} \text{ K}^{-1} \times 286 \text{ K}}{12.5 \text{ atm}} = 7.89 \text{ L}$$

$$V = \frac{nRT}{P} = \frac{4.20 \text{ mol} \times 0.08206 \text{ L atm mol}^{-1} \text{ K}^{-1} \times 286 \text{ K}}{12.5 \text{ atm}} = 7.89 \text{ L}$$

	$V = 7.89$ L	$(7.89)3 - 8.06 (7.89)2 + (5.07 \times 7.89) - 0.909 = 28.5$	> 0
Try	$V = 7.00$ L	$(7.00)3 - 8.06 (7.00)2 + (5.07 \times 7.00) - 0.909 = -17.4$	< 0
Try	$V = 7.40$ L	$(7.40)3 - 8.06 (7.40)2 + (5.07 \times 7.40) - 0.909 = 0.47$	> 0
Try	$V = 7.38$ L	$(7.38)3 - 8.06 (7.38)2 + (5.07 \times 7.38) - 0.909 = -0.53$	< 0
Try	$V = 7.39$ L	$(7.39)3 - 8.06 (7.39)2 + (5.07 \times 7.39) - 0.909 = -0.03$	< 0

The volume of CO_2 is very close to 7.39 L.

A second way is to simply disregard the last term and to solve the equation
$0 = V_3 - 8.06 \, V_2 + 5.07 \, V$

This equation simplifies to the following quadratic equation:
$0 = V_2 - 8.06 \, V + 5.07$, which is solved with the quadratic formula.

$$V = \frac{8.06 \pm \sqrt{(8.06)^2 - 4 \times 5.07}}{2} = \frac{+8.06 \pm 6.68}{2} = \frac{14.74}{2} = 7.37 \text{ L}$$

The other root, 0.69 L does not appear to be reasonable, due to its small size.

122. (D)

(a) The van der Waals gas equation is used to determine the actual pressure.

$$\left(P+\frac{n^2a}{V^2}\right)(V-nb)=nRT$$

$$P=\frac{nRT}{V-nb}-\frac{n^2a}{V^2}=\frac{(1)(0.083145)(280)}{0.2168-(1)(0.0319)}-\frac{(1^2)(1.382)}{(0.2168)^2}=96.5\text{ bar}=9.65\text{ MPa}$$

$$\%\text{ error}=\frac{(9.65-10)}{10}\times100=-3.5\%$$

(b) The volume using the ideal gas equation is given as follows:

$V=nRT/P=(1\text{ mol})(8.3145\ \text{kPa}\cdot\text{L}\cdot\text{K}^{-1}\cdot\text{mol}^{-1})(280\text{ K})/(10\times10^3\text{ kPa})=0.233\text{ L}$

$\%\text{ error}=(0.233-0.2168)/0.2168\times100=7.47\%$

123. (M)

(a) $P\bar{V}=RT\left\{1+\frac{B}{\bar{V}}+\frac{C}{\bar{V}^2}\right\}$ $\bar{V}=500\text{ cm}^3\text{mol}^{-1}$ $B=-21.89\text{ cm}^3\text{ mol}^{-1}$

$T=273\text{ K}$ $C=1230\text{ cm}^6\text{ mol}^{-2}$

$$P\left(0.500\ \frac{\text{L}}{\text{mol}}\right)=\left(0.08206\ \frac{\text{atm L}}{\text{mol K}}\right)273\text{ K}\left\{1+\frac{-21.89\text{ cm}^3\text{ mol}^{-1}}{500\text{ cm}^3\text{mol}^{-1}}+\frac{1230\text{ cm}^6\text{ mol}^{-2}}{\left(500\text{ cm}^3\text{mol}^{-1}\right)^2}\right\}$$

$$P\left(0.500\ \frac{\text{L}}{\text{mol}}\right)=22.40\frac{\text{atm L}}{\text{mol}}(0.961)$$ $$P=\frac{22.4\frac{\text{atm L}}{\text{mol}}(0.961)}{\left(0.500\frac{\text{L}}{\text{mol}}\right)}=43.1\text{ atm}$$

(b) The result is consistent with Figure 6-20. In Figure 6-20, the compressibility factor is slightly below 1 at pressures between 0 and 400 atm. At a pressure of ~50 atm, the compressibility factor is just slightly below 1. Using the data provided, a pressure of 43.1 atm has a compressibility factor of 0.961, which is slightly below 1. The data is consistent with the information provided in Fig 6-20.

124. (M)

$$P_{H_2}=(752\text{ mmHg}-21.07\text{ mmHg})\times\frac{1\text{ atm}}{760\text{ mmHg}}=0.9618\text{ atm}$$

$$\text{mol H}_2=\frac{PV}{RT}=\frac{0.9618\text{ atm}\times0.202\text{ L}}{(0.08206\text{ atm L mol}^{-1}\text{ K}^{-1})(296\text{ K})}=7.99\times10^{-3}\text{ mol}$$

$n_{H_2}=n_{H_2}\text{(from Al)}+n_{H_2}\text{(from Mg)}$ Let $x=$ mass of Al in g, therefore $0.156-x=$ mass Mg in grams

$$n_{H_2}=7.99\times10^{-3}\text{ mol H}_2=\left(x\times\frac{1\text{ mol Al}}{26.98\text{ g Al}}\times\frac{3\text{ mol H}_2}{2\text{ mol Al}}\right)+\left((0.156-x)\times\frac{1\text{ mol Mg}}{24.305\text{ g Mg}}\times\frac{1\text{ mol H}_2}{1\text{ mol Mg}}\right)$$

$7.99\times10^{-3}\text{ mol H}_2=0.0556x+0.006418-0.04114x$

$0.001572=0.01446x$ $x=0.108\underline{7}\text{ g Al}$

$\therefore\text{ mass }\%\text{ Al}=\frac{0.108\underline{7}\text{ g Al}}{0.156\text{ g mixture}}\times100\%=69.7\%\text{ Al}$

$\therefore\text{ mass }\%\text{ Mg}=100\%-69.7\%=30.3\%\text{ Mg}$

FEATURE PROBLEMS

125. (M) Boyle's law relates P and V, i.e., $P \times V$ = constant. If V is proportional to the value of A, and $P_{gas} = P_{bar} + P_{Hg}$ (i.e. the pressure of the gas equals the sum of the barometric pressure and the pressure exerted by the mercury column), then a comparison of individual $A \times P$ products should show a consistent result or a constant.

A (cm)	P_{bar} (atm)	P_{Hg} (mmHg)	P_{gas} (mmHg)	$A \times P_{gas}$ (cm × mmHg)
27.9	739.8	71	810.8	22621
30.5	739.8	0	739.8	22564
25.4	739.8	157	896.8	22779
22.9	739.8	257	996.8	22827
20.3	739.8	383	1123	22793
17.8	739.8	538	1278	22745
15.2	739.8	754	1494	22706
12.7	739.8	1056	1796	22807
10.2	739.8	1476	2216	22601
7.6	739.8	2246	2986	22692

Since consistent $A \times P_{gas}$ results are observed, these data conform reasonably well (within experimental uncertainty) to Boyle's law.

126. (E) Nitryl Fluoride $\quad 65.01 \text{ u} \left(\dfrac{49.4}{100} \right) = 32.1 \text{ u of X}$

Nitrosyl Fluoride $\quad 49.01 \text{ u} \left(\dfrac{32.7}{100} \right) = 16.0 \text{ u of X}$

Thionyl Fluoride $\quad 86.07 \text{ u} \left(\dfrac{18.6}{100} \right) = 16.0 \text{ u of X}$

Sulfuryl Fluoride $\quad 102.07 \text{ u} \left(\dfrac{31.4}{100} \right) = 32.0 \text{ u of X}$

The atomic mass of X is 16 u which corresponds to the element oxygen.
The number of atoms of X (oxygen) in each compound is given below:
Nitryl Fluoride $\quad$ = 2 atoms of O $\qquad$ Nitrosyl Fluoride $\quad$ = 1 atom of O
Thionyl Fluoride $\quad$ = 1 atom of O $\qquad$ Sulfuryl Fluoride $\quad$ = 2 atoms of O

127. (M)

(a) The $N_2(g)$ extracted from liquid air has some Ar(g) mixed in. Only $O_2(g)$ was removed from liquid air in the oxygen-related experiments.

(b) Because of the presence of Ar(g) [39.95 g/mol], the $N_2(g)$ [28.01 g/mol] from liquid air will have a greater density than $N_2(g)$ from nitrogen compounds.

(c) Magnesium will react with molecular nitrogen $[3 \text{ Mg}(s) + N_2(g) \rightarrow Mg_3N_2(s)]$ but not with Ar. Thus, magnesium reacts with all the nitrogen in the mixture, but leaves the relatively inert Ar(g) unreacted.

(d) The "nitrogen" remaining after oxygen is extracted from each mole of air (Rayleigh's mixture) contains $0.78084 + 0.00934 = 0.79018 \text{ mol}$ and has the mass calculated below.

mass of gaseous mixture $= (0.78084 \times 28.013 \text{ g/mol } N_2) + (0.00934 \times 39.948 \text{ g/mol Ar})$

mass of gaseous mixture $= 21.874 \text{ g } N_2 + 0.373 \text{ g Ar} = 22.247 \text{ g mixture}$

Then, the molar mass of the mixture can be computed: 22.247 g mixture / 0.79018 mol $= 28.154$ g/mol. Since the STP molar volume of an ideal gas is 22.414 L, we can compute the two densities.

$$d(N_2) = \frac{28.013 \text{ g/mol}}{22.414 \text{ L/mol}} = 1.2498 \text{ g/mol} \qquad d(\text{mixture}) = \frac{28.154 \text{ g/mol}}{22.414 \text{ L/mol}} = 1.2561 \text{ g/mol}$$

These densities differ by 0.50%.

128. (M)
(a) First convert pressures from mmHg to atm:

Density (g/L)	Pressure (atm)	Density/Pressure (g/L atm)
1.428962	1.0000	$1.428962 \approx 1.4290$
1.071485	0.75000	$1.428647 \approx 1.4286$
0.714154	0.50000	$1.428308 \approx 1.4283$
0.356985	0.25000	$1.42794 \approx 1.4279$

average = 1.4285 g/L atm

(b) $M_{O_2} = \dfrac{d\,RT}{P}$ $\qquad M_{O_2} = 1.4285 \text{ g/L atm} \times 0.082058 \text{ atm L/mol K} \times 273.15 \text{ K}$

$M_{O_2} = 32.018 \text{ g/mol}$ $\qquad$ Thus, the atomic mass of $O_2 = M_{O_2}/2 = 16.009$

This compares favorably with the value of 15.999 given in the textbook.

129. **(D)** Total mass = mass of payload + mass of balloon + mass of H_2

Use ideal gas equation to calculate mass of H_2: $PV = nRT = \dfrac{mRT}{M}$

$$m = \frac{PVM}{RT} = \frac{1\,\text{atm} \left(120 \text{ ft}^3 \times \dfrac{(12\,\text{in.})^3}{(1\,\text{ft})^3} \times \dfrac{(2.54\,\text{cm})^3}{(1\,\text{in.})^3} \times \dfrac{1 \times 10^{-3}\,\text{L}}{1\,\text{cm}^3} \right) 2.016\,\dfrac{\text{g}}{\text{mol}}}{\left(0.08206\,\dfrac{\text{atm L}}{\text{K mol}} \right) 273\,\text{K}} = 306 \text{ g}$$

Total mass = 1200 g + 1700 g + 306 g $\approx$ 3200 g

We know at the maximum height, the balloon will be 25 ft in diameter. Need to find out what mass of air is displaced. We need to make one assumption – the volume percent of air is unchanged with altitude. Hence we use an apparent molar mass for air of 29 g mol^{-1} (question 99). Using the data provided, we find the altitude at which the balloon displaces 3200 g of air.

Note: balloon radius = $\dfrac{25}{2}$ = 12.5 ft. volume = $\dfrac{4}{3}(\pi)r^3 = \dfrac{4}{3}(3.1416)(12.5)^3 = 8181$ ft^3

Convert to liters: $8181\,\text{ft}^3 \times \dfrac{(12\,\text{in.})^3}{(1\,\text{ft})^3} \times \dfrac{(2.54\,\text{cm})^3}{(1\,\text{in.})^3} \times \dfrac{1\times10^{-3}\,\text{L}}{1\,\text{cm}^3} = 231,660\,\text{L}$

At 10 km: $m = \dfrac{PVM}{RT} = \dfrac{\left(2.7\times10^2\,\text{mbar}\times\dfrac{1\,\text{atm}}{1013.25\,\text{mbar}}\right)(231,660\,\text{L})\left(29\dfrac{\text{g}}{\text{mol}}\right)}{\left(0.08206\dfrac{\text{atm L}}{\text{mol K}}\right)223\,\text{K}} = 97,\underline{8}27\,\text{g}$

At 20 km: $m = \dfrac{PVM}{RT} = \dfrac{\left(5.5\times10^1\,\text{mbar}\times\dfrac{1\,\text{atm}}{1013.25\,\text{mbar}}\right)(231,660\,\text{L})\left(29\dfrac{\text{g}}{\text{mol}}\right)}{\left(0.08206\dfrac{\text{atm L}}{\text{mol K}}\right)217\,\text{K}} = 20,\underline{4}78\,\text{g}$

At 30 km: $m = \dfrac{PVM}{RT} = \dfrac{\left(1.2\times10^1\,\text{mbar}\times\dfrac{1\,\text{atm}}{1013.25\,\text{mbar}}\right)(231,660\,\text{L})\left(29\dfrac{\text{g}}{\text{mol}}\right)}{\left(0.08206\dfrac{\text{atm L}}{\text{mol K}}\right)230\,\text{K}} = 4,\underline{2}15\,\text{g}$

At 40 km: $m = \dfrac{PVM}{RT} = \dfrac{\left(2.9\times10^0\,\text{mbar}\times\dfrac{1\,\text{atm}}{1013.25\,\text{mbar}}\right)(231,660\,\text{L})\left(29\dfrac{\text{g}}{\text{mol}}\right)}{\left(0.08206\dfrac{\text{atm L}}{\text{mol K}}\right)250\,\text{K}} = 93\underline{7}\,\text{g}$

The lifting power of the balloon will allow it to rise to an altitude of just over 30 km.

SELF-ASSESSMENT EXERCISES

130. (E)
   (a) atm: Pressure exerted by the atmosphere at sea level per unit area, or 760 mmHg
   (b) STP: Standard temperature and pressure, defined as a pressure of 1 bar at 273 K
   (c) R: Gas constant, which is the ratio between the product of the molar volume of a gas and pressure, and temperature
   (d) Partial pressure: The ratio between the pressure of a gas in a container and the total pressure of the container
   (e) u_{rms}: Root mean squared velocity of gas molecules in a sample

131. (E)
   (a) Absolute zero: the lowest theoretical temperature, and the temperature at which all molecular/atomic vibrations cease
   (b) Collection of gas over water: The process of isolating a gas (which does not react with water) generated by a reaction by bubbling it through a bottle and measuring its volume by the displacement of water
   (c) Effusion of a gas: the escape of gas molecules from their container through a tiny orifice or pinhole
   (d) Law of combining volumes: the volume ratio of gases consumed and generated is the same as their mole ratio, provided that temperature and pressure are kept constant throughout

132. (E)
   (a) A barometer measures atmospheric pressure, whereas a manometer measures the pressure of a generated gas in a closed vessel.
   (b) Celsius temperature uses the freezing and boiling points of water to generate a temperature scale, whereas the Kelvin scale uses the temperature below which no molecular vibrations can occur as the zero point.
   (c) The ideal gas equation states the relationship between pressure, volume, moles, and temperature in an ideal gas. The general gas equation uses the ideal gas equation to set up a linear relationship between P, V, n, and T ($P_1V_1/n_1T_1 = P_2V_2/n_2T_2$).
   (d) An ideal gas is one in which the gas molecules themselves don't occupy a volume, and that their interaction with each other is negligible. A real gas takes into account molecular volume of the gas and intermolecular/interatomic interactions.

133. (E) The answer is (d). The following shows the values for each:
   (a) $P = g \times h \times d = (9.8 \text{ m/s}^2)(0.75 \text{ m})(13,600 \text{ kg/m}^3) = 99,960 \text{ Pa}$
   (b) Just for a rough approximation, we assume the density of air to be the same as that of nitrogen (this underestimates it a bit, but is close enough). The density of N_2 is 0.02802 g/22.7 L = 1.234 g/L = 1.234 kg/m^3. $P = (9.8 \text{ m/s}^2)(16,093 \text{ m})(1.234 \text{ kg/m}^3) = 194,616 \text{ Pa}$.
   (c) $P = g \times h \times d = (9.8 \text{ m/s}^2)(5.0 \text{ m})(1590 \text{ kg/m}^3) = 77,910 \text{ Pa}$
   (d) $P = nRT/V = (10.00 \text{ g H}_2 \times 1 \text{ mol}/2.02 \text{ g})(0.083145 \text{ L bar mol}^{-1} \text{ K}^{-1})(273 \text{ K})/(22.7 \text{ L}) = 4.95 \text{ bar} = 495,032 \text{ Pa}$

134. (E) The answer is (c), because the temperature decreases from 100 °C (373 K) to 200 K.

135. (M) First, determine the amounts of both gases:

$$n_A = \frac{PV}{RT}$$

$$= \frac{(1.081 \text{ bar})(14.20 \text{ L})}{(0.083145 \text{ bar L mol}^{-1} \text{ K}^{-1})(303.1 \text{ K})}$$

$$= 0.6092 \text{ mol}$$

$$n_A = \frac{PV}{RT}$$

$$= \frac{(26.77\ \text{bar})(1.251\ \text{L})}{(0.083145\ \text{bar L mol}^{-1}\ \text{K}^{-1})(327.5\ \text{K})}$$

$$= 1.230\ \text{mol}$$

Therefore,
$n_{total} = 0.6092\ \text{mol} + 1.230\ \text{mol} = 1.839\ \text{mol}$

(a) With n_{total} obtained, we can now calculate total pressure, P_{total}:

$$P_{total} = \frac{n_{total} RT}{V}$$

$$= \frac{(1.839\ \text{mol})(0.083145\ \text{atm L mol}^{-1}\ \text{K}^{-1})(327.5\ \text{K})}{5.000\ \text{L}}$$

$$= 8.90\ \text{bar}$$

(b) The partial pressure of gas A can now be obtained from P_{total} and the mole fraction of A:

$$P_A = \left(\frac{n_A}{n_{total}}\right) P_{total} = \frac{0.6092\ \text{mol}}{1.839\ \text{mol}} \times 8.90\ \text{bar}$$

$$= 2.95\ \text{bar}$$

(c) The partial pressure of gas B can likewise be calculated:

$$P_B = \left(\frac{n_B}{n_{total}}\right) P_{total} = \frac{1.230\ \text{mol}}{1.839\ \text{mol}} \times 8.90\ \text{bar}$$

$$= 5.95\ \text{bar}$$

136. **(M)** $P_1/T_1 = P_2/T_2$. To calculate T_2, rearrange the formula:
$T_2 = 2.0\ \text{bar} / (1.0\ \text{bar} \times 273\ \text{K}) = 546\ \text{K}$

137. **(M)** The answer is (d).

$$\frac{P_1 V_1}{T_1} = \frac{P_2 V_2}{T_2}$$

$$V_2 = \frac{1\ \text{atm} \times 22.4\ \text{L} \times 298\ \text{K}}{273\ \text{K} \times 1.5\ \text{atm}} = 16.3\ \text{L}$$

138. **(M)** The answer is (b). Since the same number of moles of all ideal gases occupy the same volume, density is driven by the molar mass of the gas. Therefore, Kr has the highest density because it has a molar mass of 83 g/mol.

139. (E)

(a) Helium has the greater average molecular speed because it is the lighter gas. Recall,

$$\bar{u} = \sqrt{\frac{3RT}{M}}$$

(b) Helium strikes the container walls more frequently because it is the lighter of the two gases and has the greater average molecular speed.

(c) The gases exert equal pressure.

140. (E) The correct answer is (d). If the Kelvin temperature of the gas is doubled, it has twice the kinetic energy. Recall that

$$\bar{u}_1 = \sqrt{\frac{3RT}{M}}$$

Doubling T yields

$$\bar{u}_2 = \sqrt{\frac{3R(2T)}{M}} = \sqrt{2} \times \sqrt{\frac{3RT}{M}} = \bar{u}_1\sqrt{2}$$

We know that the average kinetic energy is given by

$$E_{k,1} = \frac{1}{2}m\,\bar{u}_1^{\,2}$$

Substituting $\bar{u}_2$,

$$E_{k,2} = \frac{1}{2}m\left(\bar{u}_1\sqrt{2}\right)^2 = \frac{1}{2}m \times 2 \times \bar{u}_1^{\,2}$$

which is twice that of $E_{k,1}$.

141. (E) The **correct** answer is (c). The statement that molecules are repelled by the walls of the container is not a postulate of the kinetic-molecular theory.

142. (M)

(a) False. They both have the same kinetic energy.

(b) True. All else being equal, the heavier molecule is slower.

(c) False. The formula $PV = nRT$ can be used to confirm this. The answer is 24.4 L.

(d) True. There is ~1.0 mole of each gas present. All else being equal, the same number of moles of any ideal gas occupies the same volume.

(e) False. Total pressure is the sum of the partial pressures. So long as there is nothing else but H_2 and O_2, the total pressure is equal to the sum of the individual partial pressures.

143. (E) The answer is (c). Partial pressures are additive, so:

$$P_{tot} = P_{H_2O} + P_{O_2}$$

$$P_{O_2}\,(\text{atm}) = \frac{P_{tot} - P_{H_2O}}{760 \text{ mmHg}} = \frac{751 - 21}{760} = 0.96 \text{ atm}$$

144. (M) The answer is (a). First, determine the # moles of NH_3 using the ideal gas equation relationship:

$n = PV/RT = (0.500 \text{ atm} \times 4.48 \text{ L}) / (0.08206 \text{ atm L K}^{-1} \times 273 \text{ K}) = 0.100 \text{ mol}$

If 1.0 mol of a substance has 6.022×10^{23} atoms, 0.100 mol has 6.022×10^{22} atoms.

145. (M) The answer is (b). Since $PV = nRT$, the number of moles of O_2 needed to satisfy the conditions of the problem is:

$$n = (2.00 \text{ atm} \times 2.24 \text{ L}) / (0.08206 \text{ L atm K}^{-1} \times 273 \text{ K}) = 0.200 \text{ mol}$$

The amount of O_2 available $= 1.60 \text{ g } O_2 \times \dfrac{1 \text{ mol } O_2}{32.0 \text{ g } O_2} = 0.050 \text{ mol } O_2$

To have an additional 0.150 mol in the system, we would add 0.6 g of He to the container.

146. (E) The volumes of both gases were measured at the same temperature and pressure. Therefore, the proportionality constant between volume and moles for both gases is the same (that is, volume can essentially replace moles in the following calculations):

$$25.0 \text{ L } H_2 \times \dfrac{3 \text{ L CO}}{7 \text{ L } H_2} = 10.7 \text{ L CO needed}$$

So, all of the H_2 and 10.7 L of CO are consumed, and 1.3 L of CO remain.

147. (M) The answer is (a), that is, the partial pressure of H_2 in the container is less than SO_2. The reasoning can be derived from the kinetic molecular theory of gases. Gas molecules with smaller molar masses travel faster, and as such can escape faster from an orifice. This is expressed in Graham's law in section 6.8.

148. (M) The answer is (c). Gases behave more ideally at high temperatures and low pressures.

149. (M)
 (a) He or Ne: Ne has higher a and b values.
 (b) CH_4 or C_3H_8: C_3H_8 has higher a and b values.
 (c) H_2 or Cl_2: Cl_2 has higher a and b values.

150. (D) We know that pressure is force per unit area, that is:
$$P = \dfrac{F}{A} = \dfrac{m \times g}{A}$$

Using the fact that area $A = \pi r^2 = \pi(D/2)^2$ and that mass $m = d \times V$, and that volume of a cylindrical tube is $V = A \times h$ (where h is the height of the liquid in the tube), we can express the pressure formula as follows:
$$P = \dfrac{F}{A} = \dfrac{d \times V \times g}{A} = \dfrac{d \times (A \times h) \times g}{A} = d \times h \times g$$

Therefore,
$$\dfrac{d \times V \times g}{A} = d \times h \times g, \text{ and,}$$

$$h = \dfrac{d}{A} = \dfrac{d}{\pi(D/2)^2}$$

As we can see, the height, h is inversely proportional to D. That is, the larger the diameter of the tube, the shorter the height of the liquid.

151. **(D)** First, convert the given information to more useful units. The pressure (752 Torr) is equivalent to 0.9895 atm (752 mmHg/760 mmHg), and the temperature is 298 K. Then, use the ideal gas relationship to determine how many moles of gas are present, assuming 1 L of gas:

$$PV = nRT$$

$$n = \frac{PV}{RT} = \frac{(0.9895 \text{ atm})(1 \text{ L})}{(0.08206 \text{ atm L mol}^{-1} \text{ K}^{-1})(298 \text{ K})} = 0.04046 \text{ mol}$$

From the problem, we know the mass of the gas per 1 L, as expressed in the density. Mass of 1 L of this gas is 2.35 g. The molar mass of this substance is therefore:

$$M = \text{g/mol} = 2.35 \text{ g}/0.04046 \text{ mol} = 58.082 \text{ g/mol}$$

Now, let's calculate the empirical formula for the hydrocarbon gas and see how it compares to the molar mass:

$$\text{mol C} = 82.7 \text{ g C} \times \frac{1 \text{ mol C}}{12.01 \text{ g C}} = 6.89 \text{ mol}$$

$$\text{mol H} = 17.3 \text{ g H} \times \frac{1 \text{ mol H}}{1.01 \text{ g H}} = 17.1 \text{ mol}$$

H:C ratio = 17.1 mol / 6.89 mol = 2.5

The ratio between H and C is 2.5:1 or 5:2, making the empirical formula C_2H_5. The mass of this formula unit is 29.07 g/mol. Comparing to the calculated molar mass of the gas, it is smaller by a factor of 2. Therefore, the gas in question in C_4H_{10} or butane.

152. **(E)** N_2 comprises 78.084% of atmosphere, oxygen 20.946%, argon 0.934%, and CO_2 0.0379%. To graphically show the scale of this difference, divide all values by the smallest one (CO_2). Therefore, for every single mark representing CO_2, we need 2060 marks for N_2, 553 marks for O_2, and 25 for Ar.

153. **(M)** To construct a concept map, one must first start with the most general concepts. These concepts are not defined by or in terms of other concepts discussed in those sections. In this chapter, pressure is the overarching concept (6-1). The topics that fall under the rubric of pressure are liquid and gas pressure, and measuring pressure. Simple gas laws are derived from the concept of pressure (6-2). Simple gas laws include Boyle's law, Charles's law, and Avogadro's law. These laws combine to form another subtopic, the ideal gas equation and the general gas equation. Take a look at the subsection headings and problems for more refining of the general and specific concepts.

CHAPTER 7
THERMOCHEMISTRY
PRACTICE EXAMPLES

1A **(E)** The heat absorbed is the product of the mass of water, its specific heat capacity $\left(4.18\ \text{J g}^{-1}\ {}^{\circ}\text{C}^{-1}\right)$, and the temperature change that occurs.

$$\text{heat energy} = 237\ \text{g} \times \frac{4.18\ \text{J}}{\text{g}\ {}^{\circ}\text{C}} \times \left(37.0\ {}^{\circ}\text{C} - 4.0\ {}^{\circ}\text{C}\right) \times \frac{1\ \text{kJ}}{1000\ \text{J}} = 32.7\ \text{kJ of heat energy}$$

1B **(E)** The heat absorbed is the product of the amount of mercury, its molar heat capacity, and the temperature change that occurs.

$$\text{heat energy} = \left(2.50\ \text{kg} \times \frac{1000\ \text{g}}{1\ \text{kg}} \times \frac{1\ \text{mol Hg}}{200.59\ \text{g Hg}}\right) \times \frac{28.0\ \text{J}}{\text{mol}\ {}^{\circ}\text{C}} \times \left[-6.0 - (-20.0)\right] {}^{\circ}\text{C} \times \frac{1\ \text{kJ}}{1000\ \text{J}}$$

$$= 4.89\ \text{kJ of heat energy}$$

2A **(E)** First calculate the quantity of heat lost by the lead. This heat energy must be absorbed by the surroundings (water). We assume 100% efficiency in the energy transfer.

$$q_{\text{lead}} = 1.00\ \text{kg} \times \frac{1000\ \text{g}}{1\ \text{kg}} \times \frac{0.13\ \text{J}}{\text{g}\ {}^{\circ}\text{C}} \times \left(35.2\ {}^{\circ}\text{C} - 100.0\ {}^{\circ}\text{C}\right) = -8.4 \times 10^3\ \text{J} = -q_{\text{water}}$$

$$8.4 \times 10^3\ \text{J} = m_{\text{water}} \times \frac{4.18\ \text{J}}{\text{g}\ {}^{\circ}\text{C}} \times \left(35.2\ {}^{\circ}\text{C} - 28.5\ {}^{\circ}\text{C}\right) = 28 m_{\text{water}} \qquad m_{\text{water}} = \frac{8.4 \times 10^3\ \text{J}}{28\ \text{J g}^{-1}} = 3.0 \times 10^2\ \text{g}$$

2B **(M)** We use the same equation, equating the heat lost by the copper to the heat absorbed by the water, except now we solve for final temperature.

$$q_{\text{Cu}} = 100.0\ \text{g} \times \frac{0.385\ \text{J}}{\text{g}\ {}^{\circ}\text{C}} \times \left(x\ {}^{\circ}\text{C} - 100.0\ {}^{\circ}\text{C}\right) = -50.0\ \text{g} \times \frac{4.18\ \text{J}}{\text{g}\ {}^{\circ}\text{C}} \times \left(x\ {}^{\circ}\text{C} - 26.5\ {}^{\circ}\text{C}\right) = -q_{\text{water}}$$

$$38.5x - 3850 = -209x + 5539 \qquad 38.5x + 209x = 5539 + 3850 \rightarrow 247.5x = 9389$$

$$x = \frac{9389\ \text{J}}{247.5\ \text{J}\ {}^{\circ}\text{C}^{-1}} = 37.9\ {}^{\circ}\text{C}$$

3A **(E)** The molar mass of $C_8H_8O_3$ is 152.14 g/mol. The calorimeter has a heat capacity of 4.90 kJ/°C.

$$q_{\text{calorim}} = \frac{4.90\ \text{kJ}\ {}^{\circ}\text{C}^{-1} \times \left(30.09\ {}^{\circ}\text{C} - 24.89\ {}^{\circ}\text{C}\right)}{1.013\ \text{g}} \times \frac{152.14\ \text{g}}{1\ \text{mol}} = 3.83 \times 10^3\ \text{kJ/mol}$$

$$\Delta_c H = -q_{\text{calorim}} = -3.83 \times 10^3\ \text{kJ/mol}$$

3B **(E)** The heat that is liberated by the benzoic acid's combustion serves to raise the temperature of the assembly. We designate the calorimeter's heat capacity by C.

$$q_r = 1.176 \text{ g} \times \frac{-26.42 \text{ kJ}}{1 \text{ g}} = -31.07 \text{ kJ} = -q_{calorim}$$

4A **(M)** The heat that is liberated by the reaction raises the temperature of the reaction mixture. We assume that this reaction mixture has the same density and specific heat capacity as pure water.

$$q_{calorim} = \left(200.0 \text{ mL} \times \frac{1.00 \text{ g}}{1 \text{ mL}}\right) \times \frac{4.18 \text{ J}}{\text{g} \,^{\circ}\text{C}} \times (30.2 - 22.4) \,^{\circ}\text{C} = 6.5 \times 10^3 \text{ J} = -q_r$$

Owing to the 1:1 stoichiometry of the reaction, the number of moles of AgCl(s) formed is equal to the number of moles of $AgNO_3$(aq) in the original sample.

$$\text{mol AgCl} = 100.0 \text{ mL} \times \frac{1 \text{ L}}{1000 \text{ mL}} \times \frac{1.00 \text{ mol AgNO}_3}{1 \text{ L}} \times \frac{1 \text{ mol AgCl}}{1 \text{ mol AgNO}_3} = 0.100 \text{ mol AgCl}$$

$$q_r = \frac{-6.5 \times 10^3 \text{ J}}{0.100 \text{ mol}} \times \frac{1 \text{ kJ}}{1000 \text{ J}} = -65. \text{ kJ/mol}$$

Because q_r is a negative quantity, the precipitation reaction is exothermic.

4B **(M)** The assumptions include no heat loss to the surroundings or to the calorimeter, a solution density of 1.00 g/mL, a specific heat capacity of 4.18 J $g^{-1}\,^{\circ}\text{C}^{-1}$, and that the initial and final solution volumes are the same. The equation for the reaction that occurs is $NaOH(aq) + HCl(aq) \rightarrow NaCl(aq) + H_2O(l)$. Since the two reactants combine in a one to one mole ratio, the limiting reactant is the one present in smaller amount (i.e. the one with a smaller molar quantity).

$$\text{amount HCl} = 100.0 \text{ mL} \times \frac{1.020 \text{ mmol HCl}}{1 \text{ mL soln}} = 102.0 \text{ mmol HCl}$$

$$\text{amount NaOH} = 50.0 \text{ mL} \times \frac{1.988 \text{ mmol NaOH}}{1 \text{ mL soln}} = 99.4 \text{ mmol NaOH}$$

Thus, NaOH is the limiting reactant.

$$q_{neutr} = 99.4 \text{ mmol NaOH} \times \frac{1 \text{ mmol H}_2\text{O}}{1 \text{ mmol NaOH}} \times \frac{1 \text{ mol H}_2\text{O}}{1000 \text{ mmol H}_2\text{O}} \times \frac{-56 \text{ kJ}}{1 \text{ mol H}_2\text{O}} = -5.57 \text{ kJ}$$

Let the final temperature of the calorimeter and its contents be $t \,^{\circ}\text{C}$. The heat absorbed by the calorimeter is:

$$q_{calorim} = (100.0 + 50.0) \text{ mL} \times \frac{1.00 \text{ g}}{1 \text{ mL}} \times \frac{4.18 \text{ J}}{\text{g} \,^{\circ}\text{C}} \times \frac{1 \text{ kJ}}{1000 \text{ J}} \times (t - 24.52) \,^{\circ}\text{C} = (0.627t - 15.37) \text{ kJ}$$

Since $q_{calorim} = -q_{neutr} = 5.57$ kJ, we have $0.627t - 15.37 = 5.57$ and

thus, $t = \dfrac{5.57 + 15.37}{0.627} = 33.4$.

5A **(E)** $w = -P\Delta V = -0.750 \text{ atm}(+1.50 \text{ L}) = -1.12\underline{5} \text{ atm L} \times \dfrac{101.33 \text{ J}}{1 \text{ atm L}} = -114 \text{ J}$

114 J of work is done by system.

5B (M) Determine the initial number of moles:

$$n = 50.0 \text{ g N}_2 \times \frac{1 \text{ mol N}_2}{28.014 \text{ g N}_2} = 1.78\underline{5} \text{ mol N}_2$$

$$V = \frac{nRT}{P} = \frac{(1.785 \text{ mol N}_2)(0.08206 \text{ atm L mol}^{-1} \text{ K}^{-1})(293.15 \text{ K})}{2.50 \text{ atm}} = 17.2 \text{ L}$$

$$\Delta V = 17.2 - 75.0 \text{ L} = -57.8 \text{ L}$$

$$w = -P\Delta V = -2.50 \text{ atm}(-57.8 \text{ L}) \times \frac{101.33 \text{ J}}{1 \text{ atm L}} \times \frac{1 \text{ kJ}}{1000 \text{ J}} = +14.6 \text{ kJ work done on system}$$

6A (E) The work is $w = +355$ J. The heat flow is $q = -185$ J. These two are related to the energy change of the system by the first law equation: $\Delta U = q + w$, which becomes

$$\Delta U = +355 \text{ J} - 185 \text{ J} = +1.70 \times 10^2 \text{ J}$$

6B (E) The internal energy change is $\Delta U = -125$ J. The heat flow is $q = +54$ J. These two are related to the work done on the system by the first law equation: $\Delta U = q + w$, which becomes $-125 \text{ J} = +54 \text{ J} + w$. The solution to this equation is $w = -125 \text{ J} - 54 \text{ J} = -179 \text{ J}$, which means that 179 J of work is done by the system to the surroundings.

7A (E) Heat that is given off has a negative sign. In addition, we use the molar mass of sucrose, 342.30 g/mol.

$$\text{sucrose mass} = -1.00 \times 10^3 \text{ kJ} \times \frac{1 \text{ mol C}_{12}\text{H}_{22}\text{O}_{11}}{-5.65 \times 10^3 \text{ kJ}} \times \frac{342.30 \text{ g C}_{12}\text{H}_{22}\text{O}_{11}}{1 \text{ mol C}_{12}\text{H}_{22}\text{O}_{11}} = 60.6 \text{ g C}_{12}\text{H}_{22}\text{O}_{11}$$

7B (E) Although the equation does not say so explicitly, the reaction of $H^+(aq) + OH^-(aq) \rightarrow H_2O(l)$ gives off 56 kJ of heat per mole of water formed. The equation then is the source of a conversion factor.

$$\text{heat flow} = 25.0 \text{ mL} \times \frac{1 \text{ L}}{1000 \text{ mL}} \times \frac{0.1045 \text{ mol HCl}}{1 \text{ L soln}} \times \frac{1 \text{ mol H}_2\text{O}}{1 \text{ mol HCl}} \times \frac{56 \text{ kJ evolved}}{1 \text{ mol H}_2\text{O}}$$

$$= 0.15 \text{ kJ heat evolved}$$

8A (M) $V_{\text{ice}} = (2.00 \text{ cm})^3 = 8.00 \text{ cm}^3$

$$m_{\text{ice}} = m_{\text{water}} = 8.00 \text{ cm}^3 \times 0.917 \text{ g cm}^{-3} = 7.34 \text{ g ice} = 7.34 \text{ g H}_2\text{O}$$

$$\text{moles of ice} = 7.34 \text{ g ice} \times \frac{1 \text{ mol H}_2\text{O}}{18.015 \text{ g H}_2\text{O}} = 0.407 \text{ mol ice}$$

$q_{\text{overall}} = q_{\text{ice}}(-10 \text{ to } 0 \text{ °C}) + q_{\text{fus}} + q_{\text{water}}(0 \text{ to } 23.2 \text{ °C})$

$q_{\text{overall}} = m_{\text{ice}} c_p(\text{ice}) \Delta T + n_{\text{ice}}\Delta H_{\text{fus}} + m_{\text{water}} c_p(\text{water}) \Delta T$

$q_{\text{overall}} = (7.34 \text{ g})(10.0 \text{ °C})(2.01 \times 10^{-3} \frac{\text{kJ}}{\text{g °C}}) + (0.407 \text{ mol ice})(6.01 \frac{\text{kJ}}{\text{mol}}) + (7.34 \text{ g})$

$(23.2 \text{ °C})(4.184 \times 10^{-3} \frac{\text{kJ}}{\text{g °C}})$

$q_{\text{overall}} = 0.148 \text{ kJ} + 2.45 \text{ kJ} + 0.712 \text{ kJ}$

$q_{\text{overall}} = +3.31 \text{ kJ}$ (the system absorbs this much heat)

8B **(M)** 5.00×10^3 kJ = $q_{ice}(-15$ to $0\ °C) + q_{fus} + q_{water}(0$ to $25\ °C) + q_{vap}$

5.00×10^3 kJ = $m_{ice}\ c_p(ice)\ \Delta T + n_{ice}\Delta H_{fus} + m_{water}\ c_p(water)\ \Delta T + n_{water}\Delta H_{vap}$

5.00×10^6 J = $m(15.0\ °C)(2.01\ \dfrac{J}{g\ °C}) + \dfrac{m}{18.015\ \text{g H}_2\text{O/mol H}_2\text{O}}(6.01 \times 10^3\ \dfrac{J}{mol})$

$\qquad + m(25.0\ °C)(4.184\ \dfrac{J}{g\ °C}) + \dfrac{m}{18.015\ \text{g H}_2\text{O/mol}}(44.0 \times 10^3\ \dfrac{J}{mol})$

5.00×10^6 J = $m(30.1\underline{5}\ \text{J/g}) + m(333.\underline{6}\ \text{J/g}) + m(104.\underline{5}\ \text{J/g}) + m(2.4\underline{4} \times 10^3\ \text{J/g})$

5.00×10^6 J = $m(2.91 \times 10^3\ \text{J/g})\ m = \dfrac{5.00 \times 10^6\ \ \text{J}}{2.91 \times 10^3\ \ \text{J/g}} = 1718$ g or 1.72 kg H_2O

9A **(M)** We combine the three combustion reactions to produce the hydrogenation reaction.

$C_3H_6(g) + \tfrac{9}{2}O_2(g) \rightarrow 3\ CO_2(g) + 3\ H_2O(l)$ $\qquad \Delta_c H = \Delta H_1 = -2058$ kJ/mol

$H_2(g) + \tfrac{1}{2}O_2(g) \rightarrow H_2O(l)$ $\qquad\qquad\qquad \Delta_c H = \Delta H_2 = -285.8$ kJ/mol

$3\ CO_2(g) + 4\ H_2O(l) \rightarrow C_3H_8(g) + 5\ O_2(g)$ $\qquad -\Delta_c H = \Delta H_3 = +2219.9$ kJ/mol

---

$C_3H_6(g) + H_2(g) \rightarrow C_3H_8(g)$ $\qquad\qquad \Delta_r H = \Delta H_1 + \Delta H_2 + \Delta H_3 = -124$ kJ/mol

9B **(M)** The combustion reaction has propanol and $O_{2(g)}$ as reactants; the products are $CO_2(g)$ and $H_2O(l)$. Reverse the reaction given and combine it with the combustion reaction of $C_3H_6(g)$.

$C_3H_7OH(l) \rightarrow C_3H_6(g) + H_2O(l)$ $\qquad\qquad \Delta H_1 = +52$ kJ/mol

$C_3H_6(g) + \tfrac{9}{2}O_2(g) \rightarrow 3\ CO_2(g) + 3\ H_2O(l)$ $\qquad \Delta H_2 = -2058$ kJ/mol

---

$C_3H_7OH(l) + \tfrac{9}{2}O_2(g) \rightarrow 3\ CO_2(g) + 4\ H_2O(l)$ $\qquad \Delta_r H = \Delta H_1 + \Delta H_2 = -2006$ kJ/mol

10A **(M)** The enthalpy of formation is the enthalpy change for the reaction in which one mole of the product, $C_6H_{13}O_2N(s)$, is produced from appropriate amounts of the reference forms of the elements (in most cases, the most stable form of the elements).

$6\ C(graphite) + \tfrac{13}{2}H_2(g) + O_2(g) + \tfrac{1}{2}N_2(g) \rightarrow C_6H_{13}O_2N(s)$

10B **(M)** The enthalpy of formation is the enthalpy change for the reaction in which one mole of the product, $NH_3(g)$, is produced from appropriate amounts of the reference forms of the elements, in this case from 0.5 mol $N_2(g)$ and 1.5 mol $H_2(g)$, that is, for the reaction:

$\tfrac{1}{2}N_2(g) + \tfrac{3}{2}H_2(g) \rightarrow NH_3(g)$

The specified reaction is twice the reverse of the formation reaction, and its enthalpy change is minus two times the enthalpy of formation of $NH_3(g)$:

$-2 \times (-46.11\ \text{kJ}) = +92.22$ kJ/mol

11A (M)

$$\Delta_r H^\circ = 2 \times \Delta_f H^\circ \left[CO_2(g) \right] + 3 \times \Delta_f H^\circ \left[H_2O(l) \right] - \Delta_f H^\circ \left[CH_3CH_2OH(l) \right] - 3 \times \Delta_f H^\circ \left[O_2(g) \right]$$

$$= \left[2 \times (-393.5 \text{ kJ/mol}) \right] + \left[3 \times (-285.8 \text{ kJ/mol}) \right] - \left[-277.7 \text{ kJ/mol} \right] - \left[3 \times 0.00 \text{ kJ/mol} \right]$$

$$= -1367 \text{ kj/mol}$$

11B (D) We write the combustion reaction for each compound, and use that reaction to determine the compound's heat of combustion.

$$C_3H_8(g) + 5 O_2(g) \rightarrow 3 CO_2(g) + 4 H_2O(l)$$

$$\Delta_c H^\circ = 3 \times \Delta_f H^\circ \left[CO_2(g) \right] + 4 \times \Delta_f H^\circ \left[H_2O(l) \right] - \Delta_f H^\circ \left[C_3H_8(g) \right] - 5 \times \Delta_f H^\circ \left[O_2(g) \right]$$

$$= \left[3 \times (-393.5 \text{ kJ}) \right] + \left[4 \times (-285.8 \text{ kJ}) \right] - \left[-103.8 \text{ kJ} \right] - \left[5 \times 0.00 \text{ kJ mol}^{-1} \right]$$

$$= -1181 \text{ kJ} - 1143 \text{ kJ} + 103.8 - 0.00 \text{ kJ mol}^{-1} = -2220. \text{ kJ/mol } C_3H_8$$

$$C_4H_{10}(g) + \tfrac{13}{2} O_2(g) \rightarrow 4 CO_2(g) + 5 H_2O(l)$$

$$\Delta_c H^\circ = 4 \times \Delta_f H^\circ \left[CO_2(g) \right] + 5 \times \Delta_f H^\circ \left[H_2O(l) \right] - \Delta_f H^\circ \left[C_4H_{10}(g) \right] - 6.5 \times \Delta_f H^\circ \left[O_2(g) \right]$$

$$= \left[4 \times (-393.5 \text{ kJ}) \right] + \left[5 \times (-285.8 \text{ kJ}) \right] - \left[-125.6 \right] - \left[6.5 \times 0.00 \text{ kJ mol}^{-1} \right]$$

$$= -1574 \text{ kJ} - 1429 \text{ kJ} + 125.6 \text{ kJ} - 0.00 \text{ kJ} = -2877 \text{ kJ/mol } C_4H_{10}$$

In 1.00 mole of the mixture there are 0.62 mol $C_3H_8(g)$ and 0.38 mol $C_4H_{10}(g)$.

$$\text{heat of combustion} = \left(0.62 \text{ mol } C_3H_8 \times \frac{-2220. \text{ kJ}}{1 \text{ mol } C_3H_8} \right) + \left(0.38 \text{ mol } C_4H_{10} \times \frac{-2877 \text{ kJ}}{1 \text{ mol } C_4H_{10}} \right)$$

$$= -1.4 \times 10^3 \text{ kJ} - 1.1 \times 10^3 \text{ kJ} = -2.5 \times 10^3 \text{ kJ/mol mixture}$$

12A (M) $6 CO_2(g) + 6 H_2O(l) \rightarrow C_6H_{12}O_6(s) + 6 O_2(g)$

$$\Delta_r H^\circ = 2803 \text{ kJ} = \Sigma \upsilon \Delta_f H^\circ_{\text{products}} - \Sigma |\upsilon| \Delta_f H^\circ_{\text{reactants}}$$

$$2803 \text{ kJ/mol} = [1 \, (\Delta_f H^\circ [C_6H_{12}O_6(s)]) + 6 \, (0 \frac{\text{kJ}}{\text{mol}})] - [6 \, (-393.5 \frac{\text{kJ}}{\text{mol}}) + 6 \, (-285.8 \frac{\text{kJ}}{\text{mol}} / \text{mol})]$$

$$2803 \text{ kJ/mol} = \Delta_f H^\circ [C_6H_{12}O_6(s)] - [-4075.8 \text{ kJ}]. \text{ Thus, } \Delta_f H^\circ [C_6H_{12}O_6(s)]$$

$$= -1273 \text{ kJ/mol } C_6H_{12}O_6(s)$$

12B (M) $\Delta_c H^\circ [CH_3OCH_3(g)] = -31.70 \dfrac{\text{kJ}}{\text{g}}$ \qquad molar mass of $CH_3OCH_3 = 46.069 \text{ g mol}^{-1}$

$$\Delta_c H^\circ [CH_3OCH_3(g)] = -31.70 \frac{\text{kJ}}{\text{g}} \times 46.069 \frac{\text{g}}{\text{mol}} = -1460 \frac{\text{kJ}}{\text{mol}} = \Delta_r H^\circ$$

$$\Delta_r H^\circ = \Sigma \upsilon \Delta_f H^\circ_{\text{products}} - \Sigma |\upsilon| \Delta_f H^\circ_{\text{reactants}} \quad \text{Reaction: } CH_3OCH_3(g) + 3 O_2(g) \rightarrow 2 CO_2(g) + 3 H_2O(l)$$

$$-1460 \text{ kJ/mol} = [2 \, (-393.5 \frac{\text{kJ}}{\text{mol}}) + 3 \, (-285.8 \frac{\text{kJ}}{\text{mol}})] - [1 \, (\Delta_f H^\circ [CH_3OCH_3(g)]) + 3 \, (0 \frac{\text{kJ}}{\text{mol}})]$$

$$-1460 \text{ kJ/mol} = -1644.4 \text{ kJ/mol} - \Delta_f H^\circ [CH_3OCH_3(g)]$$

Hence, $\Delta_f H^\circ [CH_3OCH_3(g)] = -184 \text{ kJ/mol } CH_3OCH_3(g)$

13A **(M)** The net ionic equation is: $Ag^+(aq) + I^-(aq) \rightarrow AgI(s)$ and we have the following:

$$\Delta_r H^\circ = \Delta_f H^\circ\left[AgI(s)\right] - \left[\Delta_f H^\circ\left[Ag^+(aq)\right] + \Delta_f H^\circ\left[I^-(aq)\right]\right]$$

$$= -61.84 \text{ kJ/mol} - \left[(+105.6 \text{ kJ/mol}) + (-55.19 \text{ kJ/mol})\right] = -112.3 \text{ kJ/mol AgI(s) formed}$$

13B **(M)** $2\,Ag^+(aq) + CO_3^{2-}(aq) \rightarrow Ag_2CO_3(s)$

$\Delta_r H^\circ = -39.9 \text{ kJ} = \Sigma v \Delta_f H^\circ{}_{products} - \Sigma |v| \Delta_f H^\circ{}_{reactants}$

$-39.9 \text{ kJ/mol} = \Delta_f H^\circ[Ag_2CO_3(s)] - [2\,(105.6 \text{ kJ/mol}) + 1\,(-677.1 \text{ kJ/mol})]$

$-39.9 \text{ kJ/mol} = \Delta_f H^\circ[Ag_2CO_3(s)] + 465.9 \text{ kJ/mol}$

Hence, $\Delta_f H^\circ[Ag_2CO_3(s)] = -505.8 \text{ kJ/mol Ag}_2CO_3(s)$ formed.

INTEGRATIVE EXAMPLE

A. **(M)** The combustion reactions of $C_{16}H_{32}$ and $C_{16}H_{34}$ are shown below

(1) $C_{16}H_{32} + 24\,O_2 \rightarrow 16\,CO_2 + 16\,H_2O$	$\Delta_r H_1 = -10{,}539 \text{ kJ/mol}$
(2) $2\,C_{16}H_{34} + 49\,O_2 \rightarrow 32\,CO_2 + 34\,H_2O$	$\Delta_r H_2 = -10{,}699 \text{ kJ/mol} = -21{,}398 \text{ kJ/mol}$

Since we are studying the hydrogenation of $C_{16}H_{32}$ to give $C_{16}H_{34}$, the final equation has to include the former as the reactant and the latter as the product. This is done by doubling equation 1 and reversing equation 2:

(3) $2\,C_{16}H_{32} + 48\,O_2 \rightarrow 32\,CO_2 + 32\,H_2O$	$\Delta_r H_3 = -21{,}078 \text{ kJ/mol}$
(4) $32\,CO_2 + 34\,H_2O \rightarrow 2\,C_{16}H_{34} + 49\,O_2$	$\Delta_r H_4 = +21{,}398 \text{ kJ/mol}$
(5) $2\,C_{16}H_{32} + 2\,H_2O \rightarrow 2\,C_{16}H_{34} + O_2$	$\Delta_r H_5 = +320 \text{ kJ/mol}$

Since a hydrogenation reaction involves hydrogen as a reactant, and looking at equation (5), we add the following reaction to (5):

(6) $H_2 + \frac{1}{2}\,O_2 \rightarrow H_2O$	$\Delta_r H_6 = -285.5 \text{ kJ/mol}$

Double equation (6) and add it to equation 5:

(5) $2\,C_{16}H_{32} + 2\,H_2O \rightarrow 2\,C_{16}H_{34} + O_2$	$\Delta_r H_5 = +320 \text{ kJ/mol}$
(7) $2\,H_2 + O_2 \rightarrow 2\,H_2O$	$\Delta_r H_7 = -571 \text{ kJ/mol}$
(8) $2\,C_{16}H_{32} + 2\,H_2 \rightarrow 2\,C_{16}H_{34}$	$\Delta_r H_8 = -251 \text{ kJ/mol}$

Since (8) is for 2 moles, $\Delta_f H$ is -125.5 kJ/mol

B. **(D)** This is a multistep problem. First, you must determine the amount of material that reacts, then you have to determine the amount of heat generated, and finally you have to calculate the effect of that heat on the material present in the system after the reaction.

$$CaO(s) + H_2O(l) \rightarrow Ca(OH)_2(s)$$

Note that $Ca(OH)_2$ is sparingly soluble in water, so we can safely assume that $Ca(OH)_2$ does not dissolve in water.

56 g CaO × (1 mol CaO/56.1 g CaO) = 1 mol CaO
100 g H_2O × (1 mol H_2O/18.0 g H_2O) = 5.56 mol H_2O

CaO is the limiting reactant. Therefore, the amount of unreacted H_2O is 5.56 – 1.0 = 4.6 mol. The mass of water unreacted is 4.6 mol H_2O × (18.015 g H_2O/1 mol H_2O) = 83 g H_2O. The mass of $Ca(OH)_2$ produced is calculated as follows:

$$56\ CaO \times \frac{1\ mol\ CaO}{56.1\ g\ CaO} \times \frac{1\ mol\ Ca(OH)_2}{1\ mol\ CaO} \times \frac{74.1\ g\ Ca(OH)_2}{1\ mol\ Ca(OH)_2} = 74\ g\ Ca(OH)_2$$

The enthalpy of reaction is

$$\Delta_r H = 1 \times \Delta_f H°[Ca(OH)_2(s)] - \left(1 \times \Delta_f H°[CaO(s)] + \Delta_f H°[H_2O(l)]\right)$$

$$= -987\ kJ/mol - \left(-635\ kJ/mol + (-286\ kJ/mol)\right) = -66\ kJ/mol$$

The heat released by the combustion of 1 mol CaO will raise the temperature of the $Ca(OH)_2$ and water, and if there is sufficient energy, the temperature will rise to 100 °C, and some or all of the water will evaporate. Only if there is sufficient energy to evaporate all the water will the temperature of the $Ca(OH)_2$ and the steam rise beyond 100 °C. To decide what happens, we first calculate the heat required to raise the temperature of the $Ca(OH)_2$ and water to 100 °C. To perform this calculation, we need the specific heat capacities of water (4.18 J g^{-1} °C^{-1}) and $Ca(OH)_2$. From Appendix D, the molar heat capacity at constant pressure is 87.5 J mol^{-1} °C^{-1} for $Ca(OH)_2(s)$, so we have

$$c_{P,Ca(OH)_2(s)} = \frac{87.5\ J}{mol\ °C} \times \frac{1\ mol}{74.09\ g} = 1.18\ J\ g^{-1}\ °C^{-1}$$

The heat, q, required is

$$q = m_{H_2O} \cdot c_{H_2O} \Delta T + m_{Ca(OH)_2} \cdot c_{Ca(OH)_2} \Delta T$$

$$= (83\ g)(4.18\ J \cdot g^{-1} \cdot °C^{-1})(100.0\ °C - 25.0\ °C) + (74\ g)(1.18\ J \cdot g^{-1} \cdot °C^{-1})(100.0\ °C - 25.0\ °C)$$

$$= 32,600\ J \approx 33\ kJ\ \text{energy expended}$$

With 33 kJ of energy expended to raise the temperature of $Ca(OH)_2$ and the remaining water to 100 °C, the remaining energy is 66 kJ – 33 kJ = 33 kJ, which is available to evaporate water. Since $\Delta_{vap}H° = 40.6\ kJ\ mol^{-1}$ for water at 100 °C, the mass of water evaporated is

$$33\ kJ \times \frac{1\ mol\ H_2O}{40.6\ kJ} \times \frac{18.015\ g\ H_2O}{1\ mol\ H_2O} = 15\ g\ H_2O\ \text{evaporated}$$

Therefore, the mass of H_2O remaining is 83 g – 15 g = 68 g, along with the 74 g of $Ca(OH)_2$ produced by the reaction of CaO and H_2O.

EXERCISES

Heat Capacity (Specific Heat Capacity)

1. **(E)**

   (a) $q = 9.25\,\text{L} \times \dfrac{1000\,\text{cm}^3}{1\,\text{L}} \times \dfrac{1.00\,\text{g}}{1\,\text{cm}^3} \times \dfrac{4.18\,\text{J}}{1\,\text{g}\,°\text{C}} \times \dfrac{1\,\text{kJ}}{1000\,\text{J}}(29.4\,°\text{C} - 22.0\,°\text{C}) = +2.9 \times 10^2\,\text{kJ}$

   (b) $q = 5.85\,\text{kg} \times \dfrac{1000\,\text{g}}{1\,\text{kg}} \times \dfrac{0.903\,\text{J}}{\text{g}\,°\text{C}} \times (-33.5\,°\text{C}) \times \dfrac{1\,\text{kJ}}{1000\,\text{J}} = -177\,\text{kJ}$

2. **(E)** $\text{heat} = \text{mass} \times c_p \times \Delta T$

   (a) $\Delta T = \dfrac{+875\,\text{J}}{12.6\,\text{g} \times 4.18\,\text{J}\,\text{g}^{-1}\,°\text{C}^{-1}} = +16.6\,°\text{C}$ $T_f = T_i + \Delta T = 22.9\,°\text{C} + 16.6\,°\text{C} = 39.5\,°\text{C}$

   (b) $\Delta T = \dfrac{-1.05\,\text{kcal} \times \dfrac{1000\,\text{cal}}{1\,\text{kcal}}}{\left(1.59\,\text{kg} \times \dfrac{1000\,\text{g}}{1\,\text{kg}}\right) 0.032\,\dfrac{\text{cal}}{\text{g}\,°\text{C}}} = -21\,°\text{C}$ $T_f = T_i + \Delta T = 22.9\,°\text{C} - 21.0\,°\text{C} = 8.9\,°\text{C}$

3. **(E)** heat gained by the water = heat lost by the metal; $\text{heat} = \text{mass} \times c_p \times \Delta T$

   (a) $50.0\,\text{g} \times 4.18\,\dfrac{\text{J}}{\text{g}\,°\text{C}}(38.9 - 22.0)\,°\text{C} = 3.53 \times 10^3\,\text{J} = -150.0\,\text{g} \times c_p \times (38.9 - 100.0)\,°\text{C}$

   $c_p = \dfrac{3.53 \times 10^3\,\text{J}}{150.0\,\text{g} \times 61.1\,°\text{C}} = 0.385\,\text{J}\,\text{g}^{-1}\,°\text{C}^{-1}$ for Zn

   (b) $50.0\,\text{g} \times 4.18\,\dfrac{\text{J}}{\text{g}\,°\text{C}}(28.8 - 22.0)\,°\text{C} = 1.4 \times 10^3\,\text{J} = -150.0\,\text{g} \times c_p \times (28.8 - 100.0)\,°\text{C}$

   $c_p = \dfrac{1.4 \times 10^3\,\text{J}}{150.0\,\text{g} \times 71.2\,°\text{C}} = 0.13\,\text{J}\,\text{g}^{-1}\,°\text{C}^{-1}$ for Pt

   (c) $50.0\,\text{g} \times 4.18\,\dfrac{\text{J}}{\text{g}\,°\text{C}}(52.7 - 22.0)\,°\text{C} = 6.42 \times 10^3\,\text{J} = -150.0\,\text{g} \times c_p \times (52.7 - 100.0)\,°\text{C}$

   $c_p = \dfrac{6.42 \times 10^3\,\text{J}}{150.0\,\text{g} \times 47.3\,°\text{C}} = 0.905\,\text{J}\,\text{g}^{-1}\,°\text{C}^{-1}$ for Al

4. **(E)** $50.0\,\text{g} \times 4.18\,\dfrac{\text{J}}{\text{g}\,°\text{C}}(27.6 - 23.2)\,°\text{C} = 9.2 \times 10^2\,\text{J} = -75.0\,\text{g} \times c_p \times (27.6 - 80.0)\,°\text{C}$

   $c_p = \dfrac{9.2 \times 10^2\,\text{J}}{75.0\,\text{g} \times 52.4\,°\text{C}} = 0.23\,\text{J}\,\text{g}^{-1}\,°\text{C}^{-1}$ for Ag

5. **(M)** $q_{\text{water}} = 375\,\text{g} \times 4.18\,\dfrac{\text{J}}{\text{g}\,°\text{C}}(87 - 26)\,°\text{C} = 9.5\underline{6} \times 10^4\,\text{J} = -q_{\text{iron}}$

   $q_{\text{iron}} = -9.5\underline{6} \times 10^4\,\text{J} = 465\,\text{g} \times 0.449\,\dfrac{\text{J}}{\text{g}\,°\text{C}}(87 - T_1) = 1.8\underline{16} \times 10^4\,\text{J} - 2.088 \times 10^2\,T_1$

$$T_1 = \frac{-9.5\underline{6}\times10^4 - 1.81\underline{6}\times10^4}{-2.08\underline{8}\times10^2} = \frac{-11.3\underline{8}\times10^4}{-2.08\underline{8}\times10^2} = 5.4\underline{48}\times10^2 \ ^\circ C \text{ or } 545\ ^\circ C$$

The number of significant figures in the final answer is limited by the two significant figures for the given temperatures.

6. **(M)** heat lost by steel = heat gained by water

$$-m \times 0.50\frac{J}{g\,^\circ C}(55.4 - 201)\,^\circ C = 73\ m = 150\ \text{mL} \times \frac{1.00\ g}{1\ \text{mL}} \times 4.18\frac{J}{g\,^\circ C}(55.4 - 23.2)\,^\circ C$$

$$73\ m = 2.02\times10^4\ J \qquad\qquad m = \frac{2.02\times10^4}{73} = 2.8\times10^2\ \text{g stainless steel}$$

The precision of this method of determining mass is limited by the fact that some heat leaks out of the system. When we deal with temperatures far above (or far below) room temperature, this assumption becomes less and less valid. Furthermore, the precision of the method is limited to two significant figures by the specific heat capacity of the steel. If the two specific heat capacities were known more precisely, then the temperature difference would determine the final precision of the method. It is unlikely that we could readily measure temperatures more precisely than ±0.01°C, without expensive equipment. The mass of steel in this case would be measurable to four significant figures, to ±0.1 g. This is hardly comparable to modern analytical balances which typically measure such masses to ±0.1 mg.

7. **(M)** heat lost by Mg = heat gained by water

$$-\left(1.00\ \text{kg Mg} \times \frac{1000\ g}{1\ \text{kg}}\right)1.024\frac{J}{g\,^\circ C}(T_f - 40.0\ ^\circ C) = \left(1.00\ \text{L} \times \frac{1000\ \text{cm}^3}{1\ \text{L}} \times \frac{1.00\ g}{1\ \text{cm}^3}\right)4.18\frac{J}{g\,^\circ C}(T_f - 20.0\ ^\circ C)$$

$$-1.024\times10^3\ T_f + 4.10\times10^4 = 4.18\times10^3\ T_f - 8.36\times10^4$$

$$4.10\times10^4 + 8.36\times10^4 = \left(4.18\times10^3 + 1.024\times10^3\right)T_f \ \rightarrow \ 12.46\times10^4 = 5.20\times10^3\ T_f$$

$$T_f = \frac{12.46\times10^4}{5.20\times10^3} = 24.0\ ^\circ C$$

8. **(M)** heat gained by the water = heat lost by the brass

$$150.0\ g \times 4.18\frac{J}{g\,^\circ C} \times (T_f - 22.4\ ^\circ C) = -\left(15.2\ \text{cm}^3 \times \frac{8.40\ g}{1\ \text{cm}^3}\right)0.385\frac{J}{g\,^\circ C}(T_f - 163\ ^\circ C)$$

$$6.27\times10^2\,T_f - 1.40\times10^4 = -49.2\ T_f + 8.01\times10^3; \ T_f = \frac{1.40\times10^4 + 8.01\times10^3}{6.27\times10^2 + 49.2} = 32.6\ ^\circ C$$

9. **(M)** heat lost by copper = heat gained by glycerol

$$-74.8\ g \times \frac{0.385\ J}{g\,^\circ C} \times (31.1\ ^\circ C - 143.2\ ^\circ C) = 165\ \text{mL} \times \frac{1.26\ g}{1\ \text{mL}} \times c_p \times (31.1\ ^\circ C - 24.8\ ^\circ C)$$

$$3.23\times10^3 = 1.3\times10^3 \times (c_p) \qquad c_p = \frac{3.23\times10^3}{1.3\times10^3} = 2.5\ J\ g^{-1}\,^\circ C^{-1}$$

$$\text{molar heat capacity} = 2.5\ J\ g^{-1}\,^\circ C^{-1} \times \frac{92.1\ g}{1\ \text{mol}\ C_3H_8O_3} = 2.3\times10^2\ J\ \text{mol}^{-1}\,^\circ C^{-1}$$

10. **(M)** To determine heat capacity of gold, we have to remember that heat lost by the gold is gained by the water, with both substances coming to final equilibrium temperature. That is,

$$-q_{Au} = q_{H_2O}$$

$$-m_{Au} \cdot c_{Au} \left(T_f - T_{i,Au} \right) = m_{H_2O} \cdot c_{H_2O} \left(T_f - T_{i,H_2O} \right)$$

Therefore, c_{Au} can be determined by rearranging and solving the above equation. At 25.0 °C, density of water is 0.997 g cm^{-3} or 0.997 g mL^{-1}. Therefore, the mass of 543.0 mL of water is 543.0 mL × 0.997 g mL^{-1} = 541.4 g.

$$c_{Au} = \frac{m_{H_2O} \cdot c_{H_2O} \left(T_f - T_{i,H_2O} \right)}{m_{Au} \left(T_f - T_{i,Au} \right)}$$

$$= \frac{541.4\,g \cdot 4.184\,J\,g^{-1}\,°C^{-1} \cdot \left(25.4\,°C - 25.0\,°C \right)}{-69.0\,g \left(25.4\,°C - 127.1\,°C \right)} = 0.129\,J\,g^{-1}\,°C^{-1}$$

11. **(M)** heat capacity $= \dfrac{\text{energy transferred}}{\Delta T} = \dfrac{6.052\,J}{(25.0 - 20.0\,°C)} = 1.21\,J/K$

*Note: since 1 K = 1 °C, it is not necessary to convert the temperatures to Kelvin. The change in temperature in both K and °C is the same.

12. **(E)** heat $= \text{mass} \times C_p \times \Delta T$

$$q_{water} = 6.052\,J = 1.24\ g \times 4.18\,\frac{J}{g\,°C}\,(T_f - 20.0)\,°C$$

$$T_f = 21.2\,°C$$

Heats of Reaction

13. **(E)** heat $= 283\ kg \times \dfrac{1000\ g}{1\ kg} \times \dfrac{1\ mol\ Ca(OH)_2}{74.09\ g\ Ca(OH)_2} \times \dfrac{65.2\ kJ}{1\ mol\ Ca(OH)_2} = 2.49 \times 10^5\ kJ$ of heat evolved

14. **(E)** heat energy $= 1.00\ gal \times \dfrac{3.785\ L}{1\ gal} \times \dfrac{1000\ mL}{1\ L} \times \dfrac{0.703\ g}{1\ mL} \times \dfrac{1\ mol\ C_8H_{18}}{114.2\ g\ C_8H_{18}} \times \dfrac{5.48 \times 10^3\ kJ}{1\ mol\ C_8H_{18}}$

$$= 1.28 \times 10^5\ kJ$$

15. **(M)**

(a) heat evolved $= 1.325\ g\ C_4H_{10} \times \dfrac{1\ mol\ C_4H_{10}}{58.123\ g\ C_4H_{10}} \times \dfrac{2877\ kJ}{1\ mol\ C_4H_{10}} = 3.65 \times 10^3\ kJ$

(b) heat evolved $= 28.4\ L\ C_4H_{10}\,(\text{at STP}) \times \dfrac{1\ mol\ C_4H_{10}}{22.711\ L\ C_4H_{10}\,(\text{at STP})} \times \dfrac{2877\ kJ}{1\ mol\ C_4H_{10}}$

$$= 3.65 \times 10^3\ kJ$$

(c) Use the ideal gas equation to determine the amount of propane in moles and multiply this amount by 2877 kJ heat produced per mole.

$$\text{heat evolved} = \frac{\left(738\ mmHg \times \dfrac{1\ atm}{760\ mmHg} \right) \times 12.6\ L}{\dfrac{0.08206\ atm\ L}{mol\ K} \times (23.6 + 273.2)} \times \frac{2877\ kJ}{1\ mol\ C_4H_{10}} = 1.45 \times 10^3\ kJ$$

16. **(M)**

(a) $q = \dfrac{-29.4 \text{ kJ}}{0.584 \text{ g } C_3H_8} \times \dfrac{44.10 \text{ g } C_3H_8}{1 \text{ mol } C_3H_8} = -2.22 \times 10^3 \text{ kJ/mol } C_3H_8$

(b) $q = \dfrac{-5.27 \text{ kJ}}{0.136 \text{ g } C_{10}H_{16}O} \times \dfrac{152.24 \text{ g } C_{10}H_{16}O}{1 \text{ mol } C_{10}H_{16}O} = -5.90 \times 10^3 \text{ kJ/mol } C_{10}H_{16}O$

(c) $q = \dfrac{-58.3 \text{ kJ}}{2.35 \text{ mL } (CH_3)_2 CO} \times \dfrac{1 \text{ mL}}{0.791 \text{ g}} \times \dfrac{58.08 \text{ g} (CH_3)_2 CO}{1 \text{ mol } (CH_3)_2 CO} = -1.82 \times 10^3 \text{ kJ/mol} (CH_3)_2 CO$

17. (M)

(a) $\text{mass} = 2.80 \times 10^7 \text{ kJ} \times \dfrac{1 \text{ mol } CH_4}{890.3 \text{ kJ}} \times \dfrac{16.04 \text{ g } CH_4}{1 \text{ mol } CH_4} \times \dfrac{1 \text{ kg}}{1000 \text{ g}} = 504 \text{ kg } CH_4$

(b) First determine the moles of CH_4 present, with the ideal gas equation.

$$\text{mol } CH_4 = \dfrac{\left(768 \text{ mmHg} \times \dfrac{1 \text{ atm}}{760 \text{ mmHg}}\right) 1.65 \times 10^4 \text{ L}}{0.08206 \dfrac{\text{L atm}}{\text{mol K}} \times (18.6 + 273.2) \text{ K}} = 696 \text{ mol } CH_4$$

$\text{heat energy} = 696 \text{ mol } CH_4 \times \dfrac{-890.3 \text{ kJ}}{1 \text{ mol } CH_4} = -6.20 \times 10^5 \text{ kJ of heat energy}$

(c) $V_{H_2O} = \dfrac{6.21 \times 10^5 \text{ kJ} \times \dfrac{1000 \text{ J}}{1 \text{ kJ}}}{4.18 \dfrac{\text{J}}{\text{g} \, ^\circ C} (60.0 - 8.8) ^\circ C} \times \dfrac{1 \text{ mL } H_2O}{1 \text{ g}} = 2.90 \times 10^6 \text{ mL} = 2.90 \times 10^3 \text{ L } H_2O$

18. **(M)** According to the Integrative Example synthesis gas consists of 55.0% CO(g), 33.0% H_2(g), and 12.0% non-combustible gases by volume. Keeping in mind that 1 L of gas at STP occupies a volume of 22.711 L, and that volume percent is equal to mole percent, we proceed as follows to calculate the amounts of CO and H_2 in 1 L of synthesis gas at STP:

$n_{CO} = 1 \text{ L synth. gas (at STP)} \times \dfrac{1 \text{ mol synth. gas}}{22.711 \text{ L synth. gas (at STP)}} \times \dfrac{0.550 \text{ mol CO}}{1 \text{ mol synth. gas}} = 0.02422 \text{ mol CO}$

$n_{H_2} = 1 \text{ L synth. gas (at STP)} \times \dfrac{1 \text{ mol synth. gas}}{22.711 \text{ L synth. gas (at STP)}} \times \dfrac{0.330 \text{ mol } H_2}{1 \text{ mol synth. gas}} = 0.01453 \text{ mol } H_2$

The enthalpies of combustion of CO(g) and H_2(g) at 25 °C are given as −283.0 kJ/mol and −285.8 kJ/mol, respectively. We assume that these values are the same at 0 °C. The heat released by the combustion of 1 L of synthesis gas at STP is

$q_{comb} = 0.02422 \text{ mol CO} \times \dfrac{-283.0 \text{ kJ}}{1 \text{ mol CO}} + 0.01453 \text{ mol } H_2 \times \dfrac{-285.8 \text{ kJ}}{1 \text{ mol } H_2} = -11.01 \text{ kJ (per L of synth. gas)}$

The heat needed to raise the temperature of 40.0 gallons of water from 15.2 to 65 °C is

$q_{water} = \left(40.0 \text{ gal} \times \dfrac{3.785 \text{ L}}{1 \text{ gal}} \times \dfrac{1000 \text{ mL}}{1 \text{ L}} \times \dfrac{1.00 \text{ g}}{1 \text{ mL}}\right) \left(4.184 \dfrac{\text{kJ}}{\text{g} \, ^\circ C}\right)(65.0 \, ^\circ C - 15.2 \, ^\circ C) = 3.15 \times 10^7 \text{ J}$

The volume of synthesis gas that must be burned at STP to produce 3.15×10^7 kJ of heat is

$$3.15 \times 10^7 \text{ J} \times \frac{1 \text{ L synth. gas}}{11.01 \times 10^3 \text{ J}} = 2.86 \times 10^3 \text{ L synth. gas}$$

19. **(M)** Since the molar mass of H_2 (2.0 g/mol) is $\frac{1}{16}$ of the molar mass of O_2 (32.0 g/mol) and only twice as many moles of H_2 are needed as O_2, we see that $O_2(g)$ is the limiting reactant in this reaction.

$$\frac{180.}{2} \text{ g } O_2 \times \frac{1 \text{ mol } O_2}{32.00 \text{ g } O_2} \times \frac{241.8 \text{ kJ heat}}{0.500 \text{ mol } O_2} = 1.36 \times 10^3 \text{ kJ heat}$$

20. **(M)** The amounts of the two reactants provided are the same as their stoichiometric coefficients in the balanced equation. Thus 852 kJ of heat is given off by the reaction. We can use this quantity of heat, along with the specific heat capacity of the mixture, to determine the temperature change that will occur if all of the heat is retained in the reaction mixture. We make use of the fact that $q = m \times c_p \times \Delta T$.

$$q = 8.52 \times 10^5 \text{ J} = \left(\left(1 \text{ mol } Al_2O_3 \times \frac{102 \text{ g } Al_2O_3}{1 \text{ mol } Al_2O_3} \right) + \left(2 \text{ mol Fe} \times \frac{55.8 \text{ g Fe}}{1 \text{ mol Fe}} \right) \right) \frac{0.8 \text{ J}}{\text{g °C}} \times \Delta T$$

$$\Delta T = \frac{8.52 \times 10^5 \text{ J}}{214 \text{ g} \times 0.8 \text{ J g}^{-1} \text{ °C}^{-1}} = 5 \times 10^3 \text{ °C}$$

The temperature needs to increase from 25 °C to 1530 °C or $\Delta T = 1505 \text{ °C} = 1.5 \times 10^3 \text{ °C}$. Since the actual ΔT is more than three times as large as this value, the iron indeed will melt, even if a large fraction of the heat evolved is lost to the surroundings and is not retained in the products.

21. **(M)**

(a) We first compute the heat produced by this reaction, then determine the value of ΔH in kJ/mol KOH.

$$q_{\text{calorim}} = (0.205 + 55.9) \text{ g} \times 4.18 \frac{\text{J}}{\text{g °C}} (24.4 \text{ °C} - 23.5 \text{ °C}) = 2 \times 10^2 \text{ J heat} = -q_{\text{rxn}}$$

$$\Delta H = -\frac{2 \times 10^2 \text{ J} \times \frac{1 \text{ kJ}}{1000 \text{ J}}}{0.205 \text{ g} \times \frac{1 \text{ mol KOH}}{56.1 \text{ g KOH}}} = -5 \times 10^1 \text{ kJ/mol}$$

(b) The ΔT here is known to just one significant figure (0.9 °C). Doubling the amount of KOH should give a temperature change known to two significant figures (1.6 °C) and using twenty times the mass of KOH should give a temperature change known to three significant figures (16.0 °C). This would require 4.10 g KOH rather than the 0.205 g KOH actually used, and would increase the precision from one part in five to one part in 500, or ~0.2 %. Note that as the mass of KOH is increased and the mass of H_2O stays constant, the assumption of a constant specific heat capacity becomes less valid.

22. (M) First we must determine the heat absorbed by the solute during the chemical reaction, q_{rxn}. This is the negative of the heat lost by the solution, q_{soln}. Since the solution (water plus solute) actually gives up heat, the temperature of the solution drops.

$$\text{heat of reaction} = 175.0 \text{ mL} \times \frac{1 \text{ L}}{1000 \text{ mL}} \times \frac{2.50 \text{ mol KI}}{1 \text{ L soln}} \times \frac{20.3 \text{ kJ}}{1 \text{ mol KI}} = 8.88 \text{ kJ} = q_r$$

$$-q_{rxn} = q_{soln} = \left(175.0 \text{ mL} \times \frac{1.30 \text{ g}}{1 \text{ mL}}\right) \times \frac{2.7 \text{ J}}{\text{g }^\circ\text{C}} \times \Delta T \quad \Delta T = \frac{-8.88 \times 10^3 \text{J}}{175.0 \text{ mL} \times \frac{1.30 \text{ g}}{1 \text{ mL}} \times \frac{2.7 \text{ J}}{\text{g }^\circ\text{C}}} = -14 \,^\circ\text{C}$$

final $T = $ initial $T + \Delta T = 24.3 \,^\circ\text{C} - 14 \,^\circ\text{C} = 10 \,^\circ\text{C}$

23. (M) Let x be the mass, (in grams), of NH_4Cl added to the water. heat $= \text{mass} \times c_p \times \Delta T$

$$x \times \frac{1 \text{ mol NH}_4\text{Cl}}{53.49 \text{ g NH}_4\text{Cl}} \times \frac{14.7 \text{ kJ}}{1 \text{ mol NH}_4\text{Cl}} \times \frac{1000 \text{ J}}{1 \text{ kJ}} = -\left(\left(1400 \text{ mL} \times \frac{1.00 \text{ g}}{1 \text{ mL}}\right) + x\right) 4.18 \frac{\text{J}}{\text{g }^\circ\text{C}} (10. - 25) \,^\circ\text{C}$$

$$275\,x = 8.8 \times 10^4 + 63\,x; \qquad x = \frac{8.8 \times 10^4}{275 - 63} = 4.2 \times 10^2 \text{ g NH}_4\text{Cl}$$

Our final value is approximate because of the assumed density (1.00 g/mL). The solution's density probably is a bit larger than 1.00 g/mL. Many aqueous solutions are somewhat more dense than water.

24. (M) heat $= 500 \text{ mL} \times \dfrac{1 \text{ L}}{1000 \text{ mL}} \times \dfrac{4.0 \text{ mol NaOH}}{1 \text{ L soln}} \times \dfrac{-44.5 \text{ kJ}}{1 \text{ mol NaOH}} = -89 \text{ kJ}$

$\qquad$ = heat released by reaction = $-$ heat absorbed by solution $\quad$ OR $\quad q_{rxn} = -q_{soln}$

$$\Delta T = \frac{8.9 \times 10^4 \text{ J}}{500. \text{ mL} \times \frac{1.08 \text{ g}}{1 \text{ mL}} \times \frac{4.00 \text{ J}}{\text{g }^\circ\text{C}}} = 41 \,^\circ\text{C} \qquad \text{final } T = 24 \,^\circ\text{C} + 41 \,^\circ\text{C} = 65 \,^\circ\text{C}$$

25. (E) We assume that the solution volumes are additive; that is, that 200.0 mL of solution is formed. Then we compute the heat needed to warm the solution and the cup, and finally ΔH for the reaction.

$$\text{heat} = \left(200.0 \text{ mL} \times \frac{1.02 \text{ g}}{1 \text{ mL}}\right) 4.02 \frac{\text{J}}{\text{g }^\circ\text{C}} (27.8 \,^\circ\text{C} - 21.1 \,^\circ\text{C}) + 10 \frac{\text{J}}{^\circ\text{C}} (27.8 \,^\circ\text{C} - 21.1 \,^\circ\text{C})$$

$$= 5.6 \times 10^3 \text{ J}$$

$$\Delta_{\text{neutr.}} H = \frac{-5.6 \times 10^3 \text{ J}}{0.100 \text{ mol}} \times \frac{1 \text{ kJ}}{1000 \text{ J}} = -56 \text{ kJ/mol} \left(-55.6 \text{ kJ/mol to three significant figures}\right)$$

26. (M) Neutralization reaction: $\quad \text{NaOH(aq)} + \text{HCl(aq)} \rightarrow \text{NaCl(aq)} + \text{H}_2\text{O(l)}$

Since NaOH and HCl react in a one-to-one molar ratio, and since there is twice the volume of NaOH solution as HCl solution, but the [HCl] is not twice the [NaOH], the HCl solution is the limiting reactant.

$$\text{heat released} = 25.00 \text{ mL} \times \frac{1 \text{ L}}{1000 \text{ mL}} \times \frac{1.86 \text{ mol HCl}}{1 \text{ L}} \times \frac{1 \text{ mol H}_2\text{O}}{1 \text{ mol HCl}} \times \frac{-55.84 \text{ kJ}}{1 \text{ mol H}_2\text{O}} = -2.60 \text{ kJ}$$

$\qquad$ = heat of reaction = $-$ heat absorbed by solution or $q_{rxn} = -q_{soln}$

$$\Delta T = \frac{2.60 \times 10^3 \, J}{75.00 \, mL \times \dfrac{1.02 \, g}{1 \, mL} \times \dfrac{3.98 \, J}{g \, ^\circ C}} = 8.54 \, ^\circ C \qquad \Delta T = T_{final} - T_i \qquad T_{final} = \Delta T + T_i$$

$$T_{final} = 8.54 \, ^\circ C + 24.72 \, ^\circ C = 33.26 \, ^\circ C$$

27. **(M)**

$$5.0 \, L \, C_2H_2 \times \frac{1 \, m^3}{1000 \, L} \times \frac{1.0967 \, kg}{1 \, m^3} \times \frac{1000 \, g}{1 \, kg} \times \frac{1 \, mol}{26.04 \, g} = 0.2106 \, mol \, C_2H_2$$

$$\frac{1299.5 \, kJ \, heat \, evolved}{1 \, mol \, C_2H_2} \times 0.2106 \, mol \, C_2H_2 = 272.9 \, kJ = 2.7 \times 10^2 \, kJ \, heat \, evolved$$

28. **(M)**

$$273.8 \, kJ \times \frac{1 \, mol \, propane}{2219.9 \, kJ} = 0.1233 \, mol \, propane$$

$$0.1233 \, mol \, C_3H_8 \times \frac{44.09 \, g}{1 \, mol} \times \frac{1 \, kg}{1000 \, g} \times \frac{1 \, m^3}{1.83 \, kg} \times \frac{1000 \, L}{1 \, m^3} = 2.97 \, L \, C_3H_8$$

Enthalpy Changes and States of Matter

29. **(M)** $q_{water} = q_{ice}$ $\qquad mc_p(water)\Delta T_{water} = n_{ice}\Delta_{fus}H(ice)$

$$(3.50 \, mol \, H_2O \times \frac{18.015 \, g \, H_2O}{1 \, mol \, H_2O})(4.184 \frac{J}{g \, ^\circ C})(50.0 \, ^\circ C) = (\frac{m}{18.015 \, g \, H_2O} \times 6.01 \times 10^3 \frac{J}{mol})$$

$$13.2 \times 10^3 \, J = m(333.\underline{6} \, J \, g^{-1}) \text{ Hence, } m = 39.6 \, g$$

30. **(M)** $-q_{steam} = q_{water}$

$$-[(5.00 \, g \, H_2O \times \frac{1 \, mol \, H_2O}{18.015 \, g \, H_2O})(-40.6 \times 10^3 \frac{J}{mol}) + (5.00 \, g)(4.184 \frac{J}{g \, ^\circ C})(T_f - 100.0 \, ^\circ C)]$$

$$= (100.0 \, g)(4.184 \frac{J}{g \, ^\circ C})(T_f - 25.0 \, ^\circ C)$$

$$11,2\underline{68}.4 \, J - 20.92 \frac{J}{^\circ C}(T_f) + 2092 \, J = 418.\underline{4} \frac{J}{^\circ C}(T_f) - 10,4\underline{60} \, J$$

$$11,2\underline{68}.4 \, J + 10,4\underline{60} \, J + 209\underline{2} \, J = 418.4 \frac{J}{^\circ C}(T_f) + 20.92 \frac{J}{^\circ C}(T_f) \text{ or } 23.8 \times 10^3 \, J = 439 \, J \, (T_f)$$

$$T_f = 54.2 \, ^\circ C$$

31. **(M)** Assume $H_2O(l)$ density $= 1.00 \, g \, mL^{-1}$ (at 28.5 °C) $\quad -q_{lost \, by \, ball} = q_{gained \, by \, water} + q_{vap \, water}$

$$-[(125 \, g)(0.50 \frac{J}{g \, ^\circ C})(100 \, ^\circ C - 525 \, ^\circ C)] = [(75.0 \, g)(4.184 \frac{J}{g \, ^\circ C})(100.0 \, ^\circ C - 28.5 \, ^\circ C)] + n_{H_2O}\Delta_{vap}H^\circ$$

$$26,5\underline{62}.5 \, J = 22,4\underline{36}.7 \, J + n_{H_2O}\Delta_{vap}H^\circ \text{ (Note: } n_{H_2O} = \frac{mass_{H_2O}}{molar \, mass_{H_2O}})$$

$$4\underline{125.8} \text{ J} = (m_{H_2O})(\frac{1 \text{ mol H}_2\text{O}}{18.016 \text{ g H}_2\text{O}}) (40.6 \times 10^3 \frac{\text{J}}{\text{mol}})$$

$$m_{H_2O} = 1.\underline{83} \text{ g H}_2\text{O} \cong 2 \text{ g H}_2\text{O} \text{ (1 sig. fig.)}$$

32. **(E)** $-q_{\text{lost by ball}} = q_{\text{melt ice}}$

$$-[(125 \text{ g})(0.50 \frac{\text{J}}{\text{g }^\circ\text{C}})(0 \,^\circ\text{C} - 525 \,^\circ\text{C})] = n_{H_2O}\Delta_{\text{fus}}H^\circ = (m_{H_2O})(\frac{1 \text{ mol H}_2\text{O}}{18.015 \text{ g H}_2\text{O}})(6.01 \times 10^3 \frac{\text{J}}{\text{mol}})$$

$$3\underline{2812.5} \text{ J} = m_{H_2O}(333.\underline{6} \text{ J g}^{-1}); \quad m_{H_2O} = 98.\underline{4} \text{ g H}_2\text{O} \approx 98 \text{ g H}_2\text{O}$$

<u>33.</u> **(E)**

$$\frac{571 \text{ kJ}}{1 \text{ kg}} \times \frac{1000 \text{ J}}{1 \text{ kJ}} = 5.71 \times 10^5 \text{ J/kg}$$

$$125.0 \text{ J} \times \frac{1 \text{ kg}}{5.71 \times 10^5 \text{ J}} \times \frac{1000 \text{ g}}{1 \text{ kg}} \times \frac{1 \text{ L}}{1.98 \text{ g}} = 0.111 \text{ L}$$

34. **(M)** Assume all $N_2(l)$ is converted to $N_2(g)$ when vaporized. The number of moles of $N_2(g)$ can be found by using the ideal gas equation.
$PV = nRT$

$$(1.0 \text{ atm})(1.0 \text{ L}) = n(0.08206 \text{ atm L mol}^{-1} \text{ K}^{-1})(77.36 \text{ K})$$

$$n = 0.1575 \text{ mol} = 0.16 \text{ mol (2 sig. figs)}$$

If 5.56 kJ of energy is needed to vaporize 1 mol of $N_2(l)$, then

$$0.1575 \text{ mol} \times \frac{5.56 \text{ kJ}}{1 \text{ mol}} = 0.876 \text{ kJ} = 8.8 \times 10^2 \text{ J are needed to vaporize } 0.1575 \text{ mol.}$$

Calorimetry

<u>35.</u> **(E)** Heat capacity $= \dfrac{\text{heat absorbed}}{\Delta T} = \dfrac{5228 \text{ cal}}{4.39 \,^\circ\text{C}} \times \dfrac{4.184 \text{ J}}{1 \text{ cal}} \times \dfrac{1 \text{ kJ}}{1000 \text{ J}} = 4.98 \text{ kJ/}^\circ\text{C}$

36. **(M)** heat absorbed by calorimeter $= q_c \times \text{moles} = \text{heat capacity} \times \Delta T$ or $\Delta T = \dfrac{q_c \times \text{moles}}{\text{heat capacity}}$

(a) $\Delta T = \dfrac{\left(1014.2 \dfrac{\text{kcal}}{\text{mol}} \times 4.184 \dfrac{\text{kJ}}{\text{kcal}}\right)\left(0.3268 \text{ g} \times \dfrac{1 \text{ mol C}_8\text{H}_{10}\text{O}_2\text{N}_4}{194.19 \text{ g C}_8\text{H}_{10}\text{O}_2\text{N}_4}\right)}{5.136 \text{ kJ/}^\circ\text{C}} = 1.390 \,^\circ\text{C}$

$T_f = T_i + \Delta T = 22.43 \,^\circ\text{C} + 1.390 \,^\circ\text{C} = 23.82 \,^\circ\text{C}$

(b) $\Delta T = \dfrac{2444 \dfrac{\text{kJ}}{\text{mol}}\left(1.35 \text{ mL} \times \dfrac{0.805 \text{ g}}{1 \text{ mL}} \times \dfrac{1 \text{ mol C}_4\text{H}_8\text{O}}{72.11 \text{ g C}_4\text{H}_8\text{O}}\right)}{5.136 \text{ kJ/}^\circ\text{C}} = 7.17 \,^\circ\text{C}$

$T_f = 22.43 \,^\circ\text{C} + 7.17 \,^\circ\text{C} = 29.60 \,^\circ\text{C}$

37. **(M)**

(a) $\dfrac{\text{heat}}{\text{mass}} = \dfrac{\text{heat cap.}\times \Delta t}{\text{mass}} = \dfrac{4.728 \text{ kJ/}^\circ\text{C}\times(27.19-23.29)^\circ\text{C}}{1.183 \text{ g}} = 15.6 \text{ kJ/g xylose}$

$\Delta H = \text{heat given off/g}\times M\,(\text{g/mol}) = \dfrac{-15.6 \text{ kJ}}{1 \text{ g } C_5H_{10}O_5}\times\dfrac{150.13 \text{ g } C_5H_{10}O_5}{1 \text{ mol}}$

$\Delta H = -2.34\times10^3 \text{ kJ/mol } C_5H_{10}O_5$

(b) $C_5H_{10}O_5(g)+5\,O_2(g)\rightarrow 5\,CO_2(g)+5\,H_2O(l)$ $\qquad \Delta_r H = -2.34\times10^3 \text{ kJ mol}^{-1}$

38. **(M)** This is first a limiting reactant problem. There is $0.1000 \text{ L}\times0.300 \text{ M} = 0.0300$ mol HCl and $1.82/65.39 = 0.0278$ mol Zn. Stoichiometry demands 2 mol HCl for every 1 mol Zn. Thus HCl is the limiting reactant. The reaction is exothermic. We neglect the slight excess of Zn(s), and assume that the volume of solution remains 100.0 mL and its specific heat capacity, $4.18 \text{ J g}^{-1}\,^\circ\text{C}^{-1}$. The enthalpy change, in kJ/mol Zn, is

$\Delta_r H = -\dfrac{100.0 \text{ mL}\times\dfrac{1.00 \text{ g}}{1 \text{ mL}}\times\dfrac{4.18 \text{ J}}{\text{g }^\circ\text{C}}\times(30.5-20.3)\,^\circ\text{C}}{0.0300 \text{ mol HCl}\times\dfrac{1 \text{ mol Zn}}{2 \text{ mol HCl}}}\times\dfrac{1 \text{ kJ}}{1000 \text{ J}} = -284 \text{ kJ/mol Zn}$

39. **(M)**

(a) Because the temperature of the mixture decreases, the reaction molecules (the system) must have absorbed heat from the reaction mixture (the surroundings). Consequently, the reaction must be endothermic.

(b) We assume that the specific heat capacity of the solution is $4.18 \text{ J g}^{-1}\,^\circ\text{C}^{-1}$. The enthalpy of solution in kJ/mol KCl is obtained by the heat absorbed per gram KCl.

$\Delta_{soln} H = -\dfrac{(0.75+35.0)\text{ g}\dfrac{4.18 \text{ J}}{\text{g }^\circ\text{C}}(23.6-24.8)\,^\circ\text{C}}{0.75 \text{ g KCl}}\times\dfrac{1 \text{ kJ}}{1000 \text{ J}}\times\dfrac{74.55 \text{ g KCl}}{1 \text{ mol KCl}} = +18 \text{ kJ/mol}$

40. **(M)** As indicated by the negative sign for the enthalpy change, this is an exothermic reaction. Thus the energy of the system should increase.

$q_{rxn} = 0.136 \text{ mol } KCH_3COO\times\dfrac{-15.3 \text{ kJ}}{1 \text{ mol } KCH_3COO}\times\dfrac{1000 \text{ J}}{1 \text{ kJ}} = -2.08\times10^3 \text{ J} = -q_{calorim}$

Now, we assume that the density of water is 1.00 g/mL, the specific heat capacity of the solution in the calorimeter is $4.18 \text{ J g}^{-1}\,^\circ\text{C}^{-1}$, and no heat is lost by the calorimeter.

$q_{calorim} = 2.08\times10^3 \text{ J} = \left(\left(815 \text{ mL}\times\dfrac{1.00 \text{ g}}{1 \text{ mL}}\right)+\left(0.241 \text{ mol } KCH_3COO\times\dfrac{98.14 \text{ g}}{1 \text{ mol } KCH_3COO}\right)\right)$

$\times\dfrac{4.18 \text{ J}}{\text{g }^\circ\text{C}}\times\Delta T = 3.51\times10^3\,\Delta T$

$\Delta T = \dfrac{2.08\times10^3}{2.25\times10^3} = +0.593\,^\circ\text{C}$ $\qquad T_{final} = T_{initial}+\Delta T = 25.1\,^\circ\text{C}+0.593\,^\circ\text{C} = 25.7\,^\circ\text{C}$

41. **(M)** To determine the heat capacity of the calorimeter, recognize that the heat evolved by the reaction is the negative of the heat of combustion.

$$\text{heat capacity} = \frac{\text{heat evolved}}{\Delta T} = \frac{1.620\,\text{g}\,C_{10}H_8 \times \dfrac{1\,\text{mol}\,C_{10}H_8}{128.2\,\text{g}\,C_{10}H_8} \times \dfrac{5156.1\,\text{kJ}}{1\,\text{mol}\,C_{10}H_8}}{8.44\,°C} = 7.72\,\text{kJ}/°C$$

42. **(M)** Note that the heat evolved is the negative of the heat absorbed.

$$\text{heat capacity} = \frac{\text{heat evolved}}{\Delta T} = \frac{1.201\,\text{g} \times \dfrac{1\,\text{mol}\,C_7H_6O_3}{138.12\,\text{g}\,C_7H_6O_3} \times \dfrac{3023\,\text{kJ}}{1\,\text{mol}\,C_7H_6O_3}}{(29.82 - 23.68)\,°C} = 4.28\,\text{kJ}/°C$$

43. **(M)** The temperature should increase as the result of an exothermic combustion reaction.

$$\Delta T = 1.227\ \text{g}\,C_{12}H_{22}O_{11} \times \frac{1\ \text{mol}\,C_{12}H_{22}O_{11}}{342.3\ \text{g}\,C_{12}H_{22}O_{11}} \times \frac{5.65\times10^3\ \text{kJ}}{1\ \text{mol}\,C_{12}H_{22}O_{11}} \times \frac{1\,°C}{3.87\ \text{kJ}} = 5.23\,°C$$

44. **(M)** $q_c = \dfrac{-11.23\,°C \times 4.68\,\text{kJ}/°C}{1.397\,\text{g}\,C_{10}H_{14}O \times \dfrac{1\,\text{mol}\,C_{10}H_{14}O}{150.2\,\text{g}\,C_{10}H_{14}O}} = -5.65\times10^3\ \text{kJ/mol}\,C_{10}H_{14}O$

45. **(M)**

$$5.0\ \text{g NaCl} \times \frac{1\ \text{mol}}{58.44\ \text{g}} = 0.08556\ \text{mol NaCl}$$

$$0.08556\ \text{mol NaCl} \times \frac{3.76\ \text{kJ}}{1\ \text{mol}} = 0.322\ \text{kJ} = 322\ \text{J}$$

$$q = m_{H_2O} \times \text{specific heat capacity} \times \Delta T$$

$$322\ \text{J} = m_{H_2O} \times 4.18\ \text{J/g}\,°C \times 5.0\,°C$$

$$m_{H_2O} = 15\ \text{g}$$

46. **(M)** heat lost by gold = heat gained by water

$$-10.5\ \text{g} \times \text{specific heat capacity of gold} \times (31.0 - 78.3\,°C) = 50\ \text{g} \times \frac{4.18\ \text{J}}{\text{g}\,°C} \times (31.0 - 23.7\,°C)$$

$$496.65 \times \text{specific heat capacity of gold} = 1525.7$$

$$\text{specific heat capacity of gold} = 3.07\ \text{J}/\text{g}\,°C = 3.07\ \text{J}/\text{g}\,K$$

Since the specific heat capacity of the sample does not equal the specific heat capacity of pure gold that is given in the problem, the sample is not pure gold.

Pressure-Volume Work

47. **(M)**

(a) $-P\Delta V = 3.5\ \text{L} \times (748\ \text{mmHg}) \left(\dfrac{1\ \text{atm}}{760\ \text{mmHg}} \right) = -3.4\underline{4}\ \text{atm L or } -3.4\ \text{atm L}$

(b) 1 kPa L = 1 J, hence,

$$-3.4\underline{4} \text{ atm L} \times \left(\frac{101.325 \text{ kPa}}{1 \text{ atm}}\right) \times \left(\frac{1 \text{ J}}{1 \text{ kPa L}}\right) = -3.4\underline{9} \times 10^2 \text{ J or } -3.5 \times 10^2 \text{ J}$$

(c) $-3.4\underline{9} \times 10^2 \text{ J} \times \left(\frac{1 \text{ cal}}{4.184 \text{ J}}\right) = -83.\underline{4} \text{ cal or } -83 \text{ cal}$

48. **(E)** $w = -P\Delta V = -1.23 \text{ atm} \times (3.37 \text{ L} - 5.62 \text{ L}) \times \left(\frac{101.325 \text{ kPa}}{1 \text{ atm}}\right) \times \left(\frac{1 \text{ J}}{1 \text{ kPa L}}\right) = 280. \text{ J}$

That is, 280. J of work is done on the gas by the surroundings.

49. **(E)** When the Ne(g) sample expands into an evacuated vessel it does not push aside any matter, hence no work is done.

50. **(E)** Yes, the gas from the aerosol does work. The gas pushes aside the atmosphere.

51. **(M)**
    (a) No pressure–volume work is done (no gases are formed or consumed).
    (b) $2 NO_2(g) \rightarrow N_2O_4(g)$ $\Delta n_{gas} = -1$ mol. Work is done on the system by the surroundings (compression).
    (c) $CaCO_3(s) \rightarrow CaO(s) + CO_2(g)$. Formation of a gas, $\Delta n_{gas} = +1$ mol, results in an expansion. The system does work on the surroundings.

52. **(M)**
    (a) $2 NO(g) + O_2(g) \rightarrow 2 NO_2(g)$ $\Delta n_{gas} = -1$. Work is done on the system by the surroundings (compression).
    (b) $MgCl_2(aq) + 2 NaOH(aq) \rightarrow Mg(OH)_2(s) + 2 NaCl(aq)$ $\Delta n_{gas} = 0$, no pressure–volume work is done.
    (c) $CuSO_4(s) + 5 H_2O(g) \rightarrow CuSO_4 \cdot 5 H_2O(s)$ $\Delta n_{gas} = -5$. Work is done on the system by the surroundings (compression).

53. **(E)** We can either convert pressure from atm to Pascals, or convert work from joules to atm L. We opt for the latter. Since the conversion between J and atm L is 101.33 J/(atm L), the amount of work is 325 J × (1 atm L/101.33 J) = 3.207 atm L. Therefore,
$w = -P\Delta V$
3.207 atm L = (1.0 atm) ΔV. Solving for ΔV, we get a volume of 3.21 L.

54. **(E)** We note that the work done on the object imparts a potential energy in that object after the work is done. Therefore,
work $= -E_p$

$E_p = m \times g \times h = (2.41 \text{ kg})(9.8 \text{ m/s}^2)(2.6 \text{ m}) = 61.41 \text{ J}$

work $= -61 \text{ J}$

First Law of Thermodynamics

55. **(E)**
    (a) $\Delta U = q + w = +58 \text{ J} + (-58 \text{ J}) = 0$
    (b) $\Delta U = q + w = +125 \text{ J} + (-687 \text{ J}) = -562 \text{ J}$
    (c) $280 \text{ cal} \times (4.184 \dfrac{\text{J}}{\text{cal}}) = 117\underline{1.52} \text{ J} = 1.17 \text{ kJ}$ $\Delta U = q + w = -1.17 \text{ kJ} + 1.25 \text{ kJ} = 0.08 \text{ kJ}$

56. **(E)**
    (a) $\Delta U = q + w = +235 \text{ J} + 128 \text{ J} = 363 \text{ J}$
    (b) $\Delta U = q + w = -145 \text{ J} + 98 \text{ J} = -47 \text{ J}$
    (c) $\Delta U = q + w = 0 \text{ kJ} + -1.07 \text{ kJ} = -1.07 \text{ kJ}$

57. **(E)**
    (a) Yes, the gas does work ($w < 0$).
    (b) Yes, the gas exchanges energy with the surroundings, it absorbs energy.
    (c) The temperature of the gas stays the same if the process is isothermal.
    (d) ΔU for the gas must equal zero by definition (temperature is not changing).

58. **(E)**
    (a) Yes, the gas does work ($w < 0$).
    (b) The internal energy of the gas decreases (energy is expended to do work).
    (c) The temperature of the gas should decrease, as it cannot attain thermal equilibrium with its surroundings.

59. **(E)** This situation is impossible. An ideal gas expanding isothermally means that $\Delta U = 0 = q + w$, or $w = -q$, not $w = -2q$.

60. **(E)** If a gas is compressed adiabatically, the gas will get hotter. Raise the temperature of the surroundings to an even higher temperature and heat will be transferred to the gas.

61. **(E)** We note that since the charge of the system is going from 10 to 5, the net flow of the charge is negative. Therefore, $w = (5 \text{ C} - 10 \text{ C}) = -5 \text{ C}$. Voltage ($V$) is J/C. The internal energy of the system is:
$\Delta U = q + w = -45 \text{ J} + (100 \text{ J/C})(-5 \text{ C}) = -45 \text{ J} + (-500 \text{ J}) = -545 \text{ J}$

62. **(E)** Obviously, $w = f\,\Delta l$. Plugging in the appropriate values gives the following:
$\Delta U = (10 \times 10^{-12} \text{ N})(10 \times 10^{-12} \text{ m}) = 1 \times 10^{-22} \text{ J}$

Relating ΔH and ΔU

63. **(E)** According to the First Law of Thermodynamics, the answer is (c). Both (a) q_v and (b) q_p are heats of chemical reaction carried out under conditions of constant volume and constant pressure, respectively. Both ΔU and ΔH incorporate terms related to work as well as heat.

64. **(E)**
    (a) $C_4H_{10}O(l) + 6\,O_2(g) \rightarrow 4\,CO_2(g) + 5\,H_2O(l)$ $\Delta n_{gas} = -2 \text{ mol}, \Delta H < \Delta U$
    (b) $C_6H_{12}O_6(s) + 6\,O_2(g) \rightarrow 6\,CO_2(g) + 6\,H_2O(l)$ $\Delta n_{gas} = 0 \text{ mol}, \Delta H = \Delta U$
    (c) $NH_4NO_3(s) \rightarrow 2\,H_2O(l) + N_2O(g)$ $\Delta n_{gas} = +1 \text{ mol}, \Delta H > \Delta U$

65. **(M)** $C_3H_8O(l) + 9/2\ O_2(g) \rightarrow 3\ CO_2(g) + 4\ H_2O(l)$ $\Delta n_{gas} = -1.5$ mol

    (a) $\Delta U = -33.41\ \dfrac{kJ}{g} \times \dfrac{60.096\ g\ C_3H_8O}{1\ mol\ C_3H_8O} = -2008\ \dfrac{kJ}{mol}$

    (b) $\Delta H = \Delta U - w, = \Delta U - (-P\Delta V) = \Delta U - (-\Delta n_{gas}RT) = \Delta U + \Delta n_{gas}RT$

        $\Delta H = -2008\ \dfrac{kJ}{mol} + (-1.5)(\dfrac{8.3145 \times 10^{-3}\ kJ}{mol\ K})(298.15\ K) = -2012\ \dfrac{kJ}{mol}$

66. **(M)** $C_{10}H_{14}O(l) + 13\ O_2(g) \rightarrow 10\ CO_2(g) + 7\ H_2O(l)$ $\Delta n_{gas} = -3$ mol

    $q_{bomb} = q_v = \Delta U = -5.65 \times 10^3\ kJ = \Delta U$

    $\Delta H = \Delta U - w;$ where $w = (-\Delta n_{gas}RT) = -(-3\ mol)(\dfrac{8.3145 \times 10^{-3}\ kJ}{mol\ K})(298.15\ K) = +7.4\ kJ$

    $\Delta H = -5.65 \times 10^3\ kJ - 7.4\ kJ = -5.66 \times 10^3\ kJ$

Hess's Law

67. **(E)** The formation reaction for $NH_3(g)$ is $\frac{1}{2}N_2(g) + \frac{3}{2}H_2(g) \rightarrow NH_3(g)$. The given reaction is two-thirds the reverse of the formation reaction. The sign of the enthalpy is changed and it is multiplied by two-thirds. Thus, the enthalpy of the given reaction is $-(-46.11\ kJ/mol) \times \frac{2}{3} = +30.74\ kJ/mol$.

68. **(M)**

$-(1)$	$CO(g) \rightarrow C(graphite) + \frac{1}{2}O_2(g)$	$\Delta_r H^\circ = +110.54\ kJ/mol$
$+(2)$	$C(graphite) + O_2(g) \rightarrow CO_2(g)$	$\Delta_r H^\circ = -393.51\ kJ/mol$
	$CO(g) + \frac{1}{2}O_2(g) \rightarrow CO_2(g)$	$\Delta_r H^\circ = -282.97\ kJ/mol$

69. **(M)**

$-(3)$	$3\ CO_2(g) + 4\ H_2O(l) \rightarrow C_3H_8(g) + 5\ O_2(g)$	$\Delta_r H^\circ = +2219.1\ kJ/mol$
$+(2)$	$C_3H_4(g) + 4\ O_2(g) \rightarrow 3\ CO_2(g) + 2\ H_2O(l)$	$\Delta_r H^\circ = -1937\ kJ/mol$
$2(1)$	$2\ H_2(g) + O_2(g) \rightarrow 2\ H_2O(l)$	$\Delta_r H^\circ = -571.6\ kJ/mol$
	$C_3H_4(g) + 2\ H_2(g) \rightarrow C_3H_8(g)$	$\Delta_r H^\circ = -290.\ kJ/mol$

70. **(M)** The second reaction is the only one in which $NO(g)$ appears; it must be run twice to produce $2NO(g)$.

    $2\ NH_3(g) + \frac{5}{2}O_2(g) \rightarrow 2\ NO(g) + 3\ H_2O(l)$ $2 \times \Delta_r H_2^\circ$

    The first reaction is the only one that eliminates $NH_3(g)$; it must be run twice to eliminate $2NH_3$.

    $N_2(g) + 3\ H_2(g) \rightarrow 2\ NH_3(g)$ $2 \times \Delta_r H_1^\circ$

    We triple and reverse the third reaction to eliminate $3\ H_2(g)$.

    $3\ H_2O(l) \rightarrow 3\ H_2(g) + \frac{3}{2}O_2(g)$ $-3 \times \Delta_r H_3^\circ$

    Result : $N_2(g) + O_2(g) \rightarrow 2\ NO(g)$ $\Delta_r H = 2 \times \Delta H_1 + 2 \times \Delta H_2 - 3 \times \Delta H_3$

71. (M)

$$2\,HCl(g)+C_2H_4(g)+\tfrac{1}{2}O_2(g)\rightarrow C_2H_4Cl_2(l)+H_2O(l) \qquad \Delta_rH^\circ = -318.7 \text{ kJ mol}^{-1}$$

$$Cl_2(g)+H_2O(l)\rightarrow 2\,HCl(g)+\tfrac{1}{2}O_2(g) \qquad\qquad \Delta_rH^\circ = 0.5(+202.4) = +101.2 \text{ kJ mol}^{-1}$$

$$\overline{C_2H_4(g)+Cl_2(g)\rightarrow C_2H_4Cl_2(l) \qquad\qquad\qquad\qquad \Delta_rH^\circ = -217.5 \text{ kJ mol}^{-1}}$$

72. (M)

$$N_2H_4(l)+O_2(g)\rightarrow N_2(g)+2H_2O(l) \qquad \Delta_rH^\circ = -622.2 \text{ kJ mol}^{-1}$$

$$2H_2O_2(l)\rightarrow 2H_2(g)+2O_2(g) \qquad \Delta_rH^\circ = -2(-187.8 \text{ kJ}) = +375.6 \text{ kJ mol}^{-1}$$

$$2\,H_2(g)+O_2(g)\rightarrow 2\,H_2O(l) \qquad \Delta_rH^\circ = 2(-285.8 \text{ kJ}) = -571.6 \text{ kJ mol}^{-1}$$

$$\overline{N_2H_4(l)+2H_2O_2(l)\rightarrow N_2(g)+4H_2O(l) \qquad \Delta_rH^\circ = -818.2 \text{ kJ mol}^{-1}}$$

73. (M)

$$CO(g)+\tfrac{1}{2}O_2(g)\rightarrow CO_2(g) \qquad \Delta_rH^\circ = -283.0 \text{ kJ mol}^{-1}$$

$$3\,C(graphite)+6\,H_2(g)\rightarrow 3\,CH_4(g) \qquad \Delta_rH^\circ = 3(-74.81) = -224.43 \text{ kJ mol}^{-1}$$

$$2\,H_2(g)+O_2(g)\rightarrow 2\,H_2O(l) \qquad \Delta_rH^\circ = 2(-285.8) = -571.6 \text{ kJ mol}^{-1}$$

$$3\,CO(g)\rightarrow \tfrac{3}{2}O_2(g)+3\,C(graphite) \qquad \Delta_rH^\circ = 3(+110.5) = +331.5 \text{ kJ mol}^{-1}$$

$$\overline{4\,CO(g)+8\,H_2(g)\rightarrow CO_2(g)+3\,CH_4(g)+2\,H_2O(l) \quad \Delta_rH^\circ = -747.5 \text{ kJ mol}^{-1}}$$

74. (M)

$$CS_2(l)+3\,O_2(g)\rightarrow CO_2(g)+2\,SO_2(g) \qquad \Delta_rH^\circ = -1077 \text{ kJ mol}^{-1}$$

$$2\,S(s)+Cl_2(g)\rightarrow S_2Cl_2(l) \qquad \Delta_rH^\circ = -58.2 \text{ kJ mol}^{-1}$$

$$C(s)+2\,Cl_2(g)\rightarrow CCl_4(l) \qquad \Delta_rH^\circ = -135.4 \text{ kJ mol}^{-1}$$

$$2\,SO_2(g)\rightarrow 2\,S(s)+2\,O_2(g) \qquad \Delta_rH^\circ = -2(-296.8 \text{ kJ}) = +593.6 \text{ kJ mol}^{-1}$$

$$CO_2(g)\rightarrow C(s)+O_2(g) \qquad \Delta_rH^\circ = -(-393.5 \text{ kJ}) = +393.5 \text{ kJ mol}^{-1}$$

$$\overline{CS_2(l)+3\,Cl_2(g)\rightarrow CCl_4(l)+S_2Cl_2(l) \qquad \Delta_rH^\circ = -284 \text{ kJ mol}^{-1}}$$

75. (M)

$$CH_4(g)+CO_2(g)\rightarrow 2\,CO(g)+2\,H_2(g) \qquad \Delta_rH^\circ = +247 \text{ kJ mol}^{-1}$$

$$2\,CH_4(g)+2\,H_2O(g)\rightarrow 2\,CO(g)+6\,H_2(g) \qquad \Delta_rH^\circ = 2(+206 \text{ kJ}) = +412 \text{ kJ mol}^{-1}$$

$$CH_4(g)+2\,O_2(g)\rightarrow CO_2(g)+2\,H_2O(g) \qquad \Delta_rH^\circ = -802 \text{ kJ mol}^{-1}$$

$$\overline{4\,CH_4(g)+2\,O_2(g)\rightarrow 4\,CO(g)+8\,H_2(g) \qquad \Delta_rH^\circ = -143 \text{ kJ mol}^{-1}}$$

$$\div 4 \text{ produces } CH_4(g)+\tfrac{1}{2}O_2(g)\rightarrow CO(g)+2\,H_2(g) \quad \Delta_rH^\circ = -35.8 \text{ kJ mol}^{-1}$$

76. (M)

The thermochemical combustion reactions follow.

$C_4H_6(g) + \frac{11}{2} O_2(g) \rightarrow 4 CO_2(g) + 3 H_2O(l)$ $\Delta_r H^\circ = -2540.2 \text{ kJ mol}^{-1}$

$C_4H_{10}(g) + \frac{13}{2} O_2(g) \rightarrow 4 CO_2(g) + 5 H_2O(l)$ $\Delta_r H^\circ = -2877.6 \text{ kJ mol}^{-1}$

$H_2(g) + \frac{1}{2} O_2(g) \rightarrow H_2O(l)$ $\Delta_r H^\circ = -285.85 \text{ kJ mol}^{-1}$

Then these equations are combined in the following manner.

$C_4H_6(g) + \frac{11}{2}O_2(g) \rightarrow 4CO_2(g) + 3H_2O(l)$ $\Delta_r H^\circ = -2540.2 \text{ kJ mol}^{-1}$

$4CO_2(g) + 5H_2O(l) \rightarrow C_4H_{10}(g) + \frac{13}{2}O_2(g)$ $\Delta_r H^\circ = -(-2877.6 \text{ kJ}) = +2877.6 \text{ kJ mol}^{-1}$

$2H_2(g) + O_2(g) \rightarrow 2H_2O(l)$ $\Delta_r H^\circ = 2(-285.8 \text{ kJ}) = -571.6 \text{ kJ mol}^{-1}$

$\overline{C_4H_6(g) + 2H_2(g) \rightarrow C_4H_{10}(g)}$ $\Delta_r H^\circ = -234.2 \text{ kJ mol}^{-1}$

77. (M)

$C_6H_{12}O_6(s) + 6 O_2(g) \rightarrow 6 CO_2(g) + 6 H_2O(l)$ $\Delta_r H^\circ = -2808 \text{ kJ mol}^{-1}$

$6 CO_2(g) + 6 H_2O(l) \rightarrow 2 CH_3CH(OH)COOH(s) + 6 O_2(g)$ $\Delta_r H^\circ = 2(1344) \text{ kJ mol}^{-1}$

$\overline{C_6H_{12}O_6(s) \rightarrow 2 CH_3CH(OH)COOH(s)}$ $\Delta_r H^\circ = -120. \text{ kJ mol}^{-1}$

78. (M)

$\frac{1}{2} [C_6H_{12}O_6(s) + 6 O_2(g) \rightarrow 6 CO_2(g) + 6 H_2O(l)]$ $\Delta_r H^\circ = \frac{1}{2} (-2808) \text{ kJ mol}^{-1}$

$\frac{1}{2} [2 CH_3CH_2OH(l) + 2 CO_2(g) \rightarrow C_6H_{12}O_6(s)]$ $\Delta_r H^\circ = \frac{1}{2} (72) \text{ kJ mol}^{-1}$

$\overline{CH_3CH_2OH(l) + 3 O_2(g) \rightarrow 2 CO_2(g) + 3 H_2O(l)}$ $\Delta_r H^\circ = -1368 \text{ kJ mol}^{-1}$

Standard Enthalpies of Formation

79. (M)

(a) $\Delta_r H^\circ = \Delta_f H^\circ[C_2H_6(g)] + \Delta_f H^\circ[CH_4(g)] - \Delta_f H^\circ[C_3H_8(g)] - \Delta_f H^\circ[H_2(g)]$

   $\Delta_r H^\circ = (-84.68 - 74.81 - (-103.8) - 0.00) \text{ kJ mol}^{-1} = -55.7 \text{ kJ mol}^{-1}$

(b) $\Delta_r H^\circ = 2\Delta_f H^\circ[SO_2(g)] + 2\Delta_f H^\circ[H_2O(l)] - 2\Delta_f H^\circ[H_2S(g)] - 3\Delta_f H^\circ[O_2(g)]$

   $\Delta_r H^\circ = (2(-296.8) + 2(-285.8) - 2(-20.63) - 3(0.00)) \text{ kJ mol}^{-1} = -1124 \text{ kJ mol}^{-1}$

80. (E) $\Delta_r H^\circ = \Delta_f H^\circ[H_2O(l)] + \Delta_f H^\circ[NH_3(g)] - \Delta_f H^\circ[NH_4^+(aq)] - \Delta_f H^\circ[OH^-(aq)]$

$\Delta_r H^\circ = (-285.8 + (-46.11) - (-132.5) - (-230.0)) \text{ kJ mol}^{-1} = +30.6 \text{ kJ mol}^{-1}$

81. (M)

$ZnO(s) + SO_2(g) \rightarrow ZnS(s) + \frac{3}{2}O_2(g);$ $\Delta_r H^\circ = -(-878.2 \text{ kJ})/2 = +439.1 \text{ kJ mol}^{-1}$

$439.1 \text{ kJ mol}^{-1} = \Delta_f H^\circ[ZnS(s)] + \frac{3}{2}\Delta_f H^\circ[O_2(g)] - \Delta_f H^\circ[ZnO(s)] - \Delta_f H^\circ[SO_2(g)]$

$439.1 \text{ kJ mol}^{-1} = \Delta_f H^\circ[ZnS(s)] + \frac{3}{2}(0.00 \text{ kJ mol}^{-1}) - (-348.3 \text{ kJ mol}^{-1}) - (-296.8 \text{ kJ mol}^{-1})$

$\Delta_f H^\circ[ZnS(s)] = (439.1 - 348.3 - 296.8) \text{ kJ mol}^{-1} = -206.0 \text{ kJ/mol}$

82. **(M)** Most clearly established in Figure 7-18 is the point that the enthalpies of formation for alkane hydrocarbons are negative and that they become more negative as the length of the hydrocarbon chain increases (~20 kJ per added CH_2 unit). For three hydrocarbons of comparable chain length, C_2H_6, C_2H_4, and C_2H_6, we can also infer that the one having only single bonds (C_2H_6) has the most negative enthalpy of formation. The presence of a carbon-to-carbon double bond (C_2H_4) makes the enthalpy of formation more positive, while the presence of a triple bond (C_2H_2), makes it more positive still.

83. **(E)** $\Delta_r H° = 4\Delta_f H°[HCl(g)] + \Delta_f H°[O_2(g)] - 2\Delta_f H°[Cl_2(g)] - 2\Delta_f H°[H_2O(l)]$

$= 4(-92.31) + (0.00) - 2(0.00) - 2(-285.8) = +202.4 \text{ kJ mol}^{-1}$

84. **(E)** $\Delta_r H° = 2\Delta_f H°[Fe(s)] + 3\Delta_f H°[CO_2(g)] - \Delta_f H°[Fe_2O_3(s)] - 3\Delta_f H°[CO(g)]$

$= 2(0.00) + 3(-393.5) - (-824.2) - 3(-110.5) = -24.8 \text{ kJ mol}^{-1}$

85. **(E)** Balanced equation: $C_2H_5OH(l) + 3O_2(g) \rightarrow 2CO_2(g) + 3H_2O(l)$

$\Delta_r H° = 2\Delta_f H°[CO_2(g)] + 3\Delta_f H°[H_2O(l)] - \Delta_f H°[C_2H_5OH(l)] - 3\Delta_f H°[O_2(g)]$

$= 2(-393.5) + 3(-285.8) - (-277.7) - 3(0.00) = -1366.7 \text{ kJ mol}^{-1}$

86. **(M)** First we must determine the value of $\Delta_f H°$ for $C_5H_{12}(l)$.

Balanced combustion equation: $C_5H_{12}(l) + 8O_2(g) \rightarrow 5CO_2(g) + 6H_2O(l)$

$\Delta_r H° = -3509 \text{ kJ mol}^{-1} = 5\Delta_f H°[CO_2(g)] + 6\Delta_f H°[H_2O(l)] - \Delta_f H°[C_5H_{12}(l)] - 8\Delta_f H°[O_2(g)]$

$= 5(-393.5) + 6(-285.8) - \Delta_f H°[C_5H_{12}(l)] - 8(0.00) = -3682 \text{ kJ} - \Delta_f H°[C_5H_{12}(l)]$

$\Delta_f H°[C_5H_{12}(l)] = -3682 + 3509 = -173 \text{ kJ/mol}$

Then use this value to determine the value of $\Delta H°$ for the reaction in question.

$\Delta_r H° = \Delta_f H°[C_5H_{12}(l)] + 5\Delta_f H°[H_2O(l)] - 5\Delta_f H°[CO(g)] - 11\Delta_f H°[H_2(g)]$

$= -173 + 5(-285.8) - 5(-110.5) - 11(0.00) = -1050 \text{ kJ mol}^{-1}$

87. **(E)**

$\Delta_r H° = -397.3 \text{ kJ mol}^{-1} = \Delta_f H°[CCl_4(g)] + 4\Delta_f H°[HCl(g)] - \Delta_f H°[CH_4(g)] - 4\Delta_f H°[Cl_2(g)]$

$= \Delta_f H°[CCl_4(g)] + (4(-92.31) - (-74.81) - 4(0.00)) \text{ kJ mol}^{-1} = \Delta_f H°[CCl_4(g)] - 294.4 \text{ kJ mol}^{-1}$

$\Delta_f H°[CCl_4(g)] = (-397.3 + 294.4) \text{ kJ mol}^{-1} = -102.9 \text{ kJ/mol}^{-1}$

88. **(E)**

$\Delta_r H° = -8326 \text{ kJ mol}^{-1} = 12\Delta_f H°[CO_2(g)] + 14\Delta_f H°[H_2O(g)] - 2\Delta_f H°[C_6H_{14}(l)] - 19\Delta_f H°[O_2(g)]$

$\Delta_r H° = (12(-393.5) + 14(-285.8)) \text{ kJ mol}^{-1} - 2\Delta_f H°[C_6H_{14}(l)] - 19(0 \text{ kJ mol}^{-1})$

$= -8723 \text{ kJ mol}^{-1} - 2\Delta_f H°[C_6H_{14}(l)]$

$\Delta_f H°[C_6H_{14}(l)] = \dfrac{+8326 - 8723}{2} = -199 \text{ kJ/mol}$

89. **(E)** $\Delta_r H^\circ = \Delta_f H^\circ \left[Al(OH)_3 (s) \right] - \Delta_f H^\circ \left[Al^{3+} (aq) \right] - 3\Delta_f H^\circ \left[OH^- (aq) \right]$

$$= \left((-1276) - (-531) - 3(-230.0) \right) kJ \ mol^{-1} = -55 \ kJ \ mol^{-1}$$

90. **(M)**

$\Delta_r H^\circ = \Delta_f H^\circ \left[Mg^{2+} (aq) \right] + 2\Delta_f H^\circ \left[NH_3 (g) \right] + 2\Delta_f H^\circ \left[H_2O(l) \right] - \Delta_f H^\circ \left[Mg(OH)_2 (s) \right] - 2\Delta_f H^\circ \left[NH_4^+ (aq) \right]$

$$= \left((-466.9) + 2(-46.11) + 2(-285.8) - (-924.5) - 2(-132.5) \right) kJ \ mol^{-1} = +58.8 \ kJ \ mol^{-1}$$

91. **(M)** Balanced equation: $CaCO_3 (s) \rightarrow CaO(s) + CO_2 (g)$

$$\Delta_r H^\circ = \Delta_f H^\circ \left[CaO(s) \right] + \Delta_f H^\circ \left[CO_2 (g) \right] - \Delta_f H^\circ \left[CaCO_3 (s) \right]$$

$$= \left(-635.1 - 393.5 - (-1207) \right) kJ \ mol^{-1} = +178 \ kJ \ mol^{-1}$$

$$heat = 1.35 \times 10^3 \ kg \ CaCO_3 \times \frac{1000 \ g}{1 \ kg} \times \frac{1 \ mol \ CaCO_3}{100.09 \ g \ CaCO_3} \times \frac{178 \ kJ}{1 \ mol \ CaCO_3} = 2.40 \times 10^6 \ kJ$$

92. **(M)** First we determine the heat of combustion: $C_4H_{10} (g) + \frac{13}{2} O_2 (g) \rightarrow 4 \ CO_2 (g) + 5 \ H_2O(l)$

$$\Delta_r H^\circ = 4\Delta_f H^\circ \left[CO_2 (g) \right] + 5\Delta_f H^\circ \left[H_2O(l) \right] - \Delta_f H^\circ \left[C_4H_{10} (g) \right] - \frac{13}{2} \Delta_f H^\circ \left[O_2 (g) \right]$$

$$= \left(4(-393.5) + 5(-285.8) - (-125.6) - 6.5(0.00) \right) kJ \ mol^{-1} = -2877.4 \ kJ/mol$$

Now compute the volume of gas needed, with the ideal gas equation, rearranged to: $V = \dfrac{nRT}{P}$.

$$volume = \frac{\left(5.00 \times 10^4 kJ \times \dfrac{1 \ mol \ C_4H_{10}}{2877.3 \ kJ} \right) 0.08206 \dfrac{atm \ L}{mol \ K} (24.6 + 273.2)K}{756 \ mmHg \times \dfrac{1 \ atm}{760 \ mmHg}} = 427 \ L \ CH_4$$

93. **(M)** The reaction for the combustion of formic acid is:

$HCOOH(s) + \frac{1}{2} O_2(g) \rightarrow CO_2(g) + H_2O(l)$

$$\Delta_r H^\circ = \Delta_f H^\circ \left[CO_2 (g) \right] + \Delta_f H^\circ \left[H_2O(l) \right] - \Delta_f H^\circ \left[HCOOH(s) \right] - \frac{1}{2} \Delta_f H^\circ \left[O_2 (g) \right]$$

$$-255 \ kJ \ mol^{-1} = \left(1(-393.5) + 1(-285.8) - \Delta_f H^\circ \left[HCOOH(s) \right] - 0.5(0.00) \right) kJ \ mol^{-1}$$

$$-424 \ kJ \ mol^{-1} = \Delta_f H^\circ \left[HCOOH(s) \right]$$

94. (M) The reaction for the combustion of lactic acid is:

$C_3H_6O_3(s) + 3 \ O_2(g) \rightarrow 3 \ CO_2(g) + 3 \ H_2O(l)$

$$\Delta_r H^\circ = 3\Delta_f H^\circ \left[CO_2 (g) \right] + 3\Delta_f H^\circ \left[H_2O(l) \right] - \Delta_f H^\circ \left[C_3H_6O_3 (s) \right] - 3\Delta_f H^\circ \left[O_2 (g) \right]$$

$$= \left(3(-393.5) + 3(-285.8) - (-694) - 3(0.00) \right) kJ \ mol^{-1}$$

$$= -1344 \ kJ \ mol^{-1}$$

INTEGRATIVE AND ADVANCED EXERCISES

95. (M)

(a) $\text{mass H}_2\text{O} = 40 \text{ gal} \times \dfrac{4 \text{ qt}}{1 \text{ gal}} \times \dfrac{1 \text{ L}}{1.06 \text{ qt}} \times \dfrac{1000 \text{ mL}}{1 \text{ L}} \times \dfrac{1.00 \text{ g}}{1 \text{ mL}} \times \dfrac{1 \text{ kg}}{1000 \text{ g}} \times \dfrac{2.205 \text{ lb}}{1 \text{ kg}} = 3.3 \times 10^2 \text{ lb}$

$\text{heat (Btu)} = 3.3 \times 10^2 \text{lb} \times \dfrac{1 \text{ Btu}}{\text{lb } °\text{F}} \times (145 \, °\text{F} - 48 \, °\text{F}) = 3.2 \times 10^4 \text{Btu}$

(b) $\text{heat (kcal)} = 1.5 \times 10^5 \text{g} \times \dfrac{1 \text{ cal}}{\text{g } °\text{C}} \times (145 \, °\text{F} - 48 \, °\text{F}) \times \dfrac{5 \, °\text{C}}{9 \, °\text{F}} \times \dfrac{1 \text{ kcal}}{1000 \text{ cal}} = 8.1 \times 10^3 \text{kcal}$

(c) $\text{heat (kJ)} = 8.1 \times 10^3 \text{kcal} \times \dfrac{4.184 \text{ kJ}}{1 \text{ kcal}} = 3.4 \times 10^4 \text{ kJ}$

96. (M) The additional water simply acts as a heat transfer medium. The essential relationship is heat lost by iron = heat gained by water (of unknown mass).

$-\left(1.23 \text{ kg} \times \dfrac{1000 \text{ g}}{1 \text{ kg}}\right) 0.449 \dfrac{\text{J}}{\text{g } °\text{C}} (25.6 - 68.5) \, °\text{C} = x \text{ g H}_2\text{O} \times 4.18 \dfrac{\text{J}}{\text{g } °\text{C}} (25.6 - 18.5) \, °\text{C}$

$2.37 \times 10^4 \text{ J} = 29.\underline{7} \, x \qquad x = \dfrac{2.37 \times 10^4}{29.7} = 79\underline{8} \text{ g H}_2\text{O} \times \dfrac{1 \text{ mL H}_2\text{O}}{1.00 \text{ g H}_2\text{O}} = 8.0 \times 10^2 \text{ mL H}_2\text{O}$

97. (M) Potential energy $= mgh = 7.26 \text{ kg} \times 9.81 \text{ ms}^{-2} \times 168 \text{ m} = 1.20 \times 10^4 \text{ J}$. This potential energy is converted entirely into kinetic energy just before the object hits, and this kinetic energy is converted entirely into heat when the object strikes.

$\Delta t = \dfrac{\text{heat}}{\text{mass} \times c_p} = \dfrac{1.20 \times 10^4 \text{ J}}{7.26 \text{ kg} \times \dfrac{1000 \text{ g}}{1 \text{ kg}} \times \dfrac{0.47 \text{ J}}{\text{g } °\text{C}}} = 3.5 \, °\text{C}$

This large a temperature rise is unlikely, as some of the kinetic energy will be converted into forms other than heat, such as sound and the fracturing of the object along with the surface it strikes. In addition, some heat energy would be transferred to the surface.

98. (M) $\text{heat} = \Delta t \, [\text{heat cap.} + (\text{mass H}_2\text{O} \times 4.184 \dfrac{\text{J}}{\text{g } °\text{C}})]$

$\text{heat cap.} = \dfrac{\text{heat}}{\Delta t} - (\text{mass H}_2\text{O} \times 4.184 \dfrac{\text{J}}{\text{g } °\text{C}})$

The heat of combustion of anthracene is -7067 kJ/mol, meaning that burning one mole of anthracene releases $+7067$ kJ of heat to the calorimeter.

$\text{heat cap.} = \dfrac{1.354 \text{ g C}_{14}\text{H}_{10} \times \dfrac{1 \text{ mol C}_{14}\text{H}_{10}}{178.23 \text{ g C}_{14}\text{H}_{10}} \times \dfrac{7067 \text{ kJ}}{1 \text{ mol C}_{14}\text{H}_{10}}}{(35.63 - 24.87) \, °\text{C}} - \left(983.5 \text{ g} \times 4.184 \times 10^{-3} \dfrac{\text{kJ}}{\text{g } °\text{C}}\right)$

$= (4.990 - 4.115) \text{ kJ/}°\text{C} = 0.875 \text{ kJ/}°\text{C}$

$\text{heat} = (27.19 - 25.01) \, °\text{C} \, [0.875 \text{ kJ/}°\text{C} + (968.6 \text{ g H}_2\text{O} \times 4.184 \times 10^{-3} \text{ kJ g}^{-1} \, °\text{C}^{-1})] = 10.7 \text{ kJ}$

$q_{\text{rxn}} = \dfrac{-10.7 \text{ kJ}}{1.053 \text{ g C}_6\text{H}_8\text{O}_7} \times \dfrac{192.1 \text{ g C}_6\text{H}_8\text{O}_7}{1 \text{ mol C}_6\text{H}_8\text{O}_7} = -1.95 \times 10^3 \text{ kJ/mol C}_6\text{H}_8\text{O}_7$

99. (M) heat absorbed by calorimeter and water $=$ $-$ heat of reaction

$$= -1.148 \text{ g } C_7H_6O_2 \times \frac{-26.42 \text{ kJ}}{1 \text{ g } C_7H_6O_2} \times \frac{1000 \text{ J}}{1 \text{ kJ}} = 3.033 \times 10^4 \text{ J}$$

heat absorbed by water $= 1181 \text{ g } H_2O \times \dfrac{4.184 \text{ J}}{\text{g} \,^\circ C} \times (30.25\,^\circ C - 24.96\,^\circ C) = 2.61 \times 10^4 \text{ J}$

heat absorbed by calorimeter $= 3.033 \times 10^4 \text{ J} - 2.61 \times 10^4 \text{ J} = 4.2 \times 10^3 \text{ J}$

heat capacity of the calorimeter $= \dfrac{4.2 \times 10^3 \text{ J}}{30.25\,^\circ C - 24.96\,^\circ C} = 7.9 \times 10^2 \text{ J/}^\circ C$

heat absorbed by water $= 1162 \text{ g } H_2O \times \dfrac{4.184 \text{ J}}{\text{g} \,^\circ C} \times (29.81\,^\circ C - 24.98\,^\circ C) = 2.35 \times 10^4 \text{ J}$

heat absorbed by calorimeter $= 7.9 \times 10^2 \text{ J/}^\circ C \times (29.81\,^\circ C - 24.98\,^\circ C) = 3.8 \times 10^3 \text{ J}$

heat of combustion $= \dfrac{2.35 \times 10^4 \text{ J} + 3.8 \times 10^3 \text{ J}}{0.895 \text{ g}} \times \dfrac{1 \text{ kJ}}{1000 \text{ J}} = 30.5 \text{ kJ/g}$

mass coal $= 2.15 \times 10^9 \text{ kJ} \times \dfrac{1 \text{ g coal}}{30.5 \text{ kJ}} \times \dfrac{1 \text{ kg}}{1000 \text{ g}} \times \dfrac{1 \text{ metric ton}}{1000 \text{ kg}} = 70.5 \text{ metric tons}$

100. (M) The difference is due to the enthalpy of vaporization of water. Less heat is evolved when steam is formed because some of the heat of combustion is used to vaporize the water. The difference between these two heats of vaporization is computed first.

difference $= (33.88 - 28.67) \dfrac{\text{kcal}}{\text{g } H_2} \times \dfrac{2.016 \text{ g } H_2}{1 \text{ mol } H_2} \times \dfrac{2 \text{ mol } H_2}{2 \text{ mol } H_2O} \times \dfrac{4.184 \text{ kJ}}{1 \text{ kcal}} = 43.9 \text{ kJ/mol } H_2O$

This difference should equal the heat of vaporization, that is, the enthalpy change for the following reaction.

$H_2O(l) \longrightarrow H_2O(g)$ We use values from Table 7-2.

$\Delta_r H^\circ = \Delta_f H^\circ[H_2O(g)] - \Delta_f H^\circ[H_2O(l)] = -241.8 \text{ kJ mol}^{-1} - (-285.8 \text{ kJ mol}^{-1}) = 44.0 \text{ kJ/mol}$

The two values are in good agreement.

101. (M)

(1) $N_2(g) + 2O_2(g) \longrightarrow 2NO_2$ $\quad \Delta_r H^\circ = 2\Delta_f H^\circ[NO_2(g)] = 2 \times 33.18 \text{ kJ mol}^{-1} = 66.36 \text{ kJ mol}^{-1}$

(2) $N_2(g) + 2O_2(g) \longrightarrow 2NO_2$ $\qquad\qquad\qquad \Delta_r H = 66.36 \text{ kJ mol}^{-1}$

$\underline{2 \text{ NO}_2(g) \longrightarrow N_2O_3(g) + \tfrac{1}{2}O_2(g) \qquad\qquad \Delta_r H = 16.02 \text{ kJ mol}^{-1}}$

$N_2(g) + 2 \text{ O}_2(g) \longrightarrow N_2O_3(g) + \tfrac{1}{2}O_2(g) \quad \Delta_r H = 82.38 \text{ kJ mol}^{-1}$

102. (M) First we determine the moles of gas, then the heat produced by burning each of the components.

$$n = \frac{PV}{RT} = \frac{739 \text{ mm Hg} \times \dfrac{1 \text{ atm}}{760 \text{ mmHg}} \times 385 \text{ L}}{(22.6 + 273.2) \text{ K} \times 0.08206 \text{ atm L mol}^{-1} \text{ K}^{-1}} = 15.4 \text{ mol}$$

$$CH_4 \text{ heat} = 15.4\,mol \times \frac{83.0\ mol\,CH_4}{100.0\ mol\,gas} \times \frac{-890.3\,kJ}{1\,mol\,CH_4} = -1.14 \times 10^4\,kJ$$

$$C_2H_6 \text{ heat} = 15.4\,mol \times \frac{11.2\ mol\,C_2H_6}{100.0\ mol\,gas} \times \frac{-1559.7\,kJ}{1\,mol\,C_2H_6} = -2.69 \times 10^3\,kJ$$

$$C_3H_8 \text{ heat} = 15.4\,mol \times \frac{5.8\ mol\,C_3H_8}{100.0\ mol\,gas} \times \frac{-2219.1\,kJ}{1\,mol\,C_3H_8} = -2.0 \times 10^3\,kJ$$

$$\text{total heat} = -1.14 \times 10^4\,kJ - 2.69 \times 10^3\,kJ - 2.0 \times 10^3\,kJ$$

$$= -1.61 \times 10^4\,kJ \text{ or } +1.61 \times 10^4\,kJ \text{ heat evolved}$$

103. (M)

$CO(g) + 3H_2(g) \longrightarrow CH_4(g) + H_2O(g)$	(methanation)	$-206.1\,kJ\,mol^{-1}$
$2C(s) + 2H_2O(g) \longrightarrow 2CO(g) + 2H_2(g)$	$2 \times (7.24)$	$+262.6\,kJ\,mol^{-1}$
$CO(g) + H_2O(g) \longrightarrow CO_2(g) + H_2(g)$	(7.25)	$-41.2\,kJ\,mol^{-1}$
$2C(s) + 2H_2O(g) \longrightarrow CH_4(g) + CO_2(g)$		$15.3\,kJ\,mol^{-1}$

104. (D) We first compute the heats of combustion of the combustible gases.

$$CH_4(g) + 2O_2(g) \longrightarrow CO_2(g) + 2H_2O(l)$$

$$\Delta_r H^\circ = \Delta_f H^\circ[CO_2(g)] + 2\Delta_f H^\circ[H_2O(l)] - \Delta_f H^\circ[CH_4(g)] - 2\Delta_f H^\circ[O_2(g)]$$

$$= -393.5\,kJ\,mol^{-1} + 2 \times (-285.8\,kJ\,mol^{-1}) - (-74.81\,kJ\,mol^{-1}) - 2 \times 0.00\,kJ\,mol^{-1}$$

$$= -890.3\,kJ\,mol^{-1}$$

$$C_3H_8(g) + 5O_2(g) \longrightarrow 3CO_2(g) + 4H_2O(l)$$

$$\Delta_r H^\circ = 3\Delta_f H^\circ[CO_2(g)] + 4\Delta_f H^\circ[H_2O(l)] - \Delta_f H^\circ[C_3H_8(g)] - 5\Delta_f H^\circ[O_2(g)]$$

$$= 3 \times (-393.5\,kJ\,mol^{-1}) + 4 \times (-285.8\,kJ\,mol^{-1}) - (-103.8\,kJ\,mol^{-1}) - 5 \times 0.00\,kJ\,mol^{-1}$$

$$= -2220.\,kJ\,mol^{-1}$$

$$H_2(g) + \tfrac{1}{2}O_2(g) \longrightarrow H_2O(l) \quad \Delta_r H^\circ = \Delta_f H^\circ[H_2O(l)] = -285.8\,kJ\,mol^{-1}$$

$$CO(g) + \tfrac{1}{2}O_2(g) \longrightarrow CO_2(g)$$

$$\Delta_r H^\circ = \Delta_f H^\circ[CO_2(g)] - \Delta H^\circ_f[CO(g)] - 0.5\,\Delta_f H^\circ[O_2(g)] = -393.5 + 110.5 = -283.0\,kJ\,mol^{-1}$$

Then, for each gaseous mixture, we compute the enthalpy of combustion per mole of gas. The enthalpy of combustion per liter at STP (i.e., at 1 bar and 0 °C) is 1/22.711 of this value. Recall that volume percents are equal to mole percents.

(a) H_2 combustion $= 0.497 \, mol \, H_2 \times \dfrac{-285.8 \, kJ}{1 \, mol \, H_2} = -142 \, kJ$

CH_4 combustion $= 0.299 \, mol \, CH_4 \times \dfrac{-890.3 \, kJ}{1 \, mol \, CH_4} = -266 \, kJ$

CO combustion $= 0.069 \, mol \, CO \times \dfrac{-283.0 \, kJ}{1 \, mol \, CO} = -20 \, kJ$

C_3H_8 combustion $= 0.031 \, mol \, C_3H_8 \times \dfrac{-2220. \, kJ}{1 \, mol \, C_3H_8} = -69 \, kJ$

total enthalpy of combustion $= \dfrac{(-142 - 266 - 20 - 69) \, kJ}{1 \, mol \, gas} \times \dfrac{1 \, mol \, gas}{22.711 \, L} = -21.9 \, kJ/L$

(b) CH_4 is the only combustible gas present in sewage gas.

total enthalpy of combustion $= 0.660 \, mol \, CH_4 \times \dfrac{-890.3 \, kJ}{1 \, mol \, CH_4} \times \dfrac{1 \, mol \, gas}{22.711 \, L} = -39.2 \, kJ/L$

Thus, sewage gas produces more heat per liter at STP than does coal gas.

105. (M)

(a) $CH_4(g) + 2 \, O_2(g) \longrightarrow CO_2(g) + 2 \, H_2O(l)$ is the combustion reaction

$\Delta_r H° = \Delta_f H°[CO_2(g)] + 2 \, \Delta_f H°[H_2O(l)] - \Delta_f H°[CH_4(g)] - 2 \, \Delta_f H°[O_2(g)]$

$= (-393.5 \, kJ \, mol^{-1}) + 2 \times (-285.8 \, kJ \, mol^{-1}) - (-74.81 \, kJ \, mol^{-1}) - 2 \times 0.00 \, kJ \, mol^{-1}$

$= -890.3 \, kJ \, mol^{-1}$

$n = \dfrac{PV}{RT} = \dfrac{744 \, mm \, Hg \times \dfrac{1 \, atm}{760 \, mmHg} \times 0.100 \, L}{298.2 \, K \times 0.08206 \, atm \, L \, mol^{-1} \, K^{-1}} = 0.00400 \, mol \, CH_4$

heat available from combustion $= 0.00400 \, mol \times -890.3 \, kJ/mol = -3.56 \, kJ$

heat used to melt ice $= 9.53 \, g \, ice \times \dfrac{1 \, mol \, H_2O(s)}{18.02 \, g \, ice} \times \dfrac{6.01 \, kJ}{1 \, mol \, H_2O(s)} = 3.18 \, kJ$

Since 3.56 kJ of heat was available, and only 3.18 kJ went into melting the ice, the combustion must be incomplete.

(b) One possible reaction is: $4 \, CH_4(g) + 7 \, O_2(g) \longrightarrow 2 \, CO_2(g) + 2 \, CO(g) + 8 \, H_2O(l)$, but this would generate but 3.00 kJ of energy under the stated conditions. The molar production of CO_2 (g) must be somewhat greater than that of $CO(g)$.

106. (E)

(a) The heat of reaction would be smaller (less negative) if the H_2O were obtained as a gas rather than as a liquid.

(b) The reason why the heat of reaction would be less negative is that some of the 1410.9 kJ of heat produced by the reaction will be needed to convert the H_2O from liquid to gas.

(c) $\Delta_r H° = 2\Delta_f H°[CO_2(g)] + 2\Delta_f H°[H_2O(g)] - \Delta_f H°[C_2H_4(g)] - 3\Delta_f H°[O_2(g)]$

$= [2(-393.5) + 2(-241.8) - (52.26) - 3(0.00)] \text{ kJ mol}^{-1} = -1322.9 \text{ kJ mol}^{-1}$

107. (D) First we compute the amount of butane in the cylinder before and after some is withdrawn; the difference is the amount of butane withdrawn.

$T = (26.0 + 273.2)\text{K} = 299.2 \text{ K}$

$$n_1 = \frac{PV}{RT} = \frac{2.35 \text{ atm} \times 200.0 \text{ L}}{0.08206 \text{ atm L mol}^{-1} \text{ K}^{-1} \times 299.2 \text{ K}} = 19.1 \text{ mol butane}$$

$$n_2 = \frac{PV}{RT} = \frac{1.10 \text{ atm} \times 200.0 \text{ L}}{0.08206 \text{ atm L mol}^{-1} \text{ K}^{-1} \times 299.2 \text{ K}} = 8.96 \text{ mol butane}$$

amount withdrawn $= 19.1 \text{ mol} - 8.96 \text{ mol} = 10.1 \text{ mol butane}$

Then we compute the enthalpy change for one mole of butane and from that the heat produced by burning the withdrawn butane.

$C_4H_{10}(g) + \frac{13}{2}O_2(g) \longrightarrow 4CO_2(g) + 5H_2O(l)$

$\Delta_r H° = 4\Delta_f H°[CO_2(g)] + 5\Delta_f H°[H_2O(l)] - \Delta_f H°[C_4H_{10}(g)] - \frac{13}{2}\Delta_f H°[O_2(g)]$

$= 4 \times (-393.5 \text{ kJ mol}^{-1}) + 5 \times (-285.8 \text{ kJ mol}^{-1}) - (-125.6 \text{ kJ mol}^{-1}) - 6.5 \times 0.00 \text{ kJ mol}^{-1}$

$= -2877 \text{ kJ mol}^{-1}$

Now we compute the heat produced by the combustion of the butane.

$$\text{heat} = 10.1 \text{ mol C}_4\text{H}_{10} \times \frac{-2877 \text{ kJ}}{1 \text{ mol C}_4\text{H}_{10}} = -2.91 \times 10^4 \text{ kJ}$$

To begin the calculation of the heat absorbed by the water, we compute the mass of the water.

$$\text{mass H}_2\text{O} = 132.5 \text{ L} \times \frac{1000 \text{ cm}^3}{1 \text{ L}} \times \frac{1.00 \text{ g}}{1 \text{ cm}^3} = 1.33 \times 10^5 \text{ g H}_2\text{O}$$

$$\text{heat absorbed} = 1.33 \times 10^5 \text{ g} \times \frac{4.184 \text{ J}}{\text{g °C}} \times (62.2 \text{ °C} - 26.0 \text{ °C}) \times \frac{1 \text{ kJ}}{1000 \text{ J}} = 2.01 \times 10^4 \text{ kJ}$$

$$\% \text{ efficiency} = \frac{2.01 \times 10^4 \text{ kJ absorbed}}{2.91 \times 10^4 \text{ kJ produced}} \times 100\% = 69.1\% \text{ efficient}$$

108. (M) $\text{work} = 4 \times mgh = 4 \times 58.0 \text{ kg} \times 9.807 \text{ m s}^{-2} \times 1450 \text{ m} \times \frac{1 \text{ kJ}}{1000 \text{ J}} = 3.30 \times 10^3 \text{ kJ}$

We compute the enthalpy change for the metabolism (combustion) of glucose.

$C_6H_{12}O_6(s) + 6O_2(g) \longrightarrow 6CO_2(g) + 6H_2O(l)$

$\Delta_r H° = 6\Delta_f H°[CO_2(g)] + 6\Delta_f H°[H_2O(l)] - \Delta_f H°[C_6H_{12}O_6(s)] - 6\Delta_f H°[O_2(g)]$

$= 6 \times (-393.5 \text{ kJ mol}^{-1}) - 6 \times (-285.8 \text{ kJ mol}^{-1}) - (-1273.3 \text{ kJ mol}^{-1}) - 6 \times 0.00 \text{ kJ mol}^{-1}$

$= -2802.5 \text{ kJ mol}^{-1}$

Then we compute the mass of glucose needed to perform the necessary work.

$$\text{mass } C_6H_{12}O_6 = 3.30 \times 10^3 \text{ kJ} \times \frac{1 \text{ kJ heat}}{0.70 \text{ kJ work}} \times \frac{1 \text{ mol } C_6H_{12}O_6}{2802.5 \text{ kJ}} \times \frac{180.2 \text{ g } C_6H_{12}O_6}{1 \text{ mol } C_6H_{12}O_6}$$

$$= 303 \text{ g } C_6H_{12}O_6$$

109. (M) $\Delta_f H°[C_4H_{10}(g)] = -125.6 \text{ kJ/mol}$ from Table 7-2.

The difference between C_4H_{10} and C_7H_{16} amounts to three CH_2 groups. The difference in their standard enthalpies of formation is determined as follows.

$$\text{difference} = 3 \text{ mol } CH_2 \text{ groups} \times \frac{-21 \text{ kJ}}{\text{mol } CH_2 \text{ groups}} = -63 \text{ kJ/mol}$$

Thus $\quad \Delta_f H°[C_7H_{16}(l)] \approx -125.6 \text{ kJ/mol} - 63 \text{ kJ/mol} = -189 \text{ kJ/mol}$

Now we compute the enthalpy change for the combustion of heptane.

$$C_7H_{16}(l) + 11 \ O_2(g) \longrightarrow 7 \ CO_2(g) + 8 \ H_2O(l)$$

$$\Delta_r H° = 7\Delta_f H°[CO_2(g)] + 8\Delta_f H°[H_2O(l)] - \Delta_f H°[C_7H_{16}(l)] - 11\Delta_f H°[O_2(g)]$$

$$= 7 \times (-393.5 \text{ kJ mol}^{-1}) + 8 \times (-285.8 \text{ kJ mol}^{-1}) - (-189 \text{ kJ mol}^{-1}) - 11 \times 0.00 \text{ kJ mol}^{-1}$$

$$= -4852 \text{ kJ mol}^{-1}$$

110. (M) First determine the molar heats of combustion for CH_4 and C_2H_6.

$$CH_4(g) + 2O_2(g) \longrightarrow CO_2(g) + 2H_2O(l)$$

$$\Delta_r H° = \Delta_f H°[CO_2(g)] + 2\Delta_f H°[H_2O(l)] - \Delta_f H°[CH_4(g)] - 2\Delta_f H°[O_2(g)]$$

$$= ((-393.5) + 2(-285.8) - (-74.81) - 2(0.00)) \text{ kJ mol}^{-1} = -890.3 \text{ kJ/mol}$$

$$C_2H_6(g) + \tfrac{7}{2}O_2(g) \longrightarrow 2CO_2(g) + 3H_2O(l)$$

$$\Delta_r H° = 2\Delta_f H°[CO_2(g)] + 3\Delta_f H°[H_2O(l)] - \Delta_f H°[C_2H_6(g)] - \tfrac{7}{2}\Delta_f H°[O_2(g)]$$

$$= (2(-393.5) + 3(-285.8) - (-84.68) - \tfrac{7}{2}(0.00)) \text{ kJ mol}^{-1} = -1559.7 \text{ kJ mol}^{-1}$$

Since the STP molar volume of an ideal gas is 22.7 L, there is 1/22.7 of a mole of gas present in the sample. We first compute the heat produced by one mole (that is 22.7 L at STP) of the mixed gas.

$$\text{heat} = \frac{43.6 \text{ kJ}}{1.00 \text{ L}} \times \frac{22.7 \text{ L}}{1 \text{ mol}} = 990 \text{ kJ/mol}$$

Then, if we let the number of moles of CH_4 be represented by x, the number of moles of C_2H_6 is represented by $(1.00 - x)$. Now we can construct an equation for the heat evolved per mole of mixture and solve this equation for x.

$$990 \text{ kJ} = 890.3\,x + 1559.7(1.00 - x) = 1559.7 + (890.3 - 1559.7)x = 1559.7 - 669.4\,x$$

$$x = \frac{1559.7 - 990}{669.4} = 0.851 \text{ mol } CH_4/\text{mol mixture}$$

By the ideal gas law, gases at the same temperature and pressure have the same volume ratio as their molar ratio. Hence, this gas mixture contains 85.1% CH_4 and 14.9% C_2H_6, both by volume.

111. (D)

(a) Values are not the same because enthalpies of formations in solution depend on the solute concentration.

(b) The data that we can cite to confirm that the $\Delta_f H°[H_2SO_4(aq)] = -909.3$ kJ/mol in an infinitely dilute solution is the same for the $\Delta_f H°[SO_4^{2-}]$ from Table 7.3. This is expected because an infinitely dilute solution of H_2SO_4 is $2\ H^+(aq) + SO_4^{2-}$ (aq). Since $\Delta_f H°[H^+] = 0$ kJ/mol, it is expected that SO_4^{2-} (aq) will have the same $\Delta_f H°$ as $H_2SO_4(aq)$.

(c) 500.0 mL of 1.00 M H_2SO_4 is prepared from pure H_2SO_4. Note: ½ mole H_2SO_4 used.

Reaction $\quad H_2SO_4(l) \quad \rightarrow \quad H_2SO_4(aq) \sim 1.00$ M

$\Delta_f H° \quad\quad$ –814.0 kJ/mol $\quad\quad$ –909.3 kJ/mol

q = ½ mol(–909.3 kJ/mol) – ½ mol(–814.0 kJ/mol) = –47.65 kJ

$\therefore 47{,}650$ J released by dilution and absorbed by the water.

Use $q = mc\Delta t \quad\quad \Delta t = \dfrac{47{,}650\ J}{500\ g(4.2\ J\ g^{-1}\ °C^{-1})} \approx +23\ °C$

112. (M)

$CO(g) + 3\ H_2(g)$	$\rightarrow$	$CH_4(g) + H_2O(g)$	(methanation)	–206.1 kJ mol^{-1}
$2\ C(s) + 2\ H_2O(g)$	$\rightarrow$	$2\ CO(g) + 2\ H_2(g)$	(2×7.26)	+262.6 kJ mol^{-1}
$CO(g) + H_2O(g)$	$\rightarrow$	$CO_2(g) + H_2(g)$	(7.27)	–41.2 kJ mol^{-1}
$2\ C(s) + 2\ H_2O(g)$	$\rightarrow$	$CH_4(g) + CO_2(g)$		15.3 kJ mol^{-1}

113. (M)

$n = \dfrac{(765.5/760)\text{atm}}{(0.08206\ \text{atm L mol}^{-1}\ \text{K}^{-1})} \dfrac{0.582\ L}{298.15\ K} = 2.40 \times 10^{-2}$ mol

$\text{molar mass} = \dfrac{1.103\ g}{2.40 \times 10^{-2}\ \text{mol}} = 46.0$ g/mol

moles of $CO_2 = 2.108/44.01 = 0.04790(0.0479$ mol C in unknown)

moles of $H_2O = 1.294/18.02 = 0.0719(0.144$ mol H in unknown)

$\text{moles of O in unknown} = \dfrac{1.103\ g - 0.04790\ g\ (12.011g\ C/mol) - 0.144(1.00794)}{15.9994\ g\ mol^{-1}} = 0.0239$ mol O

So C:H:O ratio is 2:6:1 and the molecular formula is C_2H_6O.

$\Delta_r T = 31.94 - 25.00 = 6.94\ °C \quad q = 6.94\ °C \times 5.015\ kJ/°C = -34.8$ kJ

$\Delta_r H = \dfrac{-34.8\ kJ}{0.0240\ mol} = -1.45 \times 10^3\ kJ/mol \quad 3\ O_2(g) + C_2H_6O(g) \rightarrow 2\ CO_2(g) + 3\ H_2O(l)$

114. (M) Energy needed = $mc\Delta T$ = (250 g)((50 – 4) °C)(4.2 J/g °C) = 4.8×10^4 J

A 700-watt oven delivers a joule of energy/sec.

$\text{time} = \left(\dfrac{4.8 \times 10^4\ J}{700\ J\ sec^{-1}} \right) = 69$ seconds

115. (M) $w = -P\Delta V$, $V_i = (3.1416)(6.00 \text{ cm})^2(8.10 \text{ cm}) = 916.1 \text{ cm}^3$

$$P = \frac{\text{force}}{\text{area}} = \frac{(3.1416)(5.00)^2(25.00)(7.75 \text{ g/cm}^3)(1 \text{ kg}/1000 \text{ g})(9.807 \text{ m/sec}^2)}{(3.1416)(6.00 \text{ cm})^2(1 \text{ m}/100\text{cm})^2}$$

$$= 1.320 \times 10^4 \text{ Pa} = \frac{1.320 \times 10^4 \text{ Pa}}{101325 \text{ Pa atm}^{-1}} = 0.130 \text{ atm difference} \quad \text{Use: } P_1V_1 = P_2V_2$$

$$V_2 = \frac{((745/760) + 0.130 \text{ atm}) \times (0.9161 \text{ L})}{(745/760)\text{atm}} = 1.04 \text{ L}$$

$$-P\Delta V = \frac{745}{760} \times (1.04 - 0.916) = -0.121 \text{ atm L} = w = (-0.121 \text{ atm L})\frac{101 \text{ J}}{\text{atm L}} = -12 \text{ J}$$

116. (M)

$Na_2CO_3 \cdot 10 H_2O(s) \rightarrow Na_2CO_3 \cdot 7 H_2O(s) + 3 H_2O(g)$	$+ 155.3 \text{ kJ mol}^{-1}$
$Na_2CO_3 \cdot 7 H_2O(s) \rightarrow Na_2CO_3 \cdot H_2O(s) + 6 H_2O(g)$	$+ 320.1 \text{ kJ mol}^{-1}$
$Na_2CO_3 \cdot H_2O(s) \rightarrow Na_2CO_3(s) + H_2O(g)$	$+ 57.3 \text{ kJ mol}^{-1}$
$Na_2CO_3 \cdot 10 H_2O(s) \rightarrow Na_2CO_3(s) + 10 H_2O(g)$	$+532.7 \text{ kJ mol}^{-1}$

Thus, using Hess's Law, $\Delta H = +532.7 \text{ kJ mol}^{-1}$. For ΔU we must assume a temperature, say, 373 K. $\Delta U = \Delta H - \Delta n_{gas}RT = +532.7 \text{ kJ mol}^{-1} - 10 (8.314472 \text{ J K}^{-1} \text{mol}^{-1})(373 \text{ L})$ $(1 \text{ kJ}/1000 \text{ J}) = + 501.7 \text{ kJ mol}^{-1}$. The value for ΔU is only an estimate because it is based on a ΔH value that has been obtained using Hess's law. Hess's law provides only an approximate value for the enthalpy change. To obtain a more precise value for the ΔU, one would use bomb calorimetry. As well, the water formed is assumed to be a vapor (gas). In reality, a portion of that water will exist as a liquid.

117. (M) First, list all of the pertinent reactions, normalizing them so that each uses the same amount of NH_3:

(rxn-1) $4 NH_3(g) + 3 O_2(g) \rightarrow 2 N_2(g) + 6 H_2O(g)$
$\Delta_r H° = 2 \times (0 \text{ kJ/mol}) + 6 \times (-241.8 \text{ kJ/mol}) - [4 \times (-46.11 \text{ kJ mol}^{-1}) + 3 \times (0 \text{ kJ/mol})]$
$\quad = -1266.4 \text{ kJ mol}^{-1}$

(rxn-2) $4 NH_3(g) + 4 O_2(g) \rightarrow 2 N_2O(g) + 6 H_2O(g)$
$\Delta_r H° = 4 \times (82.05 \text{ kJ/mol}) + 6 \times (-241.8 \text{ kJ/mol}) - [4 \times (-46.11 \text{ kJ mol}^{-1}) + 3 \times (0 \text{ kJ/mol})]$
$\quad = -938.2 \text{ kJ mol}^{-1}$

(rxn-3) $4 NH_3(g) + 5 O_2(g) \rightarrow 4 NO(g) + 6 H_2O(g)$
$\Delta_r H° = 2 \times (90.25 \text{ kJ/mol}) + 6 \times (-241.8 \text{ kJ/mol}) - [4 \times (-46.11 \text{ kJ mol}^{-1}) + 3 \times (0 \text{ kJ/mol})]$
$\quad = -1085.9 \text{ kJ mol}^{-1}$

(rxn-4) $4 NH_3(g) + 7 O_2(g) \rightarrow 4 NO_2(g) + 6 H_2O(g)$
$\Delta_r H° = 4 \times (33.18 \text{ kJ/mol}) + 6 \times (-241.8 \text{ kJ/mol}) - [4 \times (-46.11 \text{ kJ mol}^{-1}) + 3 \times (0 \text{ kJ/mol})]$
$\quad = -1133.6 \text{ kJ mol}^{-1}$

Clearly, rxn-1, the oxidation of $NH_3(g)$ to $N_2(g)$ is the most exothermic reaction.

118. (D) Let ΔH_m represent the enthalpy change per mole of N_2 when it is heated from 25 °C to 100 °C.

$$\Delta H_m = \int_{298\,K}^{373\,K} c_p\, dt = \int_{298\,K}^{373\,K} (28.58 + 0.00377T - 0.5 \times 10^5 T^{-2})dt$$

$$= 28.58 \frac{J}{mol\,K} \int_{298K}^{373\,K} dt + 0.00377 \frac{J}{K^2\,mol} \int_{298K}^{373\,K} T dt + -0.5 \times 10^5 \frac{J\,K}{mol} \int_{298K}^{373\,K} T^{-2} dt$$

$$= 28.58 \frac{J}{mol\,K} \times \left(T \Big|_{298\,K}^{373\,K} \right) + 0.00377 \frac{J}{K^2\,mol} \times \left(\frac{T^2}{2} \Big|_{298\,K}^{373\,K} \right) - 0.5 \times 10^5 \frac{J\,K}{mol} \times \left(-\frac{1}{T} \Big|_{298\,K}^{373\,K} \right)$$

$$= 28.58 \frac{J}{mol\,K} \times (373\,K - 298\,K) + 0.00377 \frac{J}{K^2\,mol} \times \left(\frac{(373\,K)^2}{2} - \frac{(298\,K)^2}{2} \right)$$

$$+ 0.5 \times 10^5 \frac{J\,K}{mol} \times \left(\frac{1}{373\,K} - \frac{1}{298\,K} \right)$$

$$= 2143.5 \frac{J}{mol} + 94.9 \frac{J}{mol} - 33.7 \frac{J}{mol} = 2205 \frac{J}{mol} = 2.205 \frac{kJ}{mol}$$

119. (D) There are several processes to consider: (1) heating the ice from −5 °C to the melting point at 0 °C; (2) melting the ice at 0 °C; (3) heating the water from 0 °C to the boiling point at 100 °C; (4) vaporizing the water at 100 °C. The following equations summarize these processes and the enthalpy changes involved. In the equations for ΔH_1 and ΔH_3, m represents the mass in kilograms.

(1) $H_2O(s, 268.15\,K) \longrightarrow H_2O(s, 273.15\,K)$ $\Delta H_1 = m \times \int_{268.15\,K}^{273.15\,K} c_{p,ice}(T)dT$

(2) $H_2O(s, 273.15\,K) \longrightarrow H_2O(l, 273.15\,K)$ $\Delta H_2 = n \times \Delta_{fus}H(ice)$

(3) $H_2O(l, 273.15\,K) \longrightarrow H_2O(l, 373.15\,K)$ $\Delta H_3 = m \times \int_{273.15\,K}^{373.15\,K} c_{p,water}(T)dT$

(4) $H_2O(l, 373.15\,K) \longrightarrow H_2O(g, 373.15\,K)$ $\Delta H_4 = n \times \Delta_{vap}H(water)$

To evaluate these enthalpy changes, we use $m = 10.0\ g = 0.010$ kg in the expressions given for $c_p(ice)$ and $c_p(water)$, $\Delta_{fus}H(ice) = 6.01$ kJ mol^{-1}, and $\Delta_{vap}H(water) = 44.0$ kJ mol^{-1}.

$$\Delta H_1/kJ = 0.010 \times \int_{268.15}^{273.15} \left[1.0187T - 1.49 \times 10^{-2} \right] dT = 0.010 \times \left[1.0187 \times \frac{T^2}{2} - 1.49 \times 10^{-2}T \right]_{268.15}^{273.15}$$

$$= 13.78$$

$$\Delta H_2 = \frac{10.0\ g}{18.016\ g\ mol^{-1}} \times 6.01\ kJ\ mol^{-1} = 3.36\ kJ$$

$$\Delta H_3/kJ = 0.010 \times \int_{268.15}^{273.15} \left[-1.0 \times 10^{-7}T^3 + 1.0 \times 10^{-4}T^2 - 3.92 \times 10^{-2}T + 8.7854 \right] dT$$

$$= 0.010 \times \left[-1.0 \times 10^{-7} \times \frac{T^4}{4} + 1.0 \times 10^{-4} \times \frac{T^3}{3} - 3.92 \times 10^{-2} \times \frac{T^2}{2} + 8.7854T \right]_{273.15}^{373.15}$$

$$= 3.19$$

$$\Delta H_4 = \frac{10.0 \text{ g}}{18.016 \text{ g mol}^{-1}} \times 44.0 \text{ kJ mol}^{-1} = 24.42 \text{ kJ}$$

The total heat required is the sum of these enthalpy changes.

$$q_{tot} = \Delta H_1 + \Delta H_2 + \Delta H_3 + \Delta H_4 = 13.78 \text{ kJ} + 3.36 \text{ kJ} + 3.19 \text{ kJ} + 24.42 \text{ kJ} = 44.75 \text{ kJ}$$

120. (D) Reaction of interest: $H_2(g) \quad + \quad \tfrac{1}{2} O_2(g) \quad \rightarrow \quad H_2O(g)$

Molar heat capacities: $\quad$ 28.84 J mol^{-1} K^{-1} $\qquad$ 29.37 J mol^{-1} K^{-1} $\qquad$ 33.58 J mol^{-1} K^{-1}

ΔT $\qquad\qquad\qquad$ 75.0 K $\qquad\qquad$ 75.0 K $\qquad\qquad$ 75.0 K

$q = n \times c_p \times \Delta T \qquad$ (1)(28.84)(75.0) J $\quad$ ($\tfrac{1}{2}$)(29.37)(75.0) J $\quad$ (1)(33.58)(75.0) J

$\qquad\qquad\qquad\qquad\qquad$ = 216$\underline{3}$ J $\qquad\qquad$ = 110$\underline{1.4}$ J $\qquad\qquad$ = 251$\underline{8.5}$ J

q_{prod} = 251$\underline{8.5}$ J = 2.52 kJ $\qquad\qquad$ q_{react} = (216$\underline{3}$ J + 110$\underline{1.4}$ J) = 326$\underline{4.4}$ J = 3.26 kJ

See diagram below.

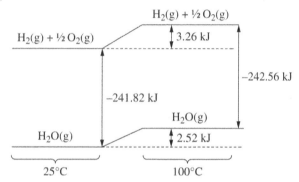

Thus, $\Delta_f H°$ $H_2O(g)$ at 100.0 °C is approximately –243 kJ/mol $H_2O(g)$ formed.

121. (M) First, calculate the enthalpy change for the combustion of 1 L of cetane by using its standard enthalpy of combustion. Then, use the standard enthalpy of combustion of methyl linoleate to determine how much methyl linoleate must be used to produce the same enthalpy change.

Cetane (or hexadecane) is $CH_3(CH_2)_{14}CH_3$ (MM = 226.45 g mol^{-1}). The equation describing its combustion is

$CH_3(CH_2)_{14}CH_3(l) + 49/2 \ O_2(g) \rightarrow 16 \ CO_2(g) + 17 \ H_2O(l)$

Methyl linoleate has the molecular formula $C_{19}H_{34}O_2$ (M = 294.48 g mol^{-1}). The equation describing its combustion is

$C_{19}H_{34}O_2(l) + 53/2 \ O_2(g) \rightarrow 19 \ CO_2(g) + 17 \ H_2O(l)$

The heat produced by the combustion of 1 L of cetane:

$$1 \text{ L cetane} \times \frac{1000 \text{ mL}}{1 \text{ L}} \times \frac{0.773 \text{ g}}{1 \text{ mL}} \times \frac{1 \text{ mol}}{226.448 \text{ g}} \times \frac{-10,699.1 \text{ kJ}}{1 \text{ mol}} = -36,523.31 \text{ kJ}$$

$$-36,523.44 \text{ kJ} \times \frac{\text{mol methyl linoleate}}{-11,690.1 \text{ kJ}} \times \frac{294.479 \text{ g}}{1 \text{ mol}} \times \frac{1 \text{ mL}}{0.885 \text{ g}} \times \frac{1 \text{ L}}{1000 \text{ mL}}$$

= 1.04 L methyl linoleate

122. (M) First, write the balanced equation for reaction of 1 mole of each substance and determine the enthalpy of reaction (or combustion), $\Delta_r H°$, for each reaction. Then use the calculated $\Delta_r H°$ and the reaction stoichiometry to determine moles of CO_2 generated per kJ of energy. Recall that

$$\Delta_r H° = \sum_{products} coefficient \times \Delta_f H° - \sum_{reactants} coefficient \times \Delta_f H°$$

To determine which fuel produces the least amount of CO_2 per equivalent energy output, divide the moles of CO_2 generated per combustion of 1 mole of each fuel by the energy produced by the combustion of 1 mole of that fuel.

Methanol

$CH_3OH(l) + 3/2\ O_2(g) \rightarrow CO_2(g) + 2\ H_2O(l)$

$\Delta_r H° = \left(-393.5\ kJ\ mol^{-1} + 2 \times -285.8\ kJ\ mol^{-1}\right) - \left(-238.7\ kJ\ mol^{-1}\right) = -726.4\ kJ\ mol^{-1}$

Since the combustion of 1 mol CH_3OH produces 1 mol CO_2 and 726.4 kJ of energy, we have 1 mol $CO_2/726.4\ kJ = 1.377 \times 10^{-3}$ mol CO_2/kJ.

Cetane

$C_{16}H_{34}(l) + 49/2\ O_2(l) \rightarrow 16\ CO_2(g) + 17\ H_2O(l)$

$\Delta_r H° = \left[\left(16 \times -393.5\ kJ\ mol^{-1}\right) + \left(17 \times -285.8\ kJ\ mol^{-1}\right)\right] - \left(-456.3\ kJ\ mol^{-1}\right) = -10,698\ kJ\ mol^{-1}$

The combustion of 1 mol $C_{16}H_{34}$ produces 16 mol CO_2, 10,698 kJ of energy, and, therefore, 16 mol $CO_2/10,698\ kJ = 1.4956 \times 10^{-3}$ mol CO_2/kJ.

Methyl linoleate

$C_{19}H_{34}O_2(l) + 53/2\ O_2(g) \rightarrow 19\ CO_2(g) + 17\ H_2O(l)$

$\Delta_r H° = \left(19 \times -393.5\ kJ\ mol^{-1} + 17 \times -285.8\ kJ\ mol^{-1}\right) - \left(-604.9\ kJ\ mol^{-1}\right) = -11,73\underline{0}\ kJ\ mol^{-1}$

The combustion of 1 mol $C_{19}H_{34}O_2$ produces 19 mol CO_2, 11,730 kJ of energy, and, therefore, 19 mol $CO_2/11,730\ kJ = 1.6198 \times 10^{-3}$ mol CO_2/kJ.

Octane

$C_8H_{18}(l) + 25/2\ O_2(g) \rightarrow 8\ CO_2(g) + 9\ H_2O(l)$

$\Delta_r H° = \left(8 \times -393.5\ kJ\ mol^{-1} + 9 \times -285.8\ kJ\ mol^{-1}\right) - \left(-250.1\ kJ\ mol^{-1}\right) = -547\underline{0}\ kJ\ mol^{-1}$

The combustion of 1 mol C_8H_{18} produces 8 mol CO_2, 5470 kJ of energy, and, therefore, 8 mol $CO_2/5470\ kJ = 1.463 \times 10^{-3}$ mol CO_2/kJ.

Therefore, methanol produces the least amount of CO_2 per unit of energy generated.

FEATURE PROBLEMS

123. (M) $1 \, °F = 5/9 \, °C = 0.555 \, °C \quad 1 \, lb = 453.6 \, g$

$E_p = mgh$

$E_p = (772 \, lb)(9.80665 \, m \, s^{-2})(1 \, ft) = 7.57 \times 10^3 \dfrac{lb \, m \, ft}{s^2}$

$E_p = 7.57 \times 10^3 \dfrac{lb \, m \, ft}{s^2} \times \dfrac{0.3048 \, m}{ft} \times \dfrac{0.4536 \, kg}{lb}$

$E_p = 1047 \dfrac{kg \, m^2}{s^2} = 1047 \, J = 1.05 \, kJ$

The statement is validated.

$q = m \times (c_p)\Delta T$

$q = 453.6 \, g (4.184 \dfrac{J}{g \, °C})(0.556 \, °C)$

$q = 1054 \, J$

$q = 1.05 \, kJ$

124. (D)

(a) We plot specific heat capacity vs. the inverse of atomic mass.

(b) The equation of the line is: specific heat capacity = 23.9 ÷ (atomic mass) + 0.0113

$0.23 \, J \, g^{-1} \, °C = 23.9 \div (atomic \, mass) + 0.0113$

$atomic \, mass = \dfrac{23.9}{0.23 - 0.0113} = 10\underline{9} \, u \, \text{ or } 110 \, u \, (2 \text{ sig fig});$

Cadmium's tabulated atomic mass is 112.4 u.

(c) $c_p = \dfrac{450 \, J}{75.0 \, g \times 15.°C} = 0.40 \, J \, g^{-1}°C^{-1} = 0.0113 + 23.9/\text{atomic mass}$

$atomic \, mass = \dfrac{23.9}{0.40 - 0.0113} = 61.\underline{5} \, u \, \text{ or } 62 \, u \quad \text{The metal is most likely Cu(63.5 u).}$

125. **(D)** The plot's maximum is the equivalence point. (Assume $\Delta T = 0$ at 0 mL of added NaOH, (i.e., only 60 mL of citric acid are present), and that $\Delta T = 0$ at 60 mL of NaOH (i.e. no citric acid added).

Plot of ΔT versus Volume of NaOH

(a) The equivalence point occurs with 45.0 mL of 1.00 M NaOH(aq) [45.0 mmol NaOH] added and 15.0 mL of 1.00 M citric acid [15.0 mmol citric acid]. Again, we assume that ΔT = zero if no NaOH added ($V_{\text{NaOH}} = 0$ mL) and $\Delta T = 0$ if no citric acid is added ($V_{\text{NaOH}} = 60$ mL).

(b) Heat is a product of the reaction, as are chemical species (products). Products are maximized at the exact stoichiometric proportions. Since each reaction mixture has the same volume, and thus about the same mass to heat, the temperature also is a maximum at this point.

(c) $H_3C_6H_5O_7(s) + 3OH^-(aq) \rightarrow 3H_2O(l) + C_6H_5O_7^{3-}(aq)$

126. **(M)**
(a) The reactions, and their temperature changes, are as follows.
(1st) $\quad NH_3(\text{conc. aq}) + HCl(aq) \rightarrow NH_4Cl(aq) \qquad \Delta T = (35.8 - 23.8)\,°C = 12.0\,°C$
(2nd,a) $\quad NH_3(\text{conc. aq}) \rightarrow NH_3(g) \qquad\qquad\qquad \Delta T = (13.2 - 19.3)\,°C = -6.1\,°C$
(2nd,b) $\quad NH_3(g) + HCl(aq) \rightarrow NH_4Cl(aq) \qquad\quad \Delta T = (42.9 - 23.8)\,°C = 19.1\,°C$
The sum of reactions $(2nd, a) + (2nd, b)$ produces the same change as the 1st reaction.

(b) We now compute the heat absorbed by the surroundings for each. Hess's law is demonstrated if $\Delta H_1 = \Delta H_{2a} + \Delta H_{2b}$, where in each case $\Delta H = -q$.

$q_1 = \left[(100.0 \text{ mL} + 8.00 \text{ mL}) \times 1.00 \text{ g/mL}\right] 4.18 \text{ J g}^{-1}\,°C^{-1} \times 12.0\,°C = 5.42 \times 10^3 \text{ J} = -\Delta H_1$

$q_{2a} = \left[(100.0 \text{ mL} \times 1.00 \text{ g/mL}) \, 4.18 \text{ J g}^{-1}\,°C^{-1} \times (-6.1\,°C)\right] = -2.55 \times 10^3 \text{ J} = -\Delta H_{2a}$

$q_{2b} = \left[(100.0 \text{ mL} \times 1.00 \text{ g/mL}) \, 4.18 \text{ J g}^{-1}\,°C^{-1} \times (19.1\,°C)\right] = 7.98 \times 10^3 \text{ J} = -\Delta H_{2b}$

$\Delta H_{2a} + \Delta H_{2b} = +2.55 \times 10^3 \text{ J} - 7.98 \times 10^3 \text{ J} = -5.43 \times 10^3 \text{ J} \cong -5.42 \times 10^3 \text{ J} = \Delta H_1 (QED)$

127. (D) According to the kinetic-molecular theory of gases, the internal energy of an ideal gas, U, is proportional to the average translational kinetic energy for the gas particles, e_k, which in turn is proportional to $3/2\ RT$. Thus the internal energy for a fixed amount of an ideal gas depends only on its temperature, i.e., $U = 3/2\ nRT$, where U is the internal energy (J), n is the number of moles of gas particles, R is the gas constant (J K^{-1} mol^{-1}), and T is the temperature (K). If the temperature of the gas sample is changed, the resulting change in internal energy is given by $\Delta U = 3/2\ nR\Delta T$.

(a) At constant volume, $q_v = nC_v\Delta T$. Assuming that no work is done $\Delta U = q_v$ so, $\Delta U = q_v = 3/2nR\Delta T = nC_v\Delta T$. (divide both sides by $n\Delta T$) $C_v = 3/2\ R = 12.5$ J/mol K.

(b) The heat flow at constant pressure q_p is the ΔH for the process (i.e., $q_p = \Delta H$) and we know that $\Delta H = \Delta U - w$ and $w = -P\Delta V = -nR\Delta T$.
Hence, $q_p = \Delta U - w = \Delta U - (-nR\Delta T) = \Delta U + nR\Delta T$ and $q_p = nC_p\Delta T$ and $\Delta U = 3/2\ nR\Delta T$ Consequently $q_p = nC_p\Delta T = nR\Delta T + 3/2\ nR\Delta T$ (divide both sides by $n\Delta T$) Now, $C_p = R + 3/2\ R = 5/2\ R = 20.8$ J/mol K.

128. (D)

(a) Here we must determine the volume between 2.40 atm and 1.30 atm using $PV = nRT$

$$V = \frac{0.100\ \text{mol} \times 0.08206\ \text{L mol}^{-1}\ \text{K}^{-1} \times 298\ \text{K}}{P} = \frac{2.44\underline{5}\ \text{atm L}}{P}$$

For $P = 2.40$ atm: $V = 1.02$ L
For $P = 2.30$ atm: $V = 1.06$ L $P\Delta V = 2.30$ atm $\times -0.04$ L $= -0.09\underline{2}$ atm L
For $P = 2.20$ atm: $V = 1.11$ L $P\Delta V = 2.20$ atm $\times -0.05$ L $= -0.1\underline{1}$ atm L
For $P = 2.10$ atm: $V = 1.16$ L $P\Delta V = 2.10$ atm $\times -0.05$ L $= -0.1\underline{1}$ atm L
For $P = 2.00$ atm: $V = 1.22$ L $P\Delta V = 2.00$ atm $\times -0.06$ L $= -0.1\underline{2}$ atm L
For $P = 1.90$ atm: $V = 1.29$ L $P\Delta V = 1.90$ atm $\times -0.06$ L $= -0.1\underline{2}$ atm L
For $P = 1.80$ atm: $V = 1.36$ L $P\Delta V = 1.80$ atm $\times -0.07$ L $= -0.1\underline{3}$ atm L
For $P = 1.70$ atm: $V = 1.44$ L $P\Delta V = 1.70$ atm $\times -0.08$ L $= -0.1\underline{4}$ atm L
For $P = 1.60$ atm: $V = 1.53$ L $P\Delta V = 1.60$ atm $\times -0.09$ L $= -0.1\underline{4}$ atm L
For $P = 1.50$ atm: $V = 1.63$ L $P\Delta V = 1.50$ atm $\times -0.10$ L $= -0.1\underline{5}$ atm L
For $P = 1.40$ atm: $V = 1.75$ L $P\Delta V = 1.40$ atm $\times -0.12$ L $= -0.1\underline{7}$ atm L
For $P = 1.30$ atm: $V = 1.88$ L $P\Delta V = 1.30$ atm $\times -0.13$ L $= -0.1\underline{7}$ atm L

total work $= -\Sigma\ P\Delta V = -1.4\underline{5}$ atm L
Expressed in joules, the work is $-1.4\underline{5}$ atm L $\times 101.325$ J/atm L $= -14\underline{7}$ J.

(b)

(c) The total work done in the two-step expansion is minus one times the total of the area of the two rectangles under the graph, which turns out to be −1.29 atm L or −131 J. In the 11-step expansion in (b), the total area of the rectangles is 1.45 atm L or −14$\underline{7}$ J. If the expansion were divided into a larger number of stages, the total area of the rectangles would be even greater. The maximum amount of work is for an expansion with an infinite number of stages and is equal to the area under the pressure–volume curve between $V = 1.02$ L and 1.88 L. This area is also obtained as the integral of the expression:

$dw = -PdV = -nRT(dV/V)$. The value obtained is:
$w = -nRT \times \ln V_f / V_i = 0.100 \text{ mol} \times 8.3145 \text{ J mol}^{-1} \text{ K}^{-1} \times 298 \text{ K} \times \ln (1.88 \text{ L}/1.02 \text{ L})$
$w = -152$ J

(d) The maximum work of compression is for a one-stage compression using an external pressure of 2.40 atm and producing a compression in volume of 1.02 L − 1.88 L = −0.86 L: $w = -P\Delta V = (2.40 \text{ atm} \times 0.86 \text{ L}) \times 101.33 \text{ J/atm L} = 209$ J

The minimum work would be that done in an infinite number of steps and would be the same as the work determined in (c) but with a positive sign, namely, +152 J.

(e) Because the internal energy of an ideal gas is a function only of temperature, and the temperature remains constant, $\Delta U = 0$. Because $\Delta U = q + w = 0$, $q = -w$. This means that −209 J corresponds to the maximum work of compression, and −152 J corresponds to the minimum work of compression.

(f) For the expansion described in part in (c),
$q = -w = nRT \ln V_f/V_i$ and $q/T = nR \ln V_f/V_i$
Because the terms on the right side are all constants or functions of state, so too is the term on the left, q/T. In Chapter 19, we learn that q/T is equal to ΔS, the change in a state function called *entropy*.

129. (D) We use the data in Table 7.1 to generate the plot, with the c_p of T_i added in to demonstrate how it fits in with the data. Below are the data table and the plot

Element	Atomic Weight (AW)	1/Aw	Cp	AW*Cp
Mg	24.3	0.041152	1.024	24.8832
Al	26.98	0.037064	0.903	24.36294
P	30.97	0.032289	0.777	24.06369
S	32.06	0.031192	0.706	22.63436
Fe	55.85	0.017905	0.449	25.07665
Cu	63.55	0.015736	0.385	24.46675
As	74.92	0.013348	0.329	24.64868
Se	78.96	0.012665	0.321	25.34616
Te	127.6	0.007837	0.202	25.7752
Pb	207.19	0.004826	0.128	26.52032
Ti	47.88	0.020886	0.523	25.04124

We can see that all the values in general center around 24 J/(mol·K) for all elements. This is known as the rule of Dulong–Petit. It is illustrated below in another way by plotting C_p versus the inverse of the atomic number. The slope of this line is ~24 J/(mol·K):

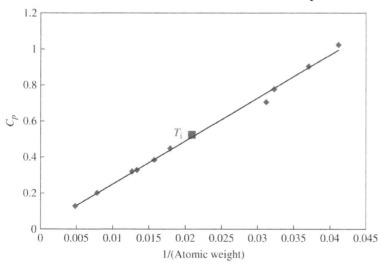

SELF-ASSESSMENT EXERCISES

130. (E)

    (a) ΔH: Enthalpy change of the system. ΔH is equal to q, the heat transferred, if the heat transfer occurs at constant pressure.

    (b) $-P\Delta V$: Work done by the system (or on the system) through volume change at constant pressure

    (c) $\Delta_f H°$: Enthalpy of formation of a compound at standard conditions

    (d) Standard State: The pure element or compound under a pressure of 1 bar at a specified temperature

    (e) Fossil fuel: A fuel source generated by the decomposition of plant and animal matter in the crust of the earth

131. (E)

    (a) Law of conservation of energy: Energy is neither created nor destroyed (or stated differently, in the interaction between the system and the surroundings, the total energy of the system remains constant).

    (b) Bomb calorimetry: A method of determining heats of reaction (mainly combustion).

    (c) Function of state: A function that only depends on the state of the system, such as initial and final conditions, and is insensitive to how the state was established

    (d) Enthalpy diagram: A diagram that represents the enthalpy change in a system

    (e) Hess's Law: The enthalpy change of a process can be determined by summation of enthalpies of individual and elementary steps

132. (E)

    (a) *System* is what we are studying. *Surroundings* is everything else.

    (b) *Heat* is the flow of thermal energy. *Work* involves physical movement of an entity (whether microscopic or macroscopic)

    (c) *Heat capacity* is the quantity of energy required to change the temperature of a substance by 1 degree. *Specific heat capacity* is the heat capacity of 1 g of a substance.

    (d) A system where the reaction is done at a constant volume to eliminate work done by the system is a *constant volume system*. In a *constant pressure system*, there can be expansion and contraction and therefore work can be done.

133. (E) The answer is (b), Al, because it has the highest heat capacity.

134. (E) The answer is (c). We know that $m_1 c\Delta T_1 = -m_2 c\Delta T_2$, where m_1 and m_2 are the masses of each quantity of water. Therefore, the equation above can be expanded and simplified as follows:

$75 (T_f - 80) = -100 (T_f - 20)$

Solving for T_f gives a value of 45.7 °C.

135. (E) The answer is (d). $U\Delta = q + w$. Since $q = -100$ J, $w = +200$ J, or the system has 200 J of work done on it.

136. **(E)** The answer is (a). The heat generated by NaOH is absorbed by the system.

137. **(E)** The answer is (b). As graphite is burned in O_2, it generates CO_2. Enthalpy of formation of CO_2 is therefore the same as enthalpy of combustion of C.

138. (E)
    (a) $Sn(s) + Cl_2(g) \rightarrow SnCl_2(s)$
    (b) $7 \ C(graphite) + 3 \ H_2(g) + O_2(g) \rightarrow C_6H_5COOH(s)$
    (c) $C(graphite) + \frac{1}{2} \ O_2(g) + Cl_2(g) \rightarrow COCl_2(g)$

139. (E)
    (a)

$$\Delta_r H^\circ = \Delta_f H^\circ \left[SiF_4(g) \right] + 2 \times \Delta_f H^\circ \left[H_2O(g) \right] - \left(\Delta_f H^\circ \left[SiO_2(s) \right] + 4 \times \Delta_f H^\circ \left[HF(g) \right] \right)$$

$$= -1615.0 + 2(-241.8) - \left[-910.9 + 4(-271.1) \right]$$

$$= -103.3 \ kJ \ mol^{-1}$$

    (b)

$$\Delta_r H^\circ = 2 \times \Delta_f H^\circ \left[CuO(s) \right] + 2 \times \Delta_f H^\circ \left[SO_2(g) \right] - \left(2 \times \Delta_f H^\circ \left[CuS(s) \right] + 3 \times \Delta_f H^\circ \left[O_2(g) \right] \right)$$

$$= 2(-157.3) + 2(-296.8) - \left[2(-53.1) + 3(0.0) \right]$$

$$= -802.0 \ kJ \ mol^{-1}$$

140. (M) First, determine the number of moles of LiCl:

$$n = 5.00 \ g \times \frac{1 \ mol}{42.391 \ g} = 0.1179 \ mol$$

Then, determine the amount of heat generated:

$$q = \frac{37.2 \ kJ}{1 \ mol} \times 0.1179 \ mol = 4.3859 \ kJ$$

Now use $q = C\Delta T$:

$$4.3859 \ kJ = 115.0 \ g \times \left(4.00 \times 10^{-3} \ kJ \ g^{-1} \ ^\circ C^{-1} \right) \times \left(T_f - 20.00 \ ^\circ C \right)$$

Solving for the final temperature, T_f:

$$T_f - 20.00 \ ^\circ C = \frac{4.3859 \ kJ}{115.0 \ g \times \left(4.00 \times 10^{-3} \ kJ \ g^{-1} \ ^\circ C^{-1} \right)}$$

$$T_f = 9.53 \ ^\circ C + 20.00 \ ^\circ C$$

$$= 29.53 \ ^\circ C$$

141. (E) The correct answer is (b).

142. (E) The correct answer is (a).

143. (E) The answer is (a), because q_V and q_P are not the same.

144. (E)

(a) We have to solve for the heat capacity (c_p) of Fe:

$m \cdot c_p \cdot \Delta T \,(H_2O) = - m \cdot c_p \cdot \Delta T \,(Fe)$

$(981\,g)(4.189)(12.3\,°C) = -(1220)(c_{P(Fe)})(-92.1\,°C)$

Solving for c_{pFe}, the heat capacity of Fe is $0.449\ J\ g^{-1}\ °C^{-1}$

(b) Now knowing the c_p of Fe, we can calculate the T_f of the iron–glycerol system:

$(409.5)(2.378)(T_f - 26.2) = -(1220)(0.4489)(T_f - 99.8)$

Solving $T_f = 52.7\ °C$

145. (E)

(a) $2\ N_2 + O_2 \rightarrow 2\ N_2O$

(b) $S + O_2 + Cl_2 \rightarrow SO_2Cl_2$

(c) $2\ CH_3CH_2COOH + 7\ O_2 \rightarrow 6\ CO_2 + 6\ H_2O$

146. (D) First, determine the $\Delta_f H°$ of CO, which is used to make $COCl_2$. This is done by using the equations for the combustion of C and CO gases:

(1) $CO + \frac{1}{2} O_2 \rightarrow CO_2$	–283.0 kJ/mol
(2) $C + O_2 \rightarrow CO_2$	–393.5 kJ/mol

To determine the $\Delta_f H°$ of CO, reverse and double equation (1) and double equation (2):

(1) $2\ CO_2 \rightarrow 2\ CO + O_2$	$566.0\ kJ\ mol^{-1}$
(2) $2\ C + 2\ O_2 \rightarrow 2\ CO_2$	$-787.0\ kJ\ mol^{-1}$
(3) $2\ C + O_2 \rightarrow 2\ CO$	$-221.0\ kJ\ mol^{-1}$
	or –110.5 kJ/mol if only 1 mole of CO is formed

Now, we use the equation for the formation of $COCl_2$ with equation (3) times ½.

(4) $CO + Cl_2 \rightarrow COCl_2$	$-108.0\ kJ\ mol^{-1}$
(3) $C + \frac{1}{2} O_2 \rightarrow CO$	$-110.5\ kJ\ mol^{-1}$
(3) $C + \frac{1}{2} O_2 + Cl_2 \rightarrow COCl_2$	$-218.5\ kJ\ mol^{-1}$

Therefore, $\Delta_f H°$ of $COCl_2$ is –218 kJ/mol.

147. **(E)** Enthalpy of formation for elements (even molecular ones, such as O_2 or Cl_2) is by convention set to 0. While it is possible for the enthalpy of formation of a compound to be near zero, it is unlikely.

148. **(M)** We note that $\Delta H = \Delta U + \Delta(PV)$. From a theoretical standpoint, one can have a situation where the $\Delta U < 0$, but there is enough work done on the system that makes $\Delta H > 0$. In reality, because the $\Delta(PV)$ is relatively small, ΔH and ΔU often have the same sign.

149. **(M)** A gas stove works by combustion of a flammable fuel. The amount of heat can be controlled by a valve. Once shut off, the heat source instantly disappears. However, an electric stove works by the principle of heat conduction, where the heat coil on the stove transfers heat to the pot through direct contact. Even after the electricity is shut off to the heating coil, it takes time for the coil to cool because of its heat capacity, and therefore it continues to supply heat to the pot.

150. **(E)** The answer is (a), 0. This is because there is no loss of energy to or gain of energy from the surroundings.

151. **(M)** The answer is (b), the temperature decreases (or at least it increases at a slower rate than it would if there was no moisture on the outside). The moisture put outside of the pot evaporates mainly because of removing heat from the pot. Therefore, the moisture on the outside of the pot removes heat from the pot as it evaporates, therefore slightly cooling the pot.

152. **(M)** To construct a concept map, one must first start with the most general concepts. These concepts are not defined by or in terms of other concepts discussed in those sections. In this case, we are constructing a map for the first law of thermodynamics. After giving the definition, the concept can be broken up into two subtopics: functions of state, path-dependent functions. Functions of state should contain a discussion of ΔU. Path-dependent functions should have a discussion of work (w) and heat (q). In the path-dependent functions subsection, there should be a discussion on the nomenclature for determining heat and work flow in and out of the system. Then, there should be a subheading for work, discussing the various forms of work (such as $P-V$ work, for instance). A discussion of heat should contain subheadings for enthalpy at constant volume and pressure.

153. **(M)** The concept map of the use of enthalpy in chemical reactions has several major subheadings. After the definition of enthalpy, there should be three major subheadings: (1) expressing enthalpy graphically using enthalpy diagrams, (2) enthalpy of change for phase transformation, and (3) standard states and standard transformations. Then, under standard states and transformations, there would be further subheadings discussing (1) enthalpy of reaction, and (2) enthalpy of formation. Hess's law would be a subtopic for #1.

154. **(M)** This concept map starts with the root term *terms in thermodynamics*. It is then split into the major subheadings, (1) path-dependent and (2) path-independent quantities. The remainder is very similar to question 144.

CHAPTER 8
ELECTRONS IN ATOMS
PRACTICE EXAMPLES

1A **(E)** Use $c = \lambda \nu$, solve for frequency. $\nu = \dfrac{2.9979 \times 10^8 \text{ m/s}}{690 \text{ nm}} \times \dfrac{10^9 \text{ nm}}{1 \text{ m}} = 4.34 \times 10^{14}$ Hz

1B **(E)** Wavelength and frequency are related through the equation $c = \lambda \nu$, which can be solved for either one.

$$\lambda = \frac{c}{\nu} = \frac{2.9979 \times 10^8 \text{ m/s}}{91.5 \times 10^6 \text{ s}^{-1}} = 3.28 \text{ m} \quad \text{Note that Hz} = \text{s}^{-1}$$

2A **(E)** The relationship $\nu = c / \lambda$ can be substituted into the equation $E = h\nu$ to obtain $E = hc / \lambda$. This energy, in J/photon, can then be converted to kJ/mol.

$$E = \frac{hc}{\lambda} = \frac{6.626 \times 10^{-34} \text{ J s photon}^{-1} \times 2.998 \times 10^8 \text{ m s}^{-1}}{230 \text{ nm} \times \dfrac{1 \text{ m}}{10^9 \text{ nm}}} \times \frac{6.022 \times 10^{23} \text{ photons}}{1 \text{ mol}} \times \frac{1 \text{ kJ}}{1000 \text{ J}} = 520 \text{ kJ/mol}$$

With a similar calculation one finds that 290 nm corresponds to 410 kJ/mol. Thus, the energy range is from 410 to 520 kJ/mol, respectively.

2B **(M)** The equation $E = h\nu$ is solved for frequency and the two frequencies are calculated.

$$\nu = \frac{E}{h} = \frac{3.056 \times 10^{-19} \text{ J/photon}}{6.626 \times 10^{-34} \text{ J s/photon}} \qquad \nu = \frac{E}{h} = \frac{4.414 \times 10^{-19} \text{ J/photon}}{6.626 \times 10^{-34} \text{ J s/photon}}$$

$$= 4.612 \times 10^{14} \text{ Hz} \qquad\qquad = 6.662 \times 10^{14} \text{ Hz}$$

To determine color, we calculate the wavelength of each frequency and compare it with *text* Figure 8-3.

$$\lambda = \frac{c}{\nu} = \frac{2.9979 \times 10^8 \text{ m/s}}{4.612 \times 10^{14} \text{ Hz}} \times \frac{10^9 \text{ nm}}{1 \text{ m}} \qquad \lambda = \frac{c}{\nu} = \frac{2.9979 \times 10^8 \text{ m/s}}{6.662 \times 10^{14} \text{ Hz}} \times \frac{10^9 \text{ nm}}{1 \text{ m}}$$

$$= 650 \text{ nm} \quad \text{orange} \qquad\qquad = 450 \text{ nm} \quad \text{indigo}$$

The colors of the spectrum that are not absorbed are what we see when we look at a plant, namely in this case blue, green, and yellow. The plant appears green.

3A **(E)** We solve the Rydberg equation for n to see if we obtain an integer.

$$n = \sqrt{n^2} = \sqrt{\frac{-R_\mathrm{H}}{E_n}} = \sqrt{\frac{-2.179 \times 10^{-18} \text{ J}}{-2.69 \times 10^{-20} \text{ J}}} = \sqrt{81.00} = 9.00 \qquad \text{This is } E_9 \text{ for } n = 9.$$

3B **(E)**

$$E_\mathrm{n} = \frac{-R_\mathrm{H}}{n^2}$$

$$-4.45 \times 10^{-20} \text{ J} = \frac{-2.179 \times 10^{-18} \text{ J}}{n^2}$$

$$n^2 = 48.97 \Rightarrow n = 7$$

4A **(E)** We first determine the energy difference, and then the wavelength of light for that energy.

$$\Delta E = R_H \left(\frac{1}{2^2} - \frac{1}{4^2} \right) = 2.179 \times 10^{-18} \text{ J} \left(\frac{1}{2^2} - \frac{1}{4^2} \right) = 4.086 \times 10^{-19} \text{ J}$$

$$\lambda = \frac{hc}{\Delta E} = \frac{6.626 \times 10^{-34} \text{ J s} \times 2.998 \times 10^8 \text{ m s}^{-1}}{4.086 \times 10^{-19} \text{ J}} = 4.862 \times 10^{-7} \text{ m or } 486.2 \text{ nm}$$

4B **(M)** The longest wavelength light results from the transition that spans the smallest difference in energy. Since all Lyman series emissions end with $n_f = 1$, the smallest energy transition has $n_i = 2$. From this, we obtain the value of ΔE.

$$\Delta E = R_H \left(\frac{1}{n_i^2} - \frac{1}{n_f^2} \right) = 2.179 \times 10^{-18} \, J \left(\frac{1}{2^2} - \frac{1}{1^2} \right) = -1.634 \times 10^{-18} \text{ J}$$

From this energy emitted, we can obtain the wavelength of the emitted light: $\Delta E = hc / \lambda$

$$\lambda = \frac{hc}{\Delta E} = \frac{6.626 \times 10^{-34} \text{ J s} \times 2.998 \times 10^8 \text{ m s}^{-1}}{1.634 \times 10^{-18} \text{ J}} = 1.216 \times 10^{-7} \text{ m or } 121.6 \text{ nm (1216 angstroms)}$$

5A **(M)**

$$E_f = \frac{-Z^2 \times R_H}{n_f^2} = \frac{-4^2 \times 2.179 \times 10^{-18} \text{ J}}{3^2}$$

$$E_f = -3.874 \times 10^{-18} \text{ J}$$

$$E_i = \frac{-Z^2 \times R_H}{n_i^2} = \frac{-4^2 \times 2.179 \times 10^{-18} \text{ J}}{5^2}$$

$$E_i = -1.395 \times 10^{-18} \text{ J}$$

$$\Delta E = E_f - E_i$$

$$\Delta E = (-3.874 \times 10^{-18} \text{ J}) - (-1.395 \times 10^{-18} \text{ J})$$

$$\Delta E = -2.479 \times 10^{-18} \text{ J}$$

To determine the wavelength, use $E = h\nu = \frac{hc}{\lambda}$; Rearrange for λ:

$$\lambda = \frac{hc}{E} = \frac{(6.626 \times 10^{-34} \text{ J s})\left(2.998 \times 10^8 \, \frac{m}{s} \right)}{2.479 \times 10^{-18} \text{ J}} = 8.013 \times 10^{-8} \text{ m or } 80.13 \text{ nm}$$

5B **(E)** Since $E = \frac{-Z^2 \times R_H}{n^2}$, the transitions are related to Z^2, hence, if the frequency is 16 times greater, then the value of the ratio $\frac{Z^2 (\text{?-atom})}{Z^2 (\text{H-atom})} = \frac{Z_?^2}{1^2} = 16$.

We can see $Z^2 = 16$ or $Z = 4$ This is a Be nucleus. The hydrogen-like ion must be Be^{3+}.

6A **(E)** Superman's de Broglie wavelength is given by the relationship $\lambda = h/mu$.

$$\lambda = \frac{h}{mu} = \frac{6.626 \times 10^{-34} \text{Js}}{91 \text{ kg} \times \frac{1}{5} \times 2.998 \times 10^8 \text{ m/s}} = 1.21 \times 10^{-43} \text{ m}$$

6B **(M)** The de Broglie wavelength is given by $\lambda = h/mu$, which can be solved for u.

$$u = \frac{h}{m\lambda} = \frac{6.626 \times 10^{-34} \text{ J s}}{1.673 \times 10^{-27} \text{ kg} \times 10.0 \times 10^{-12} \text{ m}} = 3.96 \times 10^4 \text{ m/s}$$

We used the facts that $1 \text{ J} = \text{kg m}^2 \text{s}^{-2}$, $1 \text{pm} = 10^{-12}$ m, and $1 \text{ g} = 10^{-3}$ kg

7A **(M)** $p = (91 \text{ kg})(5.996 \times 10^7 \text{ m s}^{-1}) = 5.4\underline{6} \times 10^9 \text{ kg m s}^{-1}$
$\Delta p = (0.015)(5.4\underline{6} \times 10^9 \text{ kg m s}^{-1}) = 8.2 \times 10^7 \text{ kg m s}^{-1}$

$$\Delta x = \frac{h}{4\pi \Delta p} = \frac{6.626 \times 10^{-34} \text{ J s}}{(4\pi)(8.2 \times 10^7 \frac{\text{kg m}}{\text{s}})} = 6.4 \times 10^{-43} \text{ m}$$

7B **(M)** $24 \text{ nm} = 2.4 \times 10^{-8} \text{ m} = \Delta x = \dfrac{h}{4\pi \Delta p} = \dfrac{6.626 \times 10^{-34} \text{ J s}}{(4\pi)(\Delta p)}$

Solve for Δp: $\Delta p = 2.2 \times 10^{-27} \text{ kg m s}^{-1}$
$(\Delta u)(m) = \Delta p = 2.2 \times 10^{-27} \text{ kg m s}^{-1} = (\Delta u)(1.67 \times 10^{-27} \text{ kg})$ Hence, $\Delta u = 1.3 \text{ m s}^{-1}$.

8A. **(M)** To calculate the probability percentage of finding an electron between 50 and 75 pm for an electron in level 6 ($n = 6$, # nodes $= 6 - 1 = 5$), one must integrate the probability function, which is the square of the wave function between 50 and 75 pm:

Probability function:

$$\psi_6^2 = \frac{2}{L}\sin^2\left(\frac{n\pi}{L}x\right)$$

$$\int_{50}^{75} \frac{2}{L}\sin^2\left(\frac{n\pi}{L}x\right)dx = \left[\frac{2}{L}\left(\frac{x}{2} - \frac{1}{2(n\pi/L)} \cdot \sin\left(\frac{n\pi}{L}x\right) \cdot \cos\left(\frac{n\pi}{L}x\right)\right)\right]_{50}^{75}$$

$$= 0.499\overline{9} - 0.333\overline{3} = 0.166\overline{6}$$

The probability is 0.167 out of 1, or 16.7%. Of course, we could have done this without any use of calculus by following the simple algebra used in Example 8-8. However, it is just more fun to integrate the function. The above example was made simple by giving the limits of integration at two nodes. Had the limits been in locations that were *not* nodes, you would have had no choice but to integrate.

8B. **(E)** We simply note here that at $n = 3$, the number of nodes is $n - 1 = 2$. Therefore, a box that is 300 pm long will have two nodes at 100 and 200 pm.

9A **(D)** $50. \text{ pm} \times \dfrac{1 \text{ m}}{1 \times 10^{12} \text{ pm}} = 5.0 \times 10^{-11} \text{ m}$

$\Delta E = E_{\text{excited state}} - E_{\text{ground state}}$

$E = \dfrac{n^2 h^2}{8mL^2}$ Where n = energy level, h = Planck's constant, m = mass, L = length of box

$\Delta E = \dfrac{3^2 h^2}{8 \, mL^2} - \dfrac{5^2 h^2}{8 \, mL^2}$

$\Delta E = \dfrac{-16 \, h^2}{8 \, mL^2} = \dfrac{-16(6.626 \times 10^{-34} \, Js)^2}{8(9.109 \times 10^{-31})(5.0 \times 10^{-11})^2}$

$\Delta E = -3.86 \times 10^{-16} \text{ J}$

The negative sign indicates that energy was released / emitted.

$\lambda = \dfrac{hc}{\Delta E} = \dfrac{(6.626 \times 10^{-34} \, J \, s)(3.00 \times 10^8 \, m \, s^{-1})}{3.86 \times 10^{-16} \, J}$

$\lambda = 5.15 \times 10^{-10} \, m \times \dfrac{10^9 \text{ nm}}{1 \text{ m}} = 0.515 \text{ nm} = 0.52 \text{ nm}$

9B **(D)**

$24.9 \text{ nm} \times \dfrac{1 \text{ m}}{10^9 \text{ nm}} = 2.49 \times 10^{-8} \text{ m}$

$\Delta E = \dfrac{hc}{\lambda} = \dfrac{(6.626 \times 10^{-34} \, J \, s)(3.00 \times 10^8 \text{ m s}^{-1})}{2.49 \times 10^{-8} \text{ m}}$

$\Delta E = 7.98 \times 10^{-18} \text{ J}$

$\Delta E = \dfrac{2^2 h^2}{8 \, mL^2} - \dfrac{1^2 h^2}{8 \, mL^2}$

$\Delta E = \dfrac{3 \, h^2}{8 \, mL^2}$

$7.98 \times 10^{-18} \, J = \dfrac{3(6.626 \times 10^{-34} \, J \, s)^2}{8(9.109 \times 10^{-31})(L)^2}$

$L^2 = 2.265 \times 10^{-20}$

$L = 1.50 \times 10^{-10} \text{ m} = 150. \text{ pm}$

10A **(E)** Yes, an orbital can have the quantum numbers $n = 3$, $\ell = 0$ and $m_\ell = 0$. The values of ℓ can be between 0 and $n - 1$. The values of m_ℓ m_ℓ can be between ℓ and $-\ell$ encompassing zero. The three quantum numbers given in this question represent a $3s$ orbital.

10B **(E)** For an orbital with $n = 3$ the possible values of ℓ are 0, 1, and 2. However, when $m_\ell = 0$, this would omit $\ell = 0$ because when $\ell = 0$, m_ℓ must be 0. Therefore in order for both quantum numbers of $n = 3$ and $m_\ell = 1$ to be fulfilled, the only m_ℓ values allowed would be $\ell = 1$ and 2.

11A **(E)** The magnetic quantum number, m_ℓ, is not reflected in the orbital designation. Because $\ell = 1$, this is a p orbital. Because $n = 3$, the designation is $3p$.

11B **(M)** The H-atom orbitals $3s$, $3p$, and $3d$ are degenerate. Therefore, the 9 quantum number combinations are:

	n	ℓ	m_ℓ
$3s$	3	0	0
$3p$	3	1	$-1,0,+1$
$3d$	3	2	$-2,-1,0,+1,+2$

Hence, $n = 3; 1 = 0, 1, 2; m_1 = -2, -1, 0, 1, 2$

12A **(E)**

$(3, 2, -2, 1)$	$m_s = 1$ is incorrect. The values of m_s can only be $+\frac{1}{2}$ or $-\frac{1}{2}$.
$(3, 1, -2, \frac{1}{2})$	$m_\ell = -2$ is incorrect. The values of m_ℓ can be $+1, 0, +1$ when $\ell = 1$
$(3, 0, 0, \frac{1}{2})$	All quantum numbers are allowed.
$(2, 3, 0, \frac{1}{2})$	$\ell = 3$ is incorrect. The value for ℓ can not be larger than n.
$(1, 0, 0, -\frac{1}{2})$	All quantum numbers are allowed.
$(2, -1, -1, \frac{1}{2})$	$\ell = -1$ is incorrect. The value for ℓ can not be negative.

12B **(E)**

$(2, 1, 1, 0)$	$m_s = 0$ is incorrect. The values of m_s can only be $+\frac{1}{2}$ or $-\frac{1}{2}$.
$(1, 1, 0, \frac{1}{2})$	$\ell = 1$ is incorrect. The value for ℓ is 0 when $n = 1$.
$(3, -1, 1, \frac{1}{2})$	$\ell = -1$ is incorrect. The value for ℓ can not be negative.
$(0, 0, 0, -\frac{1}{2})$	$n = 0$ is incorrect. The value for n can not be zero.
$(2, 1, 2, \frac{1}{2})$	$m_\ell = 2$ is incorrect. The values of m_ℓ can be $+1, 0, +1$ when $\ell = 1$.

13A **(E)** (a) and (c) are equivalent. The valence electrons are in two different degenerate p orbitals and the electrons are spinning in the same direction in both orbital diagrams.

13B **(E)** This orbital diagram represents an excited state of a neutral species. The ground state would follow Hund's rule and there would be one electron in each of the three degenerate p orbitals.

14A **(E)** We can simply sum the exponents to obtain the number of electrons in the neutral atom and thus the atomic number of the element. $Z = 2 + 2 + 6 + 2 + 6 + 2 + 2 = 22$, which is the atomic number for Ti.

14B **(E)** Iodine has an atomic number of 53. The first 36 electrons have the same electron configuration as $Kr: 1s^2 2s^2 2p^6 3s^2 3p^6 3d^{10} 4s^2 4p^6$. The next two electrons go into the $5s$ subshell $(5s^2)$, then 10 electrons fill the $4d$ subshell $(4d^{10})$, accounting for a total of 48 electrons. The last five electrons partially fill the $5p$ subshell $(5p^5)$.

The electron configuration of I is therefore $1s^2 2s^2 2p^6 3s^2 3p^6 3d^{10} 4s^2 4p^6 4d^{10} 5s^2 5p^5$. Each iodine atom has ten $3d$ electrons and one unpaired $5p$ electron.

15A **(E)** Iron has 26 electrons, of which 18 are accounted for by the [Ar] core configuration. Beyond [Ar] there are two $4s$ electrons and six $3d$ electrons, as shown in the following orbital diagram.

15B **(E)** Bismuth has 83 electrons, of which 54 are accounted for by the [Xe] configuration. Beyond [Xe] there are two $6s$ electrons, fourteen $4f$ electrons, ten $5d$ electrons, and three $6p$ electrons, as shown in the following orbital diagram.

16A **(E)**
   (a) Tin is in the 5th period, hence, five electronic shells are filled or partially filled.
   (b) **The** $3p$ subshell was filled with Ar; there are six $3p$ electrons in an atom of Sn.
   (c) **The** electron configuration of Sn is [Kr] $4d^{10} 5s^2 5p^2$. There are no $5d$ electrons.
   (d) **Both** of the $5p$ electrons are unpaired, thus there are two unpaired electrons in a Sn atom.

16B **(E)**
   (a) The $3d$ subshell was filled at Zn, thus each Y atom has ten $3d$ electrons.
   (b) Ge is in the $4p$ row; each germanium atom has two $4p$ electrons.
   (c) We would expect each Au atom to have ten $5d$ electrons and one $6s$ electron. Thus each Au atom should have one unpaired electron.

INTEGRATIVE EXAMPLE

A. **(M)**
(a) First, we must find the u_{rms} speed of the He atom

$$u_{rms} = \sqrt{\frac{3\,RT}{M}} = \sqrt{\frac{3\left(8.3145 \text{ J mol}^{-1}\text{K}^{-1}\right)\left(298 \text{ K}\right)}{4.003 \times 10^{-3} \text{kg mol}^{-1}}} = 1363 \text{ m/s}$$

Using the rms speed and the mass of the He atom, we can determine the momentum, and therefore the de Broglie's wavelength:

$$\text{mass He atom} = 4.003 \times 10^{-3} \frac{\text{kg}}{\text{mol}} \times \frac{1 \text{ mol}}{6.022 \times 10^{23} \text{ atoms}} = 6.647 \times 10^{-27} \text{ kg}$$

$$p = m\,u = \left(6.647 \times 10^{-27} \text{ kg}\right)\left(1363 \text{ m/s}\right) = 9.06 \times 10^{-24} \text{ kg m/s}$$

$$\lambda = \frac{h}{p} = \frac{6.6261 \times 10^{-34} \text{ J/s}}{9.06 \times 10^{-24} \text{ kg m/s}} = 7.3135 \times 10^{-11} \text{ m} = 73.14 \text{ pm}$$

(b) Since the de Broglie wavelength is known to be ~300 pm, we have to perform the above solution backwards to determine the temperature:

$$p = \frac{h}{\lambda} = \frac{6.6261 \times 10^{-34} \text{ J/s}}{300 \times 10^{-12} \text{ m}} = 2.209 \times 10^{-24} \text{ kg m/s}$$

$$u = u_{rms} = \frac{p}{m} = \frac{2.209 \times 10^{-24} \text{ kg m/s}}{6.647 \times 10^{-27} \text{ kg}} = 332.33 \text{ m/s}$$

Since $u_{rms} = \sqrt{3\,RT/M}$, solving for T yields the following:

$$T = \frac{\left(332.33 \text{ m/s}\right)^2 \left(4.003 \times 10^{-3} \text{ kg}\right)}{3\left(8.3145 \text{ J mol}^{-1}\text{K}^{-1}\right)} = 17.7 \text{ K}$$

B. **(M)** The possible combinations are $1s \rightarrow np \rightarrow nd$, for example, $1s \rightarrow 3p \rightarrow 5d$. The frequencies of these transitions are calculated as follows:

$$1s \rightarrow 3p : \nu = 3.2881 \times 10^{15} \text{ s}^{-1}\left(\frac{1}{n_i^2} - \frac{1}{n_f^2}\right) = 3.2881 \times 10^{15} \text{ s}^{-1}\left(\frac{1}{1^2} - \frac{1}{3^2}\right) = 2.92 \times 10^{15} \text{ Hz}$$

$$3p \rightarrow 5d : \nu = 3.2881 \times 10^{15} \text{ s}^{-1}\left(\frac{1}{3^2} - \frac{1}{5^2}\right) = 2.34 \times 10^{14} \text{ Hz}$$

The emission spectrum will have lines representing $5d \rightarrow 4p$, $5d \rightarrow 3p$, $5d \rightarrow 2p$, $4p \rightarrow 3s$, $4p \rightarrow 2s$, $4p \rightarrow 1s$, $3p \rightarrow 2s$, $3p \rightarrow 1s$, and $2p \rightarrow 1s$. The difference between the sodium atoms is that the positions of the lines will be shifted to higher frequencies by 11^2.

EXERCISES

Electromagnetic Radiation

1. **(E)** The wavelength is the distance between successive peaks. Thus, 4×1.17 nm $= \lambda = 4.68$ nm.

2. **(M)**

    (a) $v = \dfrac{c}{\lambda} = \dfrac{3.00 \times 10^8 \text{ m/s}}{4.68 \text{ nm} \times \dfrac{1 \text{ m}}{10^9 \text{ nm}}} = 6.41 \times 10^{16}$ Hz

    (b) $E = hv = 6.626 \times 10^{-34}$ J s $\times 6.41 \times 10^{16}$ Hz $= 4.25 \times 10^{-17}$ J

3. **(E)**
    (a) TRUE   Since frequency and wavelength are inversely related to each other, radiation of shorter wavelength has higher frequency.
    (b) FALSE   Light of wavelengths between 390 nm and 790 nm is visible to the eye.
    (c) FALSE   All electromagnetic radiation has the same speed in a vacuum.
    (d) TRUE   The wavelength of an X-ray is approximately 0.1 nm.

4.
    (E)

    (a) $v = \dfrac{c}{\lambda} = \dfrac{2.9979 \times 10^8 \text{ m/s}}{418.7 \text{ nm}} \times \dfrac{10^9 \text{ nm}}{1 \text{ m}} = 7.160 \times 10^{14}$ Hz
    (b) Light of wavelength 418.7 nm is in the visible region of the spectrum.
    (c) 418.7 nm electromagnetic radiation is visible to the human eye as violet light.

5. **(E)** The light having the highest frequency also has the shortest wavelength. Therefore, choice (c) 80 nm has the highest frequency.

6. **(E)** Increasing frequency is decreasing wavelength. Radio waves have the longest wavelengths/ lowest frequencies (b), followed by infrared light (c), followed by visible light (a), and finally UV radiation (d). Thus, the frequency increases from left to right in the following order: (b) < (c) < (a) < (d).

7. **(E)** The speed of light is used to convert the distance into an elapsed time.
    $$\text{time} = 93 \times 10^6 \text{ mi} \times \frac{5280 \text{ ft}}{1 \text{ mi}} \times \frac{12 \text{ in.}}{1 \text{ ft}} \times \frac{2.54 \text{ cm}}{1 \text{ in.}} \times \frac{1 \text{ s}}{3.00 \times 10^{10} \text{ cm}} \times \frac{1 \text{ min}}{60 \text{ s}} = 8.3 \text{ min}$$

8. **(E)** The speed of light is used to convert the time into a distance spanned by light.
    $$1 \text{ light-year} = 1 \text{ y} \times \frac{365.25 \text{ d}}{1 \text{ y}} \times \frac{24 \text{ h}}{1 \text{ d}} \times \frac{3600 \text{ s}}{1 \text{ h}} \times \frac{2.9979 \times 10^8 \text{ m}}{1 \text{ s}} \times \frac{1 \text{ km}}{1000 \text{ m}} = 9.4607 \times 10^{12} \text{ km}$$

Photons and the Photoelectric Effect

9. **(E)**

(a) $E = h\nu = 6.626 \times 10^{-34} \text{ J s} \times 7.39 \times 10^{15} \text{ s}^{-1} = 4.90 \times 10^{-18}$ J/photon

(b) $E_m = 6.626 \times 10^{-34} \text{ J s} \times 1.97 \times 10^{14} \text{ s}^{-1} \times \dfrac{6.022 \times 10^{23} \text{ photons}}{1 \text{ mol}} \times \dfrac{1 \text{ kJ}}{1000 \text{ J}} = 78.6$ kJ/mol

10. **(M)**

(a) $\nu = \dfrac{E}{h} = \dfrac{8.62 \times 10^{-21} \text{ J}}{6.626 \times 10^{-34} \text{ J s}} = 1.30 \times 10^{13} \text{ s}^{-1} = 1.30 \times 10^{13}$ Hz

(b) $E = h\nu = \dfrac{hc}{\lambda}; \quad \lambda = \dfrac{hc}{E} = \dfrac{6.626 \times 10^{-34} \text{ J s} \times 3.00 \times 10^{8} \text{ m/s}}{360 \text{ kJ/mol} \times \dfrac{1000 \text{ J}}{1 \text{ kJ}} \times \dfrac{1 \text{ mol}}{6.022 \times 10^{23} \text{ photons}}} = 3.33 \times 10^{-7} \text{ m} = 333$ nm

11. **(E)**

(a) Here we combine $E = h\nu$ and $c = \nu\lambda$ to obtain $E = hc/\lambda$

$E = \dfrac{6.626 \times 10^{-34} \text{J s} \times 2.998 \times 10^{8} \text{ m/s}}{574 \text{ nm} \times \dfrac{1 \text{ m}}{10^{9} \text{ nm}}} = 3.46 \times 10^{-19}$ J/photon

(b) $E_m = 3.46 \times 10^{-19} \dfrac{\text{J}}{\text{photon}} \times 6.022 \times 10^{23} \dfrac{\text{photons}}{\text{mol}} = 2.08 \times 10^{5}$ J/mol

12. **(M)** First we determine the energy of an individual photon, and then its wavelength in nm.

$E = \dfrac{2112 \dfrac{\text{kJ}}{\text{mol}} \times \dfrac{1000 \text{ J}}{1 \text{ kJ}}}{6.022 \times 10^{23} \dfrac{\text{photons}}{\text{mol}}} = 3.507 \times 10^{-18} \dfrac{\text{J}}{\text{photon}} = \dfrac{hc}{\lambda} \quad \text{or} \quad \dfrac{hc}{E} = \lambda$

$\lambda = \dfrac{6.626 \times 10^{-34} \text{ J s} \times 2.998 \times 10^{8} \text{ m/s}}{3.507 \times 10^{-18} \text{ J}} \times \dfrac{10^{9} \text{ nm}}{1 \text{ m}} = 56.64 \text{ nm}$ This is ultraviolet radiation.

13. **(E)** The easiest way to answer this question is to convert all of (b) through (d) into nanometers. The radiation with the smallest wavelength will have the greatest energy per photon, while the radiation with the largest wavelength has the smallest amount of energy per photon.

(a) 6.62×10^{2} nm

(b) $2.1 \times 10^{-5} \text{ cm} \times \dfrac{1 \times 10^{7} \text{ nm}}{1 \text{ cm}} = 2.1 \times 10^{2}$ nm

(c) $3.58 \ \mu\text{m} \times \dfrac{1 \times 10^{3} \text{ nm}}{1 \ \mu\text{m}} = 3.58 \times 10^{3}$ nm

(d) $\quad 4.1 \times 10^{-6} \, \text{m} \times \dfrac{1 \times 10^{9} \;\; \text{nm}}{1 \;\; \text{m}} = 4.1 \times 10^{3} \, \text{nm}$

So, 2.1×10^{-5} nm radiation, by virtue of possessing the smallest wavelength in the set, has the greatest energy per photon. Conversely, since 4.1×10^{3} nm has the largest wavelength, it possesses the least amount of energy per photon.

14. **(M)** This time, let's express each type of radiation in terms of its frequency (ν).
   (a) $\quad \nu = 3.0 \times 10^{15} \, \text{s}^{-1}$

   (b) $\quad$ The maximum frequency for infrared radiation is $\sim 3 \times 10^{14} \, \text{s}^{-1}$.

   (c) $\quad$ Here, $\lambda = 7000 \, \text{Å}$ (where $1 \, \text{Å} = 1 \times 10^{-10}$ m), so $\lambda = 7000 \, \text{Å} \times \dfrac{1 \times 10^{-10} \, \text{m}}{1 \, \overset{\circ}{\text{A}}} = 7.000 \times 10^{-7} \, \text{m}$.

   Calculate the frequency using the equation: $\nu = c/\lambda$

   $$\nu = \frac{2.998 \times 10^{8} \, \text{m s}^{-1}}{7.000 \times 10^{-7} \, \text{m}} = 4.283 \times 10^{14} \, \text{s}^{-1}$$

   (d) $\quad$ X-rays have frequencies that range from $10^{17} \, \text{s}^{-1}$ to $10^{21} \, \text{s}^{-1}$. Recall that for all forms of electromagnetic radiation, the energy per mole of photons increases with increasing frequency. Consequently, the correct order for the energy per mole of photons for the various types of radiation described in this question is:

   infrared radiation (b) $< \lambda = 7000 \, \text{Å}$ radiation (c) $< \nu = 2.0 \times 10^{15} \, \text{s}^{-1}$ (a) $<$ X-rays (d)

   $\xrightarrow{\hspace{3cm} \text{increasing energy per mole of photons} \hspace{3cm}}$

15. **(E)** Notice that energy and wavelength are inversely related: $E = \dfrac{hc}{\lambda}$. Therefore radiation that is 100 times as energetic as radiation with a wavelength of 988 nm will have a wavelength one-hundredth as long, namely 9.88 nm. The frequency of this radiation is found by employing the wave equation.

   $\nu = \dfrac{c}{\lambda} = \dfrac{2.998 \times 10^{8} \, \text{m/s}}{9.88 \, \text{nm} \times \dfrac{1 \text{m}}{10^{9} \text{nm}}} = 3.03 \times 10^{16} \, \text{s}^{-1}$ From Figure 8-3, we can see that this is UV radiation.

16. **(M)**

   $E_{1} = h\nu = \dfrac{hc}{\lambda} = \dfrac{6.62607 \times 10^{-34} \, \text{J s} \times 2.99792 \times 10^{8} \, \text{m s}^{-1}}{589.00 \, \text{nm} \times \dfrac{1 \, \text{m}}{10^{9} \, \text{nm}}} = 3.3726 \times 10^{-19} \, \text{J/photon}$

   $E_{2} = \dfrac{6.62607 \times 10^{-34} \, \text{J s} \times 2.99792 \times 10^{8} \, \text{m s}^{-1}}{589.59 \, \text{nm} \times \dfrac{1 \, \text{m}}{10^{9} \, \text{nm}}} = 3.3692 \times 10^{-19} \, \text{J/photon}$

   $\Delta E = E_{1} - E_{2} = 3.3726 \times 10^{-19} \, \text{J} - 3.3692 \times 10^{-19} \, \text{J} = 0.0034 \times 10^{-19} \, \text{J/photon} = 3.4 \times 10^{-22} \, \text{J/photon}$

17. **(M)**

(a) $E = hv = 6.63 \times 10^{-34}$ J s $\times 9.96 \times 10^{14}$ s^{-1} $= 6.60 \times 10^{-19}$ J/photon

(b) Indium will display the photoelectric effect when exposed to ultraviolet light since ultraviolet light has a maximum frequency of 1×10^{16} s^{-1}, which is above the threshold frequency of indium. It will not display the photoelectric effect when exposed to infrared light since the maximum frequency of infrared light is $\sim 3 \times 10^{14}$ s^{-1}, which is below the threshold frequency of indium.

18. **(M)** We are given the work function of potassium in terms of the minimum energy required for photoelectron ejection. The minimum energy that an impinging photon must have to cause ejection of the photoelectron is:

$eV_0 = hv_0 = 3.69 \times 10^{-19}$ J

The photon frequency is therefore:

$v_0 = 3.69 \times 10^{-19}$ J$/6.6261 \times 10^{-34}$ J s$^{-1} = 5.57 \times 10^{14}$ s^{-1}

And the wavelength of photon is:

$\lambda = c/v_0 = \left(2.998 \times 10^8 \text{ m/s}\right)/\left(5.57 \times 10^{14} \text{s}^{-1}\right) = 5.38 \times 10^{-7}$ m $= 538$ nm

Since the visible spectrum covers 390 to 750 nm, wavelengths covering the green to blue portion of the spectrum have enough energy to eject a photoelectron from potassium.

Provided that the energy of the impinging photon exceeds the minimum threshold, the extra energy is transferred to the photoelectron in form of kinetic energy. That is:

$$K_e = \frac{1}{2}m_e u^2 = hv - eV_0$$

Therefore, if potassium is exposed to light with $\lambda = 400$ nm, the speed of the photoelectron is determined using the above equation. But first, determine the frequency of the photon:

$v_0 = c/\lambda = \left(2.998 \times 10^8 \text{ m/s}\right)/\left(520 \times 10^{-9} \text{m}\right) = 5.765 \times 10^{14}$ s^{-1}

Then, enter the requisite information in the kinetic energy equation provided:

$$K_e = \frac{1}{2}m_e u^2 = hv - eV_0 = \left(6.6261 \times 10^{-34} \text{J s}^{-1}\right)\left(5.765 \times 10^{14} \text{s}^{-1}\right) - 3.69 \times 10^{-19} \text{J} = 1.30 \times 10^{-19} \text{J}$$

$$\frac{1}{2}m_e u^2 = 1.30 \times 10^{-19} \text{J}$$

so,

$$u = \sqrt{\frac{2 \times 1.30 \times 10^{-19} \text{J}}{9.109 \times 10^{-34} \text{kg}}} = 1.69 \times 10^7 \text{ m/s}$$

Atomic Spectra

19. **(M)**

(a) $v = 3.2881 \times 10^{15}$ s$^{-1}\left(\dfrac{1}{2^2} - \dfrac{1}{5^2}\right) = 6.9050 \times 10^{14}$ s^{-1}

(b) $\qquad v = 3.2881 \times 10^{15} \text{ s}^{-1} \left(\dfrac{1}{2^2} - \dfrac{1}{7^2} \right) = 7.5492 \times 10^{14} \text{ s}^{-1}$

$$\lambda = \frac{2.9979 \times 10^8 \text{ m/s}}{7.5492 \times 10^{14} \text{ s}^{-1}} = 3.9711 \times 10^{-7} \text{ m} \times \frac{10^9 \text{ nm}}{1 \text{ m}} = 397.11 \text{ nm}$$

(c) $\qquad v = \dfrac{3.00 \times 10^8 \text{ m/s}}{380 \text{ nm} \times \dfrac{1 \text{ m}}{10^9 \text{ nm}}} = 7.89 \times 10^{14} \text{ s}^{-1} = 3.2881 \times 10^{15} \text{ s}^{-1} \left(\dfrac{1}{2^2} - \dfrac{1}{n^2} \right)$

$$0.250 - \frac{1}{n^2} = \frac{7.89 \times 10^{14} \text{ s}^{-1}}{3.2881 \times 10^{15} \text{ s}^{-1}} = 0.240 \qquad \frac{1}{n^2} = 0.250 - 0.240 = 0.010 \qquad n = 10$$

20. **(E)** The frequencies of hydrogen emission lines in the infrared region of the spectrum other than the visible region would be predicted by replacing the constant "2" in the Balmer equation by the variable m, where m is an integer smaller than n: $m = 3, 4, \ldots$

   The resulting equation is $v = 3.2881 \times 10^{15} \text{ s}^{-1} \left(\dfrac{1}{m^2} - \dfrac{1}{n^2} \right)$

21. **(E)** $\Delta E = -2.179 \times 10^{-18} \text{ J} \left(\dfrac{1}{n_f^2} - \dfrac{1}{n_i^2} \right) = -2.179 \times 10^{-18} \text{ J} \left(\dfrac{1}{3^2} - \dfrac{1}{6^2} \right) = -1.816 \times 10^{-19} \text{ J}$

   $E_{\text{photon emitted}} = 1.816 \times 10^{-19} \text{ J} = hv \qquad v = \dfrac{E}{h} = \dfrac{1.550 \times 10^{-19} \text{ J}}{6.626 \times 10^{-34} \text{ J s}} = 2.740 \times 10^{14} \text{ s}^{-1}$

22. **(E)** $\Delta E = 2.179 \times 10^{-18} \text{ J} \left(\dfrac{1}{5^2} - \dfrac{1}{2^2} \right) = -4.576 \times 10^{-19} \text{ J}$ (negative denotes energy release)

   $v = \dfrac{E_{\text{photon emitted}}}{h} = \dfrac{4.576 \times 10^{-19} \text{ J}}{6.6260755 \times 10^{-34} \text{ J s}} = 6.906 \times 10^{14} \text{ s}^{-1}$

23. **(M)** First we determine the frequency of the radiation, and then match it with the Balmer equation.

   $$v = \frac{c}{\lambda} = \frac{2.9979 \times 10^8 \text{ m s}^{-1} \times \dfrac{10^9 \text{ nm}}{1 \text{ m}}}{389 \text{ nm}} = 7.71 \times 10^{14} \text{ s}^{-1} = 3.2881 \times 10^{15} \text{ s}^{-1} \left(\frac{1}{2^2} - \frac{1}{n^2} \right)$$

   $$\left(\frac{1}{2^2} - \frac{1}{n^2} \right) = \frac{7.71 \times 10^{14} \text{ s}^{-1}}{3.2881 \times 10^{15} \text{ s}^{-1}} = 0.234 = 0.2500 - \frac{1}{n^2} \qquad \frac{1}{n^2} = 0.016 \qquad n = 7.9 \approx 8$$

24. **(M)**

(a) The maximum wavelength occurs when $n = 2$ and the minimum wavelength occurs at the series convergence limit, namely, when n is exceedingly large (and $1/n^2 \approx 0$).

$$v = 3.2881 \times 10^{15} \text{ s}^{-1} \left(\frac{1}{1^2} - \frac{1}{2^2} \right) = 2.4661 \times 10^{15} \text{ s}^{-1} \quad \lambda = \frac{c}{v} = \frac{2.9979 \times 10^8 \text{ m/s}}{2.4661 \times 10^{15} \text{ s}^{-1}} = 1.2156 \times 10^{-7} \text{ m}$$

$$= 121.56 \text{ nm}$$

$$v = 3.2881 \times 10^{15} \text{ s}^{-1} \left(\frac{1}{1^2} - 0 \right) = 3.2881 \times 10^{15} \text{ s}^{-1} \quad \lambda = \frac{c}{v} = \frac{2.9979 \times 10^8 \text{ m/s}}{3.2881 \times 10^{15} \text{ s}^{-1}} = 9.1174 \times 10^{-8} \text{ m}$$

$$= 91.174 \text{ nm}$$

(b) First we determine the frequency of this spectral line, and then the value of n to which it corresponds.

$$v = \frac{c}{\lambda} = \frac{2.9979 \times 10^8 \text{ m/s}}{95.0 \text{ nm} \times \dfrac{1 \text{m}}{10^9 \text{nm}}} = 3.16 \times 10^{15} \text{s}^{-1} = 3.2881 \times 10^{15} \text{s}^{-1} \left(\frac{1}{1^2} - \frac{1}{n^2} \right)$$

$$\left(\frac{1}{1^2} - \frac{1}{n^2} \right) = \frac{3.16 \times 10^{15} \text{ s}^{-1}}{3.2881 \times 10^{15} \text{ s}^{-1}} = 0.961 \qquad \frac{1}{n^2} = 1.000 - 0.961 = 0.039 \qquad n = 5$$

(c) Let us use the same approach as the one in part (b).

$$v = \frac{c}{\lambda} = \frac{2.9979 \times 10^8 \text{ m/s}}{108.5 \text{ nm} \times \dfrac{1 \text{m}}{10^9 \text{nm}}} = 2.763 \times 10^{15} \text{s}^{-1} = 3.2881 \times 10^{15} \text{s}^{-1} \left(\frac{1}{1^2} - \frac{1}{n^2} \right)$$

$$\left(\frac{1}{1^2} - \frac{1}{n^2} \right) = \frac{2.763 \times 10^{15} \text{ s}^{-1}}{3.2881 \times 10^{15} \text{ s}^{-1}} = 0.8403 \qquad \frac{1}{n^2} = 1.000 - 0.8403 = 0.1597$$

This gives as a result $n = 2.502$. Since n is not an integer, there is no line in the Lyman spectrum with a wavelength of 108.5 nm.

25. **(M)** The longest wavelength component has the lowest frequency (and thus, the smallest energy).

$$v = 3.2881 \times 10^{15} \text{ s}^{-1} \left(\frac{1}{2^2} - \frac{1}{3^2} \right) = 4.5668 \times 10^{14} \text{ s}^{-1} \quad \lambda = \frac{c}{v} = \frac{2.9979 \times 10^8 \text{ m/s}}{4.5668 \times 10^{14} \text{ s}^{-1}} = 6.5646 \times 10^{-7} \text{ m}$$

$$= 656.46 \text{ nm}$$

$$v = 3.2881 \times 10^{15} \text{ s}^{-1} \left(\frac{1}{2^2} - \frac{1}{4^2} \right) = 6.1652 \times 10^{14} \text{ s}^{-1} \quad \lambda = \frac{c}{v} = \frac{2.9979 \times 10^8 \text{ m/s}}{6.1652 \times 10^{14} \text{ s}^{-1}} = 4.8626 \times 10^{-7} \text{ m}$$

$$= 486.26 \text{ nm}$$

$$v = 3.2881 \times 10^{15} \text{ s}^{-1} \left(\frac{1}{2^2} - \frac{1}{5^2} \right) = 6.9050 \times 10^{14} \text{ s}^{-1} \quad \lambda = \frac{c}{v} = \frac{2.9979 \times 10^8 \text{ m/s}}{6.9050 \times 10^{14} \text{ s}^{-1}} = 4.3416 \times 10^{-7} \text{ m}$$

$$= 434.16 \text{ nm}$$

$$v = 3.2881 \times 10^{15} \text{ s}^{-1} \left(\frac{1}{2^2} - \frac{1}{6^2} \right) = 7.3069 \times 10^{14} \text{ s}^{-1} \quad \lambda = \frac{c}{v} = \frac{2.9979 \times 10^8 \text{ m/s}}{7.3069 \times 10^{14} \text{ s}^{-1}} = 4.1028 \times 10^{-7} \text{ m}$$

$$= 410.28 \text{ nm}$$

26. **(E)** $\lambda = 1880 \text{ nm} \times \dfrac{1 \text{ m}}{10^9 \text{ nm}} = 1.88 \times 10^{-6}$ m. From Exercise 17, we see that wavelengths in the

Balmer series range downward from 6.5646×10^{-7} m. Since this is less than 1.88×10^{-6} m, we conclude that light with a wavelength of 1880 nm cannot be in the Balmer series.

Energy Levels and Spectrum of the Hydrogen Atom

<u>**27.**</u> **(E)**

$$E = -R_H / n^2 = \dfrac{-2.179 \times 10^{-18} \text{ J}}{6^2} = -6.053 \times 10^{-18} \text{ J}$$

28. **(E)**

$$\Delta E = -R_H \left(\dfrac{1}{n_f^2} - \dfrac{1}{n_i^2} \right) = -2.179 \times 10^{-18} \text{ J} \left(\dfrac{1}{3^2} - \dfrac{1}{1^2} \right) = 1.937 \times 10^{-18} \text{ J}$$

<u>**29.**</u> **(M)**

(a) $\quad v = \dfrac{2.179 \times 10^{-18} \text{ J}}{6.626 \times 10^{-34} \text{ J s}} \left(\dfrac{1}{4^2} - \dfrac{1}{7^2} \right) = 1.384 \times 10^{14} \text{ s}^{-1}$

(b) $\quad \lambda = \dfrac{c}{v} = \dfrac{2.998 \times 10^8 \text{ m/s}}{1.384 \times 10^{14} \text{ s}^{-1}} = 2.166 \times 10^{-6} \text{ m} \times \dfrac{10^9 \text{ nm}}{1 \text{ m}} = 2166 \text{ nm}$

(c) This is infrared radiation.

30. **(E)** The greatest quantity of energy is absorbed in the situation where the difference between the inverses of the squares of the two quantum numbers is the largest, and the system begins with a lower quantum number than it finishes with. The second condition eliminates answer (d) from consideration. Now we can consider the difference of the inverses of the squares of the two quantum numbers in each case.

(a) $\left(\dfrac{1}{1^2} - \dfrac{1}{2^2} \right) = 0.75$ **(b)** $\left(\dfrac{1}{2^2} - \dfrac{1}{4^2} \right) = 0.1875$ **(c)** $\left(\dfrac{1}{3^2} - \dfrac{1}{9^2} \right) = 0.0988$

Thus, the largest amount of energy is absorbed in the transition from $n = 1$ to $n = 2$, answer **(a)**, among the four choices given.

<u>**31.**</u> **(E)**
(a) To determine the energy corresponding to $n = 8$,

$$E = -R_H / n^2 = \dfrac{-2.179 \times 10^{-18} \text{ J}}{8^2} = -3.405 \times 10^{-20} \text{ J}$$

(b) Recall that the quantum number n must be an integer. We have
$$E = -R_H / n^2$$

$$-2.500 \times 10^{-19} \text{ J} = \dfrac{-2.179 \times 10^{-18} \text{ J}}{n^2}$$

$$n = \sqrt{0.08716} = 0.2952$$

Since n is not an integer, there is no energy level at -2.500×10^{-19} J.

(c) In this case, the ionization energy corresponds to the energy change for the transition from $n_i = 6$ to $n_f = \infty$. Therefore,

$$\Delta E = -R_{\mathrm{H}}\left(\frac{1}{n_f^2} - \frac{1}{n_i^2}\right) = -2.179\times10^{-18}\,\mathrm{J}\left(0 - \frac{1}{6^2}\right) = 6.053\times10^{-20}\,\mathrm{J}$$

$$E_{i(\text{from } n = 6)} = 6.053\times10^{-20}\,\mathrm{J}$$

32. **(M)** Only transitions (a) and (d) result in the emission of a photon ((b) and (c) involve absorption, not the emission of light). In the Bohr model, the energy difference between two successive energy levels decreases as the value of n increases. Thus, the $n = 3 \rightarrow n = 2$ electron transition involves a greater loss of energy than the $n = 4 \rightarrow n = 3$ transition. This means that the photon emitted by the $n = 4 \rightarrow n = 3$ transition will be lower in energy and, hence, longer in wavelength than the photon produced by the $n = 3 \rightarrow n = 2$ transition. Consequently, among the four choices given, the electron transition in (a) is the one that will produce light of the longest wavelength.

33. **(M)** If infrared light is produced, the quantum number of the final state must have a lower value (i.e., be of lower energy) than the quantum number of the initial state. First we compute the frequency of the transition being considered (from $\nu = c / \lambda$), and then solve for the final quantum number.

$$\nu = \frac{c}{\lambda} = \frac{3.00\times10^8\ \mathrm{m/s}}{410\,\mathrm{nm}\times\dfrac{1\,\mathrm{m}}{10^9\,\mathrm{nm}}} = 7.32\times10^{14}\ \mathrm{s^{-1}}$$

$$7.32\times10^{14}\ \mathrm{s^{-1}} = \frac{2.179\times10^{-18}\ \mathrm{J}}{6.626\times10^{-34}\ \mathrm{J\,s}}\left(\frac{1}{n^2} - \frac{1}{7^2}\right) = 3.289\times10^{15}\ \mathrm{s^{-1}}\left(\frac{1}{n^2} - \frac{1}{7^2}\right)$$

$$\left(\frac{1}{n^2} - \frac{1}{7^2}\right) = \frac{7.32\times10^{14}\ \mathrm{s^{-1}}}{3.289\times10^{15}\ \mathrm{s^{-1}}} = 0.2226 \qquad \frac{1}{n^2} = 0.2226 + \frac{1}{7^2} = 0.2429 \qquad n = 2$$

34. **(M)** If infrared light is produced, the quantum number of the final state must have a lower value (i.e., be of lower energy) than the quantum number of the initial state. First we compute the frequency of the transition being considered (from $\nu = c / \lambda$), and then solve for the initial quantum number, n.

$$\nu = \frac{c}{\lambda} = \frac{3.00\times10^8\ \mathrm{m/s}}{1090\,\mathrm{nm}\times\dfrac{1\,\mathrm{m}}{10^9\,\mathrm{nm}}} = 2.75\times10^{14}\,\mathrm{s^{-1}}$$

$$2.75\times10^{14}\,\mathrm{s^{-1}} = \frac{2.179\times10^{-18}\ \mathrm{J}}{6.626\times10^{-34}\ \mathrm{J\,s}}\left(\frac{1}{5^2} - \frac{1}{n^2}\right) = 3.289\times10^{15}\ \mathrm{s^{-1}}\left(\frac{1}{5^2} - \frac{1}{n^2}\right)$$

$$\left(\frac{1}{3^2} - \frac{1}{n^2}\right) = \frac{2.75\times10^{14}\ \mathrm{s^{-1}}}{3.289\times10^{15}\ \mathrm{s^{-1}}} = 0.0836_1 \qquad \frac{1}{n^2} = -0.0836_1 + \frac{1}{3^2} = 0.0275_0 \qquad n = 6$$

35. **(M)**

    (a) Line A is for the transition $n = 3 \rightarrow n = 1$, while Line B is for the transition $n = 4 \rightarrow n = 1$

    (b) This transition corresponds to the $n = 3$ to $n = 1$ transition. Hence, $\Delta E = hc/\lambda$

$\Delta E = (6.626 \times 10^{-34} \text{ J s}) \times (2.998 \times 10^{8} \text{ m s}^{-1}) \div (103 \times 10^{-9} \text{ m}) = 1.92\underline{9} \times 10^{-18} \text{ J}$

$\Delta E = -Z^2 R_\text{H}/n_1^2 - -Z^2 R_\text{H}/n_2^2$

$1.92\underline{9} \times 10^{-18} \text{ J} = -Z^2(2.179 \times 10^{-18})/(3)^2 + Z^2(2.179 \times 10^{-18})/(1)^2$

$Z^2 = 0.996$ and $Z = 0.998$ Thus, this is the spectrum for the hydrogen atom.

36. **(M)**

    (a) Line A is for the transition $n = 5 \rightarrow n = 2$, while Line B is for the transition $n = 6 \rightarrow n = 2$

    (b) This transition corresponds to the $n = 5$ to $n = 2$ transition. Hence, $\Delta E = hc/\lambda$

$\Delta E = (6.626 \times 10^{-34} \text{ J s}) \times (2.998 \times 10^{8} \text{ m s}^{-1}) \div (434 \times 10^{-9} \text{ m}) = 4.57\underline{7} \times 10^{-19} \text{ J}$

$\Delta E = -Z^2 R_\text{H}/n_1^2 - (-Z^2 R_\text{H}/n_2^2)$

$4.57\underline{7} \times 10^{-19} \text{ J} = -Z^2(2.179 \times 10^{-18})/(5)^2 + Z^2(2.179 \times 10^{-18})/(2)^2$

$Z^2 = 1.00$ and $Z = 1.00$ Thus, this is the spectrum for the hydrogen atom.

37. **(M)**

    (a) Line A is for the transition $n = 5 \rightarrow n = 2$, while Line B is for the transition $n = 6 \rightarrow n = 2$

    (b) This transition corresponds to the $n = 5$ to $n = 2$ transition. Hence, $\Delta E = hc/\lambda$.

$\Delta E = (6.626 \times 10^{-34} \text{ J s}) \times (2.998 \times 10^{8} \text{ m s}^{-1}) \div (27.1 \times 10^{-9} \text{ m}) = 7.33 \times 10^{-18} \text{ J}$

$\Delta E = -Z^2 R_\text{H}/n_1^2 - -Z^2 R_\text{H}/n_2^2$

$4.57\underline{7} \times 10^{-19} \text{ J} = -Z^2(2.179 \times 10^{-18})/(5)^2 + Z^2(2.179 \times 10^{-18})/(2)^2$

$Z^2 = 16.0\underline{2}$ and $Z = 4.00$ Thus, this is the spectrum for the Be^{3+} cation.

38. **(M)**

    (a) Line A is for the transition $n = 4 \rightarrow n = 1$, whereas Line B is for the transition $n = 5 \rightarrow n = 1$

    (b) This transition corresponds to the $n = 4$ to $n = 1$ transition. Hence, $\Delta E = hc/\lambda$.

$\Delta E = (6.626 \times 10^{-34} \text{ J s}) \times (2.998 \times 10^{8} \text{ m s}^{-1}) \div (10.8 \times 10^{-9} \text{ m}) = 1.84 \times 10^{-17} \text{ J}$

$\Delta E = -Z^2 R_\text{H}/n_1^2 - -Z^2 R_\text{H}/n_2^2$

$4.57\underline{7} \times 10^{-19} \text{ J} = -Z^2(2.179 \times 10^{-18})/(5)^2 + Z^2(2.179 \times 10^{-18})/(2)^2$

$Z^2 = 9.00\underline{4}$ and $Z = 3.00$ Thus, this is the spectrum for the Li^{2+} cation.

Wave–Particle Duality

39. **(E)** The de Broglie equation is $\lambda = h/mu$. This means that, for a given wavelength to be produced, a lighter particle would have to be moving faster. Thus, electrons would have to move faster than protons to display matter waves of the same wavelength.

40. **(M)** First, we rearrange the de Broglie equation, and solve it for velocity: $u = h/m\lambda$. Then we compute the velocity of the electron. From Table 2-1, we see that the mass of an electron is 9.109×10^{-28} g.

$$u = \frac{h}{m\lambda} = \frac{6.626 \times 10^{-34}\,\text{J s}}{\left(9.109 \times 10^{-28}\,\text{g} \times \dfrac{1\,\text{kg}}{1000\,\text{g}}\right)\left(850\,\text{nm} \times \dfrac{1\,\text{m}}{10^9\,\text{nm}}\right)} = 8.6 \times 10^2\,\text{m/s}$$

41. **(M)**

$$\lambda = \frac{h}{mu} = \frac{6.626 \times 10^{-34}\,\text{J s}}{\left(145\,\text{g} \times \dfrac{1\,\text{kg}}{1000\,\text{g}}\right)\left(168\,\text{km/h} \times \dfrac{1\,\text{h}}{3600\,\text{s}} \times \dfrac{1000\,\text{m}}{1\,\text{km}}\right)} = 9.79 \times 10^{-35}\,\text{m}$$

The diameter of a nucleus approximates 10^{-15} m, which is far larger than the baseball's wavelength.

42. **(E)**

$$\lambda = \frac{h}{mu} = \frac{6.626 \times 10^{-34}\,\text{J s}}{0.0097\,\text{kg} \times 887\,\text{m/s}} = 7.7 \times 10^{-35}\,\text{m}$$

Because the bullet's wavelength is smaller than the Planck limit ($\sim 10 - 33$ cm), which is the scale at which quantum fluctuations occur, its experimental measurement is impossible.

The Heisenberg Uncertainty Principle

43. **(M)** The uncertainty relation $\Delta r \Delta p \geq h/(4\pi)$ indicates that it is not possible to specify exact values for both the radial position and the momentum along the radial direction. For an electron moving in a circular orbit, the radius is exactly known. And because the distance between the electron and the nucleus is constant, the electron has no velocity along the radial direction. Therefore, the momentum along the radial direction is exactly zero. The specification of exact values for both r and p violates the Heisenberg uncertainty principle. Alternatively, because r and p are precisely known, the corresponding uncertainties are $\Delta r = 0$ and $\Delta p = 0$. However, the product of Δr and Δp cannot be zero; it must be greater than or equal to $h/(4\pi)$.

44. **(M)** Einstein believed very strongly in the law of cause and effect, what is known as a deterministic view of the universe. He felt that the need to use probability and chance ("playing dice") in describing atomic structure resulted because a suitable theory had not yet been developed to permit accurate predictions. He believed that such a theory could be developed, and had good reason for his belief: The developments in the theory of atomic structure came very rapidly during the first thirty years of this century, and those, such as Einstein, who had lived through this period had seen the revision of a number of theories and explanations that were thought to be the final answer. Another viewpoint in this area is embodied in another famous quotation: "Nature is subtle, but not malicious." The meaning of this statement is that the causes of various effects may be obscure but they exist nonetheless. Bohr was stating that we should accept theories as they are revealed by experimentation and logic, rather than attempting to make these theories fit our preconceived notions of what we believe they should be. In other words, Bohr was telling Einstein to keep an open mind.

45. **(M)**

$$\Delta u = \left(\frac{1}{100}\right)(0.1)\left(2.998 \times 10^8 \frac{m}{s}\right) = 2.\underline{9}98 \times 10^5 \text{ m/s} \quad m = 1.673 \times 10^{-27} \text{ kg}$$

$$\Delta p = m\Delta u = (1.673 \times 10^{-27} \text{ kg})(2.998 \times 10^5 \text{ m/s}) = 5.\underline{0} \times 10^{-22} \text{ kg m s}^{-1}$$

$$\Delta x = \frac{h}{4\pi\Delta p} = \frac{6.626 \times 10^{-34} \text{ J s}}{(4\pi)(5.0 \times 10^{-22} \frac{\text{kg m}}{s})} = \sim 1 \times 10^{-13} \text{ m } (\sim 100 \text{ times the diameter of a nucleus})$$

46. **(E)** Assume a mass of 1000 kg for the automobile and that its position is known to 1 cm (0.01 m).

$$\Delta u = \frac{h}{4\pi m\Delta x} \frac{6.626 \times 10^{-34} \text{ J s}}{(4\pi)(1000 \text{ kg})(0.01 \text{ m})} = 5 \times 10^{-36} \text{ m s}^{-1}$$

This represents an undetectable uncertainty in the velocity.

47. **(M)** Electron mass $= 9.109 \times 10^{-31}$ kg, $\lambda = 0.53$ Å (1 Å $= 1 \times 10^{-10}$ m), hence $\lambda = 0.53 \times 10^{-10}$ m

$$\lambda = \frac{h}{mu} \text{ or } u = \frac{h}{m\lambda} = \frac{6.626 \times 10^{-34} \text{ J s}}{(9.109 \times 10^{-31} \text{ kg})(0.53 \times 10^{-10} \text{ m})} = 1.4 \times 10^7 \text{ m s}^{-1}$$

48. **(M)** $\Delta E = hu = \dfrac{hc}{\lambda}$ or $\lambda = \dfrac{hc}{E} = \dfrac{(6.626 \times 10^{-34} \text{ J s})(2.998 \times 10^8 \text{ m s}^{-1})}{(-5.45 \times 10^{-19} \text{ J}) - (-2.179 \times 10^{-18} \text{ J})}$

$$= 1.216 \times 10^{-7} \text{ m}$$

$$u = \frac{h}{m\lambda} = \frac{6.626 \times 10^{-34} \text{ J s}}{(9.109 \times 10^{-31} \text{ kg})(1.216 \times 10^{-7} \text{ m})} = 5.983 \times 10^3 \text{ m s}^{-1}$$

Wave Mechanics

49. **(M)** A sketch of this situation is presented at right. We see that 2.50 waves span the space of the 42 cm. Thus, the length of each wave is obtained by equating: $2.50\lambda = 42$ cm, giving $\lambda \approx 17$ cm.

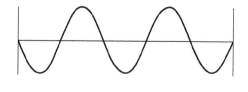

50. **(E)** If there are four nodes, then there are three half-wavelengths within the string: one between the first and second nodes, the second half-wavelength between nodes 2 and 3, and the third between nodes 3 and 4. Therefore, $3 \times \lambda/2 = \text{length} = 3 \times 17 \text{ cm}/2 = 26$ cm long string.

51. **(D)** $50.\ \text{pm} \times \dfrac{1\ \text{m}}{1 \times 10^{12}\ \text{pm}} = 5.0 \times 10^{-11}\ \text{m}$

$$E = \frac{n^2 h^2}{8\ mL^2}$$

Where n = energy level, h = Planck's constant, m = mass, L = length of box

$$\Delta E = E_{\text{excited state}} - E_{\text{ground state}}$$

$$\Delta E = \left[\frac{4^2(6.626 \times 10^{-34}\ \text{J s})^2}{8(9.109 \times 10^{-31}\text{kg})(5.0 \times 10^{-11}\text{m})^2}\right] - \left[\frac{1^2(6.626 \times 10^{-34}\ \text{J s})^2}{8(9.109 \times 10^{-31}\text{kg})(5.0 \times 10^{-11}\text{m})^2}\right]$$

$$\Delta E = 3.856 \times 10^{-16}\ \text{J} - 2.410 \times 10^{-17}\ \text{J}$$

$$\Delta E = 3.615 \times 10^{-16}\ \text{J}$$

$$\lambda = \frac{hc}{\Delta E} = \frac{(6.626 \times 10^{-34}\ \text{J s})(3.00 \times 10^8\ \text{m s}^{-1})}{3.615 \times 10^{-16}\ \text{J}}$$

$$\lambda = 5.499 \times 10^{-10}\ \text{m} \times \frac{10^9\ \text{nm}}{1\ \text{m}} = 0.5499\ \text{nm} = 0.55\ \text{nm}$$

52. **(D)**

$618\ \text{nm} \times \dfrac{1\ \text{m}}{10^9\ \text{nm}} = 6.18 \times 10^{-7}\ \text{m}$

$$\Delta E = \frac{hc}{\lambda} = \frac{(6.626 \times 10^{-34}\ \text{J s})(3.00 \times 10^8\ \text{m s}^{-1})}{6.18 \times 10^{-7}\ \text{m}}$$

$$\Delta E = 3.127 \times 10^{-19}\ \text{J}$$

$$\Delta E = E_{\text{excited state}} - E_{\text{ground state}}$$

$$E = \frac{n^2 h^2}{8\ mL^2}$$

Where n = energy level, h = Planck's constant, m = mass, L = length of box

$$3.217 \times 10^{-19}\ J = \left[\frac{4^2(6.626 \times 10^{-34}\ \text{J s})^2}{8(9.109 \times 10^{-31}\text{kg})(L)^2}\right] - \left[\frac{2^2(6.626 \times 10^{-34}\ \text{J s})^2}{8(9.109 \times 10^{-31}\text{kg})(L)^2}\right]$$

$$3.217 \times 10^{-19}\ J = \frac{9.6397 \times 10^{-37}}{L^2} - \frac{2.410 \times 10^{-37}}{L^2}$$

$$L^2 = 2.247 \times 10^{-18}$$

$$L = 1.499 \times 10^{-9}\ \text{m} \times \frac{1012\ \text{pm}}{1\ \text{m}} = 1499\ \text{pm} = 1.50 \times 10^3\ \text{pm}$$

53. **(D)**

$$20.0 \text{ nm} \times \frac{1 \text{ m}}{10^9 \text{ nm}} = 2.00 \times 10^{-8} \text{ m} = \text{length of the box}$$

$$\Delta E = \frac{hc}{\lambda} = \frac{(6.626 \times 10^{-34} \text{ J s})(3.00 \times 10^8 \text{ m s}^{-1})}{8.60 \times 10^{-5} \text{ m}}$$

$$\Delta E = 2.311 \times 10^{-21} \text{ J}$$

$$\Delta E = E_{\text{excited state}} - E_{\text{ground state}}$$

$$E = \frac{n^2 h^2}{8 m L^2}$$

Where n = energy level, h = Planck's constant, m = mass, L = length of box

$$2.311 \times 10^{-21} \text{ J} = \left[\frac{n^2 (6.626 \times 10^{-34} \text{ J s})^2}{8(9.109 \times 10^{-31} \text{ kg})(2.00 \times 10^{-8} \text{ m})^2} \right] - \left[\frac{1^2 (6.626 \times 10^{-34} \text{ J s})^2}{8(9.109 \times 10^{-31} \text{ kg})(2.00 \times 10^{-8} \text{ m})^2} \right]$$

$$2.311 \times 10^{-21} \text{ J} = 1.506 \times 10^{-22} n^2 - 1.506 \times 10^{-22}$$

$$n^2 = 16.35$$

$$n = 4.0$$

54. **(D)** Mass of a proton = 1.6726×10^{-27} kg

$$50. \text{ pm} \times \frac{1 \text{ m}}{1 \times 10^{12} \text{ pm}} = 5.0 \times 10^{-11} \text{ m}$$

$$E = \frac{n^2 h^2}{8 m L^2}$$

Where n = energy level, h = Planck's constant, m = mass, L = length of box

$$\Delta E = E_{\text{excited state}} - E_{\text{ground state}}$$

$$\Delta E = \left[\frac{4^2 (6.626 \times 10^{-34} \text{ J s})^2}{8(1.6726 \times 10^{-27} \text{ kg})(5.0 \times 10^{-11} \text{ m})^2} \right] - \left[\frac{1^2 (6.626 \times 10^{-34} \text{ J s})^2}{8(1.6726 \times 10^{-27} \text{ kg})(5.0 \times 10^{-11} \text{ m})^2} \right]$$

$$\Delta E = 1.969 \times 10^{-19} \text{ J}$$

$$\lambda = \frac{hc}{\Delta E} = \frac{(6.626 \times 10^{-34} \text{ J s})(3.00 \times 10^8 \text{ m s}^{-1})}{1.969 \times 10^{-19} \text{ J}}$$

$$\lambda = 1.010 \times 10^{-6} \text{ m} \times \frac{10^9 \text{ nm}}{1 \text{ m}} = 1.0 \times 10^3 \text{ nm}$$

55. **(M)** The differences between Bohr orbits and wave mechanical orbitals are given below.

(a) The first difference is that of shape. Bohr orbits, as originally proposed, are circular (later, Sommerfeld proposed elliptical orbits). Orbitals, on the other hand, can be spherical, or shaped like two tear drops or two squashed spheres, or shaped like four tear drops meeting at their points.

(b) Bohr orbits are planar pathways, while orbitals are three-dimensional regions of space in which there is a high probability of finding electrons.

(c) The electron in a Bohr orbit has a definite trajectory. Its position and velocity are known at all times. The electron in an orbital, however, does not have a well-known position or velocity. In fact, there is a small but definite probability that the electron may be found outside the boundaries generally drawn for the orbital. Orbits and orbitals are similar in that the radius of a Bohr orbit is comparable to the average distance of the electron from the nucleus in the corresponding wave mechanical orbital.

56. **(E)** We must be careful to distinguish between probability density—the chance of finding the electron within a definite volume of space—and the probability of finding the electron at a certain distance from the nucleus. The probability density—that is, the probability of finding the electron within a small volume element (such as 1 pm^3)—at the nucleus may well be high, in fact higher than the probability density at a distance 0.53 Å from the nucleus. But the probability of finding the electron at a fixed distance from the nucleus is this probability density multiplied by all of the many small volume elements that are located at this distance. (Recall the dartboard analogy of Figure 8-35.)

Quantum Numbers and Electron Orbitals

57. **(E)** Answer (a) is incorrect because the values of m_s may be either $+\frac{1}{2}$ or $-\frac{1}{2}$. Answers (b) and (d) are incorrect because the value of ℓ may be any integer $\geq |m_\ell|$, and less than n. Thus, answer (c) is the only one that is correct.

58. **(E)**

   (a) $n = 3, \ell = 2, m_\ell = 2, m_s = +\frac{1}{2}$ (ℓ must be smaller than n and $\geq |m_\ell|$.)

                                       This is a $3d$ orbital.

   (b) $n \geq 3, \ell = 2, m_\ell = -1, m_s = -\frac{1}{2}$ (n must be larger than ℓ.)

                                         This is any d orbital, namely
                                               $3d, 4d, 5d, \ldots$ etc.

   (c) $n = 4, \ell = 2, m_\ell = 0, m_s = +\frac{1}{2}$ (m_s can be either $+\frac{1}{2}$ or $-\frac{1}{2}$.) This is a $4d$ orbital.

   (d) $n \geq 1, \ell = 0, m_\ell = 0, m_s = +\frac{1}{2}$ (n can be any positive integer, m_s could also
                                             equal $-\frac{1}{2}$.) This is a $1s$ orbital.

59. **(E)**

   (a) $n = 5, \ \ell = 1, \ m_\ell = 0$ designates a $5p$ orbital. ($\ell = 1$ for all p orbitals.)

   (b) $n = 4, \ \ell = 2, \ m_\ell = -2$ designates a $4d$ orbital. ($\ell = 2$ for all d orbitals.)

   (c) $n = 2, \ \ell = 0, \ m_\ell = 0$ designates a $2s$ orbital. ($\ell = 0$ for all s orbitals.)

60. **(E)**

   (a)   TRUE; The fourth principal shell has $n = 4$.

   (b)   TRUE; A d orbital has $\ell = 2$. Since $n = 4$, ℓ can be $= 3, 2, 1, 0$. Since $m_\ell = -2$, ℓ can be equal to 2 or 3.

(c)   FALSE; A p orbital has $\ell = 1$. But we demonstrated in part (b) that the only allowed values for ℓ are 2 and 3.

(d)   FALSE Either $+\dfrac{1}{2}$ or $-\dfrac{1}{2}$ is permitted as a value of m_s.

61. **(E)**
    (a)   1 electron   (All quantum numbers are allowed and each electron has a unique set of four quantum numbers)
    (b)   2 electrons   ($m_s = + \frac{1}{2}$ and $-\frac{1}{2}$)
    (c)   10 electrons   ($m_\ell = -2, -1, 0, 1, 2$ and $m_s = + \frac{1}{2}$ and $-\frac{1}{2}$ for each m_ℓ orbital)
    (d)   32 electrons   ($\ell = 0, 1, 2, 3$ so there are one s, three p, five d, and seven f orbitals in $n = 4$ energy level. Each orbital has 2 electrons.)
    (e)   5 electrons   (There are five electrons in the $4d$ orbital that are spin up.)

62. **(E)**
    (a)   3 subshells
    (b) $3s, 3p, 3d$
    (c)   7 orbitals
    (d)   1 orbital
    (e)   16 orbitals

The Shapes of Orbitals and Radial Probabilities

63. **(M)** The wave function for the 2s orbital of a hydrogen atom is:

$$\psi_{2s} = \frac{1}{4}\left(\frac{1}{2\pi a_0{}^3}\right)^{1/2}\left(2 - \frac{r}{a_0}\right) e^{-\frac{r}{2a_0}}$$

Where $r = 2a_0$, the $\left(2 - \dfrac{r}{a_0}\right)$ term becomes zero, thereby making $\psi_{2s} = 0$. At this point, the wave function has a radial node (i.e., the electron density is zero). The finite value of r is $2\,a_0$ at the node, which is equal to 2×53 pm or 106 pm. Thus at 106 pm, there is a nodal surface with zero electron density.

64. **(M)** The radial part for the 2s wave function in the Li^{2+} cation is:

$$R_{2s} = \left(\frac{Z}{2\pi a_0}\right)^{3/2}\left(2 - \frac{Zr}{a_0}\right) e^{-\frac{Zr}{2a_0}}$$

(Z is the atomic number for the element, and, in Li^{2+} $Z = 3$). At $Zr = 2a_0$, the pre-exponential term for the 2s orbital of Li^{2+} is zero. The Li^{2+} 2s orbital has a nodal sphere at $\dfrac{2a_0}{3}$ or 35 pm.

65. **(M)** The angular part of the $2p_y$ wave function is $Y(\theta, \phi)_{py} = \sqrt{\dfrac{3}{4\pi}}\sin\theta\sin\phi$. The two lobes of the $2p_y$ orbital lie in the xy plane and perpendicular to this plane is the xz plane. For all points in the xz plane $\phi = 0$, and since the sine of $0°$ is zero, this means that the entire xz plane is a node. Thus, the probability of finding a $2p_y$ electron in the xz plane is zero.

66. **(M)** The angular component of the wave function for the $3d_{xz}$ orbital is

$$Y(\theta, \phi)_{d_{xz}} = \sqrt{\dfrac{15}{4\pi}}\sin\theta\cos\theta\cos\phi.$$

The four lobes of the d_{xz} orbital lie in the xz plane. The xy plane is perpendicular to the xz plane, and thus the angle for θ is $90°$. The cosine of $90°$ is zero, so at every point in the xy plane the angular function has a value of zero. In other words, the entire xy plane is a node and, as a result, the probability of finding a $3d_{xz}$ electron in the xy plane is zero.

67./68. **(D)** The $2p_y$ orbital $Y(\theta, \phi) = \sqrt{\dfrac{3}{4\pi}}\sin\theta\sin\phi$, however, in the xy plane $\theta = 90°$ and $\sin\theta = 1$. Plotting in the xy plane requires that we vary only ϕ.

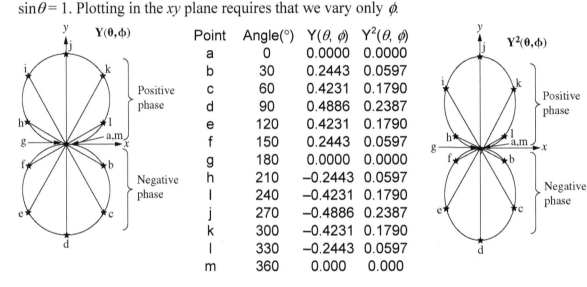

Point	Angle(°)	$Y(\theta, \phi)$	$Y^2(\theta, \phi)$
a	0	0.0000	0.0000
b	30	0.2443	0.0597
c	60	0.4231	0.1790
d	90	0.4886	0.2387
e	120	0.4231	0.1790
f	150	0.2443	0.0597
g	180	0.0000	0.0000
h	210	−0.2443	0.0597
I	240	−0.4231	0.1790
j	270	−0.4886	0.2387
k	300	−0.4231	0.1790
l	330	−0.2443	0.0597
m	360	0.000	0.000

69. **(D)** A plot of radial probability distribution versus r/a_0 for a H_{1s} orbital shows a maximum at 1.0 (that is, $r = a_0$ or $r = 53$ pm). The plot is shown below:

70. **(D)** A plot of radial probability distribution versus r/a_o for a Li^{2+} $1s$ orbital shows a maximum at 0.33 (that is, $r = a_o/3$ or $r = 18$ pm). The plot is shown below:

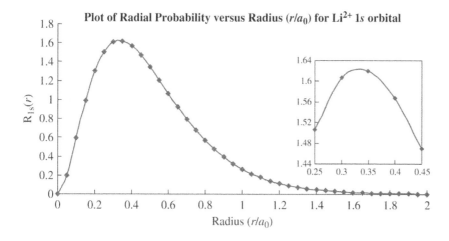

Plot of Radial Probability versus Radius (r/a_0) for Li^{2+} $1s$ orbital

71. **(E)**

(a) To answer this question, we must keep two simple rules in mind.
1. Value of ℓ is the number of angular nodes.
2. Total number of nodes $= n - 1$.

From this we see that this is a p-orbital (1 angular node $\rightarrow \ell = 1$) and because there are a total of 2 nodes, $n = 3$. This must be a $3p$ orbital.

(b) From this we see that this is a d-orbital (2 angular nodes $\rightarrow \ell = 2$) and because there are a total of 2 nodes, $n = 3$. This must be a $3d$ orbital.

(c) From this we see that this is an f-orbital (3 angular nodes $\rightarrow \ell = 2$) and because there are a total of 5 nodes, $n = 6$. This must be a $6f$ orbital.

72. **(E)**

(a) To answer this question, we must keep two simple rules in mind.
1. Value of ℓ is the number of angular nodes.
2. Total number of nodes $= n - 1$.

From this we see that this is a p-orbital (1 angular node $\rightarrow \ell = 1$) and because there are a total of 3 nodes, $n = 4$. This must be a $4p$ orbital.

(b) From this we see that this is an s-orbital (0 angular nodes $\rightarrow \ell = 0$) and because there are a total of 5 nodes, $n = 6$. This must be a $6s$ orbital.

(c) From this we see that this is a g-orbital (4 angular nodes $\rightarrow \ell = 4$) and because there are a total of 5 nodes, $n = 6$. This must be a $6g$ orbital.

73. **(E)** The orbital is in the xy plane and has two angular nodes (d-orbital) and 2 spherical nodes (total nodes = 4, hence $n = 5$). Since the orbital points between the x-axis and y-axis, this is a $5d_{xyz}$ orbital. The second view of the same orbital is just a 90° rotation about the x-axis.

74. **(E)** The orbital in the xy plane has three angular nodes (*f*-orbital) and 1 spherical node (total nodes = 4, hence $n = 5$). This is one of the 5*f* orbitals. The second view of the same orbital is just a 90° rotation about the *x*-axis.

Electron Configurations

<u>**75.**</u> **(E)**

(a) N is the third element in the *p* block of the second period. It has three 2*p* electrons.

(b) Rb is the first element in the *s* block of the *fifth* period. It has two 4*s* electrons.

(c) As is in the *p* block of the fourth period. The 3*d* subshell is filled with ten electrons, but no 4*d* electrons have been added.

(d) Au is in the *d* block of the sixth period; the 4*f* subshell is filled. Au has fourteen 4*f* electrons.

(e) Pb is the second element in the *p* block of the sixth period; it has two 6*p* electrons. Since these two electrons are placed in separate 6*p* orbitals, they are unpaired. There are two unpaired electrons.

(f) Group 14 of the periodic table is the group with the elements C, Si, Ge, Sn, and Pb. This group currently has five named elements.

(g) The sixth period begins with the element Cs $(Z = 55)$ and ends with the element Rn $(Z = 86)$. This period is 32 elements long.

76. **(E)**

(a) Sb is in group 15, with an outer shell electron configuration ns^2np^3. Sb has five outer-shell electrons.

(b) Pt has an atomic number of $Z = 78$. The fourth principal shell fills as follows: 4*s* from $Z = 19$ (K) to $Z = 20$ (Ca); 4*p* from $Z = 31$ (Ga) to $Z = 36$ (Kr); 4*d* from $Z = 39$ (Y) to $Z = 48$ (Cd); and 4*f* from $Z = 58$ (Ce) to $Z = 71$ (Lu). Since the atomic number of Pt is greater than $Z = 71$, the entire fourth principal shell is filled, with 32 electrons.

(c) The five elements with six outer-shell electrons are those in group 16: O, S, Se, Te, Po.

(d) The outer-shell electron configuration is ns^2np^4, giving the following as a partial orbital diagram: $_{s^2}$ ⊞ $_{p^4}$ ⊞⊞⊞ . There are two unpaired electrons in an atom of Te.

(e) The sixth period begins with Cs and ends with Rn. There are 10 outer transition elements in this period (La, and Hf through Hg) and there are 14 inner transition elements in the period (Ce through Lu). Thus, there are 10 + 14 or 24 transition elements in the sixth period.

77. **(E)** Configuration (b) is correct for phosphorus. The reasons why the other configurations are incorrect are given below.

(a) The two electrons in the $3s$ subshell must have opposed spins, or different values of m_s.

(c) The three $3p$ orbitals must each contain one electron, before a pair of electrons is placed in any one of these orbitals.

(d) The three unpaired electrons in the $3p$ subshell must all have the same spin, either all spin up or all spin down.

78. **(E)**

The electron configuration of Mo is [Kr] $4d$ [↑|↑|↑|↑|↑] $5s$ [↑]

(a) [Ar] $3d$ [↑↓|↑↓|↑↓|↑↓|↑↓] $3f$ [↑↓|↑↓|↑↓|↑↓|↑↓|↑↓|↑↓]   This configuration has the correct number of electrons, but it incorrectly assumes that there is a $3f$ subshell ($n = 3$, $\ell = 3$).

(b) [Kr] $4d$ [↑|↑|↑|↑|↑] $5s$ [↑]   This is the correct electron configuration.

(c) [Kr] $4d$ [↑|↑|↑|↑|↑] $5s$ [↑↓]   This configuration has one electron too many.

(d) [Ar] $3d$ [↑↓|↑↓|↑↓|↑↓|↑↓] $4s$ [↑↓] $4p$ [↑↓|↑↓|↑]   This configuration incorrectly assumes that electrons
$4d$ [↑↓|↑|↑|↑|↑]   enter the $4d$ subshell before they enter the $5s$ subshell.

79. **(E)** We write the correct electron configuration first in each case.

(a) P: $[\text{Ne}]3s^2 3p^3$ There are 3 unpaired electrons in each P atom.

(b) Br: $[\text{Ar}]3d^{10} 4s^2 4p^5$ There are ten $3d$ electrons in an atom of Br.

(c) Ge: $[\text{Ar}]3d^{10} 4s^2 4p^2$ There are two $4p$ electrons in an atom of Ge.

(d) Ba: $[\text{Xe}]6s^2$ There are two $6s$ electrons in an atom of Ba.

(e) Au: $[\text{Xe}]4f^{14}5d^{10}6s^1$ (exception)   There are fourteen $4f$ electrons in an atom of Au.

80. **(E)**

(a) The $4p$ subshell of Br contains 5 electrons: [Ar] $3d$ [↑↓|↑↓|↑↓|↑↓|↑↓] $4s$ [↑↓] $4p$ [↑↓|↑↓|↑]

(b) The $3d$ subshell of Co^{2+} contains 7 electrons: [Ar] $3d$ [↑↓|↑↓|↑|↑|↑] $4s$ [ ]

(c) The $5d$ subshell of Pb contains 10 electrons:
[Xe] $4f$ [↑↓|↑↓|↑↓|↑↓|↑↓|↑↓|↑↓] $5d$ [↑↓|↑↓|↑↓|↑↓|↑↓] $6s$ [↑↓] $6p$ [↑↓|↑↓|↑↓]

81. **(E)** Since the periodic table is based on electron structure, two elements in the same group (Pb and element 114) should have similar electron configurations.

(a) Pb: $[\text{Xe}]\, 4f^{14}5d^{10}6s^2 6p^2$ **(b)** 114: $[\text{Rn}]\, 5f^{14}6d^{10}7s^2 7p^2$

82. **(E)**

(a) The fifth period noble gas in group 18 is the element Xe.

(b) A sixth period element whose atoms have three unpaired electrons is an element in group 15, which has an outer electron configuration of $ns^2 np^3$, and thus has three unpaired p electrons. This is the element Bi.

(c) One *d*-block element that has one $4s$ electron is Cu: [Ar] $3d^{10}4s^1$. Another is Cr: [Ar] $3d^5 4s^1$.

(d) There are several *p*-block elements that are metals, namely Al, Ga, In, Tl, Sn, Pb, and Bi.

83. **(E)**

(a) This is an excited state; the $2s$ orbital should fill before any electrons enter the $2p$ orbital.

(b) This is an excited state; the electrons in the $2p$ orbitals should have the same spin (Hund's rule).

(c) This is the ground-state configuration of N.

(d) This is an excited state; there should be one set of electrons paired up in the $2p$ orbital (Hund's rule is violated).

84. **(E)**

(a) This is an excited-state silicon atom ($3p$ electrons should remain unpaired with same spin).

(b) This is an excited-state phosphorus atom; the three $3p$ orbital electrons should have the same spin (violates Hund's rule).

(c) This is a ground-state sulfur atom.

(d) This is an excited-state sulfur atom. The two unpaired electrons should have the same spin.

85. **(E)**

(a) Hg: $[Xe]4f^{14}5d^{10}6s^2$

(b) Ca: $[Ar]4s^2$

(c) Po: $[Xe]4f^{14}5d^{10}6s^26p^4$

(d) Sn: $[Kr]4d^{10}5s^25p^2$

(e) Ta: $[Xe]4f^{14}5d^36s^2$

(f) I: $[Kr]4d^{10}5s^25p^5$

86. **(E)**

(a) Te: $[Kr]4d^{10}5s^25p^4$

(b) Cs: $[Xe]6s^1$

(c) Se: $[Ar]3d^{10}4s^24p^4$

(d) *Pt: $[Xe]6s^2 4f^{14} 5d^8$

(e) Os: $[Xe]4f^{14}5d^66s^2$

(f) Cr: $[Ar]3d^54s^1$

*Note that this is the expected electron configuration of Pt based on its position in the periodic table. Experiment reveals that the true ground-state configuration is in fact $[Xe]4f^{14} 5d^96s^1$. Ultimately, it is experiment and not the position of the element in the periodic table that has the final say on the true ground-state electronic configuration.

87. **(E) (a)** rutherfordium; **(b)** carbon; **(c)** vanadium; **(d)** tellurium; **(e)** not an element

88. **(E) (a)** arsenic; **(b)** sulfur; **(c)** scandium; **(d)** ruthenium*; **(e)** not an element

*Note that this is the expected electron configuration of Ru based on its position in the periodic table. Experiment reveals that the true ground-state electron configuration is in fact $[Kr]5s^14d^7$.

INTEGRATIVE AND ADVANCED EXERCISES

89. (M) We begin with $\Delta E = 2.179 \times 10^{-18}$ J $\left(\dfrac{1}{n_i^2} - \dfrac{1}{n_f^2} \right)$ and wish to produce the Balmer

equation, which is $v = 3.2881 \times 10^{15}$ s^{-1} $\left(\dfrac{1}{2^2} - \dfrac{1}{n^2} \right)$. First we set $n_i = 2$ and $n_f = n$. Then we

recognize that all that remains is to demonstrate that the energy $E = 2.179 \times 10^{-18}$ J is associated with electromagnetic radiation of frequency $v = 3.2881 \times 10^{15}$ s^{-1}. For this, we use Planck's equation.

$E = hv = 6.626 \times 10^{-34}$ J s $\times 3.2881 \times 10^{15}$ s^{-1} $= 2.178_7 \times 10^{-18}$ J The transformation is complete.

90. (E) By definition, heat is the transfer of energy via disorderly molecular motion. Thus the transfer of heat occurs through translational movement of atoms or molecules. The exception to this is radiant heat, which is actually infrared radiation. Therefore, heat cannot be transferred through a vacuum unless it is first converted to electromagnetic radiation and then converted back to original form after transmission.

<u>**91.**</u> **(M)**
(a) We first must determine the wavelength of light that has an energy of 435 kJ/mol and compare that wavelength with those known for visible light.

$$E = \dfrac{435 \dfrac{\text{kJ}}{\text{mol}} \times \dfrac{1000 \text{ J}}{1 \text{ kJ}}}{6.022 \times 10^{23} \text{ photons/mol}} = 7.22 \times 10^{-19} \text{ J/photon} = hv$$

$$v = \dfrac{E}{h} = \dfrac{7.22 \times 10^{-19} \text{ J}}{6.626 \times 10^{-34} \text{ J s}} = 1.09 \times 10^{15} \text{ s}^{-1} \qquad \lambda = \dfrac{c}{v} = \dfrac{2.9979 \times 10^8 \text{ m s}^{-1}}{1.09 \times 10^{15} \text{ s}^{-1}} \times \dfrac{10^9 \text{ nm}}{1 \text{ m}} = 275 \text{ nm}$$

Because the shortest wavelength of visible light is 390 nm, the photoelectric effect for mercury cannot be obtained with visible light.

(b) We first determine the energy per photon for light with 215 nm wavelength.

$$E = hv = \dfrac{hc}{\lambda} = \dfrac{6.626 \times 10^{-34} \text{ J s} \times 2.9979 \times 10^8 \text{ m s}^{-1}}{215 \text{ nm} \times \dfrac{1 \text{ m}}{10^9 \text{ nm}}} = 9.24 \times 10^{-19} \text{ J/photon}$$

Excess energy, over and above the threshold energy, is imparted to the electron as kinetic

energy. Electron kinetic energy $= 9.24 \times 10^{-19}$ J $- 7.22 \times 10^{-19}$ J $= 2.02 \times 10^{-19}$ J $= \dfrac{mu^2}{2}$

(c) We solve for the velocity $u = \sqrt{\dfrac{2 \times 2.02 \times 10^{-19} \text{ J}}{9.109 \times 10^{-31} \text{ kg}}} = 6.66 \times 10^5 \text{ m s}^{-1}$

92. (M) We first determine the energy of an individual photon.

$$E = \frac{hc}{\lambda} = \frac{6.626 \times 10^{-34} \text{ J s} \times 2.998 \times 10^8 \text{ m/s}}{1525 \text{ nm} \times \dfrac{1 \text{ m}}{10^9 \text{ nm}}} = 1.303 \times 10^{-19} \text{ J}$$

$$\frac{\text{no. photons}}{\text{sec}} = \frac{95 \text{ J}}{\text{s}} \times \frac{1 \text{ photon}}{1.303 \times 10^{-19} \text{ J}} \times \frac{14 \text{ photons produced}}{100 \text{ photons theoretically possible}} = 1.0 \times 10^{20} \text{ photons/s}$$

93. (M) A watt = joule/second, so joules = watts $\times$ seconds J = 75 watts $\times$ 5.0 seconds = $37\underline{5}$ Joules
E = (number of photons) $h\nu$ and $\nu = c/\lambda$, so E = (number of photons)hc/λ and

$$\lambda = (\text{number of photons})\frac{hc}{E} = \frac{(9.91 \times 10^{20} \text{ photons})(6.626 \times 10^{-34} \text{ J s})(3.00 \times 10^8 \text{ m/s})}{37\underline{5} \text{ watts}}$$

$\lambda = 5.3 \times 10^{-7}$ m or 530 nm   The light will be green in color.

94. (D) A He$^+$ ion is a hydrogen-like ion for which $Z = 2$. The energy levels are given by

$$E_n = -R_H Z^2/n^2 = -R_H \times 2^2/n^2 = -4R_H/n^2$$

The ionization energy for removing the electron from the ground state ($n = 1$) is

$$E_i(\text{He}^+) = -E_1 = 4R_H/1^2 = 4 \times 2.179 \times 10^{-18} \text{ J} = 8.716 \times 10^{-18} \text{ J}$$

For light of wavelength 209 nm,

$$E_{\text{photon}} = h\nu = hc/\lambda = (6.626 \times 10^{-34} \text{ J s})(2.998 \times 10^8 \text{ m s}^{-1})/(208 \times 10^{-9} \text{ m}) = 9.550 \times 10^{-19} \text{ J}$$

The kinetic energy of the ionized electron is

$$E_k = E_{\text{photon}} - E_i(\text{He}^+) = 8.716 \times 10^{-18} \text{ J} - 0.955 \times 10^{-18} \text{ J} = 7.761 \times 10^{-18} \text{ J}$$

Since $E_k = \frac{1}{2}m_e u^2$ and 1 J = 1 kg m^2 s^{-2}, we have

$$u = \sqrt{2E_k/m_e} = \sqrt{2 \times 7.761 \times 10^{-18} \text{ kg m}^2 \text{ s}^{-2}/9.109 \times 10^{-31} \text{ kg}} = 4.128 \times 10^6 \text{ m s}^{-1}$$

The de Broglie wavelength, $\lambda = h/(m_e u)$, is

$$\lambda = \frac{6.626 \times 10^{-34} \text{ kg m}^2 \text{ s}^{-1}}{9.109 \times 10^{-31} \text{ kg} \times 4.128 \times 10^6 \text{ m s}^{-1}} = 1.76 \times 10^{-10} \text{ m} = 0.176 \text{ nm}$$

95. **(M)** The longest wavelength line in a series is the one with the lowest frequency. It is the one with the two quantum numbers separated by one unit. First we compute the frequency of the line.

$$v = \frac{c}{\lambda} = \frac{2.9979 \times 10^8 \text{ m s}^{-1} \times \dfrac{10^9 \text{ nm}}{1 \text{ m}}}{7400 \text{ nm}} = 4.051 \times 10^{13} \text{ s}^{-1} = 3.2881 \times 10^{15} \text{ s}^{-1} \left(\frac{1}{m^2} - \frac{1}{n^2}\right)$$

$$\left(\frac{1}{m^2} - \frac{1}{n^2}\right) = \frac{4.051 \times 10^{13} \text{ s}^{-1}}{3.2881 \times 10^{15} \text{ s}^{-1}} = 0.01232 = \left(\frac{1}{m^2} - \frac{1}{(m+1)^2}\right)$$

Since this is a fourth-order equation, it is best solved by simply substituting values.

$$\frac{1}{1^2} - \frac{1}{2^2} = 0.75 \quad \frac{1}{2^2} - \frac{1}{3^2} = 0.13889 \quad \frac{1}{3^2} - \frac{1}{4^2} = 0.04861 \quad \frac{1}{4^2} - \frac{1}{5^2} = 0.02250$$

$$\frac{1}{5^2} - \frac{1}{6^2} = 0.01222 \qquad \frac{1}{6^2} - \frac{1}{7^2} = 0.00737 \qquad \text{Pfund series has } m = 5 \text{ and } n = 6, 7, 8, 9, \ldots \infty$$

96. **(M)** First we determine the frequency of the radiation. Then rearrange the Rydberg equation (generalized from the Balmer equation) and solve for the parenthesized expression.

$$v = \frac{c}{\lambda} = \frac{2.9979 \times 10^8 \text{ m s}^{-1} \times \dfrac{10^9 \text{ nm}}{1 \text{ m}}}{1876 \text{ nm}} = 1.598 \times 10^{14} \text{ s}^{-1} = 3.2881 \times 10^{15} \text{ s}^{-1} \left(\frac{1}{m^2} - \frac{1}{n^2}\right)$$

$$\left(\frac{1}{m^2} - \frac{1}{n^2}\right) = \frac{1.598 \times 10^{14} \text{ s}^{-1}}{3.2881 \times 10^{15} \text{ s}^{-1}} = 0.0486$$

We know that $m < n$, and both numbers are integers. Furthermore, we know that $m \neq 2$ (the Balmer series) which is in the visible region, and $m \neq 1$ which is in the ultraviolet region, since the wavelength 1876 nm is in the infrared region. Let us try $m = 3$ and $n = 4$.

$$\frac{1}{3^2} - \frac{1}{4^2} = 0.04861 \text{ These are the values we want.}$$

97. **(M)**

$$E_5 = \frac{-Z^2}{n^2} R_H = \frac{(+2)^2 \, 2.179 \times 10^{-18} \text{ J}}{5^2} \qquad\qquad E_2 = \frac{-Z^2}{n^2} R_H = -\frac{(+2)^2 \, 2.179 \times 10^{-18} \text{ J}}{2^2}$$

$$= -3.486 \times 10^{-19} \text{ J} \qquad\qquad\qquad\qquad = -2.179 \times 10^{-18} \text{ J}$$

$$E_5 - E_2 = \Delta E = \frac{hc}{\lambda} = -3.486 \times 10^{-19} \text{ J} - (-2.179 \times 10^{-18} \text{ J}) = 1.830 \times 10^{-18} \text{ J}$$

$$\lambda = \frac{hc}{\Delta E} = \frac{6.626 \times 10^{-34} \text{ J s} \times 2.998 \times 10^8 \text{ m/s}}{1.830 \times 10^{-18} \text{ J}} \times \frac{10^9 \text{ nm}}{1 \text{ m}} = 108.6 \text{ nm}$$

98. **(M)** The lines observed consist of

    (a) the transitions starting at $n = 5$ and ending at $n = 4, 3, 2,$ and 1;

    (b) the transitions starting at $n = 4$ and ending at $n = 3, 2,$ and 1;

    (c) the transitions starting at $n = 3$ and ending at $n = 2$ and 1;

    (d) the transition starting at $n = 2$ and ending at $n = 1$.

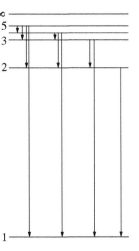

The energy level diagram is shown on the right hand side of this page.

99. **(M)** When the outermost electron is very far from the inner electrons, it no longer is affected by them individually. Rather, all of the inner electrons and the nucleus affect this outermost electron as if they are one composite entity, a nucleus with a charge of 1+, in other words, a hydrogen nucleus.

100. **(M)**

    (a) If there were three possibilities for electron spin, then each orbital could accommodate three electrons. Thus, an s subshell, with one orbital, could hold three electrons. A p subshell, with three orbitals, could hold 9 electrons. A d subshell, with five orbitals, could hold 15 electrons. And an f subshell, with seven orbitals, could hold 21 electrons. Therefore, the electron configuration for cesium, with 55 electrons, becomes the following.

    ordered by energy: $1s^3 2s^3 2p^9 3s^3 3p^9 4s^3 3d^{15} 4p^9 5s^1$
    ordered by shells: $1s^3 2s^3 2p^9 3s^3 3p^9 3d^{15} 4s^3 4p^9 5s^1$

    (b) If ℓ could have the value n, then there could be orbitals such as $1p$, $2d$, $3f$, etc. In this case, the electron configuration for cesium, with 55 electrons, would be:

    ordered by energy: $1s^2 1p^6 2s^2 2p^6 3s^2 2d^{10} 3p^6 4s^2 3d^{10} 4p^6 5s^2 3f^1$
    ordered by shells: $1s^2 1p^6 2s^2 2p^6 2d^{10} 3s^2 3p^6 3d^{10} 3f^1 4s^2 4p^6 5s^2$

101. **(D)** First we must determine the energy per photon of the radiation, and then calculate the number of photons needed, (i.e., the number of ozone molecules (with the ideal gas equation)). (Parts per million O_3 are assumed to be by volume.) The product of these two numbers is total energy in joules.

$$E_1 = h\nu = \frac{hc}{\lambda} = \frac{6.626 \times 10^{-34} \text{ J s} \times 2.9979 \times 10^8 \text{ m s}^{-1}}{254 \text{ nm} \times \dfrac{1 \text{ m}}{10^9 \text{ nm}}} = 7.82 \times 10^{-19} \text{ J/photon}$$

$$\text{no. photons} = \frac{\left(748 \text{ mmHg} \times \dfrac{1 \text{ atm}}{760 \text{ mmHg}}\right) \times \left(1.00 \text{ L} \times \dfrac{0.25 \text{ L O}_3}{10^6 \text{ L air}}\right)}{\dfrac{0.08206 \text{ atm L}}{\text{mol K}} \times (22 + 273) \text{ K}} \times \frac{6.022 \times 10^{23} \text{ molecules}}{1 \text{ mol O}_3}$$

$$\times \frac{1 \text{ photon}}{1 \text{ molecule O}_3} = 6.1 \times 10^{15} \text{ photons}$$

energy needed $= 7.82 \times 10^{-19}$ J/photon $\times 6.1 \times 10^{15}$ photons $= 4.8 \times 10^{-3}$ J or 4.8 mJ

102. (M) First we compute the energy per photon, and then the number of photons received per second.

$$E = h\nu = 6.626 \times 10^{-34} \text{J s} \times 8.4 \times 10^9 \text{ s}^{-1} = 5.6 \times 10^{-24} \text{ J/photon}$$

$$\frac{\text{photons}}{\text{second}} = \frac{4 \times 10^{-21} \text{ J/s}}{5.6 \times 10^{-24} \text{ J/photon}} = 7 \times 10^2 \text{ photons/s}$$

103. (M)

(a) The average kinetic energy is given by the following expression.

$$\bar{E}_k = \frac{3}{2} \cdot \frac{R}{N_A} \cdot T = \frac{3 \times 8.314 \text{ J mol}^{-1} \text{ K}^{-1}}{2 \times 6.022 \times 10^{23} \text{ mol}^{-1}} \times 1023 \text{ K} = 2.12 \times 10^{-20} \text{ J molecule}^{-1}$$

Then we determine the energy per photon of visible light. $E = h\nu = \dfrac{hc}{\lambda}$

$$E_{\text{max}} = \frac{6.626 \times 10^{-34} \text{ J s} \times 2.9979 \times 10^8 \text{ m s}^{-1}}{390 \text{ nm} \times \dfrac{1 \text{ m}}{10^9 \text{ nm}}} = 5.09 \times 10^{-19} \text{ J/photon}$$

$$E_{\text{min}} = \frac{6.626 \times 10^{-34} \text{ J s} \times 2.9979 \times 10^8 \text{ m s}^{-1}}{760 \text{ nm} \times \dfrac{1 \text{ m}}{10^9 \text{ nm}}} = 2.61 \times 10^{-19} \text{ J/photon}$$

We see that the average kinetic energy of molecules in the flame is not sufficient to account for the emission of visible light.

(b) The reason why visible light is emitted is that the atoms in the flame do not all have the same energy. Some of them have energy considerably greater than the average, which is sufficiently high to account for the emission of visible light.

104. (M) If the angular momentum (*mur*) is restricted to integral values of $h/2\pi$, then we have *mur = nh*/2π. The circumference of a circular orbit equals its diameter times π, or twice its radius multiplied by π: 2πr. When *mur = nh*/2π is rearranged, we obtain $2\pi r = nh/mu = n\lambda$, where $\lambda = h/mu$ is the de Broglie wavelength, which is the result requested.

105. **(D)** First, we must calculate the energy of the 300 nm photon. Then, using the amount of energy required to break a Cl–Cl bond energy and the energy of the photon, we can determine how much excess energy there is after bond breakage.

Energy of a single photon at 300 nm is:

$$E = h\nu = hc/\lambda$$

$$E = \frac{(6.6261\times10^{-34} \text{ J s})(2.998\times10^{8} \text{ m s}^{-1})}{(300\overline{\times}10^{-9} \text{ m})} = 6.6215\times10^{-19} \text{ J}$$

The bond energy of a single Cl–Cl bond is determined as follows:

$$\text{Cl}-\text{Cl B.E.} = \frac{242.6\times10^{3} \text{ J}}{1 \text{ mol Cl}_2} \times \frac{1 \text{ mol Cl}_2}{6.022\times10^{23} \text{ molecules}} \times \frac{1 \text{ molecules}}{1 \text{ Cl}-\text{Cl bond}} = 4.028\times10^{-19} \text{ J/Cl}-\text{Cl bond}$$

Therefore, the excess energy after splitting a Cl–Cl bond is $(6.6215 - 4.028) \times 10^{-19}$ J $= 2.59 \times 10^{-19}$ J. Statistically, this energy is split evenly between the two Cl atoms and imparts a kinetic energy of 1.29×10^{-19} J to each.

The velocity of each atom is determined as follows:

$$\text{mass of Cl} = \frac{35.45 \text{ g Cl}}{1 \text{ mol Cl}} \times \frac{1 \text{ mol Cl}}{6.022\times10^{23} \text{ molecules}} = 5.887\times10^{-23} \text{ kg/Cl atom}$$

$$E_k = \frac{1}{2}mu^2$$

$$u = \sqrt{\frac{2E_k}{m}} = \sqrt{\frac{2(1.29\times10^{-19} \text{ J})}{5.887\times10^{-23} \text{ kg}}} = 66.2 \text{ m/s}$$

106. **(M)** The $n = 138$ level is a high Rydberg state (excited state). It is a bound state that lies in the continuum and is very close to the energy required to ionize the electron.

$$\text{radius} = n^2 a_0 = (138)^2(53\times10^{-12} \text{m}) = 1.01\times10^{-6}\text{m}$$

$$u = \frac{nh}{2\pi mr} = \frac{nh}{2\pi mn^2 a_0} = \frac{138(6.626\times10^{-34}\text{J s})}{2(3.1416)(9.11\times10^{-31}\text{kg})(138)^2(53\times10^{-12}\text{m})} = 1.6\times10^{5}\text{m/s}$$

$$\text{rev/s} = \frac{u}{2\pi r} = \frac{u}{2\pi n^2 a_0} = \frac{(1.6\times10^{5} \text{ m/sec})}{2(3.1416)(138)^2(53\times10^{-12}\text{m})} = 2.5\times10^{10}\text{rev/s}$$

107. (D) For the 3s orbital of Hydrogen ($Z = 1$ and $n = 3$):

$$R(3s) = \frac{1}{9\sqrt{3}}\left(\frac{1}{a_0}\right)^{3/2}\left(6 - \frac{4r}{a_0} + \frac{4r^2}{9a_0{}^2}\right)e^{\frac{-r}{3a_0}}$$

To find the nodes, we need only find the values of r that result in $R(3s) = 0$.
Note that for r = infinity, $R(3s) = 0$. However this is not a node; rather, this result indicates that the e^- must be near the nucleus for it to be associated with the atom (r = infinity suggests electron has ionized). Basically we have to find the roots of the equation $(6 - 4r/a_0 + 4r^2/9a_0{}^2)$ = 0. This is a quadratic where $x = r/a_0$ and $a = 4/9$, $b = -4$ and $c = 6$. It can be solved using the quadratic roots expression and it yields two roots, $r/a_0 = 7.098$ and $r/a_0 = 1.902$. The nodes occur at $r = 1.902\ a_0$ and $7.098\ a_0$.

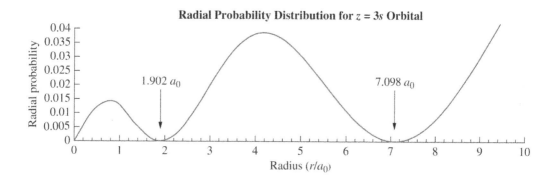

108. (D) For a 2s orbital on hydrogen ($Z = 1$, $n = 2$):
$$R(2s) = \frac{1}{2\sqrt{2}}\left(\frac{1}{a_0}\right)^{3/2}\left(2 - \frac{r}{a_0}\right)e^{\frac{-r}{2a_0}}$$

To find the radius where the probability of finding a 2s orbital electron (on H) is a maximum or a minimum), we need to set the first derivative of $4\pi r^2 R^2(2s) = 0$ and solve for r in terms of a_0.

$$4\pi r^2 (R^2(2s)) = 4\pi r^2 \left(\frac{1}{2\sqrt{2}}\left(\frac{1}{a_0}\right)^{3/2}\right)^2 \left(2 - \frac{r}{a_0}\right)^2\left(e^{\frac{-r}{2a_0}}\right)^2$$

$$4\pi r^2 \left(\frac{1}{8a_0^3}\right)\left(4 - 4\frac{r}{a_0} + \frac{r^2}{a_0^2}\right)e^{\frac{-r}{a_0}} = \left(\frac{\pi r^2}{2a_0^3}\right)\left(4 - 4\frac{r}{a_0} + \frac{r^2}{a_0^2}\right)e^{\frac{-r}{a_0}} = \left(\frac{2\pi r^2}{a_0^3} - \frac{2\pi r^3}{a_0^4} + \frac{\pi r^4}{2a_0^5}\right)e^{\frac{-r}{a_0}}$$

Next, we take the derivative and set this equal to zero. This will give the points where the wave function is a maximum or minimum.

$$\frac{d\left[4\pi r^2 (R^2(2s))\right]}{dr} = \left(\frac{2\pi r^2}{a_0^3} - \frac{2\pi r^3}{a_0^4} + \frac{\pi r^4}{2a_0^5}\right)\left(-\frac{1}{a_0}\right)e^{\frac{-r}{a_0}} + \left(\frac{4\pi r}{a_0^3} - \frac{6\pi r^2}{a_0^4} + \frac{2\pi r^3}{a_0^5}\right)e^{\frac{-r}{a_0}} = 0$$

$$\left(-\frac{2\pi r^2}{a_0^4} + \frac{2\pi r^3}{a_0^5} - \frac{\pi r^4}{2a_0^6}\right)e^{\frac{-r}{a_0}} + \left(\frac{4\pi r}{a_0^3} - \frac{6\pi r^2}{a_0^4} + \frac{2\pi r^3}{a_0^5}\right)e^{\frac{-r}{a_0}} = 0 \quad \text{multiply through by } \frac{-2a_0^6}{\pi r e^{-r/a_0}}$$

$$4a_0^2 r - 4a_0 r^2 + r^3 - 8a_0^2 r + 12a_0^2 r - 4a_0 r^2 = 0$$

$$r^3 - 8a_0 r^2 + 16a_0^2 r - 8a_0^3 = 0 \qquad \text{Set} \quad r = xa_0$$

$$x^3 a_0^3 - 8a_0 \left(x^2 a_0^2 \right) + 16a_0^2 \left(xa_0 \right) - 8a_0^3 = 0 \qquad \text{Divide through by } a_0^3$$

$$x^3 - 8x^2 + 16x - 8 = 0$$

This is a cubic equation, which has three possible roots. Using the method of successive approximations, we can find the following three roots:

$$x_1 = 0.764 = \frac{r}{a_0} \qquad\qquad x_2 = 2 = \frac{r}{a_0} \qquad\qquad x_3 = 5.236 = \frac{r}{a_0}$$

$$r_1 = 0.764a_0 = 0.405 \ \overset{o}{\text{A}} \qquad r_2 = 2a_0 = 1.06 \ \overset{o}{\text{A}} \qquad r_3 = 5.236a_0 = 2.775 \ \overset{o}{\text{A}}$$

109. (D) The $4p_x$ orbital has electron density in the xy plane that is directed primarily along the x axis. Since it is a p-orbital, there is one angular plane. Since $n = 4$, a total of 3 nodes are present, one angular and two radial. A sketch of this orbital is shown below.

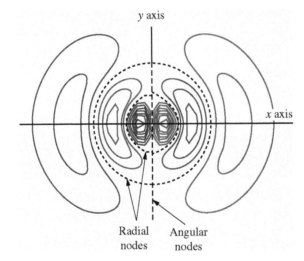

y axis

x axis

Radial   Angular
nodes   nodes

110. (D) Recall, the volume of a sphere is $4/3\pi r^3$. One way of solving this problem is to find the difference in the volumes of two spheres, one with a radius of r and the other with a radius of $r + dr$, where dr is an infinitesimal increment in r. The difference in the volumes would be given by: $dV = 4/3\pi(r + dr)^3 - 4/3\pi r^3 = (4/3)\pi(3r^2 dr + 3rdr^2 + dr^3)$. For very small values of dr, the terms $3rdr^2 + dr^3$ are negligible in comparison to $3r^2 dr$. Thus for small values of dr, the volume expression simplifies to $dV = (4/3)\pi(3r^2 dr) = 4\pi r^2 dr$.

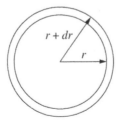

r + dr

r

The expression above for dV can also be obtained by differentiating $V = (4/3)\pi r^3$ with respect to r. Since $dV/dr = 4\pi r^2$, then $dV = 4\pi r^2 dr$.

111. (D)

(a) To calculate the probability of finding a $1s$ electron anywhere within a sphere of radius a_0, we must integrate the probability density distribution $4\pi r^2 \psi^2$ from 0 to a_0 with respect to r.

$$\psi^2(1s) = \frac{1}{\pi a_0^{3}} e^{-\frac{2r}{a_0}} \qquad \text{Let } P_{a_0} = \text{probability of finding electron out to a radius of } a_0$$

$$P_{a_0} = \int_0^{a_0} 4\pi r^2 \psi^2 \, dr = \int_0^{a_0} 4\pi r^2 \frac{1}{\pi a_o^{3}} e^{-\frac{2r}{a_0}} \, dr = \int_0^{a_0} 4r^2 \frac{1}{a_0^{3}} e^{-\frac{2r}{a_0}} \, dr$$

$$\text{Let } x = \frac{2r}{a_0} \quad \text{then} \quad dx = \frac{2}{a_0} dr \quad \text{Then } r = 0 \to x = 0 \quad \text{and} \quad r = a_o \to x = 2$$

The integral then becomes: $P_{a_o} = \int_0^2 4\left(\frac{a_0 x}{2}\right)^2 \frac{1}{a_0^{3}} e^{-x} \left(\frac{a_0}{2}\right) dx = \int_0^2 \frac{x^2 e^{-x}}{2} dx$

This simplifies to $P_{a_0} = \frac{1}{2}\int_0^2 x^2 e^{-x} dx$

We now calculate the antiderivative of $F(x) = \int x^2 e^{-x} dx$ by using integration by parts (twice):

$$F(x) = \int x^2 e^{-x} dx = \int x^2 \left(-e^{-x}\right) dx = -x^2 e^{-x} + \int 2x \left(-e^{-x}\right) dx = -x^2 e^{-x} - 2xe^{-x} + \int 2e^{-x} dx$$

$$F(x) = \int x^2 e^{-x} dx = -x^2 e^{-x} - 2xe^{-x} - 2e^{-x} + \text{constant}$$

(We don't need the constant of integration because we will be solving the definite integral.)

Using the fundamental theorem of calculus and the antiderivative we just found, we return to:

$$P_{a_o} = \frac{1}{2}\int_0^2 x^2 e^{-x} dx = \frac{1}{2}\left(F(2) - F(0)\right) = \frac{1}{2}\left(-4e^{-2} - 4e^{-2} - 2e^{-2}\right) - \frac{1}{2}\left(-0 - 0 - 2e^{-0}\right)$$

$$P_{a_o} = -\frac{1}{2}\left(10e^{-2}\right) + 1 = 1 - 5e^{-2} = 0.32$$

This suggests that there is a 32% probability of finding the $1s$ electron within a radius of a_0 in a ground-state hydrogen atom.

(b) Performing the same calculation as before but with $r = 0 \to r = 2a_0 (x = 4)$ we obtain

$$P_{2a_0} = F(4) - F(0) = \frac{1}{2}\left(-16e^{-4} - 8e^{-4} - 2e^{-4}\right) - \frac{1}{2}\left(-0 - 0 - 2e^{-0}\right)$$

$$= -\frac{1}{2}\left(26e^{-4}\right) + 1 = 1 - 13e^{-4} = 0.76$$

This suggests that there is a 76% probability of finding the $1s$ electron within a radius of $2a_0$ in a ground-state hydrogen atom.

112. (D) The energy available from the excited state hydrogen atom is 1.634×10^{-18} J $(-R_H/2^2 - (-R_H/1^2))$ This energy is then used to excite an He$^+$ ion $(Z = 2)$.

Hence, 1.634×10^{-18} J $= -Z^2 R_H/n_{low}^2 - (-Z^2 R_H/n_{high}^2)$ $n_{low} = 1$, $Z = 2$ and $R_H = 2.179 \times 10^{-18}$ J

Substituting we find, 1.634×10^{-18} J $= (-4 \times 2.179 \times 10^{-18}$ J$/1^2) - (-4 \times 2.179 \times 10^{-18}$ J$/n_{high}^2)$ $0.1875 = (1 - 1/n_{high}^2)$ or $1/n_{high}^2 = 1 - 0.1875 = 0.8125$ rearrange to give $n_{high}^2 = 1.231$. From this, $n_{high} = 1.11$. This suggests that far more energy is required to excite a He$^+$ atom to the first excited state than is available from excited-state H atoms. Thus, the energy transfer described here is not possible. One can calculate that the energy required to reach the first excited state in He$^+$ is $-2^2(2.179 \times 10^{-18}$ J$)/1^2 - (-2^2(2.179 \times 10^{-18}$ J$)/2^2 = 6.537 \times 10^{-18}$ J. This is 4 times larger than the available energy from a H atom's $2s^1 \rightarrow 1s^1$ transition.

FEATURE PROBLEMS

113. (M) By carefully scanning the diagram, we note that there are no spectral lines in the area of 304 nm and 309 nm, nor at 318 nm and 327 nm. Likewise, there are none between 435 and 440 nm. We conclude that V is absent. There are spectral lines that correspond to each of the Cr spectral lines—between 355 nm and 362 nm, and between 425 nm and 430 nm. Cr is present. There are no spectral lines close to 403 nm; Mn is absent. There are spectral lines at about 344 nm, 358 nm, 372 nm, 373 nm, and 386 nm. Fe is present. There are spectral lines at 341 nm, 344 nm to 352 nm, and 362 nm. Ni is present. There are spectral lines between 310 and 315 nm and at about 415 nm. Another element is present. Thus, Cr, Fe, and Ni are present. V and Mn are absent. Also, there is an additional element present.

114. (D) The equation of a straight line is $y = mx + b$, where m is the slope of the line and b is its y-intercept. The Balmer equation is $\nu = 3.2881 \times 10^{15}$ Hz $\left(\dfrac{1}{2^2} - \dfrac{1}{n^2}\right) = \dfrac{c}{\lambda}$. In this equation, one plots ν on the vertical axis, and $1/n^2$ on the horizontal axis. The slope is $b = -3.2881 \times 10^{15}$ Hz and the intercept is 3.2881×10^{15} Hz $\div 2^2 = 8.2203 \times 10^{14}$ Hz. The plot of the data for Figure 8-12 follows.

λ	656.3 nm	486.1 nm	434.0 nm	410.1 nm
ν	4.568×10^{14} Hz	6.167×10^{14} Hz	6.908×10^{14} Hz	7.310×10^{14} Hz
n	3	4	5	6

We see that the slope (-3.2906×10^{15}) and the y-intercept (8.2240×10^{14}) are almost exactly what we had predicted from the Balmer equation.

115. (D)

(a) Use Balmer's original equation, and take the ratio of the first two lines:

$$\lambda = \frac{Bm^2}{(m^2 - n^2)} \qquad\qquad v_{m,n} = \frac{c}{\lambda} = \frac{(m^2 - n^2)}{m^2} \times \frac{c}{B}$$

(b) For the Lyman series, $\dfrac{v_{2,1}}{v_{3,1}} = \dfrac{(4-1)/4}{(9-1)/9} = \dfrac{3/4}{8/9} = \dfrac{27}{32} = 0.84375$

For the Balmer series, $\dfrac{v_{3,2}}{v_{4,2}} = \dfrac{(9-4)/9}{(16-4)/16} = \dfrac{5/9}{12/16} = \dfrac{80}{72} = 1.1111$

For the Paschen series, $\dfrac{v_{4,3}}{v_{5,3}} = \dfrac{(16-9)/9}{(25-9)/25} = \dfrac{7/9}{16/25} = \dfrac{175}{144} = 1.2153$

Comparing these ratios with the ratio of the first two lines,
$2.465263/2.921793 = 0.843750$, we identify the series as the Lyman series.

(c) Using equation (8.2), we can write

$$v_{2,1} = cR_H(1/1^2 - 1/2^2) \qquad v_{3,2} = cR_H(1/2^2 - 1/3^2) \qquad v_{3,1} = cR_H(1/1^2 - 1/3^2)$$

Hence, $v_{2,1} + v_{3,2} = cR_H(1/1^2 - 1/2^2) + cR_H(1/2^2 - 1/3^2) = cR_H(1/1^2 - 1/3^2) = v_{3,1}$

and $v_{3,1} - v_{2,1} = cR_H(1/1^2 - 1/3^2) - cR_H(1/1^2 - 1/2^2) = cR_H(1/2^2 - 1/3^2) = v_{3,2}$

(d) To construct the Balmer series from the Lyman series, we subtract $v_{2,1}$ from $v_{3,1}$ to get the first frequency for $v_{3,2}$. We can then proceed to generate the next frequencies. A similar procedure will give the Paschen series, that is $v_{4,3} = v_{4,1} - v_{3,1}$.

(e) The line observed by Humphreys is of low frequency, so we expect that a combination of the low frequency lines of the Lyman series will be involved. Let us try $v_{6,5} = v_{6,1} - v_{5,1} = 3.195711 \times 10^{15} - 3.155536 \times 10^{15} = 0.0040175 \times 10^{15}$, which is not correct. Let us try $v_{7,6} = v_{7,1} - v_{6,1} = 3.219935 \times 10^{15} - 3.195711 \times 10^{15} = 0.0024224 \times 10^{15}$, which is correct.

116. (D)

(a) First we calculate the range of energies for the incident photons used in the absorption experiment. Remember: $E_{photon} = hv$ and $v = c/\lambda$. At one end of the range, $\lambda = 100$ nm.
Therefore, $v = 2.998 \times 10^8$ m s^{-1} ÷ $(1.00 \times 10^{-7}$ m$) = 2.998 \times 10^{15}$ s^{-1}.
So $E_{photon} = 6.626 \times 10^{-34}$ J s$(2.998 \times 10^{15}$ s$^{-1}) = 1.98 \times 10^{-18}$ J.
At the other end of the range, $\lambda = 1000$ nm.
Therefore, $v = 2.998 \times 10^8$ m s^{-1} ÷ 1.00×10^{-6} m $= 2.998 \times 10^{14}$ s^{-1}.
So $E_{photon} = 6.626 \times 10^{-34}$ J s$(2.998 \times 10^{14}$ s$^{-1}) = 1.98 \times 10^{-19}$ J.

Next, we will calculate what excitations are possible using photons with energies between 1.98×10^{-18} J and 1.98×10^{-19} J and the electron initially residing in the $n = 1$ level. The photon energies for these transitions can be found with the equation

$$\Delta E = E_f - E_i = -2.179 \times 10^{-18} \left(\frac{1}{(1)^2} - \frac{1}{(n_f)^2} \right). \text{ For the lowest energy photon}$$

$$1.98 \times 10^{-19} \text{ J} = -2.179 \times 10^{-18} \left(\frac{1}{(1)^2} - \frac{1}{(n_f)^2} \right) \text{ or } 0.0904 = 1 - \frac{1}{(n_f)^2}$$

From this $-0.9096 = -\dfrac{1}{(n_f)^2}$ and $n_f = 1.05$

Thus, the lowest energy photon is not capable of promoting the electron above the $n = 1$ level. For the highest energy level:

$$1.98 \times 10^{-18} \text{ J} = -2.179 \times 10^{-18} \left(\frac{1}{(1)^2} - \frac{1}{(n_f)^2} \right) \text{ or } 0.9114 = 1 - \frac{1}{(n_f)^2}$$

From this $-0.0886 = -\dfrac{1}{(n_f)^2}$ and $n_f = 3.35$ Thus, the highest energy photon can promote a ground-state electron to both the $n = 2$ and $n = 3$ levels. This means that we would see two lines in the absorption spectrum, one corresponding to the $n = 1 \rightarrow n = 2$ transition and the other to the $n = 1 \rightarrow n = 3$ transition.

Energy for the $n = 1 \rightarrow n = 2$ transition $= -2.179 \times 10^{-18} \left(\dfrac{1}{(1)^2} - \dfrac{1}{(2)^2} \right) = 1.634 \times 10^{-18}$ J

$$v = \frac{1.634 \times 10^{-18} \text{ J}}{6.626 \times 10^{-34} \text{ J s}} = 2.466 \times 10^{15} \text{ s}^{-1} \quad \lambda = \frac{2.998 \times 10^8 \text{ m s}^{-1}}{2.466 \times 10^{15} \text{ s}^{-1}} = 1.215 \times 10^{-7} \text{ m}$$

$\lambda = 121.5$ nm

Thus, we should see a line at 121.5 nm in the absorption spectrum.

Energy for the $n = 1 \rightarrow n = 3$ transition $= -2.179 \times 10^{-18} \left(\dfrac{1}{(1)^2} - \dfrac{1}{(3)^2} \right) = 1.937 \times 10^{-18}$ J

$$v = \frac{1.937 \times 10^{-18} \text{ J}}{6.626 \times 10^{-18} \text{ J}} = 2.923 \times 10^{15} \text{ s}^{-1} \quad \lambda = \frac{2.998 \times 10^8 \text{ m s}^{-1}}{2.923 \times 10^{15} \text{ s}^{-1}} = 1.025 \times 10^{-7} \text{ m}$$

$\lambda = 102.5$ nm

Consequently, the second line should appear at 102.6 nm in the absorption spectrum.

(b) An excitation energy of 1230 kJ mol^{-1} to 1240 kJ mol^{-1} works out to 2×10^{-18} J per photon. This amount of energy is sufficient to raise the electron to the $n = 4$ level. Consequently, six lines will be observed in the emission spectrum. The calculation for each emission line is summarized below:

$$E_{4 \rightarrow 1} = \frac{2.179 \times 10^{-18} \text{ J}}{6.626 \times 10^{-34} \text{ J s}} \left(\frac{1}{1^2} - \frac{1}{4^2} \right) = 3.083 \times 10^{15} \text{ s}^{-1} \quad \lambda = \frac{2.998 \times 10^8 \text{ m s}^{-1}}{3.083 \times 10^{15} \text{ s}^{-1}} = 9.724 \times 10^{-8} \text{ m}$$

$\lambda = 97.2$ nm

$$E_{4\rightarrow2} = \frac{2.179\times10^{-18}\text{ J}}{6.626\times10^{-34}\text{ J s}}\left(\frac{1}{2^2}-\frac{1}{4^2}\right) = 6.167\times10^{14}\text{ s}^{-1} \quad \lambda = \frac{2.998\times10^{8}\text{ ms}^{-1}}{6.167\times10^{14}\text{ s}^{-1}} = 4.861\times10^{-7}\text{ m}$$
$$\lambda = 486.1\text{ nm}$$

$$E_{4\rightarrow3} = \frac{2.179\times10^{-18}\text{ J}}{6.626\times10^{-34}\text{ J s}}\left(\frac{1}{3^2}-\frac{1}{4^2}\right) = 1.599\times10^{14}\text{ s}^{-1} \quad \lambda = \frac{2.998\times10^{8}\text{ ms}^{-1}}{1.599\times10^{14}\text{ s}^{-1}} = 1.875\times10^{-6}\text{ m}$$
$$\lambda = 1875\text{ nm}$$

$$E_{3\rightarrow1} = \frac{2.179\times10^{-18}\text{ J}}{6.626\times10^{-34}\text{ J s}}\left(\frac{1}{1^2}-\frac{1}{3^2}\right) = 2.924\times10^{15}\text{ s}^{-1} \quad \lambda = \frac{2.998\times10^{8}\text{ ms}^{-1}}{2.924\times10^{15}\text{ s}^{-1}} = 1.025\times10^{-7}\text{ m}$$
$$\lambda = 102.5\text{ nm}$$

$$E_{3\rightarrow2} = \frac{2.179\times10^{-18}\text{ J}}{6.626\times10^{-34}\text{ J s}}\left(\frac{1}{2^2}-\frac{1}{3^2}\right) = 4.568\times10^{14}\text{ s}^{-1} \quad \lambda = \frac{2.998\times10^{8}\text{ ms}^{-1}}{4.568\times10^{14}\text{ s}^{-1}} = 6.563\times10^{-7}\text{ m}$$
$$\lambda = 656.3\text{ nm}$$

$$E_{2\rightarrow1} = \frac{2.179\times10^{-18}\text{ J}}{6.626\times10^{-34}\text{ J s}}\left(\frac{1}{1^2}-\frac{1}{2^2}\right) = 2.467\times10^{15}\text{ s}^{-1} \quad \lambda = \frac{2.998\times10^{8}\text{ ms}^{-1}}{2.467\times10^{15}\text{ s}^{-1}} = 1.215\times10^{-7}\text{ m}$$
$$\lambda = 121.5\text{ nm}$$

(c) The number of lines observed in the two spectra is not the same. The absorption spectrum has two lines, while the emission spectrum has six lines. Notice that the 102.5 nm and 1021.5 nm lines are present in both spectra. This is not surprising since the energy difference between each level is the same whether it is probed by emission or absorption spectroscopy.

117. (M)

(a) The wavelength associated with each helium-4 atom must be close to 100 pm $(1.00\times10^{-10}$ m) in order for diffraction to take place. To find the necessary velocity for the He atoms, we need to employ the de Broglie equation: $\lambda = \dfrac{h}{mu}$.

Rearrange to give $u = \dfrac{h}{m\lambda}$ where:

$\lambda = 1.00\times10^{-10}$ m, $h = 6.626\times10^{-34}$ kg m^{2}s^{-1} and $m_{\text{He nucleus}} = 6.647\times10^{-27}$ kg

So, $u = \dfrac{6.626\times10^{-34}\text{ kg m}^2\text{ s}^{-1}}{6.647\times10^{-27}\text{ kg}(1.00\times10^{-10}\text{ m})} = 9.97\times10^{2}\text{ m s}^{-1}$

(b) The de Broglie wavelength for the beam of protons would be too small for any diffraction to occur. Instead, most of the protons would simply pass through the film of gold and have little or no interaction with the constituent gold atoms. Keep in mind, however, that some of the protons will end up being deflected or bounced back by either passing too close to a nucleus or colliding with a gold nucleus head on, respectively.

118. (D) The emission lines are due to transitions from $n_{high} \rightarrow n_{low}$ where $n_{high} = 6, 5, 4, 3, 2$ and $n_{low} = 5, 4, 3, 2, 1$ (with the restriction $n_{high} > n_{low}$). Consider the emission resulting from $n_{high} = 6 \rightarrow n_{low} = 5$. The orbital types allowed for $n = 6$ are s, p, d, f, g, h and for $n = 5$ are s, p, d, f, g. We can have $6s \rightarrow 5p$ ($5s$ is not allowed because of the selection rule $\Delta \ell = \pm 1$). $6p \rightarrow 5s, 6p \rightarrow 5d, 6d \rightarrow 5p, 6d \rightarrow 5f, 6f \rightarrow 5g, 6f \rightarrow 5d, 6g \rightarrow 5f, 6h \rightarrow 5g$.

In the absence of a magnetic field, all of these transitions occur at the same frequency or wavelength for a hydrogen atom. In the hydrogen atom the $6 \rightarrow 5$ occurs at the longest wavelength, which is the rightmost line in the spectrum. We can calculate the wavelength of this emission by using the following relationship:

$$\Delta E = 2.179 \times 10^{-18} \text{ J} \times \left(\frac{1}{n_{high}^2} - \frac{1}{n_{low}^2} \right) \quad \text{and} \quad \Delta E = \frac{hc}{\lambda} \quad \text{or} \quad \lambda = \frac{hc}{\Delta E}$$

For the transition $n_{high} = 6 \rightarrow n_{low} = 5$. We calculate the following values for ΔE and λ.

$$\Delta E = 2.179 \times 10^{-18} \text{ J} \times \left(\frac{1}{6^2} - \frac{1}{5^2} \right) = 2.663 \times 10^{-20} \text{ J}$$

$$\lambda = \frac{hc}{\Delta E} = \frac{(6.626 \times 10^{-34} \text{ J s}) \times (2.998 \times 10^8 \text{ m s}^{-1})}{2.663 \times 10^{-20} \text{ J}} = 7.459 \times 10^{-6} \text{ m or 7459 nm}$$

We can similarly repeat the procedure for the remaining 14 lines and obtain the following data.

n(initial)	n(final)	ΔE(Joules)	λ (nm)	Line Number
6	5	2.663×10^{-20}	7459	1
6	4	7.566×10^{-20}	2625	3
6	3	1.816×10^{-19}	1094	6
6	2	4.842×10^{-19}	410	10
6	1	2.118×10^{-18}	94	15
5	4	4.903×10^{-20}	4052	2
5	3	1.550×10^{-19}	1282	5
5	2	4.576×10^{-19}	434	9
5	1	2.092×10^{-18}	95	14
4	3	1.059×10^{-19}	1875	4
4	2	4.086×10^{-19}	486	8
4	1	2.043×10^{-18}	97	13
3	2	3.026×10^{-19}	656	7
3	1	1.937×10^{-18}	103	12
2	1	1.634×10^{-18}	122	11

When a magnetic field is applied, the levels with $\ell > 0$ split into the $2\ell + 1$ sublevels. The line that splits into the most lines is the one that contains the greatest number levels with $\ell > 0$, this is the $6 \rightarrow 5$ transition, the rightmost or longest wavelength emission.

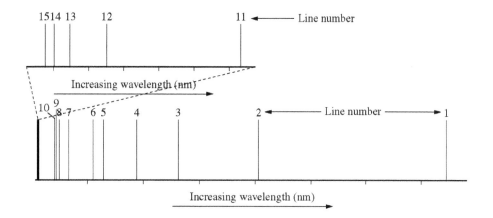

119. (D)

(a) Using $V(x) = 0$, we can rearrange $-\dfrac{h^2}{8\pi^2 m}\dfrac{d^2\psi}{dx^2} + V(x)\psi = E\psi$ as $\dfrac{d^2\psi}{dx^2} = -\dfrac{8\pi^2 mE}{h^2}\psi$.

If we define $a^2 = 8\pi^2 mE/h^2$, then $d^2\psi/dx^2 = -a^2\psi^2$.

(b) If $\psi = A\sin(ax)$, then $d\psi/dx = aA\cos(ax)$ and $d^2\psi/dx^2 = -a^2 A\sin(ax) = -a^2\psi$.

Therefore, $\psi = A\sin(ax)$ is a solution to the equation $d^2\psi/dx^2 = -a^2\psi^2$.

(c) If $\psi = A\cos(ax)$, then $d\psi/dx = -aA\sin(ax)$ and $d^2\psi/dx^2 = -a^2 A\cos(ax) = -a^2\psi$.

Therefore, $\psi = A\cos(ax)$ is a solution to the equation $d^2\psi/dx^2 = -a^2\psi^2$.

(d) If $\psi = A\sin(ax)$, then $\psi(0) = A\sin(0) = 0$ and $\psi^2(0) = 0$, as required by the boundary condition. Therefore, $\psi = A\sin(ax)$ satisfies the boundary condition at $x = 0$. If $\psi = A\cos(ax)$, then $\psi(0) = A\cos(0) = A$ and $\psi^2(0) = A^2$. The only way for $\psi = A\cos(ax)$ to satisfy the boundary condition at $x = 0$ is to set $A = 0$. However, if $A = 0$, then $\psi = 0$ at all points, which means that there is zero probability of finding the particle anywhere in the box. This is an unacceptable result. Therefore, $\psi = A\cos(ax)$ is an unacceptable solution.

(e) The boundary condition $\psi(L) = 0$ ensures that the probability density is equal to zero at $x = L$: $\psi^2(L) = 0$. From (d), we know that $\psi = A\sin(ax)$. Thus, $\psi(L) = A\sin(aL)$. This boundary condition $\psi(L) = 0$ can be satisfied only if $\sin(aL) = 0$, which means that aL must be an integer multiple of π, that is, $aL = n\pi$ with $n = 1, 2, 3$, and so on. The value n is excluded because, if $n = 0$, then $\psi = 0$ at all points, which, as discussed in part (d), is unacceptable. Since we have determined that $a = n\pi/L$, we can write $\psi = A\sin(ax) = A\sin(n\pi x/L)$.

(f) From part (a), we have $a^2 = 8\pi^2 mE/h^2$, which we can rearrange to give $E = h^2 a^2/(8\pi^2 m)$. In part (d), we established that $a = n\pi/L$. Therefore, the expression for E becomes $E = h^2(n\pi/L)^2/(8\pi^2 m) = h^2 n^2/(8mL^2)$, with $n = 1, 2, 3$, and so on.

(g) Using $\psi = A\sin(n\pi x/L)$, we find that $\int_0^L \psi^2 dx = A^2 \int_0^L \sin^2(n\pi x/L)dx = A^2 \times L/2$.

The requirement to have $\int_0^L \psi^2 dx = 1$ means that $A^2 \times L/2 = 1$, or $A = \sqrt{2/L}$.

The final form for the wave function is $\psi = A\sin(n\pi x/L) = \sqrt{2/L}\sin(n\pi x/L)$, which is equation (8.13).

120. (D)

(a) Since $E_k = (1/2)m_e u^2$ and $PE = (+e)(-e)/(4\pi\varepsilon_0 r) = -e^2/(4\pi\varepsilon_0 r)$, the total energy is $E = (1/2)m_e u^2 - e^2/(4\pi\varepsilon_0 r)$.

(b) According to equation (8.13), the magnitude of the force of attraction between the electron and the proton is $e^2/(4\pi\varepsilon_0 r^2)$. Since we must have $e^2/(4\pi\varepsilon_0 r^2) = m_e u^2/r$, then $m_e u^2 = m_e e^2/(4\pi\varepsilon_0 r)$. Therefore,

$$E = (1/2)m_e u^2 - e^2/(4\pi\varepsilon_0 r)$$
$$= (1/2)e^2/(4\pi\varepsilon_0 r) - e^2/(4\pi\varepsilon_0 r)$$
$$= e^2/(4\pi\varepsilon_0 r)[-(1/2)+1]$$
$$= -(1/2)e^2/(4\pi\varepsilon_0 r)$$

(c) From the condition $m_e u r = nh/(2\pi)$, we obtain $u = nh/(2\pi m_e r)$. Since $e^2/(4\pi\varepsilon_0 r^2) = m_e u^2/r$, from part (b), we obtain $r = e^2/(4\pi\varepsilon_0 m_e u^2)$, and using $u = nh/(2\pi m_e r)$, we get $r = \dfrac{e^2}{4\pi\varepsilon_0 m_e} \times \dfrac{(2\pi m_e r)^2}{n^2 h^2} = \dfrac{\pi e^2 m_e r^2}{\varepsilon_0 n^2 h^2}$. This expression can be simplified to $1 = \dfrac{\pi e^2 m_e r}{\varepsilon_0 n^2 h^2}$, from which we obtain

$$r = \underbrace{\left(\dfrac{\varepsilon_0 h^2}{\pi e^2 m_e}\right)}_{a_0} \times n^2$$

Using this expression for r in the equation $E = -(1/2)e^2/(4\pi\varepsilon_0 r)$, from part (b), we

obtain $E = -\dfrac{1}{2} \times \dfrac{e^2}{4\pi\varepsilon_0} \times \dfrac{\pi m_e e^2}{\varepsilon_0 h^2} \times \dfrac{1}{n^2} = -\underbrace{\left(\dfrac{m_e e^4}{8\varepsilon_0^2 h^2}\right)}_{R_\infty} \times \dfrac{1}{n^2}$

Using the values $m_e = 9.10938291 \times 10^{-31}$ kg, $e = 1.602176565 \times 10^{-19}$ C, $h = 6.62606957 \times 10^{-34}$ J s and $\varepsilon_0 = 8.854187817 \times 10^{-12}$ C^2 J^{-1} m^{-1}, we get

$$R_\infty = \dfrac{m_e e^4}{8\varepsilon_0^2 h^2} = 2.17987 \times 10^{-18} \text{ J} \quad \text{and} \quad a_0 = \dfrac{\varepsilon_0 h^2}{\pi e^2 m_e} = 5.29177 \times 10^{-11} \text{ m}$$

(d) $\mu = \dfrac{m_e m_p}{m_e + m_p} = \dfrac{(9.10938291 \times 10^{-31}\ \text{kg})(1.672621777 \times 10^{-27}\ \text{kg})}{9.10938291 \times 10^{-31}\ \text{kg} + 1.672621777 \times 10^{-27}\ \text{kg}}$

$= 9.10442449 \times 10^{-31}\ \text{kg}$

$R_H = \dfrac{\mu e^4}{8\varepsilon_0^2 h^2} = 2.17869 \times 10^{-18}\ \text{J}$

SELF-ASSESSMENT EXERCISES

121. (E)

(a) λ: Wavelength, the distance between two identical points on two adjacent waves

(b) v: Frequency, the number of crests or troughs that pass through a point per a given unit of time

(c) h: Planck's constant, which is the proportionality constant between energy of an object and its frequency

(d) ψ: Standing wave within the boundary of the system

(e) n: The period in the periodic table in which an atom resides, which also relates to the energy and the most probable distance of the outer electrons from the nucleus

122. (M)

(a) Atomic (line) spectrum: Photons of distinct energy emitted by an atom as it relaxes back to ground state.

(b) Photoelectric effect: A phenomenon in which electrons are ejected from a material when exposed to photons. The photons must have a minimum energy to overcome the energy barrier for the electron ejection.

(c) Matter wave: A term coined by Louis de Broglie to describe the observation that beams of matter (e.g., electrons) exhibit wave-like behavior.

(d) Heisenberg's Uncertainty Principle postulates that the position and the momentum of a particle cannot be simultaneously measured with great precision.

(e) Electron spin: The fourth principal quantum number, with values of $+\frac{1}{2}$ and $-\frac{1}{2}$.

(f) Pauli Exclusion Principle: No two electrons can have an identical set of four quantum numbers. Stated differently, an orbital can only contain two electrons, and they must have opposite spins.

(g) Hund's Rule: So long as degenerate orbitals are available, electrons fill each orbital singly.

(h) Orbital diagram: A shorthand graphical means of representing electron configurations in occupied molecular orbitals which also shows the spin of each electron.

(i) Electron charge density: The product of the square of the electron's wave function, ψ^2, which is a measure of the probability of finding an electron in a given volume.

(j) Radial electron density: The measure of probability of finding an electron at a certain distance from the nucleus

123. (M)
  (a) *Frequency* is the number of times waves pass through a certain point, whereas *wavelength* is the crest-to-crest or trough-to-trough length of the said wave.
  (b) *Ultraviolet radiation* is a range of photon energies with wavelengths shorter than violet light but longer than X-rays, whereas *infrared radiation* is a range of photon energies longer in the length than red light but shorter than microwaves.
  (c) *Continuous spectra* are emitted by blackbody radiators and cover the entirety of a certain range of electromagnetic radiation spectrum, whereas *discontinuous spectra* only have several wavelengths characteristic of specific electronic transitions.
  (d) In *traveling waves,* a waveform actually travels physically in the longitudinal direction as well as oscillating in the transverse; that is, the crest and the trough of each wave travel the entire length of the system. In a *standing wave,* oscillations of a wave are in one place and the crests and troughs happen at the same location.
  (e) *Quantum numbers* are a set of numbers that define the shell, orbital angular momentum, magnetic momentum, and spin of an electron. On the other hand, *orbitals* are wave functions that describe the probability of finding an electron with a certain quantum number at a given location in the atom.
  (f) The *spdf notation* is a shorthand method of writing gross orbital occupancy of an atom by combining orbitals of the same type and shell (for example, combining $2p_x$, $2p_y$, and $2p_z$ into a generic $2p$). The *orbital diagram,* however, is a shorthand graphical means of representing electron configurations in occupied molecular orbitals that also shows the spin of each electron.
  (g) The *s block* are orbitals with an orbital angular momentum of zero ($l = 0$), whereas the *p block* are those with $l = 1$.
  (h) In *main group elements,* the *p* block is the valence shell, whereas in *transition elements*, the *d* block is the valence shell.
  (i) *Ground state* is the lowest possible energy state of the H atom, whereas the *excited state* is any higher energy state.

124. (M) Atomic orbitals of multielectron atoms resemble those of the H atom in having both angular and radial nodes. They differ in that subshell energy levels are not degenerate and their radial wave functions no longer conform to the expressions in Table 8.2.

125. (E) Effective nuclear charge is the amount of positive charge from the nucleus that the valence shell of the electrons actually experiences. This amount is less than the actual nuclear charge, because electrons in other shells shield the full effect.

126. (E) The p_x, p_y, and p_z orbitals are triply degenerate (they are the same energy), and they have the same shape. Their difference lies in their orientation with respect to the arbitrarily assigned x, y, and z axes of the atom, as shown in Figure 8-28 of the textbook.

127. (E) The difference between the $2p$ and $3p$ orbitals is that the $2p$ orbital has only one node ($n = 2 - 1$) which is angular, whereas the $3p$ orbital has two nodes, angular and radial. See the figures below, which are extracted from the text.

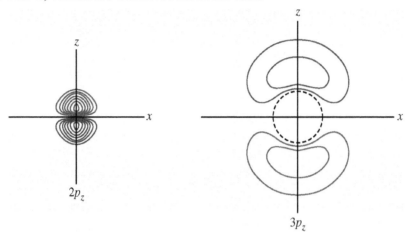

128. (E) The answer is (a). If the speed is the same for all particles, the lightest particle will have the longest wavelength.

129. (E)
(a) Velocity of the electromagnetic radiation is fixed at the speed of light in a vacuum.
(b) Wavelength is inversely proportional to frequency, because $v = c/\lambda$.
(c) Energy is directly proportional to frequency, because $E = hv$.

130. (M) The concept map for modern quantum mechanics encompasses the second half of the chapter. To create it, one must first start with the most general concepts. These concepts define or encompass the other concepts discussed in those sections. The major concepts in the chapter are particle–wave duality and the uncertainty principle. While these two concepts are part of larger concepts, within the confines of the question they are the most general topics. The concept of particle–wave duality gives rise to the discussion of wave mechanics, which itself gives rise to wave functions and quantum particles. The concept of wave functions covers wave forms and probabilities. Wave functions in turn can be further broken down into quantum numbers and orbitals.

131. (M) The concept map for the atomic orbitals of hydrogen is an amalgam of many of the topics already discussed in other sections. The overarching topic which gives rise to the others is Schrödinger's equation. From there, it splits into the subtopics of the wave function, which can be used to define the probability function. The probability function (which is the square of the wave function) explains the topic of orbitals, which is divided into s, p, and d orbitals.

132. (E) The concept map for a multielectron atom is very similar to that of a hydrogen atom, except that under the topic of orbitals, there is another topic describing effective nuclear charge, and electron configuration.

CHAPTER 9

THE PERIODIC TABLE AND SOME ATOMIC PROPERTIES

PRACTICE EXAMPLES

1A (E) Atomic size decreases from left to right across a period, and from bottom to top in a family. We expect the smallest elements to be in the upper right corner of the periodic table. S is the element closest to the upper right corner and thus should have the smallest atom. S = 104 pm   As = 121 pm   I = 133 pm

1B (E) From the periodic table inside the front cover, we see that Na is in the same period as Al (period 3), but in a different group from K, Ca, and Br (period 4), which might suggest that Na and Al are about the same size. However, there is a substantial decrease in size as one moves from left to right in a period due to an increase in effective nuclear charge. Enough in fact, that Ca should be about the same size as Na.

2A (E) Ti^{2+} and V^{3+} are isoelectronic; the one with higher positive charge should be smaller: $V^{3+} < Ti^{2+}$. Sr^{2+} and Br^- are isoelectronic; again, the one with higher positive charge should be smaller: $Sr^{2+} < Br^-$. In addition Ca^{2+} and Sr^{2+} both are ions of Group 2A; the one of lower atomic number should be smaller. $Ca^{2+} < Sr^{2+} < Br^-$. Finally, we know that the size of atoms decreases from left to right across a period; we expect sizes of like-charged ions to follow the same trend: $Ti^{2+} < Ca^{2+}$. The species are arranged below in order of increasing size.

$$V^{3+}(64 \text{ pm}) < Ti^{2+}(86 \text{ pm}) < Ca^{2+}(100 \text{ pm}) < Sr^{2+}(113 \text{ pm}) < Br^-(196 \text{ pm})$$

2B (E) Br^- clearly is larger than As since Br^- is an anion in the same period as As. In turn, As is larger than N since both are in the same group, with As lower down in the group. As also should be larger than P, which is larger than Mg^{2+}, an ion smaller than N. All that remains is to note that Cs is a truly large atom, one of the largest in the periodic table. The As atom should be in the middle. Data from Figure 9-11 shows:

$$Mg^{2+} < N < As < Br^- < Cs$$

3A (E) Ionization increases from bottom to top of a group and from left to right through a period. The first ionization energy of K is less than that of Mg and the first ionization energy of S is less than that of Cl. We would expect also that the first ionization energy of Mg is smaller than that of S, because Mg is a metal.

3B (E) We would expect an alkali metal (Rb) or an alkaline earth metal (Sr) to have a low first ionization energy and nonmetals (e.g., Br) to have relatively high first ionization energies. Metalloids (such as Sb and As) should have intermediate ionization energies. Since the first ionization energy for As is larger than that for Sb, the first ionization energy of Sb should be in the middle.

4A **(E)** Cl and Al must be paramagnetic, since each has an odd number of electrons. The electron configurations of K^+ ([Ar]) and O^{2-} ([Ne]) are those of the nearest noble gas. Because all of the electrons are paired, they are diamagnetic species. In Zn: [Ar] $3d^{10}4s^2$ all electrons are paired and so the atom is diamagnetic.

4B **(E)** The electron configuration of Cr is [Ar] $3d^54s^1$; it has six unpaired electrons. The electron configuration of Cr^{2+} is [Ar] $3d^4$; it has four unpaired electrons. The electron configuration of Cr^{3+} is [Ar] $3d^3$; it has three unpaired electrons. Thus, of the two ions, Cr^{2+} has the greater number of unpaired electrons.

INTEGRATIVE EXAMPLE

A. **(M)** The physical properties of elements in the same period follow general trends. Below is a tabulation of the melting points, densities, and atomic radii of the alkali earth metals.

	Z	M.P. (°C)	Density (g/cc)	Metallic Radii (Å)
Li	3	180.54	0.53	2.05
Na	11	97.81	0.97	2.23
K	19	63.25	0.86	2.77
Rb	37	38.89	1.53	2.98
Cs	55	28.4	1.87	3.34

Accompanying this table is the plot of the data. Based on rough approximations of the trends of data, the properties of francium can be approximated as follows:

Melting point: 22 °C, density: 2.75 g/cc, atomic radius: 4.25 Å

B. **(M)** Element 168 should be a solid since the trend in boiling point and melting point would put the boiling point temperature above 298 K. The electronic configuration is [Unk] $8s^2$ $5g^{18}$ $6f^{14}$ $7d^{10}$ $8p^6$, where Unk represents element 118.

EXERCISES

The Periodic Law

1. **(E)** Element 114 will be a metal in the same group as Pb, element 82 ($18 \ cm^3/mol$); Sn, element 50 ($18 \ cm^3/mol$); and Ge, element 32 ($14 \ cm^3/mol$). We note that the atomic volumes of Pb and Sn are essentially equal, probably due to the lanthanide contraction. If there is also an actinide contraction, element 114 will have an atomic volume of $18 \ cm^3 / mol$. If there is no actinide contraction, we would predict a molar volume of $\sim$ $22 \ cm^3 / mol$. This need to estimate atomic volume is what makes the value for density questionable.

$$\text{density}\left(\frac{g}{cm^3}\right) = \frac{298 \ \dfrac{g}{mol}}{18 \ \dfrac{cm^3}{mol}} = 16 \ \frac{g}{cm^3} \qquad \text{density}\left(\frac{g}{cm^3}\right) = \frac{298 \ \dfrac{g}{mol}}{22 \ \dfrac{cm^3}{mol}} = 14 \ \frac{g}{cm^3}$$

2. **(E)** Lanthanum has an atomic number of $Z = 57$, and thus its atomic volume is somewhat less than $25 \ cm^3 / mol$. Let us assume $23 \ cm^3 / mol$.

atomic mass $=$ density $\times$ atomic volume $= 6.145 \ g/cm^3 \times 23 \ cm^3 / mol = 141 \ g/mol$

This compares very well with the listed value of 139 for La.

3. **(M)** The following data are plotted at right. Density clearly is a periodic property for these two periods of main group elements. It rises, falls a bit, rises again, and falls back to the axis, in both cases.

Element	Atomic Number Z	Density g/cm³
Na	11	0.968
Mg	12	1.738
Al	13	2.699
Si	14	2.336
P	15	1.823
S	16	2.069
Cl	17	0.0032
Ar	18	0.0018
K	19	0.856
Ca	20	1.550
Ga	31	5.904
Ge	32	5.323
As	33	5.778
Se	34	4.285
Br	35	3.100
Kr	36	0.0037

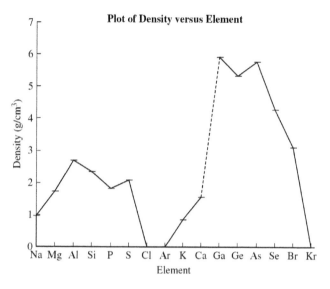

4. **(M)** The following data are plotted at right below. Melting point clearly is a periodic property for these two periods. It rises to a maximum and then falls off in each case.

Element	Atomic Number Z	Melting Point °C
Li	3	179
Be	4	1278
B	5	2300
C	6	3350
N	7	−210
O	8	−218
F	9	−220
Ne	10	−249
Na	11	98
Mg	12	651
Al	13	660
Si	14	1410
P	15	590
S	16	119
Cl	17	−101
Ar	18	−189

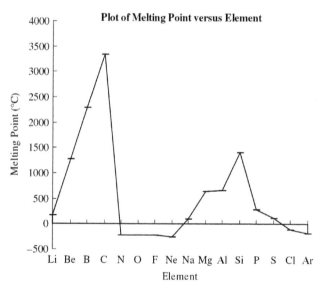

The Periodic Table

5. **(E)** Mendeleev arranged elements in the periodic table in order of increasing atomic weight. Of course, atomic masses with non-integral values are permissible. Hence, there always is room for an added element between two elements that already are present in the table. On the other hand, Moseley arranged elements in order of increasing atomic number. Only integral (whole number) values of atomic number are permitted. Thus, when elements with all possible integral values in a certain range have been discovered, no new elements are possible in that range.

6. **(E)** For there to be the same number of elements in each period of the periodic table, each shell of an electron configuration would have to contain the same number of electrons. This, however, is not the case; the shells have 2 (K shell), 8 (L shell), 18 (M shell), and 32 (N shell) electrons each. This is because each of the periods of the periodic table begins with one s electron beyond a noble gas electron configuration, and the noble gas electron configuration corresponds to either s^2 (He) or s^2p^6, with various other full subshells.

7. **(E)**
The noble gas following radon $(Z = 86)$ will have an atomic number of $(86 + 32 =) 118$. The alkali metal following francium $(Z = 87)$ will have an atomic number of $(87 + 32 =) 119$.

The mass number of radon $(A = 222)$ is $(222 \div 86 =) 2.58$ times its atomic number. The mass number of Lr $(A = 262)$ is $(262 \div 103 =) 2.54$ times its atomic number. Thus, we would expect the mass numbers, and hence approximate atomic masses, of elements 118 and 119 to be about 2.5 times their atomic numbers, that is, $A_{119} \approx 298$ u and $A_{118} \approx 295$ u.

8. **(E)**
(a) The $6d$ subshell will be complete with an element in the same group as Hg. This is three elements beyond Une (Z = 109) and thus this element has an atomic number of Z = 112.

(b) The element in this period that will most closely resemble bismuth is six elements beyond Mt (Z=109) and thus has $Z = 115$.

(c) The element in this period that would be a noble gas would fall below Rn, nine elements beyond Mt (Z=109) and thus has $Z = 118$.

Atomic Radii and Ionic Radii

9. **(E)** In general, atomic size in the periodic table increases from top to bottom for a group and increases from right to left through a period, as indicated in Figure 9-4. The larger element is indicated first, followed by the reason for making the choice.

(a) Te: Te is to the left of Br and also in the period below that of Br in the 4th period.

(b) K: K is to the left of Ca within the same period, Period 4.

(c) Cs : Cs is both below and to the left of Ca in the periodic table.

(d) N: N is to the left of O within the same period, Period 2.

(e) P: P is both below and to the left of O in the periodic table.

(f) Au: Au is both below and to the left of Al in the periodic table.

10. **(E)** An Al atom is larger than a F atom since Al is both below and to the left of F in the periodic table. As is larger than Al, since As is below Al in the periodic table. (Even though As is to the right of Al, we would not conclude that As is smaller than Al, since increases in size down a group are more pronounced than decreases in size across a period (from left to right). A Cs^+ ion is isoelectronic with an I^- ion, and in an isoelectronic series, anions are larger than cations, thus I^- is larger than Cs^+. I^- also is larger than As, since I is below As in the periodic table (and increases in size down a group are more pronounced than those across a period). Finally, N is larger than F, since N is to the left of F in the periodic table. Therefore, we conclude that F is the smallest species listed and I^- is the largest. In fact, with the exception of Cs^+, we can rank the species in order of decreasing size.

$I^- >$ As$>$ Al$>$ N $>$ F and also $I^- > Cs^+$

11. **(E)** Sizes of atoms do not simply increase with atomic number is because electrons often are added successively to the same subshell. These electrons do not fully screen each other from the nuclear charge (they do not effectively get between each other and the nucleus). Consequently, as each electron is added to a subshell and the nuclear charge increases by one unit, all of the electrons in this subshell are drawn more closely into the nucleus, because of the ineffective shielding.

12. **(E)** Atomic sizes are uncertain because the electron cloud that surrounds an atom has no fixed limit. It can be pictured as gradually fading away, rather like the edge of a town. In both cases we pick an arbitrary boundary.

13. **(E)**
    (a)   The smallest atom in Group 13 is the first: B
    (b)   Po is in the sixth period, and is larger than the others, which are rewritten in the following list from left to right in the fifth period, that is, from largest to smallest: Sr, In, Sb, Te. Thus, Te is the smallest of the elements given.

14. **(M)** The hydrogen ion contains no electrons, only a nucleus. It is exceedingly tiny, much smaller than any other atom or electron-containing ion. Both H and H^- have a nuclear charge of +1, but H^- has two electrons to H's one, and thus is larger. Both He and H^- contain two electrons, but He has a nuclear charge of +2, while H^- has one of only +1. The smaller nuclear charge of H^- is less effective at attracting electrons than the more positive nuclear charge of He. The only comparison left is between H and He; we expect He to be smaller since atomic size decreases from left to right across a period. Thus, the order by increasing size: $H^+ <$ He$<$ H$<$ H$^-$.

15. **(E)** Li^+ is the smallest; it not only is in the second period, but also is a cation. I^- is the largest, an anion in the fifth period. Next largest is Se in the previous (the fourth) period. We expect Br to be smaller than Se because it is both to the right of Se and in the same period.

$Li^+ <$ Br$<$ Se $< I^-$

16. **(E)** Size decreases from left to right in the periodic table. On this basis I should be smaller than Al. But size increases from top to bottom in the periodic table. On this basis, I should be larger than Al. There really is no good way of resolving these conflicting predictions.

17. **(M)** In the literal sense, isoelectronic means having the same number and types of electrons. (In another sense, not used in the text, it means having the same electron configuration.) We determine the total number of electrons and the electron configuration for each species and make our decisions based on this information.

Fe^{2+}	24 electrons	$[Ar]\,3d^6$	Sc^{3+}	18 electrons	$[Ar]$
Ca^{2+}	18 electrons	$[Ar]$	F^-	10 electrons	$[He]\,2s^2 2p^6$
Co^{2+}	25 electrons	$[Ar]\,3d^7$	Co^{3+}	24 electrons	$[Ar]\,3d^6$
Sr^{2+}	36 electrons	$[Ar]\,3d^{10} 4s^2 4p^6$	Cu^+	28 electrons	$[Ar]\,3d^{10}$
Zn^{2+}	28 electrons	$[Ar]\,3d^{10}$	Al^{3+}	10 electrons	$[He]\,2s^2 2p^6$

Thus the species with the same number of electrons and the same electron configuration are the following. Fe^{2+} and Co^{3+} Sc^{3+} and Ca^{2+} F^- and Al^{3+} Zn^{2+} and Cu^+

18. **(E)** In an isoelectronic series, all of the species have the same number and types of electrons. The size is determined by the nuclear charge. Those species with the largest (positive) nuclear charge are the smallest. Those with smaller nuclear charges are larger in size. Thus, the more positively charged an ion is in an isoelectronic series, the smaller it will be.

$$Y^{3+} < Sr^{2+} < Rb^+ < Br^- < Se^{2-}$$

19. **(E)** Ions can be isoelectronic without having noble-gas electron configurations. Take, for instance, Cu^+ and Zn^{2+}. Both of these ions have the electron configuration $[Ar]\,3d^{10}$.

20. **(E)** Isoelectronic species must have the same number of electrons, and each element has a different atomic number. Thus, atoms of different elements cannot be isoelectronic. Two different cations may be isoelectronic, as may two different anions, or an anion and a cation. In fact, there are many sets of different cations and anions that have a common configuration. For example, all of the ions listed below share the same electron configuration, namely that of the noble gas Ne: O^{2-} and F^-, Na^+ and Mg^{2+}, or F^- and Na^+.

Ionization Energies; Electron Affinities

21. **(E)** Ionization energy in the periodic table decreases from top to bottom for a group, and increases from left to right for a period, as summarized in Figure 9-12. Cs has the lowest ionization energy as it is farthest to the left and nearest to the bottom of the periodic table. Next comes Sr, followed by As, then S, and finally F, the most nonmetallic element in the group (and in the periodic table). Thus, the elements listed in order of increasing ionization energy are:

$$Cs < Sr < As < S < F$$

22. **(E)** The second ionization energy for an atom cannot be smaller than the first ionization energy for the same atom. The reason is that, when the first electron is removed it is being separated from a species with a charge of zero. On the other hand, when the second electron is removed, it is being separated from a species with a charge of +1. Since the force between two charged particles is proportional to $q_+ q_- / r^2$ (r is the distance between the particles), the higher the positive charge, the more difficult it will be to remove an electron.

23. **(E)** In the case of a first electron affinity, a negative electron is being added to a neutral atom. This process may be either exothermic or endothermic depending upon the electronic configuration of the atom. Energy tends to be released when filled shells or filled subshells are generated. In the case of an ionization potential, however, a negatively charged electron is being separated from a positively charged cation, a process that must always require energy, because unlike charges attract each other.

24. **(E)** First we convert the mass of Na given to an amount in moles of Na. Then we compute the energy needed to ionize this much Na.

$$\text{Energy} = 1.00 \text{ mg Na} \times \frac{1 \text{ g}}{1000 \text{ mg}} \times \frac{1 \text{ mol Na}}{22.99 \text{ g Na}} \times \frac{495.8 \text{ kJ}}{1 \text{ mol Na}} = 0.0216 \text{ kJ} \times \frac{1000 \text{ J}}{1 \text{ kJ}} = 21.6 \text{ J}$$

25. **(E)** Ionization energies for Si: $E_{i,1} = 786.5$ kJ/mol, $E_{i,2} = 1577$ kJ/mol, $E_{i,3} = 3232$ kJ/mol, $E_{i,4} = 4356$ kJ/mol. To remove all four electrons from the third shell ($3s^2 3p^2$) would require the sum of all four ionization energies or 9951.5 kJ/mol. This would be 9.952×10^6 J per mole of Si atoms.

26. **(E)** Data ($E_i = 375.7$ kJ/mol) are obtained from Table 9.3.

$$\text{no. Cs}^+ \text{ ions} = 1 \text{ J} \times \frac{1 \text{ kJ}}{1000 \text{ J}} \times \frac{1 \text{ mol Cs}^+}{375.7 \text{ kJ}} \times \frac{6.022 \times 10^{23} \text{ Cs}^+ \text{ ions}}{1 \text{ mol Cs}^+ \text{ ions}} = 1.603 \times 10^{18} \text{ Cs}^+ \text{ ions}$$

27. **(M)** The electron affinity of bromine is −324.6 kJ/mol (Figure 9-15). We use Hess's law to determine the heat of reaction for $Br_2(g)$ becoming $2 Br^-(g)$.

$Br_2(g) \rightarrow 2 Br(g)$ $\Delta H = +193$ kJ

$2 Br(g) + 2 e^- \rightarrow 2 Br^-(g)$ $2 \times \Delta_{ea} H = 2(-324.6)$ kJ

$Br_2(g) + 2 e^- \rightarrow 2 Br^-(g)$ $\Delta H = -456$ kJ   Overall process is *exothermic*.

28. **(M)** The electron affinity of fluorine is −328.0 kJ/mol (Figure 9-15) and the first and second ionization energies of Mg (Table 9.4) are 737.7 kJ/mol and 1451 kJ/mol, respectively.

$Mg(g) \rightarrow Mg^+(g) + e^-$ $E_i(Mg) = 737.7$ kJ/mol

$Mg^+(g) \rightarrow Mg^{2+}(g) + e^-$ $E_i(Mg_+) = 1451$ kJ/mol

$2 F(g) + 2 e^- \rightarrow 2 F^-(g)$ $2 \Delta_{ea} H = 2(-328.0)$ kJ/mol

$Mg(g) + 2 F(g) \rightarrow Mg^{2+}(g) + 2 F^-(g)$ $\Delta H = +1533$ kJ/mol Endothermic.

29. **(E)** The electron is being removed from a species with a neon electron configuration. But in the case of Na^+, the electron is being removed from a species that is left with a +2 charge, while in the case of Ne, the electron is being removed from a species with a +1 charge. The more highly charged the resulting species, the more difficult it is to produce it by removing an electron.

30. **(M)** The electron affinity of Li is −59.6 kJ/mol. The smallest ionization energy listed in Table 9.3 (and, except for Fr, displayed in Figure 9-12) is that of Cs, 375.7 kJ/mol. Thus, insufficient energy is produced by the electron affinity of Li to account for the ionization of Cs. As a result, we would predict that Li^-Cs^+ will not be stable and hence Li^-Li^+ and Li^-Na^+, owing to the larger ionization energies of Li and Na, should be even less stable. (One other consideration not dealt with here is the energy released when the positive and negative ion combine to form an ion pair. This is an exothermic process, but we have no way of assessing the value of this energy.)

31. **(M)**
    (a) Ionization energy in the periodic table decreases from top to bottom in a group, and increases from left to right across a period, as summarized in Figure 9-12. Therefore, the elements listed in order of increasing ionization energy are:

$$Al < Si < S < Cl$$

    (b) Electron affinity is the measure of the energy change that occurs when a gaseous atom gains an electron. If energy is given off when this occurs, the process is exothermic and the electron affinity is negative. It is harder to make generalizations about electron affinities. If an atom has a high affinity for an electron, the electon affinity tends to be a large negative value. Chlorine hast the greatest affinity for an electron, becuase it will have a noble gas configuration when this occurs. In this series, aluminum has the smallest affinity for an electron. Therefore, the elements listed in order of increasing electron affinity are:

$$Al < Si < S < Cl$$

    (c) Polarizability increases with increasing size and, as a result, decreases going from left to right across a period. Al, Si, S, and Cl are in the same period, which means that Cl has the lowest polarizability and Al has the highest polarizability. Since Si is larger than S, Si will have a larger polarizability. Therefore, polarizability increases as follows: Cl < S < Si < Al.

32. **(M)**
    (a) Ionization energy in the periodic table decreases from top to bottom in a group, and increases from left to right across a period, as summarized in Figure 9-10. Therefore, the elements listed in order of increasing ionization energy are:

$$Na < Mg < P < O$$

    (b) If an atom has a high affinity for an electron, the electon affinity tends to be a large negative value. Non-metals have a greater affinity to gain electrons compared with metals. Metals prefer to lose electrons to form cations.

Oxygen has the greatest affinity since it would only have to add two electrons to reach a noble gas configuration, as compared with phosphorus. Sodium has more affinity for an electron than magnesium because sodium's $3s$ orbital would be full upon addition of an electron. Magnesium is less likely to add an electron because its electron would populate the higher energy $3p$ orbital.

Therefore, the elements listed in order of increasing electron affinity are:

$$Mg < Na < P < O$$

(c) Polarizability decreases going from left to right across a period and increases from top to bottom within a group. Since O is in the second period and P, Mg, and Na are in the third, O has the lowest polarizability. Because P, Mg, and Na are all in the same period, Na will have the highest polarizability since it is the largest, followed by Mg and then P. Therefore, the order of increasing polarizability is $O < P < Mg < Na$.

Magnetic Properties

33. **(E)** Three of the ions have noble gas electron configurations and thus have no unpaired electrons: F^- is $1s^2 2s^2 2p^6$ $\qquad$ Ca^{2+} and S^{2-} are $[Ne]3s^2 3p^6$

Only Fe^{2+} has unpaired electrons. Its electron configuration is $[Ar]3d^6$.

34. **(E)**
(a) Ge$[Ar]3d^{10}4s^2 4p^2$ with two unpaired electrons
(b) Cl $[Ne]3s^2 3p^5$ with one unpaired electron
(c) $Cr^{3+}[Ar]3d^3$ with three unpaired electrons
(d) Br$[Ar]3d^{10}4s^2 4p^6$ with no unpaired electrons
Clearly, (c) Cr^{3+} has the most unpaired electrons of the four elements listed.

35. **(E)**
(a) K^+ is isoelectronic with Ar, with no unpaired electrons. It is diamagnetic.
(b) Cr^{3+} has the configuration $[Ar]3d^3$ with three unpaired electrons. It is paramagnetic.
(c) Zn^{2+} has the configuration $[Ar]3d^{10}$, with no unpaired electrons. It is diamagnetic.
(d) Cd has the configuration $[Kr]4d^{10}5s^2$, with no unpaired electrons. It is diamagnetic.
(e) Co^{3+} has the configuration $[Ar]3d^6$ with four unpaired electrons. It is paramagnetic
(f) Sn^{2+} has the configuration $[Kr]4d^{10}5s^2$, with no unpaired electrons. It is diamagnetic.
(g) Br has the configuration $[Ar]3d^{10}4s^2 5p^5$ with one unpaired electron. It is paramagnetic. From this, we see that (a), (c), (d), and (f) are diamagnetic and (b), (e), and (g) are paramagnetic.

36. **(E)** First we write the electron configuration of the element, then that of the ion. In each case, the number of unpaired electrons written beside the configuration agrees with the data given in the statement of the problem.

(a) Ni $\quad$ [Ar] $3d^8 4s^2$ $\longrightarrow$ Ni^{2+} [Ar] $3d^8$ $\quad$ Two unpaired e^-

(b) Cu $\quad$ [Ar] $3d^{10}4s^1$ $\longrightarrow$ Cu^{2+} [Ar] $3d^9$ $\quad$ One unpaired e^-

(c) Cr $\quad$ [Ar] $3d^5 4s^1$ $\longrightarrow$ Cr^{3+} [Ar] $3d^3$ $\quad$ Three unpaired e^-

37. **(E)** All atoms with an odd number of electrons must be paramagnetic. There is no way to pair all of the electrons up if there is an odd number of electrons. Many atoms with an even number of electrons are diamagnetic, but some are paramagnetic. The one of lowest atomic number is carbon $(Z = 6)$, which has two unpaired p-electrons producing the paramagnetic behavior: [He] $2s^2 2p^2$.

38. **(E)** The electron configuration of each iron ion can be determined by starting with the electron configuration of the iron atom. $[Fe] = [Ar]3d^6 4s^2$ Then the two ions result from the loss of both $4s$ electrons, followed by the loss of a $3d$ electron in the case of Fe^{3+}.

$$\left[Fe^{2+} \right] = \left[Ar \right] 3d^6 \qquad \text{four unpaired electrons}$$
$$\left[Fe^{3+} \right] = \left[Ar \right] 3d^5 \qquad \text{five unpaired electrons}$$

Predictions Based on the Periodic Table

39. **(M)**
    (a) Elements that one would expect to exhibit the photoelectric effect with visible light should be ones that have a small value of their first ionization energy. Based on Figure 9-12, the alkali metals have the lowest first ionization energies of these. Cs, Rb, and K are three suitable metals. Metals that would not exhibit the photoelectric effect with visible light are those that have high values of their first ionization energy. Again from Figure 9-9, Zn, Cd, and Hg seem to be three metals that would not exhibit the photoelectric effect with visible light.

    (b) From Figure 9-1, we notice that the atomic (molar) volume increases for the solid forms of the noble gases as we travel down the group (the data points just before the alkali metal peaks). But it seems to increase less rapidly than the molar mass. This means that the density should increase with atomic mass, and Rn should be the densest solid in the group. We expect densities of liquids to follow the same trend as densities of solids.

    (c) To estimate the first ionization energy of fermium, we note in Figure 9-12 that the ionization energies of the lanthanides (following the Cs valley) are approximately the same. We expect similar behavior of the actinides, and estimate a first ionization energy of about +600 kJ/mol.

    (d) We can estimate densities of solids from the information in Figure 9-1. Radium has $Z = 88$ and an approximate atomic volume of 40 cm^3/mol. Then we use the molar mass of radium to determine its density:

$$\text{density} = \frac{1 \text{ mol}}{40 \text{ cm}^3} \times \frac{226 \text{ g Ra}}{1 \text{ mol}} = 5.7 \text{ g/cm}^3$$

40. **(E)** Recall that polarizability decreases going from left to right across a period and increases from top to bottom within a group. Therefore, the least polarizable atom is F. P and Na are both in the same period, and since polarizability decreases from left to right, P will be less polarizable than Na. Finally, Br and As are also in the same period, and applying the same logic, Br is less polarizable than As. Therefore, the order of increasing polarizability is F < P < Na < Br < As.

41. **(E)** Polarizability decreases going from left to right across a period and increases from top to bottom within a group. Be, N, and O are in the same period, which means that O has the lowest polarizability and Be has the highest polarizability in this period. S belongs to period 3 and is farther to the right than K, which is in period 4. Therefore, S is less polarizable than K. In order of increasing polarizability, they are O < N < Be < S < K.

42. **(E)**

    (a) Size increases down a group and from right to left in a period. Ba is closest to the lower left corner of the periodic table and thus has the largest size.

    (b) Ionization energy decreases down a group and from right to left in a period. Although Pb is closest to the bottom of its group, Sr is farthest left in its period (and only one period above Pb). Sr should have the lowest first ionization energy.

    (c) Electron affinity becomes more negative from left to right in a period and from bottom to top in a group. Cl is closest to the upper right in the periodic table and has the most negative (smallest) electron affinity.

    (d) The number of unpaired electrons can be determined from the orbital diagram for each species. Atomic nitrogen ($[He]2s^2 2p^3$), by virtue of having three half-filled p-orbitals, possesses the greatest number of unpaired electrons.

43. **(E)** Polarizability increases with increasing size. Given the choice of Cl, Cl^+, and Cl^-, size depends on the number of electrons in the valence shell. Therefore, polarizability increases as follows: $Cl^+ < Cl < Cl^-$.

44. **(E)** Polarizability increases with increasing size, which for a given atom is also dictated by the number of electrons in the valence shell. For the given atom–ion pairs, F^- is more polarizable than F, and Na^+ is less polarizable than Na. Both Na^+ and F^- have the same electron configuration, but Na^+ has a higher nuclear charge. Therefore, Z_{eff} for Na^+ is larger than that of F^-, which means that Na^+ holds its valence electrons more tightly. Therefore, Na^+ is the least polarizable and F^- most polarizable.

45. **(E)**

    (a) $Z = 32$ 1. This is the element Ge, with an outer electron configuration of $3s^2 3p^2$. Thus, Ge has two unpaired p electrons.

    (b) $Z = 8$ 1. This is the element O. Each atom has an outer electron configuration of $2s^2 2p^4$. Thus, O has two unpaired p electrons.

    (c) $Z = 53$ 3. This is the element I, with an electron affinity more negative than that of the adjacent atoms: Xe and Te.

    (d) $Z = 38$ 4. This is the element Sr, which has two $5s$ electrons. It is easier to remove one $5s$ electron than to remove the outermost $4s$ electron of Ca, but harder than removing the outermost $6s$ electron of Cs.

    (e) $Z = 48$ 2. This is the element Cd. Its outer electron configuration is s^2 and thus it is diamagnetic.

    (f) $Z = 20$ 2. This is the element Ca. Since its electron configuration is $[Ar]4s^2$, all electrons are paired and it is diamagnetic.

46. **(E)**

(a) 6. Tl's electron configuration [Xe] $4f^{14}5d^{10}6s^{2}6p^{1}$ has one p electron in its outermost shell.

(b) 8. $Z = 70$ identifies the element as Yb, an f block of the periodic table, or an inner transition element.

(c) 5. Ni has the electron configuration [Ar] $4s^{2}3d^{8}$. It also is a d block element.

(d) 1. An s^{2} outer electron configuration, with the underlying configuration of a noble gas, is characteristic of elements of group 2(2A), the alkaline earth elements. Since the noble gas core is [Ar], the element must be Ca.

(e) 2. The element in the fifth period and Group 15 is Sb, a metalloid.

(f) 4 and 6. The element in the fourth period and Group 16 is Se, a nonmetal. (Note, B is a nonmetal with electron configuration $1s^{2}2s^{2}2p^{1}$ (having one p electron in the shell of highest n). 6 is also a possible answer.

47. **(M)** Ga^{4+} and Ge^{5+} are unlikely to be found in chemical compounds because these ions are unstable. Atoms tend to gain or lose electrons such that they achieve a noble gas configuration. Removing 4 electrons from Ga and 5 from Ge does not give these atoms a noble gas configuration due to the electrons populating the 3d orbitals.

48. **(E)** Li^{+} and Te^{2-} are likely to be found in chemical compounds because these are the most stable ions that lithium and tellurium form. Both Li^{+} and Te^{2-} have noble gas configurations.

INTEGRATIVE AND ADVANCED EXERCISES

49. **(M)**

(a) Not possible. C (77 pm) and Ca^{2+}(100 pm) are very different in size; however the diagram requires these to be nearly the same size

(b) This is a possibility. Na^{+} is approximately the same size as Sr (99 pm). Cl^{-} (181 pm) and Br^{-}(196 pm) are comparable, with one being slightly smaller.

(c) Not possible. There are three large atoms and only one small one. Y (165 pm), K (227 pm), Ca (197 pm), and the small Na^{+} (99 pm).

(d) Not possible. The smaller atoms are of noticeably different sizes: Zr^{2+} (95 pm) and Mg^{2+} (72 pm).

(e) This is possible. Fe and Co are of comparable sizes (~125 pm), and Cs (265 pm) and Rb (248 pm) are comparable, with one being slightly smaller.

Thus, the answer is that both (b) and (e) are compatible with the sketch.

50. **(M)** This periodic table would have to have the present width of 18 elements plus the width of the 14 lanthanides or actinides. That is, the periodic table would be (18 + 14 =) 32 elements wide.

51. **(E)** We can determine the atomic mass of indium by beginning with the atomic mass of oxygen, and using the chemical formula of InO to determine the amount (in moles) of indium in 100.0 g InO. In 100.0 g InO there is 82.5 g In and also 17.5 g O.

$$17.5\,\text{g O} \times \frac{1\,\text{mol O}}{16.0\,\text{g O}} \times \frac{1\,\text{mol In}}{1\,\text{mol O}} = 1.09\,\text{mol In} \quad \text{Atomic mass of In} = \frac{82.5\,\text{g In}}{1.09\,\text{mol In}} = 75.7\,\text{g In/mol}$$

With this value of the atomic mass of indium, Mendeleev might well have placed the element between As (75 g/mol) and Se (78 g/mol), that is, in his "Gruppe V" or "Gruppe VI."

52. **(E)** For In_2O_3: atomic mass of $In = \dfrac{82.5\,\text{g In}}{17.5\,\text{g O}} \times \dfrac{16.00\,\text{g O}}{1\,\text{mol O}} \times \dfrac{3\,\text{mol O}}{2\,\text{mol In}} = 113\,\text{g In/mol In}$

Indium now falls between Cd (112 g/mol) and Sn (118 g/mol), which places the element in "Gruppe III,", where it remains in the modern periodic table (Group 3A).

53. **(M)** Sizes of atoms do not simply increase uniformly with atomic number because electrons do not effectively screen each other from the nuclear charge (they do not effectively get between each other and the nucleus). Consequently, as each electron is added and the nuclear charge increases, all of the electrons in the subshell are drawn more closely. As well, in a particular group, atomic size does not increase uniformly owing to the penetration of electrons of a particular shell. Penetration is very dependent on the magnitude of the positive charge in the nucleus and how tightly held electrons are to that nucleus. For instance, a 2p electron will have a different penetration when compared to a 5p electron because the core electrons are more tightly held for an atom with 5p orbitals than those with only the 2p orbitals filled. Finally, electron-electron repulsion is not constant for the outer electrons as one goes down a particular group owing to the volume of the orbital occupied by the electron. 2p orbitals are smaller and have a higher electron-electron repulsion than do electrons in a 5p orbital.

54. **(M)** The ground-state electron configuration of Li is $1s^2\,2s^1$. The third ionization energy of Li(g) corresponds to the removal of the last remaining electron (from the $1s$ orbital). For a one-electron atom or atomic ion, the energy levels are given by equation (8.9).

$$E_n = -\frac{R_H Z^2}{n^2}$$

The energy of the last remaining electron in a lithium atom is

$$E_1 = -\frac{2.179 \times 10^{-18} \text{ J} \times 3^2}{1^2} = -1.96 \times 10^{-17} \text{ J} = -1.96 \times 10^{-20} \text{ kJ (per ion)}$$

Removing this electron requires the input of 1.96×10^{-20} kJ of energy (per ion). For one mole of ions, we require 1.96×10^{-20} kJ ion^{-1} × 6.022×10^{23} ions/mol = 1.18×10^4 kJ mol^{-1}.

The energy formula given above for E_n is sometimes applied to atoms or ions containing more than one electron by replacing Z by Z_{eff}, as we did in the Integrative Example. However, accurate values of Z_{eff} are not easily calculated or readily available. In fact, one way of estimating Z_{eff} values is to calculate them from the measured ionization energies.

55. **(E)**
   (a) A; Element "A" (K) has an electron configuration consistent with group 1A, which is the alkali metals.
   (b) B; Element "B" (As) is a non-metal. It is easier for As to gain an electron to form As$^-$ than for K to form K$^-$.
   (c) A; Element "A" (K) has the larger atomic radius. In general, size decreases going across a period.
   (d) B; Element "B" (As) has the greatest electron affinity. Non-metals have a greater tendency to add electrons compared with metals.

56. **(M)**
   (a) A; Element "A" (Sr) has an electron configuration consistent with group 1A which are the alkali metals.
   (b) B; Element "B" (Br) is a non-metal. It is easier for Br to gain an electron to form Br$^-$ than for Sr to form Sr$^-$.
   (c) A; Element "A" (Sr) has the larger atomic radius. In general, size decreases going across a period and increases going down a group. Since Sr has valence electrons in the higher energy 5s orbital, which is farther from the nucleus, Sr will be larger in size.
   (d) B; Element "B" (Br) has the greatest electron affinity. Non-metals have a greater tendency to add electrons compared with metals.

57. **(M)** Since (0.3734)(382) = 143 u, if we subtract 143 from 382 we get 239 u, which is very close to the correct value of 238 u.
   First we convert to J/g°C: 0.0276 × (4.184 J/cal) = 0.1155 J/g°C, so:
   0.1155 = 0.011440 + (23.967/atomic mass); solving for atomic mass yields a value of 230 u, which is within about 3% of the correct value.

58. **(M)** The volume of a sphere is given by

$$V = \frac{4}{3}\pi r^3 = \frac{4}{3} \times 3.142 \times (186 \text{ pm})^3 = 2.70 \times 10^7 \text{ pm}^3 = V_{\text{Na atom}}$$ One would then expect the

volume of a mole of sodium (atoms) to be Avogadro's constant times the volume of one atom.

$$\text{Na molar volume} = 6.022 \times 10^{23} \frac{\text{Na atoms}}{\text{mole Na}} \times 2.70 \times 10^7 \frac{\text{pm}^3}{\text{Na atom}} \times \left(\frac{100 \text{ cm}}{10^{12} \text{ pm}}\right)^3 = 16.3 \text{ cm}^3/\text{mol}$$

This value is about two-thirds of the value of 23 cm³/mole in Figure 9-1. An explanation for the great disagreement is that we have assumed that the entire volume of the solid is occupied by the spherical atoms. In fact, spheres leave some free space when they are packed together. (Recall how marbles do not completely fill the space when they are placed in a box.)

59. (E) The reaction given is the sum of the reverse of two reactions: those for the first ionization energy of Na and for the electron affinity of Cl.

$$Na^+(g) + e^- \rightarrow Na(g) \qquad -E_i(Na) \qquad = -495.8 \text{ kJ/mol}$$
$$\underline{Cl^-(g) \rightarrow Cl(g) + e^- \qquad -EA_{ea}(Cl) \qquad = +349.0 \text{ kJ/mol}}$$
$$Na^+(g) + Cl^-(g) \rightarrow Na(g) + Cl(g) \text{ Energy} = -146.8 \text{ kJ/mol}$$

Thus this is clearly an exothermic reaction.

60. (M) $E_1 = \dfrac{-2^2 \times 2.179 \times 10^{-18} \text{ J}}{1^2} = -8.716 \times 10^{-18} \text{ J/atom}$

This is the energy released when an electron combines with an alpha particle (He^{2+}) to the nucleus to form the ion He^+. The energy absorbed when the electron is removed from He^+, the ionization energy of He^+ or the *second* ionization energy of He, is the negative of this value. Then the energy per mole, E_m, is computed.

$$E_1 = E_1 \times N_A = \frac{8.716 \times 10^{-18}}{1 \text{ atom}} \times \frac{6.022 \times 10^{23}}{1 \text{ mol}} \times \frac{1 \text{ kJ}}{1000 \text{J}} = 5249 \text{ kJ/mol}$$

This is in excellent agreement with the tabulated value of 5251 kJ/mol.

61. (M) It should be relatively easy to remove electrons from ions of metallic elements, if the metal does not have a noble gas electron configuration. Thus, the third ionization energy for Sc and the second ionization energy for Ba should be small, with the second being smaller, since the electron is being removed from a more highly charged species in the case of the third ionization energy for Sc. The first ionization energy for F might be smaller than either of these because it involves removing only the first electron from a neutral atom, rather than removing an electron from a cation. There is some uncertainty here, because the electron being removed from F is not well shielded from the nuclear charge, and this value could be larger than the other two. The remaining ionization energies are both substantially larger than the other three because they both involve disrupting a noble gas electron configuration. The third ionization energy for Mg is larger than the second ionization energy for Na because it is more difficult to remove an electron from a more highly charged species.

Literature values (in kJ/mol) are given below.

First ionization energy of F:	1681 kJ/mol
Second ionization energy of Ba:	965
Third ionization energy of Sc:	2389
Second ionization energy of Na:	4562
Third ionization energy of Mg:	7733

Note that we have overestimated the difficulty of removing a second electron from Ba (a relatively large metal atom) and underestimated the difficulty of removing the first electron from F (a small nonmetal atom).

62. (M) $\dfrac{1 \text{ eV}}{1 \text{ atom}} \times \dfrac{6.02214 \times 10^{23} \text{ atoms}}{1 \text{ mol}} \times \dfrac{1.60218 \times 10^{-19} \text{ C}}{1 \text{ electron}} \times \dfrac{1 \text{ J}}{1 \text{ V} \cdot \text{C}} \times \dfrac{1 \text{ kJ}}{1000 \text{ J}} = 96.4855 \text{ kJ/mol}$

63. **(D)** Ionization energy (I.E.) data is tabulated below and plotted in the graphs below.

GRAPH 1

Atom/Ion	I.E. (kJ)	Z	root of I.E.
Na	495.8	11	22.26657
Mg^+	1451	12	38.09199
Al^{2+}	2745	13	52.39275
Si^{3+}	4356	14	66

GRAPH 2

Atom/Ion	I.E. (kJ)	Z	root of I.E.
Li	520	3	22.80351
Be^+	1757	4	41.91658
B^{2+}	3659	5	60.48967
C^{3+}	6221	6	78.87332

Graph 1 caption: Square root ionization energy vs atomic number
$y = 14.55x - 137.19$
$R^2 = 0.9988$

Graph 2 caption: Square root ionization energy vs atomic number
$y = 18.68x - 33.03$
$R^2 = 1.00$

From the Bohr model: $\text{I.E.} = R_H \times \dfrac{Z_{eff}^2}{n^2} = 1312.1\,\text{kJ}\,\text{mol}^{-1}\,\dfrac{Z_{eff}^2}{n^2}$

If we take the root of both sides, we obtain the following expression

$$\sqrt{\text{I.E.}} = \dfrac{Z_{eff}^2}{n^2} = \sqrt{1312.1\,\text{kJ}\,\text{mol}^{-1}\,\dfrac{Z_{eff}^2}{n^2}} = 36.22\,\dfrac{Z_{eff}}{n}$$

For graph 1: $n = 3$ hence $\sqrt{\text{I.E.}} = 36.22\,\dfrac{Z_{eff}}{3}$ Hence: $\sqrt{\text{I.E.}} = 12.1\,Z_{eff}$

The expected slope for the graph is 12.1, while the actual slope from data is 14.55. Although the y-intercept is not zero, we do see a linear relationship ($R = 0.9988$).

For graph 2: $n = 2$ hence $\sqrt{\text{I.E.}} = 36.22\,\dfrac{Z_{eff}}{2}$ Hence: $\sqrt{\text{I.E.}} = 18.1\,Z_{eff}$

The expected slope for the graph is 18.1, while the actual slope from data is 18.68. Although the y-intercept is not zero, we do see a linear relationship ($R = 1.00$)

The apparent discrepancy lies in the fact that there are electrons in lower shells. For the series plotted in graph 1, there are electrons in the $n = 1$ and $n = 2$ shells. This results in deviation from the theoretical slope and explains why the y-intercept is not zero. We have assumed that the nuclear charge is also the effective nuclear charge. For the series plotted in graph 2, there are electrons in the $n = 1$ shell. This results in a much smaller deviation from the theoretical slope and a y-intercept that is closer to zero. Again, we have made the assumption that the nuclear charge is also the effective nuclear charge, which is not correct.

A plot using H and He$^+$ yields a slope of 36.24 (theoretical = 36.22) and a y-intercept of 0.014. There is excellent agreement here because both are Bohr atoms, with no underlying electrons. In this case, the nuclear charge is also the effective nuclear charge. This is an excellent assumption as can be seen by the agreement with the theoretical slope and y-intercept.

64. (M)

Fl	114	Unp	115	Lv	116
$7s^27p^2$	289	$7s^27p^3$	291	$7s^27p^4$	293
2 upe	215	3 upe	175	1 upe	240
20	-37	24	79	25	190
723	15	572	13	755	12

FEATURE PROBLEMS

65. (M)

(a) The work function is the energy required for an electron to escape from the solid surface of an element.

(b) Work functions tend to decrease down a group and increase across a period in the periodic table. The work function increases across the periodic table from left to right following the steady increase in effective nuclear charge. As one proceeds down a given group, the principal quantum number increases and so does the distance of the outer electrons from the nucleus. The farther the electrons are from the nucleus, the more easily they can be removed from the solid surface of the element, and hence, the smaller will be the value of the work function for the element.

(c) Through the process of interpolation, one would predict that the work function for potassium should fall somewhere close to 3.9. The published value for the work function of potassium is 3.69 (CRC handbook). Had we been provided more information on the nature of the bonding in each of these metals, and had we been told what type of crystalline lattice each metal adopts, we would have been able to come up with a more accurate estimate of the work function.

(d) The periodic trends in work function closely follow those in ionization energy. This should come as no surprise since both ionization and the work function involve the loss of electrons from neutral atoms.

66. **(D)** The Moseley equation, $v = A(Z - b)^2$, where v is the frequency of the emitted X-ray radiation, Z is the atomic number, and A and b are constants, relates the frequency of emitted X-rays to the nuclear charge for the atoms that make up the target of the cathode ray tube. X-rays are emitted by the element after one of its K-level electrons has been knocked out of the atom by collision with a fast moving electron. In this question, we have been asked to determine the values for the constants A and b. The simplest way to find these values is to plot $\sqrt{v}$ vs. Z. This plot provides $\sqrt{A}$ as the slope and $-\sqrt{A}$ (b) as the y-intercept. Starting with $v = A(Z - b)^2$, we first take the square root of both sides. This affords $\sqrt{v} = \sqrt{A}$ $(Z - b)$. Multiplying out this expression gives $\sqrt{v} = \sqrt{A}$ $(Z) - \sqrt{A}$ (b). This expression follows the equation of a straight line $y = mx + b$, where $y = \sqrt{v}$, $m = \sqrt{A}$, $x = Z$ and $b = -\sqrt{A}$ (b). So a plot of $\sqrt{v}$ vs. Z will provide us with A and b, after a small amount of mathematical manipulation. Before we can construct the plot, we need to convert the provided X-ray wavelengths into their corresponding frequencies. For instance, Mg has an X-ray wavelength = 987 pm. The corresponding frequency for this radiation = c/λ, hence,

$$v = \frac{2.998 \times 10^8 \text{ m s}^{-1}}{9.87 \times 10^{-10} \text{ m}} = 3.04 \times 10^{17} \text{ s}^{-1}$$

Performing similar conversions on the rest of the data allows for the construction of the following table and plot (below).

(Z)	$\sqrt{v}$
12	5.51×10^8
16	7.48×10^8
20	9.49×10^8
24	1.14×10^9
30	1.45×10^9
37	1.80×10^9

Plot of square root (v) versus atomic number

Equation of the Line
$y = 4.98E+07x - 4.83E+07$

The slope of the line is $4.98 \times 10^7 = \sqrt{A}$ and the y-intercept is $-4.83 \times 10^7 = -\sqrt{A}$ (b).

Thus, $A = 2.30 \times 10^{15}$ Hz and $b = \dfrac{-4.83 \times 10^7}{-4.98 \times 10^7} = 0.969$.

According to Bohr's theory, the frequencies that correspond to the lines in the emission

spectrum are given by the equation: $(3.2881 \times 10^{15} \text{ s}^{-1}) \left(\dfrac{1}{(n_i)^2} - \dfrac{1}{(n_f)^2} \right)$,

where $(3.2881 \times 10^{15} \text{ s}^{-1})$ represents the frequency for the lowest energy photon that is capable of completely removing (ionizing) an electron from a hydrogen atom in its ground state. The value of A (calculated in this question) is close to the Rydberg frequency ($3.2881 \times 10^{15} \text{ s}^{-1}$), so it is probably the equivalent term in the Moseley equation. The constant b, which is close to unity, could represent the number of electrons left in the K shell after one K-shell electron has been ejected by a cathode ray. Thus, one can think of b as representing the screening afforded by the remaining electron in the K-shell. Of course screening of the nucleus is only be possible for those elements with $Z > 1$.

67. **(D)**

(a) The table provided in this question shows the energy changes associated with the promotion of the outermost valence electron of sodium into the first four excited states above the highest occupied ground state atomic orbital. In addition, we have been told that the energy needed to completely remove one mole of $3s$ electrons from one mole of sodium atoms in the ground state is 496 kJ. The ionization energy for each excited state can be found by subtracting the "energy quanta" entry for the excited state from 496 kJ mol^{-1}.

e.g., for $[Ne]3p^1$, the first ionization energy $= 496\ \dfrac{kJ}{mol} - 203\ \dfrac{kJ}{mol} = 293\ \dfrac{kJ}{mol}$

Thus, the rest of the ionization energies are:
$[Ne]4s^1$, $= 496$ kJ mol^{-1} $- 308$ kJ mol^{-1} $= 188$ kJ mol^{-1}
$[Ne]3d^1$, $= 496$ kJ mol^{-1} $- 349$ kJ mol^{-1} $= 147$ kJ mol^{-1}
$[Ne]4p^1$, $= 496$ kJ mol^{-1} $- 362$ kJ mol^{-1} $= 134$ kJ mol^{-1}

(b) Z_{eff} (the effective nuclear charge) for each state can be found by using the equation:

ionization energy in kJ mol^{-1} (I.E.) $= \dfrac{A(Z_{eff})^2}{n^2}$

Where $n =$ starting principal quantum level for the electron that is promoted out of the atom and $A = 1.3121 \times 10^3$ kJ mol^{-1} (Rydberg constant).

For $[Ne]3p^1$ ($n = 3$) 2.93×10^2 kJmol^{-1} $= \dfrac{1.3121\times10^3\ \frac{kJ}{mol}(Z_{eff})^2}{3^2}$ $Z_{eff} = 1.42$

For $[Ne]4s^1$ ($n = 4$) 1.88×10^2 kJmol^{-1} $= \dfrac{1.3121\times10^3\ \frac{kJ}{mol}(Z_{eff})^2}{4^2}$ $Z_{eff} = 1.51$

For $[Ne]3d^1$ ($n = 3$) 1.47×10^2 kJmol^{-1} $= \dfrac{1.3121\times10^3\ \frac{kJ}{mol}(Z_{eff})^2}{3^2}$ $Z_{eff} = 1.00$

For $[Ne]4p^1$ ($n = 4$) 1.34×10^2 kJmol^{-1} $= \dfrac{1.3121\times10^3\ \frac{kJ}{mol}(Z_{eff})^2}{4^2}$ $Z_{eff} = 1.28$

(c) $\bar{r}_{nl}$, which is the average distance of the electron from the nucleus for a particular orbital, can be calculated with the equation:

$\bar{r}_{nl} = \dfrac{n^2 a_o}{Z_{eff}}\left(1 + \dfrac{1}{2}\left(1 - \dfrac{\ell(\ell+1)}{n^2}\right)\right)$ Where $a_o = 52.9$ pm,
$n =$ principal quantum number
$\ell =$ angular quantum number for the orbital

For $[Ne]3p^1$ ($n = 3$, $\ell = 1$) $\bar{r}_{3p} = \dfrac{3^2(52.9\ \text{pm})}{1.42}\left(1 + \dfrac{1}{2}\left(1 - \dfrac{1(1+1)}{3^2}\right)\right) = 466$ pm

For $[Ne]4s^1$ ($n = 4$, $\ell = 0$) $\bar{r}_{4s} = \dfrac{4^2(52.9\ \text{pm})}{1.51}\left(1 + \dfrac{1}{2}\left(1 - \dfrac{0(0+1)}{4^2}\right)\right) = 823$ pm

$$\text{For [Ne]}3d^1 \ (n=3, \ \ell=2) \ \overline{r}_{3d} = \frac{3^2(52.9 \text{ pm})}{1.00}\left(1+\frac{1}{2}\left(1-\frac{2(2+1)}{3^2}\right)\right) = 555 \text{ pm}$$

$$\text{For [Ne]}4p^1 \ (n=4, \ \ell=1) \ \overline{r}_{4p} = \frac{4^2(52.9 \text{ pm})}{1.28}\left(1+\frac{1}{2}\left(1-\frac{1(1+1)}{4^2}\right)\right) = 950 \text{ pm}$$

(d) The results from the Z_{eff} calculations show that the greatest effective nuclear charge is experienced by the $4s$ orbital ($Z_{eff} = 1.51$). Next are the two p-orbitals, $3p$ and $4p$, which come in at 1.42 and 1.28 respectively. Coming in last is the $3d$ orbital, which has a $Z_{eff} = 1.00$. These results are precisely in keeping with what we would expect. First of all, only the s-orbital penetrates all the way to the nucleus. Both the p- and d-orbitals have nodes at the nucleus. Also p-orbitals penetrate more deeply than do d-orbitals. Recall that the more deeply an orbital penetrates (i.e., the closer the orbital is to the nucleus), the greater is the effective nuclear charge felt by the electrons in that orbital. It follows then that the $4s$ orbital will experience the greatest effective nuclear charge and that the Z_{eff} values for the $3p$ and $4p$ orbitals should be larger than the Z_{eff} for the $3d$ orbital.

The results from the $\overline{r}_{nl}$ calculations for the four excited state orbitals show that the largest orbital in the set is the $4p$ orbital. This is exactly as expected because the $4p$ orbital is highest in energy and hence, on average farthest from the nucleus. The $4s$ orbital has an average position closer to the nucleus because it experiences a larger effective nuclear charge. The $3p$ orbital, being lowest in energy and hence on average closest to the nucleus, is the smallest orbital in the set. The $3p$ orbital has an average position closer to the nucleus than the $3d$ orbital (which is in the same principal quantum level), because it penetrates more deeply into the atom.

68. (D)

(a) First of all, we need to find the ionization energy (I.E.) for the process: $F^-(g) \rightarrow F(g) + e^-$. To accomplish this, we need to calculate Z_{eff} for the species in the left hand column and plot the number of protons in the nucleus against Z_{eff}. By extrapolation, we can estimate the first ionization energy for $F^-(g)$. The electron affinity for F is equal to the first ionization energy of F^- multiplied by minus one (i.e., by reversing the ionization reaction, one can obtain the electron affinity).
For $Ne(g) \rightarrow Ne^+(g) + e^-$ (I.E. = 2080 kJ mol^{-1}; $n=2$; 10 protons)

$$\text{I.E. (kJ mol}^{-1}) = \frac{1312.1\frac{\text{kJ}}{\text{mol}}(Z_{eff})^2}{4} = 2080 \text{ kJ mol}^{-1} \quad Z_{eff} = 2.518$$

For $Na^+(g) \rightarrow Na^{2+}(g) + e^-$ (I.E. = 4565 kJ mol^{-1}; $n=2$; 11 protons)

$$\text{I.E. (kJ mol}^{-1}) = \frac{1312.1\frac{\text{kJ}}{\text{mol}}(Z_{eff})^2}{4} = 4565 \text{ kJ mol}^{-1} \quad Z_{eff} = 3.730$$

For $Mg^{2+}(g) \rightarrow Mg^{3+}(g) + e^-$ (I.E. = 7732 kJ mol^{-1}; $n=2$; 12 protons)

$$\text{I.E. (kJ mol}^{-1}) = \frac{1312.1\frac{\text{kJ}}{\text{mol}}(Z_{eff})^2}{4} = 7732 \text{ kJ mol}^{-1} \quad Z_{eff} = 4.855$$

For $Al^{3+}(g) \rightarrow Al^{4+}(g) + e^-$ (I.E. = 11,577 kJ mol^{-1}; $n = 2$; 13 protons)

$$\text{I.E. (kJ mol}^{-1}) = \frac{1312.1 \frac{kJ}{mol}(Z_{eff})^2}{4} = 11,577 \text{ kJ mol}^{-1} \quad Z_{eff} = 5.941$$

A plot of the points (10, 2.518), (11, 3.730), (12, 4.855), and (13,5.941) gives a straight line that follows the equation: $Z_{eff} = 1.1394(Z) - 8.8421$.
For F^-, $Z = 9$; so $Z_{eff} = 1.1394(9) - 8.8421 = 1.413$ and $n = 2$. Hence,

$$\text{I.E. (kJ mol}^{-1}) = \frac{1312.1 \frac{kJ}{mol}(1.413)^2}{4} = 654.9 \text{ kJ mol}^{-1} \text{ for } F^-$$

The electron affinity for F must equal the reverse of the first ionization energy, or −654.9 kJ. The actual experimental value found for the first electron affinity of F is −328 kJ/mol.

(b) Here, we will use the same method of solution as we did for part (a). To find the electron affinity for the process: $O(g) + e^- \rightarrow O^-(g)$, we first need to calculate the I.E. for $O^-(g)$. This is available from a plot of the number of protons in the nucleus vs. Z_{eff} for the four species in the central column.

For $F(g) \rightarrow F^+(g) + e^-$ (I.E. = 1681 kJ mol^{-1}; n = 2; 9 protons)

$$\text{I.E. (kJ mol}^{-1}) = \frac{1312.1 \frac{kJ}{mol}(Z_{eff})^2}{4} = 1681 \text{ kJ mol}^{-1} \quad Z_{eff} = 2.264$$

For $Ne^+(g) \rightarrow Ne^{2+}(g) + e^-$ (I.E. = 3963 kJ mol^{-1}; $n = 2$; 10 protons)

$$\text{I.E. (kJ mol}^{-1}) = \frac{1312.1 \frac{kJ}{mol}(Z_{eff})^2}{4} = 3963 \text{ kJ mol}^{-1} \quad Z_{eff} = 3.476$$

For $Na^{2+}(g) \rightarrow Na^{3+}(g) + e^-$ (I.E. = 6912 kJ mol^{-1}; $n = 2$; 11 protons)

$$\text{I.E. (kJ mol}^{-1}) = \frac{1312.1 \frac{kJ}{mol}(Z_{eff})^2}{4} = 6912 \text{ kJ mol}^{-1} \quad Z_{eff} = 4.590$$

For $Mg^{3+}(g) \rightarrow Mg^{4+}(g) + e^-$ (I.E. = 10,548 kJ mol^{-1}; $n = 2$; 12 protons)

$$\text{I.E. (kJ mol}^{-1}) = \frac{1312.1 \frac{kJ}{mol}(Z_{eff})^2}{4} = 10,548 \text{ kJ mol}^{-1} \quad Z_{eff} = 5.671$$

A plot of the points (9, 2.264), (10, 3.476). (11, 4.590), and (12, 5.671) gives a straight line that follows the equation: $Z_{eff} = 1.134(Z) - 7.902$.
For O^-, $Z = 8$; so $Z_{eff} = 1.134(8) - 7.902 = 1.170$ and $n = 2$. Hence,

$$\text{I.E. (kJ mol}^{-1}) = \frac{1312.1 \frac{kJ}{mol}(1.170)^2}{4} = 449 \text{ kJ mol}^{-1} \text{ for } O^-$$

The Electron affinity for O must equal the reverse of the first ionization energy, or – 449 kJ. Again we will use the same method of solution as was used for part (a). To find the electron affinity for the process: $N(g) + e^- \rightarrow N^-(g)$, we first need to calculate the I.E. for $N^-(g)$. This is accessible from a plot of the number of protons in the nucleus vs. Z_{eff} for the four species in the last column.

For $O(g) \rightarrow O^+(g) + e^-$ (I.E. = 1314 kJ mol^{-1}; $n = 2$; 8 protons)

$$\text{I.E. (kJ mol}^{-1}) = \frac{1312.1 \frac{kJ}{mol}(Z_{eff})^2}{4} = 1314 \text{ kJ mol}^{-1} \quad Z_{eff} = 2.001$$

For $F^+(g) \rightarrow F^{2+}(g) + e^-$ (I.E. = 3375 kJ mol^{-1}; $n = 2$; 9 protons)

$$\text{I.E. (kJ mol}^{-1}) = \frac{1312.1 \frac{kJ}{mol}(Z_{eff})^2}{4} = 3375 \text{ kJ mol}^{-1} \quad Z_{eff} = 3.208$$

For $Ne^{2+}(g) \rightarrow Ne^{3+}(g) + e^-$ (I.E. = 6276 kJ mol^{-1}; $n = 2$; 10 protons)

$$\text{I.E. (kJ mol}^{-1}) = \frac{1312.1 \frac{kJ}{mol}(Z_{eff})^2}{4} = 6276 \text{ kJ mol}^{-1} \quad Z_{eff} = 4.374$$

For $Na^{3+}(g) \rightarrow Na^{4+}(g) + e^-$ (I.E. = 9,540 kJ mol^{-1}; $n = 2$; 11 protons)

$$\text{I.E. (kJ mol}^{-1}) = \frac{1312.1 \frac{kJ}{mol}(Z_{eff})^2}{4} = 9,540 \text{ kJ mol}^{-1} \quad Z_{eff} = 5.393$$

A plot of the points (8, 2.001), (9, 3.204), (10, 4.374). and (11, 5.393), gives a straight line that follows the equation: $Z_{eff} = 1.1346(Z) - 7.0357$.

For N^-, $Z = 7$; so $Z_{eff} = 1.1346 (7) - 7.0357 = 0.9065$ and $n = 2$. Hence,

$$\text{I.E. (kJ mol}^{-1}) = \frac{1312.1 \frac{kJ}{mol}(0.9065)^2}{4} = 269.6 \text{ kJ mol}^{-1} \text{ for } N^-$$

The electron affinity for N must equal the reverse of the first ionization energy, or –269.6 kJ.

(c) For N, O, and F, the additional electron ends up in a $2p$ orbital. In all three instances the nuclear charge is well shielded by the filled $2s$ orbital located below the $2p$ set of orbitals. As we proceed from N to F, electrons are placed, one by one, in the $2p$ subshell and these electrons do afford some additional shielding, but this extra screening is more than offset by the accompanying increase in nuclear charge. Thus, the increase in electron affinity observed upon moving from N via oxygen to fluorine is the result of the steady increase in Z_{eff} that occurs upon moving farther to the right in the periodic table.

69. (D)

(a) An oxygen atom in the ground state has the valence shell configuration $2s^2 2p^4$. Thus there are a total of six electrons in the valence shell. The amount of shielding experienced by one electron in the valence shell is the sum of the shielding provided by the other five electrons in the valence shell and the shielding afforded by the two electrons in the filled 1s orbital below the valence shell. Shielding from electrons in the same shell contributes $5 \times 0.35 = 1.75$ and the shielding from the electrons in the $n = 1$ shell contributes $2 \times 0.85 = 1.70$. The total shielding is 3.45 ($=1.75 + 1.70$). For O, $Z = 8$, hence, $Z_{eff} = 8 - 3.45 = 4.55$.

(b) A ground state Cu atom has the valence shell configuration $3d^9 4s^2$. According to Slater's rules, the nine $3d$ electrons do not shield the $4s^2$ electrons from the nucleus. Thus the total amount of shielding experienced by a $4s$ electron in Cu is:
Shielding from the other $4s$ electron $= 1 \times 0.35 \qquad = 0.35$
$+$ shielding from the electrons in the $3d$ subshell $= 9 \times 0.85 = 7.65$
$+$shielding from the electrons in the $3s/3p$ orbitals $= 8 \times 1.00 \quad = 8.00$
$+$shielding from the electrons in the $2s/2p$ orbitals $= 8 \times 1.00 \quad = 8.00$
$+$shielding from the electrons in the $1s$ orbital $= 2 \times 1.00 \qquad = \underline{2.00}$
Total shielding for the $4s$ electrons $= (0.35 + 7.65 + 8 + 8 + 2) = 26.00$
Copper has $Z = 29$, so $Z_{eff} = 29 - 26.00 = 3.00$

(c) $3d$ electron in a ground state Cu atom will be shielded by the eight other $3d$ electrons and by the electrons in the lower principal quantum levels. Thus the total amount of shielding for a $3d$ electron is equal to
shielding from the eight electrons in the $3d$ subshell $= 8 \times 0.35 \qquad = 2.80$
$+$shielding from the electrons in the $3s/3p$ orbitals $= 8 \times 1.00 \qquad = 8.00$
$+$shielding from the electrons in the $2s/2p$ orbitals $= 8 \times 1.00 \qquad = 8.00$
$+$shielding from the electrons in the $1s$ orbital $= 2 \times 1 \qquad = \underline{2.00}$
Total shielding for the $3d$ electrons $= (2.80 + 8.00 + 8.00 + 2.00) \quad = 20.80$
Copper has $Z = 29$, so $Z_{eff} = 29 - 20.80 = 8.2$

(d) To find Z_{eff} for the valence electron in each Group I element, we first calculate the screening constant for the electron.
For H: $S = 0$, so $Z_{eff} = Z$ and $Z = 1$; thus $Z_{eff} = 1$
For Li: $S = 2(0.85) = 1.70$ and $Z = 3$; thus $Z_{eff} = 3 - 1.70 = 1.30$
For Na: $S = 8(0.85) + 2(1) = 8.80$ and $Z = 11$; thus $Z_{eff} = 11 - 8.80 = 2.20$
For K: $S = 8(0.85) + 8(1) + 2(1) = 16.80$, $Z = 19$; thus $Z_{eff} = 19 - 16.80 = 2.20$
For Rb: $S = 8(0.85) + 10(1) + 8(1) + 8(1) + 2(1) = 34.80$, $Z = 37$;
thus $Z_{eff} = 37 - 34.80 = 2.20$
For Cs: $S = 8(0.85) + 10(1) + 8(1) + 10(1) + 8(1) + 8(1) + 2(1) = 52.80$; $Z = 55$,
Thus $Z_{eff} = 2.20$

Based upon Slater's rules, we have found that the effective nuclear charge increases sharply between periods one and three and then stays at 2.20 for the rest of the alkali metal group. You may recall that the ionization energy for an element can be calculated by using the equation:

$$\text{I.E. (kJ mol}^{-1}) = \frac{1312.1 \, \frac{\text{kJ}}{\text{mol}} (Z_{eff})^2}{n^2} \qquad \text{Where } n = \text{principal quantum number.}$$

By plugging the results from our Z_{eff} calculations into this equation, we would find that the ionization energy decreases markedly as we descend the alkali metal group, in spite of the fact that the Z_{eff} remains constant after Li. The reason that the ionization energy drops is, of course, because the value for n becomes larger as we move down the periodic table and, according to the ionization energy equation given above, larger n values translate into smaller ionization energies (this is because n^2 appears in the denominator). Put another way, even though Z_{eff} remains constant throughout most of Group I, the valence s-electrons become progressively easier to remove as we move down the group because they are farther and farther away from the nucleus. Of course, the further away an electron is from the nucleus, the weaker is its attraction to the nucleus and the easier it is to remove.

(e) As was the case in part (d), to evaluate Z_{eff} for a valence electron in each atom, we must first calculate the screening experienced by the electron with Slater's rules

For Li: $S = 2(0.85) = 1.70$ and $Z = 3$, thus $Z_{eff} = 3 - 1.70 = 1.30$
For Be: $S = 1(0.35) + 2(0.85) = 2.05$ and $Z = 4$; thus $Z_{eff} = 4 - 2.05 = 1.95$
For B: $S = 2(0.35) + 2(0.85) = 2.40$ and $Z = 5$; thus $Z_{eff} = 5 - 2.40 = 2.60$
For C: $S = 3(0.35) + 2(0.85) = 2.75$ and $Z = 6$; thus $Z_{eff} = 6 - 2.75 = 3.25$
For N: $S = 4(0.35) + 2(0.85) = 3.10$ and $Z = 7$; thus $Z_{eff} = 7 - 3.10 = 3.90$
For O: $S = 5(0.35) + 2(0.85) = 3.45$ and $Z = 8$; thus $Z_{eff} = 8 - 3.45 = 4.55$
For F: $S = 6(0.35) + 2(0.85) = 3.80$ and $Z = 9$; thus $Z_{eff} = 9 - 3.80 = 5.20$
For Ne: $S = 7(0.35) + 2(0.85) = 4.15$ and $Z = 10$; thus $Z_{eff} = 10 - 4.15 = 5.85$

The results from these calculations show that the Z_{eff} increases from left to right across the periodic table. Apart from small irregularities, the first ionization energies for the elements within a period also increase with increasing atomic number. Based upon our calculated Z_{eff} values, this is exactly the kind of trend for ionization energies that we would have anticipated. The fact is, a larger effective nuclear charge means that the outer electron(s) is/are held more tightly and this leads to a higher first ionization energy for the atom.

(f) First we need to calculate the Z_{eff} values for an electron in the 3s, 3p, and 3d orbitals of both a hydrogen atom and a sodium atom, by using Slater's rules. Since there is only one electron in a H atom, there is no possibility of shielding, and thus the effective nuclear charge for an electron in a 3s, 3p or 3d orbital of a H atom is one. The picture for Na is more complicated because it contains intervening electrons that shield the outermost electrons from the attractive power of the nucleus. The Z_{eff} calculations (based on Slater's Rules) for an electron in i) the 3s orbital, ii) the 3p orbital, and iii) the 3d orbital of a Na atom are shown below:

Na (3s electron; $n = 3$) $Z_{eff} = 11.0 - [(8e^- \text{ in the } n = 2 \text{ shell} \times 0.85/e^-) + (2e^- \text{ in the } n = 1 \text{ shell} \times 1.00/e^-)] = [11.0 - 8.8] = 2.2$

Na (3p electron; $n = 3$; e^- was originally in the 3s orbital)) $Z_{eff} = 11.0 - [(8e^- \text{ in the } n = 2 \text{ shell} \times 0.85/e^-) + (2e^- \text{ in the } n = 1 \text{ shell} \times 1.00/e^-)] = [11.0 - 8.8] = 2.2$

Na (3d electron; $n = 3$; e⁻ was originally in the 3s orbital)) $Z_{eff} = 11.0 - [(8e^-$ in the $n = 2$ shell $\times 1.00/e^-) + (2e^-$ in the $n = 1$ shell $\times 1.00/e^-)] = [11.0 - 10.0] = 1.0$

Next, we insert these Z_{eff} values into their appropriate radial functions, which are gathered in Table 8.1, and use the results from these calculations to construct radial probability plots for an electron in the 3s, 3p and 3d orbitals of H and Na. The six plots that result are collected in the two figures presented below:

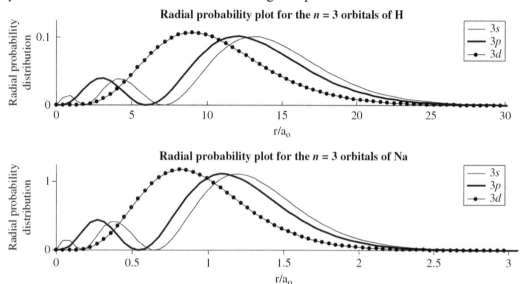

Notice that the 3s and 3p orbitals of sodium are much closer to the nucleus, on average, than the 3s and 3p orbitals of hydrogen. Because they are pulled more strongly towards the nucleus, the 3s and 3p orbitals of sodium end up being much smaller than the corresponding orbitals on hydrogen. Put another way, since the 3s and 3p electrons in sodium experience a larger effective nuclear charge, they are more tightly bound to the nucleus and, hence, are lower in energy than s and p electrons in the third principal shell of a hydrogen atom. If we want to express this in terms of shielding, we can say that the radial probability distributions for the 3s and 3p orbitals of sodium are smaller than those of hydrogen because the 3s and 3p orbitals of sodium are more poorly shielded. The graphs also show that the radial probability plot for the 3d orbital of a hydrogen atom is identical to that for a 3d orbital of a Na atom. This is what one would expect since a 3d electron in H and a 3d electron in Na both experience an effective nuclear charge of one.

SELF-ASSESSMENT EXERCISES

70. **(E)**
   (a) Isoelectronic: Two elements having the same number of electrons in identical configuration (through the gain or loss of electrons by either).
   (b) Valence shell electrons: The subshell of highest energy in an atom. They are principally responsible for bonding and chemical reaction.

(c) Metals: Elements that are generally characterized by high electrical and thermal conductivity, ductility, and luster.

(d) Non-metals: Elements that are generally characterized by properties the exact opposite of metals.

(e) Metalloids: Elements in the "transition" region where the metals and non-metals meet in the periodic table. They generally have the physical appearance of a metal, but, exhibit some properties of non-metals as well.

71. (E)

(a) The periodic law: The original law by Mendeleev and Meyer stated that "When the elements are arranged in order of increasing atomic mass, certain sets of properties recur periodically." The updated version replaces atomic mass with atomic number.

(b) Ionization energy: The energy required to remove one electron from the valence shell of an atom in the gas phase.

(c) Electron affinity: The enthalpy change that occurs when an atom in the gas phase gains and electron (essentially, the reverse of ionization energy).

(d) Paramagnetism: A magnetic phenomenon occurring in atoms that have unpaired electrons and the magnetic effects of the unpaired electrons don't cancel each other out.

72. (E)

(a) Actinide and lanthanide element: Both rare earth elements. Lanthanides have a $4f$ subshell for their valence band and are generally found in nature (albeit at very small quantities), and actinides have a $5f$ subshell for their valence and, with the exception of two elements, are all synthetic.

(b) Covalent and metallic radius: Covalent radius is the distance between the nuclei of two identical atoms in a covalent bond, whereas metallic radius is the distance between two nuclei of metal atoms, where there is no sharing of electrons with adjacent atoms.

(c) Atomic number and effective nuclear charge: Atomic number is the number of protons in the nucleus of the atom, whereas effective nuclear charge is the amount of the charge of the nucleus that is actually experienced by valence electrons after some shielding by core and other valence electrons.

(d) Ionization energy and electron affinity: Ionization energy is the energy required to remove one electron from the valence shell of an atom in the gas phase; electron affinity is the exact opposite.

(e) Paramagnetic and diamagnetic: Paramagnetism rises from unpaired electrons in the valence shell of an atom, whereas diamagnetism results from fully paired valence shell.

73. (E) The answer is (b). The element in question is antimony (Sb), which is in the same group as Bi.

74. (E) The answer is (a), K. This is because atomic radius decreases going from left to right of the period.

75. (E) The answer is (a), Cl^-. All of the choices have the same electron configuration as Ar, but Cl^- has an extra electron in the valence shell, which expands the ionic radius.

76. (E) The answer is (b), because it has the smallest radius (and highest electron affinity). Therefore, the valence electrons are held more tightly, hence a higher first ionization energy.

77. **(E)** The answer is (a), Br. This is because electron affinities increase across the periodic table, and are greatest for nonmetallic main group elements. The other choices are for metals.

78. **(E)** The answer is (d), Sr^{2+}. They both have the electron configuration of Kr.

79. **(E)** The electron configurations of the first and second ionization products of Cs are as follows:
Cs^+: [Xe], or [Kr] $4d^{10}5s^25p^6$
Cs^{2+}: [Kr] $4d^{10}5s^25p^5$
The second ionization energy is much greater because one has to overcome the extra energy required to remove an electron from a stable, filled subshell (which resembles that of a stable noble atom Xe).

80. **(M)** The first ionization energy of Mg is higher than Na because, in the case of Mg, an electron from a filled subshell is being removed, whereas in Na, the removing of one electron leads to the highly stable electron configuration of Ne. The second ionization of Mg is lower than Na, because in the case Mg, the electron configuration of Ar is achieved, whereas in Na, the stable [Ar] configuration is being lost by removing an electron from the filled subshell.

81. **(M)**
(a) As, because it is the left and bottom-most element in the choices given
(b) F^-. Xe valence shell has $n = 5$, so it would be the largest and therefore not correct. Among those with shells with $n = 2$, F^- is the smallest because it has the highest nuclear charge and therefore more attraction of the orbitals to the nucleus
(c) Cl^-, because it is the most electronegative, and is being farther removed from the ideal filled subshell electron configuration
(d) Carbon, because it is the smallest, and hence has the least amount of shielding of the nucleus from the valence band, and the greatest attraction between the valence electrons and the nucleus
(e) Carbon, because electron affinity increases going across a period

82. **(M)** The trends would generally follow higher first ionization energy values for a fuller subshell. The exception is the case of S and P, where P has a slightly higher value. This is because there is a slight energy advantage to having a half-filled subshell with an electron in each of p_x, p_y and p_z orbitals as in the case of P, whereas the S has one extra electron.

83. **(E)** The pairs are Ar/Ca, Co/Ni, Te/I and Th/Pa. The periodic table must be arranged by atomic number because only this order is consistent with the regularity in electron configurations that is the ultimate basis of the table.

84. **(E)**
(a) protons = 50
(b) neutrons = 69
(c) $4d$ electrons = 10
(d) $3s$ electrons = 2
(e) $5p$ electrons = 2
(f) valence shell electrons = 4

85. **(E)**
(a) F; it is the top right-most reactive element and has the highest electron affinity
(b) Sc
(c) Si

86. **(E)**
(a) C
(b) Rb
(c) At

87. **(E)**
(a) Ba
(b) S
(c) Bi, because Ba < Ca < Bi < As < S

88. **(E)** Rb > Ca > Sc > Fe > Te > Br > O > F

89. **(M)**
(a) False. The s orbitals have a higher probability of being near the nucleus (whereas the probability is zero for p and d orbitals), so they are more effective at shielding.
(b) True. The s orbitals have much better penetration than p or d orbitals and therefore are better at shielding nuclear charge.
(c) True for all atoms except hydrogen. Z_{eff} has a maximum theoretical value equal to Z. In practice, it is always less in a multi-electron atom, because there is always some shielding of the nuclear charge by the electrons.
(d) True. Electrons in p orbitals penetrate better than those in d orbitals.
(e) True. To understand this, remember that ionization energy, $I = R_H \times Z_{eff}^2 / n^2$. Use the data in Table 9-4 to determine Z_{eff} for these elements.

90. **(M)**
(a) False. The $1s$ orbital has more penetration with the nucleus than the $2s$ orbital, and feels nearly the entire charge of the nucleus (higher Z_{eff}).
(b) False. The Z_{eff} of a $2s$ orbital is greater than a $2p$ because of higher penetration.
(c) True, because the electron in an s orbital has greater penetration with the nucleus and is more tightly attracted.
(d) True. Because of the greater penetration of the $2s$ electrons, the $2p$ electrons are more effectively shielded from the full nuclear charge.

91. **(M)** These ionization energies are the reverse of electron affinities, for example, the ionization energy, E_i, for Li^- is $-(-59.6$ kJ/mol$)$. The variations in these anions follow those seen in Figure 9-15.

92. **(M)** Ionization energy generally increases with Z for a given period (and decreases going to higher periods) with the exception of the small deviation observed going from N to O because N has a slightly more stable configuration for N where half of the orbitals are filled.

93. **(E)** Mg would have the more positive electron affinity, because Mg has the electron configuration [Ne]$3s^2$. Therefore, the added electron would need to occupy the higher energy level $3p$ orbitals, compared with Na (electron configuration = [Ne]$3s^1$), which has a partially filled $3s$ orbital that can accommodate another electron.

94. **(E)** The addition of an electron is usually exothermic because the electrons in the atom do not completely shield the incoming electron from the nuclear charge. Therefore, the incoming electron is attracted by the nucleus. The reverse process is easier to think about. Given a valence electron in an atom, energy (such as heat) must be expended to remove that electron.

95. **(E)** The answer is (a) atomic radius. Metallic elements tend to occur earlier in a period than nonmetals and have larger radii. Compared with nonmetal atoms, metal atoms have low ionization energies and low electron affinities.

96. **(E)** The answer is (c) Ge. On the periodic table, Ge falls on the boundary line between metals and nonmetals.

97. **(E)** The answer is (a) Mg^{2+}. When Mg loses two electrons, it has the same electron configuration as Ne. However, because Mg has two more protons in its nucleus, the effective nuclear charge experienced by the electrons is greater, which decreases the radius.

98. **(E)** The answer is (c) the outer-shell electron with the highest orbital quantum number. When an atom is ionized, it loses its electron(s) in the valence shell, which is the outer-most shell and has the highest energy electrons. The electrons in the valence shell with highest orbital quantum number have the highest energy. Hence, they are the first to be removed when the atom ionizes.

99. **(E)** The answer is (c) $4s$. The electron configuration of Fe is $1s^2 2s^2 2p^6 3s^2 3p^6 3d^6 4s^2$, whereas the electron configuration for Fe^{2+} is $1s^2 2s^2 2p^6 3s^2 3p^6 3d^6$.

100. **(M)** To construct a concept map, one must first start with the most general concepts. These concepts define and encompass other concepts discussed in those sections. In this chapter, the concept of periodicity of the elements is the overarching concept. There are two inter-related concepts that dominate periodicity: nuclear charge and electron configuration. Most other periodic properties can be derived from the combination of these two concepts. Two intermediary concepts derived from nuclear charge and electron configuration are electron penetration and screening (together, they form the concept of effective nuclear charge, Z_{eff}). From these concepts, we can derive trends in atomic, covalent, and ionic radii, electron affinity, and ionization energy. Directly coming from the electron configuration is the concept of magnetism. Take a look at the subsection headings and problems for more refining of the general and specific concepts.

CHAPTER 10
CHEMICAL BONDING I: BASIC CONCEPTS
PRACTICE EXAMPLES

1A **(E)** Mg is in group 2(2A), and thus has 2 valence electrons and 2 dots in its Lewis symbol. Ge is in group 14(4A), and thus has 4 valence electrons and 4 dots in its Lewis symbol. K is in group 1(1A), and thus has 1 valence electron and 1 dot in its Lewis symbol. Ne is in group 18(8A), and thus has 8 valence electrons and 8 dots in its Lewis symbol.

$$\cdot \text{Mg} \cdot \qquad \cdot \text{Ge} \cdot \qquad \text{K} \cdot \qquad : \text{Ne} :$$

1B **(E)** Sn is in Family 4A, and thus has 4 electrons and 4 dots in its Lewis symbol. Br is in Family 7A with 7 valence electrons. Adding an electron produces an ion with 8 valence electrons. Tl is in Family 3A with 3 valence electrons. Removing an electron produces a cation with 2 valence electrons.
S is in Family 6A with 6 valence electrons. Adding 2 electrons produces an anion with 8 valence electrons.

$$\cdot \text{Sn} \cdot \qquad [: \text{Br} :]^- \qquad [\cdot \text{Tl} \cdot]^+ \qquad [: \text{S} :]^{2-}$$

2A **(E)** The Lewis structures for the cation, the anion, and the compound follows the explanation.

(a) Na loses one electron to form Na^+, while S gains two to form S^{2-}.

$$\text{Na} \cdot - 1 e^- \rightarrow [\,\text{Na}\,]^+ \qquad \cdot \text{S} \cdot + 2e^- \rightarrow [: \text{S} :]^{2-} \quad \text{Lewis Structure: } [\text{Na}]^+ [: \text{S} :]^{2-} [\text{Na}]^+$$

(b) Mg loses two electrons to form Mg^{2+}, while N gains three to form N^{3-}.

$$\cdot \text{Mg} \cdot - 2 e^- \rightarrow [\,\text{Mg}\,]^{2+} \qquad \cdot \text{N} \cdot + 3e^- \rightarrow [: \text{N} :]^{3-}$$

$$\text{Lewis Structure: } [\text{Mg}]^{2+} [: \text{N} :]^{3-} [\text{Mg}]^{2+} [: \text{N} :]^{3-} [\text{Mg}]^{2+}$$

2B **(E)** Below each explanation are the Lewis structures for the cation, the anion, and the compound.

(a) In order to acquire a noble-gas electron configuration, Ca loses two electrons, and I gains one, forming the ions Ca^{2+} and I^-. The formula of the compound is CaI_2.

$$\cdot \text{Ca} \cdot - 2 e^- \rightarrow [\,\text{Ca}\,]^{2+} \qquad : \text{I} \cdot + e^- \rightarrow [: \text{I} :]^- \quad \text{Lewis Structure: } \quad [: \text{I} :]^- [\text{Ca}]^{2+} [: \text{I} :]^-$$

(b) Ba loses two electrons and S gains two to acquire a noble-gas electron configuration, forming the ions Ba^{2+} and S^{2-}. The formula of the compound is BaS.

$$\cdot \text{Ba} \cdot - 2 e^- \rightarrow [\,\text{Ba}\,]^{2+} \qquad \cdot \text{S} \cdot + 2e^- \rightarrow [: \text{S} :]^{2-} \quad \text{Lewis Structure: } \quad [\text{Ba}]^{2+} [: \text{S} :]^{2-}$$

(c) Each Li loses one electron and each O gains two to attain a noble-gas electron configuration, producing the ions Li^+ and O^{2-}. The formula of the compound is Li_2O.

$$\cdot \text{Li} - 1 e^- \rightarrow [\,\text{Li}\,]^+ \qquad \cdot \text{O} \cdot + 2e^- \rightarrow [: \text{O} :]^{2-} \quad \text{Lewis Structure:} [\text{Li}]^+ [: \text{O} :]^{2-} [\text{Li}]^+$$

3A   **(M)** In the Br_2 molecule, the two Br atoms are joined by a single covalent bond. This bonding arrangement gives each Br atom a closed valence shell configuration that is equivalent to that for a Kr atom.

$$: \ddot{Br} - \ddot{Br} :$$

In CH_4, the carbon atom is covalently bonded to four hydrogen atoms. This arrangement gives the carbon atom a valence shell octet and each H atom a valence shell duet.

$$\begin{matrix} & H & \\ & | & \\ H- & C & -H \\ & | & \\ & H & \end{matrix}$$

In HOCl, the hydrogen and chlorine atoms are attached to the central oxygen atom through single covalent bonds. This bonding arrangement provides each atom in the molecule with a closed valence shell.

$$H - \ddot{O} - \ddot{Cl}:$$

3B   **(M)** The Lewis structure for NI_3 is similar to that of NH_3. The central nitrogen atom is attached to each iodine atom by a single covalent bond. All of the atoms in this structure get a closed valence shell.

$$:\ddot{I} - \ddot{N} - \ddot{I}:$$
$$:\ddot{I}:$$

The Lewis diagram for N_2H_4 has each nitrogen with one lone pair of electrons, two covalent bonds to hydrogen atoms, and one covalent bond to the other nitrogen atom. With this arrangement, the nitrogen atoms complete their octets while the hydrogen atoms complete their duets.

$$\begin{matrix} & \ddot{~} & \ddot{~} & \\ H- & N & -N & -H \\ & | & | & \\ & H & H & \end{matrix}$$

In the Lewis structure for C_2H_6, each carbon atom shares four pairs of electrons with three hydrogen atoms and the other carbon atom. With this arrangement, the carbon atoms complete their octets while the hydrogen atoms complete their duets.

$$\begin{matrix} & H & H & \\ & | & | & \\ H- & C & -C & -H \\ & | & | & \\ & H & H & \end{matrix}$$

4A   **(E)** The bond with the most ionic character is the one in which the two bonded atoms are the most different in their electronegativities. We find electronegativities in Figure 10-6 and calculate ΔEN for each bond.
Electronegativities: H = 2.1   Br = 2.8   N = 3.0   O= 3.5   P = 2.1   Cl = 3.0

Bonds :	H—Br	N—H	N—O	P—Cl
ΔEN values :	0.7	0.9	0.5	0.9

Therefore, the N—H and P—Cl bonds are the most polar of the four bonds cited.

4B   **(E)** The most polar bond is the one with the greatest electronegativity difference.
Electronegativities: C = 2.5   S = 2.5   P = 2.1   O = 3.5   F = 4.0

Bonds:	C—S	C—P	P—O	O—F
ΔEN values:	0.0	0.4	1.4	0.5

Therefore, the P—O bond is the most polar of the four bonds cited.

5A **(E)** The electrostatic potential map that corresponds to IF is the one with the most red in it. This suggests polarization in the molecule. Specifically, the red region signifies a build-up of negative charge that one would expect with the very electronegative fluorine. The other electrostatic potential map corresponds to IBr. The electronegativities are similar, resulting in a relatively non-polar molecule (i.e., little in the way of charge build-up in the molecule).

5B **(E)** The electrostatic potential map that corresponds to CH_3OH is the one with the most red in it. This suggests polarization in the molecule. Specifically, the red region signifies a build-up of negative charge that one would expect with the very electronegative oxygen atom. The other electrostatic potential map corresponds to CH_3SH. The carbon and sulfur electronegativities are similar, resulting in a relatively non-polar molecule (i.e., little in the way of charge build-up in the molecule).

6A **(M)**

(a) C has 4 valence electrons and each S has 6 valence electrons: $4 + (2 \times 6) = 16$ valence electrons or 8 pairs of valence electrons. We place C between two S, and use two electron pairs to hold the molecule together, one between C and each S. We complete the octet on each S with three electron pairs for each S. This uses up six more electron pairs, for a total of eight electron pairs used. $:\overset{..}{\underset{..}{S}} - C - \overset{..}{\underset{..}{S}}:$ But C does not have an octet. We correct this situation by moving one lone pair from each S into a bonding position between C and S. $:\overset{..}{S} = C = \overset{..}{S}:$

(b) C has 4 valence electrons, N has 5 valence electrons and hydrogen has 1 valence electron: Total number of valence electrons = 4 + 5 + 1 = 10 valence electrons or 5 pairs of valence electrons. We place C between H and N, and use two electron pairs to hold the molecule together, one between C and N, as well as one between C and H. We complete the octet on N using three lone pairs. This uses up all five valence electron pairs ($H - C - \overset{..}{\underset{..}{N}}:$). But C does not yet have an octet. We correct this situation by moving two lone pairs from N into bonding position between C and N. $H - C \equiv N:$

(c) C has 4 valence electrons, each Cl has 7 valence electrons, and oxygen has 6 valence electrons: Thus, the total number of valence electrons = 4 + 2(7) + 6 = 24 valence electrons or 12 pairs of valence electrons. We choose C as the central atom, and use three electron pairs to hold the molecule together, one between C and O, as well as one between C and each Cl. We complete the octet on Cl and O using three lone pairs. This uses all twelve electron pairs. But C does not have an octet. We correct this situation by moving one lone pair from O into a bonding position between C and O.

$$:\overset{..}{\underset{..}{O}} - C(-\overset{..}{\underset{..}{Cl}}:)_2 \rightarrow :\overset{..}{O} = C(-\overset{..}{\underset{..}{Cl}}:)_2$$

6B   **(a)**

$$:\overset{\displaystyle :O:}{\underset{\displaystyle}{\parallel}}$$

H—C—Ö—H

(b)

H   :O:

H—C—C—H

H

7A   **(E)**

(a)   A plausible Lewis structure for the nitrosonium cation, NO^+, is drawn below:

$$:N{\equiv}\overset{\oplus}{O}:$$

The nitrogen atom is triply bonded to the oxygen atom and both atoms in the structure possess a lone pair of electrons. This gives each atom an octet and a positive formal charge appears on the oxygen atom.

(b)   A plausible Lewis structure for $N_2H_5^+$ is given below:

H H

H—$\overset{\oplus}{N}$—N:

H H

The two nitrogen atoms have each achieved an octet. The right hand side N atom is surrounded by three bonding pairs and one lone pair of electrons, while the left hand side N atom is surrounded by four bonding pairs of electrons. Each hydrogen atom has completed its duet by sharing a pair of electrons with a nitrogen atom. A formal 1+ charge has been assigned to the left hand side nitrogen atom because it is bonded to four atoms (one more than its usual number) in this structure.

(c)   In order to achieve a noble gas configuration, oxygen gains two electrons, forming the stable dianion. The Lewis structure for O^{2-} is shown below.

$$:\overset{..}{\underset{..}{O}}:\overset{(2-)}{}$$

7B   **(M)**

(a)   The most likely Lewis structure for BF_4^- is drawn below:

:F:

:F—$\overset{\ominus}{B}$—F:

:F:

Four bonding pairs of electrons surround the central boron atom in this structure. This arrangement gives the boron atom a complete octet and a formal charge of –1. By virtue of being surrounded by three lone pairs and one bonding electron pair, each fluorine achieves a full octet.

(b)   A plausible Lewis structural form for NH_3OH^+, the hydroxylammonium ion, has been provided below:

H

H—$\overset{\oplus}{N}$—Ö—H

H

By sharing bonding electron pairs with three hydrogen atoms and the oxygen atom, the nitrogen atom acquires a full octet and a formal charge of 1+. The oxygen atom shares one bonding electron pair with the nitrogen and a second bonding pair with a hydrogen atom.

(c) Three plausible resonance structures can be drawn for the isocyanate ion, NCO⁻. The nitrogen contributes five electrons, the carbon four, oxygen six, and one more electron is added to account for the negative charge, giving a total of 16 electrons or eight pairs of electrons. In the first resonance contributor, structure 1 below, the carbon atom is joined to the nitrogen and oxygen atoms by two double bonds, thereby creating an octet for carbon. To complete the octet of nitrogen and oxygen, each atom is given a lone pair of electrons. Since nitrogen is sharing just two bonding pairs of electrons in this structure, it must be assigned a formal charge of 1–. In structure 2, the carbon atom is again surrounded by four bonding pairs of electrons, but this time, the carbon atom forms a triple bond with oxygen and just a single bond with nitrogen. The octet for the nitrogen atom is closed with three lone pairs of electrons, while that for oxygen is closed with one lone pair of electrons. This bonding arrangement necessitates giving nitrogen a formal charge of 2– and the oxygen atom a formal charge of 1+. In structure 3, which is the dominant contributor because it has a negative formal charge on oxygen (the most electronegative element in the anion), the carbon achieves a full octet by forming a triple bond with the nitrogen atom and a single bond with the oxygen atom. The octet for oxygen is closed with three lone pairs of electrons, while that for nitrogen is closed with one lone pair of electrons.

$$:\ddot{N}{=}C{=}\ddot{O}: \qquad :\ddot{N}{-}C{\equiv}O: \qquad :N{\equiv}C{-}\ddot{O}:$$

Structure 1   Structure 2   Structure 3

8A **(M)** The total number of valence electrons in NOCl is 18 (5 from nitrogen, 6 from oxygen and 7 from chlorine). Four electrons are used to covalently link the central oxygen atom to the terminal chlorine and nitrogen atoms in the skeletal structure: N—O—Cl. Next, we need to distribute the remaining electrons to achieve a noble gas electron configuration for each atom. Since four electrons were used to form the two covalent single bonds, fourteen electrons remain to be distributed. By convention, the valence shells for the terminal atoms are filled first. If we follow this convention, we can close the valence shells for both the nitrogen and the chlorine atoms with twelve electrons.

$$:\ddot{N}{-}O{-}\ddot{\underset{..}{Cl}}:$$

Oxygen is moved closer to a complete octet by placing the remaining pair of electrons on oxygen as a lone pair.

$$:\ddot{N}{-}\ddot{O}{-}\ddot{\underset{..}{Cl}}:$$

The valence shell for the oxygen atom can then be closed by forming a double bond between the nitrogen atom and the oxygen atom.

$$:\ddot{N}{=}\ddot{O}{-}\ddot{\underset{..}{Cl}}:$$

380

This structure obeys the requirement that all of the atoms end up with a filled valence shell, but is much poorer than the one derived in Example 10-8 because it has a positive formal charge on oxygen, which is the most electronegative atom in the molecule. In other words, this structure can be rejected on the grounds that it does not conform to the third rule for determining plausibility of a Lewis structure based on formal charges, which states that "negative formal charges should appear on the most electronegative atom, while any positive formal charge should appear on the least electronegative atom."

8B **(D)** There are a total of sixteen valence electrons in the cyanamide molecule (five from each nitrogen atom, four from carbon and one electron from each hydrogen atom). The formula has been written as NH_2CN to remind us that carbon, the most electropositive p-block element in the compound, should be selected as the central atom in the skeletal structure.

$$H-N-C-N$$
$$|$$
$$H$$

To construct this skeletal structure we use 8 electrons. Eight electrons remain to be added to the structure. Note: each hydrogen atom at this stage has achieved a duet by forming a covalent bond with the nitrogen atom in the NH_2 group. The octet for the NH_2 nitrogen is completed by giving it a lone pair of electrons.

$$H-\ddot{N}-C-N$$
$$|$$
$$H$$

The remaining six electrons can then be given to the terminal nitrogen atom, affording structure 1, shown below. Alternatively, four electrons can be assigned to the terminal nitrogen atom and the last two electrons can be given to the central carbon atom, to produce structure 2 below:

$$H-\ddot{N}-C-\ddot{N}:\qquad\qquad H-\ddot{N}-\ddot{C}-\ddot{N}:$$
$$|\qquad\qquad\qquad\qquad\qquad |$$
$$H\qquad\qquad\qquad\qquad\qquad H$$

(Structure 1)   (Structure 2)

The octet for the carbon atom in structure 1 can be completed by converting two lone pairs of electrons on the terminal nitrogen atom into two more covalent bonds to the central carbon atom.

$$H-\ddot{N}-C\equiv N:$$
$$|$$
$$H$$

Structure 3

Each atom in structure 3 has a closed-shell electron configuration and a formal charge of zero. We can complete the octet for the carbon and nitrogen atoms in structure 1 by converting a lone pair of electrons on each nitrogen atom into a covalent bond to the central carbon atom.

$$H-\overset{\oplus}{N}=C=\overset{\ominus}{\ddot{N}}$$
$$|$$
$$H$$

Structure 4

The resulting structure has a formal charge of 1– on the terminal nitrogen atom and a 1+ formal charge on the NH_2 nitrogen atom. Although structures 3 and 4 both satisfy the octet and duet rules, structure 3 is the better of the two structures because it has no formal charges. A third structure which obeys the octet rule (depicted below), can be rejected on the grounds that it has formal charges of the same type (two 1+ formal charges) on adjacent atoms, as well as negative formal charges on carbon, which is not the most electronegative element in the molecule.

$$H{-}\overset{\oplus}{\underset{\underset{H}{|}}{N}}{=}\overset{\oplus}{N}{=}\overset{\cdot\cdot}{\underset{\cdot\cdot}{C}}{}^{\scriptsize\textcircled{\tiny -2}}$$

9A **(D)** The skeletal structure for SO_2 has two terminal oxygen atoms bonded to a central sulfur atom. Sulfur has been selected as the central atom by virtue of its being the most electropositive atom in the molecule. Two different Lewis structures of identical energy can be derived from the skeletal structure described above. First we determine that SO_2 has 18 valence electrons (6 from each atom). Four of the valence electrons must be used to covalently bond the three atoms together. The remaining 14 electrons are used to close the valence shell of each atom. Twelve electrons are used to give the terminal oxygen atoms a closed shell. The remaining two electrons (14 – 12 = 2) are placed on the sulfur atom, affording the structure depicted below:

$$:\overset{\cdot\cdot}{\underset{\cdot\cdot}{O}}{-}\overset{\cdot\cdot}{S}{-}\overset{\cdot\cdot}{\underset{\cdot\cdot}{O}}:$$

At this stage, the valence shells for the two oxygen atoms are closed, but the sulfur atom is two electrons short of a complete octet. If we complete the octet for sulfur by converting a lone pair of electrons on the right hand side oxygen atom into a sulfur-to-oxygen π-bond, we end up generating the resonance contributor (A) shown below:

$$:\overset{\cdot\cdot}{\underset{\cdot\cdot}{O}}{}^{\ominus}{-}\overset{\cdot\cdot}{\underset{\oplus}{S}}{=}\overset{\cdot\cdot}{O}: \quad \text{(A)}$$

Notice that the structure has a positive formal charge on the sulfur atom (most electropositive element) and a negative formal charge on the left-hand oxygen atom. Remember that oxygen is more electronegative than sulfur, so these charges are plausible.

The second completely equivalent contributor, (B), is produced by converting a lone pair on the left-most oxygen atom in the structure into a π-bond, resulting in conversion of a sulfur-oxygen single bond into a sulfur-oxygen double bond:

$$:\overset{\cdot\cdot}{O}{=}\overset{\cdot\cdot}{\underset{\oplus}{S}}{-}\overset{\cdot\cdot}{\underset{\cdot\cdot}{O}}{}^{\ominus}: \quad \text{(B)}$$

We obtain a third resonance structure from structure A or B by converting a lone pair on the singly bonded oxygen to a π bonding pair. In the resulting structure, the formal charges on the S and O atoms are all zero.

$$\overset{\cdot\cdot}{\underset{\cdot\cdot}{O}}{=}\overset{\cdot\cdot}{S}{=}\overset{\cdot\cdot}{\underset{\cdot\cdot}{O}}$$

The true structure of SO_2 is a resonance hybrid of three structures.

As a result, the sulfur–oxygen bond lengths in SO_2 are equal. (In the first structure, the two sulfur–oxygen bond lengths are the same, and the last two structures contribute equally.)

9B **(D)** The skeletal structure for the NO_3^- ion has three terminal oxygen atoms bonded to a central nitrogen atom. Nitrogen has been chosen as the central atom by virtue of being the most electropositive atom in the ion. It turns out that three contributing resonance structures of identical energy can be derived from the skeletal structure described here. We begin the process of generating these three structures by counting the total number of valence electrons in the NO_3^- anion. The nitrogen atom contributes five electrons, each oxygen contributes six electrons, and an additional electron must be added to account for the 1– charge on the ion. In total, we must account for 24 electrons. Six electrons are used to draw single covalent bonds between the nitrogen atom and three oxygen atoms. The remaining 18 electrons are used to complete the octet for the three terminal oxygen atoms:

At this stage the valence shells for the oxygen atoms are filled, but the nitrogen atom is two electrons short of a complete octet. If we complete the octet for nitrogen by converting a lone pair on O_1 into a nitrogen-to-oxygen π-bond, we end up generating resonance contributor (A):

Notice the structure has a 1+ formal charge on the nitrogen atom and a 1– on two of the oxygen atoms (O_2 and O_3). These formal charges are quite reasonable energetically. The second and third equivalent structures are generated similarly; by moving a lone pair from O_2 to form a nitrogen to oxygen (O_2) double bond, we end up generating resonance contributor (B), shown below. Likewise, by converting a lone pair from oxygen (O_3) into a π-bond with the nitrogen atom, we end up generating resonance contributor (C), also shown below.

None of these individual structures ((A), (B), or (C)) correctly represents the actual bonding in the nitrate anion. The actual structure, called the resonance hybrid, is the equally weighted average of all three structures (i.e. 1/3(A) + 1/3(B) + 1/3(C)):

These three resonance forms give bond lengths that are comparable to nitrogen- nitrogen double bonds.

10A **(E)** The Lewis structure of NCl_3 has three Cl atoms bonded to N and one lone pair attached to N. These four electron groups around N produce a tetrahedral electron-group geometry. The fact that one of the electron groups is a lone pair means that the molecular geometry is trigonal pyramidal.

10B **(E)** The Lewis structure of $POCl_3$ has three single P—Cl bonds and one P—O bond. These four electron groups around P produce a tetrahedral electron-group geometry. No lone pairs are attached to P and thus the molecular geometry is tetrahedral.

11A **(E)** The Lewis structure of COS has one S doubly-bonded to C and an O doubly-bonded to C. There are no lone pairs attached to C. The electron-group and molecular geometries are the same: linear. $:\!\ddot{S} = C = \ddot{O}\!:$. We can draw other resonance forms, however, the molecular geometry is unaffected.

11B **(E)** N is the central atom. $:\!N \equiv N — \ddot{O}\!:$ This gives an octet on each atom, a formal charge of 1+ on the central N, and a 1– on the O atom. There are two bonding pairs of electrons and no lone pairs on the central N atom. The N_2O molecule is linear. We can draw other resonance forms, however, the molecular geometry is unaffected.

12A **(E)** In the Lewis structure of methanol, each H atom contributes 1 valence electron, the C atom contributes 4, and the O atom contributes 6, for a total of $(4 \times 1) + 4 + 6 = 14$ valence electrons, or 7 electron pairs. 4 electron pairs are used to connect the H atoms to the C and the O, 1 electron pair is used to connect C to O, and the remaining 2 electron pairs are lone pairs on O, completing its octet.

$$
\begin{array}{c}
\text{H} \\
| \\
\text{H} - \text{C} - \ddot{\text{O}} - \text{H} \\
| \\
\text{H}
\end{array}
$$

The resulting molecule has two central atoms. Around the C there are four bonding pairs, resulting in a tetrahedral electron-group geometry and molecular geometry. The H—C—H bond angles are ~109.5°, as are the H—C—O bond angles. Around the O there are two bonding pairs of electrons and two lone pairs, resulting in a tetrahedral electron-group geometry and a bent molecular shape around the O atom, with a C—O—H bond angle of slightly less than 109.5°.

12B **(M)** The Lewis structure is drawn below. With four electron groups surrounding each, the electron-group geometries of N, the central C, and the right-hand O are all tetrahedral. The H—N—H bond angle and the H—N—C bond angles are almost the tetrahedral angle of 109.5°, made a bit smaller by the lone pair. The H—C—N angles, the H—C—H angle and the H—C—C angles all are very close to 109.5°. The C—O—H bond angle is made somewhat smaller than 109.5° by the presence of two lone pairs on O. Three electron groups surround the right-hand C, making its electron-group and molecular geometries trigonal planar. The O—C—O bond angle and the O—C—C bond angles all are very close to 120°.

$$
\begin{array}{c}
\quad\;\; \text{H} \quad \text{H} \quad \ddot{\text{O}} \\
\quad\;\; | \qquad | \qquad \| \\
\text{H} - \text{N} - \text{C} - \text{C} - \ddot{\text{O}} - \text{H} \\
\quad\;\; \ddot{\;} \qquad | \\
\qquad\qquad \text{H}
\end{array}
$$

13A **(M)** Lewis structures of the three molecules are drawn below. Around the S in the SF_6 molecule are six bonding pairs of electrons, and no lone pairs. The molecule is octahedral; each of the S-F bond moments is cancelled by one on the other side of the molecule.

SF_6 is nonpolar. The OF_2 molecule is bent; the bond dipoles do not cancel. OF_2 is polar. H_2O_2 is polar. Around each C in C_2H_4 are three bonding pairs of electrons; the molecule is planar around each C and planar overall. The polarity of each —CH_2 group is cancelled by the polarity of the other H_2C— group. C_2H_2 is nonpolar.

13B **(M)** Lewis structures of the four molecules are drawn below and we can consider the three C — H bonds and the one C — C bond to be nonpolar. The three C — Cl bonds are tetrahedrally oriented.

If there were a fourth C — Cl bond on the left-hand C, the bond dipoles would cancel out, producing a nonpolar molecule. Since it is not there, the molecule is polar. A similar argument is made for NH_3, where three tetrahedrally-oriented N — H polar bonds are not balanced by a fourth, and for CH_2Cl_2, where two tetrahedrally oriented C — Cl bonds are not balanced by two others. This leaves PCl_5 as the only nonpolar species; it is a highly symmetrical molecule in which individual bond dipoles cancel out.

14A **(M)** The Lewis structure of CH_3Br has all single bonds. From Table 10.2, the length of a C — H bond is 110 pm. The length of a C — Br bond is not given in the table. A reasonable value is the average of the C — C and Br — Br bond lengths.

$$C—Br = \frac{C—C + Br—Br}{2} = \frac{154 \text{ pm} + 228 \text{ pm}}{2} = 191 \text{ pm}$$

14B **(E)** In Table 10.2, the C=N bond length is 128 pm, while the C≡N bond length is 116 pm. The observed C—N bond length of 115 pm is much closer to a carbon-nitrogen triple bond. This can be explained by using the following Lewis structure: $:\ddot{S}- C \equiv N:$ where there is a formal negative charge on the sulfur atom. This molecule is linear according to VSEPR theory.

15A **(M)** We first draw Lewis structures for all of the molecules involved in the reaction.

$$2 \text{ H—H} + \ddot{O}=\ddot{O} \longrightarrow 2\text{H}-\ddot{O}-\text{H}$$

Break 1 O=O + 2H—H = 498 kJ/mol + (2 × 436 kJ/mol) = 1370 kJ/mol absorbed
Form 4H—O = (4 × 464 kJ/mol) = 1856 kJ/mol given off
Enthalpy change = 1370 kJ / mol − 1856 kJ / mol = −486 kJ / mol

15B **(M)** The chemical equation, with Lewis structures, is:

$$1/2 :N \equiv N: \quad + \quad 3/2 \text{ H—H} \quad \longrightarrow \quad \text{H}-\ddot{N}-\text{H}$$

Energy required to break bonds $= \frac{1}{2}N \equiv N + \frac{3}{2}H—H$

$= (0.5 \times 946 \text{ kJ / mol}) + (1.5 \times 436 \text{ kJ / mol}) = 1.13 \times 10^3 \text{ kJ / mol}$

Energy realized by forming bonds = 3 N — H = 3 × 389 kJ / mol = 1.17×10^3 kJ / mol

$\Delta_r H = 1.13 \times 10^3$ kJ/mol $- 1.17 \times 10^3$ kJ/mol $= -4 \times 10^1$ kJ/mol of NH_3.

Thus, $\Delta_f H = -4 \times 10^1$ kJ/mol NH_3 (Appendix D value is $\Delta_f H = -46.11$ kJ/mol NH_3)

16A **(M)** The reaction below,

$$CH_3(C=O)CH_3(g) + H_2(g) \rightarrow (CH_3)_2 CH(OH)(g)$$

Involves the following bond breakages and formations:
Broken: 1 C=O bond (736 kJ/mol)
Broken: 1 H–H bond (436 kJ/mol)
Formed: 1 C–O bond (360 kJ/mol)
Formed: 1 C–H bond (414 kJ/mol)
Formed: 1 O–H bond (464 kJ/mol)

Therefore, the energy of the reaction is:
$$\Delta_r H = \Delta H(\text{bond breakage}) + \Delta_r H(\text{bond formation})$$
$$\Delta_r H = \left[(1 \times 736) + (1 \times 436)\right] + \left[(1 \times -360) + (1 \times -414) + (1 \times -464)\right]$$
$$\Delta_r H = -66 \text{ kJ/mol}$$
Therefore, the reaction is exothermic.

16B **(E)** First we will double the chemical equation, and represent it in terms of Lewis structures:

$$2 \text{ H–O–H } + 2 \text{ :Cl–Cl: } \rightarrow \text{ O=O } + 4 \text{ H–Cl:}$$

Energy required to break bonds $= 2 \text{ Cl—Cl} + 4\text{H—O}$
$$= (2 \times 243 \text{ kJ/mol}) + (4 \times 464 \text{ kJ/mol}) = 2342 \text{ kJ/mol}$$

Energy realized by forming bonds $= 1 \text{ O}=\text{O} + 4 \times \text{ H—Cl}$
$$= 498 \text{ kJ/mol} + (4 \times 431 \text{ kJ/mol}) = 2222 \text{ kJ/mol}$$

$$\Delta H = \tfrac{1}{2}(2342 \text{ kJ/mol} - 2222 \text{ kJ/mol}) = +60 \text{ kJ/mol}; \text{ The reaction is endothermic.}$$

Important Note: In this and subsequent chapters, a lone pair of electrons in a Lewis structure can be shown as a line or a pair of dots. Thus, the Lewis structure of Be is both Be| and Be:.

INTEGRATIVE EXAMPLE

A. **(M)** The reaction is as follows: $PCl_3 + Cl_2 \rightarrow PCl_5$
$$\Delta_r H = \sum \Delta H_{\text{prod}} - \sum \Delta H_{\text{react}}$$
$$\Delta_r H = (-374.9) - (-287.0 + 0) = -87.9 \text{ kJ/mol}$$
To determine the P–Cl bond energy, we must first deduce the Cl–Cl bond energy:
$$2Cl \rightarrow Cl_2 \quad \Delta_r H = 0 - 2(121.7) = -243 \text{ kJ/mol, which is in reasonable agreement with}$$
Table 10-3.

Using the above information, we can determine the P–Cl bond energy:

$\Delta_r H = \Delta_r H(\text{bond breakage}) + \Delta_r H(\text{bond formation})$

$\Delta_r H = 1\,\text{Cl} - \text{Cl (broken)} + 2\,\text{P} - \text{Cl (formed)}$

$-87.9 = 243 + 2\,\text{P} - \text{Cl}$

$\text{P} - \text{Cl} = -165.5\;\text{kJ/mol}$

The Lewis structures of PCl_3 and PCl_5 are shown below.

Since the geometries of the two molecules differ, the orbital overlap between P and the surrounding Cl atoms will be different and therefore the P–Cl bonds in these two compounds will also be slightly different.

B. (M)

(a) The structures are shown below, with appropriate geometries:

Formamide

Formaldoxime

$\sum BE\,(H_2NCOH) = 2(N-H) + 1(N-C) + 1(C=O) + 1(C-H)$

$= 2(389) + 305 + 736 + 414 = 2233\;\text{kJ/mol}$

$\sum BE\,(H_2C=N-OH) = 2(C-H) + 1(C=N) + 1(N-O) + 1(O-H)$

$= 2(414) + 615 + 222 + 464 = 2129\;\text{kJ/mol}$

Since BE of formamide is greater than that of formaldoxime, it is more stable, and its conversion endothermic.

(b) The experiment shows that the geometry around C is trigonal planar, and around N is trigonal pyramidal.

EXERCISES

Lewis Theory

<u>**1.**</u>   **(E)**

   (a) $:\overset{\cdot\cdot}{\underset{\cdot\cdot}{Kr}}:$ **(b)** $\cdot\overset{\cdot}{\underset{\cdot}{Ge}}\cdot$ **(c)** $\cdot\overset{\cdot}{\underset{\cdot}{N}}:$ **(d)** $\cdot\overset{\cdot}{Ga}$ **(e)** $\cdot\overset{\cdot}{\underset{\cdot}{As}}:$ **(f)** $Rb\cdot$

2.   **(E)**

   (a) $\left[H: \right]^-$ **(b)** $\left[\cdot Sn \cdot \right]^{2+}$ **(c)** $\left[K \right]^+$ **(d)** $\left[:\overset{\cdot\cdot}{\underset{\cdot\cdot}{Br}}: \right]^-$ **(e)** $\left[:\overset{\cdot\cdot}{\underset{\cdot\cdot}{Se}}: \right]^{2-}$ **(f)** $\left[Sc \right]^{3+}$

<u>**3.**</u>   **(E)**
   (a)   **(b)**   **(c)**

   (d)   **(e)**

4.   **(E)** For simplicity, the 3 lone pairs on halogens are not shown in the structures below. Add 6 electrons per halogen atom.

   (a)   **(b)**   **(c)**

   $H-C\equiv N:$

   (d)   **(e)**   **(f)**

<u>**5.**</u>   **(E)**

   (a) $Cs^{\oplus} \ :\overset{\cdot\cdot}{\underset{\cdot\cdot}{Br}}:^{\ominus}$ CsBr, cesium bromide **(b)**

H_3Sb , hydrogen antimonide or trihydrogen antimonide

(c) :Cl̈—B—Cl̈: BCl_3, boron trichloride   **(d)** $Cs^{\oplus}$:Cl̈:$^{\ominus}$ CsCl, cesium chloride

(e) $Li^{\oplus}$:Ö:$^{\textcircled{2-}}$ $Li^{\oplus}$ Li_2O, lithium oxide   **(f)** :Ï—Cl̈: ICl, iodine monochloride

6. **(E)** $B(OH)_3$, SiF_6^{2-}, SO_3, PO_4^{3-}, ClO_2, and $SO(CH_3)_2$ do not follow the octet rule. For simplicity, where possible, the 3 lone pairs on halogens are not shown in the structures below.

7. **(M)**

NH_3 $5+(3\times1)=8$ v.e.$=4$ pairs BF_3 $3+(3\times7)=24$ v.e.$=12$ pairs

SF_6 $6+(6\times7)=48$ v.e.$=24$ pairs SO_3 $6+(3\times6)=24$ v.e.$=12$ pairs

NH_4^+ $5+(4\times1)-1=8$ v.e.$=4$ pairs SO_4^{2-} $6+(4\times6)+2=32$ v.e.$=16$ pairs

NO_2 $5+(2\times6)=17$ v.e.$=8.5$ pairs

NO_2 cannot obey the octet rule; there is no way to pair all electrons when the number of electrons is odd.

All of these Lewis structures obey the octet rule except for BF_3, which is electron deficient, and SF_6, which has an expanded octet.

8. **(M)**

(a) In order to construct an H_3 molecule, one H would have to bridge the other two. This would place 3 electrons around the central H atom, which is more than the stable pair found around H in most Lewis structures. As well, one bond would be the normal 2 e⁻ bond and the other would be a one electron bond, which is beyond Lewis theory (i.e., H–H · H).

(b) In HHe there would be three electrons between the two atoms, or three electrons around the He atom, one of which would be a nonbonding electron. Neither of these is a particularly stable situation.

(c) He$_2$ would have either a double bond between two He atoms and thus four electrons around each He atom, or three electrons around each He atom (2 e$^-$ in a bond and an unpaired electron on each atom). Neither situation achieves the electron configuration of a noble gas.

(d) H$_3$O has an expanded octet (9 electrons) on oxygen; expanded octets are not possible for elements in the second period. Other structures place a multiple bond between O and H. Both situations are unstable.

$$H-\overset{\overset{\displaystyle H}{|}}{\underset{\cdot\cdot}{O}}-H$$

9. **(E)**

(a) $H-H-\overset{\cdot\cdot}{\underset{\cdot\cdot}{N}}-\overset{\cdot\cdot}{\underset{\cdot\cdot}{O}}-H$ has two bonds to (four electrons around) the second hydrogen, and only six electrons around the nitrogen. A better Lewis structure is shown below.

$$H-\overset{\overset{\displaystyle H}{|}}{\underset{\cdot\cdot}{N}}-\overset{\cdot\cdot}{\underset{\cdot\cdot}{O}}-H$$

(b) Here, $Ca-\overset{\cdot\cdot}{\underset{\cdot\cdot}{O}}:$ is improperly written as a covalent Lewis structure. CaO is actually an ionic compound. $[Ca]^{2+} \left[:\overset{\cdot\cdot}{\underset{\cdot\cdot}{O}}:\right]^{2-}$ is a more plausible Lewis structure for CaO.

10. **(E)**

(a) $:\overset{\cdot\cdot}{\underset{\cdot\cdot}{O}}-\overset{\cdot\cdot}{\underset{\cdot\cdot}{Cl}}-\overset{\cdot\cdot}{\underset{\cdot\cdot}{O}}:$ has 20 valence electrons, whereas the molecule ClO$_2$ has 19 valence electrons. This is a proper Lewis structure for the chlorite ion, although the brackets and the minus charge are missing. A plausible Lewis structure for the molecule ClO$_2$ is $:\overset{\cdot\cdot}{\underset{\cdot\cdot}{O}}-\overset{\cdot}{\underset{\cdot\cdot}{Cl}}-\overset{\cdot\cdot}{\underset{\cdot\cdot}{O}}:$

(b) $\left[\cdot\overset{\cdot}{C}=\overset{\cdot\cdot}{\underset{\cdot\cdot}{N}}\right]^-$ has only six electrons around the C atom and two too few overall.

$\left[:C\equiv N:\right]^-$ is a more plausible Lewis structure for the cyanide ion.

11. **(M)** The answer is (c), hypochlorite ion. The flaws with the other answers are as follows:

(a) $\ominus:\overset{\cdot\cdot}{\underset{\cdot\cdot}{O}}-\overset{\oplus}{C}=\overset{\cdot\cdot}{\underset{\cdot\cdot}{N}}\ominus$ – does not have an octet of electrons around C.

(b) $[C=C:]^-$ does not have an octet around either C. Moreover, it has only 6 valence electrons in total while it should have 10, and finally, the sum of the formal charges on the two carbons doesn't equal the charge on the ion.

(d) The total number of valence electrons in NO is incorrect. No, being an odd-electron species should have 11 valence electrons, not 12.

12. **(M)**

(a) $Mg-\overset{..}{\underset{..}{O}}:$ is incorrectly written as a covalent structure. One expects an ionic Lewis structure, namely $[Mg]^{2+}[:\overset{..}{\underset{..}{O}}:]^{2-}$

(b) $[:\overset{..}{\underset{..}{O}}-\overset{.}{N}=\overset{..}{\underset{..}{O}}]^+$ has too many valence electrons—8.5 electron pairs or 17 valence electrons—it should have $(2\times6)+5-1=16$ valence electrons or 8 electron pairs. A a plausible Lewis structure is $[\overset{..}{\underset{..}{O}}=N=\overset{..}{\underset{..}{O}}]^{2+}$, which has 1+ formal charge on N and 0 formal charge of zero on each oxygen.

(c) $[\overset{..}{\underset{..}{Cl}}:]^+[:\overset{..}{\underset{..}{O}}:]^{2-}[:\overset{..}{\underset{..}{Cl}}]^+$ is written as an ionic structure, even though we expect a covalent structure between nonmetallic atoms. A more plausible structure is $:\overset{..}{\underset{..}{Cl}}-\overset{..}{\underset{..}{O}}-\overset{..}{\underset{..}{Cl}}:$

(d) In the structure $[\overset{..}{\underset{..}{S}}-C=\overset{..}{N}]^-$ neither S nor C possesses an octet of electrons. In addition, there are only 7 pairs of valence electrons in this structure or 14 valence electrons. There should be $6+4+5+1=16$ valence electrons, or 8 electron pairs. Two structures are possible. $\overset{..}{\underset{..}{S}}=C=\overset{..}{\underset{..}{N}}$ has a formal charge of 1– on N and is preferred over $:\overset{..}{\underset{..}{S}}-C\equiv N:$, with its formal charge of 1– on S, which is less electronegative than N.

Ionic Bonding

<u>**13.**</u> **(E)**

(a) $[:\overset{..}{\underset{..}{Cl}}:]^-[Ca]^{2+}[:\overset{..}{\underset{..}{Cl}}:]^-$ (b) $[Ba]^{2+}[:\overset{..}{\underset{..}{S}}:]^{2-}$ (c) $[Li]^+[:\overset{..}{\underset{..}{O}}:]^{2-}[Li]^+$ (d) $[Na]^+[:\overset{..}{\underset{..}{F}}:]^-$

14. **(E)** The Lewis symbols are $[H:]^-$ for the hydride ion, $[:\overset{..}{\underset{..}{N}}:]^{3-}$ for the nitride ion.

(a) $[Li]^+[H:]^-$
Lithium hydride

(b) $[H:]^-[Ca]^{2+}[H:]^-$
Calcium hydride

(c) $\left[Mg\right]^{2+}\left[:\overset{..}{\underset{..}{N}}:\right]^{3-}\left[Mg\right]^{2+}\left[:\overset{..}{\underset{..}{N}}:\right]^{3-}\left[Mg\right]^{2+}$
Magnesium nitride

<u>**15.**</u> **(E)**

(a) $[Li]^+[:\overset{..}{\underset{..}{S}}:]^{2-}[Li]^+ : Li_2S$

(b) $[Na]^+[:\overset{..}{\underset{..}{F}}:]^- : NaF$

(c) $[:\overset{..}{\underset{..}{I}}:]^-[Ca]^{2+}[:\overset{..}{\underset{..}{I}}:]^- : CaI_2$

(d) $[:\overset{..}{\underset{..}{Cl}}:]^-$
$[:\overset{..}{\underset{..}{Cl}}:]^-[Sc]^{3+}[:\overset{..}{\underset{..}{Cl}}:]^-$ $: ScCl_3$

16. (M)

(a)

Al^{3+} 3 [:Ö—H]⁻

(b)

Ca^{2+} 2 [:C≡N:]⁻

(c)

$$\begin{bmatrix} \quad H \quad \\ H—N\cdots\backslash\!\backslash\!\backslash H \\ \quad H \quad \end{bmatrix}^{+} \quad F^{-}$$

(d)

$$K^{+} \quad \begin{bmatrix} \quad :\ddot{O}: \quad \\ :\ddot{O}=Cl=\ddot{O}: \end{bmatrix}^{-}$$

(e)

$$3\ Ba^{2+} \quad 2 \quad \begin{bmatrix} \quad :\ddot{O}: \quad \\ :\ddot{O}—P\cdots\backslash\!\backslash\!\backslash \ddot{O}: \\ \quad :\ddot{O}: \quad \end{bmatrix}^{3-}$$

Formal Charge

17. (M)

(a) computations for:

	H—	—C≡	≡C
no. valence e⁻	1	4	4
− no. lone-pair e⁻	−0	−0	−2
− ½ no. bond-pair e⁻	−1	−4	−3
formal charge	0	0	−1

(b) computations for:

	=O	—O(×2)	C
no. valence e⁻	6	6	4
− no. lone-pair e⁻	−4	−6	−0
− ½ no. bond-pair e⁻	−2	−1	−4
formal charge	−0	−1	0

(c) computations for:

	—H(×7)	side C(×2)	central C
no. valence e⁻	1	4	4
− no. lone-pair e⁻	−0	−0	−0
− ½ no. bond-pair e⁻	−1	−4	−3
formal charge	0	0	+1

18. **(M)**

   (a) The formal charge on each I is 0,

      computed as follows:

      no. valence $e^- = 7$

      $-$no. lone-pair $e^- = -6$

      $-\frac{1}{2}$ no. bond-pair $e^- = \underline{-1}$

      formal charge $= 0$

   (b) computations for:

	=O	—O	=S—
no. valence e^-	6	6	6
$-$ no. lone-pair e^-	-4	-6	-2
$-\frac{1}{2}$ no. bond-pair e^-	$\underline{-2}$	$\underline{-1}$	$\underline{-3}$
formal charge	0	-1	$+1$

   (c) computations for:

	=O	—O	=N—
no. valence e^-	6	6	5
$-$ no. lone-pair e^-	-4	-6	-1
$-\frac{1}{2}$ no. bond-pair e^-	$\underline{-2}$	$\underline{-1}$	$\underline{-3}$
formal charge	0	-1	$+1$

19. **(M)** There are three features common to formal charge and oxidation state. First, both indicate how the bonding electrons are distributed in the molecule. Second, negative formal charge (in the most plausible Lewis structure) and negative oxidation state are generally assigned to the more electronegative atoms. And third, both numbers are determined by a set of rules, rather than being determined experimentally. Bear in mind, however, that there are also significant differences. For instance, there are cases where atoms of the same type with the same oxidation state have different formal charges, such as oxygen in ozone, O_3. Another is that formal charges are used to decide between alternative Lewis structures, while oxidation state is used in balancing equations and naming compounds. Also, the oxidation state in a compound is invariant, while the formal charge can change. The most significant difference, though, is that whereas the oxidation state of an element in its compounds is usually not zero, its formal charge usually is.

20. **(M)** The most common instance in which formal charge is not kept to a minimum occurs in the case of ionic compounds. For example, in $Mg\!-\!\ddot{O}\!:$ the formal charge on Mg is 1+ and on O it is 1^-, while in the ionic version $[Mg]^{2+}$ $[:\!\ddot{O}\!:]^{2-}$, formal charges are 2+ and 2^-, respectively. Additionally, in some resonance hybrids, formal charge is not minimized. In order to have bond lengths agree with experimental results, it may not be acceptable to create multiple bonds. Yet a third instance is when double bonds are created to lower formal charge, particularly when this results in the octet rule being violated. For instance, all the $Cl\!-\!O$ bonds in ClO_4^- are best represented using single bonds. Although including some double bonds would minimize formal charges, the resulting structure is less desirable because the octet for Cl has been exceeded and this requires the input of additional energy.

21. **(E)** FC = # valence e⁻ in free atom – number lone-pair e⁻ – ½ # bond pair e⁻
(a) Central O in O_3: 6 – 2 – 3 = +1
(b) Al in AlH_4^- : 3 – 0 – 4 = –1
(c) Cl in ClO_3^- : 7 – 2 – 5 = 0
(d) Si in SiF_6^{2-} : 4 – 0 – 6 = –2
(e) Cl in ClF_3 : 7 – 4 – 3 = 0

22. **(M)**
(a) H_2NOH is favored because opposite charges don't reside adjacent to each other.

FC(N) = 5 – 2 – 3 = 0   FC(N) = 5 – 4 – 2 = –1
FC(O) = 6 – 4 – 2 = 0   FC(O) = 6 – 2 – 3 = +1

(b) S=C=S is favored, because FC on everything is zero.

FC(C) = 4 – 0 – 4 = 0   FC(C) = 4 – 4 – 2 = –2
FC(S) = 6 – 4 – 2 = 0   FC(=S=) = 6 – 0 – 4 = +2;
                               FC(=S) = 6 – 4 – 2 = 0

(c) F–N=O is favored.

0   1+   –1   0   0   0

:N—F—O: :F—N=O:

(d) $OSCl_2$ is favored. Even though the formal charges of all elements on both $OSCl_2$ and OCl_2S are zero, $OSCl_2$ represents a much more realistic structure because the O and Cl atoms are in their normal bonding configuration.

(e) F_3SN is favored.

395

23. **(M)** We begin by counting the total number of valence electrons that must appear in the Lewis structure of the ion CO_2H^+: one from hydrogen, four from carbon, and six from each of the two oxygen (12 in all from the oxygen atoms). One electron is lost to establish the 1+ charge on the ion. In all, sixteen electrons are in the valence shell of the cation. If the usual rules for constructing valid Lewis structures are applied to HCO_2^+, we come up with the following structures:

In structure (A), the internal oxygen atom caries the positive charge, while in structure (B), the positive charge is located on the terminal oxygen atom. A third structure can also be drawn, however, due to an unacceptably large charge build-up, this form can be neglected. Thus, in this case of A and B, we cannot use the concept of formal charge to pick one structure over the other because the positive formal charge in both structures is located on the same type of atom, namely, an oxygen atom. In other words, based on formal charge rules alone, we must conclude that structures (A) and (B) are equally plausible.

24. **(M)** The intention of this question is to make the student aware of the fact that on occasion, one can obtain a better Lewis structure *"from the standpoint of formal charge minimization"* by using chain-like structures rather than the expected compact, symmetrical structures. The two linear Lewis structures for the ClO_4^- (I) and (II) and a compact structure (III) are shown below:

All of these structures have the required 32 valence electrons. Structure I has only one formal charge, 1– on the terminal oxygen atom. Structure II has a total of three formal charges, 1– on each of the terminal oxygen atoms and 1+ on the central chlorine atom. The compact structure, structure III, has formal charges on all of the atoms, 1– on all oxygen atoms and a formal charge of 3+ on the central chlorine atom. From the standpoint of minimizing formal charge, structure I would be deemed the most appropriate. Nevertheless, structure III is the one that is actually adopted by the ClO_4^- ion, despite the fact that better minimization is achieved with the linear structure. By using an expanded valence shell with 14 electrons for the central atom, as in structure IV below, one can achieve the same minimum set of formal charges as in structure I:

The chlorine atom presumably uses available $3d$ orbitals to accommodate the six additional electrons in its valence shell. Structure IV would appear to be the best structure yet, because it has the minimum number of formal charges and is close to the true shape seen in the ClO_4^- ion. In light of recent quantum mechanical calculations, however, many chemists now believe that d-orbital involvement in expanded octets should only be invoked when there is no way to avoid them, as in PCl_5 or SF_6. This means that whenever possible, octet structures should be used, even though at times they afford unsettlingly large formal charges. Thus, structure III is now considered by most chemists as being superior to structure IV.

Lewis Structures

25. **(E)**

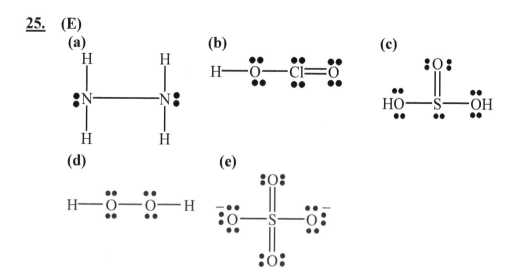

26. **(M)** The total valence electrons for C_2O_4 (a neutral molecule) are $(4 \times 6) + (2 \times 4) = 32$, or 16 electron pairs. Assuming a conventional maximum of 2 lone electron pairs and 2 bonds for each O, 16 electrons are used as lone pairs, leaving 16 electrons left for bonding.

27. **(M)**

(a) The total number of valence electrons in SO_3^{2-} is $6 + (3 \times 6) + 2 = 26$, or 13 electron pairs. A plausible Lewis structure is:

(b) The total number of valence electrons in NO_2^- is $5+(2\times6)+1=18$, or 9 electron pairs. There are two resonance forms for the nitrite ion:

$$\overset{\ominus}{\overset{\bullet\bullet}{\underset{\bullet\bullet}{O}}}-\overset{\bullet\bullet}{N}=\overset{\bullet\bullet}{\underset{\bullet\bullet}{O}} \longleftrightarrow \overset{\bullet\bullet}{\underset{\bullet\bullet}{O}}=\overset{\bullet\bullet}{N}-\overset{\bullet\bullet}{\underset{\bullet\bullet}{O}}\overset{\ominus}{}$$

(c) The total number of valence electrons in CO_3^{2-} is $4+(3\times6)+2=24$, or 12 electron pairs. There are three resonance forms for the carbonate ion:

(d) The total number of valence electrons in HO_2^- is $1+(2\times6)+1=14$, or 7 electron pairs. A plausible Lewis structure is $H-\overset{\bullet\bullet}{\underset{\bullet\bullet}{O}}-\overset{\bullet\bullet}{\underset{\bullet\bullet}{O}}\overset{\ominus}{}$

28. **(M)** Each of the cations has an empty valence shell as the result of ionization. The main task is to determine the Lewis structure of each anion.

(a) The total number of valence electrons in OH^- is $6+1+1=8$, or 4 electron pairs. A plausible Lewis structure for barium hydroxide is $[:\overset{\bullet\bullet}{\underset{\bullet\bullet}{O}}-H]^-[Ba]^{2+}[:\overset{\bullet\bullet}{\underset{\bullet\bullet}{O}}-H]^-$

(b) The total number of valence electrons in NO_2^- is $5+(2\times6)+1=18$, or 9 electron pairs. A plausible Lewis structure for sodium nitrite is

$$[Na]^+[:\overset{\bullet\bullet}{\underset{\bullet\bullet}{O}}-\overset{\bullet\bullet}{N}=\overset{\bullet\bullet}{\underset{\bullet\bullet}{O}}]^- \longleftrightarrow [Na]^+[\overset{\bullet\bullet}{\underset{\bullet\bullet}{O}}=\overset{\bullet\bullet}{N}-\overset{\bullet\bullet}{\underset{\bullet\bullet}{O}}:]^-$$

(c) The total number of valence electrons in IO_3^- is $7+(3\times6)+1=26$, or 13 electron pairs. A plausible Lewis structure for magnesium iodate is

(d) The total number of valence electrons in SO_4^{2-} is $6+(4\times6)+2=32$, or 16 electron pairs. A plausible structure for aluminum sulfate is $[SO_4]^{2-}[Al]^{3+}[SO_4]^{2-}[Al]^{3+}[SO_4]^{2-}$. Because of the ability of S to expand its octet, SO_4^{2-} has several resonance forms, a few of which are:

The first structure, without S expanded octet, is preferred.

29. **(M)** In $CH_3CHCHCHO$ there are $(4 \times 4) + (6 \times 1) + 6 = 28$ valence electrons, or 14 electron pairs. We expect that the carbon atoms bond to each other. A plausible Lewis structure is:

$$
\begin{array}{c}
\text{H} \quad \text{H} \quad \text{H} \quad :\!\overset{\displaystyle ..}{\text{O}}\!: \\
\mid \qquad \mid \qquad \mid \qquad \|\! \\
\text{H}\!-\!\overset{\displaystyle \mid}{\underset{\displaystyle \mid}{\text{C}}}\!-\!\text{C}\!=\!\text{C}\!-\!\text{C}\!-\!\text{H} \\
\mid \\
\text{H}
\end{array}
$$

30. **(E)** In C_3O_2 there are $(3 \times 4) + (2 \times 6) = 24$ valence electrons or 12 valence electron pairs.

A plausible Lewis structure follows: $\overset{..}{\underset{..}{\text{O}}}=C=C=C=\overset{..}{\underset{..}{\text{O}}}$

31.
(E)

(a)

$$
\begin{array}{c}
:\!\overset{\displaystyle ..}{\text{O}}\!: \\
\|\! \\
\text{H}\!-\!\text{C}\!-\!\text{H}
\end{array}
$$

(b)

$$
\begin{array}{c}
\text{H} \quad :\!\overset{\displaystyle ..}{\text{Cl}}\!: \quad \text{H} \\
\mid \qquad \mid \qquad \mid \\
\text{H}\!-\!\text{C}\!-\!\text{C}\!-\!\text{C}\!-\!\overset{..}{\underset{..}{\text{O}}}\!-\!\text{H} \\
\mid \qquad \mid \qquad \mid \\
\text{H} \quad \text{H} \quad \text{H}
\end{array}
$$

32.
(E)

(a)

$$
\begin{array}{c}
\text{H} \quad \text{H} \quad :\!\overset{\displaystyle ..}{\text{O}}\!: \\
\mid \qquad \mid \qquad \|\! \\
\text{H}\!-\!\text{C}\!-\!\text{C}\!-\!\text{C}\!-\!\text{H} \\
\mid \qquad \mid \\
\text{H} \quad \text{H}
\end{array}
$$

(b)

$$
\begin{array}{c}
\text{H} \qquad \text{H} \quad \text{H} \\
\mid \qquad \qquad \mid \qquad \mid \\
\text{H}\!-\!\text{C}\!-\!\overset{..}{\underset{..}{\text{O}}}\!-\!\text{C}\!-\!\text{C}\!-\!\text{H} \\
\mid \qquad \qquad \mid \qquad \mid \\
\text{H} \qquad \qquad \text{H} \quad \text{H}
\end{array}
$$

33.
(E)

(a)

$$
\begin{array}{c}
\text{H} \quad :\!\overset{\displaystyle ..}{\text{O}}\!: \\
\mid \qquad \|\! \\
:\!\overset{..}{\underset{..}{\text{Cl}}}\!-\!\text{C}\!-\!\text{C}\!-\!\overset{..}{\underset{..}{\text{O}}}\!-\!\text{H} \\
\mid \\
\text{H}
\end{array}
$$

(b)

$$
\begin{array}{c}
\text{H} \quad \text{H} \quad :\!\overset{\displaystyle ..}{\text{O}}\!: \\
\mid \qquad \mid \qquad \|\! \\
\text{H}\!-\!\overset{..}{\underset{..}{\text{O}}}\!-\!\text{C}\!-\!\text{C}\!-\!\text{C}\!-\!\overset{..}{\underset{..}{\text{O}}}\!-\!\text{H} \\
\mid \qquad \mid \\
\text{H} \quad \text{H}
\end{array}
$$

34. **(E)**

(a)

$$
\begin{array}{c}
\text{H} \quad \text{H} \quad \overset{\displaystyle ..}{\underset{\displaystyle ..}{\text{O}}} \quad \text{H} \\
\mid \qquad \mid \qquad \|\! \qquad \mid \\
\text{H}\!-\!\text{C}\!-\!\text{C}\!-\!\text{C}\!-\!\text{C}\!-\!\text{H} \\
\mid \qquad \mid \qquad \qquad \mid \\
\text{H} \quad \text{H} \qquad \quad \text{H}
\end{array}
$$

(b)

$$
\begin{array}{c}
\text{H} \quad \text{H} \quad \text{H} \\
\mid \qquad \mid \qquad \mid \\
:\!\overset{..}{\underset{..}{\text{Cl}}}\!-\!\text{C}\!-\!\text{C}\!-\!\text{N}\!-\!\text{H} \\
\mid \qquad \mid \qquad \overset{..}{} \\
\text{H} \quad \text{H}
\end{array}
$$

35. **(M)**
(a) Group 16

(b) Group 16 except oxygen

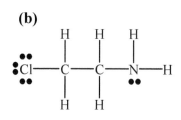

(c) Group 17 except fluorine

(d) Group 13

36. **(M)**

  (a) Group 14

  (b) Group 16 except oxygen

(c) Group 17 except fluorine

(d) Group 13

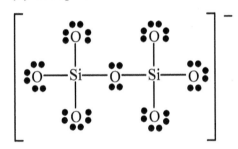

Polar Covalent Bonds and Electrostatic Potential Maps

37. **(M)** Na — Cl and K — F both possess bonds between a metal and a nonmetal. Thus, they have the largest ionic character, with the ionic character of K — F being greater than that of Na — Cl, both because K is more metallic (closer to the lower left of the periodic table) than Na and because F is more nonmetallic (closer to the upper right) than Cl. The remaining three bonds are covalent bonds to H. Since H and C have about the same electronegativity (a fact you need to memorize), the H — C bond is the most covalent (or the least ionic). Br is somewhat more electronegative than is C, while F is considerably more electronegative than C, making the F — H bond the most polar of the three covalent bonds. Thus, ranked in order of increasing ionic character, these five bonds are:

C — H < Br — H < F — H < Na — Cl < K — F

The actual electronegativity differences follow:

$C(2.5) - H(2.1) < Br(2.8) - H(2.1) < F(4.0) - H(2.1) < Na(0.9) - Cl(3.0) < K(0.8) - F(4.0)$
$\Delta EN = 0.4 = 0.7 = 1.9 = 2.1 = 3.2$

38. **(M)**

  (a) F_2 cannot possess a dipole moment, since both of the atoms in the diatomic molecule are the same. This means that there is no electronegativity difference between atoms, and hence no polarity in the F—F bond.

(b) $\overset{..}{O}=\overset{.}{N}-\overset{..}{\underset{..}{O}}$: Each nitrogen-to-oxygen bond in this molecule is polarized toward oxygen, the more electronegative element. The molecule is of the AX_2E category and hence is bent. Therefore the two bond dipoles do not cancel, and the molecule is polar.

(c) Although each B—F bond is polarized toward F in this trigonal planar AX_3 molecule, these bond dipoles cancel. The molecule is nonpolar.

(d) $H-\overset{..}{\underset{..}{Br}}$: The H—Br bond is polar toward Br, and this molecule is polar as well.

(e) There is a tetrahedral arrangement of groups around the central C atom. The groups are not identical; there are two H atoms and two Cl atoms. Therefore, the bond dipoles do not cancel. The molecule is polar.

(f) Although each Si—F bond is polarized toward F, in this tetrahedral AX_4 molecule these bond dipoles oppose and cancel each other. As a result, the molecule is nonpolar.

(g) $\overset{..}{\underset{..}{O}}=C=\overset{..}{\underset{..}{S}}$ In this linear molecule, the two bonds from carbon both are polarized away from carbon. But the C=O bond is more polar than the C=S bond, and hence the molecule is polar.

39. **(M)** The percent ionic character of a bond is based on the difference in electronegativity of its constituent atoms and Figure 10.7.

(a) $S(2.5)-H(2.1)$	**(b)** $O(3.5)-Cl(3.0)$	**(c)** $Al(1.5)-O(3.5)$	**(d)** $As(2.0)-O(3.5)$
Δ EN 0.4	0.5	2.0	1.5
%ionic = 4%	= 5 %	=60 %	=33 %

40. **(D)**

The property of electronegativity does indeed conform to the periodic law. Each of the "low points" corresponds to an alkali metal, and the end of each trend corresponds to a halogen. This is not unexpected and follows the general trend of increasing Z_{eff} from left to right, across the periodic table.

41. (M)

Cl+⟶F

$$\delta = \frac{\mu}{d} = \frac{0.8881\,\text{D} \times 3.34 \times 10^{-30}\ \text{C} \cdot \text{m/D}}{162.8 \times 10^{-12}\ \text{m}} \times \frac{1e}{1.602 \times 10^{-19}\ \text{C}} = 0.114e,\ \text{towards F.}$$

Rb+⟶F

$$\delta = \frac{\mu}{d} = \frac{8.547\,\text{D} \times 3.34 \times 10^{-30}\ \text{C} \cdot \text{m/D}}{227.0 \times 10^{-12}\ \text{m}} \times \frac{1e}{1.602 \times 10^{-19}\ \text{C}} = 0.785e,\ \text{towards F.}$$

Sn+⟶O

$$\delta = \frac{\mu}{d} = \frac{4.3210\,\text{D} \times 3.34 \times 10^{-30}\ \text{C} \cdot \text{m/D}}{183.3 \times 10^{-12}\ \text{m}} \times \frac{1e}{1.602 \times 10^{-19}\ \text{C}} = 0.491e,\ \text{towards O.}$$

Ba+⟶O

$$\delta = \frac{\mu}{d} = \frac{7.954\,\text{D} \times 3.34 \times 10^{-30}\ \text{C} \cdot \text{m/D}}{194.0 \times 10^{-12}\ \text{m}} \times \frac{1e}{1.602 \times 10^{-19}\ \text{C}} = 0.855e,\ \text{towards O.}$$

42. (M)

O⟵+H

$$\delta = \frac{\mu}{d} = \frac{1.66\,\text{D} \times 3.34 \times 10^{-30}\ \text{C} \cdot \text{m/D}}{98.0 \times 10^{-12}\ \text{m}} \times \frac{1e}{1.602 \times 10^{-19}\ \text{C}} = 0.353e,\ \text{towards O.}$$

C⟵+H

$$\delta = \frac{\mu}{d} = \frac{1.46\,\text{D} \times 3.34 \times 10^{-30}\ \text{C} \cdot \text{m/D}}{131.1 \times 10^{-12}\ \text{m}} \times \frac{1e}{1.602 \times 10^{-19}\ \text{C}} = 0.232e,\ \text{towards C.}$$

C+⟶N

$$\delta = \frac{\mu}{d} = \frac{117.5\,\text{D} \times 3.34 \times 10^{-30}\ \text{C} \cdot \text{m/D}}{1.45 \times 10^{-12}\ \text{m}} \times \frac{1e}{1.602 \times 10^{-19}\ \text{C}} = 0.257e,\ \text{towards N.}$$

C+⟶S

$$\delta = \frac{\mu}{d} = \frac{1.96\,\text{D} \times 3.34 \times 10^{-30}\ \text{C} \cdot \text{m/D}}{194.4 \times 10^{-12}\ \text{m}} \times \frac{1e}{1.602 \times 10^{-19}\ \text{C}} = 0.210e,\ \text{towards S.}$$

43. (M) When looking at the electrostatic potential map, we expect similar structures. However, in the case of $F_2C = O$, the carbon should be more electropositive than in $H_2C=O$ due to the presence of very electronegative fluorine atoms (as opposed to H atoms). Thus, for $F_2C = O$, one expects the center of the molecule to appear blue. As well, the electronegative oxygen atom should have less electron density associated with it, thus $H_2C = O$ should have a greater amount of red (electron rich) than the corresponding $F_2C = O$, again, as a result of the presence of highly electronegative fluorine atoms. $F_2C = O$ is represented on the left, while $H_2C = O$ is represented on the right.

44. **(M)** HOCl, HOF, and FOCl have similar structural features, however, they differ in terms of their electron density maps. O, Cl, and F have similar electronegativities, thus FOCl should be fairly neutral (mostly yellow coloration), in terms of the electrostatic potential map. Thus, the molecule on the far right is FOCl. In the molecule HOF, the H atom will be very electropositive (blue coloring), owing to the presence of the very electronegative O and F atoms. Therefore, the molecule on the far right is HOF. This means that HOCl is the center molecule, which, as expected, should have a relatively electropositive H atom (blue coloration, however, not as blue as in the case of HOF).

45. **(M)** The molecular formulas for the compounds are SF_4 and SiF_4. SiF_4 is a symmetric molecule (tetrahedral). It is expected that the fluorine atoms should have the same electron density (same coloration). Since Si is more electropositive, it should have a greater blue coloration (more positive center). This suggests the electrostatic potential map on the right is for SiF_4. SF_4 is not a symmetric molecule. It has a trigonal bipyramidal electron geometry, where a lone pair occupies an equatorial position. It has a saw-horse or see-saw molecular shape in which the two axial fluorine atoms are nearly 180° to one another, while the two equatorial fluorine atoms are ~120° to one another. Owing to the lone pair in the equatorial position, the equatorial fluorine atoms will not be as electronegative as the axial fluorine atoms. This is certainly the case for the representation on the left.

46. **(M)** The molecular formulas are ClF_3 and PF_3. Since P is more electropositive than Cl, we can easily argue that the right hand representation in which the central atom has a greater positive charge associated with it (blue coloration) is PF_3. As well, the molecular geometries are different. PF_3 is expected to be trigonal pyramidal while ClF_3 is T-shaped. It is relatively clear that the molecular geometries of the two molecules are different in the electrostatic potential maps. Thus the representation on the left, which is nearly planar, is that for ClF_3, while the non-planar map on the right is that for PF_3.

Resonance

47. **(E)** In NO_2^-, the total number of valence electrons is $1+5+(2\times6)=18$ valence electrons, or 9 electron pairs. N is the central atom. The two resonance forms are shown below:

$$[\overset{\ominus}{\underset{\cdot\cdot}{\overset{\cdot\cdot}{O}}}-\overset{\cdot\cdot}{N}=\underset{\cdot\cdot}{\overset{\cdot\cdot}{O}}]^- \longleftrightarrow [\underset{\cdot\cdot}{\overset{\cdot\cdot}{O}}=\overset{\cdot\cdot}{N}-\overset{\cdot\cdot}{\underset{\cdot\cdot}{O}}\overset{\ominus}{:}]^-$$

48. **(M)** The only one of the four species that requires resonance forms to correctly describe the intramolecular bonding is CO_3^{2-}. Resonance forms of equal energy cannot be generated for the other species. All four Lewis structures are drawn below.

    (a) In CO_2, there are $4+(2\times6)=16$ valence electrons, or 8 electron pairs. $\overset{\cdot\cdot}{O}=C=\overset{\cdot\cdot}{O}$

    (b) In OCl^-, there are $6+7+1=14$ valence electrons, or 7 electron pairs, $\overset{\ominus}{\underset{\cdot\cdot}{\overset{\cdot\cdot}{O}}}-\overset{\cdot\cdot}{\underset{\cdot\cdot}{Cl}}:$

(c) In CO_3^{2-}, there are $4 + (3 \times 6) + 2 = 24$ valence electrons, or 12 electron pairs (see below).

$$\left[\overset{\displaystyle :\ddot{O}:}{\underset{\displaystyle \ddot{O}=C-\ddot{O}:}{|}} \right]^{2-} \longleftrightarrow \left[\overset{\displaystyle :O:}{\underset{\displaystyle :\ddot{O}-C-\ddot{O}:}{||}} \right]^{2-} \longleftrightarrow \left[\overset{\displaystyle :\ddot{O}:}{\underset{\displaystyle :\ddot{O}-C=\ddot{O}}{|}} \right]^{2-}$$

(d) In OH^-, there are $6 + 1 + 1 = 8$ valence electrons, or 4 electron pairs. $^{\ominus}\ddot{O}-H$

49. **(M)** Bond length data from Table 10.2 follow:

$N \equiv N$ 109.8 pm $N = N$ 123 pm $N - N$ 145 pm $N = O$ 120 pm $N - O$ 136 pm

The experimental $N - N$ bond length of 113 pm approximates that of the $N \equiv N$ triple bond, which appears in structure (a). The experimental $N - O$ bond length of 119 pm approximates that of the $N=O$ double bond, which appears in structure (b). Structure (d) is highly unlikely because it contains no nitrogen-to-nitrogen bonds, and a N—N bond was found experimentally. Structure (c) also is unlikely, because it contains a very long (145 pm) $N - N$ single bond, which does not agree at all well with the experimental N-to-N bond length. The molecule seems best represented as a resonance hybrid of (a) and (b).

$$^{\ominus}\ddot{N} = \overset{\oplus}{N} = \ddot{O} \longleftrightarrow :N \equiv \overset{\oplus}{N} - \ddot{O}\overset{\ominus}{:}$$

50. **(M)** We begin by drawing all three valid resonance forms of HNO_3 and then analyzing their distributions of formal charge to determine which is the most plausible.

$$\begin{array}{ccc} \overset{\displaystyle :\ddot{O}:^{\ominus}}{H-\overset{\oplus}{\ddot{O}}-N=\ddot{O}} & \overset{\displaystyle :\ddot{O}:}{H-\ddot{O}-\overset{\oplus}{N}-\ddot{O}\overset{\ominus}{:}} & \overset{\displaystyle :\ddot{O}\overset{\ominus}{:}}{H-\overset{\oplus}{O}=\overset{\oplus}{N}-\ddot{O}\overset{\ominus}{:}} \\ \textbf{(a)} & \textbf{(b)} & \textbf{(c)} \end{array}$$

In all three structures, the formal charges of N and H are the same:
f.c. of $H = 1 - 1 - 0 = 0$ f.c. of $N = 5 - 4 - 0 = +1$

For an oxygen that forms two bonds (either 2 single or one double), $f.c. = 6 - 2 - (2 \times 2) = 0$

For an oxygen that forms only one bond, $f.c. = 6 - 1 - (3 \times 2) = -1$

For the oxygen that forms three bonds (a single and a double), $f.c. = 6 - 3 - (1 \times 2) = +1$

Thus, structures (a) and (b) are equivalent in their distributions of formal charges, zero on all atoms except 1+ on N and 1- on one O. These are degenerate resonance forms (i.e., they are of equal energy). Structure (c) is quite different, with formal charges of 1- on two O's, and 1+ on the other, and a formal charge of 1+ on N. Structure (c) is thus the least plausible, because of the adjacent like charges.

51. (M)

(a) Both structures are equivalent.

(b) Structures A and C are the most important, and they are equivalent.

(c) Structure B is more important.

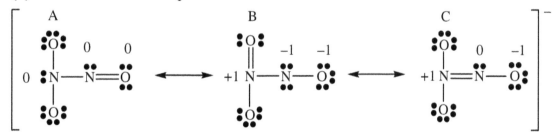

(d) Structure A is more important.

52. (M)

(a) Structures A and B are equivalent and most important.

(b) Structure A is the most important.

(c) Both structures are equivalent.

(d) All structures are equivalent.

Odd-electron species

53. (M)

(a) CH_3 has a total of $(3 \times 1) + 4 = 7$ valence electrons, or 3 electron pairs and a lone electron. C is the central atom. A plausible Lewis structure is shown on the right.

(b) ClO_2 has a total of $(2 \times 6) + 7 = 19$ valence electrons, or 9 electron pairs and a lone electron. Cl is the central atom. A plausible Lewis structure is:

(c) NO_3 has a total of $(3\times6)+5=23$ valence electrons, or 11 electron pairs, plus a lone electron. N is the central atom. A plausible Lewis structure is shown to the right. Other resonance forms can also be drawn.

54. (M)

(a)

C_2H_5 has a total of $(5\times1)+(2\times4)=13$ valence electrons or 6 electron pairs and a lone electron on C. A plausible Lewis structure is given to the right.

(b)

HO_2 has a total of $(2\times6)+1=13$ valence electrons or 6 electron pairs (2 bonding and 4 non-bonding) and a lone electron on O. A plausible Lewis structure is given to the right.

(c)

ClO has a total of $7+6=13$ valence electrons or 6 electron pairs (1 bonding and 5 non-bonding) and a lone electron on either Cl or O. A plausible Lewis structure is given to the right.

55. (E) Since electrons pair up (if at all possible) in plausible Lewis structures, a species will be paramagnetic if it has an odd number of (valence) electrons.

(a) OH^- $6+1+1=8$ valence electrons   diamagnetic

(b) OH $6+1=7$ valence electrons   paramagnetic

(c) NO_3 $5+(3\times6)=23$ valence electrons   paramagnetic

(d) SO_3 $6+(3\times6)=24$ valence electrons   diamagnetic

(e) SO_3^{2-} $6+(3\times6)+2=26$ valence electrons   diamagnetic

(f) HO_2 $1+(2\times6)=13$ valence electrons   paramagnetic

56. (D) In NO_2, there are $5+(2\times6)=17$ valence electrons, 8 electron pairs and a lone electron. N is the central atom and it carries the lone electron. A plausible Lewis structure is (A) which has a formal charge of 1+ on N and 1– on the single-bonded O. Another Lewis structure, with zero formal charge on each atom, is (B). The major difference is that one of the oxygen atoms carries the lone electron. In both cases, due to the unpaired electron we expect NO_2 to be paramagnetic. We would expect a bond to form between two NO_2 molecules as a result of the pairing of the lone unpaired electrons in the NO_2 molecules. If the second Lewis structure for NO_2 is used, the one with zero formal charge on each atom and the lone electron on oxygen, a plausible structure for N_2O_4 is (C). If the first Lewis structure for NO_2 where there are formal charges and a lone electron on nitrogen is used to form a bond between molecules, a plausible Lewis structure containing a N — N bond results (D). Resonance structures can be drawn for this second version of N_2O_4. A N — N bond is observed experimentally in N_2O_4. In either structure, the product N_2O_4, has all electrons paired up in bonding and non-bonding lone pairs; the molecule is expected to be (and is) diamagnetic. Lewis structures for (A) – (D) are shown below.

$$\overset{\ominus}{:}\overset{..}{O}\!-\!\overset{\oplus}{N}\!=\!\overset{..}{O}: \textbf{(A)} \qquad :\overset{..}{O}\!-\!N\!=\!\overset{..}{O}: \textbf{(B)}$$

$$\downarrow \qquad\qquad\qquad\qquad \downarrow$$

$$\overset{\ominus}{:}\overset{..}{O}\!-\!\overset{\oplus}{N}\!=\!O: \qquad :\overset{..}{O}\!-\!N\!=\!O:$$

$$\overset{..}{O}\!-\!N\!=\!\overset{..}{O}: \qquad :O\!-\!\overset{..}{N}\!=\!\overset{..}{O}:$$

$$\downarrow \qquad\qquad\qquad\qquad \downarrow$$

$$\overset{\ominus}{:}\overset{..}{O}\!-\!\overset{\oplus}{N}\!=\!O: \qquad \overset{..}{O}\!=\!\overset{..}{N}\!-\!\overset{..}{O}\!-\!\overset{..}{O}\!-\!\overset{..}{N}\!=\!\overset{..}{O} \textbf{ (C)}$$

$$:\overset{..}{O}\!-\!N\!=\!\overset{..}{O}: \quad\textbf{(D)}$$

Expanded Octets

57. **(M)** In PO_4^{3-}: $5 + (4 \times 6) + 3 = 32$ valence electrons or 16 electron pairs. An expanded octet is not needed.

In PI_3: $5 + (3 \times 7) = 26$ valence electrons or 13 electron pairs. An expanded octet is not needed.

In ICl_3: $7 + (3 \times 7) = 28$ valence electrons or 14 electron pairs. An expanded octet is necessary.

In $OSCl_2$: $6 + 6 + (2 \times 7) = 26$ valence electrons or 13 electron pairs. An expanded octet is not needed.

In SF_4: $6 + (4 \times 7) = 34$ valence electrons or 17 electron pairs. An expanded octet is necessary.

In ClO_4^-: $7 + (4 \times 6) + 1 = 32$ valence electrons or 16 electron pairs. An expanded octet is not needed.

58. **(M)** Let us draw the Lewis structure of H_2CSF_4. The molecule has $(2 \times 1) + 4 + 6 + (4 \times 7) = 40$ valence electrons, or 20 electron pairs. With only single bonds and all octets complete, there is a 1– formal charge on C and 1+ on S, as in the left structure below . The right structure below avoids an undesirable separation of charge by creating a carbon-to-sulfur double bond (charge separation requires the input of energy).

The bond can be described either as a single bond with ionic contributions or a double bond in which the formal charges are eliminated.

Molecular Shapes

59. **(M)** The AX_nE_m designations that are cited below are to be found in Table 10.1 of the text, along with a sketch and a picture of a model of each type of structure.

(a) Dinitrogen is linear; two points define a line.

$$:N\equiv N:$$

(b) Hydrogen cyanide is linear. The molecule belongs to the AX_2 category, and these species are linear.

$$H-C\equiv N:$$

(c) NH_4^+ is tetrahedral. The ion is of the AX_4 type, which has a tetrahedral electron-group geometry and a tetrahedral shape.

$$\left[\begin{array}{c} H \\ | \\ H-\overset{\oplus}{N}-H \\ | \\ H \end{array} \right]^+$$

(d) NO_3^- is trigonal planar. The ion is of the AX_3 type, which has a trigonal planar electron-group geometry and a trigonal planar shape. The other resonance forms are of the same type.

$$\left[\begin{array}{c} :O: \\ \| \\ ^{\ominus}:O-\overset{\oplus}{N}-O:^{\ominus} \end{array} \right]^-$$

(e) NSF is bent. The molecule is of the AX_2E type, which has a trigonal planar electron-group geometry and a bent shape.

$$^{\ominus}\ddot{N}=\underset{\oplus}{S}-\ddot{F}:$$

60. **(M)** The AX_nE_m designations that are cited below are to be found in Table 11.1 of the text, along with a sketch and a picture of a model of each type of structure.

(a) PCl_3 is a trigonal pyramid. The molecule is of the AX_3E type, and has a tetrahedral electron-group geometry and a trigonal pyramid shape.

$$\begin{array}{c} :\ddot{Cl}: \\ | \\ :\ddot{Cl}-P-\ddot{Cl}: \end{array}$$

(b) SO_4^{2-} has a tetrahedral shape. The ion is of the type AX_4, and has a tetrahedral electron-group geometry and a tetrahedral shape. The other resonance forms of the sulfate ion have the same shape.

$$\left[\begin{array}{c} :\ddot{O}:^{\ominus} \\ | \\ ^{\ominus}:\ddot{O}-\underset{2+}{S}-\ddot{O}:^{\ominus} \\ | \\ :O:^{\ominus} \end{array} \right]^{2-}$$

(c) $SOCl_2$ has a trigonal pyramidal shape. This molecule is of the AX_3E type and has a tetrahedral electron-group geometry and a trigonal pyramidal shape.

$$\begin{array}{c} :O: \\ \| \\ :\ddot{Cl}-\ddot{S}-\ddot{Cl}: \end{array}$$

(d) SO_3 has a trigonal planar shape. The molecule is of the AX_3 type, with a trigonal planar electron-group geometry and molecular shape. The other resonance contributors have the same shape.

$$\begin{array}{c} :O: \\ \| \\ ^{\ominus}:\ddot{O}-\underset{2+}{S}-\ddot{O}:^{\ominus} \end{array}$$

(e) BrF_4^+ has a distorted see-saw shape. The molecule is of the AX_4E type, with a trigonal bipyramid electron-group geometry and a see-saw molecular shape.

$$\left[\begin{array}{c} :\ddot{F}: \\ | \\ :\ddot{F}-\overset{}{\underset{\oplus}{Br}}-\ddot{F}: \\ | \\ :\ddot{F}: \end{array} \right]^+$$

61. **(M)** We first draw all the Lewis structures. From each, we can deduce the electron-group geometry and the molecular shape.

(a) H_2S tetrahedral electron-group geometry, bent (angular) molecular geometry

(b) N_2O_4 trigonal planar electron-group geometry around each N, (planar molecule)

(c) HCN   linear electron-group geometry, linear molecular geometry

(d) $SbCl_6^-$ octahedral electron-group geometry, octahedral geometry

(e) BF_4^- tetrahedral electron-group geometry, tetrahedral molecular geometry

62. **(M)** In each case, a plausible Lewis structure is given first, followed by the AX_nE_m notation for each species followed by the electron-group geometry and, finally, the molecular geometry.

(a) CO   linear electron-group geometry, linear molecular geometry

(b) $SiCl_4$ tetrahedral electron-group geometry, tetrahedral molecular geometry

(c) PH_3 tetrahedral electron-group geometry, trigonal pyramidal molecular geometry

(d) ICl_3 trigonal bipyramidal electron-group geometry, T- shape molecular geometry

(e) $SbCl_5$ electron-group geometry and molecular geometry, trigonal bipyramidal

(f) SO₂   trigonal planar electron-group geometry,
          bent molecular geometry

(g) AlF₆³⁻   octahedral electron-group geometry,
          octahedral geometry

63. **(M)** A trigonal planar shape requires that three groups and no lone pairs be bonded to the central atom. Thus PF_6^- cannot have a trigonal planar shape, since six atoms are attached to the central atom. In addition, PO_4^{3-} cannot have a trigonal planar shape, since four O atoms are attached to the central P atom. We now draw the Lewis structure of each of the remaining ions, as a first step in predicting their shapes. The SO_3^{2-} ion is of the AX_3E type. It has a tetrahedral electron-group geometry and a trigonal pyramidal shape. The CO_3^{2-} ion is of the AX_3 type, and has a trigonal planar electron-group geometry and a trigonal planar shape.

64. **(E)** We can predict shapes by first of all drawing the Lewis structures for the species. Thus, SO_3^{2-} and NI_3 both have the same shape.

Lewis
Structure

AX_nE_m	AX_3E_1	AX_2E_0	AX_3E_1	AX_3E_0
shape	trigonal pyramid	linear	trigonal pyramid	trigonal planar

65. **(M)**

(a) In CO_2 there are a total of $4+(2\times6)=16$ valence electrons, or 8 electron pairs. The following Lewis structure is plausible. $\overset{\cdot\cdot}{O} = C = \overset{\cdot\cdot}{O}$ This is a molecule of type AX_2. CO_2 has a linear electron-shape geometry and a linear shape.

(b) In Cl_2CO there are a total of $(2\times7)+4+6=24$ valence electrons, or 12 electron pairs. The molecule can be represented by a Lewis structure with C as the central atom. This molecule is of the AX_3 type. It has a trigonal planar electron-group geometry and molecular shape.

(c) In $ClNO_2$ there are a total of $7+5+(2\times6)=24$ valence electrons, or 12 electron pairs. N is the central atom. A plausible Lewis structure is shown to the right: This molecule is of the AX_3 type. It has a trigonal planar electron-group geometry and a trigonal planar shape.

66. (M) Lewis structures enable us to determine molecular shapes.

(a) N_2O_4 has $(2\times5)+(4\times6)=34$ valence electrons, or 17 electron pairs.

There are three atoms bound to each N in N_2O_4, making the molecule triangular planar around each N. The entire molecule does not have to be planar, however, since there is free rotation around the N—N bond.

(b) C_2N_2 has $(2\times4)+(2\times5)=18$ valence electrons, or 9 electron pairs. There are two atoms attached to each C, requiring a linear geometry. The entire molecule is linear.

$$:N\equiv C-C\equiv N:$$

(c) C_2H_6 has $(2\times4)+(6\times1)=14$ valence electrons, or 7 electron pairs. There are four atoms attached to each C. The molecular geometry around each C is tetrahedral, as shown in the sketch above.

(d) CH_3OCH_3 has 6 more valence electrons than $C_2H_6 = 20$ valence e^- or 10 electron pairs. Around the central O, the electron-group geometry is tetrahedral. With two of the electron groups being lone pairs, the molecular geometry around the central atom is bent.

67. (M) First we draw the Lewis structure of each species, then use it to predict the molecular shape. The structures are provided below.

(a) In ClO_4^- there are $7+(4\times6)+1=32$ valence electrons or 16 electron pairs.

A plausible Lewis structure follows. Since there are four atoms and no lone pairs bonded to the central atom, the molecular shape and the electron-group geometry are the same: tetrahedral.

(b) In $S_2O_3^{2-}$ there are $(2 \times 6) + (3 \times 6) + 2 = 32$ valence electrons or 16 electron pairs. A plausible Lewis structure follows. Since there are four atoms and no lone pairs bonded to the central atom, both the electron-group geometry and molecular shape are tetrahedral.

(c) In PF_6^- there are $5 + (6 \times 7) + 1 = 48$ valence electrons or 24 electron pairs. Since there are six atoms and no lone pairs bonded to the central atom, the electron-group geometry and molecular shape are octahedral.

(d) In I_3^- there are $(3 \times 7) + 1 = 22$ valence electrons or 11 electron pairs. There are three lone pairs and two atoms bound to the central atom. The electron-group geometry is trigonal bipyramidal, thus, the molecular shape is linear.

68. (D)

(a) In OSF_2, there are a total of $6 + 6 + (2 \times 7) = 26$ valence electrons, or 13 electron pairs. S is the central atom. A plausible Lewis structure is shown to the right. This molecule is of the type AX_3E_1. It has a tetrahedral electron-group geometry and a trigonal pyramidal shape.

(b) In O_2SF_2, there are a total of $(2 \times 6) + 6 + (2 \times 7) = 32$ valence electrons, or 16 electron pairs. S is the central atom. One plausible Lewis structure is shown to the right. The molecule is of the AX_4 type. It has a tetrahedral electron-group geometry and a tetrahedral shape. The structure with all single bonds is preferred because it avoids an expanded octet.

(c) In SF_5^-, there are $6 + (5 \times 7) + 1 = 42$ valence electrons, or 21 electron pairs. A plausible Lewis structure is shown to the right. The ion is of the AX_5E type. It has an octahedral electron-group geometry and a square pyramidal molecular shape.

(d) In ClO_4^-, there are a total of $1 + 7 + (4 \times 6) = 32$ valence electrons, or 16 electron pairs. Cl is the central atom. A plausible Lewis structure is shown to the right. This ion is of the AX_4 type. It has a tetrahedral electron-group geometry and a tetrahedral shape.

(e) In ClO_3^-, the total number of valence electrons is $1 + (3 \times 6) + 7 = 26$ valence electrons, or 13 electron pairs. A plausible Lewis structure is shown to the right. The molecule is of the type AX_3E. It has a tetrahedral electron-group geometry and a trigonal pyramidal molecular shape.

413

69. **(M)** In BF_4^-, there are a total of $1+3+(4\times7)=32$ valence electrons, or 16 electron pairs. A plausible Lewis structure has B as the central atom. This ion is of the type AX_4. It has a tetrahedral electron-group geometry and a tetrahedral shape.

70. **(M)** The molecular geometry is indicated by the VSEPR notation (i.e., AX_3E_2). Formal charge is reduced by moving lone pairs of electrons from the terminal atoms and forming multiple bonds to the central atom. The VSEPR notation is unchanged, however, when formal charge is increased or decreased. For example, consider SO_2:

VSEPR notation AX_2E shape: bent   VSEPR notation AX_2E shape: bent   VSEPR notation AX_2E shape: bent

71. **(M)** Looking at the structures, the molecular angle/shape depends on the number of valence electron pairs on the central atom. The more pairs there are, the more acute the angle becomes.

$180°$ $120°$ $120°$ $109°$

72. **(M)** CO_3^{2-} and NO_3^- are trigonal planar, because the central atom has no lone pairs. SO_3^{2-} and ClO_3^- are trigonal pyramidal, because the lone pair on the central atom forces a shape change.

$120°$ $120°$ $109°$ $109°$

73. **(M)**

	(a)	**(b)**	**(c)**	**(d)**
e^- group geometry	Trigonal Bipyramidal	Trigonal Bipyramidal	Octahedral	Octahedral
Molecular geometry	Linear	T-Shaped	Square Planar	Square Pyramidal

74. (M)

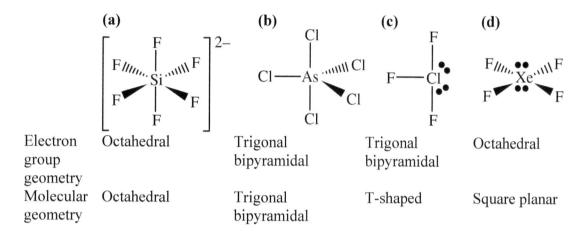

Electron group geometry	(a) Octahedral	(b) Trigonal bipyramidal	(c) Trigonal bipyramidal	(d) Octahedral
Molecular geometry	Octahedral	Trigonal bipyramidal	T-shaped	Square planar

Shapes of Molecules with More Than One Central Atom

75. (E)

A maximum of 5 atoms can be in the same plane

76. (E)

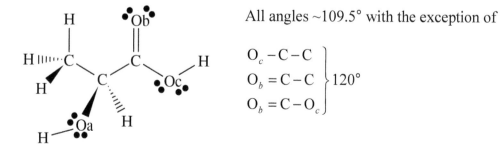

A maximum of 8 atoms can be on the same plane.

77. (E)

All angles ~109.5° with the exception of

$$O_c - C - C$$
$$O_b = C - C \quad \Big\} 120°$$
$$O_b = C - O_c$$

78. (E)

All angles ~ 109.5° with the exception of

$$
\left.\begin{array}{l}
O_c\text{---}C_b\text{---}C \\
O_b\text{==}C_b\text{---}O_c \\
O_b\text{==}C_b\text{---}C \\
O_a\text{==}C_a\text{---}C \\
C\text{---}C_a\text{---}C
\end{array}\right\} \sim 120°
$$

79. (M)

80. (M)

Polar Molecules

81. **(D)** For each molecule, we first draw the Lewis structure, which we use to predict the shape.

(a) SO_2 has a total of $6 + (2 \times 6) = 18$ valence electrons, or 9 electron pairs. The molecule has three resonance forms.

Each of these resonance forms is of the type AX_2E. Thus it has a trigonal planar electron-group geometry and a bent shape. Since each S—O bond is polar toward O, and since the bond dipoles do not cancel, the molecule has a resultant dipole moment, pointing from S through a point midway between the two O atoms. Consequently, SO_2 is polar.

(b) NH_3 has a total of $5 + (3 \times 1) = 8$ valence electrons, or 4 electron pairs. N is the central atom. A plausible Lewis structure is shown to the right. The molecule is of the AX_3E type; it has a tetrahedral electron-group geometry and a trigonal pyramidal shape. Each N-H bond is polar toward N. Since the bonds do not symmetrically oppose each other, there is a resultant molecular dipole moment, pointing from the triangular base (formed by the three H atoms) through N. Consequently, the molecule is polar.

(c) H_2S has a total of $6 + (2 \times 1) = 8$ valence electrons, or 4 electron pairs. S is the central atom and a plausible Lewis structure is H-S̈-H. This molecule is of the AX_2E_2 type; it has a tetrahedral electron-group geometry and a bent shape. Each H—S bond is polar toward S. Since the bonds do not symmetrically oppose each other, the molecule has a net dipole moment, pointing through S from a point midway between the two H atoms. H_2S is polar.

(d) C_2H_4 consists of atoms that all have about the same electronegativities. Of course, the C—C bond is not polar and essentially neither are the C—H bonds. The molecule is planar. Thus, the entire molecule is nonpolar.

(e) SF_6 has a total of $6 + (6 \times 7) = 48$ valence electrons, or 24 electron pairs. S is the central atom. All atoms have zero formal charge in the Lewis structure. This molecule is of the AX_6 type. It has an octahedral electron-group geometry and an octahedral shape. Even though each S—F bond is polar toward F, the bonds symmetrically oppose each other, resulting in a molecule that is nonpolar.

(f) CH_2Cl_2 has a total of $4 + (2 \times 1) + (2 \times 7) = 20$ valence electrons, or 10 electron pairs. A plausible Lewis structure is shown to the right. The molecule is tetrahedral and polar, since the two polar bonds $(C—Cl)$ do not cancel the effect of each other.

82. (D)

(a) HCN is a linear molecule, which can be derived from its Lewis structure $H—C \equiv N:$. The $C \equiv N$ bond is strongly polar toward N, while the H—C bond is generally considered to be nonpolar. Thus, the molecule has a dipole moment, pointed from C toward N.

(b) SO_3 is a trigonal planar molecule, which can be derived from its Lewis structure. Each sulfur-oxygen bond is polar from S to O, but the three bonds are equally polar and are pointed in symmetrical opposition so that they cancel. The SO_3 molecule has a dipole moment of zero.

(c) CS_2 is a linear molecule, which can be derived from its Lewis structure $S̈=C=S̈$. Each carbon-sulfur bond is polar from C to S, but the two bonds are equally polar and are pointed in opposition to each other so that they cancel. The CS_2 molecule has a dipole moment of zero.

(d) OCS also is a linear molecule. Its Lewis structure is $\ddot{\text{O}} = \text{C} = \ddot{\ddot{\text{S}}}$. But the carbon-oxygen bond is more polar than the carbon-sulfur bond. Although both bond dipoles point from the central atom to the bonded atom, these two bond dipoles are unequal in strength. Thus, the molecule is polar in the direction from C to O.

(e) $SOCl_2$ is a trigonal pyramidal molecule. Its Lewis structure is shown to the right. The lone pair on S is at one corner of the tetrahedron. Each bond in the molecule is polar, with the dipole moments pointing away from the central atom. The sulfur-chlorine bond is less polar than the sulfur-oxygen bond, and this makes the molecule polar. The dipole moment of the molecule points from the sulfur atom to the base of the trigonal pyramid, not toward the center of the base but slightly toward the O apex of that base.

(f) SiF_4 is a tetrahedral molecule, with the following Lewis structure. Each $Si — F$ bond is polar, with its negative end away from the central atom toward F in each case. These four $Si - F$ bond dipoles oppose each other and thus cancel. SiF_4, as a result, has no dipole moment.

(g) POF_3 is a tetrahedral molecule. A valid Lewis structure is shown to the right. All four bonds are polar, with their dipole moments pointing away from the central atom. The $P — F$ bond polarity is greater than that of the $P — O$ bond. Thus, POF_3 is a polar molecule with its dipole moment pointing away from the P toward the center of the triangle formed by the three F atoms.

83. **(M)** In H_2O_2, there are a total of $(2 \times 1) + (2 \times 6) = 14$ valence electrons, 7 electron pairs. The two O atoms are central atoms. A plausible Lewis structure has zero formal charge on each atom: $H–\ddot{\ddot{\text{O}}}–\ddot{\ddot{\text{O}}}–H$. In the hydrogen peroxide molecule, the $O — O$ bond is non-polar, while the $H — O$ bonds are polar, with the dipole moment pointing toward O. Since the molecule has a resultant dipole moment, it cannot be linear, for, if it were linear the two polar bonds would oppose each other and their polarities would cancel.

84. **(M)**

(a) FNO has a total of $7 + 5 + 6 = 18$ valence electrons, or 9 electron pairs. N is the central atom. A plausible Lewis structure is $:\ddot{\ddot{\text{F}}} – \ddot{\text{N}} = \ddot{\text{O}}$. The formal charge on each atom in this structure is zero.

(b) FNO is of the AX_2E type. It has a trigonal planar electron-group geometry and a bent shape.

(c) The $N — F$ bond is polar toward F and the $N—O$ bond is polar toward O. In FNO, these two bond dipoles point in the same general direction, producing a polar molecule. In FNO_2, however, the additional $N—O$ bond dipole partially opposes the polarity of the other two bond dipoles, resulting in a smaller net dipole moment.

Bond Lengths

85. **(E)** The answer is c. Br_2 possess the longest bond. Single bonds are generally longer than multiple bonds. Of the two molecules with single bonds, Br_2 is expected to have longer bonds than BrCl, since Br is larger than Cl.

(a) $\overset{\cdot\cdot}{\underset{\cdot\cdot}{O}} = \overset{\cdot\cdot}{\underset{\cdot\cdot}{O}}$ (b) $:N\equiv N:$ (c) $:\overset{\cdot\cdot}{\underset{\cdot\cdot}{Br}} - \overset{\cdot\cdot}{\underset{\cdot\cdot}{Br}}:$ (d) $:\overset{\cdot\cdot}{\underset{\cdot\cdot}{Br}} - \overset{\cdot\cdot}{\underset{\cdot\cdot}{Cl}}:$

86. **(M)** The bond lengths predicted will be larger than the actual bond lengths. This is because we do not take into account polarity of the bond. In the case of the I-Cl bond, the electronegativity difference is small, thus the predicted bond length should be close to the experimental value. In the case of the C-F bond, the electronegativity difference is quite large, thus it is expected that the actual bond length will be shorter than the one predicted.

    (a)   I—Cl bond length   = [(I—I bond length) + (Cl—Cl bond length)] ÷ 2
                                        $= \left[266\ \text{pm} + 199\ \text{pm}\right] \div 2 = 233\ \text{pm}$ (literature 232 pm)

    (b)   C — F bond length $= \left[\left(\text{C—C bond length}\right) + \left(\text{F—F bond length}\right)\right] \div 2$
                                        $= \left[154\ \text{pm} + 143\ \text{pm}\right] \div 2 = 149\ \text{pm}$ (literature 135 pm)

87. **(M)** A heteronuclear bond length (one between two different atoms) is approximately equal to the average of two homonuclear bond lengths (one between two like atoms) of the same order (both single, both double, or both triple).

    (a)   I—Cl bond length   = [(I—I bond length) + (Cl—Cl bond length)] ÷ 2
                                        $= \left[266\ \text{pm} + 199\ \text{pm}\right] \div 2 = 233\ \text{pm}$

    (b)   O — Cl bond length $= \left[\left(\text{O—O bond length}\right) + \left(\text{Cl—Cl bond length}\right)\right] \div 2$
                                        $= \left[145\ \text{pm} + 199\ \text{pm}\right] \div 2 = 172\ \text{pm}$

    (c)   C — F bond length $= \left[\left(\text{C—C bond length}\right) + \left(\text{F—F bond length}\right)\right] \div 2$
                                        $= \left[154\ \text{pm} + 143\ \text{pm}\right] \div 2 = 149\ \text{pm}$

    (d)   C — Br bond length $= \left[\left(\text{C—C bond length}\right) + \left(\text{Br—Br bond length}\right)\right] \div 2$
                                        $= \left[154\ \text{pm} + 228\ \text{pm}\right] \div 2 = 191\ \text{pm}$

88. **(M)** First we need to draw the Lewis structure of each of the compounds cited, so that we can determine the order, and hence the relative length, of each O-to-O bond.

    (a)   In H_2O_2, there are $(2\times1)+(2\times6)=14$ valence electrons or 7 electron pairs. A plausible Lewis structure is $H - \overset{\cdot\cdot}{\underset{\cdot\cdot}{O}} - \overset{\cdot\cdot}{\underset{\cdot\cdot}{O}} - H$.

    (b)   In O_2, the total number of valence electrons is $(2\times6 =)12$ valence electrons, or 6 electron pairs. A plausible Lewis structure is $\overline{O} = \overline{O}$.

(c) In O_3, the total number of valence electrons is $(3 \times 6) = 18$ valence electrons, or 9 electron pairs. A plausible Lewis structure is $\ddot{O}=\ddot{O}-\ddot{O}: \leftrightarrow :\ddot{O}-\ddot{O}=\ddot{O}$ (two most stable resonance contributors).

Thus, O_2 should have the shortest O-to-O bond, because the O atoms are joined via a double bond. The single $O-O$ bond in H_2O_2 should be longest.

89. **(E)** The $N-F$ bond is a single bond. Its bond length should be the average of the $N-N$ single bond (145 pm) and the $F-F$ single bond (143 pm). Thus, the average $N-F$ bond length $= (145+143) \div 2 = 144$ pm.

90. **(M)** In H_2NOH, there are $(3 \times 1) + 5 + 6 = 14$ valence electrons total, or 7 electron pairs. N and O are the two central atoms. A plausible Lewis structure has zero formal charge on each atom. The $N-H$ bond lengths are 100 pm, the $O-H$ bond is 97 pm long, and the $N-O$ bond is 136 pm in length. All values are taken from Table 10.2. All bond angles approximate the tetrahedral bond angle of $109.5°$, but are expected to be somewhat smaller, perhaps by $2°$ to $4°$ each.

Bond Energies

91. **(E)** The reaction $O_2(g) \rightarrow 2\, O(g)$ is an endothermic reaction since it requires the breaking of the bond between two oxygen atoms without the formation of any new bonds. Since bond breakage is endothermic and the process involves only bond breakage, the entire process must be endothermic.

92. **(M)**
(a) The net result of this reaction involves breaking one mole of $C-H$ bonds (which requires 414 kJ) and forming one mole of $H-I$ bonds (which produces 297 kJ). Thus, this reaction is endothermic (i.e., a net infusion of energy is necessary).

(b) The net result of this reaction involves breaking one mole of $H-H$ bonds (which requires 436 kJ) and one mole of $I-I$ bonds (which requires 151 kJ), along with forming two moles of $H-I$ bonds (which produces $2 \times 297 = 594$ kJ). Thus, this reaction is exothermic (just barely, mind you).

93. **(M)**

Analysis of the Lewis structures of products and reactants indicates that a $C-H$ bond and a $Cl-Cl$ bond are broken, and a $C-Cl$ and a $H-Cl$ bond are formed.

Energy required to break bonds $= C-H + Cl-Cl = 414 \dfrac{kJ}{mol} + 243 \dfrac{kJ}{mol} = 657 \dfrac{kJ}{mol}$

Energy realized by forming bonds $= C-Cl + H-Cl = 339 \dfrac{kJ}{mol} + 431 \dfrac{kJ}{mol} = 770 \dfrac{kJ}{mol}$

$\Delta_r H = 657 \text{ kJ/mol} - 770 \text{ kJ/mol} = -113 \text{ kJ/mol}$

94. **(M)** The reaction in terms of Lewis structures is $\ddot{\underset{..}{O}}=\ddot{O}-\ddot{\underset{..}{O}}: + \ddot{\underset{..}{O}}=\ddot{N}\cdot \longrightarrow \ddot{O}=N-\ddot{\underset{..}{O}}\cdot + \ddot{\underset{..}{O}}=\ddot{O}$

The net result is the breakage of an O—O bond (142 kJ/mol) and the formation of a N—O bond (222 kJ/mol). $\Delta_r H = 142$ kJ/mol $- 222$ kJ/mol $= -80.$ kJ/mol

95. **(M)** In each case we write the formation reaction, but specify reactants and products with their Lewis structures. All species are assumed to be gases.

(a) $\frac{1}{2}\left(\ddot{\underset{..}{O}}=\ddot{\underset{..}{O}}\right) + \frac{1}{2}(H-H) \longrightarrow \cdot\ddot{\underset{..}{O}}-H$

Bonds broken: $\frac{1}{2}(O=O) + \frac{1}{2}(H-H) = 0.5(498 \text{ kJ} + 436 \text{ kJ}) = 467 \text{ kJ}$

Bonds formed: O—H $= 464$ kJ $\qquad \Delta_r H° = 467$ kJ $- 464$ kJ $= 3$ kJ/mol

If the O — H bond dissociation energy of 428.0 kJ/mol from Figure 10-16 is used, $\Delta_f H° = 39$ kJ/mol.

(b) $:N\equiv N: + \ 2\,H-H \longrightarrow \begin{array}{c} H-\ddot{N}-\ddot{N}-H \\ \mid \quad \mid \\ H \quad H \end{array}$

Bonds broken $= N \equiv N + 2\,H - H = 946 \text{ kJ} + 2 \times 436 \text{ kJ} = 1818 \text{ kJ}$
Bonds formed $= N-N + 4\,N-H = 163 \text{ kJ} + 4 \times 389 \text{ kJ} = 1719 \text{ kJ}$
$\Delta_f H° = 1818 \text{ kJ} - 1719 \text{ kJ} = 99 \text{ kJ}$

96. **(M)** The reaction of Example 10-15 is $CH_4(g) + Cl_2(g) \rightarrow CH_3Cl(g) + HCl(g)$

$\Delta_r H = -113$ kJ. In Appendix D are the following values:

$\Delta_f H°\left[CH_4(g)\right] = -74.81 \text{ kJ}, \Delta_f H°\left[HCl(g)\right] = -92.31 \text{ kJ}, \Delta_f H°\left[Cl_2(g)\right] = 0$

Thus, we have

$\Delta_r H = \Delta_f H°\left[CH_3Cl(g)\right] + \Delta_f H°\left[HCl(g)\right] - \Delta_f H°\left[CH_4(g)\right] - \Delta_f H°\left[Cl_2(g)\right]$

$-113 \text{ kJ} = \Delta_f H°\left[CH_3Cl(g)\right] - 92.31 \text{ kJ} - (-74.81 \text{ kJ}) - (0.00)$

$\Delta_f H°\left[CH_3Cl(g)\right] = -113 \text{ kJ} + 92.31 \text{ kJ} - 74.81 \text{ kJ} = -96 \text{ kJ}$

97.

(M)

$H-C\equiv C-H \ + \ H-H \longrightarrow \begin{array}{c} H \qquad \quad H \\ \diagdown \qquad \diagup \\ C=C \\ \diagup \qquad \diagdown \\ H \qquad \quad H \end{array}$

Bonds broken	Energy change	Bonds formed	Energy change
1 mol C≡C	1×837 kJ	1 mol C=C	1×-611 kJ
1 mol H—H	1×436 kJ	2 mol C-H	2×-414 kJ

Energy required
to break bonds $\qquad +1273$ kJ

Energy obtained
upon bond formation $\qquad -1439$ kJ

Overall energy change $= 1273$ kJ $- 1439$ kJ $= -166$ kJ/mol $= \Delta_r H°$

98. **(M)** First we must determine the value of $\Delta_r H$ for reaction (2).

(1) $\quad$ C(s) $\longrightarrow$ C(g) $\qquad\qquad\qquad \Delta_r H° = 717$ kJ/mol

(2) $\quad$ C(g) + 2 H$_2$(g) $\longrightarrow$ CH$_4$(g) $\quad \Delta_r H° = ?$

Net: $\quad$ C(s) + 2H$_2$(g) $\longrightarrow$ CH$_4$(g) $\Delta_f H° = -75$ kJ/mol

717 kJ + ? kJ = −75 kJ $\quad$ or $\quad$? kJ = −75 kJ − 717 kJ = −792 kJ

To determine the energy of a C — H bond, we need to analyze reaction (2) in some detail.

$$\text{C} + 2\ \text{H—H} \longrightarrow \text{H—C—H (with H above and below)}$$

In this reaction, 2 H — H bonds are broken and 4 C — H bonds are formed, resulting in the production of 792 kJ/mol.

−792 kJ/mol $\quad$ = energy of broken bonds − energy of formed bonds
$\qquad\qquad\qquad = (2 \times 436$ kJ / mol$) - (4 \times$ C — H$)$

4 × C—H $\qquad$ = 792 kJ/mol + (2 × 436 kJ/mol) = 1664 kJ/mol

C—H $\qquad\qquad$ = 1662 ÷ 4 = 416 kJ/mol (compares favorably to the literature value of 414 kJ/mol)

99. **(M)**

$\Delta_f H° = (0 + 90.25) - (33.18 + 249.2) = -192.1$ kJ/mol

Using the calculated $\Delta_f H°$, we can calculate the O---N bond energy:

$\Delta_f H° = -(2 \times (\text{O:::N}) + 0) - (590 + 498) = -192.1$

O---N = 448 kJ/mol, which is between the values for N=O and N–O.

100. **(M)**

$\Delta_f H° = -394$ kJ

$\Delta_f H° = 2(\text{O:::O}) - 2(498) = -394$ kJ/mol

O---O = (−394 + 996)/2 = 301 kJ/mol, which is an intermediate value between O = O and O–O bond energies.

INTEGRATIVE AND ADVANCED EXERCISES

Important Note: In this and subsequent chapters, a lone pair of electrons in a Lewis structure often is shown as a line rather than a pair of dots. Thus, the Lewis structure of Be is Be| or Be:

101. (M) Recall that bond breaking is endothermic, while bond making is exothermic.
Break 2 N-O bonds requires 2(631 kJ/mol) = +1262 kJ
Break 5 H-H bonds requires 4(436 kJ/mol) = +2180 kJ
Make 6 N-H bonds yields 5(−389 kJ/mol) = −2334 kJ
Make 4 O-H bonds yields 4(−463 kJ/mol) = −1852 kJ

$$\Sigma(\text{bond energies}) = \Delta_r H = -744 \text{ kJ/mol reaction}$$

102. (M)

(a) There is at least one instance in which one atom must bear a formal charge—a polyatomic ion. In these cases, formal charges must be invoked to ensure that there be no more than one unpaired electron in the structure.

(b) Since three points define a plane, stating that a triatomic molecule is planar is just stating a reiteration of a fundamental tenet of geometry. In fact, it is misleading, for some triatomic molecules are actually linear. HCN is one example of a linear triatomic molecule, as is CO_2. Of course, some molecules with more than three atoms are also planar; two examples are XeF_4 and $H_2C=CH_2$.

(c) This statement is incorrect because in some molecules that contain polar bonds, the bonds are so oriented in space that there is no resulting molecular dipole moment. Examples of such molecules are CO_2, $BeCl_3$, CCl_4, PCl_5, and SF_6.

103. (M) First we determine the empirical formula of the compound, based on 100 g of compound.

$$\text{Amount N} = 42.44 \text{ g N} \times \frac{1 \text{ mol N}}{14.01 \text{ g N}} = 3.029 \text{ mol N}$$

$$\text{Amount F} = 57.56 \text{ g F} \times \frac{1 \text{ mol F}}{19.00 \text{ g F}} = 3.026 \text{ mol N}$$

$$\frac{3.029 \text{ mol}}{3.026 \text{ mol}} = 1.00 \text{ N}$$

$$\frac{3.026 \text{ mol}}{3.026 \text{ mol}} = 1.00 \text{ F}$$

Therefore, N and F exist in this compound in equimolar amounts. Based on the relative mole ratios of N and F in the compound, and the fact that F can only make one bond, the structure cannot contain just one N and F and still satisfy the octet rule for N. The next possibility is a compound with two N and F atoms each, and a total of 24 electrons. The structure is shown below and satisfies the octet rule:

:F̈—N=N—F̈:

104. **(M)**

$$\text{amount of gas} = \frac{PV}{RT} = \frac{749 \text{ mmHg} \times \dfrac{1 \text{ atm}}{760 \text{ mmHg}} \times 0.193 \text{ L}}{0.08206 \text{ L atm mol}^{-1} \text{ K}^{-1} \times 299.3 \text{ K}} = 0.00774 \text{ mol}$$

$$M = \frac{\text{mass}}{\text{amount}} = \frac{0.325 \text{ g}}{0.00774 \text{ mol}} = 42.0 \text{ g/mol}$$

Because three moles of C weigh 36.0 g and four moles weigh 48.0 g, this hydrocarbon is

C_3H_6. A possible Lewis structure is
$$\begin{array}{c} \qquad\quad H \\ \quad\;\; | \\ H-C-C=C-H \\ \quad | \quad | \quad | \\ \quad H \;\; H \;\; H \end{array}$$

There is another possible Lewis structure: the three C atoms are arranged in a ring, with two H atoms bonded to each C atom (see below).

105. (D) First we determine the empirical formula of this C, H compound.

$$\text{amount C} = 4.04 \text{ g CO}_2 \times \frac{1 \text{ mol CO}_2}{44.01 \text{ g CO}_2} \times \frac{1 \text{ mol C}}{1 \text{ mol CO}_2} = 0.0.0918 \text{ mol C} \div 0.0.0918 \longrightarrow 1.00 \text{ mol C}$$

$$\text{amount C} = 1.24 \text{ g H}_2\text{O} \times \frac{1 \text{ mol H}_2\text{O}}{18.02 \text{ g H}_2\text{O}} \times \frac{2 \text{ mol H}}{1 \text{ mol H}_2\text{O}} = 0.138 \text{ mol H} \div 0.0918 \longrightarrow 1.50 \text{ mol H}$$

empirical formula = C_2H_3 possible molecular formula = C_4H_6

Lewis structure
$$\begin{array}{c} H-C=C\cdot \\ \;\; | \quad | \\ \;\; H \;\; H \end{array}$$
Lewis structures

$$\begin{array}{ccc} & \quad H \qquad\qquad H \\ & \quad | \qquad\qquad | \\ H-C=C-C=C-H \qquad H-C-C\equiv C-C-H \\ \;\; | \quad | \quad | \quad | \qquad\qquad | \qquad\qquad | \\ \;\; H \;\; H \;\; H \;\; H \qquad\qquad H \qquad\qquad H \end{array}$$

There are several other isomers that share this molecular formula.

106. **(M)** The two isomers are
$$\begin{array}{c} H \qquad\qquad H \\ \backslash \qquad\qquad / \\ C=C=C \\ / \qquad\qquad \backslash \\ H \qquad\qquad H \end{array}$$
and
$$\begin{array}{c} H \\ | \\ H-C-C\equiv C-H \\ | \\ H \end{array}$$

The left-hand isomer is planar around the first and third C atoms, but we cannot predict with VSEPR theory whether the molecule is planar overall; in other words, the two H—C—H planes may be at 90° to each other. (They are, in fact.) In the right-hand isomer, the C—C≡C—H chain is linear, but the H_3C— molecular geometry is tetrahedral.

107. **(M)** There are three valid resonance forms for the N_3^- ion; all three are shown below:

$$\ominus \ddot{N}\!=\!\!=\!\!\overset{\oplus}{N}\!=\!\!=\!\!\ddot{N} \ominus \qquad\qquad :N\!\!\equiv\!\!\overset{\oplus}{N}\!\!—\!\!\ddot{\ddot{N}}: -2 \qquad\qquad -2 : \ddot{\ddot{N}}\!\!—\!\!\overset{\oplus}{N}\!\!\equiv\!\!N:$$

$$\quad\quad\; \mathbf{1} \qquad\qquad\qquad\qquad \mathbf{2} \qquad\qquad\qquad\qquad \mathbf{3}$$

The best resonance form is the one with the lowest formal charge (all N have octets). Thus, resonance form **1** is the greatest contributor (probably the only contributor). The bond length give (116 pm) has a bond order between 2.0 (123 pm) and 3.0 (110 pm). This deviation from a bond order or 2 (double bond) can be explained by the formal charges in the ion which gives the bonds within the ion some partial ionic character.

108. **(M)** Because $\Delta_f H°[NO(g)] = +90.25$ kJ/mol, thus $\frac{1}{2}N_2(g) + \frac{1}{2}O_2(g) \longrightarrow NO(g)$

has a $\Delta_r H = 90.25$ kJ/mol. $\Delta_r H = \Delta_r H(N\!=\!O) - \frac{1}{2}\Delta_r H(N \equiv N) - \frac{1}{2}\Delta_r H(O = O)$

The heat of reaction will be the algebraic sum of bonds broken (N_2 and O_2) and bonds formed (NO). Note that bond breaking requires energy, while bond making releases energy.

$$+90.25\,\text{kJ} = -\Delta_r H(N\!=\!O) - \left(\frac{946\,\text{kJ}}{2}\right) - \left(\frac{498\,\text{kJ}}{2}\right)$$

$$\Delta_r H(N\!=\!O) = (-90.25 + 473 + 249)\,\text{kJ/mol} = +632\,\text{kJ/mol}$$

109. **(M)** The HN_3 molecule has $1 + (3 \times 5) = 16$ valence electrons, or 8 pairs. Average bond lengths are 136 pm for N—N, 123 pm for N=N, and 110 pm for N≡N. Thus it seems that one nitrogen-to-nitrogen bond is a double bond, while the other is a triple bond. A plausible Lewis structure is H–$\ddot{N}$=N=$\ddot{N}$ The three N's lie on a line, with a $120°$ H —N— N

bond angle: $\overset{H}{\underset{\ddot{N}=N=\ddot{N}}{\diagdown}}$ Another valid resonance form is H–$\ddot{\ddot{N}}$–N≡N: which would have one N—N separation consistent with a nitrogen-nitrogen triple bond. It would also predict a tetrahedral H—N—N bond angle of 109.5°. Thus, the resulting resonance hybrid should have a bond angle between 120° and 109.5°, which is in good agreement with the observed 112° H — N — N bond angle.

110. **(D)** For N_5^+ the number of valence electrons is $(5 \times 5) - 1 = 24$. There are four possible Lewis structures with formal charges that are not excessive ($<\pm 2$).

$$:\ddot{N}\!=\!\overset{\oplus}{N}\!=\!\overset{\oplus}{N}\!=\!\overset{\oplus}{N}\!=\!\ddot{N}: \quad :\ddot{N}\!=\!\overset{\oplus}{N}\!=\!\ddot{N}\!-\!\overset{\oplus}{N}\!\equiv\!N: \quad :N\!\equiv\!\overset{\oplus}{N}\!-\!\ddot{N}\!=\!\overset{\oplus}{N}\!=\!\ddot{N}: \quad :N\!\equiv\!\overset{\oplus}{N}\!-\!\overset{\ominus}{\ddot{N}}\!-\!\overset{\oplus}{N}\!\equiv\!N:$$
$$\;\;\ominus \qquad\qquad\qquad\quad \ominus \qquad\quad \ominus \qquad\qquad\qquad\qquad\quad \ominus$$
$$\qquad \mathbf{1} \qquad\qquad\qquad \mathbf{2} \qquad\qquad\qquad \mathbf{3} \qquad\qquad\qquad\qquad \mathbf{4}$$

Structure **1** has three adjacent atoms possessing formal charges of the same sign. Energetically, this is highly unfavorable. Structure **2 & 3** are similar and highly unsymmetrical but these are energetically more favorable than **1** Structure **4** is probably best of all, as all of the charges are close together with no two adjacent charges of the same sign. If structures **2, 3,** or **4** are chosen, the central nitrogen has one or two lone pairs. Thus, the structure of N_5^+ will be angular. (Note: an angle of 107.9° has been experimentally observed for the angle about the central nitrogen, as well, the bond length of the terminal N—N bonds is very close to that seen in N_2, suggesting a triple bond. This suggests that resonance form **4** best describes the structure of the ion.)

111. **(M)** The carbon-carbon distances of 130 pm are close to those of a $C = C$ double bond, (134 pm). The carbon-oxygen distances of 120 pm are close to that of a $C = O$ double bond, 123 pm. In C_3O_2 there are $3 \times 4 + 2 \times 6 = 24$ valence electrons or 12 valence electron pairs. The molecule is almost certainly linear. A plausible Lewis structure follows.

$$\ddot{\underset{\cdot\cdot}{O}} = C = C = C = \ddot{\underset{\cdot\cdot}{O}}$$

112. **(M)** In PCl_5 there are $5 + 5 \times 7 = 40$ valence electrons = 20 pairs. The Lewis structures are shown below. Since there are five atoms and no lone pairs attached to the central atom, the electron-group geometry and molecular shape of the molecule are the same, namely, trigonal bipyramidal. In PCl_4^+ there are $5 + 4 \times 7 - 1 = 32$ valence electrons = 16 pairs. Since there are four atoms and no lone pairs bonded to the central atom, the electron-group geometry and molecular shape of the species are the same, namely, tetrahedral. In PCl_6^- there are $5 + 6 \times 7 + 1 = 48$ valence electrons = 24 pairs. Since there are six atoms and no lone pairs bonded to the central atom, the electron-group geometry and molecular shape of the species are the same, namely, octahedral.

113. **(D)** The Lewis structures for the species in reaction (2) follow.

$$:N \equiv N: \quad H - H \quad H - C \equiv N:$$

Bonds broken $= \dfrac{1}{2} \; N \equiv N + \dfrac{1}{2} \; H - H = \dfrac{1}{2} \; (946 \; kJ + 436 \; kJ) = 691 \; kJ$

Bonds formed $= H - C + C \equiv N = 414 \; kJ + 891 \; kJ = 1305 \; kJ$

$\Delta_r H = 691 \; kJ - 1305 \; kJ = -614 \; kJ$

Then we determine $\Delta_f H°$

(a) $C(s) \longrightarrow C(g)$ $\Delta_r H = +717 \; kJ$

(b) $\underline{C(g) + \frac{1}{2} \, N_2(g) + \frac{1}{2} \, H_2(g) \longrightarrow HCN(g) \quad \Delta_r H = -614 \; kJ}$

Net: $C(s) + \frac{1}{2} \, N_2(g) + \frac{1}{2} H_2(g) \longrightarrow HCN(g) \qquad \Delta_f H° = +103 \; kJ$

This compares favorably to the value of 135.1 kJ/mol given in Appendix D-2.

114. **(M)** We analyze the formation reaction for $H_2O_2(g)$ via the use of Lewis structures.

$$H - H + \ddot{\underset{\cdot\cdot}{O}} = \ddot{\underset{\cdot\cdot}{O}} \longrightarrow H - \ddot{\underset{\cdot\cdot}{O}} - \ddot{\underset{\cdot\cdot}{O}} - H$$

Bonds broken $= H - H + O = O$

Energy required: $436 \; kJ + 498 \; kJ = 934 \; kJ$

426

Bonds formed = 2(H — O) + O — O

Energy released: 2×464 kJ + O — O = 928 kJ + O — O

$\Delta_f H° = -136$ kJ = 934 kJ $-$ 928 kJ $-$ O — O

Bond energy (O — O) = 142 kJ

This is the same as the value in Table 10.3.

115. **(D)** Ambiguity arises because of uncertainly over (i) bond order between C and S and (ii) the position of the H atoms

H in equatorial or axial positions on S

Both H in equatorial positions on S or both in the axial positions on S

H in equatorial or axial positions on S

Both H in equatorial positions on S or one hydrogen is axial and one is equatorial

116. **(M)** We first compute the heats of reaction.

$$CH_3OH(g) + H_2S(g) \longrightarrow CH_3SH(g) + H_2O(g)$$

$$\Delta_r H° = \Delta_f H°[H_2O(g)] + \Delta_f H°[CH_3SH(g)] - [\Delta_f H°[CH_3OH(g)] + \Delta_f H°[H_2S(g)]]$$
$$= -241.8 \text{ kJ} + (-22.9 \text{ kJ}) - [(-200.7 \text{ kJ} - 20.63 \text{ kJ})] = -43.4 \text{ kJ}$$

Breaking of one mole of C—O bond requires (360 kJ) = +360 kJ

Breaking of one mole of H—S bond requires (368 kJ) = + 368 kJ

Breaking of one mole of O—H bond requires (464 kJ) = + 464 kJ

Making of one mole of C—S bond yields = $-x$ kJ

Making 2 moles of O—H bonds yields 2(–464 kJ) =   –928 kJ

$$\Sigma(\text{bond energies}) = \Delta_r H^\circ = -43.4 \text{ kJ}$$

Then… $264 - x = -43.4$ and $x = 307$ kJ, which is the C-S bond energy for the C—S bond in methanethiol (estimate only).

117. (M)

$$\text{Li} \underset{}{\overset{217 \text{ pm}}{\rule{2cm}{0.4pt}}} \text{Br} \qquad \mu = 7.268 \text{ D} \qquad \Delta EN = 1.7$$

$$\text{Na} \underset{}{\overset{236 \text{ pm}}{\rule{2cm}{0.4pt}}} \text{Cl} \qquad \mu = 7.268 \text{ D} \qquad \Delta EN = 2.1$$

(a)

$$\delta_{Li-Br} = \frac{\mu \times 3.34 \times 10^{-30} \, CmD^{-1}}{d} = \frac{7.268 \, D \times 3.34 \times 10^{-30} \, CmD^{-1}}{217 \times 10^{-12} \, m} = 1.12 \times 10^{-19} \, C \ (\approx 70\% \, ionic)$$

$$\delta_{Na-Cl} = \frac{\mu \times 3.34 \times 10^{-30} \, CmD^{-1}}{d} = \frac{9.001 \, D \times 3.34 \times 10^{-30} \, CmD^{-1}}{236 \times 10^{-12} \, m} = 1.27 \times 10^{-19} \, C \ (\approx 80\% \, ionic)$$

(b) Using the ΔEN values for each gas phase species and Figure 10-7, we can estimate that Li-Br ~ 50% ionic and Na-Cl ~ 70% ionic.

(c) The value for NaCl agrees quite well, however, LiBr does not show as good an agreement. This is probably due to the large lone pairs on Br, the small size of the Li atom (especially relative to the Br atom), and the fact that the Li atom does not have much shielding. As well, bear in mind that these are very loosely associated atoms.

118. **(M)** IF_7 has a pentagonal bipyramidal structure, with the following internal angles:

180° angle for F_a–I–F_a
90° angle for F_a–I–F_b
72° angle for F_b–I–F_b

119. **(D)** Consider the possible resonance forms for each acid (shown below).

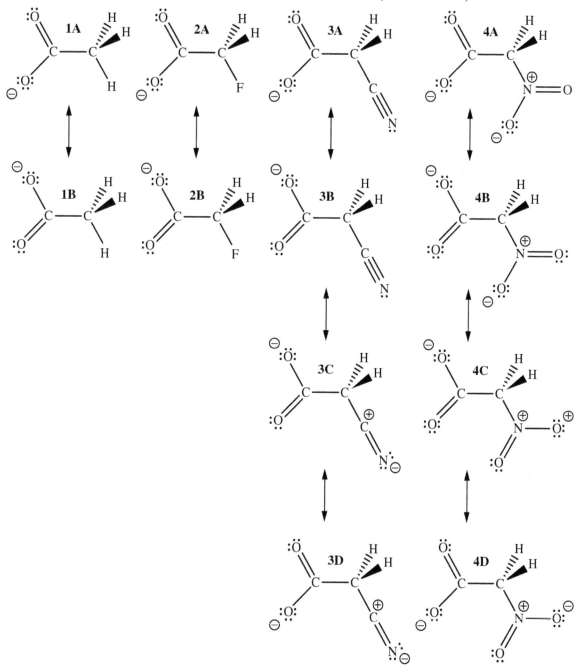

Note: All of these carboxylic acids display delocalization of the negative charge across the carboxylate group. Let's consider each acid in turn, to assess the stability of the anion/acidity of the acid.

Acetic acid

In the case of acetic acid (1A and 1B), the hydrogen atoms do not contribute to the stability of the anion. In fact, one might argue that the hydrogen atoms with an electronegativity of 2.1, donates electron density to the adjacent (α) carbon and thus offsets delocalization of the negative charge on the anion.

Fluoroacetic acid

In the case of fluoroacetic acid (2A and 2B), other than the carboxylate resonance forms, the fluorine atom does not contribute significantly to the stability of the anion by way of resonance. However, fluorine is quite electronegative compared to carbon, resulting in the development of a partial positive charge on the α-carbon. This allows for more extensive delocalization of the negative charge on the anions, which leads to greater stability for the anion.

Cyanoacetic acid

In the case of cyanoacetic acid (3A to 3D), we clearly see the carboxylate resonance delocalization.. However, there are resonance forms in the cyano group that result in a formally positively charged carbon (carbocation) being directly bonded to the α-carbon. This will allow for more complete delocalization of negative charge on the anion. There is one problem, however. The resonance forms for the cyano group do not leave the carbon atom with the formal positive charge in the cyano group with a complete octet. Although the cyano group is electron withdrawing, it behaves very much like a very electronegative halide by virtue of the fact that a very electronegative nitrogen is directly bonded to carbon in the cyano group. This results in a slightly positive charge on the carbon attached to the α-carbon, resulting in significant delocalization of the negative charge on the anion.

Nitroacetic acid

In the case of nitroacetic acid (4A to 4B), we clearly see the carboxylate resonance delocalization. However, there are resonance forms in the nitro group that result in the development of a positive formal charge on the nitrogen atom directly bonded to the α-carbon. This will significantly allow for the delocalization of negative charge on the anion. Unlike the cyano group, the nitro group has a formal positive charge on nitrogen and complete octets for all the second row atoms in the acid. Thus, the nitro group will allow for the most delocalization of the negative charge on the anion, which makes nitroacetic acid the strongest of the four acids and the nitroacetate ion the most stable conjugate base.

The acids in order of strength should be: nitroacetic > cyanoacetic > fluoroacetic > acetic.

120. **(M)** For the halogens we have the following data:

Atom	Electronegativity	Ionization Energy (kJ/mol)	Electron Affinity (kJ/mol)
F	4.0	1680	–328
Cl	3.0	1256	–349
Br	2.8	1143	–324.6
I	2.5	1009	–295.2

From the data above and using $EN = k \times (E_i - E_{ea})$ for the halogens, we find the following values for k: F = 0.00199   Cl = 0.00187   Br = 0.00191   I = 0.00192 We shall assume that the value of k for astatine is 0.0019. As well, from the data, we can estimate the ionization energy for astatine to be ~900 kJ/mol. The text gives 2.2 as the electronegativity for astatine. We can now estimate a value for the electron affinity of At.

$$EN = k \times (E_i - E_{ea}) = 2.2 = 0.0019(900 - E_{ea}) \quad E_{ea} \sim -260 \text{ kJ/mol}$$

121. (M) Structure (a) has too many electrons, resulting in a molecule with an overall charge of –2 (each sulfur has a formal charge of –1). Structure (b) has formal charges of +1 on each sulfur atom and -1 on each Cl atom. Structure (c) has considerable formal charge built up in this Lewis structure (each sulfur carries a formal charge of –2 and each chlorine carries a formal charge of +2). Both structures (d) and (e) have no formal charges in the Lewis structure and may be considered "good" Lewis structures, however, structure (d) has 10 electrons around each sulfur (expanded octet), while in structure (e), all atoms have an octet. Given this information, structure (e) best represents the molecule, however, one cannot rule out structure (d) completely based solely on the expanded octet, especially since S has vacant 3 d orbitals that may be used in expanding its octet. Read Section 10-6: Expanded Octets.

122. (D) The molecules hydrogen azide, nitrosyl azide and trifluoromethyl azide share some common structural elements. They can be viewed as N_3^- attached to H, NO, and CF_3 respectively. There are numerous resonance structures that can be written for these molecules. Some of the resonance forms are better than others for several reasons, including such factors as the lack of a full octet and unacceptably large charge separations. Drawn below are the various resonance forms for the molecules. The Lewis diagrams have been modified to include geometric considerations that are imposed on the molecule by hybridization and the effects of lone pairs.

Let's consider each molecule in turn.

Hydrogen azide (linear N—N—N):

Resonance forms (A) and (B) are the best, owing to low formal charges. (C) is clearly not an important an resonance contributor because it possess two adjacent like charges. Note that the molecule should be bent at the hydrogen bonded nitrogen.

Hydrogen azide(cyclic form):

Resonance form (D) is clearly favored because all of the atoms have a formal charge of zero. This structural isomer would be highly reactive owing to the very strained ring which imposes internal N—N—N angles that approach ~ 60° and a hybridization scheme that tries to accommodate both 120 or 109.5° angles.

Trifluoromethyl azide:

| (G) | (H) | (I) |

Good resonance forms Poor resonance form
(charge buildup)

Resonance forms (G) and (H) are the best, owing to low formal charges for the constituent atoms. Structure (I) is clearly not as important a resonance contributor because it contains destabilizing adjacent positive charges. The molecule is expected to be very reactive and hence hard to isolate.

Nitrosyl azide

Best resonance forms (small distance between charge separation)

Good resonance forms (however, large charge separation)

Poor resonance forms (charge buildup)

Nitrosyl azide is a bent molecule. Based on the best two Lewis structures, we expect that the molecule is bent at the two leftmost nitrogen atoms ($\sim 115\,^{\circ} \pm 20\,^{\circ}$).

123. (M) Consider each molecule separately:

B_2F_4: A total of 34 electrons. Neutral molecule. There are no formal charges in the molecule. Free rotation about single bond, with the possibility of all atoms being planar. There are no valid resonance forms.

N_2O_4: A total of 34 electrons. Neutral molecule with formal charges. Free rotation about single bond, with the possibility of all atoms being planar. There are 3 valid resonance forms.

$C_2O_4^{2-}$: A total of 34 electrons Must be the dianion where the formal charges add to the overall charge of the anion.
Free rotation about single bond, with the possibility of all atoms being planar. There are 3 valid resonance forms.

124. (M) Shown below is the deprotonation and the expected resonance stabilized enolate product, which has two forms (**A** and **B** below). In structure **A,** the negative charge is on the CH_2 carbon atom and in structure **B** it is on the oxygen atom. Both of these resonance forms will contribute to the hybrid structure of the anion. Structure **A** is desirable in that it possess a very strong C = O bond (relative to the weaker C = C bond in **B**). Structure **B** has the negative charge on oxygen, the more electronegative atom, which is better able to accommodate the negative charge.

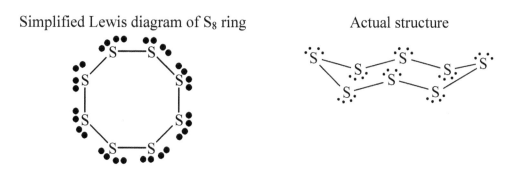

125. (M) The anion PBr_4^- has 34 electrons. Its electronic geometry is trigonal bypyramidal, while ideally, its molecular geometry is expected to be a see-saw. Since phosphorus is a relatively small atom and bromine is a relatively large atom, significant distortions may exist in the anion such that the bromine atoms distribute themselves more evenly around the phosphorus centre. With extensive delocalization of the phosphorus lone pair over the four bromine atoms, the structure will approach a pure tetrahedron. Even if the lone pair stays localized on the phosphorus, the geometry may well appear to be tetrahedral, albeit distorted (see below).

126. (a) Sulfur in the form of S_8 is not planar, because each sulfur atom in the S_8 ring has a tetrahedral electron group geometry. Below is the drawing of a flat S_8 ring, which is provided to show a simplified Lewis structure, accompanied with the actual shape of the S_8 ring:

Simplified Lewis diagram of oxidized
S_8 ring

Actual structure

127. (M)

(a)

(b)

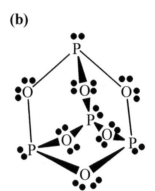

The O atoms in P_4O_6 are surrounded by 4 groups and so the geometry around each O is tetrahedral. Therefore, the P–O–P bond is not linear.

FEATURE PROBLEMS

128. (M) The table containing the constants used for the calculations is reproduced below. In all cases, a sample calculation is worked out for F.

	Atom, X				
	H	F	Cl	Br	I
E_i/eV	13.5985	17.423	12.9677	11.8139	10.4513
E_{ea}/eV	0.7542	3.399	3.617	3.365	3.059
$D(HX)$/eV	4.44	6.39	4.38	3.74	3.07
$D(X_2)$/eV	4.44	2.80	2.468	1.962	1.535
Z_{eff}	1	4.86	5.75	7.25	7.25
r_{cov}/pm	–	71.5	99.4	114.2	133.4

Electronegativity using the Pauling method, calculated relative to EN_H, is shown below. The general formula is

$$EN_A - EN_B = \sqrt{\frac{D_{A-B} - \frac{1}{2}\left(D_{A-A} + D_{B-B}\right)}{1\ eV}}$$

For F, the relative χ is calculated as follows:

$$EN_F - EN_H = \sqrt{\frac{6.39 \text{ eV} - \frac{1}{2}(2.8 + 4.44)\text{ eV}}{1 \text{ eV}}} = 1.7$$

Assuming a EN_H value of 2.1, the absolute value of EN_F is 3.8. Electronegativity values for Cl, Br, and I are provided in the table at the end of this problem.

Electronegativity using the Mullikan method for F is calculated as follows:

$$EN = 0.336 \times \left(\frac{E_i + E_{ea}}{2 \text{ eV}}\right) - 0.165$$

$$EN = 0.336 \times \left(\frac{17.423 + 3.399}{2 \text{ eV}}\right) - 0.165 = 3.33$$

Electronegativity using the Allred-Rochow method is calculated as follows:

$$EN = \frac{3590 \, Z_{eff}}{(r_{cov}/1 \text{ pm})^2} + 0.744$$

$$EN = \frac{3590 \times 4.86}{(71.5/1 \text{ pm})^2} + 0.744 = 4.16$$

The calculation results for all the nuclides are shown in the table below.

	F	Cl	Br	I
Pauling (relative to H)	1.7	1.0	0.7	0.3
Pauling (absolute)	3.8	3.1	2.8	2.4
Mulliken	3.3	2.6	2.3	2.1
Allred–Rochow	4.2	2.8	2.7	2.2

129. (D)

(a) The two bond dipole moments can be added geometrically, by placing the head of one at the tail of the other, as long as we do not change the direction or the length of the moved dipole. The resultant molecular dipole moment is represented by the arrow drawn from the tail of one bond dipole to the head of the other. This is shown in the figure to the right. The 52.0° angle in the figure is one-half of the 104° bond angle in water. The length is given as 1.84 D. We can construct a right angled triangle by bisecting the 76.0° angle. The right angled triangle has a hypotenuse = O — H bond dipole and the two other angles are 52° and 38°. The side opposite the bisected 76.0 ° angles is ½ (1.84 D) = 0.92 D. We can calculate the bond dipole using: sin

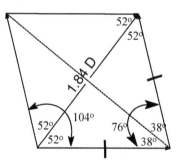

$$38.0° = \frac{0.92 \text{ D}}{\text{O-H bond dipole}} = 0.61566, \text{ hence O—H bond dipole} = 1.49 \text{ D}.$$

(b) For H_2S, we do not know the bond angle. We shall represent this bond angle as 2α. Using a similar procedure to that described in part (a), above, a diagram can be constructed and the angle 2α calculated as follows:

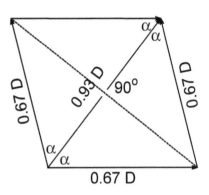

$$\cos\alpha = \frac{\frac{1}{2}(0.93\,D)}{0.67\,D} = 0.694 \quad \alpha = 46.05°$$

or $2\alpha = 92.\underline{1}°$

The H—S—H angle is approximately 92°.

(c)

Molecule and associated individual bond dipoles	Relationship between dipole moment(molecular) and bond dipoles(Vector addition)	Geometric Relationship

$\mu_{C-H} + 3(\mu_{C-Cl}) = 1.04\,D$
$0.30\,D + 3(x) = 1.04\,D$
$x = 0.25\,D = \mu_{C-Cl}$

Mathematical solution: $\sin(\phi) = \dfrac{0.25\,D}{1.87\,D}$

$\phi = 7.6°$

The H-C-Cl bond angle is $(90 + \phi)° = 90° + 7.6° = 97.6°$

130. (D) Step 1 in the alternative approach is similar to the first step in the method used for drawing Lewis structures. The only significant difference is that "electron pairs" rather than the total number of valence electrons are counted in this alternative approach. The second step in the alternative strategy is also similar to the second step for writing Lewis structures. By counting the number of bonding electron pairs in the alternative method, one is effectively working out the number of bonds present in the skeletal structure of the Lewis diagram. In step 3, the number of electron pairs surrounding the central atom is calculated. This is basically the same procedure as completing the octets for the terminal atoms and assigning the remaining electrons to the central atom in the Lewis structure. Finally, in step 4 of the alternative method, the number of lone pair electrons on the central atom is calculated. This number, together with the result from step 3, allows one to establish the VSEPR class. Consequently, both the alternative strategy and the Lewis diagram provide the number of bonding electron pairs and lone pairs on the central atom for the species whose shape is being predicted. Since the shape of the molecule or ion in the VSEPR approach is determined solely by the number and types of electron pairs on the central atom (i.e., the VSEPR class) both methods end up giving the same result.

Included in the "alternative strategy" is the assumption that the central atom does not form double bonds with any of the terminal atoms. This means that in many instances, the central atom does not possess a complete octet. The presence or absence of an octet is, however, of no consequence to the VSEPR method because, according to the tenets of this theory, the shape adopted by the molecule is determined solely by the number and types of electron pairs on the central atom. Examples follow on the next two pages.

(a) PCl_5

    1. Total e^- pairs $= \dfrac{(1 \times 5e^- \text{ from P atom}) + (5 \times 7e^- \text{ from the 5 Cl atoms})}{2} = 20$ pairs of e^-

    2. Number of bonding e^- pairs = 6 atoms ($5 \times Cl + 1 \times P$) $- 1 = 5$ bonding e^- pairs.

    3. Number of e^- pairs around the central atom = (20(total) e^- pairs) $- 3 \times$(5 terminal Cl)
                                              $= 5$ e^- pairs around P atom.

    4. Number of lone pair $e^- = 5$ e^- pairs around P $- 5$ bonding pairs of $e^- = 0$

Thus, according to this alternative approach, PCl_5 belongs to the VSEPR class AX_5. Molecules of this type adopt a trigonal bipyramidal structure.

(b) NH_3

    1. Total e^- pairs $= \dfrac{(1 \times 5e^- \text{ from N atom}) + (3 \times 1e^- \text{ from the 3 H atoms})}{2} = 4$ pairs of e^-

    2. Number of bonding e^- pairs = 4 atoms ($1 \times N + 3 \times H$) $- 1 = 3$ bonding e^- pairs.

    3. Number of e^- pairs around the central atom = 4(total) e^- pairs $- 0$
                                              $= 4$ e^- pairs around N atom.

    4. Number of lone pair $e^- = 4$ e^- pairs around N $- 3$ bonding pairs of $e^- = 1$ lone pair of e^-

Thus, according to this alternative approach, NH_3 belongs to the VSEPR class AX_3E. Molecules of this type adopt a trigonal pyramidal structure.

(c) ClF_3

    1. Total e^- pairs $= \dfrac{(1 \times 7e^- \text{ from Cl atom}) + (3 \times 7e^- \text{ from the 3 F atoms})}{2} = 14$ e^- pairs

    2. Number of bonding e^- pairs = 4 atoms ($1 \times Cl + 3 \times F$) $- 1 = 3$ bonding e^- pairs.

    3. Number of e^- pairs around the central atom = 14(total) pairs $- 3 \times$ (3 terminal F atoms)
                                              $= 5$ e^- pairs around Cl atom.

    4. Number of lone pair $e^- = 5$ e^- pairs around Cl $- 3$ bonding pairs of
                              $e^- = 1$ lone pair of e^-

Thus, according to this alternative approach, ClF_3 belongs to the VSEPR class AX_3E_2. Molecules of this type adopt a T-shaped structure.

(d) SO_2

1. Total e^- pairs $= \dfrac{(1 \times 6e^- \text{ from S atom}) + (2 \times 6e^- \text{ from the 2 O atoms})}{2} = 9 \; e^- \text{ pairs}$

2. Number of bonding e^- pairs $= 3$ atoms $(1 \times S + 2 \times O) - 1 = 2$ bonding e^- pairs.

3. Number of e^- pairs around the central atom $= 9$(total) pairs $- 3 \times (2$ terminal O atoms$)$
$= 3 \; e^-$ pairs around S atom.

4. Number of lone pair $e^- = 3 \; e^-$ pairs around S $- 2$ bonding pairs of $e^- = 1$ lone pair of e^-

Thus, according to this alternative approach, SO_2 belongs to the VSEPR class AX_2E. Molecules of this type adopt a bent structure.

(e) ClF_4^-

1. Total e^- pairs $= \dfrac{(1 \times 7e^- \text{ from Cl}) + (4 \times 7e^- \text{ from the 4 F}) + (1e^- \text{ for charge of } -1))}{2}$
$= 18$ pairs of e^-

2. Number of bonding e^- pairs $= 5$ atoms $(1 \times Cl + 4 \times F) - 1 = 4$ bonding e^- pairs.

3. Number of e^- pairs around the central atom $= 18$(total) pairs $- 3 \times (4$ terminal F atoms$)$
$= 6 \; e^-$ pairs around Cl atom.

4. Number of lone pair $e^- = 6 \; e^-$ pairs around Cl $- 4$ bonding pairs of $e^- = 2$ lone pair of e^-

Thus, according to this alternative approach, ClF_4^- belongs to the VSEPR class AX_4E_2. Molecules of this type adopt a square planar structure.

(f) PCl_4^+

1. Total e^- pairs $= \dfrac{(1 \times 5e^- \text{ from P}) + (4 \times 7e^- \text{ from the 4 Cl}) - (1e^- \text{ for } +1 \text{ charge})}{2}$
$= 16$ pairs of e^-

2. Number of bonding e^- pairs $= 5$ atoms $(4 \times Cl + 1 \times P) - 1 = 4$ bonding e^- pairs.

3. Number of e^- pairs around the central atom $= 16$(total) pairs $- 3(4$ terminal Cl atoms$)$
$= 4 \; e^-$ pairs around P atom.

4. Number of lone pair $e^- = 4 \; e^-$ pairs around P $- 4$ bonding pairs of $e^- = 0$

Thus, according to this alternative approach, ClF_4^+ belongs to the VSEPR class AX_4. Molecules of this type adopt a tetrahedral structure.

SELF-ASSESSMENT EXERCISES

131. (E)

(a) Valence electrons: Electrons in the outermost shell of an atom which are involved in the bonding

(b) Electronegativity: A measure of atoms competing for electrons with other atoms

(c) Bond dissociation energy: The energy required to break a covalent bond

(d) Double covalent bond: A sharing of two pairs of electrons between two atoms

(e) Coordinate covalent bond: A covalent bond in which one atom contributes both electrons to make a bond

132. (E)

(a) Formal charge: The apparent (but not necessarily actual) charge on an atom derived from the Lewis structure based on the number of valence, shared, and unshared electrons

(b) Resonance: For a given compound, resonance means two or more Lewis structures, which contribute to the final "correct" structure

(c) Expanded valence shell: When an atom in a molecule can accommodate more than 8 electrons in its valence shell (happens usually with p-block atoms in the 3p or higher subshells such as S, P, As, etc., because they can use their empty d subshells for the extra electrons)

(d) Bond energy: The energy released when a bond is formed.

133. (E)

(a) Ionic and covalent bonds: In ionic bonds, there is no sharing of electrons, but rather a complete transfer of electrons from one atom to another. In covalent bonds, there is sharing of a pair (or more) of electrons between two atoms.

(b) Lone-pair and bond-pair electrons: Lone pairs are electron pairs entirely localized on one atom. Bond pairs are pairs of electrons shared between two atoms.

(c) Molecular geometry and electron-group geometry: Molecular geometry only considers arrangement of atoms, and is influenced by the lone pairs. An electron-group geometry ignores the atoms and determines the ultimate geometry using electron pairs only.

(d) Bond dipole and resultant dipole moment: Bond dipole is a measure of the difference in electron densities between two bonded atoms as a result of the difference in their electronegativities. The resultant dipole moment is a measure of the polarity of the molecule derived from individual bond dipoles and the molecular geometry.

(e) Polar molecules and non-polar molecules: Polar molecules have a net dipole moment, whereas non-polar molecules do not.

134. (E) The answer is (b). The structure is:

135. (E) The answer is (c). The structure is:

Formal charge on O is: $6 - 4 - 2 = 0$

136. (E) The answer is (a), SO_2. NO is linear by definition since there are only two atoms. The other molecules have the following structures:

137. (E) The answer is (a), SO_3. The other choices are polar, because: CH_2Cl_2 has a non-uniform field of atoms around the central atom C; NH_3 is trigonal pyramidal and has a lone pair of electrons on N; in FNO, there are three different atoms with different electron affinities.

138. **(E)** The answer is (b), N_2, because one has to break three covalent bonds to dissociate the two N atoms from each other.

139. **(E)** The answer is (c), Br_2, because the greater the covalent radii of the two atoms involved, the longer the bond length. Br is the largest atom and therefore, Br–Br bond would be the longest.

140. **(M)**
(a)   (b)

(c)   (d)

141. **(M)**

	(a)	(b)	(c)
e^- group geometry	Trigonal planar	Tetrahedral	Tetrahedral
Molecular geometry	Bent	Trigonal pyramidal	Tetrahedral

142. **(E)** The answer is (a). Although all the other compounds are ionic, they all contain metals.

143. **(E)** The answer is (d). It does not obey the octet rule since a full set of eight electrons cannot be placed around both atoms because of the odd number of valence electrons. The correct Lewis structure is shown below.

·N̈=Ö

144. (E) The answer is (e). All the choices have a polar bond, which arises from the difference in electronegativity of the atoms making the bond.

145. (E) The answer is (a). The oxygen atom in H_2O has two bonds and two lone electron pairs, which gives it a tetrahedral electron-group geometry and a bent (or V-shaped) molecular structure.

146. (M)

Electron-Group Geometry	Molecular Shape	
Tetrahedral	Tetrahedral	
Tetrahedral	Trigonal pyramidal	
Trigonal pyramidal	Seesaw	
Octahedral	Square pyramidal	

147. (M) The total enthalpy change for each reaction is the difference between the sum of the bond energies for the bonds broken (which consumes energy) and the sum of the bond energies for the bonds formed (which releases energy).

(a) CH_4: The balanced reaction is

$$CH_4(g) + 2\, O_2 \rightarrow CO_2(g) + 2\, H_2O(g)$$

The oxidation state of C in CH_4 is −4.

Bonds broken: 4 C–H + 2 O=O

$$4(414) + 2(498) = 2642 \text{ kJ mol}^{-1}$$

Bonds formed: 2 C=O + 4 H–O

$$2(799) + 4(464) = 3454 \text{ kJ mol}^{-1}$$

Therefore, the total energy change for combustion of CH_4 is $2642 - 3454 = -812 \text{ kJ mol}^{-1}$
The energy change per gram is

$$\frac{-812 \text{ kJ mol}^{-1}}{16.05 \text{ g mol}^{-1}} = -50.6 \text{ kJ g}^{-1}$$

(b) CH_3OH: The balanced reaction is

$$2\ CH_3OH(g) + 3\ O_2 \rightarrow 2\ CO_2(g) + 4\ H_2O(g)$$

The oxidation state of C in CH_3OH is −2.

Bonds broken: 6 C–H + 2 C–O + 2 O–H + 3 O=O

$$6(414) + 2(360) + 2(464) + 3(498) = 5626 \text{ kJ mol}^{-1}$$

Bonds formed: 4 C=O + 8 H–O

$$4(799) + 8(464) = 6908 \text{ mol}^{-1}$$

Therefore, the total energy change for combustion of CH_4 is $5626 - 6908 = -1282 \text{ kJ mol}^{-1}$

The energy change per gram is

$$\frac{-1282 \text{ kJ mol}^{-1}}{2(32.05 \text{ g mol}^{-1})} = -20.0 \text{ kJ g}^{-1}$$

(c) H_2CO: The balanced reaction is

$$H_2CO(g) + O_2 \rightarrow CO_2(g) + H_2O(g)$$

The oxidation state of C in H_2CO is 0.

Bonds broken: 2 C–H + C=O + O=O

$$2(414) + (799) + (498) = 2125 \text{ kJ mol}^{-1}$$

Bonds formed: 2 C=O + 2 H–O

$$2(707) + 2(464) = 2342 \text{ kJ mol}^{-1}$$

Therefore, the total energy change for combustion of CH_4 is $2125 - 2342 = -217 \text{ kJ mol}^{-1}$

The energy change per gram is

$$\frac{-217 \text{ kJ mol}^{-1}}{30.03 \text{ g mol}^{-1}} = -7.23 \text{ kJ g}^{-1}$$

(d) H_2CO: The balanced reaction is

$$2\ HCOOH(g) + O_2 \rightarrow 2\ CO_2(g) + 2\ H_2O(g)$$

The oxidation state of C in HCOOH is +2.

Bonds broken: 2 O–H + C–H + 2 C = O + 2 C–O + O = O

$$2(464) + 2(414) + 2(799) + 2(360) + (498) = 4572 \text{ kJ mol}^{-1}$$

Bonds formed: 4 C=O + 4 H–O

$$4(707) + 4(464) = 4684 \text{ kJ mol}^{-1}$$

Therefore, the total energy change for combustion of HCOOH is

$$4572 - 4684 = -112 \text{ kJ mol}^{-1}$$

The energy change per gram is

$$\frac{-112 \text{ kJ mol}^{-1}}{2(46.03 \text{ g mol}^{-1})} = -1.22 \text{ kJ g}^{-1}$$

There is a trend with respect to the oxidation state and energy generated per gram of combusted material. The more negative the oxidation state of the carbon, the more energy that is generated per gram of that material.

148. **(E)** Ba and Mg are active metals with a low EN, S is the most electronegative (and non-metallic) as indicated by its location on the periodic table. In comparing Bi and As, Bi has lower EN value, as indicated by its location. Therefore, Bi has the middle position: Ba < Mg < Bi < As < S

149. **(E)**

Bond	Bond Energy (kJ/mol)	Bond Length (pm)
C–H	414	110
C=O	736	120
C–C	347	154
C–Cl	339	178

150. **(E)** VSEPR theory is valence shell electron pair repulsion theory. It is based on the premise that electron pairs assume orientations about an atom to minimize electron pair repulsions.

151. **(E)** The structure of the NH_3 molecule and the arrangement of electrons is shown below:

As can be seen, there are 4 pairs of electrons around the nitrogen atoms. Three pairs are in the form of covalent bonds with hydrogen atoms, and one is a lone pair. Since there are 4 electron pairs around the central atom, the way to maximize the distance between them is to set up a tetrahedral electron group geometry. However, since there are only three atoms bonding to the central atom, the molecular geometry is trigonal pyramidal.

152. **(E)** A pyramidal geometry is observed when an atom has one lone pair and is bonded to three other atoms (AX_3E). A bent geometry is observed when an atom has two lone pairs and is bonded to two other atoms (AX_2E_2). For both, the bond angles will be approximately (usually smaller than) $109°$.

153. **(M)**

154. **(M)** The way to approach this concept map is to break it down to three major topics: Lewis dot structures, shape of molecule, and polarity. Lewis dot structures can be divided into simpler subtopics, such as Lewis symbols, the 8-electron rule, and the expanded valence shell. Molecular shape can be divided into molecular geometry and electron-group geometry. Polarity can be described in terms of dipole moment of the molecule, which can itself be described in terms of bond dipole and molecular geometry.

CHAPTER 11
CHEMICAL BONDING II: VALENCE BOND AND MOLECULAR ORBITAL THEORIES
PRACTICE EXAMPLES

1A **(M)** The valence-shell orbital diagrams of N and I are as follows:

N [He]$_{2s}$⊞ $_{2p}$⊞⊞⊞   I [Kr] 4d^{10} $_{5s}$⊞ $_{5p}$⊞⊞⊞

There are three half-filled $2p$ orbitals on N, and one half-filled $5p$ orbital on I. Each half-filled $2p$ orbital from N will overlap with one half-filled $5p$ orbital of an I. Thus, there will be three N—I bonds. The I atoms will be oriented in the same direction as the three $2p$ orbitals of N: toward the $x-$, $y-$, and z-directions of a Cartesian coordinate system. Thus, the I—N—I angles will be approximately 90° (probably larger because the I atoms will repel each other). The three I atoms will lie in the same plane at the points of a triangle, with the N atom centered above them. The molecule is trigonal pyramidal. (The same molecular shape is predicted if N is assumed to be sp^3 hybridized, but with 109.5° rather than 90° bond angles.)

1B **(M)** The valence-shell orbital diagrams of N and H are as follows. N: [He]$_{2s}$⊞ $_{2p}$⊞⊞⊞ H: $_{1s}$⊞
There are three half-filled orbitals on N and one half-filled orbital on each H. There will be three N—H bonds, with bond angles of approximately 90°. The molecule is trigonal pyramid. (We obtain the same molecular shape if N is assumed to be sp^3 hybridized, but bond angles are closer to 109.5°, the tetrahedral bond angle.) VSEPR theory begins with the Lewis structure and notes that there are three bond pairs and one lone pair attached to N. This produces a tetrahedral electron pair geometry and a trigonal pyramidal molecular shape with bond angles a bit less than the tetrahedral angle of 109.5° because of the lone pair downward repulsion of the bonded pairs of electrons. Since VSEPR theory makes a prediction closer to the experimental bond angle of 107°, it seems more appropriate in this case.

2A **(D)** Following the strategy outlined in the textbook, we begin by drawing a plausible Lewis structure for the cation in question. In this case, the Lewis structure must contain 20 valence electrons. The skeletal structure for the cation has a chlorine atom, the least electronegative element present, in the central position. Next we join the terminal chlorine and fluorine atoms to the central chlorine atom via single covalent bonds and then complete the octets for all three atoms by placing three lone pairs around the terminal atoms and two lone pairs around the central atom.

$$:\overset{..}{\underset{..}{F}}—\overset{..}{\underset{..}{Cl}}{}^{\oplus}—\overset{..}{\underset{..}{Cl}}:$$

With this bonding arrangement, the central chlorine atom ends up with a 1+ formal charge.

Once the Lewis diagram is complete, we can then use the VSEPR method to establish the geometry for the electron pairs on the central atom. The Lewis structure has two bonding electron pairs and two lone pairs of electrons around the central chlorine atom. These four pairs of electrons assume a tetrahedral geometry to minimize electron-electron repulsions. The VSEPR notation for the Cl_2F^+ ion is AX_2E_2. According to Table 10.1, molecules of this type exhibit a tetrahedral geometric orientation. Our next task is to select a hybridization scheme that is consistent with the predicted shape. It turns out that the only way we can end up with a tetrahedral array of electron groups is if the central chlorine atom is sp^3 hybridized. In this scheme, two of the sp^3 hybrid orbitals are filled, while the remaining two are half occupied.

$$\boxed{\uparrow\downarrow}\ \boxed{\uparrow\downarrow}\ \boxed{\uparrow}\ \boxed{\uparrow}\ \ sp^3 \text{ hybridized central chlorine atom } (Cl^+)$$

The Cl—F and Cl—Cl bonds in the cation are then formed by the overlap of the half-filled sp^3 hybrid orbitals of the central chlorine atom with the half-filled p-orbitals of the terminal Cl and F atoms. Thus, by using sp^3 hybridization, we end up with the same <u>bent</u> molecular geometry for the ion as that predicted by VSEPR theory (when the lone pairs on the central atom are ignored)

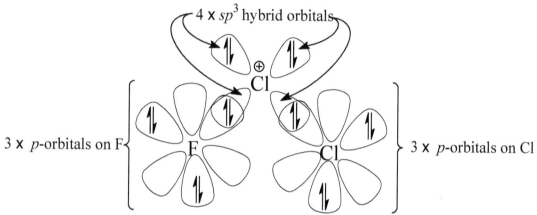

2B   **(D)** As was the case in 2A, we begin by drawing a plausible Lewis structure for the cation in question. This time, the Lewis structure must contain 34 valence electrons. The skeletal structure has bromine, the least electronegative element present, as the central atom. Next, we join the four terminal fluorine atoms to the central bromine atom via single covalent bonds and complete the octets for all of the fluorine atoms by assigning three lone pairs to each fluorine atom. Placing the last two electrons on the central bromine atom completes the diagram.

In order to accommodate ten electrons, the bromine atom is forced to expand its valence shell. Notice that the Br ends up with a 1+ formal charge in this structure. With the completed Lewis structure in hand, we can then use VSEPR theory to establish the geometry for the electron pairs around the central atom. The Lewis structure has four bonding pairs and one lone pair of electrons around the central bromine atom. These five pairs of electrons assume a trigonal bipyramidal geometry to minimize electron-electron repulsions. The VSEPR notation for the BrF_4^+ cation is AX_4E. According to Table 10.1, molecules of this type exhibit a see-saw molecular geometry.

Next we must select a hybridization scheme for the Br atom that is compatible with the predicted shape. It turns out that only sp^3d hybridization will provide the necessary trigonal bipyramidal distribution of electron pairs around the bromine atom. In this scheme, one of the sp^3d hybrid orbitals is filled, while the remaining four are half-occupied.

| ⇅ | ↑ | ↑ | ↑ | ↑ | sp^3d hybridized central bromine atom (Br$^+$)

The four Br—F bonds in the cation are then formed by the overlap of the four half-filled sp^3d hybrid orbitals of the bromine atom with the half-filled p-orbitals of the four separate terminal fluorine atoms. Thus, by using sp^3d hybridization, we end up with the same see-saw molecular geometry for the cation as that predicted by VSEPR theory (when the lone pair on Br is ignored).

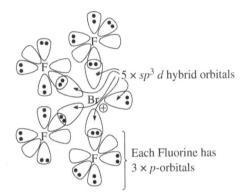

$5 \times sp^3 d$ hybrid orbitals

Each Fluorine has $3 \times p$-orbitals

3A **(M)** We begin by writing the Lewis structure. The H atoms are terminal atoms. There are three central atoms and $(3\times1)+4+6+4+(3\times1)=20$ valence electrons, or 10 pairs. A plausible Lewis structure is drawn at right. Each central atom is surrounded by four electron pairs, requiring sp^3 hybridization. The valence-shell orbital diagrams for the atoms follow.

H$_{1s}$[↑]   C [He] $_{2s}$[⇅] $_{2p}$[↑|↑|]   O [He] $_{2s}$[⇅] $_{2p}$[⇅|↑|↑]

The valence-shell orbital diagrams for the hybridized central atoms then are:

C$_{sp^3}$[↑|↑|↑|↑]   O$_{sp^3}$[⇅|⇅|↑|↑]

All bonds in the molecule are σ bonds. The H—C—H bond angles are 109.5°, as are the H—C—O bond angles. The C—O—C bond angle is possibly a bit smaller than 109.5° because of the repulsion of the two lone pairs of electrons on O. A wedge-and-dash sketch of the molecule is at right.

3B **(M)** The H atoms and one O are terminal atoms in the Lewis structure, which has $3\times1+4+4+2\times6+1=24$ valence electrons, or 12 pairs. The left-most C and the right-most O are surrounded by four electron pairs, and thus require sp^3 hybridization. The central carbon is surrounded by three electron groups and is sp^2 hybridized. The orbital diagrams for the un-hybridized atoms are:

H:$_{1s}$[↑]   C: [He] $_{2s}$[⇅] $_{2p}$[↑|↑|]   O: [He] $_{2s}$[⇅] $_{2p}$[⇅|↑|↑]

Hybridized orbital diagrams:

C: [He]$_{sp3}$ ⬚⬚⬚⬚   C: [He] $_{sp2}$ ⬚⬚⬚ $_{2p}$ ⬚   O:[He] $_{sp3}$ ⬚⬚⬚⬚   terminal O: [He] $_{sp2}$ ⬚⬚⬚ $_{2p}$ ⬚

There is one π bond in the molecule: between the $2p$ on the central C and the $2p$ on the terminal O. The remaining bonds are σ bonds. The H—C—H and H—C—C bond angles are 109.5°. The H—O—C angle is somewhat less, perhaps 105° because of lone pair repulsion. The C—C—O bond angles and O—C—O bond angles are all 120°.

4A **(M)** There are four bond pairs around the left-hand C, requiring sp^3 hybridization. Three of the bonds that form are C—H sigma bonds resulting from the overlap of a half-filled sp^3 hybrid orbital on C with a half-filled $1s$ orbital on H. The other C has two attached electron groups, utilizing sp hybridization.

C: [He]$_{sp}$ ⬚⬚ $_{2p}$ ⬚⬚ The N atom is sp hybridized. N: [He] $_{2s}$ ⬚ $_{2p}$ ⬚⬚⬚

The two C atoms join with a sigma bond: overlap of sp^2 on the left-hand C with sp on the right-hand C. The three bonds between C and N consist of a sigma bond (sp on C with sp on N), and two pi bonds ($2p$ on C with $2p$ on N).

4B **(M)** The bond lengths that are given indicate that N is the central atom. The molecule has $(2\times5)+6=16$ valence electrons, or 8 pairs. Average bond lengths are: N—N = 145 pm, N═N = 123 pm, N≡N = 110 pm, N—O = 136 pm, N═O = 120 pm. Plausible resonance structures are (with subscripts for identification):

structure(1) $:N_a\equiv N_b^{\oplus}-\ddot{\underset{..}{O}}:^{\ominus}$ ↔ $^{\ominus}\ddot{\underset{..}{N}}_a=N_b^{\oplus}=\ddot{\underset{..}{O}}$ structure(2)

In both structures, the central N is attached to two other atoms, and possesses no lone pairs. The geometry of the molecule thus is linear and the hybridization on this central N is sp. N_b [He] $_{sp}$ ⬚⬚ $_{2p}$ ⬚⬚ We will assume that the terminal atoms are not hybridized in either structure. Their valence-shell orbital diagrams are:

terminal N: N_a [He]$_{2s}$ ⬚ $_{2p}$ ⬚⬚⬚ O [He] $_{2s}$ ⬚ $_{2p}$ ⬚⬚⬚

In structure (1) the N≡N bond results from the overlap of three pairs of half-filled orbitals: (1) sp_x on N_b with $2p_x$ on N_a forming a σ bond, (2) $2p_y$ on N_b with $2p_y$ on N_a forming a π bond, and (3) $2p_z$ on N_b with $2p_z$ on N_a also forming a π bond. The N—O bond is a coordinate covalent bond, and requires that the electron configuration of O be written as O [He] $_{2s}$ ⬚ $_{2p}$ ⬚⬚⬚. The N—O bond then forms by the overlap of the full sp_x orbital on N_b with the empty $2p$ orbital on O.

In structure (2) the N═O bond results from the overlap of two pairs of half-filled orbitals: (1) sp_y on N_b with $2p_y$ on O forming a σ bond and (2) $2p_z$ on N_b with $2p_z$ on O forming a π bond. The N═N σ bond is a coordinate covalent bond, and requires that the configuration of N_a be written N_a [He] $_{2s}$ ⬚ $_{2p}$ ⬚⬚⬚. The N═N bond is formed by two overlaps: (1) the overlap of the full sp_y orbital on N_b with the empty $2p_y$ orbital on N_a to form a σ bond, and (2) the overlap of the half-filled $2p_x$ orbital on N_b with the half-filled $2p_x$ orbital on N_a to form a π bond. Based on formal charge arguments, structure (1) is preferred, because the negative formal charge is on the more electronegative atom, O.

5A **(M)** An electron from Li_2 removes a bonding electron because the valence molecular orbital diagram for Li_2 is the same as that for H_2, only it is just moved up a principal quantum level: $\sigma_{1s}{}^b \boxed{\uparrow\downarrow}\ \sigma_{1s}{}^* \boxed{\uparrow\downarrow}\ \sigma_{2s}{}^b \boxed{\uparrow\downarrow}\ \sigma_{2s}{}^* \boxed{\ }$.

The molecular orbital diagram for Li2+ is: $\sigma_{1s}{}^b \boxed{\uparrow\downarrow}\ \sigma_{1s}{}^* \boxed{\uparrow\downarrow}\ \sigma_{2s}{}^b \boxed{\uparrow}\ \sigma_{2s}{}^* \boxed{\ }$

The bond order in $Li_2{}^+$ is: 1/2, while that in Li_2 is one. Thus, the Li-Li bond in $Li_2{}^+$ should be one half as strong as the Li-Li bond in Li_2 : 106 kJ/mol $\div 2 = 53$ kJ/mol $Li_2{}^+$

5B **(M)** The $H_2{}^-$ ion contains 1 electron from each H plus 1 electron for the negative charge for a total of three electrons. Its molecular orbital diagram is $\sigma_{1s} \boxed{\uparrow\downarrow}\ \sigma_{1s}{}^* \boxed{\uparrow}$. There are two bonding and one antibonding electrons. The bond order in $H_2{}^-$ is obtained as follows:

$$\text{bond order} = \frac{(2\ \text{bonding e}^- - 1\ \text{antibonding e}^-)}{2} = \frac{1}{2}$$

Thus, we would expect the ion $H_2{}^-$ to be stable, with a bond strength about half that of a hydrogen molecule.

6A **(M)** For each case, the empty molecular-orbital diagram has the following appearance. (KK indicates that the molecular orbitals formed from $1s$ atomic orbitals are full: KK = $\sigma_{1s} \boxed{\uparrow\downarrow}\ \sigma_{1s}{}^* \boxed{\uparrow\downarrow}$

KK = $\sigma_{2s} \boxed{\ }\ \sigma_{2s}{}^* \boxed{\ }\quad \sigma_{2p} \boxed{\ }\ \pi_{2p} \boxed{\ \ }\ \pi_{2p}{}^* \boxed{\ \ }\sigma_{2p}{}^* \boxed{\ }$. We need to simply count up the total number of electrons in each species, and place them in the valence-shell molecular-orbital diagram.

(a) $N_2{}^+$ has $(2 \times 5) - 1 = 9$ valence electrons. Its molecular orbital diagram is

$N_2{}^+\quad$ KK $\sigma_{2s} \boxed{\uparrow\downarrow}\ \sigma_{2s}{}^* \boxed{\uparrow\downarrow}\quad \pi_{2p} \boxed{\uparrow\downarrow\,|\,\uparrow\downarrow}\ \sigma_{2p} \boxed{\uparrow}\ \pi_{2p}{}^* \boxed{\ \ }\ \sigma_{2p}{}^* \boxed{\ }$

bond order = (7 bonding electrons -2 antibonding electrons) $\div 2 = 2.5$

(b) $Ne_2{}^+$ has $(2 \times 8) - 1 = 15$ valence electrons. Its molecular orbital diagram is

$Ne_2{}^+$ KK $\quad \sigma_{2s} \boxed{\uparrow\downarrow}\ \sigma_{2s}{}^* \boxed{\uparrow\downarrow}\ \sigma_{2p} \boxed{\uparrow\downarrow}\ \pi_{2p} \boxed{\uparrow\downarrow\,|\,\uparrow\downarrow}\ \pi_{2p}{}^* \boxed{\uparrow\downarrow\,|\,\uparrow\downarrow}\ \sigma_{2p}{}^* \boxed{\uparrow}$

bond order = (8 bonding electrons -7 antibonding electrons) $\div 2 = 0.5$

(c) $C_2{}^{2-}$ has $(2 \times 4) + 2 = 10$ valence electrons. Its molecular orbital diagram is

$C_2{}^{2-}$ KK $\sigma_{2s} \boxed{\uparrow\downarrow}\ \sigma_{2s}{}^* \boxed{\uparrow\downarrow}\quad \pi_{2p} \boxed{\uparrow\downarrow\,|\,\uparrow\downarrow}\ \sigma_{2p} \boxed{\uparrow\downarrow}\ \pi_{2p}{}^* \boxed{\ \ }\ \sigma_{2p}{}^* \boxed{\ }$

bond order = (8 bonding electrons -2 antibonding electrons) $\div 2 = 3.0$

6B **(M)** For each case, the empty molecular-orbital diagram has the following appearance. (KK indicates that the molecular orbitals formed from $1s$ atomic orbitals are full:

KK = σ_{1s}⥮ $\sigma_{1s}{}^{*}$⥮

KK σ_{2s}☐ $\sigma_{2s}{}^{*}$☐ σ_{2p}☐ π_{2p}☐☐ $\pi_{2p}{}^{*}$☐☐ $\sigma_{2p}{}^{*}$☐ . All of these species are based on O_2, which has $2\times6 = 12$ valence electrons. We simply put the appropriate number of valence electrons in each diagram and determine the bond order.

$O_2{}^{+}$ 11 v.e.   KK σ_{2s}⥮ $\sigma_{2s}{}^{*}$⥮ σ_{2p}⥮ π_{2p}⥮⥮ $\pi_{2p}{}^{*}$⥯☐ $\sigma_{2p}{}^{*}$☐

bond order = (8 bonding e^{-} –5 antibonding e^{-}) ÷ 2 = 2.5; bond length = 112 pm

O_2 12 v.e.   KK

bond order = (8 bonding e^{-} – 4 antibonding e^{-}) ÷ 2 = 2.0; bond length = 121 pm

$O_2{}^{-}$ 13 v.e.   KK

bond order = (8 bonding e^{-} –5 antibonding e^{-}) ÷ 2 = 1.5; bond length = 128 pm

$O_2{}^{2-}$ 14 v.e.   KK σ_{2s}⥮ $\sigma_{2s}{}^{*}$⥮ σ_{2p}⥮ π_{2p}⥮⥮ $\pi_{2p}{}^{*}$⥮⥮ $\sigma_{2p}{}^{*}$☐

bond order = (8 bonding electrons –6 antibonding electrons) ÷ 2 = 1.0; bond length = 149 pm. We see that the bond length does indeed increase as the bond order decreases. Longer bonds are weaker bonds.

7A **(M)** There are 8 valence electrons that must be placed into the valence molecular orbital diagram for CN^{+} (5 electrons from nitrogen, four electrons from carbon and one electron is removed to produce the positive charge). Since both C and N precede oxygen and they are not far apart in atomic number, we must use the modified molecular-orbital energy-level diagram to get the correct configuration. We will assume that the order of the MOs for CN^{+} is the same as for CO, shown in Figure 11-28. By following the Aufbau orbital filling method, one obtains the ground state diagram asked for in the question.

Before calculating the bond order, the MOs must be classified as bonding, antibonding, or nonbonding. Both the 3σ and 1π MOs are bonding, the 2π and 6σ are antibonding, and the 4σ and 5σ are nonbonding.

The bond order for the C–N bond in CN^+ is

$$\frac{6 \text{ bonding electrons} - 0 \text{ antibonding electrons}}{2} = 3$$

Thus, the C and N atoms in CN^+ are joined by a triple bond.

7B **(M)** There are 8 valence electrons that must be placed in the molecular orbital diagram for BN (3 electrons from boron and five electrons from nitrogen). Since both B and N precede oxygen and they are not far apart in atomic numbers, we must use the modified molecular-orbital energy-level diagram to get the correct configuration. We will assume that the order of the MOs for CN^+ is the as as for CO, shown in Figure 11-28. By following the Aufbau orbital filling method, one obtains the ground-state diagram asked for in the question.

Before calculating the bond order, the MOs must be classified as bonding, antibonding, or nonbonding. Both the 3σ and 1π MOs are bonding, the 2π and 6σ are antibonding, and the 4σ and 5σ are nonbonding.

The bond order for the B–N bond in BN is

$$\frac{6 \text{ bonding electrons} - 0 \text{ antibonding electrons}}{2} = 3$$

Thus, the B and N atoms in BN are joined by a triple bond.

8A **(D)** In this exercise we will combine valence-bond and molecular orbital methods to describe the bonding in the SO_3 molecule. By invoking a π-bonding scheme, we can replace the three resonance structures for SO_3 (shown below) with just <u>one</u> structure that exhibits both σ-bonding and delocalized π-bonding.

We will use structure (i) to develop a combined localized/delocalized bonding description for the molecule. (Note: Any one of the three resonance contributors can be used as the starting structure.) We begin by assuming that every atom in the molecule is sp^2 hybridized to produce the σ-framework for the molecule. The half-filled sp^2 hybrid orbitals of the oxygen atoms will each be overlapped with a half-filled sp^2 hybrid orbital on sulfur. By contrast, to generate a set of π molecular orbitals, we will combine one unhybridized $2p$ orbital from each of three oxygen atoms with an unhybridized $3p$ orbital on the sulfur atom. This will generate four π molecular orbitals: a bonding molecular orbital, two nonbonding molecular orbitals, and an antibonding orbital. Remember that the number of valence electrons assigned to each atom must reflect the formal charge for that atom. Accordingly, sulfur, with a 2+ formal charge, can have only four valence electrons, the two oxygens with a 1– formal charge must each end up with 7 electrons and the oxygen with a zero formal charge must have its customary six electrons

Let's begin assigning valence electrons by half-filling three sp^2 hybrid orbitals on the sulfur atom (atom A) and one sp^2 hybrid orbital on each of the oxygen atoms (atoms B, C and D) Next, we half-fill the lone unhybridized $3p$ orbital on sulfur and the lone $2p$ orbital on the oxygen atom with a formal charge of zero (atom B). Following this, the $2p$ orbital of the other two oxygen atoms (atoms C and D), are filled and then lone pairs are placed in the sp^2 hybrid orbitals that are still empty. At this stage, then, all 24 valence electrons have been put into atomic and hybrid orbitals on the four atoms. Now we overlap the six half-filled sp^2 hybrid orbitals to generate the σ-bond framework and combine the three $2p$ orbitals (2 filled, one half-filled) and the $3p$ orbital (half-filled) to form the four π-molecular orbitals, as shown below

F.C. Atom Label sp^2 hybrids np orbitals

2+ A(S) (3p)

0 B(O) (2p)

(1−) C(O) (2p)

(1−) D(O) (2p)

$120°$

σ-framework

$3 \times sp^2 - sp^2$ σ-bonds

π*

non-bonding π-orbitals

π

π-molecular orbitals

Overall bond order for this set of π-molecular orbitals $\dfrac{2 \text{ bonding e}^- - 0 \text{ antibonding e}^-}{2} = 1$

The π-bond is spread out evenly over the three S—O linkages. This leads to an average bond order of 1.33 for the three S—O bonds in SO_3. By following this "combined approach", we end up with a structure that has the σ-bond framework sandwiched within the delocalized π-molecular orbital framework:

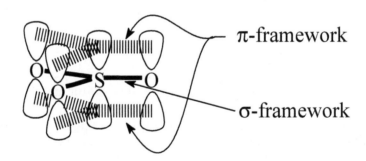

π-framework

σ-framework

This is a much more accurate description of the bonding in SO_3 than that provided by any one of the three Lewis diagrams shown above.

8B **(D)** We will use the same basic approach to answer this question as was used to solve Practice Example 11-8A. This time, the bonding in NO_2^- will be described by combining valence-bond and molecular orbital theory. With this approach we will be able to generate a structure that more accurately describes the bonding in NO_2^- than either of the two equivalent Lewis diagrams that can be drawn for the nitrate ion (below).

(i)   (ii)

Structure (i) will be used to develop the combined localized/delocalized bonding description for the anion (either structure could have been used as the starting structure). We begin by assuming that every atom in the molecule is sp^2 hybridized. To produce the σ-framework for the molecule, the half-filled sp^2 orbitals of the oxygen atoms will be overlapped with a half-filled sp^2 orbital of nitrogen. By contrast, to generate a set of π-molecular orbitals, we will combine one unhybridized $2p$ orbital from each of the two oxygen atoms with an unhybridized $2p$ orbital on nitrogen. This will generate three π molecular orbitals: a bonding molecular orbital, a non-bonding molecular orbital and an antibonding molecular orbital.

(i)

Remember that the number of valence electrons assigned to each atom must reflect the formal charge for that atom. Accordingly, the oxygen with a 1– formal charge (atom C) must end up with 7 electrons, whereas the nitrogen atom (atom A) and the other oxygen atom (atom B) must have their customary 5 and 6 valence electrons, respectively, because they both have a formal charge of zero. Let's begin assigning valence electrons by half-filling two sp^2 hybrid orbitals on the nitrogen atom (atom A) and one sp^2 hybrid orbital on each oxygen atom (atoms B and C). Next, we half-fill the lone $2p$ orbital on nitrogen (atom A) and the lone $2p$ orbital on the oxygen atom with a formal charge of zero (atom B). Following this, the $2p$ orbital for the remaining oxygen (atom C) is filled and then lone pairs are placed in the sp^2 hybrid orbitals that are still empty. At this stage, then, all 18 valence electrons have been put into atomic and hybrid orbitals on the three atoms. Now, we overlap the four half-filled sp^2 hybrid orbitals to generate the σ-bond framework and combine the three $2p$ orbitals (two half-filled, one filled) to form three π-molecular orbitals as shown below

F.C. Atom Label sp^2 hybrids $2p$ orbitals

0   A(N)

0   B(O)

(1–)   C(O)

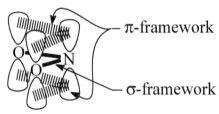

σ-framework

$2 \times sp^2$-sp^2 σ-bonds

Overall bond order for this set of π-molecular orbitals $\dfrac{2 \text{ bonding e}^- - 0 \text{ antibonding e}^-}{2} = 1$

The π bond is spread out evenly over the two N—O linkages. This leads to an average bond order of 1.5 for each of the two N—O bonds in NO_2^-. By following this combined approach, we end up with a structure that has the σ-bond framework sandwiched within the delocalized π-molecular orbitals:

π-framework

σ-framework

This is a much more accurate depiction of the bonding in NO_2^- than that provided by one of the two Lewis diagrams given above.

INTEGRATIVE EXAMPLE

<u>A.</u> **(M)** We will assume 100 g of the compound and find the empirical formula in the usual way.
moles of carbon = 28.57 g(1 mole/12.011g) = 2.379 mol
moles of hydrogen = 4.80 g(1 mole/1.008g) = 4.76 mol
moles of nitrogen = 66.64 g(mole/14.01g) = 4.76 mol
Dividing by 2.38 we get: C(2.379/2.379) H(4.76/2.379) N(4.758/2.379)
This yields an empirical formula of: CH_2N_2 From the description given in the question
(6-membered ring), the molecular formula is $C_3N_6H_6$

(a)   Lewis structure for $C_3N_6H_6$ (based on info provided)

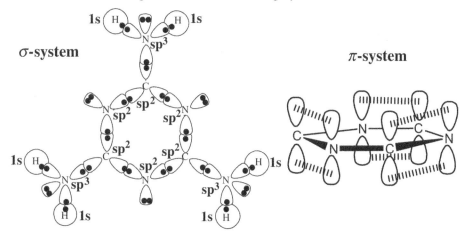

(b)   Valence-bond description σ and π-bonding systems

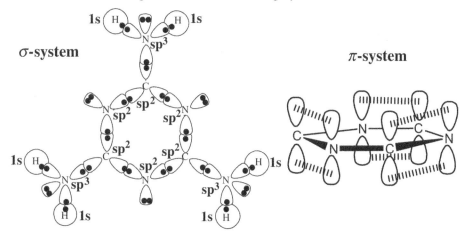

(c)   The bonds in the ring system are similar to those seen in benzene (C_6H_6) and pyridine (C_5H_5N), namely

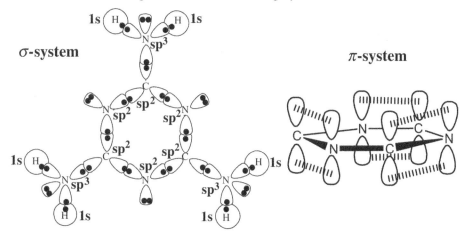

Antibonding π moleclar orbitals

Bonding π moleclar orbitals

One $2p$ electron from each of the atoms is placed in the ring

B.   **(D)** We have 2.464 g of dimethylglyoxime (DMG)

moles C : 3.735(1 mol C/44.01g CO_2) = 0.08487 mol C
moles H : 1.530(2 mol H/18.01g H_2O) = 0.1698 mol C

First we find the excess H_2SO_4 left over from the nitrogen determination:

$$18.6 \text{ mL} \times \frac{1 \text{ L}}{1000 \text{ mL}} \times \frac{0.2050 \text{ mol NaOH}}{1 \text{ L}} \times \frac{1 \text{ mol } H_2SO_4}{2 \text{ mol NaOH}} = 1.910 \times 10^{-3} \text{mol } H_2SO_4 \text{ in excess}$$

Next we find the moles of H_2SO_4 initially added:

$$50.00 \text{ mL} \times \frac{1 \text{ L}}{1000 \text{ mL}} \times \frac{0.3600 \text{ mol } H_2SO_4}{1 \text{ L}} = 1.800 \times 10^{-2} \text{mol } H_2SO_4 \text{ used}$$

Now we find the moles of H_2SO_4 that reacted:

mole H_2SO_4 that reacted $= 1.800 \times 10^{-2}$ mol H_2SO_4

initially used -1.910×10^{-3} mol H_2SO_4 in excess

mole H_2SO_4 that reacted $= 1.609 \times 10^{-2}$ mol H_2SO_4
Therefore, the moles of nitrogen in 1.868 g DMG sample is:

0.01609 mol $H_2SO_4 \times \dfrac{2 \text{ mol } NH_3}{1 \text{ mol } H_2SO_4} \times \dfrac{1 \text{ mol } N}{1 \text{ mol } NH_3} = 3.218 \times 10^{-2}$ mol nitrogen (0.4507 g nitrogen)

For a 1.868 g sample, moles of C and H present are fond as follows:
C: (1.868/2.464)(0.08487) = 0.06434 mol C (0.7728 g C)
H: (1.868/2.464)(0.1698) = 0.1287 mol H (0.1297 g H)

Mass of oxygen in 1.868 g DMG sample is $1.868 - 0.4507 - 0.7728 - 0.1298 = 0.515$ g oxygen (0.0322 mol O)

Empirical formula: C(0.0643/0.0322) H(0.1287/0.0322) N(0.03218/0.0322) O(0.0322/0.0322) or C_2H_4 NO The empirical molecular mass is 58 u and the true molecular mass is 116.12 u so we multiply the empirical formula by two to get the molecular formula of $C_4H_8 N_2O_2$. The structure is $H_3C–C(=NOH)–C(=NOH)–CH_3$

Hybrid orbitals used:
$C_b - H$: σ H(1s) $- C_b(sp^3)$
$C_a = N$: σ $C_a(sp^2) - N(sp^2)$, π: $C_a(2p) - N(2p)$
$N - O$: σ N$(sp^2) - O(sp^3)$
$C_a - C_a$: σ $C_a(sp^2) - C_a(sp^2)$
$C_a - C_b$: σ $C_b(sp^3) - C_a(sp^2)$
$O - H$: σ H(1s) $- O(sp^3)$

EXERCISES

Valence-Bond Method

Note: In VSEPR theory, the term *"bond pair"* is used for a single bond, a double bond, or a triple bond, even though a single bond consists of one pair of electrons, a double bond two pairs of electrons, and a triple bond three pairs of electrons. To avoid any confusion between the number of electron pairs actually involved in the bonding to a central atom, and the number of atoms bonded to that central atom, we shall occasionally use the term *"ligand"* to indicate an atom or a group of atoms attached to the central atom.

1.   **(E)** There are several ways in which valence-bond theory is superior to Lewis structures in describing covalent bonds. *First*, valence-bond theory clearly distinguishes between sigma and pi bonds. In Lewis theory, a double bond appears to be just two bonds and it is not clear why a double bond is not simply twice as strong as a single bond. In valence-bond theory, it is clear

that a sigma bond must be stronger than a pi bond, for the orbitals overlap more effectively in a sigma bond (end-to-end) than they do in a pi bond (side-to-side). *Second*, molecular geometries are more directly obtained in valence-bond theory than in Lewis theory. Although valence-bond theory requires the introduction of hybridization to explain these geometries, Lewis theory does not predict geometries at all; it simply provides the basis from which VSEPR theory predicts geometries. *Third*, Lewis theory does not explain hindered rotation about double bonds. With valence-bond theory, any rotation about a double bond involves cleavage of the π-bond, which would require the input of considerable energy.

2. **(E)** The overlap of pure atomic orbitals gives bond angles of 90° or 180°. These bond angles are suitable only for 3- and 4-atom compounds in which the central atom is an atom of the third (or higher) period of the periodic table. For central atoms from the second period of the periodic table, 3- and 4-atom compounds have bond angles closer to 180°, 120°, and 109.5° than to 90°. These other bond angles can only be explained well through hybridization. *Second*, hybridization clearly distinguishes between the (hybrid) orbitals that form σ bonds and the p orbitals that form π bonds. It places those p orbitals in their proper orientation so that they can overlap side-to-side to form π bonds. *Third*, the bond angles of 90° and 120° that result when the octet of the central atom is expanded cannot be produced with pure atomic orbitals. Hybrid orbitals are necessary. *Finally*, the overlap of pure atomic orbitals does not usually result in all σ bonds being equivalent. Overlaps with hybrid orbitals produce equivalent bonds.

<u>3.</u> **(E)**

   (a) Lewis theory does not describe the shape of the water molecule. It does indicate that there is a single bond between each H atom and the O atom, and that there are two lone pairs attached to the O atom, but it says nothing about molecular shape.

   (b) In valence-bond theory using simple atomic orbitals, each H—O bond results from the overlap of a $1s$ orbital on H with a $2p$ orbital on O. The angle between $2p$ orbitals is 90° so this method initially predicts a 90° bond angle. The observed 104° bond angle is explained as arising from repulsion between the two slightly positively charged H atoms.

   (c) In VSEPR theory the H_2O molecule is categorized as being of the AX_2E_2 type, with two atoms and two lone pairs attached to the central oxygen atom. The lone pairs repel each other more than do the bond pairs, explaining the smaller than 109.5° tetrahedral bond angle.

   (d) In valence-bond theory using hybrid orbitals, each H—O bond results from the overlap of a $1s$ orbital on H with an sp^3 orbital on O. The angle between sp^3 orbitals is 109.5°. The observed bond angle of 104° is rationalized based on the greater repulsion of lone pair electrons when compared to bonding pair electrons.

4. **(E)**

   (a) Lewis theory really does not describe the shape of the molecule. It does indicate that there is a single bond between each H atom and the N atom, but it says nothing about molecular shape.

(b) In valence-bond theory using simple atomic orbitals, each N—H bond results from the overlap of a $1s$ orbital on H with a $2p$ orbital on N. Since the angle between $2p$ orbitals is 90°, this method initially predicts a 90° bond angle. The observed 107.8° bond angle is explained as resulting from the repulsion between the lone electron pair and the N—H bonds.

(c) In VSEPR theory, the NH_3 molecule is categorized as being of the AX_4 type, with three atoms and one lone electron pair attached to the central nitrogen atom.

(d) In valence-bond theory, each N—H bond results from the overlap of a $1s$ orbital on H with an sp^3 orbital on N. The angle between the sp^3 orbitals is 109.5°, but because of the repulsion created by the lone electron pair, the H—N—H bond angle is 107.8°.

5. **(M)** Determining hybridization is made easier if we begin with Lewis structures. Only one resonance form is drawn for CO_3^{2-}, SO_2, and NO_2^{-}.

The C atom is attached to three ligands and no lone pairs and thus is sp^2 hybridized in CO_3^{2-}. The S atom is attached to two ligands and one lone pair and thus is sp^2 hybridized in SO_2. The C atom is attached to four ligands and no lone pairs and thus is sp^3 hybridized in CCl_4. Both the oxygen and the carbon in CO are sp hybridized. The N atom is attached to two ligands and one lone pair in NO_2^{-} and thus is sp^2 hybridized. Thus, the central atom is sp^2 hybridized in SO_2, CO_3^{2-}, and NO_2^{-}.

6. **(M) (a)** HI: H $\quad 1s\,\boxed{\uparrow}$ I [Kr]$4d^{10}$ $5s\,\boxed{\uparrow\downarrow}$ $5p\,\boxed{\uparrow\downarrow}\boxed{\uparrow\downarrow}\boxed{\uparrow}$

The $1s$ orbital of H overlaps the half-filled $5p$ orbital of I to produce a linear molecule.

(b) BrCl: Br [Ar]$3d^{10}$ $\quad 4s\,\boxed{\uparrow\downarrow}$ $4p\,\boxed{\uparrow\downarrow}\boxed{\uparrow\downarrow}\boxed{\uparrow}$ $\quad$ Cl [Ne]$3s\,\boxed{\uparrow\downarrow}$ $3p\,\boxed{\uparrow\downarrow}\boxed{\uparrow\downarrow}\boxed{\uparrow}$

The half-filled $3p$ orbital of Cl overlaps the half-filled $4p$ orbital of Br to produce a linear molecule.

(c) H_2Se: H $\quad 1s\,\boxed{\uparrow}$ Se [Ar]$3d^{10}$ $\quad 4s\,\boxed{\uparrow\downarrow}$ $4p\,\boxed{\uparrow\downarrow}\boxed{\uparrow}\boxed{\uparrow}$

Each half-filled $4p$ orbital of Se overlaps with a half-filled $1s$ orbital of a H atom to produce a bent molecule, with a bond angle of approximately 90°.

(d) OCl_2: O $1s\,\boxed{\uparrow\downarrow}$ $2s\,\boxed{\uparrow\downarrow}$ $2p\,\boxed{\uparrow\downarrow}\boxed{\uparrow}\boxed{\uparrow}$ $\quad$ Cl [Ne] $3s\,\boxed{\uparrow\downarrow}$ $3p\,\boxed{\uparrow\downarrow}\boxed{\uparrow\downarrow}\boxed{\uparrow}$

Each half-filled $2p$ orbital of O overlaps with a half-filled $3p$ orbital of a Cl atom to produce a bent molecule, with a bond angle of approximately 90°.

7. **(M)** For each species, we first draw the Lewis structure, to help explain the bonding.

(a) In CO_2, there are a total of $4+(2\times6)=16$ valence electrons, or 8 pairs. C is the central atom. The Lewis structure is $\overset{..}{\underset{..}{O}}=C=\overset{..}{\underset{..}{O}}$ The molecule is linear and C is sp hybridized.

(b) In $HONO_2$, there are a total of $1+5+(3\times6)=24$ valence electrons, or 12 pairs. N is the central atom, and a plausible Lewis structure is shown on the right The molecule is trigonal planar around N which is sp^2 hybridized. The O in the H—O—N portion of the molecule is sp^3 hybridized.

$$H-\overset{..}{\underset{..}{O}}-N=\overset{..}{\underset{..}{O}}$$
$$\underset{\overset{|}{:\overset{..}{O}H}}{}$$

(c) In ClO_3^-, there are a total of $7+(3\times6)+1=26$ valence electrons, or 13 pairs. Cl is the central atom, and a plausible Lewis structure is shown on the right. The electron-group geometry around Cl is tetrahedral, indicating that Cl is sp^3 hybridized.

$$\left(\overset{0\quad\;0\quad\;1-}{\overset{..}{O}-\overset{..}{\underset{||}{Cl}}-\overset{..}{O}:}\right)^{-}$$
$$\underset{\underset{0}{:\overset{..}{O}:}}{}$$

(d) In BF_4^-, there are a total of $3+(4\times7)+1=32$ valence electrons, or 16 pairs. B is the central atom, and a plausible Lewis structure is shown on the right. The electron-group geometry is tetrahedral, indicating that B is sp^3 hybridized.

$$\left(\begin{array}{c}:\overset{..}{F}:\\|\\:\overset{..}{F}-B-\overset{..}{F}:\\|\\:\overset{..}{F}:\end{array}\right)^{-}$$

8. **(E)** In ONF, there are $6 + 5 + 7 = 18$ valence electrons or 9 electron pairs. In the following Lewis structure, $:\overset{..}{O}=N—\overset{..}{\underset{..}{F}}:$, there are two atoms bonded to the central N, which has a lone pair. Thus, the electron group geometry around the central N is trigonal planar (with sp^2 hybridization), and the molecular shape is bent.

9. **(E)** The Lewis structure of ClF_3 is shown on the right. There are three atoms and two lone pairs attached to the central atom, its hybridization is sp^3d, which is achieved as follows. $Cl_{unhyb}[Ne]\,3s\boxed{↑↓}\;3p\boxed{↑↓}\boxed{↑↓}\boxed{↑}\;3d\boxed{\;}\boxed{\;}\boxed{\;}\boxed{\;}\boxed{\;} \longrightarrow Cl_{hyb}\,[Ne]\;_{dsp^3}\boxed{↑↓}\boxed{↑↓}\boxed{↑}\boxed{↑}\boxed{↑}\;3d\boxed{\;}\boxed{\;}\boxed{\;}\boxed{\;}$

$$\overset{..\;..\;..}{:F-Cl-F:}$$
$$\underset{:\overset{..}{F}:}{|}$$

The orbital diagram of F is $[He]\,2s\boxed{↑↓}\;2p\boxed{↑↓}\boxed{↑↓}\boxed{↑}$ Each of the three sigma bonds are formed by the overlap of a $2p$ orbital on F with one of the half-filled sp^3d orbitals on Cl. Since the sp^3d hybridization has a trigonal bipyramidal shape, and the two lone pairs occupy the equatorial positions in the molecule, ClF_3 is T-shaped.

10. **(E)** In SF_4 there are $6+(4\times7)=34$ valence electrons, or 17 pairs. A plausible Lewis structure has zero formal charge on each atom (structure drawn on right). This molecule has a see-saw shape. There are four atoms and one lone pair attached to S, requiring sp^3d hybridization. Each sigma S—F bond results from the overlap of two half-filled orbitals: namely, an sp^3d on S and $2p$ on F.

$$\begin{array}{c}:\overset{..}{F}:\\|\\:\overset{..}{F}-\overset{..}{S}-\overset{..}{F}:\\|\\:\overset{..}{F}:\end{array}$$

The orbital diagram of F is $[He]2s\boxed{↑↓}\;2p\boxed{↑↓}\boxed{↑↓}\boxed{↑}$. The hybridization diagram for S follows:

$S_{unhyb}[Ne]\,3s\boxed{↑↓}\;3p\boxed{↑↓}\boxed{↑}\boxed{↑}\;3d\boxed{\;}\boxed{\;}\boxed{\;}\boxed{\;}\boxed{\;} \longrightarrow S_{hyb}\,[Ne]\;sp^3d\boxed{↑↓}\boxed{↑}\boxed{↑}\boxed{↑}\boxed{↑}\;3d\boxed{\;}\boxed{\;}\boxed{\;}$

11. **(M)**

(a) In PF_6^- there are a total of $5 + (6 \times 7) + 1 = 48$ valence electrons, or 24 pairs. A plausible Lewis structure is shown below. In order to form the six P—F bonds, the hybridization on P must be sp^3d^2.

(b) In COS there are a total of $4 + 6 + 6 = 16$ valence electrons, or 8 pairs. A plausible Lewis structure is shown below. In order to bond two atoms to the central C, the hybridization on that C atom must be sp.

(c) In $SiCl_4$, there are a total of $4 + (4 \times 7) = 32$ valence electrons, or 16 pairs. A plausible Lewis structure is given below. In order to form four Si—Cl bonds, the hybridization on Si must be sp^3.

(d) In NO_3^-, there are a total of $5 + (3 \times 6) + 1 = 24$ valence electrons, or 12 pairs. A plausible Lewis structure is given below. In order to bond three O atoms to the central N atom, with no lone pairs on that N atom, its hybridization must be sp^2.

(e) In AsF_5, there are a total of $5 + (5 \times 7) = 40$ valence electrons, or 20 pairs. A plausible Lewis structure is shown below. This is a molecule of the type AX_5. To form five As—F bonds, the hybridization on As must be sp^3d.

12. **(M)** We base each hybridization scheme on the Lewis structure for the molecule.

(a) $H—C{\equiv}N\!:$ There are two atoms bonded to C and no lone pairs on C. Thus, the hybridization for C must be sp.

(b) There are four atoms bonded to C and no lone pairs in this molecule. Thus, the hybridization for C must be sp^3. (O atom is also sp^3 hybridized).

(c) There are four atoms bonded to each terminal C and no lone pairs on these C atoms. Thus, the hybridization for each terminal C must be sp^3. There are three atoms and no lone pairs bonded to the central C. The hybridization for the central C must be sp^2.

(d) There are three atoms bonded to C and no lone pairs on C. This requires sp^2 hybridization.

13. **(M)**

(a) This is a planar molecule. The hybridization on C is sp^2
(one bond to each of the three attached atoms).

(b) $:N\equiv C—C\equiv N:$ is a linear molecule. The hybridization for each C is sp
(one bond to each of the N atoms).

(c) Trifluoroacetonitrile is neither linear nor planar. The shape around
the left-hand C is tetrahedral and that C has sp^3 hybridization.
The shape around the right-hand carbon is linear and that C has sp
hybridization.(N atom is sp hybridized).

$$:\overset{\cdot\cdot}{\underset{\cdot\cdot}{F}}:$$
$$:\overset{\cdot\cdot}{F}—\overset{|}{\underset{|}{C}}—C\equiv N:$$
$$:\overset{\cdot\cdot}{\underset{\cdot\cdot}{F}}:$$

(d) $\left[:\overset{\cdot\cdot}{\underset{\cdot\cdot}{S}}—C\equiv N:\right]^{-}$ is a linear molecule. The hybridization for C is sp and N is sp.
The hybridization of the S atom is sp^3.

14. **(M)**

(a) The central C atom employs four sp^3 hybrid orbitals; these have a tetrahedral
geometry. Each of the two H atoms employs a $1s$ orbital, and each of the two Cl
atoms employs a half-filled $3p$ orbital. A diagram of this follows:

(b) The ground state C atom has the electron configuration [He] $2s$⬆⬇ $2p$⬆⬆☐ Based on this
ground state electron configuration, we would expect a bent molecule. To produce the
two half-filled orbitals required to form two linear bonds a hybridized electron
configuration (which corresponds to an excited state for the individual atoms) is
required: C* $1s$⬆⬇ $2s$⬆ $2p$⬆⬆⬆ $\longrightarrow$ C*$_{hyb}$ $1s$⬆⬇ sp⬆⬆ $2p$⬆⬆
The overlap of the two half-filled sp orbitals of C, one with a half-filled $2p$ orbital
on O and the other with a half-filled $2p$ orbital on N$^-$, produces the σ bond
framework. O $1s$⬆⬇ $2s$⬆⬇ $2p$⬆⬇⬆⬆   N$^-$ $1s$⬆⬇ $2s$⬆⬇ $2p$⬆⬇⬆⬆
The π bonds are produced by the sidewise overlap of the two half-filled $2p$ orbitals
on C, one with a half-filled $2p$ orbital on O, the other with a half-filled $2p$ orbital
on N$^-$. A diagram of the bonding follows:

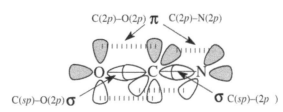

(c) The ground-state electron configuration of B suggests an ability to form one B—F bond, rather than three. $1s$⊞ $2s$⊞ $2p$⊡⊡ Again, excitation, or promotion of an electron to a higher energy orbital, followed by hybridization is required to form three equivalent half-filled B orbitals.

B* $1s$⊞ $2s$↿ $2p$↿↿⊡ $\longrightarrow$ B*$_{\text{hyb}}$ $1s$⊞ $sp2$↿↿↿ $2p$☐

Recall that the ground-state electron configuration of F is $[He]2s$⊞ $2p$⊞⊞↿ Bonds are produced through overlap of the half-filled sp^2 orbitals on B with the half filled F $2p$ orbitals. The BF_3 molecule is trigonal planar, with F—B—F bond angles of 120° A diagram of the bonding follows:

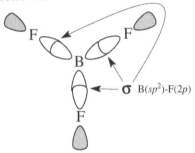

σ B(sp^2)-F($2p$)

15. **(M)**

(a) In HCN, there are a total of $1+4+5=10$ valence electrons, or 5 electron pairs. A plausible Lewis structure follows. H—C≡N|. The H—C bond is a σ bond, and the C≡N bond is composed of 1 σ and 2 π bonds.

(b) In C_2N_2, there are a total of $(2\times4)+(2\times5)=18$ valence electrons, or 9 electron pairs. A plausible Lewis structure follows: |N≡C—C≡N| The C—C bond is a σ bond, and each C≡N bond is composed of 1 σ and 2 π bonds.

(c) In $CH_3CHCHCCl_3$, there are a total of 42 valence electrons, or 21 electron pairs. A plausible Lewis structure is shown to the right. All bonds are σ bonds except one of the bonds that comprise the C=C bond. The C=C bond is composed of one σ and one π bond.

```
     H            :Cl:
     |             |
H—C—C=C—C—Cl:
     |   |   |   |
     H  H  H :Cl:
```

(d) In HONO, there is a total of $1+5+(2\times6)=18$ valence electrons, or 9 electron pairs. A plausible Lewis structure is shown below:

H—Ö—N̈=Ö

All single bonds in this structure are σ bonds. The double bond is composed of one σ and one π bond.

16. **(E)**

(a) In CO, there are $4 + 6 = 10$ valence electrons, or 5 electron pairs. A plausible Lewis structure is :O≡C:.

(b) The molecule is linear, and the hybridization on the C atom is sp. The triple bond between C and O comprises a σ bond, which is the overlap between the half-filled $2p_z$ orbital on C with a $2p_z$ orbital on O, and two π bonds, which are the result of the overlap of the partially filled $2p_x$ and $2p_y$ orbitals of C and O.

17. **(M)**

(a) In CCl_4, there are a total of $4+(4\times7)=32$ valence electrons, or 8 electron pairs. C is the central atom. A plausible Lewis structure is shown to the right. The geometry at C is tetrahedral; C is sp^3 hybridized. Cl—C—Cl bond angles are 109.5°. Each C—Cl bond is represented by σ: $C(sp^3)^1$ — $Cl(3p)^1$

(b) In ONCl, there are a total of $6+5+7=18$ valence electrons, or 9 electron pairs. N is the central atom. A plausible Lewis structure is $\ddot{O}=\ddot{N}-\ddot{\ddot{Cl}}:$. The e⁻ group geometry around N is triangular planar, and N is sp^2 hybridized. The O—N—C bond angle is about 120°. The bonds are: σ: $O(2p_y)^1$—$N(sp^2)^1$ σ: $N(sp^2)^1$—$Cl(3p_z)^1$

π: $O(2p_z)^1$—$N(2p_z)^1$

(c) In HONO, there are a total of $1+(2\times6)+5=18$ valence electrons, or 9 electron pairs. A plausible Lewis structure is $H-\ddot{O}_a-\ddot{N}=\ddot{O}_b$. The geometry of O_a is tetrahedral, O_a is sp^3 hybridized and the $H-O_a-N$ bond angle is (at least close to)109.5°. The e⁻ group geometry at N is trigonal planar, N is sp^2 hybridized, and the O_a-N-O_b bond angle is120°. The four bonds are represented as follows. σ: $H(1s)^1$—$O_a(sp^3)^1$

σ: $O_a(sp^3)^1$—$N(sp^2)^1$ σ: $N(sp^2)^1$—$O_b(2p_y)^1$ π: $N(2p_z)^1$—$O_b(2p_z)^1$.

(d) In $COCl_2$, there are a total of $4+6+(2\times7)=24$ valence electrons, or 12 electron pairs. A plausible Lewis structure is shown to the right. The e⁻ group geometry around C is trigonal planar; all bond angles around C are 120º, and the hybridization of C is sp^2. The four bonds in the molecules are:

$2\times\sigma$: $Cl(3p_x)^1$—$C(sp^2)^1$ σ: $O(2p_y)^1$—$C(sp^2)^1$ π: $O(2p_z)^1$—$C(2p_z)^1$.

18. **(D)**

(a) In NO_2^-, there are a total of $5+(2\times6)+1=18$ valence electrons, or 9 electron pairs. A plausible Lewis structure follows $\ddot{O}_a=\ddot{N}-\ddot{O}_b:$. The e⁻ group geometry around N is trigonal planar, all bond angles around that atom are 120°, and the hybridization of N is sp^2. The three bonds in this molecule are:

σ: $O_a(2p_y)^1$—$N(sp^2)^1$ σ: $O_b(2p_x)^1$—$N(sp^2)^1$ and π: $O_a(2p_z)^1$—$N(2p_z)^1$

(b) In I_3^-, there are a total of $(3\times7)+1=22$ valence electrons, or 11 electron pairs. A plausible Lewis structure follows. $[:\ddot{I}-\ddot{I}-\ddot{I}:]^-$ Since there are three lone pairs and two I atoms attached to the central I, the electron-group geometry around that atom is trigonal bipyramidal; its hybridization is sp^3d. Since the two I atoms are located in the axial positions due to each of the lone pairs occupying the equitorial position of the trigonal bipyramid, the I—I—I bond angle is 180°. Each I—I sigma bond is the result of the overlap of a $5p$ orbital on a terminal I with an sp^3d hybrid orbital on the central I.

(c) In $C_2O_4^{2-}$, there are a total of $(2\times4)+(4\times6)+2=34$ valence electrons, or 17 electron pairs. A plausible Lewis structure is shown on the right. As we see, the ion is symmetrical. There are three atoms or groups of atoms attached to each C, the bond angles around each C are $120°$, and the hybridization on each C is sp^2. The bonding to one of these carbons (the right-hand one) is represented as follows.

$$\sigma:\ C\left(sp^2\right)^1-C\left(sp^2\right)^1\quad \sigma:\ C\left(sp^2\right)^1-O_a\left(2p_z\right)^1\quad \sigma:\ C\left(sp^2\right)^1-O_b\left(2p_x\right)^1\quad \pi:\ C\left(2p_y\right)^1-O_a\left(2p_y\right)^1$$

(d) In HCO_3^-, there are $1+4+(3\times6)+1=24$ valence electrons, or 12 electron pairs. A plausible Lewis structure is shown on the right. The e^- group geometry around C is trigonal planar, with a bond angle of $120°$; the hybridization is sp^2. The geometry around O_a is bent with a bond angle less than $109.5°$; the hybridization is sp^3. The five bonds are represented as follows:

$$\sigma:\ O_a\left(sp^3\right)^1-H(1s)^1,\ \sigma:\ C\left(sp^2\right)^1-O_a\left(sp^3\right)^1,\quad \sigma:\ C\left(sp^2\right)^1-O_b(2p)^1,$$

$$\sigma:\ C\left(sp^2\right)^1-O_c\left(2p_x\right)^1,\ \pi:\ C\left(2p_z\right)^1-O_c\left(2p_z\right)^1$$

19. **(D)** Citric acid has the molecular structure shown below. Using Figure 11-18 as a guide, the flowing hybridization and bonding scheme is obtained for citric acid:

① $\sigma(O(sp^3)$ - $H(1s))$
② $\sigma(C(sp^3)$ - $H(1s))$
③ $\sigma(C(sp^2)$ - $O(sp^3))$
④ $\sigma(C(sp^2)$ - $O(2p))$
      +
   $\pi(C(2p)$ - $O(2p))$
⑤ $\sigma(C(sp^3)$ - $C(sp^2))$
⑥ $\sigma(C(sp^3)$ - $C(sp^3))$
⑦ $\sigma(C(sp^3)$ - $O(sp^3))$

20. **(M)** All interior atoms are sp^3 hybridized except C_a and C_d, which are sp^2 hybridized. The overlaps in the sixteen bonds of the molecule are represented as follows.

$$\sigma:O_e\left(sp^3\right)^1-H(1s)^1\quad \sigma:C_d\left(sp^2\right)^1-O_e\left(sp^3\right)^1\quad \sigma:C_a\left(sp^2\right)^1-O_b\left(2p_x\right)^1\quad \pi:C_d-\left(2p_z\right)^1-O_d\left(2p_z\right)^1.$$

$$\sigma:O_a\left(sp^3\right)^1-H(1s)^1\quad \sigma:C_a\left(sp^2\right)^1-O_a\left(sp^3\right)^1\quad \sigma:C_d\left(sp^2\right)^1-O_d\left(2p_x\right)^1\quad \pi:C_a-\left(2p_z\right)^1-O_b\left(2p_z\right)^1$$

$$\sigma:C_b\left(sp^3\right)^1-H(1s)^1\quad \sigma:C_b\left(sp^3\right)^1-H(1s)^1\quad \sigma:C_a\left(sp^2\right)^1-C_b\left(sp^3\right)^1\quad \sigma:C_b\left(sp^3\right)^1-C_c\left(sp^3\right)^1$$

$$\sigma:C_c\left(sp^3\right)^1-H(1s)^1\quad \sigma:C_c\left(sp^3\right)^1-O_c\left(sp^3\right)^1\quad \sigma:C_c\left(sp^3\right)^1-C_d\left(sp^2\right)^1\quad \sigma:O_c\left(sp^3\right)^1-H(1s)^1$$

21. **(M)**

(a)

Central S is sp^2 hybridized and the terrminal O and S atoms are unhybridized

$\sigma(S(sp^2)\text{-}S(3p_x))$

$\pi(S(3p_z)\text{-}S(3p_z))$

$\sigma(S(sp^2)\text{-}O(2p_z))$

(b)

Br atom is sp^3d hybridized. F atoms are unhybridized.

$3\times\sigma(Br(sp^3d) - F(2p))$

22. **(M)** Model A is XeF_2
VSEPR class: AX_2E_3
Therefore XeF_2 is a linear molecule
The central Xe atom in XeF_2 is sp^3d hybridized

Lewis Diagram:

$2 \times \sigma(Xe(sp^3d) \text{-} F(2p))$

Model B is IF_6^+
VSEPR class: AX_6
Therefore IF_6^+ is an octahedral molecule
The central I atom in IF_6^+ is sp^3d^2 hybridized

Lewis Diagram:
all I-F bonds in IF_6 are
$\sigma(I(sp^3d^2)\text{-}F(sp^3))$

23. **(M)** The bond lengths are consistent with the left-hand C—C bond being a triple bond (120 pm), the other C—C bond being a single bond (154 pm) rather than a double bond (134 pm), and the C—O bond being a double bond (123 pm). Of course, the two C—H bonds are single bonds (110 pm). All of this is depicted in the Lewis structure on the right. The overlap that produces each bond follows:

$\sigma: C_a(sp)^1 —H_a(1s)^1 \qquad \sigma: C_a(sp)^1 —C_b(sp)^1 \qquad \sigma: C_b(sp)^1 — C_c(sp^2)^1$

$\sigma: C_c(sp^2)^1 — H_b(1s)^1 \qquad \sigma: C_c(sp^2)^1 —O(2p_y)^1 \qquad \pi: C_a(2p_y)^1 —C_b(2p_y)^1$

$\pi: C_a(2p_z)^1 —C_b(2p_z)^1 \qquad \pi: C_c(2p_z)^1 —O(2p_z)^1$

24. **(E)** All of the valence electron pairs in the molecule are indicated in the sketch for the problem; there are no lone pairs. The two terminal carbon atoms have three atoms attached to them; they are sp^2 hybridized. This means there is one half-filled $2p$ orbital available on each of these terminal carbon atoms that can be used for the formation of a π bond. The central carbon atom has two atoms attached to it; it is sp hybridized. Thus there are two (perpendicular) half-filled $2p$ orbitals (such as $2p_y$ and $2p_z$) on this central carbon atom available for the formation of π bonds. One π bond is formed from the central carbon atom to each of the terminal carbon atoms. Because the two $2p$ orbitals on the central carbon atom are perpendicular to each other, these two π bonds are also mutually orthogonal. Thus, the two H—C—H planes are at 90° from each other, because of the π bonding in the molecule.

<u>25.</u> **(M)** The structure is shown below:

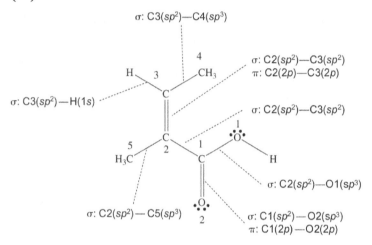

There are 8 atoms that are on the same plane (O1, O2, C1-5, H attached to C3). Furthermore, depending on the angle of rotation of the –CH$_3$ groups (C4 and C5), two H atoms can also be added to this total.

26. **(M)**

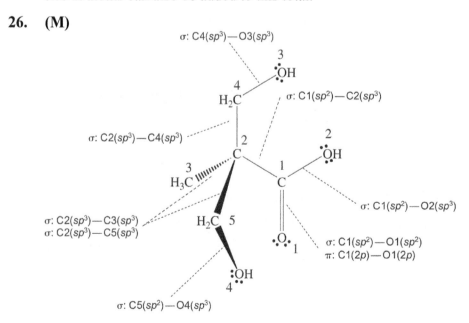

There are 7 atoms that are on the same plane (C1–4, O1–3).

Molecular–Orbital Theory

27. **(E)** The valence-bond method describes a covalent bond as the result of the overlap of atomic orbitals. The more complete the overlap, the stronger the bond. Molecular orbital theory describes a bond as a region of space in a molecule where there is a good chance of finding the bonding electrons. The molecular orbital bond does not have to be created from atomic orbitals (although it often is) and the orientations of atomic orbitals do not have to be manipulated to obtain the correct geometric shape. There is little concept of the relative energies of bonding in valence-bond theory. In molecular orbital theory, bonds are ordered energetically. These energy orderings, in fact, provide a means of checking the predictions of the theory through the spectroscopic analysis of the molecules.

28. **(E)** C_2 has $(2 \times 4) = 8$ valence electrons. A plausible Lewis structure, which obeys the octet rule and has zero formal charge for each C atom, incorporates a quadruple bond C::::C or C≡C. Molecular orbital theory, on the other hand, distributes those same 8 electrons as shown below, with a resulting bond order of $(6-2) \div 2 = 2$, (i.e., a double bond).

29. **(E)** The two molecular orbital diagrams follow:

N_2^- no. valence $e^- = (2 \times 5) + 1 = 11$

N_2^{2-} no. valence $e^- = (2 \times 5) + 2 = 12$

N_2^- bond order $= (8-3) \div 2 = 2.5$ (stable) N_2^{2-} bond order $= (8-4) \div 2 = 2$ (stable)

30. **(M)** B_2 has $(2 \times 5 =)10$ electrons. We compare the number of unpaired electrons predicted if the order is π_{2p}^b before σ_{2p}^b with the number predicted if the σ_{2p}^b orbital is before the π_{2p}^b orbital. (^{b} indicates a bonding orbital)

B_2 π_{2p}^b before σ_{2p}^b

B_2 σ_{2p}^b before π_{2p}^b

The order of orbitals with π_{2p}^b below σ_{2p}^b in energy results in B_2 being paramagnetic, with two unpaired electrons, as observed experimentally. However, if σ_{2p}^b comes before the π_{2p}^b orbital in energy, a diamagnetic B_2 molecule is predicted, which is in contradiction to experimental evidence.

31. **(E)** In order to have a bond order higher than three, there would have to be a region in a molecular orbital diagram where four bonding orbitals occur together in order of increasing energy, with no intervening antibonding orbitals. No such region exists in any of the molecular orbital diagrams in Figure 11-25. Alternatively, three bonding orbitals would have to occur together energetically, following an electron configuration which, when full, results in a bond order greater than zero. This arrangement does not occur in any of the molecular orbital diagrams in Figure 11-25.

32. **(E)** The statement is not true, for there are many instances when the bond is strengthened when a diatomic molecule loses an electron. Specifically, whenever the electron that is lost is an antibonding electron (as is the case for $F_2 \rightarrow F_2^+$ and $O_2 \rightarrow O_2^+$), the bond will actually be stronger in the resulting cation than it was in the starting neutral molecule.

33. **(M)**

(a) A σ_{1s} orbital must be lower in energy than a σ_{1s}^* orbital. The bonding orbital always is lower than the antibonding orbital if they are derived from the same atomic orbitals.

(b) The σ_{2s} orbital is derived from the 2s atomic orbitals while the σ_{2p} molecular orbitals are constructed from 2p atomic orbitals. Since the 2s orbitals are lower in energy than the 2p orbitals, we would expect that the σ_{2p} molecular orbital would be higher in energy than the σ_{2s} molecular orbital.

(c) A σ_{1s}^* orbital should be lower than a σ_{2s} orbital, since the 1s atomic orbital is considerably lower in energy than is the 2s orbital.

(d) A σ_{2p} orbital should be lower in energy than a σ_{2p}^* orbital. Both orbitals are from atomic orbitals in the same subshell but we expect a bonding orbital to be more stable than an antibonding orbital.

34. **(M)**

(a) In each case, the number of valence electrons in the species is determined first; this is followed by the valence molecular orbital diagram for each species.

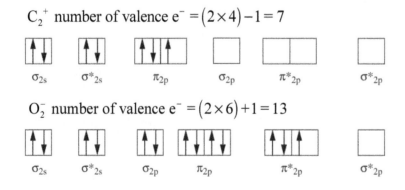

C_2^+ number of valence $e^- = (2 \times 4) - 1 = 7$

σ_{2s} σ^*_{2s} π_{2p} σ_{2p} π^*_{2p} σ^*_{2p}

O_2^- number of valence $e^- = (2 \times 6) + 1 = 13$

σ_{2s} σ^*_{2s} σ_{2p} π_{2p} π^*_{2p} σ^*_{2p}

F_2^+ number of valence $e^- = (2 \times 7) - 1 = 13$

$\sigma_{2s} \quad \sigma^*_{2s} \quad \sigma_{2p} \quad \pi_{2p} \quad \pi^*_{2p} \quad \sigma^*_{2p}$

NO^+ number of valence $e^- = 5 + 6 - 1 = 10$

$1\sigma \quad 2\sigma \quad 1\pi \quad 3\sigma \quad 2\pi \quad 4\sigma$

(b) Bond order = (no. bonding electrons – no. antibonding electrons) ÷ 2

C_2^+ bond order $= (5 - 2) \div 2 = 1.5$ \qquad This species is stable.

O_2^- bond order $= (8 - 5) \div 2 = 1.5$ \qquad This species is stable.

F_2^+ bond order $= (8 - 5) \div 2 = 1.5$ \qquad This species is stable.

NO^+ bond order $= (6 - 0) \div 2 = 3.0$ \qquad This species is stable.

(In NO^+, both the 3σ and 1π MOs are bonding, the 2π and 6σ are antibonding, and the 4σ and 5σ are nonbonding.)

(c) C_2^+ has an odd number of electrons and is paramagnetic, with one unpaired electron.
O_2^- has an odd number of electrons and is paramagnetic, with one unpaired electron.
F_2^+ has an odd number of electrons and is paramagnetic, with one unpaired electron.
NO^+ has an even number of electrons and is diamagnetic.

35. **(M)** For each of the following heteronuclear species, the valence number of electrons and valence molecular orbital diagram is listed.

(a) NO: $5 + 6 = 11$

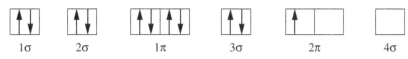

$1\sigma \quad 2\sigma \quad 1\pi \quad 3\sigma \quad 2\pi \quad 4\sigma$

(b) NO^+: $5 + 6 - 1 = 10$

$1\sigma \quad 2\sigma \quad 1\pi \quad 3\sigma \quad 2\pi \quad 4\sigma$

(c) CO: $4 + 6 = 10$

$1\sigma \quad 2\sigma \quad 1\pi \quad 3\sigma \quad 2\pi \quad 4\sigma$

(d) CN: $4+5=9$

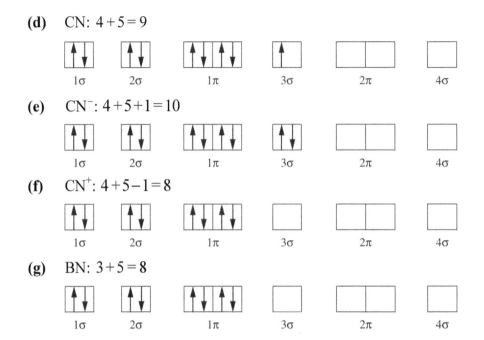

(e) CN⁻: $4+5+1=10$

(f) CN⁺: $4+5-1=8$

(g) BN: $3+5=8$

36. In Exercise 33, the species that are isoelectronic are those with 8 electrons: CN^+, BN; with 10 electrons: NO^+, CO, CN^-.

37. **(M)**

(a) NO^+ has ten valence electrons ($5+6-1=10$). The valence MO diagram is

The molecular orbital configuration is $1\sigma^2 2\sigma^2 1\pi^4 3\sigma^2$.
N_2^+ has nine valence electrons ($5+5-1=9$). The valence MO occupancy diagram is

The molecular orbital configuration is $\sigma_{2s}^2 \sigma*_{2s}^2 \pi_{2p}^4 \sigma_{2p}^1$.

(b) In heteronuclear diatomic species, both the 3σ and 1π MOs are bonding, the 2π and 6σ are antibonding, and the 4σ and 5σ are nonbonding. The bond order is calculated by subtracting the number of antibonding electrons from the number of bonding electrons and dividing by two. The bond order is 3 for NO^+ and 2.5 for N_2^+.

(c) NO^+ is diamagnetic (all paired electrons). N_2^+ is paramagnetic.

(d) N_2^+ has the greater bond length because there is less electron density between the two nuclei.

38. (M)

(a) The MO occupancy diagrams for CO^+ and CN^- are similar to that for CO as shown in the textbook in Figure 11-27. CO^+ has 9 valence electrons $(4 + 6 - 1)$ and CN^- has ten valence electrons $(4 + 5 + 1)$. The diagrams showing the occupancy of the valence molecular orbitals are shown below:

CO^+

| 1σ | 2σ | 1π | 3σ | 2π | 4σ |

$CN-$

| 1σ | 2σ | 1π | 3σ | 2π | 4σ |

(b) In heteronuclear diatomic species, both the 3σ and 1π MOs are bonding, the 2π and 6σ are antibonding, and the 4σ and 5σ are nonbonding. The bond order is calculated by subtracting the number of antibonding electrons from the number of bonding electrons and dividing by two. The bond order for CO^+ is 3 and for CN^- is 3.

(c) CO^+ is paramagnetic. CN^- is diamagnetic (all electrons are paired).

(d) Both have the same bond order; therefore, the bond length is expected to be the same for CO^+ and CN^-.

39. **(M)** The valence molecular orbital occupancy diagram for CF is shown below:

| 1σ | 2σ | 1π | 3σ | 2π | 4σ |

Both the 3σ and 1π MOs are bonding, the 2π and 6σ are antibonding, and the 4σ and 5σ are nonbonding. The bond order is calculated by subtracting the number of antibonding electrons from the number of bonding electrons and dividing by two.

The bond order for CF is 2.5 $[(6 - 1)/2]$. In CF^+, the electron in the antibonding 2π is removed, so its bond order is 3 $[(6 - 0)/2]$. Therefore, the bond length in CF^+ will be shorter, which means greater electron overlap and bonding between the two atoms.

40. **(D)** $SrCl^+$ bond will be shorter since the bond order of $SrCl^+$ is 1 and that for $SrCl$ is 0.5.

Delocalized Molecular Orbitals

41. **(E)** With either Lewis structures or the valence-bond method, two structures must be drawn (and "averaged") to explain the π bonding in C_6H_6. The σ bonding is well explained by assuming sp^2 hybridization on each C atom. But the π bonding requires that all six C—C π bonds must be equivalent. This can be achieved by creating six π molecular orbitals—three bonding and three antibonding—into which the 6π electrons are placed. This creates a single delocalized structure for the C_6H_6 molecule.

42. **(E)** Resonance is replaced in molecular orbital theory with delocalized molecular orbitals. These orbitals extend over the entire molecule, rather than being localized between two atoms. Because Lewis theory represents all bonds as being localized, the only way to depict a situation in which a pair of electrons spreads over a larger region of the molecule is to draw several Lewis structures and envision the molecule as the weighted combination or average of these (localized) Lewis structures.

43. **(M)** We expect to find delocalized orbitals in those species for which bonding cannot be represented thoroughly by one Lewis structure, that is, for compounds that require several resonance forms.

(a) In C_2H_4, there are a total of $(2\times4)+(4\times1)=12$ valence electrons, or 6 pairs. C atoms are the central atoms. Thus, the bonding description of C_2H_4 does not involve the use of delocalized orbitals.

(b) In SO_2, there are a total of $6 + (2 \times 6) = 18$ valence electrons, or 9 pairs. N is the central atom. A plausible Lewis structure has two resonance forms. The bonding description of SO_2 will require the use of delocalized molecular orbitals.

$$\overset{\cdot\cdot}{\underset{\cdot\cdot}{O}} = \overset{\cdot\cdot}{S} - \overset{\cdot\cdot}{\underset{\cdot\cdot}{O}} \colon \longleftrightarrow \colon \overset{\cdot\cdot}{\underset{\cdot\cdot}{O}} - \overset{\cdot\cdot}{S} = \overset{\cdot\cdot}{\underset{\cdot\cdot}{O}}$$

(c) In H_2CO, there are a total of $(2 \times 1) + 4 + 6 = 12$ valence electrons, or 6 pairs. C is the central atom. A plausible Lewis structure is shown on the right. Because one Lewis structure adequately represents the bonding in the molecule, the bonding description of H_2CO does not involve the use of delocalized molecular orbitals.

44. **(M)** We expect to find delocalized orbitals in those species for which bonding cannot be represented thoroughly by one Lewis structure, that is, for species that require several resonance forms.

(a) In HCO_2^-, there are $1 + 4 + (2 \times 6) + 1 = 18$ valence electrons, or 9 pairs. A plausible Lewis structure has two resonance forms. The bonding description of HCO_2^- requires the use of delocalized molecular orbitals.

(b) In CO_3^{2-}, there are $4 + (3 \times 6) + 2 = 24$ valence electrons, or 12 pairs. A plausible Lewis structure has three resonance forms. The bonding description of CO_3^{2-} requires the use of delocalized molecular orbitals.

(c) In CH_3^+, there are $4 + (3 \times 1) - 1 = 6$ valence electrons, or 3 pairs. The ion is adequately represented by one Lewis structure; no resonance forms exist.

INTEGRATIVE AND ADVANCED EXERCISES

45. **(M)**

(a) Since N_2 is symmetrical, each N atom has the same hybridization scheme [He] $sp\ \boxed{\uparrow\downarrow\ \uparrow}\ 2p\ \boxed{\uparrow\ \uparrow}$ The sigma bond results from the overlap of an sp orbital on each N. Each of the two π bonds results from the overlap of a half-filled $2p$ orbital on one nitrogen atom with a half-filled $2p$ orbital on the other nitrogen atom. The lone pair on each N is in a hybrid sp orbital. The Lewis structure is $\colon N \equiv N \colon$

(b) Although we have to stretch the concepts of valence-bonding considerably, the bonding in the N_2 molecule indeed can be described in each of the manners proposed. Consider sp^2 hybridization in detail and sketch descriptions of the others. sp^2 hybridization for N is [He] sp^2 ⬆⬇|↑|↑ $2p$ |↑| A sketch of the overlap of the hybrid orbitals appears at below. This overlap forms two of the three bonds in N_2. The third overlap occurs between the two $2p$ orbitals, affording a traditional π–bond.

For sp^3 hybridization, the lone pair resides in one of the four hybrid orbitals, and the other three overlap, rather like the thumb and spread index and middle fingers on your left and right hands can touch at their points. Finally, for simple atomic orbitals, the lone pair resides in the $2s$ orbital, and the three $2p$ orbitals are half-filled and overlap to form three bonds. This is virtually the same as the bonding description for CO or CN⁻.

46. **(M)** We begin with the orbital diagram for Na to describe the valence-bond picture for Na_2. [Ne] $_{3s}$|↑| The half-filled $3s$ orbital on each Na overlaps with another to form a σ covalent bond. There are 22 electrons in Na_2. These electrons are distributed in the molecular orbitals as follows.

σ_{1s} $\quad$ σ_{1s}^* $\quad$ σ_{2s} $\quad$ σ_{2s}^* $\qquad$ $\sigma_{2p}\, \pi_{2p}$ $\quad$ $\pi_{2p}^*\,\sigma_{2p}^*$ $\quad$ σ_{3s}
⬆⬇ $\quad$ ⬆⬇ $\quad$ ⬆⬇ $\quad$ ⬆⬇ $\qquad$ ⬆⬇|⬆⬇⬆⬇| $\quad$ |⬆⬇⬆⬇|⬆⬇| $\quad$ ⬆⬇ $\quad$ Again, we predict a single bond for Na_2. A Lewis-theory picture of the bonding would have the two Lewis symbols for two Na atoms uniting to form a bond: Na· ·Na $\longrightarrow$ Na — Na Thus, the bonding in Na_2 is very much like that in H_2.

47. **(M)**

Species	NeF	NeF⁺	NeF⁻
Orbital Diagram	↑ σ_{2p}^* ⬆⬇ ⬆⬇ π_{2p}^* ⬆⬇ ⬆⬇ π_{2p} ⬆⬇ σ_{2p} ⬆⬇ σ_{2s}^* ⬆⬇ σ_{2s}	— σ_{2p}^* ⬆⬇ ⬆⬇ π_{2p}^* ⬆⬇ ⬆⬇ π_{2p} ⬆⬇ σ_{2p} ⬆⬇ σ_{2s}^* ⬆⬇ σ_{2s}	⬆⬇ σ_{2p}^* ⬆⬇ ⬆⬇ π_{2p}^* ⬆⬇ ⬆⬇ π_{2p} ⬆⬇ σ_{2p} ⬆⬇ σ_{2s}^* ⬆⬇ σ_{2s}
Bond Order	0.5	1.0	0
Magnetic Property	Paramagnetic (1 e⁻)	Diamagnetic	Diamagnetic (atoms)

From the MO diagrams, it is expected that NeF and NeF⁺ should be observable species since they have non-zero bond orders. NeF⁻ has a bond order of zero, hence it is unlikely that it will be observed, or at best, we would expect a very loose association between the atoms (long/weak bond).

48. **(M)** The superoxide ion, O_2^-, has 17 electrons, while the peroxide ion, O_2^{2-}, has a total of 18 electrons,

(a) The molecular orbital diagrams for these two ions are given below.

$$\sigma_{1s} \quad \sigma_{1s}^* \quad \sigma_{2s} \quad \sigma_{2s}^* \qquad \sigma_{2p} \quad \pi_{2p} \quad \pi_{2p}^* \quad \sigma_{2p}^*$$

$$O_2^- \;\; \boxed{\uparrow\downarrow}\; \boxed{\uparrow\downarrow}\; \boxed{\uparrow\downarrow}\; \boxed{\uparrow\downarrow}\;\;\; \boxed{\uparrow\downarrow}\; \boxed{\uparrow\downarrow\,|\,\uparrow\downarrow}\; \boxed{\uparrow\downarrow\,|\,\uparrow}\; \boxed{\;}$$

bond order = (no. bonding electrons – no. antibonding electrons) ÷2 = (10 – 7) ÷2 = 1.5

$$\sigma_{1s} \quad \sigma_{1s}^* \quad \sigma_{2s} \quad \sigma_{2s}^* \qquad \sigma_{2p} \quad \pi_{2p} \quad \pi_{2p}^* \quad \sigma_{2p}^*$$

$$O_2^{2-} \;\; \boxed{\uparrow\downarrow}\; \boxed{\uparrow\downarrow}\; \boxed{\uparrow\downarrow}\; \boxed{\uparrow\downarrow}\;\;\; \boxed{\uparrow\downarrow}\; \boxed{\uparrow\downarrow\,|\,\uparrow\downarrow}\; \boxed{\uparrow\,|\,\uparrow\downarrow}\; \boxed{\;}$$

bond order = (no. bonding electrons – no. antibonding electrons) ÷2 = (10 – 8) ÷2 = 1.0

(b) O_2^- has $(2 \times 6) + 1 = 13$ electrons, 6 electron pairs plus one electron. O_2^{2-} has $(2 \times 6) + 2 = 14$ electrons, 7 electron pairs. Plausible Lewis structures are

$$O_2^- \quad [\,:\!\ddot{O}\!-\!\ddot{O}\!\cdot\,]^- \qquad O_2^{2-} \quad [\,:\!\ddot{O}\!-\!\ddot{O}\!:\,]^{2-}$$

49. **(M)** K_2O_3 contains two K^+ ions, and thus the total charge of the anions must be 2^-: O_3^{2-}. There is no simple way to do this with peroxide(O_2^{2-}) and superoxide (O_2^-) ions. But if we take a hint from the word "empirical" in the statement of the problem and try K_4O_6, we have O_6^{4-}, which will be a combination of one O_2^{2-} and two O_2^- ions. Thus a nice symmetrical Lewis structure is $[K^+] \; [\,:\!\ddot{O}\!-\!\ddot{O}\!\cdot\,]^- \; [K^+] \; [\,:\!\ddot{O}\!-\!\ddot{O}\!:\,]^{2-} \; [K^+] \; [\,:\!\ddot{O}\!-\!\ddot{O}\!\cdot\,]^- \; [K^+]$.

50. **(D)** Urea has $4 + 6 + 2 \times [5 + (2 \times 1)] = 24$ valence electrons, or 12 pairs. C is at the very center, bonded to O and 2 N's. Each N is bonded to 2 H's. A plausible Lewis structure is

$$\begin{array}{ccccc} H-\!\!\!\!&\overset{\cdot\cdot}{N}&\!\!\!\!-C-\!\!\!\!&\overset{\cdot\cdot}{N}&\!\!\!\!-H \\ & | & \| & | & \\ & H & :\!\ddot{O}\!: & H & \end{array}$$

A VSEPR treatment of this Lewis structure suggests that the geometry around C is trigonal planar, as experimentally observed. But VSEPR theory predicts trigonal pyramidal geometry around each N, rather than the observed trigonal planar geometry. Because all of the bond angles are 120°, the hybridization on each central atom must be sp^2. The orbital diagram for each type of atom follows

$$H_{1s}\,\boxed{\uparrow} \qquad O\,[He]\; {}_{2s}\boxed{\uparrow\downarrow}\; {}_{2p}\boxed{\uparrow\downarrow\,|\,\uparrow\,|\,\uparrow}$$

$$N\,[He]\; {}_{2s}\boxed{\uparrow\downarrow}\; {}_{2p}\boxed{\uparrow\,|\,\uparrow\,|\,\uparrow} \;\rightarrow\; N\,[He]\; {}_{sp^2}\boxed{\uparrow\,|\,\uparrow\,|\,\uparrow}\; {}_{2p}\boxed{\uparrow\downarrow}$$

$$C\,[He]\; {}_{2s}\boxed{\uparrow\downarrow}\; {}_{2p}\boxed{\uparrow\,|\,\uparrow\,|\,} \;\rightarrow\; C\,[He]\; {}_{sp^2}\boxed{\uparrow\,|\,\uparrow\,|\,\uparrow}\; {}_{2p}\boxed{\uparrow}$$

The bonding scheme is as follows. There are four N — H sigma bonds, each formed by the overlap of an sp^2 hybrid orbital on N with a $1s$ orbital on H. There are two C — N sigma bonds, each formed by the end-to-end overlap of the remaining sp^2 hybrid orbital on N with an sp^2 orbital on C. There is also one C — O sigma bond, formed by the end-to-end overlap of the remaining sp^2 orbital on C with the $2p_y$ orbital on O. There is one pi bond, formed by the side-to-side overlap of the $2p_z$ orbital on C with the side-to-side overlap of the $2p_z$ orbital on O. The lone pairs reside in $2p_z$ orbitals on each N; they each probably interact with the electrons in the pi bond to stabilize the molecule. Contributing Lewis resonance forms follow.

$$\begin{array}{ccc}
H-\!\overset{\cdot\cdot}{N}\!-C-\!\overset{\cdot\cdot}{N}\!-H & H-\!\overset{\oplus}{N}\!=C-\!\overset{\cdot\cdot}{N}\!-H & H-\!\overset{\cdot\cdot}{N}\!-C=\!\overset{\oplus}{N}\!-H \\
| \;\;\; \| \;\;\; | & | \;\;\; | \;\;\; | & | \;\;\; | \;\;\; | \\
H \;\; :\!\ddot{O}\!: \;\; H & H \;\; :\!\ddot{O}\!: \;\; H & H \;\; :\!\ddot{O}\!: \;\; H \\
& \ominus & \ominus
\end{array}$$

51. (M)

(a) A sketch of the molecule is: [structure: O–N–O–C–H with H and O below, H and O on C] The CH₃ group is tetrahedral.

(b) Each of the C—H bonds is a sigma bond, as are the C—O bond and the next N—O bond. There are of course, a sigma bonds connecting the N to the other two O's. But there is also a pi bond. In fact, if Lewis structures are drawn to represent the bonding in the molecule, two resonance forms must be drawn.

[Lewis resonance structures: $\ddot{O}=N-\ddot{O}_c-C-H$ with charges 1–, 1+, 0, 0 ⟷ $\ddot{O}-N-\ddot{O}_c-C-H$ with charges 0, 1+, 0, 0, 1–]

All three C—H bonds are σ bonds: $C(sp^3)^1 — H(1s)^1$

The C—O_c bond is a σ bond: $C(sp^3)^1 — O_c(sp^3)^1$

There are two lone pairs on the O_c atom: $O_c(sp^3)^2$.

The bonds from N to the terminal atoms are σ bonds: $N(sp^2) – O(sp^3)$ and $N(sp^2) –O(sp^2)$

And there is one π bond: $N(2p_z)^1 — O(2p_z)^1$

The subscript is on O_c to distinguish this central oxygen from the two terminal oxygens.

(c) The N—O_c bond is a single bond in both resonance forms (136 pm). The other N-to-O bonds are single bonds in one resonance form and double bonds in the other, making them about one-and-a-half bonds, which would be significantly shorter (126 pm) than the N—O_c bond, but longer than typical N=O bonds (120 pm, see Table 11.1).

52. (M) The O—N—O bond angle of 125° indicates the N atom is sp^2 hybridized, while the F—O_a—N bond angle of 105° indicates the O_a atom is sp^3 hybridized. The orbital diagrams of the atoms follow.

O [He] $2s$ [↑↓] $2p$ [↑↓][↑][↑] O_a [He] $2s$ [↑↓] $2p$ [↑↓][↑][↑] ⟶ O [He] sp^3 [↑↓][↑↓][↑][↑]

F [He] $2s$ [↑↓] $2p$ [↑↓][↑↓][↑]   N [He] $2s$ [↑↓] $2p$ [↑][↑][↑] ⟶ N [He] sp^2 [↑][↑][↑] $2p$ [↑]

Electron transfer from N to the terminal oxygen atom results in a +1 formal charge for nitrogen, a –1 formal charge for O and a single bond being developed between these two atoms.

O [He] $2s$[↑↓] $2p$[↑↓][↑][↑] $\xrightarrow{+e^-}$ O⁻ [He] $2s$[↑↓] $2p$[↑↓][↑↓][↑]

Bonds are formed by the following overlaps.

$$\sigma: F(2p) — O_a(sp^3) \quad \sigma: O_a(sp^3) — N(sp^2) \quad \sigma: N(sp^2) — O(2p_y) \quad \pi: N(2p_z) — O(2p_z)$$

Two resonance structures are required $\ddot{F}-\ddot{O}_a-N-\ddot{O}$ [with :O: above N] ⟷ $\ddot{F}-\ddot{O}_a-N=\ddot{O}$ [with :Ö: above N]

With the wedge-and-dash representation, a sketch of the molecule is [structure: N bonded to O (up), O (down-left), and O–F (wedge)]

53. **(M)** NO_2^- has $5 + 2 \times 6 + 1 = 18$ valence electrons = 9 electron pairs. The singly bonded oxygen has a formal charge of -1 while the other two atoms have an octet of electrons and no formal charge.

$$\left[\overset{..}{\underset{..}{O}}=\overset{..}{N}-\overset{..}{\underset{..}{O}}:\right]^- \longleftrightarrow \left[:\overset{..}{\underset{..}{O}}-\overset{..}{N}=\overset{..}{\underset{..}{O}}\right]^-$$ The N atom is sp^2 hybridized. Orbital diagrams for the atoms follow.

O [He] $_{2s}\boxed{\uparrow\downarrow}$ $_{2p}\boxed{\uparrow\downarrow|\uparrow|\uparrow}$ N [He] $_{2s}\boxed{\uparrow\downarrow}$ $_{2p}\boxed{\uparrow|\uparrow|\uparrow}$ $\longrightarrow$ N [He] $_{sp^2}\boxed{\uparrow\downarrow|\uparrow|\uparrow}$ $_{2p}\boxed{\uparrow}$

There are two N-O sigma bonds, each formed by the end-to-end overlap of an sp^2 hybrid orbital on N with a $2p_y$ orbital on O. The pi bonding system is constructed from three $2p_z$ orbitals: (1) the $2p_z$ orbital on one O, (2) the $2p_z$ orbital on N, and (3) the $2p_z$ orbital on the other O. There are four π electrons in this system (the three $2p_z$ electrons shown in the orbital diagrams above, plus an extra electron due to the negative charge on the anion). There should be three π molecular orbitals formed: bonding, nonbonding, and an antibonding orbital, which fill as follows:

. π antibonding orbital $\boxed{}$

                    π nonbonding orbital $\boxed{\uparrow\downarrow}$ π bond order $= (2-0) \div 2 = 1$

                    π bonding orbital $\boxed{\uparrow\downarrow}$

54. **(M)** Let us begin by drawing Lewis structures for the species concerned.

(a) For ClF_3 there are three atoms and two lone pairs attached to the central atom. The electron group geometry is trigonal bipyramidal and the molecule is T-shaped. For As F_5 there are five atoms attached to the central atom; its electron group geometry and molecular shape are trigonal bipyramidal. For ClF_2^+ there are two lone pairs and two atoms attached to the central atom. Its electron group geometry is tetrahedral and the ion is bent in shape. For AsF_6^- there are six atoms and no lone pairs attached to the central atom. Thus, the electron group geometry and the shape of this ion are octahedral.

(b) Trigonal bipyramidal electron group geometry is associated with sp^3d hybridization. The Cl in ClF_3 and As in AsF_5 both have sp^3d hybridization. Tetrahedral electron group geometry is associated with sp^3 hybridization. Thus Cl in ClF_2^+ has sp^3 hybridization. Octahedral electron group geometry is associated with sp^3d^2 hybridization, which is the hybridization adopted by As in AsF_6^-.

55. **(M)** The two shorter nitrogen-oxygen bond distances indicate partial double bond character; a N=O bond is 120 pm long, while a N—O bond is 136 pm long. There are two resonance forms for HNO_3 that represent these facts.

The H—O sigma bond is formed by the overlap of a half-filled $1s$ orbital on H with a half-filled sp^3 orbital on O. The HO—N sigma bond is formed by the overlap of the remaining half-filled sp^3 orbital on O with a half-filled sp^2 orbital on N. Both of the remaining N—O sigma bonds are formed by the overlap of a half-filled sp^2 orbital on N with a half-filled $2p_y$ orbital on O. Each of the structures has a N-O π bond formed by the side-to-side overlap of half-filled $2p_z$ orbitals.

56. **(E)** Suppose two He atoms in the excited state $1s^1 2s^1$ unite to form an He_2 molecule. One possible configuration is $\sigma_{1s}^2 \sigma_{1s}^{*0} \sigma_{2s}^2 \sigma_{2s}^{0*}$. The bond order would be (4-0)/2 = 2.

57. **(M)** Since all angles ~ 120°, and since the bond angles around C total 360° (= 123° + 113° + 124°), we postulate that both the C and N atoms have sp^2 hybridization. Two resonance forms follow.

The structure on the right would be predicted to have sp^2 hybridization on both the C and N atoms. For structure on the right hand side, the overlaps that form the bonds are as follows.

σ: H($1s$)—C(sp^2) σ: C(sp^2)—O($2p$)

σ: C(sp^2)—N(sp^2) σ: N(sp^2)—H($1s$) σ: N(sp^2)—H($1s$) π: C($2p_z$)—N($2p_z$)

The structure on the left is predicted to have sp^2 hybridization on C and sp^3 hybridization on N. In this structure, the following overlaps result in bonds.

σ: H($1s$)—C(sp^2) σ: C(sp^2)—O($2p$)

σ: C(sp^2)—N(sp^3) σ: N(sp^3)—H($1s$) σ: N(sp^3)—H($1s$) π: C($2p_z$)— O($2p_z$)

From Table 10-2 we see the C−N bond length of 138 pm is intermediate between a single C—N bond length (147 pm) and a double C=N bond length (128 pm), just as we would expect for the resonance hybrid of the two structures written above.

58. **(E)** The orbital diagrams for C and N are as follows. C [He] sp^2 [↑][↑][↑] $2p$[↑]

N [He] sp^2 [↑↓][↑][↑] $2p$[↑]

The sp^2 electrons are involved in σ bonding. For N, the lone pair is in one sp^2 orbital; the remaining two half-filled sp^2 orbitals bond to adjacent C atoms. For C, one sp^2 orbital forms a σ bond by overlap with a half-filled $1s$ H atom. The remaining two half-filled sp^2 orbitals bond to either adjacent C or N atoms. The $2p$ electrons are involved in π bonding. The six $2p$ orbitals form six delocalized π molecular orbitals, three bonding and three antibonding. These six π orbitals are filled as shown in the π molecular orbital diagram sketched below.

antibonding
π molecular orbitals

bonding
π molecular orbitals

Number of π-bonds $= \dfrac{6-0}{2} = 3$

This π-bonding scheme produces three π-bonds, which is identical to the number predicted by Lewis theory.

59. (E) Both of the π_{2p} orbitals have a nodal plane. This plane passes through both nuclei and between the two lobes of the π bond. The difference between nodes in the two types of orbitals is that, in an antibonding orbital, the node lies between the two nuclei and is perpendicular to the internuclear axis, whereas in the bonding orbital, the two nuclei lie in the plane of the node, which plane therefore contains the internuclear axis. The deciding factor in determining whether an orbital is bonding or not is whether it places more electron density in the region between the two nuclei than does the combination of two atomic orbitals. All of the bonding orbitals fulfill this criterion.

60. (M) We draw the Lewis structure of each species to account for the electron pairs around each central atom, which is Cl in each species. In F_2Cl^-, there are a total of $7 + (2 \times 7) + 1 = 22$ valence electrons, or 11 electron pairs. In F_2Cl^+, there are a total of $7 + (2 \times 7) - 1 = 20$ valence electrons, or 10 electron pairs. Plausible Lewis structures follow. $[:\!\ddot{F}\!-\!\ddot{C}l\!-\!\ddot{F}\!:]^-$ $[:\!\ddot{F}\!-\!\ddot{C}l\!-\!\ddot{F}\!:]^+$ Since there are two atoms and three lone pairs attached to Cl in F_2Cl^-, the electron-group geometry around the Cl atom is trigonal bipyramidal, the Cl atom hybridization is sp^3d, and the shape of the species is linear. There are two atoms and only two lone pairs attached to the Cl atom in F_2Cl^+, which produces a tetrahedral electron-group geometry, a hybridization of sp^3 for Cl, and a bent shape for the species.

61. (M) We will assume 100 g of the compound and find the empirical formula in the usual way.

moles of carbon $= 53.09 \text{ g C} \times \dfrac{1 \text{ mole C}}{12.011 \text{g C}} = 4.424$ mol

moles of hydrogen $= 6.24 \text{ g} \times \dfrac{1 \text{ mole H}}{1.008 \text{ g H}} = 6.19$ mol

moles of nitrogen $= 12.39 \text{ g} \times \dfrac{1 \text{ mole N}}{14.007 \text{ g N}} = 0.885$ mol

moles of oxygen $= 28.29 \text{ g} \times \dfrac{1 \text{ mole O}}{15.999 \text{ g O}} = 1.768$ mol

Dividing all result by 0.885 we get: 5.00 moles C, 6.99$\underline{5}$ moles H, 1.00 mole N and 2.00 moles O. This yields an empirical formula of $C_5H_7NO_2$.
Structure: $N{\equiv}C{-}CH_2(C{=}O)OC_2H_5$

Hybrid orbitals used:

C_b—H , C_d—H, C_e—H : σ H($1s$) – C(sp^3) (all tetrahedral carbon uses sp^3 hybrid orbitals)

C_c=O_b: σ C_c (sp^2) –O_b ($2p$ or sp^2), π: C_c ($2p$) – O_b ($2p$)

C_c-O_a: σ C_c (sp^2) –O_a ($2p$ or sp^3)

C_d-O_a: σ C_d (sp^3) –O_a ($2p$ or sp^3)

C_a≡N: σ C_a (sp) –N(sp)

Two mutually perpendicular π-bonds: C($2p$) – N($2p$)

C_a-C_b: σ C_b(sp^3) –C_a(sp)

C_d-C_e: σ C_d(sp^3) –C_e(sp^3)

C_c-C_b: σ C_b(sp^3) –C_c(sp^2)

62. **(M)** We will assume 100 g of the compound and find the empirical formula in the usual way.

$$\text{moles of carbon} = 67.90 \text{ g} \times \frac{1 \text{ mole C}}{12.011 \text{g C}} = 5.653 \text{ mol}$$

$$\text{moles of hydrogen} = 5.70 \text{ g} \times \frac{1 \text{ mole H}}{1.008 \text{ g H}} = 5.65\underline{5} \text{ mol}$$

$$\text{moles of nitrogen} = 26.40 \text{ g} \times \frac{1 \text{ mole N}}{14.007 \text{ g N}} = 1.885 \text{ mol}$$

Dividing all results by 1.885, we get: 2.999 moles C, 3.00 moles H, and 1.00 mole N. This yields an empirical formula of C_3H_3N.

There are three possible molecules (Lewis structures) with this formula:

63. **(E)**

(a) power output = $(1.00 \text{ kW/m}^2) \times (1000 \text{ W/kW}) \times (40.0 \text{ cm}^2) \times (1 \text{m}^2/10^4 \text{ cm}^2) = 4.00$ watts

amps = $i = w/v$

(b) $i = 4.00 \text{ watts} = 4.00 \dfrac{\text{J}}{\text{s}} \times \dfrac{1 \text{ C}}{0.45 \text{ J}} = 8.9 \dfrac{\text{C}}{\text{s}} = 8.9$ amps

64. **(M)** See structures below:

N is sp^2 hybridized with ~120° C – N = C angle. C is sp hybridized with a N = C = O angle of ~180°.

The CH$_3$ group has an sp^3 hybridized C with 3 × H – C – H angles of ~109.5°.

65. **(E)** The expanded Lewis structure of histidine is shown below on the right.

The N(1) atom in histidine has an sp^2 hybridization. The N(2) atom is sp^3 hybridized (it has three single bonds). The C(3) carbon is sp^2 hybridized. The angles α and β are determined by noting the hybridization of the atom at the vertex of the angle: The carbon atom at the vertex of α is sp^3 hybridized, so α is 109.5°, while the carbon at the vertex of β is sp^2 hybridized, so β is 120°.

66. **(M)** The Lewis structures below and the valence-bond diagrams explain the differences in the shapes.

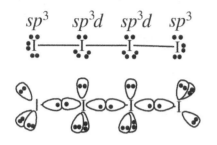

67. **(M)** The five isomers with shapes derived from VSEPR theory are shown below, along with the explanation for the geometry of each carbon in the structure. In the structures below, carbons with an AX_4 configuration are sp^3 hybridized and have a bond angle of 109.5°, those with AX_3 are sp^2 hybridized and have a bond angle of 120°, and those with AX_2 are sp hybridized with a bond angle of 180°.

C(1) has an AX_3 configuration: trigonal planar geometry
C(2) is AX_3 also: trigonal planar geometry
C(3) is AX_4 configuration: tetrahedral geometry
C(4) is AX_3 as well: trigonal planar geometry
C(5) is AX_3 configuration: trigonal planar geometry

C(1) has an AX_3 configuration: trigonal planar geometry
C(2) is AX_3 also: trigonal planar geometry
C(3) is AX_3 also: trigonal planar geometry
C(4) is AX_3 as well: trigonal planar geometry
C(5) is an AX_4 configuration: tetrahedral geometry

C(1) has an AX_4 configuration: tetrahedral geometry
C(2) has an AX_3 configuration: trigonal planar geometry
C(3) has an AX_2 configuration: linear geometry
C(4) is AX_3 as well: trigonal planar geometry
C(5) has an AX_4 configuration: tetrahedral geometry
** See the solution to Exercise 24 for an explanation of why the groups bonded to C(2) and C(4) do not lie in the same plane.

The valence bond method derives structure from overlap of individual atomic orbitals with each other. Because the $2p$ orbitals of carbon are at 90° to each other, the valence bond method, without hybridization, allows for 90° and 180° bond angles only. However, by using the appropriate hybridization scheme, the valence bond method can be used to describe bonding for the shapes and geometries predicted by using VSEPR theory.

Of the structures above, the second one has a partially delocalized π system because it has alternating single and double bonds. An energy-level diagram, including the molecular orbitals, of the delocalized π system is shown below. It is important to note that for $H_2C=CH-CH=CH-CH_3$, the $2p$ orbitals from the four sp^2 hybridized carbon atoms contribute to the π system. The carbon atom in the CH_3 group is sp^3 hybridized and does not contribute a $2p$ electron to the π system.

68. **(M)** The molecular orbital occupancy diagrams of the π system for 1,3,5-hexatriene and 1,3,5,7-octatetraene are shown below, derived from Figure 11-34 in the text.

As is seen, the HOMO-LUMO gap in 1,3,5,7-ocatetraene is smaller than the gap for 1,3,5-hexatriene. Therefore, the wavelength corresponding to the excitation of the former would be longer. Energy and wavelength are related according to the equation below:

$$E = hc/\lambda$$

Since the energy gap needed to overcome for 1,3,5,7-octatetraene is smaller, the wavelength is larger.

For 1,3,4-hexatriene, there are three bonding orbitals and three nonbonding molecular orbitals. The combinations of atomic orbitals contributing to each molecular orbital are illustrated below.

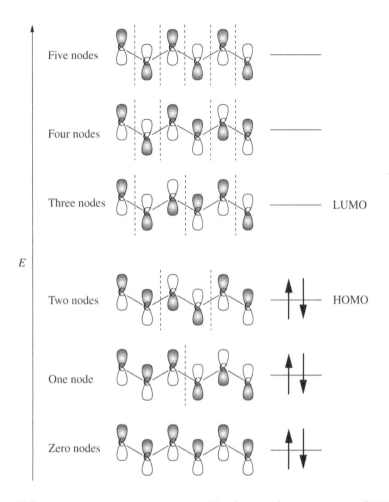

69. (D) Some plausible resonance structures contributing to the structure of HOON are shown below.

Radical-pair structure (major contributor) Molecular structure (significant contributor) Ion-pair structure (minor contributor)

FEATURE PROBLEMS

70. **(D)**

(a) $C_6H_6(l) + 3 H_2(g) \rightarrow C_6H_{12}(l)$ $\Delta H° = \Sigma\Delta_f H°$, products $- \Sigma\Delta_f H°$, reactants

$\Delta H° = -156.4$ kJ mol^{-1} $- [3 \times 0$ kJ mol^{-1} + 49.0 kJ mol^{-1}] $= -205.4$ kJ mol^{-1} $= \Delta H°(a)$

(b) $C_6H_{10}(l) + H_2(g) \rightarrow C_6H_{12}(l)$ $\Delta H° = \Sigma\Delta_f H°$ products $- \Sigma\Delta_f H°$ reactants

$\Delta H° = -156.4$ kJ mol^{-1} $- [1 \times 0$ kJ mol^{-1} + $(-38.5$ kJ mol$^{-1})$] $= -117.9$ kJ mol^{-1} $= \Delta H°(b)$

(c) Enthalpy of hydrogenation for 1,3,5-cyclohexatriene $= 3 \times \Delta H°(b)$
Enthalpy of hydrogenation $= 3 (-117.9$ kJ mol$^{-1})$ $= -353.7$ kJ mol^{-1} $= \Delta H°(c)$
$\Delta_f H°_{cyclohexene} = -38.5$ kJ/mole (given in part b of this question).
Resonance energy is the difference between $\Delta H°(a)$ and $\Delta H°(c)$.
Resonance energy $= -353.7$ kJ mol^{-1} $- (-205.4$ kJ mol$^{-1})$ $= -148.3$ kJ mol^{-1}

(d) Using bond energies:
$\Delta H°_{atomization} = 6(C—H) + 3(C—C) + 3(C=C)$
$\Delta H°_{atomization} = 6(414$ kJ mol$^{-1})$ + 3(347 kJ mol$^{-1})$ + 3(611 kJ mol$^{-1})$
$\Delta H°_{atomization} = 5358$ kJ mol^{-1}

$C_6H_6(g) \rightarrow 6 C(g) + 6 H(g)$
$\Delta H° = [6(716.7$ kJ mol$^{-1})$ + 6(218 kJ mol$^{-1})$] $- 82.6$ kJ mol^{-1} $= 5525.6$ kJ mol^{-1}
Resonance energy $= 5358$ kJ mol^{-1} $- 5525.6$ kJ mol^{-1} $= -168$ kJ mol^{-1}

71. **(D)**

(a) Five valid resonance forms can be drawn for furan:

These individual resonance forms do not exist. The actual structure is a hybrid possessing characteristics of all five individual contributors.

(b) Furan is an aromatic five-membered heterocycle. Its four carbon atoms and lone oxygen atom are sp^2 hybridized in the classical bonding description. One of the lone pairs on oxygen occupies an unhybridized p-orbital, and this lone pair overlaps with the half-filled $2p$ orbitals on the four carbon atoms to form an aromatic sextet:

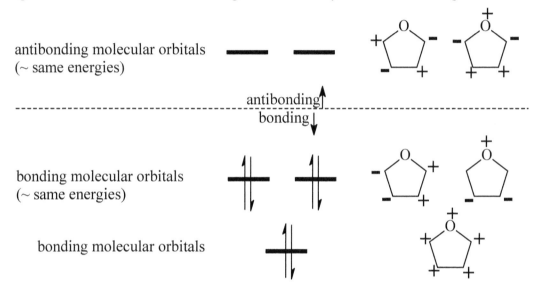

6 π-e⁻ is shown as $6 \, \pi\text{-e}^-$

$(4n + 2) \, \pi\text{-e}^-$ where n = 1
Therefore, aromatic ring

The ground-state molecular orbital diagram for the π-system in furan is depicted below:

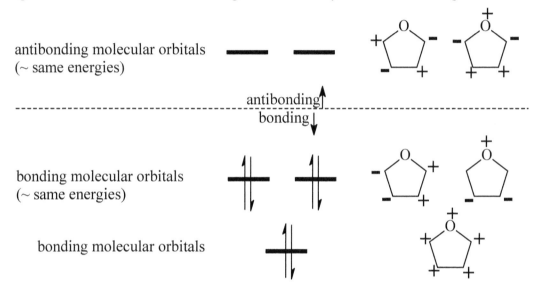

The diagram shows that the six π-electrons fill the three bonding molecular orbitals for the π-system. Keep in mind that the ensemble of π-molecular orbitals is superimposed on the sp^2 framework for the molecule.

(c) All five resonance structures for furan (structures a-e) have six electrons involved in π-bonding. In structure (a), a lone pair in a $2p$ orbital on the oxygen atom along with the four π-electrons in unhybridized $2p$ orbitals that form the two C=C bonds are combined to give the π-system. In structures (b) to (e) inclusive, the π-system is produced by the combination of a lone pair in a $2p$ orbital on a carbon atom with the four π-electrons from the C=O and C=C bonds.

72. (D)

(a) In order to see the shape of the *sp* hybrid, the simplest approach is to combine just the angular parts of the *s* and *p* orbitals. Including the radial part makes the plot more challenging (see below). The angular parts for the 2s and $2p_z$ orbitals are

$$Y(s) = \left(\frac{1}{4\pi}\right)^{1/2} \text{ and } \quad Y\left(p_z\right) = \left(\frac{3}{4\pi}\right)^{1/2} \cos\theta$$

Combining the two angular parts:

$$\psi_1(sp) = \frac{1}{\sqrt{2}}\left[Y(2s) + Y(2p)\right]$$

$$\psi_1(sp) = \frac{1}{\sqrt{2}}\left[\left(\frac{1}{4\pi}\right)^{1/2} + \left(\frac{3}{4\pi}\right)^{1/2}\cos\theta\right]$$

$$\psi_1(sp) = \frac{1}{\sqrt{2}}\left(\frac{1}{4\pi}\right)^{1/2}\left[1 + \sqrt{3}\cos\theta\right]$$

We now evaluate this function (ignoring the constants in front of the square brackets) for various values of θ

Theta(deg)	Theta(rad)	sp_1	sp_2
0	0	2.732	−0.732
30	0.5236	2.500	−0.500
45	0.7854	2.225	−0.225
60	1.0472	1.866	0.134
90	1.5708	1.000	1.000
120	2.0944	0.134	1.866
135	2.3562	−0.225	2.225
150	2.6180	−0.500	2.500
170	2.9670	−0.706	2.706
180	3.1416	−0.732	2.732
190	3.3161	−0.706	2.706
210	3.6652	−0.500	2.500
225	3.9270	−0.225	2.225
240	4.1888	0.134	1.866
270	4.7124	1.000	1.000
300	5.2360	1.866	0.134
315	5.4978	2.225	−0.225
330	5.7596	2.500	−0.500
360	6.2832	2.732	−0.732

A plot of these values in the form of Figure 8.24 gives the general shape of the *sp* hybrid.

This is a plot in the *xz*-plane, for $\Psi_1(sp)$.

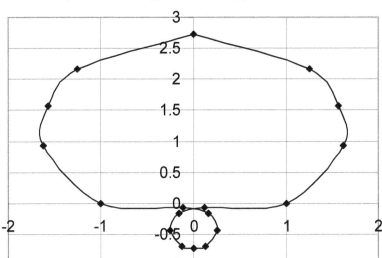

The other *sp* hybrid is

$$\psi_2(sp) = \frac{1}{\sqrt{2}}\left[Y(2s) - Y(2p)\right]$$

$$\psi_2(sp) = \frac{1}{\sqrt{2}}\left[\left(\frac{1}{4\pi}\right)^{1/2} - \left(\frac{3}{4\pi}\right)^{1/2}\cos\theta\right]$$

$$\psi_2(sp) = \frac{1}{\sqrt{2}}\left(\frac{1}{4\pi}\right)^{1/2}\left[1 - \sqrt{3}\cos\theta\right]$$

Graphically, $\Psi_2(sp)$ is generated as follows:

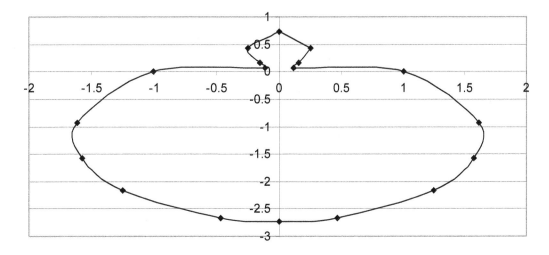

We now see that the second *sp* hybrid, $\Psi_2(sp)$, points in a direction opposite to the first $\Psi_1(sp)$.

(b) Figure 12-10 pictorially shows the hybridization of a 2s orbital and a 2p (there is no mention of whether it is a $2p_x$, $2p_y$ or $2p_z$ orbital). When one of the degenerate 2p-orbitals and the 2s orbital are hybridized, we expect that there should be no difference in shape or energy of the resulting sp-hybrid orbitals. The only difference between the $2p_x$, $2p_y$ and $2p_z$ orbitals is the direction in which these atomic orbitals are oriented. Similarly, the only difference in the resulting hybrid orbitals should be their directional properties. Mathematically, we have shown (part (a)), that an sp_z hybrid orbital is proportional to $1 - \sqrt{3}\cos\theta$. Similar calculations for an sp_x hybrid orbital result in an analogous relationship, namely one proportional to $1 - \sqrt{3}\sin\theta\cos\phi$. (Note: in the xz plane, $\phi = 90°$, therefore $\cos\phi = 1$). In the xz plane, this expression simplifies to $1 - \sqrt{3}\sin\theta$. (Note: $\sin\theta = \cos(90° - \theta)$.) These two relationships result in similar answers (i.e., same shape), the only difference being a shift by an expected 90°. Similar arguments can be made for an sp_y hybrid orbital expression.

(c) The sp^2 hybrids. To show the spatial distribution of the sp^2 hybrids, we will again use the angular functions only. Thus

$$Y(p_x) = \left(\frac{3}{4\pi}\right)^{1/2}\sin\theta\cos\phi \qquad\qquad Y(s) = \left(\frac{1}{4\pi}\right)^{1/2}$$

Combining these functions

$$\psi_1(sp^2) = \frac{1}{\sqrt{3}}\psi(2s) + \frac{\sqrt{2}}{\sqrt{3}}\psi(2p_x) \quad \psi_1(sp^2) = \frac{1}{\sqrt{3}}\left(\frac{1}{4\pi}\right)^{1/2} + \frac{\sqrt{2}}{\sqrt{3}}\left(\frac{3}{4\pi}\right)^{1/2}\sin\theta\cos\phi$$

$$\psi_1(sp^2) = \left(\frac{1}{4\pi}\right)^{1/2}\left[\frac{1}{\sqrt{3}} + \sqrt{2}\sin\theta\cos\phi\right]$$

In the xy-plane $\theta = 90°$ so that the function becomes $(\sin(90°) = 1)$

$$\psi_1(sp^2) = \left(\frac{1}{4\pi}\right)^{1/2}\left[\frac{1}{\sqrt{3}} + \sqrt{2}\cos\phi\right]$$

We now evaluate the functional form of one of the other sp^2 hybrids.

$$Y(p_y) = \left(\frac{3}{4\pi}\right)^{1/2}\sin\theta\sin\phi \qquad \psi_2(sp^2) = \frac{1}{\sqrt{3}}\psi(2s) - \frac{1}{\sqrt{6}}\psi(2p_x) + \frac{1}{\sqrt{2}}\psi(2p_y)$$

$$\psi_2(sp^2) = \frac{1}{\sqrt{3}}\left(\frac{1}{4\pi}\right)^{1/2} - \frac{1}{\sqrt{6}}\left(\frac{3}{4\pi}\right)^{1/2}\sin\theta\cos\phi + \frac{1}{\sqrt{2}}\left(\frac{3}{4\pi}\right)^{1/2}\sin\theta\sin\phi$$

$$\psi_2(sp^2) = \left(\frac{1}{4\pi}\right)^{1/2}\left[\frac{1}{\sqrt{3}} - \frac{1}{\sqrt{6}}\sqrt{3}\sin\theta\cos\phi + \frac{1}{\sqrt{2}}\sqrt{3}\sin\theta\sin\phi\right]$$

$$\psi_2(sp^2) = \left(\frac{1}{4\pi}\right)^{1/2}\left[\frac{1}{\sqrt{3}} - \frac{1}{\sqrt{2}}\sin\theta\cos\phi + \frac{\sqrt{3}}{\sqrt{2}}\sin\theta\sin\phi\right]$$

Again in the xy plane we have

$$\psi_2\left(sp^2\right)=\left(\frac{1}{4\pi}\right)^{1/2}\left[\frac{1}{\sqrt{3}}-\frac{1}{\sqrt{2}}\cos\phi+\frac{\sqrt{3}}{\sqrt{2}}\sin\phi\right]$$

The third sp^2 hybrid is

$$\psi_3\left(sp^2\right)=\left(\frac{1}{4\pi}\right)^{1/2}\left[\frac{1}{\sqrt{3}}-\frac{1}{\sqrt{2}}\sin\theta\cos\phi-\frac{\sqrt{3}}{\sqrt{2}}\sin\theta\sin\phi\right]$$

and in the xy plane

$$\psi_3\left(sp^2\right)=\left(\frac{1}{4\pi}\right)^{1/2}\left[\frac{1}{\sqrt{3}}-\frac{1}{\sqrt{2}}\cos\phi-\frac{\sqrt{3}}{\sqrt{2}}\sin\phi\right]$$

We can evaluate these functions and obtain sp^2 angular values:

Phi(deg)	Phi(rad)	$sp^2(1)$	$sp^2(2)$	$sp^2(3)$
0	0	1.992	−0.130	−0.647
30	0.5236	1.802	0.577	−0.837
45	0.7854	1.577	0.943	−0.789
60	1.0472	1.284	1.284	−0.647
90	1.5708	0.577	1.802	−0.130
120	2.0944	−0.123	1.992	0.577
135	2.3562	−0.423	1.943	0.943
150	2.6180	−0.647	1.802	1.284
170	2.9671	−0.815	1.486	1.661
180	3.1416	−0.837	1.284	1.802
190	3.3161	−0.815	1.061	1.906
210	3.6652	−0.647	0.577	1.992
225	3.9270	−0.423	0.211	1.943
240	4.1888	−0.130	−0.130	1.802
270	4.7124	0.577	−0.647	1.284
300	5.2360	1.284	−0.837	0.577
315	5.4978	1.577	−0.789	0.211
330	5.7596	1.802	−0.647	−0.130
360	6.2832	1.992	−0.130	−0.647

The graphs are as follows:

Part (a) INCLUDING THE RADIAL PART

If we combine the angular and radial parts of the $2s$ and $2p$ orbitals, the situation becomes more complicated because we now have to deal with two variables. The angular and radial parts of the $2s$ and $2p$ orbitals are:

$$Y(s) = \left(\frac{1}{4\pi}\right)^{1/2} \qquad R(2s) = \frac{1}{2\sqrt{2}}\left(\frac{Z}{a_0}\right)^{3/2}(2-\sigma)e^{-\sigma/2}$$

$$Y(p_z) = \left(\frac{3}{4\pi}\right)^{1/2}\cos\theta \qquad R(2p) = \frac{1}{2\sqrt{6}}\left(\frac{Z}{a_0}\right)^{3/2}\sigma e^{-\sigma/2}$$

Combining these

$$\psi(2s) = \left(\frac{1}{4\pi}\right)^{1/2}\times\frac{1}{2\sqrt{2}}\left(\frac{Z}{a_0}\right)^{3/2}(2-\sigma)e^{-\sigma/2} \qquad \psi(2p_z) = \left(\frac{3}{4\pi}\right)^{1/2}\cos\theta\times\frac{1}{2\sqrt{6}}\left(\frac{Z}{a_0}\right)^{3/2}\sigma e^{-\sigma/2}$$

We now combine these to form the sp-hybrids

$$\psi_1(sp) = \frac{1}{\sqrt{2}}\left[\psi(2s)+\psi(2p)\right]$$

$$\psi_1(sp) = \frac{1}{\sqrt{2}}\left[\left(\frac{1}{4\pi}\right)^{1/2}\times\frac{1}{2\sqrt{2}}\left(\frac{Z}{a_0}\right)^{3/2}(2-\sigma)e^{-\sigma/2}+\left(\frac{3}{4\pi}\right)^{1/2}\cos\theta\times\frac{1}{2\sqrt{6}}\left(\frac{Z}{a_0}\right)^{3/2}\sigma e^{-\sigma/2}\right]$$

$$\psi_1(sp) = \frac{1}{\sqrt{2}}\left(\frac{1}{4\pi}\right)^{1/2}\left[\frac{1}{2\sqrt{2}}\left(\frac{Z}{a_0}\right)^{3/2}(2-\sigma)e^{-\sigma/2}+\sqrt{3}\times\cos\theta\times\frac{1}{2\sqrt{6}}\left(\frac{Z}{a_0}\right)^{3/2}\sigma e^{-\sigma/2}\right]$$

$$\psi_1(sp) = \frac{1}{\sqrt{2}}\left(\frac{1}{4\pi}\right)^{1/2}\left(\frac{Z}{a_0}\right)^{3/2}\frac{1}{2\sqrt{2}}\left[(2-\sigma)e^{-\sigma/2}+\sqrt{3}\times\cos\theta\times\frac{1}{\sqrt{3}}\sigma e^{-\sigma/2}\right]$$

$$\psi_1(sp) = \frac{1}{\sqrt{2}}\left(\frac{1}{4\pi}\right)^{1/2}\left(\frac{Z}{a_0}\right)^{3/2}\frac{e^{-\sigma/2}}{2\sqrt{2}}\left[(2-\sigma)+\cos\theta\times\sigma\right]$$

$$\psi_1(sp) = \frac{1}{\sqrt{2}}\left(\frac{1}{4\pi}\right)^{1/2}\left(\frac{Z}{a_0}\right)^{3/2}\frac{e^{-\sigma/2}}{2\sqrt{2}}\left[2+\sigma(\cos\theta-1)\right]$$

Similarly

$$\psi_2(sp) = \frac{1}{\sqrt{2}}\left[\psi(2s)-\psi(2p)\right] \qquad \psi_2(sp) = \frac{1}{\sqrt{2}}\left(\frac{1}{4\pi}\right)^{1/2}\left(\frac{Z}{a_0}\right)^{3/2}\frac{e^{-\sigma/2}}{2\sqrt{2}}\left[2-\sigma(\cos\theta+1)\right]$$

We are dealing with orbitals with $n = 2$, so that

$$\sigma = \frac{2Zr}{na_0} = \frac{Zr}{a_0}$$

In order to proceed further, we have to choose values of r and θ, but how do we plot this? The way to do this is to evaluate the function for various values of (r/a_0) and θ and plot points in the xz-plane with values of x and z derived from the polar coordinates

$$z = r\cos\theta \qquad x = r\sin\theta\cos\phi$$

choosing $\phi=0$ in the xz plane so that $x = r\sin\theta$

Thus, we evaluate the probability as the square of the functions

$$\psi_1(sp) = \frac{1}{\sqrt{2}}\left(\frac{1}{4\pi}\right)^{1/2}\left(\frac{Z}{a_0}\right)^{3/2}\frac{e^{-Zr/2a_0}}{2\sqrt{2}}\left[2+\frac{Zr}{a_0}(\cos\theta-1)\right]$$

$$\psi_2(sp) = \frac{1}{\sqrt{2}}\left(\frac{1}{4\pi}\right)^{1/2}\left(\frac{Z}{a_0}\right)^{3/2}\frac{e^{-Zr/2a_0}}{2\sqrt{2}}\left[2-\frac{Zr}{a_0}(\cos\theta+1)\right]$$

and plot the value of the function at the x,z coordinate and join points of equal value of the probability in the manner of a contour plot.. The shape of the sp hybrid will then be revealed. Choose a value of Z (or Z_{eff}) that is convenient.

This is suitable for a class team project using *Microsoft Excel*. A primitive spreadsheet is available upon request.

73. **(M)** The ozone molecule, O_3, has no bond dipoles because all of the atoms are alike. The Lewis structure below shows the two equivalent structures contributing to the resonance hybrid. The electron-group geometry around the central oxygen atom is trigonal planar (it is bonded to two oxygen atoms and a lone pair). This results in a molecule that has a bent geometry. The zero bond dipoles in O_3 signify that the centers of negative and positive charge coincide along the oxygen-to-oxygen bonds. However, the lone pair electrons on the central oxygen atom constitute another center of negative charge that is offset from the oxygen-to-oxygen bonds. The dipole moment in the O_3 molecule is directed toward this charge center. The electrostatic potential map shows evidence of this. As well, because of the formal charges found on each resonance form, the hybrid indicates that there should be a formal charge of +1 on the central oxygen atom and a -1 charge distributed on the terminal oxygen atoms. This is supported by the electrostatic potential map provided as well.

Resonance form A   Resonance form B   Resonance hyhbrid

74. **(M)** Borazine has a delocalized π system that resembles benzene. Both benzene and borazine have 6 electrons in a conjugated π system and thus, have similar molecular orbitals of comparable shape and energy.

Benzene Resonance Structures   Borazine Resonance Structures

The molecular orbital diagram for borazine is drawn below. Both the HOMO and LUMO are labeled. Note that the LUMO is an antibonding orbital with two nodes (degenerate set) while the HOMO is a bonding orbital (degenerate set) with only one node.

75. **(E)**
(a) non-bonding, **(b)** non-bonding, **(c)** non-bonding **(d)** bonding, σ **(e)** bonding, π.

76. **(M)**

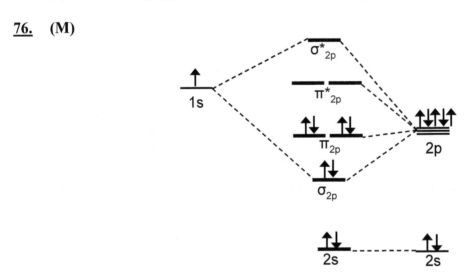

SELF-ASSESSMENT EXERCISES

77. **(E)**

(a) sp^2: The result of hybridization of one s and $2p$ orbitals, giving a trigonal planar geometry

(b) σ^*_{2p}: The anti-bonding σ orbital created by the combination of two p orbitals

(c) Bond order: One-half the difference between the number of bonding and antibonding orbitals

(d) π-bond: A side-to-side overlap of the unhybridized orbitals (such as the p_x and p_y orbitals interacting on their sides.) In this bond, there is a region of high electron charge density above and below the plane of the bond.

78. **(E)**

(a) Hybridization of atomic orbitals: a mathematical process of adding wavefunctions of atomic orbitals to obtain the wavefunction of the combination molecular orbital

(b) σ-bond framework: σ bonds of all the atoms in an entire molecule of a molecular subunit, creating a framework

(c) Kekulé structures of benzene: The C_6H_6 molecule is a flat hexagonal ring, with a σ-bond framework. The electrons comprising the alternating double bonds are distributed equally among all six bonds.

79. **(E)**

(a) σ and π bonds: σ bond is a head-to-head overlap of two atomic orbitals to make a single bond (such as the s or p_z), whereas a π bond is created between two atoms via a side-to-side overlap of two atomic orbitals (such as p_x and p_y).

(b) Localized and delocalized electrons: A localized electron is in an orbital on one single atom, whereas a delocalized electron travels freely between multiple atoms

(c) Bonding and anti-bonding molecular orbitals: Bonding orbitals are orbitals whose wavefunctions are in phase, and as such constructively interfere to give a very high probability of electron being found there (i.e., a bond). Anti bonding orbitals are the opposite: the wavefunctions of the orbitals destructively interfere such that the probability of finding the electron at certain locations is zero, therefore there is no bond.

80. **(E)** The answer is (c). It is the only option that has three species attached to the central atom (2 oxygen atoms, one electron pair):

81. **(E)** The answer is (c). H_2Se has the same geometry as H_2S and H_2O. It is sp^3 hybridized, and the bond angle is less than H_2S, but it has to be more than $90°$.

82. **(E)** The answer is (a). The Lewis structure of I_3^- is shown below:

$$:\ddot{I}\!\!-\!\!\ddot{I}\!\!-\!\!\ddot{I}:$$

There are $1s$ and $3p$ orbitals for the central atom. However, there are 5 groups around it, which means that the d orbital needs to be used.

83. **(E)** The answer is (b). Each Li has the electron configuration $1s^2 2s^1$. The valence electrons occupy the 2σ orbitals completely, and not the $2\sigma^*$, so the bond order is $(4 - 2)/2 = 1$

84. **(E)** The answer is (c). The Lewis structure of XeF_2 is shown below:

Since there are 5 groups around Xe, the hybridization is $sp^3 d$.

85. **(E)** The answer is (d). The Lewis structure of CO_3^{2-} and the result of its resonance structures is shown below:

86. **(M)** From VSEPR theory we conclude that BF_3 is a trigonal planar molecule (as seen in Table 11.1). The valence-bond method using pure *s* and *p* orbitals incorrectly predicts a trigonal pyramidal shape with 90° F—B—F bond angles.

87. **(E)** BrF_5 has six constituents around it; five are fluorine atoms, and the sixth is a lone pair. Therefore, the hybridization is $sp^3 d^2$, but the geometry is square pyramidal. The structure is shown below:

88. **(E)** The structure of CH_3NCO is shown below:

There are two double bonds, which means that there are **(a)** 6 σ and **(b)** 2 π bonds.

89. **(M)** All three are paramagnetic, because all three have unpaired electrons. The one with the strongest bond is **(b)**. The molecular orbital diagrams for all three are shown below. B_2^- has 3 bonding electrons, so the B–B bond is the strongest.

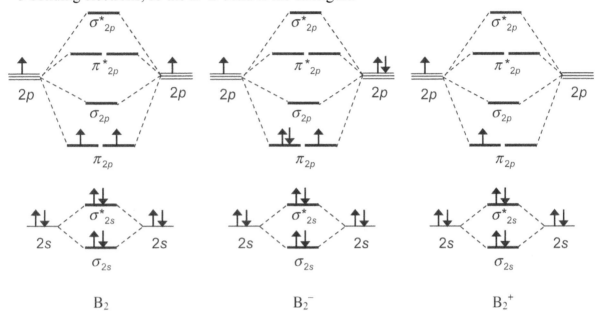

90. **(E)** The answer is (c), because C_2^- has an unpaired electron in the $\sigma(2s)$ bonding orbital, which is easier to remove than one already paired up because there is no pairing energy to overcome. The other two have electrons in the bonding orbitals, which require more energy to remove.

91. **(M)**

92. **(E)** The bond order in C_2 is two, whereas in Li_2 is one. Therefore, C_2 has the greater bond energy.

93. **(E)** A particular structure has resonance structures if its structure cannot be adequately represented by just one Lewis structure. The structures of the compounds are shown below, along with resonance structures when appropriate.

Several resonance structures contribute to the structure of the oxalate anion. Three of the structures are shown next.

(a) Formaldehyde, or H_2CO, does not have any resonance structures.

(b) The structure of the NO_3^- ion is a hybrid of three equivalent resonance structures.

94. **(M)** We draw the Lewis structure of each species to account for the electron pairs around each central atom, which is N in both species. In NO_2^-, there are $5 + (2 \times 6) + 1 = 18$ valence electrons, or 9 pairs of electrons. In NO_2^+, there are $5 + (2 \times 6) - 1 = 16$ valence electron, or 8 pairs. Plausible Lewis structures for both are shown below:

$$NO_2^- \qquad NO_2^+$$

In case of NO_2^-, N has two bonds (one single, one double) and a lone pair. Its hybridization is sp^2, it has a trigonal pyramidal electron group geometry (AX_2E), and its shape is bent. In case of NO_2^+, N has two double bonds and a positive charge. Its hybridization is sp, it has a linear electron group geometry (AX_2), and its shape is therefore straight.

95. **(E)** The answer is (a). In $BeCl_2$, sp hybridization involves the combination of an s and a p orbital from Be, which yields two hybrid sp orbitals for bonding with two Cl atoms. Boron is sp^2 hybridized in BCl_3. Carbon and nitrogen are sp^3 hybridized in CCl_4 and NCl_3, respectively.

96. **(E)** Bond hybridization is used to explain why all C—H bonds have equal length in methane. The C atom in CH_4 is sp^3 hybridized. The sp^3 hybrid orbitals have identical shapes and point toward the corners of a tetrahedron. Therefore, the C—H bonds are identical, and the H—C—H bond angles are all $109.5°$. Since the C—H bonds are single bonds, there is no resonance or delocalization of electrons. The electronegativities of C and H are similar, and therefore the C—H bond is considered nonpolar.

97. **(M)** The peroxide ion has $(6 + 6 + 2) = 14$ valence electrons. The valence molecular orbital occupancy diagram is shown below:

σ_{2s} σ^*_{2s} σ_{2p} π_{2p} π^*_{2p} σ^*_{2p}

All the electrons are paired. The bond order of O_2^{2-} is one $[(8-6)/2]$. The highest energy electron is in the π^*_{2p} MO. The correct answer is (d) because the peroxide ion has electrons in sigma and pi molecular orbitals and not in an atomic $2s$ orbital.

98. **(E)** The correct answer is (b). Three hybrid orbitals (sp^2) are formed by the combination of a $2s$ and two $2p$ orbitals; therefore, the angle between the hybrid orbitals is 120°.

99. **(M)**

$$:N\equiv C^a - C^b - \overset{..}{\underset{..}{O}} - H$$
with :S: double-bonded to C^b

(a) There are five σ bonds: C^a—C^b, C^b—O, O—H are easily assigned. The double and triple bonds have one sigma bond each. There are three π bonds: one in the C=S bond and two in the C≡N bond.

(b) C^a is sp hybridized, C^b is sp^2 hybridized and O is sp^3 hybridized.

(c) The lone pairs on the nitrogen are in one of the sp hybrid orbitals on N. Both lone pairs on the sulfur are in two of the sp^2 hybrid orbitals on S. The lone pairs on the oxygen are in two of the sp^3 hybrid orbitals on O.

(d) N—C^a—C^b; C^a is sp hybridized, so the ideal bond angle is 180°
C^a—C^b=S; C^b is sp^2 hybridized, so the ideal bond angle is 120°.
C^a—C^b—O; C^b is sp^2 hybridized, so the ideal bond angle is 120°.
C^b—O—H; O is sp^3 hybridized, so the ideal bond angle is 109.5°.

100. **(E)** The concept map for valence-bond theory gives rise to the overarching concept of orbital hybridization. Orbital hybridization is then divided into various hybrid orbitals, sp, sp^2, sp^3, sp^3d, sp^3d^2. The next major topic is VSEPR theory.

101. **(M)** The basic ideas of molecular orbital theory are discussed on pages 486 to 488. The terms that comprise the concept map are atomic orbitals, combination of atomic orbitals to form molecular orbitals, bonding and anti-bonding orbitals, ground state and excited state, and the Pauli Exclusion Principle.

102. **(E)** Apply the terms discussed above to the concepts of σ-bond framework, π bonds, and electron delocalization.

CHAPTER 12

INTERMOLECULAR FORCES: LIQUIDS AND SOLIDS

PRACTICE EXAMPLES

1A **(E)** The substance with the highest boiling point will have the strongest intermolecular forces. The weakest of van der Waals forces are London forces, which depend on molar mass (and surface area): C_3H_8 is 44 g/mol, CO_2 is 44 g/mol, and CH_3CN is 41 g/mol. Thus, the London forces are approximately equal for these three compounds. Next to consider are dipole–dipole forces. C_3H_8 is essentially nonpolar; its bonds are not polarized to an appreciable extent. CO_2 is nonpolar; its two bond moments cancel each other. CH_3CN is polar and thus has the strongest intermolecular forces and should have the highest boiling point. The actual boiling points are –78.44° C for CO_2, –42.1° C for C_3H_8, and 81.6° C for CH_3CN.

1B **(M)** Dispersion forces, which depend on the number of electrons (molar mass) and structure, are one of the determinants of boiling point. The molar masses are: C_8H_{18} (114.2 g/mol), $CH_3CH_2CH_2CH_3$ (58.1 g/mol), $(CH_3)_3CH$ (58.1 g/mol), C_6H_5CHO (106.1 g/mol), and SO_3 (80.1 g/mol). We would expect $(CH_3)_3CH$ to have the lowest boiling point because it has the lowest molar mass and the most compact (ball-like) shape, whereas $CH_3CH_2CH_2CH_3$, which has the same mass but is longer and hence has more surface area (more chances for intermolecular interactions), should have the second highest boiling point. We would expect SO_3 to be next in line as it is also non-polar, but more massive than C_4H_{10}. C_6H_5CHO should have a boiling point higher than the more massive C_8H_{18} because benzaldehyde is polar while octane is not. Actual boiling points are given in parentheses in the following ranking.
$(CH_3)_3CH$ (–11.6 °C) < $CH_3CH_2CH_2CH_3$ (–0.5 °C) < SO_3 (44.8 °C) C_8H_{18} (125.7 °C) < C_6H_5CHO (178°C)

2A **(E)** Values of $\Delta_{vap}H$ are in kJ/mol so we first determine the amount in moles of diethyl ether.

$$\text{Heat} = 2.35 \text{ g } (C_2H_5)_2O \times \frac{1 \text{ mol } (C_2H_5)_2O}{74.12 \text{ g } (C_2H_5)_2O} \times \frac{29.1 \text{ kJ}}{1 \text{ mol } (C_2H_5)_2O} = 0.923 \text{ kJ}$$

2B **(M)**

$$\Delta_{overall}H = \Delta_{cond}H + \Delta_{cooling}H$$

$$\Delta_{cond}H = 0.0245 \text{ mol} \times (-40.7 \text{ kJ mol}^{-1}) = -0.997 \text{ kJ} = -997 \text{ J}$$

$$\Delta_{cooling}H = 0.0245 \text{ mol} \times (4.21 \text{ J g}^{-1} \, {}^{\circ}C^{-1})(85.0 \, {}^{\circ}C - 100.0 \, {}^{\circ}C)(18.0153 \text{ g mol}^{-1}) = -27.9 \text{ J}$$

$$\Delta_{overall}H = -997 \text{ J} + -27.9 \text{ J} = -1025 \text{ J or } -1.025 \text{ kJ}$$

3A **(E)** $d = 0.701$ g/L at 25 °C for C_6H_{14} (molar mass = 86.177 g mol^{-1})
Consider a 1.00 L sample. This contains 0.701 g C_6H_{14}.

$$\text{moles } C_6H_{14} \text{ in 1.00 L sample} = 0.701 \text{ g } C_6H_{14} \times \frac{1\,\text{mol}\,C_6H_{14}}{86.177\,\text{g}\,C_6H_{14}} = 8.13 \times 10^{-3} \text{ mol } C_6H_{14}$$

Find pressure using the ideal gas law: $P = \dfrac{nRT}{V} = \dfrac{(8.31 \times 10^{-3} \text{ mol})\left(\dfrac{0.08206 \text{ L atm}}{\text{K mol}}\right)(298 \text{ K})}{1.00 \text{ L}}$

$$P = 0.199 \text{ atm or } 151 \text{ Torr}$$

3B **(M)** From Figure 12-9, the vapor pressure is ≈ 420 mmHg or

$$420 \text{ mmHg} \times \frac{1 \text{ atm}}{760 \text{ Torr}} = 0.553 \text{ atm}$$

molar mass = 74.123 g mol^{-1}. $P = \dfrac{nRT}{V} = \dfrac{\left(\dfrac{\text{mass}}{\text{molar mass}}\right)RT}{V} = \dfrac{(\text{density})RT}{\text{molar mass}}$

or $d = \dfrac{(\text{molar mass})P}{RT} = \dfrac{\left(74.123\,\dfrac{\text{g}}{\text{mol}}\right)(0.553 \text{ atm})}{\left(0.08206\,\dfrac{\text{L atm}}{\text{K mol}}\right)(293 \text{ K})} = 1.70 \text{ g } L^{-1} \approx 1.7 \text{ g/L}$

4A **(E)** We first calculate pressure created by the water at 80.0 °C, assuming all 0.132 g H_2O vaporizes.

$$P_2 = \frac{nRT}{V} = \frac{\left(0.132 \text{ g } H_2O \times \dfrac{1 \text{ mol } H_2O}{18.02 \text{ g } H_2O}\right) \times 0.08206\,\dfrac{\text{L atm}}{\text{mol K}} \times 353.2 \text{ K}}{0.525 \text{ L}} \times \frac{760 \text{ mmHg}}{1 \text{ atm}}$$

$$= 307 \text{ mmHg}$$

At 80.0 °C, the vapor pressure of water is 355.1 mmHg, thus, all the water exists as vapor.

4B **(E)** The result of Example 12-3 is that 0.132 g H_2O would exert a pressure of 281 mmHg if it all existed as a vapor. Since that 281 mmHg is greater than the vapor pressure of water at this temperature, some of the water must exist as liquid. The calculation of the example is based on the equation $P = nRT/V$, which means that the pressure of water is proportional to its mass. Thus, the mass of water needed to produce a pressure of 92.5 mmHg under this situation is

$$\text{mass of water vapor} = 92.5 \text{ mmHg} \times \frac{0.132 \text{ g } H_2O}{281 \text{ mmHg}} = 0.0435 \text{ g } H_2O$$

mass of liquid water = 0.132 g H_2O total − 0.0435 g H_2O vapor = 0.089 g liquid water

5A **(M)** From Table 12.4 we know that $\Delta_{vap}H = 37.4$ kJ/mol for methanol. We now can use the Clausius-Clapeyron equation to determine the vapor pressure at $25.0\,°C = 298.2$ K.

$$\ln\frac{P}{100\ \text{mmHg}} = -\frac{37.4\times10^3\ \text{J mol}^{-1}}{8.3145\ \text{J mol}^{-1}\ \text{K}^{-1}}\left(\frac{1}{298.2\text{K}} - \frac{1}{(273.2+21.2)\ \text{K}}\right) = +0.195$$

$$\frac{P}{100\ \text{mmHg}} = e^{+0.195} = 1.22 \qquad P = 1.22\times100\ \text{mmHg} = 122\ \text{mmHg}$$

5B **(M)** The vapor pressure at the normal boiling point $(99.2\,°C = 372.4\ \text{K})$ is 760 mmHg precisely. We can use the Clausius-Clapeyron equation to determine the vapor pressure at $25\,°C = 298$ K.

$$\ln\frac{P}{760\ \text{mmHg}} = -\frac{35.76\times10^3\ \text{J mol}^{-1}}{8.3145\ \text{J mol}^{-1}\ \text{K}^{-1}}\left(\frac{1}{298.2\ \text{K}} - \frac{1}{372.4\ \text{K}}\right) = -2.874$$

$$\frac{P}{760\ \text{mmHg}} = e^{-2.874} = 0.0565 \quad P = 0.0565\times760\ \text{mmHg} = 42.9\ \text{mmHg}$$

6A **(M)** We first look to molar masses: Ne (20.2 g/mol), He (4.0 g/mol), Cl_2 (70.9 g/mol), $(CH_3)_2CO$ (58.1 g/mol), O_2 (32.0 g/mol), and O_3 (48.0 g/mol). Both $(CH_3)_2CO$ and O_3 are polar, O_3 weakly so (because of its uneven distribution of electrons). We expect $(CH_3)_2CO$ to have the highest boiling point, followed by Cl_2, O_3, O_2, Ne, and He. In the following ranking, actual boiling points are given in parentheses. He (–268.9 °C), Ne (–245.9 °C), O_2 (–183.0 °C), O_3 (–111.9 °C), Cl_2 (–34.6 °C), and $(CH_3)_2CO$ (56.2 °C).

6B **(M)** The magnitude of the enthalpy of vaporization is strongly related to the strength of intermolecular forces: the stronger these forces, the more endothermic the vaporization process. The first three substances all are nonpolar and, therefore, their only intermolecular forces are London forces, whose strength primarily depends on molar mass. The substances are arranged in order of increasing molar mass: $H_2 = 2.0$ g / mol, $CH_4 = 16.0$ g / mol, $C_6H_6 = 78.1$ g/mol, and also in order of increasing heat of vaporization. The last substance has a molar mass of 61.0 g/mol, which would produce intermolecular forces smaller than those of C_6H_6 if CH_3NO_2 were nonpolar. But the molecule is definitely polar. Thus, the strong dipole–dipole forces developed between CH_3NO_2 molecules make the enthalpy of vaporization for CH_3NO_2 larger than that for C_6H_6, which is, of course, essentially non-polar.

7A **(M)** Moving from point R to P we begin with $H_2O(g)$ at high temperature (>100 °C). When the temperature reaches the point on the vaporization curve, OC, water condenses at constant temperature (100 °C). Once all of the water is in the liquid state, the temperature drops. When the temperature reaches the point on the fusion curve, OD, ice begins to form at constant temperature (0 °C). Once all of the water has been converted to $H_2O(s)$, the temperature of the sample decreases slightly until point P is reached.

Since solids are not very compressible, very little change occurs until the pressure reaches the point on the fusion curve OD. Here, melting begins. A significant decrease in the volume occurs ($\approx$10%) as ice is converted to liquid water. After melting, additional pressure produces very little change in volume because liquids are not very compressible.

7B **(M)**

1.00 mol H_2O. At point R, $T = 374.1$ °C or 647.3 K

$$V_{\text{point R}} = \frac{nRT}{P} = \frac{(1.00\,\text{mol})\left(0.08206\,\dfrac{\text{L atm}}{\text{K mol}}\right)(647.3\,\text{K})}{1.00\,\text{atm}} = 53.1\ \text{L}$$

1.00 mol H_2O on P-R line, if 1/2 of water is vaporized, $T = 100$ °C (273.015 K)

$$V_{\text{1/2 vap(PR)}} = \frac{nRT}{P} = \frac{(0.500\,\text{mol})\left(0.08206\,\dfrac{\text{L atm}}{\text{K mol}}\right)(373.15\,\text{K})}{1.00\,\text{atm}} = 15.3\ \text{L}$$

A much smaller volume results when just 1/2 of the sample is vaporized (moles of gas smaller as well, temperature is smaller). 53.1 L vs 15.3 L (about 28.8 % of the volume as that seen at point R).

> 51. 3 L
>
> At
>
> Point
>
> R

> 15.3 L
> at 100C
> 1/2 vap

6A **(M)** We first look to molar masses: Ne (20.2 g/mol), He (4.0 g/mol), Cl_2 (70.9 g/mol), $(CH_3)_2 CO$ (58.1 g/mol), O_2 (32.0 g/mol), and O_3 (48.0 g/mol). Both $(CH_3)_2 CO$ and O_3 are polar, O_3 weakly so (because of its uneven distribution of electrons). We expect $(CH_3)_2 CO$ to have the highest boiling, followed by Cl_2, O_3, O_2, Ne, and He. In the following ranking, actual boiling points are given in parentheses. He (–268.9 °C), Ne (–245.9 °C), O_2 (–183.0 °C), O_3 (–111.9 °C), Cl_2 (–34.6 °C), and $(CH_3)_2CO$ (56.2°C)

6B **(M)** The magnitude of the enthalpy of vaporization is strongly related to the strength of intermolecular forces: the stronger these forces are, the more endothermic the vaporization process. The first three substances all are nonpolar and, therefore, their only intermolecular forces are London forces, whose strength primarily depends on molar mass. The substances are arranged in order of increasing molar mass: $H_2 = 2.0$ g / mol, $CH_4 = 16.0$ g / mol, $C_6H_6 = 78.1$ g/mol, and also in order of increasing heat of vaporization. The last substance has a molar mass of 61.0 g/mol, which would produce intermolecular forces smaller than those of C_6H_6 if CH_3NO_2 were nonpolar. But the molecule is definitely polar. Thus, the strong dipole-dipole forces developed between CH_3NO_2 molecules make the enthalpy of vaporization for CH_3NO_2 larger than that for C_6H_6, which is, of course, essentially non-polar.

8A **(E)** Strong interionic forces lead to high melting points. Strong interionic forces are created by ions with high charge and of small size. Thus, for a compound to have a lower melting point than KI it must be composed of ions of larger size, such as RbI or CsI. A compound with a melting point higher than CaO would have either smaller ions, such as MgO, or more highly charged ions, such as Ga_2O_3 or Ca_3N_2, or both, such as AlN or Mg_3N_2.

8B **(E)** Mg^{2+} has a higher charge and a smaller size than does Na^+. In addition, Cl^- has a smaller size than I^-. Thus, interionic forces should be stronger in $MgCl_2$ than in NaI. We expect $MgCl_2$ to have lower solubility and, in fact, 12.3 mol (1840 g) of NaI dissolves in a liter of water, compared to just 5.7 mol (543 g) of $MgCl_2$, confirming our prediction.

9A **(E)** The length (l) of a bcc unit cell and the radius (r) of the atom involved are related by $4r = l\sqrt{3}$. For potassium, $r = 227$ pm. Then $l = 4 \times 227 \, pm / \sqrt{3} = 524 \, pm$

9B **(M)** Consider just the face of Figure 12-46. Note that it is composed of one atom at each of the four corners and one in the center. The four corner atoms touch the atom in the center, but not each other. Thus, the atoms are in contact across the diagonal of the face. If each atomic radius is designated r, then the length of the diagonal is $4r$ ($= r$ for one corner atom $+2r$ for the center atom $+r$ for the other corner atom). The diagonal also is related to the length of a side, l, by the Pythagorean theorem: $d^2 = l^2 + l^2 = 2l^2$ or $d = \sqrt{2}l$. We have two quantities equal to the diagonal, and thus to each other.

$$\sqrt{2}l = \text{diagonal} = 4r = 4 \times 143.1 \, pm = 572.4 \, pm$$

$$l = \frac{572.4}{\sqrt{2}} = 404.7 \, pm$$

The cubic unit cell volume, V, is equal to the cube of one side.

$$V = l^3 = (404.7 \, pm)^3 = 6.628 \times 10^7 \, pm^3$$

10A **(M)** In a bcc unit cell, there are eight corner atoms, of which $\frac{1}{8}$ of each is apportioned to the unit cell. There is also one atom in the center. The total number of atoms per unit cell is:

$$= 1 \, \text{center} + 8 \, \text{corners} \times \frac{1}{8} = 2 \text{ atoms.}$$ The density, in g/cm^3, for this cubic cell:

$$\text{density} = \frac{2 \text{ atoms}}{(524 \, pm)^3} \times \left(\frac{10^{12} \, pm}{10^2 \, cm}\right)^3 \times \frac{1 \, mol}{6.022 \times 10^{23} \text{ atoms}} \times \frac{39.10 \, g \, K}{1 \, mol \, K} = 0.903 \, g / cm^3$$

The tabulated density of potassium at 20 °C is $0.86 \, g/cm^3$.

10B **(M)** In a fcc unit cell the number of atoms is computed as 1/8 atom for each of the eight corner atoms (since each is shared among eight unit cells) plus 1/2 atom for each of the six face atoms (since each is shared between two unit cells). This gives the total number of atoms per unit cell as: atoms/unit cell = (1/8 corner atom × 8 corner atoms/unit cell) + (1/2 face atom × 6 face atoms/unit cell) = 4 atoms / unit cell

Now we can determine the mass per Al atom, and a value for the Avogadro constant.

$$\frac{\text{mass}}{\text{Al atom}} = \frac{2.6984 \, g \, Al}{1 \, cm^3} \times \left(\frac{100 \, cm}{1 \, m} \times \frac{1 \, m}{10^{12} \, pm}\right)^3 \times \frac{6.628 \times 10^7 \, pm^3}{1 \, \text{unit cell}} \times \frac{1 \, \text{unit cell}}{4 \, Al \, \text{atoms}}$$

$$= 4.471 \times 10^{-23} \, g/Al \, \text{atom}$$

Therefore,

$$N_A = \frac{26.9815 \text{ g Al}}{1 \text{ mol Al}} \times \frac{1 \text{ Al atom}}{4.471 \times 10^{-23} \text{ g Al}} = 6.035 \times 10^{23} \frac{\text{atoms Al}}{\text{mol Al}}$$

11A **(E)** Across the diagonal of a CsCl unit cell are Cs^+ and Cl^- ions, so that the body diagonal equals $2r(Cs^+) + 2r(Cl^-)$. This body diagonal equals $\sqrt{3}l$, where l is the length of the unit cell.

$$l = \frac{2r(Cs^+) + 2r(Cl^-)}{\sqrt{3}} = \frac{2(167 + 181) \text{ pm}}{\sqrt{3}} = 402 \text{ pm}$$

11B **(M)** Since NaCl is fcc, the Na^+ ions are in the same locations as were the Al atoms in Practice Example 12-10B, and there are 4 Na^+ ions per unit cell. For stoichiometric reasons, there must also be 4 Cl^- ions per unit cell. These are accounted for as follows: there is one Cl^- along each edge, and each of these edge Cl^- ions are shared among four unit cells, and there is one Cl^- precisely in the body center of the unit cell, not shared with any other unit cells. Thus, the number of Cl^- ions is given by: Cl^- ions/unit cell = $(1/4 \; Cl^- \text{ on edge} \times 12 \text{ edges per unit cell}) + 1 \; Cl^-$ in body center = 4 Cl^-/ unit cell.

The volume of this cubic unit cell is the cube of its length. The density is:

$$\text{NaCl density} = \frac{4 \text{ formula units}}{1 \text{ unit cell}} \times \frac{1 \text{ unit cell}}{(560 \text{ pm})^3} \times \left(\frac{10^{12} \text{ pm}}{1 \text{ m}} \times \frac{1 \text{ m}}{100 \text{ cm}} \right)^3 \times \frac{1 \text{ mol NaCl}}{6.022 \times 10^{23} \text{ f.u.}}$$

$$\times \frac{58.44 \text{ g NaCl}}{1 \text{ mol NaCl}} = 2.21 \text{ g/cm}^3$$

12A **(M)**

Sublimation of Cs:	$Cs(s) \rightarrow Cs(g)$	$\Delta_{sub}H = +78.2$ kJ/mol
Ionization of Cs(g):	$Cs(g) \rightarrow Cs^+(g) + e^-$	$E_1 = +375.7$ kJ/mol (Table 9.3)
$\frac{1}{2}$ Dissociation of $Cl_2(g)$:	$\frac{1}{2} Cl_2(g) \rightarrow Cl(g)$	$DE = \frac{1}{2} \times 243$ kJ = 121.5 kJ/mol (Table 10.3)
Cl(g) electron affinity:	$Cl(g) + e^- \rightarrow Cl^-(g)$	$E_{ea1} = -349.0$ kJ/mol (Figure 9–12)
Lattice energy:	$Cs^+(g) + Cl^-(g) \rightarrow CsCl(s)$	L.E.

Enthalpy of formation: $Cs(s) + \frac{1}{2} Cl_2(s) \rightarrow CsCl(s)$ $\Delta_f H^\circ = -442.8$ kJ/mol

-442.8 kJ/mol $= +78.2$ kJ/mol $+ 375.7$ kJ/mol $+ 121.5$ kJ/mol $- 349.0$ kJ/mol $+$ L.E.

$= +226.4$ kJ/mol $+$ L.E.

L.E. $= -442.8$ kJ $- 226.4$ kJ $= -669.2$ kJ/mol

12B **(M)** Sublimation: $\qquad$ $Ca(s) \rightarrow Ca(g)$ $\qquad$ $\Delta_{sub}H = +178.2$ kJ/mol

First ionization energy: $\qquad$ $Ca(g) \rightarrow Ca^+(g) + e^-$ $\qquad$ $E_{i,1} = +590$ kJ/mol

Second ionization energy: $\qquad$ $Ca^+(g) \rightarrow Ca^{2+}(g) + e^-$ $\qquad$ $E_{i,2} = +1145$ kJ/mol

Dissociation energy: $\qquad$ $Cl_2(g) \rightarrow 2Cl(g)$ $\qquad$ $D.E. = (2 \times 122)$ kJ / mol

Electron Affinity: $\qquad$ $2\,Cl(g) + 2\,e^- \rightarrow 2Cl^-(g)$ $\qquad$ $2 \times E_{ea} = 2(-349)$ kJ/mol

Lattice energy: $\qquad$ $Ca^{2+}(g) + 2\,Cl^-(g) \rightarrow CaCl_2(s)$ L.E. $= -2223$ kJ/mol

---

Enthalpy of formation: $\qquad$ $Ca(s) + Cl_2(s) \rightarrow CaCl_2(s)$ $\qquad$ $\Delta_f H° = ?$

$\Delta_f H° = \Delta_{sub}H + E_{i,1} + E_{i,2} + D.E. + (2 \times E_{ea}) + L.E.$

$= 178.2$ kJ/mol $+ 590$ kJ/mol $+ 1145$ kJ/mol $+ 244$ kJ/mol $- 698$ kJ/mol $- 2223$ kJ/mol

$= -764$ kJ/mol

INTEGRATIVE EXAMPLE

A. **(M)** At 25.0 °C, the vapor pressure of water is 23.8 mmHg. We calculate the vapor pressure for isooctane with the Clausius-Clapeyron equation.

$$\ln \frac{P}{760 \text{ mmHg}} = \frac{35.76 \times 10^3 \text{J/mol}}{8.3145 \text{ J mol}^{-1} \text{K}^{-1}} \left(\frac{1}{(99.2 + 273.2) \text{ K}} - \frac{1}{298.2 \text{ K}} \right) = -2.87$$

$P = e^{-2.87} \times 760$ mmHg $= 43.1$ mmHg which is higher than H_2O's vapor pressure.

B. **(D) (a)** and **(b)** We will work both parts simultaneously.

Sublimation of Mg(s): $\qquad$ $Mg(s) \longrightarrow Mg(g)$ $\qquad$ $\Delta_{sub}H = +146$ kJ

First ionization of Mg(g): $\qquad$ $Mg(g) \longrightarrow Mg^+(g) + e^-$ $\qquad$ $E_{i,1} = +737.7$ kJ

Second ionization of Mg(g): $\qquad$ $Mg^+(g) \longrightarrow Mg^{2+}(g) + e^-$ $\qquad$ $E_{i,2} = +1451$ kJ

$\frac{1}{2}$ Dissociation of $O_2(g)$: $\qquad$ $\frac{1}{2} O_2(g) \longrightarrow O(g)$ $\qquad$ $\Delta_{dis}H = +249$ kJ

First electron affinity: $\qquad$ $O(g) + e^- \longrightarrow O^-(g)$ $\qquad$ $E_{ea,1} = -141.0$ kJ

Second electron affinity: $\qquad$ $O^-(g) + e^- \rightarrow O^{2-}(g)$ $\qquad$ $E_{ea,2}$

Lattice energy: $\qquad$ $Mg^{2+}(g) + O^{2-}(g) \longrightarrow MgO(s)$ L.E. $= -3925$ kJ

Enthalpy of formation: $\qquad$ $Mg(s) + \frac{1}{2} O_2(g) \longrightarrow MgO(s)$ $\qquad$ $\Delta_f H° = -601.7$ kJ

-601.7 kJ $= +146$ kJ $+ 737.7$ kJ $+ 1451$ kJ $+ 249$ kJ $- 141.0$ kJ $+ E_{ea,2} - 3925$ kJ

$E_{ea,2} = +881$ kJ

EXERCISES

Intermolecular Forces

1. **(M)**

    (a) HCl is not a very heavy diatomic molecule. Thus, the London forces between HCl molecules are expected to be relatively weak. Hydrogen bonding is weak in the case of H–Cl bonds; Cl is not one of the three atoms (F, O, N) that form strong hydrogen bonds. Finally, because Cl is an electronegative atom, and H is only moderately electronegative, dipole–dipole interactions should be relatively strong.

    (b) In Br_2 neither hydrogen bonds nor dipole–dipole attractions can occur (there are no H atoms in the molecule, and homonuclear molecules are nonpolar). London forces are more important in Br_2 than in HCl since Br_2 has more electrons (i.e., is more polarizable).

    (c) In ICl there are no hydrogen bonds since there are no H atoms in the molecule. The London forces are as strong as in Br_2 since the two molecules have the same number of electrons. However, dipole–dipole interactions are important in ICl, due to the polarity of the I–Cl bond.

    (d) In HF London forces are not very important; the molecule has only 10 electrons and thus is quite small. Hydrogen bonding is obviously the most important interaction developed between HF molecules.

    (e) In CH_4, H bonds are not important (the H atoms are not bonded to F, O, or N). In addition the molecule is not polar, so there are no dipole-dipole interactions. Finally, London forces are quite weak since the molecule contains only 10 electrons. For these reasons CH_4 has a very low critical temperature.

2. **(M)** Substituting Cl for H makes the molecule heavier (and thus increases London forces) and polar, which results in the formation of dipole–dipole interactions. Both of these effects make it more difficult to disrupt the forces of attraction between molecules, increasing the boiling point. Substitution of Br for Cl increases the London forces, but makes the molecule less polar. Since London forces in this case are more important than dipole–dipole interactions, the boiling point increases yet again. Finally, substituting OH for Br decreases London forces but both increases the dipole-dipole interactions and creates opportunities for hydrogen bonding. Since hydrogen bonds are much stronger than London forces, the boiling point increases even further.

3. **(E)**

(c)	<	(b)	<	(d)	<	(a)
(ethane thiol)		(ethanol)		(butanol)		(acetic acid)

    Viscosity will depend on the intermolecular forces. The stronger the intermolecular bonding, the more viscous the substance.

4.   **(E)**

(d)	<	(b)	<	(a)	<	(c)
(butane)		(carbon disulfide)		(ethanol)		(1,2-dihydroxyethane)

The boiling point is dependent on the intermolecular forces. Hence, hydrogen bonding produces the strongest interactions (highest boiling point) and non-polar molecules like butane and CS_2 have the lowest boiling point. We must also consider the effect of Van der Waals forces.

5.   **(E)** We expect CH_3OH to be a liquid from among the four substances listed. Of these four molecules, C_3H_8 has the most electrons and should have the strongest London forces. However, only CH_3OH satisfies the conditions for hydrogen bonding (H bonded to and attracted to N, O, or F) and thus its intermolecular attractions should be much stronger than those of the other substances.

6.   **(E)**

(a)   The conditions for hydrogen bonding are not satisfied in this molecule (i.e., hydrogen bonding requires an H atom covalently bonded to a N, an O, or an F atom, and that H atom is also attracted to another N, O, or F atom). Although there is an O in this molecule, none of the H atoms are bonded to it. The molecule forms neither intramolecular nor intermolecular hydrogen bonds.

(b)   Intramolecular hydrogen bonding is probably not important in CH_3NH_2. The two H atoms will interact with the lone pair on the N atom in another molecule. Therefore, intermolecular hydrogen bonding will be more important than intramolecular hydrogen bonding.

(c)   Intramolecular hydrogen bonding is probably important in $CH_3CH_2CHFCH_2OH$. The H atom of the hydroxyl group can interact with the lone pairs on the nearby F atom.

(d)   In orthophthalic acid, intramolecular hydrogen bonds can occur. The H of one —COOH group can be attracted to one of the O atoms of the other —COOH group. The resulting ring is seven atoms around and thus should not cause substantial bond angle strain.

7.   **(M)** Three water molecules: the two lone pairs on the oxygen will interact with two hydrogens on two different water molecules, and one will interact with the hydrogen attached to O itself.

8.   **(M)** Two hydrogen bonds can occur between two acetic acid molecules. The interaction is shown below:

9. **(M)** There are three H-bonds:

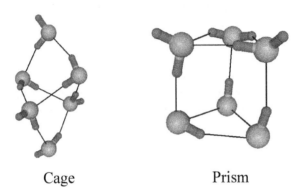

10. **(D)** See the figures below:

Cage   Prism

Surface Tension and Viscosity

11. **(E)** Since both the silicone oil and the cloth or leather are composed of relatively nonpolar molecules, they attract each other. The oil thus adheres well to the material. Water, on the other hand is polar and adheres very poorly to the silicone oil (actually, the water is repelled by the oil), much more poorly, in fact, than it adheres to the cloth or leather. This is because the oil is more nonpolar than is the cloth or the leather. Thus, water is repelled from the silicone-treated cloth or leather.

12. **(E)** Both surface tension and viscosity deal with the work needed to overcome the attractions between molecules. Increasing the temperature of a liquid sample causes the molecules to move faster. Some of the work has been done by adding thermal energy (heat) and less work needs to be done by the experimenter, consequently, both surface tension and viscosity decrease. The vapor pressure is a measure of the concentration of molecules that have broken free of the surface. As thermal energy is added to the liquid sample, more and more molecules have enough energy to break free of the surface, and the vapor pressure increases.

13. **(E)**
Molasses, like honey, is a very viscous liquid (high resistance to flow). The coldest temperatures are generally in January (in the northern hemisphere). Viscosity generally increases as the temperature decreases. Hence, molasses at low temperature is a very slow flowing liquid. Thus there is indeed a scientific basis for the expression "slower than molasses in January."

14. **(E)** The product can lower the surface tension of water. Then the water can more easily wet a solid substance, because a greater surface area of water can be created with the same energy. (Surface tension equals the work needed to create a given quantity of surface area.) This greater water surface area means a greater area of contact with a solid object, such as a piece of fabric. More of the fabric being in contact with the water means that the water is indeed wetter.

<u>15.</u> **(E)** $CH_3CH_2OCH_2CH_3 < CH_3OH < HOCH_2CH_2OH$. Although all three substances are polar, the CH_3OH and $HOCH_2CH_2OH$ molecules form hydrogen bonds. The surface tension of $HOCH_2CH_2OH$ is higher than that of CH_3OH because the $HOCH_2CH_2OH$ molecule is not only larger (more polarizable) but also able to form a greater number of hydrogen bonds because of the OH groups at either end.

16. **(E)** One would expect the surface tension in t-butyl alcohol to be less than *n*-butyl alcohol, because *t*-butyl alcohol is a more compact/spherical molecule, it has less molecular "surface area" for interaction with other *t*-butyl alcohol molecules, and therefore its van der Waals forces are weaker than *n*-butyl alcohol's.

<u>17.</u> **(E)** The intermolecular interactions in butanol are dominated by H-bonding, which is much stronger than the London dispersion forces dominant in pentane.

18. **(E)** Simply put, if two substances (in this case, CCl_4 and Hg) have the same viscosity, that means that the magnitudes of their intramolecular/atomic interactions have to be about the same, even though the nature of these interactions can be significantly different. The intermolecular interactions in CCl_4 are primarily London dispersion, for Hg mainly metallic.

Vaporization

<u>19.</u> **(E)** The process of evaporation is endothermic, meaning it requires energy. If evaporation occurs from an uninsulated container, this energy is obtained from the surroundings, through the walls of the container. However, if the evaporation occurs from an insulated container, the only source of the needed energy is the liquid that is evaporating. Therefore, the temperature of the liquid will decrease as the liquid evaporates.

20. **(E)** Vapor cannot form throughout the liquid at temperatures below the boiling point because, for vapor to form, it must overcome the atmospheric pressure (≈ 1 atm) or slightly more due to the pressure of the liquid. Formation of a bubble of vapor in the liquid, requires that it must push the liquid out of the way. This is not true at the surface. The vapor molecules simply move into the gas phase at the surface, which is mostly empty space.

<u>21.</u> **(E)** We use the quantity of heat to determine the number of moles of benzene that vaporize.

$$V = \frac{nRT}{P} = \frac{\left(1.54\,kJ \times \dfrac{1\,mol}{33.9\,kJ}\right) \times 0.08206 \dfrac{L\,atm}{mol\,K} \times 298\,K}{95.1\,mmHg \times \dfrac{1\,atm}{760\,mmHg}} = 8.88\,L\,C_6H_6(l)$$

22. (E) $n_{\text{acetonitrile}} = \dfrac{PV}{RT} = \dfrac{1.00 \text{ atm} \times 1.17 \text{ L}}{0.08206 \text{ L atm mol}^{-1}\text{K}^{-1} \times (273.2 + 81.6) \text{ K}} = 0.0402 \text{ mol acetonitrile}$

$\Delta_{\text{vap}}H = \dfrac{1.00 \text{ kJ}}{0.0402 \text{ mol}} = 24.9 \text{ kJ/mol acetonitrile}$

23. (M)

25.00 mL of N_2H_4 (25 °C) density (25°C) = 1.0036 g mL^{-1} (molar mass = 32.0452 g mol^{-1})

mass of N_2H_4 = (volume) × (density) = (25.00 mL) × (1.0036 g mL^{-1}) = 25.09 g N_2H_4

$n_{\text{N2H4}} = 25.09 \text{ g } N_2H_4 \times \dfrac{1 \text{ mol } N_2H_4}{32.0452 \text{ g } N_2H_4} = 0.7830 \text{ mol}$

Energy required to increase temperature from 25.0 °C to 113.5 °C (Δt =88.5 °C)

$q_{\text{heating}} = (n)(C)(\Delta t) = (0.78295 \text{ mol } N_2H_4)\left(\dfrac{98.84 \text{ J}}{1 \text{ mol } N_2H_4 \text{ °C}}\right)(88.5 \text{ °C}) = 6848.7 \text{ J or } 6.85 \text{ kJ}$

$q_{\text{vap}} = (n_{N_2H_4})(\Delta_{\text{vap}}H) = (0.78295 \text{ mol } N_2H_4)\left(\dfrac{43.0 \text{ kJ}}{1 \text{ mol } N_2H_4}\right) = 33.7 \text{ kJ}$

$q_{\text{overall}} = q_{\text{heating}} + q_{\text{vap}} = 6.85 \text{ kJ} + 33.7 \text{ kJ} = 40.5 \text{ kJ}$

24. (M) $\Delta_{\text{vap}}H$ for $CH_3OH(l)$ = 38.0 kJ mol^{-1} at 298 K (assumes ΔH does not depend on temperature)
Δt = 30.0 °C – 20.0 °C = 10.0 °C

$n_{\text{CH}_3\text{OH}} = 215 \text{ g } CH_3OH \times \left(\dfrac{1 \text{ mol } CH_3OH}{32.0422 \text{ g } CH_3OH}\right) = 6.71 \text{ mol } CH_3OH$

Raise temperature of liquid from 20.0 °C to 30.0 °C

$q = (n)(C)(\Delta t) = (6.71 \text{ mol } CH_3OH)\left(\dfrac{81.1 \text{ J}}{1 \text{ mol } CH_3OH \text{ °C}}\right)(10.0 \text{ °C}) = 5441.8 \text{ J or } 5.44 \text{ kJ}$

Vaporize liquid at 30 °C (Use $\Delta_{\text{vap}}H$ at 25 °C and assume value is the same at 30 °C)

$q_{\text{vap}} = (n_{\text{CH}_3\text{OH}})(\Delta_{\text{vap}}H) = (6.71 \text{ mol } CH_3OH)\left(\dfrac{38.0 \text{ kJ}}{1 \text{ mol } CH_3OH}\right) = 255 \text{ kJ}$

$q_{\text{overall}} = q_{\text{heating}} + q_{\text{vap}} = 5.44 \text{ kJ} + 255 \text{ kJ} = 260. \text{ kJ}$

25. (M)

heat needed = $3.78 \text{ L } H_2O \times \dfrac{1000 \text{ cm}^3}{1 \text{ L}} \times \dfrac{0.958 \text{ g } H_2O}{1 \text{ cm}^3} \times \dfrac{1 \text{ mol } H_2O}{18.02 \text{ g } H_2O} \times \dfrac{40.7 \text{ kJ}}{1 \text{ mol } H_2O} = 8.18 \times 10^3 \text{ kJ}$

amount CH_4 needed = $8.18 \times 10^3 \text{ kJ} \times \dfrac{1 \text{ mol } CH_4}{890 \text{ kJ}} = 9.19 \text{ mol } CH_4$

$V = \dfrac{nRT}{P} = \dfrac{9.19 \text{ mol} \times 0.08206 \text{ L atm mol}^{-1}\text{K}^{-1} \times 296.6 \text{ K}}{768 \text{ mmHg} \times \dfrac{1 \text{ atm}}{760 \text{ mmHg}}} = 221 \text{ L methane}$

26. **(M)** If not all of the water vaporizes, the final temperature of the system will be $100.00\,°C$. Let us proceed on that assumption and modify our final state if this is not true. First we determine the heat available from the iron in cooling down, and then the heat needed to warm the water to boiling, and finally the mass of water that vaporizes.

$$\text{heat from Fe} = \text{mass} \times \text{sp.ht.} \times \Delta t = 50.0 \text{ g} \times \frac{0.45 \text{ J}}{\text{g} \, °C} \times (100.00\,°C - 152\,°C) = -1.17 \times 10^3 \text{ J}$$

$$\text{heat to warm water} = 20.0 \text{ g} \times \frac{4.21 \text{ J}}{\text{g} \, °C} \times (100.00\,°C - 89\,°C) = 9.3 \times 10^2 \text{ J}$$

mass of water vaporized:

$$= \left(11.7 \times 10^2 \text{ J available} - 9.3 \times 10^2 \text{ J used}\right) \times \frac{1 \text{ mol } H_2O \text{ vaporized}}{40.7 \times 10^3 \text{ J}} \times \frac{18.02 \text{ g } H_2O}{1 \text{ mol } H_2O}$$

$$= 0.11 \text{ g of water vaporize}$$

Clearly, all of the water does not vaporize and our initial assumption was valid.

Vapor Pressure and Boiling Point

27. **(E)**

(a) We read up the $100\,°C$ line until we arrive at C_6H_7N curve (e). This occurs at about 45 mmHg.

(b) We read across the 760 mmHg line until we arrive at the C_7H_8 curve (d). This occurs at about $110\,°C$.

28. **(E)**

(a) The normal boiling point occurs where the vapor pressure is 760 mmHg, and thus $\ln P = 6.63$. For aniline, this occurs at about the uppermost data point (open circle) on the aniline line. This corresponds to $1/T = 2.18 \times 10^{-3} \text{ K}^{-1}$. Thus,

$$T_{nbp} = \frac{1}{2.18 \times 10^{-3} \text{ K}^{-1}} = 459 \text{ K}.$$

(b) $25\,°C = 298 \text{ K} = T$ and thus $1/T = 3.36 \times 10^{-3} \text{ K}^{-1}$. This occurs at about $\ln P = 6.25$. Thus, $P = e^{6.25} = 518$ mmHg.

29. **(E)** Use the ideal gas equation, $n = \text{moles } Br_2 = 0.486 \text{ g } Br_2 \times \frac{1 \text{ mol } Br_2}{159.8 \text{ g } Br_2} = 3.04 \times 10^{-3} \text{ mol } Br_2$.

$$P = \frac{nRT}{V} = \frac{3.04 \times 10^{-3} \text{ mol } Br_2 \times 0.08206 \text{ L atm mol}^{-1} \text{ K}^{-1} \times 298.2 \text{ K}}{0.2500 \text{ L}} \times \frac{760 \text{ mmHg}}{1 \text{ atm}}$$

$$= 226 \text{ mmHg}$$

30. **(M)** We can determine the vapor pressure by using the ideal gas law.

$$P = \frac{nRT}{V} = \frac{\left(0.876 \text{ g } (CH_3)_2CO \times \dfrac{1 \text{ mol } (CH_3)_2CO}{58.08 \text{ g } (CH_3)_2CO}\right) \times \left(\dfrac{0.08206 \text{ L atm}}{K \text{ mol}}\right) \times (32 + 273.15) \text{ K}}{1 \text{ L}}$$

$$= 0.378 \text{ atm}$$

$$P = 0.378 \text{ atm} \times \frac{101.325 \text{ kPa}}{1 \text{ atm}} = 38.3 \text{ kPa}$$

31. **(E)**

(a) In order to vaporize water in the outer container, heat must be applied (i.e., vaporization is an endothermic process). When this vapor (steam) condenses on the outside walls of the inner container, that same heat is liberated. Thus condensation is an exothermic process.

(b) Liquid water, condensed on the outside wall, is in equilibrium with the water vapor that fills the space between the two containers. This equilibrium exists at the boiling point of water. We assume that the pressure is 1.000 atm, and thus, the temperature of the equilibrium must be 373.15 K or 100.00 °C. This is the maximum temperature that can be realized without pressurizing the apparatus.

32. **(E)** When the can is heated, the vapor pressure of water inside the can is ~ 760 mm Hg. As the can cools, most of the water vapor in the can condenses to liquid and the pressure inside the can drops sharply to the vapor pressure of water at room temperature ($\approx$ 25 mmHg). The pressure on the outside of the can is still near 760 mmHg. It is this huge difference in pressure that is responsible for the can being crushed.

33. **(M)** Use the Clausius-Clapeyron equation, and the vapor pressure of water at 100.0 °C (373.2 K) and 120.0 °C (393.2 K) to determine $\Delta_{vap}H$ of water near its boiling point. We then use the equation again, to determine the temperature at which water's vapor pressure is 2.00 atm.

$$\ln \frac{1489.1 \text{ mmHg}}{760.0 \text{ mmHg}} = \frac{\Delta_{vap}H}{8.3145 \text{ J mol}^{-1}\text{ K}^{-1}}\left(\frac{1}{373.2 \text{ K}} - \frac{1}{393.2 \text{ K}}\right) = 0.6726 = 1.639 \times 10^{-5}\Delta_{vap}H$$

$$\Delta_{vap}H = 4.104 \times 10^4 \text{ J/mol} = 41.04 \text{ kJ/mol}$$

$$\ln \frac{2.00 \text{ atm}}{1.00 \text{ atm}} = 0.6931 = \frac{41.04 \times 10^3 \text{ J mol}}{8.3145 \text{ J mol}^{-1}\text{ K}^{-1}}\left(\frac{1}{373.2 \text{ K}} - \frac{1}{T}\right)$$

$$\left(\frac{1}{373.2 \text{ K}} - \frac{1}{T_{bp}}\right) = 0.6931 \times \frac{8.1345 \text{ K}^{-1}}{41.03 \times 10^3} = 1.404 \times 10^{-4} \text{ K}^{-1}$$

$$\frac{1}{T_{bp}} = \frac{1}{373.2 \text{ K}} - 1.404 \times 10^{-4} \text{ K}^{-1} = 2.539 \times 10^{-3} \text{ K}^{-1} \quad T_{bp} = 393.9 \text{ K} = 120.7 \text{ °C}$$

34. (E)

(a) We need the temperature at which the vapor pressure of water is 640 mmHg. This is a temperature between 95.0 °C (633.9 mmHg) and 96.0 °C (657.6 mmHg. We estimate a boiling point of 95.3 °C.

(b) If the observed boiling point is 94 °C, the atmospheric pressure must equal the vapor pressure of water at 94 °C, which is, 611 mmHg.

35. (M) The 25.0 L of He becomes saturated with aniline vapor, at a pressure equal to the vapor pressure of aniline.

$$n_{aniline} = (6.220\ g - 6.108\ g) \times \frac{1\ mole\ aniline}{93.13\ g\ aniline} = 0.00120\ mol\ aniline$$

$$P = \frac{nRT}{V} = \frac{0.00120\ mol \times 0.08206\ L\ atm\ mol^{-1}K^{-1} \times 303.2\ K}{25.0\ L} = 0.00119\ atm = 0.907\ mmHg$$

36. (M) The final pressure must be 742 mm Hg and the partial pressure of $CCl_4(g)$ is constant at 261 mm Hg, thus, the partial pressure of N_2 must be 481 mm Hg. Using Dalton's law of partial pressures, $P_{N_2}/P_{total} = V_{N_2}/V_{total}$, the total and final pressures are known. Since the temperature does not change, the volume occupied by N_2 is constant at 7.53 L.

Hence, $V_{total} = V_{N_2} \times \dfrac{P_{total}}{P_{N_2}} = 7.53\ L \times \dfrac{742\ mmHg}{481\ mmHg} = 11.6\ L.$

**37.
(M)**

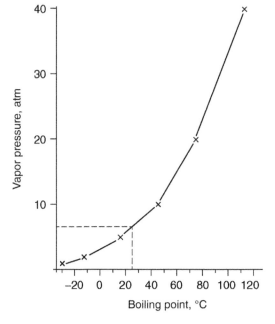

The graph of pressure vs. boiling point for Freon-12 is shown.

At a temperature of 25 °C the vapor pressure is approximately 6.5 atm for Freon-12. Thus the compressor must be capable of producing a pressure greater than 6.5 atm.

38. **(M)** At 27 °C, the vapor pressure of water is 26.7 mmHg. We use this value to determine the mass of water that can exist within the container as vapor.

$$\text{mass of water vapor} = \frac{\left(26.7\,\text{mmHg} \times \dfrac{1\,\text{atm}}{760\,\text{mmHg}}\right) \times \left(1515\,\text{mL} \times \dfrac{1\,\text{L}}{1000\,\text{mL}}\right)}{\dfrac{0.08206\,\text{L atm}}{\text{mol K}} \times (27+273)\,\text{K}} = 0.00216\,\text{mol H}_2\text{O(g)}$$

$$\text{mass of water vapor} = 0.00216\,\text{mol H}_2\text{O(g)} \times \frac{18.02\,\text{g H}_2\text{O}}{1\,\text{mol H}_2\text{O}} = 0.0389\,\text{g H}_2\text{O(g)}$$

The Clausius-Clapeyron Equation

39. **(M)** We use the Clausius-Clapeyron equation (12.2) to answer this question.

$T_1 = (56.0+273.2)\,\text{K} = 329.2\,\text{K}$ $T_2 = (103.7+273.2)\,\text{K} = 376.9\,\text{K}$

$$\ln\frac{10.0\,\text{mmHg}}{100.0\,\text{mmHg}} = \frac{\Delta_{vap}H}{8.3145\,\text{J mol}^{-1}\,\text{K}^{-1}}\left(\frac{1}{376.9\,\text{K}} - \frac{1}{329.2\,\text{K}}\right) = -2.30 = -4.624\times10^{-5}\Delta_{vap}H$$

$\Delta_{vap}H = 4.97\times10^{4}\,\text{J/mol} = 49.7\,\text{kJ/mol}$

40. **(M)** We use the Clausius-Clapeyron equation (12.2), to answer this question.

$T_1 = (5.0+273.2)\,\text{K} = 278.2\,\text{K}$

$$\ln\frac{760.0\,\text{mmHg}}{40.0\,\text{mmHg}} = 2.944 = \frac{38.0\times10^{3}\,\text{J/mol}}{8.3145\,\text{J mol}^{-1}\,\text{K}^{-1}}\left(\frac{1}{278.2\,\text{K}} - \frac{1}{T_{nbp}}\right)$$

$$\left(\frac{1}{278.2\,\text{K}} - \frac{1}{T_{nbp}}\right) = 2.944 \times \frac{8.3145\,\text{K}^{-1}}{38.0\times10^{3}} = 6.44\times10^{-4}\,\text{K}^{-1}$$

$$\frac{1}{T_{nbp}} = \frac{1}{278.2} - 6.44\times10^{-4}\,\text{K}^{-1} = 2.95\times10^{-3}\,\text{K}^{-1} \qquad T_{nbp} = 339\,\text{K}$$

41. **(M)** Once again, we will employ the Clausius-Clapeyron equation.

$T = 56.2\,°\text{C}$ is $T = 329.4\,\text{K}$

$$\ln\frac{760\,\text{mmHg}}{375\,\text{mmHg}} = \frac{25.5\times10^{3}\,\text{J/mol}}{8.3145\,\text{J mol}^{-1}\,\text{K}^{-1}}\left(\frac{1}{T} - \frac{1}{329.4\,\text{K}}\right) = 0.706$$

$$\left(\frac{1}{T} - \frac{1}{329.4\,\text{K}}\right) = \frac{0.706\times8.3145}{25.5\times10^{3}}\,\text{K}^{-1} = 2.30\times10^{-4}\,\text{K}^{-1} = 1/T - 3.03_6\times10^{-3}\,\text{K}^{-1}$$

$1/T = (3.03_6 + 0.230)\times10^{-3}\,\text{K}^{-1} = 3.266\times10^{-3}\,\text{K}^{-1} \qquad T = 306\,\text{K} = 33\,°\text{C}$

42. **(M)** $P_1 = 40.0$ Torr $T_1 = -7.1\,°\text{C}$ (266 K) and $\Delta_{vap}H = 29.2\,\text{kJ mol}^{-1}$

$P_2 = 760.0$ Torr $T_2 = ?$

$$\ln\left(\frac{760.0}{40.0}\right) = \frac{29{,}200\,\text{J}}{8.31451\dfrac{\text{J}}{\text{K mol}}}\left(\frac{1}{266\,\text{K}} - \frac{1}{T_2}\right) \qquad T_2 = 342.\underline{3}\,\text{K or } \sim69\,°\text{C}$$

(The literature boiling point for trichloromethane is 61 °C.)

43. **(M)** Normal boiling point = 179 °C and critical point = 422 °C and 45.9 atm

$$\ln\left(\frac{P_2}{P_1}\right)=\frac{\Delta_{vap}H}{R}\left(\frac{1}{T_1}-\frac{1}{T_2}\right) \qquad \ln\left(\frac{45.9}{1}\right)=\frac{\Delta_{vap}H}{8.3145\ \text{J}\,\text{K}^{-1}\text{mol}^{-1}}\left(\frac{1}{452.2\,\text{K}}-\frac{1}{695.2\,\text{K}}\right)$$

$\Delta_{vap}H = 41.2$ kJ mol^{-1}

$$\ln\left(\frac{1}{P}\right)=\frac{41,200\,\text{J}\,\text{mol}^{-1}}{8.3145\,\text{J}\,\text{K}^{-1}\text{mol}^{-1}}\left(\frac{1}{373.2}-\frac{1}{452.2\,\text{K}}\right) \qquad P = 0.0981 \text{ atm or } 74.6 \text{ Torr}$$

44. **(E)**

(a) The plot of ln P vs 1/T for benzene is located to the right of that for toluene. This tells us that, for a given temperature, the vapor pressure for toluene is lower than that for benzene, and thus benzene is a more volatile liquid than toluene.

(b) According to Figure 12-20, at 65 °C, the vapor pressure for benzene is ~ 450 mm Hg or 0.60 atm. We have been asked to estimate the temperature at which toluene has a vapor pressure of 0.60 atm. First, we find ln 450 = 6.11 on the benzene curve of Figure 12-20. Then, we move horizontally to the left along ln P = 6.11 until we reach the toluene curve. At this point on the toluene curve, the value of 1/T = 0.00273. This corresponds to T = 366 K.

Critical Point

45. **(E)** Substances that can exist as a liquid at room temperature (about 20 °C) have critical temperature above 20 °C, 293 K. Of the substances listed in Table 12.6, $CO_2(T_c = 304.2$ K), $HCl(T_c = 324.6$ K), $NH_3(T_c = 405.7$ K), $SO_2(T_c = 431.0$ K), and $H_2O(T_c = 647.3$ K) can exist in liquid form at 20 °C. In fact, CO_2 exists as a liquid in CO_2 fire extinguishers.

46. **(E)** The critical temperature of SO_2, 431.0 K, is above the temperature of 0 °C, 273 K. The critical pressure of SO_2 is 77.7 atm, which is below the pressure of 100 atm. Thus, SO_2 can be maintained as a liquid at 0 °C and 100 atm. The critical temperature of methane, CH_4, is 191.1 K, which is below the temperature of 0 °C, 273 K. Thus, CH_4 cannot exist as a liquid at 0 °C, no matter what pressure is applied.

Melting and Freezing

47. **(M)**

(a) heat evolved = 3.78 kg Cu $\times \dfrac{1000\text{ g}}{1\text{ kg}} \times \dfrac{1\text{ mol Cu}}{63.55\text{ g Cu}} \times \dfrac{13.05\text{ kJ}}{1\text{ mol Cu}} = 776$ kJ evolved or

$\Delta H = -776$ kJ

(b) heat absorbed = $(75\text{ cm} \times 15\text{ cm} \times 12\text{ cm}) \times \dfrac{8.92\text{ g}}{1\text{ cm}^3} \times \dfrac{1\text{ mol Cu}}{63.55\text{ g Cu}} \times \dfrac{13.05\text{ kJ}}{1\text{ mol Cu}} = 2.5 \times 10^4$ kJ

48. **(M)** The relevant reaction is $C_3H_8(g) + 5\ O_2(g) \rightarrow 3\ CO_2(g) + 4\ H_2O(g)$

$\Delta_r H = \Delta_c H = [4(-285.8\ \text{kJ mol}^{-1}) + 3(-393.5\ \text{kJ mol}^{-1})] - (-103.8\ \text{kJ mol}^{-1})$

$\qquad = -2219.9\ \text{kJ mol}^{-1}\ C_3H_8(g)$

$$n = \dfrac{PV}{RT} = \dfrac{\left(735\ \text{mmHg} \times \dfrac{1.013\ \text{bar}}{760\ \text{mm Hg}}\right)(1.60\ \text{L})}{\left(0.083145\ \text{L bar K}^{-1}\right)(20 + 273.15\ \text{K})} = 0.0643\ \text{mol}$$

$q_{\text{combustion}} = n\,\Delta_c H = 0.0643\ \text{mol}\ C_3H_8(g) \times \left(-2219.9\ \text{kJ mol}^{-1}\ C_3H_8(g)\right)$

$\qquad\qquad = -142.74\ \text{kJ}$

From equation (12.3), the $\Delta_{\text{fus}}H$ of ice is 6.01 kJ mol^{-1}. Therefore, the moles of ice melted can be calculated from the available energy, and the mass of ice can be determined:

$$142.74\ \text{kJ} \times \dfrac{1\ \text{mol ice}}{6.01\ \text{kJ}} \times \dfrac{18.02\ \text{g ice}}{1\ \text{mol ice}} = 428\ \text{g ice melted}$$

States of Matter and Phase Diagrams

49. **(M)** Let us use the ideal gas law to determine the final pressure in the container, assuming that all of the dry ice vaporizes. We then locate this pressure, at a temperature of 25 °C, on the phase diagram of Figure 12-28.

$$P = \dfrac{nRT}{V} = \dfrac{\left(80.0\ \text{g CO}_2 \times \dfrac{1\,\text{mol CO}_2}{44.0\,\text{g CO}_2}\right) \times 0.08206\dfrac{\text{L atm}}{\text{mol K}} \times 298\ \text{K}}{0.500\ \text{L}} = 88.9\ \text{atm}$$

Although this point (25 °C and 88.9 atm) is most likely in the region labeled "liquid" in Figure 12–28, we computed its pressure assuming the CO_2 is a gas. Some of this gas should condense to a liquid. Thus, both liquid and gas are present in the container. Solid would not be present unless the temperature is below –50 °C at ~ 88.9 atm.

50. **(M)** The phase diagram for hydrazine is sketched below. The triple point is shown on the diagram at 0.00445 atm (3.4 mmHg) and 2 °C. The normal boiling point is shown at 113.5 °C and the critical point at 380 °C and 145 atm. We are not certain of the slope and curvature of the lines in the diagram.

518

51. (M)

(a) The upper-right region of the phase diagram is the liquid region, while the lower-right region is the region of gas.

(b) Melting involves converting the solid into a liquid. As the phase diagram shows, the lowest pressure at which liquid exists is at the triple point pressure, namely, 43 atm. 1.00 atm is far below 43 atm. Thus, liquid cannot exist at this pressure, and solid sublimes to gas instead.

(c) As we move from point *A* to point *B* by lowering the pressure, initially nothing happens. At a certain pressure, the solid liquefies. The pressure continues to drop, with the entire sample being liquid while it does, until another, lower pressure is reached. At this lower pressure the entire sample vaporizes. The pressure then continues to drop, with the gas becoming less dense as the pressure falls, until point *B* is reached.

52. (D)

(a) As heat is added initially, the temperature of the ice rises from –20 °C to 0 °C. At (or just slightly below) 0 °C, ice begins to melt to liquid water. The temperature remains at 0 °C until all of the ice has melted. Adding heat then warms the liquid until a temperature of about 93.5 °C is reached, at which point the liquid begins to vaporize to steam. The temperature remains fixed until all the water is converted to steam. Adding heat then warms the steam to 200 °C. (Data for this part are taken from Figure 12-30 and Table 12.5.)

(b) As the pressure is raised, initially gaseous iodine is just compressed. At ~ 91 mmHg, liquid iodine appears. As the pressure is pushed above 99 mmHg, more liquid condenses until eventually all the vapor is converted to a liquid. Increasing the pressure further simply compresses the liquid until a high pressure is reached, perhaps 50 atm, where solid iodine appears. Again the pressure remains fixed with further compression until all of the iodine is converted to its solid form. After this has occurred further compression raises the pressure on the solid until 100 atm is reached. (Data for this part are from Figure 12-27 and the surrounding text.)

(c) Cooling of gaseous CO_2 simply lowers the temperature until a temperature of perhaps 20 °C is reached. At this point, liquid CO_2 appears. The temperature remains constant as more heat is removed until all the gas is converted to liquid. Further cooling then lowers the temperature of the liquid until a temperature of slightly higher than –56.7 °C is reached, where solid CO_2 appears. At this point, further cooling simply converts liquid to solid at constant temperature, until all liquid has been converted to solid. From this point, further cooling lowers the temperature of the solid. (Data for this part are taken from Figure 12-28 and Table 12.6.)

53. **(D)** 0.240 g of H_2O corresponds to 0.0133 mol H_2O. If the water does not vaporize completely, the pressure of the vapor in the flask equals the vapor pressure of water at the indicated temperature. However, if the water vaporizes completely, the pressure of the vapor is determined by the ideal gas law.

(a) 30.0°C, vapor pressure of H_2O = 31.8 mmHg = 0.0418 atm

$$n = \frac{PV}{RT} = \frac{0.0418 \text{ atm} \times 3.20 \text{ L}}{0.08206 \text{ L atm mol}^{-1} \text{ K}^{-1} \times 303.2 \text{ K}}$$

n = 0.00538 mol H_2O vapor, which is less than 0.0133 mol H_2O;

This represents a non-eqilibrium condition, since not all the H_2O vaporizes.

The pressure in the flask is 0.0418 atm. (from tables)

(b) 50.0 °C, vapor pressure of H_2O = 92.5 mmHg = 0.122 atm

$$n = \frac{PV}{RT} = \frac{0.122 \text{ atm} \times 3.20 \text{ L}}{0.08206 \text{ L atm mol}^{-1} \text{ K}^{-1} \times 323.2 \text{ K}}$$

= 0.0147 mol H_2O vapor > 0.0133 mol H_2O; all the H_2O vaporizes. Thus,

$$P = \frac{nRT}{V} = \frac{0.0133 \text{ mol} \times 0.08206 \text{ L atm mol}^{-1} \text{ K}^{-1} \times 323.2 \text{ K}}{3.20 \text{ L}} = 0.110 \text{ atm} = 83.8 \text{ mmHg}$$

(c) 70.0 °C All the H_2O must vaporize, as this temperature is higher than that of part (b). Thus,

$$P = \frac{nRT}{V} = \frac{0.0133 \text{ mol} \times 0.08206 \text{ L atm mol}^{-1} \text{ K}^{-1} \times 343.2 \text{ K}}{3.20 \text{ L}} = 0.117 \text{ atm} = 89.0 \text{ mmHg}$$

54. **(M)**
(a) If the pressure exerted by 2.50 g of H_2O (vapor) is less than the vapor pressure of water at 120 °C (393 K), then the water must exist entirely as a vapor.

$$P = \frac{nRT}{V} = \frac{\left(2.50 \text{ g} \times \dfrac{1 \text{ mol } H_2O}{18.02 \text{ g } H_2O}\right) \times 0.08206 \text{ L atm mol}^{-1}\text{K}^{-1} \times 393 \text{ K}}{5.00 \text{ L}} = 0.895 \text{ atm}$$

Since this is less than the 1.00 atm vapor pressure at 100 °C, it must be less than the vapor pressure of water at 120 °C. Thus, the water exists entirely as a vapor.

(b) 0.895 atm = 680 mmHg. From Table 12.3, we see that this corresponds to a temperature of 97.0 °C (at which temperature the vapor pressure of water is 682.1 mmHg). Thus, at temperatures slightly less than 97.0 °C the water will begin to condense to liquid. But we have forgotten that, in this constant-volume container, the pressure (of water) will decrease as the temperature decreases. Calculating the precise decrease in both involves linking the Clausius-Clapeyron equation with the expression $P = kT$, but we can estimate the final temperature. First, we determine the pressure if we lower the temperature from 393 K to 97.0 °C (370 K).

$P_f = \dfrac{370\ K}{393\ K} \times 680\ \text{mmHg} = 640\ \text{mmHg}$ From Table 12.3, this pressure occurs at a temperature of about 95 °C (368 K). We now determine the final pressure at this temperature. $P_f = \dfrac{368\ K}{393\ K} \times 680\ \text{mmHg} = 637\ \text{mmHg}$ This is just slightly above the vapor pressure of water (633.9 mmHg) at 95 °C, which we conclude must be the temperature at which liquid water appears.

55. **(M)**

(a) According to Figure 12-28, $CO_2(s)$ exists at temperatures below –78.5 °C when the pressure is 1 atm or less. We do not expect to find temperatures this low and partial pressures of $CO_2(g)$ of 1 atm on the surface of Earth.

(b) According to Table 12.6, the critical temperature of CH_4, the maximum temperature at which $CH_4(l)$ can exist, is 191.1 K = –82.1 °C. We do not expect to find temperatures this low on the surface of Earth.

(c) Since, according to Table 12.6, the critical temperature of SO_2 is 431.0 K = 157.8 °C, $SO_2(g)$ can be found on the surface of Earth.

(d) According to Figure 12–27, $I_2(l)$ can exist at pressures less than 1.00 atm between the temperatures of 114 °C and 184 °C. There are very few places on Earth that reach temperatures this far above the boiling point of water at pressures below 1 atm. One example of such a place would be the mouth of a volcano high above sea level. Essentially, $I_2(l)$ is not found on the surface of Earth.

(e) According to Table 12.6, the critical temperature – the maximum temperature at which $O_2(l)$ exists – is 154.8 K = –118.4 °C. Temperatures this low do not exist on the surface of Earth.

56. **(E)** The final pressure specified (100. atm) is below the ice III-ice I-liquid water triple point, according to the text adjacent to Figure 12–30; no ice III is formed. The starting point is that of $H_2O(g)$. When the pressure is increased to about 4.5 mmHg, the vapor condenses to ice I.

As the pressure is raised, the melting point of ice I decreases–by 1 °C for every 125 atm increase in pressure. Thus, somewhere between 10 and 15 atm, the ice I melts to liquid water, and it remains in this state until the final pressure is reached.

57. **(D)**

(a) heat lost by water = $q_{\text{water}} = (m)(C)(\Delta t)$

$$q_{\text{water}} = (100.0\ \text{g})\left(4.18\dfrac{J}{\text{g °C}}\right)(0.00\ °C - 20.00\ °C)\left(\dfrac{1\text{kJ}}{1000\text{J}}\right) = -8.36\ \text{kJ}$$

Using $\Delta_{\text{cond}}H = -\Delta_{\text{vap}}H$ and heat lost by system = heat loss of condensation + cooling

$$q_{steam} = (175 \text{ g H}_2\text{O})\left(4.18\frac{\text{J}}{\text{g °C}}\right)(0.0 \text{ °C} - 100.0 \text{ °C})\left(\frac{1\text{kJ}}{1000\text{ J}}\right)$$

$$+ (175 \text{ g H}_2\text{O})\left(\frac{1\text{mol H}_2\text{O}}{18.015\text{g H}_2\text{O}}\right)\left(\frac{-40.7\text{kJ}}{1\text{mol H}_2\text{O}}\right)$$

$q_{steam} = -395.4 \text{ kJ} + (-73.2 \text{ kJ}) = -468.6 \text{ kJ or } \sim -469 \text{ kJ}$

total energy to melt the ice $= q_{water} + q_{steam} = -8.37 \text{ kJ} + (-469 \text{ kJ}) = -477 \text{ kJ}$

$$\text{moles of ice melted} = (477 \text{ kJ})\left(\frac{1\text{mol ice}}{6.01\text{kJ}}\right) = 79.4 \text{ mol ice melted}$$

$$\text{mass of ice melted} = (79.4 \text{ mol H}_2\text{O})\left(\frac{18.015\text{g H}_2\text{O}}{1\text{mol H}_2\text{O}}\right)\left(\frac{1\text{kg H}_2\text{O}}{1000\text{g H}_2\text{O}}\right) = 1.43 \text{ kg}$$

mass of unmelted ice $= 1.65 \text{ kg} - 1.43 \text{ kg} = 0.22 \text{ kg}$

(b) mass of unmelted ice $= 0.22 \text{ kg}$ (from above)
heat required to melt ice $= n\Delta_{fus}H$

$$\text{heat required} = (0.22 \text{ kg ice})\left(\frac{1000\text{g H}_2\text{O}}{1\text{kg H}_2\text{O}}\right)\left(\frac{1\text{mol H}_2\text{O}}{18.015\text{g H}_2\text{O}}\right)\left(\frac{6.01\text{kJ}}{1\text{mol H}_2\text{O}}\right) = 73.\underline{4} \text{ kJ}$$

Next we need to determine heat produced when 1 mole of steam (18.015 g) condenses and cools from 100 °C to 0.0 °C.
Heat evolved can be calculated as shown below:

$$= (1 \text{ mol H}_2\text{O})\left(\frac{-40.7\text{kJ}}{1\text{mol H}_2\text{O}}\right) + (18.015 \text{ g})\left(4.18\frac{\text{J}}{\text{g °C}}\right)(0.0 \text{ °C} - 100 \text{ °C})\left(\frac{1\text{kJ}}{1000\text{ J}}\right)$$

$= -40.7 \text{ kJ} + -7.53 \text{ kJ} = -48.2 \text{ kJ per mole of H}_2\text{O(g) or per 18.015 g H}_2\text{O(g)}$

$$\text{mass of steam required} = (73.\underline{4} \text{ kJ})\left(\frac{1\text{mol H}_2\text{O(g)}}{48.2\text{kJ}}\right)\left(\frac{18.015\text{g H}_2\text{O}}{1\text{mol H}_2\text{O}}\right) = 27 \text{ g steam}$$

58. **(M)** The heat gained by the ice equals the negative of the heat lost by the water. Let us use this fact in a step-by-step approach. We first compute the heat needed to raise the temperature of the ice to 0.0 °C and then the heat given off when the temperature of the water is lowered to 0.0 °C.

$$\text{to heat the ice} = 54 \text{ cm}^3 \times \frac{0.917 \text{ g}}{1 \text{ cm}^3} \times 2.01 \text{ J g}^{-1}\text{ °C}^{-1} \times (0 \text{ °C} + 25.0 \text{ °C}) = 2.5 \times 10^3 \text{ J}$$

$$\text{to cool the water} = -400.0 \text{ cm}^3 \times \frac{0.998 \text{ g}}{1 \text{ cm}^3} \times 4.18 \text{ J g}^{-1}\text{ °C}^{-1} \times (0 \text{ °C} - 32.0 \text{ °C}) = 53.4 \times 10^3 \text{ J}$$

$$\text{Mass of ice} = 54 \text{ cm}^3 \times \frac{0.917 \text{ g}}{1 \text{ cm}^3} = 49.5 \text{ g} = 50. \text{ g ice}$$

$$\text{Mass of water} = 400.0 \text{ cm}^3 \times \frac{0.998 \text{ g}}{1 \text{ cm}^3} = 399 \text{ g water}$$

Thus, at $0\,^\circ C$, we have 50. g ice, 399 g water, and $(53.4-2.5)\times10^3$ J $=50.9$ kJ of heat available. Since 50.0 g of ice is a bit less than 3 moles of ice and 50.9 kJ is enough heat to melt at least 8 moles of ice, all of the ice will melt. The heat needed to melt the ice is

$$50.\ \text{g ice}\times\frac{1\ \text{mol H}_2\text{O}}{18.0\ \text{g H}_2\text{O}}\times\frac{6.01\ \text{kJ}}{1\ \text{mol ice}}=17\ \text{kJ}$$

We now have 50.9 kJ -17 kJ $=34$ kJ of heat, and 399 g $+50.$ g $=449$ g of water at $0\,^\circ C$. We compute the temperature change that is produced by adding the heat to the water.

$$\Delta T=\frac{34\times10^3\ \text{J}}{449\ \text{g}\times4.18\ \text{J g}^{-1}\ ^\circ\text{C}^{-1}}=18\ ^\circ\text{C}\quad\text{The final temperature is }18\ ^\circ\text{C}.$$

59. **(E)** The liquid in the can is supercooled. When the can is opened, gas bubbles released from the carbonated beverage serve as sites for the formation of ice crystals. The condition of supercooling is destroyed and the liquid reverts to the solid phase. An alternative explanation follows. The process of the gas coming out of solution is endothermic (heat is required). (We know this to be true because the reaction solution of gas in water $\rightarrow$ gas + liquid water proceeds to the right as the temperature is raised, a characteristic direction of an endothermic reaction.) The required heat is taken from the cooled liquid, causing it to freeze.

60. **(E)** Both the melting point of ice and the boiling point of water are temperatures that vary as the pressure changes, and the boiling point changes more substantially than the melting point. The triple point, however, does not vary with pressure. Solid, liquid, and vapor coexist only at one fixed temperature and pressure.

Network Covalent Solids

61. **(E)** One would expect diamond to have a greater density than graphite. Although the bond distance in graphite, "one-and-a-half" bonds, would be expected to be shorter than the single bonds in diamond, the large spacing between the layers of C atoms in graphite makes its crystals much less dense than those of diamond.

62. **(E)** Diamond works well in glass cutters because of its extreme hardness. Its hardness is due to the crystal being held together entirely by covalent bonds. Graphite will not function effectively in a glass cutter, since it is quite soft, soft enough to flake off in microscopic pieces when used in pencils. The bonding in between layers of graphite is weak, which leads to it being a softer material. In fact, graphite is so soft that pure graphite is rarely used in common wooden pencils. Often clay or some other substance is mixed with the graphite to produce a mechanically strong pencil "lead."

63. (a) We expect Si and C atoms to alternate in the structure, as shown at the right. The C atoms are on the corners ($8 \times 1/8 = 1$ C atom) and on the faces ($6 \times 1/2 = 3$ C atoms), a total of four C atoms/unit cell. The Si atoms are each totally within the cell, a total of four Si atoms/unit cell.

(M)

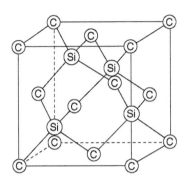

(b) To have a graphite structure, we expect sp^2 hybridization for each atom. The hybridization schemes for B and N atoms are shown to the right. The half-filled sp^2 hybrid orbitals of the boron and nitrogen atoms overlap to form the σ bonding structure, and a hexagonal array of atoms. The $2p_z$ orbitals then overlap to form the π bonding orbitals. Thus, there will be as many π electrons in a sample of BN as there are in a sample of graphite, assuming both samples have the same number of atoms.

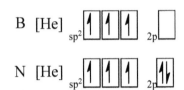

64. (M) Buckminsterfullerene is composed of C_{60} spheres. These molecules of carbon are rather like the N_2, P_4, and S_8 molecules in that they produce a nonpolar molecular solid. The chain of alternating single and triple bonds could be a network covalent solid, and hence another allotrope of carbon. The long carbon chain would be linear and these rods of carbon ($-C \equiv C - C \equiv C - C \equiv C - C \equiv C - C \equiv C - C \equiv C -$) could fit together rather like spaghetti in a box, with the π electrons of the triple bonds from adjacent rods attracting each other.

Ionic Bonding and Properties

65. (E) We expect forces in ionic compounds to increase as the sizes of ions become smaller and as ionic charges become greater. As the forces between ions become stronger, a higher temperature is required to melt the crystal. In the series of compounds NaF, NaCl, NaBr, and NaI, the anions are progressively larger, and thus the ionic forces become weaker. We expect the melting points to decrease in this series from NaF to NaI. This is precisely what is observed.

66. (M) Coulomb's law (Appendix B) states that the force between two particles of charges Q_1 and Q_2 that are separated by a distance r is given by $F = Q_1 Q_2 / 4\pi\varepsilon r^2$ where ε, the dielectric constant, equals 1 in a vacuum. Since we are comparing forces, we can use $+1, -1, +2$, and -2 for the charges on ions. The length r is equal to the sum of the cation and anion radii, which are taken from Figure 12-36.

For NaCl, $r_+ = 99$ pm, $r_- = 181$ pm $\quad F = (+1)(-1)/(99+181)^2 = -1.3 \times 10^{-5}$

For MgO, $r_+ = 72$ pm, $r_- = 140$ pm $\quad F = (+2)(-2)/(72+140)^2 = -8.9 \times 10^{-5}$

Thus, it is clear that interionic forces are about seven times stronger in MgO than in NaCl.

67. **(E)** NaF will give the highest Mohs value, because hardness is a function of stronger bonds, which are also shorter, and are affected by charge and size of the anions and cations. NaF has the smallest anion, and is tied with NaCl for the smallest cation.

68. **(E)** MgO will have the higher Mohs constant, because the distance between Mg^{2+} and O^{2-} is the smallest (and hence the bond is strongest) because both the anion and cation are divalent.

Crystal Structures

69. **(M)** In each layer of a closest packing arrangement of spheres, there are six spheres surrounding and touching any given sphere. A second similar layer then is placed on top of this first layer so that its spheres fit into the indentations in the layer below. The two different closest packing arrangements arise from two different ways of placing the third layer on top of these two, with its spheres fitting into the indentations of the layer below. In one case, one can look down into these indentations and see a sphere of the bottom (first) layer. If these indentations are used, the closest packing arrangement *abab* results (hexagonal closest packing). In the other case, no first layer sphere is visible through the indentation; the closest packing arrangement *abcabc* results (cubic closest packing).

70. **(E)** Physical properties are determined by the type of bonding between atoms in a crystal or the types of interactions between ions or molecules in the crystal. Different types of interactions can produce the same geometrical relationships of unit cell components. In both Ar and CO_2, London forces hold the particles in the crystal. In NaCl, the forces are interionic attractions, while metallic bonds hold Cu atoms in their crystals. It is the type of force, not the geometric arrangement of the components, that largely determines the physical properties of the crystalline material.

71. **(M)**

(a) We naturally tend to look at crystal structures in right-left, up-down terms. If we do that here, we might be tempted to assign a unit cell as a square, with its corners at the centers of the light-colored squares. But the crystal does not "know" right and left or top and bottom. If we look at this crystal from the lower right corner, we see a unit cell that has its corners at the centers of dark-colored diamonds. These two types of unit cells are outlined at the top of the diagram below.

(b) The unit cell has one light-colored square fully inside it. It has four light-colored "circles" (which the computer doesn't draw as very round) on the edges, each shared with one other unit cell. So there are a total of $4 \times 1/2 = 2$ circles per unit cell. Also, the unit cell has four dark-colored diamonds, one at each corner, and each diamond is shared with four other unit cells, for a total of $4 \times 1/4 = 1$ diamond per unit cell.

(c) One example of an erroneous unit cell is the small square outlined near the center of the figure drawn in part (a). Notice that simply repeatedly translating this unit cell toward the right, so that its left edge sits where its right edge is now, will not generate the lattice.

72. **(M)** This question reduces to asking what percentage of the area of a square remains uncovered by a circle inscribed within it. First, calculate the area that is covered by the circles, and then subtract from 100% to determine the area that is uncovered. The diameter of the circle equals the side of the square. Since $\text{diameter} = 2 \times \text{radius}$, we have

$$\frac{\text{area of circle}}{\text{area of square}} = \frac{\pi r^2}{(2r)^2} = \frac{\pi}{4} = \frac{3.14159}{4} = 0.7854 \quad \text{or} \quad 78.54\% \text{ covered}$$

$100\% - 78.54\% = 21.46\%$ uncovered

73. **(M)** In Figure 12–45 we see that the body diagonal of a cube has a length of $\sqrt{3}l$, where l is the length of one edge of the cube. The length of this body diagonal also equals $4r$, where r is the radius of the atom in the structure. Hence $4r = \sqrt{3}l$ or $l = 4r \div \sqrt{3}$. Recall that the volume of a cube is l^3, and $\sqrt{3} = 1.732$.

$$\text{density} = \frac{\text{mass}}{\text{volume}} = \frac{\dfrac{2 \text{ W atoms}}{1 \text{ unit cell}} \times \dfrac{1 \text{ mol W}}{6.022 \times 10^{23} \text{ W atoms}} \times \dfrac{183.85 \text{ g W}}{1 \text{ mol W}}}{\left(\dfrac{4 \times 139 \text{ pm}}{1.732} \times \dfrac{1 \text{ m}}{10^{12} \text{ pm}} \times \dfrac{100 \text{ cm}}{1 \text{ m}} \right)^3} = 18.5 \text{ g}/\text{cm}^3$$

This compares well with a tabulated density of 19.25 g/cm^3.

74. **(M)** One atom lies entirely within the hcp unit cell and there are eight corner atoms, each of which are shared among eight unit cells. Thus, there are a total of two atoms per unit cell. The volume of the unit cell is given by the product of its height and the area of its base. The base is a parallelogram, which can be subdivided along its shorter diagonal into two triangles. The height of either triangle, equivalent to the perpendicular distance between the parallel sides of the parallelogram, is given by $320. \text{ pm} \times \sin(60°) = 277 \text{ pm}$.

$\text{area of base} = 2 \times \text{area of triangle} = 2 \times (1/2 \times \text{base} \times \text{height})$

$$= 277 \text{ pm} \times 320. \text{ pm} = 8.86 \times 10^4 \text{ pm}^2$$

$\text{volume of unit cell} = 8.86 \times 10^4 \text{ pm}^2 \times 520. \text{ pm} = 4.61 \times 10^7 \text{ pm}^3$

$$\text{density} = \frac{\text{mass}}{\text{volume}} = \frac{2 \text{ Mg atoms} \times \dfrac{1 \text{ mol Mg}}{6.022 \times 10^{23} \text{ Mg atoms}} \times \dfrac{24.305 \text{ g Mg}}{1 \text{ mol Mg}}}{4.61 \times 10^7 \text{ pm}^3 \times \left(\dfrac{1 \text{ m}}{10^{12} \text{ pm}} \times \dfrac{100 \text{ cm}}{1 \text{ m}} \right)^3} = 1.75 \text{ g/cm}^3$$

This is in reasonable agreement with the experimental value of 1.738 g/cm^3.

75. **(M)**

(a) 335 pm = 2 radii or 1 diameter. Hence Po diameter = 335 pm

(b) 1 Po unit cell = $(335 \text{ pm})^3 = 3.76 \times 10^7 \text{ pm}^3$ $(3.76 \times 10^{-23} \text{ cm}^3)$ per unit cell.

$$\text{density} = \frac{m}{V} = \frac{3.47 \times 10^{-22} \text{ g}}{3.76 \times 10^{-23} \text{ cm}^3} = 9.23 \text{ g cm}^{-3}$$

(c) $n = 1$, $d = 335$ pm and $\lambda = 1.785 \times 10^{-10}$ or 178.5 pm Solve for sin θ, then determine θ.

$$\sin \theta = \frac{n\lambda}{2d} = \frac{(1)(1.785 \times 10^{-10})}{2(335 \times 10^{-12})} = 0.266\underline{4} \text{ or } \theta = 15.4\underline{5}°$$

76. **(M)** Ge unit cell has a length of 565 pm. volume = (length)^3 = $(565 \text{ pm})^3 = 1.80 \times 10^8 \text{ pm}^3$

Next we convert to cm^3: $1.80 \times 10^8 \text{ pm}^3 \left(\frac{1 \times 10^{-12} \text{ m}}{1 \text{ pm}} \right)^3 \left(\frac{100 \text{ cm}}{1 \text{ m}} \right)^3 = 1.80\underline{4} \times 10^{-22} \text{ cm}^3$

Now we determine the number of Ge atoms per unit cell.
Method: Find number of atoms of Ge per cm^3, then using the unit cell volume (calculation above), determine number of Ge atoms in the unit cell.

$$\frac{\text{atoms Ge}}{\text{cm}^3} = \left(\frac{5.36 \text{ g Ge}}{\text{cm}^3} \right) \left(\frac{1 \text{ mol Ge}}{72.61 \text{ g Ge}} \right) \left(\frac{6.022 \times 10^{23}}{1 \text{ mol Ge}} \right) = 4.44\underline{5} \times 10^{22} \frac{\text{atoms Ge}}{\text{cm}^3}$$

$$\frac{\text{atoms Ge}}{\text{unit cell}} = (1.80\underline{4} \times 10^{-22} \text{ cm}^3) \left(4.445 \times 10^{22} \frac{\text{atoms Ge}}{\text{cm}^3} \right) = 8.02 \frac{\text{atoms Ge}}{\text{unit cell}}$$

There are 8 atoms of Ge per unit cell. Ge must adopt a face centered cubic structure with the 4 tetrahedral holes filled (diamond structure).

77. **(E)** There are 8 SiF_4 molecules with the Si atoms at each corner of the cube, and one molecule in the center. Therefore, there are 8 × 1/8 + 1 = 2 Si atoms per unit cell.

78. **(E)** 1.5 Ti atoms (4 × 1/8 + 1) and 3 O atoms (6 × 1/2) per unit cell

Ionic Crystal Structures

79. **(M)** CaF_2: There are eight Ca^{2+} ions on the corners, each shared among eight unit cells, for a total of one $(8 \times 1/8)$ corner ion per unit cell. There are six Ca^{2+} ions on the faces, each shared between two unit cells, for a total of three $(6 \times 1/2)$ face ions per unit cell. This gives a total of four Ca^{2+} ions per unit cell. There are eight F^- ions, each wholly contained within the unit cell. The ratio of Ca^{2+} ions to F^- ions is 4 Ca^{2+} ions per 8 F^- ions: Ca_4F_8 or CaF_2. TiO_2. There are eight Ti^{4+} ions on the corners, each shared among eight unit cells, for a total of one Ti^{4+} corner ion $(8 \times 1/8)$ per unit cell. There is one Ti^{4+} ion in the center, wholly contained within the unit cell. Thus, there are a total of two Ti^{4+} ions per unit cell. There are four O^{2-} ions on the faces of the unit cell, each shared between two unit cells, for a total of two $(4 \times 1/2)$ face atoms per unit cells. There are two O^{2-} ions totally contained within the unit cell. This gives a total of four O^{2-} ions per unit cell. The ratio of Ti^{4+} ions to O^{2-} ions is 2 Ti^{4+} ions per 4 O^{2-} ion: Ti_2O_4 or TiO_2.

80. **(M)** The unit cell of CsCl is pictured in Figure 12–49. The length of the body diagonal equals $2r_+ + 2r_-$. For Cl^-, $r_- = 181$ pm. Thus, the length of the body diagonal equals $2(169 \text{ pm} + 181 \text{ pm}) = 700.$ pm. From Figure 12–45, the length of this body diagonal is $\sqrt{3}l = 700.$ pm. The volume of the unit cell is $V = l^3$. ($\sqrt{3} = 1.732$).

$$V = \left(\frac{700. \text{ pm}}{1.732} \times \frac{1 \text{ m}}{10^{12} \text{ pm}} \times \frac{100 \text{ cm}}{1 \text{ m}} \right)^3 = 6.60 \times 10^{-23} \text{ cm}^3$$

Per unit cell, there is one Cs^+ and one Cl^- (8 corner ions $\times 1/8$ corner ion per unit cell).

$$\text{density} = \frac{\text{mass}}{\text{volume}} = \frac{\left(1 \text{ f.u. CsCl} \times \dfrac{1 \text{ mol CsCl}}{6.022 \times 10^{23} \text{CsCl f.u.'s}} \times \dfrac{168.4 \text{ g CsCl}}{1 \text{ mol CsCl}} \right)}{6.60 \times 10^{-23} \text{ cm}^3} = 4.24 \text{ g / cm}^3$$

<u>**81.**</u> **(D)**

    (a) In a sodium chloride type of lattice, there are six cations around each anion and six anions around each cation. These oppositely charged ions are arranged as follows: one above, one below, one in front, one in back, one to the right, and one to the left. Thus the coordination number of Mg^{2+} is 6 and that of O^{2-} is 6 also.

    (b) In the unit cell, there is an oxide ion at each of the eight corners; each of these is shared between eight unit cells. There also is an oxide ion at the center of each of the six faces; each of these oxide ions is shared between two unit cells. Thus, the total number of oxide ions is computed as follows.

$$\text{total \# of oxide ions} = 8 \text{ corners} \times \frac{1 \text{ oxide ion}}{8 \text{ unit cells}} + 6 \text{ faces} \times \frac{1 \text{ oxide ion}}{2 \text{ unit cells}} = 4 \text{ } O^{2-} \text{ ions}$$

There is a magnesium ion on each of the twelve edges; each of these is shared between four unit cells. There also is a magnesium ion in the center which is not shared with another unit cell.

$$\text{total \# of Mg}^{2+} \text{ ions} = 12 \text{ adjoining cells} \times \frac{1 \text{ magnesium ion}}{4 \text{ unit cells}} + 1 \text{ central Mg}^{2+} \text{ ion}$$

$$= 4 \text{ Mg}^{2+} \text{ ions (Thus, there are four formula units per unit cell of MgO.)}$$

    (c) Along the edge of the unit cell, Mg^{2+} and O^{2-} ions are in contact. The length of the edge is equal to the radius of one O^{2-}, plus the diameter of Mg^{2+}, plus the radius of another O^{2-}.

edge length $= 2 \times O^{2-}$ radius $+ 2 \times Mg^{2+}$ radius $= 2 \times 140$ pm $+ 2 \times 72$ pm $= 424$ pm

The unit cell is a cube; its volume is the cube of its length.

$$\text{volume} = (424 \text{ pm})^3 = 7.62 \times 10^7 \text{ pm} \left(\frac{1 \text{ m}}{10^{12} \text{ pm}} \times \frac{100 \text{ cm}}{1 \text{ m}} \right)^3 = 7.62 \times 10^{-23} \text{ cm}^3$$

    (d) $\quad \text{density} = \dfrac{\text{mass}}{\text{volume}} = \dfrac{4 \text{ MgO f.u.}}{7.62 \times 10^{-23} \text{ cm}^3} \times \dfrac{1 \text{ mol MgO}}{6.022 \times 10^{23} \text{ f.u.}} \times \dfrac{40.30 \text{ g MgO}}{1 \text{ mol MgO}} = 3.51 \text{ g/cm}^3$

Thus, there are four formula units (f.u.) per unit cell of MgO.

82. **(M)** According to Figure 12-48, there are four formula units of KCl in a unit cell and the length of the edge of that unit cell is twice the internuclear distance between K^+ and Cl^- ions. The unit cell is a cube; its volume is the cube of its length.

length $= 2 \times 314.54$ pm $= 629.08$ pm

$$\text{volume} = (629.08 \text{ pm})^3 = 2.4895 \times 10^8 \text{ pm}^3 \left(\frac{1 \text{ m}}{10^{12} \text{ pm}} \times \frac{100 \text{ cm}}{1 \text{ m}} \right)^3 = 2.4895 \times 10^{-22} \text{ cm}^3$$

unit cell mass $=$ volume $\times$ density $= 2.4895 \times 10^{-22} \text{ cm}^3 \times 1.9893 \text{ g/cm}^3 = 4.9524 \times 10^{-22}$ g

$=$ mass of 4 KCl formula units

$$N_A = \frac{4 \text{ KCl formula unit}}{4.9524 \times 10^{-22} \text{ g KCl}} \times \frac{74.5513 \text{ g KCl}}{1 \text{ mol KCl}} = 6.0214 \times 10^{23} \text{ formula unit/mol}$$

83. **(M)**

(a) CaO $\rightarrow$ radius ratio $= \dfrac{r_{Ca^{2+}}}{r_{O^{2-}}} = \dfrac{100 \text{ pm}}{140 \text{ pm}} = 0.714$

Cations occupy octahedral holes of a face centered cubic array of anions.

(b) CuCl $\rightarrow$ radius ratio $= \dfrac{r_{Cu^+}}{r_{Cl^-}} = \dfrac{96 \text{ pm}}{181 \text{ pm}} = 0.530$

Cations occupy octahedral holes of a face centered cubic array of anions.

(c) LiO$_2$ $\rightarrow$ radius ratio $= \dfrac{r_{Li^+}}{r_{O_2^-}} = \dfrac{59 \text{ pm}}{128 \text{ pm}} = 0.461$

Cations occupy octahedral holes of a face centered cubic array of anions.

84. **(M)** BaO $\rightarrow$ radius ratio $= \dfrac{r_{Ba^{2+}}}{r_{O^{2-}}} = \dfrac{135 \text{ pm}}{140 \text{ pm}} = 0.964$

Cations occupy cubic hole of a simple cubic array of anions.

CuI $\rightarrow$ radius ratio $= \dfrac{r_{Cu^+}}{r_{I^-}} = \dfrac{96 \text{ pm}}{220 \text{ pm}} = 0.436$

Cations occupy octahedral holes of a face centered cubic array of anions.

LiS$_2$ $\rightarrow$ radius ratio $= \dfrac{r_{Li^+}}{r_{S_2^-}} = \dfrac{59 \text{ pm}}{198 \text{ pm}} = 0.298$

Cations occupy tetrahedral holes of a face centered cubic array of anions.

Lattice Energy

85. **(E)** Lattice energies of a series such as LiCl(s), NaCl(s), KCl(s), RbCl(s), and CsCl(s) will vary approximately with the size of the cation. A smaller cation will produce a more exothermic lattice energy. Thus, the lattice energy for LiCl(s) should be the most exothermic and CsCl(s) the least in this series, with NaCl(s) falling in the middle of the series.

86. **(D)** The cycle of reactions is shown. Recall that Hess's law (a state function), states that the enthalpy change is the same, whether a chemical change is produced by one reaction or several.

Formation reaction:	$K(s) + \frac{1}{2} F_2(g) \rightarrow KF(s)$	$\Delta_f H° = -567.3$ kJ/mol
Sublimation:	$K(s) \rightarrow K(g)$	$\Delta_{sub} H = 89.24$ kJ/mol
Ionization:	$K(s) \rightarrow K^+(g) + e^-$	$E_i = 418.9$ kJ/mol
Dissociation:	$\frac{1}{2} F_2(g) \rightarrow F(g)$	D.E. $= (159/2)$ kJ / mol F
Electron affinity:	$F(g) + e^- \rightarrow F^-(g)$	$E_{ea} = -328$ kJ/mol

$\Delta_f H° = \Delta_{sub} H + E_i + \text{D.E.} + E_{ea} + \text{lattice energy (L.E.)}$

-567.3 kJ/mol $= 89.24$ kJ/mol $+ 418.9$ kJ/mol $+ (159/2)$ kJ/mol $- 328$ kJ/mol $+$ L.E.

L.E. $= -827$ kJ/mol

87. **(D)**

Second ionization energy:	$Mg^+(g) \rightarrow Mg^{2+}(g) + e^-$	$E_{i,2} = 1451$ kJ/mol
Lattice energy:	$Mg^{2+}(g) + 2\,Cl^-(g) \rightarrow MgCl_2(s)$	L.E. $= -2526$ kJ / mol
Sublimation:	$Mg(s) \rightarrow Mg(g)$	$\Delta_{sub} H = 146$ kJ/mol
First ionization energy	$Mg(g) \rightarrow Mg^+(g) + e^-$	$E_{i,1} = 738$ kJ/mol
Dissociation energy:	$Cl_2(g) \rightarrow 2\,Cl(g)$	D.E. $= (2 \times 122)$ kJ/mol
Electron affinity:	$2\,Cl(g) + 2\,e^- \rightarrow 2\,Cl^-(g)$	$2 \times E_{ea} = 2(-349)$ kJ/mol

$\Delta_f H° = \Delta_{sub} H + E_{i,1} + E_{i,2} + \text{D.E.} + (2 \times E_{ea}) + \text{L.E.}$

$= 146 \dfrac{\text{kJ}}{\text{mol}} + 738 \dfrac{\text{kJ}}{\text{mol}} + 1451 \dfrac{\text{kJ}}{\text{mol}} 1 + 244 \dfrac{\text{kJ}}{\text{mol}} - 698 \dfrac{\text{kJ}}{\text{mol}} - 2526 \dfrac{\text{kJ}}{\text{mol}} = -645 \dfrac{\text{kJ}}{\text{mol}}$

In Example 12-12, the value of $\Delta_f H°$ for MgCl is calculated as -19 kJ/mol. Therefore, $MgCl_2$ is much more stable than MgCl, since considerably more energy is released when it forms. $MgCl_2(s)$ is more stable than MgCl(s)

88. **(D)**

Formation reaction:	$Na(s) + \frac{1}{2} H_2(g) \rightarrow NaH(s)$	$\Delta_f H° = -57$ kJ/mol
Heat of sublimation:	$Na(s) \rightarrow Na(g)$	$\Delta_{sub} H = +107$ kJ/mol
Ionization energy:	$Na(g) \rightarrow Na^+(g) + e^-$	$E_{i,1} = +496$ kJ/mol
Dissociation energy:	$\frac{1}{2} H_2(g) \rightarrow H(g)$	D.E. $= +218$ kJ/mol H

Electron affinity: $H(g) + e^- \rightarrow H^-(g)$ $E_{ea} = ?$

Lattice energy: $Na^+(g) + H^-(g) \rightarrow NaH(s)$ L.E. $= -812\,kJ/mol$

$\Delta_f H° = \Delta_{sub} H + E_{i,1} + D.E. + E_{ea} + \text{lattice energy (L.E.)}$

$-57\,kJ/mol = 107\,kJ/mol + 496\,kJ/mol + E_{ea} + 218\,kJ/mol - 812\,kJ/mol$

$E_{ea} = -66\,kJ/mol$ (compares favorably to the literature value of $-72.8\,kJ$)

INTEGRATIVE AND ADVANCED EXERCISES

89. **(E)** The heat of the flame melts the solid wax, converting it to a liquid. Still closer to the flame the temperature is higher, and the liquid wax vaporizes to the gaseous hydrocarbons, which are then burned. The liquid wax is drawn up the wick toward the flame by capillary action, where it is vaporized and burns, producing the heat needed to melt the solid wax, and the process continues until all the wax is burned.

90. **(M)** We know that 1.00 atm = 101,325 Pa and 1 Bar = 100,000 Pa. The enthalpy of vaporization is given as 40,657 J/mol in the chapter. These numbers are substituted into the Clapeyron equation.

$$\ln\frac{101,325\,Pa}{100,000\,Pa} = \frac{40,657\,J\,mol^{-1}}{8.3145\,J\,mol^{-1}\,K^{-1}}\left(\frac{1}{T} - \frac{1}{373.15}\right)$$

$T = 372.78\,K$

91. **(M)** In many instances, with CO_2 being one, the substance in the tank is not present as a gas only, but as a liquid in equilibrium with its vapor. As gas is released from the tank, the liquid will vaporize to replace it, maintaining a pressure in the tank equal to the vapor pressure of the substance at the temperature at which the cylinder is stored. This will continue until all of the liquid vaporizes, after which only gas will be present. The remaining gas will be quickly consumed, and hence the reason for the warning. However, the situation of gas in equilibrium with liquid only applies to substances that have a critical temperature above room temperature (20 °C or 293 K). Thus, substances in Table 12.6 for which gas pressure does serve as a measure of the quantity of gas in the tank are H_2 ($T_c = 33.3$ K), N_2 ($T_c = 126.2$ K), O_2 ($T_c = 154.8$ K), and CH_4 ($T_c = 191.1$ K).

92. **(D)** $m = 15.0$ g Hg(s) or $n = 0.0748$ mol Hg(s) 24.3 J K^{-1}mol^{-1} Hg(l) 28.0 J K^{-1} mol^{-1} (Hg melting point $= -38.87$ °C and $\Delta_{fusion}H = 2.33$ kJ mol^{-1})

Here we need to calculate (using Appendix D), $\Delta_{vap}H$ at 25 °C. That is: $Hg(l) \rightarrow Hg(g)$ at 25 °C. Simply use $\Delta_f H°$ values from Appendix D. $\Delta_{vap}H = \Delta_f H°\ Hg(g) - \Delta_f H°Hg(l)$
$\Delta_{vap}H = 61.32$ kJ/mol $- 0$ kJ/mol $= 61.32$ kJ/mol.
Next we calculate each of the four quantities shown in the schematic.
$nC_{solid}\Delta T + \Delta = 0.0748$ mol$(24.3$ J K^{-1}mol$^{-1})(-38.87$ °C $- -50.0$ °C$)(1$ kJ/1000J$) = 0.0202\underline{3}$ kJ
$n\Delta_{fus}H = 0.0748$ mol$(2.33$ kJ mol$^{-1}) = 0.174$ kJ
$nC_{liquid}\Delta T = 0.0748$ mol$(28.0$ J K^{-1} mol$^{-1})(25.0$ °C $- -38.87$ °C$)(1$ kJ/1000J$) = 0.134$ kJ
$n\Delta_{vap}H = 0.0748$ mol$(61.32$ kJ/mol$) = 4.58\underline{7}$ kJ
$q = nC_{solid}\Delta T + n\Delta_{fus}H + nC_{solid}\Delta T + n\Delta_{vap}H = 0.020.2\underline{3}$ kJ $+ 0.174$ kJ $+ 0.134$ kJ $+ 4.58\underline{7}$ kJ
$q = 4.91\underline{5}$ kJ

93. (M) For this question we need to determine the quantity of heat required to vaporize 1.000 g H_2O at each temperature. At 20 °C, 2447 J of heat is needed to vaporize each 1.000 g H_2O. At 100 °C., the quantity of heat needed is

$$\frac{10.00 \quad kJ}{4.430 \quad g \ H_2O} \times \frac{1000 \quad J}{1 \quad kJ} = 2257 \quad J/g \ H_2O$$

Thus, less heat is needed to vaporize 1.000 g of H_2O at the higher temperature of 100 °C. This makes sense, for at the higher temperature the molecules of the liquid already are in rapid motion. Some of this energy of motion or vibration will contribute to the energy needed to break the cohesive forces and vaporize the molecules.

94. (M) 1.00 g of Car Kooler (10 % C_2H_5OH) is used to cool 55 °C air which has a heat capacity of 29 J K^{-1}mol^{-1}. Hence, 0.100 g C_2H_5OH is evaporated, (with $\Delta_{vap}H = 42.6$ kJ.mol^{-1}) and 0.900 g of H_2O (with $\Delta_{vap}H = 44.0$ kJ.mol^{-1}), is also evaporated.
Energy required to evaporate

$$0.100\,g\,C_2H_5OH \times \frac{1\,mol\,C_2H_5OH}{46.068\,g\,C_2H_5OH} \times \frac{42.6\,kJ}{1\,mol\,C_2H_5OH} = 0.092\underline{5}\,kJ$$

Energy required to evaporate the water $0.900\,g\,H_2O \times \dfrac{1\,mol\,H_2O}{18.015\,g\,H_2O} \times \dfrac{44.0\,kJ}{1\,mol\,H_2O} = 2.20\,kJ$

Thus, most of the energy($> 95\%$), absorbed by Car Kooler goes toward the evaporation of water. In fact, if one were to replace the C_2H_5OH with water, it would be even more effective.

95. (M) In this case, we use the Clausius-Clapeyron equation to determine the sublimation pressure at 25 °C. We also need the enthalpy of sublimation and the sublimation pressure at another temperature. We can closely estimate the sublimation pressure at the triple point with the following three step process. First, assume that the triple point temperature and the melting point temperature are the same (53.1 °C or 326.3 K). Second, realize that the vapor pressure and the sublimation pressure are the same at the triple point. Third, use the Clausius-Clapeyron equation to determine the vapor pressure at the triple point.

$$\ln\frac{P}{10.0\,mmHg} = \frac{72,220\,J\,mol^{-1}}{8.3145\,J\,K^{-1}\,mol^{-1}}\left(\frac{1}{328.0\,K} - \frac{1}{326.3\,K}\right) = -0.138 \quad P = 10.0e^{-0.138} = 8.71\,mmHg$$

$\Delta_{sub}H$ is determined by: $\Delta_{sub}H = \Delta_{fus}H + \Delta_{vap}H = 17.88$ kJ mol^{-1} + 72.22 kJ mol^{-1} = 90.10 kJ mol^{-1}

Use the Clausius-Clapeyron equation to determine the sublimation pressure at 25 °C.

$$\ln \frac{P}{8.71 \text{ mmHg}} = \frac{90{,}100 \text{ J mol}^{-1}}{8.3145 \text{ J K}^{-1}\text{ mol}^{-1}}\left(\frac{1}{326.3 \text{ K}} - \frac{1}{298.0 \text{ K}}\right) = -3.15 \quad P = 8.71 e^{-3.15} = 0.37 \text{ mmHg}$$

96. **(E)** If only gas were present, the final pressure would be 10 atm. This is far in excess of the vapor pressure of water at 30.0 °C (~ 0.042 atm). Most of the water vapor condenses to liquid water. (It cannot all be liquid, because the liquid volume is only about 20 mL and the system volume is 2.61 L.) The final condition is a point on the vapor pressure curve at 30.0 °C.

97. **(M)** At the triple point, the sublimation pressure equals the vapor pressure. We need to also realize that Celsius temperature, t, is related to Kelvin temperature, T, by $t = T - 273.15$. Thus,

$$9.846 - 2309/T = 6.90565 - 1211.033/(220.790 + t) = 6.90565 - 1211.033/(220.790 + T - 273.15)$$
$$= 6.90565 - 1211.033/(T - 52.36)$$

$$9.846 - 6.90565 = 2.940 = \frac{2309}{T} - \frac{1211.033}{T - 52.36} = \frac{2309\,(T - 52.36) - 1211.033\,T}{T(T - 52.36)}$$

$$2.940T(T - 52.36) = 2.940T^2 - 153.9T = 2309T - 1.209 \times 10^5 - 1211.033T = 1098T - 1.209 \times 10^5$$

$$2.940T^2 - 153.9T - 1098T + 1.209 \times 10^5 = 0 = 2.940T^2 - 1252T + 1.209 \times 10^5$$

The quadratic formula is used to solve this equation.

$$T = \frac{-b \pm \sqrt{b^2 - 4\,a\,c}}{2a} = \frac{1252 \pm \sqrt{(1252)^2 - (4 \times 2.940 \times 1.209 \times 10^5)}}{2 \times 2.940}$$

$$T = 212.9 \pm 64.9 = 277.8 \text{ K} \quad \text{or} \quad 148.0 \text{ K} \qquad \therefore \ T = 4.6 \,°\text{C} \quad \text{or} \quad -125.2 \,°\text{C}$$

The acceptable result from the quadratic equation is 4.6 °C; below this temperature liquid benzene can only exist as a metastable supercooled liquid, not as a stable liquid and thus –125.2 °C is not a reasonable value. The calculated value, 4.6 °C, compares favorably to the listed value of 5.5 °C.

98. **(D)** First, we need to calculate ln P and $1/T$ for the given data points.

t, °C	76.6	128.0	166.7	197.3	251.0
P, mmHg	1	10	40	100	400
T, K	349.8	401.2	439.9	470.5	524.2
$1/T \times 10^3$ K^{-1}	2.859	2.493	2.273	2.125	1.908
Ln P	0	2.303	3.689	4.605	5.991

NOTE: Graphs are given on the following page

(a) The normal boiling point of phosphorus occurs at a pressure of 760 mmHg, where ln P = 6.63. Based on the graph below (left), this occurs when $1/T = 1.81 \times 10^{-3}$ K^{-1}, or $T = 552$ K, 279 °C.

(b) When $\ln P$ is plotted vs $1/T$, (see below), the slope of the line equals $-\Delta_{vap}H/R$. For the graph on the left, the slope (by linear regression) is -6.30×10^3 K. Thus, $\Delta_{vap}H = 6.30 \times 10^3$ K $\times 8.3145$ J mol^{-1} K^{-1} $= 5.24 \times 10^4$ J/mol.

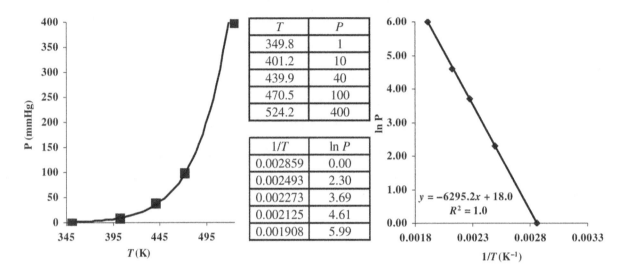

T	P
349.8	1
401.2	10
439.9	40
470.5	100
524.2	400

$1/T$	$\ln P$
0.002859	0.00
0.002493	2.30
0.002273	3.69
0.002125	4.61
0.001908	5.99

$y = -6295.2x + 18.0$
$R^2 = 1.0$

99. (M)

(a) $\text{pressure} = \dfrac{\text{force}}{\text{area}} = \dfrac{80.\ \text{kg} \times 9.8067\ \text{m s}^{-2}}{2.5\ \text{cm}^2 \times \dfrac{1\ \text{m}^2}{10^4\ \text{cm}^2}} \times \dfrac{1\ \text{N}}{1\ \text{kg m s}^{-2}} \times \dfrac{1\ \text{atm}}{101325\ \text{N m}^{-2}} = 31\ \text{atm}$

(b) $\text{decrease in melting point} = 31\ \text{atm} \times \dfrac{1.0\ °\text{C}}{125\ \text{atm}} = 0.25\ °\text{C}$

The ice under the skates will melt at $-0.25\ °\text{C}$.

100. (M) $P = P_0 \times 10^{-Mgh/2.303RT}$ Assume ambient temperature is $10.0\ °\text{C} = 283.2\ \text{K}$

$\dfrac{Mgh}{2.303\ RT} = \dfrac{0.02896\ \text{kg/mol air} \times 9.8067\ \text{m/s}^2 \times 3170\ \text{m}}{2.303 \times 8.3145\ \text{Jmol}^{-1}\text{K}^{-1} \times 283.2\ \text{K}} = 0.166$

$P = P_0 \times 10^{-0.166} = 1\ \text{atm} \times 0.682 = 0.682\ \text{atm} = \text{atmospheric pressure in Leadville, CO.}$

$\ln \dfrac{0.682\ \text{atm}}{1.000\ \text{atm}} = \dfrac{-41 \times 10^3\ \text{J/mol}}{8.3145\ \text{J mol}^{-1}\ \text{K}^{-1}} \left(\dfrac{1}{T} - \dfrac{1}{373.2\ \text{K}} \right) = -0.383$

$\left(\dfrac{1}{T} - \dfrac{1}{373.2\ \text{K}} \right) = -0.383 \times \dfrac{8.3145}{-41 \times 10^3} = +7.8 \times 10^{-5}\ \text{K}^{-1}$

$\dfrac{1}{T} = +7.77 \times 10^{-5}\ \text{K}^{-1} + 2.68 \times 10^{-3}\ \text{K}^{-1} = 2.76 \times 10^{-3}\ \text{K}^{-1}$ $T = 360\ \text{K} = 87\ °\text{C}$

101. (M) From the graphs in Figure 12-20, choose two points for benzene and two points for water. Set $\ln P_{benzene} = \ln P_{water}$ Hence: $-4.10 \times 10^3 (1/T) + 18.3 = -5.35 \times 10^3 (1/T) + 21.0$

Compound	ln P	1/T (K⁻¹)	Equation of Line
Benzene	5.99	0.00300	$\ln P_{benzene} = -4.10 \times 10^3 (1/T) + 18.3$
	4.35	0.00340	
Water	6.55	0.00270	$\ln P_{water} = -5.35 \times 10^3 (1/T) + 21.0$
	4.41	0.00310	

$1250(1/T) = 2.7 \ (1/T) = 0.00216$ or $T = 463$ K.

We can calculate the pressures for both benzene and water using this temperature.

Note: If the pressures for both benzene and water are close, this will serve as a double check.

$\ln P_{benzene} = -4.10 \times 10^3 (1/T) + 18.3 = -4.10 \times 10^3 (0.00216) + 18.3 = 9.44\underline{4}$

$\ln P_{water} = -5.35 \times 10^3 (1/T) + 21.0 = -5.35 \times 10^3 (0.00216) + 21.0 = 9.44\underline{4}$

$\ln P = 9.44\underline{4}$, hence $p = e^{9.444} = 126\underline{32}$ mmHg or 16.6 atm.

102. (M) We first compute the volume of the cylinder, and then the mass of Cl_2 present as vapor.

$$V = \pi r^2 h = 3.1416 \times (5.0 \text{ in.})^2 \times 45 \text{ in.} \left(\frac{2.54 \text{ cm}}{1 \text{ in.}} \right)^3 = 5.8 \times 10^4 \text{cm}^3 = 58 \text{ L}$$

$$\text{amount } Cl_2 = \frac{PV}{RT} = \frac{100. \text{ psi} \times \frac{1 \text{ atm}}{14.7 \text{ psi}} \times 58 \text{ L}}{0.08206 \text{ L atm mol}^{-1} \text{ K}^{-1} \times 293 \text{ K}} = 16 \text{ mol } Cl_2$$

$$\text{mass } Cl_2 = 16 \text{ mol } Cl_2 \times \frac{70.9 \text{ g } Cl_2}{1 \text{ mol } Cl_2} \times \frac{1 \text{ lb}}{453.6 \text{ g}} = 2.5 \text{ lb } Cl_2(g)$$

Thus, the mass of gas does not account for all of the 151 lb of chlorine in the cylinder. Since 20 °C is below the critical temperature of Cl_2, liquid chlorine can exist, provided that the pressure is high enough. That is the case in this instance. Both liquid and gaseous chlorine are present in the cylinder. There is almost certainly no solid present; 20 °C is too far above chlorine's melting point of −103 °C for any reasonable pressure to produce the solid.

<u>103.</u> (M) The molar mass of acetic acid monomer is 60.05 g/mol. We first determine the volume occupied by 1 mole of molecules of the vapor, assuming that the vapor consists only of monomer molecules: CH_3COOH.

$$\text{volume of vapor} = 60.05 \text{ g} \times \frac{1 \text{ L}}{3.23 \text{ g}} = 18.6 \text{ L}$$

Next, we can determine the actual number of moles of vapor in 18.6 L at 350 K.

$$\text{moles of vapor} = \frac{PV}{RT} = \frac{1 \text{ atm} \times 18.6 \text{ L}}{0.08206 \text{ L atm mol}^{-1} \text{ K}^{-1} \times 350 \text{ K}} = 0.648 \text{ mol vapor}$$

Then, we can determine the number of moles of dimer and monomer, starting with 1.00 mole of monomer, and producing a final mixture of 0.648 moles total (monomer and dimer together).

Reaction:	2 $CH_3COOH(g) \longrightarrow (CH_3COOH)_2 (g)$	
Initial:	1.00 mol	0
Changes:	$-2x$ mol	$+x$ mol
Final:	$(1.00 - 2x)$ mol	x mol

The line labeled "Changes" indicates that 2 moles of monomer are needed to form each mole of dimer. The line labeled "Final" results from adding the "Initial" and "Changes" lines.

total number of moles $= 1.00 - 2x + x = 1.00 - x = 0.648$ mol

$x = 0.352$ mol dimer $\qquad\qquad (1.00 - 2x) = 0.296$ mol monomer

$\% \text{ dimer} = \dfrac{0.352 \text{ mol dimer}}{0.648 \text{ mol total}} \times 100\% = 54.3\% \text{ dimer}$

We would expect the % dimer to decrease with temperature. Higher temperatures will provide the energy (as translational energy (heat)) needed to break the relatively weak hydrogen bonds that hold the dimers together.

104. **(M)** First we compute the mass and the amount of mercury.

$\text{mass Hg} = 685 \text{ mL} \times \dfrac{13.6 \text{ g}}{1 \text{ mL}} = 9.32 \times 10^3 \text{ g} \qquad n_{Hg} = 9.32 \times 10^3 \text{ g} \times \dfrac{1 \text{ mol Hg}}{200.59 \text{ g}} = 46.5 \text{ mol Hg}$

Then we calculate the heat given up by the mercury in lowering its temperature, as the sum of the following three terms.

cool liquid $= 9.32 \times 10^3 \text{ g} \times 0.138 \text{ J g}^{-1}\text{°C}^{-1} \times (-39 \text{ °C} - 20 \text{ °C}) = -7.6 \times 10^4 \text{ J} = -76 \text{ kJ}$

freeze liquid $= 46.5 \text{ mol Hg} \times (-2.30 \text{ kJ/mol}) = -107 \text{ kJ}$

cool solid $= 9.32 \times 10^3 \text{g} \times 0.126 \text{ J g}^{-1} \text{ °C}^{-1} \times (-196 + 39) \text{ °C} = -1.84 \times 10^5 \text{ J} = -184 \text{ kJ}$

total heat lost by Hg $= -76 \text{ kJ} - 107 \text{ kJ} - 184 \text{ kJ} = -367 \text{kJ} = -\text{heat gained by N}_2$

$\text{mass of N}_2(l) \text{ vaporized} = 367 \text{ kJ} \times \dfrac{1 \text{mol N}_2}{5.58 \text{ kJ}} \times \dfrac{28.0 \text{g N}_2}{1 \text{ mol N}_2} = 1.84 \times 10^3 \text{ g N}_2(l) = 1.84 \text{ kg N}_2$

105. **(M)** In the phase diagram on the left, the liquid-vapor curve dips down and then rises. This means that there can be a situation where raising the temperature will cause the vapor to condense to liquid – this is counterintuitive and does not correspond to the laws of thermodynamics as they operate in our universe. Also, a negative slope for the vapor pressure curve would correspond to a negative value of $\Delta_{vap}H$, but this quantity must always have a positive sign (vaporization is an endothermic process). In the diagram on the right, the liquid-vapor line has the same curvature as the solid–vapor line. This means that the heat of vaporization is the same as the heat of sublimation. This would mean that the heat of fusion is zero. Therefore no energy is needed to melt the solid, which is again counterintuitive and a physical impossibility.

106. (M) The normal boiling point is that temperature at which the vapor pressure is 760 mmHg. We have been provided with the following expression to solve for T, the normal boiling point.

$\text{Log}_{10}(760) = 2.88081 = 9.95028 - 0.003863T - 1473.17(T^{-1})$
$0 = 7.06947 - 0.003863T - 1473.17(T^{-1})$ Multiply through by T to get
$0 = 7.06947T - 0.003863T^2 - 1473.17$

By solving the quadratic equation, we get the roots 239.8 K or 1590 K. The second of these temperatures makes no physical sense, since we know that NH_3 is a gas at room temperature. Thus the normal boiling point of $NH_3(l)$ is 239.8 K.

107. (D) We need to calculate five different times. They are shown below.
1. Heat the solid to its melting point $T_1 =$

$$1 \text{ mol Bi} \times \frac{0.028 \text{ kJ}}{\text{K mol}} \times (554.5 \text{ K} - 300 \text{ K}) \times \frac{1 \text{ min}}{1.00 \text{ kJ}} = 7.1 \text{ min}$$

2. Melt the solid $T_2 = 1 \text{ mol Bi} \times \dfrac{10.9 \text{ kJ}}{\text{K mol}} \times \dfrac{1 \text{ min}}{1.00 \text{ kJ}} = 10.9 \text{ min}$

3. Heat the liquid to its boiling point $T_3 =$

$$1 \text{ mol Bi} \times \frac{0.031 \text{ kJ}}{\text{K mol}} \times (1832 \text{ K} - 554.5 \text{ K}) \times \frac{1 \text{ min}}{1.00 \text{ kJ}} = 39.6 \text{ min}$$

4. Vaporize the liquid $\quad T_4 = 1 \text{ mol Bi} \times \dfrac{151.5 \text{ kJ}}{\text{K mol}} \times \dfrac{1 \text{ min}}{1.00 \text{ kJ}} = 151.5 \text{ min}$

5. Heat the gas to 2000 K $T_5 = 1 \text{ mol Bi} \times \dfrac{0.021 \text{ kJ}}{\text{K mol}} \times (2000 \text{ K} - 1832 \text{ K}) \times \dfrac{1 \text{ min}}{1.00 \text{ kJ}} = 3.5 \text{ min}$

A plot is shown below:

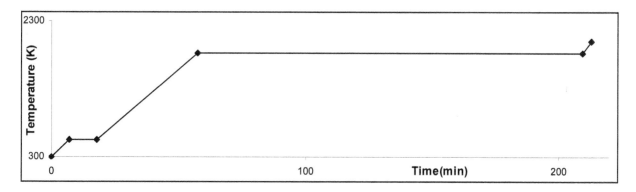

108. (M)
  (a) The coordination number for S^{2-} is 8, while for Li^+ it is 4 (tetrahedral holes).
  (b) $8 \times Li^+$ within the unit cell (tetrahedral holes) and $4 \times S^{2-}$ (8 corners $\times$ 1/8) + (6 faces $\times$ ½) = 1 + 3 = 4 formula units per unit cell.

(c) Note: $1 \text{ pm}^3 = \dfrac{\left(1 \times 10^{-12} \text{ m}\right)^3}{(1 \text{ pm})^3} \times \dfrac{(100 \text{ cm})^3}{(1 \text{ m})^3} = 1 \times 10^{-30} \text{ cm}^3$

$V = \ell^3 = (5.88 \times 10^2 \text{ pm})^3 \times \dfrac{1 \times 10^{-30} \text{ cm}^3}{1 \text{ pm}^3} = 2.03\underline{3} \times 10^{-22} \text{ cm}^3$

In a unit cell there are 4 Li_2S formula units.

($Li_2S \rightarrow 45.948 \text{ g mol}^{-1}$ or 4 mol $Li_2S \rightarrow 183.792$ g)

Consider one mole of unit cells. This contains 45.948 g of Li_2S and has a volume of

$(2.03 \times 10^{-22} \text{ cm}^3) \times (6.022 \times 10^{23}) = 122.\underline{4} \text{ cm}^3$

$\text{density} = \dfrac{\text{mass}}{\text{volume}} = \dfrac{183.792 \text{ g}}{122.4 \text{ cm}^3} = 1.50 \text{ g cm}^3$

109. (E) The edge length of the NaCl unit cell is 560 pm (from Example 12-11), and thus the distance between the top and the middle layers in the NaCl unit cell is 560 pm ÷ 2 = 280 pm. This is equal to the value of d in the Bragg equation (12.5). We first solve for $\sin \theta$ and then for θ.

$$\sin \theta = \frac{n\lambda}{2d} = \frac{1 \times 154.1 \text{ pm}}{2 \times 280 \text{ pm}} = 0.275 \qquad \theta = \sin^{-1}(0.275) = 16.0°$$

110. (M) In a bcc cell, there are two atoms per unit cell. The length of an edge of the unit cell is $4r \div \sqrt{3}$, where $\sqrt{3} = 1.732$. In a fcc cell, there are four particles per unit cell. The length of an edge of the unit cell is $4r \div \sqrt{2}$, where $\sqrt{2} = 1.414$. Now, the volume of a cube is $V = \ell^3$. Thus,

$$V_{bcc} = \left(\frac{4r}{1.732}\right)^3 = 12.32\, r^3 \qquad \text{and} \qquad V_{fcc} = \left(\frac{4r}{1.414}\right)^3 = 22.63\, r^3$$

The volume of an individual sphere is $\frac{4}{3}\pi r^3 = 4.189\, r^3$

Then the fraction, F, of occupied volume in each unit cell can be computed.

$$F_{bcc} = \frac{\text{volume of spheres}}{\text{volume of unit cell}} = \frac{2 \times 4.189\, r^3}{12.317\, r^3} = 0.6800 \text{ or } 68.00\% \text{ occupied, } 32.00\% \text{ void}$$

$$F_{fcc} = \frac{\text{volume of spheres}}{\text{volume of unit cell}} = \frac{4 \times 4.189\, r^3}{22.627\, r^3} = 0.7404 \text{ or } 74.04\% \text{ occupied, } 25.96\% \text{ void}$$

The volume of an individual sphere is $\frac{4}{3}\pi r^3 = 4.189\, r^3$.

Then the fraction, F, of occupied volume in each unit cell can be computed.

111. (D) Consider the two limits

CASE I (Square planar arrangement of anions around a cation)	CASE II (Tetrahedral arrangement of anions around a cation)
	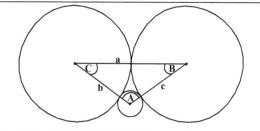
$a = 2(r_{anion})$ $b = c = r_{anion} + r_{cation}$ $A = 90°$ $a^2 = b^2 + c^2 = (2(r_{anion}))^2 = (r_{anion} + r_{cation})^2 + (r_{anion} + r_{cation})^2$ $(2(r_{anion}))^2 = 2(r_{anion} + r_{cation})^2$ (take root of both sides) $2(r_{anion}) = \sqrt{2}\,(r_{anion} + r_{cation})$ $2(r_{anion}) = \sqrt{2}\,r_{anion} + \sqrt{2}\,r_{cation}$ $2(r_{anion}) - \sqrt{2}\,r_{anion} = \sqrt{2}\,r_{cation}$ $(2 - \sqrt{2})r_{anion} = \sqrt{2}\,r_{cation}$ $\dfrac{r_{cation}}{r_{anion}} = \dfrac{2 - \sqrt{2}}{\sqrt{2}} = 0.414$	$a = 2(r_{anion})$ $b = c = r_{anion} + r_{cation}$ $A = 109.47°$ Use cosine law: $a^2 = b^2 + c^2 - 2bc(\cos A)$ & $\cos A = -1/3$ $2(r_{anion})^2 = (r_{anion} + r_{cation})^2 + (r_{anion} + r_{cation})^2 - 2((r_{anion} + r_{cation})^2)(-1/3)$ $(2(r_{anion}))^2 = 2(r_{anion} + r_{cation})^2 + (2/3)(r_{anion} + r_{cation})^2$ $(2(r_{anion}))^2 = (8/3)(r_{anion} + r_{cation})^2$ (take root of both sides) $2(r_{anion}) = \sqrt{8/3}\,(r_{anion} + r_{cation}) = \sqrt{8/3}\,r_{anion} + \sqrt{8/3}\,r_{cation}$ $2(r_{anion}) - \sqrt{8/3}\,r_{anion} = \sqrt{8/3}\,r_{cation} = (2 - \sqrt{8/3})r_{anion}$ $\dfrac{r_{cation}}{r_{anion}} = \dfrac{2 - \sqrt{8/3}}{\sqrt{8/3}} = 0.225$

112. (D) Diamond is a face centered cubic structure + ½ filled tetrahedral holes.
Therefore, in the unit cell there are $8 \times (1/8) + 6 \times (1/2) + 4 \times 1 = 8$ atoms.
Need to find the length of the edge of the unit cell to determine the volume.

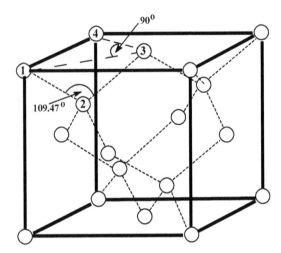

Structure of diamond is shown at the left. The carbon atoms of interest are numbered. Note that the tetrahedral angle (109.47°) around carbon 2 and right angle (90°) around carbon 3.

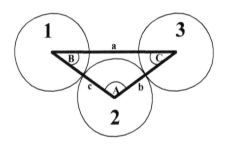

Close-up of carbons 1, 2 and 3.
angle A = 109.47°, c = b = 154.45 pm
Use cosine law: $a^2 = b^2 + c^2 - 2bc(\cos A)$ &
$\cos A = -1/3$
$a^2 = (154.45)^2 + (154.45)^2 - 2(154.45)^2(-1/3)$
$a^2 = 63,612.8$ pm². Take the square root of both sides a = 252.2 pm

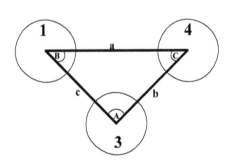

Close-up of carbons 1, 3 and 4.
angle A = 90.00°, c = b = 252.2 pm
$a^2 = b^2 + c^2 = (252.2 \text{ pm})^2 + (252.2 \text{ pm})^2$
$a^2 = 127,209.7$ pm². Take the square root of both sides a = 356.7 pm = ℓ (length of unit cell)

$V = \ell^3 = (356.7 \text{ pm})^3 = 4.538 \times 10^7 \text{ pm}^3$ (1 pm³ = 1 ×10⁻³⁰ cm³) $V = 4.538 \times 10^{-23} \text{ cm}^3$
Consider one mol of unit cells. This contains 8 moles of carbon atoms or 96.088 g.
The volume of one mole of unit cells = $4.538 \times 10^{-23} \text{ cm}^3 (6.022 \times 10^{23}) = 27.33 \text{ cm}^3$.

density = $\dfrac{\text{mass}}{\text{volume}} = \dfrac{96.088 \text{ g}}{27.33 \text{ cm}^3} = 3.516 \text{ g cm}^{-3}$ (literature value = 3.52 g cm⁻³)

113.

(D)

Sublimation of Na(s):	$Na(s) \longrightarrow Na(g)$	$\Delta_{vap}H = +107.3$ kJ mol^{-1} (Appendix D)
Ionization of Na(g):	$Na(g) \longrightarrow Na^+(g) + e^-$	$\Delta E_{i,1} = +495.8$ kJ mol^{-1}
$\frac{1}{2}$ Sublimation of I$_2$(s):	$\frac{1}{2} I_2(s) \longrightarrow \frac{1}{2} I_2(g)$	$\Delta_{sub}H = \frac{1}{2}\{\Delta_f H°[I_2(g)] - \Delta_f H°[I_2(s)]\}$
		$= 0.5 \times (62.44 - 0.00) = 31.22$ kJ mol^{-1}
$\frac{1}{2}$ Dissociation of I$_2$(g):	$\frac{1}{2} I_2(g) \longrightarrow I(g)$	$DE = \frac{1}{2} \times 151 = 75.5$ kJ mol^{-1}
I(g) electron affinity:	$I(g) + e^- \longrightarrow I^-(g)$	$E_{ea} = -295.2$ kJ mol^{-1} (Figure 10-11)
Lattice energy:	$Na^+(g) + I^-(g) \longrightarrow NaI(s)$	L.E.
Enthalpy of formation:	$Na(s) + \frac{1}{2} I_2(s) \longrightarrow NaI(s)$	$\Delta_f H° = -288$ kJ mol^{-1}

$$-288 \text{ kJ mol}^{-1} = (-107.3 + 495.8 + 31.22 + 75.5 - 295.2) \text{ kJ mol}^{-1} + \text{L.E.} = 415 \text{ kJ mol}^{-1} + \text{L.E.}$$

$$\text{L.E.} = (-288 - 415) \text{ kJ mol}^{-1} = -703 \text{ kJ mol}^{-1}$$

114.

(D)

Sublimation of Na(s):	$Na(s) \longrightarrow Na(g)$	$\Delta_{sub}H = +107.3$ kJ mol^{-1} (App. D)
First ionization of Na(g):	$Na(g) \longrightarrow Na^+(g) + e^-$	$E_{i,1} = +495.8$ kJ mol^{-1}
Second ionization of Na(g):	$Na^+(g) \longrightarrow Na^{2+}(g) + e^-$	$E_{i,2} = +4562$ kJ mol^{-1}
Dissociation of Cl$_2$(g):	$Cl_2(g) \longrightarrow 2 Cl(g)$	$D.E. = +243$ kJ mol^{-1}
Electron affinity of Cl(g):	$2 Cl(g) + 2 e^- \longrightarrow 2 Cl^-(g)$	$E_{ea} = -698$ kJ mol^{-1}
Lattice energy of NaCl(s):	$Na^{2+}(g) + 2 Cl^-(g) \longrightarrow NaCl_2(s)$	L.E. $= -2.5 \times 10^3$ kJ mol^{-1}
Enthalpy of formation:	$Na(s) + Cl_2(g) \longrightarrow NaCl_2(s)$	$\Delta_f H° = +2.2 \times 10^3$ kJ mol^{-1}

This highly endothermic process is quite unlikely. Thus NaCl$_2$ will not form under normal conditions.

115. (M) The Na$^+$ ions on the 6 faces are shared by 2 cells; the O^{2-} ions on the 8 corners are shared by 8 cells; the Cl$^-$ is unique to each cell. Thus, the formula is Na$_3$ClO. The coordination numbers of O^{2-} and Cl$^-$ are both 6. The shortest distance from the center of Na$^+$ to the center of O^{2-} is half the length of a face diagonal, which is $\sqrt{2} \times (a/2)$. The shortest distance from the center of a Cl$^-$ to the center of O^{2-} is half the length of a cell diagonal, namely, $\sqrt{3} \times (a/2)$.

116. (M) The two representations are shown below:

Corner position Ca $= 8 \times (1/8) = 1$
Face center O $= 6 \times (1/2) = 3$
Body center Ti $= 1 \times 1 = 1$

Formula is CaTiO$_3$

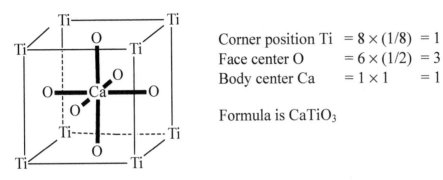

Corner position Ti $= 8 \times (1/8) = 1$
Face center O $= 6 \times (1/2) = 3$
Body center Ca $= 1 \times 1 \quad = 1$

Formula is $CaTiO_3$

Note: In each representation, there are six oxygen atoms around each Ti atom and Ca atom.

117. (M) From Chapter 10, Ca^{2+} radius = 100 pm, F^- radius = 133 pm.

$$\text{radius ratio} = \frac{r_{\text{cation}}}{r_{\text{anion}}} = \frac{100\,\text{pm}}{133\,\text{pm}} = 0.752$$

This is a fairly large value suggesting a structure in which the anions adopt a simple cubic structure so that the cations can be accommodated in the cubic holes. For CaF_2, the cations must occupy every other cubic hole so as to maintain the formula unit of CaF_2. Essentially CaF_2 has the CsCl structure, however every second cell has the cation missing.

118. (M)
(a) Three $(6 \times 1/2)$
(b) One $(8 \times 1/8)$
(c) One (1×1)
(d) Determine the volume of the unit cell and the mass of the atoms in each cell:

$$\text{volume} = \left(0.403 \times 0.398 \times 0.398\right)\text{nm}^3 \times \frac{1\,\text{cm}^3}{\left(10^7\,\text{nm}\right)^3} = 6.384 \times 10^{-23}\,\text{cm}^3$$

$$\text{mass of atoms} = \frac{1\,\text{mol}}{6.022 \times 10^{23}\,\text{atoms}} \left(\begin{array}{l} 3\,\text{O atoms} \times 16.0\,\text{g}\cdot\text{mol}^{-1} \\ + 1\,\text{Pb atom} \times 207.19\,\text{g}\cdot\text{mol}^{-1} \\ + 1\,\text{Ti atom} \times 47.88\,\text{g}\cdot\text{mol}^{-1} \end{array} \right) = 5.0327 \times 10^{-22}\,\text{g}$$

$$\text{density} = \frac{m}{V} = \frac{5.0327 \times 10^{-22}\,\text{g}}{6.384 \times 10^{-23}\,\text{cm}^3} = 7.87\,\text{g/cm}^3$$

119. (E)

(a) [Bmim][BF$_4$]   [Amim]Cl

(b) m.p.([Bmim][BF$_4$]) = −80 °C
m.p.(Amim]Cl = 49 − 51 °C

(c) To a first approximation, the melting point of an ionic compound depends on the charges and sizes of the cations and anions involved. As suggested by Figure 12-36, the smaller the charges and the larger the ions, the weaker the interaction, the lower the lattice enthalpy, and the lower the melting temperature. Another factor may be that the interactions among the ions have a larger contribution from van der Waals forces (because of the large size of the cations). Since van der Waals forces are typically much weaker than "pure" ionic interactions, the lattice enthalpy of an IL is further reduced.

120. (M) In reality, a nanocrystal has many faces. However, for simplicity, this problem assumes the nanocrystal is spherical. The volume of a 2 nm diameter nanocrystal is

$$V_{nc} = \frac{4}{3}\pi r^3 = \frac{4}{3}\pi \times \left(\frac{2\ nm}{2}\right)^3 = 4.189\ nm^3$$

Now, calculate the volume of the unit cell:

$$V_{uc} = a \times a \times a = \left(6.097 \times 10^{-1}\ nm\right)^3 = 0.2266\ nm^3/unit\ cell$$

Now determine how many unit cells fit into the nanocrystal:

$$\frac{V_{nc}}{V_{uc}} = \frac{4.189\ nm^3}{0.2266\ nm^3} = 18.48\ unit\ cell$$

Finally, determine the number of atoms: 20 atoms/unit cell × 18.46 unit cells = 369 atoms

121. Sample calculations are shown below for the H$_2$O—H$_2$O interaction.

$$E(dipole\text{-}dipole) = -\frac{1}{r^6} \cdot \frac{2\mu^4}{3k_5T} \cdot \frac{1}{(4\pi\varepsilon_0)^2}$$

$$= -\frac{1}{(4\times10^{-10}\ m)^6} \times \frac{2(1.8546\ D \times 3.33564\times10^{-30}\ C\ m\ D^{-1})^4}{3(1.3807\times10^{-23}\ JK^{-1})(298\ K)}$$

$$\times \frac{1}{(4\pi(8.854\times10^{-12}\ J^{-1}C^2m^{-1}))^2} - 4.86\times10^{-21}\ J$$

(a) To express this result in kJ mol^{-1}, we multiply by the Avogadro constant and divide by 1000:

$$E(\text{dipole-dipole}) = -4.68 \times 10^{-21} \text{ J} \times 6.022 \times 10^{23} \text{ mol}^{-1} \times \frac{\text{kJ}}{1000 \text{ J}} = -2.82 \text{ kJ mol}^{-1}$$

$$E(\text{dipole-induced dipole}) = -\frac{1}{r^6} \cdot 2\mu^2 a' \cdot \frac{1}{4\pi\varepsilon_0}$$

$$= -\frac{1}{(4.00 \times 10^{-10} \text{ m})^6} \times 2(1.8546 \text{ D} \times 3.33564$$

$$\times 10^{-30} \text{ C m D}^{-1})^2 (14.5 \times 10^{-25} \text{ cm}^3 \times 10^{-6} \text{ m}^3 \text{cm}^3)$$

$$\times \frac{1}{4\pi(8.854 \times 10^{-12} \text{ J}^{-1} \text{C}^2 \text{m}^{-1})}$$

$$= -2.435 \times 10^{-22} \text{ J}$$

$$E(\text{dipole-induced dipole}) = -2.435 \times 10^{-22} \text{ J} \times 6.022 \times 10^{23} \text{ mol}^{-1} \times \frac{\text{kJ}}{1000 \text{ J}} = -0.15 \text{ kJ mol}^{-1}$$

$$E(\text{dispersion}) = -\frac{1}{r^6} \cdot \frac{3}{4} \alpha^2 E_i$$

$$= \frac{1}{(4.00 \times 10^{-10} \text{m})^6} \times \frac{3}{4} (14.5 \times 10^{-25} \text{ cm}^3 \times 10^{-6} \text{ m}^3 \text{cm}^{-3})^2 \times (1218 \text{ kJ mol}^{-1})$$

$$= -4.689 \times 10^{-2} \text{ kJ mol}^{-1}$$

The sum of these contributions is

$$E = E(\text{dipole-dipole}) + E(\text{dipole-induced dipole}) + E(\text{dispersion})$$

$$= -2.82 \text{ kJ mol}^{-1} + (-0.15 \text{ kJ mol}^{-1}) + (-0.47 \text{ kJ mol}^{-1})$$

$$= -3.44 \text{ kJ mol}^{-1}$$

(b) The percent contributions are

$$\% \text{ dipole} = \frac{E(\text{dipole-dipole})}{E} \times 100\%$$

$$= \frac{-2.82 \text{ kJ mol}^{-1}}{-3.44 \text{ kJ mol}^{-1}} \times 100\%$$

$$= 82.0\%$$

$$\% \text{ induced} = \frac{E(\text{dipole-induced dipole})}{E} \times 100\%$$

$$= \frac{2(-0.15 \text{ kJ mol}^{-1})}{-3.44 \text{ kJ mol}^{-1}} \times 100\%$$

$$= 4.3\%$$

$$\% \text{ dispersion} = \frac{E(\text{dispersion})}{E} \times 100\%$$

$$= \frac{-0.47 \text{ kJ mol}^{-1})}{-3.44 \text{ kJ mol}^{-1}} \times 100\%$$

$$= 13.6\%$$

Results for the other substances are obtained in the same manner. The following table provides a summary:

	E(dipole–dipole) (kJ mol^{-1})	E(dipole–induced dipole) (kJ mol^{-1})	E(dispersion) (kJ mol^{-1})	E (kJ mol^{-1})	Percent		
					Dipole–Dipole	Dipole–Induced Dipole	Dispersion
HF	−2.65	−0.08	−0.18	−2.91	91.1	2.7	6.2
HCl	−0.36	−0.10	−1.56	−2.01	17.9	4.7	77.4
HBr	−0.11	−0.07	−2.68	−2.87	3.9	2.5	93.6
HI	−0.01	−0.03	−5.43	−5.47	0.2	0.6	99.2
H_2O	−2.82	−0.15	−0.47	−3.44	82.1	4.3	13.6
CH_3OH	−1.99	−0.28	−2.08	−4.35	45.8	6.4	47.8
CH_3CH_2OH	−1.94	−0.45	−5.39	−7.79	25.0	5.8	69.2
$CH_3(CH_2)_2OH$	−1.38	−0.48	−8.17	−10.02	3.7	4.8	81.5
$CH_3(CH_2)_3OH$	−1.81	−0.72	−13.92	−16.45	11.0	4.4	84.6
CH_4	0.00	0.00	−1.50	−1.50	0.0	0.0	100.0
CH_3CH_3	0.00	0.00	−4.08	−4.08	0.0	0.0	100.0
$CH_3CH_2CH_3$	0.00	0.00	−7.66	−7.66	0.0	0.0	100.0
$(CH_3)_3CH$	0.00	0.00	−12.38	−12.38	0.0	0.0	100.0
$CH_3(CH_2)_2CH_3$	0.00	0.00	−12.51	−12.51	0.0	0.0	100.0
$CH_3(CH_2)_3CH_3$	0.00	0.00	−18.13	−18.13	0.0	0.0	100.0

(c) The values range from tenths of a kJ mol^{-1} to approximately 12 kJ mol^{-1}. Intermolecular interaction energies are typically ten to a thousand times smaller than the energy of a covalent bond.

(d) The plot for the halogen acids   The plot for the alcohols

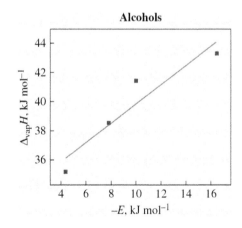

The plot for the alkanes

These plots show that as the magnitude of the intermolecular interaction energies increases, the enthalpy of vaporization increases.

(e) For low temperatures, when thermal energies are small, the majority of molecules will have their dipoles aligned head-to-tail. However, at very high temperatures, the molecules will be able to "jiggle" out of alignment, with their dipoles more randomly oriented. Therefore, the attraction arising from a favorable alignment of dipole moments is less significant at higher temperatures.

FEATURE PROBLEMS

122. **(E)** We obtain the surface tension by substituting the experimental values into the equation for surface tension.

$$h = \frac{2\gamma}{dgr} \quad \gamma = \frac{hdgr}{2} = \frac{1.1 \text{ cm} \times 0.789 \text{ g cm}^{-3} \times 981 \text{ cm s}^{-2} \times 0.050 \text{ cm}}{2} = 21 \text{ g/s}^2 = 0.021 \text{ J/m}^2$$

123. **(D)**

(a) $\dfrac{dP}{dT} = \dfrac{\Delta_{vap}H}{T(V_g - V_l)} = \dfrac{\Delta_{vap}H}{T(V_g)}$ Note: $V_l \approx 0$ Rearrange expression, Use $V_g = \dfrac{nRT}{P}$

$$\frac{dP}{dT} = \frac{\Delta_{vap}H}{T(\frac{nRT}{P})} = \frac{\Delta_{vap}H}{\frac{nRT^2}{P}} = \frac{P\Delta_{vap}H}{nRT^2} \quad or \quad \frac{dP}{P} = \frac{\Delta_{vap}H \times dT}{nRT^2}$$

Consider 1 mole (n = 1) and substitute in $\Delta_{vap}H = 15{,}971 + 14.55 \text{ T} - 0.160 \text{ T}^2$

$$\frac{dP}{P} = \frac{(15{,}971 + 14.55\,T - 0.160\,T^2)dT}{RT^2} = \frac{(15{,}971)dT}{RT^2} + \frac{(14.55\,T)dT}{RT^2} - \frac{(0.160\,T^2)dT}{RT^2}$$

Simplify and collect constants

$$\frac{dP}{P} = \frac{(15,971)}{R}\frac{dT}{T^2} + \frac{(14.55)}{R}\frac{dT}{T} - \frac{(0.160)}{R}dT \quad \text{Integrate from } P_1 \to P_2 \text{ and } T_1 \to T_2$$

$$\ln\left(\frac{P_2}{P_1}\right) = \frac{(15,971)}{R}\left(\frac{1}{T_1} - \frac{1}{T_2}\right) + \frac{(14.55)}{R}\ln\left(\frac{T_2}{T_1}\right) - \frac{(0.160)}{R}(T_2 - T_1)$$

(b) First we consider 1 mole ($n = 1$) $P_1 = 10.16$ torr (0.01337 atm) and $T_1 = 120$ K
Find the boiling point (T_2) when the pressure (P_2) is 1 atm.

$$\ln\left(\frac{1}{0.01337}\right) = \frac{15971}{8.3145}\left(\frac{1}{120} - \frac{1}{T_2}\right) + \frac{14.55}{8.3145}\ln\left(\frac{T_2}{120}\right) - \frac{0.160}{8.3145}(T_2 - 120)$$

Then we solve for T_2 using the method of successive approximations: $T_2 = 169$ K

124. (M)

(a) 1 NaCl unit missing from the NaCl unit cell → overall stoichiometry is the same. The unit cell usually has 4 Na^+ and 4 Cl^- in the unit cell. Now the unit cell will have 3 Na^+ and 3 Cl^-. Accordingly, the density will decrease by a factor of 25% (1/4) if 1 Na^+ and 1 Cl^- are consistently absent throughout the structure. Thus, the density will be $0.75(d_{NaCl, normal})$.

(b) No change in stoichiometry or density, as this is just a simple displacement of an ion within the unit cell.

(c) Unit cell should contain 4 Ti^{2+} and 4 O^{2-} ions (same as in the NaCl unit cell).
4 TiO ions have a mass of :

$$4 \text{ formula units} \times \left(\frac{1\,\text{mol TiO}}{6.022 \times 10^{23}\,\text{formula units}}\right)\left(\frac{63.88\,\text{g TiO}}{1\,\text{mol TiO}}\right) = 4.243 \times 10^{-22}\,\text{g TiO}$$

$$V = (418\,\text{pm})^3 \times \left(\frac{1 \times 10^{-12}\,\text{m}}{1\,\text{pm}}\right)^3 \left(\frac{100\,\text{cm}}{1\,\text{m}}\right)^3 = 7.30 \times 10^{-23}\,\text{cm}^3$$

$$\text{Calculated density} = \frac{m}{V} = \frac{4.243 \times 10^{-22}\,\text{g}}{7.30 \times 10^{-23}\,\text{cm}^3} = 5.81\,\text{g cm}^{-3}\,(\text{actual density} = 4.92\,\text{g cm}^{-3})$$

This indicates the presence of vacancies, and these could be Schottky-type defects.

125. (D)

(a) For a uniformly spaced (separation = r) one dimensional linear "crystal" of alternating cations and anions (having the same unipositive charge $Q_1 = Q_2 = Q_3$ (see diagram below)), the interaction of one ion with all of the other ions is proportional to

$$V = \frac{Q^2 e^2}{d_{12}} \qquad \text{where} \qquad \frac{1}{d_{12}} = \frac{2}{R} - \frac{2}{2R} + \frac{2}{3R} - \frac{2}{4R} + \frac{2}{5R} - \frac{2}{6R} \ldots\ldots$$

Note: The factor of 2 comes from the fact that the same set of ions appears on both sides of the central ion and it does not matter if you start with a cation or an anion.

$$\frac{1}{d_{12}} = \frac{2}{R} \times \left(1 - \frac{1}{2} + \frac{1}{3} - \frac{1}{4} + \frac{1}{5} - \frac{1}{6} \ldots\ldots \right) \qquad \frac{1}{d_{12}} = \frac{1}{R} \times 2 \left(\ln 2 \right) \qquad V = \frac{Q^2 e^2}{R} \times 2 \left(\ln 2 \right)$$

(b) Consider the crystal lattice for NaCl.

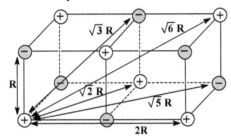

The 4 closest distances are marked to the reference Na^+ ion in the bottom left.

At a distance of R, there are 6 Cl^- ions which are attracted to the Na^+ ion.

At a distance of $\sqrt{2}$ R, there are 12 Na^+ ions which are repelled by the Na^+ ion.

At a distance of $\sqrt{3}$ R, there are 8 Cl^- ions which are attracted to the Na^+ ion.

At a distance of 2R or $\sqrt{4}$ R, there are 6 Na^+ ions which are repelled by the Na^+ ion.

The value of $k_M = \left(\frac{6}{1} - \frac{12}{\sqrt{2}} + \frac{8}{\sqrt{3}} - \frac{6}{\sqrt{4}} + \ldots.. \right)$

(c) If we carry out the same calculation for the CsCl structure, we would see that the Madelung constant is not the same. This is because the crystal structure is not the same. Notable is the fact that there are 8 nearest neighbors in CsCl and only 6 in NaCl.

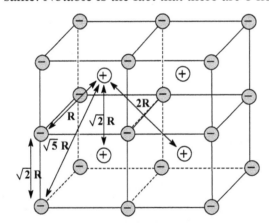

The 4 closest distances are marked to the reference Cs^+ ion in the top left cell.

At a distance of R, there are 8 Cl^- ions which are attracted to the Cs^+ ion.

At a distance of $\sqrt{2}$ R, there are 6 Cs^+ ions which are repelled by the Cs^+ ion.

At a distance of $\sqrt{5}$ R, there are 24 Cl^- ions which are attracted to the Cs^+ ion.

At a distance of 2R or $\sqrt{4}$ R, there are 8 Cs^+ ions which are repelled by the Cs^+ ion.

The value of $k_M = \left(\frac{8}{1} - \frac{6}{\sqrt{2}} + \frac{24}{\sqrt{5}} - \frac{8}{\sqrt{4}} + \ldots.. \right)$

126. (M) There is a better linear correlation between polarizability and boiling point (as demonstrated by the linear regression fit) than between mass and boiling point. Therefore, interatomic/molecular interaction drive the boiling point, not mass.

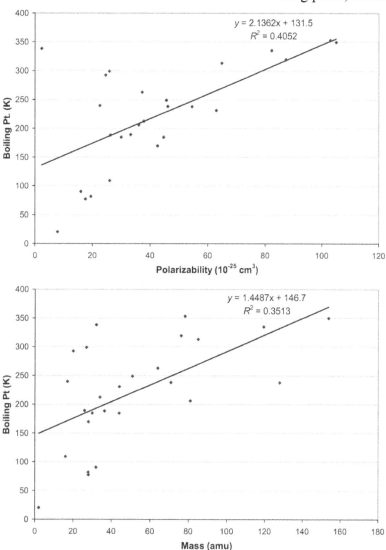

127. (M) The first two entries are obtained by simple plugging in:

$$\text{NaCl}: \frac{\left(120,250 \text{ kJ pm mol}^{-1}\right)(2)(+1 \times -1)}{(181+99)\text{pm}} \times \left(1 - \frac{34.5 \text{ pm}}{(181+99)\text{pm}}\right) = -753 \text{ kJ mol}^{-1}$$

$$\text{LaF}_3: \frac{\left(120,250 \text{ kJ pm mol}^{-1}\right)(4)(+3 \times -1)}{(133+117)\text{pm}} \times \left(1 - \frac{34.5 \text{ pm}}{(133+117)\text{pm}}\right) = -4975 \text{ kJ mol}^{-1}$$

The case of Na_2SO_4 is more difficult, and is approached as follows:

$$\text{Na}_2\text{SO}_4: \frac{\left(120,250 \text{ kJ pm mol}^{-1}\right)(3)(+1 \times -2)}{(r_0)\text{pm}} \times \left(1 - \frac{34.5 \text{ pm}}{(r_0)\text{pm}}\right) = -3389 \text{ kJ mol}^{-1}$$

Expanding the above term, we get the following expression:

$$\frac{-721500}{r_0}\left(\frac{r_0 - 34.5}{r_0}\right) = -3389$$

$$3389 \cdot r_0^2 - 721500 r_0 + 24891750 = 0$$

Solving r_0 using the quadratic formula, we get $r_0 = 169$ pm
Since $r_0 = r_+ + r_-$, and $r_+ = 99$ pm, $r_- = 70$ pm.
This ionic radius for sulfate seems small. One would expect SO_4^{2-} to have a significantly higher radius than an Na^+. What this suggests is that the Kapustinksii relationship does not do a good enough job for polyatomic anions, and thus would need to be modified.

SELF-ASSESSMENT EXERCISES

128. (E)

(a) $\Delta_{vap}H$: Enthalpy of vaporization, the amount of heat needed to convert one mole of liquid to a gas

(b) T_c: Critical temperature, the temperature at which the boundary between gas and liquid phase disappears (and beyond which, the gas cannot be compressed into a liquid no matter the pressure)

(c) Instantaneous dipole: Purely based on chance at some point in time, electrons can be concentrated in one region of an atom or a molecule. This displacement of electrons causes a weak and instantaneous dipole in the molecule, making a normally non-polar species momentarily polar.

(d) Coordination number: The number of atoms that are in contact with a central atom

(e) Unit cell: In a crystalline substance, a unit cell is the smallest parallelepiped that can be used to represent the entire crystal by translation in the x, y and z directions.

129. (E)

(a) Capillary action: See Figure 12-14. A thin film of water spreads up the inside walls of the capillary because of strong adhesive forces between water and glass (water wets glass). The pressure below the meniscus falls slightly. Atmospheric pressure then pushes a column of water up the tube to eliminate the pressure difference. The smaller the diameter of the capillary, the higher the liquid rises.

(b) Polymorphism: The phenomenon of the pure solid of a substance existing in more than one form.

(c) Sublimation: The phase transformation process involving the direct conversion of a solid to a gas.

(d) Supercooling: If, during the cooling of a liquid, the temperature drops below the freezing point without any solid forming

(e) Determining the freezing point of a liquid from a cooling curve: A cooling curve plots heat released by the system as a function of temperature. If, during the cooling of the system, the temperature of the liquid does not change, that is the freezing point. After the solid phase is formed and the liquid is frozen, the temperature will resume decreasing again.

130. (E)

    (a) Adhesive and cohesive forces: Cohesive forces are forces between the molecules of a substance in a certain phase that holds the phase together (such as the forces holding together a droplet of water). Adhesive forces are the forces between molecules of a substance and another substance (such as a droplet of water sticking to glass).

    (b) Vaporization and condensation: Vaporization is the process of converting a liquid into a gas. It is endothermic, because a net amount of energy has to be expended for this conversion. Condensation is the reverse process, where a gas forms a liquid.

    (c) Triple point and critical point: Triple point is the temperature and pressure where all three phases of the matter exist simultaneously. Critical point is the temperature beyond which the gas cannot be condensed into a liquid no matter what the pressure (and also, the meniscus between the gas and liquid phase disappears.

    (d) Face-centered and body-centered cubic unit cell: A face centered cubic unit cell has an atom at each corner of the cube, and an atom at each face. Body centered cubic has an atom at each corner, and one atom in the center of the cubic lattice.

    (e) Tetrahedral and octahedral hole: tetrahedral holes are voids between packed layers of atoms were the void has 4 nearest atom neighbors. An octahedral hole is a void with 6 nearest neighbor atoms.

131. (E) The correct answer is (e) because all these properties depend on the strength of the intermolecular forces. Surface tension is the tendency of matter to resist an external force. The strength of the intermolecular attractions directly affects the ability of the surface of the liquid to resist this external force. Boiling point and vapor pressure are likewise affected. The stronger the intermolecular attractions, the lower the vapor pressure at a given temperature, and the higher the boiling temperature. Similarly, heat of vaporization of the substance also increases with increasing intermolecular attractions; more energy is required to take 1 mole of the substance from the liquid phase to the gas phase.

132. (E) The correct answer is (b). As the vapor escapes, there is less vapor over the liquid available for condensation, so the immediate effect is a lower condensation rate. More vapor will be produced because the vaporization rate will be greater than the condensation rate, until finally the two rates are again equal.

133. (E) The answer is (c). As temperature increases, more molecules from a liquid get sufficient energy to escape, and thus vapor pressure increases.

134. (E) The answer is (c). HF, CH_3OH, and N_2H_4 all participate in hydrogen bonding.

135. (E) The correct answer is (d). The normal boiling point is defined as the temperature where the vapor pressure of the liquid is the same as normal (sea level) atmospheric pressure of 760 Torr (1 atm).

136. **(M)** The van't Hoff equation can be used to calculate the vapor pressure at a given temperature:

$$\ln\frac{p_2}{p_1} = -\frac{\Delta_{vap}H°}{R}\left[\frac{1}{T_2} - \frac{1}{T_1}\right]$$

Plugging in the values, we have

$$\ln\frac{50.0 \text{ mmHg}}{760 \text{ mmHg}} = -\frac{\Delta_{vap}H°}{8.3145 \text{ J}\cdot\text{K}^{-1}\cdot\text{mol}^{-1}}\left[\frac{1}{T_2} - \frac{1}{329.4 \text{ K}}\right]$$

T_2 can be solved as follows:

$$T_2 = -\left[\ln\frac{50.0 \text{ mmHg}}{760 \text{ mmHg}} \times \left(\frac{8.3145 \text{ J}\cdot\text{K}^{-1}\cdot\text{mol}^{-1}}{32.0\times10^3 \text{ J mol}^{-1}}\right) - \frac{1}{329.4 \text{ K}}\right]^{-1} = 267.17 \text{ K or } -6.0 \text{ °C}$$

137. **(E)** The answer is (b). Refer to Table 12.9.

138. **(E)** The anwer is (a).

139. **(M)** The answers are (d) and (f).

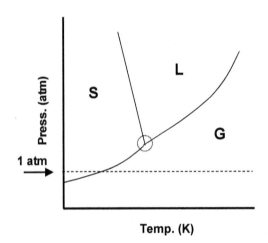

140. **(E)** The species with higher boiling points are underlined.
  (a) C_7H_{16} v. $\underline{C_{10}H_{22}}$: The only interaction is London dispersion. $C_{10}H_{22}$ because it has the higher mass
  (b) C_3H_8 v. $\underline{(CH_3)_2O}$: because dipole–dipole interactions are predominant, versus just London dispersion for C_3H_8.
  (c) CH_3CH_2SH v. $\underline{CH_3CH_2OH}$: because H-bonding dominates the inter-molecular interactions. This interaction is much weaker for CH_3CH_2SH.

141. **(E)** O_3 is the one that is out of place. The correct order of boiling points based on molar masses is: $N_2 < F_2 < Ar < O_3 < Cl_2$. O_3 is the only polar molecule in the group, but this is not important enough to put it after the more massive Cl_2 (bp: 162 K for O_3 and 239 K for Cl_2).

142. (E) The following listing reflects that organic compounds are lower melting than inorganic compounds, hydrogen bonding is an important intermolecular force for two of the compounds, and melting points of inorganic compounds are affected by ionic sizes and charges:

$Ne < C_3H_8 < CH_3CH_2OH < CH_2OHCHOHCH_2OH < KI < K_2SO_4 < MgO$

143. (M) Refer to the photograph on page 538 of water boiling under a reduced pressure. If the vapor is evacuated fast enough, to supply the required $\Delta_{vap}H$, the water may cool to 0 °C and ice may begin to form.

144. (M) If there is too little benzene(l) in the sealed tube in Figure 12-22 initially, the liquid will all be converted to benzene(g) before T_c is reached. If too much is present initially, the liquid will expand and cause the benzene(l) to condense, and therefore only benzene(l) will be present at the time T_c is reached.

145. (D)

    (a) To determine whether any CCl_4 remains in the flask, we have to determine how many moles of CCl_4 are placed in the vessel, determine that how much CCl_4 is in the vapor phase in a vessel of 8.21 L if the vapor pressure is 110 Torr at 25 °C, and then figure out if there will be more or less CCl_4 in the vapor phase compared to the amount of liquid given.

$$\text{mol } CCl_4 = 3.50 \text{ g } CCl_4 \times \frac{1 \text{ mol } CCl_4}{153.80 \text{ g } CCl_4} = 0.02276 \text{ mol of liquid } CCl_4 \text{ placed in vessel}$$

Assuming a pressure of 110 Torr at 25 °C:

vol CCl_4 = 3.50 g CCl_4 / 1.59 g mol^{-1} = 2.20 mL
vol inside the vessel = 8.210 L – 0.00220 L = 8.208 L
pressure = 110 Torr/760 Torr = 0.145 atm.

Moles of CCl_4 in the gas phase in this closed container:

$$\text{mol } CCl_4 = \frac{PV}{RT} = \frac{(0.145 \text{ atm})(8.208 \text{ L})}{(0.08206 \text{ L atm K}^{-1})(298 \text{ K})} = 0.0486 \text{ mol in the vapor phase}$$

0.0486 mol > 0.0228 mol, therefore at equilibrium, all the CCl_4 will be in the vapor phase.

    (b) To determine the amount of energy required to vaporize a certain amount of CCl_4, we have to first determine the enthalpy of vaporization, or $\Delta_{vap}H$:

$$\ln\left(\frac{P_2}{P_1}\right) = \frac{-\Delta_{vap}H}{R}\left(\frac{1}{T_2} - \frac{1}{T_1}\right)$$

$$\ln\left(\frac{760}{110}\right) = \frac{-\Delta_{vap}H}{8.3145 \text{ J mol}^{-1} K}\left(\frac{1}{350 \text{ K}} - \frac{1}{298 \text{ K}}\right)$$

$\Delta_{vap}H = 32.2$ kJ/mol

The energy required to vaporize 2.00 L of CCl_4 is therefore determined as follows:

$$\text{energy} = 2000 \text{ mL} \times \frac{1.59 \text{ g}}{1 \text{ mL}} \times \frac{1 \text{ mol } CCl_4}{153.80 \text{ g } CCl_4} \times \frac{32.2 \text{ kJ}}{\text{mol}} = 666 \text{ kJ}$$

146. (M)

(a) Unit cell length: we note from the picture that the hypotenuse of the right triangle equals $4 \times r$.

$$L^2 + L^2 = (4r)^2 = 16 \cdot (128 \text{ pm})^2 = 2.621 \times 10^5$$

$$L = \sqrt{2.621 \times 10^5 / 2} = 362 \text{ pm}$$

(b) volume $= (362 \text{ pm})^3 = 4.74 \times 10^7 \text{ pm}^3$

(c) 8 corners $\times 1/8 + 6$ faces $\times \frac{1}{2} = 4$ atoms/unit cell.

(d) Volume % is the ratio between the volume taken up by the atoms and the volume of the unit cell.

$$\frac{\text{vol of atoms}}{\text{vol of cells}} = \frac{4 \times (4/3)\pi (128 \text{ pm})^3}{4.74 \times 10^7 \text{ pm}^3} \times 100 = 74\%$$

(e)

$$\frac{\text{mass of Cu}}{\text{unit cell}} = \frac{4 \text{ atoms}}{\text{unit cell}} \times \frac{1 \text{ mol Cu}}{6.022 \times 10^{23} \text{ atoms}} \times \frac{63.546 \text{ g Cu}}{1 \text{ mol Cu}} = 4.221 \times 10^{-22} \text{ g}$$

(f) $D = m/V$

$$D = \frac{4.221 \times 10^{-22} \text{ g Cu}}{4.74 \times 10^7 \text{ pm}^3} \times \frac{(1 \times 10^{-10} \text{ pm})^3}{(1 \text{ cm})^3} = 8.91 \text{ g/cm}^3$$

147. (E) The answer is (a). All of these liquids participate in hydrogen-bonding. Therefore, higher van der Waals interactions translate to higher surface tensions. Methanol, CH_3OH, is the smallest molecule, therefore has the least amount of van der Waals forces, and the lowest surface tension.

148. (E) The answer is (d). All of these compounds are straight-chain hydrocarbons. Their only major intermolecular interaction is London dispersion. The lower this interaction, the lower the viscosity. *N*-pentane is the lightest, and therefore has the lowest viscosity.

149. (E) A network covalent solid will have a higher melting point, because it takes much more energy to overcome the covalent bonds in the solid (such as, for example, diamond) than to overcome ionic interactions.

150. (E) MgO would have the highest melting point. Lattice energy increases as the magnitude of the charges on the ions increases and as the sizes (radii) of the ions decreases. Large lattice energies result from highly charged ions with the smallest radii.

151. (M) The Li^+ and I^- have an fcc structure. Because I^- is much larger, the iodide ions touch. The structure is shown below.

Since the Li–I distance is 3.02 Å, the length of the cube is 2 × 3.02 Å = 6.04 Å. Therefore, the face diagonal of the cube is:

$$D = \sqrt{6.04^2 + 6.04^2} = 8.54 \ \text{Å}$$

Since there are 4 I^- radii in the face diagonal of the cube, radius of I^- is 8.54/4 = 2.13 Å

152. (E) The answer is (c), because of increased pressure, the transformation that causes the greatest packing efficiency change is likely to prevail.

153. (M) The intermolecular forces can be broken down into two categories: dipole and induced dipole. The dipole interactions can be further subdivided to dipole–dipole, which originates from the attraction between two molecules that have a dipole moment, to the more specific case of hydrogen bonding, where the hydrogen in one molecule attached to F, O, and N interacts with the F, O, and N atom from another molecule. Induced dipole or van der Waals forces are between non-polar molecules, where the momentary changes in the electron cloud distribution in the molecule creates a temporary dipole, which interacts with other molecules for a weak interaction.

154. (M) The concept of sphere packing can be described by the following packing types: hexagonal closed packing (HCP), cubic closed packing (CCP), body centered cubic (BCC) and simple cubic (SC). With the concepts of HCP and CCP come the concepts of interstitial sites, manifested in forms of octahedral and tetrahedral holes.

155. (M) The phase diagram is the overarching concept (obviously), which needs to be broken down further. The major sub-topics are the three phases: gas, liquid, solid. Deriving from the three phases is phase transformation as a function of temperature and pressure. Phase transformations also give rise to two other topics: triple point and critical point.

CHAPTER 13

SPONTANEOUS CHANGE:
ENTROPY AND GIBBS ENERGY

PRACTICE EXAMPLES

1A **(M)** The energy levels for the 905 pm box are given by

$$E_n = \frac{(6.626 \times 10^{-34} \text{ J})^2}{(8)(3.351 \times 10^{-26} \text{ kg})(905 \times 10^{-12} \text{ m})^2} \times n^2 = (2.00 \times 10^{-24} \text{ J}) \times n^2$$

The energies of the first four levels are

n	$E_n / 10^{-24}$ J
1	2.00
2	8.00
3	18.0
4	32.0

As shown in the diagrams below, there are 6 microstates for the system in the 905 pm box, each having a total energy of 20.0×10^{-24} J.

1B **(E)** A volume change causes a change in the spacing between the (translational) energy levels. (In an expansion, the energy levels become more closely spaced. In a compression, the energy levels are more widely spaced.) Part (b) illustrates a volume change, more specifically a compression. There is a larger change in energy from one level to the next in the final state than in the initial state. Part (a) represents an increase in total energy, with no change in volume.

2A **(E)** In general, $\Delta_r S > 0$ if $\Delta n_{gas} > 0$. This is because gases are very dispersed compared to liquids or solids; (gases possess large entropies). Recall that Δn_{gas} is the difference between the sum of the stoichiometric coefficients of the gaseous products and a similar sum for the reactants.

(a) $\Delta n_{\text{gas}} = 2 + 0 - (2 + 1) = -1$. One mole of gas is consumed here. We predict $\Delta_r S < 0$.

(b) $\Delta n_{\text{gas}} = 1 + 0 - 0 = +1$. Since one mole of gas is produced, we predict $\Delta_r S > 0$.

2B (E) (a) The outcome is uncertain in the reaction between ZnS(s) and $Ag_2O(s)$. We have used Δn_{gas} to estimate the sign of entropy change. There is no gas involved in this reaction and thus our prediction is uncertain.

(b) In the chlor-alkali process the entropy increases because two moles of gas have formed where none were originally present ($\Delta n_{\text{gas}} = (1 + 1 + 0) - (0 + 0) = 2$

3A **(E)** For a vaporization which occurs at the usual or normal vaporization temperature, $\Delta_{\text{vap}} G^\circ = 0 = \Delta_{\text{vap}} H^\circ - T \Delta_{\text{vap}} S^\circ$. Thus, $\Delta_{\text{vap}} S^\circ = \Delta_{\text{vap}} H^\circ / T_{\text{vap}}$.

We substitute the given values. $\Delta_{\text{vap}} S^\circ = \dfrac{\Delta_{\text{vap}} H^\circ}{T_{\text{vap}}} = \dfrac{20.2 \text{ kJ mol}^{-1}}{(-29.79 + 273.15) \text{ K}} = 83.0 \text{ J mol}^{-1} \text{ K}^{-1}$

3B **(E)** For a phase change which occurs at the normal transition temperature, $\Delta_{\text{tr}} G^\circ = 0 = \Delta_{\text{tr}} H^\circ - T \Delta_{\text{tr}} S^\circ$. Thus, $\Delta_{\text{tr}} H^\circ = T \Delta_{\text{tr}} S^\circ$. We substitute in the given values.
$\Delta_{\text{tr}} H^\circ = T \Delta_{\text{tr}} S^\circ = (95.5 + 273.15) \text{ K} \times 1.09 \text{ J mol}^{-1} \text{ K}^{-1} = 402 \text{ J/mol}$

4A **(E)** Here, we use $\Delta S = C_p \ln(T_f / T_i) - nR \ln(P_f / P_i)$, with $T_f = 240$ K, $T_i = 300$ K, $P_f = 0.50$ bar, $P_i = 1.00$ bar, $C_p = 20.8 \text{ J K}^{-1}$, and $n = 1$ mol. We get $\Delta S = 20.8 \text{ J K}^{-1} \ln(240 / 300) - 8.3145 \text{ J K}^{-1} \ln(0.5) = -4.64 \text{ J K}^{-1} + 5.76 \text{ J K}^{-1} = 1.12 \text{ J K}^{-1}$

4B **(E)** We use $\Delta S = C_p \ln(T_f / T_i) - nR \ln(P_f / P_i)$, with $T_f = T_i = 300$ K, $P_f = 0.5$ bar, $P_i = 1.00$ bar, $C_p = 20.8 \text{ J K}^{-1}$, and $n = 1$ mol. We get
$\Delta S = 20.8 \text{ J K}^{-1} \ln(300 / 300) - 8.3145 \text{ J K}^{-1} \ln(0.5) = (0 + 5.76) \text{ J K}^{-1} = 5.76 \text{ J K}^{-1}$

5A **(M)** The standard entropy change of reaction is expressed in terms of the standard entropies of the reagents.
$\Delta_r S^\circ = 2S^\circ[NH_3(g)] - S^\circ[N_2(g)] - 3S^\circ[H_2(g)]$
$= 2 \times 192.5 \text{ J mol}^{-1}\text{K}^{-1} - 191.6 \text{ J mol}^{-1} \text{ K}^{-1} - 3 \times 130.7 \text{ J mol}^{-1} \text{ K}^{-1} = -198.7 \text{ J mol}^{-1} \text{ K}^{-1}$
Thus to form *one* mole of $NH_3(g)$, the standard entropy of reaction is $-99.4 \text{ J mol}^{-1} \text{ K}^{-1}$

5B **(M)** The standard entropy of reaction is expressed in terms of the standard entropies of the reagents.

$$\Delta_r S° = S°\left[NO(g)\right] + S°\left[NO_2(g)\right] - S°\left[N_2O_3(g)\right]$$

$$138.5 \text{ J mol}^{-1} \text{ K}^{-1} = 210.8 \text{ J mol}^{-1} \text{ K}^{-1} + 240.1 \text{ J mol}^{-1} \text{ K}^{-1} - S°\left[N_2O_3(g)\right]$$

$$= 450.9 \text{ J mol}^{-1} \text{ K}^{-1} - S°\left[N_2O_3(g)\right]$$

$$S°\left[N_2O_3(g)\right] = 450.9 \text{ J mol}^{-1} \text{ K}^{-1} - 138.5 \text{ J mol}^{-1} \text{ K}^{-1} = 312.4 \text{ J mol}^{-1} \text{ K}$$

6A **(E)**

(a) Because $\Delta n_{gas} = 2 - (1+3) = -2$ for the synthesis of ammonia, we would predict $\Delta_r S < 0$ for the reaction. We already know that $\Delta_r H < 0$. Thus, the reaction falls into case 2, namely, a reaction that is spontaneous at low temperatures and non-spontaneous at high temperatures.

(b) For the formation of ethylene $\Delta n_{gas} = 1 - (2+0) = -1$ and thus $\Delta_r S < 0$. We are given that $\Delta_r H > 0$ and, thus, this reaction corresponds to case 4, namely, a reaction that is non-spontaneous at all temperatures.

6B **(E)**

(a) Because $\Delta n_{gas} = +1$ for the decomposition of calcium carbonate, $CaCO_3(s) \rightarrow CaO(s) + CO_2(g)$, we would predict $\Delta_r S > 0$ for the reaction, favoring the reaction at high temperatures. High temperatures also favor this endothermic $(\Delta H° > 0)$ reaction.

(b) The "roasting" of $ZnS(s)$, $2\,ZnS(s) + 3\,O_2(g) \rightarrow 2\,ZnO(s) + 2\,SO_2(g)$, has $\Delta n_{gas} = 2 - 3 = -1$ and, thus, $\Delta_r S < 0$. We are given that $\Delta_r H < 0$; thus, this reaction corresponds to case 2, namely, a reaction that is spontaneous at low temperatures, and non-spontaneous at high ones.

7A **(E)** The expression $\Delta_r G° = \Delta_r H° - T\Delta_r S°$ is used with $T = 298.15$ K.

$$\Delta_r G° = \Delta_r H° - T\Delta_r S° = -1648 \text{ kJ} - 298.15 \text{ K} \times \left(-549.3 \text{ J K}^{-1}\right) \times \left(1 \text{ kJ}/1000 \text{ J}\right)$$

$$= -1648 \text{ kJ} + 163.8 \text{ kJ} = -1484 \text{ kJ}$$

7B **(M)** We just need to substitute values from Appendix D into the supplied expression.

$$\Delta_r G° = 2\Delta_f G°\left[NO_2(g)\right] - 2\Delta_f G°\left[NO(g)\right] - \Delta_f G°\left[O_2(g)\right]$$

$$= 2 \times 51.31 \text{ kJ mol}^{-1} - 2 \times 86.55 \text{ kJ mol}^{-1} - 0.00 \text{ kJ mol}^{-1} = -70.48 \text{ kJ mol}^{-1}$$

8A **(M)** Using equation (13.14), the balanced chemical equation, and the value for $\Delta_r G° = -32.90$ kJ mol^{-1} from Example 13-8, it follows that

$$\Delta_r G = \Delta_r G° + RT \ln Q$$

$$-82.00 \text{ kJ mol}^{-1} = -32.90 \text{ kJ mol}^{-1} + 8.314 \times 10^{-3} \text{ kJ K}^{-1} \text{ mol}^{-1} \times 298.15 \text{ K} \ln \frac{\left(P_{NH_3}/P°\right)^2}{\left(P_{N_2}/P°\right)\left(P_{H_2}/P°\right)^3}$$

$$-82.00 \text{ kJ mol}^{-1} = -32.90 \text{ kJ mol}^{-1} + 2.479 \text{ kJ mol}^{-1} \ln \frac{\left(P_{NH_3}/P°\right)^2}{(0.5)(0.5)^3}$$

Solving for P_{NH_3}, we obtain

$$2.478 \text{ kJ mol}^{-1} \ln \frac{\left(P_{NH_3}/P°\right)^2}{(0.5)(0.5)^3} = -82.00 \text{ kJ mol}^{-1} + 32.90 \text{ kJ mol}^{-1} = -49.10 \text{ kJ mol}^{-1}$$

$$\ln \frac{\left(P_{NH_3}/P°\right)^2}{(0.5)(0.5)^3} = \frac{-49.10 \text{ kJ mol}^{-1}}{2.478 \text{ kJ mol}^{-1}} = 19.81 \Rightarrow \frac{\left(P_{NH_3}/P°\right)^2}{(0.5)(0.5)^3} = e^{19.81} = 4.0 \times 10^8$$

$$P_{NH_3} = P° \times \sqrt{4.0 \times 10^8} = 5.0 \times 10^3 \text{ bar}$$

8B **(M)** The minimum value of Q required to make the reverse reaction, conversion of ammonia to nitrogen and hydrogen, spontaneous implies that $\Delta_r G > 0$. Therefore,

$$\Delta_r G° + RT \ln Q > 0 \Rightarrow RT \ln Q > -\Delta_r G° \Rightarrow \ln Q > \frac{-\Delta_r G°}{RT}$$

$$Q > e^{\frac{-\Delta_r G°}{RT}} = e^{\frac{+32.90 \text{ kJ mol}^{-1}}{8.314 \times 10^{-3} \text{ kJ mol}^{-1} \text{ K}^{-1} \times 298.15 \text{ K}}} = 5.81 \times 10^5$$

9A **(M)** Pressures of gases and molarities of solutes in aqueous solution appear in thermodynamic equilibrium constant expressions. Pure solids and liquids (including solvents) do not appear.

(a) $\quad K = \dfrac{P_{SiCl_4}}{P_{Cl_2}^2} = K_p$ **(b)** $\quad K = \dfrac{[HOCl][H^+][Cl^-]}{P_{Cl_2}}$

$\quad K = K_p$ for (a) because all terms in the K expression are gas pressures.

9B **(M)** We need the balanced chemical equation in order to write the equilibrium constant expression. We start by translating names into formulas.

$$PbS(s) + HNO_3(aq) \rightarrow Pb(NO_3)_2(aq) + S(s) + NO(g)$$

The equation then is balanced with the ion-electron method.

oxidation : $\{PbS(s) \rightarrow Pb^{2+}(aq) + S(s) + 2e^- \qquad \} \times 3$

reduction : $\{NO_3^-(aq) + 4H^+(aq) + 3e^- \rightarrow NO(g) + 2H_2O(l) \quad \} \times 2$

net ionic : $3 PbS(s) + 2NO_3^-(aq) + 8H^+(aq) \rightarrow 3Pb^{2+}(aq) + 3S(s) + 2NO(g) + 4H_2O(l)$

In writing the thermodynamic equilibrium constant, recall that neither pure solids (PbS(s) and S(s)) nor pure liquids $(H_2O(l))$ appear in the thermodynamic equilibrium constant expression. Note also that we have written $H^+(aq)$ here for brevity even though we understand that $H_3O^+(aq)$ is the acidic species in aqueous solution.

$$K = \frac{[Pb^{2+}]^3 \, p_{NO}^2}{[NO_3^-]^2 [H^+]^8}$$

10A **(D)** We first determine the value of $\Delta_r G°$ and then set $\Delta_r G° = -RT \ln K$ to determine K.

$$\Delta_r G = \Delta_f G°\left[Ag^+(aq)\right] + \Delta_f G°[I^-(aq)] - \Delta_f G°\left[AgI(s)\right]$$

$$= [(77.11 - 51.57) - (-66.19)] \text{ kJ/mol} = +91.73 \text{ kJ mol}^{-1}$$

$$\ln K = \frac{-\Delta_r G°}{RT} = -\frac{-91.73 \text{ kJ/mol}}{8.3145 \text{ J mol}^{-1} \text{ K}^{-1} \times 298.15 \text{ K}} \times \frac{1000 \text{ J}}{1 \text{ kJ}} = -37.00$$

$$K = e^{-37.00} = 8.5 \times 10^{-17}$$

This is precisely equal to the value for the K_{sp} of AgI listed in Appendix D.

10B **(D)** We begin by translating names into formulas: $MnO_2(s) + HCl(aq) \rightarrow Mn^{2+}(aq) + Cl_2(aq)$. Then we produce a balanced net ionic equation with the ion–electron method:

oxidation: $2Cl^-(aq) \quad\quad\quad\quad\quad \rightarrow Cl_2(aq) + 2e^-$

reduction: $\underline{MnO_2(s) + 4YH^+(aq) + 2e^- \quad \rightarrow Mn^{2+}(aq) + 2H_2O(l)}$

net ionic: $MnO_2(s) + 4H^+(aq) + 2Cl^-(aq) \rightarrow Mn^{2+}(aq) + Cl_2(g) + 2H_2O(l)$

Next we determine the value of $\Delta_r G°$ for the reaction and then the value of K.

$$\Delta_r G° = \Delta_f G°\left[Mn^{2+}(aq)\right] + \Delta_f G°\left[Cl_2(g)\right] + 2\Delta_f G°\left[H_2O(l)\right]$$

$$-\Delta_f G°\left[MnO^{2+}(s)\right] - 4\Delta_f G°\left[H^+(aq)\right] - 2\Delta_f G°\left[Cl^-(aq)\right]$$

$$= -228.1 \text{ kJ mol}^{-1} + 0.0 \text{ kJ mol}^{-1} + 2\times(-237.1 \text{ kJ mol}^{-1})$$

$$-(-465.1 \text{ kJ mol}^{-1}) - 4\times 0.0 \text{ kJ mol}^{-1} - 2\times(-131.2 \text{ kJ mol}^{-1})$$

$$= +25.2 \text{ kJ mol}^{-1}$$

$$\ln K = \frac{-\Delta_r G°}{RT} = \frac{-(+25.2\times 10^3 \text{ J mol}^{-1})}{8.3145 \text{ J mol}^{-1} \text{ K}^{-1} \times 298.15 \text{ K}} = -10.1\underline{7} \quad K = e^{-10.2} = 4\times 10^{-5}$$

Because the value of K is so much smaller than 1, we expect the reaction will proceed in the forward direction only to a very limited extent.

11A **(M)** We set equal the two expressions for $\Delta_r G°$ and solve for the absolute temperature.

$$\Delta_r G° = \Delta_r H° - T\Delta_r S° = -RT \ln K \qquad \Delta_r H° = T\Delta_r S° - RT \ln K = T\left(\Delta_r S° - R \ln K\right)$$

$$T = \frac{\Delta_r H°}{\Delta_r S° - R \ln K} = \frac{-114.1\times10^3 \text{ J/mol}}{\left[-146.4 - 8.3145 \ \ln(150)\right] \text{J mol}^{-1} \text{ K}^{-1}} = 607 \text{ K}$$

11B **(D)** We expect the value of the equilibrium constant to increase as the temperature decreases since this is an exothermic reaction and exothermic reactions will have a larger equilibrium constant (shift right to form more products), as the temperature decreases. Thus, we expect K to be larger than 1000, which is its value at 4.3×10^2 K.

(a) The value of the equilibrium constant at 25 °C is obtained directly from the value of $\Delta_r G°$, since that value is also for 25 °C. Note:

$$\Delta_r G° = \Delta_r H° - T\Delta_r S° = -77.1 \text{ kJ/mol} - 298.15 \text{ K}\left(-0.1213 \text{ kJ/mol}\cdot\text{K}\right) = -40.9 \text{ kJ/mol}$$

$$\ln K = \frac{-\Delta_r G°}{RT} = \frac{-(-40.9\times10^3 \text{ J mol}^{-1})}{8.3145 \text{ J mol}^{-1} \text{ K}^{-1}\times298.15 \text{ K}} = 16.5 \qquad K = e^{+16.5} = 1.5\times10^7$$

(b) First, we solve for $\Delta_r G°$ at $75\,°C = 348$ K

$$\Delta_r G° = \Delta_r H° - T\Delta_r S° = -77.1 \frac{\text{kJ}}{\text{mol}}\times\frac{1000 \text{ J}}{1 \text{ kJ}} - \left(348.15 \text{ K}\times\left(-121.3\frac{\text{J}}{\text{mol K}}\right)\right)$$

$$= -34.87\times10^3 \text{ J/mol}$$

Then we use this value to obtain the value of the equilibrium constant, as in part (a).

$$\ln K = \frac{-\Delta_r G°}{RT} = \frac{-(-34.87\times10^3 \text{ J mol}^{-1})}{8.3145 \text{ J mol}^{-1} \text{ K}^{-1}\times348.15 \text{ K}} = 12.05 \qquad K = e^{+12.05} = 1.7\times10^5$$

As expected, K for this exothermic reaction decreases with increasing temperature.

12A **(M)** We use the value of $K = 9.1\times10^2$ at 800 K and $\Delta_r H° = -1.8\times10^5$ J/mol, for the appropriate terms, in the van't Hoff equation.

$$\ln\frac{5.8\times10^{-2}}{9.1\times10^2} = \frac{-1.8\times10^5 \text{ J/mol}}{8.3145 \text{ J mol}^{-1} \text{ K}^{-1}}\left(\frac{1}{800 \text{ K}} - \frac{1}{T \text{ K}}\right) = -9.66; \quad \frac{1}{T} = \frac{1}{800} - \frac{9.66\times8.3145}{1.8\times10^5}$$

$$1/T = 1.25\times10^{-3} - 4.5\times10^{-4} = 8.0\times10^{-4} \qquad T = 1240 \text{ K} \approx 970 \text{ °C}$$

This temperature is an estimate because it is an extrapolated point beyond the range of the data supplied.

12B **(M)** The temperature we are considering is $235\,°C = 508$ K. We substitute the value of $K = 9.1\times10^2$ at 800 K and $\Delta_r H° = -1.8\times10^5$ J/mol, for the appropriate terms, in the van't Hoff equation.

$$\ln\frac{K}{9.1\times10^2} = \frac{-1.8\times10^5 \text{ J/mol}}{8.3145 \text{ J mol}^{-1} \text{ K}^{-1}}\left(\frac{1}{800 \text{ K}} - \frac{1}{508 \text{ K}}\right) = +15_{.6}; \quad \frac{K}{9.1\times10^2} = e^{+15.6} = 6\times10^6$$

$$K = 6\times10^6 \times 9.1\times10^2 = 5\times10^9$$

INTEGRATIVE EXAMPLE

A. **(D)** The value of $\Delta_r G^\circ$ can be calculated by finding the value of the equilibrium constant K_p at 25 °C. The equilibrium constant for the reaction is simply given by $K_p = p\{N_2O_5(g)\}$. The vapor pressure of $N_2O_5(g)$ can be determined from the Clausius-Clapeyron eqution, which is a specialized version of the van't Hoff equation.

$$\ln\frac{P_2}{P_1} = \frac{\Delta_{sub}H}{R}\left(\frac{1}{T_1} - \frac{1}{T_2}\right) \Rightarrow \Delta_{sub}H = \frac{R\ln\frac{P_2}{P_1}}{\left(\frac{1}{T_1} - \frac{1}{T_2}\right)}$$

$$\Delta_{sub}H = \frac{8.314\ \mathrm{Jmol^{-1}K^{-1}} \times \ln\frac{760\ \mathrm{mmHg}}{100\ \mathrm{mmHg}}}{\left(\frac{1}{7.5+273.15} - \frac{1}{32.4+273.15}\right)} = \frac{2.028}{3.49\times10^{-5}}\ \mathrm{Jmol^{-1}} = 5.81\times10^4\ \mathrm{Jmol^{-1}}$$

$$\ln\frac{P_3}{P_1} = \frac{\Delta_{sub}H}{R}\left(\frac{1}{T_1} - \frac{1}{T_2}\right) \Rightarrow P_3 = P_1 e^{\frac{\Delta_{sub}H}{R}\left(\frac{1}{T_1} - \frac{1}{T_2}\right)}$$

$$P_3 = 100\ \mathrm{mmHg} \times e^{\frac{5.81\times10^4\ \mathrm{J\,mol^{-1}}}{8.314\ \mathrm{J\,K^{-1}\,mol^{-1}}}\left(\frac{1}{280.7} - \frac{1}{298.2}\right)\mathrm{K^{-1}}} = 431\ \mathrm{mmHg} \times \frac{1\ \mathrm{atm}}{760\ \mathrm{mmHg}} = 0.567\ \mathrm{atm} = K_p$$

$$\Delta_r G^\circ = -RT\ln K_p = -(8.314\times10^{-3}\ \mathrm{kJ\ mol^{-1}\ K^{-1}} \times 298.15\ \mathrm{K})\ln(0.567) = 1.42\ \mathrm{kJ/mol}$$

B. **(D)** The standard entropy change for the reaction $(\Delta_r S^\circ)$ can be calculated from the known values of $\Delta_r H^\circ$ and $\Delta_r G^\circ$.

$$\Delta_r G^\circ = \Delta_r H^\circ - T\Delta_r S^\circ \Rightarrow \Delta_r S^\circ = \frac{\Delta_r H^\circ - \Delta_r G^\circ}{T} = \frac{-454.8\ \mathrm{kJ\ mol^{-1}} - (-323.1\ \mathrm{kJ\ mol^{-1}})}{298.15\ \mathrm{K}}$$

$$= -441.7\ \mathrm{J\ K^{-1}\ mol^{-1}}$$

Plausible chemical reaction for the production of ethylene glycol can also be written as:

$$2\,C(s) + 3\,H_2(g) + O_2(g) \longrightarrow CH_2OHCH_2OH(l)$$

Since $\Delta_r S^\circ = \sum\{S^\circ_{products}\} - \sum\{S^\circ_{reactants}\}$ it follows that:

$$\Delta_r S^\circ = S^\circ(CH_2OHCH_2OH(l)) - [2\times S^\circ(C(s)) + 3\times S^\circ(H_2(g)) + S^\circ(O_2(g))]$$

$$-441.7\ \mathrm{J\ K^{-1}\ mol^{-1}} = S^\circ(CH_2OHCH_2OH(l)) - [2\times5.74\ \mathrm{J\ K^{-1}\ mol^{-1}} + 3\times130.7\ \mathrm{J\ K^{-1}\ mol^{-1}}$$
$$+ 205.1\ \mathrm{J\ K^{-1}\ mol^{-1}}]$$

$$S^\circ(CH_2OHCH_2OH(l)) = -441.7\ \mathrm{J\ K^{-1}\ mol^{-1}} + 608.68\ \mathrm{J\ K^{-1}\ mol^{-1}} = 167\ \mathrm{J\ K^{-1}\ mol^{-1}}$$

EXERCISES

Spontaneous Change and Entropy

1. **(M)**

(a) If the length of the box is increased to $2L$ for a fixed total energy, the number of possible microstates will increase. Hence, the entropy of the system will increase.

(b) If the total energy of the box is increased at constant length L, the number of energy levels and number of microstates that are accessible to the particles will increase. Hence, the entropy of the system will increase.

2. **(M)**

(a) Generally speaking, the entropy of an ideal gas will increase as the space available to the particles increases. Therefore, $\Delta S > 0$ for an isothermal expansion of an ideal gas. This result can be verified by using the appropriate equation from Table 13.1. For an

isothermal process involving an ideal gas, $\Delta S = nR\ln\left(\dfrac{V_f}{V_i}\right)$. This equation shows that

ΔS is greater than zero when the ratio V_f/V_i is greater than 1. For example, when (V_f/V_i) = 2, the entropy change is $\Delta S = nR\ln 2 = 0.693 \times nR > 0$. In other words, S increases.

(b) An increase in pressure at constant temperature will cause a decrease in volume. The entropy of an ideal gas will decrease as the space available to the particles decreases. Therefore, $\Delta S < 0$ when the pressure of an ideal gas increases at constant temperature. This result can also be verified by using the appropriate equation from Table 13.1. For

an isothermal process involving an ideal gas, $\Delta S = nR\ln\left(\dfrac{P_i}{P_f}\right) = -nR\ln\left(\dfrac{P_f}{P_i}\right)$.

This equation shows that ΔS is less than zero when the ratio P_f/P_i is greater than 1. For example, when $(P_f/P_i) = 2$, the entropy change is $\Delta S = -nR\ln 2 = -0.693 \times nR < 0$. In other words, S decreases.

(c) When an ideal gas is heated at constant pressure, the temperature will increase and so too will the average kinetic energy of the molecules. Therefore, total energy of the molecules will increase and so too will the number of (accessible) microstates. As a result, the entropy of the system will increase. This result can also be verified by using the appropriate equation from Table 13.1. For a constant pressure process involving an ideal gas, $\Delta S = C_p\ln(T_f/T_i)$. This equation shows that ΔS is greater than zero when the ratio T_f/T_i is greater than 1. For example, when $(T_f/T_i) = 2$, the entropy change is $\Delta S = C_p\ln 2 = 0.693 \times C_p > 0$. In other words, S increases.

3. **(D)** The entropy of one mole of H_2 molecules is $S = 1\ \text{mol} \times 130.7\ \text{J K}^{-1}\ \text{mol}^{-1} = 130.7\ \text{J K}^{-1}$. Using $S = k\ln W$, we can calculate

$$\ln W = \frac{S}{k} = \frac{130.7\ \text{J K}^{-1}}{1.3807 \times 10^{-23}\ \text{J K}^{-1}} = 9.466 \times 10^{24}$$

Since $\ln W = 2.030 \log W$, we can write $\log W = \dfrac{9.466 \times 10^{24}}{2.303} = 4.111 \times 10^{24}$. Therefore,

$W = 10^{4.111 \times 10^{24}}$. To write this number in decimal form, we would write 1 followed by 4.111×10^{24} zeros.

4. **(D)** $S = (1 \times 10^{-12} \text{ g}/183.52 \text{ g mol}^{-1}) \times 0.012 \text{ J K}^{-1} \text{ mol}^{-1} = 6.54 \times 10^{-17} \text{ J K}^{-1}$
   Using $S = k \ln W$, we can calculate $\ln W = S/k = 6.54 \times 10^{-17} \text{ J K}^{-1}/(1.3807 \times 10^{-23} \text{ J K}^{-1}) = 4.74 \times 10^{6}$.

   Since $\ln W = 2.303 \log W$, we can write $\log W = 4.74 \times 10^{6}/2.303 = 2.1 \times 10^{6}$, and so $W = 10^{2.1 \times 10^{6}}$.

   To write this number in decimal form, we would write a 1 followed by 2.1×10^{6} zeros.

5. **(E)**
   (a) The freezing of ethanol involves a *decrease* in the entropy of the system. There is a reduction in mobility and in the number of forms in which their energy can be stored when they leave the solution and arrange themselves into a crystalline state.
   (b) The sublimation of dry ice involves converting a solid that has little mobility into a highly dispersed vapor which has a number of ways in which energy can be stored (rotational, translational). Thus, the entropy of the system *increases* substantially.
   (c) The burning of rocket fuel involves converting a liquid fuel into the highly dispersed mixture of the gaseous combustion products. The entropy of the system *increases* substantially.

6. **(E)** Although there is a substantial change in entropy involved in **(a)** changing H_2O (liq., 1 atm) to H_2O (g, 1 atm), it is not as large as **(c)** converting the liquid to a gas at 10 mmHg. The gas is more dispersed, (less ordered), at lower pressures. In **(b)**, if we start with a solid and convert it to a gas at the lower pressure, the entropy change should be even larger, since a solid is more ordered (concentrated) than a liquid. Thus, in order of increasing ΔS, the processes are: **(a)** < **(c)** < **(b)**.

7. **(E)** The first law of thermodynamics states that energy is neither created nor destroyed (thus, "The energy of the universe is constant"). A consequence of the second law of thermodynamics is that entropy of the universe increases for all spontaneous, that is, naturally occurring, processes (and therefore, "the entropy of the universe increases toward a maximum").

8. **(E)** When pollutants are produced they are usually dispersed throughout the environment. These pollutants thus start in a relatively compact form and end up dispersed throughout a large volume mixed with many other substances. The pollutants are highly dispersed, thus, they have a high entropy. Returning them to their original compact form requires reducing this entropy, which is a highly non-spontaneous process. If we have had enough foresight to retain these pollutants in a reasonably compact form, such as disposing of them in a *secure* landfill, rather than dispersing them in the atmosphere or in rivers and seas, the task of permanently removing them from the environment, and perhaps even converting them to useful forms, would be considerably easier.

9. **(E)**

(a) Increase in entropy because a gas has been created from a liquid, a condensed phase.

(b) Decrease in entropy as a condensed phase, a solid, is created from a solid and a gas.

(c) For this reaction we cannot be certain of the entropy change. Even though the number of moles of gas produced is the same as the number that reacted, we cannot conclude that the entropy change is zero because not all gases have the same molar entropy.

(d) $2H_2S(g) + 3O_2(g) \rightarrow 2H_2O(g) + 2SO_2(g)$ Decrease in entropy since five moles of gas with high entropy become only four moles of gas, with about the same quantity of entropy per mole.

10. **(E)**
(a) At $75°$ C, 1 mol H_2O (g, 1 atm) has a greater entropy than 1 mol H_2O (liq., 1 atm) since a gas is much more dispersed than a liquid.

(b) $50.0 \text{ g Fe} \times \dfrac{1 \text{ mol Fe}}{55.8 \text{ g Fe}} = 0.896$ mol Fe has a higher entropy than 0.80 mol Fe, both (s)

at 1 atm and 5 °C, because entropy is an extensive property that depends on the amount of substance present.

(c) 1 mol Br_2 (liq., 1 atm, 8 °C) has a higher entropy than 1 mol Br_2 (s, 1atm, –8 °C) because solids are more ordered (concentrated) substances than are liquids, and furthermore, the liquid is at a higher temperature.

(d) 0.312 mol SO_2 (g, 0.110 atm, 32.5 °C) has a higher entropy than 0.284 mol O_2 (g, 15.0 atm, 22.3 °C) for at least three reasons. First, entropy is an extensive property that depends on the amount of substance present (more moles of SO_2 than O_2). Second, entropy increases with temperature (temperature of SO_2 is greater than that for O_2. Third, entropy is greater at lower pressures (the O_2 has a much higher pressure). Furthermore, entropy generally is higher per mole for more complicated molecules.

11. **(E)**

(a) Negative; A liquid (moderate entropy) combines with a solid to form another solid.

(b) Positive; One mole of high entropy gas forms where no gas was present before.

(c) Positive; One mole of high entropy gas forms where no gas was present before.

(d) Uncertain; The number of moles of gaseous products is the same as the number of moles of gaseous reactants.

(e) Negative; Two moles of gas (and a solid) combine to form just one mole of gas.

12. **(M)** The entropy of formation of a compound would be the difference between the absolute entropy of one mole of the compound and the sum of the absolute entropies of the appropriate amounts of the elements constituting the compound, with each species in its most stable form.

It seems as though $CS_2(l)$ would have the highest molar entropy of formation of the compounds listed, since it is the only substance whose formation does not involve the consumption of high entropy gaseous reactants. This prediction can be checked by determining $\Delta_f S°$ values from the data in Appendix D:

(a) $C(graphite) + 2H_2(g) \rightleftharpoons CH_4(g)$

$$\Delta_f S°[CH_4(g)] = S°[CH_4(g)] - S°[C(graphite)] - 2S°[H_2(g)]$$
$$= 186.3 \text{ J mol}^{-1}\text{K}^{-1} - 5.74 \text{ J mol}^{-1}\text{K}^{-1} - 2 \times 130.7 \text{ J mol}^{-1}\text{K}^{-1}$$
$$= -80.8 \text{ J mol}^{-1}\text{K}^{-1}$$

(b) $2C(graphite) + 3H_2(g) + \frac{1}{2}O_2(g) \rightleftharpoons CH_3CH_2OH(l)$

$$\Delta_f S°[CH_3CH_2OH(l)] = S°[CH_3CH_2OH(l)] - 2S°[C(graphite)] - 3S°[H_2(g)] - \frac{1}{2}S°[O_2(g)]$$
$$= 160.7 \text{ J mol}^{-1}\text{K}^{-1} - 2 \times 5.74 \text{ J mol}^{-1}\text{K}^{-1} - 3 \times 130.7 \text{ J mol}^{-1}\text{K}^{-1} - \frac{1}{2} \times 205.1 \text{ J mol}^{-1}\text{K}^{-1}$$
$$= -345.4 \text{ J mol}^{-1}\text{K}^{-1}$$

(c) $C(graphite) + 2S(rhombic) \rightleftharpoons CS_2(l)$

$$\Delta_f S°[CS_2(l)] = S°[CS_2(l)] - S°[C(graphite)] - 2S°[S(rhombic)]$$
$$= 151.3 \text{ J mol}^{-1}\text{K}^{-1} - 5.74 \text{ J mol}^{-1}\text{K}^{-1} - 2 \times 31.80 \text{ J mol}^{-1}\text{K}^{-1}$$
$$= 82.0 \text{ J mol}^{-1}\text{K}^{-1}$$

13. **(M)**

(a) For an isothermal gas expansion, $\Delta S = nR \ln\left(\dfrac{V_f}{V_i}\right)$. Therefore,

$$\Delta S = 1 \text{ mol} \times 8.3145 \text{ J K}^{-1} \text{ mol}^{-1} \ln\left(\frac{2V}{V}\right) = 5.76 \text{ J K}^{-1}$$

(b) This is a constant pressure heating process for which $\Delta S \approx C_p \ln\left(\dfrac{T_f}{T_i}\right)$. Using 35.69 J K^{-1} mol^{-1} for the molar heat capacity of methane, we obtain

$$\Delta S \approx 1 \text{ mol} \times 35.69 \text{ J K}^{-1} \text{ mol}^{-1} \times \ln\left(\frac{325 \text{ K}}{298 \text{ K}}\right) = 3.10 \text{ J K}^{-1}$$

14. **(M)**

(a) For an isothermal gas expansion, $\Delta S = -nR \ln\left(\dfrac{P_f}{P_i}\right)$. Therefore,

$$\Delta S = -1 \text{ mol} \times 8.3145 \text{ J K}^{-1} \text{ mol}^{-1} \ln\left(\frac{2P}{P}\right) = -5.76 \text{ J K}^{-1}$$

(b) Here, we can use the equation $\Delta S = C_p \ln(T_f/T_i) - nR \ln(P_f/P_i)$. The pressure of the gas changes in this process. We have

$$P_i = \frac{(1 \text{ mol})(0.083145 \text{ bar L}^{-1} \text{ K}^{-1} \text{ mol}^{-1})(298 \text{ K})}{20.0 \text{ L}} = 1.24 \text{ bar}$$

$$P_f = \frac{(1 \text{ mol})(0.083145 \text{ bar L}^{-1} \text{ K}^{-1} \text{ mol}^{-1})(355 \text{ K})}{20.0 \text{ L}} = 1.48 \text{ bar}$$

Therefore,

$$\Delta S = (1 \text{ mol})(29.1 \text{ J K}^{-1} \text{ mol}^{-1}) \ln(355 \text{ K}/298 \text{ K})$$

$$-(1 \text{ mol})(8.3145 \text{ J K}^{-1} \text{ mol}^{-1}) \ln(1.48 \text{ bar}/1.24 \text{ bar})$$

$$= (5.09 - 1.47) \text{ J K}^{-1} = 3.62 \text{ J K}^{-1}$$

15. (M)

(a) $\Delta_{vap}H = \Delta_f H°[H_2O(g)] - \Delta_f H°[H_2O(l)] = -241.8 \text{ kJ/mol} - (-285.8 \text{ kJ/mol})$

$$= +44.0 \text{ kJ/mol}$$

$\Delta_{vap}S° = S°[H_2O(g)] - S°[H_2O(l)] = 188.8 \text{ J mol}^{-1} \text{ K}^{-1} - 69.91 \text{ J mol}^{-1}\text{K}^{-1}$

$$= 118.9 \text{ J mol}^{-1} \text{ K}^{-1}$$

There is an alternate, but incorrect, method of obtaining $\Delta_{vap}S°$.

$$\Delta_{vap}S° = \frac{\Delta_{vap}H°}{T} = \frac{44.0 \times 10^3 \text{ J/mol}}{298.15 \text{ K}} = 148 \text{ J mol}^{-1} \text{ K}^{-1}$$

This method is invalid because the temperature in the denominator of the equation must be the temperature at which the liquid-vapor transition is at equilibrium. Liquid water and water vapor at 1 atm pressure (standard state, indicated by °) are in equilibrium only at $100 °C = 373$ K.

(b) The reason why $\Delta_{vap}H°$ is different at 25 °C from its value at 100 °C has to do with the heat required to bring the reactants and products down to 298 K from 373 K. The specific heat of liquid water is higher than the heat capacity of steam. Thus, more heat is given off by lowering the temperature of the liquid water from 100 °C to 25 °C than is given off by lowering the temperature of the same amount of steam. Another way to think of this is that hydrogen bonding is more disrupted in water at 100 °C than at 25 °C (because the molecules are in rapid—thermal—motion), and hence, there is not as much energy needed to convert liquid to vapor (thus $\Delta_{vap}H°$ has a smaller value at 100 °C. The reason why $\Delta_{vap}S°$ has a larger value at 25 °C than at 100 °C has to do with dispersion. A vapor at 1 atm pressure (the case at both temperatures) has about the same entropy. On the other hand, liquid water is more disordered (better able to disperse energy) at higher temperatures since more of the hydrogen bonds are disrupted by thermal motion. (The hydrogen bonds are totally disrupted in the two vapors).

16. **(M)** In this problem we are given standard enthalpies of the formation ($\Delta_f H°$) of liquid and gas pentane at 298.15 K and asked to estimate the normal boiling point of pentane, $\Delta_{vap} G°$ and furthermore comment on the significance of the sign of $\Delta_{vap} G°$. The general strategy in solving this problem is to first determine $\Delta_{vap} H°$ from the known enthalpies of formation. Trouton's rule can then be used to determine the normal boiling point of pentane. Lastly, $\Delta_{vap, 298K} G°$ can be calculated using $\Delta_{vap} G° = \Delta_{vap} H° - T\Delta_{vap} S°$.

Calculate $\Delta_{vap} H°$ from the known values of $\Delta_f H°$ (part a):

$$C_5H_{12}(l) \rightleftharpoons C_5H_{12}(g)$$

$$\Delta_f H° - 173.5 \text{ kJ mol}^{-1} -146.9 \text{ kJ mol}^{-1}$$

$$\Delta_{vap} H° = (-146.9 - (-173.5))\text{kJ mol}^{-1} = 26.6 \text{ kJ mol}^{-1}$$

Determine normal boiling point using Trouton's rule (part a):

$$\Delta_{vap} S° = \frac{\Delta_{vap} H°}{T_{nbp}} = 87 \text{ J mol}^{-1} \text{ K}^{-1}$$

$$T_{nbp} = \frac{\Delta_{vap} H°}{\Delta_{vap} S°} = \frac{26.6 \text{ kJ mol}^{-1}}{\dfrac{87 \text{ kJ K}^{-1}\text{mol}^{-1}}{1000}} = 306 \text{ K}$$

$$T_{nbp} = 32.9 \text{ °C}$$

Use $\Delta_{vap} G° = \Delta_{vap} H° - T\Delta_{vap} S°$ to calculate $\Delta_{vap, 298K} G°$ (part b):

$$\Delta_{vap} G° = \Delta_{vap} H° - T\Delta_{vap} S°$$

$$\Delta_{vap, 298K} G° = 26.6 \text{ kJ mol}^{-1} - 298.15 \text{ K} \times \frac{87 \text{ kJ mol}^{-1}\text{K}^{-1}}{1000}$$

$$\Delta_{vap, 298K} G° = 0.66 \text{ kJ mol}^{-1}$$

Comment on the value of $\Delta_{vap, 298K} G°$ (part c):

The positive value of $\Delta_{vap} G°$ indicates that normal boiling (having a vapor pressure of 1.00 atm) for pentane should be non-spontaneous (will not occur) at 298. The vapor pressure of pentane at 298 K should be less than 1.00 atm.

17. **(M)** Trouton's rule is obeyed most closely by liquids that do not have a high degree of order within the liquid. In both HF and CH_3OH, hydrogen bonds create considerable order within the liquid. In $C_6H_5CH_3$, the only attractive forces are non-directional London forces, which have no preferred orientation as hydrogen bonds do. Thus, of the three choices, liquid $C_6H_5CH_3$ would most closely follow Trouton's rule.

18. **(E)** $\Delta_{vap}H° = \Delta_f H°\,[Br_2(g)] - \Delta_f H°\,[Br_2(l)] \approx 30.91 \text{ kJ/mol} - 0.00 \text{ kJ/mol} = 30.91 \text{ kJ/mol}$

$$\Delta_{vap}S° = \frac{\Delta_{vap}H°}{T_{vap}} \approx 87 \text{ J mol}^{-1}\text{ K}^{-1} \text{ or } T_{vap} = \frac{\Delta_{vap}H°}{\Delta_{vap}S°} \approx \frac{30.91 \times 10^3 \text{ J/mol}}{87 \text{ J mol}^{-1}\text{K}^{-1}} = 3.5 \times 10^2 \text{ K}$$

The accepted value of the boiling point of bromine is $58.8\,°C = 332 \text{ K} = 3.32 \times 10^2 \text{ K}$. Thus, our estimate is in reasonable agreement with the measured value.

19. **(M)** The liquid water-gaseous water equilibrium H_2O (l, 0.50 atm) $\rightleftharpoons H_2O$ (g, 0.50 atm) can only be established at <u>one temperature</u>, namely the boiling point for water under 0.50 atm external pressure. We can estimate the boiling point for water under 0.50 atm external pressure by using the Clausius-Clapeyron equation:

$$\ln\frac{P_2}{P_1} = \frac{\Delta_{vap}H°}{R}\left(\frac{1}{T_1} - \frac{1}{T_2}\right)$$

We know that at 373 K, the pressure of water vapor is 1.00 atm and $\Delta_{vap}H = 40.7 \text{ kJ mol}^{-1}$ (see footnote b in Table 12.4). Let's make $P_1 = 1.00$ atm, $P_2 = 0.50$ atm and $T_1 = 373$ K. Thus, the boiling point under 0.50 atm pressure is T_2. To find T_2 we simply insert the appropriate information into the Clausius-Clapeyron equation and solve for T_2:

$$\ln\frac{0.50 \text{ atm}}{1.00 \text{ atm}} = \frac{40.7 \text{ kJ mol}^{-1}}{8.3145 \times 10^{-3} \text{ kJ K}^{-1}\text{ mol}^{-1}}\left(\frac{1}{373 \text{ K}} - \frac{1}{T_2}\right)$$

$$-1.4\underline{16} \times 10^{-4} \text{ K} = \left(\frac{1}{373 \text{ K}} - \frac{1}{T_2}\right)$$

Solving for T_2 we find a temperature of 354 K or 81°C. Consequently, to achieve an equilibrium between gaseous and liquid water under 0.50 atm pressure, the temperature must be set at 354 K.

20. **(M)** Figure 12-28 (phase diagram for carbon dioxide) shows that at −60 °C and under 1 atm of external pressure, carbon dioxide exists as a gas. In other words, neither solid nor liquid CO_2 can exist at this temperature and pressure. Clearly, of the three phases, gaseous CO_2 must be the most stable and, hence, have the lowest Gibbs energy when $T = -60\,°C$ and $P_{ext} = 1.00$ atm.

Gibbs Energy and Spontaneous Change

21. **(E)** Answer (b) is correct. Br—Br bonds are broken in this reaction, meaning that it is endothermic, with $\Delta_r H > 0$. Since the number of moles of gas increases during the reaction, $\Delta_r S > 0$. And, because $\Delta_r G = \Delta_r H - T\,\Delta_r S$, this reaction is non-spontaneous $(\Delta_r G > 0)$ at low temperatures where the $\Delta_r H$ term predominates and spontaneous $(\Delta_r G < 0)$ at high temperatures where the $T\,\Delta_r S$ term predominates.

22. **(E)** Answer (d) is correct. A reaction that proceeds only through electrolysis is a reaction that is non-spontaneous. Such a reaction has $\Delta_r G > 0$.

23. **(E)**

(a) $\Delta_r H^\circ < 0$ and $\Delta_r S^\circ < 0$ (since $\Delta n_{gas} < 0$) for this reaction. Thus, this reaction is case 2 of Table 13-3. It is spontaneous at low temperatures and non-spontaneous at high temperatures.

(b) We are unable to predict the sign of $\Delta_r S^\circ$ for this reaction, since $\Delta n_{gas} = 0$. Thus, no strong prediction as to the temperature behavior of this reaction can be made. Since $\Delta_r H^\circ > 0$, we can, however, conclude that the reaction will be non-spontaneous at low temperatures.

(c) $\Delta_r H^\circ > 0$ and $\Delta_r S^\circ > 0$ (since $\Delta n_{gas} > 0$) for this reaction. This is case 3 of Table 13-3. It is non-spontaneous at low temperatures, but spontaneous at high temperatures.

24. **(E)**

(a) $\Delta_r H^\circ > 0$ and $\Delta_r S^\circ < 0$ (since $\Delta n_{gas} < 0$) for this reaction. This is case 4 of Table 13-3. It is non-spontaneous at all temperatures.

(b) $\Delta_r H^\circ < 0$ and $\Delta_r S^\circ > 0$ (since $\Delta n_{gas} > 0$) for this reaction. This is case 1 of Table 13-3. It is spontaneous at all temperatures.

(c) $\Delta_r H^\circ < 0$ and $\Delta_r S^\circ < 0$ (since $\Delta n_{gas} < 0$) for this reaction. This is case 2 of Table 13-3. It is spontaneous at low temperatures and non-spontaneous at high temperatures.

25. **(E)** First of all, the process is clearly spontaneous, and therefore $\Delta G < 0$. In addition, the gases are more dispersed when they are at a lower pressure and therefore $\Delta S > 0$. We also conclude that $\Delta H = 0$ because the gases are ideal and thus there are no forces of attraction or repulsion between them.

26. **(E)** Because an ideal solution forms spontaneously, $\Delta G < 0$. Also, the molecules of solvent and solute that are mixed together in the solution are in a more dispersed state than the separated solvent and solute. Therefore, $\Delta S > 0$. However, in an ideal solution, the attractive forces between solvent and solute molecules equal those forces between solvent molecules and those between solute molecules. Thus, $\Delta H = 0$. There is no net energy of interaction.

27. **(M)**

(a) An exothermic reaction (one that gives off heat) may not occur spontaneously if, at the same time, the system becomes more ordered (concentrated) that is, $\Delta_r S^\circ < 0$. This is particularly true at a high temperature, where the $T\Delta_r S$ term dominates the $\Delta_r G$ expression. An example of such a process is freezing water (clearly exothermic because the reverse process, melting ice, is endothermic), which is not spontaneous at temperatures above $0\,^\circ C$.

(b) A reaction in which $\Delta_r S > 0$ need not be spontaneous if that process also is endothermic. This is particularly true at low temperatures, where the $\Delta_r H$ term dominates the $\Delta_r G$ expression. An example is the vaporization of water (clearly an endothermic process, one that requires heat, and one that produces a gas, so $\Delta_r S > 0$), which is not spontaneous at low temperatures, that is, below 100 °C (assuming $P_{ext} = 1.00$ atm).

28. **(M)** In this problem we are asked to explain whether the reaction $AB(g) \rightarrow A(g) + B(g)$ is always going to be spontaneous at high rather than low temperatures. In order to answer this question, we need to determine the signs of $\Delta_r H$, $\Delta_r S$ and consequently $\Delta_r G$. Recall that $\Delta_r G = \Delta_r H - T\Delta_r S$.

Determine the sign of $\Delta_r S$:
We are generating two moles of gas from one mole. The entropy of the system increases and $\Delta_r S$ must be greater than zero.

Determine the sign of $\Delta_r H$:
In this reaction, we are breaking A-B bond. Bond breaking requires energy, so the reaction must be endothermic. Therefore, $\Delta_r H$ is also greater than zero.

Use $\Delta_r G = \Delta_r H - T\Delta_r S$ to determine the sign of $\Delta_r G$:

$\Delta_r G = \Delta_r H - T\Delta_r S$. Since $\Delta_r H$ is positive and $\Delta_r S$ is positive there will be a temperature at which $T\Delta_r S$ will become greater than $\Delta_r H$. The reaction will be favored at high temperatures and disfavored at low temperatures.

Standard Gibbs Energy of Reaction, $\Delta_r G°$

29. **(M)** $\Delta_r H° = \Delta_f H°\left[NH_4Cl(s)\right] - \Delta_f H°\left[NH_3(g)\right] - \Delta_f H°\left[HCl(g)\right]$

$= -314.4 \text{ kJ/mol} - (-46.11 \text{ kJ/mol} - 92.31 \text{ kJ/mol}) = -176.0 \text{ kJ/mol}$

$\Delta_r G° = \Delta_f G°\left[NH_4Cl(s)\right] - \Delta_f G°\left[NH_3(g)\right] - \Delta_f G°\left[HCl(g)\right]$

$= -202.9 \text{ kJ/mol} - (-16.48 \text{ kJ/mol} - 95.30 \text{ kJ/mol}) = -91.1 \text{ kJ/mol}$

$\Delta_r G° = \Delta_r H° - T\Delta_r S°$

$\Delta_r S° = \dfrac{\Delta_r H° - \Delta_r G°}{T} = \dfrac{-176.0 \text{ kJ/mol} + 91.1 \text{ kJ/mol}}{298 \text{ K}} \times \dfrac{1000 \text{ J}}{1 \text{ kJ}} = -285 \text{ J mol}^{-1}$

30. **(M)**

(a) $\Delta_r G° = \Delta_f G°\left[C_2H_6(g)\right] - \Delta_f G°\left[C_2H_2(g)\right] - 2\Delta_f G°\left[H_2(g)\right]$

$= -32.82 \text{ kJ/mol} - 209.2 \text{ kJ/mol} - 2(0.00 \text{ kJ/mol}) = -242.0 \text{ kJ/mol}$

(b) $\Delta_r G° = 2\Delta_f G°\left[SO_2(g)\right] + \Delta_f G°\left[O_2(g)\right] - 2\Delta_f G°\left[SO_3(g)\right]$

$= 2(-300.2 \text{ kJ/mol}) + 0.00 \text{ kJ/mol} - 2(-371.1 \text{ kJ/mol}) = +141.8 \text{ kJ/mol}$

(c) $\Delta_r G° = 3\Delta_f G°\left[\text{Fe(s)}\right] + 4\Delta_f G°\left[\text{H}_2\text{O(g)}\right] - \Delta_f G°\left[\text{Fe}_3\text{O}_4\text{(s)}\right] - 4\Delta_f G°\left[\text{H}_2\text{(g)}\right]$

$= 3(0.00 \text{ kJ/mol}) + 4(-228.6 \text{ kJ/mol}) - (-1015 \text{ kJ/mol}) - 4(0.00 \text{ kJ/mol})$

$= 101 \text{ kJ/mol}$

(d) $\Delta_r G° = 2\Delta_f G°\left[\text{Al}^{3+}\text{(aq)}\right] + 3\Delta_f G°\left[\text{H}_2\text{(g)}\right] - 2\Delta_f G°\left[\text{Al(s)}\right] - 6\Delta_f G°\left[\text{H}^+\text{(aq)}\right]$

$= 2(-485 \text{ kJ/mol}) + 3(0.00 \text{ kJ/mol}) - 2(0.00\text{kJ/mol}) - 6(0.00 \text{ kJ/mol})$

$= -970. \text{ kJ/mol}$

31. **(M)**

(a) $\Delta_r S° = 2 S°\left[\text{POCl}_3\text{(1)}\right] - 2 S°\left[\text{PCl}_3\text{(g)}\right] - S°\left[\text{O}_2\text{(g)}\right]$

$= 2(222.4 \text{ J K}^{-1}\text{ mol}^{-1}) - 2(311.7 \text{ J K}^{-1}\text{ mol}^{-1}) - 205.1 \text{ J K}^{-1}\text{ mol}^{-1}$

$= -383.7 \text{ J K}^{-1}\text{ mol}^{-1}$

$\Delta_r G° = \Delta_r H° - T\Delta_r S° = -620.2\times10^3 \text{ J mol}^{-1} - (298 \text{ K})(-383.7 \text{ J K}^{-1}\text{ mol}^{-1})$

$= -506\times10^3 \text{ J mol}^{-1} = -506 \text{ kJ mol}^{-1}$

(b) The reaction proceeds spontaneously in the forward direction when reactants and products are in their standard states, because the value of $\Delta_r G°$ is less than zero.

32. **(M)**

(a) $\Delta_r S° = S°\left[\text{Br}_2\text{(1)}\right] + 2 S°\left[\text{HNO}_2\text{(aq)}\right] - 2 S°\left[\text{H}^+\text{(aq)}\right]$

$- 2 S°\left[\text{Br}^-\text{(aq)}\right] - 2 S°\left[\text{NO}_2\text{(g)}\right]$

$= 152.2 \text{ J K}^{-1}\text{ mol}^{-1} + 2(135.6 \text{ J K}^{-1}\text{ mol}^{-1}) - 2(0 \text{ J K}^{-1}\text{ mol}^{-1})$

$- 2(82.4 \text{ J K}^{-1}\text{ mol}^{-1}) - 2(240.1 \text{ J K}^{-1}\text{ mol}^{-1}) = -221.6 \text{ J/K}$

$\Delta_r G° = \Delta_r H° - T\Delta_r S° = -61.6\times10^3\text{ J mol}^{-1} - (298\text{ K})(-221.6 \text{ JK}^{-1}\text{ mol}^{-1})$

$= +4.4\times10^3 \text{ J} = +4.4\text{ kJ mol}^{-1}$

(b) The reaction does not proceed spontaneously in the forward direction when reactants and products are in their standard states, because the value of $\Delta_r G°$ is greater than zero.

33. **(M)** We combine the reactions in the same way as for any Hess's law calculations.

(a) $\text{N}_2\text{O(g)} \rightarrow \text{N}_2\text{(g)} + \tfrac{1}{2}\text{O}_2\text{(g)}$ $\quad\quad \Delta_r G° = -\tfrac{1}{2}(+208.4\text{ kJ mol}^{-1}) = -104.2\text{ kJ mol}^{-1}$

$\text{N}_2\text{(g)} + 2\text{O}_2\text{(g)} \rightarrow 2\text{NO}_2\text{(g)}$ $\quad\quad \Delta_r G° = +102.6\text{ kJ mol}^{-1}$

Net: $\text{N}_2\text{O(g)} + \tfrac{3}{2}\text{O}_2\text{(g)} \rightarrow 2\text{NO}_2\text{(g)}$ $\quad \Delta_r G° = -104.2 + 102.6 = -1.6\text{ kJ mol}^{-1}$

This reaction reaches an equilibrium condition, with significant amounts of all species being present. This conclusion is based on the relatively small absolute value of $\Delta_r G°$.

(b)

$$2N_2(g) + 6H_2(g) \rightarrow 4NH_3(g) \qquad \Delta_rG^\circ = 2(-33.0 \text{ kJ mol}^{-1}) = -66.0 \text{ kJ mol}^{-1}$$

$$4NH_3(g) + 5O_2(g) \rightarrow 4NO(g) + 6H_2O(l) \quad \Delta_rG^\circ = -1010.5 \text{ kJ mol}^{-1}$$

$$4NO(g) \rightarrow 2N_2(g) + 2O_2(g) \qquad \Delta_rG^\circ = -2(+173.1 \text{ kJ mol}^{-1}) = -346.2 \text{ kJ mol}^{-1}$$

Net: $6H_2(g) + 3O_2(g) \rightarrow 6H_2O(l) \quad \Delta_rG^\circ = -66.0 \text{ kJ mol}^{-1} - 1010.5 \text{ kJ mol}^{-1}$

$$-346.2 \text{ kJ mol}^{-1} = -1422.7 \text{ kJ mol}^{-1}$$

This reaction is three times the desired reaction, which therefore has
$\Delta_rG^\circ = -1422.7 \text{ kJ mol}^{-1} \div 3 = -474.3 \text{ kJ mol}^{-1}$.

The large negative Δ_rG° value indicates that this reaction will go to completion at 25 °C.

(c)

$$4NH_3(g) + 5O_2(g) \rightarrow 4NO(g) + 6H_2O(l) \quad \Delta_rG^\circ = -1010.5 \text{ kJ mol}^{-1}$$

$$4NO(g) \rightarrow 2N_2(g) + 2O_2(g) \qquad \Delta_rG^\circ = -2(+173.1 \text{ kJ mol}^{-1}) = -346.2 \text{ kJ mol}^{-1}$$

$$2N_2(g) + O_2(g) \rightarrow 2N_2O(g) \qquad \Delta_rG^\circ = +208.4 \text{ kJ mol}^{-1}$$

$4NH_3(g) + 4O_2(g) \rightarrow 2N_2O(g) + 6H_2O(l) \quad \Delta_rG^\circ = -1010.5 \text{ kJ mol}^{-1} - 346.2 \text{ kJ mol}^{-1}$

$$+208.4 \text{ kJ mol}^{-1}$$

$$= -1148.3 \text{ kJ mol}^{-1}$$

This reaction is twice the desired reaction, which, therefore, has $\Delta_rG^\circ = -574.2 \text{ kJ mol}^{-1}$.
The very large negative value of the Δ_rG° for this reaction indicates that it will go to completion.

34. **(M)** We combine the reactions in the same way as for any Hess's law calculations.

(a) $COS(g) + 2CO_2(g) \rightarrow SO_2(g) + 3CO(g) \qquad \Delta_rG^\circ = -(-246.4 \text{ kJ mol}^{-1}) = +246.6 \text{ kJ mol}^{-1}$

$2CO(g) + 2H_2O(g) \rightarrow 2CO_2(g) + 2H_2(g) \qquad \Delta_rG^\circ = 2(-28.6 \text{ kJ mol}^{-1}) = -57.2 \text{ kJ mol}^{-1}$

$COS(g) + 2H_2O(g) \rightarrow SO_2(g) + CO(g) + 2H_2(g) \quad \Delta_rG^\circ = +246.6 - 57.2 = +189.4 \text{ kJ mol}^{-1}$

This reaction is spontaneous in the reverse direction, because of the large positive value of Δ_rG°.

(b) $COS(g) + 2CO_2(g) \rightarrow SO_2(g) + 3CO(g) \qquad \Delta_rG^\circ = -(-246.4 \text{ kJ mol}^{-1}) = +246.6 \text{ kJ mol}^{-1}$

$3CO(g) + 3H_2O(g) \rightarrow 3CO_2(g) + 3H_2(g) \qquad \Delta_rG^\circ = 3(-28.6 \text{ kJ mol}^{-1}) = -85.8 \text{ kJ mol}^{-1}$

$COS(g) + 3H_2O(g) \rightarrow CO_2(g) + SO_2(g) + 3H_2(g) \quad \Delta_rG^\circ = +246.6 - 85.8 = +160.8 \text{ kJ mol}^{-1}$

This reaction is spontaneous in the reverse direction, because of the large positive value of Δ_rG°.

(c) $COS(g) + H_2(g) \rightarrow CO(g) + H_2S(g) \qquad \Delta_rG^\circ = -(+1.4) \text{ kJ mol}^{-1}$

$CO(g) + H_2O(g) \rightarrow CO_2(g) + H_2(g) \qquad \Delta_rG^\circ = -28.6 \text{ kJ mol}^{-1} = -28.6 \text{ kJ mol}^{-1}$

$COS(g) + H_2O(g) \rightarrow CO_2(g) + H_2S(g) \qquad \Delta_rG^\circ = -1.4 \text{ kJ mol}^{-1} - 28.6 \text{ kJ mol}^{-1}$

$$= -30.0 \text{ kJ mol}^{-1}$$

The negative value of the Δ_rG° for this reaction indicates that it is spontaneous in the forward direction.

35. **(D)** The combustion reaction is : $C_6H_6(l) + \frac{15}{2}O_2(g) \rightarrow 6CO_2(g) + 3H_2O(g \text{ or } l)$

(a) $\Delta_r G° = 6\Delta_f G°[CO_2(g)] + 3\Delta_f G°[H_2O(l)] - \Delta_f G°[C_6H_6(l)] - \frac{15}{2}\Delta_f G°[O_2(g)]$

$= 6(-394.4\,\text{kJ mol}^{-1}) + 3(-237.1\,\text{kJ mol}^{-1}) - (+124.5\,\text{kJ mol}^{-1}) - \frac{15}{2}(0.00\,\text{kJ mol}^{-1})$

$= -3202\,\text{kJ mol}^{-1}$

(b) $\Delta_r G° = 6\Delta_f G°[CO_2(g)] + 3\Delta_f G°[H_2O(g)] - \Delta_f G°[C_6H_6(l)] - \frac{15}{2}\Delta_f G°[O_2(g)]$

$= 6(-394.4\,\text{kJ mol}^{-1}) + 3(-228.6\,\text{kJ mol}^{-1}) - (+124.5\,\text{kJ mol}^{-1}) - \frac{15}{2}(0.00\,\text{kJ mol}^{-1})$

$= -3177\,\text{kJ mol}^{-1}$

We could determine the difference between the two values of $\Delta_r G°$ by noting the difference between the two products: $3H_2O(l) \rightarrow 3H_2O(g)$ and determining the value of $\Delta_r G°$ for this difference:

$\Delta_r G° = 3\Delta_f G°[H_2O(g)] - 3\Delta_f G°[H_2O(l)] = 3[-228.6 - (-237.1)]\,\text{kJ mol}^{-1}$

$= 25.5\,\text{kJ mol}^{-1}$

36. **(M)** We wish to find the value of the $\Delta H°$ for the given reaction: $F_2(g) \rightarrow 2F(g)$

$\Delta_r S° = 2S°[F(g)] - S°[F_2(g)] = 2(158.8\,\text{J K}^{-1}\,\text{mol}^{-1}) - (202.8\,\text{J K}^{-1}\,\text{mol}^{-1})$

$= +114.8\,\text{J K}^{-1}\,\text{mol}^{-1}$

$\Delta_r H° = \Delta_r G° + T\Delta_r S° = 123.9 \times 10^3\,\text{J mol}^{-1} + (298\,\text{K} \times 114.8\,\text{J K}^{-1}\,\text{mol}^{-1})$

$= 158.1\,\text{kJ/mole of bonds}$

The value in Table 10.3 is 159 kJ/mol, which is in quite good agreement with the value found here.

37. **(M)**

(a) $\Delta_r S° = \Sigma S°_{\text{products}} - \Sigma S°_{\text{reactants}}$

$= [1 \times 301.2\,\text{J K}^{-1}\text{mol}^{-1} + 2 \times 188.8\,\text{J K}^{-1}\text{mol}^{-1}] - [2 \times 247.4\,\text{J K}^{-1}\text{mol}^{-1} + 1 \times 238.5\,\text{J K}^{-1}\text{mol}^{-1}] = -54.5\,\text{J K}^{-1}\,\text{mol}^{-1}$

$\Delta_r S° = -0.0545\,\text{kJ K}^{-1}\,\text{mol}^{-1}$

(b) $\Delta_r H° = \Sigma$ (bonds broken in reactants (kJ/mol)) $-\Sigma$(bonds broken in products(kJ/ mol))

$= [4 \times (389\,\text{kJ mol}^{-1})_{\text{N-H}} + 4 \times (222\,\text{kJ mol}^{-1})_{\text{O-F}}] -$
$[4 \times (301\,\text{kJ mol}^{-1})_{\text{N-F}} + 4 \times (464\,\text{kJ mol}^{-1})_{\text{O-H}}]$

$\Delta_r H° = -616\,\text{kJ mol}^{-1}$

(c) $\Delta_r G° = \Delta_r H° - T\Delta_r S° = -616\,\text{kJ mol}^{-1} - 298\,\text{K}(-0.0545\,\text{kJ K}^{-1}\text{mol}^{-1})$

$= -600\,\text{kJ mol}^{-1}$

Since the $\Delta_r G°$ is <u>negative</u>, the reaction is <u>spontaneous</u>, and hence feasible (at 25 °C). Because both the entropy and enthalpy changes are *negative*, this reaction will be more highly favored at low temperatures (i.e., the reaction is enthalpy driven)

38. **(D)** In this problem we are asked to find $\Delta_r G^\circ$ at 298 K for the decomposition of ammonium nitrate to yield dinitrogen oxide gas and liquid water. Furthermore, we are asked to determine whether the decomposition will be favored at temperatures above or below 298 K. In order to answer these questions, we first need the balanced chemical equation for the process. From the data in Appendix D, we can determine $\Delta_r H^\circ$ and $\Delta_r S^\circ$. Both quantities will be required to determine $\Delta_r G^\circ$ ($\Delta_r G^\circ = \Delta_r H^\circ - T\Delta_r S^\circ$). Finally the magnitude of $\Delta_r G^\circ$ as a function of temperature can be judged depending on the values of $\Delta_r H^\circ$ and $\Delta_r S^\circ$.

From the balanced chemical equation for the process

$$\text{NH}_4\text{NO}_3(s) \xrightarrow{\Delta} \text{N}_2\text{O}(g) + 2\text{H}_2\text{O}(l)$$

we can determine $\Delta_r H^\circ$ and $\Delta_r S^\circ$ by utilizing $\Delta_f H^\circ$ and S° values provided in Appendix D:

$\Delta_r H^\circ = [2 \, (-285.8 \text{ kJ mol}^{-1}) + 1 \, (82.05 \text{ kJ mol}^{-1})] - [1 \, (-365.6 \text{ kJ mol}^{-1})]$

$\Delta_r H^\circ = -124.0 \text{ kJ mol}^{-1}$

$\Delta_r S^\circ = [2 \times 69.91 \text{ J K}^{-1} \text{ mol}^{-1} + 1 \times 219.9 \text{ J K}^{-1} \text{ mol}^{-1}] - [1 \times 151.1 \text{ J K}^{-1} \text{ mol}^{-1}]$

$\Delta_r S^\circ = 208.6 \text{ J K}^{-1} \text{mol}^{-1} = 0.2086 \text{ J K}^{-1} \text{ mol}^{-1}$

$\Delta_r G^\circ = \Delta_r H^\circ - T\Delta_r S^\circ = -124.0 \text{ kJ mol}^{-1} - 298.15 \text{ K} \times 0.2086 \text{ J K}^{-1} \text{ mol}^{-1}$

$\Delta_r G^\circ = -186.1 \text{ kJ mol}^{-1}$

Since $\Delta_r H^\circ$ is <u>negative</u> and $\Delta_r S^\circ$ is <u>positive</u>, the decomposition of ammonium nitrate is spontaneous at all temperatures. However, as the temperature increases, the $T\Delta S$ term gets larger and as a result, the decomposition reaction shift towards producing more products. The reaction is highly favored above 298 K (it will also be faster).

The Thermodynamic Equilibrium Constant

39. **(E)** In all three cases, $K_{eq} = K_p$ because only gases, pure solids, and pure liquids are present in the chemical equations. There are no factors for solids and liquids in K_{eq} expressions, and gases appear as partial pressures in atmospheres. That makes K_{eq} the same as K_p for these three reactions.

We now recall that $K_p = K_c (RT)^{\Delta n}$. Hence, in these three cases we have:

(a) $2\text{SO}_2(g) + \text{O}_2(g) \rightleftharpoons 2\text{SO}_3(g)$; $\Delta n_{gas} = 2 - (2+1) = -1$; $K = K_p = K_c (RT)^{-1}$

(b) $\text{HI}(g) \rightleftharpoons \frac{1}{2}\text{H}_2(g) + \frac{1}{2}\text{I}_2(g)$; $\Delta n_{gas} = 1 - (\frac{1}{2} + \frac{1}{2}) = 0$; $K = K_p = K_c$

(c) $\text{NH}_4\text{HCO}_3(s) \rightleftharpoons \text{NH}_3(g) + \text{CO}_2(g) + \text{H}_2\text{O}(l)$;

$\Delta n_{gas} = 2 - (0) = +2$ $\quad K = K_p = K_c (RT)^2$

40. **(M)**

(a) $K = \dfrac{P\{\text{H}_2(g)\}^4}{P\{\text{H}_2\text{O}(g)\}^4}$

(b) Terms for both solids, Fe(s) and $\text{Fe}_3\text{O}_4(s)$, are properly excluded from the thermodynamic equilibrium constant expression. (Actually, each solid has an activity of 1.00.) Thus, the equilibrium partial pressures of both $\text{H}_2(g)$ and $\text{H}_2\text{O}(g)$ do not depend on the amounts of the two solids present, as long as some of each solid is present. One way to understand this is that any chemical reaction occurs on the surface of the solids, and thus is unaffected by the amount present.

(c) We can produce $H_2(g)$ from $H_2O(g)$ without regard to the proportions of $Fe(s)$ and $Fe_3O_4(s)$ with the qualification, that there must always be some $Fe(s)$ present for the production of $H_2(g)$ to continue.

41. **(M)** In this problem, we are asked to determine the equilibrium constant and Δ_rG° for the reaction between carbon monoxide and hydrogen to yield methanol. To calculate Δ_rG°, we can use the equation $\Delta_rG^\circ = -RT \ln K$, where K is the thermodynamic equilibrium constant. Our first task is to use the given data to obtain the value of the thermodynamic equilibrium constant. For the given reaction, $K = \dfrac{(P_{CH_3OH}/P^\circ)}{(P_{CO}/P^\circ)(P_{H_2}/P^\circ)^2}$ with $P^\circ = 1$ bar

The equilibrium concentrations at 483 K were provided. We proceed by first converting the molar concentrations to pressures by using the ideal gas law, and then calculating the thermodynamic equilibrium constant, K. The standard Gibbs energy of reaction can then be determined by using $\Delta_rG^\circ = -RT \ln K$.

$$CO(g) + 2H_2(g) \rightleftharpoons CH_3OH(g)$$

$$pV = nRT \Rightarrow p = \frac{n}{V}RT = cRT$$

$$p_{CO} = 0.0911 \text{ mol L}^{-1} \times 0.08314 \text{ L bar K}^{-1} \text{ mol}^{-1} \times 483 \text{ K} = 3.66 \text{ bar}$$

$$p_{H_2} = 0.0822 \text{ mol L}^{-1} \times 0.08314 \text{ L bar K}^{-1} \text{ mol}^{-1} \times 483 \text{ K} = 3.30 \text{ bar}$$

$$p_{CH_3OH} = 0.00892 \text{ mol L}^{-1} \times 0.08314 \text{ L bar K}^{-1} \text{ mol}^{-1} \times 483 \text{ K} = 0.358 \text{ bar}$$

$$K = \frac{p_{CH_3OH}}{p_{CO} \times p_{H_2}^2} = \frac{0.358}{3.66 \times 3.30^2} = 8.98 \times 10^{-3}$$

$$\Delta_rG^\circ = -RT \ln K = -8.314 \text{ J K}^{-1} \text{ mol}^{-1} \times 483 \text{ K} \times \ln(8.98 \times 10^{-3}) = 1.89 \times 10^4 \text{ J mol}^{-1}$$

$$\Delta_rG^\circ = 18.9 \text{ kJ mol}^{-1}$$

42. **(M)** Gibbs energy for the reaction ($\Delta_rG^\circ = \Delta_rH^\circ - T\Delta_rS^\circ$) can be calculated using Δ_fH° and S° values for $CO(g)$, $H_2(g)$ and $CH_3OH(g)$ from Appendix D.

$$\Delta_rH^\circ = \Delta_fH^\circ(CH_3OH(g)) - [\Delta_fH^\circ(CO(g)) + 2\Delta_fH^\circ(H_2(g)]$$

$$\Delta_rH^\circ = -200.7 \text{ kJ mol}^{-1} - (-110.5 \text{ kJ mol}^{-1} + 0 \text{ kJ mol}^{-1}) = -90.2 \text{ kJ mol}^{-1}$$

$$\Delta_rS^\circ = S^\circ(CH_3OH(g)) - [S^\circ(CO(g)) + 2S^\circ(H_2(g)]$$

$$\Delta_rS^\circ = 239.8 \text{ JK}^{-1} \text{ mol}^{-1} - (197.7 \text{ JK}^{-1} \text{ mol}^{-1} + 2 \times 130.7 \text{ JK}^{-1} \text{ mol}^{-1}) = -219.3 \text{ J K}^{-1} \text{ mol}^{-1}$$

$$\Delta_rG^\circ = -90.2 \text{ kJ mol}^{-1} - \frac{483K \times (-219.3) \text{ kJ K}^{-1}\text{mol}^{-1}}{1000} = 15.7 \text{ kJ mol}^{-1}$$

Equilibrium constant for the reaction can be calculated using $\Delta_rG^\circ = -RT \ln K$

$$\ln K = \frac{-\Delta_rG^\circ}{RT} \Rightarrow \ln K = \frac{-15.7 \times 1000 \text{ J mol}^{-1}}{8.314 \text{ JK}^{-1}\text{mol}^{-1} \times 483 \text{ K}} = -3.9 \Rightarrow K = e^{-3.9} = 2.0 \times 10^{-2}$$

Relationships Involving $\Delta_r G$, $\Delta_r G°$, Q and K

43. **(M)** $\Delta_r G° = 2\Delta_f G°\left[NO(g)\right] - \Delta_f G°\left[N_2O(g)\right] - 0.5\,\Delta_f G°\left[O_2(g)\right]$

$$= 2(86.55\text{ kJ/mol}) - (104.2\text{ kJ/mol}) - 0.5(0.00\text{ kJ/mol}) = 68.9\text{ kJ/mol}$$

$$= -RT\ln K = -(8.3145\times10^{-3}\text{ kJ mol}^{-1}\text{ K}^{-1})(298\text{ K})\ln K$$

$$\ln K = -\frac{68.9\text{ kJ/mol}}{8.3145\times10^{-3}\text{ kJ mol}^{-1}\text{ K}^{-1}\times298\text{ K}} = -27.8 \qquad K = e^{-27.8} = 8\times10^{-13}$$

44. **(M) (a)** $\Delta_r G° = 2\Delta_f G°\left[N_2O_5(g)\right] - 2\Delta_f G°\left[N_2O_4(g)\right] - \Delta_f G°\left[O_2(g)\right]$

$$= 2(115.1\text{ kJ/mol}) - 2(97.89\text{ kJ/mol}) - (0.00\text{ kJ/mol}) = 34.4\text{ kJ/mol}$$

(b) $\Delta_r G° = -RT\ln K \qquad \ln K = -\dfrac{\Delta_r G°}{RT} = -\dfrac{34.4\times10^3\text{ J/mol}}{8.3145\text{ J mol}^{-1}\text{ K}^{-1}\times298\text{ K}} = -13.9$

$$K = e^{-13.9} = 9\times10^{-7}$$

45. **(M)** We first balance each chemical equation, then calculate the value of $\Delta_r G°$ with data from Appendix D, and finally calculate the value of K_{eq} with the use of $\Delta_r G° = -RT\ln K$.

(a) $4HCl(g) + O_2(g) \rightleftharpoons 2H_2O(g) + 2Cl_2(s)$

$$\Delta_r G° = 2\Delta_f G°\left[H_2O(g)\right] + 2\Delta_f G°\left[Cl_2(g)\right] - 4\Delta_f G°\left[HCl(g)\right] - \Delta_f G°\left[O_2(g)\right]$$

$$= 2\times\left(-228.6\,\frac{kJ}{mol}\right) + 2\times0\,\frac{kJ}{mol} - 4\times\left(-95.30\,\frac{kJ}{mol}\right) - 0\,\frac{kJ}{mol} = -76.0\,\frac{kJ}{mol}$$

$$\ln K = \frac{-\Delta_r G°}{RT} = \frac{+76.0\times10^3\text{ J/mol}}{8.3145\text{ J mol}^{-1}\text{ K}^{-1}\times298\text{ K}} = +30.7 \qquad K = e^{+30.7} = 2\times10^{13}$$

(b) $3Fe_2O_3(s) + H_2(g) \rightleftharpoons 2Fe_3O_4(s) + H_2O(g)$

$$\Delta_r G° = 2\Delta_f G°\left[Fe_3O_4(s)\right] + \Delta_f G°\left[H_2O(g)\right] - 3\Delta_f G°\left[Fe_2O_3(s)\right] - \Delta_f G°\left[H_2(g)\right]$$

$$= 2\times(-1015\text{ kJ/mol}) - 228.6\text{ kJ/mol} - 3\times(-742.2\text{ kJ/mol}) - 0.00\text{ kJ/mol}$$

$$= -32\text{ kJ/mol}$$

$$\ln K = \frac{-\Delta_r G°}{RT} = \frac{32\times10^3\text{ J/mol}}{8.3145\text{ J mol}^{-1}\text{ K}^{-1}\times298\text{ K}} = 13; \quad K = e^{+13} = 4\times10^5$$

(c) $2Ag^+(aq) + SO_4{}^{2-}(aq) \rightleftharpoons Ag_2SO_4(s)$

$$\Delta_r G° = \Delta_f G°\left[Ag_2SO_4(s)\right] - 2\Delta_f G°\left[Ag^+(aq)\right] - \Delta_f G°\left[SO_4{}^{2-}(aq)\right]$$

$$= -618.4\text{ kJ/mol} - 2\times77.11\text{ kJ/mol} - (-744.5\text{ kJ/mol}) = -28.1\text{ kJ/mol}$$

$$\ln K = \frac{-\Delta_r G°}{RT} = \frac{28.1\times10^3\text{ J/mol}}{8.3145\text{ J mol}^{-1}\text{ K}^{-1}\times298\text{ K}} = 11.3; \quad K = e^{+11.3} = 8\times10^4$$

46. **(E)** $\Delta_r S^\circ = S^\circ\{CO_2(g)\} + S^\circ\{H_2(g)\} - S^\circ\{CO(g)\} - S^\circ\{H_2O(g)\}$

$= 213.7 \text{ J mol}^{-1} \text{ K}^{-1} + 130.7 \text{ J mol}^{-1} \text{ K}^{-1} - 197.7 \text{ J mol}^{-1} \text{ K}^{-1} - 188.8 \text{ J mol}^{-1} \text{ K}^{-1}$

$= -42.1 \text{ J mol}^{-1} \text{ K}^{-1}$

47. **(M)** In this problem we need to determine in which direction the reaction

$2SO_2(g) + O_2(g) \rightleftharpoons 2SO_3(g)$ is spontaneous when the partial pressure of SO_2, O_2, and SO_3 are 1.0×10^{-4}, 0.20 and 0.10 atm, respectively. We proceed by first determining the standard Gibbs energy of reaction ($\Delta_r G^\circ$) using tabulated data in Appendix D. The Gibbs energy of reaction for the given conditions ($\Delta_r G$) is then calculated by employing the equation $\Delta_r G = \Delta_r G^\circ + RT \ln Q$, where Q is the reaction quotient. Based on the sign of $\Delta_r G$, we can determine in which direction is the reaction spontaneous.

$\Delta_r G^\circ = 2\Delta_f G^\circ[SO_3(g)] - 2\Delta_f G^\circ[SO_2(g)] - \Delta_f G^\circ[O_2(g)]$

$\Delta_r G^\circ = 2\times(-371.1 \text{ kJ/mol}) - 2\times(-300.2 \text{ kJ/mol}) - 0.0 \text{ kJ/mol} = -141.8 \text{ kJ mol}^{-1}$

$\Delta_r G = \Delta_r G^\circ + RT \ln Q$

$$Q_p = \frac{P\{SO_3(g)\}^2}{P\{O_2(g)\} P\{SO_2(g)\}^2} = \frac{(0.10)^2}{(0.20)(1.0\times10^{-4})^2} = 5.0\times10^6$$

$\Delta_r G = -141.8 \text{ kJ mol}^{-1} + (8.3145 \times 10^{-3} \text{ kJ/K·mol})(298 \text{ K})\ln(5.0 \times 10^6) = -104 \text{ kJ mol}^{-1}$.

Since $\Delta_r G$ is negative, the reaction is spontaneous in the forward direction.

48. **(M)** We begin by calculating the standard Gibbs energy of reaction:

$H_2(g) + Cl_2(g) \rightleftharpoons 2HCl(g)$

$\Delta_r G^\circ = 2\Delta_f G^\circ[HCl(g)] - \Delta_f G^\circ[Cl_2(g)] - \Delta_f G^\circ[H_2(g)]$

$= 2\times(-95.30 \text{ kJ/mol}) - 0.0 \text{ kJ/mol} - 0.0 \text{ kJ/mol} = -190.6 \text{ kJ mol}^{-1}$

Now we can calculate ΔG by employing the equation $\Delta_r G = \Delta_r G^\circ + RT \ln Q$, where

$$Q = \frac{P\{HCl(g)\}^2}{P\{H_2(g)\}P\{Cl_2(g)\}}; \quad Q = \frac{(0.5)^2}{(0.5)(0.5)} = 1$$

$\Delta_r G = -190.6 \text{ kJ mol}^{-1} + (8.3145 \times 10^{-3} \text{ kJ/K·mol})(298 \text{ K})\ln(1)$

$\Delta_r G = -190.6 \text{ kJ mol}^{-1} + 0 \text{ kJ mol}^{-1} = -190.6 \text{ kJ mol}^{-1}$.

Since $\Delta_r G$ is negative, the reaction is spontaneous in the forward direction.

49. **(M)** In order to determine the direction in which the reaction is spontaneous, we need to calculate the non-standard Gibbs energy of reaction. To accomplish this, we will employ the equation $\Delta_r G = \Delta_r G^\circ + RT \ln Q$, where

$$Q = \frac{[H_3O^+(aq)][CH_3CO_2^-(aq)]}{[CH_3CO_2H(aq)]}; \quad Q = \frac{(1.0\times10^{-3})^2}{(0.10)} = 1.0\times10^{-5}$$

$\Delta_r G = 27.07 \text{ kJ mol}^{-1} + (8.3145 \times 10^{-3} \text{ kJ/K·mol})(298 \text{ K})\ln(1.0 \times 10^{-5})$

$\Delta_r G = 27.07 \text{ kJ mol}^{-1} + (-28.53 \text{ kJ mol}^{-1}) = -1.46 \text{ kJ mol}^{-1}$.

Since $\Delta_r G$ is negative, the reaction is spontaneous in the forward direction.

50. **(M)** As was the case for Exercise 45, we need to calculate the non-standard Gibbs energy of reaction. Once again, we will employ the equation $\Delta_r G = \Delta_r G^\circ + RT \ln Q$, but this time

$$Q = \frac{[NH_4^+(aq)][OH^-(aq)]}{[NH_3(aq)]}; \quad Q = \frac{(1.0 \times 10^{-3})^2}{(0.10)} = 1.0 \times 10^{-5}$$

$\Delta_r G = 29.05 \text{ kJ mol}^{-1} + (8.3145 \times 10^{-3} \text{ kJ/K·mol})(298 \text{ K})\ln(1.0 \times 10^{-5})$
$\Delta_r G = 29.05 \text{ kJ mol}^{-1} + (-28.53 \text{ kJ mol}^{-1}) = 0.52 \text{ kJ mol}^{-1}$.

Since $\Delta_r G$ is positive, the reaction is spontaneous in the reverse direction.

51. **(E)** The relationship $\Delta_r S^\circ = (\Delta_r G^\circ - \Delta_r H^\circ)/T$ (Equation (b)) is incorrect. Rearranging this equation to put $\Delta_r G^\circ$ on one side by itself gives $\Delta_r G^\circ = \Delta_r H^\circ + T\Delta_r S^\circ$. This equation is not valid. The $T\Delta_r S^\circ$ term should be subtracted from the $\Delta_r H^\circ$ term, not added to it.

52. **(E)** The $\Delta_r G^\circ$ value is a powerful thermodynamic parameter because it can be used to determine the equilibrium constant for the reaction at each and every chemically reasonable temperature via the equation $\Delta_r G^\circ = -RT \ln K$.

53. **(M)**
    (a) To determine K_p we need the equilibrium partial pressures. In the ideal gas law, each partial pressure is defined by $P = nRT/V$. Because R, T, and V are the same for each gas, and because there are the same number of partial pressure factors in the numerator as in the denominator of the K_p expression, we can use the ratio of amounts to determine K_p.

$$K_p = \frac{P\{CO(g)\}P\{H_2O(g)\}}{P\{CO_2(g)\}P\{H_2(g)\}} = \frac{n\{CO(g)\}n\{H_2O(g)\}}{n\{CO_2(g)\}n\{H_2(g)\}} = \frac{0.224 \text{ mol CO} \times 0.224 \text{ mol H}_2O}{0.276 \text{ mol CO}_2 \times 0.276 \text{ mol H}_2} = 0.659$$

    (b) $\Delta_r G^\circ{}_{1000K} = -RT \ln K_p = -8.3145 \text{ J mol}^{-1}K^{-1} \times 1000. \text{ K} \times \ln(0.659)$

$$= 3.467 \times 10^3 \text{ J/mol} = 3.467 \text{ kJ/mol}$$

    (c) $Q_p = \dfrac{0.0340 \text{ mol CO} \times 0.0650 \text{ mol H}_2O}{0.0750 \text{ mol CO}_2 \times 0.095 \text{ mol H}_2} = 0.31 < 0.659 = K_p$

    Since Q_p is smaller than K_p, the reaction will proceed to the right, forming products, to attain equilibrium, i.e., $\Delta_r G = 0$.

54. **(M)**
    (a) We know that $K_p = K_c (RT)^{\Delta n}$. For the reaction $2SO_2(g) + O_2(g) \rightleftharpoons 2SO_3(g)$,

    $\Delta n_{gas} = 2 - (2+1) = -1$, and therefore a value of K_p can be obtained.

$$K_p = K_c(RT)^{-1} = \frac{2.8 \times 10^2}{\dfrac{0.08206 \text{ L atm}}{\text{mol K}} \times 1000 \text{ K}} = 3.41 = K$$

    We recognize that $K = K_p$ since all of the substances involved in the reaction are gases. We can now evaluate $\Delta_r G^\circ$.

$$\Delta_r G^\circ = -RT \ln K = -\frac{8.3145 \text{ J}}{\text{mol K}} \times 1000 \text{ K} \times \ln(3.41) = -1.02 \times 10^4 \text{ J/mol} = -10.2 \text{ kJ/mol}$$

(b) We can evaluate Q_c for this situation and compare the value with that of $K_c = 2.8 \times 10^2$ to determine the direction of the reaction to reach equilibrium.

$$Q_c = \frac{[SO_3]^2}{[SO_2]^2[O_2]} = \frac{\left(\dfrac{0.72 \text{ mol SO}_3}{2.50 \text{ L}}\right)^2}{\left(\dfrac{0.40 \text{ mol SO}_2}{2.50 \text{ L}}\right)^2 \times \left(\dfrac{0.18 \text{ mol O}_2}{2.50 \text{ L}}\right)} = 45 < 2.8 \times 10^2 = K_c$$

Since Q_c is smaller than K_c the reaction will shift right, producing sulfur trioxide and consuming sulfur dioxide and molecular oxygen, until the two values are equal.

55. (E)

(a) $\Delta_r G^\circ = -RT \ln K = -8.314 \times 10^{-3} \text{kJ mol}^{-1}\text{K}^{-1} \times 718.15 \text{ K} \times \ln(50.2) = -23.4 \text{ kJ mol}^{-1}$

(b) $\Delta_r G^\circ = -RT \ln K = -8.314 \times 10^{-3} \text{kJ mol}^{-1}\text{K}^{-1} \times 298.15 \text{ K} \times \ln(8.5 \times 10^{-13})$
$$= +69 \text{ kJ mol}^{-1}$$

(c) $\Delta_r G^\circ = -RT \ln K = -8.314 \times 10^{-3} \text{kJ mol}^{-1}\text{K}^{-1} \times 298.15 \text{ K} \times \ln(0.114) = +5.38 \text{ kJ mol}^{-1}$

(d) $\Delta_r G^\circ = -RT \ln K = -8.314 \times 10^{-3} \text{kJ mol}^{-1}\text{K}^{-1} \times 298.15 \text{ K} \times \ln(9.14 \times 10^{-6})$
$$= +28.8 \text{ kJ mol}^{-1}$$

56. (M)

(a) The first equation involves the formation of one mole of $Mg^{2+}(aq)$ from $Mg(OH)_2(s)$ and $2H^+(aq)$, while the second equation involves the formation of only half-a-mole of $Mg^{2+}(aq)$. We would expect a Gibbs energy change of half the size if only half as much product is formed.

(b) The value of K for the first reaction is the square of the value of K for the second reaction. The equilibrium constant expressions are related in the same fashion.

$$K_1 = \frac{\left[Mg^{2+}\right]}{\left[H^+\right]^2} = \left(\frac{\left[Mg^{2+}\right]^{1/2}}{\left[H^+\right]}\right)^2 = \left(K_2\right)^2$$

(c) The equilibrium solubilities will be the same regardless which expression is used. The equilibrium conditions (solubilities in this instance) are the same no matter how we choose to express them in an equilibrium constant expression.

57. **(E)** $\Delta_r G^\circ = -RT\ln K = -\left(8.3145\times10^{-3}\,\text{kJ mol}^{-1}\text{K}^{-1}\right)(298\,\text{K})\ln\left(6.5\times10^{11}\right) = -67.4\,\text{kJ/mol}$

$CO(g)+Cl_2(g)\rightarrow COCl_2(g)$ $\qquad\qquad\qquad\qquad \Delta_r G^\circ = -67.4\,\text{kJ/mol}$

$C(\text{graphite})+\tfrac{1}{2}O_2(g)\rightarrow CO(g)$ $\qquad\qquad\qquad \Delta_f G^\circ = -137.2\,\text{kJ/mol}$

$C(\text{graphite})+\tfrac{1}{2}O_2(g)+Cl_2(g)\rightarrow COCl_2(g)$ $\qquad \Delta_f G^\circ = -204.6\,\text{kJ/mol}$

$\Delta_f G^\circ$ of $COCl_2(g)$ given in Appendix D is -204.6 kJ/mol, thus the agreement is excellent.

58. **(M)** In each case, we first determine the value of $\Delta_r G^\circ$ for the dissolution reaction. From that, we calculate the value of the equilibrium constant, K, for the reaction.

(a) $AgBr(s)\rightleftharpoons Ag^+(aq)+Br^-(aq)$

$\Delta_r G^\circ = \Delta_f G^\circ\left[Ag^+(aq)\right]+\Delta_f G^\circ\left[Br^-(aq)\right]-\Delta_f G^\circ\left[AgBr(s)\right]$

$\qquad = 77.11\,\text{kJ/mol}-104.0\,\text{kJ/mol}-(-96.90\,\text{kJ/mol}) = +70.0\,\text{kJ/mol}$

$\ln K = \dfrac{-\Delta_r G^\circ}{RT} = \dfrac{-70.0\times10^3\,\text{J/mol}}{8.3145\,\text{J mol}^{-1}\text{K}^{-1}\times298.15\,\text{K}} = -28.2;\qquad K = e^{-28.2} = 6\times10^{-13}$

(b) $CaSO_4(s)\rightleftharpoons Ca^{2+}(aq)+SO_4^{2-}(aq)$

$\Delta_r G^\circ = \Delta_f G^\circ\left[Ca^{2+}(aq)\right]+\Delta_f G^\circ\left[SO_4^{2-}(aq)\right]-\Delta_f G^\circ\left[CaSO_4(s)\right]$

$\qquad = -553.6\,\text{kJ/mol}-744.5\,\text{kJ/mol}-(-1332\,\text{kJ/mol}) = +34\,\text{kJ/mol}$

$\ln K = \dfrac{-\Delta_r G^\circ}{RT} = \dfrac{-34\times10^3\,\text{J/mol}}{8.3145\,\text{J mol}^{-1}\text{K}^{-1}\times298.15\,\text{K}} = -14; K = e^{-14} = 8\times10^{-7}$

(c) $Fe(OH)_3(s)\rightleftharpoons Fe^{3+}(aq)+3OH^-(aq)$

$\Delta_r G^\circ = \Delta_f G^\circ\left[Fe^{3+}(aq)\right]+3\Delta_f G^\circ\left[OH^-(aq)\right]-\Delta_f G^\circ\left[Fe(OH)_3(s)\right]$

$\qquad = -4.7\,\text{kJ/mol}+3\times(-157.2\,\text{kJ/mol})-(-696.5\,\text{kJ/mol}) = +220.2\,\text{kJ/mol}$

$\ln K = \dfrac{-\Delta_r G^\circ}{RT} = \dfrac{-220.2\times10^3\,\text{J/mol}}{8.3145\,\text{J mol}^{-1}\,\text{K}^{-1}\times298.15\,\text{K}} = -88.83\qquad K = e^{-88.83} = 2.6\times10^{-39}$

59. **(M)**

(a) We can determine the equilibrium partial pressure from the value of the equilibrium constant.

$\Delta_r G^\circ = -RT\ln K\qquad \ln K = -\dfrac{\Delta_r G^\circ}{RT} = -\dfrac{58.54\times10^3\,\text{J/mol}}{8.3145\,\text{J mol}^{-1}\,\text{K}^{-1}\times298.15\,\text{K}} = -23.63$

$K = P\{O_2(g)\}^{1/2} = e^{-23.63} = 5.5\times10^{-11}\qquad P\{O_2(g)\} = \left(5.5\times10^{-11}\right)^2 = 3.0\times10^{-21}\,\text{atm}$

(b) Lavoisier did two things to increase the quantity of oxygen that he obtained. First, he ran the reaction at a high temperature, which favors the products (i.e., the side with molecular oxygen.) Second, the molecular oxygen was removed immediately after it was formed, which causes the equilibrium to shift to the right continuously (the shift towards products as result of the removal of the O_2 is an example of Le Châtelier's principle).

60. (D)

(a) We determine the values of $\Delta_r H^\circ$ and $\Delta_r S^\circ$ from the data in Appendix D, and then the value of $\Delta_r G^\circ$ at $25\,°C = 298$ K.

$$\Delta_r H^\circ = \Delta_f H^\circ\left[CH_3OH(g)\right] + \Delta_f H^\circ\left[H_2O(g)\right] - \Delta_f H^\circ\left[CO_2(g)\right] - 3\,\Delta_f H^\circ\left[H_2(g)\right]$$

$$= -200.7\,kJ/mol + (-241.8\,kJ/mol) - (-393.5\,kJ/mol) - 3(0.00\,kJ/mol) = -49.0\,kJ/mol$$

$$\Delta_r S^\circ = S^\circ\left[CH_3OH(g)\right] + S^\circ\left[H_2O(g)\right] - S^\circ\left[CO_2(g)\right] - 3S^\circ\left[H_2(g)\right]$$

$$= (239.8 + 188.8 - 213.7 - 3\times130.7)\,J\,mol^{-1}K^{-1} = -177.2\,J\,mol^{-1}K^{-1}$$

$$\Delta_r G^\circ = \Delta_r H^\circ - T\Delta_r S^\circ = -49.0\,kJ/mol - 298\,K\left(-0.1772\,kJ\,mol^{-1}K^{-1}\right) = +3.81\,kJ/mol$$

Because the value of $\Delta_r G^\circ$ is positive, this reaction does not proceed in the forward direction at 25°C.

(b) Because the value of $\Delta_r H^\circ$ is negative and that of $\Delta_r S^\circ$ is negative, the reaction is *non-spontaneous* at high temperatures, if reactants and products are *in their standard states*. The reaction will proceed slightly in the forward direction, however, to produce an equilibrium mixture with small quantities of $CH_3OH(g)$ and $H_2O(g)$. Also, because the forward reaction is exothermic, this reaction is favored by lowering the temperature. That is, the value of K increases with decreasing temperature.

(c) $\Delta_r G^\circ_{500K} = \Delta_r H^\circ - T\Delta_r S^\circ = -49.0\,kJ/mol - 500.K\left(-0.1772\,kJ\,mol^{-1}\,K^{-1}\right) = 39.6\,kJ/mol$

$$= 39.6\times10^3\,J/mol = -RT\ln K_p$$

$$\ln K = \frac{-\Delta_r G^\circ}{RT} = \frac{-39.6\times10^3\,J/mol}{8.3145\,J\,mol^{-1}K^{-1}\times500.\,K} = -9.53; \quad K = e^{-9.53} = 7.3\times10^{-5}$$

(d)

Reaction:	$CO_2(g)+$	$3H_2(g)$	$\rightleftharpoons$	$CH_3OH(g)$	$+H_2O(g)$
Initial:	1.00 atm	1.00 atm		0 atm	0 atm
Changes:	$-x$ atm	$-3x$ atm		$+x$ atm	$+x$ atm
Equil:	$(1.00-x)$ atm	$(1.00-3x)$ atm		x atm	x atm

$$K_p = 7.3\times10^{-5} = \frac{P\{CH_3OH\}\,P\{H_2O\}}{P\{CO_2\}\,P\{H_2\}^3} = \frac{x\cdot x}{(1.00-x)(1.00-3x)^3} \approx x^2$$

$$x = \sqrt{7.3\times10^{-5}} = 8.5\times10^{-3}\,atm = P\{CH_3OH\}\quad\text{Our assumption, that }3x \ll 1.00\text{ atm,}$$

is valid.

$\Delta_r G^\circ$ and K as Function of Temperature

61. (M)

(a) $\Delta_r S^\circ = S^\circ\left[Na_2CO_3(s)\right] + S^\circ\left[H_2O(l)\right] + S^\circ\left[CO_2(g)\right] - 2S^\circ\left[NaHCO_3(s)\right]$

$$= 135.0\frac{J}{K\,mol} + 69.91\frac{J}{K\,mol} + 213.7\frac{J}{K\,mol} - 2\left(101.7\frac{J}{K\,mol}\right) = +215.2\frac{J}{K\,mol}$$

(b) $\Delta_r H° = \Delta_f H°\left[Na_2CO_3(s)\right] + \Delta_f H°\left[H_2O(l)\right] + \Delta_f H°\left[CO_2(g)\right] - 2\Delta_f H°\left[NaHCO_3(s)\right]$

$= -1131\dfrac{kJ}{mol} - 285.8\dfrac{kJ}{mol} - 393.5\dfrac{kJ}{mol} - 2\left(-950.8\dfrac{kJ}{mol}\right) = +91\dfrac{kJ}{mol}$

(c) $\Delta_r G° = \Delta_r H° - T\Delta_r S° = 91\,kJ/mol - (298\,K)(215.2\times10^{-3}\,kJ\,mol^{-1}K^{-1})$

$= 91\,kJ/mol - 64.13\,kJ/mol = 27\,kJ/mol$

(d) $\Delta_r G° = -RT\ln K \qquad \ln K = -\dfrac{\Delta_r G°}{RT} = -\dfrac{27\times10^3\,J/mol}{8.3145\,J\,mol^{-1}\,K^{-1}\times298\,K} = -10.\underline{9}$

$K = e^{-10.9} = 2\times10^{-5}$

62. (M)

(a) $\Delta_r S° = S°\left[CH_3CH_2OH(g)\right] + S°\left[H_2O(g)\right] - S°\left[CO(g)\right] - 2S°\left[H_2(g)\right] - S°\left[CH_3OH(g)\right]$

$\Delta_r S° = 282.7\dfrac{J}{K\,mol} + 188.8\dfrac{J}{K\,mol} - 197.7\dfrac{J}{K\,mol} - 2\left(130.7\dfrac{J}{K\,mol}\right) - 239.8\dfrac{J}{K\,mol}$

$\Delta_r S° = -227.4\dfrac{J}{K\,mol}$

$\Delta_r H° = \Delta_f H°\left[CH_3CH_2OH(g)\right] + \Delta_f H°\left[H_2O(g)\right] - \Delta_f H°\left[CO(g)\right]$
$\qquad - 2\Delta_f H°\left[H_2(g)\right] - \Delta_f H°\left[CH_3OH(g)\right]$

$\Delta_r H° = -235.1\dfrac{kJ}{mol} - 241.8\dfrac{kJ}{mol} - \left(-110.5\dfrac{kJ}{mol}\right) - 2\left(0.00\dfrac{kJ}{mol}\right) - \left(-200.7\dfrac{kJ}{mol}\right)$

$\Delta_r H° = -165.7\dfrac{kJ}{mol}$

$\Delta_r G° = -165.7\dfrac{kJ}{mol} - (298\,K)\left(-227.4\times10^{-3}\dfrac{kJ}{K\,mol}\right)$

$= -165.4\dfrac{kJ}{mol} + 67.8\dfrac{kJ}{mol} = -97.9\dfrac{kJ}{mol}$

(b) $\Delta_r H° < 0$ for this reaction. Thus it is favored at low temperatures. Also, because $\Delta n_{gas} = +2 - 4 = -2$, which is less than zero, the reaction is favored at high pressures.

(c) First we assume that neither $\Delta_r S°$ nor $\Delta_r H°$ varies significantly with temperature. Then we compute a value for $\Delta_r G°$ at 750 K. From this value of $\Delta_r G°$, we compute a value for K.

$\Delta_r G° = \Delta_r H° - T\Delta_r S° = -165.7\,kJ/mol - (750.\,K)(-227.4\times10^{-3}\,kJ\,mol^{-1}K^{-1})$

$= -165.7\,kJ/mol + 170.6\,kJ/mol = +4.9\,kJ/mol = -RT\ln K$

$\ln K = -\dfrac{\Delta G°}{RT} = -\dfrac{4.9\times10^3\,J/mol}{8.3145\,J\,mol^{-1}\,K^{-1}\times750.\,K} = -0.79 \qquad K = e^{-0.79} = 0.5$

63. **(E)** In this problem we are asked to determine the temperature for the reaction between iron(III) oxide and carbon monoxide to yield iron and carbon dioxide given $\Delta_r G°$, $\Delta_r H°$, and $\Delta_r S°$. We proceed by rearranging $\Delta_r G° = \Delta_r H° - T\Delta_r S°$ in order to express the temperature as a function of $\Delta_r G°$, $\Delta_r H°$, and $\Delta_r S°$.

$$\Delta_r G° = \Delta_r H° - T\Delta_r S° \Rightarrow T = \frac{\Delta_r H° - \Delta_r G°}{\Delta_r S°} = \frac{-24.8\times10^3 \text{ J} - (-45.5\times10^3 \text{ J})}{15.2 \text{ J/K}} = 1.36\times10^3 \text{ K}$$

64. **(E)** We use the van't Hoff equation with $\Delta_r H° = -1.8\times10^5$ J/mol, $T_1 = 800.$ K,

$T_2 = 100.°C = 373$ K, and $K_1 = 9.1\times10^2$.

$$\ln\frac{K_2}{K_1} = \frac{\Delta_r H°}{R}\left(\frac{1}{T_1} - \frac{1}{T_2}\right) = \frac{-1.8\times10^5 \text{ J/mol}}{8.3145 \text{ J mol}^{-1}\text{K}^{-1}}\left(\frac{1}{800 \text{ K}} - \frac{1}{373 \text{ K}}\right) = 31$$

$$\frac{K_2}{K_1} = e^{31} = 2.9\times10^{13} = \frac{K_2}{9.1\times10^2} \qquad K_2 = (2.9\times10^{13})(9.1\times10^2) = 3\times10^{16}$$

65. **(M)** We first determine the value of $\Delta_r G°$ at $400°C$, from the values of $\Delta_r H°$ and $\Delta_r S°$, which are calculated from information listed in Appendix D.

$$\Delta_r H° = 2\Delta_f H°\left[NH_3\,(g)\right] - \Delta_f H°\left[N_2\,(g)\right] - 3\Delta_f H°\left[H_2\,(g)\right]$$
$$= 2(-46.11\text{kJ/mol}) - (0.00\text{kJ/mol}) - 3(0.00 \text{ kJ/mol}) = -92.22\text{kJ/mol N}_2$$

$$\Delta_r S° = 2S°\left[NH_3\,(g)\right] - S°\left[N_2\,(g)\right] - 3S°\left[H_2\,(g)\right]$$
$$= 2(192.5 \text{ J mol}^{-1}\text{ K}^{-1}) - (191.6 \text{ J mol}^{-1}\text{ K}^{-1}) - 3(130.7 \text{ J mol}^{-1}\text{ K}^{-1}) = -198.7 \text{ J mol}^{-1}\text{ K}^{-1}$$

$$\Delta_r G° = \Delta_r H° - T\Delta_r S° = -92.22 \text{ kJ/mol} - 673 \text{ K}\times(-0.1987 \text{ kJ mol}^{-1}\text{ K}^{-1})$$
$$= +41.51 \text{ kJ/mol} = -RT \ln K_p$$

$$\ln K_p = \frac{-\Delta_r G°}{RT} = \frac{-41.51\times10^3 \text{ J/mol}}{8.3145 \text{ J mol}^{-1}\text{K}^{-1}\times673\text{K}} = -7.42; \quad K_p = e^{-7.42} = 6.0\times10^{-4}$$

66. **(M)**

(a) $\Delta_r H° = \Delta_f H°\left[CO_2\,(g)\right] + \Delta_f H°\left[H_2\,(g)\right] - \Delta_f H°\left[CO\,(g)\right] - \Delta_f H°\left[H_2O\,(g)\right]$

$$= -393.5 \text{ kJ/mol} - 0.00 \text{ kJ/mol} - (-110.5 \text{ kJ/mol}) - (-241.8 \text{ kJ/mol})$$
$$= -41.2 \text{ kJ/mol}$$

$$\Delta_r S^\circ = S^\circ\left[CO_2(g)\right] + S^\circ\left[H_2(g)\right] - S^\circ\left[CO(g)\right] - S^\circ\left[H_2O(g)\right]$$

$$= 213.7\ \text{J mol}^{-1}\ \text{K}^{-1} + 130.7\ \text{J mol}^{-1}\ \text{K}^{-1} - 197.7\ \text{J mol}^{-1}\ \text{K}^{-1} - 188.8\ \text{J mol}^{-1}\ \text{K}^{-1}$$

$$= -42.1\ \text{J mol}^{-1}\ \text{K}^{-1}$$

$$\Delta_r G^\circ = \Delta_r H^\circ - T\Delta_r S^\circ = -41.2\ \text{kJ/mol} - 298.15\ \text{K} \times (-42.1 \times 10^{-3})\ \text{kJ/mol K}$$

$$\Delta_r G^\circ = -41.2\ \text{kJ/mol} + 12.6\ \text{kJ/mol} = -28.6\ \text{kJ/mol}$$

(b) $\quad \Delta_r G^\circ = \Delta_r H^\circ - T\Delta_r S^\circ = -41.2\ \text{kJ/mol} - (875\ \text{K})(-42.1 \times 10^{-3}\ \text{kJ mol}^{-1}\ \text{K}^{-1})$

$$= -41.2\ \text{kJ/mol} + 36.8\ \text{kJ/mol} = -4.4\ \text{kJ/mol} = -RT \ln K_p$$

$$\ln K_p = -\frac{\Delta_r G^\circ}{RT} = -\frac{-4.4 \times 10^3\ \text{J/mol}}{8.3145\ \text{J mol}^{-1}\ \text{K}^{-1} \times 875\ \text{K}} = +0.60 \qquad K_p = e^{+0.60} = 1.8$$

67. **(M)** We assume that both $\Delta_r H^\circ$ and $\Delta_r S^\circ$ are constant with temperature.

$$\Delta_r H^\circ = 2\Delta_f H^\circ\left[SO_3(g)\right] - 2\Delta_f H^\circ\left[SO_2(g)\right] - \Delta_f H^\circ\left[O_2(g)\right]$$

$$= 2(-395.7\ \text{kJ/mol}) - 2(-296.8\ \text{kJ/mol}) - (0.00\ \text{kJ/mol}) = -197.8\ \text{kJ/mol}$$

$$\Delta_r S^\circ = 2S^\circ\left[SO_3(g)\right] - 2S^\circ\left[SO_2(g)\right] - S^\circ\left[O_2(g)\right]$$

$$= 2(256.8\ \text{J mol}^{-1}\ \text{K}^{-1}) - 2(248.2\ \text{J mol}^{-1}\ \text{K}^{-1}) - (205.1\ \text{J mol}^{-1}\ \text{K}^{-1})$$

$$= -187.9\ \text{J mol}^{-1}\ \text{K}^{-1}$$

$$\Delta_r G^\circ = \Delta_r H^\circ - T\Delta_r S^\circ = -RT \ln K \qquad \Delta_r H^\circ = T\Delta_r S^\circ - RT \ln K \qquad T = \frac{\Delta_r H^\circ}{\Delta_r S^\circ - R \ln K}$$

$$T = \frac{-197.8 \times 10^3\ \text{J/mol}}{-187.9\ \text{J mol}^{-1}\ \text{K}^{-1} - 8.3145\ \text{J mol}^{-1}\ \text{K}^{-1} \ln(1.0 \times 10^6)} \approx 650\ \text{K}$$

This value compares very favorably with the value of $T = 6.37 \times 10^2\ \text{K}$ that was obtained in Example 13-10.

68. **(E)** We use the van't Hoff equation to determine the value of $\Delta_r H^\circ$($448\ °C = 721\ \text{K}$ and $350\ °C = 623\ \text{K}$).

$$\ln \frac{K_1}{K_2} = \frac{\Delta_r H^\circ}{R}\left(\frac{1}{T_2} - \frac{1}{T_1}\right) = \ln \frac{50.0}{66.9} = -0.291 = \frac{\Delta_r H^\circ}{R}\left(\frac{1}{623} - \frac{1}{721}\right) = \frac{\Delta_r H^\circ}{R}(2.2 \times 10^{-4})$$

$$\frac{\Delta_r H^\circ}{R} = \frac{-0.291}{2.2 \times 10^{-4}\ \text{K}^{-1}} = -1.3 \times 10^3\ \text{K};$$

$$\Delta_r H^\circ = -1.3 \times 10^3\ \text{K} \times 8.3145\ \text{J K}^{-1}\ \text{mol}^{-1} = -11 \times 10^3\ \text{J mol}^{-1} = -11\ \text{kJ mol}^{-1}$$

69. **(M)**

(a) $\quad \ln \frac{K_2}{K_1} = \frac{\Delta_r H^\circ}{R}\left(\frac{1}{T_1} - \frac{1}{T_2}\right) = \frac{57.2 \times 10^3\ \text{J/mol}}{8.3145\ \text{J mol}^{-1}\ \text{K}^{-1}}\left(\frac{1}{298\ \text{K}} - \frac{1}{273\ \text{K}}\right) = -2.11$

$$\frac{K_2}{K_1} = e^{-2.11} = 0.121 \qquad K_2 = 0.121 \times 0.113 = 0.014\ \text{at}\ 273\ \text{K}$$

(b) $\ln\dfrac{K_2}{K_1} = \dfrac{\Delta_r H°}{R}\left(\dfrac{1}{T_1} - \dfrac{1}{T_2}\right) = \dfrac{57.2\times10^3\text{ J/mol}}{8.3145\text{ J mol}^{-1}\text{ K}^{-1}}\left(\dfrac{1}{T_1} - \dfrac{1}{298\text{ K}}\right) = \ln\dfrac{0.113}{1.00} = -2.180$

$\left(\dfrac{1}{T_1} - \dfrac{1}{298\text{K}}\right) = \dfrac{-2.180\times8.3145}{57.2\times10^3}\text{K}^{-1} = -3.17\times10^{-4}\text{K}^{-1}$

$\dfrac{1}{T_1} = \dfrac{1}{298} - 3.17\times10^{-4} = 3.36\times10^{-3} - 3.17\times10^{-4} = 3.04\times10^{-3}\text{ K}^{-1}; \quad T_1 = 329\text{ K}$

70. **(D)** First we calculate $\Delta_r G°$ at 298 K to obtain a value for K_{eq} at that temperature.

$\Delta_r G° = 2\Delta_f G°\left[NO_2(g)\right] - 2\Delta_f G°\left[NO(g)\right] - \Delta_f G°\left[O_2(g)\right]$

$= 2(51.31\text{ kJ/mol}) - 2(86.55\text{ kJ/mol}) - 0.00\text{ kJ/mol} = -70.48\text{ kJ/mol}$

$\ln K = \dfrac{-\Delta_r G°}{RT} = -\dfrac{-70.48\times10^3\text{ J/mol K}}{\dfrac{8.3145\text{ J}}{\text{mol K}}\times298.15\text{ K}} = 28.43 \qquad K = e^{28.43} = 2.2\times10^{12}$

Now we calculate $\Delta H°$ for the reaction, which then will be inserted into the van't Hoff equation.

$\Delta_r H° = 2\Delta_f H°\left[NO_2(g)\right] - 2\Delta_f H°\left[NO(g)\right] - \Delta_f H°\left[O_2(g)\right]$

$= 2(33.18\text{ kJ/mol}) - 2(90.25\text{ kJ/mol}) - 0.00\text{ kJ/mol} = -114.14\text{ kJ/mol}$

$\ln\dfrac{K_2}{K_1} = \dfrac{\Delta_r H°}{R}\left(\dfrac{1}{T_1} - \dfrac{1}{T_2}\right) = \dfrac{-114.14\times10^3\text{ J/mol}}{8.3145\text{ J mol}^{-1}\text{ K}^{-1}}\left(\dfrac{1}{298\text{ K}} - \dfrac{1}{373\text{ K}}\right) = -9.26$

$\dfrac{K_2}{K_1} = e^{-9.26} = 9.5\times10^{-5}; \quad K_2 = 9.5\times10^{-5}\times2.2\times10^{12} = 2.1\times10^{8}$

Another way to find K at 100 °C is to compute $\Delta_r H°(-114.14\text{ kJ/mol})$ from $\Delta_f H°$ values and $\Delta_r S°(-146.5\text{ J mol}^{-1}\text{ K}^{-1})$ from $S°$ values. Then determine $\Delta G°(-59.5\text{ kJ/mol})$, and find K_p with the expression $\Delta_r G° = -RT\ln K_p$. Not surprisingly, we obtain the same result, $K_p = 2.2\times10^{8}$.

71. **(M)** First, the van't Hoff equation is used to obtain a value of $\Delta_r H°$. $200\text{ °C} = 473\text{ K}$ and $260\text{ °C} = 533\text{ K}$.

$\ln\dfrac{K_2}{K_1} = \dfrac{\Delta_r H°}{R}\left(\dfrac{1}{T_1} - \dfrac{1}{T_2}\right) = \ln\dfrac{2.15\times10^{11}}{4.56\times10^8} = 6.156 = \dfrac{\Delta_r H°}{8.3145\text{ J mol}^{-1}\text{ K}^{-1}}\left(\dfrac{1}{533\text{ K}} - \dfrac{1}{473\text{ K}}\right)$

$6.156 = -2.9\times10^{-5}\Delta_r H° \qquad \Delta_r H° = \dfrac{6.156}{-2.9\times10^{-5}} = -2.1\times10^5\text{ J/mol} = -2.1\times10^2\text{ kJ/mol}$

Another route to $\Delta_r H°$ is the combination of standard enthalpies of formation.

$CO(g) + 3\,H_2(g) \rightleftharpoons CH_4(g) + H_2O(g)$

$$\Delta_r H^\circ = \Delta_f H^\circ \left[CH_4(g) \right] + \Delta_f H^\circ \left[H_2O(g) \right] - \Delta_f H^\circ \left[CO(g) \right] - 3\Delta_f H^\circ \left[H_2(g) \right]$$

$$= -74.81 \text{ kJ/mol} - 241.8 \text{ kJ/mol} - (-110.5) - 3 \times 0.00 \text{ kJ/mol} = -206.1 \text{ kJ/mol}$$

Within the precision of the data supplied, the results are in good agreement.

72. (D) (a)

$t, ^\circ C$	T, K	$1/T, K^{-1}$	K_p	$\ln K_p$
30.	303	3.30×10^{-3}	1.66×10^{-5}	-11.006
50.	323	3.10×10^{-3}	3.90×10^{-4}	-7.849
70.	343	2.92×10^{-3}	6.27×10^{-3}	-5.072
100.	373	2.68×10^{-3}	2.31×10^{-1}	-1.465

Plot of ln(K_p) versus 1/T

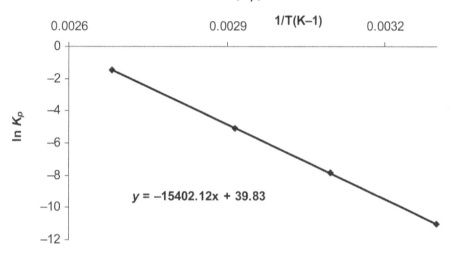

The slope of this graph is $-\Delta H^\circ / R = -1.54 \times 10^4 \text{ K}$

$$\Delta_r H^\circ = -\left(8.3145 \text{ J mol}^{-1} K^{-1} \right) \left(-1.54 \times 10^4 K \right) = 128 \times 10^3 \text{ J/mol} = 128 \text{ kJ/mol}$$

(b) When the total pressure is 2.00 atm, and both gases have been produced from $NaHCO_3(s)$,

$$P\{H_2O(g)\} = P\{CO_2(g)\} = 1.00 \text{ atm}$$

$$K_p = P\{H_2O(g)\}P\{CO_2(g)\} = (1.00)(1.00) = 1.00$$

Thus, $\ln K_p = \ln(1.00) = 0.000$. The corresponds to $1/T = 2.59 \times 10^{-3} \text{ K}^{-1}$; $T = 386 \text{ K}$.

We can compute the same temperature from the van't Hoff equation.

$$\ln \frac{K_2}{K_1} = \frac{\Delta_r H^\circ}{R} \left(\frac{1}{T_1} - \frac{1}{T_2} \right) = \frac{128 \times 10^3 \text{ J/mol}}{8.3145 \text{ J mol}^{-1} \text{ K}^{-1}} \left(\frac{1}{T_1} - \frac{1}{303 \text{ K}} \right) = \ln \frac{1.66 \times 10^{-5}}{1.00} = -11.006$$

$$\left(\frac{1}{T_1} - \frac{1}{303 \text{ K}}\right) = \frac{-11.006 \times 8.3145}{128 \times 10^3} \text{ K}^{-1} = -7.15 \times 10^{-4} \text{ K}^{-1}$$

$$\frac{1}{T_1} = \frac{1}{303} - 7.15 \times 10^{-4} = 3.30 \times 10^{-3} - 7.15 \times 10^{-4} = 2.59 \times 10^{-3} \text{ K}^{-1}; \quad T_1 = 386 \text{ K}$$

This temperature agrees well with the result obtained from the graph.

Coupled Reactions

73. **(E)**

(a) We compute $\Delta_r G°$ for the given reaction in the following manner

$$\Delta_r H° = \Delta_f H°\left[\text{TiCl}_4\,(l)\right] + \Delta_f H°\left[\text{O}_2\,(g)\right] - \Delta_f H°\left[\text{TiO}_2\,(s)\right] - 2\Delta_f H°\left[\text{Cl}_2\,(g)\right]$$

$$= -804.2 \text{ kJ/mol} + 0.00 \text{ kJ/mol} - (-944.7 \text{ kJ/mol}) - 2(0.00 \text{ kJ/mol})$$

$$= +140.5 \text{ kJ/mol}$$

$$\Delta_r S° = S°\left[\text{TiCl}_4\,(l)\right] + S°\left[\text{O}_2\,(g)\right] - S°\left[\text{TiO}_2\,(s)\right] - 2S°\left[\text{Cl}_2\,(g)\right]$$

$$= 252.3 \text{ J mol}^{-1} \text{ K}^{-1} + 205.1 \text{ J mol}^{-1} \text{ K}^{-1} - \left(50.33 \text{ J mol}^{-1} \text{ K}^{-1}\right) - 2\left(223.1 \text{ J mol}^{-1} \text{ K}^{-1}\right)$$

$$= -39.1 \text{ J mol}^{-1} \text{ K}^{-1}$$

$$\Delta_r G° = \Delta_r H° - T\,\Delta_r S° = +140.5 \text{ kJ/mol} - (298 \text{ K})\left(-39.1 \times 10^{-3} \text{ kJ mol}^{-1} \text{ K}^{-1}\right)$$

$$= +140.5 \text{ kJ/mol} + 11.6 \text{ kJ/mol} = +152.1 \text{ kJ/mol}$$

Thus the reaction is non-spontaneous at 25 °C. (we also could have used values of $\Delta_f G°$ to calculate $\Delta_r G°$).

(b) For the cited reaction, $\Delta_r G° = 2\Delta_f G°\left[\text{CO}_2\,(g)\right] - 2\Delta_f G°\left[\text{CO}\,(g)\right] - \Delta_f G°\left[\text{O}_2\,(g)\right]$

$\Delta_r G° = 2(-394.4 \text{ kJ/mol}) - 2(-137.2 \text{ kJ/mol}) - 0.00 \text{ kJ/mol} = -514.4 \text{ kJ/mol}$

Then we couple the two reactions.

$$\text{TiO}_2\,(s) + 2\text{Cl}_2\,(g) \longrightarrow \text{TiCl}_4\,(l) + \text{O}_2\,(g) \qquad\qquad \Delta_r G° = +152.1 \text{ kJ/mol}$$
$$2\text{CO}\,(g) + \text{O}_2\,(g) \longrightarrow 2\text{CO}_2\,(g) \qquad\qquad \Delta_r G° = -514.4 \text{ kJ/mol}$$

$$\overline{\text{TiO}_2\,(s) + 2\text{Cl}_2\,(g) + 2\text{CO}\,(g) \longrightarrow \text{TiCl}_4\,(l) + 2\text{CO}_2\,(g); \Delta_r G° = -362.3 \text{ kJ/mol}}$$

The coupled reaction has $\Delta_r G° < 0$, and, therefore, is spontaneous.

74. **(E)** If $\Delta_r G° < 0$ for the sum of coupled reactions, the reduction of the oxide with carbon is spontaneous.

(a)
$$\text{NiO}\,(s) \rightarrow \text{Ni}\,(s) + \tfrac{1}{2}\text{O}_2\,(g) \qquad\qquad \Delta_r G° = +115 \text{ kJ mol}^{-1}$$
$$\text{C}\,(s) + \tfrac{1}{2}\text{O}_2\,(g) \rightarrow \text{CO}\,(g) \qquad\qquad \Delta_r G° = -250 \text{ kJ mol}^{-1}$$

$$\overline{\text{Net}: \text{NiO}\,(s) + \text{C}\,(s) \rightarrow \text{Ni}\,(s) + \text{CO}\,(g) \qquad \Delta_r G° = +115 \text{ kJ mol}^{-1} - 250 \text{ kJ mol}^{-1}}$$
$$= -135 \text{ kJ mol}^{-1}$$

Therefore the coupled reaction is spontaneous

(b) $MnO(s) \rightarrow Mn(s) + \frac{1}{2}O_2(g)$ $\Delta_r G^\circ = +280 \text{ kJ mol}^{-1}$

$C(s) + \frac{1}{2}O_2(g) \rightarrow CO(g)$ $\Delta_r G^\circ = -250 \text{ kJ mol}^{-1}$

$Net: MnO(s) + C(s) \longrightarrow Mn(s) + CO(g)$ $\Delta_r G^\circ = +280 \text{ kJ mol}^{-1} - 250 \text{ kJ mol}^{-1}$

$$= +30 \text{ kJ mol}^{-1}$$

Therefore the coupled reaction is non-spontaneous

(c) $TiO_2(s) \longrightarrow Ti(s) + O_2(g)$ $\Delta_r G^\circ = +630 \text{ kJ mol}^{-1}$

$2C(s) + O_2(g) \longrightarrow 2CO(g)$ $\Delta_r G^\circ = 2(-250 \text{ kJ mol}^{-1})$

$$= -500 \text{ kJ mol}^{-1}$$

$Net: TiO_2(s) + 2C(s) \longrightarrow Ti(s) + 2CO(g)$ $\Delta_r G^\circ = +630 \text{ kJ mol}^{-1} - 500 \text{ kJ mol}^{-1}$

$$= +130 \text{ kJ mol}^{-1}$$

Therefore the coupled reaction is non-spontaneous

75. **(E)** In this problem we need to determine if the phosphorylation of arginine with ATP is a spontaneous reaction. We proceed by coupling the two given reactions in order to calculate $\Delta_r G^\circ$ for the overall reaction. The sign of $\Delta_r G^\circ$ can then be used to determine whether the reaction is spontaneous or not.

Stepwise approach:

First determine $\Delta_r G^\circ$ for the coupled reaction:

$ATP + H_2O \longrightarrow ADP + P$ $\Delta_r G^\circ = -31.5 \text{ kJ mol}^{-1}$

$arginine + P \longrightarrow phosphorarginine + H_2O$ $\Delta_r G^\circ = -33.2 \text{ kJ mol}^{-1}$

$ATP + arginine \longrightarrow phosphorarginine + ADP$

$\Delta_r G^\circ = (-31.5 + 33.2) \text{ kJ mol}^{-1} = 1.7 \text{ kJ mol}^{-1}$

Examine the sign of $\Delta_r G^\circ$:

$\Delta_r G^\circ > 0$. Therefore, the reaction is not spontaneous.

Conversion pathway approach:

$\Delta_r G^\circ$ for the coupled reaction is:

$ATP + arginine \longrightarrow phosphorarginine + ADP$

$\Delta_r G^\circ = (-31.5 + 33.2) \text{ kJ mol}^{-1} = 1.7 \text{ kJ mol}^{-1}$

Since $\Delta_r G^\circ > 0$, the reaction is not spontaneous.

76. **(E)** By coupling the two reactions, we obtain:

$Glu^- + NH_4^+ \longrightarrow G \ln + H_2O$ $\Delta_r G^\circ = 14.8 \text{ kJ mol}^{-1}$

$ATP + H_2O \longrightarrow ADP + P$ $\Delta_r G^\circ = -31.5 \text{ kJ mol}^{-1}$

$Glu^- + NH_4^+ + ATP \longrightarrow Gln + ADP + P$ $\Delta_r G^\circ = (14.8 - 31.5) \text{ kJ mol}^{-1} = -16.7 \text{ kJ mol}^{-1}$

Therefore, the reaction is spontaneous.

INTEGRATIVE AND ADVANCED EXERCISES

77. **(D)** For an adiabatic process, no heat is exchanged with the surroundings. Therefore, $\Delta S_{surr} = 0$. For a spontaneous process, we must have $\Delta S_{univ} = \Delta S + \Delta S_{surr} > 0$. If $\Delta S_{surr} = 0$, then we must have $\Delta S > 0$ for the system. In other words, for a spontaneous adiabatic process only, ΔS_{surr} is equal to zero. Only for a reversible, adiabatic process will we have $\Delta S = \Delta S_{surr} = \Delta S_{univ} = 0$.

78. **(D)** We begin by constructing a thermodynamic cycle consisting of three steps:

$$
\begin{array}{ccc}
\text{H}_2\text{O (1, 283.15 K)} & \xrightarrow{\ \Delta S = ?,\ \Delta H = ?\ } & \text{H}_2\text{O (g, 398.15 K)} \\
\Big\downarrow \Delta S_1, \Delta H_1\ \text{①} & & \text{③}\ \Big\uparrow \Delta S_3, \Delta H_3 \\
\text{H}_2\text{O (1, 373.15 K)} & \xrightarrow[\text{②}]{\ \Delta S_2, \Delta H_2\ } & \text{H}_2\text{O (g, 373.15 K)}
\end{array}
$$

The enthalpy and entropy changes for the three steps can be calculated by using equations presented in Table 13.1

1. Reversible heating of water from 283.15 K to 373.15 K

$$\Delta H_1 = C_p(\text{H}_2\text{O, 1})\Delta T = 1\ \text{mol} \times 75.3\ \text{J K}^{-1}\ \text{mol}^{-1} \times (373.15\ \text{K} - 283.15\ \text{K}) = 6777\ \text{J}$$

$$\Delta S_1 = C_p(\text{H}_2\text{O, 1})\ln\frac{T_f}{T_i} = 1\ \text{mol} \times 75.3\ \text{J K}^{-1}\ \text{mol}^{-1}\ln\frac{373.15\ \text{K}}{283.15\ \text{K}} = 20.8\ \text{J K}^{-1}$$

2. Reversible vaporization of water at 373.15 K

$$\Delta H_2 = \Delta_{vap}H^\circ = 1\ \text{mol} \times 40.66\ \text{kJ mol}^{-1} = 40.66\ \text{kJ} = 40{,}660\ \text{J}$$

$$\Delta S_2 = \frac{\Delta_{vap}H^\circ}{T_{vap}} = \frac{1\ \text{mol} \times 40.66\ \text{kJ mol}^{-1}}{373.15\ \text{K}} = 0.109\ \text{kJ K}^{-1} = 109\ \text{J K}^{-1}$$

3. Reversible heating of water gas from 373.15 to 398.15 K

$$\Delta H_3 = C_p(\text{H}_2\text{O, g})\Delta T = 1\ \text{mol} \times 33.6\ \text{J K}^{-1}\ \text{mol}^{-1} \times (398.15\ \text{K} - 373.15\ \text{K}) = 840\ \text{J}$$

$$\Delta S_3 = C_p(\text{H}_2\text{O, g})\ln\frac{T_f}{T_i} = 1\ \text{mol} \times 33.6\ \text{J K}^{-1}\ \text{mol}^{-1}\ln\frac{398.15\ \text{K}}{373.15\ \text{K}} = 2.2\ \text{J K}^{-1}$$

Notice that the enthalpy and entropy changes are both positive for the heating processes. The values of ΔH and ΔS for the overall process are obtained by adding the corresponding values for the individual steps. Therefore,

$\Delta H = \Delta H_1 + \Delta H_2 + \Delta H_3 = 6777\ \text{J} + 40{,}660\ \text{J} + 840\ \text{J} = 48{,}277\ \text{J}$

$\Delta S = \Delta S_1 + \Delta S_2 + \Delta S_3 = 20.8\ \text{J K}^{-1} + 109\ \text{J K}^{-1} + 2.2\ \text{J K}^{-1} = 132\ \text{J K}^{-1}$

The entropy change for the surroundings is determined by the total amount of heat that flows into the surroundings, as well as the temperature of the surroundings.

$$\Delta S_{surr} = -\frac{q_{sys}}{T_{surr}} = -\frac{\Delta H}{T_{surr}} = \frac{48{,}277\ \text{J}}{398.15\ \text{K}} = -121.2\ \text{J K}^{-1}$$

Therefore, the entropy change of the universe is

$\Delta S_{univ} = \Delta S + \Delta S_{surr} = 132\ \text{J K}^{-1} - 121.2\ \text{J K}^{-1} = 10.8\ \text{J K}^{-1}$

79. (D)

(a) Let's first calculate the heat released by 0.20 kg of copper and the heat absorbed by 1.5 kg of copper.

$$q_{0.20 \text{ kg}} = C_p \Delta T = 0.20 \text{ kg} \times \frac{1000 \text{ g}}{1 \text{ kg}} \times \frac{1}{63.55 \text{ g mol}^{-1}} \times 0.385 \text{ J K}^{-1} \text{ mol}^{-1} \times (225 \text{ K} - 300 \text{ K})$$

$$= -90.9 \text{ J}$$

$$q_{1.5 \text{ kg}} = C_p \Delta T = 1.5 \text{ kg} \times \frac{1000 \text{ g}}{1 \text{ kg}} \times \frac{1}{63.55 \text{ g mol}^{-1}} \times 0.385 \text{ J K}^{-1} \text{ mol}^{-1} \times (410 \text{ K} - 400 \text{ K})$$

$$= 90.9 \text{ J}$$

Notice that the heat absorbed by the warmer block of copper is equal to the heat released from the colder block.

(b) To determine ΔS_{univ}, we first need to calculate ΔS and ΔS_{surr}. We start by calculating the entropy changes for the 0.20 kg and 1.5 kg blocks.

$$\Delta S_{0.20 \text{ kg}} = C_p (0.20 \text{ kg Cu}) \ln \frac{T_f}{T_i}$$

$$= 0.20 \text{ kg} \times \frac{1000 \text{ g}}{1 \text{ kg}} \times \frac{1}{63.55 \text{ g mol}^{-1}} \times 0.385 \text{ J K}^{-1} \text{ mol}^{-1} \times \ln \frac{225 \text{ K}}{300 \text{ K}}$$

$$\Delta S_{0.20 \text{ kg}} = -0.349 \text{ J K}^{-1}$$

$$\Delta S_{1.5 \text{ kg}} = C_p (1.5 \text{ kg Cu}) \ln \frac{T_f}{T_i}$$

$$= 1.5 \text{ kg} \times \frac{1000 \text{ g}}{1 \text{ kg}} \times \frac{1}{63.55 \text{ g mol}^{-1}} \times 0.385 \text{ J K}^{-1} \text{ mol}^{-1} \times \ln \frac{410 \text{ K}}{400 \text{ K}}$$

$$\Delta S_{1.5 \text{ kg}} = 0.224 \text{ J K}^{-1}$$

Therefore, $\Delta S = \Delta S_{0.20 \text{ kg}} + \Delta S_{1.5 \text{ kg}} = -0.349 \text{ J K}^{-1} + 0.224 \text{ J K}^{-1} = -0.125 \text{ J K}^{-1}$. Similarly, the entropy change for the surroundings (ΔS_{surr}) is determined by the total amount of heat that flows into the surroundings, as well as the temperature of the surroundings. Since we assumed that there is no heat lost to the surroundings, $\Delta S_{surr} = 0$.

Finally, $\Delta S_{univ} = \Delta S + \Delta S_{surr} = -0.125 \text{ J K}^{-1} + 0.182 \text{ J K}^{-1} = -0.125 \text{ J K}^{-1} < 0$, indicating that the process is indeed nonspontaneous.

80. Assuming that argon behaves as an ideal gas, the initial and final temperatures are

$$pV = nRT \Rightarrow T = \frac{pV}{nR}$$

$$T_i = \frac{0.877 \text{ bar} \times \frac{1 \text{ atm}}{1.01325 \text{ bar}} \times 25.6 \text{ L}}{1 \text{ mol} \times 0.08206 \text{ L atm mol}^{-1} \text{ K}^{-1}} = 270 \text{ K}$$

$$T_f = \frac{2.42 \text{ bar} \times \frac{1 \text{ atm}}{1.01325 \text{ bar}} \times 15.1 \text{ L}}{1 \text{ mol} \times 0.08206 \text{ L atm mol}^{-1} \text{ K}^{-1}} = 439 \text{ K}$$

The entropy and enthalpy changes can be calculated by using equations presented in Table 13.1 and the molar heat capacity of argon (20.79 J K^{-1} mol^{-1}).

$$\Delta H = C_p \Delta T = 1 \text{ mol} \times 20.79 \text{ J K}^{-1} \text{ mol}^{-1} \times (439 \text{ K} - 270 \text{ K}) = 3.51 \times 10^3 \text{ J} = 3.51 \text{ kJ}$$

$$\Delta S = C_p \ln\left(\frac{T_f}{T_i}\right) - nR \ln\left(\frac{P_f}{P_i}\right)$$

$$\Delta S = 1 \text{ mol} \times 20.79 \text{ J K}^{-1} \text{ mol}^{-1} \ln\left(\frac{439 \text{ K}}{270 \text{ K}}\right) \quad -1 \text{ mol} \times \text{J K}^{-1} \text{ mol}^{-1} \ln\left(\frac{2.42 \text{ bar}}{0.877 \text{ bar}}\right)$$

$$\Delta S = 10.1 \text{ J K}^{-1} - 8.4 \text{ J K}^{-1} = 1.7 \text{ J K}^{-1}$$

81. **(M)**

(a) The normal boiling point of mercury is that temperature at which the mercury vapor pressure is 1.00 atm, or where the equilibrium constant for the vaporization equilibrium reaction has a numerical value of 1.00. This is also the temperature where $\Delta_r G° = 0$, since $\Delta_r G° = -RT \ln K_{eq}$ and $\ln(1.00) = 0$.

$$Hg(l) \rightleftharpoons Hg(g)$$

$$\Delta_r H° = \Delta_f H°[Hg(g)] - \Delta_f H°[Hg(l)] = 61.32 \text{ kJ/mol} - 0.00 \text{ kJ/mol} = 61.32 \text{ kJ/mol}$$

$$\Delta_r S° = S°[Hg(g)] - S°[Hg(l)] = 175.0 \text{ J mol}^{-1} \text{ K}^{-1} - 76.02 \text{ J mol}^{-1} \text{ K}^{-1} = 99.0 \text{ J mol}^{-1} \text{ K}^{-1}$$

$$0 = \Delta_r H° - T \Delta_r S° = 61.32 \times 10^3 \text{ J/mol} - T \times 99.0 \text{ J mol}^{-1} \text{ K}^{-1}$$

$$T = \frac{61.32 \times 10^3 \text{ J/mol}}{99.0 \text{ J mol}^{-1} \text{ K}^{-1}} = 619 \text{ K}$$

(b) The vapor pressure in atmospheres (atm) is the value of the equilibrium constant, which is related to the value of the Gibbs energy change for formation of Hg vapor.

$$\Delta_f G°[Hg(g)] = 31.82 \text{ kJ/mol} = -RT \ln K$$

$$\ln K = \frac{-31.82 \times 10^3 \text{ J/mol}}{8.3145 \text{ J mol}^{-1} \text{ K}^{-1} \times 298.15 \text{ K}} = -12.84 \qquad K = e^{-12.84} = 2.65 \times 10^{-6} \text{ atm}$$

Therefore, the vapor pressure of Hg at 25°C is 2.65×10^{-6} atm.

82. **(M)**

(a) **TRUE;** It is the change in Gibbs energy for a process in which reactants and products are all in their standard states (regardless of whatever states might be mentioned in the statement of the problem). When liquid and gaseous water are each at 1 atm at 100 °C (the normal boiling point), they are in equilibrium, so that $\Delta_r G = \Delta_r G° = 0$ is only true when the difference of the standard free energies of products and reactants is zero. A reaction with $\Delta_r G° = 0$ would be at equilibrium when products and reactants were all present under standard state conditions and the pressure of $H_2O(g) = 2.0$ atm is not the standard pressure for $H_2O(g)$.

(b) **FALSE;** $\Delta_r G \neq 0$. The system is not at equilibrium.

(c) **FALSE;** $\Delta_r G°$ can have only one value at any given temperature, and that is the value corresponding to all reactants and products in their standard states, so at the normal boiling point $\Delta_r G° = 0$ [as was also the case in answering part (a)]. Water will not vaporize spontaneously under standard conditions to produce water vapor with a pressure of 2 atm.

(d) **TRUE;** $\Delta_r G > 0$. The process of transforming water to vapor at 2.0 atm pressure at 100°C is not a spontaneous process; the condensation (reverse) process is spontaneous. (i.e. for the system to reach equilibrium, some $H_2O(l)$ must form)

83. **(D)** $\Delta_r G° = +\frac{1}{2}\Delta_f G°[Br_2(g)] + \frac{1}{2}\Delta_f G°[Cl_2(g)] - \Delta_f G°[BrCl(g)]$

$= +\frac{1}{2}(3.11\,kJ/mol) + \frac{1}{2}(0.00\,kJ/mol) - (-0.98\,kJ/mol) = +2.54\,kJ/mol = -RT\ln K_p$

$\ln K_p = -\dfrac{\Delta G°}{RT} = -\dfrac{2.54\times10^3\,J/mol}{8.3145\,J\,mol^{-1}\,K^{-1}\times298.15\,K} = -1.02 \quad K_p = e^{-1.02} = 0.361$

For ease of solving the problem, we double the reaction, which squares the value of the equilibrium constant. $K_{eq} = (0.357)^2 = 0.130$

Reaction: $2\,BrCl(g) \rightleftharpoons Br_2(g) + Cl_2(g)$

Initial: 1.00 mol   0 mol   0 mol

Changes: $-2x$ mol $+x$ mol $+x$ mol

Equil: $(1.00-2x)$mol x mol x mol

$K_p = \dfrac{P\{Br_2(g)\}\,P\{Cl_2(g)\}}{P\{BrCl(g)\}^2} = \dfrac{[n\{Br_2(g)\}RT/V][n\{Cl_2(g)\}RT/V]}{[n\{BrCl(g)\}RT/V]^2}$

$= \dfrac{n\{Br_2(g)\}\,n\{Cl_2(g)\}}{n\{BrCl(g)\}^2}$

$= \dfrac{x^2}{(1.00-2x)^2} = (0.361)^2 \qquad \dfrac{x}{1.00-2x} = 0.361 \qquad x = 0.361 - 0.722\,x$

$x = \dfrac{0.361}{1.722} = 0.210\,mol\,Br_2 = 0.210\,mol\,Cl_2 \quad 1.00-2x = 0.580\,mol\,BrCl$

84. **(M)** First we determine the value of K_p for the dissociation reaction. If $I_2(g)$ is 50% dissociated, then for every mole of undissociated $I_2(g)$, one mole of $I_2(g)$ has dissociated, producing two moles of $I(g)$. Thus, the partial pressure of $I(g)$ is twice the partial pressure of $I_2(g)$ ($I_2(g) \rightleftharpoons 2\,I(g)$).

$P_{total} = 1.00\,atm = P_{I_2(g)} + P_{I(g)} = P_{I_2(g)} + 2\times P_{I_2(g)} = 3\,P_{I_2(g)} \qquad P_{I_2(g)} = 0.333\,atm$

$K_p = \dfrac{P_{I(g)}^2}{P_{I_2(g)}} = \dfrac{(0.667)^2}{0.333} = 1.34 \quad \ln K_p = 0.293$

$\Delta_r H° = 2\,\Delta_f H°[I(g)] - \Delta_f H°[I_2(g)] = 2\times106.8\,kJ/mol - 62.44\,kJ/mol = 151.2\,kJ/mol$

$\Delta_r S° = 2\,S°[I(g)] - S°[I_2(g)] = 2\times180.8\,J\,mol^{-1}\,K^{-1} - 260.7\,J\,mol^{-1}\,K^{-1} = 100.9\,J\,mol^{-1}\,K^{-1}$

Now we equate two expressions for $\Delta_r G°$ and solve for T.

$$\Delta_r G° = \Delta_r H° - T \Delta_r S° = -RT \ln K_p = 151.2 \times 10^3 - 100.9T = -8.3145 \times T \times 0.293$$

$$151.2 \times 10^3 = 100.9T - 2.44T = 98.4T \qquad T = \frac{151.2 \times 10^3}{98.5} = 1535\,\text{K} \approx 1.5 \times 10^3\,\text{K}$$

85. **(M)**

(a) The oxide with the most positive (least negative) value of $\Delta_f G°$ is the one that most readily decomposes to the free metal and $O_2(g)$, since the decomposition is the reverse of the formation reaction. Thus the oxide that decomposes most readily is $Ag_2O(s)$.

(b) The decomposition reaction is $2\,Ag_2O(s) \longrightarrow 4\,Ag(s) + O_2(g)$ For this reaction $K_p = P_{O_2(g)}$. Thus, we need to find the temperature where $K_p = 1.00$. Since $\Delta_r G° = -RT \ln K_p$ and $\ln(1.00) = 0$, we wish to know the temperature where $\Delta_r G° = 0$. Note also that the decomposition is the reverse of the formation reaction. Thus, the following values are valid for the decomposition reaction at 298 K.

$$\Delta_r H° = +31.05\,\text{kJ/mol} \qquad\qquad \Delta_r G° = +11.20\,\text{kJ/mol}$$

We use these values to determine the value of $\Delta_r S°$ for the reaction.

$$\Delta_r G° = \Delta_r H° - T \Delta_r S° \quad T \Delta_r S° = \Delta_r H° - \Delta_r G° \quad \Delta_r S° = \frac{\Delta_r H° - \Delta_r G°}{T}$$

$$\Delta_r S° = \frac{31.05 \times 10^3\,\text{J/mol} - 11.20 \times 10^3\,\text{J/mol}}{298\,\text{K}} = +66.6\,\text{J mol}^{-1}\,\text{K}^{-1}$$

Now we determine the value of T where $\Delta_r G° = 0$.

$$T = \frac{\Delta_r H° - \Delta_r G°}{\Delta_r S°} = \frac{31.05 \times 10^3\,\text{J/mol} - 0.0\,\text{J/mol}}{+66.6\,\text{J mol}^{-1}\,\text{K}^{-1}} = 466\,\text{K} = 193\,°\text{C}$$

86. **(M)** At $127\,°\text{C} = 400\,\text{K}$, the two phases are in equilibrium, meaning that
$$\Delta_r G° = 0 = \Delta_r H° - T\Delta_r S° = [\Delta_f H°(\text{yellow}) - \Delta_f H°(\text{red})] - T[S°(\text{yellow}) - S°(\text{red})]$$
$$= [-102.9 - (-105.4)] \times 10^3\,\text{J} - 400\,\text{K} \times [S°(\text{yellow}) - 180\,\text{J mol}^{-1}\,\text{K}^{-1}]$$
$$= 2.5 \times 10^3\,\text{J/mol} - 400\,\text{K} \times S°(\text{yellow}) + 7.20 \times 10^4\,\text{J/mol}$$

$$S°(\text{yellow}) = \frac{(7.20 \times 10^4 + 2.5 \times 10^3)\,\text{J/mol}}{400\,\text{K}} = 186\,\text{J mol}^{-1}\,\text{K}^{-1}$$

Then we compute the value of the "entropy of formation" of the yellow form at 298 K.
$$\Delta_f S° = S°[HgI_2] - S°[Hg(l)] - S°[I_2(s)] = [186 - 76.02 - 116.1]\,\text{J mol}^{-1}\,\text{K}^{-1} = -6\,\text{J mol}^{-1}\,\text{K}^{-1}$$

Now we can determine the value of the Gibbs energy of formation for the yellow form.
$$\Delta_f G° = \Delta_f H° - T\Delta_f S° = -102.9\,\frac{\text{kJ}}{\text{mol}} - [298\,\text{K} \times (-6\,\frac{\text{J}}{\text{K mol}}) \times \frac{1\text{kJ}}{1000\,\text{J}}] = -101.1\,\frac{\text{kJ}}{\text{mol}}$$

87. **(M)** First we need a value for the equilibrium constant. 1% conversion means that 0.99 mol $N_2(g)$ are present at equilibrium for every 1.00 mole present initially.

$$K = K_p = \frac{P_{NO(g)}^2}{P_{N_2(g)}P_{O_2(g)}} = \frac{[n\{NO(g)\}RT/V]^2}{[n\{N_2(g)\}RT/V][n\{O_2(g)\}RT/V]} = \frac{n\{NO(g)\}^2}{n\{N_2(g)\}\,n\{O_2(g)\}}$$

Reaction:	$N_2(g)$	$+$	$O_2(g)$	$\rightleftharpoons$	$2NO(g)$	
Initial:	1.00 mol		1.00 mol		0 mol	
Changes(1% rxn):	-0.010 mol		-0.010 mol		$+0.020$ mol	$K = \dfrac{(0.020)^2}{(0.99)(0.99)} = 4.1\times10^{-4}$
Equil:	0.99 mol		0.99 mol		0.020 mol	

The cited reaction is twice the formation reaction of NO(g), and thus

$$\Delta_r H^\circ = 2\Delta_f H^\circ[NO(g)] = 2\times90.25\,kJ/mol = 180.50\,kJ/mol$$
$$\Delta_r S^\circ = 2S^\circ[NO(g)] - S^\circ[N_2(g)] - S^\circ[O_2(g)]$$
$$= 2(210.7\,J\,mol^{-1}\,K) - 191.5\,J\,mol^{-1}\,K^{-1} - 205.0\,J\,mol^{-1}\,K^{-1} = 24.9\,J\,mol^{-1}\,K^{-1}$$
$$\Delta_r G^\circ = -RT\ln K = -8.31447\,JK^{-1}mol^{-1}(T)\ln(4.1\times10^{-4}) = 64.85(T)$$
$$\Delta_r G^\circ = \Delta_r H^\circ - T\Delta_r S^\circ = 64.85(T) = 180.5\,kJ/mol - (T)24.9\,J\,mol^{-1}\,K^{-1}$$
$$180.5\times10\,J/mol = 64.85(T) + (T)24.9\,J\,mol^{-1}\,K^{-1} = 89.75(T) \qquad T = 2.01\times10^3\,K$$

88. **(M)** $P_{H_2O} = 75$ torr or $0.098\underline{7}$ atm. $\qquad K = \left(P_{H_2O}\right)^2 = (0.098\underline{7})^2 = 9.7\underline{4}\times10^{-3}$

$$\Delta_r G^\circ = (2\times(-228.6\,kJ/mol) + (1)\times-918.1\,kJ/mol) - (1)\times-1400.0\,kJ/mol$$
$$= 309.0\,kJ\,mol^-$$
$$\Delta_r H^\circ = (2\times(-241.8\,kJ/mol) + (1)\times-1085.8.1\,kJ/mol) - (1)\times-1684.3\,kJ/mol$$
$$= 114.9\,kJ\,mol^{-1}$$
$$\Delta_r S^\circ = (2\times(188.\,J/K\,mol) + (1\times146.\,J/K\,mol) + (1)\times221.3.\,J/K\,mol = 302.3\,J\,K^{-1}\,mol^{-1}$$
$$\Delta_r G^\circ = -RT\ln K = -8.3145\,J\,mol^{-1}\,K^{-1}\times T\times\ln(9.74\times10^{-3}) = 38.\underline{5}(T)$$
$$\Delta_r G^\circ = 38.\underline{5}(T) = \Delta_r H^\circ - T\Delta S^\circ = 114,900\,J\,mol^{-1} - (T)\times302.3\,J\,K^{-1}\,mol^{-1}$$
$$114,900\,J\,mol^{-1} = 340.8\,J\,mol^{-1}\,K^{-1}(T) \quad \text{Hence: } T = 337\,K = 64\,°C$$

89. **(M)** The value of $\Delta_r H^\circ$ determined in Exercise 70 is $\Delta_r H^\circ = +128\,kJ/mol$. We use any one of the values of $K_p = K_{eq}$ to determine a value of $\Delta_r G^\circ$. At 30 °C = 303 K,

$$\Delta_r G^\circ = -RT\ln K_{eq} = -(8.3145\,J\,mol^{-1}\,K^{-1})(303\,K)\ln(1.66\times10^{-5}) = +2.77\times10^4\,J/mol$$

Now we determine $\Delta_r S^\circ$. $\Delta_r G^\circ = \Delta_r H - T\Delta_r S^\circ$

$$\Delta_r S^\circ = \frac{\Delta_r H - \Delta_r G^\circ}{T} = \frac{128\times10^3\,J/mol - 2.77\times10^4\,J/mol}{303\,K} = +331\,J\,mol^{-1}\,K^{-1}$$

By using the appropriate S° values in Appendix D, we calculate $\Delta_r S^\circ = +334\,J\,mol^{-1}\,K^{-1}$.

90. **(M)** In this problem we are asked to estimate the temperature at which the vapor pressure of cyclohexane is 100 mmHg. We begin by using Trouton's rule to determine the value of $\Delta_{vap}H$ for cyclohexane. The temperature at which the vapor pressure is 100.00 mmHg can then be determined using Clausius–Clapeyron equation.

Use Trouton's rule to find the value of $\Delta_{vap}H$:

$$\Delta_{vap}H = T_{nbp}\,\Delta_{vap}S = 353.9\,\mathrm{K} \times 87\,\mathrm{J\,mol^{-1}\,K^{-1}} = 31 \times 10^3\,\mathrm{J/mol}$$

Next, use Clausius–Clapeyron equation to find the required temperature:

$$\ln\frac{P_2}{P_1} = \frac{\Delta_{vap}H}{R}\left(\frac{1}{T_1} - \frac{1}{T_2}\right) = \ln\frac{100\,\mathrm{mmHg}}{760\,\mathrm{mmHg}}$$

$$= \frac{31 \times 10^3\,\mathrm{J/mol}}{8.3145\,\mathrm{J\,mol^{-1}\,K^{-1}}}\left(\frac{1}{353.9\,\mathrm{K}} - \frac{1}{T}\right) = -2.028$$

$$\frac{1}{353.9} - \frac{1}{T} = \frac{-2.028 \times 8.3145}{31 \times 10^3} = -5.4 \times 10^{-4} =$$

$$2.826 \times 10^{-3} - \frac{1}{T} \qquad \frac{1}{T} = 3.37 \times 10^{-3}\,\mathrm{K^{-1}}$$

$$T = 297\,\mathrm{K} = 24\,°\mathrm{C}$$

91. **(M)**

(a) $2\mathrm{Ag(s)} + \dfrac{1}{2}\mathrm{O}_2\mathrm{(g)} \rightarrow \mathrm{Ag}_2\mathrm{O}$

$$\Delta_f G° = \Delta_f G°(\mathrm{Ag}_2\mathrm{O(s)}) - \{2\Delta_f G°(\mathrm{Ag(s)}) + \frac{1}{2}\Delta_f G°(\mathrm{O}_2)\}$$

$$\Delta_f G° = -11.2\,\mathrm{kJ\,mol^{-1}} - \{2(0) + \frac{1}{2}(0)\} = -11.2\,\mathrm{kJ\,mol^{-1}} \Rightarrow \mathrm{Ag}_2\mathrm{O}$$

is thermodynamically stable at 25 °C

(b) Assuming $\Delta_r H°$, $\Delta_r S°$ are constant from 25–200°C (not so, but a reasonable assumption !)

$$\Delta_r S° = S°(\mathrm{Ag}_2\mathrm{O}) - \{2\,S°(\mathrm{Ag(s)}) + \frac{1}{2}S°(\mathrm{O}_2)\} = 121.3 - (2(42.6) + \frac{1}{2}(205.1))$$

$$= -66.5\,\mathrm{J\,K^{-1}\,mol^{-1}}$$

$$\Delta_r G° = -31.0\,\mathrm{kJ\,mol^{-1}} - \frac{(473\,\mathrm{K})(-66.5\,\mathrm{J\,K^{-1}mol^{-1}})}{1000\,\mathrm{J/kJ}} = \Delta_r H° - T\Delta_r S° = +0.45\,\mathrm{kJ\,mol^{-1}}$$

$\Rightarrow$ thermodynamically *unstable* at 200°C

92. **(M)** $\Delta_r G = 0$ since the system is at equilibrium. As well, $\Delta_r G° = 0$ because this process is under standard conditions. Since $\Delta_r G° = \Delta_r H° - T\Delta_r S° = 0. = \Delta_r H° = T\Delta_r S° = 273.15\,\mathrm{K} \times 21.99\,\mathrm{J\,K^{-1}\,mol^{-1}} = 6.007\,\mathrm{kJ\,mol^{-1}}$. Since we are dealing with 2 moles of ice melting, the values of $\Delta_r H°$ and $\Delta_r S°$ are doubled. Hence, $\Delta_r H° = 12.01\,\mathrm{kJ}$ and $\Delta_r S° = 43.98\,\mathrm{J\,K^{-1}}$. Note: The densities are not necessary for the calculations required for this question.

93. **(D)** First we determine the value of K_p that corresponds to 15% dissociation. We represent the initial pressure of phosgene as x atm.

Reaction: $COCl_2(g)$ $\rightleftharpoons$ $CO(g)$ + $Cl_2(g)$

Initial : x atm   0 atm   0 atm

Changes: $-0.15x$ atm $+0.15x$ atm $+0.15x$ atm

Equil: $0.85x$ atm $0.15x$ atm $0.15x$ atm

$P_{total} = 0.85x \text{ atm} + 0.15x \text{ atm} + 0.15x \text{ atm} = 1.15x \text{ atm} = 1.00 \text{ atm}$

$x = \dfrac{1.00}{1.15} = 0.870 \text{ atm}$

$K_p = \dfrac{P_{CO} P_{Cl_2}}{P_{COCl_2}} = \dfrac{(0.15 \times 0.870)^2}{0.85 \times 0.870} = 0.0230$

Next we find the value of $\Delta H°$ for the decomposition reaction.

$\ln \dfrac{K_1}{K_2} = \dfrac{\Delta_r H°}{R} \left(\dfrac{1}{T_2} - \dfrac{1}{T_1} \right) = \ln \dfrac{6.7 \times 10^{-9}}{4.44 \times 10^{-2}} = -15.71 = \dfrac{\Delta_r H°}{R} \left(\dfrac{1}{668} - \dfrac{1}{373.0} \right)$

$= \dfrac{\Delta_r H°}{R} (-1.18 \times 10^{-3})$

$\dfrac{\Delta_r H°}{R} = \dfrac{-15.71}{-1.18 \times 10^{-3}} = 1.33 \times 10^4,$

$\Delta_r H° = 1.33 \times 10^4 \times 8.3145 = 111 \times 10^3 \text{ J/mol} = 111 \text{ kJ/mol}$

And finally we find the temperature at which $K = 0.0230$.

$\ln \dfrac{K_1}{K_2} = \dfrac{\Delta_r H°}{R} \left(\dfrac{1}{T_2} - \dfrac{1}{T_1} \right) = \ln \dfrac{0.0230}{0.0444} = \dfrac{111 \times 10^3 \text{ J/mol}}{8.3145 \text{ J mol}^{-1}\text{K}^{-1}} \left(\dfrac{1}{668 \text{ K}} - \dfrac{1}{T} \right) = -0.658$

$\dfrac{1}{668} - \dfrac{1}{T} = \dfrac{-0.658 \times 8.3145}{111 \times 10^3} = -4.93 \times 10^{-5} = 1.497 \times 10^{-3} - \dfrac{1}{T} \qquad \dfrac{1}{T} = 1.546 \times 10^{-3}$

$T = 647 \text{ K} = 374°C$

94. From the given expressions for $S°$ and $\Delta_r H°$, we can calculate the ratio $S°/\Delta_r H°$:

$$\dfrac{S°}{\Delta_r H°} = \dfrac{\displaystyle\int_{0K}^{298.15K} \dfrac{aT}{T} dT}{\displaystyle\int_{0K}^{298.15K} aT \, dT} = \dfrac{a \displaystyle\int_{0K}^{298.15K} dT}{a \displaystyle\int_{0K}^{298.15K} T \, dT} = \dfrac{aT \big|_{0K}^{298.15K}}{\dfrac{1}{2} aT^2 \big|_{0K}^{298.15K}} =$$

$$= \dfrac{2}{T} \big|_{0K}^{298.15K} = \dfrac{2}{(298.15 \text{ K} - 0 \text{ K})} = \dfrac{2}{298.15 \text{ K}} = 0.0067 \text{ K}^{-1}$$

95. (M) $S^\circ_{298.15} = S^\circ_{274.68} + \Delta_{fus}S + \Delta_{heating}S$

$$S^\circ_{298.15} = 67.15 \text{ J K}^- \text{ mol}^{-1} + \frac{12{,}660 \text{ J mol}^{-1}}{274.68 \text{ K}} + \int_{274.68}^{298.15} 97.78 \frac{\text{J}}{\text{mol K}}$$

$$+ 0.0586 \frac{\text{J}}{\text{mol K}^2} \times (T - 274.68)$$

$$S^\circ_{298.15} = 67.15 \text{ J K}^{-1} \text{ mol}^{-1} + 46.09 \text{ J K}^{-1} \text{ mol}^{-1} + 8.07 \text{ J K}^{-1} \text{ mol}^{-1} = 121.3 \text{ J K}^{-1} \text{ mol}^{-1}$$

96. (M) $S^\circ = S^\circ_{solid} + \Delta_{fus}S + \Delta_{heating}S + \Delta_{vap}S + \Delta_{pressure\ change}S$

$$S^\circ = 128.82 \text{ J K}^{-1} \text{ mol}^{-1} + \frac{9866 \text{ J mol}^{-1}}{278.68 \text{ K}} + \int_{278.68}^{298.15} \frac{134.0 \frac{\text{J}}{\text{mol K}} dT}{T} + \frac{33{,}850 \text{ J mol}^{-1}}{298.15 \text{ K}}$$

$$+ 8.3145 \text{ J K}^{-1} \text{ mol}^{-1} \times \ln\left(\frac{95.13 \text{ torr}}{760 \text{ torr}}\right)$$

$$S^\circ = 128.82 \text{ J K}^{-1} \text{ mol}^{-1} + 35.40 \text{ J K}^{-1} \text{ mol}^{-1} + 9.05 \text{ J K}^{-1} \text{ mol}^{-1}$$

$$+ 113.5 \text{ J K}^{-1} \text{ mol}^{-1} + (-17.28 \text{ J K}^{-1} \text{ mol}^{-1})$$

$$S^\circ = 269.53 \text{ J K}^{-1} \text{ mol}^{-1}$$

97. (D) Start by labeling the particles A, B and C. Now arrange the particles among the states. One possibility includes A, B, and C occupying one energy state ($\varepsilon = 0,1,2$ or 3). This counts as one microstate. Another possibility is two of the particles occupying one energy state with the remaining one being in a different state. This possibility includes a total of three microstates. The final set of combinations is one with each particle being in different energy state. This combination includes a total of six microstates. Therefore, the total number of microstates in the system is 10. See pictorial representation on the following page illustrating the three different cases.

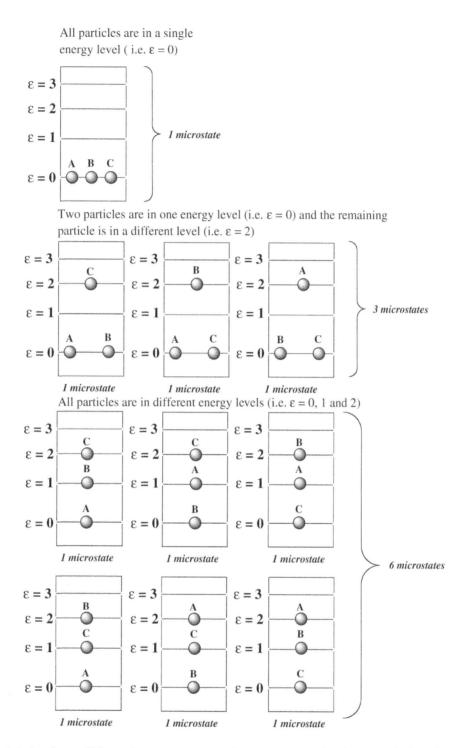

All particles are in a single energy level (i.e. $\varepsilon = 0$)

1 microstate

Two particles are in one energy level (i.e. $\varepsilon = 0$) and the remaining particle is in a different level (i.e. $\varepsilon = 2$)

3 microstates

1 microstate   1 microstate   1 microstate

All particles are in different energy levels (i.e. $\varepsilon = 0$, 1 and 2)

6 microstates

1 microstate   1 microstate   1 microstate

1 microstate   1 microstate   1 microstate

98. **(M) (a)** In the solid as the temperature increases, so do the translational, rotational, and vibrational degrees of freedom. In the liquid, most of the vibrational degrees of freedom are saturated and only translational and rotational degrees of freedom can increase. In the gas phase, all degrees of freedom are saturated. **(b)** The increase in translation and rotation on going from solid to liquid is much less than on going from liquid to gas. This is where most of the change in entropy is derived.

99. **(D)** Because KNO_3 is a strong electrolyte, its solution reaction will be:

$$KNO_3(s) + H_2O \rightleftharpoons K^+(aq) + NO_3^-(aq)$$

This reaction can be considered to be at equilibrium when the solid is in contact with a saturated solution, i.e. the conditions when crystallization begins. The solubility, s, of the salt, in moles per liter, can be calculated from the amount of salt weighted out and the volume of the solution. The equilibrium constant K for the reaction will be:

$$K = [K^+(aq)][NO_3^-(aq)] = (s)(s) = s^2$$

In the case of 25.0 mL solution at 340 K, the equilibrium constant K is:

$$n(KNO_3) = \frac{m}{M} = \frac{20.2 \text{ g}}{101.103 \text{ g mol}^{-1}} = 0.200 \text{ mol} \Rightarrow s = \frac{n}{V} = \frac{0.200 \text{ mol}}{0.0250 \text{ L}} = 8.0 \text{ mol L}^{-1}$$

$$K = s^2 = 8^2 = 64$$

The equilibrium constant K can be used to calculate $\Delta_r G$ for the reaction using $\Delta_r G = -RT \ln K$:

$$\Delta_r G = -8.314 \text{ JK}^{-1}\text{mol}^{-1} \times 340 \text{ K} \times \ln 64 = -12 \text{ kJ mol}^{-1}$$

The values for K and $\Delta_r G$ at all other temperatures are summarized in the table below.

Volume (mL)	$T/(K)$	$1/T\,(K^{-1})$	s (mol L^{-1})	K	$\ln K$	$\Delta_r G$ (kJ mol^{-1})
25.0	340	0.00294	8.0	64	4.2	−12
29.2	329	0.00304	6.9	48	3.9	−11
33.4	320	0.00312	6.0	36	3.6	−9.6
37.6	313	0.00320	5.3	28	3.3	−8.6
41.8	310	0.00322	4.8	23	3.1	−8.0
46.0	306	0.00327	4.3	18.5	2.9	−7.4
51.0	303	0.00330	3.9	15	2.7	−6.8

The plot of $\ln K$ v.s. $1/T$ provides $\Delta_r H$ (slope $= -\Delta_r H/R$) and $\Delta_r S$ (y-intercept $= \Delta_r S/R$) for the reaction:

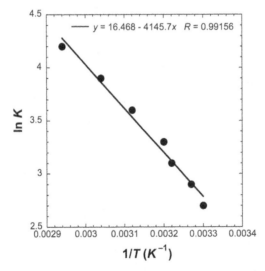

$$\Delta_r H = -\text{slope} \times R = 4145.7 \times 8.314 \text{ JK}^{-1}\text{mol}^{-1} = 34.5 \text{ kJmol}^{-1}$$

$$\Delta_r S = y - \text{intercept} \times R = 16.468 \times 8.314 \text{ JK}^{-1}\text{mol}^{-1} = 136.9 \text{ JK}^{-1}\text{mol}^{-1}$$

$\Delta_r H$ for the crystallization process is -35.4 kJ mol^{-1}. It is negative as expected because crystallization is an exothermic process. Furthermore, the positive value for $\Delta_r S$ shows that crystallization is a process that decreases the entropy of a system.

FEATURE PROBLEMS

100. (M)

(a) The first method involves combining the values of $\Delta_f G°$. The second uses

$$\Delta_r G° = \Delta_r H° - T\Delta_r S°$$

$$\Delta_r G° = \Delta_f G°\left[H_2O(g)\right] - \Delta_f G°\left[H_2O(l)\right]$$

$$= -228.572 \text{ kJ/mol} - \left(-237.129 \text{ kJ/mol}\right) = +8.557 \text{ kJ/mol}$$

$$\Delta_r H° = \Delta_f H°\left[H_2O(g)\right] - \Delta_f H°\left[H_2O(l)\right]$$

$$= -241.818 \text{ kJ/mol} - \left(-285.830 \text{ kJ/mol}\right) = +44.012 \text{ kJ/mol}$$

$$\Delta_r S° = S°\left[H_2O(g)\right] - S°\left[H_2O(l)\right]$$

$$= 188.825 \text{ J mol}^{-1}\text{ K}^{-1} - 69.91 \text{ J mol}^{-1}\text{ K}^{-1} = +118.92 \text{ J mol}^{-1}\text{ K}^{-1}$$

$$\Delta_r G° = \Delta_r H° - T\Delta_r S°$$

$$= 44.012 \text{ kJ/mol} - 298.15 \text{ K} \times 118.92 \times 10^{-3} \text{ kJ mol}^{-1}\text{ K}^{-1} = +8.556 \text{ kJ/mol}$$

(b) We use the average value: $\Delta_r G° = +8.558 \times 10^3$ J/mol $= -RT \ln K$

$$\ln K = -\frac{8558 \text{ J/mol}}{8.3145 \text{ J mol}^{-1}\text{ K}^{-1} \times 298.15 \text{ K}} = -3.452; \quad K = e^{-3.452} = 0.0317 \text{ bar}$$

(c) $P\{H_2O\} = 0.0317 \text{ bar} \times \dfrac{1 \text{ atm}}{1.01325 \text{ bar}} \times \dfrac{760 \text{ mmHg}}{1 \text{ atm}} = 23.8 \text{ mmHg}$

(d) $\ln K = -\dfrac{8590 \text{ J/mol}}{8.3145 \text{ J mol}^{-1}\text{ K}^{-1} \times 298.15 \text{ K}} = -3.465;$

$K = e^{-3.465} = 0.0312_7 \text{ atm};$

$P\{H_2O\} = 0.0313 \text{ atm} \times \dfrac{760 \text{ mmHg}}{1 \text{ atm}} = 23.8 \text{ mmHg}$

101. (D)

(a) When we combine two reactions and obtain the overall value of $\Delta_r G°$, we subtract the value on the plot of the reaction that becomes a reduction from the value on the plot of the reaction that is an oxidation. Thus, to reduce ZnO with elemental Mg, we subtract the values on the line labeled "$2Zn + O_2 \rightarrow 2ZnO$" from those on the line labeled "$2Mg + O_2 \rightarrow 2MgO$". The result for the overall $\Delta G°$ will always be negative because every point on the "zinc" line is above the corresponding point on the "magnesium" line

(b) In contrast, the "carbon" line is only below the "zinc" line at temperatures above about 1000 °C. Thus, only at these elevated temperatures can ZnO be reduced by carbon.

(c) The decomposition of zinc oxide to its elements is the reverse of the plotted reaction, the value of $\Delta_r G°$ for the decomposition becomes negative, and the reaction becomes spontaneous, where the value of $\Delta_r G°$ for the plotted reaction becomes positive. This occurs above about 1850 °C.

(d) The "carbon" line has a negative slope, indicating that carbon monoxide becomes more stable as temperature rises. The point where CO(g) would become less stable than 2C(s) and O_2(g) looks to be below −1000 °C (by extrapolating the line to lower temperatures). Based on this plot, it is not possible to decompose CO(g) to C(s) and O_2(g) in a spontaneous reaction.

(e)

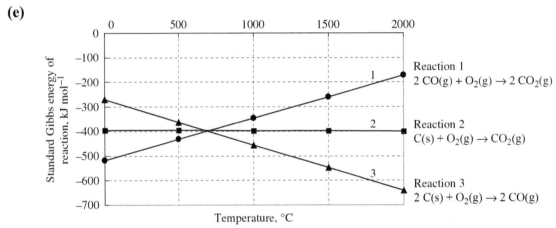

All three lines are straight-line plots of $\Delta_r G°$ vs. T following the equation $\Delta_r G° = \Delta_r H° - T\Delta_r S°$.

The general equation for a straight line is given below with the slightly modified Gibbs energy equation as a reference: $\Delta_r G° = -\Delta_r S° \, T + \Delta_r H°$ (here $\Delta_r H°$ assumed constant)

$y = mx + b$ (m = $-\Delta_r S°$ = slope of the line)

Thus, the slope of each line multiplied by minus one is equal to the $\Delta_r S°$ for the oxide formation reaction. It is hardly surprising, therefore, that the slopes for these lines differ so markedly because these three reactions have quite different $\Delta_r S°$ values ($\Delta_r S°$ for Reaction 1 = −173 J K^{-1}, $\Delta_r S°$ for Reaction 2 = 2.86 J K^{-1}, $\Delta_r S°$ for Reaction 3 = 178.8 J K^{-1})

(f) Since other metal oxides apparently have positive slopes similar to Mg and Zn, we can conclude that in general, the stability of metal oxides <u>decreases</u> as the temperature increases. Put another way, the decomposition of metal oxides to their elements becomes more spontaneous as the temperature is increased. By contrast, the two reactions involving elemental carbon, namely Reaction 2 and Reaction 3, have negative slopes, indicating that the formation of CO_2(g) and CO(g) from graphite becomes more favorable as the temperature rises. This means that the $\Delta_r G°$ for the reduction of metal oxides by carbon becomes more and more negative with increasing temperature. Moreover, there must exist a threshold temperature for each metal oxide above which the reaction with carbon will occur spontaneously. Carbon would appear to be an excellent reducing agent, therefore, because it will reduce virtually <u>any</u> metal oxide to its corresponding metal as long as the temperature chosen for the reaction is higher than the threshold temperature (the threshold temperature is commonly referred to as the transition temperature).

Consider for instance the reaction of MgO(s) with graphite to give CO_2(g) and Mg metal:

2 MgO(s) + C(s) → 2 Mg(s) + CO_2(g) $\Delta_r S° = 219.4$ J/K and $\Delta_r H° = 809.9$ kJ

$$T_{transition} = \frac{\Delta_r H°}{\Delta_r S°} = \frac{809.9 \text{ kJ}}{0.2194 \text{ kJ K}^{-1}} = 3691 \text{ K} = T_{threshold}$$

Consequently, above 3691 K, carbon will spontaneously reduce MgO to Mg metal.

102. (D)

(a) With a 36% efficiency and a condenser temperature (T_l) of 41 °C = 314 K,

$$\text{efficiency} = \frac{T_h - T_l}{T_h} \times 100\% = 36\% \qquad \frac{T_h - 314}{T_h} = 0.36 ;$$

$T_h = (0.36 \times T_h) + 314$ K; 0.64 $T_h = 314$ K; $T_h = 4.9 \times 10^2$ K

(b) The overall efficiency of the power plant is affected by factors other than the thermodynamic efficiency. For example, a portion of the heat of combustion of the fuel is lost to parts of the surroundings other than the steam boiler; there are frictional losses of energy in moving parts in the engine; and so on. To compensate for these losses, the thermodynamic efficiency must be greater than 36%. To obtain this higher thermodynamic efficiency, T_h must be greater than 4.9×10^2 K.

(c) The steam pressure we are seeking is the vapor pressure of water at 4.9×10^2 K. We also know that the vapor pressure of water at 373 K (100 °C) is 1 atm. The enthalpy of vaporization of water at 298 K is $\Delta_r H° = \Delta_f H°[H_2O(g) - \Delta_f H°[H_2O(l)] = -241.8$ kJ/mol − (−285.8 kJ/mol) = 44.0 kJ/mol. Although the enthalpy of vaporization is somewhat temperature dependent, we will assume that this value holds from 298 K to 4.9×10^2 K, and make appropriate substitutions into the Clausius-Clapeyron equation.

$$\ln\left(\frac{P_2}{1 \text{ atm}}\right) = \frac{44.0 \text{ kJ mol}^{-1}}{8.3145 \times 10^{-3} \text{ kJ mol}^{-1}}\left(\frac{1}{373 \text{ K}} - \frac{1}{490 \text{ K}}\right)$$

$$= 5.29 \times 10^{-3}\left(2.68 \times 10^{-3} - 2.04 \times 10^{-3}\right)$$

$$\ln\left(\frac{P_2}{1 \text{ atm}}\right) = 3.39 ; \left(\frac{P_2}{1 \text{ atm}}\right) = 29.7 ; P_2 \approx 30 \text{ atm}$$

The answer cannot be given with greater certainty because of the weakness of the assumption of a constant $H°_{vapn}$.

(d) It is not possible to devise a heat engine with 100% efficiency or greater. For 100% efficiency, $T_l = 0$ K, which is unattainable. To have an efficiency greater than 100 % would require a *negative* T_l, which is also unattainable.

103. (D)

(a) Under biological standard conditions:

$$ADP^{3-} + HPO_4^{2-} + H^+ \rightarrow ATP^{4-} + H_2O \quad \Delta_r G^{\circ\prime} = 32.4 \text{ kJ/mol}$$

If all of the energy of combustion of 1 mole of glucose is employed in the conversion of ADP to ATP, then the maximum number of moles ATP produced is

$$\text{Maximum number} = \frac{2870 \text{ kJ mol}^{-1}}{32.4 \text{ kJ mol}^{-1}} = 88.6 \text{ moles ATP}$$

(b) In an actual cell the number of ATP moles produced is 38, so that the efficiency is:

$$\text{Efficiency} = \frac{\text{number of ATP's actually produced}}{\text{Maximum number of ATP's that can be produced}} = \frac{38}{88.6} = 0.43$$

Thus, the cell's efficiency is about 43%.

(c) The previously calculated efficiency is based upon the biological standard state. We now calculate the Gibbs energies involved under the actual conditions in the cell. To do this we require the relationship between $\Delta_r G$ and $\Delta_r G^{\circ\prime}$ for the two coupled reactions. For the combustion of glucose we have

$$\Delta_r G = \Delta_r G^{\circ\prime} + RT \ln\left(\frac{a_{CO_2}^6 a_{H_2O}^6}{a_{glu} a_{O_2}^6}\right)$$

For the conversion of ADP to ATP we have

$$\Delta_r G = \Delta_r G^{\circ\prime} + RT \ln\left(\frac{a_{ATP} a_{H_2O}}{a_{ADP} a_{P_i}\left(\left[H^+\right]/10^{-7}\right)}\right)$$

Using the concentrations and pressures provided we can calculate the Gibbs energy for the combustion of glucose under biological conditions. First, we need to replace the activities by the appropriate effective concentrations. That is,

$$\Delta_r G = \Delta_r G^{\circ\prime} + RT \ln\left(\frac{\left(p/p^{\circ}\right)_{CO_2}^6 a_{H_2O}^6}{[glu]/[glu]^{\circ}\left(p/p^{\circ}\right)_{O_2}^6}\right)$$

using $a_{H_2O} \approx 1$ for a dilute solution we obtain

$$\Delta_r G = \Delta_r G^{\circ\prime} + RT \ln\left(\frac{\left(0.050 \text{ bar}/1 \text{ bar}\right)^6 \times 1^6}{[glu]/1\times\left(0.132 \text{ bar}/1 \text{ bar}\right)^6}\right)$$

The concentration of glucose is given in mg/mL and this has to be converted to molarity as follows:

$$[glu] = \frac{1.0 \text{ mg}}{mL} \times \frac{g}{1000 \text{ mg}} \times \frac{1000 \text{ mL}}{L} \times \frac{1}{180.16 \text{ g mol}^{-1}} = 0.00555 \text{ mol L}^{-1},$$

where the molar mass of glucose is 180.16 g mol^{-1}.

Assuming a temperature of 37 °C for a biological system we have, for one mole of glucose:

$$\Delta_r G = -2870 \times 10^3 \,\mathrm{J\,mol^{-1}} + 8.314 \,\mathrm{J\,K^{-1}\,mol^{-1}} \times 310\,\mathrm{K} \times \ln\left(\frac{(0.050\ )^6 \times 1^6}{0.00555/1 \times (0.132)^{\mathrm{mol^{-1}6}}}\right)$$

$$\Delta_r G = -2870 \times 10^3 \,\mathrm{J\,mol^{-1}} + 8.314 \,\mathrm{J\,K^{-1}\,mol^{-1}} \times 310\,\mathrm{K} \times \ln\left(\frac{2.954 \times 10^{-3}}{0.00555}\right)$$

$$\Delta_r G = -2870 \times 10^3 \,\mathrm{J\,mol^{-1}} + 8.314 \,\mathrm{J\,K^{-1}\,mol^{-1}} \times 310\,\mathrm{K} \times \ln\left(0.5323\right)$$

$$\Delta_r G = -2870 \times 10^3 \,\mathrm{J\,mol^{-1}} + 8.314 \,\mathrm{J\,K^{-1}\,mol^{-1}} \times 310\,\mathrm{K} \times (-0.6305)$$

$$\Delta_r G = -2870 \times 10^3 \,\mathrm{J\,mol^{-1}} - 1.625 \times 10^3 \,\mathrm{J\,mol^{-1}}$$

$$\Delta_r G = -2872 \times 10^3 \,\mathrm{J\,mol^{-1}}$$

In a similar manner we calculate the Gibbs energy change for the conversion of ADP to ATP:

$$\Delta_r G = \Delta_r G^{\circ\prime} + RT \ln\left(\frac{[ATP]/1 \times 1}{[ADP]/1 \times [P_i]/1 \times ([H^+]/10^{-7})}\right)$$

$$\Delta_r G = 32.4 \times 10^3 \,\mathrm{J\,mol^{-1}} + 8.314 \,\mathrm{J\,K^{-1}\,mol^{-1}} \times 310\,\mathrm{K} \times \ln\left(\frac{0.0001}{0.0001 \times 0.0001 \times (10^{-7}/10^{-7})}\right)$$

$$\Delta_r G = 32.4 \times 10^3 \,\mathrm{J\,mol^{-1}} + 8.314 \,\mathrm{J\,K^{-1}\,mol^{-1}} \times 310\,\mathrm{K} \times \ln\left(10^4\right)$$

$$\Delta_r G = 32.4 \times 10^3 \,\mathrm{J\,mol^{-1}} + 8.314 \,\mathrm{J\,K^{-1}\,mol^{-1}} \times 310\,\mathrm{K} \times (9.2103))$$

$$= 32.4 \times 10^3 \,\mathrm{J\,mol^{-1}} + 23.738 \times 10^3 \,\mathrm{J\,mol^{-1}} = 56.2 \times 10^3 \,\mathrm{J\,mol^{-1}}$$

(d) The efficiency under biological conditions is

$$\text{Efficiency} = \frac{\text{number of ATP's actually produced}}{\text{Maximum number of ATP's that can be produced}} = \frac{38}{2872/56.2} = 0.744$$

Thus, the cell's efficiency is about 74%.

The theoretical efficiency of the diesel engine is:

$$\text{Efficiency} = \frac{T_h - T_l}{T_h} \times 100\% = \frac{1923 - 873}{1923} \times 100\% = 55\%$$

Thus, the diesel's actual efficiency is $0.78 \times 55\% = 43\%$.
The cell's efficiency is 74% whereas that of the diesel engine is only 43%. Why is there such a large discrepancy? The diesel engine supplies heat to the surroundings, which is at a lower temperature than the engine. This dissipation of energy raises the temperature of the surroundings and the entropy of the surroundings. A cell operates under isothermal conditions and the energy not utilized goes only towards changing the entropy of the cell's surroundings. The cell is more efficient since it does not heat the surroundings.

104. (E)

(a) In this case CO can exist in two states, therefore, W = 2. There are N of these states in the crystal, and so we have

$$S = k \ln 2^N = 1.381 \times 10^{-23} \text{JK}^{-1} \times 6.022 \times 10^{23} \text{mol}^{-1} \ln 2 = 5.8 \text{JK}^{-1}\text{mol}^{-1}$$

(b) Let's calculate W. A mole of water has $2N$ hydrogen nuclei. If each nucleus had the choice of two positions along its O—O axis, one close to one oxygen atom and the other closer to the second oxygen atom, there would be 2^{2N} configurations. Many of these configurations are ruled out by the condition that each oxygen atom has two attached hydrogen atoms. Let's consider a particular oxygen atom and the four surrounding hydrogen atoms. There are a total of 16 arrangements of this OH_4 group; one with all four hydrogen atoms close to the oxygen atom, corresponding to $(H_4O)^{2+}$, four corresponding to $(H_3O)^+$, six to H_2O, four to OH^-, and one to O^{2-}. The acceptable arrangements assigning two strongly bonded hydrogen atoms to this oxygen atom accordingly compose six-sixteenths or three-eighths of the total possible arrangements. Of these arrangements, only three-eighths are suitable with respect to the second oxygen atom, and so forth; the number of configurations, W, is hence $2^{2N}(3/8)^N = (3/2)^N$. For water, W = 3/2, which leads to

$$S = k \ln(\frac{3}{2})^N = 1.381 \times 10^{-23} \text{JK}^{-1} \times 6.022 \times 10^{23} \text{mol}^{-1} \ln 1.5 = 3.4 \text{JK}^{-1}\text{mol}^{-1}$$

SELF-ASSESSMENT EXERCISES

105. (E)

(a) $\Delta_r S_{univ}$ or total entropy contains contributions from the entropy change of the system ($\Delta_r S_{sys}$) and the surroundings ($\Delta_r S_{surr}$). According to the second law of thermodynamics, $\Delta_r S_{univ}$ is always greater then zero.

(b) $\Delta_f G°$ or standard Gibbs energy of formation is the Gibbs energy change for a reaction in which a substances in its standard state is formed from its elements in their reference forms in their standard states.

(c) For a hypothetical chemical reaction $a\text{A} + b\text{B} \rightleftharpoons c\text{C} + d\text{D}$, the equilibrium constant K is defined as $K = \dfrac{a_C^c a_D^d}{a_A^a a_B^b}$, where a is the activity. For a substance in solution, activity is equal to the dimensionless ratio, $\gamma[\text{X}]/c°$, where γ is referred to as the activity coefficient, [X] represents a particular concentration, and $c°$ corresponds to the concentration in a chosen reference state (1 mol L^{-1}). For gases, the activity is equal to the dimensionless ratio $\gamma P/P°$, where P is the particular partial pressure and $P°$ is the partial pressure in the reference state (1 bar).

(d) $S°$ is the specific entropy of a substance at 298.15 K. The value for $S°$ is always positive.

(e) $\Delta_r G°$ is the standard Gibbs energy of a reaction. It is based on the conversion of stoichiometric amounts of reactants in their standard states to stoichiometric amounts of products in their standard states. The value of $\Delta_r G°$ is often calculated from tabulated values of standard Gibbs energies of formation, $\Delta_f G°$ at 298.15 K.

106. (E)

   (a) Absolute molar entropy is the entropy at zero-point energy (lowest possible energy state) and it is equal to zero.

   (b) Coupled reactions are spontaneous reactions ($\Delta_r G < 0$) that are obtained by pairing reactions with positive $\Delta_r G$ with the reactions with negative $\Delta_r G$.

   (c) Trouton's rule states that for many liquids at their normal boiling points, the standard molar entropy of vaporization has a value of approximately 87 J mol^{-1} K^{-1}.

   (d) Equilibrium constant K for a certain chemical reaction can be evaluated using either $\Delta_r G°$ or $\Delta_f G°$ in conjunction with $S°$ (which are often tabulated). The relationship used to calculate K is $\Delta_r G° = -RT \ln K$.

107. (E)

   (a) A spontaneous process is a process that occurs in a system left to itself; once started, no external action form outsize the system is necessary to make the process continue. A nonspontaneous process is a process that will not occur unless some external action is continuously applied.

   (b) Second law of thermodynamics states that the entropy of universe is always greater than zero or in other words that all spontaneous processes produce an increase in the entropy of the universe. The third law of thermodynamics states that the entropy of perfect pure crystal at 0 K is zero.

   (c) $\Delta_r G$ is the Gibbs energy of reaction for arbitrary (including nonstandard) conditions. $\Delta_r G°$ is the standard Gibbs energy of reaction.

   (d) $\Delta_r G$ is the Gibbs energy change of a system, usually expressed in units of J or kJ. $\Delta_r G$ is the Gibbs energy of reaction, usually expressed in units of J mol^{-1} or kJ mol^{-1}. $\Delta_r G$ refers to the rate of change of Gibbs with respect to the extent of the reaction.

108. (E) Second law of thermodynamics states that all spontaneous processes produce an increase in the entropy of the universe. In other words, $\Delta_r S_{univ} = \Delta_r S_{sys} + \Delta_r S_{surr} > 0$. Therefore, the correct answer is (d).

109. (E) The Gibbs energy of reaction cannot be used to determine how much heat is absorbed from the surroundings or how much work the system does on the surroundings. Furthermore, it also cannot be used to determine the proportion of the heat evolved in an exothermic reaction that can be converted to various forms of work. The sign of the Gibbs energy of reaction can be used to determine whether forward or reverse reaction is spontaneous for the given conditions: If $\Delta_r G < 0$, the forward reaction is spontaneous; if $\Delta_r G > 0$, the reverse reaction is spontaneous. Therefore, the correct answer is (c).

110. (M) To answer this question, we must first determine whether the entropy change for the given reaction is positive or negative. The reaction produces three moles of gas from two moles; therefore, the entropy change for the reaction is positive. The Gibbs energy of a reaction is a function of enthalpy, entropy, and temperature ($\Delta_r G = \Delta_r H - T\Delta_r S$). Since $\Delta_r H < 0$ and $\Delta_r S > 0$, this reaction will be spontaneous at any temperature. The correct answer is (a).

111. (M) Recall that $\Delta_r G° = -RT \ln K$. If $\Delta_r G° = 0$, then it follows that $\Delta_r G° = -RT \ln K = 0$. Solving for K yields: $\ln K = 0 \Rightarrow K = e^0 = 1$. Therefore, the correct answer is (b).

112. (E) In this reaction, the number of moles of reactants equals the number of moles of products. Therefore, K is equal to K_p and K_c. The correct answers are (a) and (d).

113. (M)

(a) No reaction is expected because of the decrease in entropy and the expectation that the reaction is endothermic. As a check with data from Appendix D, $\Delta_r G° = 326.4$ kJ mol^{-1} for the reaction as written—a very large value.

(b) Based on the increase in entropy, the forward reaction should occur, at least to some extent. For this reaction $\Delta_r G° = 75.21$ kJ mol^{-1}.

(c) $\Delta_r S$ is probably small, and $\Delta_r H$ is probably also small (one Cl-Cl bond and one Br-Br bonds are broken and two Br-Cl bonds are formed). $\Delta_r G°$ should be small and the forward reaction should occur to a significant extent. For this reaction $\Delta_r G° = -5.07$ kJmol^{-1}.

114. (M)

(a) Entropy change must be accessed for the system and its surroundings ($\Delta_r S_{univ}$), not just for the system alone.

(b) Equilibrium constant can be calculated from $\Delta_r G°$ ($\Delta_r G° = -RT \ln K$), and K permits equilibrium calculations for nonstandard conditions.

115. (D)

(a) First we need to determine $\Delta_{vap} H°$ which is simply equal to:
$$\Delta_{vap} H° = \Delta_f H°[(C_5H_{10}(g)] - \Delta_f H°[(C_5H_{10}(l)] = -77.2\text{kJ/mol} - (-105.9\text{kJ/mol})$$
$= 28.7$kJ/mol. Now we use Trouton's rule to calculate the boiling point of cyclopentane:
$$\Delta_{vap} S° = \frac{\Delta_{vap} H°}{T_{bp}} = 87 \text{ J mol}^{-1}\text{ K}^{-1} \Rightarrow T_{bp} = \frac{\Delta_{vap} H°}{87 \text{ J mol}^{-1}\text{ K}^{-1}} = \frac{28.7 \times 1000 \text{ J mol}^{-1}}{87 \text{ J mol}^{-1}\text{ K}^{-1}} = 330 \text{ K}$$
$$T_{bp} = 330 \text{ K} - 273.15 \text{ K} = 57 \text{ °C}$$

(b) If we assume that $\Delta_{vap} H°$ and $\Delta_{vap} S°$ are independent of T we can calculate $\Delta_{vap} G°$:
$$\Delta_{vap, 298 K} G° = \Delta_{vap} H° - T\Delta_{vap} S° = 28.7 \text{ kJ mol}^{-1} - 298.15 K \times \frac{87}{1000} \text{kJK}^{-1}\text{mol}^{-1} = 2.8 \text{ kJ mol}^{-1}$$

(c) Because $\Delta_{vap, 298 K} G° > 0$, the vapor pressure is less than 1 atm at 298 K, consistent with $T_{bp} = 57$ °C.

116. **(M)**

(a) We can use the data from Appendix D to determine the change in enthalpy and entropy for the reaction:

$$\Delta_r H^\circ = \Delta_f H^\circ(N_2O(g)) + 2\Delta_f H^\circ(H_2O(l)) - \Delta_f H^\circ(NH_4NO_3(s))$$

$$\Delta_r H^\circ = 82.05 \text{ kJ mol}^{-1} + 2 \times (-285.8 \text{ kJ mol}^{-1}) - (-365.6 \text{ kJ mol}^{-1}) = -124 \text{ kJ mol}^{-1}$$

$$\Delta_r S^\circ = S^\circ(N_2O(g)) + 2S^\circ(H_2O(l)) - S^\circ(NH_4NO_3(s))$$

$$\Delta_r S^\circ = 219.9 \text{ J K}^{-1} \text{ mol}^{-1} + 2 \times 69.91 \text{ J K}^{-1} \text{ mol}^{-1} - 151.1 \text{ J K}^{-1} \text{ mol}^{-1} = 208.6 \text{ J K}^{-1} \text{ mol}^{-1}$$

The forward reaction is exothermic.

(b) From the values of $\Delta_r H^\circ$ and $\Delta_r S^\circ$ determined in part (a) we can calculate $\Delta_r G^\circ$ at 298 K:

$$\Delta_r G^\circ = \Delta_r H^\circ - T\Delta_r S^\circ$$

$$\Delta_r G^\circ = -124 \text{ kJ mol}^{-1} - 298 \, K \times \frac{208.6 \text{ kJ mol}^{-1} \text{ K}^{-1}}{1000} = -186.1 \text{ kJ mol}^{-1}$$

Alternatively, $\Delta_r G^\circ$ can also be calculated directly using $\Delta_f G^\circ$ values tabulated in Appendix D.

(c) The equilibrium constant for the reaction is calculated using $\Delta_r G^\circ = -RT \ln K$:

$$\Delta_r G^\circ = -RT \ln K \Rightarrow -186.1 \times 1000 \text{ J mol}^{-1} = -8.314 \text{ J K}^{-1} \text{ mol}^{-1} \times 298 \text{ K} \times \ln K$$

$$-186100 \text{ J mol}^{-1} = -2477.6 \ln K \Rightarrow \ln K = 75.1 \Rightarrow K = e^{75.1} = 4.1 \times 10^{32}$$

(d) The reaction has $\Delta_r H^\circ < 0$ and $\Delta_r S^\circ > 0$. Because $\Delta_r G^\circ = \Delta_r H^\circ - T\Delta_r S^\circ$, the reaction will be spontaneous at all temperatures.

117. **(M)** Recall from Exercise 110 that $\Delta_r G^\circ = 0$ when K = 1. Therefore, we are looking for the graph with smallest change in Gibbs energy between the products and the reactants. The correct answer is graph (a). Notice that graphs (b) and (c) represent chemical reactions with small and large values of equilibrium constants, respectively.

118. **(M)** Carbon dioxide is a gas at room temperature. The melting point of carbon dioxide is expected to be very low. At room temperature and normal atmospheric pressure this process is spontaneous. The entropy of the universe if positive.

CHAPTER 14

SOLUTIONS AND THEIR PHYSICAL PROPERTIES

PRACTICE EXAMPLES

1A **(E)** To determine mass percent, we need both the mass of ethanol and the mass of solution. From volume percent, we know that 100.0 mL of solution contains 20.0 mL pure ethanol. The density of pure ethanol is 0.789 g/mL. We now can determine the mass of solute (ethanol) and solution. We perform the calculation in one step.

$$\text{mass percent ethanol} = \frac{20.0 \text{ mL ethanol} \times \dfrac{0.789 \text{ g}}{1 \text{ mL ethanol}}}{100.0 \text{ mL soln} \times \dfrac{0.977 \text{ g}}{1 \text{ mL soln}}} \times 100\% = 16.2\% \text{ ethanol by mass}$$

1B **(M)**

(a) The molarity of CO_2 refers to the number of moles of CO_2 in 1 L of solution. If we focus on 1 L of solution (= 1 L solvent, since we assume no volume change when the CO_2 is added), we can write

$$m(\text{IL}) = 1000 \text{ mL} \times 1.380 \text{ g/mL}$$
$$= 1380 \text{ g}$$

$$n(\text{IL}) = 1380 \text{ g}/284.1 \text{ g mol}^{-1}$$
$$= 4.857 \text{ mol}$$

Since the mole fraction of CO_2 is 0.60, we may write

$$n(CO_2)/[n(CO_2) + 4.857 \text{ mol}] = 0.6$$

which we can solve to obtain

$$n(CO_2) = 4.857 \text{ mol} \times 0.6/0.4$$
$$= 7.286 \text{ mol}$$

Therefore, the molarity of CO_2 is about 7.3 mol/L.

(b) The molality refers to the number of moles of CO_2 in 1 kg of solvent. We know that 1 kg of solvent has a volume of 1000 g × 1 mL/1.38 g = 724.6 mL, or 0.7246 L. Since the addition of CO_2 does not change the volume, then 0.7246 L is also the volume of solution containing 1 kg of solvent.

We established in (a) that the molarity of CO_2 is 7.286 mol/L, so the number of moles of CO_2 in 1 kg of solvent (and 0.7246 L of solution) is

$$n(CO_2) = 7.286 \text{ mol/L} \times 0.7246 \text{ L} = 5.2797 \text{ mol}$$

The molality of CO_2 is about 5.3 mol/kg.

2A **(M)** First we need to find the amount of each component in solution. Let us consider a 100.00-g sample of solution, in which there are 16.00 g glycerol and 84.00 g water. The shorthand notation for glycerol, $HOCH_2CH(OH)CH_2OH$, is $C_3H_5(OH)_3$

$$\text{amount of glycerol} = 16.00 \text{ g } C_3H_5(OH)_3 \times \frac{1 \text{ mol } C_3H_5(OH)_3}{92.10 \text{ g } C_3H_5(OH)_3} = 0.1737 \text{ mol } C_3H_5(OH)_3$$

$$\text{amount of water} = 84.00 \text{ g } H_2O \times \frac{1 \text{ mol } H_2O}{18.02 \text{ g } H_2O} = 4.661 \text{ mol } H_2O$$

$$\text{mole fraction of } C_3H_5(OH)_3 = \frac{n_{C_3H_5(OH)_3}}{n_{C_3H_5(OH)_3} + n_{H_2O}} = \frac{0.1737 \text{ mol } C_3H_5(OH)_3}{0.1737 \text{ mol } C_3H_5(OH)_3 + 4.661 \text{ mol } H_2O}$$

$$\text{mole fraction of } C_3H_5(OH)_3 = 0.03593$$

2B **(M)** First we need the amount of sucrose in solution. We use a 100.00-g sample of solution, in which there are 10.00 g sucrose and 90.00 g water.

$$\text{amount } C_{12}H_{22}O_{11} = 10.00 \text{ g } C_{12}H_{22}O_{11} \times \frac{1 \text{ mol } C_{12}H_{22}O_{11}}{342.30 \text{ g } C_{12}H_{22}O_{11}} = 0.02921 \text{ mol } C_{12}H_{22}O_{11}$$

(a) Molarity is amount of solute in moles per liter of solution. Convert the 100.00 g of solution to L with density as a conversion factor.

$$C_{12}H_{22}O_{11} \text{ molarity} = \frac{0.02921 \text{ mol } C_{12}H_{22}O_{11}}{1000. \text{ g soln}} \times \frac{1.040 \text{ g soln}}{1 \text{ mL}} \times \frac{1000 \text{ mL}}{1 \text{ L}} = 0.3038 \text{ M}$$

(b) Molality is amount of solute in moles per kilogram of solvent. Convert 90.00 g of solvent to kg.

$$C_{12}H_{22}O_{11} \text{ molality} = \frac{0.02921 \text{ mol } C_{12}H_{22}O_{11}}{90.00 \text{ g } H_2O} \times \frac{1000 \text{ g}}{1 \text{ kg}} = 0.3246 \text{ mol kg}^{-1}$$

(c) Mole fraction is the moles of solute per moles of solution. First compute the moles in 90.00 g H_2O.

$$n_{H_2O} = 90.00 \text{ g} \times \frac{1 \text{ mol } H_2O}{18.02 \text{ g } H_2O} = 4.994 \text{ mol } H_2O$$

$$\text{mole fraction } C_{12}H_{22}O_{11} = \frac{0.02921 \text{ mol } C_{12}H_{22}O_{11}}{0.02921 \text{ mol } C_{12}H_{22}O_{11} + 4.994 \text{ mol } H_2O} = 0.005815$$

3A **(E)** Water is a highly polar compound. In fact, water molecules bond to each other through hydrogen bonds, which are unusually strong dipole–dipole interactions. Thus, water should mix well with other polar, hydrogen bonding compounds. (a) Toluene is nonpolar and should not be very soluble in water. (c) Benzaldehyde can form hydrogen bonds to water through its O atom. However, most of the molecule is nonpolar and, as a result, it has limited solubility in water. (b) Oxalic acid is polar and can form hydrogen bonds. Of these three compounds, oxalic acid should be the most readily soluble in water. Actual solubilities (w/w%) are: toluene (0.067%) < benzaldehyde (0.28%) < oxalic acid (14%).

3B **(E)** Both I_2 and CCl_4 are nonpolar molecules. It does not take much energy to break the attractions among I_2 molecules, or among CCl_4 molecules. Also, there is not a strong I_2-CCl_4 attraction created when a solution forms. Thus, I_2 should dissolve well in CCl_4 by simple mixing. H_2O is extensively hydrogen bonded with strong intermolecular forces that are difficult to break, but there is not a strong I_2-H_2O attraction created when a solution forms. Thus, we expect I_2 to dissolve poorly in water. Actual solubilities are: 2.603 g I_2/100 g CCl_4 and 0.033 g I_2/100 g H_2O.

4A **(M)** The two suggestions are quoted first, followed by the means for achieving each one.
(1) Dissolve the 95 g NH_4Cl in just enough water to produce a saturated solution (55 g NH_4Cl/100 g H_2O) at 60 °C.

$$\text{mass of water needed} = 95 \text{ g } NH_4Cl \times \frac{100 \text{ g } H_2O}{55 \text{ g } NH_4Cl} = 173 \text{ g } H_2O$$

The mass of NH_4Cl in the saturated solution at 20 °C will be smaller.

$$\text{mass } NH_4Cl \text{ dissolved} = 173 \text{ g } H_2O \times \frac{37 \text{ g } NH_4Cl}{100 \text{ g } H_2O} = 64 \text{ g } NH_4Cl \text{ dissolved}$$

$$\text{crystallized mass } NH_4Cl = 95 \text{ g } NH_4Cl \text{ total} - 64 \text{ g } NH_4Cl \text{ dissolved at } 20 \,°C$$
$$= 31 \text{ g } NH_4Cl \text{ crystallized}$$

(2) Lower the final temperature to 0 °C, rather than 20 °C. From Figure 14-10, at 0 °C, the solubility of NH_4Cl is 28.5 g NH_4Cl/100 g H_2O. From this (and knowing that there are 173 g H_2O present in the solution) we calculate the mass of NH_4Cl dissolved at this lower temperature.

$$\text{mass dissolved } NH_4Cl = 173 \text{ g } H_2O \times \frac{28.5 \text{ g } NH_4Cl}{100 \text{ g } H_2O} = 49.3 \text{ g } NH_4Cl \text{ dissolved}$$

The mass of NH_4Cl recrystallized is 95 g $-$ 49.3 g $=$ 46 g

$$\text{yield} = \left(\frac{46 \text{ g}}{95 \text{ g}}\right) \times 100\% = 48\%$$

4B **(M)** Percent yield for the recrystallization can be defined as:

$$\% \text{ yield} = \frac{\text{mass crystallized}}{\text{mass dissolved} \left(40 \,°C\right)} \times 100\%$$

$$\% \text{ yield} = \frac{\text{mass dissolved} \left(\text{at } 40 \,°C\right) - \text{mass dissolved} \left(\text{at } 20 \,°C\right)}{\text{mass dissolved} \left(\text{at } 40 \,°C\right)} \times 100\%$$

Figure 14-10 solubilities per 100 g H_2O are followed by percent yield calculations. Solubility of $KClO_4$: 4.84 g at 40 °C and 3.0 g at 20 °C

$$\text{Percent yield of } KClO_4 = \frac{4.84 \text{ g} - 3.0 \text{ g}}{4.84 \text{ g}} \times 100\% = 38\% \ KClO_4$$

Solubility of KNO_3: 60.7 g at 40 °C and 32.3 g at 20 °C

$$\text{Percent Yield of } KNO_3 = \frac{60.7 \text{ g} - 32.3 \text{ g}}{60.7 \text{ g}} \times 100\% = 47\% \ KNO_3$$

Solubility of K_2SO_4: 15.1 g at 40 °C and 11.9 g at 20 °C

$$\text{Percent yield of } K_2SO_4 = \frac{15.1 \text{ g} - 11.9 \text{ g}}{15.1 \text{ g}} \times 100\% = 21\% \ K_2SO_4$$

Ranked in order of decreasing percent yield we have:
$$KNO_3 \,(47\%) > KClO_4 \,(38\%) > K_2SO_4 \,(21\%)$$

5A **(M)** From Example 14-5, we know that the Henry's law constant for O_2 dissolved in water is $k = 2.18 \times 10^{-3}$ M atm^{-1}. Consequently,

$$P_{\text{gas}} = \frac{C}{k} = \frac{\dfrac{5.00 \times 10^{-3} \text{ g} \times \dfrac{1 \text{ mol } O_2}{32.00 \text{ g } O_2}}{0.100 \text{ L}}}{2.18 \times 10^{-3} \text{ M atm}^{-1}} = 0.717 \text{ atm } O_2 \text{ pressure}$$

5B **(M)** We note the relationship between gas partial pressure over a liquid and its dissolved concentration is given by Henry's Law: $C = k\,P$, where C is the concentration (given in dimensionless "volume parts" unit, akin to ppm), k is the Henry's Law constant, and P is the partial pressure of CO, which is given by: $\chi_{P_{\text{CO}}} = P_{\text{CO}}/P_{\text{total}}$. Assuming a CO partial pressure of 1.0 (100% at 1 atm), the k value is 0.0354 mL mL^{-1} atm^{-1}.

First, since the concentration of CO is 0.0100 mol CO/1.000 L of H_2O, we have to find the volume of CO at 273 K and 1.0 atm. That is,

$$V = \frac{nRT}{P} = \frac{(0.0100 \text{ mol})(0.08206 \text{ L} \cdot \text{atm} \cdot \text{mol}^{-1} \cdot \text{K}^{-1})(273 \text{ K})}{1.0 \text{ atm}} = 0.224 \text{ L}$$

Therefore, the concentration of CO may be expressed as follows:

$$\text{v/v concentration of CO} = \frac{0.224 \text{ L CO}}{1.000 \text{ L } H_2O} = 0.224 \text{ L/L or } 0.224 \text{ mL/mL}$$

$$P_{\text{CO}} = \frac{C}{k} = \frac{0.224 \text{ mL} \cdot \text{mL}^{-1}}{0.0354 \text{ mL} \cdot \text{mL}^{-1} \cdot \text{atm}^{-1}} = 6.328 \text{ atm}$$

6A **(E)** Raoult's law enables us to determine the vapor pressure of each component.
$$P_{\text{hex}} = \chi_{\text{hex}} P^*_{\text{hex}} = 0.750 \times 149.1 \text{ mmHg} = 112 \text{ mmHg}$$
$$P_{\text{pen}} = \chi_{\text{pen}} P^*_{\text{pen}} = 0.250 \times 508.5 \text{ mmHg} = 127 \text{ mmHg}.$$
We use Dalton's law to determine the total vapor pressure:
$$P_{\text{total}} = P_{\text{hex}} + P_{\text{pen}} = 112 \text{ mmHg} + 127 \text{ mmHg} = 239 \text{ mmHg}$$

6B **(M)** The masses of solution components need to be converted to amounts in moles through the use of molar masses. Let us choose as our amount precisely 1.0000 mole of $C_6H_6 = 78.11$ g C_6H_6 and an equal mass of toluene.

$$\text{amount of toluene} = 78.11 \text{ g } C_7H_8 \times \frac{1 \text{ mol } C_7H_8}{92.14 \text{ g } C_7H_8} = 0.8477 \text{ mol } C_7H_8$$

$$\text{mole fraction toluene} = \chi_{tol} = \frac{0.8477 \text{ mol } C_7H_8}{0.8477 \text{ mol } C_7H_8 + 1.0000 \text{ mol } C_6H_6} = 0.4588$$

$$\text{toluene vapor pressure} = \chi_{tol} P^*_{tol} = 0.4588 \times 28.4 \text{ mmHg} = 13.0 \text{ mmHg}$$

$$\text{benzene vapor pressure} = \chi_{benz} P^*_{benz} = (1.0000 - 0.4588) \times 95.1 \text{ mmHg} = 51.5 \text{ mmHg}.$$

$$\text{total vapor pressure} = 13.0 \text{ mmHg} + 51.5 \text{ mmHg} = 64.5 \text{ mmHg}$$

7A **(E)** The vapor pressure composition of each component is that component's partial pressure divided by the total pressure. Again, we note that the vapor is richer in the more volatile component.

$$y_{hexane} = \frac{P_{hexane}}{P_{total}} = \frac{112 \text{ mmHg hexane}}{239 \text{ mmHg total}} = 0.469 \qquad y_{pentane} = \frac{P_{pentane}}{P_{total}} = \frac{127 \text{ mmHg pentane}}{239 \text{ mmHg total}} = 0.531$$

or simply $1.000 - 0.469 = 0.531$

7B **(E)** The vapor pressure composition of each component is that component's partial pressure divided by the total pressure. Again we note that the vapor is richer in the more volatile component.

$$y_t = \frac{P_{toluene}}{P_{total}} = \frac{13.0 \text{ mmHg toluene}}{64.5 \text{ mmHg total}} = 0.202 \qquad y_b = \frac{P_{benzene}}{P_{total}} = \frac{51.5 \text{ mmHg benzene}}{64.5 \text{ mmHg total}} = 0.798$$

or simply $1.000 - 0.202 = 0.798$

8A **(M)** We use the osmotic pressure equation, converting the mass of solute to amount in moles, the temperature to Kelvin, and the solution volume to liters.

$$\pi = \frac{nRT}{V} = \frac{\left(1.50 \text{ g } C_{12}H_{22}O_{11} \times \dfrac{1 \text{ mol } C_{12}H_{22}O_{11}}{342.3 \text{ g } C_{12}H_{22}O_{11}}\right) \times 0.08206 \dfrac{L \text{ atm}}{\text{mol K}} \times 298 \text{ K}}{125 \text{ mL} \times \dfrac{1 \text{ L}}{1000 \text{ mL}}} = 0.857 \text{ atm}$$

8B **(E)** We use the osmotic pressure equation to determine the molarity of the solution.

$$\frac{n}{V} = \frac{\pi}{RT} = \frac{0.015 \text{ atm}}{0.08206 \text{ L atm mol}^{-1} \text{ K}^{-1} \times 298 \text{ K}} = 6.1 \times 10^{-4} \text{ M}$$

Now, we can calculate the mass of urea.

$$\text{urea mass} = 0.225 \text{ L} \times \frac{6.1 \times 10^{-4} \text{ mol urea}}{1 \text{ L soln}} \times \frac{60.06 \text{ g } CO(NH_2)_2}{1 \text{ mol } CO(NH_2)_2} = 8.2\underline{4} \times 10^{-3} \text{ g}$$

9A **(M)** We could substitute directly into the equation for molar mass derived in Example 14-9, but let us rather think our way through each step of the process. First, we find the concentration of the solution, by rearranging $\pi = \dfrac{n}{V}RT$. We need to convert the osmotic pressure to atmospheres.

$$\frac{n}{V} = \frac{\pi}{RT} = \frac{8.73 \text{ mmHg} \times \dfrac{1 \text{ atm}}{760 \text{ mmHg}}}{0.08206 \dfrac{\text{L atm}}{\text{mol K}} \times 298 \text{ K}} = 4.70 \times 10^{-4} \text{ M}$$

Next we determine the amount in moles of dissolved solute.

$$\text{amount of solute} = 100.0 \text{ mL} \times \frac{1 \text{ L}}{1000 \text{ mL}} \times \frac{4.70 \times 10^{-4} \text{ mol solute}}{1 \text{ L solution}} = 4.70 \times 10^{-5} \text{ mol solute}$$

We use the mass of solute, 4.04 g, to determine the molar mass. $\rightarrow$ $M = \dfrac{4.04 \text{ g}}{4.70 \times 10^{-5} \text{ mol}} = 8.60 \times 10^{4} \text{ g/mol}$

9B **(M)** We use the osmotic pressure equation along with the molarity of the solution.

$$\pi = \frac{n}{V}RT = \frac{2.12 \text{ g} \times \dfrac{1 \text{ mol}}{6.86 \times 10^{4} \text{ g}}}{75.00 \text{ mL} \times \dfrac{1 \text{ L}}{1000 \text{ mL}}} \times \frac{0.08206 \text{ L atm}}{\text{mol K}} \times (310.2)\text{K} = 0.0105 \text{ atm} = 7.97 \text{ mmHg}$$

10A **(M)**

(a) The freezing point depression constant for water is $K_f = 1.86 \,^\circ\text{C mol}^{-1} \text{ kg}$.

$$\text{molality} = \frac{\Delta T_f}{-K_f} = \frac{-0.227 \,^\circ\text{C}}{-1.86 \,^\circ\text{C mol}^{-1} \text{ kg}} = 0.122 \text{ mol kg}^{-1}$$

(b) We will use the definition of molality to determine the number of moles of riboflavin in 0.833 g of dissolved riboflavin.

$$\text{amount of riboflavin} = 18.1 \text{ g solvent H}_2\text{O} \times \frac{1 \text{ kg solvent}}{1000 \text{ g}} \times \frac{0.122 \text{ mol solute}}{1 \text{ kg solvent}}$$

$$\text{amount of riboflavin} = 2.21 \times 10^{-3} \text{ mol riboflavin}$$

$$\text{molar mass} = \frac{0.833 \text{ g riboflavin}}{2.21 \times 10^{-3} \text{ mol}} = 377 \text{ g/mol}$$

(c) We use the method of Chapter 3 to find riboflavin's empirical formula, starting with a 100.00-g sample.

$$54.25 \text{ g C} \times \frac{1 \text{ mol C}}{12.01 \text{ g C}} = 4.517 \text{ mol C} \quad \div 1.063 \quad \rightarrow \quad = 4.249 \text{ mol C}$$

$$5.36 \text{ g H} \times \frac{1 \text{ mol H}}{1.008 \text{ g H}} = 5.32 \text{ mol H} \quad \div 1.063 \quad \rightarrow \quad = 5.00 \text{ mol H}$$

$$25.51 \text{ g O} \times \frac{1 \text{ mol O}}{16.00 \text{ g O}} = 1.594 \text{ mol O} \div 1.063 \quad \rightarrow \quad = 1.500 \text{ mol O}$$

$$14.89 \text{ g N} \times \frac{1 \text{ mol N}}{14.01 \text{ g N}} = 1.063 \text{ mol N} \div 1.063 \quad \rightarrow \quad = 1.000 \text{ mol N}$$

If we multiply each of these amounts by 4 (because 4.249 is almost equal to $4\frac{1}{4}$), the empirical formula is found to be $C_{17}H_{20}O_6N_4$ with a molar mass of 376 g/mol. The molecular formula is $C_{17}H_{20}O_6N_4$.

10B **(M)** The boiling point of pure water at 760.0 mmHg is 100.000 °C. For higher pressures, the boiling point occurs at a higher temperature; for lower pressures, a lower boiling point is observed. The boiling point elevation for the urea solution is calculated as follows.

$$\Delta T_b = K_b \times m = 0.512 \text{ °C mol}^{-1} \text{ kg} \times 0.205 \text{ m} = 0.105 \text{ °C}$$

We would expect this urea solution to boil at $(100.00 + 0.105 =)100.105 \text{ °C}$ under 760.0 mmHg atmospheric pressure. Since it boils at a lower temperature, the atmospheric pressure must be lower than 760.0 mmHg.

11A **(M)** We assume a van't Hoff factor of $i = 3.00$ and convert the temperature to Kelvin, 298 K.

$$\pi = iMRT = \frac{3.00 \text{ mol ions}}{1 \text{ mol MgCl}_2} \times \frac{0.0530 \text{ mol MgCl}_2}{1 \text{ L soln}} \times 0.08206 \frac{\text{L atm}}{\text{mol K}} \times 298 \text{ K} = 3.89 \text{ atm}$$

11B **(M)** We first determine the molality of the solution, and assume a van't Hoff factor of $i = 2.00$.

$$m = \frac{\Delta T_f}{-K_f \times i} = \frac{-0.100 \text{ °C}}{-1.86 \text{ °C mol}^{-1} \text{ kg} \times 2.00} = 0.0269 \text{ mol kg}^{-1} \approx 0.0269 \text{ M}$$

$$\text{volume of HCl(aq)} = 250.0 \text{ mL final soln} \times \frac{0.0269 \text{ mmol HCl}}{1 \text{ mL soln}} \times \frac{1 \text{ mL conc soln}}{12.0 \text{ mmol HCl}}$$

$$\text{volume of HCl(aq)} = 0.560 \text{ mL conc soln}$$

INTEGRATIVE EXAMPLE

A.   **(M)** We determine the mass of each component in the water-rich phase.

$$\text{mass } H_2O = 32.8 \text{ g phase} \times \frac{92.50 \text{ g } H_2O}{100.00 \text{ g phase}} = 30.3 \text{ g } H_2O$$

mass phenol = 32.8 g phase – 30.3 g H_2O = 2.5 g phenol

Then we determine the mass of each component in the other phase.

mass phenol = 50.0 g – 2.5 g = 47.5 g phenol   mass H_2O = 50.0 g – 30.3 g = 19.7 g H_2O

$$\% H_2O = \frac{19.7 \text{ g } H_2O}{19.7 \text{ g } H_2O + 47.5 \text{ g phenol}} \times 100\% = 29.3\% H_2O$$

Above 66.8 °C phenol and water are completely miscible. Consequently, for temperatures above 66.8 °C, the mixture will be a homogeneous solution consisting of 50.0 g of H_2O and 50.0 g of phenol. To calculate the mole fraction of phenol in the mixture, we must first determine the number of moles of each component.

$$\text{number of moles of } H_2O = 50.0 \text{ g } H_2O \times \frac{1 \text{ mol } H_2O}{18.016 \text{ g } H_2O} = 2.77\underline{5} \text{ mol } H_2O$$

$$\text{number of moles of } H_2O = 50.0 \text{ g phenol} \times \frac{1 \text{ mol phenol}}{94.11 \text{ g phenol}} = 0.531 \text{ mol phenol}$$

$$\text{Thus } \chi_{\text{phenol}}(\text{mol fraction}) = \frac{0.531 \text{ mol phenol}}{2.775 \text{ mol phenol} + 0.531 \text{ mol } H_2O} = 0.161$$

B.   **(D)**

(a)   Rearrange Raoult's law (Equation 14.3) to the form $\dfrac{P_A^* - P_A}{P_A^*} = x_B$. The mass of H_2O absorbed by D_1 is proportional to P_A^*; the mass of H_2O absorbed by D_2 is proportional to P_A. Hence,

$$\frac{11.7458 - 11.5057}{11.7458} = x_B = 0.0204. \quad x_A = 0.9796,$$

$$P_A = 0.9796 \times 23.76 \text{ mmHg} = 23.28 \text{ mmHg}.$$

The observed vapor pressure lowering = 23.76 mmHg – 23.28 mmHg = 0.48 mmHg.

(b)   Calculate x_B for a 1.00 mol kg^{-1} solution. $x_B = 0.0177$; $x_A = 0.9823$. Calculate P_A using Raoult's law. $P_A = 23.34$ mmHg. The expected vapor pressure lowering = (23.76 – 23.34) mmHg = 0.42 mmHg.

EXERCISES

Homogeneous and Heterogeneous Mixtures

1. **(E)** $NH_2OH(s)$ should be the most soluble in water. Both $C_6H_6(l)$ and $C_{10}H_8(s)$ are composed of essentially nonpolar molecules, which are barely (if at all) soluble in water. Both $NH_2OH(s)$ and $CaCO_3(s)$ should be able to interact with water molecules. But $CaCO_3(s)$ contains ions of high charge, and thus it dissolves with great difficulty because of the high lattice energy. (Recall the solubility rules of Chapter 5: most carbonates are insoluble in water.)

2. **(E)** 1-Butanol should be moderately soluble in both water and benzene. A solute that is moderately soluble in both solvents will have some properties in common with each solvent. Both naphthalene and hexane are nonpolar molecules, like benzene, but interact only weakly with water molecules. Not surprisingly, they are soluble in benzene but not in water. Sodium chloride consists of charged ions, similar to the charges in the polar bonds of water. Thus, as expected NaCl is very soluble in water. 1-Butanol, on the other hand, possesses both a nonpolar part (C_4H_9-) like benzene, and a polar bond ($-O-H$) like water. Consequently 1-Butanol is expected to be soluble in both water and benzene.

3. **(E)** (b) Salicyl alcohol probably is moderately soluble in both benzene and water. The reason for this assertion is that salicyl alcohol contains a benzene ring, which would make it soluble in benzene, and also can use its $-OH$ groups to hydrogen bond to water molecules. On the other hand, (c) diphenyl contains only nonpolar benzene rings; it should be soluble in benzene but not in water. (a) *para*-dichlorobenzene contains a benzene ring, making it soluble in benzene, and two polar C–Cl bonds, which oppose each other, producing a nonpolar—and thus water-insoluble—molecule. (d) Hydroxyacetic acid is a very polar molecule with many opportunities for hydrogen bonding. Its polar nature would make it insoluble in benzene, while the prospective hydrogen bonding will enhance aqueous solubility.

4. **(E)** Vitamin C is a water-soluble molecule. It contains a number of polar $-OH$ groups, capable of hydrogen bonding with water, making these molecules soluble in water. Vitamin E is fat-soluble. Its molecules are composed of largely non-polar hydrocarbon chains, with few polar groups and thus it should be soluble in nonpolar solvents.

5. **(E)** (c) Formic acid and (f) propylene glycol are soluble in water. They both can form hydrogen bonds with water, and they both have small nonpolar portions. (b) Benzoic acid and (d) 1-Butanol are only slightly soluble in water. Although they both can form hydrogen bonds with water, both molecules contain reasonably large nonpolar portions, which will not interact strongly with water. (a) Iodoform and (e) chlorobenzene are insoluble in water. Although both molecules have polar groups, their influence is too small to enable the molecules to disrupt the hydrogen bonds in water and form a homogeneous liquid mixture.

6. **(E)** Benzoic acid will react with NaOH to form a solution of sodium ions and benzoate ions. Both of these charged species are highly soluble in strongly polar solvents such as water. In this equation, ϕ represents the benzene ring with one hydrogen omitted, C_6H_5- .

$$Na^+(aq) + OH^-(aq) + \phi\text{-COOH} \rightarrow Na^+(aq) + \phi\text{-COO}^-(aq) + H_2O\,(l)$$

The result of this reaction is that the concentration of molecular benzoic acid decreases, and thus more of the acid can be dissolved before the solution is saturated.

7. **(M)** We expect small, highly charged ions to form crystals with large lattice energies, which tends to decrease their solubility in water. Based on this information, we would expect MgF_2 to be insoluble and KF to be soluble. It is also probable that CaF_2 is insoluble due to its high lattice energy, but that NaF, with smaller lattice energy, is soluble. Of all of the fluorides listed, KF is probably the most water soluble. The actual solubilities at 25 °C are:
0.00020 M CaF_2 < 0.0021 M MgF_2 < 0.95 M NaF < 16 M KF.

8. **(M)** The nitrate ion is reasonably large and has a small negative charge. It thus should produce crystals with small lattice energies. In contrast, S^{2-} is highly charged, small and easily polarized. It should form crystals with relatively high lattice energies. In fact, partial covalent bonding occurs in many metal sulfides, as predicted from the polarizability of the anion, making these partially covalent solids difficult to break apart. We would expect the sulfide ion to be most polarized by small, highly charged cations. Thus the sulfides of small metal cations should be the least soluble. The most soluble sulfides thus should be those that have large cations of low charge: K_2S, Rb_2S, Cs_2S, to name but three.

Percent Concentration

9. **(E)** $\% \text{ NaBr} = \dfrac{116 \text{ g NaBr}}{116 \text{ g NaBr} + 100 \text{ g H}_2\text{O}} \times 100\% = 53.7\% = 53.7 \text{ g NaBr}/100 \text{ g solution}$

10. **(M)**

    (a) $\% \text{ by volume} = \dfrac{12.8 \text{ mL CH}_3\text{CH}_2\text{CH}_2\text{OH}}{75.0 \text{ mL soln}} \times 100\% = 17.1\% \text{ CH}_3\text{CH}_2\text{CH}_2\text{OH}$

    (b) $\text{percent by mass} = \dfrac{12.8 \text{ mL CH}_3\text{CH}_2\text{CH}_2\text{OH} \times \dfrac{0.803 \text{ g}}{1 \text{ mL}}}{75.0 \text{ mL} \times \dfrac{0.988 \text{ g}}{1 \text{ mL}}} \times 100\%$

    $= 13.5\% \text{ CH}_3\text{CH}_2\text{CH}_2\text{OH by mass}$

    (c) $\text{percent}(\text{mass}/\text{vol}) = \dfrac{12.8 \text{ mL CH}_3\text{CH}_2\text{CH}_2\text{OH} \times \dfrac{0.803 \text{ g}}{1 \text{ mL}}}{75.0 \text{ mL}} \times 100\%$

    $= 13.7 \dfrac{\text{mass}}{\text{vol}}\% \text{ CH}_3\text{CH}_2\text{CH}_2\text{OH}$

11. **(E)**

$$\text{soln. volume} = 725 \text{ kg NaCl} \times \frac{1000 \text{ g NaCl}}{1 \text{ kg NaCl}} \times \frac{100.00 \text{ g soln}}{3.87 \text{ g NaCl}} \times \frac{75.0 \text{ mL soln}}{76.9 \text{ g soln}} \times \frac{1 \text{ L soln}}{1000 \text{ mL soln}}$$

$$= 1.83 \times 10^4 \text{ L sol'n}$$

12. **(E)**

$$\text{mass AgNO}_3 = 0.1250 \text{ L soln} \times \frac{0.0321 \text{ mol AgNO}_3}{1 \text{ L soln}} \times \frac{169.9 \text{ g AgNO}_3}{1 \text{ mol AgNO}_3} \times \frac{100.00 \text{ g mixt.}}{99.81 \text{ g AgNO}_3}$$

$$= 0.683 \text{ g mixture}$$

13. **(E)** For water, the mass in grams and the volume in mL are about equal; the density of water is close to 1.0 g/mL. For ethanol, on the other hand, the density is about 0.8 g/mL. As long as the final solution volume after mixing is close to the sum of the volumes for the two pure liquids, the percent by volume of ethanol will have to be larger than its percent by mass. This would not necessarily be true of other ethanol solutions. It would only be true in those cases where the density of the other component is greater than the density of ethanol.

14. **(M)** We assume that blood has a density of 1.0 g/mL.

$$\text{mass \% cholesterol} = \frac{176 \text{ mg}}{\text{dL}} \times \frac{1 \text{ dl}}{100 \text{ mL}} \times \frac{100 \text{ ml}}{1.0 \times 10^2 \text{ g}} \times \frac{1 \text{ g}}{1000 \text{ mg}} \times 100\% = 0.17\underline{6} \%$$

We are only able to provide two significant figures at best owing to the initial assumption, namely, that blood has a density of 1.0 g/mL. Blood density will vary depending on a number of factors, for instance, percent water (i.e., blood alcohol level), disease (high white blood cell count), and the sex of the person, to name a few.

15. **(E)**

$$\text{mass HC}_2\text{H}_3\text{O}_2 = 355 \text{ mL vinegar} \times \frac{1.01 \text{ g vinegar}}{1 \text{ mL}} \times \frac{6.02 \text{ g HC}_2\text{H}_3\text{O}_2}{100.00 \text{ g vinegar}} = 21.6 \text{ g HC}_2\text{H}_3\text{O}_2$$

16. **(M)** We start with the molarity and convert both solute amount (numerator) and solution volume (denominator) to mass in order to obtain the mass percent.

$$\text{mass \% H}_2\text{SO}_4 = \frac{6.00 \text{ mol H}_2\text{SO}_4 \times \dfrac{98.08 \text{ g H}_2\text{SO}_4}{1 \text{ mol H}_2\text{SO}_4}}{1 \text{ L soln} \times \dfrac{1000 \text{ mL}}{1 \text{ L}} \times \dfrac{1.338 \text{ g}}{1 \text{ mL}}} \times 100\% = 44.0\% \text{ H}_2\text{SO}_4$$

17. **(M)** $46.1 \text{ ppm} = \dfrac{46.1 \text{ mg SO}_4^{2-}}{1 \text{ L solution}}$ (Assumes density of water $\sim 1.00 \text{ g mL}^{-1}$)

$$[\text{SO}_4^{2-}] = \frac{46.1 \text{ mg SO}_4^{2-}}{1 \text{ L solution}} \times \frac{1 \text{ g SO}_4^{2-}}{1000 \text{ mg SO}_4^{2-}} \times \frac{1 \text{ mol SO}_4^{2-}}{96.06 \text{ g SO}_4^{2-}} = 4.80 \times 10^{-4} \text{ M}$$

18. **(M)** 9.4 ppb $CHCl_3 = \dfrac{9.4 \; \mu g \;\; CHCl_3}{1 \; L \; solution}$ (Assumes density of water ~ 1.00 g mL^{-1})

$$mass \; CHCl_3 = \dfrac{9.4 \; \mu g \;\; CHCl_3}{1 \; L \; solution} \times \dfrac{1 \; g \;\; CHCl_3}{1 \times 10^6 \; \mu g \;\; CHCl_3} \times \dfrac{1 \; L \; solution}{1000 \; g \; solution} \times 250 \; g \; solution$$

$$= 2.4 \times 10^{-6} \; g$$

Molarity

19. **(E)**

$$molarity = \dfrac{6.00 \; g \; CH_3OH \times \dfrac{1 \; mol \; CH_3OH}{32.04 \; g \; CH_3OH}}{100.00 \; g \; soln \times \dfrac{1 \; mL}{0.988 \; g} \times \dfrac{1 \; L}{1000 \; mL}} = 1.85 \; M = [CH_3OH]$$

20. **(E)**

$$H_3PO_4 \; molarity = \dfrac{75 \; g \; H_3PO_4 \times \dfrac{1 \; mol \; H_3PO_4}{98.00 \; g \; H_3PO_4}}{100.0 \; g \; soln \times \dfrac{1 \; mL}{1.57 \; g} \times \dfrac{1 \; L}{1000 \; mL}} = 12 \; M$$

21. **(E)** The solution of Example 14-1 is 1.71 M C_2H_5OH, or 1.71 mmol C_2H_5OH in each mL of solution.

$$volume \; conc. \; soln = 825 \; mL \times \dfrac{0.235 \; mmol \; C_2H_5OH}{1 \; mL \; soln} \times \dfrac{1 \; mL \; conc. \; soln}{1.71 \; mmol \; C_2H_5OH}$$

$$= 113 \; mL \; conc. \; soln$$

22. **(E)**

$$HNO_3 \; molarity = \dfrac{30.00 \; g \; HNO_3 \times \dfrac{1 \; mol \; HNO_3}{63.01 \; g \; HNO_3}}{100.0 \; g \; soln \times \dfrac{1 \; mL}{1.18 \; g} \times \dfrac{1 \; L}{1000 \; mL}} = 5.62 \; M \; at \; 20 \; ^\circ C$$

23. **(E)** The easiest way to work with ppm is to think of it in terms of mg of a substance in a kg of solvent. The molarity of CO_2 is calculated as follows:

$$molarity \; of \; CO_2 = \dfrac{280 \; mg \; CO_2}{1 \; kg \; H_2O} \times \dfrac{1 \; g \; CO_2}{1000 \; mg \; CO_2} \times \dfrac{1 \; mol \; CO_2}{44.0 \; g \; CO_2} \times \dfrac{1027 \; kg \; H_2O}{1000 \; L \; H_2O}$$

$$= 0.00654 \; M$$

24. (E)

$$\text{mol O}_2 = \frac{PV}{RT} = \frac{(1\,\text{atm})(0.00577\,\text{L})}{(0.08206\,\text{L atm K}^{-1})(298\,\text{K})} = 2.360\times10^{-4}\,\text{mol}$$

$$\text{molarity of O}_2 = \frac{2.360\times10^{-4}\,\text{mol O}_2}{1\,\text{L H}_2\text{O}}$$

Molality

25. (M)

$$\text{molality} = \frac{2.65\,\text{g C}_6\text{H}_4\text{Cl}_2 \times \dfrac{1\,\text{mol C}_6\text{H}_4\text{Cl}_2}{147.0\,\text{g C}_6\text{H}_4\text{Cl}_2}}{50.0\,\text{mL} \times \dfrac{0.879\,\text{g}}{1\,\text{mL}} \times \dfrac{1\,\text{kg}}{1000\,\text{g}}} = 0.410\,\text{mol kg}^{-1}$$

26. (M) Consider a 1 L (1000 mL) sample. This sample has a mass of 1338 g (1000 mL × 1.338 g mL^{-1}). The mass of H_2SO_4 is 588.$\underline{47}$ g (1 L × 6 mol L^{-1} × 98.078 g mol^{-1}). The mass of solvent = 749.$\underline{53}$ g (1338 g – 588.$\underline{47}$ g). Molality is defined as moles of solute per kg of solvent.

$$\text{molality} = \frac{588.\underline{47}\,\text{g H}_2\text{SO}_4 \times \dfrac{1\,\text{mol H}_2\text{SO}_4}{98.078\,\text{g H}_2\text{SO}_4}}{(749.\underline{53})\ \text{g solvent} \times \dfrac{1\,\text{kg}}{1000\,\text{g}}} = 8.01\,\text{mol kg}^{-1}$$

27. (E) The mass of solvent in kg multiplied by the molality gives the amount in moles of the solute.

$$\text{mass I}_2 = \left(725.0\,\text{mL CS}_2 \times \frac{1.261\,\text{g}}{1\,\text{mL}} \times \frac{1\,\text{kg}}{1000\,\text{g}}\right) \times \frac{0.236\,\text{mol I}_2}{1\,\text{kg CS}_2} \times \frac{253.8\,\text{g I}_2}{1\,\text{mol I}_2} = 54.8\,\text{g I}_2$$

28. (M) In the original solution, the mass of CH_3OH associated with each 1.00 kg or 1000 g of water is:

$$\text{mass CH}_3\text{OH} = 1.00\,\text{kg H}_2\text{O} \times \frac{1.38\,\text{mol CH}_3\text{OH}}{1\,\text{kg H}_2\text{O}} \times \frac{32.04\,\text{g CH}_3\text{OH}}{1\,\text{mol CH}_3\text{OH}} = 44.2\,\text{g CH}_3\text{OH}$$

Then we compute the mass of methanol in 1.0000 kg = 1000.0 g of the original solution.

$$\text{mass CH}_3\text{OH} = 1000.0\,\text{g soln} \times \frac{44.2\,\text{g CH}_3\text{OH}}{1044.2\,\text{g soln}} = 42.3\,\text{g CH}_3\text{OH}$$

Thus, 1.0000 kg of this original solution contains (1000.0 – 42.3 =) 957.7 g H_2O)

Now, a 1.00 mol kg^{-1} CH_3OH solution contains 32.04 g CH_3OH (one mole) for every 1000.0 g H_2O. We can compute the mass of H_2O associated with 42.3 g CH_3OH in such a solution.

$$\text{mass } H_2O = 42.3 \text{ g } CH_3OH \times \frac{1000.0 \text{ g } H_2O}{32.04 \text{ g } CH_3OH} = 1320 \text{ g } H_2O$$

(We have temporarily retained an extra significant figure in the calculation.) Since we already have 957.7 g H_2O in the original solution, the mass of water that must be added equals $1320 \text{ g} - 957.7 \text{ g} = 362 \text{ g } H_2O = 3.6 \times 10^2 \text{ g } H_2O$.

29. **(M)**

$$H_3PO_4 \text{ molarity} = \frac{34.0 \text{ g } H_3PO_4 \times \dfrac{1 \text{ mol } H_3PO_4}{98.00 \text{ g } H_3PO_4}}{100.0 \text{ g soln} \times \dfrac{1 \text{ mL}}{1.209 \text{ g}} \times \dfrac{1 \text{ L}}{1000 \text{ mL}}} = 4.19 \text{ M}$$

$$H_3PO_4 \text{ molality} = \frac{34.0 \text{ g } H_3PO_4 \times \dfrac{1 \text{ mol } H_3PO_4}{98.00 \text{ g } H_3PO_4}}{66.0 \text{ g solvent} \times \dfrac{1 \text{ kg}}{1000 \text{ g}}} = 5.26 \text{ mol kg}^{-1}$$

30. **(M)**

$$C_2H_5OH \text{ molarity} = \frac{10.00 \text{ g } C_2H_5OH \times \dfrac{1 \text{ mol } C_2H_5OH}{46.069 \text{ g } C_2H_5OH}}{90.00 \text{ g } H_2O \times \dfrac{1 \text{ kg}}{1000 \text{ g}}} = 2.412 \text{ mol kg}^{-1}$$

The molality of this solution does not vary with temperature. We would, however, expect the solution's molarity to vary with temperature because the solution's density, and thus the volume of solution that contains one mole, varies with temperature. Unlike the volume, the mass of the solution does not vary with temperature, and so the solution's molality doesn't vary with temperature either.

Mole Fraction, Mole Percent

31. **(M)** The total number of moles
$= 1.28 \text{ mol } C_7H_{16} + 2.92 \text{ mol } C_8H_{18} + 2.64 \text{ mol } C_9H_{20} = 6.84 \text{ moles}$

(a) $\quad \chi_{C_7H_{16}} = \dfrac{1.28 \text{ mol } C_7H_{16}}{6.84 \text{ moles total}} = 0.187$ **(b)** $\quad \times 100\% = 18.7 \text{ mol\% } C_7H_{16}$

$\quad \chi_{C_8H_{18}} = \dfrac{2.92 \text{ mol } C_8H_{18}}{6.84 \text{ moles total}} = 0.427$ $\quad \times 100\% = 42.7 \text{ mol\% } C_8H_{18}$

$\quad \chi_{C_9H_{20}} = \dfrac{2.64 \text{ mol } C_9H_{20}}{6.84 \text{ moles total}} = 0.386$ $\quad \times 100\% = 38.6 \text{ mol\% } C_9H_{20}$

or $1.00 - 0.187 - 0.427 = 0.386$ $\quad$ or $100 - 18.7 - 42.7 = 38.6 \%$

32. **(M)**

(a) moles of $C_2H_5OH = 21.7$ g $C_2H_5OH \times \dfrac{1 \text{ mol } C_2H_5OH}{46.07 \text{ g } C_2H_5OH} = 0.471$ mol C_2H_5OH

$n_{H_2O} = 78.3$ g $H_2O \times \dfrac{1 \text{ mol } H_2O}{18.02 \text{ g } H_2O} = 4.35$ mol H_2O $\chi_{ethanol} = \dfrac{0.471 \text{ mol } C_2H_5OH}{(0.471 + 4.35) \text{ total moles}} = 0.0977$

(b) $n_{H_2O} = 1000.$ g $\times \dfrac{1 \text{ mol } H_2O}{18.02 \text{ g } H_2O} = 55.49$ mol H_2O $\chi_{urea} = \dfrac{0.684 \text{ mol urea}}{(55.49 + 0.684) \text{ total moles}} = 0.0122$

33. **(M)**

(a) The amount of solvent is found after the solute's mass is subtracted from the total mass of the solution.

$$\text{solvent amount} = \left(\left(1 \text{ L soln} \times \dfrac{1000 \text{ mL}}{1 \text{ L}} \times \dfrac{1.006 \text{ g}}{1 \text{ mL}}\right) - \left(0.112 \text{ mol } C_6H_{12}O_6 \times \dfrac{180.2 \text{ g } C_6H_{12}O_6}{1 \text{ mol } C_6H_{12}O_6}\right)\right)$$

$$= [1006 \text{ g solution} - 20.2 \text{ g } C_6H_{12}O_6] \times \dfrac{1 \text{ mol } H_2O}{18.02 \text{ g } H_2O} = 54.7 \text{ mol } H_2O$$

$$\chi_{solute} = \dfrac{0.112 \text{ mol } C_6H_{12}O_6}{0.112 \text{ mol } C_6H_{12}O_6 + 54.7 \text{ mol } H_2O} = 0.00204$$

(b) First we must determine the mass and the number of moles of ethanol. The number of moles of solvent is calculated after the ethanol's mass is subtracted from the solution's mass. Use a 100.00-mL sample of solution for computation. This 100 mL sample would contain 3.20 mL of C_2H_5OH. We calculate the mass of ethanol first, followed by the number of moles:

$$\text{mass}_{C_2H_5OH} = 3.20 \text{ mL } C_2H_5OH \times \dfrac{0.789 \text{ g}}{1 \text{ mL } C_2H_5OH} = 2.52 \text{ g } C_2H_5OH$$

$$\text{moles } C_2H_5OH = 2.52 \text{ g } C_2H_5OH \times \dfrac{1 \text{ mol } C_2H_5OH}{46.07 \text{ g } C_2H_5OH} = 0.0547 \text{ mol } C_2H_5OH$$

$$\text{mass of } H_2O = \left(\left(100.0 \text{ mL soln} \times \dfrac{0.993 \text{ g}}{1 \text{ mL}}\right) - 2.52 \text{ g } C_2H_5OH\right) = 96.8 \text{ g } H_2O$$

$$\text{amount of } H_2O = 96.8 \text{ g } H_2O \times \dfrac{1 \text{ mol } H_2O}{18.02 \text{ g } H_2O} = 5.37 \text{ mol } H_2O$$

$$\chi_{solute} = \dfrac{0.0547 \text{ mol } C_2H_5OH}{0.0547 \text{ mol } C_2H_5OH + 5.37 \text{ mol } H_2O} = 0.0101$$

34. **(M)** Solve the following relationship for $n_{ethanol}$, the number of moles of ethanol, C_2H_5OH. The number of moles of water calculated in Example is 5.01 moles, that of ethanol is 0.171 moles.

$$\chi_{ethanol} = \dfrac{n_{ethanol}}{n_{ethanol} + 5.01 \text{ mol } H_2O} = 0.0525 \qquad n_{ethanol} = 0.0525\, n_{ethanol} + 0.263$$

$$n_{ethanol} = \dfrac{0.263}{1.0000 - 0.0525} = 0.278 \text{ mol ethanol}$$

moles of added ethanol $= (0.278 - 0.171)$ mol $C_2H_5OH = 0.107$ mol C_2H_5OH

mass added ethanol $= 0.107$ mol $C_2H_5OH \times \dfrac{46.07 \text{ g } C_2H_5OH}{1 \text{ mol } C_2H_5OH} = 4.93$ g C_2H_5OH

35. **(M)** The amount of water present in 1 kg is

$n_{water} = 1000$ g $H_2O \times \dfrac{1 \text{ mol } H_2O}{18.02 \text{ g } H_2O} = 55.49$ mol H_2O. Now, solve the following expression

for n_{gly}, the amount of glycerol. $4.85\% = 0.0485$ mole fraction.

$$\chi_{gly} = 0.0485 = \dfrac{n_{gly}}{n_{gly} + 55.49} \qquad\qquad n_{gly} = 0.0485 \; n_{gly} + 2.69$$

$$n_{gly} = \dfrac{2.69}{(1.0000 - 0.0485)} = 2.83 \text{ mol glycerol}$$

volume glycerol $= 2.83$ mol $C_3H_8O_3 \times \dfrac{92.09 \text{ g } C_3H_8O_3}{1 \text{ mol } C_3H_8O_3} \times \dfrac{1 \text{ mL}}{1.26 \text{ g}} = 207$ mL glycerol

36. **(D)** Consider 100.0 mL of solution 1 (0.1487 M $C_{12}H_{22}O_{11}$, d =1.018 g/mL) and solution 2 (10.00% $C_{12}H_{22}O_{11}$, d = 1.038g/mL). We first determine the moles of $C_{12}H_{22}O_{11}$ (342.30 g mol^{-1}) and H_2O (18.0153 g mol^{-1}) in each of the solutions.

Solution 1: $n_{C_{12}H_{22}O_{11}} = 0.1000$ L solution $\times \dfrac{0.1487 \text{ mol } C_{12}H_{22}O_{11}}{\text{L solution}} = 0.01487$ mol $C_{12}H_{22}O_{11}$

$mass_{H_2O}$ = mass of solution − mass of $C_{12}H_{22}O_{11}$

$\qquad = 100$ mL solution $\times \dfrac{1.018 \text{ g solution}}{1 \text{ mL solution}} - 0.01487$ mol $C_{12}H_{22}O_{11} \times \dfrac{342.30 \text{ g } C_{12}H_{22}O_{11}}{1 \text{ mol } C_{12}H_{22}O_{11}}$

$\qquad = 101.8$ g solution $- 5.090$ g $C_{12}H_{22}O_{11} = 96.7$ g H_2O

$n_{H_2O} = 96.7$ g $H_2O \times \dfrac{1 \text{ mol } H_2O}{18.0153 \text{ g } H_2O} = 5.36\underline{8}$ mol H_2O

Solution 2: mass of solution = = 100 mL solution $\times \dfrac{1.038 \text{ g solution}}{1 \text{ mL solution}} = 103.8$ g solution

$mass_{C_{12}H_{22}O_{11}} = 103.8$ g soluton $\times \dfrac{10.00 \text{ g } C_{12}H_{22}O_{11}}{100 \text{ g solution}} = 10.38$ g $C_{12}H_{22}O_{11}$

$n_{C_{12}H_{22}O_{11}} = 10.38$ g $C_{12}H_{22}O_{11} \times \dfrac{1 \text{ mol } C_{12}H_{22}O_{11}}{342.30 \text{ g } C_{12}H_{22}O_{11}} = 0.03032$ mol $C_{12}H_{22}O_{11}$

$mass_{H_2O}$ = mass of solution − mass of $C_{12}H_{22}O_{11}$

$\qquad = 103.8$ g solution $- 10.38$ g $C_{12}H_{22}O_{11} = 93.4$ g H_2O

$n_{H_2O} = 93.4$ g $H_2O \times \dfrac{1 \text{ mol } H_2O}{18.0153 \text{ g } H_2O} = 5.18\underline{4}$ mol H_2O

Next we calculate the mole fraction

$$\chi_{C_{12}H_{22}O_{11}} = \frac{n_{C_{12}H_{22}O_{11}}}{n_{C_{12}H_{22}O_{11}} + n_{H_2O}} = \frac{0.01487 + 0.03022}{5.38\underline{6} + 5.18\underline{4}} = \frac{0.04509}{10.57} = 0.004266$$

Finally we calculate mole percent simply by multiplying mole fraction by 100%.
mole percent = 0.004266 × 100% = 0.4266%

37. **(E)** We assume that density of water is 1.000 g/mL, so 1.000 mL of water has a mass of 1.000 g. First, determine the number of moles of Pb, and then the number of moles of water:

$$\text{mol Pb} = \frac{15\ \mu g\ \text{Pb}}{1.000\ \text{g } H_2O} \times \frac{1\ \text{g}}{10^6\ \mu g} \times \frac{1\ \text{mol Pb}}{207.19\ \text{g Pb}} = 7.24 \times 10^{-8}\ \text{mol}$$

$$\text{\# Pb atoms} = 7.24 \times 10^{-8}\ \text{mol Pb} \times \frac{6.022 \times 10^{23}\ \text{atoms}}{1\ \text{mol Pb}} = 4.36 \times 10^{16}\ \text{atoms}$$

$$\text{mol } H_2O = 1.000\ \text{g } H_2O \times \frac{1\ \text{mol } H_2O}{18.0\ \text{g } H_2O} = 0.05556\ \text{mol}$$

$$\chi_{Pb} = \frac{7.24 \times 10^{-8}}{0.05556 + 7.24 \times 10^{-8}} = 1.303 \times 10^{-6}$$

38. **(M)** Perform the same type of calculation as above to determine the mole fraction of CO_2 in ocean water. Assume a 1 kg sample of ocean water.

$$\text{mol } CO_2 = \frac{280\ \text{mg } CO_2}{1.0\ \text{kg } H_2O} \times \frac{1\ \text{g}}{10^3\ \text{mg}} \times \frac{1\ \text{mol } CO_2}{44.0\ \text{g } CO_2} = 0.00636\ \text{mol}$$

$$\text{mol } H_2O = 1\overline{0}00\ \text{g } H_2O \times \frac{1\ \text{mol } H_2O}{18.0\ \text{g } H_2O} = 55.56\ \text{mol} \approx 56\ \text{mol}$$

$$\chi_{CO_2} = \frac{0.00636}{55.56 + 0.00636} = 1.1 \times 10^{-4}$$

Solubility Equilibrium

39. **(E)** At 40 °C the solubility of NH_4Cl is 46.3 g per 100 g of H_2O. To determine molality, we calculate amount in moles of the solute and the solvent mass in kg.

$$\text{molality} = \frac{46.3\ \text{g} \times \dfrac{1\ \text{mol } NH_4Cl}{53.49\ \text{g } NH_4Cl}}{100\ \text{g } H_2O \times \dfrac{1\ \text{kg}}{1000\ \text{g}}} = 8.66\ \text{mol kg}^{-1}$$

40. **(M)** The data in Figure 14-10 are given in mass of solute per 100 g H_2O.

0.200 mol kg^{-1} $KClO_4$ contains 0.200 mol $KClO_4$ associated with each

1 kg (=1000 g) of H_2O. The mass of $KClO_4$ dissolved in 100 g H_2O is:

$$\text{mass } KClO_4 = 100 \text{ g } H_2O \times \frac{0.200 \text{ mol } KClO_4}{1000 \text{ g } H_2O} \times \frac{138.5 \text{ g } KClO_4}{1 \text{ mol } KClO_4} = 2.77 \text{ g } KClO_4.$$

This concentration is realized at a temperature of about 32 °C. At this temperature a saturated solution has $KClO_4 \approx 0.200$ mol kg^{-1}.

41. **(M)**

(a) The concentration for $KClO_4$ in this mixture is calculated first.

$$\frac{\text{mass solute}}{100 \text{ g } H_2O} = 100 \text{ g } H_2O \times \frac{20.0 \text{ g } KClO_4}{500.0 \text{ g water}} = 4.00 \text{ g } KClO_4$$

At 40 °C a saturated $KClO_4$ solution has a concentration of about 4.6 g $KClO_4$ dissolved in 100 g water. Thus, the solution is unsaturated.

(b) The mass of $KClO_4$ that must be added is the difference between the mass now present in the mixture and the mass that is dissolved in 500 g H_2O to produce a saturated solution.

$$\text{mass to be added} = \left(500.0 \text{ g } H_2O \times \frac{4.6 \text{ g } KClO_4}{100 \text{ g } H_2O} \right) - 20.0 \text{ g } KClO_4 = 3.0 \text{ g } KClO_4$$

42. **(M)** From Figure 14-10, the solubility of KNO_3 in water is 38 g KNO_3 per 100 g water at 25.0 °C, while at 0.0 °C its solubility is 15 g KNO_3 per 100 g water. At 25.0 °C, every 138 g of solution contains 38 g of KNO_3 and 100.0 g water. At 0.0 °C every 115 g solution contains 15 g KNO_3 and 100.0 g water. We calculate the mass of water and of KNO_3 present at 25.0 °C.

$$\text{mass water} = 335 \text{ g soln} \times \frac{100.0 \text{ g water}}{138 \text{ g soln}} = 243 \text{ g water}$$

$$\text{mass } KNO_3 = 335 \text{ g soln} - 243 \text{ g water} = 92 \text{ g } KNO_3$$

At 0.0 °C the mass of water has been reduced 55 g by evaporation to $(243 \text{ g} - 55 \text{ g} =) 188$ g. The mass of KNO_3 soluble in this mass of water at 0.0 °C is

$$\text{mass } KNO_3 \text{ dissolved} = 188 \text{ g } H_2O \times \frac{15 \text{ g } KNO_3}{100.0 \text{ g } H_2O} = 28 \text{ g } KNO_3$$

Thus, of the 92 g KNO_3 originally present in solution, the mass that recrystallizes is

$$KNO_3 \text{ recrystallized (g)} = 92 \text{ g } KNO_3 \text{ (orig. dissol.)} - 28 \text{ g } KNO_3 \text{ (still dissol.)} = 64 \text{ g } KNO_3$$

Solubility of Gases

43. **(M)** We first determine the number of moles of O_2 that have dissolved.

$$\text{moles of } O_2 = \frac{PV}{RT} = \frac{1.00 \text{ atm} \times 0.02831 \text{ L}}{0.08206 \text{ L atm mol}^{-1} \text{ K}^{-1} \times 298 \text{ K}} = 1.16 \times 10^{-3} \text{ mol } O_2$$

$$\left[O_2 \right] = \frac{1.16 \times 10^{-3} \text{ mol } O_2}{1.00 \text{ L soln}} = 1.16 \times 10^{-3} \text{ M}$$

The oxygen concentration now is computed at the higher pressure.

$$\left[O_2 \right] = \frac{1.16 \times 10^{-3} \text{ M}}{1 \text{ atm } O_2} \times 3.86 \text{ atm } O_2 = 4.48 \times 10^{-3} \text{ M}$$

44. **(E)** If we assume that the normal atmospheric pressure is 1 atm, then the partial pressure of O_2 can be determined by using Dalton's law of partial pressures. Since the volume % O_2 is 20.95%, the partial pressure of O_2 is 0.2095 atm (for ideal gases, volume % and mole % are equal).

$$\left[O_2 \right] = \frac{1.16 \times 10^{-3} \text{ M}}{1 \text{ atm } O_2} \times 0.2095 \text{ atm } O_2 = 2.43 \times 10^{-4} \text{ M}$$

45. **(E)** $\text{mass of } CH_4 = 1.00 \times 10^3 \text{ kg H}_2\text{O} \times \dfrac{0.02 \text{ g CH}_4}{1 \text{ kg H}_2\text{O} \cdot \text{ atm}} \times 20 \text{ atm} = 4 \times 10^2 \text{ g CH}_4$ (natural gas)

46. **(M)** We first compute the amount of O_2 dissolved in 515 mL = 0.515 L at each temperature.

$$\text{amount } O_2 = 0.515 \text{ L} \times \frac{2.18 \times 10^{-3} \text{ mol } O_2}{1 \text{ L}} = 1.12 \times 10^{-3} \text{ mol } O_2 \text{ at } 0 \,^\circ\text{C}$$

$$\text{amount } O_2 = 0.515 \text{ L} \times \frac{1.26 \times 10^{-3} \text{ mol } O_2}{1 \text{ L}} = 6.49 \times 10^{-4} \text{ mol } O_2 \text{ at } 25 \,^\circ\text{C}$$

Next, we determine the difference between these amounts, and the corresponding volume of gas expelled.

$$V_{O_2} = \frac{(11.2 - 6.49) \times 10^{-4} \text{ mol } O_2 \times \dfrac{0.08206 \text{ L atm}}{\text{mol 1 K}} \times 298 \text{ K}}{1 \text{ atm}} = 1.2 \times 10^{-2} \text{ L} = 12 \text{ mL expelled}$$

47. **(M)** We use the STP molar volume $\left(22.414 \text{ L} = 22{,}414 \text{ mL} \right)$ to determine the molarity of Ar under 1 atmosphere of pressure and then use Henry's law.

$$k_{Ar} = \frac{C}{P_{Ar}} = \frac{\dfrac{33.7 \text{ mL Ar}}{1 \text{ L soln}} \times \dfrac{1 \text{ mol Ar}}{22{,}414 \text{ mL at STP}}}{1 \text{ atm pressure}} = \frac{0.00150 \text{ M}}{\text{atm}}$$

In the atmosphere, the partial pressure of argon is $P_{Ar} = 0.00934$ atm. (Recall that pressure fractions equal volume fractions for ideal gases.) We now compute the concentration of argon in aqueous solution.

$$C = k_{Ar} P_{Ar} = \frac{0.00150 \text{ M}}{\text{atm}} \times 0.00934 \text{ atm} = 1.40 \times 10^{-5} \text{ M Ar}$$

48. **(M)** We use the STP molar volume $(22.414 \text{ L} = 22,414 \text{ mL})$ to determine the molarity of CO_2 under 1 atm pressure and then the Henry's law constant.

$$k_{CO_2} = \frac{C}{P_{CO_2}} = \frac{\dfrac{87.8 \text{ mL } CO_2}{0.1 \text{ L soln}} \times \dfrac{1 \text{ mol } CO_2}{22,414 \text{ mL at STP}}}{1 \text{ atm pressure}} = \frac{0.0392 \text{ M}}{\text{atm}}$$

In the atmosphere, the partial pressure of CO_2 is $P_{CO_2} = 0.000360$ atm. (Recall that pressure fractions equal volume fractions for ideal gases.) We now compute the concentration of carbon dioxide in aqueous solution.

$$C = k_{CO_2} P_{CO_2} = \frac{0.0392 \text{ M } CO_2}{\text{atm}} \times 0.000360 \text{ atm} = 1.41 \times 10^{-5} \text{ M } CO_2$$

49. **(M)** Because of the low density of molecules in the gaseous state, the solution volume remains essentially constant as a gas dissolves in a liquid. Changes in concentrations in the solution result from changes in the number of dissolved gas molecules (recall Figure 14-13). This number is directly proportional to the mass of dissolved gas.

50. **(M)** Although this statement initially may seem quite different, we need to remember that at constant volume, the partial pressure of the gas increases as more moles of gas are added. Thus, increasing the partial pressure means that more moles of gas are forced into the same volume of solvent. Thus, at higher pressure, more moles of gas are absorbed by the solvent, but the volume of the "pressurized" gas absorbed is the same as the volume of gas absorbed at lower pressure. This statement is equivalent to Equation 14.2.

$$kP_{gas} = c_{gas} = \frac{n_{gas}}{V_{solvent}} = \frac{P_{gas} V_{gas}}{RT_{gas} V_{solvent}} \quad \text{or} \quad V_{gas} = kRT_{gas} V_{solvent}$$

Thus, V_{gas} is constant at fixed temperature for a given volume of solvent. At the higher pressure V_{gas} contains more moles of gas. This statement is not valid if the ideal gas law is not obeyed or if the gas reacts with the solvent.

Raoult's Law and Liquid–Vapor Equilibrium

51. **(M)** First we determine the number of moles of each component, its mole fraction in the solution, the partial pressure due to that component above the solution, and finally the total pressure.

amount benzene $= n_b = 35.8 \text{ g } C_6H_6 \times \dfrac{1 \text{ mol } C_6H_6}{78.11 \text{ g } C_6H_6} = 0.458 \text{ mol } C_6H_6$

amount toluene $= n_t = 56.7 \text{ g } C_7H_8 \times \dfrac{1 \text{ mol } C_7H_8}{92.14 \text{ g } C_7H_8} = 0.615 \text{ mol } C_7H_8$

$\chi_b = \dfrac{0.458 \text{ mol } C_6H_6}{(0.458 + 0.615) \text{ total moles}} = 0.427 \qquad \chi_t = \dfrac{0.615 \text{ mol } C_7H_8}{(0.458 + 0.615) \text{ total moles}} = 0.573$

$P_b = 0.427 \times 95.1 \text{ mmHg} = 40.6 \text{ mmHg} \qquad P_t = 0.573 \times 28.4 \text{ mmHg} = 16.3 \text{ mmHg}$

total pressure $= 40.6 \text{ mmHg} + 16.3 \text{ mmHg} = 56.9 \text{ mmHg}$

52. **(M)** vapor fraction of benzene $= f_b = \dfrac{40.6 \text{ mmHg}}{56.9 \text{ mmHg}} = 0.714$

vapor fraction of toluene $= f_t = \dfrac{16.3 \text{ mmHg}}{56.9 \text{ mmHg}} = 0.286$

These are both pressure fractions, as calculated, and also the mole fractions in the vapor phase.

53. **(M)** We need to determine the mole fraction of water in this solution.

$n_{glucose} = 165 \text{ g } C_6H_{12}O_6 \times \dfrac{1 \text{ mol } C_6H_{12}O_6}{180.2 \text{ g } C_6H_{12}O_6} = 0.916 \text{ mol } C_6H_{12}O_6$

$n_{water} = 685 \text{ g } H_2O \times \dfrac{1 \text{ mol } H_2O}{18.02 \text{ g } H_2O} = 38.0 \text{ mol } H_2O$ $\quad \chi_{water} = \dfrac{38.0 \text{ mol } H_2O}{(38.0 + 0.916) \text{ total moles}} = 0.976$

$P_{sol'n} = \chi_{water} P^*_{water} = 0.976 \times 23.8 \text{ mmHg} = 23.2 \text{ mmHg}$

54. **(M)** We need to determine the mole fraction of methanol in this solution.

$n_{urea} = 17 \text{ g } CO(NH_2)_2 \times \dfrac{1 \text{ mol } CO(NH_2)_2}{60.06 \text{ g } CO(NH_2)_2} = 0.28\underline{3} \text{ mol } CO(NH_2)_2$

$n_{methanol} = 100 \text{ mL } CH_3OH \times \dfrac{0.792 \text{ g}}{1 \text{ mL}} \times \dfrac{1 \text{ mol } CH_3OH}{32.04 \text{ g } CH_3OH} = 2.47 \text{ mol } CH_3OH$

$\chi_{methanol} = \dfrac{2.47 \text{ mol } CH_3OH}{(2.47 + 0.28\underline{3}) \text{ total moles}} = 0.897$

$P_{sol'n} = \chi_{methanol} P^*_{methanol} = 0.897 \times 95.7 \text{ mmHg} = 85.8 \text{ mmHg}$

55. **(M)** We consider a sample of 100.0 g of the solution and determine the number of moles of each component in this sample. From this information and the given vapor pressures, we determine the vapor pressure of each component. Note that styrene, $C_6H_5C{=}CH_2$, is represented by the simplified molecular formula C_8H_8 in this problem.

amount of styrene $= n_s = 38 \text{ g styrene} \times \dfrac{1 \text{ mol } C_8H_8}{104 \text{ g } C_8H_8} = 0.37 \text{ mol } C_8H_8$

amount of ethylbenzene $= n_e = 62 \text{ g ethylbenzene} \times \dfrac{1 \text{ mol } C_8H_{10}}{106 \text{ g } C_8H_{10}} = 0.58 \text{ mol } C_8 H_{10}$

$\chi_s = \dfrac{n_s}{n_s + n_e} = \dfrac{0.37 \text{ mol styrene}}{(0.37 + 0.58) \text{ total moles}} = 0.39;$ $P_s = 0.39 \times 134 \text{ mmHg} = 52 \text{ mmHg for } C_8H_8$

$\chi_e = \dfrac{n_e}{n_s + n_e} = \dfrac{0.58 \text{ mol ethylbenzene}}{(0.37 + 0.58) \text{ total moles}} = 0.61;$ $P_e = 0.61 \times 182 \text{ mmHg} = 111 \text{ mmHg for } C_8H_{10}$

Then the mole fraction in the vapor can be determined.

$y_e = \dfrac{P_e}{P_e + P_s} = \dfrac{111 \text{ mmHg}}{(111 + 52) \text{ mmHg}} = 0.68$ $\qquad y_s = 1.00 - 0.68 = 0.32$

56. **(D)** The vapor pressures of the pure liquids are: for benzene $P_b^* = 95.1$ mmHg, and for toluene $P_t^* = 28.4$ mmHg. We know that $P_t = \chi_t P_t^*$ and $P_b = \chi_b P_b^*$. We also know that $\chi_t + \chi_b = 1.000$. We solve for χ_b in the following expression.

$$0.620 = \frac{P_b}{P_b + P_t} = \frac{\chi_b P_b^*}{\chi_b P_b^* + \chi_t P_t^*} = \frac{\chi_b P_b^*}{\chi_b P_b^* + (1-\chi_b)P_t^*} = \frac{\chi_b 95.1}{\chi_b 95.1 + (1-\chi_b)28.4}$$

$$95.1\chi_b = 0.620\left[\chi_b 95.1 + (1-\chi_b)28.4\right] = 59.0\chi_b + 17.6 - 17.6\chi_b$$

$$17.6 = (95.1 - 59.0 + 17.6)\chi_b = 53.7\chi_b \qquad \chi_b = \frac{17.6}{53.7} = 0.328$$

57. **(M)** The total vapor pressure above the solution at its normal boiling point is 760 mm Hg. The vapor pressure due to toluene is given by the following equation.
$P_{toluene} = \chi_{toluene} \cdot P^*_{toluene} = 0.700 \times 533$ mm Hg = 373 mm Hg. Next, the vapor pressure due to benzene is determined, followed by the vapor pressure for pure benzene.
$P_{benzene} = P_{total} - P_{toluene} = 760$ mm Hg $- 373$ mm Hg $= 387$ mm Hg $= \chi_{benzene} \cdot P^*_{benzene}$
387 mm Hg $= 0.300 \times P^*_{benzene}$ and hence, $P^*_{benzene} = 1.29 \times 10^3$ mm Hg

58. **(E)**

(a) The vapor pressure of water is greater above the solution that has the higher mole fraction of water, according to Raoult's law. This also is the solution that has the smaller mole fraction of NaCl, namely, the unsaturated Solution 2.

(b) As water evaporates from the unsaturated solution, its concentration changes and so does its vapor pressure, according to Raoult's law. This does not happen with the saturated solution (Solution 1). Its concentration and thus its vapor pressure remains constant as the solvent evaporates.

(c) The solution with the higher boiling point is the more concentrated solution (the saturated solution, Solution 1) because the boiling point increases as the amount of dissolved solute increases.

Osmotic Pressure

59. **(M)** We first compute the concentration of the solution. Then, assuming that the solution volume is the same as that of the solvent (0.2500 L), we determine the amount of solute dissolved, and finally the molar mass.

$$\frac{n}{V} = \frac{\pi}{RT} = \frac{1.67 \text{ mmHg} \times \dfrac{1 \text{ atm}}{760 \text{ mmHg}}}{0.08206 \text{ L atm mol}^{-1} \text{ K}^{-1} \times 298.2 \text{ K}} = 8.98 \times 10^{-5} \text{ M}$$

$$\begin{array}{l}\text{solute} \\ \text{amount}\end{array} = 0.2500 \text{ L} \times \frac{8.98 \times 10^{-5} \text{ mol}}{1 \text{ L}} = 2.25 \times 10^{-5} \text{ mol}$$

$$M = \frac{0.72 \text{ g}}{2.25 \times 10^{-5} \text{ mol}} = 3.2 \times 10^4 \text{ g/mol}$$

60. **(M)** We assume the density of the solution to be 1.00 g/mL and calculate the $[C_{12}H_{22}O_{11}]$.

$$[C_{12}H_{22}O_{11}] = \frac{20. \text{ g } C_{12}H_{22}O_{11} \times \dfrac{1 \text{ mol } C_{12}H_{22}O_{11}}{342.3 \text{ g } C_{12}H_{22}O_{11}}}{100 \text{ g solution} \times \dfrac{1 \text{ mL solution}}{1 \text{ g solution}} \times \dfrac{1 \text{ L solution}}{1000 \text{ mL solution}}} = 0.58\underline{4} \text{ M}$$

We now compute the osmotic pressure, assuming a temperature of 25 °C.

$$\pi = CRT = 0.58\underline{4} \text{ M} \times \frac{0.08206 \text{ L atm}}{\text{K mol}} \times 298 \text{ K} = 14.\underline{3} \text{ atm}$$

Next we need to determine the height of a column of sucrose (density = water).

$$\text{height} = 14.\underline{3} \text{ atm} \times \frac{760 \text{ mmHg}}{1 \text{ atm}} \times \frac{13.6 \text{ mm solution}}{1 \text{ mmHg}} \times \frac{1 \text{ m solution}}{1000 \text{ mm solution}} = 14\underline{8} \text{ m} \sim 150 \text{ m solution}$$

We have assumed a density of 1.00 g/mL and a conversion of 13.6 mm of solution per mmHg. If the solution were more dense, say 1.06 g/mL, this would correspond to a higher concentration and a larger osmotic pressure. At the same time, an increase in the density would result in a slight decrease in the conversion factor between mmHg and mm solution (we used 13.6 mm solution per mmHg , resulting in a slight decrease in the osmotic pressure). Overall, an increase in density would result in a slight increase in the osmotic pressure.

61. **(E)** Both the flowers and the cucumber contain ionic solutions (plant sap), but both of these solutions are less concentrated than the salt solution. Thus, the solution in the plant material moves across the semipermeable membrane in an attempt to dilute the salt solution, leaving behind wilted flowers and shriveled pickles (wilted/shriveled plants have less water in their tissues).

62. **(E)** The main purpose of drinking water is to provide H_2O for living tissues. In freshwater, water should move across the semipermeable membranes into the fish's body as water moves past the gills for breathing. Thus, it should not be necessary for freshwater fish to drink. In contrast, the concentration of solutes in saltwater is about the same as their concentration in a fish's blood plasma. In this case, osmotic pressure will not be effective in moving water into a fish's tissues. The purpose of drinking for a saltwater fish is to isolate the ingested water within the fish. Then mechanisms within the fish's body can move water across membranes into the fish's tissues. Or possibly, the fish has a means of desalinating the ingested water, in which case osmotic pressure would carry water into the fish's tissues.

63. **(E)** We first determine the molarity of the solution. Let's work the problem out with three significant figures.

$$\frac{n}{V} = \frac{\pi}{RT} = \frac{1.00 \text{ atm}}{0.08206 \text{ L atm mol}^{-1} \text{ K}^{-1} \times 273 \text{ K}} = 0.0446 \text{ M}$$

$$\text{volume} = 1 \text{ mol} \times \frac{1 \text{ L}}{0.0446 \text{ mol solute}} = 22.4 \text{ L solution} \approx 22.4 \text{ L solvent}$$

We have assumed that the solution is so dilute that its volume closely approximates the volume of the solvent constituting it. Note that this volume corresponds to the STP molar volume of an ideal gas. The osmotic pressure equation also resembles the ideal gas equation.

64. **(E)** First we calculate the concentration of solute in the solution, then the mass of solute in 100.0 mL of that solution.

$$\left[\text{solute}\right] = \frac{\pi}{RT} = \frac{7.25\,\text{mmHg}\times\left(\dfrac{1\,\text{atm}}{760\,\text{mmHg}}\right)}{0.08206\ \text{L atm mol}^{-1}\ \text{K}^{-1}\times 298\ \text{K}} = 3.90\times10^{-4}\ \text{M}$$

$$\text{mass of hemoglobin} = 0.1000\,\text{L}\times\frac{3.90\times10^{-4}\ \text{mol hemoglobin}}{1\ \text{L soln}}\times\frac{6.86\times10^{4}\ \text{g}}{1\ \text{mol hemoglobin}}$$

$$= 2.68\ \text{g hemoglobin}$$

65. **(M)** First we determine the concentration of the solution from the osmotic pressure, then the amount of solute dissolved, and finally the molar mass of that solute.

$$\pi = 5.1\ \text{mm soln}\times\frac{0.88\ \text{mmHg}}{13.6\ \text{mm soln}}\times\frac{1\ \text{atm}}{760\ \text{mmHg}} = 4.3\times10^{-4}\ \text{atm}$$

$$\frac{n}{V} = \frac{\pi}{RT} = \frac{4.3\times10^{-4}\ \text{atm}}{0.08206\ \text{L atm mol}^{-1}\ \text{K}^{-1}\times 298\ \text{K}} = 1.8\times10^{-5}\ \text{M}$$

$$\text{amount solute} = 100.0\ \text{mL}\times\frac{1\ \text{L}}{1000\ \text{mL}}\times1.8\times10^{-5}\ \text{M} = 1.8\times10^{-6}\ \text{mol solute}$$

$$\text{molar mass} = \frac{0.50\ \text{g}}{1.8\times10^{-6}\ \text{mol}} = 2.8\times10^{5}\ \text{g/mol}$$

66. **(M)** We need the molar concentration of ions in the solution to determine its osmotic pressure. We assume that the solution has a density of 1.00 g/mL.

$$\left[\text{ions}\right] = \frac{0.92\ \text{g NaCl}\times\dfrac{1\ \text{mol NaCl}}{58.4\ \text{g NaCl}}\times\dfrac{2\ \text{mol ions}}{1\ \text{mol NaCl}}}{100.0\ \text{mL soln}\times\dfrac{1\ \text{L soln}}{1000\ \text{mL}}} = 0.32\ \text{M}$$

$$\pi = \frac{n}{V}RT = 0.32\,\frac{\text{mol}}{\text{L}}\times0.08206\ \text{L atm mol}^{-1}\ \text{K}^{-1}\times\left(37.0+273.2\right)\ \text{K} = 8.1\ \text{atm}$$

67. **(M)** The reverse osmosis process requires a pressure equal to or slightly greater than the osmotic pressure of the solution. We assume that this solution has a density of 1.00 g/mL. First, we determine the molar concentration of ions in the solution.

$$\left[\text{ions}\right] = \frac{2.5\ \text{g NaCl}\times\dfrac{1\ \text{mol NaCl}}{58.4\ \text{g NaCl}}\times\dfrac{2\ \text{mol ions}}{1\ \text{mol NaCl}}}{100.0\ \text{mL soln}\times\dfrac{1\ \text{mL soln}}{1.00\ \text{g}}\times\dfrac{1\ \text{L soln}}{1000\ \text{mL}}} = 0.86\ \text{M}$$

$$\pi = \frac{n}{V}RT = 0.86\,\frac{\text{mol}}{\text{L}}\times0.08206\ \text{L atm mol}^{-1}\ \text{K}^{-1}\times\left(25+273.2\right)\ \text{K} = 21\ \text{atm}$$

68. **(M)** We need to determine the molarity of each solution. The solution with the higher molarity has the higher osmotic pressure, and water will flow from the more dilute into the more concentrated solution, in an attempt to create two solutions of equal concentrations.

$$[C_3H_8O_3] = \frac{14.0 \text{ g } C_3H_8O_3 \times \dfrac{1 \text{ mol } C_3H_8O_3}{92.09 \text{ g } C_3H_8O_3}}{55.2 \text{ mL soln} \times \dfrac{1 \text{ L}}{1000 \text{ mL}}} = 2.75 \text{ M}$$

$$[C_{12}H_{22}O_{11}] = \frac{17.2 \text{ g } C_{12}H_{22}O_{11} \times \dfrac{1 \text{ mol } C_{12}H_{22}O_{11}}{342.3 \text{ g } C_{12}H_{22}O_{11}}}{62.5 \text{ mL soln} \times \dfrac{1 \text{ L}}{1000 \text{ mL}}} = 0.804 \text{ M}$$

Thus, water will move from the $C_{12}H_{22}O_{11}$ solution into the $C_3H_8O_3$ solution, that is, from right to left.

Freezing-Point Depression and Boiling-Point Elevation

69. **(M)** First we compute the molality of the benzene solution, then the number of moles of solute dissolved, and finally the molar mass of the unknown compound.

$$m = \frac{\Delta T_f}{-K_f} = \frac{4.92 \, °C - 5.53 \, °C}{-5.12 \, °C/\text{mol kg}^{-1}} = 0.12 \text{ mol kg}^{-1}$$

$$\text{amount solute} = 0.07522 \text{ kg benzene} \times \frac{0.12 \text{ mol solute}}{1 \text{ kg benzene}} = 9.0 \times 10^{-3} \text{ mol solute}$$

$$\text{molecular weight} = \frac{1.10 \text{ g unknown compound}}{9.0 \times 10^{-3} \text{ mol}} = 1.2 \times 10^2 \text{ g/mol}$$

70. **(M)** We compute the value of the van't Hoff factor first, then use this value to compute the boiling-point elevation.

$$i = \frac{\Delta T_f}{-K_f m} = \frac{-0.072 \, °C}{-1.86 \, °C/\text{mol kg}^{-1} \times 0.010 \text{ mol kg}^{-1}} = 3.9$$

$$\Delta T_b = i \, K_b m = 3.9 \times 0.512 \, °C \text{ mol}^{-1} \text{ kg} \times 0.010; \text{ mol kg}^{-1} = 0.020 \, °C$$

Thus, the solution begins to boil at 100.02 °C.

71. **(M)**

(a) First we determine the molality of the solution, then the value of the freezing-point depression constant.

$$m = \frac{1.00 \text{ g } C_6H_6 \times \dfrac{1 \text{ mol } C_6H_6}{78.11 \text{ g } C_6H_6}}{80.00 \text{ g solvent} \times \dfrac{1 \text{ kg}}{1000 \text{ g}}} = 0.160 \text{ mol kg}^{-1}$$

$$K_f = \frac{\Delta T_f}{-m} = \frac{3.3 \, °C - 6.5 \, °C}{-0.160 \text{ mol kg}^{-1}} = 20. \, °C/(\text{mol kg}^{-1})$$

(b) For benzene, $K_f = 5.12 \text{ °C mol}^{-1}\text{ kg}$. Cyclohexane is the better solvent for freezing-point depression determinations of molar mass, because a less concentrated solution will still give a substantial freezing-point depression. For the same concentration, cyclohexane solutions will show a freezing-point depression approximately four times that of benzene. Also, one should steer clear of benzene because it is a known carcinogen.

72. **(M)** The solution's boiling point is 0.40 °C above the boiling point of pure water. First we must compute the molality of the solution, then the mass of sucrose that must be added to 1 kg (1000 g) H_2O, and finally the mass% sucrose in the solution.

$$m = \frac{\Delta T_b}{K_b} = \frac{0.40 \text{ °C}}{0.512 \text{ °C/(mol kg}^{-1})} = 0.78 \text{ mol kg}^{-1}. \rightarrow \frac{0.78 \text{ mol C}_{12}\text{H}_{22}\text{O}_{11}}{1 \text{kg H}_2\text{O}} \times \frac{342.3 \text{ g C}_{12}\text{H}_{22}\text{O}_{11}}{1 \text{ mol C}_{12}\text{H}_{22}\text{O}_{11}} = \frac{267 \text{g C}_6\text{H}_{12}\text{O}_6}{1 \text{ kg H}_2\text{O}}$$

$$\text{mass\% C}_{12}\text{H}_{22}\text{O}_{11} = \frac{267 \text{ g C}_{12}\text{H}_{22}\text{O}_{11}}{(1000. + 267) \text{ g total}} \times 100\% = 21\% \text{ C}_{12}\text{H}_{22}\text{O}_{11}$$

73. **(M)** Here we determine the molality of the solution, then the number of moles of solute present, and the molar mass of the solute to start things off. Then we determine the compound's empirical formula, and combine this with the molar mass to determine the molecular formula.

$$m = \frac{\Delta T_f}{-K_f} = \frac{1.37 \text{ °C} - 5.53 \text{ °C}}{-5.12 \text{ °C/(mol kg}^{-1})} = 0.813 \text{ mol kg}^{-1}$$

$$\text{amount} = \left(50.0 \text{ mL C}_6\text{H}_6 \times \frac{0.879 \text{ g}}{1 \text{ mL}} \times \frac{1 \text{ kg}}{1000 \text{ g}}\right) \times \frac{0.813 \text{ mol solute}}{1 \text{ kg C}_6\text{H}_6} = 3.57 \times 10^{-2} \text{ mol}$$

$$\text{molecular weight} = \frac{6.45 \text{ g}}{3.57 \times 10^{-2} \text{ mol}} = 181 \text{ g/mol}$$

Now, calculate the empirical formula from the provided mass percents for C, H, N, and O.

$$42.9 \text{ g C} \times \frac{1 \text{ mol C}}{12.01 \text{ g C}} = 3.57 \text{ mol C} \quad \div 1.19 \rightarrow 3.00 \text{ mol C}$$

$$2.4 \text{ g H} \times \frac{1 \text{ mol H}}{1.01 \text{ g H}} = 2.4 \text{ mol H} \quad \div 1.19 \rightarrow 2.0 \text{ mol H}$$

$$16.7 \text{ g N} \times \frac{1 \text{ mol N}}{14.01 \text{ g N}} = 1.19 \text{ mol N} \quad \div 1.19 \rightarrow 1.00 \text{ mol N}$$

$$38.1 \text{ g O} \times \frac{1 \text{ mol O}}{16.00 \text{ g O}} = 2.38 \text{ mol O} \quad \div 1.19 \rightarrow 2.00 \text{ mol O}$$

The empirical formula is $C_3H_2NO_2$, with a formula mass of 84.0 g/mol. This is one-half the experimentally determined molar mass. Thus, the molecular formula is $C_6H_4N_2O_4$.

74. **(M)** We determine the molality of the nitrobenzene $\left(K_f = 8.1 \,^\circ\text{C/m}\right)$ solution first, then the solute's molar mass.

$$m = \frac{\Delta T_f}{-K_f} = \frac{-1.4\,^\circ\text{C} - 5.7\,^\circ\text{C}}{-8.1\,^\circ\text{C/(mol kg}^{-1})} = 0.88 \text{ mol kg}^{-1}$$

$$\text{amount solute} = 30.0 \text{ mL nitrobenzene} \times \frac{1.204 \text{ g}}{1 \text{ mL}} \times \frac{1 \text{ kg}}{1000 \text{ g}} \times \frac{0.88 \text{ mol solute}}{1 \text{ kg nitrobenzene}} = 0.032 \text{ mol solute}$$

$$\text{molar mass} = \frac{3.88 \text{ g nicotinamide}}{0.032 \text{ mol nicotinamide}} = 1.2 \times 10^2 \text{ g/mol}$$

Then we determine the compound's empirical formula, and combine this with the molar mass to determine the molecular formula.

$$59.0 \text{ g C} \times \frac{1 \text{ mol C}}{12.01 \text{ g C}} = 4.91 \text{ mol C} \quad \div 0.819 \rightarrow 6.00 \text{ mol C}$$

$$5.0 \text{ g H} \times \frac{1 \text{ mol H}}{1.01 \text{ g H}} = 5.0 \text{ mol H} \quad \div 0.819 \rightarrow 6.0 \text{ mol H}$$

$$22.9 \text{ g N} \times \frac{1 \text{ mol N}}{14.01 \text{ g N}} = 1.63 \text{ mol N} \quad \div 0.819 \rightarrow 2.00 \text{ mol N}$$

$$13.1 \text{ g O} \times \frac{1 \text{ mol O}}{16.00 \text{ g O}} = 0.819 \text{ mol O} \quad \div 0.819 \rightarrow 1.00 \text{ mol O}$$

The empirical formula is $C_6H_6N_2O$, with a molar mass of 122 g/mol. Since this is the same as the experimentally determined molar mass, the molecular formula of nicotinamide is $C_6H_6N_2O$.

75. **(M)** We determine the molality of the benzene solution first, then the molar mass of the solute.

$$m = \frac{\Delta T_f}{-K_f} = \frac{-1.183\,^\circ\text{C}}{-5.12\,^\circ\text{C/(mol kg}^{-1})} = 0.231 \text{ mol kg}^{-1}$$

$$\text{amount solute} = 0.04456 \text{ kg benzene} \times \frac{0.231 \text{ mol solute}}{1 \text{ kg benzene}} = 0.0103 \text{ mol solute}$$

$$\text{molar mass} = \frac{0.867 \text{ g thiophene}}{0.0103 \text{ mol thiophene}} = 84.2 \text{ g/mol}$$

Next, we determine the empirical formula from the masses of the combustion products.

$$\text{amount C} = 4.913 \text{ g CO}_2 \times \frac{1 \text{ mol CO}_2}{44.010 \text{ g CO}_2} \times \frac{1 \text{ mol C}}{1 \text{ mol CO}_2} = 0.1116 \text{ mol C} \div 0.02791 \rightarrow 4.000 \text{ mol C}$$

$$\text{amount H} = 1.005 \text{ g H}_2\text{O} \times \frac{1 \text{ mol H}_2\text{O}}{18.015 \text{ g H}_2\text{O}} \times \frac{2 \text{ mol H}}{1 \text{ mol H}_2\text{O}} = 0.1116 \text{ mol H} \div 0.02791 \rightarrow 4.000 \text{ mol H}$$

$$\text{amount S} = 1.788 \text{ g SO}_2 \times \frac{1 \text{ mol SO}_2}{64.065 \text{ g SO}_2} \times \frac{1 \text{ mol S}}{1 \text{ mol SO}_2} = 0.02791 \text{ mol S} \div 0.02791 \rightarrow 1.000 \text{ mol S}$$

A reasonable empirical formula is C_4H_4S, which has an empirical mass of 84.1 g/mol. Since this is the same as the experimentally determined molar mass, the molecular formula of thiophene is C_4H_4S.

76. (D) First we determine the empirical formula of coniferin from the combustion data.

$$0.698 \text{ g H}_2\text{O}\times\frac{1 \text{ mol H}_2\text{O}}{18.015 \text{ g H}_2\text{O}}\times\frac{2 \text{ mol H}}{1 \text{ mol H}_2\text{O}}=0.0775 \text{ mol H}\times\frac{1.008 \text{ g H}}{1 \text{ mol H}}=0.0781 \text{ g H}$$

$$2.479 \text{ g CO}_2\times\frac{1 \text{ mol CO}_2}{44.010 \text{ g CO}_2}\times\frac{1 \text{ mol C}}{1 \text{ mol CO}_2}=0.05633 \text{ mol C}\times\frac{12.011 \text{ g C}}{1 \text{ mol C}}=0.6766 \text{ g C}$$

$$\left(1.205 \text{ g}-0.0781 \text{ g H}-0.6766 \text{ g C}\right)\times\frac{1 \text{ mol O}}{16.00 \text{ g O}}=0.0281 \text{ mol O}$$

0.0775 mol H ÷ 0.0281 = 2.76 mol H	×4 → 11.04 mol H
0.05633 mol C ÷ 0.0281 = 2.00 mol C	×4 → 8.00 mol C
0.0281 mol O ÷ 0.0281 = 1.00 mol O	×4 → 4.00 mol O

Empirical formula = $C_8H_{11}O_4$ with a formula weight of 171 g/mol.

Now we determine the molality of the boiling solution, the number of moles of solute present in that solution, and the molar mass of the solute.

$$m=\frac{\Delta T_b}{K_b}=\frac{0.068\,°\text{C}}{0.512\,°\text{C}/(\text{mol kg}^{-1})}=0.13 \text{ mol kg}^{-1}$$

$$\text{amount solute}=48.68 \text{ g H}_2\text{O}\times\frac{1 \text{ kg solvent}}{1000 \text{ g}}\times\frac{0.13 \text{ mol solute}}{1 \text{ kg solvent}}=6.3\times10^{-3} \text{ mol solute}$$

$$\text{molar mass}=\frac{2.216 \text{ g solute}}{6.3\times10^{-3} \text{ mol solute}}=3.5\times10^2 \text{ g/mol}$$

This molar mass is twice the formula weight of the empirical formula. Thus, the molecular formula is twice the empirical formula: Molecular formula = $C_{16}H_{22}O_8$.

77. **(M)** The boiling point must go up by 2 °C, so $\Delta T_b = 2$ °C. We know that $K_b = 0.512$ °C/(mol kg^{-1}) for water. We assume that the mass of a liter of water is 1.000 kg and the van't Hoff factor for NaCl is $i = 2$. We first determine the molality of the saltwater solution and then the mass of solute needed.

$$m=\frac{\Delta T_b}{i\,K_b}=\frac{2\,°\text{C}}{2.00\times0.512\,°\text{C}/(\text{mol kg}^{-1})}=2 \text{ mol kg}^{-1}$$

$$\text{solute mass}=1.00 \text{ L H}_2\text{O}\times\frac{1 \text{ kg H}_2\text{O}}{1 \text{ L H}_2\text{O}}\times\frac{2 \text{ mol NaCl}}{1 \text{ kg H}_2\text{O}}\times\frac{58.4 \text{ g NaCl}}{1 \text{ mol NaCl}}=120 \text{ g NaCl}$$

This is at least ten times the amount of salt one would typically add to a liter of water for cooking purposes!

78. (M)

(a) The impure compound begins to melt at a temperature lower than that of the pure compound because the compound acts as a solvent for the impurity. The impurity thus causes a depression of the freezing point for the compound. Actually, the compound freezes (or melts) over a range of temperatures because once some of the pure compound freezes out, the remaining solution is a more concentrated solution of the impurity and thus has an even lower freezing point. It is this range of freezing points (or melting points) rather than a single freezing point—a so called "sharp" melting point—that is the true characteristic of an impure solid.

(b) The melting point of the impure compound can be higher than the melting point of the pure compound if two conditions are met. First, the impurity must have a higher melting point than the pure compound. Second, the impurity and the compound of interest must be soluble in each other. Third, the amount of impurity should be as much as or greater than the desired compound, so the melting point is dominated by the higher melting point impurity.

79. **(E)** Assume that 1 L of ocean water has a mass of 1 kg.

$$\Delta T_f = -K_f\, m$$

$$-1.94\,°C = \left(-1.86\,°C \cdot mol^{-1}\, kg\right) \times mol\, kg^{-1}$$

$$m = 1.04$$

80. **(E)** Ocean water is 3.5% NaCl, or 35 g of NaCl per 1 kg of ocean water:

$$m\, NaCl = 35.0\, g\, NaCl \times \frac{1\, mol\, NaCl}{58.443\, g\, NaCl} \times \frac{2\, mol\, ions}{1\, mol\, NaCl} = 1.20\, mol\, kg^{-1}$$

$$\Delta T_f = -K_f\, m = \left(-1.86\,°C\, mol^{-1}\, kg\right)\left(1.20\, mol\, kg^{-1}\right) = -2.23\,°C$$

Strong Electrolytes, Weak Electrolytes, and Nonelectrolytes

81. **(M)** The freezing-point depression is given by $\Delta T_f = -iK_f m$. Since $K_f = 1.86\,°C/(mol\, kg^{-1})$ for water, $\Delta T_f = -i0.186\,°C$ for this group of $0.10\, mol\, kg^{-1}$ solutions.

(a) $T_f = -0.186\,°C$. Urea is a nonelectrolyte, and $i = 1$.

(b) $T_f = -0.372\,°C$. NH_4NO_3 is a strong electrolyte, composed of two ions per formula unit; $i = 2$.

(c) $T_f = -0.372\,°C$. HCl is a strong electrolyte, composed of two ions per formula unit; $i = 2$.

(d) $T_f = -0.558\,°C$. $CaCl_2$ is a strong electrolyte, composed of three ions per formula unit; $i = 3$.

(e) $T_f = -0.372\,°C$. $MgSO_4$ is a strong electrolyte, composed of two ions per formula unit; $i = 2$.

(f) $T_f = -0.186\,°C$. Ethanol is a nonelectrolyte; $i = 1$.

(g) $T_f < -0.186\,°C$. $HC_2H_3O_2$ is a weak electrolyte; i is somewhat larger than 1.

82. **(M)**

    (a) First calculate the freezing point for a 0.050 *m* solution of a nonelectrolyte.

$$\Delta T_{f,calc} = -K_f m = -1.86 \,°\text{C/(mol kg}^{-1}) \times 0.050 \text{ mol kg}^{-1} = -0.093 \,°\text{C}$$

$$i = \frac{\Delta T_{f,obs}}{\Delta T_{f,calc}} = \frac{-0.0986 \,°\text{C}}{-0.093 \,°\text{C}} = 1.1$$

    (b) $\left[H^+ \right] = \left[NO_2^- \right] = 6.91 \times 10^{-3} \text{ M} = 0.00691 \text{ M}$

$$\left[HNO_2 \right] = 0.100 \text{ M} - 0.00691 \text{ M} = 0.093 \text{ M}$$

$$[\text{particles}] = 0.00691 \text{ M} + 0.00691 \text{ M} + 0.093 \text{ M} = 0.107 \text{ M} \qquad i = \frac{0.107 \text{ M}}{0.100 \text{ M}} = 1.07$$

83. **(E)** The combination of $NH_3\,(aq)$ with CH_3COOH (aq), results in the formation of NH_4CH_3COO (aq), which is a solution of the ions NH_4^+ and CH_3COO^-.

$$NH_3\left(aq\right) + CH_3COOH\left(aq\right) \rightarrow NH_4CH_3COO\left(aq\right) \rightarrow NH_4^+\left(aq\right) + CH_3COO^-\left(aq\right)$$

This solution of ions or strong electrolytes conducts a current very well.

84. **(E)** For two solutions to be isotonic, they must contain the same concentration of particles. For the solutions to also have the same % mass/volume would mean that each solution must possess the same number of particles per unit mass, typically per gram of solution. This would be true if they had the same molar mass and the same van't Hoff factor. It would also be true if the quotient of molar mass and van't Hoff factor were the same. While this condition is not impossible to meet, it is highly improbable.

85. **(E)** The answer is (d). The other options describe (a) a gas dissolved in water, (b) a gas which when dissolved in water fully dissociates and is a strong electrolyte, and (c) a non-electrolytic molecule in water.

86. **(E)** The answer is (b); see notes for Exercise 85.

INTEGRATIVE AND ADVANCED EXERCISES

87. (M)

$$\text{mass P} = 12 \text{ fl oz} \times \frac{29.6 \text{ mL}}{1 \text{ fl oz}} \times \frac{1.00 \text{ g}}{1 \text{ mL}} \times \frac{0.13 \text{ g acid soln}}{100.0 \text{ g root beer}} \times \frac{75 \text{ g H}_3\text{PO}_4}{100 \text{ g acid soln}}$$

$$\times \frac{1 \text{ mol H}_3\text{PO}_4}{98.00 \text{ g H}_3\text{PO}_4} \times \frac{1 \text{ mol P}}{1 \text{ mol H}_3\text{PO}_4} \times \frac{30.97 \text{ g P}}{1 \text{ mol P}} \times \frac{1000 \text{ mg P}}{1 \text{ g P}} = 1.1 \times 10^2 \text{ mg P}$$

88. **(M)** The molarity of the original solution is computed first.

$$\text{KOH molarity} = \frac{109.2 \text{ g KOH} \times \dfrac{1 \text{ mol KOH}}{56.010 \text{ g KOH}}}{1 \text{ L soln}} = 1.950 \text{ M}$$

A 1.950 M solution is more concentrated than a 0.250 m solution. Thus, we must dilute the original solution. First we determine the mass of water produced in the final solution, and the mass of water present in the original solution, and finally the mass of water we must add.

$$\text{mass } H_2O \text{ in final soln} = 0.1000 \text{ L orig. soln} \times \frac{1.950 \text{ mol KOH}}{1 \text{ L soln}} \times \frac{1 \text{ kg } H_2O}{0.250 \text{ mol KOH}} = 0.780 \text{ kg } H_2O$$

$$\text{mass original solution} = 100.0 \text{ mL} \times \frac{1.09 \text{ g}}{1 \text{ mL}} = 109 \text{ g original solution}$$

$$\text{mass KOH} = 100.0 \text{ mL} \times \frac{1 \text{ L}}{1000 \text{ mL}} \times \frac{109.2 \text{ g KOH}}{1 \text{ L soln}} = 10.92 \text{ g KOH}$$

original mass of water = 109 g soln $-$ 10.92 g KOH = 98 g H_2O

mass added H_2O = 780.g H_2O $-$ 98 g H_2O = 682 g H_2O

89. **(M)** A quick solution to this problem is to calculate the molarity of a 50% by volume solution, using the density of 0.789 g/mL for ethanol.

$$\text{ethanol molarity} = \frac{50 \text{ mL } C_2H_5OH \times \dfrac{0.789 \text{ g}}{1 \text{ mL}} \times \dfrac{1 \text{ mol } C_2H_5OH}{46.07 \text{ g } C_2H_5OH}}{100 \text{ mL soln} \times \dfrac{1 \text{ L}}{1000 \text{ mL}}} = 8.6 \text{ M}$$

Thus, solutions that are more than 8.6 M are more than 100 proof.

90. **(D)** At the outset, we observe that the solution having the highest mole fraction of water (the most dilute solution) will have the highest partial pressure of water in its equilibrium vapor. Also, the solution with the lowest mole fraction of water (the most concentrated solution) will have the lowest freezing point. We need to identify these two solutions, and to achieve this we need a simple way to compare concentrations, which are given here in disparate units. Let's look at the solutions one at a time. Keep in mind that 1 L of water contains about 1000 g H_2O $\div$ 18.02 g/mol $\approx$ 55.49 mol H_2O (55.49 M).

Solution (a): The concentration 0.100% CH_3COCH_3 by mass is equivalent to 1.00 g CH_3COCH_3/1000 g solution, which in turn is about 1.00 g CH_3COCH_3/L solution. (The density of the solution will be very nearly the same as that of water.) A 1.00-g sample of CH_3COCH_3 is the same as 1.00 g/58.1 g /mol $\ll$ 0.10 mol CH_3COCH_3 .

Solution (b): The 0.100 M CH_3COCH_3 has 0.100 mol CH_3COCH_3 per liter. Solution (b) is more concentrated than (a), so (b) cannot be the solution with the highest water vapor pressure.

Solution (c): The 0.100 mol kg^{-1} CH_3COCH_3 has 0.100 mol CH_3COCH_3 per kg H_2O. Because water is the preponderant component in the solution, the density of the solution will be very nearly that of water, and the 0.100 mol kg^{-1} CH_3COCH_3 $\approx$ 0.100 M CH_3COCH_3. So, as with (b), solution (c) cannot be the solution with the highest water vapor pressure.

Solution (d): In the solution $\chi_{acetone}$ = 0.100, acetone molecules comprise one-tenth of all the molecules, or there is one acetone molecule for every nine water molecules. In a liter of this solution there would be about 55.5 ÷ 9 ≈ 6 mol CH_3COCH_3. This is clearly the most concentrated of the solutions.

To summarize, solution (a) has the highest water vapor pressure and solution (d) has the lowest freezing point. Our next task is to apply Raoult's law to solution (a), which requires the mole fraction of water in solution (a). One kilogram of this solution contains 1.00 g per 58.1 g /mol = 0.0172 mol CH_3COCH_3 and 999 g per 18.02 g/ mol = 55.44 mol H_2O. The mole fraction of the water is χ_{water} = 55.44/(55.44 + 0.0172) ≈ 1.00. The mole fraction is only very slightly less than 1.00, so the water vapor pressure above this solution will be only very slightly less than the vapor pressure of pure water at 25 °C, namely, 23.8 mmHg.

To apply Equation 14.5 for freezing-point depression to solution (d), we must first express its concentration in molality. In a solution that has 1.00 mol CH_3COCH_3 for every 9.00 mol H_2O, there is 1.00 mol of the solute for every (9.00 mol × 18.02 g/mol=) 162 g H_2O. The molality of the solution is 1.00 mol CH_3COCH_3/0.162 kg H_2O = 6.17 mol kg^{-1} CH_3COCH_3. The approximate freezing-point depression for this solution is

$$T_f = -K_f \times m = -1.86 \text{ °C} \times 6.17 \text{ mol kg}^{-1} \approx -11.5 \text{ °C}$$

and the approximate freezing point of the solution is −11.5 °C. This result is only approximate because we have used Equation 14.5 for a much more concentrated solution than that for which the equation is intended.

91. We assume that the presence of the second solute will not substantially affect the solubility of the first solute in the solution. To get around this assumption, solubility data often are given in grams of solute per 100 g of solvent, as in Figure 14-10. This only partially avoids the problem because the interaction of the solutes can mutually affect their solubilities.

(a) We determine the solution concentration of each solute in the mixture, and compare these values to the solubilities at 60 °C obtained from Figure 14-10: greater than 100 g/100g H_2O for KNO_3 and 18.2 g/100 g water for K_2SO_4.

$$\text{conc. } KNO_3 = \frac{0.850 \times 60.0 \text{ g solid}}{130.0 \text{ g water}} \times 100 \text{ g water} = 39.2 \text{ g } KNO_3/100 \text{ g water}$$

$$\text{conc. } K_2SO_4 = \frac{0.150 \times 60.0 \text{ g solid}}{130.0 \text{ g water}} \times 100 \text{ g water} = 6.92 \text{ g } K_2SO_4/100 \text{ g water}$$

Thus, all of the solid dissolves.

(b) At 0 °C, the solubility of KNO_3 is 14.0 g/100 g water. The mass of KNO_3 that crystallizes is obtained by difference.

$$m_{KNO_3} = 130.0 \text{g water} \times \frac{39.2 \text{ g(dissolved at 60 °C)} - 14.0 \text{ g (dissolved at 0 °C)}}{100 \text{ g water}}$$

$$m_{KNO_3} = 32.8 \text{g } KNO_3 \text{ crystallized}$$

(c) At 0 °C, the solubility of K_2SO_4 is 7.4 g/100 g water. Since this is greater than the 6.92 g K_2SO_4/100 g water that is dissolved at 60 °C, all of the K_2SO_4 remains dissolved.

92. **(M)** First determine the molality of the solution with the desired freezing point and compare it to the molality of the supplied solution to determine if ethanol or water needs to be added.

$$m = \frac{\Delta T_f}{-K_f} = \frac{-2.0 \text{ °C}}{-1.86 \text{ °C/(mol kg}^{-1})} = 1.1 \text{ mol kg}^{-1} \text{ (desired)}$$

$$\text{mass solution} = 2.50 \text{ L} \times \frac{1000 \text{ mL}}{1 \text{ L}} \times \frac{0.9767 \text{ g}}{1 \text{ mL}} = 2.44 \times 10^3 \text{ g solution}$$

$$\text{mass solute} = 2.44 \times 10^3 \text{ g soln} \times \frac{13.8 \text{ g } C_2H_5OH}{100.0 \text{ g soln}} = 337 \text{ g } C_2H_5OH$$

$$\text{mass } H_2O = (2.44 \times 10^3 \text{ g} - 337 \text{ g } C_2H_5OH) \times \frac{1 \text{ kg}}{1000 \text{ g}} = 2.10 \text{ kg } H_2O$$

$$m = \frac{337 \text{ g } C_2H_5OH \times \dfrac{1 \text{ mol } C_2H_5OH}{46.07 \text{ g } C_2H_5OH}}{2.10 \text{ kg } H_2O} = 3.48 \text{ mol kg}^{-1} \text{ (available)}$$

Thus we need to dilute the solution with water. We must find the mass of water needed in the final solution, then the mass of water that must be added.

$$\text{final mass of water} = 337 \text{ g } C_2H_5OH \times \frac{1 \text{ mol } C_2H_5OH}{46.07 \text{ g } C_2H_5OH} \times \frac{1 \text{ kg } H_2O}{1.1 \text{ mol } C_2H_5OH} = 6.6 \text{ kg } H_2O$$

$$\text{mass } H_2O \text{ needed} = 6.6 \text{ kg total} - 2.10 \text{ kg already present} = 4.5 \text{ kg } H_2O$$

93. **(E)** HCl is very soluble in water and the reaction with water is highly exothermic. Concentrated HCl gives off small quantities of HCl(g) which react with water vapor in the atmosphere. The reaction between HCl and water is sufficiently exothermic that the room temperature water vapor changes to steam and then recondenses as the solution returns to room temperature.

94. (M)

(a) First we will determine the effect of an increase in pressure from the triple point pressure of 4.58 mmHg to 1 atm pressure on the melting point of ice.

$$\Delta T = -0.00750\,^{\circ}\text{C/atm} \times \frac{(760 - 4.58)\,\text{Torr}}{760\,\text{Torr/atm}} = -0.00746\,^{\circ}\text{C}$$

(b) Next we will determine the molarity of dissolved air in water:

$$\text{molarity} = \frac{29.18\,\text{mL} \times \dfrac{1\,\text{mol air}}{22{,}414\,\text{mL}}}{1\,\text{L}} = 0.0013\,\text{M.}$$

The molality of the solution is also 0.0013 mol kg^{-1}. The freezing-point depression by this dissolved air is $\Delta T_f = -1.86\,^{\circ}\text{C mol}^{-1}\,\text{kg} \times 0.0013\,\text{mol kg}^{-1} = -0.0024\,^{\circ}\text{C}$.

The effect of lowering the pressure on the system and removing the dissolved air would be to raise the melting point of the ice by $(0.00745 + 0.0024)\,^{\circ}\text{C} \approx 0.0098\,^{\circ}\text{C}$, which is what we set out to show.

95. **(M)** First we determine the molality of the benzene solution, and then the number of moles of solute in the sample.

$$\text{molality} = \frac{\Delta T_f}{-K_f} = \frac{5.072\,^{\circ}\text{C} - 5.533\,^{\circ}\text{C}}{-5.12\,^{\circ}\text{C/(mol kg}^{-1})} = 0.0900\,\text{mol kg}^{-1}$$

$$\text{amount of solute} = 50.00\,\text{mL} \times \frac{0.879\,\text{g}}{1\,\text{mL}} \times \frac{1\,\text{kg}}{1000\,\text{g}} \times \frac{0.0900\,\text{mol solute}}{1\,\text{kg solvent}} = 0.00396\,\text{mol solute}$$

We use this amount to determine the amount of each acid in the solute, with the added data of the molar masses of stearic acid, $C_{18}H_{36}O_2$, 284.5 g/mol, and palmitic acid, $C_{18}H_{36}O_2$, 256.4 g/mol. We let x represent the amount in moles of palmitic acid.

$$1.115\,\text{g sample} = (0.00396 - x)\,\text{mol} \times 284.5\,\text{g/mol} + x\,\text{mol} \times 256.4\,\text{g/mol}$$
$$= 1.12\underline{7} - 284.5\,x + 256.4\,x = 1.12\underline{7} - 28.1\,x$$

$$x = \frac{1.12\underline{7} - 1.115}{28.1} = 0.0004\underline{3}\,\text{mol palmitic acid}$$

$$0.00396 - 0.0004\underline{3} = 0.0035\underline{3}\,\text{mol stearic acid}$$

mass palmitic acid = $0.00043\,\text{mol} \times 256.4\,\text{g/mol} = 0.11\,\text{g palmitic acid}$

$$\% \text{ palmitic acid} = \frac{0.11\,\text{g palmitic acid}}{1.115\,\text{g sample}} \times 100\% = 1 \times 10^1\,\%\text{ palmitic acid (about 10\%)}$$

96. **(M)** Let us first consider a solution in which nitrobenzene, $K_f = 8.1$ °C/(mol kg^{-1}), is the solvent. For this solution to freeze at 0.0 °C,. $\Delta T_f = -5.7$°C

$$\text{molality} = \frac{\Delta T_f}{K_f} = \frac{-5.7\,°C}{-8.1\,°C/(mol\ kg^{-1})} = 0.70\ mol\ kg^{-1} = \frac{0.70\ mol\ C_6H_6}{1\ kg\ C_6H_5NO_2}$$

$$\%\ C_6H_5NO_2 = \frac{1000\ g\ C_6H_5NO_2}{1000\ g\ C_6H_5NO_2 + 0.70\ mol\ C_6H_6 \times \dfrac{78.1\ g\ C_6H_6}{1\ mol\ C_6H_6}} \times 100\%$$

$$= 95\%\ C_6H_5NO_2\,(\text{by mass})$$

Then we consider a solution in which benzene, $K_f = 5.12$ °C/(mol kg^{-1}), is the solvent. For this solution to freeze at 0.0 °C, $\Delta T_f = -5.5$ °C.

$$\text{molality} = \frac{\Delta T_f}{K_f} = \frac{-5.5\,°C}{-5.12\,°C/(mol\ kg^{-1})} = 1.07\ mol\ kg^{-1} = \frac{1.07\ mol\ C_6H_5NO_2}{1\ kg\ C_6H_6}$$

$$\%\ C_6H_5NO_2 = \frac{1.07\ mol\ C_6H_5NO_2 \times \dfrac{123.1\ g\ C_6H_5NO_2}{1\ mol\ C_6H_5NO_2}}{1.07\ mol\ C_6H_5NO_2 \times \dfrac{123.1\ g\ C_6H_5NO_2}{1\ mol\ C_6H_5NO_2} + 1000\ g\ C_6H_6} \times 100\%$$

$$= 12\%\ C_6H_5NO_2\,(\text{by mass})$$

97. **(D)** We first determine the amount in moles of each substance.

$$\text{amount } CO(NH_2)_2 = 0.515\ g\ CO(NH_2)_2 \times \frac{1\ mol\ CO(NH_2)_2}{60.06\ g\ CO(NH_2)_2} = 0.00858\ mol\ CO(NH_2)_2$$

$$\text{amount } H_2O \text{ with urea} = 92.5\ g\ H_2O \times \frac{1\ mol\ H_2O}{18.015\ g\ H_2O} = 5.13\ mol\ H_2O$$

$$\text{amount } C_{12}H_{22}O_{11} = 2.50\ g\ C_{12}H_{22}O_{11} \times \frac{1\ mol\ C_{12}H_{22}O_{11}}{342.3\ g\ C_{12}H_{22}O_{11}} = 0.00730\ mol\ C_{12}H_{22}O_{11}$$

$$\text{amount } H_2O \text{ with sucrose} = 85.0\ g\ H_2O \times \frac{1\ mol\ H_2O}{18.015\ g\ H_2O} = 4.72\ mol\ H_2O$$

The vapor pressure of water will be the same above both solutions when their mole fractions are equal. We assume that the amount of water present as water vapor is negligible. The total amount of water in the two solutions is (4.72 + 5.13 =) 9.85 mol H_2O. We let n_{water} designate the amount of water in the urea solution. The amount of water in the sucrose solution is then 9.85 mole − n_{water}. Note that we can compute the mole fraction of solute for comparison, since when the two solute mole fractions are equal, the mole fractions of solvent will also be equal ($\chi_{solvent} = 1.0000 - \chi_{solute}$).

$$\frac{0.00857 \text{ mol urea}}{0.00858 \text{ mol urea} + n_{water}} = \chi_{urea} = \chi_{sucrose} = \frac{0.00730 \text{ mol sucrose}}{0.00730 \text{ mol sucrose} + (9.85 - n_{water})}$$

We "cross multiply'' to begin the solution for n_{water}.

$$0.00857 (0.00730 + 9.85 - n_{water}) = 0.00730 (0.00858 + n_{water})$$
$$0.0845 - 0.00857 \, n_{water} = 0.0000626 + 0.00730 \, n_{water} \quad n_{water}$$
$$= \frac{0.0845 - 0.0000626}{0.00730 + 0.00857} = 5.32 \text{ mol}$$

We check the answer by substitution into the mole fraction equation.

$$\frac{0.00857 \text{ mol urea}}{0.00857 \text{ mol} + 5.32\underline{4}} = 0.00161 = \chi_{urea} = \chi_{sucrose} = 0.00161$$
$$= \frac{0.00730 \text{ mol sucrose}}{0.00730 \text{ mol} + (9.85 - 5.32\underline{4})\text{mol}}$$

The mole fraction of water in each solution is (1.00000 − 0.00161 =) 0.99839, or 99.839 mol%

98. **(M)** We would expect the movement of the solvent molecules across the semipermeable membrane to cease as soon as the concentration of solute particles becomes the same on both sides of the membrane. This equality of concentration is achieved in two ways. (1) The solvent molecules move across the membrane into the sucrose solution and dilute it. (2) the sucrose solution overflows out of the funnel into the liquid that originally was pure water. In order to overflow the funnel, the water moving across the membrane must push the solution up the funnel. This requires a small pressure, an osmotic pressure, that is generated by a difference in concentration of the two solutions. Because this difference in concentration is required, the flow of water will stop when the concentrations are almost the same. At that point, the difference in concentrations will be insufficient to raise the solution to the top of the tube.

99. **(E)** The reason that the cooling curve is not horizontal at the freezing point is that as the solution freezes, the composition of the liquid changes. The solid phase which forms at the freezing point is pure solvent. Consequently, as freezing occurs, the concentration of the solution increases, and the freezing point decreases.

100. (M)

    (a) Surface area of a particle $= 4\pi r^2 = 4(3.1416)(1 \times 10^{-7}m)^2 = 1.26 \times 10^{-13}$ m²/particle. We need to find the number of particles present (not atoms!)

$$\text{particle volume} = \frac{4\pi r^3}{3} = \frac{4\pi (1\times 10^{-7}m)^3}{3} = 4.19\times 10^{-21} m^3$$

$$\text{particle mass} = \text{density} \times \text{volume} = \frac{19.3\ g}{cm^3}\frac{(100\ cm)^3}{(1\ m)^3}\times 4.19\times 10^{-21} m^3 = 8.09\times 10^{-14}\ g/\text{particle}$$

$$\text{number of Au particles} = \frac{\text{mass of Au}}{\text{particle mass}} = \frac{1.00\times 10^{-3} g\ Au}{8.09\times 10^{-14} g/\text{particle}} = 1.24\times 10^{10}\ \text{particles}$$

$$\text{total surface area} = (1.26\times 10^{-13} m^2/\text{particle})(1.24\times 10^{10}\ \text{particles}) = 1.56\times 10^{-3} m^2$$

    (b) For 1.00 mg Au the volume of Au is: $(1.00\ mg)(1\ g/1000\ mg)/(19.3\ g/cm^3) = 5.18 \times 10^{-5}$ cm³

    Volume of a cube is L^3, where L is the edge length, so

$$L = \sqrt[3]{5.18\times 10^{-5}\ cm^3} = 3.73\times 10^{-2}\ cm$$

$$\text{area} = 6 \times L^2 = 6 \times (3.73 \times 10^{-2}\ cm)^2 \times (1\ m/100\ cm)^2 = 8.34 \times 10{-7}\ m^2$$

101. (D)

    (a) Assume that there is 100.00 mL of solution. Then, since the volumes of the components are additive, the volume of benzene in the solution is numerically equal to its volume percent, V. The volume of toluene is 100.00 mL $- V$. Now we determine the mass of the solution.

$$\text{solution mass} = V\ \text{mL benzene}\times \frac{0.879\ g\ \text{benzene}}{1\ \text{mL benzene}} + (100.00-V)\ \text{mL toluene}\times\frac{0.867\ g\ \text{toluene}}{1\ \text{mL toluene}}$$

The density of the solution is given by its mass divided by its volume, 100.00 mL.

$$\text{density} = \frac{\text{mass}}{\text{volume}} = \frac{V(\text{mL})\times 0.879(g/mL)+(100.00-V)\text{mL}\times 0.867(g/mL)}{100.00\ \text{mL}}$$

This is the equation requested in (c).

We now calculate the density for a number of solutions of varying volume percent benzene

20% by volume =

$$\frac{20.0 \text{ mL} \times 0.879 \text{ g mL}^{-1} + (100.0 - 20) \text{ mL} \times 0.869 \text{ g/mL}}{100 \text{ mL}} = 0.871 \text{ g/mL}$$

40% by volume =

$$\frac{40.0 \text{ mL} \times 0.879 \text{ g mL}^{-1} + (100.0 - 40) \text{ mL} \times 0.869 \text{ g/mL}}{100 \text{ mL}} = 0.873 \text{ g/mL}$$

60% by volume =

$$\frac{60.0 \text{ mL} \times 0.879 \text{ g mL}^{-1} + (100.0 - 60) \text{ mL} \times 0.869 \text{ g/mL}}{100 \text{ mL}} = 0.875 \text{ g/mL}$$

80% by volume =

$$\frac{80.0 \text{ mL} \times 0.879 \text{ g mL}^{-1} + (100.0 - 80.0) \text{ mL} \times 0.869 \text{ g/mL}}{100 \text{ mL}} = 0.877 \text{ g/mL}$$

(b) The data is plotted below and includes the density of pure benzene (100%) and toluene (0%)

(c) The equation relating density of solution with volume percent Benzene was developed above and reprinted here.

$$\text{density} = \frac{\text{mass}}{\text{volume}} = \frac{V(\text{mL}) \times 0.879(\text{g/mL}) + (100.00 - V)\text{mL} \times 0.867(\text{g/mL})}{100.00 \text{ mL}}$$

102. **(M)** Separation by fractional distillation is based on a difference in the boiling points of the two substances being separated. Since the boiling points of *meta*- and *para*-xylene differ by only 0.7 °C, their separation by fractional distillation is impractical. However, the freezing points of these two isomers differ by more than 60 °C. Separation by fractional solidification should be possible, freezing out primarily pure *para*-xylene at 13.3 °C, thereby leaving a solution rich in *meta*-xylene.

103. **(M)** As the fraction of ethylene glycol in the solution increases, we eventually reach a point where the ethylene glycol, rather than water, is the solvent in the solution. After the fraction of ethylene glycol in the solution has increased past this point, the solution will freeze at the depressed freezing point of ethylene glycol, rather than at the depressed freezing point of water. That is, solid ethylene glycol, rather than solid water, will freeze out of the solution. The freezing point of ethylene glycol (–13 °C) is higher than –34 °C.

104. **(D)**

   (a) Let's begin with the definition of molality for an aqueous solution. We assume that the mass of the solvent is essentially equal to the mass of the solution, since the solution is a dilute one.
   Next we assume that the density of this dilute solution is that of pure water, 1.00 g/mL, and then apply some definitions (1 kg = 1000 g and 1 L = 1000 mL).

   $$\text{molality} \approx \frac{\text{moles solute}}{1 \text{ kg solution}} \times \frac{1 \text{ kg solution}}{1000 \text{ g solution}} \times \frac{1.00 \text{ g solution}}{1 \times 10^{-3} \text{ L solution}} \approx \frac{\text{moles solute}}{1 \text{ L solution}} = \text{molarity}$$

   (b) We begin with the definition of mole fraction for the solute. Then we assume that the amount of solute is quite small compared to the amount of solvent, and use the molar mass (M) of the solvent, along with the fact that 1 kg = 1000 g.

   $$\chi_{\text{solute}} = \frac{\text{moles solute}}{\text{moles solute} + \text{moles solvent}} \approx \frac{\text{moles solute}}{\text{moles solvent}} \times \frac{1 \text{ mol solvent}}{M \text{ g solvent}} \times \frac{1000 \text{ g solvent}}{1 \text{ kg solvent}}$$

   $$\approx \frac{1000 \text{ g/kg} \times \text{moles solute}}{M_{\text{solvent}} \times 1 \text{ kg solvent}} = \frac{\text{moles solute}}{1 \text{ kg solvent}} \times \frac{1000 \text{ g/kg}}{M_{\text{solvent}}} = \text{molality} \times \frac{1000 \text{ g/kg}}{M_{\text{solvent}}}$$

   Thus, mole fraction of a solute indeed is proportional to its molality in a dilute solution.

   (c) For a dilute aqueous solution, we begin with the result of part (b) and first use the definition of molality and then assume that the mass of the solvent is essentially equal to the mass of the solution.

   $$\chi_{\text{solute}} \approx \text{molality} \times \frac{1000 \text{ g/kg}}{M_{\text{solvent}}} \approx \frac{\text{moles solute}}{1 \text{ kg solvent}} \times \frac{1000 \text{ g/kg}}{M_{\text{solvent}}} \times \frac{1 \text{ kg solvent}}{1 \text{ kg solution}}$$

   Now we assume that the density of this dilute solution is that of pure water, 1.00 g/mL, and then apply some definitions (1 kg = 1000 g and 1 L = 1000 mL).

$$\chi_{solute} \approx \frac{\text{moles solute}}{1\ \text{kg solvent}} \times \frac{1000\ \text{g/kg}}{M_{solvent}} \times \frac{1\ \text{kg solvent}}{1\ \text{kg soln}} \times \frac{1\ \text{kg soln}}{1000\ \text{g soln}} \times \frac{1.00\ \text{g soln}}{1\ \text{mL soln}} \times \frac{1000\ \text{mL soln}}{1\ \text{L soln}}$$

$$\approx \frac{\text{moles solute}}{1\ \text{L solution}} \times \frac{1000\ \text{g/kg}}{M_{solvent}} = \text{molarity} \times \frac{1000\ \text{g/kg}}{M_{solvent}}$$

Thus molarity of dilute aqueous solutions is proportional to mole fraction of the solute.

105. (M) We determine the volumes of O_2 and N_2 that dissolve under the appropriate partial pressures of 0.2095 atm O_2 and 0.7808 atm N_2, and at a temperature of 25 °C, with both gas volumes measured at 1.00 atm and 25 °C. Note that the percent by volume and the percent by partial pressures of the atmosphere are numerically the same.

$$O_2\ \text{volume} = 0.2095\ \text{atm} \times \frac{28.31\ \text{mL}\ O_2}{1\ \text{atm} \cdot \text{L soln}} = 5.931\ \frac{\text{mL}\ O_2}{\text{L solution}}$$

$$N_2\ \text{volume} = 0.7808\ \text{atm} \times \frac{14.34\ \text{mL}\ N_2}{1\ \text{atm} \cdot \text{L soln}} = 11.20\ \frac{\text{mL}\ N_2}{\text{L solution}}$$

$$\text{volume}\ \%\ N_2 = \frac{11.20\ \dfrac{\text{mL}\ N_2}{\text{L solution}}}{11.20\ \dfrac{\text{mL}\ N_2}{\text{L solution}} + 5.931\ \dfrac{\text{mL}\ O_2}{\text{L solution}}} \times 100\% = 65.38\%\ N_2\ \text{by volume}$$

$$\text{volume}\ \%\ O_2 = 100.00\% - 65.38\% = 34.62\%\ O_2\ \text{by volume}$$

106. (D) The vapor pressure values at 100 °C, that is, 1350.5 mmHg for benzene and 556.3 for toluene, can be found in data tables, or estimated from the graphs in Figure 14-16 on page 663.

If the curve representing the liquid composition in Figure 14-17 were a straight line, the two end points on the curve (111 °C, mole fraction of benzene = 0 and 80 °C, mole fraction of benzene = 1) would have to lie on this line. But then all other liquid composition points would also have to be on this line, since two points determine a straight line. The basic requirement is to choose one or a few conditions on the graph and show that they do <u>not</u> fall on the line just mentioned.

The normal boiling point of a liquid mixture of the two volatile components, benzene and toluene, is given by the expression

$$x_{benz}P^*_{benz} + x_{tol}P^*_{tol} = x_{benz}P^*_{benz} + (1 - x_{benz})P^*_{tol} = 760\ \text{mmHg}$$

Thus, for a normal boiling point of 100 °C,

$$1350.5 x_{benz} + 556.3(1 - x_{benz}) = 760$$

resulting in

$$x_{benz} = 0.256 \text{ and } x_{tol} = (1 - x_{benz}) = 0.744$$

The expected result at a boiling point of 100 °C for a straight-line liquid composition graph would be about $x_{benz} = 0.33$ and $x_{tol} = 0.67$

Additionally, the calculated results at a temperature of 90 °C were found to be

$$1021 x_{benz} + 406.7(1 - x_{benz}) = 760 \text{ and } x_{benz} = 0.575 \text{ and } x_{tol} = 0.425$$

Again, these results are different than the straight-line estimates at 90 °C, which are

$$x_{benz} = 0.67 \text{ and } x_{tol} = 0.33.$$

Thus, the graph of boiling point versus liquid composition cannot be a straight line.

107. **(D)** First we determine the mass of $CuSO_4$ in the original solution at 70 °C.

$$335 \text{ g sample} \times \frac{32.0 \text{ g } CuSO_4}{100.0 \text{ g soln}} = 107.\underline{2} \text{ g } CuSO_4$$

We let x represent the mass of $CuSO_4$ removed from the solution when the $CuSO_4 \cdot 5H_2O$ recrystallizes. Then the mass of H_2O present in the recrystallized product is determined.

$$\text{mass } H_2O = x \text{ g } CuSO_4 \times \frac{1 \text{ mol } CuSO_4}{159.6 \text{ g } CuSO_4} \times \frac{5 \text{ mol } H_2O}{1 \text{ mol } CuSO_4} \times \frac{18.02 \text{ g } H_2O}{1 \text{ mol } H_2O} = 0.565x \text{ g } H_2O$$

Now we determine the value of x by using the concentration of the saturated solution at 0 °C.

$$\frac{12.5 \text{ g } CuSO_4}{100.0 \text{ g soln}} = \frac{(107.\underline{2} - x) \text{ g } CuSO_4}{(335 - x - 0.565\,x) \text{ g soln}}$$

$$1.07\underline{2} \times 10^4 - 100.0x = 4.19 \times 10^3 - 19.6x \qquad (100.0 - 19.6)x = 1.07\underline{2} \times 10^4 - 4.19 \times 10^3$$

$$x = \frac{6.5\underline{3} \times 10^3}{80.4} = 81 \text{ g } CuSO_4$$

$$\text{mass } CuSO_4 \cdot 5H_2O = 81 \text{ g } CuSO_4 \times \frac{1.000 \text{ g } CuSO_4 + 0.565 \text{ g } H_2O}{1.000 \text{ g } CuSO_4} = 1.3 \times 10^2 \text{ g } CuSO_4 \cdot 5H_2O$$

108. (E)

$$\text{mass of Ar} = \frac{11.5 \times 10^{-6} \text{mol Ar}}{\text{L of seawater}} \times \frac{40.0 \text{ g Ar}}{1 \text{ mol}} = 4.60 \times 10^{-4} \frac{\text{g}}{\text{L}}$$

Partial pressure can be determined from Henry's Law:

$$C = k_H P$$

$$11.5 \times 10^{-6} \text{ M} = \left(1.5 \times 10^{-3} \text{M} \cdot \text{atm}^{-1}\right) P$$

$$P = \frac{11.5 \times 10^{-6} \text{ M}}{1.5 \times 10^{-3} \text{M} \cdot \text{atm}^{-1}} = 0.0077 \text{ atm}$$

109. (E)

$$\text{mass of N}_2 = \frac{445 \times 10^{-6} \text{mol N}_2}{\text{L of seawater}} \times \frac{28.0 \text{ g N}_2}{1 \text{ mol}} = 0.0125 \frac{\text{g}}{\text{L}}$$

Partial pressure can be determined from Henry's Law:

$$C = k_H P$$

$$445 \times 10^{-6} \text{ M} = \left(0.61 \times 10^{-3} \text{M} \cdot \text{atm}^{-1}\right) P$$

$$P = \frac{445 \times 10^{-6} \text{ M}}{0.61 \times 10^{-3} \text{M} \cdot \text{atm}^{-1}} = 0.73 \text{ atm}$$

110. (M)

(a) density = m/V

$$D = \frac{750 \text{g} + 85.0 \text{g}}{810.0 \text{ mL}} = 1.03 \text{ g/mL}$$

(b) $\text{wt\%} = \dfrac{\text{mass}_{\text{sucrose}}}{\text{mass}_{\text{sucrose}} + \text{mass}_{\text{ethanol}}} \times 100\% = \dfrac{85.0 \text{ g}}{85.0 \text{ g} + 750 \text{ g}} \times 100\% = 10.2\%$

(c) $\text{mol}_{\text{suc.}} = 85.0 \text{ g} \times \dfrac{1 \text{mol}}{180.0 \text{ g}} = 0.4722 \text{ mol}$

$$\text{mol}_{\text{EtOH}} = 750.0 \text{ g} \times \frac{1 \text{mol}}{34.07 \text{ g}} = 22.01 \text{ mol}$$

$$\chi_{\text{suc.}} = \frac{0.4722 \text{ mol}}{0.4722 \text{ mol} + 22.01 \text{ mol}} = 0.0210 \text{ mol}$$

(d) molality = mol kg^{-1} solvent. We note that the density of ethanol is 0.789 g/mL or 0.789 kg/L.

$$\text{molality} = \frac{0.4722 \text{ mol}}{0.810 \text{ L} \times 0.789 \text{ kg L}^{-1}} = 0.740 \text{ mol kg}^{-1}$$

(e) molarity = mol/Vol solvent

$$\text{Molarity} = \frac{0.4722 \text{ mol}}{0.810 \text{ L}} = 0.583 \text{ M}$$

111. **(M)** First, determine what molality of ethylene glycol is needed to cause a 10.0 °C freezing-point depression:

$$\Delta T_f = -K_f \cdot m$$

$$-10 \, ^{\circ}C = \left(-1.86 \, ^{\circ}C \cdot \text{mol}^{-1} \text{kg}\right) \cdot m$$

$$m = 5.376 \text{ mol kg}^{-1}$$

Then, determine the number of moles of ethylene glycol, which can be used to determine the volume, using the density of ethylene glycol given.

$$\text{mol } C_2H_6O_2 = \frac{5.376 \text{ mol } C_2H_6O_2}{1 \text{ kg } H_2O} \times \frac{1 \text{ kg } H_2O}{1 \text{ L } H_2O} \times \frac{20.0 \text{ L } H_2O}{\text{sample}} = 107.53 \text{ mol } C_2H_6O_2/\text{sample}$$

$$\text{Vol } C_2H_6O_2 = 107.53 \text{ mol } C_2H_6O_2 \times \frac{62.09 \text{ g } C_2H_6O_2}{1 \text{ mol } C_2H_6O_2} \times \frac{1 \text{ mL}}{1.12 \text{ g } C_2H_6O_2} = 5961 \text{ mL} = 5.96 \text{ L}$$

112. **(E)**

(a) $\chi_{\text{solute}} = 5/36 = 0.14$

(b) Solvent has the higher vapor pressure

(c) %solute vapor = $1/6 \times 100 = 16.7\%$

FEATURE PROBLEMS

113. **(D)**

(a) The temperature at which the total vapor pressure is equal to 760 mm Hg corresponds to the boiling point for the cinnamaldehyde/H_2O mixture. Consequently, to find the temperature at which steam distillation begins under 1 atm pressure, we must construct a plot of P_{total} against the temperature. The data needed for this graph and a separate graph required for the answer to part (c) are given in the table below.

Temperature (°C)	P_{H_2O} (mmHg)	$P_{C_9H_8O}$ (mmHg)	P_{total} (mmHg)	Mole fraction of C_9H_8O
76.1	308	1	309	3.24×10^{-3}
105.8	942	5	947	5.28×10^{-3}
120.0	1489	10	1499	6.67×10^{-3}

The graph of total vapor pressure vs temperature is drawn below:

According to this plot, when the barometric pressure is 1 atm. (i.e., 760 mmHg), distillation occurs at 99.6 °C. Thus, as one would expect for a steam distillation, the boiling point for the mixture is below the boiling point for the lower boiling point component, viz. water. Moreover, the graph shows that the boiling point for this mixture is close to that for pure water and, once again, this is the anticipated result since the mixture contains very little cinnamaldehyde.

(b) The condensate that is collected in a steam distillation is the liquefied form of the gaseous mixture generated in the distillation pot. The composition of the gaseous mixture and that of the derived condensate is determined not by the composition of the liquid mixture but rather by the vapor pressure for each component at the boiling point. The boiling point of the cinnamaldehyde/H$_2$O mixture will stay fixed at 99.6 °C and the composition will remain at 99.5$\underline{4}$ mole % H$_2$O and 0.46$\underline{4}$ % cinnamaldehyde as long as there is at least a modicum of each component present.

(c) To answer this part of the question, we must construct a plot of the mole fraction of cinnamaldehyde against temperature. The graph, which is drawn below, shows that the mole fraction for cinnamaldehyde at the boiling point (99.6 °C) is 0.0046$\underline{4}$. in the vapor is directly proportional
to its vapor pressure, the number of moles of component A divided by the moles of component B is equal to the partial pressure for component A divided by the partial pressure of component B.

$$\frac{n_A}{n_B} = \frac{P_{\text{component A}}}{P_{\text{component B}}} = \frac{\text{mass A}}{\text{mass B}} = \frac{P_{\text{component A}}}{P_{\text{component B}}} \times \frac{\text{molar mass component A}}{\text{molar mass component B}}$$

If we make cinnamaldehyde component A and water component B, and then plug in the appropriate numbers into the second equation involving masses, we obtain

$P_{\text{cinn}} = 0.00464 \times (760 \text{ mmHg}) = {\sim}3.53 \text{ mmHg};$
$P_{\text{H}_2\text{O}} = (760 - 3.53) \text{ mmHg} = {\sim} 756 \text{ mmHg}$

$$\frac{\text{mass C}_9\text{H}_8\text{O}}{\text{mass H}_2\text{O}} = \frac{3.53 \text{ mmHg}}{756 \text{ mm Hg}} \times \frac{\dfrac{132 \text{ g C}_9\text{H}_8\text{O}}{1 \text{ mol} \quad \text{C}_9\text{H}_8\text{O}}}{\dfrac{18.0 \text{ g} \quad \text{H}_2\text{O}}{1 \text{ mol} \quad \text{H}_2\text{O}}} = 3.42 \times 10^{-2}$$

Clearly then, water condenses in the greater quantity by mass. In fact, every gram of cinnamaldehyde that condenses is accompanied by ~29 g of water in the collection flask!

114. (D)

(a) A solution with $\chi_{\text{HCl}} = 0.50$ begins to boil at about 18 °C. At that temperature, the composition of the vapor is about $\chi_{\text{HCl}} = 0.63$, reading directly across the tie line at 18 °C. The vapor has $\chi_{\text{HCl}} > 0.50$.

(b) The composition of HCl(aq) changes as the solution boils in an open container because the vapor has a different composition than does the liquid. Thus, the component with the lower boiling point is depleted as the solution boils. The boiling point of the remaining solution must change as the vapor escapes due to changing composition.

(c) The azeotrope occurs at the maximum of the curve: at $\chi_{\text{HCl}} = 0.12$ and a boiling temperature of 110 °C.

(d) We first determine the amount of HCl in the sample.

$$\text{amount HCl} = 30.32 \text{ mL NaOH} \times \frac{1 \text{ L}}{1000 \text{ mL}} \times \frac{1.006 \text{ mol NaOH}}{1 \text{ L}} \times \frac{1 \text{ mol HCl}}{1 \text{ mol NaOH}}$$

amount HCl = 0.03050 mol HCl

The mass of water is the difference between the mass of solution and that of HCl.

$$\text{mass H}_2\text{O} = \left(5.00 \text{ mL soln} \times \frac{1.099 \text{ g}}{1 \text{ mL}}\right) - \left(0.03050 \text{ mol HCl} \times \frac{36.46 \text{ g HCl}}{1 \text{ mol HCl}}\right) = 4.38 \text{ g}$$

Now we determine the amount of H_2O and then the mole fraction of HCl.

$$\text{amount H}_2\text{O} = 4.38 \text{ g H}_2\text{O} \times \frac{1 \text{ mol H}_2\text{O}}{18.02 \text{ g H}_2\text{O}} = 0.243 \text{ mol H}_2\text{O}$$

$$\chi_{\text{HCl}} = \frac{0.03050 \text{ mol HCl}}{0.03050 \text{ mol HCl} + 0.243 \text{ mol H}_2\text{O}} = 0.112$$

115. (M)

(a) At 20 °C, the solubility of NaCl is 35.9 g NaCl / 100 g H_2O. We determine the mole fraction of H_2O in this solution

$$\text{amount } H_2O = 100 \text{ g } H_2O \times \frac{1 \text{ mol } H_2O}{18.02 \text{ g } H_2O} = 5.549 \text{ mol } H_2O$$

$$\text{amount NaCl} = 35.9 \text{ g NaCl} \times \frac{1 \text{ mol NaCl}}{58.44 \text{ g NaCl}} = 0.614 \text{ mol NaCl}$$

$$\chi_{\text{water}} = \frac{5.549 \text{ mol } H_2O}{0.614 \text{ mol NaCl} + 5.549 \text{ mol } H_2O} = 0.9004$$

The approximate relative humidity then will be 90% (90.04%), because the water vapor pressure above the NaCl saturated solution will be 90.04% of the vapor pressure of pure water at 20 °C.

(b) $CaCl_2 \cdot 6\, H_2O$ deliquesces if the relative humidity is over 32%. Thus, $CaCl_2 \cdot 6\, H_2O$ will deliquesce (i.e., it will absorb water from the atmosphere).

(c) If the substance in the bottom of the desiccator has high water solubility, its saturated solution will have a low χ_{water}, which in turn will produce a low relative humidity. Thus, a relative humidity lower than 32% is needed to keep $CaCl_2 \cdot 6\, H_2O$ dry.

116. (D)

(a) We first compute the molality of a 0.92% mass/volume solution, assuming the solution's density is about 1.00 g/mL, meaning that 100.0 mL solution has a mass of 100.0 g.

$$\text{molality} = \frac{0.92 \text{ g NaCl} \times \dfrac{1 \text{ mol NaCl}}{58.44 \text{ g NaCl}}}{(100.0 \text{ g soln} - 0.92 \text{ g NaCl}) \times \dfrac{1 \text{ kg solvent}}{1000 \text{ g}}} = 0.16 \text{ mol kg}^{-1}$$

Then we compute the freezing-point depression of this solution.

$$\Delta T_f = -iK_f m = \frac{-2.0 \text{ mol ions}}{\text{mol NaCl}} \times \frac{1.86 \text{ °C}}{\text{mol kg}^{-1}} \times 0.16 \text{ mol kg}^{-1} = -0.60 \text{ °C}$$

The van't Hoff factor of NaCl most likely is not equal to 2.0, but a bit less and thus the two definitions are in fair agreement.

(b) We calculate the amount of each solute, assume 1.00 L of solution has a mass of 1000 g, and subtract the mass of all solutes to determine the mass of solvent.

$$\text{amount NaCl ions} = 3.5 \text{ g NaCl} \times \frac{1 \text{ mol NaCl}}{58.44 \text{ g NaCl}} \times \frac{2 \text{ mol ions}}{1 \text{ mol NaCl}} = 0.12 \text{ mol ions}$$

$$\text{amount KCl ions} = 1.5 \text{ g} \times \frac{1 \text{ mol KCl}}{74.55 \text{ g KCl}} \times \frac{2 \text{ mol ions}}{1 \text{ mol KCl}} = 0.040 \text{ mol ions}$$

amount $Na_3C_6H_5O_7$ ions = $2.9 \text{ g} \times \dfrac{1 \text{ mol } Na_3C_6H_5 \ O_7}{258.07 \text{ g } Na_3C_6H_5O_7} \times \dfrac{4 \text{ mol ions}}{1 \text{ mol } Na_3C_6H_5O_7}$

amount $Na_3C_6H_5O_7$ ions = 0.045 mol ions

amount $C_6H_{12}O_6$ = $20.0 \text{ g } C_6H_{12}O_6 \times \dfrac{1 \text{ mol } C_6H_{12}O_6}{180.2 \text{ g } C_6H_{12}O_6}$ = $0.111 \text{ mol } C_6H_{12}O_6$

solvent mass = $1000.0 \text{ g} - (3.5 \text{ g} + 1.5 \text{ g} + 2.9 \text{ g} + 20.0 \text{ g}) = 972.1 \text{ g } H_2O$

solvent mass = $0.9721 \text{ kg } H_2O$

solution molality = $\dfrac{(0.120 + 0.040 + 0.045 + 0.111) \text{ mol}}{0.9721 \text{ kg } H_2O}$ = $0.325 \text{ mol kg}^{-1}$

$\Delta T_f = -K_f m = -1.86 \text{ °C/(mol kg}^{-1}) \times 0.325 \text{ mol kg}^{-1} = -0.60 \text{ °C}$

This again is close to the defined freezing point of –0.52 °C, with the error most likely arising from the van't Hoff factors not being integral. We can conclude, therefore, that the solution is isotonic.

SELF-ASSESSMENT EXERCISES

117. (E)

(a) x_B: Mole fraction of solute B

(b) P_A^*: Vapor pressure of pure solvent A

(c) K_f: Molal freezing point constant

(d) i: van't Hoff factor, a designation for the number of components per formula unit

(e) Activity: The effective (as opposed to stoichiometric) concentration of a solution, which takes into account solute-solute and solute-solvent interactions

118. (E)

(a) Henry's law: A law stating that, at a given temperature, the ratio between the concentration of a gas in a liquid and the partial pressure of that gas above the liquid is a constant

(b) Freezing-point depression: The decrease in the freezing point of a solvent compared to its normal freezing point because of the presence of a solute

(c) Recrystallization: A process of purifying a solid, whereby a solution saturated in the species that we need to purify is cooled just enough to fractionally crystallize the pure solid, while the impurities remain in the solution because the temperature is too high for them to crystallize

(d) Hydrated ion: An anion or cation surrounded by a cluster of water molecules which interact electrostatically

(e) Deliquescence: A phenomenon in which a solid begins to dissolve by the moisture that condenses on its surface from the water vapor in air

119. (E)

   (a) Molality and molarity: Molality is a measure of concentration expressed as the ratio of moles of solute and kilograms of solvent. Molarity is a measure of concentration expressed as the ratio between the moles of solute and the volume of the final solution.

   (b) Ideal and non-ideal solutions: In an ideal solution, the properties of the solution can be determined from the properties of the bulk phases of solutes and solvent. Furthermore, there are no interactions between solute particles. In case of non-ideal solutions, forces of attraction between unlike molecules exceed those between like molecules, and the properties of such solutions generally cannot be predicted from bulk pure components.

   (c) Unsaturated and supersaturated solution: An unsaturated solution is one that can still accommodate the dissolution of more solute in it. A supersaturated solution is one that for various reasons has more solute dissolved in it than otherwise would be possible at that given temperature.

   (d) Fractional crystallization and fractional distillation: Fractional crystallization is a process of purifying a solid, whereby a solution saturated in the species that we need to purify is cooled just enough to fractionally crystallize the pure solid. Fractional distillation is a process of purifying a mixture of solvents by raising and/or lowering the temperature just enough to selectively distill away a lower boiling point component of a solution.

   (e) Osmosis and reverse osmosis: Osmosis is the process by which water migrates across a water-permeable membrane from one side with lower molality to the side with higher ionic molality. Reverse osmosis is the process of forcing water to go from a region of high molality to a lower one by exerting a pressure greater than the osmotic pressure, thereby concentrating the solution with the higher molality.

120. (E) The answer is (b), because molality is moles solute/kg solvent. Assuming a volume of 1 L, at a concentration of 0.010 mol kg^{-1}, the mass of the water ($\sim$1 kg) is nearly the same as the volume of the solution (1 L).

121. (E) The answer is (d), because the other choices either don't form a solution because they are immiscible or the solute-solvent interactions are stronger than intramolecular interactions for either of the pure solute or solvent, making the solutions non-ideal.

122. (E) The answer is (a). As partial pressure of the gas increases, Henry's law shows that the concentration of the gas in the liquid increases.

123. (E) The answer is (d), because the total ionic molality of the $MgCl_2$ is $3 \times 0.008 = 0.024$.

124. (E) The answer is (c), because nothing in the information provided suggests that the concentrations of the two volatile species are the same.

125. (E) The mass of NH_4Cl is: 1.12 mol $NH_4Cl \times$ (53.45 g/mol) = 59.86 g. Solubility is 59.86 g NH_4Cl / 150.0 g H_2O = 0.40, or 40 g/100 g.

   Based on Figure 14-10, the concentration limit of NH_4Cl is 42 g per 100 g of H_2O. Since the amount of NH_4Cl is below the solubility limit, no crystals will form.

126. (M)

(a) $\left[Na^+\right] = \dfrac{0.92 \text{ g NaCl}}{100 \text{ mL } H_2O} \times \dfrac{1 \text{ mol NaCl}}{58.45 \text{ g NaCl}} \times \dfrac{1 \text{ mol Na}^+}{1 \text{ mol NaCl}} \times \dfrac{1000 \text{ mL}}{1 \text{ L}} = 0.16 \text{ M Na}^+$

(b) total molarity of ions $= 0.16 \text{ M Na}^+ \times \dfrac{1 \text{ mol NaCl}}{1 \text{ mol Na}^+} \times \dfrac{2 \text{ mol ions}}{1 \text{ mol NaCl}} = 0.32 \text{ M}$

(c) $\Pi = MRT = (0.32 \text{ M})(0.08206 \text{ L} \cdot \text{atm} \cdot \text{K}^{-1})(310 \text{ K}) = 8.1 \text{ atm}$

(d) Determine the solution molality first, then determine freezing-point depression.

molality $H_2O = \dfrac{0.32 \text{ mol ions}}{1 \text{ L solution}} \times \dfrac{1 \text{ L solution}}{1.005 \text{ kg solution}} = 0.3184 \text{ mol kg}^{-1}$

$\Delta_f T = \left(-1.86 \, {}^\circ\text{C}/(\text{mol kg}^{-1})\right)\left(0.3184 \text{ mol kg}^{-1}\right) = -0.60 \, {}^\circ\text{C}$

127. (M)

(a)

$[C_3H_8O_3] = \dfrac{62.0 \text{ g } C_3H_8O_3}{100 \text{ g sol'n}} \times \dfrac{1.159 \text{ g sol'n}}{1 \text{ mL sol'n}} \times \dfrac{1000 \text{ mL sol'n}}{1 \text{ L sol'n}} \times \dfrac{1 \text{ mol } C_3H_8O_3}{92.11 \text{ g } C_3H_8O_3}$

$= 7.80 \text{ M } C_3H_8O_3$

(b)

$[H_2O] = \dfrac{38.0 \text{ g } H_2O}{100 \text{ g sol'n}} \times \dfrac{1.159 \text{ g sol'n}}{1 \text{ mL sol'n}} \times \dfrac{1000 \text{ mL sol'n}}{1 \text{ L sol'n}} \times \dfrac{1 \text{ mol } H_2O}{18.02 \text{ g } H_2O}$

$= 24.4 \text{ M } H_2O$

(c)

$[H_2O] = \dfrac{38.0 \text{ g } H_2O}{62.0 \text{ g } C_3H_8O_3} \times \dfrac{1000 \text{ g solvent}}{1 \text{ kg solvent}} \times \dfrac{1 \text{ mol } H_2O}{18.02 \text{ g } H_2O}$

$= 34.0 \text{ mol kg}^{-1} H_2O$

(d) We can determine the moles of $C_3H_8O_3$ and H_2O from the above calculations.
moles of $H_2O = 2.11$ mol.
moles of $C_3H_8O_3 = 0.673$ mol.

$x_{C_3H_8O_3} = \dfrac{0.673 \text{ mol } C_3H_8O_3}{0.673 \text{ mol } C_3H_8O_3 + 2.11 \text{ mol } H_2O} = 0.242$

(e) mol% $H_2O = \dfrac{2.11 \text{ mol } H_2O}{0.673 \text{ mol } C_3H_8O_3 + 2.11 \text{ mol } H_2O} \times 100 = 75.8\%$

128. (E)

(1) Solution with lowest conductivity: (b) 0.15 mol kg^{-1} $C_{12}H_{22}O_{11}$, because it is a non-electrolyte.

(2) Lowest boiling point: (d) 0.05 m NaCl, because the molality of the solute is the smallest, making boiling-point elevation the smallest value.

(3) Highest vapor pressure of water: (d), for the same reason as above.

(4) Lowest freezing point: (a), because the molality of the solute is the highest (2×0.10 m).

129. (E) The answer is (c). It shows solvation of individual ions by oriented water molecules.

130. (E) The answer is (b), because the charge in all species is the same (+1 or –1), but F$^-$ is the smallest.

131. (E) The magnitude of $\Delta_{lattice}H$ is larger than the sum of the $\Delta_{hydration}H$ of the individual ions. Since the test tube turns cold, dissolution of NH_4Cl is endothermic, which means that the final energy of the system, the hydration of the individual ions, is less than the initial energy of the system, which is the lattice energy of the solid.

132. (E) The answer is (a). Lowering temperature increases solubility.

133. (E) The answer is (b), because the HCl dissociates completely in water to give cations and anions, which are then solvated with water (and are none-volatile).

134. (E) The answer is (a). Use Raoult's law to determine the mole fraction:

$$P_{C_6H_{14}} = x_{C_6H_{14}} \cdot P^*_{C_6H_{14}}$$
$$600 \text{ mmHg} = x_{solute} \cdot 760 \text{ mmHg}$$
$$x_{C_6H_{14}} = 0.789$$
$$x_{solute} = 1 - 0.789 = 0.211$$

135. (M) The answer is (e).
$$\Pi = MRT$$
$$\Pi = (0.312 \text{ M})(0.08206 \text{ L atm K}^{-1})(348 \text{ K}) = 8.91 \text{ atm}$$
$$P(\text{bar}) = 8.91 \text{ atm} \times \frac{1.0135 \text{ bar}}{1 \text{ atm}} = 9.03 \text{ bar}$$

136. (E) The answer is (c).
$$10.5 \text{ mol H}_2\text{O} \times \frac{18.0 \text{ g H}_2\text{O}}{1 \text{ mol H}_2\text{O}} = 189 \text{ g H}_2\text{O}$$
$$\text{mass\%} = \frac{23.4}{189 + 23.4} \times 100 = 11.0\%$$

137. (M) Clearly the concept of concentration is overarching in this discussion. It can be broken down into several subtopics: mass percent, volume percent, mass/volume percent, parts per million/trillion, mole fraction/percent, molarity, molality. These concepts can be further defined with the more basic terms of mole, mass and volume.

138. (M) The concept of colligative properties has four major components: boiling-point elevation, freezing-point depression, vapor pressure lowering, and osmotic pressure. They are all related to each other by the effects of solute concentration.

CHAPTER 15
PRINCIPLES OF CHEMICAL EQUILIBRIUM
PRACTICE EXAMPLES

1A **(E)** The reaction is as follows:

$2\,Cu^{2+}(aq) + Sn^{2+}(aq) \rightleftharpoons 2\,Cu^{+}(aq) + Sn^{4+}(aq)$

Therefore, the equilibrium expression is as follows:

$$K = \frac{\left[Cu^{+}\right]^2 \left[Sn^{4+}\right]}{\left[Cu^{2+}\right]^2 \left[Sn^{2+}\right]}$$

Rearranging and solving for Cu^{2+}, the following expression is obtained:

$$\left[Cu^{2+}\right] = \left(\frac{\left[Cu^{+}\right]^2 \left[Sn^{4+}\right]}{K \left[Sn^{2+}\right]}\right)^{1/2} = \left(\frac{x^2 \cdot x}{(1.48)\,x}\right)^{1/2} = \frac{x}{1.22}$$

1B **(E)** The reaction is as follows:

$2\,Fe^{3+}(aq) + Hg_2^{2+}(aq) \rightleftharpoons 2\,Fe^{2+}(aq) + 2\,Hg^{2+}(aq)$

Therefore, the equilibrium expression is as follows:

$$K = \frac{\left[Fe^{2+}\right]^2 \left[Hg^{2+}\right]^2}{\left[Fe^{3+}\right]^2 \left[Hg_2^{2+}\right]} = \frac{(0.0025)^2 (0.0018)^2}{(0.015)^2 (x)} = 9.14 \times 10^{-6}$$

Rearranging and solving for Hg_2^{2+}, the following expression is obtained:

$$\left[Hg_2^{2+}\right] = \frac{\left[Fe^{2+}\right]^2 \left[Hg^{2+}\right]^2}{\left[Fe^{3+}\right]^2 \cdot K} = \frac{(0.0025)^2 (0.0018)^2}{(0.015)^2 (9.14 \times 10^{-6})} = 0.009847 \approx 0.0098\ M$$

2A **(E)** The example gives $\underline{K_c} = 5.8 \times 10^5$ for the reaction $N_2(g) + 3\,H_2(g) \rightleftharpoons 2\,NH_3(g)$.

The reaction we are considering is one-third of this reaction. If we divide the reaction by 3, we should take the cube root of the equilibrium constant to obtain the value of the equilibrium constant for the "divided" reaction: $K_{c3} = \sqrt[3]{K_c} = \sqrt[3]{5.8 \times 10^5} = 8.3 \times 10^2$

2B **(E)** First we reverse the given reaction to put $NO_2(g)$ on the reactant side. The new equilibrium constant is the inverse of the given one.

$NO_2(g) \rightleftharpoons NO(g) + \tfrac{1}{2}O_2(g)$ $\qquad$ $K_c' = 1/(1.2 \times 10^2) = 0.0083$

Then we double the reaction to obtain 2 moles of $NO_2(g)$ as reactant. The equilibrium constant is then raised to the second power.

$2\,NO_2(g) \rightleftharpoons 2\,NO(g) + O_2(g)$ $\qquad$ $K_c = (0.00833)^2 = 6.9 \times 10^{-5}$

3A **(E)** We remember that neither solids, such as $Ca_5(PO_4)_3OH(s)$, nor liquids, such as $H_2O(l)$, appear in the equilibrium constant expression. Concentrations of products appear in the numerator, those of reactants in the denominator. $K_c = \dfrac{\left[Ca^{2+} \right]^5 \left[HPO_4^{\,2-} \right]^3}{\left[H^+ \right]^4}$

3B **(E)** First we write the balanced chemical equation for the reaction. Then we write the equilibrium constant expression, remembering that gases appear in the K_p expression, but pure liquids and pure solids do not.

$$3\,Fe(s) + 4\,H_2O(g) \rightleftharpoons Fe_3O_4(s) + 4\,H_2(g)$$

$$K_p = \frac{\{P(H_2)\}^4}{\{P(H_2O)\}^4}$$

4A **(E)** We use the expression $K_p = K_c(RT)^{\Delta v_{gas}}$. In this case, $\Delta v_{gas} = 3 + 1 - 2 = 2$ and thus we have

$$K_p = K_c(RT)^2 = 2.8 \times 10^{-9} \times (0.08314 \times 298)^2 = 1.7 \times 10^{-6}$$

4B **(M)** We begin by writing the K_p expression. We then substitute $P = (n/V)RT = [concentration]RT$ for each pressure. We collect terms to obtain an expression relating K_c and K_p, into which we substitute to find the value of K_c.

$$K_p = \frac{\{P(H_2)\}^2\{P(S_2)\}}{\{P(H_2S)\}^2} = \frac{([H_2]RT)^2([S_2]RT)}{([H_2S]RT)^2} = \frac{[H_2]^2[S_2]}{[H_2S]^2}RT = K_cRT$$

The same result can be obtained by using $K_p = K_c(RT)^{\Delta v_{gas}}$, since $\Delta v_{gas} = 2 + 1 - 2 = +1$.

$$K_c = \frac{K_p}{RT} = \frac{1.2 \times 10^{-2}}{0.08314 \times (1065 + 273)} = 1.1 \times 10^{-4}$$

But the reaction has been reversed and halved. Thus $K_{final} = \sqrt{\dfrac{1}{K_c}} = \sqrt{\dfrac{1}{1.1 \times 10^{-4}}} = \sqrt{9091} = 95$

5A **(M)** We compute the value of Q_c. Each concentration equals the mass (m) of the substance divided by its molar mass (this quotient is the amount of the substance in moles) and further divided by the volume of the container.

$$Q_c = \frac{[CO_2][H_2]}{[CO][H_2O]} = \frac{\dfrac{m \times \dfrac{1\ mol\ CO_2}{44.0\ g\ CO_2}}{V} \times \dfrac{m \times \dfrac{1\ mol\ H_2}{2.0\ g\ H_2}}{V}}{\dfrac{m \times \dfrac{1\ mol\ CO}{28.0\ g\ CO}}{V} \times \dfrac{m \times \dfrac{1\ mol\ H_2O}{18.0\ g\ H_2O}}{V}} = \frac{\dfrac{1}{44.0 \times 2.0}}{\dfrac{1}{28.0 \times 18.0}} = \frac{28.0 \times 18.0}{44.0 \times 2.0} = 5.7 > 1.00 = K_c$$

(In evaluating the expression above, we cancelled the equal values of V, and we also cancelled the equal values of m.) Because the value of Q_c is larger than the value of K_c, the reaction will proceed to the left to reach a state of equilibrium. Thus, at equilibrium there will be greater quantities of reactants, and smaller quantities of products than there were initially.

5B **(M)** We compare the value of the reaction quotient, Q_p, to that of K_p.

$$Q_p = \frac{\{P(PCl_3)\}\{P(Cl_2)\}}{\{P(PCl_5)\}} = \frac{2.19 \times 0.88}{19.7} = 0.098$$

$$K_p = K_c (RT)^{2-1} = K_c (RT)^1 = 0.0454 \times (0.08314 \times (261 + 273))^1 = 2.02$$

Because $Q_c < K_c$, the net reaction will proceed to the right, forming products and consuming reactants.

6A **(E)** $O_2(g)$ is a reactant. The equilibrium system will shift right, forming product in an attempt to consume some of the added $O_2(g)$ reactant. Looked at in another way, $[O_2]$ is increased above its equilibrium value by the addition of oxygen. This makes Q_c smaller than K_c. (The $[O_2]$ is in the denominator of the expression.) And the system shifts right to drive Q_c back up to K_c, at which point equilibrium will have been achieved.

6B **(M)**

(a) The position of an equilibrium mixture is affected only by changing the concentration of substances that appear in the equilibrium constant expression, $K_c = [CO_2]$. Since $CaO(s)$ is a pure solid, its concentration does not appear in the equilibrium constant expression and thus adding extra $CaO(s)$ will have no direct effect on the position of equilibrium.

(b) The addition of $CO_2(g)$ will increase $[CO_2]$ above its equilibrium value. The reaction will shift left to alleviate this increase, causing some $CaCO_3(s)$ to form.

(c) Since $CaCO_3(s)$ is a pure solid like $CaO(s)$, its concentration does not appear in the equilibrium constant expression and thus the addition of any solid $CaCO_3$ to an equilibrium mixture will not have an effect upon the position of equilibrium.

7A **(E)** We know that a decrease in volume or an increase in pressure of an equilibrium mixture of gases causes a net reaction in the direction producing the smaller number of moles of gas. In the reaction in question, that direction is to the left: one mole of $N_2O_4(g)$ is formed when two moles of $NO_2(g)$ combine. Thus, decreasing the cylinder volume would have the initial effect of doubling both $[N_2O_4]$ and $[NO_2]$. In order to reestablish equilibrium, some NO_2 will then be converted into N_2O_4. Note, however, that the NO_2 concentration will still ultimately end up being higher than it was prior to pressurization.

7B **(E)** In the balanced chemical equation for the chemical reaction, $\Delta v_{gas} = (1+1) - (1+1) = 0$.

As a consequence, a change in overall volume or total gas pressure will have no effect on the position of equilibrium. In the equilibrium constant expression, the two partial pressures in the numerator will be affected to exactly the same degree, as will the two partial pressures in the denominator, and, as a result, Q_p will continue to equal K_p.

8A **(E)** The cited reaction is endothermic. Raising the temperature on an equilibrium mixture favors the endothermic reaction. Thus, $N_2O_4(g)$ should decompose more completely at higher temperatures and the amount of $NO_2(g)$ formed from a given amount of $N_2O_4(g)$ will be greater at high temperatures than at low ones.

8B **(E)** The $NH_3(g)$ formation reaction is $\frac{1}{2}N_2(g) + \frac{3}{2}H_2(g) \rightarrow NH_3(g)$, $\Delta_r H^\circ = -46.11$ kJ/mol. This reaction is an exothermic reaction. Lowering temperature causes a shift in the direction of this exothermic reaction to the right toward products. Thus, the equilibrium $[NH_3(g)]$ will be greater at 100°C.

9A **(E)** We write the expression for K_c and then substitute expressions for molar concentrations.

$$K_c = \frac{[H_2]^2[S_2]}{[H_2S]^2} = \frac{\left(\dfrac{0.22}{3.00}\right)^2 \dfrac{0.11}{3.00}}{\left(\dfrac{2.78}{3.00}\right)^2} = 2.3 \times 10^{-4}$$

9B **(M)** We write the equilibrium constant expression and solve for $[N_2O_4]$.

$$K_c = 4.61 \times 10^{-3} = \frac{[NO_2]^2}{[N_2O_4]} \qquad [N_2O_4] = \frac{[NO_2]^2}{4.61 \times 10^{-3}} = \frac{(0.0236)^2}{4.61 \times 10^{-3}} = 0.121 \text{ M}$$

Then we determine the mass of N_2O_4 present in 2.26 L.

$$N_2O_4 \text{ mass} = 2.26 \text{ L} \times \frac{0.121 \text{ mol } N_2O_4}{1 \text{ L}} \times \frac{92.01 \text{ g } N_2O_4}{1 \text{ mol } N_2O_4} = 25.2 \text{ g } N_2O_4$$

10A **(M)** We use the initial-change-equilibrium setup to establish the amount of each substance at equilibrium. We then label each entry in the table in the order of its determination (1st, 2nd, 3rd, 4th, 5th), to better illustrate the technique. We know the initial amounts of all substances (1st). There are no products at the start.

Because "initial" + "change" = "equilibrium", the equilibrium amount (2nd) of $Br_2(g)$ enables us to determine "change" (3rd) for $Br_2(g)$. We then use stoichiometry to write other entries (4th) on the "change" line. And finally, we determine the remaining equilibrium amounts (5th).

Reaction:	$2 \text{ NOBr}(g)$	$\rightleftharpoons$	$2 \text{ NO}(g)$	$+$	$Br_2(g)$
Initial:	1.86 mol (1st)		0.00 mol (1st)		0.00 mol (1st)
Change:	−0.164 mol (4th)		+0.164 mol (4th)		+0.082 mol (3rd)
Equil.:	1.70 mol (5th)		0.164 mol (5th)		0.082 mol (2nd)

$$K_c = \frac{[NO]^2[Br_2]}{[NOBr]^2} = \frac{\left(\dfrac{0.164}{5.00}\right)^2\left(\dfrac{0.082 \text{ mol}}{5.00}\right)}{\left(\dfrac{1.70}{5.00}\right)^2} = 1.5\times10^{-4}$$

Here, $\Delta v_{gas} = 2+1-2 = +1$. $K_p = K_c(RT)^{+1} = 1.5\times10^{-4}\times(0.08314\times298) = 3.7\times10^{-3}$

10B (M) Use the amounts stated in the problem to determine the equilibrium concentration for each substance.

Reaction:	$2\,SO_3(g)$	$\rightleftharpoons$	$2\,SO_2(g)$	$+$	$O_2(g)$
Initial:	0 mol		0.100 mol		0.100 mol
Changes:	+0.0916 mol		−0.0916 mol		−0.0916/2 mol
Equil.:	0.0916 mol		0.0084 mol		0.0542 mol
Concentrations:	$\dfrac{0.0916 \text{ mol}}{1.52 \text{ L}}$		$\dfrac{0.0084 \text{ mol}}{1.52 \text{ L}}$		$\dfrac{0.0542 \text{ mol}}{1.52 \text{ L}}$
Concentrations:	0.0603 M		0.0055 M		0.0357 M

We use these values to compute K_c for the reaction and then the relationship $K_p = K_c(RT)^{\Delta v_{gas}}$ (with $\Delta v_{gas} = 2+1-2 = +1$) to determine the value of K_p.

$$K_c = \frac{[SO_2]^2[O_2]}{[SO_3]^2} = \frac{(0.0055)^2(0.0357)}{(0.0603)^2} = 3.0\times10^{-4}$$

$$K_p = 3.0\times10^{-4}\times(0.08314\times900) \simeq 0.022$$

11A (M) The equilibrium constant expression is $K_p = P\{H_2O\}P\{CO_2\} = 0.231$ at 100 °C. From the balanced chemical equation, we see that one mole of $H_2O(g)$ is formed for each mole of $CO_2(g)$ produced. Consequently, $P\{H_2O\} = P\{CO_2\}$ and $K_p = (P\{CO_2\})^2$. We solve this expression for $P\{CO_2\}$: $P\{CO_2\} = \sqrt{(P\{CO_2\})^2} = \sqrt{K_p} = \sqrt{0.231} = 0.481$ bar.

11B (M) The equation for the reaction is $NH_4HS(s) \rightleftharpoons NH_3(g) + H_2S(g)$, $K_p = 0.108$ at 25 °C. The two partial pressures do not have to be equal at equilibrium. The only instance in which they must be equal is when the two gases come solely from the decomposition of $NH_4HS(s)$. In this case, some of the $NH_3(g)$ has come from another source. We can obtain the pressure of $H_2S(g)$ by substitution into the equilibrium constant expression, since we are given the equilibrium pressure of $NH_3(g)$.

$$K_p = P\{H_2S\}P\{NH_3\} = 0.108 = P\{H_2S\}\times0.500 \text{ bar } NH_3 \quad P\{H_2S\} = \frac{0.108}{0.500} = 0.216 \text{ bar}$$

So, $P_{total} = P_{H_2S} + P_{NH_3} = 0.216 \text{ bar} + 0.500 \text{ bar} = 0.716$ bar

12A **(M)** We set up this problem in the same manner that we have previously employed, namely designating the equilibrium amount of HI as $2x$. (Note that we have used the same multipliers for x as the stoichiometric coefficients.)

Equation:	$H_2(g)$	$+$	$I_2(g)$	$\rightleftharpoons$	$2\,HI(g)$
Initial:	0.150 mol		0.200 mol		0 mol
Changes:	$-x$ mol		$-x$ mol		$+2x$ mol
Equil:	$(0.150-x)$ mol		$(0.200-x)$ mol		$2x$ mol

$$K_c = \frac{\left(\dfrac{2x}{15.0}\right)^2}{\dfrac{0.150-x}{15.0} \times \dfrac{0.200-x}{15.0}} = \frac{(2x)^2}{(0.150-x)(0.200-x)} = 50.2$$

We substitute these terms into the equilibrium constant expression and solve for x.

$$4x^2 = (0.150-x)(0.200-x)50.2 = 50.2(0.0300 - 0.350x + x^2) = 1.51 - 17.6x + 50.2x^2$$

$$0 = 46.2x^2 - 17.6x + 1.51 \qquad \text{Now we use the quadratic equation to determine the value of } x.$$

$$x = \frac{-b \pm \sqrt{b^2 - 4ac}}{2a} = \frac{17.6 \pm \sqrt{(17.6)^2 - 4 \times 46.2 \times 1.51}}{2 \times 46.2} = \frac{17.6 \pm 5.54}{92.4} = 0.250 \text{ or } 0.131$$

The first root cannot be used because it would afford a negative amount of H_2 (namely, $0.150 - 0.250 = -0.100$). Thus, we have $2 \times 0.131 = 0.262$ mol HI at equilibrium. We check by substituting the amounts into the K_c expression. (Notice that the volumes cancel.) The slight disagreement in the two values (52 compared to 50.2) is the result of rounding error.

$$K_c = \frac{(0.262)^2}{(0.150-0.131)(0.200-0.131)} = \frac{0.0686}{0.019 \times 0.069} = 52$$

12B **(D)**

(a) The equation for the reaction is $N_2O_4(g) \rightleftharpoons 2\,NO_2(g)$ and $K_c = 4.61 \times 10^{-3}$ at 25 °C. In the example, this reaction is conducted in a 0.372 L flask. The effect of moving the mixture to the larger, 10.0 L container is that the reaction will be shifted to produce a greater number of moles of gas. Thus, $NO_2(g)$ will be produced and $N_2O_4(g)$ will dissociate. Consequently, the amount of N_2O_4 will decrease.

(b) The equilibrium constant expression, substituting 10.0 L for 0.372 L, follows.

$$K_c = \frac{[NO_2]^2}{[N_2O_4]} = \frac{\left(\dfrac{2x}{10.0}\right)^2}{\dfrac{0.0240-x}{10.0}} = \frac{4x^2}{10.0(0.0240-x)} = 4.61 \times 10^{-3}$$

This can be solved with the quadratic equation, and the sensible result is $x = 0.0118$ moles. We can attempt the method of successive approximations. *First*, assume that $x \ll 0.0240$. We obtain:

$$x = \frac{\sqrt{4.61 \times 10^{-3} \times 10.0\,(0.0240 - 0)}}{4} = \sqrt{4.61 \times 10^{-3} \times 2.50\,(0.0240 - 0)} = 0.0166$$

Clearly x is not much smaller than 0.0240. So, *second*, assume $x \approx 0.0166$. We obtain:

$$x = \sqrt{4.61 \times 10^{-3} \times 2.50\,(0.0240 - 0.0166)} = 0.00925$$

This assumption is not valid either. So, *third*, assume $x \approx 0.00925$. We obtain:

$$x = \sqrt{4.61 \times 10^{-3} \times 2.50\,(0.0240 - 0.00925)} = 0.0130$$

Notice that after each cycle the value we obtain for x gets closer to the value obtained from the roots of the equation. The values from the next several cycles follow.

Cycle	4th	5th	6th	7th	8th	9th	10th	11th
x value	0.0112	0.0121	0.0117	0.0119	0.01181	0.01186	0.01183	0.01184

The amount of N_2O_4 at equilibrium is 0.0118 mol, less than the 0.0210 mol N_2O_4 at equilibrium in the 0.372 L flask, as predicted.

13A **(M)** Again we base our solution on the balanced chemical equation.

Equation: $Ag^+(aq) + Fe^{2+}(aq) \rightleftharpoons Fe^{3+}(aq) + Ag(s)$ $K_c = 2.98$

Initial:	0 M	0 M	1.20 M
Changes:	$+x$ M	$+x$ M	$-x$ M
Equil:	x M	x M	$(1.20 - x)$ M

$$K_c = \frac{\left[Fe^{3+}\right]}{\left[Ag^+\right]\left[Fe^{2+}\right]} = 2.98 = \frac{1.20 - x}{x^2} \quad 2.98\,x^2 = 1.20 - x \quad 0 = 2.98x^2 + x - 1.20$$

We use the quadratic formula to obtain a solution.

$$x = \frac{-b \pm \sqrt{b^2 - 4ac}}{2a} = \frac{-1.00 \pm \sqrt{(1.00)^2 + 4 \times 2.98 \times 1.20}}{2 \times 2.98} = \frac{-1.00 \pm 3.91}{5.96} = 0.488 \text{ M or } -0.824 \text{ M}$$

A negative root makes no physical sense. We obtain the equilibrium concentrations from x.

$$\left[Ag^+\right] = \left[Fe^{2+}\right] = 0.488 \text{ M} \qquad \left[Fe^{3+}\right] = 1.20 - 0.488 = 0.71 \text{ M}$$

13B **(M)** We first calculate the value of Q_c to determine the direction of the reaction.

$$Q_c = \frac{\left[V^{2+}\right]\left[Cr^{3+}\right]}{\left[V^{3+}\right]\left[Cr^{2+}\right]} = \frac{0.150 \times 0.150}{0.0100 \times 0.0100} = 225 < 7.2 \times 10^2 = K_c$$

Because the reaction quotient has a smaller value than the equilibrium constant, a net reaction to the right will occur. We now set up this solution as we have others, heretofore, based on the balanced chemical equation.

	$V^{3+}(aq)$	+	$Cr^{2+}(aq)$	$\rightleftharpoons$	$V^{2+}(aq)$	+	$Cr^{3+}(aq)$
initial	0.0100 M		0.0100 M		0.150 M		0.150 M
changes	$-x$ M		$-x$ M		$+x$ M		$+x$ M
equil	$(0.0100 - x)$M		$(0.0100 - x)$M		$(0.150 + x)$M		$(0.150 + x)$M

$$K_c = \frac{\left[V^{2+}\right]\left[Cr^{3+}\right]}{\left[V^{3+}\right]\left[Cr^{2+}\right]} = \frac{(0.150+x) \times (0.150+x)}{(0.0100-x) \times (0.0100-x)} = 7.2 \times 10^2 = \left(\frac{0.150+x}{0.0100-x}\right)^2$$

If we take the square root of both sides of this expression, we obtain

$$\sqrt{7.2 \times 10^2} = \frac{0.150 + x}{0.0100 - x} = 27$$

$0.150 + x = 0.27 - 27x$ which becomes $28x = 0.12$ and yields 0.0043 M. Then the equilibrium concentrations are: $\left[V^{3+}\right] = \left[Cr^{2+}\right] = 0.0100\ M - 0.0043\ M = 0.0057\ M$

$$\left[V^{2+}\right] = \left[Cr^{3+}\right] = 0.150\ M + 0.0043\ M = 0.154\ M$$

INTEGRATIVE EXAMPLE

A. **(E)** We will determine the concentration of F6P and the final enthalpy by adding the two reactions:

$$C_6H_{12}O_6 + ATP \rightleftharpoons G6P + ADP$$

$$\underline{\phantom{C_6H_{12}O_6 + ATP} G6P \rightleftharpoons F6P }$$

$$C_6H_{12}O_6 + ATP \rightleftharpoons ADP + F6P$$

$$\Delta H_{TOT} = -19.74\ kJ\ mol^{-1} + 2.84\ kJ\ mol^{-1} = -16.9\ kJ\ mol^{-1}$$

Since the overall reaction is obtained by adding the two individual reactions, then the overall reaction equilibrium constant is the product of the two individual K values. That is, $K = K_1 \cdot K_2 = 1278$

The equilibrium concentrations of the reactants and products is determined as follows:

	$C_6H_{12}O_6$	+	ATP	$\rightleftharpoons$	ADP	+	F6P
Initial	1.20×10^{-6}		1×10^{-4}		1×10^{-2}		0
Change	$-x$		$-x$		$+x$		$+x$
Equil	$1.20 \times 10^{-6} - x$		$1 \times 10^{-4} - x$		$1 \times 10^{-2} + x$		x

$$K = \frac{[ADP][F6P]}{[C_6H_{12}O_6][ATP]}$$

$$1278 = \frac{(1\times10^{-2}+x)(x)}{(1.20\times10^{-6}-x)(1\times10^{-4}-x)} = \frac{1.0\times10^{-2}x+x^2}{1.2\times10^{-10}-1.012\times10^{-4}x+x^2}$$

Expanding and rearranging the above equation yields the following second-order polynomial:

$1277\, x^2 - 0.1393\, x + 1.534 \times 10^{-7} = 0$

Using the quadratic equation to solve for x, we obtain two roots: $x = 1.113\times10^{-6}$ and 1.080×10^{-4}. Only the first one makes physical sense, because it is less than the initial value of $C_6H_{12}O_6$. Therefore, $[F6P]_{eq} = 1.113 \times 10^{-6}$.

During a fever, the body generates heat. Since the net reaction above is exothermic, Le Châtelier's principle would force the equilibrium to the left, reducing the amount of F6P generated.

B. **(E)**

(a) The ideal gas law can be used for this reaction, since we are relating vapor pressure and concentration. Since $K = 3.3 \times 10^{-29}$ for decomposition of Br_2 to Br (very small), then it can be ignored.

$$V = \frac{nRT}{P} = \frac{(0.100\text{ mol})(0.08206\text{ L atm K}^{-1})(298.15\text{ K})}{0.289\text{ atm}} = 8.47\text{ L}$$

(b) At 1000 K, there is much more Br being generated from the decomposition of Br_2. However, K is still rather small, and this decomposition does not notably affect the volume needed.

EXERCISES

Writing Equilibrium Constants Expressions

1. **(E)**

(a) $2\, COF_2(g) \rightleftharpoons CO_2(g) + CF_4(g)$ $\qquad K_c = \dfrac{[CO_2][CF_4]}{[COF_2]^2}$

(b) $Cu(s) + 2\, Ag^+(aq) \rightleftharpoons Cu^{2+}(aq) + 2\, Ag(s)$ $\qquad K_c = \dfrac{[Cu^{2+}]}{[Ag^+]^2}$

(c) $S_2O_8^{2-}(aq) + 2\, Fe^{2+}(aq) \rightleftharpoons 2\, SO_4^{2-}(aq) + 2\, Fe^{3+}(aq)$ $\qquad K_c = \dfrac{[SO_4^{2-}]^2[Fe^{3+}]^2}{[S_2O_8^{2-}][Fe^{2+}]^2}$

2. **(E)**

(a) $4 NH_3(g) + 3 O_2(g) \rightleftharpoons 2 N_2(g) + 6 H_2O(g)$

$$K_p = \frac{P\{N_2\}^2 \cdot P\{H_2O\}^6}{P\{NH_3\}^4 \cdot P\{O_2\}^3}$$

(b) $7 H_2(g) + 2 NO_2(g) \rightleftharpoons 2 NH_3(g) + 4 H_2O(g)$

$$K_p = \frac{P\{NH_3\}^2 \cdot P\{H_2O\}^4}{P\{H_2\}^7 \cdot P\{NO_2\}^2}$$

(c) $N_2(g) + Na_2CO_3(s) + 4 C(s) \rightleftharpoons 2 NaCN(s) + 3 CO(g)$

$$K_c = \frac{[CO]^3}{[N_2]}$$

3. **(E)**

(a) $K_c = \dfrac{[NO_2]^2}{[NO]^2[O_2]}$ **(b)** $K_c = \dfrac{[Zn^{2+}]}{[Ag^+]^2}$ **(c)** $K_c = \dfrac{[OH^-]^2}{[CO_3^{2-}]}$

4. **(E)**

(a) $K_p = \dfrac{P\{CH_4\}P\{H_2S\}^2}{P\{CS_2\}P\{H_2\}^4}$ **(b)** $K_p = P\{O_2\}^{1/2}$ **(c)** $K_p = P\{CO_2\}P\{H_2O\}$

5. **(E)** In each case we write the equation for the formation reaction and then the equilibrium constant expression, K_c, for that reaction.

(a) $\frac{1}{2}H_2(g) + \frac{1}{2}F_2(g) \rightleftharpoons HF(g)$ $K_c = \dfrac{[HF]}{[H_2]^{1/2}[F_2]^{1/2}}$

(b) $N_2(g) + 3 H_2(g) \rightleftharpoons 2 NH_3(g)$ $K_c = \dfrac{[NH_3]^2}{[N_2][H_2]^3}$

(c) $2 N_2(g) + O_2(g) \rightleftharpoons 2 N_2O(g)$ $K_c = \dfrac{[N_2O]^2}{[N_2]^2[O_2]}$

(d) $\frac{1}{2}Cl_2(g) + \frac{3}{2}F_2(g) \rightleftharpoons ClF_3(l)$ $K_c = \dfrac{1}{[Cl_2]^{1/2}[F_2]^{3/2}}$

6. **(E)** In each case we write the equation for the formation reaction and then the equilibrium constant expression, K_p, for that reaction.

(a) $\frac{1}{2}N_2(g) + \frac{1}{2}O_2(g) + \frac{1}{2}Cl_2(g) \rightleftharpoons NOCl(g)$ $K_p = \dfrac{[P_{NOCl}]}{[P_{N_2}]^{1/2}[P_{O_2}]^{1/2}[P_{Cl_2}]^{1/2}}$

(b) $N_2(g) + 2 O_2(g) + Cl_2(g) \rightleftharpoons 2 ClNO_2(g)$ $K_p = \dfrac{[P_{ClNO_2}]^2}{[P_{N_2}][P_{O_2}]^2[P_{Cl_2}]}$

(c) $\quad N_2(g) + 2 H_2(g) \rightleftharpoons N_2H_4(g) \qquad\qquad K_p = \dfrac{P_{N_2H_4}}{\left[P_{N_2}\right]\left[P_{H_2}\right]^2}$

(d) $\quad \frac{1}{2} N_2(g) + 2 H_2(g) + \frac{1}{2} Cl_2(g) \rightleftharpoons NH_4Cl(s) \qquad K_p = \dfrac{1}{\left[P_{N_2}\right]^{1/2}\left[P_{H_2}\right]^2\left[P_{Cl_2}\right]^{1/2}}$

7. **(E)** Since $K_p = K_c\left(RT\right)^{\Delta v_{gas}}$, it is also true that $K_c = K_p\left(RT\right)^{-\Delta v_{gas}}$.

(a) $\quad K_c = \dfrac{[SO_2][Cl_2]}{[SO_2Cl_2]} = K_p\left(RT\right)^{-(+1)} = 2.9\times10^{-2}(0.08314\times303)^{-1} = 0.0012$

(b) $\quad K_c = \dfrac{[NO_2]^2}{[NO]^2[O_2]} = K_p\left(RT\right)^{-(-1)} = 1.48\times10^4\times(0.08314\times457.15) = 5.63\times10^5$

(c) $\quad K_c = \dfrac{[H_2S]^3}{[H_2]^3} = K_p\left(RT\right)^0 = K_p = 0.429$

8. **(E)** $K_p = K_c\left(RT\right)^{\Delta v_{gas}}$, with $R = 0.08314\ \text{L}\cdot\text{bar mol}^{-1}\ \text{K}^{-1}$

(a) $\quad K_p = \dfrac{P\{NO_2\}^2}{P\{N_2O_4\}} = K_c(RT)^{+1} = 4.61\times10^{-3}(0.08314\times298)^1 = 0.114$

(b) $\quad K_p = \dfrac{P\{C_2H_2\}P\{H_2\}^3}{P\{CH_4\}^2} = K_c(RT)^{(+2)} = (0.154)(0.08314\times2000)^2 = 4.26\times10^3$

(c) $\quad K_p = \dfrac{P\{H_2\}^4 P\{CS_2\}}{P\{H_2S\}^2 P\{CH_4\}} = K_c(RT)^{(+2)} = (5.27\times10^{-8})(0.08314\times973)^2 = 3.45\times10^{-4}$

9. **(E)** The equilibrium reaction is $H_2O(l) \rightleftharpoons H_2O(g)$ with $\Delta v_{gas} = +1$. $K_p = K_c\left(RT\right)^{\Delta v_{gas}}$ gives

$K_c = K_p\left(RT\right)^{-\Delta v_{gas}}$. $K_p = P\{H_2O\} = 23.8\ \text{mmHg}\times\dfrac{1\ \text{atm}}{760\ \text{mmHg}} = 0.0313$

$K_c = K_p\left(RT\right)^{-1} = \dfrac{K_p}{RT} = \dfrac{0.0313}{0.08206\times298} = 1.28\times10^{-3}$

10. **(E)** The equilibrium rxn is $C_6H_6(l) \rightleftharpoons C_6H_6(g)$ with $\Delta v_{gas} = +1$. Using $K_p = K_c\left(RT\right)^{\Delta v_{gas}}$,

$K_p = K_c\left(RT\right) = 5.12\times10^{-3}\left(0.08206\times298\right) = 0.125 = P\{C_6H_6\}$

$P\{C_6H_6\} = 0.125\ \text{atm}\times\dfrac{760\ \text{mmHg}}{1\ \text{atm}} = 95.0\ \text{mmHg}$

11. **(E)** Add one-half of the reversed 1st reaction with the 2nd reaction to obtain the desired reaction.

$\frac{1}{2}N_2(g) + \frac{1}{2}O_2(g) \rightleftharpoons NO(g)$ $\qquad\qquad K_c = \dfrac{1}{\sqrt{2.1\times10^{30}}}$

$NO(g) + \frac{1}{2}Br_2(g) \rightleftharpoons NOBr(g)$ $\qquad\qquad K_c = 1.4$

net : $\frac{1}{2}N_2(g) + \frac{1}{2}O_2(g) + \frac{1}{2}Br_2(g) \rightleftharpoons NOBr(g)$ $\qquad K_c = \dfrac{1.4}{\sqrt{2.1\times10^{30}}} = 9.7\times10^{-16}$

12. **(M)** We combine the several given reactions to obtain the net reaction.

$2\,N_2O(g) \rightleftharpoons 2\,N_2(g) + O_2(g)$ $\qquad\qquad K_c = \dfrac{1}{\left(2.7\times10^{-18}\right)^2}$

$4\,NO_2(g) \rightleftharpoons 2\,N_2O_4(g)$ $\qquad\qquad K_c = \dfrac{1}{\left(4.6\times10^{-3}\right)^2}$

$2\,N_2(g) + 4\,O_2(g) \rightleftharpoons 4\,NO_2(g)$ $\qquad\qquad K_c = (4.1\times10^{-9})^4$

net : $2\,N_2O(g) + 3\,O_2(g) \rightleftharpoons 2\,N_2O_4(g)$ $\quad K_{c(Net)} = \dfrac{\left(4.1\times10^{-9}\right)^4}{\left(2.7\times10^{-18}\right)^2\left(4.6\times10^{-3}\right)^2} = 1.8\times10^6$

13. **(M)** We combine the K_c values to obtain the value of K_c for the overall reaction, and then convert this to a value for K_p.

$2\,CO_2(g) + 2H_2(g) \rightleftharpoons 2\,CO(g) + 2\,H_2O(g)$ $\qquad K_c = \left(1.4\right)^2$

$2\,C(graphite) + O_2(g) \rightleftharpoons 2\,CO(g)$ $\qquad K_c = \left(1\times10^8\right)^2$

$4\,CO(g) \rightleftharpoons 2\,C(graphite) + 2\,CO_2(g)$ $\qquad K_c = \dfrac{1}{\left(0.64\right)^2}$

Overall: $2H_2(g) + O_2(g) \rightleftharpoons 2H_2O(g)$ $\qquad K_{c(overall)} = \dfrac{(1.4)^2(1\times10^8)^2}{(0.64)^2} = 5\times10^6$

$K_p = K_c\left(RT\right)^{\Delta n} = \dfrac{K_c}{RT} = \dfrac{5\times10^{16}}{0.08206\times1200} = 5\times10^{14}$

14. **(M)** We combine the K_p values to obtain the value of K_p for the overall reaction, and then convert this to a value for K_c.

$2\,NO_2Cl(g) \rightleftharpoons 2\,NOCl(g) + O_2(g)$ $\qquad\qquad K_p = \left(\dfrac{1}{1.1\times10^2}\right)^2$

$2\,NO_2(g) + Cl_2(g) \rightleftharpoons 2\,NO_2Cl(g)$ $\qquad\qquad K_p = \left(0.3\right)^2$

$N_2(g) + 2\,O_2(g) \rightleftharpoons 2\,NO_2(g)$ $\qquad\qquad K_p = (1.0\times10^{-9})^2$

Overall: $N_2(g) + O_2(g) + Cl_2(g) \rightleftharpoons 2\,NOCl(g)$ $\qquad K_{p(overall)} = \dfrac{(0.3)^2(1.0\times10^{-9})^2}{(1.1\times10^2)^2} = 7.\underline{4}\times10^{-24}$

$K_p = K_c\left(RT\right)^{\Delta n}$ $\qquad K_c = \dfrac{K_p}{\left(RT\right)^{\Delta n}} = \dfrac{7.\underline{4}\times10^{-24}}{(0.08206\times298)^{2-3}} = 2\times10^{-22}$

15. **(E)** $CO_2(g) + H_2O(l) \rightleftharpoons H_2CO_3(aq)$

In terms of activities, $K = a(H_2CO_3)/a(CO_2)$

In terms of concentration and partial pressure, $K = \dfrac{[H_2CO_3]/c^\circ}{P_{CO_2}/P^\circ}$

16. **(E)** $2\,Fe(s) + 3\,O_2(g) \rightleftharpoons Fe_2O_3(s)$

$K = \dfrac{a_{Fe_2O_3}}{a_{Fe} \cdot a_{O_2}}$. Since activity of solids and liquids is defined as 1, then the expression

simplifies to $K = \dfrac{1}{a_{O_2}}$

Similarly, in terms of pressure and concentration, $K = 1\big/\left(P_{O_2}/P^\circ\right)$

Experimental Determination of Equilibrium Constants

17. **(M)** First, we determine the concentration of PCl_5 and of Cl_2 present initially and at equilibrium, respectively. Then we use the balanced equation to help us determine the concentration of each species present at equilibrium.

$$[PCl_5]_{initial} = \frac{1.00 \times 10^{-3}\ mol\ PCl_5}{0.250\ L} = 0.00400\ M \qquad [Cl_2]_{equil} = \frac{9.65 \times 10^{-4}\ mol\ Cl_2}{0.250\ L} = 0.00386\ M$$

Equation:	$PCl_5(g)$	$\rightleftharpoons$	$PCl_3(g)$	$+$	$Cl_2(g)$
Initial:	0.00400M		0 M		0 M
Changes:	$-x$M		$+x$M		$+x$M
Equil:	0.00400M-xM		xM		xM ← 0.00386 M (from above)

At equilibrium, $[Cl_2] = [PCl_3] = 0.00386\ M$ and $[PCl_5] = 0.00400M - xM = 0.00014\ M$

$$K_c = \frac{[PCl_3][Cl_2]}{[PCl_5]} = \frac{(0.00386\,M)(0.00386\,M)}{0.00014\,M} = 0.10\underline{6}$$

18. **(M)** First we determine the partial pressure of each gas.

$$P_{initial}\{H_2(g)\} = \frac{nRT}{V} = \frac{1.00\,g\,H_2 \times \dfrac{1\,mol\,H_2}{2.016\,g\,H_2} \times \dfrac{0.08206\,L\,atm}{mol\,K} \times 1670\,K}{0.500\,L} = 136\,atm$$

$$P_{initial}\{H_2S(g)\} = \frac{nRT}{V} = \frac{1.06\,g\,H_2S \times \dfrac{1\,mol\,H_2S}{34.08\,g\,H_2S} \times \dfrac{0.08206\,L\,atm}{mol\,K} \times 1670\,K}{0.500\,L} = 8.52\,atm$$

$$P_{equil}\{S_2(g)\} = \frac{nRT}{V} = \frac{8.00 \times 10^{-6}\,mol\,S_2 \times \dfrac{0.08206\,L\,atm}{mol\,K} \times 1670\,K}{0.500\,L} = 2.19 \times 10^{-3}\,atm$$

Equation: $\quad 2\,H_2(g) \quad + \quad S_2(g) \quad \rightleftharpoons \quad 2\,H_2S(g)$

Initial: $\quad\quad$ 136 atm $\quad\quad$ 0 atm $\quad\quad\quad$ 8.52 atm

Changes: $\quad$ +0.00438 atm $\;$ 0.00219 atm $\;$ −0.00438 atm

Equil: $\quad\quad$ 136 atm $\quad\quad$ 0.00219 atm $\;$ 8.52 atm

$$K_p = \frac{P\{H_2S(g)\}^2}{P\{H_2(g)\}^2\,P\{S_2(g)\}} = \frac{(8.52)^2}{(136)^2\,0.00219} = 1.79$$

19. (M)

(a) $\quad K_c = \dfrac{[PCl_5]}{[PCl_3][Cl_2]} = \dfrac{\dfrac{0.105\ g\ PCl_5}{2.50\ L} \times \dfrac{1\ mol\ PCl_5}{208.2\ g}}{\left(\dfrac{0.220\ g\ PCl_3}{2.50\ L} \times \dfrac{1\ mol\ PCl_3}{137.3\ g}\right) \times \left(\dfrac{2.12\ g\ Cl_2}{2.50\ L} \times \dfrac{1\ mol\ Cl_2}{70.9\ g}\right)} = 26.3$

(b) $\quad K_p = K_c(RT)^{\Delta v} = 26.3\,(0.08206 \times 523)^{-1} = 0.613$

20. (M)

$$[ICl]_{initial} = \frac{0.682\ g\ ICl \times \dfrac{1\ mol\ ICl}{162.36\ g\ ICl}}{0.625\ L} = 6.72 \times 10^{-3}\ M$$

Reaction: $\quad 2\,ICl(g) \quad\quad\quad \rightleftharpoons \quad I_2(g) \quad + \quad Cl_2(g)$

Initial: $\quad\quad 6.72 \times 10^{-3}\ M \quad\quad\quad\quad 0\ M \quad\quad\quad 0\ M$

Change: $\quad\quad -2x \quad\quad\quad\quad\quad\quad\quad\quad +x \quad\quad\quad +x$

Equilibrium: $\quad 6.72 \times 10^{-3}\ M - 2x \quad\quad x \quad\quad\quad\quad x$

$$[I_2]_{equil} = \frac{0.0383\ g\ I_2 \times \dfrac{1\ mol\ I_2}{253.808\ g\ I_2}}{0.625\ L} = 2.41 \times 10^{-4}\ M\ = x$$

$$K_c = \frac{x \cdot x}{(6.72 \times 10^{-3} - 2x)} = \frac{(2.41 \times 10^{-4})^2}{(6.72 \times 10^{-3} - 2(2.41 \times 10^{-4}))} = 9.31 \times 10^{-6}$$

21. (E)

$$K = \frac{[Fe^{3+}]}{[H^+]^3} \Rightarrow 9.1 \times 10^3 = \frac{[Fe^{3+}]}{(1.0 \times 10^{-7})^3}$$

$$[Fe^{3+}] = 9.1 \times 10^{-18}\ M$$

22. (E)

$$K = \frac{[NH_3(aq)]}{P_{NH_3(g)}} \Rightarrow 57.5 = \frac{5 \times 10^{-9}}{P_{NH_3(g)}}$$

$$P_{NH_3(g)} = 5 \times 10^{-9}/57.5 = 8.7 \times 10^{-11}$$

Equilibrium Relationships

23. **(M)** $K_c = 281 = \dfrac{[SO_3]^2}{[SO_2]^2[O_2]} = \dfrac{[SO_3]^2}{[SO_2]^2} \times \dfrac{0.185\,L}{0.00247\,mol}$ $\dfrac{[SO_2]}{[SO_3]} = \sqrt{\dfrac{0.185}{0.00247 \times 281}} = 0.516$

24. **(M)** $K_c = 0.011 = \dfrac{[I]^2}{[I_2]} = \dfrac{\left(\dfrac{0.37\,mol\,I}{V}\right)^2}{\dfrac{1.00\,mol\,I_2}{V}} = \dfrac{1}{V} \times 0.14$ $V = \dfrac{0.14}{0.011} = 13\,L$

25. **(M)**

(a) A possible equation for the oxidation of $NH_3(g)$ to $NO_2(g)$ follows.

$$NH_3(g) + \tfrac{7}{4}O_2(g) \rightleftharpoons NO_2(g) + \tfrac{3}{2}H_2O(g)$$

(b) We obtain K_p for the reaction in part (a) by appropriately combining the values of K_p given in the problem.

$NH_3(g) + \tfrac{5}{4}O_2(g) \rightleftharpoons NO(g) + \tfrac{3}{2}H_2O(g)$ $K_p = 2.11 \times 10^{19}$

$NO(g) + \tfrac{1}{2}O_2(g) \rightleftharpoons NO_2(g)$ $K_p = \dfrac{1}{0.524}$

net: $NH_3(g) + \tfrac{7}{4}O_2(g) \rightleftharpoons NO_2(g) + \tfrac{3}{2}H_2O(g)$ $K_p = \dfrac{2.11 \times 10^{19}}{0.524} = 4.03 \times 10^{19}$

26. **(D)**

(a) We first determine $[H_2]$ and $[CH_4]$ and then $[C_2H_2]$. $[CH_4] = [H_2] = \dfrac{0.10\,mol}{1.0\,L} = 0.10\,M$

$$K_c = \dfrac{[C_2H_2][H_2]^3}{[CH_4]^2} \quad [C_2H_2] = \dfrac{K_c[CH_4]^2}{[H_2]^3} = \dfrac{0.154 \times 0.10^2}{0.10^3} = 1.54\,M$$

In a 1.00 L container, each concentration numerically equals the molar quantities of the substance.

$$\chi\{C_2H_2\} = \dfrac{1.54\,mol\,C_2H_2}{1.54\,mol\,C_2H_2 + 0.10\,mol\,CH_4 + 0.10\,mol\,H_2} = 0.89$$

(b) The conversion of $CH_4(g)$ to $C_2H_2(g)$ is favored at low pressures, since the conversion reaction has a larger sum of the stoichiometric coefficients of gaseous products (4) than of reactants (2).

(c) Initially, all concentrations are halved when the mixture is transferred to a flask that is twice as large. To re-establish equilibrium, the system reacts to the right, forming more moles of gas (to compensate for the drop in pressure). We base our solution on the balanced chemical equation, in the manner we have used before.

Equation:	$2\,CH_4(g)$	$\rightleftharpoons$	$C_2H_2(g)$	$+$	$3\,H_2$
Initial:	$\dfrac{0.10\,mol}{2.00\,L}$		$\dfrac{1.5\,mol}{2.00\,L}$		$\dfrac{0.10\,mol}{2.00\,L}$
	$=0.050\ M$		$=0.75\ M$		$=0.050\ M$
Changes:	$-2x\ M$		$+x\ M$		$+3x\ M$
Equil:	$(0.050-2x)\ M$		$(0.0750+x)\ M$		$(0.050+3x)\ M$

$$K_c = \frac{[C_2H_2][H_2]^3}{[CH_4]^2} = \frac{(0.050+3x)^3(0.750+x)}{(0.050-2x)^2} = 0.154$$

We can solve this 4th-order equation by successive approximations.
First guess: $x = 0.010$ M.

$$x=0.010 \quad Q_c = \frac{(0.050+3(0.010))^3(0.750+0.010)}{(0.050-2(0.010))^2} = \frac{(0.080)^3(0.760)}{(0.030)^2} = 0.433 > 0.154$$

$$x=0.020 \quad Q_c = \frac{(0.050+3(0.020))^3(0.750+0.020)}{(0.050-2(0.020))^2} = \frac{(0.110)^3(0.770)}{(0.010)^2} = 10.2 > 0.154$$

$$x=0.005 \quad Q_c = \frac{(0.050+3(0.005))^3(0.750+0.005)}{(0.050-2(0.005))^2} = \frac{(0.065)^3(0.755)}{(0.040)^2} = 0.129 < 0.154$$

$$x=0.006 \quad Q_c = \frac{(0.050+3(0.006))^3(0.750+0.006)}{(0.050-2(0.006))^2} = \frac{(0.068)^3(0.756)}{(0.038)^2} = 0.165 > 0.154$$

This is the maximum number of significant figures our system permits. We have
$x = 0.006$ M. $[CH_4] = 0.038$ M; $[C_2H_2] = 0.756$ M; $[H_2] = 0.068$ M
Because the container volume is 2.00 L, the molar amounts are double the values of
molarities.

$$2.00\ L \times \frac{0.756\ mol\ C_2H_2}{1\ L} = 1.51\ mol\ C_2H_2 \quad 2.00\ L \times \frac{0.038\ mol\ CH_4}{1\ L} = 0.076\ mol\ CH_4$$

$$2.00\ L \times \frac{0.068\ mol\ H_2}{1\ L} = 0.14\ mol\ H_2$$

Thus, the increase in volume results in the production of some additional C_2H_2.

27. **(M)**

(a) $K_c = \dfrac{[CO][H_2O]}{[CO_2][H_2]} = \dfrac{\dfrac{n\{CO\}}{V} \times \dfrac{n\{H_2O\}}{V}}{\dfrac{n\{CO_2\}}{V} \times \dfrac{n\{H_2\}}{V}}$

Since V is present in both the denominator and the numerator, it can be stricken from the expression. This happens here because $\Delta v_g = 0$. Therefore, K_c is independent of V.

(b)   Note that $K_p = K_c$ for this reaction, since $\Delta v_{gas} = 0$.

$K_c = K_p = \dfrac{0.224 \text{ mol CO} \times 0.224 \text{ mol H}_2O}{0.276 \text{ mol CO}_2 \times 0.276 \text{ mol H}_2} = 0.659$

28. **(M)** For the reaction $CO(g) + H_2O(g) \rightleftharpoons CO_2(g) + H_2(g)$ the value of $K_p = 23.2$

The expression for Q_p is $\dfrac{[CO_2][H_2]}{[CO][H_2O]}$. Consider each of the provided situations

(a) $P_{CO} = P_{H_2O} = P_{H_2} = P_{CO_2}$; $Q_p = 1$ Not an equilibrium position

(b) $\dfrac{P_{H_2}}{P_{H_2O}} = \dfrac{P_{CO_2}}{P_{CO}} = x$; $Q_p = x^2$ If $x = \sqrt{23.2}$, this is an equilibrium position.

(c) $(P_{CO} \times P_{H_2O}) = (P_{CO_2} \times P_{H_2})$; $Q_p = 1$ Not an equilibrium position

(d) $\dfrac{P_{H_2}}{P_{CO}} = \dfrac{P_{CO_2}}{P_{H_2O}} = x$; $Q_p = x^2$ If $x = \sqrt{23.2}$, this is an equilibrium position.

Direction and Extent of Chemical Change

29. **(M)** We compute the value of Q_c for the given amounts of product and reactants.

$Q_c = \dfrac{[SO_3]^2}{[SO_2]^2[O_2]} = \dfrac{\left(\dfrac{1.8 \text{ mol SO}_3}{7.2 \text{ L}}\right)^2}{\left(\dfrac{3.6 \text{ mol SO}_2}{7.2 \text{ L}}\right)^2 \dfrac{2.2 \text{ mol O}_2}{7.2 \text{ L}}} = 0.82 < K_c = 100$

The mixture described cannot be maintained indefinitely. In fact, because $Q_c < K_c$, the reaction will proceed to the right, that is, toward products, until equilibrium is established. We do not know how long it will take to reach equilibrium.

30. **(M)** We compute the value of Q_c for the given amounts of product and reactants.

$$Q_c = \frac{[NO_2]^2}{[N_2O_4]} = \frac{\left(\dfrac{0.0205\,mol\,NO_2}{5.25\,L}\right)^2}{\dfrac{0.750\,mol\,N_2O_4}{5.25\,L}} = 1.07 \times 10^{-4} < K_c = 4.61 \times 10^{-3}$$

The mixture described cannot be maintained indefinitely. In fact, because $Q_c < K_c$, the reaction will proceed to the right, that is, toward products, until equilibrium is established. If E_a is large, however, it may take some time to reach equilibrium.

31. **(M)**

(a) We determine the concentration of each species in the gaseous mixture, use these concentrations to determine the value of the reaction quotient, and compare this value of Q_c with the value of K_c.

$$[\,SO_2\,] = \frac{0.455\,mol\,SO_2}{1.90\,L} = 0.239\,M \qquad [\,O_2\,] = \frac{0.183\,mol\,O_2}{1.90\,L} = 0.0963\,M$$

$$[\,SO_3\,] = \frac{0.568\,mol\,SO_3}{1.90\,L} = 0.299\,M \qquad Q_c = \frac{[\,SO_3\,]^2}{[\,SO_2\,]^2[\,O_2\,]} = \frac{(0.299)^2}{(0.239)^2\,0.0963} = 16.3$$

Since $Q_c = 16.3 \neq 2.8 \times 10^2 = K_c$, this mixture is not at equilibrium.

(b) Since the value of Q_c is smaller than that of K_c, the reaction will proceed to the right, forming product and consuming reactants to reach equilibrium.

32. **(M)** We compute the value of Q_c. Each concentration equals the mass (m) of the substance divided by its molar mass and further divided by the volume of the container.

$$Q_c = \frac{[CO_2][H_2]}{[CO][H_2O]} = \frac{\dfrac{m \times \dfrac{1\,mol\,CO_2}{44.0\,g\,CO_2}}{V} \times \dfrac{m \times \dfrac{1\,mol\,H_2}{2.0\,g\,H_2}}{V}}{\dfrac{m \times \dfrac{1\,mol\,CO}{28.0\,g\,CO}}{V} \times \dfrac{m \times \dfrac{1\,mol\,H_2O}{18.0\,g\,H_2O}}{V}} = \frac{\dfrac{1}{44.0 \times 2.0}}{\dfrac{1}{28.0 \times 18.0}} = \frac{28.0 \times 18.0}{44.0 \times 2.0} = 5.7 < 31.4(\text{value of } K_c)$$

(In evaluating the expression above, we cancelled the equal values of V, along with, the equal values of m.) Because the value of Q_c is smaller than the value of K_c, (a) the reaction is not at equilibrium and (b) the reaction will proceed to the right (formation of products) to reach a state of equilibrium.

33. (M) The information for the calculation is organized around the chemical equation. Let $x = $ mol H_2 (or I_2) that reacts. Then use stoichiometry to determine the amount of HI formed, in terms of x, and finally solve for x.

Equation: $H_2(g) \quad + \quad I_2(g) \rightleftharpoons \quad 2\, HI(g)$

Initial: 0.150 mol   0.150 mol   0.000 mol

Changes: $-x$ mol $-x$ mol $+2x$ mol

Equil: $0.150 - x$ $0.150 - x$ $2x$

$$K_c = \frac{[HI]^2}{[H_2][I_2]} = \frac{\left(\dfrac{2x}{3.25\,L}\right)^2}{\dfrac{0.150 - x}{3.25\,L} \times \dfrac{0.150 - x}{3.25\,L}}$$

Then take the square root of both sides: $\sqrt{K_c} = \sqrt{50.2} = \dfrac{2x}{0.150 - x} = 7.09$

$2x = 1.06 - 7.09x \qquad x = \dfrac{1.06}{9.09} = 0.117$ mol, amount HI $= 2x = 2 \times 0.117$ mol $= 0.234$ mol HI

amount $H_2 = $ amount $I_2 = (0.150 - x)$ mol $= (0.150 - 0.117)$ mol $= 0.033$ mol H_2 (or I_2)

34. (M) We use the balanced chemical equation as a basis to organize the information

Equation: $\qquad SbCl_5(g) \rightleftharpoons SbCl_3(g) \quad + \quad Cl_2(g)$

Initial: $\dfrac{0.00\ \text{mol}}{2.50\ \text{L}}$ $\dfrac{0.280\ \text{mol}}{2.50\ \text{L}}$ $\dfrac{0.160\ \text{mol}}{2.50\ \text{L}}$

Initial: 0.000 M   0.112 M   0.0640 M

Changes: $+x$ M $-x$ M $-x$ M

Equil: x M $(0.112 - x)$ M $(0.0640 - x)$ M

$$K_c = 0.025 = \frac{[SbCl_3][Cl_2]}{[SbCl_5]} = \frac{(0.112 - x)(0.0640 - x)}{x} = \frac{0.00717 - 0.176x + x^2}{x}$$

$0.025x = 0.00717 - 0.176x + x^2 \qquad x^2 - 0.201x + 0.00717 = 0$

$$x = \frac{-b \pm \sqrt{b^2 - 4ac}}{2a} = \frac{0.201 \pm \sqrt{0.0404 - 0.0287}}{2} = 0.0464 \text{ or } 0.155$$

The second of the two values for x gives a negative value of $[Cl_2] (= -0.091\ M)$, and thus is physically meaningless in our universe. Thus, concentrations and amounts follow.

$[SbCl_5] = x = 0.0464\ M \qquad$ amount $SbCl_5 = 2.50\ L \times 0.0464\ M = 0.116$ mol $SbCl_5$

$[SbCl_3] = 0.112 - x = 0.066\ M \qquad$ amount $SbCl_3 = 2.50\ L \times 0.066\ M = 0.17$ mol $SbCl_3$

$[Cl_2] = 0.0640 - x = 0.0176\ M \qquad$ amount $Cl_2 = 2.50\ L \times 0.0176\ M = 0.0440$ mol Cl_2

35. (M) We use the chemical equation as a basis to organize the information provided about the reaction, and then determine the final number of moles of $Cl_2(g)$ present.

Equation: $CO(g)$ + $Cl_2(g)$ $\rightleftharpoons$ $COCl_2(g)$

Initial: 0.3500 mol   0.0000 mol   0.05500 mol

Changes: $+x$ mol $+x$ mol $-x$ mol

Equil.: $(0.3500+x)$ mol x mol $(0.05500-x)$ mol

$$K_c = 1.2 \times 10^3 = \frac{[COCl_2]}{[CO][Cl_2]} = \frac{\dfrac{(0.0550-x)\,\text{mol}}{3.050\,\text{L}}}{\dfrac{(0.3500+x)\text{mol}}{3.050\,\text{L}} \times \dfrac{x\,\text{mol}}{3.050\ \text{L}}}$$

$$\frac{1.2\times10^3}{3.050} = \frac{0.05500-x}{(0.3500+x)\,x}\quad \text{Assume } x \ll 0.0550 \text{ This produces the following expression.}$$

$$\frac{1.2\times10^3}{3.050} = \frac{0.05500}{0.3500\,x}\qquad x = \frac{3.050\times0.05500}{0.3500\times1.2\times10^3} = 4.0\times10^{-4}\ \text{mol Cl}_2$$

We use the first value we obtained, 4.0×10^{-4} (= 0.00040), to arrive at a second value.

$$x = \frac{3.050\times(0.0550-0.00040)}{(0.3500+0.00040)\times1.2\times10^3} = 4.0\times10^{-4}\ \text{mol Cl}_2$$

Because the value did not change on the second iteration, we have arrived at a solution.

36. (M) Compute the initial concentration of each species present. Then determine the equilibrium concentrations of all species. Finally, compute the mass of CO_2 present at equilibrium.

$$[CO]_{int} = \frac{1.00\ \text{g}}{1.41\ \text{L}} \times \frac{1\ \text{mol CO}}{28.01\ \text{g CO}} = 0.0253\ \text{M} \quad [H_2O]_{int} = \frac{1.00\ \text{g}}{1.41\ \text{L}} \times \frac{1\ \text{mol H}_2O}{18.02\ \text{g H}_2O} = 0.0394\ \text{M}$$

$$[H_2]_{int} = \frac{1.00\ \text{g}}{1.41\ \text{L}} \times \frac{1\ \text{mol H}_2}{2.016\ \text{g H}_2} = 0.352\ \text{M}$$

Equation: $CO(g)$ + $H_2O(g)$ $\rightleftharpoons$ $CO_2(g)$ + $H_2(g)$

Initial: 0.0253 M   0.0394 M   0.0000 M   0.352 M

Changes: $-x$ M $-x$ M $+x$ M $+x$ M

Equil: $(0.0253-x)$ M $(0.0394-x)$ M x M $(0.352+x)$ M

$$K_c = \frac{[CO_2][H_2]}{[CO][H_2O]} = 23.2 = \frac{x(0.352+x)}{(0.0253-x)(0.0394-x)} = \frac{0.352x+x^2}{0.000997-0.0647x+x^2}$$

$$0.0231-1.50x+23.2x^2 = 0.352x+x^2 \qquad 22.2x^2 -1.852x+0.0231 = 0$$

$$x = \frac{-b \pm \sqrt{b^2-4ac}}{2a} = \frac{1.852 \pm \sqrt{3.430-2.051}}{44.4} = 0.0682\ \text{M},\ \ 0.0153\ \text{M}$$

The first value of x gives negative concentrations for reactants ([CO] = –0.0429 M and [H$_2$O] = –0.0288 M). Thus, x = 0.0153 M = $\left[\text{CO}_2\right]$. Now we can find the mass of CO$_2$.

$$1.41\,\text{L} \times \frac{0.0153\,\text{mol CO}_2}{1\,\text{L mixture}} \times \frac{44.01\,\text{g CO}_2}{1\,\text{mol CO}_2} = 0.949\,\text{g CO}_2$$

37. **(D)** We base each of our solutions on the balanced chemical equation.

(a)

Equation :	PCl$_5$ (g)	$\rightleftharpoons$	PCl$_3$ (g)	+	Cl$_2$ (g)
Initial :	$\dfrac{0.550\ \text{mol}}{2.50\ \text{L}}$		$\dfrac{0.550\ \text{mol}}{2.50\ \text{L}}$		$\dfrac{0\ \text{mol}}{2.50\ \text{L}}$
Changes :	$\dfrac{-x\ \text{mol}}{2.50\ \text{L}}$		$\dfrac{+x\ \text{mol}}{2.50\ \text{L}}$		$\dfrac{+x\ \text{mol}}{2.50\ \text{L}}$
Equil :	$\dfrac{(0.550-x)\ \text{mol}}{2.50\ \text{L}}$		$\dfrac{(0.550+x)\ \text{mol}}{2.50\ \text{L}}$		$\dfrac{x\ \text{mol}}{2.50\ \text{L}}$

$$K_c = \frac{[\text{PCl}_3][\text{Cl}_2]}{[\text{PCl}_5]} = 3.8 \times 10^{-2} = \frac{\dfrac{(0.550+x)\,\text{mol}}{2.50\,\text{L}} \times \dfrac{x\,\text{mol}}{2.50\,\text{L}}}{\dfrac{(0.550-x)\,\text{mol}}{2.50\,\text{L}}} \qquad \frac{x(0.550+x)}{2.50(0.550-x)} = 3.8\times10^{-2}$$

$$x^2 + 0.550x = 0.052 - 0.095x \qquad x^2 + 0.645x - 0.052 = 0$$

$$x = \frac{-b \pm \sqrt{b^2 - 4ac}}{2a} = \frac{-0.645 \pm \sqrt{0.416 + 0.208}}{2} = 0.0725\,\text{mol},\ -0.717\,\text{mol}$$

The second answer gives a negative quantity. of Cl$_2$, which makes no physical sense.

$$n_{\text{PCl}_5} = (0.550 - 0.0725) = 0.478\ \text{mol PCl}_5 \quad n_{\text{PCl}_3} = (0.550 + 0.0725) = 0.623\ \text{mol PCl}_3$$

$$n_{\text{Cl}_2} = x = 0.0725\ \text{mol Cl}_2$$

(b)

Equation :	PCl$_5$ (g)	$\rightleftharpoons$	PCl$_3$ (g)	+	Cl$_2$ (g)
Initial :	$\dfrac{0.610\ \text{mol}}{2.50\ \text{L}}$		0 M		0 M
Changes :	$\dfrac{-x\ \text{mol}}{2.50\ \text{L}}$		$\dfrac{+x\ \text{mol}}{2.50\ \text{L}}$		$\dfrac{+x\ \text{mol}}{2.50\ \text{L}}$
Equil :	$\dfrac{0.610-x\ \text{mol}}{2.50\ \text{L}}$		$\dfrac{(x\ \text{mol})}{2.50\ \text{L}}$		$\dfrac{(x\ \text{mol})}{2.50\ \text{L}}$

$$K_c = \frac{[\text{PCl}_3][\text{Cl}_2]}{[\text{PCl}_5]} = 3.8 \times 10^{-2} = \frac{\dfrac{(x\,\text{mol})}{2.50\,\text{L}} \times \dfrac{(x\,\text{mol})}{2.50\,\text{L}}}{\dfrac{0.610-x\,\text{mol}}{2.50\,\text{L}}}$$

$$2.50 \times 3.8 \times 10^{-2} = \frac{x^2}{0.610 - x} = 0.095 \qquad 0.058 - 0.095x = x^2 \quad x^2 + 0.095x - 0.058 = 0$$

$$x = \frac{-b \pm \sqrt{b^2 - 4ac}}{2a} = \frac{-0.095 \pm \sqrt{0.0090 + 0.23}}{2} = 0.20\,\text{mol},\ -0.29\,\text{mol}$$

amount PCl$_3$ = 0.20 mol = amount Cl$_2$; amount PCl$_5$ = 0.610 – 0.20 = 0.41 mol

38. (D)

(a) We use the balanced chemical equation as a basis to organize the information we have about the reactants and products.

Equation:	$2\,COF_2\,(g)$	$\rightleftharpoons$	$CO_2\,(g)$	$+$	$CF_4\,(g)$
Initial:	$\dfrac{0.145\ mol}{5.00\ L}$		$\dfrac{0.262\ mol}{5.00\ L}$		$\dfrac{0.074\ mol}{5.00\ L}$
Initial:	0.0290 M		0.0524 M		0.0148 M

And we now compute a value of Q_c and compare it to the given value of K_c.

$$Q_c = \frac{[CO_2][CF_4]}{[COF_2]^2} = \frac{(0.0524)(0.0148)}{(0.0290)^2} = 0.922 < 2.00 = K_c$$

Because Q_c is not equal to K_c, the mixture is not at equilibrium.

(b) Because Q_c is smaller than K_c, the reaction will shift right, that is, products will be formed at the expense of COF_2, to reach a state of equilibrium.

(c) We continue the organization of information about reactants and products.

Equation:	$2\,COF_2\,(g)$	$\rightleftharpoons$	$CO_2\,(g)$	$+$	$CF_4\,(g)$
Initial:	0.0290 M		0.0524 M		0.0148 M
Changes:	$-2x$ M		$+x$ M		$+x$ M
Equil:	$(0.0290 - 2x)$ M		$(0.0524 + x)$ M		$(0.0148 + x)$ M

$$K_c = \frac{[CO_2][CF_4]}{[COF_2]^2} = \frac{(0.0524 + x)(0.0148 + x)}{(0.0290 - 2x)^2} = 2.00 = \frac{0.000776 + 0.0672x + x^2}{0.000841 - 0.1160x + 4x^2}$$

$$0.00168 - 0.232x + 8x^2 = 0.000776 + 0.0672x + x^2 \quad 7x^2 - 0.299x + 0.000904 = 0$$

$$x = \frac{-b \pm \sqrt{b^2 - 4ac}}{2a} = \frac{0.299 \pm \sqrt{0.0894 - 0.0253}}{14} = 0.0033\ M, 0.0394\ M$$

The second of these values for x (0.0394) gives a negative $[COF_2]\,(= -0.0498\ M)$, clearly a nonsensical result. We now compute the concentration of each species at equilibrium, and check to ensure that the equilibrium constant is satisfied.

$$[COF_2] = 0.0290 - 2x = 0.0290 - 2(0.0033) = 0.0224\ M$$

$$[CO_2] = 0.0524 + x = 0.0524 + 0.0033 = 0.0557\ M$$

$$\left[CF_4\right] = 0.0148 + x = 0.0148 + 0.0033 = 0.0181 \text{ M}$$

$$K_c = \frac{\left[CO_2\right]\left[CF_4\right]}{\left[COF_2\right]^2} = \frac{0.0557 \text{ M} \times 0.0181 \text{ M}}{\left(0.0224 \text{ M}\right)^2} = 2.01$$

The agreement of this value of K_c with the cited value (2.00) indicates that this solution is correct. Now we determine the number of moles of each species at equilibrium.

$$\text{mol } COF_2 = 5.00 \text{ L} \times 0.0224 \text{ M} = 0.112 \text{ mol } COF_2$$

$$\text{mol } CO_2 = 5.00 \text{ L} \times 0.0557 \text{ M} = 0.279 \text{ mol } CO_2$$

$$\text{mol } CF_4 = 5.00 \text{ L} \times 0.0181 \text{ M} = 0.0905 \text{ mol } CF_4$$

But suppose we had incorrectly concluded, in part (b), that reactants would be formed in reaching equilibrium. What result would we obtain? The set-up follows.

Equation: $2 COF_2 (g) \rightleftharpoons CO_2 (g) + CF_4 (g)$

Initial: 0.0290 M 0.0524 M 0.0148 M

Changes: $+2y \text{ M}$ $-y \text{ M}$ $-y \text{ M}$

Equil: $(0.0290+2y)\text{M}$ $(0.0524-y)\text{M}$ $(0.0148-y) \text{ M}$

$$K_c = \frac{\left[CO_2\right]\left[CF_4\right]}{\left[COF_2\right]^2} = \frac{(0.0524-y)(0.0148-y)}{(0.0290+2y)^2} = 2.00 = \frac{0.000776 - 0.0672y + y^2}{0.000841 + 0.1160y + 4y^2}$$

$$0.00168 + 0.232y + 8y^2 = 0.000776 - 0.0672y + y^2 \quad 7y^2 + 0.299y + 0.000904 = 0$$

$$y = \frac{-b \pm \sqrt{b^2 - 4ac}}{2a} = \frac{-0.299 \pm \sqrt{0.0894 - 0.0253}}{14} = -0.0033 \text{ M}, -0.0394 \text{ M}$$

The second of these values for $x(-0.0394)$ gives a negative $\left[COF_2\right](= -0.0498 \text{ M})$, clearly a nonsensical result. We now compute the concentration of each species at equilibrium, and check to ensure that the equilibrium constant is satisfied.

$$\left[COF_2\right] = 0.0290 + 2y = 0.0290 + 2(-0.0033) = 0.0224 \text{ M}$$

$$\left[CO_2\right] = 0.0524 - y = 0.0524 + 0.0033 = 0.0557 \text{ M}$$

$$\left[CF_4\right] = 0.0148 - y = 0.0148 + 0.0033 = 0.0181 \text{ M}$$

These are the same equilibrium concentrations that we obtained by making the correct decision regarding the direction that the reaction would take. Thus, you can be assured that, if you perform the algebra correctly, it will guide you even if you make the incorrect decision about the direction of the reaction.

39. **(D)**

(a) We calculate the initial amount of each substance.

$$n \{C_2H_5OH\} = 17.2 \text{ g } C_2H_5OH \times \frac{1 \text{ mol } C_2H_5OH}{46.07 \text{ g } C_2H_5OH} = 0.373 \text{ mol } C_2H_5OH$$

$$n\{CH_3CO_2H\} = 23.8 \text{ g } CH_3CO_2H \times \frac{1 \text{ mol } CH_3CO_2H}{60.05 \text{ g } CH_3CO_2H} = 0.396 \text{ mol } CH_3CO_2H$$

$$n\{CH_3CO_2C_2H_5\} = 48.6 \text{ g } CH_3CO_2C_2H_5 \times \frac{1 \text{ mol } CH_3CO_2C_2H_5}{88.11 \text{ g } CH_3CO_2C_2H_5}$$

$$n\{CH_3CO_2C_2H_5\} = 0.552 \text{ mol } CH_3CO_2C_2H_5$$

$$n\{H_2O\} = 71.2 \text{ g } H_2O \times \frac{1 \text{ mol } H_2O}{18.02 \text{ g } H_2O} = 3.95 \text{ mol } H_2O$$

All of the substances involved are liquids and they form a liquid solution. Since we would divide each amount by the total volume, and since there are the same numbers of product and reactant stoichiometric coefficients, we can use moles rather than concentrations in the Q_c expression.

$$Q_c = \frac{n\{CH_3CO_2C_2H_5\}\,n\{H_2O\}}{n\{C_2H_5OH\}\,n\{CH_3CO_2H\}} = \frac{0.552 \text{ mol} \times 3.95 \text{ mol}}{0.373 \text{ mol} \times 0.396 \text{ mol}} = 14.8 > K_c = 4.0$$

Since $Q_c > K_c$ the reaction will shift to the left, forming reactants, as it attains equilibrium.

(b)

Equation:	C_2H_5OH	+	CH_3CO_2H	$\rightleftharpoons$	$CH_3CO_2C_2H_5$	+	H_2O
Initial	0.373 mol		0.396 mol		0.552 mol		3.95 mol
Changes	$+x$ mol		$+x$ mol		$-x$ mol		$-x$ mol
Equil	$(0.373 + x)$ mol		$(0.396 + x)$ mol		$(0.552 - x)$ mol		$(3.95 - x)$ mol

$$K_c = \frac{(0.552 - x)(3.95 - x)}{(0.373 + x)(0.396 + x)} = \frac{2.18 - 4.50x + x^2}{0.148 + 0.769x + x^2} = 4.0$$

$$x^2 - 4.50x + 2.18 = 4x^2 + 3.08x + 0.59 \qquad 3x^2 + 7.58x - 1.59 = 0$$

$$x = \frac{-b \pm \sqrt{b^2 - 4ac}}{2a} = \frac{-7.58 \pm \sqrt{57 + 19}}{6} = 0.19 \text{ moles}, -2.72 \text{ moles}$$

Negative amounts do not make physical sense. We compute the equilibrium amount of each substance with $x = 0.19$ moles.

$$n\{C_2H_5OH\} = 0.373 \text{ mol} + 0.19 \text{ mol} = 0.56 \text{ mol } C_2H_5OH$$

$$\text{mass } C_2H_5OH = 0.56 \text{ mol } C_2H_5OH \times \frac{46.07 \text{ g } C_2H_5OH}{1 \text{ mol } C_2H_5OH} = 26 \text{ g } C_2H_5OH$$

$n\{CH_3CO_2H\} = 0.396 \text{ mol} + 0.19 \text{ mol} = 0.59 \text{ mol } CH_3CO_2H$

$\text{mass } CH_3CO_2H = 0.59 \text{ mol } CH_3CO_2H \times \dfrac{60.05 \text{ g } CH_3CO_2H}{1 \text{ mol } CH_3CO_2H} = 35 \text{ g } CH_3CO_2H$

$n\{CH_3CO_2C_2H_5\} = 0.552 \text{ mol} - 0.19 \text{ mol} = 0.36 \text{ } CH_3CO_2C_2H_5$

$\text{mass } CH_3CO_2C_2H_5 = 0.36 \text{ mol } CH_3CO_2C_2H_5 \times \dfrac{88.10 \text{ g } CH_3CO_2C_2H_5}{1 \text{ mol } CH_3CO_2C_2H_5} = 32 \text{ g } CH_3CO_2C_2H_5$

$n\{H_2O\} = 3.95 \text{ mol} - 0.19 \text{ mol} = 3.76 \text{ mol } H_2O$

$\text{mass } H_2O = 3.76 \text{ mol } H_2O \times \dfrac{18.02 \text{ g } H_2O}{1 \text{ mol } H_2O} = 68 \text{ g } H_2O$

$\text{To check } K_c = \dfrac{n\{CH_3CO_2C_2H_5\}n\{H_2O\}}{n\{C_2H_5OH\}n\{CH_3CO_2H\}} = \dfrac{0.36 \text{ mol} \times 3.76 \text{ mol}}{0.56 \text{ mol} \times 0.59 \text{ mol}} = 4.1$

40. **(M)** The final volume of the mixture is $0.750 \text{ L} + 2.25 \text{ L} = 3.00 \text{ L}$. Then use the balanced chemical equation to organize the data we have concerning the reaction. The reaction should shift to the right, that is, form products in reaching a new equilibrium, since the volume is greater.

Equation:	$N_2O_4(g)$	$\rightleftharpoons$	$2 NO_2(g)$
Initial:	$\dfrac{0.971 \text{ mol}}{3.00 \text{ L}}$		$\dfrac{0.0580 \text{ mol}}{3.00 \text{ L}}$
Initial:	0.324 M		0.0193 M
Changes:	$-x \text{ M}$		$+2x \text{ M}$
Equil:	$(0.324 - x) \text{M}$		$(0.0193 + 2x) \text{M}$

$K_c = \dfrac{[NO_2]^2}{[N_2O_4]} = \dfrac{(0.0193 + 2x)^2}{0.324 - x} = \dfrac{0.000372 + 0.0772x + 4x^2}{0.324 - x} = 4.61 \times 10^{-3}$

$0.000372 + 0.0772x + 4x^2 = 0.00149 - 0.00461x \qquad 4x^2 + 0.0818x - 0.00112 = 0$

$x = \dfrac{-b \pm \sqrt{b^2 - 4ac}}{2a} = \dfrac{-0.0818 \pm \sqrt{0.00669 + 0.0179}}{8} = 0.00938 \text{ M}, \ -0.0298 \text{ M}$

$[NO_2] = 0.0193 + (2 \times 0.00938) = 0.0381 \text{ M}$

$\text{amount } NO_2 = 0.0381 \text{ M} \times 3.00 \text{ L} = 0.114 \text{ mol } NO_2$

$[N_2O_4] = 0.324 - 0.00938 = 0.3146 \text{ M}$

$\text{amount } N_2O_4 = 0.3146 \text{ M} \times 3.00 \text{ L} = 0.944 \text{ mol } N_2O_4$

41. **(M)** $[HCONH_2]_{init} = \dfrac{0.186 \text{ mol}}{2.16 \text{ L}} = 0.0861 \text{ M}$

Equation: $HCONH_2(g) \rightleftharpoons NH_3(g) + CO(g)$

Initial:	0.0861 M	0 M	0 M
Changes:	$-x$ M	$+x$ M	$+x$ M
Equil:	$(0.0861 - x)$ M	x M	x M

$K_c = \dfrac{[NH_3][CO]}{[HCONH_2]} = \dfrac{x \cdot x}{0.0861 - x} = 4.84 \qquad x^2 = 0.417 - 4.84x \qquad 0 = x^2 + 4.84x - 0.417$

$x = \dfrac{-b \pm \sqrt{b^2 - 4ac}}{2a} = \dfrac{-4.84 \pm \sqrt{23.4 + 1.67}}{2} = 0.084 \text{ M}, \; -4.92 \text{ M}$

The negative concentration obviously is physically meaningless. We determine the total concentration of all species, and then the total pressure with $x = 0.084$.

$[\text{total}] = [NH_3] + [CO] + [HCONH_2] = x + x + 0.0861 - x = 0.0861 + 0.084 = 0.170 \text{ M}$

$P_{tot} = 0.170 \text{ mol L}^{-1} \times 0.08206 \text{ L atm mol}^{-1} \text{ K}^{-1} \times 400. \text{ K} = 5.58 \text{ atm}$

42. **(E)** Compare Q_p to K_p. We assume that the added solids are of negligible volume so that the initial partial pressures of $CO_2(g)$ and $H_2O(g)$ do not significantly change.

$P\{H_2O\} = \left(715 \text{ mmHg} \times \dfrac{1 \text{ atm}}{760 \text{ mmHg}}\right) = 0.941 \text{ atm H}_2O$

$Q_p = P\{CO_2\} P\{H_2O\} = 2.10 \text{ atm } CO_2 \times 0.941 \text{ atm H}_2O = 1.98 > 0.23 = K_p$

Because Q_p is larger than K_p, the reaction will proceed left toward reactants to reach equilibrium. Thus, the partial pressures of the two gases will decrease.

43. **(M)**

We organize the solution around the balanced chemical equation.

Equation: $2\,Cr^{3+}(aq) + Cd(s) \rightleftharpoons 2\,Cr^{2+}(aq) + Cd^{2+}(aq)$

Initial:	1.00 M	0 M	0 M
Changes:	$-2x$ M	$+2x$	$+x$
Equil:	$(1.00 - 2x)$ M	$2x$	x

$K_c = \dfrac{[Cr^{2+}]^2[Cd^{2+}]}{[Cr^{3+}]^2} = \dfrac{(2x)^2(x)}{(1.00 - 2x)^2} = 0.288 \qquad$ *Via successive approximations, one obtains* $x = 0.257 \text{ M}$

Therefore, at equilibrium, $[Cd^{2+}] = 0.257 \text{ M}$, $[Cr^{2+}] = 0.514 \text{ M}$ and $[Cr^{3+}] = 0.486 \text{ M}$

Minimum mass of Cd(s) = 0.350L $\times$ 0.257 M $\times$ 112.41 g/mol = 10.1 g of Cd metal

44. **(M)** Again we base the set-up of the problem around the balanced chemical equation.

Equation: $\qquad$ $Pb(s) + 2\,Cr^{3+}(aq)$ $\xrightleftharpoons{\quad K_c = 3.2 \times 10^{-10} \quad}$ $Pb^{2+}(aq) \ + \ 2\,Cr^{2+}(aq)$

Initial: $\qquad\qquad$ $-$ $\qquad$ 0.100 M $\qquad\qquad\qquad\qquad\qquad$ 0 M $\qquad\qquad$ 0 M

Changes: $\qquad\quad$ $-$ $\qquad$ $-2x$ M $\qquad\qquad\qquad\qquad\qquad$ $+x$M $\qquad\quad$ $+2x$ M

Equil: $\qquad\qquad$ $-$ $\qquad$ $(0.100 - 2x)$M $\qquad\qquad\qquad\quad$ xM $\qquad\qquad$ $2x$ M

$$K_c = \frac{x(2x)^2}{(0.100)^2} = 3.2 \times 10^{-10} \qquad\qquad 4x^3 = (0.100)^2 \times 3.2 \times 10^{-10} = 3.2 \times 10^{-12}$$

$$x = \sqrt[3]{\frac{3.2 \times 10^{-12}}{4}} = 9.3 \times 10^{-5} \text{ M Assumption that } 2x \ll 0.100, \text{ is valid and thus}$$

$$\left[Pb^{2+}\right] = x = 9.3 \times 10^{-5} \text{ M, } [Cr^{2+}] = 1.9 \times 10^{-4} \text{ M and } [Cr^{3+}] = 0.100 \text{ M}$$

45. **(M)** We are told in this question that the reaction $SO_2(g) + Cl_2(g) \rightleftharpoons SO_2Cl_2(g)$ has $K_c = 4.0$ at a certain temperature T. This means that at the temperature T, $[SO_2Cl_2] = 4.0 \times [Cl_2] \times [SO_2]$. Careful scrutiny of the three diagrams reveals that sketch (b) is the best representation because it contains numbers of SO_2Cl_2, SO_2, and Cl_2 molecules that are consistent with the K_c for the reaction. In other words, sketch (b) is the best choice because it contains 12 SO_2Cl_2 molecules (per unit volume), 1 Cl_2 molecule (per unit volume) and 3 SO_2 molecules (per unit volume), which is the requisite number of each type of molecule needed to generate the expected K_c value for the reaction at temperature T.

46. **(M)** In this question we are told that the reaction $2\,NO(g) + Br_2(g) \rightleftharpoons 2\,NOBr(g)$ has $K_c = 3.0$ at a certain temperature T. This means that at the temperature T, $[NOBr]^2 = 3.0 \times [Br_2][NO]^2$. Sketch (c) is the most accurate representation because it contains 18 NOBr molecules (per unit volume), 6 NO molecules (per unit volume), and 3 Br_2 molecules (per unit volume), which is the requisite number of each type of molecule needed to generate the expected K_c value for the reaction at temperature T.

47. **(E)**

$$K = \frac{[\text{aconitate}]}{[\text{citrate}]}$$

$$Q = \frac{4.0 \times 10^{-5}}{(0.00128)} = 0.031$$

Since $Q = K$, the reaction is at equilibrium,

48. **(E)**

$$K = \frac{[CO_2][NAD_{red}][oxoglut.]}{[citrate][NAD_{ox}]}$$

$$Q = \frac{(0.00868)(0.00132)(0.00868)}{(0.00128)(0.00868)} = 0.00895$$

Since $Q < K$, the reaction needs to proceed to the right (products).

Partial Pressure Equilibrium Constant, K_p

49. **(M)** The $I_2(s)$ maintains the presence of I_2 in the flask until it has all vaporized. Thus, if enough $HI(g)$ is produced to completely consume the $I_2(s)$, equilibrium will not be achieved.

$$P\{H_2S\} = 747.6 \text{ mmHg} \times \frac{1 \text{ atm}}{760 \text{ mmHg}} = 0.9837 \text{ atm}$$

Equation:	$H_2S(g) +$	$I_2(s)$	$\rightleftharpoons$	$2\,HI(g) + S(s)$
Initial:	0.9837 atm			0 atm
Changes:	$-x$ atm			$+2x$ atm
Equil:	$(0.9837 - x)$ atm			$2x$ atm

$$K_p = \frac{P\{HI\}^2}{P\{H_2S\}} = \frac{(2x)^2}{(0.9837 - x)} = 1.34 \times 10^{-5} = \frac{4x^2}{0.9837}$$

$$x = \sqrt{\frac{1.34 \times 10^{-5} \times 0.9837}{4}} = 1.82 \times 10^{-3} \text{ atm}$$

The assumption that $0.9837 \gg x$ is valid. Now we verify that sufficient $I_2(s)$ is present by computing the mass of I_2 needed to produce the predicted pressure of $HI(g)$. Initially, 1.85 g I_2 is present (given).

$$\text{mass } I_2 = \frac{1.82 \times 10^{-3} \text{ atm} \times 0.725 \text{ L}}{0.08206 \text{ L atm mol}^{-1} \text{ K}^{-1} \times 333 \text{ K}} \times \frac{1 \text{ mol } I_2}{2 \text{ mol HI}} \times \frac{253.8 \text{ g } I_2}{1 \text{ mol } I_2} = 0.00613 \text{ g } I_2$$

$$P_{tot} = P\{H_2S\} + P\{HI\} = (0.9837 - x) + 2x = 0.9837 + x = 0.9837 + 0.00182 = 0.9855 \text{ atm}$$

$$P_{tot} = 749.0 \text{ mmHg}$$

50. **(M)** We first determine the initial pressure of NH_3.

$$P\{NH_3(g)\} = \frac{nRT}{V} = \frac{0.100 \text{ mol } NH_3 \times 0.08206 \text{ L atm mol}^{-1} \text{ K}^{-1} \times 298 \text{ K}}{2.58 \text{ L}} = 0.948 \text{ atm}$$

Equation:	$NH_4HS(s)$	$\rightleftharpoons$	$NH_3(g)$	$+$	$H_2S(g)$
Initial:			0.948 atm		0 atm
Changes:			$+x$ atm		$+x$ atm
Equil:			$(0.948 + x)$ atm		x atm

$$K_p = P\{NH_3\}P\{H_2S\} = 0.108 = (0.948 + x)x = 0.948x + x^2 \quad 0 = x^2 + 0.948x - 0.108$$

$$x = \frac{-b \pm \sqrt{b^2 - 4ac}}{2a} = \frac{-0.948 \pm \sqrt{0.899 + 0.432}}{2} = 0.103 \text{ atm}, \; -1.05 \text{ atm}$$

The negative root makes no physical sense. The total gas pressure is obtained as follows.

$$P_{tot} = P\{NH_3\} + P\{H_2S\} = (0.948 + x) + x = 0.948 + 2x = 0.948 + 2 \times 0.103 = 1.154 \text{ atm}$$

51. **(M)** We substitute the given equilibrium pressure into the equilibrium constant expression and solve for the other equilibrium pressure. $K_p = \dfrac{P\{O_2\}^3}{P\{CO_2\}^2} = 28.5 = \dfrac{P\{O_2\}^3}{(0.0721 \text{ atm CO}_2)^2}$

$$P\{O_2\} = \sqrt[3]{P\{O_2\}^3} = \sqrt[3]{28.5(0.0712 \text{ atm})^2} = 0.529 \text{ atm O}_2$$

$$P_{total} = P\{CO_2\} + P\{O_2\} = 0.0721 \text{ atm CO}_2 + 0.529 \text{ atm O}_2 = 0.601 \text{ atm total}$$

52. **(M)** The composition of dry air is given in volume percent. Division of these percentages by 100 gives the volume fraction, which equals the mole fraction and also the partial pressure in atmospheres, if the total pressure is 1.00 atm. Thus, we have $P\{O_2\} = 0.20946$ atm and $P\{CO_2\} = 0.00036$ atm. We substitute these two values into the expression for Q_p.

$$Q_p = \frac{P\{O_2\}^3}{P\{CO_2\}^2} = \frac{(0.20946 \text{ atm O}_2)^3}{(0.00036 \text{ atm CO}_2)^2} = 6.4 \times 10^4 > 28.5 = K_p$$

The value of Q_p is much larger than the value of K_p. Thus this reaction should be spontaneous in the reverse direction until equilibrium is achieved. It will only be spontaneous in the forward direction when the pressure of O_2 drops or that of CO_2 rises (as would be the case in self-contained breathing devices).

53. **(M)**

(a) We first determine the initial pressure of each gas.

$$P\{CO\} = P\{Cl_2\} = \frac{nRT}{V} = \frac{1.00 \text{ mol} \times 0.08206 \text{ L atm mol}^{-1} \text{ K}^{-1} \times 668 \text{ K}}{1.75 \text{ L}} = 31.3 \text{ atm}$$

Then we calculate equilibrium partial pressures, organizing our calculation around the balanced chemical equation. We see that the equilibrium constant is not very large, meaning that we must solve the polynomial exactly (or by successive approximations).

Equation	CO(g)	+ Cl$_2$(g)	$\rightleftharpoons$	COCl$_2$(g)	$K_p = 22.5$
Initial:	31.3 atm	31.3 atm		0 atm	
Changes:	$-x$ atm	$-x$ atm		$+x$ atm	
Equil:	$31.3 - x$ atm	$31.3 - x$ atm		x atm	

$$K_p = \frac{P\{COCl_2\}}{P\{CO\}P\{Cl_2\}} = 22.5 = \frac{x}{(31.3 - x)^2} = \frac{x}{(979.\underline{7} - 62.6x + x^2)}$$

$$22.5(979.\underline{7} - 62.6x + x^2) = x = 22043 - 1408.\underline{5}x + 22.5x^2 = x$$

$$22043 - 1409.\underline{5}x + 22.5x^2 = 0 \quad \text{(Solve by using the quadratic equation)}$$

689

$$x = \frac{-b \pm \sqrt{b^2 - 4ac}}{2a} = \frac{-(-1409.5) \pm \sqrt{(-1409.5)^2 - 4(22.5)(22043)}}{2(22.5)}$$

$$x = \frac{1409.5 \pm \sqrt{2818}}{45} = 30.1\underline{4},\ 32.5\,(\text{too large})$$

$$P\{CO\} = P\{Cl_2\} = 31.3\ \text{atm} - 30.1\underline{4}\ \text{atm} = 1.16\ \text{atm} \qquad P\{COCl_2\} = 30.1\underline{4}\ \text{atm}$$

(b) $P_{\text{total}} = P\{CO\} + P\{Cl_2\} + P\{COCl_2\} = 1.1\underline{6}\ \text{atm} + 1.1\underline{6}\ \text{atm} + 30.14\ \text{atm} = 32.46\ \text{atm}$

54. **(M)** We first find the value of K_p for the reaction.

$$2\ NO_2(g) \rightleftharpoons 2\ NO(g) + O_2(g), \qquad K_c = 1.8 \times 10^{-6}\ \text{at } 184\ °C = 457\ K.$$

For this reaction $\Delta v_{\text{gas}} = 2 + 1 - 2 = +1$.

$$K_p = K_c(RT)^{\Delta v_{\text{gas}}} = 1.8 \times 10^{-6}\,(0.08206 \times 457)^{+1} = 6.8 \times 10^{-5}$$

To obtain the required reaction $NO(g) + \frac{1}{2}O_2(g) \rightleftharpoons NO_2(g)$ from the initial reaction, that initial reaction must be reversed and then divided by two. Thus, in order to determine the value of the equilibrium constant for the final reaction, the value of K_p for the initial reaction must be inverted, and the square root taken of the result.

$$K_{p,\text{final}} = \sqrt{\frac{1}{6.8 \times 10^{-5}}} = 1.2 \times 10^2$$

Le Châtelier's Principle

55. **(E)** Continuous removal of the product, of course, has the effect of decreasing the concentration of the products below their equilibrium values. Thus, the equilibrium system is disturbed by removing the products and the system will attempt (in vain, as it turns out) to re-establish the equilibrium by shifting toward the right, that is, to generate more products.

56. **(E)** We notice that the density of the solid ice is smaller than is that of liquid water. This means that the same mass of liquid water is present in a smaller volume than an equal mass of ice. Thus, if pressure is placed on ice, attempting to force it into a smaller volume, the ice will be transformed into the less-space-occupying water at 0 °C. Thus, at 0 °C under pressure, $H_2O(s)$ will melt to form $H_2O(l)$. This behavior is *not* expected in most cases because generally a solid is *more* dense than its liquid phase.

57. **(M)**
(a) This reaction is exothermic with $\Delta_r H° = -150.\ \text{kJ mol}^{-1}$. Thus, high temperatures favor the reverse reaction (endothermic reaction). The amount of $H_2(g)$ present at high temperatures will be less than that present at low temperatures.

(b) $H_2O(g)$ is one of the reactants involved. Introducing more will cause the equilibrium position to shift to the right, favoring products. The amount of $H_2(g)$ will increase.

(c) Doubling the volume of the container will favor the side of the reaction with the largest sum of gaseous stoichiometric coefficients. The sum of the stoichiometric coefficients of gaseous species is the same (4) on both sides of this reaction. Therefore, increasing the volume of the container will have no effect on the amount of $H_2(g)$ present at equilibrium.

(d) A catalyst merely speeds up the rate at which a reaction reaches the equilibrium position. The addition of a catalyst has no effect on the amount of $H_2(g)$ present at equilibrium.

58. (M)

(a) This reaction is endothermic, with $\Delta_r H° = +92.5$ kJ mol^{-1}. Thus, a higher temperature will favor the forward reaction and increase the amount of HI(g) present at equilibrium.

(b) The introduction of more product will favor the reverse reaction and decrease the amount of HI(g) present at equilibrium.

(c) The sum of the stoichiometric coefficients of gaseous products is larger than that for gaseous reactants. Increasing the volume of the container will favor the forward reaction and increase the amount of HI(g) present at equilibrium.

(d) A catalyst merely speeds up the rate at which a reaction reaches the equilibrium position. The addition of a catalyst has no effect on the amount of HI(g) present at equilibrium.

(e) The addition of an inert gas to the constant-volume reaction mixture will not change any partial pressures. It will have no effect on the amount of HI(g) present at equilibrium.

59. (M)

(a) The formation of NO(g) from its elements is an endothermic reaction ($\Delta_r H° = +$ 181 kJ/mol). Since the equilibrium position of endothermic reactions is shifted toward products at higher temperatures, we expect more NO(g) to be formed from the elements at higher temperatures.

(b) Reaction rates always are enhanced by higher temperatures, since a larger fraction of the collisions will have an energy that surmounts the activation energy. This enhancement of rates affects both the forward and the reverse reactions. Thus, the position of equilibrium is reached more rapidly at higher temperatures than at lower temperatures.

60. **(M)** If the reaction is endothermic ($\Delta H° > 0$), the forward reaction is favored at high temperatures. If the reaction is exothermic ($\Delta H° < 0$), the forward reaction is favored at low temperatures.

(a) $\Delta_r H° = \Delta_f H°\left[PCl_5(g)\right] - \Delta_f H°\left[PCl_3(g)\right] - \Delta_f H°\left[Cl_2(g)\right]$

$\Delta_r H° = -374.9\,\text{kJ mol}^{-1} - \left(-287.0\,\text{kJ mol}^{-1}\right) - 0.00\,\text{kJ mol}^{-1} = -87.9$ kJ/mol

(favored at low temperatures)

(b) $\Delta_r H^\circ = 2\Delta_f H^\circ[\text{H}_2\text{O}(g)] + 3\Delta_f H^\circ[\text{S(rhombic)}] - \Delta_f H^\circ[\text{SO}_2(g)] - 2\Delta_f H^\circ[\text{H}_2\text{S}(g)]$

$\Delta_r H^\circ = 2(-241.8\,\text{kJ mol}^{-1}) + 3(0.00\,\text{kJ mol}^{-1}) - (-296.8\,\text{kJ mol}^{-1}) - 2(-20.63\,\text{kJ mol}^{-1})$

$\Delta_r H^\circ = -145.5$ kJ/mol (favored at low temperatures)

(c) $\Delta_r H^\circ = 4\Delta_f H^\circ\left[\text{NOCl}(g)\right] + 2\Delta_f H^\circ\left[\text{H}_2\text{O}(g)\right]$

$\quad -2\Delta_f H^\circ\left[\text{N}_2(g)\right] - 3\Delta_f H^\circ\left[\text{O}_2(g)\right] - 4\Delta_f H^\circ\left[\text{HCl}(g)\right]$

$\Delta_r H^\circ = 4(51.71\,\text{kJ mol}^{-1}) + 2(-241.8\,\text{kJ mol}^{-1}) - 2(0.00\,\text{kJ mol}^{-1}) - 3(0.00\,\text{kJ mol}^{-1})$

$\quad -4(-92.31\,\text{kJ mol}^{-1})$

$\Delta_r H^\circ = +92.5$ kJ/mol (favored at higher temperatures)

61. **(E)** If the total pressure of a mixture of gases at equilibrium is doubled by compression, the equilibrium will shift to the side with fewer moles of gas to counteract the increase in pressure. Thus, if the pressure of an equilibrium mixture of $\text{N}_2(g)$, $\text{H}_2(g)$, and $\text{NH}_3(g)$ is doubled, the reaction involving these three gases, i.e., $\text{N}_2(g) + 3\,\text{H}_2(g) \rightleftharpoons 2\,\text{NH}_3(g)$, will proceed in the forward direction to produce a new equilibrium mixture that contains additional ammonia and less molecular nitrogen and molecular hydrogen. In other words, $P\{\text{N}_2(g)\}$ will have decreased when equilibrium is re-established. It is important to note, however, that the final equilibrium partial pressure for the N_2 will, nevertheless, be higher than its original partial pressure prior to the doubling of the total pressure.

62. **(M)**

(a) Because $\Delta_r H^\circ = 0$, the position of the equilibrium for this reaction will not be affected by temperature. Since the equilibrium position is expressed by the value of the equilibrium constant, we expect K_p to be unaffected by, or to remain constant with, temperature.

(b) From part (a), we know that the value of K_p will not change when the temperature is changed. The pressures of the gases, however, will change with temperature. (Recall the ideal gas law: $P = nRT/V$.) In fact, all pressures will increase. The stoichiometric coefficients in the reaction are such that at higher pressures the formation of more reactant will be favored (the reactant side has fewer moles of gas). Thus, the amount of $\text{D}(g)$ will be smaller when equilibrium is reestablished at the higher temperature for the cited reaction.

$$\text{A}(s) \rightleftharpoons \text{B}(s) + 2\,\text{C}(g) + \frac{1}{2}\,\text{D}(g)$$

63. **(M)** Increasing the volume of an equilibrium mixture causes that mixture to shift toward the side (reactants or products) where the sum of the stoichiometric coefficients of the gaseous species is the larger. That is: shifts to the right if $\Delta v_{gas} > 0$, shifts to the left if $\Delta v_{gas} > 0$, and does not shift if $\Delta v_{gas} > 0$.

(a) $C(s) + H_2O(g) \rightleftharpoons CO(g) + H_2(g), \Delta v_{gas} > 0$, shift right, toward products

(b) $Ca(OH)_2(s) + CO_2(g) \rightleftharpoons CaCO_3(s) + H_2O(g), \quad \Delta v_{gas} = 0$, no shift, no change in equilibrium position.

(c) $4\,NH_3(g) + 5\,O_2(g) \rightleftharpoons 4\,NO(g) + 6\,H_2O(g), \quad \Delta v_{gas} > 0$, shifts right, towards products

64. **(M)** The equilibrium position for a reaction that is exothermic shifts to the left (reactants are favored) when the temperature is raised. For one that is endothermic, it shifts right (products are favored) when the temperature is raised.

(a) $NO(g) \rightleftharpoons \frac{1}{2}\,N_2(g) + \frac{1}{2}\,O_2(g) \quad \Delta_r H° = -90.2\ kJ\,mol^{-1}$ shifts left, % dissociation $\downarrow$

(b) $SO_3(g) \rightleftharpoons SO_2(g) + \frac{1}{2}\,O_2(g) \quad \Delta_r H° = +98.9\,kJ\,mol^{-1}$ shifts right, % dissociation $\uparrow$

(c) $N_2H_4(g) \rightleftharpoons N_2(g) + 2\,H_2(g) \quad \Delta_r H° = -95.4\,kJ\,mol^{-1}$ shifts left, % dissociation $\downarrow$

(d) $COCl_2(g) \rightleftharpoons CO(g) + Cl_2(g) \quad \Delta_r H° = +108.3\ kJ\,mol^{-1}$ shifts right, % dissociation $\uparrow$

65. **(E)**

(a) Conceptually, to increase the temperature, we add heat. The equilibrium shifts in the direction that consumes heat. There will be net reaction to the left and the $Hb:O_2$ level decreases.

(b) Net reaction to the left, replacing some of the O_2 that was removed. The $Hb:O_2$ level decreases.

(c) Net reaction to the right, using up some of the added Hb. The $Hb:O_2$ level increases.

66. **(E)**

(a) CO_2 (g) increases as the equilibrium is pushed toward the reactant side

(b) Increase CO_2 (aq) levels, which then pushes the equilibrium to the product side

(c) It has no effect, but it helps establish the final equilibrium more quickly

(d) CO_2 increases, as the equilibrium shifts to the reactants

67. **(E)** The pressure on N_2O_4 will initially increase as the crystal melts and then vaporizes, but over time the new concentration decreases as the equilibrium is shifted toward NO_2.

68. **(E)** If the equilibrium is shifted to the product side by increasing temperature, that means that heat is a "reactant" (or being consumed). Therefore, HI decomposition is endothermic.

69. **(E)** Since $\Delta_r H$ is >0, the reaction is endothermic. If we increase the temperature of the reaction, we are adding heat to the reaction, which shifts the reaction toward the decomposition of calcium carbonate. While the amount of calcium carbonate will decrease, its concentration will remain the same because it is a solid.

70. **(E)** The amount of N_2 increases in the body. As the pressure on the body increases, the equilibrium shifts from N_2 gas to N_2 (aq).

Reactions with Very Small or Very Large *K* Values

71. **(M)** The reaction of excess CuS in acid is shown below:

$$CuS(s) + 2\,H_3O^+(aq) \rightleftharpoons Cu^{2+}(aq) + H_2S(aq) + 2\,H_2O(l)$$

We can set up the equilibrium table as follows:

	CuS(s) +	2 H₃O⁺(aq)	⇌	Cu²⁺(aq)	+ H₂S(aq)	+ H₂O(l)
I		0.30 M		0 M	0.10 M	
C		− 2x M		+ x M	+ x M	
E		(0.30 − 2x) M		x M	(0.10 + x) M	

At equilibrium, we must have

$$K = \frac{(x)(0.10+x)}{(0.30-2x)^2}$$

Although the expression can be solved exactly by rearranging it and using the quadratic formula, an approximate solution can be obtained rather easily. Because $K \ll 1$, we expect only a small amount of CuS to dissolve. Thus, we anticipate that $2x \ll 0.30$ and $x \ll 0.10$. Therefore,

$$K \approx \frac{(x)(0.10)}{(0.30)^2} \quad \Rightarrow \quad x \approx \frac{(0.30)^2 K}{(0.10)} = 5.4 \times 10^{-16}\ M$$

The calculated value of *x* is much less than 0.10, so the assumption is justified. The equilibrium concentration of Cu^{2+} is about 5×10^{-16} M.

72. **(M)** The equilibrium summary (ICE table) is as follows.

	C₂H₂(g) +	3 H₂(g)	⇌	2 CH₄(g)	$K_c = 4.9 \times 10^{-11}$ at 1100 K
I	0.0200 M	0.200 M		0 M	
C	− x M	− 3x M		+ 2x M	
E	(0.0200 − x) M	(0.200 − 3x) M		2x M	

At equilibrium, we must have

$$K = \frac{(2x)^2}{(0.0200-x)(0.200-3x)^3}$$

We can simplify the expression above considerably by noting that $K \ll 1$. Thus, we expect the extent of reaction to be small. Let's assume $x \ll 0.0200$ and $3x \ll 0.200$. Therefore,

$$K_c \approx \frac{4x^2}{(0.0200)(0.200)^3} \quad \Rightarrow \quad x \approx \sqrt{\frac{(0.0200)(0.200)^3 K_c}{4}} = 4.43 \times 10^{-8}$$

The calculated value of *x* is much less than 0.0200, so the assumption is justified. The equilibrium concentration of CH₄ is

$$[CH_4]_{eq} = 2x = 8.9 \times 10^{-8}\ M$$

73. **(M)** The reaction of CH_3COOH and $NaOH$ is shown below:

$$CH_3COOH(aq) + OH^-(aq) \rightleftharpoons CH_3COO^-(aq) + H_2O(l)$$

Because $K_c \gg 1$, for simplicity we can view the reaction reaching true equilibrium by going to completion by completely forming CH_3COO^- and H_2O, and then backing up by a small extent as the CH_3COO^- and H_2O react to form CH_3COOH and OH^-.

	$CH_3COOH(aq)$	$+$ $OH^-(aq)$	$\rightleftharpoons$	$CH_3COO^-(aq)$	$+$ H_2O (l)
I	0.100 M	0.100 M		0 M	
100%	0 M	0 M		0.100 M	
C	$+ x$ M	$+x$ M		$- x$ M	
E	x M	x M		$(0.100 - x)$ M	

Because K_c is so large for the forward reaction, we expect the reverse reaction to happen to a very slight extent. Therefore, the concentration of CH_3COO^- remains essentially unchanged from its final value; that is, $0.100 - x \approx 0.100$.

$$K_c = \frac{[CH_3COO^-]}{[CH_3COOH][OH^-]} \approx \frac{0.100}{(x)(x)} \quad \Rightarrow \quad x \approx \sqrt{\frac{0.100}{K_c}} = 7.45 \times 10^{-6}$$

$[CH_3COOH]_{eq} = 7.5 \times 10^{-6}$ M

Of the initial amount of CH_3COOH, only 0.0075% remains at equilibrium. Therefore, 99.9925% reacted. The reaction goes essentially to completion.

74. **(M)** The reaction of NH_2^- with water is shown below:

$$NH_2^-(aq) + H_2O(l) \rightleftharpoons NH_3(aq) + OH^-(l)$$

Because $K_c \gg 1$, for simplicity we can view the reaction reaching true equilibrium by going to completion by completely forming NH_3 and OH^-, and then backing up by a small extent as the NH_3 and OH^- react and form CH_3COOH and H_2O.

	$NH_2^-(aq)$	$+ H_2O(l)$	$\rightleftharpoons$	$NH_3(aq)$	$+$ OH^- (l)
I	0.0125 M			0 M	0 M
100%	0 M			0.0125 M	0.0125 M
C	$+ x$ M			$- x$ M	$- x$ M
E	x M			$(0.0125 - x)$ M	$(0.0125 - x)$ M

Because K_c is so large for the forward reaction, we expect the reverse reaction to happen to a very slight extent. Therefore, the concentration of NH_3 and OH^- remains essentially unchanged from their final values; that is, $0.0125 - x \approx 0.0125$

$$K_c = \frac{[NH_3][OH^-]}{[NH_2^-]} \approx \frac{(0.0125)^2}{x} \quad \Rightarrow \quad x \approx \frac{0.0125^2}{K_c} = 1.6 \times 10^{-24}$$

$[NH_2^-]_{eq} = 1.6 \times 10^{-24}$ M

If we use this result to calculate the number of NH_2^- ions present at equilibrium in 1.0 L of solution, we obtain:

$$1.6 \times 10^{-24} \frac{\text{mol}}{\text{L}} \times 1\,\text{L} \times \frac{6.022 \times 10^{23} \text{ ions}}{1 \text{ mol}} = 0.96 \text{ ions} \approx 1 \text{ ion}$$

We cannot have less than one ion in solution, so the calculated concentration must be considered a very rough estimate. The main point is that, at equilibrium, relatively few NH_2^- ions will be present in solution. The reaction goes essentially to completion.

INTEGRATIVE AND ADVANCED EXERCISES

75. **(E)** In a reaction of the type $I_2(g) \rightarrow 2\,I(g)$ the bond between two iodine atoms, the I—I bond, must be broken. Since $I_2(g)$ is a stable molecule, this bond breaking process must be endothermic. Hence, the reaction cited is an endothermic reaction. The equilibrium position of endothermic reactions will be shifted toward products when the temperature is raised.

76. **(M)**
   (a) In order to determine a value of K_c, we first must find the CO_2 concentration in the gas phase. Note, the total volume for the gas is 1.00 L (moles and molarity are numerically equal)

$$[CO_2] = \frac{n}{V} = \frac{P}{RT} = \frac{1.00 \text{ atm}}{0.08206 \frac{\text{L atm}}{\text{mol K}} \times 298 \text{ K}} = 0.0409 \text{ M} \qquad K_c = \frac{[CO_2(aq)]}{[CO_2(g)]} = \frac{3.29 \times 10^{-2} \text{ M}}{0.0409 \text{ M}} = 0.804$$

   (b) It does not matter to which phase the radioactive $^{14}CO_2$ is added. This is an example of a Le Châtelier's principle problem in which the stress is a change in concentration of the reactant $CO_2(g)$. To find the new equilibrium concentrations, we must solve and I.C.E. table. Since $Q_c < K_c$, the reaction shifts to the product, CO_2 (aq) side.

Reaction:	$CO_2(g)$	$\rightleftharpoons$	$CO_2(aq)$
Initial:	0.0409 mol		3.29×10^{-3} mol
Stress	+0.01000 mol		−
Changes:	− x mol		+ x mol
Equilibrium:	$(0.05090 - x)$ mol		$3.29 \times 10^{-3} + x$ mol

$$K_c = \frac{[CO_2(aq)]}{[CO_2(g)]} = \frac{\dfrac{3.29 \times 10^{-3} + x \text{ mol}}{0.1000 \text{ L}}}{\dfrac{(0.05090 - x) \text{ mol}}{1.000 \text{ L}}} = 0.804 = \frac{3.29 \times 10^{-2} + 10x}{0.05090 - x} \qquad x = 7.43 \times 10^{-4} \text{mol } CO_2$$

   Total moles of CO_2 in the aqueous phase $(0.1000 \text{ L})(3.29 \times 10^{-2} + 7.43 \times 10^{-3})$
   $= 4.03 \times 10^{-3}$ mol

   Total moles of CO_2 in the gaseous phase $(1.000 \text{ L})(5.090 \times 10^{-2} - 7.43 \times 10^{-4})$
   $= 5.02 \times 10^{-2}$ mol

   Total moles of $CO_2 = 5.02 \times 10^{-2}$ mol $+ 4.03 \times 10^{-3}$ mol $= 5.42 \times 10^{-2}$ mol

There is continuous mixing of the ^{12}C and ^{14}C such that the isotopic ratios in the two phases is the same. This ratio is given by the mole fraction of the two isotopes.

For $^{14}CO_2$ in either phase its mole fraction is $\dfrac{0.01000 \text{ mol}}{5.419 \times 10^{-2} \text{ mol}} \times 100 = 18.4\underline{5}$ %

Moles of $^{14}CO_2$ in the gaseous phase $= 5.02 \times 10^{-2}$ mol $\times 0.1845 = 0.00926$ mol

Moles of $^{14}CO_2$ in the aqueous phase $= 4.03 \times 10^{-3}$ mol $\times 0.1845 = 0.000744$ mol

77. **(M)** Dilution makes Q_c larger than K_c. Thus, the reaction mixture will shift left in order to regain equilibrium. We organize our calculation around the balanced chemical equation.

Equation: $Ag^+(aq)$ $+$ $Fe^{2+}(aq)$ $\rightleftharpoons$ $Fe^{3+}(aq) + Ag(s)$ $K_c = 2.98$

Equil: 0.31 M   0.21 M   0.19 M   –

Dilution: 0.12 M   0.084 M   0.076 M   –

Changes: $+x$ M $+x$ M $-x$ M   –

New equil: $(0.12 + x)$ M $(0.084 + x)$ M $(0.076 - x)$ M   –

$K_c = \dfrac{[Fe^{3+}]}{[Ag^+][Fe^{2+}]} = 2.98 = \dfrac{0.076 - x}{(0.12 + x)(0.084 + x)}$ $2.98\,(0.12 + x)(0.084 + x) = 0.076 - x$

$0.076 - x = 0.030 + 0.61x + 2.98\,x^2$ $2.98\,x^2 + 1.61 \quad x - 0.046 = 0$

$x = \dfrac{-1.61 \pm \sqrt{2.59 + 0.55}}{5.96} = 0.027, -0.57$ Note that the negative root makes no physical sense; it gives $[Fe^{2+}] = 0.084 - 0.57 = -0.49$ M.

Thus, the new equilibrium concentrations are

$[Fe^{2+}] = 0.084 + 0.027 = 0.111$ M $[Ag^+] = 0.12 + 0.027 = 0.15$ M

$[Fe^{3+}] = 0.076 - 0.027 = 0.049$ M   We can check our answer by substitution.

$K_c = \dfrac{0.049 \text{ M}}{0.111 \text{ M} \times 0.15 \text{ M}} = 2.94 \approx 2.98$ (within precision limits)

78. **(M)** The percent dissociation should increase as the pressure is lowered, according to Le Châtelier's principle. Thus the total pressure in this instance should be more than in Example 15-12, where the percent dissociation is 12.5%. The total pressure in Example 15-12 was computed starting from the total number of moles at equilibrium.

The total amount $= (0.0240 - 0.00300)$ moles $N_2O_4 + 2 \times 0.00300$ mol $NO_2 = 0.027$ mol gas.

$P_{\text{total}} = \dfrac{nRT}{V} = \dfrac{0.0270 \text{ mol} \times 0.08206 \text{ L atm K}^{-1} \text{ mol}^{-1} \times 298 \text{ K}}{0.372 \text{ L}} = 1.77 \text{ atm}$ (Example 15-12)

We base our solution on the balanced chemical equation. We designate the initial pressure of N_2O_4 as P. The change in $P\{N_2O_4\}$ is given as $-0.10\,P$ atm. to represent the 10.0 % dissociation.

Equation: $N_2O_4(g)$ $\rightleftharpoons$ $2\,NO_2(g)$

Initial: P atm   0 atm

Changes: $-0.10\,P$ atm $+2(0.10\,P$ atm$)$

Equil: $0.90\,P$ atm $0.20\,P$ atm

$$K_p = \frac{P\{NO_2\}^2}{P\{N_2O_4\}} = \frac{(0.20\,P)^2}{0.90\,P} = \frac{0.040\,P}{0.90} = 0.113 \qquad P = \frac{0.113 \times 0.90}{0.040} = 2.54 \text{ atm.}$$

Thus, the total pressure at equilibrium is $0.90\,P + 0.20\,P$ and $1.10\,P$ (where $P = 2.54$ atm) Therefore, total pressure at equilibrium = 2.79 atm.

79. **(M)** Equation: $2\,SO_3(g)$ $\rightleftharpoons$ $2\,SO_2(g)$ $+$ $O_2(g)$

Initial: 1.00 atm   0 atm   0 atm

Changes: $-2x$ atm $+2x$ atm $+x$ atm

Equil: $(1.00-2x)$atm $2x$ atm x atm

Because of the small value of the equilibrium constant, the reaction does not proceed very far toward products in reaching equilibrium. Hence, we assume that $x \ll 1.00$ atm and calculate an approximate value of x (small K problem).

$$K_P = \frac{P\{SO_2\}^2\,P\{O_2\}}{P\{SO_3\}^2} = \frac{(2x)^2\,x}{(1.00-2x)^2} = 1.6 \times 10^{-5} \approx \frac{4x^3}{(1.00)^2} \qquad x = 0.016 \text{ atm}$$

A second cycle may get closer to the true value of x.

$$1.6 \times 10^{-5} \approx \frac{4x^3}{(1.00-0.032)^2} = x = 0.016 \text{ atm}$$

Our initial value was sufficiently close. We now compute the total pressure at equilibrium.

$$P_{\text{total}} = P\{SO_3\} + P\{SO_2\} + P\{O_2\} = (1.00-2x) + 2x + x = 1.00 + x = 1.00 + 0.016 = 1.02 \text{ atm}$$

80. **(M)** Let us start with one mole of air, and let $2x$ be the amount in moles of NO formed.

Equation: $N_2(g)$ $+$ $O_2(g)$ $\rightleftharpoons$ $2\,NO(g)$

Initial: 0.79 mol   0.21 mol   0 mol

Changes: $-x$ mol $-x$ mol $+2x$ mol

Equil: $(0.79-x)$mol $(0.21-x)$mol $2x$ mol

$$\chi_{NO} = \frac{n\{NO\}}{n\{N_2\} + n\{O_2\} + n\{NO\}} = \frac{2x}{(0.79-x)+(0.21-x)+2x} = 0.018 = \frac{2x}{1.00}$$

$x = 0.0090$ mol $0.79 - x = 0.78$ mol N_2 $0.21 - x = 0.20$ mol O_2

$2x = 0.018$ mol NO

$$K_p = \frac{P\{NO\}^2}{P(N_2)\,P\{O_2\}} = \frac{\left(\dfrac{n\{NO\}\,RT}{V_{\text{total}}}\right)^2}{\dfrac{n\{N_2)\,RT}{V_{\text{total}}}\,\dfrac{n\{O_2\}\,RT}{V_{\text{total}}}} = \frac{n\{NO\}^2}{n\{N_2\}\,n\{O_2\}} = \frac{(0.018)^2}{0.78 \times 0.20} = 2.1 \times 10^{-3}$$

81. **(D)** We organize the data around the balanced chemical equation. Note that the reaction is stoichimoetrically balanced.

(a)

Equation:	$2\,SO_2(g)\ +$	$O_2(g)\ \rightleftharpoons$	$2\,SO_3(g)$
Equil :	0.32 mol	0.16 mol	0.68 mol
Add SO_3	0.32 mol	0.16 mol	1.68 mol
Initial :	$\dfrac{0.32\text{ mol}}{10.0\text{ L}}$	$\dfrac{0.16\text{ mol}}{10.0\text{ L}}$	$\dfrac{1.68\text{ mol}}{10.0\text{ L}}$
Initial :	0.032 M	0.016 M	0.168 M
To right :	0.000 M	0.000 M	0.200 M
Changes :	$+\,2x$ M	$+\,x$ M	$-\,2x$ M
Equil :	$2x$ M	x M	$(0.200-2x)$M

In setting up this problem, we note that solving this question exactly involves finding the roots for a cubic equation. Thus, we assumed that all of the reactants have been converted to products. This gives the results in the line labeled "To right." We then reach equilibrium from this position by converting some of the product back into reactants. Now, we substitute these expressions into the equilibrium constant expression, and we solve this expression approximately by assuming that $2x \ll 0.200$.

$$K_c = \frac{[SO_3]^2}{[SO_2]^2[O_2]} = \frac{(0.200-2x)^2}{(2x)^2\,x} = 2.8\times10^2 \approx \frac{(0.200)^2}{4x^3}\ \text{or}\ x = 0.033$$

We then substitute this approximate value into the expression for K_c.

$$K_c = \frac{(0.200-0.066)^2}{4x^3} = 2.8\times10^2\ \text{or}\ x = 0.025$$

Let us try one more cycle. $K_c = \dfrac{(0.200-0.050)^2}{4x^3} = 2.8\times10^2\ \text{or}\ x = 0.027$

This gives the following concentrations and amounts of each species.

$[SO_3] = 0.200 - (2\times0.027) = 0.146$ M   amount $SO_3 = 10.0$ L $\times$ 0.146 M $= 1.46$ mol SO_3

$[SO_2] = 2\times0.027 = 0.054$ M   amount $SO_2 = 10.0$ L $\times$ 0.054 M $= 0.54$ mol SO_2

$[O_2] = 0.027$ M   amount $O_2 = 10.0$ L $\times$ 0.027 M $= 0.27$ mol O_2

(b)

Equation:	$2\ SO_2(g)\ +$	$O_2(g)\ \rightleftharpoons$	$2\,SO_3(g)$
Equil :	0.32 mol	0.16 mol	0.68 mol
Equil :	$\dfrac{0.32\text{ mol}}{10.0\text{ L}}$	$\dfrac{0.16\text{ mol}}{10.0\text{ L}}$	$\dfrac{0.68\text{ mol}}{10.0\text{ L}}$
Equil :	0.032 M	0.016 M	0.068 M
0.10 V :	0.32 M	0.16 M	0.68 M
To right :	0.00 M	0.00 M	1.00 M
Changes :	$+\,2x$ M	$+x$ M	$-2x$ M
Equil :	$2x$ M	x M	$(1.00-2x)$M

Again, notice that an exact solution involves finding the roots of a cubic. So we have taken the reaction 100% in the forward direction and then sent it back in the reverse direction to a small extent to reach equilibrium. We now solve the K_c expression for x, obtaining first an approximate value by assuming $2x \ll 1.00$.

$$K_c = \frac{[SO_3]^2}{[SO_2]^2[O_2]} = \frac{(1.00 - 2x)^2}{(2x)^2 x} = 2.8 \times 10^2 \approx \frac{(1.00)^2}{4x^3} \text{ or } x = 0.096$$

We then use this approximate value of x to find a second approximation for x.

$$K_c = \frac{(1.00 - 0.19)^2}{4x^3} = 2.8 \times 10^2 \qquad \text{or} \qquad x = 0.084$$

Another cycle gives $K_c = \dfrac{(1.00 - 0.17)^2}{4x^3} = 2.8 \times 10^2 \quad$ or $\quad x = 0.085$

Then we compute the equilibrium concentrations and amounts.

$[SO_3] = 1.00 - (2 \times 0.085) = 0.83$ M   amount $SO_3 = 1.00$ L $\times 0.83$ M $= 0.83$ mol SO_3

$[SO_2] = 2 \times 0.085 = 0.17$ M   amount $SO_2 = 1.00$ L $\times 0.17$ M $= 0.17$ mol SO_2

$[O_2] = 0.085$ M   amount $O_2 = 1.00$ L $\times 0.085$ M $= 0.085$ mol O_2

82. (M)

Equation: $HOC_6H_4COOH(g) \rightleftharpoons C_6H_5OH(g) + CO_2(g)$

$$n_{CO_2} = \frac{PV}{RT} = \frac{\left(\dfrac{730 \text{ mmHg}}{760 \text{ mmHg/atm}}\right)\left(\left(\dfrac{48.2 + 48.5}{2}\right) \times \dfrac{1 \text{ L}}{1000 \text{ mL}}\right)}{0.0821 \text{ L atm mol K} \, (293 \text{ K})} = 1.93 \times 10^{-3} \text{ mol } CO_2$$

Note that moles of CO_2 = moles phenol

$$n_{\text{salicylic acid}} = \frac{0.300 \text{ g}}{138 \text{ g/mol}} = 2.17 \times 10^{-3} \text{ mol salicylic acid}$$

$$K_c = \frac{[C_6H_5OH][CO_2(g)]}{[HOC_6H_4COOH]} = \frac{\left(\dfrac{1.93 \text{ mmol}}{50.0 \text{ mL}}\right)^2}{\dfrac{(2.17 - 1.93) \text{ mmol}}{50.0 \text{ mL}}} = 0.310$$

$$K_p = K_c(RT)^{(2-1)} = (0.310) \times (0.08206) \times (473) = 12.0$$

83. (D)

(a) This reaction is exothermic and thus, conversion of synthesis gas to methane is favored at lower temperatures. Since $\Delta v_{\text{gas}} = (1+1) - (1+3) = -2$, high pressure favors the products.

(b) The value of K_c is a large number, meaning that almost all of the reactants are converted to products (note that the reaction is stoichiometrically balanced). Thus, after we set up the initial conditions we force the reaction to products and then allow the system to reach equilibrium.

Equation: $3\,H_2(g)\ +\ CO(g)\ \rightleftharpoons\ CH_4(g)\ +\ H_2O(g)$

Initial:	$\dfrac{3.00\ \text{mol}}{15.0\ \text{L}}$	$\dfrac{1.00\ \text{mol}}{15.0\ \text{L}}$	0 M	0 M
Initial:	0.200 M	0.0667 M	0 M	0 M
To right:	0.000 M	0.000 M	0.0667 M	0.0667 M
Changes:	$+3x$ M	$+x$ M	$-x$ M	$-x$ M
Equil:	$3x$ M	x M	$(0.0667-x)$M	$(0.0667-x)$M

$$K_c = \frac{[CH_4][H_2O]}{[H_2]^3[CO]} = \frac{(0.0667-x)^2}{(3x)^3\,x} = 190. \qquad \sqrt{190.} = \frac{0.0667-x}{\sqrt{27}\ x^2}$$

$$\sqrt{190 \times 27}\ x^2 = 0.0667 - x = 71.6\ x^2 \qquad 71.6\,x^2 + x - 0.0667 = 0$$

$$x = \frac{-b \pm \sqrt{b^2 - 4ac}}{2a} = \frac{-1.00 \pm \sqrt{1.00 + 19.1}}{143} = 0.0244\ M$$

$[CH_4] = [H_2O] = 0.0667 - 0.0244 = 0.0423$ M

$[H_2] = 3 \times 0.0244 = 0.0732$ M

$[CO] = 0.0244$ M

We check our calculation by computing the value of the equilibrium constant.

$$K_c = \frac{[CH_4]\,[H_2O]}{[H_2]^3\,[CO]} = \frac{(0.0423)^2}{(0.0732)^3\ 0.0244} = 187$$

Now we compute the amount in moles of each component present at equilibrium, and finally the mole fraction of CH_4.

amount CH_4 = amount $H_2O = 0.0423\ M \times 15.0\ L = 0.635$ mol

amount $H_2 = 0.0732\ M \times 15.0\ L = 1.10$ mol

amount $CO = 0.0244\ M \times 15.0\ L = 0.366$ mol

$$\chi_{CH_4} = \frac{0.635\ \text{mol}}{0.635\ \text{mol} + 0.635\ \text{mol} + 1.10\ \text{mol} + 0.366\ \text{mol}} = 0.232$$

84. (M) We base our calculation on 1.00 mole of PCl_5 being present initially.

Equation: $PCl_5(g) \rightleftharpoons PCl_3(g)\ +\ Cl_2(g)$

Initial:	1.00 mol	0 M	0 M
Changes:	$-\alpha$ mol	$+\alpha$ mol	$+\alpha$ mol
Equil:	$(1.00-\alpha)$ mol	α mol	α mol

$n_{\text{total}} = 1.00 - \alpha + \alpha + \alpha = 1.00 + \alpha$

Equation: $\qquad PCl_5(g) \ \rightleftharpoons \ PCl_3(g) \ + \ Cl_2(g)$

Mol fract. $\qquad \dfrac{1.00-\alpha}{1.00+\alpha} \qquad\qquad \dfrac{\alpha}{1.00+\alpha} \qquad\qquad \dfrac{\alpha}{1.00+\alpha}$

$$K_p = \frac{P\{Cl_2\}\,P\{PCl_3\}}{P\{PCl_5\}} = \frac{[\chi\{Cl_2\}P_{total}]\,[\chi\{PCl_3\}P_{total}]}{[\chi\{PCl_5\}P_{total}]} = \frac{\left(\dfrac{\alpha}{1.00+\alpha}P_{total}\right)^2}{\dfrac{1.00-\alpha}{1.00+\alpha}P_{total}} = \frac{\alpha^2\,P_{total}}{(1.00+\alpha)(1.00-\alpha)} = \frac{\alpha^2\,P_{total}}{1-\alpha^2}$$

85. **(M)** We assume that the entire 5.00 g is N_2O_4 and reach equilibrium from this starting point.

$$[N_2O_4]_i = \frac{5.00\text{ g}}{0.500\text{ L}} \times \frac{1\text{ mol }N_2O_4}{92.01\text{ g }N_2O_4} = 0.109\text{ M}$$

Equation: $\quad N_2O_4(g) \qquad\rightleftharpoons\qquad 2\,NO_2(g)$
Initial: $\qquad 0.109 \qquad\qquad\qquad 0\text{ M}$
Changes: $\qquad -x\text{ M} \qquad\qquad\qquad +2x\text{ M}$
Equil: $\qquad (0.0109-x)\text{ M} \qquad\qquad 2x\text{ M}$

$$K_c = \frac{[NO_2]^2}{[N_2O_4]} = 4.61\times10^{-3} = \frac{(2x)^2}{0.109-x} \qquad 4x^2 = 5.02\times10^{-4} - 4.61\times10^{-3}\,x$$

$$4x^2 + 0.00461\,x - 0.000502 = 0$$

$$x = \frac{-b\pm\sqrt{b^2-4ac}}{2a} = \frac{-0.00461\pm\sqrt{2.13\times10^{-5}+8.03\times10^{-3}}}{8} = 0.0106\text{ M}, \ -0.0118\text{ M}$$

(The method of successive approximations yields 0.0106 after two iterations)

amount $N_2O_4 = 0.500$ L $(0.109-0.0106)$ M $= 0.0492$ mol N_2O_4

amount $NO_2 = 0.500$ L $\times 2 \times 0.0106$ M $= 0.0106$ mol NO_2

$$\text{mol fraction }NO_2 = \frac{0.0106\text{ mol }NO_2}{0.0106\text{ mol }NO_2 + 0.0492\text{ mol }N_2O_4} = 0.177$$

86. **(M)** We let P be the initial pressure in atmospheres of $COCl_2(g)$.

Equation: $COCl_2(g) \qquad\rightleftharpoons\qquad CO(g) \ + \ Cl_2(g)$
Initial: $\qquad P \qquad\qquad\qquad 0\text{ M} \qquad\qquad 0\text{ M}$
Changes: $\qquad -x \qquad\qquad\qquad +x \qquad\qquad +x$
Equil: $\qquad P-x \qquad\qquad\qquad x \qquad\qquad x$

Total pressure $= 3.00$ atm $= P-x+x+x = P+x \qquad P = 3.00-x$

$P\{COCl_2\} = P-x = 3.00-x-x = 3.00-2x$

$$K_p = \frac{P\{CO\}P\{Cl_2\}}{P(COCl_2)} = 0.0444 = \frac{x\cdot x}{3.00-2x}$$

$$x^2 = 0.133 - 0.0888\,x \qquad x^2 + 0.0888\,x - 0.133 = 0$$

$$x = \frac{-b\pm\sqrt{b^2-4ac}}{2a} = \frac{-0.0888\pm\sqrt{0.00789+0.532}}{2} = 0.323, \ -0.421$$

Since a negative pressure is physically meaningless, $x = 0.323$ atm.
(The method of successive approximations yields $x = 0.323$ after four iterations.)
$P\{CO\} = P\{Cl_2\} = 0.323$ atm

$P\{COCl_2\} = 3.00 - 2 \times 0.323 = 2.35$ atm

The mole fraction of each gas is its partial pressure divided by the total pressure. And the contribution of each gas to the apparent molar mass of the mixture is the mole fraction of that gas multiplied by the molar mass of that gas.

$$M_{avg} = \frac{P\{CO\}}{P_{tot}} M\{CO\} + \frac{P\{Cl_2\}}{P_{tot}} M\{Cl_2\} + \frac{P\{COCl_2\}}{P_{tot}} M\{COCl_2\}$$

$$= \left(\frac{0.323\ \text{atm}}{3.00\ \text{atm}} \times 28.01\ \text{g/mol} \right) + \left(\frac{0.323\ \text{atm}}{3.00\ \text{atm}} \times 70.91\ \text{g/mol} \right) + \left(\frac{2.32\ \text{atm}}{3.00\ \text{atm}} \times 98.92\ \text{g/mol} \right)$$

$$= 87.1\ \text{g/mol}$$

87. (M) Each mole fraction equals the partial pressure of the substance divided by the total pressure. Thus $\chi\{NH_3\} = P\{NH_3\}/P_{tot}$ or $P\{NH_3\} = \chi\{NH_3\}\, P_{tot}$

$$K_p = \frac{P\{NH_3\}^2}{P\{N_2\}\, P\{H_2\}^3} = \frac{(\chi\{NH_3\}P_{tot})^2}{(\chi\{N_2\}P_{tot})\,(\chi\{H_2\}P_{tot})^3} = \frac{\chi\{NH_3\}^2}{\chi\{N_2\}\,\chi\{H_2\}^3}\frac{(P_{tot})^2}{(P_{tot})^4}$$

$$= \frac{\chi\{NH_3\}^2}{\chi\{N_2\}\,\chi\{H_2\}^3}\frac{1}{(P_{tot})^2}$$

This is the expression we were asked to derive.

88. (D) Since the mole ratio of N_2 to H_2 is 1:3, $\chi\{H_2\} = 3\chi\{N_2\}$. Since $P_{tot} = 1.00$ atm, it follows.

$$K_p = \frac{\chi\{NH_3\}^2}{\chi\{N_2\}(3\chi\{N_2\})^3}\frac{1}{(1.00)^2} = 9.06 \times 10^{-2} = 0.0906$$

$$3^3 \times 0.0906 = \frac{\chi\{NH_3\}^2}{\chi\{N_2\}\,\chi\{N_2\}^3} = \frac{\chi\{NH_3\}^2}{\chi\{N_2\}^4} \quad \frac{\chi\{NH_3\}}{\chi\{N_2\}^2} = \sqrt{3^3 \times 0.0906} = 1.56$$

We realize that $\chi\{NH_3\} + \chi\{N_2\} + \chi\{H_2\} = 1.00 = \chi\{NH_3\} + \chi\{N_2\} + 3\chi\{N_2\}$

This gives $\chi\{NH_3\} = 1.00 - 4\chi\{N_2\}$ And we have

$$1.56 = \frac{1.00 - 4\chi\{N_2\}}{\chi\{N_2\}^2} \quad \text{For ease of solving, we let } x = \chi\{N_2\}$$

$$1.56 = \frac{1.00 - 4x}{x^2} \qquad 1.56\,x^2 = 1.00 - 4x \qquad 1.56\,x^2 + 4x - 1.00 = 0$$

$$x = \frac{-b \pm \sqrt{b^2 - 4ac}}{2a} = \frac{-4.00 \pm \sqrt{16.00 + 6.24}}{3.12} = 0.229,\ -2.794$$

Thus $\chi\{N_2\} = 0.229$ Mole % NH_3 = (1.000 mol –(4 × 0.229 mol)) × 100% = 8.4%

89. **(M)** Since the initial mole ratio is 2 $H_2S(g)$ to 1 $CH_4(g)$, the reactants remain in their stoichiometric ratio when equilibrium is reached. Also, the products are formed in their stoichiometric ratio.

$$\text{amount } CH_4 = 9.54 \times 10^{-3} \text{ mol } H_2S \times \frac{1 \text{ mol } CH_4}{2 \text{ mol } H_2S} = 4.77 \times 10^{-3} \text{ mol } CH_4$$

$$\text{amount } CS_2 = 1.42 \times 10^{-3} \text{ mol } BaSO_4 \times \frac{1 \text{ mol } S}{1 \text{ mol } BaSO_4} \times \frac{1 \text{ mol } CS_2}{2 \text{ mol } S} = 7.10 \times 10^{-4} \text{ mol } CS_2$$

$$\text{amount } H_2 = 7.10 \times 10^{-4} \text{ mol } CS_2 \times \frac{4 \text{ mol } H_2}{1 \text{ mol } CS_2} = 2.84 \times 10^{-3} \text{ mol } H_2$$

$$\text{total amount} = 9.54 \times 10^{-3} \text{mol } H_2S + 4.77 \times 10^{-3} \text{ mol } CH_4 + 7.10 \times 10^{-4} \text{mol } CS_2 + 2.84 \times 10^{-3} \text{ mol } H_2$$

$$= 17.86 \times 10^{-3} \text{ mol}$$

The partial pressure of each gas equals its mole fraction times the total pressure.

$$P\{H_2S\} = 1.00 \text{ atm} \times \frac{9.54 \times 10^{-3} \text{ mol } H_2S}{17.86 \times 10^{-3} \text{ mol total}} = 0.534 \text{ atm}$$

$$P\{CH_4\} = 1.00 \text{ atm} \times \frac{4.77 \times 10^{-3} \text{ mol } CH_4}{17.86 \times 10^{-3} \text{ mol total}} = 0.267 \text{ atm}$$

$$P\{CS_2\} = 1.00 \text{ atm} \times \frac{7.10 \times 10^{-4} \text{ mol } CS_2}{17.86 \times 10^{-3} \text{ mol total}} = 0.0398 \text{ atm}$$

$$P\{H_2\} = 1.00 \text{ atm} \times \frac{2.84 \times 10^{-3} \text{ mol } H_2}{17.86 \times 10^{-3} \text{ mol total}} = 0.159 \text{ atm}$$

$$K_p = \frac{P\{H_2\}^4 \, P\{CS_2\}}{P\{H_2S\}^2 \, P\{CH_4\}} = \frac{0.159^4 \times 0.0398}{0.534^2 \times 0.267} = 3.34 \times 10^{-4}$$

90. **(D)** We base our calculation on an I.C.E. table, after we first determine the direction of the reaction by computing :

$$Q_c = \frac{[Fe^{2+}]^2[Hg^{2+}]^2}{[Fe^{3+}]^2[Hg_2^{2+}]} = \frac{(0.03000)^2(0.03000)^2}{(0.5000)^2(0.5000)} = 6.48 \times 10^{-6}$$

Because this value is smaller than K_c, the reaction will shift to the right to reach equilibrium. Since the value of the equilibrium constant for the forward reaction is quite small, let us assume that the reaction initially shifts all the way to the left (line labeled "to left:"), and then reacts back in the forward direction to reach a position of equilibrium.

Equation:	$2\,Fe^{3+}(aq)$	$+$	$Hg_2^{2+}(aq)$	$\rightleftharpoons$	$2\,Fe^{2+}(aq)$	$+$	$2\,Hg^{2+}(aq)$
Initial:	0.5000 M		0.5000 M		0.03000 M		0.03000 M
$\longleftarrow$	$+0.03000$ M		$+0.0150$ M		-0.03000 M		-0.03000 M
To left:	0.5300 M		0.5150 M		0 M		0 M
Changes:	$-2x$ M		$-x$ M		$+2x$ M		$+2x$ M
Equil:	$(0.5300-2x)$M		$(0.5150-x)$M		$2x$ M		$2x$ M

$$K_c = \frac{[Fe^{2+}]^2[Hg^{2+}]^2}{[Fe^{3+}]^2[Hg_2^{2+}]} = 9.14 \times 10^{-6} = \frac{(2x)^2(2x)^2}{(0.5300-2x)^2(0.5150-x)} \approx \frac{4x^2 \, 4x^2}{(0.5300)^2 \, 0.5150}$$

Note that we have assumed that $2x << 0.5300$ and $x < 0.5150$

$$x^4 = \frac{9.14 \times 10^{-6} \ (0.5300)^2 \ (0.5150)}{4 \times 4} = 8.26 \times 10^{-8} \qquad x = 0.0170$$

Our assumption, that $2x \ (= 0.0340) << 0.5300$, is reasonably good.

$[Fe^{3+}] = 0.5300 - 2 \times 0.0170 = 0.4960$ M $\qquad [Hg_2^{2+}] = 0.5150 - 0.0170 = 0.4980$

$[Fe^{2+}] = [Hg^{2+}] = 2 \times 0.0170 = 0.0340$ M

We check by substituting into the K_c expression.

$$9.14 \times 10^{-6} = K_c = \frac{[Fe^{2+}]^2 [Hg^{2+}]^2}{[Fe^{3+}]^2 [Hg_2^{2+}]} = \frac{(0.0340)^2 (0.0340)^2}{(0.4960)^2 \ 0.4980} = 11 \times 10^{-6} \text{ Not a substantial difference.}$$

Mathematica (version 4.0, Wolfram Research, Champaign, IL) gives a root of 0.0163.

91. **(D)** Again we base our calculation on an I.C.E. table. In the course of solving the Integrative Example, we found that we could obtain the desired equation by reversing equation (2) and adding the result to equation (1)

$-(2)$	$H_2O(g)$	$+$	$CH_4(g)$	$\rightleftharpoons$	$CO(g)$	$+$	$3\,H_2(g)$	$K = 1/190$
$+(1)$	$CO(g)$	$+$	$H_2O(g)$	$\rightleftharpoons$	$CO_2(g)$	$+$	$H_2(g)$	$K = 1.4$

Equation: $CH_4(g) + 2\,H_2O(g) \rightleftharpoons CO_2(g) + 4\,H_2(g) \quad K = 1.4/190 = 0.0074$

$-(2)$	$H_2O(g)$	$+$	$CH_4(g)$	$\rightleftharpoons$	$CO(g)$	$+$	$3\,H_2(g)$	$K = 1/190$
$+(1)$	$CO(g)$	$+$	$H_2O(g)$	$\rightleftharpoons$	$CO_2(g)$	$+$	$H_2(g)$	$K = 1.4$

Equation: $CH_4(g) + 2\,H_2O(g) \rightleftharpoons CO_2(g) + 4\,H_2(g) \quad K = 1.4/190 = 0.0074$

Initial:	0.100 mol	0.100 mol		0.100 mol	0.100 mol
$\longleftarrow$	$+0.025$ mol	$+0.050$ mol		-0.025 mol	-0.100 mol
To left:	0.125 mol	0.150 mol		0.075 mol	0.000 mol
Concns:	0.0250 M	0.0300 M		0.015 M	0.000 M
Changes:	$-x$ M	$-2x$ mol		$+x$ mol	$+4x$ mol
Equil:	$(0.0250-x)$ M	$(0.0300-2x)$		$(0.015+x)$ M	$4x$ mol

Notice that we have a fifth order polynomial to solve. Hence, we need to try to approximate its final solution as closely as possible. The reaction favors the reactants because of the small size of the equilibrium constant. Thus, we approach equilibrium from as far to the left as possible.

$$K_c = 0.0074 = \frac{[CO_2][H_2]^4}{[CH_4][H_2O]^2} = \frac{(0.0150+x)(4x)^4}{(0.0250-x)\ (0.0300-2x)^2} \approx \frac{0.0150\ (4x)^4}{0.0250\ (0.0300)^2}$$

$$x \approx \sqrt[4]{\frac{0.0250\ (0.0300)^2\ 0.0074}{0.0150 \times 256}} = 0.014 \text{ M}$$

Our assumption is terrible. We substitute to continue successive approximations.

$$0.0074 = \frac{(0.0150 + 0.014)(4x)^4}{(0.0250 - 0.014)(0.0300 - 2 \times 0.014)^2} = \frac{(0.029)(4x)^4}{(0.011)(0.002)^2}$$

Next, try $x_2 = 0.0026$

$$0.074 = \frac{(0.0150 + 0.0026)(4x)^4}{(0.0250 - 0.0026)(0.0300 - 2 \times 0.0026)^2}$$

then, try $x_3 = 0.0123$.

After 18 iterations, the x value converges to 0.0080.

Considering that the equilibrium constant is known to only two significant figures, this is a pretty good result. Recall that the total volume is 5.00 L. We calculate amounts in moles.

$CH_4(g)$ $\quad$ $(0.0250 - 0.0080) \times 5.00\ L = 0.017\ M \times 5.00\ L = 0.085$ moles $CH_4(g)$

$H_2O(g)$ $\quad$ $(0.0300 - 2 \times 0.0080)\ M \times 5.00\ L = 0.014\ M \times 5.00\ L = 0.070$ moles $H_2O(g)$

$CO_2(g)$ $\quad$ $(0.015 + 0.0080)\ M \times 5.00\ L = 0.023\ M \times 5.00\ L = 0.12$ mol CO_2

$H_2(g)$ $\quad$ $(4 \times 0.0080)\ M \times 5.00\ L = 0.032\ M \times 5.00\ L = 0.16$ mol H_2

92. **(M)** The initial mole fraction of C_2H_2 is $\chi_i = 0.88$. We use molar amounts at equilibrium to compute the equilibrium mole fraction of C_2H_2, χ_{eq}. Because we have a 2.00-L container, molar amounts are double the molar concentrations.

$$\chi_{eq} = \frac{(2 \times 0.756)\ mol\ C_2H_2}{(2 \times 0.756)\ mol\ C_2H_2 + (2 \times 0.038)\ mol\ CH_4 + (2 \times 0.068)\ mol\ H_2} = 0.87\underline{7}$$

Thus, there has been only a slight decrease in mole fraction.

93. **(M)**

(a) $K_{eq} = 3.7 \times 10^8 \dfrac{P\{NOCl\}^2}{P\{NO\}^2 P\{Cl_2\}} = \dfrac{(4.125)^2}{P\{NO\}^2 (0.1125)}$

$$P\{NO\} = \sqrt{\frac{(4.125)^2}{3.7 \times 10^8 (0.1125)}} = 6.4 \times 10^{-4}\ atm$$

(b) $P_{total} = P_{NO} + P_{Cl_2} + P_{NOCl} = 6.4 \times 10^{-4}\ atm + 0.1125\ atm + 4.125\ atm = 4.238\ atm$

94. **(M)** We base our calculation on an I.C.E. table.

Reaction:	$N_2(g)$	$+$	$3\ H_2(g)$	$\rightleftharpoons$	$2\ NH_3(g)$
Initial:	$\dfrac{0.424\ mol}{10.0\ L}$		$\dfrac{1.272\ mol}{10.0\ L}$		$\dfrac{0\ mol}{10.0\ L}$
Change	$\dfrac{-x\ mol}{10.0\ L}$		$\dfrac{-3x\ mol}{10.0\ L}$		$\dfrac{+2x\ mol}{10.0\ L}$
Equilibrium	$\dfrac{(0.424 - x)\ mol}{10.0\ L}$		$\dfrac{(1.272 - 3x)\ mol}{10.0\ L}$		$\dfrac{2x\ mol}{10.0\ L}$

$$K_c = \frac{[NH_3]^2}{[N_2][H_2]^3} = 152 = \frac{\left(\dfrac{2x\,mol}{10.0\,L}\right)^2}{\left(\dfrac{(0.424-x)\,mol}{10.0\,L}\right)\left(\dfrac{(1.272-3x)\,mol}{10.0\,L}\right)^3}$$

$$K_c = \frac{100(2x\,mol)^2}{((0.424-x)\,mol)(3(0.424-x)\,mol)^3}$$

$$K_c = \frac{100(2x\,mol)^2}{3^3\,(0.424-x)\,mol)^4} = 152\frac{(2x\,mol)^2}{(0.424-x)\,mol)^4} = 41.0\underline{4}\quad \text{Take root of both sides}$$

$$\frac{(2x\,mol)}{(0.424-x)\,mol)^2} = 6.41 \qquad 6.41(0.424-x)^2 = 2x$$

$3.20(0.180-0.848x+x^2) = x = 3.20x^2 - 2.71x + 0.576 \qquad 3.20x^2 - 3.71x + 0.576 = 0$

Now solve using the quadratic equation: $x = 0.184\underline{6}$ mol or $0.975\underline{6}$ mol (too large)

amount of $NH_3 = 2x = 2(0.1846\,mol) = 0.369\,mol$ in 10.0 L or 0.0369 M

$([H_2] = 0.0718\,M$ and $[N_2] = 0.0239\,M)$

95. (D)

Equation: $2\,H_2(g) \quad + \quad CO(g) \quad \rightleftharpoons \quad CH_3OH(g) \quad K_c = 14.5$ at 483 K

$$K_p = K_c(RT)^{\Delta v} = 14.5\left(0.08206\,\frac{L\,atm}{mol\,K} \times 483K\right)^{-2} = 9.23\times10^{-3}$$

We know that mole percents equal pressure percents for ideal gases.

$P_{CO} = 0.350\times100\,atm = 35.0\,atm$

$P_{H_2} = 0.650\times100\,atm = 65.0\,atm$

Equation: $2\,H_2(g) \quad + \quad CO(g) \quad \rightleftharpoons \quad CH_3OH(g)$

Initial: 65 atm   35 atm

Changes: $-2\,P$ atm $-P$ atm $+P$ atm

Equil: $65-2\,P$ $35-P$ P

$$K_p = \frac{P_{CH_3OH}}{P_{CO}\times P_{H_2}^2} = \frac{P}{(35.0-P)(65.0-2P)^2} = 9.23\times10^{-3}$$

By successive approximations, $P = 24.6\,atm = P_{CH_3OH}$ at equilibrium.

Mathematica (version 4.0, Wolfram Research, Champaign, IL) gives a root of 24.5.

96. (M)

(a)

$$Q_p = \frac{P_{NH_3}^2}{P_{N_2} P_{H_2}^3}$$

$$P_{NH_3} = x_{NH_3} P; \quad P_{N_2} = x_{N_2} P; \quad P_{H_2} = x_{H_2} P$$

$$Q_p = \frac{(x_{NH_3} P)^2}{(x_{N_2} P)(x_{H_2} P)^3} = \frac{x_{NH_3}^2 P^2}{x_{N_2} x_{H_2}^3 P^4}$$

$$Q_p = \frac{x_{NH_3}^2}{x_{N_2} x_{H_2}^3 P^2}$$

(b) Mixture A:

$$x_{N_2} = \frac{n_{N_2}}{n_{tot}} = \frac{0.0424}{0.3544} = 0.11\underline{9}64$$

$$x_{H_2} = \frac{n_{H_2}}{n_{tot}} = \frac{0.136}{0.3544} = 0.38\underline{3}75$$

$$x_{NH_3} = \frac{n_{NH_3}}{n_{tot}} = \frac{0.176}{0.3544} = 0.49\underline{6}61$$

$$Q_p = \frac{x_{NH_3}^2}{x_{N_2} x_{H_2}^3 P^2} = \frac{(0.49\underline{6}61)^2}{(0.11\underline{9}6)(0.38\underline{3}7)^3 (1.00)^2}$$

$$Q_p = 36.47793 = 36.5$$

$$K_p = 36.5$$

Mixture B:

$$x_{N_2} = \frac{n_{N_2}}{n_{tot}} = \frac{0.194}{0.3049} = 0.63\underline{6}27$$

$$x_{H_2} = \frac{n_{H_2}}{n_{tot}} = \frac{0.403}{0.3049} = 0.13\underline{2}17$$

$$x_{NH_3} = \frac{n_{NH_3}}{n_{tot}} = \frac{0.0706}{0.3049} = 0.23\underline{1}55$$

$$Q_p = \frac{x_{NH_3}^2}{x_{N_2} x_{H_2}^3 P^2} = \frac{(0.23\underline{1}55)^2}{(0.63\underline{6}27)(0.13\underline{2}17)^3 (1.00)^2}$$

$$Q_p = 36.49282 = 36.5$$

$$K_p = 36.5$$

(c) Mixture A:

	N$_2$(g)	+ 3 H$_2$(g) $\rightleftharpoons$	2 NH$_3$(g)
Initial moles	0.0424 + 0.100	0.136	0.176

$$x_{N_2} = \frac{n_{N_2}}{n_{tot}} = \frac{0.14\underline{24}}{0.4544} = 0.31\underline{3}39$$

$$x_{H_2} = \frac{n_{H_2}}{n_{tot}} = \frac{0.136}{0.4544} = 0.299\underline{3}0$$

$$x_{NH_3} = \frac{n_{NH_3}}{n_{tot}} = \frac{0.176}{0.4544} = 0.387\underline{3}2$$

$$Q_p = \frac{x_{NH_3}^2}{x_{N_2} x_{H_2}^3 P^2} = \frac{(0.387\underline{3}2)^2}{(0.31339)(0.299\underline{3}0)^3 (1.00)^2}$$

$$Q_p = 17.8540 = 17.9$$

$$K_p = 36.5$$

Since $Q_p < K_p$, net reaction is to the right.

Mixture B:

	N$_2$(g)	+ 3 H$_2$(g) $\rightleftharpoons$	2 NH$_3$(g)
Initial moles	0.194 + 0.100	0.0403	0.0706

$$x_{N_2} = \frac{n_{N_2}}{n_{tot}} = \frac{0.294}{0.4049} = 0.72\underline{6}11$$

$$x_{H_2} = \frac{n_{H_2}}{n_{tot}} = \frac{0.0403}{0.4049} = 0.099\underline{5}3$$

$$x_{NH_3} = \frac{n_{NH_3}}{n_{tot}} = \frac{0.0706}{0.4049} = 0.17\underline{4}36$$

$$Q_p = \frac{x_{NH_3}^2}{x_{N_2} x_{H_2}^3 P^2} = \frac{(0.17\underline{4}36)^2}{(0.72\underline{6}11)(0.099\underline{5}3)^3 (1.00)^2}$$

$$Q_p = 42.4648 = 42.5$$

$$K_p = 36.5$$

Since $Q_p > K_p$, net reaction is to the left.

97. **(M)** We are given densities (ρ) of water at 300 K for various pressures. The molar volume ($\bar{V}$) of water at each pressure is calculated using $\bar{V} = M/\rho$ where $M = 18.016$ g mol^{-1} is the molar mass of water. The activity at each pressure is calculated using $a = \exp[\bar{V}(P - P°)/(RT)]$, with $P° = 1$ bar. The results below indicate that $a \approx 1$ for liquid water at 300 K for pressures up to about 100 bar.

P/bar	ρ/g mL^{-1}	V_m/mL	V/L	$\bar{V}(P - P°)/(RT)$	a
1	0.99656	18.07819	0.018078	0	1.0000
10	0.99696	18.07094	0.018071	0.00652	1.0065
100	1.001	17.99800	0.017998	0.071434	1.0740
1000	1.0372	17.36984	0.017370	0.695671	2.0051

98. **(M)** Let c_o represent the initial concentrations of A and B. The equilibrium summary (ICE table) is as follows.

	A	+	B	$\rightleftharpoons$	C	+	D
I	c_o		c_o		0		0
C	$-x$		$-x$		$+x$		$+x$
E	$c_o - x$		$c_o - x$		x		x

The equilibrium condition is $K = \dfrac{[C]_{eq}[D]_{eq}}{[A]_{eq}[B]_{eq}} = \dfrac{x^2}{(c_o - x)^2}$, which may be solved for x as follows.

$$\sqrt{K} = \frac{x}{c_o - x} \Rightarrow c_o\sqrt{K} - x\sqrt{K} = x \Rightarrow c_o\sqrt{K} = x(\sqrt{K} + 1) \Rightarrow x = \frac{c_o\sqrt{K}}{\sqrt{K} + 1}$$

The fraction of A and B that reacts is calculated as follows.

$$\text{fraction that reacts} = \frac{x}{c_o} = \frac{\sqrt{K}}{\sqrt{K} + 1}$$

Therefore,

$$\text{percentage that reacts} = c \times 100 = \frac{100\sqrt{K}}{\sqrt{K} + 1}$$

For $K = 10^{10}$: $\text{percentage that reacts} = \dfrac{100\sqrt{10^{10}}}{\sqrt{10^{10}} + 1} = \dfrac{100 \times 10^5}{10^5 + 1} = 99.999$

For $K = 10^{-10}$: $\text{percentage that reacts} = \dfrac{100\sqrt{10^{-10}}}{\sqrt{10^{-10}} + 1} = \dfrac{100 \times 10^{-5}}{10^{-5} + 1} = 0.001$, and therefore

99.999% of the reactants remain.

FEATURE PROBLEMS

99. **(M)** We first determine the amount in moles of acetic acid in the equilibrium mixture.

$$\text{amount } CH_3CO_2H = 28.85 \text{ mL} \times \frac{1 \text{ L}}{1000 \text{ mL}} \times \frac{0.1000 \text{ mol } Ba(OH)_2}{1 \text{ L}} \times \frac{2 \text{ mol } CH_3CO_2H}{1 \text{ mol } Ba(OH)_2}$$

$$\times \frac{\text{complete equilibrium mixture}}{0.01 \text{ of equilibrium mixture}} = 0.5770 \text{ mol } CH_3CO_2H$$

$$K_c = \frac{[CH_3CO_2C_2H_5][H_2O]}{[C_2H_5OH][CH_3CO_2H]} = \frac{\dfrac{0.423 \text{ mol}}{V} \times \dfrac{0.423 \text{ mol}}{V}}{\dfrac{0.077 \text{ mol}}{V} \times \dfrac{0.577 \text{ mol}}{V}} = \frac{0.423 \times 0.423}{0.077 \times 0.577} = 4.0$$

100. **(D)** In order to determine whether or not equilibrium has been established in each bulb, we need to calculate the concentrations for all three species at the time of opening. The results from these calculations are tabulated below and a typical calculation is given beneath this table.

Bulb No.	Time Bulb Opened (hours)	Initial Amount HI(g) (in mmol)	Amount of I_2(g) and H_2(g) at Time of Opening (in mmol)	Amount HI(g) at Time of Opening (in mmol)	[HI] (mM)	[I_2] & [H_2] (mM)	$\dfrac{[H_2][I_2]}{[HI]^2}$
1	2	2.34<u>5</u>	0.1572	2.03	5.08	0.393	0.00599
2	4	2.51<u>8</u>	0.2093	2.10	5.25	0.523	0.00992
3	12	2.46<u>3</u>	0.2423	1.98	4.95	0.606	0.0150
4	20	3.17<u>4</u>	0.3113	2.55	6.38	0.778	0.0149
5	40	2.18<u>9</u>	0.2151	1.76	4.40	0.538	0.0150

Consider, for instance, bulb #4 (opened after 20 hours).

Initial moles of HI(g) $= 0.406 \text{ g HI(g)} \times \dfrac{1 \text{ mole HI}}{127.9 \text{ g HI}} = 0.00317\underline{4} \text{ mol HI(g) or } 3.17\underline{4} \text{ mmol}$

moles of I_2(g) present in bulb when opened.

$= 0.04150 \text{ L } Na_2S_2O_3 \times \dfrac{0.0150 \text{ mol } Na_2S_2O_3}{1 \text{ L } Na_2S_2O_3} \times \dfrac{1 \text{ mol } I_2}{2 \text{ mol } Na_2S_2O_3} = 3.113 \times 10^{-4} \text{ mol } I_2$

millimoles of I_2(g) present in bulb when opened $= 3.113 \times 10^{-4} \text{mol } I_2$

moles of H_2 present in bulb when opened = moles of I_2(g) present in bulb when opened.

HI reacted $= 3.113 \times 10^{-4} \text{ mol } I_2 \times \dfrac{2 \text{ mole HI}}{1 \text{ mol } I_2} = 6.226 \times 10^{-4} \text{ mol HI } (0.6226 \text{ mmol HI})$

moles of HI(g) in bulb when opened $= 3.17\underline{4} \text{ mmol HI} - 0.6226 \text{ mmol HI} = 2.55 \text{ mmol HI}$

Concentrations of HI, I_2, and H_2

[HI] = 2.55 mmol HI ÷ 0.400 L = 6.38 mM

$[I_2] = [H_2]$ = 0.3113 mmol ÷ 0.400 L = 0.778 mM

Ratio: $\dfrac{[H_2][I_2]}{[HI]^2} = \dfrac{(0.778 \text{ mM})(0.778 \text{ mM})}{(6.38 \text{ mM})^2} = 0.0149$

As the time increases, the ratio $\dfrac{[H_2][I_2]}{[HI]^2}$ initially climbs sharply, but then plateaus at 0.0150 somewhere between 4 and 12 hours. Consequently, it seems quite reasonable to conclude that the reaction $2\,HI(g) \rightleftharpoons H_2(g) + I_2(g)$ has a $K_c \sim 0.015$ at 623 K.

101. **(D)** We first need to determine the number of moles of ammonia that were present in the sample of gas that left the reactor. This will be accomplished by using the data from the titrations involving HCl(aq).

Original number of moles of HCl(aq) in the 20.00 mL sample

$= 0.01872$ L of KOH $\times \dfrac{0.0523 \text{ mol KOH}}{1 \text{ L KOH}} \times \dfrac{1 \text{ mol HCl}}{1 \text{ mol KOH}}$

$= 9.79\underline{06} \times 10^{-4}$ moles of $HCl_{(initially)}$

Moles of unreacted HCl(aq)

$= 0.01542$ L of KOH $\times \dfrac{0.0523 \text{ mol KOH}}{1 \text{ L KOH}} \times \dfrac{1 \text{ mol HCl}}{1 \text{ mol KOH}} =$

$8.06\underline{47} \times 10^{-4}$ moles of $HCl_{(unreacted)}$

Moles of HCl that reacted and /or moles of NH_3 present in the sample of reactor gas $= 9.79\underline{06} \times 10^{-4}$ moles $- 8.06\underline{47} \times 10^{-4}$ moles $= 1.73 \times 10^{-4}$ mole of NH_3 (or HCl).

The remaining gas, which is a mixture of $N_2(g)$ and $H_2(g)$ gases, was found to occupy 1.82 L at 273.2 K and 1.00 atm. Thus, the total number of moles of N_2 and H_2 can be found via the ideal gas law:

$n_{H_2 + N_2} = \dfrac{PV}{RT} = \dfrac{(1.00 \text{ atm})(1.82 \text{ L})}{(0.08206 \frac{\text{L atm}}{\text{K mol}})(273.2 \text{ K})} = 0.0811\underline{8}$ moles of $(N_2 + H_2)$

According to the stoichiometry for the reaction, 2 parts NH_3 decompose to give 3 parts H_2 and 1 part N_2. Thus the non-reacting mixture must be 75% H_2 and 25% N_2.

So, the number of moles of $N_2 = 0.25 \times 0.0811\underline{8}$ moles = 0.0203 moles N_2 and the number of moles of $H_2 = 0.75 \times 0.0811\underline{8}$ moles = 0.0609 moles H_2.

Before we can calculate K_c, we need to determine the volume that the NH_3, N_2, and H_2 molecules occupied in the reactor. Once again, the ideal gas law ($PV = nRT$) will be employed. $v_{gas} = 0.08118$ moles ($N_2 + H_2$) $+ 1.73 \times 10^{-4}$ moles $NH_3 = 0.08135$ moles

$$V_{gases} = \frac{nRT}{P} = \frac{(0.08135 \text{ mol})(0.08206 \frac{\text{L atm}}{\text{K mol}})(1174.2 \text{ K})}{30.0 \text{ atm}} = 0.2613 \text{ L}$$

So, $K_c = \dfrac{\left[\dfrac{1.73 \times 10^{-4} \text{ moles}}{0.2613 \text{ L}}\right]^2}{\left[\dfrac{0.0609 \text{ moles}}{0.2613 \text{ L}}\right]^3 \left[\dfrac{0.0203 \text{ moles}}{0.2613 \text{ L}}\right]^1} = 4.46 \times 10^{-4}$

To calculate K_p at 901 °C, we need to employ the equation $K_p = K_c (RT)^{\Delta v_{gas}}$; $\Delta v_{gas} = -2$

$K_p = 4.46 \times 10^{-4} [(0.08206 \text{ L atm K}^{-1}\text{mol}^{-1})] \times (1174.2 \text{ K})]^{-2} = 4.80 \times 10^{-8}$ at 901°C for the reaction $N_2(g) + 3 H_2(g) \rightleftharpoons 2 NH_3(g)$

102. **(M)** The equilibrium expressions for the two reactions are:

$K_1 = \dfrac{\left[H^+\right]\left[HCO_3^-\right]}{\left[H_2CO_3\right]}$; $K_2 = \dfrac{\left[H^+\right]\left[CO_3^{2-}\right]}{\left[HCO_3^-\right]}$

First, start with $[H^+] = 0.1$ and $[HCO_3^-] = 1$. This means that $[H^+]/[HCO_3^-] = 0.1$, which means that $[CO_3^{2-}] = 10K_2$. By adding a small amount of H_2CO_3 we shift $[H^+]$ by 0.1 and $[HCO_3^-]$ by 0.1. This leads to $[H^+]/[HCO_3^-] \approx 0.2$, which means that $[CO_3^{2-}] = 5K_2$. Note that $[CO_3^{2-}]$ has *decreased* as a result of adding H_2CO_3 to the solution.

103. **(D)** First, it is most important to get a general feel for the direction of the reaction by determining the reaction quotient:

$$Q = \frac{[C(aq)]}{[A(aq)]\cdot[B(aq)]} = \frac{0.1}{0.1 \times 0.1} = 10$$

Since $Q \gg K$, the reaction proceeds toward the reactants. Looking at the reaction in the aqueous phase only, the equilibrium can be expressed as follows:

	A(aq)	+	B(aq)	⇌	C(aq)
Initial	0.1		0.1		0.1
Change	$-x$		$-x$		$+x$
Equil.	$0.1 - x$		$0.1 - x$		$0.1 + x$

We will do part (b) first, which assumes the absence of an organic layer for extraction:

$$K = \frac{(0.1+x)}{(0.1-x)(0.1-x)} = 0.01$$

Expanding the above equation and using the quadratic formula, $x = -0.0996$. Therefore, the concentration of C(aq) and equilibrium is $0.1 + (-0.0996) = 4 \times 10^{-4}$ M.

If the organic layer is present for extraction, we can add the two equations together, as shown below:

$$
\begin{array}{cccc}
A(aq) & + \ B(aq) & \rightleftharpoons & C(aq) \\
 & C(aq) & \rightleftharpoons & C(or) \\
\hline
A(aq) & + \ B(aq) & \rightleftharpoons & C(or)
\end{array}
$$

$K = K_1 \times K_2 = 0.1 \times 15 = 0.15$.

Since the organic layer is present with the aqueous layer, and K_2 is large, we can expect that the vast portion of C initially placed in the aqueous phase will go into the organic phase. Therefore, the initial [C] = 0.1 can be assumed to be for C(or). The equilibrium can be expressed as follows

	A(aq)	+	B(aq)	$\rightleftharpoons$	C(or)
Initial	0.1		0.1		0.1
Change	$-x$		$-x$		$+x$
Equil.	$0.1-x$		$0.1-x$		$0.1+x$

We will do part (b) first, which assumes the absence of an organic layer for extraction:

$$K = \frac{(0.1+x)}{(0.1-x)(0.1-x)} = 0.15$$

Expanding the above equation and using the quadratic formula, $x = -0.0943$. Therefore, the concentration of C(or) and equilibrium is $0.1 + (-0.0943) = 6 \times 10^{-4}$ M. This makes sense because the K for the overall reaction is < 1, which means that the reaction favors the reactants.

SELF-ASSESSMENT EXERCISES

104. (E)

(a) K_p: The equilibrium constant of a reaction where the pressures of gaseous reactants and products are used instead of their concentrations

(b) Q_c: The reaction quotient using the molarities of the reactants and products

(c) Δv_{gas}: The difference between the number of moles (as determined from a balanced reaction) of product and reactant gases

105. (E)

(a) Dynamic equilibrium: In a dynamic equilibrium (which is to say, real equilibrium), the forward and reverse reactions happen, but at a constant rate

(b) Direction of net chemical change: In a reversible reaction, if the reaction quotient $Q_c > K_c$, then the net reaction will go toward the reactants, and vice versa

(c) Le Châtelier's principle: When a system at equilibrium is subjected to external change (change in partial pressure of reactants/products, temperature or concentration), the equilibrium shifts to a side to diminish the effects of that external change

(d) Effect of catalyst on equilibrium: A catalyst does not affect the final concentrations of the reactants and products. However, since it speeds up the reaction, it allows for the equilibrium concentrations to be established more quickly

106. (E)

(a) Reaction that goes to completion and reversible reaction: In a reversible reaction, the products can revert back to the reactants in a dynamic equilibrium. In a reaction that goes to completion, the formation of products is so highly favored that there is practically no reverse reaction (or the reverse is practically impossible, such as a combustion reaction).

(b) K_p and K_c: K_p is the equilibrium constant using pressures of products and reactants, while K_c is the constant for reaction using concentrations.

(c) Reaction quotient (Q) and equilibrium constant expression (K): The reaction quotient Q is the ratio of the concentrations of the reactants and products expressed in the same format as the equilibrium expression. The equilibrium constant expression is the ratio of concentrations at equilibrium.

(d) Homogeneous and heterogeneous reaction: In a homogeneous reaction, the reaction happens within a single phase (either aqueous or gas). In a heterogeneous reaction, there is more than one phase present in the reaction.

107. **(E)** The answer is (c). Because the limiting reagent is I_2 at one mole, the theoretical yield of HI is 2 moles. However, because there is an established equilibrium, there is a small amount of HI which will decompose to yield H_2 and I_2. Therefore the total moles of HI created is close, but less than 2.

108. **(E)** The answer is (d). The equilibrium expression is:

$$K = \frac{P(SO_3)^2}{P(SO_2)^2 P(O_2)} = 100$$

If equilibrium is established, moles of SO_3 and SO_2 cancel out of the equilibrium expression. Therefore, if $K = 100$, the moles of O_2 have to be 0.01 to make $K = 100$.

109. **(E)** The answer is (a). As the volume of the vessel is expanded (i.e., pressure is reduced), the equilibrium shifts $_{toward}$ the side with more moles of gas.

110. **(E)** The answer is (b). At half the stoichiometric values, the equilibrium constant is $K^{1/2}$. If the equation is reversed, it is K^{-1}. Therefore, the $K' = K^{-1/2} = (1.8 \times 10^{-6})^{-1/2} = 7.5 \times 10^{-2}$.

111. **(E)** The answer is (a). We know that $K_p = K_c (RT)^{\Delta v}$. Since $\Delta v = (3-2) = 1$, $K_p = K_c (RT)$. Therefore, $K_p > K_c$.

112. **(E)** The answer is (c). Since the number of moles of gas of products is more than the reactants, increasing the vessel volume will drive the equilibrium more toward the product side. The other options: (a) has no effect, and (b) drives the equilibrium to the reactant side.

113. **(E)** The equilibrium expression is:

$$K = \frac{[C]^2}{[B]^2 [A]} = \frac{(0.43)^2}{(0.55)^2 (0.33)} = 1.9$$

114. **(E)**
   (a)   As more O_2 (a reactant) is added, more Cl_2 is produced.
   (b)   As HCl (a reactant) is removed, equilibrium shifts to the left and less Cl_2 is made.
   (c)   Since there are more moles of reactants, equilibrium shifts to the left and less Cl_2 is made.
   (d)   No change. However, the equilibrium is reached faster.
   (e)   Since the reaction is exothermic, increasing the temperature causes less Cl_2 to be made.

115. **(E)** SO_2 (g) will be less than SO_2 (aq), because $K > 1$, so the equilibrium lies to the product side, SO_2 (aq).

116. **(E)** Since $K \gg 1$, there will be much more product than reactant

117. **(M)** The equilibrium expression for this reaction is:

$$K = \frac{[SO_3]^2}{[SO_2]^2 [O_2]} = 35.5$$

   (a)   If $[SO_3]_{eq} = [SO_2]_{eq}$, then $[O_2] = 1/35.5 = 0.0282$ M.
         moles of $O_2 = 0.0282 \times 2.05$ L $= 0.0578$ mol
   (b)   Plugging in the new concentration values into the equilibrium expression:

$$K = \frac{[SO_3]^2}{[SO_2]^2 [O_2]} = \frac{[2 \times SO_2]^2}{[SO_2]^2 [O_2]} = \frac{4}{[O_2]} = 35.5$$

   $[O_2] = 0.113$ M
   moles of $O_2 = 0.113 \times 2.05$ L $= 0.232$ mol

118. **(M)** This concept map involves the various conditions that affect equilibrium of a reaction, and those that don't. Under the category of conditions that do cause a change, there is changing the partial pressure of gaseous products and reactants, which includes pressure and vessel volume. The changes that do not affect partial pressure are changing the concentration of reactants or products in an aqueous solution, through dilution or concentration. Changing the temperature can affect both aqueous and gaseous reactions. Under the category of major changes that don't affect anything is the addition of a non-reactive gas.

CHAPTER 16
ACIDS AND BASES

PRACTICE EXAMPLES

1A **(E)**

(a) In the forward direction, HF is the acid (proton donor; forms F^-), and H_2O is the base (proton acceptor; forms H_3O^+). In the reverse direction, F^- is the base (forms HF), accepting a proton from H_3O^+, which is the acid (forms H_2O).

(b) In the forward direction, HSO_4^- is the acid (proton donor; forms SO_4^{2-}), and NH_3 is the base (proton acceptor; forms NH_4^+). In the reverse direction, SO_4^{2-} is the base (forms HSO_4^-), accepting a proton from NH_4^+, which is the acid (forms NH_3).

(c) In the forward direction, HCl is the acid (proton donor; forms Cl^-), and CH_3COO^- is the base (proton acceptor; forms CH_3COOH). In the reverse direction, Cl^- is the base (forms HCl), accepting a proton from CH_3COOH, which is the acid (forms CH_3COO^-).

1B **(E)** We know that the formulas of most acids begin with H. Thus, we identify HNO_2 and HCO_3^- as acids.

$$HNO_2\,(aq) + H_2O(l) \rightleftharpoons NO_2^-\,(aq) + H_3O^+\,(aq);$$
$$HCO_3^-\,(aq) + H_2O(l) \rightleftharpoons CO_3^{2-}\,(aq) + H_3O^+\,(aq)$$

A negatively charged species will attract a positively charged proton and act as a base. Thus PO_4^{3-} and HCO_3^- can act as bases. We also know that PO_4^{3-} must be a base because it cannot act as an acid—it has no protons to donate—and we know that all three species have acid-base properties.

$$PO_4^{3-}\,(aq) + H_2O(l) \rightleftharpoons HPO_4^{2-}\,(aq) + OH^-\,(aq);$$
$$HCO_3^-\,(aq) + H_2O(l) \rightleftharpoons H_2CO_3(aq) \rightarrow CO_2 \cdot H_2O\,(aq) + OH^-\,(aq)$$

Notice that HCO_3^- is the amphiprotic species, acting as both an acid and a base.

2A **(M)** $\left[H_3O^+\right]$ is readily computed from pH: $\left[H_3O^+\right] = 10^{-pH}$ $\left[H_3O^+\right] = 10^{-2.85} = 1.4 \times 10^{-3}$ M. $\left[OH^-\right]$ can be found in two ways: (1) from $K_w = \left[H_3O^+\right]\left[OH^-\right]$, giving

$$\left[OH^-\right] = \frac{K_w}{\left[H_3O^+\right]} = \frac{1.0 \times 10^{-14}}{1.4 \times 10^{-3}} = 7.1 \times 10^{-12}\,M, \text{ or (2) from pH} + pOH = 14.00, \text{ giving}$$

$pOH = 14.00 - pH = 14.00 - 2.85 = 11.15$, and then $\left[OH^-\right] = 10^{-pOH} = 10^{-11.15} = 7.1 \times 10^{-12}$ M.

2B **(M)** The concentration of hydronium ion can be calculated from the pH.
$[H_3O^+] = 10^{-pH} = 10^{-2.50} = 3.16 \times 10^{-6}$ M

The concentration of hydroxide ion can be calculated by using the formula
$K_w = [H_3O^+][OH^-]$
$[OH^-] = K_w/[H_3O^+] = 1.0 \times 10^{-14}/3.16 \times 10^{-6} = 3.16 \times 10^{-9}$ M

Because the self-ionization of water produces equal amounts of H_3O^+ and OH^-, we can say $[H_3O^+]_{water} = [OH^-] = 3.16 \times 10^{-9}$ M. Therefore,

$$
\begin{aligned}
\% \ H_3O^+ \text{ from water} \ &= \ ([H_3O^+]_{water}/[H_3O^+]) \times 100 \\
&= \ (3.16 \times 10^{-9} \text{ M})/(3.16 \times 10^{-6} \text{ M}) \times 100 \\
&= \ 0.1
\end{aligned}
$$

Only 0.1% of the H_3O^+ in solution comes from the self-ionization of water. Also, because $[H_3O^+]_{water} = [OH^-] = 3.16 \times 10^{-9}$ M $< 1.0 \times 10^{-7}$ M, we have also verified that the self-ionization of water is partially suppressed by the addition of acid to the water.

3A **(M)** Since the K_a of HNO_3 is larger than 1, we expect most of the nitric acid to react and x is a very small number.

	$HNO_3 +$	$H_2O(l) \rightleftharpoons$	$NO_3^-(aq) +$	$H_3O^+(aq)$
initial concns:	0.010 M			
to completion:	0 M		0.010 M	0.010 M
to the left:	$+ x$ M		$- x$ M	$- x$ M
equil concns:	x M		$(0.010 - x)$ M	$(0.010 - x)$ M

By assuming $x \ll 1$, we can write the following:

$$K_a = \frac{[NO_3^-][H_3O^+]}{[HNO_3]} = \frac{(0.010)(0.010)}{x}$$

$$x = \frac{(0.010)^2}{K_a} = \frac{0.0001}{20} = 5.0 \times 10^{-6}$$

Therefore, $[HNO_3] = x$ M $= 5.0 \times 10^{-6}$ M

$$\text{fraction of } HNO_3 \text{ remaining} = \frac{5.0 \times 10^{-6} \text{M}}{0.010 \text{ M}} \times 100\% = 0.05 \ \%$$

percent ionization $= 100 - 0.05 = 99.95\%$

3B **(M)** Since the K_a of HOCl is $\ll 1$, HOCl is considered a weak acid and we expect a very small amount of the HOCl to react.

	HOCl (aq) +	**$H_2O(l)$** $\rightleftharpoons$	**OCl^- (aq) +**	**H_3O^+ (aq)**
initial concns:	0.010 M			
change:	$-x$ M		$+x$ M	$+x$ M
equil concns:	$(0.010-x)$ M		x M	x M

$$K_a = \frac{[H_3O^+][OCl^-]}{[HOCl]} = \frac{(x)(x)}{0.010-x}$$

By assuming that $x \ll 0.010$, we can simplify the denominator of the equation:

$$K_a = \frac{(x)(x)}{0.010}$$

$$x = \sqrt{0.010 \times K_a}$$

$$x = \sqrt{0.010 \times 2.9 \times 10^{-8}}$$

$$x = 1.70 \times 10^{-5}$$

Therefore, $[HOCl] = (0.010 - 1.70 \times 10^{-5}) = 9.98 \times 10^{-3}$ M

$$\text{percent ionization} = \frac{1.70 \times 10^{-5} \text{M}}{0.010 \text{ M}} \times 100\% = 0.17\%$$

$$pH = -\log(1.70 \times 10^{-5} \text{ M}) = 4.77$$

4A **(M)** We organize the solution around the balanced chemical equation; a M is $[HF]_{initial}$.

Equation:	HF(aq) +	$H_2O(l)$ $\rightleftharpoons$	H_3O^+ (aq) +	F^- (aq)
Initial:	a M	—	≈ 0 M	0 M
Changes:	$-x$ M	—	$+x$ M	$+x$ M
Equil:	$(a-x)$ M	—	x M	x M

$$K_a = \frac{[H_3O^+][F^-]}{[HF]} = \frac{(x)(x)}{a-x} \approx \frac{x^2}{a} = 6.6 \times 10^{-4} \quad x = \sqrt{a \times 6.6 \times 10^{-4}}$$

For 0.20 M HF, $a = 0.20$ M $\qquad x = \sqrt{0.20 \times 6.6 \times 10^{-4}} = 0.011$ M

$$\% \text{ dissoc} = \frac{0.011 \text{ M}}{0.20 \text{ M}} \times 100\% = 5.5\%$$

For 0.020 M HF, $a = 0.020$ M $\qquad x = \sqrt{0.020 \times 6.6 \times 10^{-4}} = 0.0036$ M

We need another cycle of approximation: $x = \sqrt{(0.020 - 0.0036) \times 6.6 \times 10^{-4}} = 0.0033$ M

Yet another cycle with $x \approx 0.0033$ M : $x = \sqrt{(0.020 - 0.0033) \times 6.6 \times 10^{-4}} = 0.0033$ M

$$\% \text{ dissoc} = \frac{0.0033\text{M}}{0.020\text{M}} \times 100\% = 17\%$$

As expected, the weak acid is more dissociated.

4B   **(E)** Since both H_3O^+ and $CH_3CH(OH)COO^-$ come from the same source in equimolar amounts, their concentrations are equal. $\left[H_3O^+ \right] = \left[CH_3CH(OH)COO^- \right] = 0.067 \times 0.0284\,\text{M} = 0.0019\,\text{M}$

$$K_a = \frac{\left[H_3O^+ \right]\left[CH_3CH(OH)COO^- \right]}{\left[HC_3H_5CH_3CH(OH)COOH \right]} = \frac{(0.0019)(0.0019)}{0.0284 - 0.0019} = 1.4 \times 10^{-4}$$

5A   **(E)** pH is computed directly from the equation below.

$\left[H_3O^+ \right]$, $\text{pH} = -\log \left[H_3O^+ \right] = -\log(0.0025) = 2.60$.

We know that HI is a strong acid and, thus, is completely dissociated into H_3O^+ and I^-. The consequence is that $\left[I^- \right] = \left[H_3O^+ \right] = 0.0025$ M. $\left[OH^- \right]$ is most readily computed from pH: $\text{pOH} = 14.00 - \text{pH} = 14.00 - 2.60 = 11.40$; $\left[OH^- \right] = 10^{-\text{pOH}} = 10^{-11.40} = 4.0 \times 10^{-12}$ M

5B   **(M)** The number of moles of HCl(g) is calculated from the ideal gas law. Then $\left[H_3O^+ \right]$ is calculated, based on the fact that HCl(aq) is a strong acid (1 mol H_3O^+ is produced from each mole of HCl).

$$\text{moles HCl(g)} = \frac{\left(747\,\text{mmHg} \times \dfrac{1\,\text{atm}}{760\,\text{mmHg}} \right) \times 0.535\,\text{L}}{\dfrac{0.08206\,\text{L atm}}{\text{mol K}} \times (26.5 + 273.2)\,\text{K}}$$

moles HCl(g) = 0.0214 mol HCl(g) = 0.0214 mol H_3O^+ when dissolved in water

$[H_3O^+] = 0.0214\,\text{mol}$ $\text{pH} = -\log(0.0214) = 1.670$

6A   **(E)** pH is most readily determined from $\text{pOH} = -\log \left[OH^- \right]$. Assume $Mg(OH)_2$ is a strong base.

$$\left[OH^- \right] = \frac{9.63\text{ mg } Mg(OH)_2}{100.0\text{ mL soln}} \times \frac{1000\text{ mL}}{1\text{ L}} \times \frac{1\text{g}}{1000\text{ mg}} \times \frac{1\text{ mol } Mg(OH)_2}{58.32\text{ g } Mg(OH)_2} \times \frac{2\text{ mol } OH^-}{1\text{ mol } Mg(OH)_2}$$

$\left[OH^- \right] = 0.00330\,\text{M};\ \text{pOH} = -\log(0.00330) = 2.481$

$\text{pH} = 14.000 - \text{pOH} = 14.000 - 2.481 = 11.519$

6B **(E)** KOH is a strong base, which means that each mole of KOH that dissolves produces one mole of dissolved OH^- (aq). First we calculate $\left[OH^-\right]$ and the pOH. We then use $pH + pOH = 14.00$ to determine pH.

$$\left[OH^-\right] = \frac{3.00\,g\,KOH}{100.00\,g\,soln} \times \frac{1\,mol\,KOH}{56.11\,g\,KOH} \times \frac{1\,mol\,OH^-}{1\,mol\,KOH} \times \frac{1.0242\,g\,soln}{1\,mL\,soln} \times \frac{1000\,mL}{1\,L} = 0.548\,M$$

$$pOH = -\log(0.548) = 0.261 \quad pH = 14.000 - pOH = 14.000 - 0.261 = 13.739$$

7A **(M)** $\left[H_3O^+\right] = 10^{-pH} = 10^{-4.18} = 6.6 \times 10^{-5}$ M.

Organize the solution using the balanced chemical equation.

Equation:	$HOCl(aq)$	$+$	$H_2O(l)$	$\rightleftharpoons$	$H_3O^+(aq)\ +$	$OCl^-(aq)$
Initial:	0.150 M		—		≈ 0 M	0 M
Changes:	-6.6×10^{-5} M		—		$+6.6 \times 10^{-5}$ M	$+6.6 \times 10^{-5}$ M
Equil:	≈ 0.150 M		—		6.6×10^{-5} M	6.6×10^{-5} M

$$K_a = \frac{\left[H_3O^+\right]\left[OCl^-\right]}{\left[HOCl\right]} = \frac{\left(6.6 \times 10^{-5}\right)\left(6.6 \times 10^{-5}\right)}{0.150} = 2.9 \times 10^{-8}$$

7B **(M)** First, we use pH to determine $\left[OH^-\right]$. $pOH = 14.00 - pH = 14.00 - 10.08 = 3.92$.

$\left[OH^-\right] = 10^{-pOH} = 10^{-3.92} = 1.2 \times 10^{-4}$ M. We determine the initial concentration of cocaine and then organize the solution around the balanced equation in the manner we have used before.

$$[C_{17}H_{21}O_4N] = \frac{0.17\,g\,C_{17}H_{21}O_4N}{100\,mL\,soln} \times \frac{1000\,mL}{1\,L} \times \frac{1\,mol\,C_{17}H_{21}O_4N}{303.36\,g\,C_{17}H_{21}O_4N} = 0.0056\,M$$

Equation:	$C_{17}H_{21}O_4N(aq)\ +$	$H_2O(l)$	$\rightleftharpoons$	$C_{17}H_{21}O_4NH^+(aq)\ +$	$OH^-(aq)$
Initial:	0.0056 M	—		0 M	≈ 0 M
Changes:	-1.2×10^{-4} M	—		$+1.2 \times 10^{-4}$ M	$+1.2 \times 10^{-4}$ M
Equil:	≈ 0.0055 M	—		1.2×10^{-4} M	1.2×10^{-4} M

$$K_b = \frac{\left[C_{17}H_{21}O_4NH^+\right]\left[OH^-\right]}{\left[C_{17}H_{21}O_4N\right]} = \frac{\left(1.2 \times 10^{-4}\right)\left(1.2 \times 10^{-4}\right)}{0.0055} = 2.6 \times 10^{-6}$$

8A **(M)** Again we organize our solution around the balanced chemical equation.

Equation: $CH_2FCOOH(aq)$ + $H_2O(l)$ $\rightleftharpoons$ $H_3O^+(aq)$ + $CH_2FCOO^-(aq)$
Initial: 0.100 M — $\approx 0M$ 0 M
Changes: $-x$ M — $+x$ M $+x$ M
Equil: $(0.100 - x)$ M — x M x M

$$K_a = \frac{[H_3O^+][C_2H_2FO_2^-]}{[HC_2H_2FO_2^-]} \text{ ; therefore, } 2.6 \times 10^{-3} = \frac{x \cdot x}{(0.100 - x)}$$

We can use the 5% rule to ignore x in the denominator. Therefore, $x = [H_3O^+] = 0.016$ M, and pH $= -\log(0.016) = 1.8$. Thus, the calculated pH is considerably lower than 2.89 (Example 16-6).

8B **(M)** We first determine the concentration of undissociated acid. We then use this value in a set-up that is based on the balanced chemical equation.

$$2 \text{ aspirin tablets} \times \frac{0.500 \text{ g } C_6H_4(OOCCH_3)COOH}{\text{tablet}} \times \frac{1 \text{ mol } C_6H_4(OOCCH_3)COOH}{180.155 \text{ g } C_6H_4(OOCCH_3)COOH}$$

$$\times \frac{1}{0.325 \text{ L}} = 0.0171 \text{ M}$$

Equation: $C_6H_4(OOCCH_3)COOH(aq)$ + $H_2O(l)$ $\rightleftharpoons$ $H_3O^+(aq)$ + $C_6H_4(OOCCH_3)COO^-(aq)$
Initial: 0.0171 M — 0 M 0 M
Changes: $-x$ M — $+x$ M $+x$ M
Equil: $(0.0171 - x)$ M — x M x M

$$K_a = \frac{[H_3O^+][C_6H_4(OOCCH_3)COO^-]}{[C_6H_4(OOCCH_3)COOH]} = 3.3 \times 10^{-4} = \frac{x \cdot x}{0.0171 - x}$$

$x^2 + 3.3 \times 10^{-4} - 5.6\underline{4} \times 10^{-6} = 0$ (find the physically reasonable roots of the quadratic equation)

$$x = \frac{-3.3 \times 10^{-4} \pm \sqrt{1.1 \times 10^{-7} + 2.3 \times 10^{-5}}}{2} = 0.0022 \text{ M}; \quad pH = -\log(0.0022) = 2.66$$

9A **(M)** Again we organize our solution around the balanced chemical equation.

Equation: $CH_2FCOOH(aq)$ + $H_2O(l)$ $\rightleftharpoons$ $H_3O^+(aq)$ + $CH_2FCOOH^-(aq)$
Initial: 0.015 M — $\approx 0M$ 0 M
Changes $-x$ M — $+x$ M $+x$ M
Equil: $(0.015 - x)$ M — x M x M

$$K_a = \frac{[H_3O^+][CH_2FCOOH^-]}{[CH_2FCOOH]} = 2.6 \times 10^{-3} = \frac{(x)(x)}{0.015 - x} \approx \frac{x^2}{0.015}$$

$x = \sqrt{x^2} = \sqrt{0.015 \times 2.6 \times 10^{-3}} = 0.0062 \text{ M} = [H_3O^+]$ Our assumption is invalid:

0.0062 is not quite small enough compared to 0.015 for the 5% rule to hold. Thus we use another cycle of successive approximations.

$$K_a = \frac{(x)(x)}{0.015 - 0.0062} = 2.6 \times 10^{-3} \quad x = \sqrt{(0.015 - 0.0062) \times 2.6 \times 10^{-3}} = 0.0048 \text{ M} = [\text{H}_3\text{O}^+]$$

$$K_a = \frac{(x)(x)}{0.015 - 0.0048} = 2.6 \times 10^{-3} \quad x = \sqrt{(0.015 - 0.0048) \times 2.6 \times 10^{-3}} = 0.0051 \text{ M} = [\text{H}_3\text{O}^+]$$

$$K_a = \frac{(x)(x)}{0.015 - 0.0051} = 2.6 \times 10^{-3} \quad x = \sqrt{(0.015 - 0.0051) \times 2.6 \times 10^{-3}} = 0.0051 \text{ M} = [\text{H}_3\text{O}^+]$$

Two successive identical results indicate that we have the solution.

$\text{pH} = -\log[\text{H}_3\text{O}^+] = -\log(0.0051) = 2.29.$ The quadratic equation gives the same result (0.0051 M) as this method of successive approximations.

9B **(M)** First we find [$C_5H_{10}NH$]. We then use this value as the starting base concentration in a set-up based on the balanced chemical equation.

$$[C_5H_{10}NH] = \frac{114 \text{ mg } C_5H_{10}NH}{315 \text{ mL soln}} \times \frac{1 \text{ mmol } C_5H_{10}NH}{85.15 \text{ mg } C_5H_{10}NH} = 0.00425 \text{ M}$$

Equation: $\quad C_5H_{10}NH(aq) \quad + \quad H_2O(l) \quad \rightleftharpoons \quad C_5H_{10}NH_2^+(aq) + \quad OH^-(aq)$

	$C_5H_{10}NH$	H_2O	$C_5H_{10}NH_2^+$	OH^-
Initial:	0.00425 M	—	0 M	≈ 0 M
Changes:	−x M	—	+x M	+x M
Equil:	(0.00425 − x) M	—	x M	x M

$$K_b = \frac{[C_5H_{10}NH_2^+][OH^-]}{[C_5H_{10}NH]} = 1.6 \times 10^{-3} = \frac{x \cdot x}{0.00425 - x} \approx \frac{x \cdot x}{0.00425} \quad \text{We assumed that } x \ll 0.00425$$

$x = \sqrt{0.0016 \times 0.00425} = 0.0026 \text{ M}$ The assumption is not valid. Let's assume $x \approx 0.0026$

$x = \sqrt{0.0016(0.00425 - 0.0026)} = 0.0016$ Let's try again, with $x \approx 0.0016$

$x = \sqrt{0.0016(0.00425 - 0.0016)} = 0.0021$ Yet another try, with $x \approx 0.0021$

$x = \sqrt{0.0016(0.00425 - 0.0021)} = 0.0019$ The last time, with $x \approx 0.0019$

$x = \sqrt{0.0016(0.00425 - 0.0019)} = 0.0019 \text{ M} = [OH^-]$

$\text{pOH} = -\log[\text{H}_3\text{O}^+] = -\log(0.0019) = 2.72 \quad \text{pH} = 14.00 - \text{pOH} = 14.00 - 2.72 = 11.28$

We could have solved the problem with the quadratic formula roots equation rather than by successive approximations. The same answer is obtained. In fact, if we substitute $x = 0.0019$ into the K_b expression, we obtain $(0.0019)^2 / (0.00425 - 0.0019) = 1.5 \times 10^{-3}$ compared to $K_b = 1.6 \times 10^{-3}$. The error is due to rounding, not to an incorrect value. Using $x = 0.0020$ gives a value of 1.8×10^{-3}, while using $x = 0.0018$ gives 1.3×10^{-3}.

10A **(M)** For an aqueous solution of a diprotic acid, the concentration of the divalent anion is very close to the second ionization constant: $\left[{}^{-}OOCCH_2COO^{-} \right] \approx K_{a_2} = 2.0 \times 10^{-6} M$. We organize around the chemical equation.

Equation:	$CH_2(COOH)_2$ (aq)	+ $H_2O(l)$	$\rightleftharpoons$	H_3O^+ (aq)	+	$HOOCCH_2COO^-$ (aq)
Initial:	1.0 M	—		$\approx 0\,M$		0 M
Change:	$-x$ M	—		$+x$ M		$+x$ M
Equil:	$(1.0 - x)$ M	—		x M		x M

$$K_a = \frac{[H_3O^+][HOOCCH_2COO^-]}{[CH_2(COOH)_2]} = \frac{(x)(x)}{1.0 - x} \approx \frac{x^2}{1.0} = 1.4 \times 10^{-3}$$

$x = \sqrt{1.4 \times 10^{-3}} = 3.7 \times 10^{-2}$ M $= [H_3O^+] = [HOOCCH_2COO^-]$ $x \ll 1.0$ M is a valid assumption.

10B **(M)** We know $K_{a_2} \approx \left[\text{doubly charged anion} \right]$ for a polyprotic acid. Thus, $K_{a_2} = 5.3 \times 10^{-5} \approx \left[C_2O_4^{2-} \right]$. From the pH, $\left[H_3O^+ \right] = 10^{-pH} = 10^{-0.67} = 0.21$ M. We also recognize that $\left[HC_2O_4^- \right] = \left[H_3O^+ \right]$, since the second ionization occurs to only a very small extent. We note as well that $HC_2O_4^-$ is produced by the ionization of $H_2C_2O_4$. Each mole of $HC_2O_4^-$ present results from the ionization of 1 mole of $H_2C_2O_4$. Now we have sufficient information to determine the K_{a_1}.

$$K_{a_1} = \frac{\left[H_3O^+ \right]\left[HC_2O_4^- \right]}{\left[H_2C_2O_4 \right]} = \frac{0.21 \times 0.21}{1.05 - 0.21} = 5.3 \times 10^{-2}$$

11A **(M)** H_2SO_4 is a strong acid in its first ionization, and somewhat weak in its second, with $K_{a_2} = 1.1 \times 10^{-2} = 0.011$. Because of the strong first ionization step, this problem involves determining concentrations in a solution that initially is 0.20 M H_3O^+ and 0.20 M HSO_4^-. We base the set-up on the balanced chemical equation.

Equation:	HSO_4^- (aq)	+ H_2O (l)	$\rightleftharpoons$	H_3O^+ (aq)	+	SO_4^{2-} (aq)
Initial:	0.20 M	—		0.20 M		0 M
Changes:	$-x$ M	—		$+x$ M		$+x$ M
Equil:	$(0.20 - x)$ M	—		$(0.20 + x)$ M		x M

$$K_{a_2} = \frac{\left[H_3O^+ \right]\left[SO_4^{2-} \right]}{\left[HSO_4^- \right]} = \frac{(0.20 + x)x}{0.20 - x} = 0.011 \approx \frac{0.20 \times x}{0.20}, \text{ assuming that } x \ll 0.20 M.$$

$x = 0.011$ M   Try one cycle of approximation:

$$0.011 \approx \frac{(0.20+0.011)x}{(0.20-0.011)} = \frac{0.21x}{0.19} \qquad x = \frac{0.19 \times 0.011}{0.21} = 0.010 \text{ M}$$

The next cycle of approximation produces the same answer $0.010 \text{M} = \left[SO_4^{2-} \right]$,

$\left[H_3O^+ \right] = 0.010 + 0.20 \text{ M} = 0.21 \text{ M}, \qquad \left[HSO_4^- \right] = 0.20 - 0.010 \text{ M} = 0.19 \text{ M}$

11B **(M)** We know that H_2SO_4 is a strong acid in its first ionization, and a somewhat weak acid in its second, with $K_{a_2} = 1.1 \times 10^{-2} = 0.011$. Because of the strong first ionization step, the problem essentially reduces to determining concentrations in a solution that initially is 0.020 M H_3O^+ and 0.020 M HSO_4^-. We base the set-up on the balanced chemical equation. The result is solved using the quadratic equation.

Equation: $\quad HSO_4^-(aq) + H_2O(l) \rightleftharpoons H_3O^+(aq) \quad + \quad SO_4^{2-}(aq)$

Initial: $\qquad$ 0.020 M $\qquad$ — $\qquad$ 0.020 M $\qquad$ 0 M

Changes: $\quad$ $-x$ M $\qquad$ — $\qquad$ $+x$ M $\qquad$ $+x$ M

Equil: $\qquad$ $(0.020-x)$ M $\quad$ — $\quad$ $(0.020+x)$ M $\qquad$ x M

$$K_{a_2} = \frac{\left[H_3O^+ \right]\left[SO_4^{2-} \right]}{\left[HSO_4^- \right]} = \frac{(0.020+x)x}{0.020-x} = 0.011 \qquad\qquad 0.020x + x^2 = 2.2 \times 10^{-4} - 0.011x$$

$$x^2 + 0.031x - 0.00022 = 0 \qquad x = \frac{-0.031 \pm \sqrt{0.00096 + 0.00088}}{2} = 0.0060 \text{ M} = \left[SO_4^{2-} \right]$$

$\left[HSO_4^- \right] = 0.020 - 0.0060 = 0.014 \text{ M} \qquad \left[H_3O^+ \right] = 0.020 + 0.0060 = 0.026 \text{ M}$

(The method of successive approximations converges to $x = 0.006$ M in 8 cycles.)

12A **(E)**

(a) $CH_3NH_3^+NO_3^-$ is the salt of the cation of a weak base. The cation, $CH_3NH_3^+$, will hydrolyze to form an acidic solution $\left(CH_3NH_3^+ + H_2O \rightleftharpoons CH_3NH_2 + H_3O^+ \right)$, while NO_3^-, by virtue of being the conjugate base of a strong acid will not hydrolyze to a detectable extent. The aqueous solutions of this compound will thus be acidic.

(b) NaI is the salt composed of the cation of a strong base and the anion of a strong acid, neither of which hydrolyzes in water. Solutions of this compound will be pH neutral.

(c) $NaNO_2$ is the salt composed of the cation of a strong base that will not hydrolyze in water and the anion of a weak acid that will hydrolyze to form an alkaline solution $\left(NO_2^- + H_2O \rightleftharpoons HNO_2 + OH^- \right)$. Thus aqueous solutions of this compound will be basic (alkaline).

12B **(E)** Even without referring to the K values for acids and bases, we can predict that the reaction that produces H_3O^+ occurs to the greater extent. This, of course, is because the pH is less than 7, thus acid hydrolysis must predominate.

We write the two reactions of $H_2PO_4^-$ with water, along with the values of their equilibrium constants.

$$H_2PO_4^-(aq) + H_2O(l) \rightleftharpoons H_3O^+(aq) + HPO_4^{2-}(aq) \qquad K_{a_2} = 6.3 \times 10^{-8}$$

$$H_2PO_4^-(aq) + H_2O(l) \rightleftharpoons OH^-(aq) + H_3PO_4(aq) \qquad K_b = \frac{K_w}{K_{a_1}} = \frac{1.0 \times 10^{-14}}{7.1 \times 10^{-3}} = 1.4 \times 10^{-12}$$

As predicted, the acid ionization occurs to the greater extent.

13A **(M)** From the value of pK_b we determine the value of K_b and then K_a for the cation.

cocaine: $\qquad K_b = 10^{-pK} = 10^{-8.41} = 3.9 \times 10^{-9} \qquad K_a = \frac{K_w}{K_b} = \frac{1.0 \times 10^{-14}}{3.9 \times 10^{-9}} = 2.6 \times 10^{-6}$

codeine: $\qquad K_b = 10^{-pK} = 10^{-7.95} = 1.1 \times 10^{-8} \qquad K_a = \frac{K_w}{K_b} = \frac{1.0 \times 10^{-14}}{1.1 \times 10^{-8}} = 9.1 \times 10^{-7}$

(This method may be a bit easier:

$pK_a = 14.00 - pK_b = 14.00 - 8.41 = 5.59, K_a = 10^{-5.59} = 2.6 \times 10^{-6}$) The acid with the larger K_a will produce the higher $[H^+]$, and that solution will have the lower pH. Thus, the solution of codeine hydrochloride will have the higher pH (i.e., codeine hydrochloride is the weaker acid).

13B **(E)** Both of the ions of $NH_4CN(aq)$ react with water in hydrolysis reactions.

$$NH_4^+(aq) + H_2O(l) \rightleftharpoons NH_3(aq) + H_3O^+(aq) \qquad K_a = \frac{K_w}{K_b} = \frac{1.0 \times 10^{-14}}{1.8 \times 10^{-5}} = 5.6 \times 10^{-10}$$

$$CN^-(aq) + H_2O(l) \rightleftharpoons HCN(aq) + OH^-(aq) \qquad K_b = \frac{K_w}{K_a} = \frac{1.0 \times 10^{-14}}{6.2 \times 10^{-10}} = 1.6 \times 10^{-5}$$

Since the value of the equilibrium constant for the hydrolysis reaction of cyanide ion is larger than that for the hydrolysis of ammonium ion, the cyanide ion hydrolysis reaction will proceed to a greater extent and thus the solution of $NH_4CN(aq)$ will be basic (alkaline).

14A **(M)** NaF dissociates completely into sodium ions and fluoride ions. The released fluoride ion hydrolyzes in aqueous solution to form hydroxide ion. The determination of the equilibrium pH is organized around the balanced equation.

Equation:	$F^-(aq)$	$+$	$H_2O(l)$	$\rightleftharpoons$	$HF(aq)$	$+$	$OH^-(aq)$
Initial:	0.10 M		—		0 M		0 M
Changes:	$-x$ M		—		$+x$ M		$+x$ M
Equil:	$(0.10-x)$ M		—		x M		x M

$$K_b = \frac{K_w}{K_a} = \frac{1.0 \times 10^{-14}}{6.6 \times 10^{-4}} = 1.5 \times 10^{-11} = \frac{[HF][OH^-]}{[F^-]} = \frac{(x)(x)}{(0.10-x)} = \frac{x^2}{0.10}$$

$$x = \sqrt{0.10 \times 1.5 \times 10^{-11}} = 1.2 \times 10^{-6} \text{ M} = [OH^-]; \text{ pOH} = -\log(1.2 \times 10^{-6}) = 5.92$$

$$\text{pH} = 14.00 - \text{pOH} = 14.00 - 5.92 = 8.08 \quad (\text{As expected, pH} > 7)$$

14B **(M)** The cyanide ion hydrolyzes in solution, as indicated in Practice Example 16-12B. As a consequence of the hydrolysis, $[OH^-] = [HCN]$ $[OH^-]$ can be found from the pH of the solution, and then values are substituted into the K_b expression for CN^-, which is then solved for $[CN^-]$.

$$\text{pOH} = 14.00 - \text{pH} = 14.00 - 10.38 = 3.62$$

$$[OH^-] = 10^{-\text{pOH}} = 10^{-3.62} = 2.4 \times 10^{-4} \text{ M} = [HCN]$$

$$K_b = \frac{[HCN][OH^-]}{[CN^-]} = 1.6 \times 10^{-5} = \frac{(2.4 \times 10^{-4})^2}{[CN^-]} \qquad [CN^-] = \frac{(2.4 \times 10^{-4})^2}{1.6 \times 10^{-5}} = 3.6 \times 10^{-3} \text{ M}$$

15A **(M)** First we draw the Lewis structures of the four acids. Lone pairs have been omitted since we are interested only in the arrangements of atoms.

$HClO_4$ should be stronger than HNO_3. Although Cl and N have similar electronegativities, there are more terminal oxygen atoms attached to the chlorine in perchloric acid than to the nitrogen in nitric acid. By virtue of having more terminal oxygens, perchloric acid, when ionized, affords a more stable conjugate base. The more stable the anion, the more easily it is formed and hence the stronger is the conjugate acid from which it is derived. CH_2FCOOH will be a stronger acid than $CH_2BrCOOH$ because F is a more electronegative atom than Br. The F atom withdraws additional electron density from the O—H bond, making the bond easier to break, which leads to increased acidity.

15B **(M)** First we draw the Lewis structures of the first two acids. Lone pairs are not depicted since we are interested in the arrangements of atoms.

H_3PO_4 and H_2SO_3 both have one terminal oxygen atom, but S is more electronegative than P. This suggests that $H_2SO_3 (K_{a_1} = 1.3 \times 10^{-2})$ should be a stronger acid than $H_3PO_4 (K_{a_1} = 7.1 \times 10^{-3})$, and it is. The only difference between CCl_3CH_2COOH and CCl_2FCH_2COOH is the replacement of Cl by F. Since F is more electronegative than Cl, CCl_3CH_2COOH should be a weaker acid than CCl_2FCH_2COOH.

16A **(M)** We draw Lewis structures to help us decide.

(a) Clearly, BF_3 is an electron pair acceptor, a Lewis acid, and NH_3 is an electron pair donor, a Lewis base.

(b) H_2O certainly has electron pairs (lone pairs) to donate and thus it can be a Lewis base. It is unlikely that the cation Cr^{3+} has any accessible valence electrons that can be donated to another atom, thus, it is the Lewis acid. The product of the reaction, $[Cr(H_2O)_6]^{3+}$, is described as a water adduct of Cr^{3+}.

16B **(M)** The Lewis structures of the six species follow.

Both the hydroxide ion and the chloride ion have lone pairs of electrons that can be donated to electron-poor centers. These two are the electron pair donors, or the Lewis bases. $Al(OH)_3$ and $SnCl_4$ have additional spaces in their structures to accept pairs of electrons, which is what occurs when they form the complex anions $[Al(OH)_4]^-$ and $[SnCl_6]^{2-}$. Thus, $Al(OH)_3$ and $SnCl_4$ are the Lewis acids in these reactions.

INTEGRATIVE EXAMPLE

A. (D) To confirm the pH of rainwater, we have to calculate the concentration of $CO_2(aq)$ in water and then use simple acid-base equilibrium to calculate pH.

Concentration of CO_2 in water at 1 atm pressure and 298 K is 1.45 g/L, or

$$\frac{1.45 \text{ g CO}_2}{\text{L}} \times \frac{1 \text{ mol CO}_2}{44.0 \text{ g CO}_2} = 0.0329 \text{ M CO}_2$$

Furthermore, if the atmosphere is 0.037% by volume CO_2, then the mole fraction of CO_2 is 0.00037, and the partial pressure of CO_2 also becomes 0.00037 atm (because $P_{CO_2} = x_{CO_2} P_{atm}$)

From Henry's law, we know that concentration of a gas in a liquid is proportional to its partial pressure.
$C(\text{mol/L}) = k \, P_{CO_2}$, which can rearrange to solve for k:

$$k = \frac{0.0329 \text{ M}}{1 \text{ atm}} = 0.0329 \text{ mol L}^{-1} \text{ atm}^{-1}$$

Therefore, concentration of $CO_2(aq)$ in water under atmospheric pressures at 298 K is:

$$C_{CO_2} (\text{mol}/\text{L}) = 0.0329 \text{ mol L}^{-1} \text{ atm}^{-1} \, 0.00037 \text{ atm} = 1.217 \times 10^{-5} \text{ M}$$

Using the equation for reaction of CO_2 with water:

CO_2 (aq)	+	2 H_2O (l)	$\rightleftharpoons$	H_3O^+ (aq)	+	HCO_3^- (aq)
1.217×10^{-5}				0		0
$-x$				$+x$		$+x$
$1.217 \times 10^{-5} - x$				x		x

$$K_{a1} = \frac{x^2}{\left(1.217 \times 10^{-5} - x\right)} = 4.4 \times 10^{-7}$$

Using the quadratic formula, $x = 2.104 \times 10^{-6}$ M

$$pH = -\log\left[H_3O^+\right] = -\log\left(2.104 \times 10^{-6}\right) = 5.68 \approx 5.7$$

We can, of course, continue to refine the value of $[H_3O^+]$ further by considering the dissociation of HCO_3^-, but the change is too small to matter.

B. (D)

   (a) For the acids given, we determine values of m and n in the formula $EO_m(OH)_n$. HOCl or Cl(OH) has $m = 0$ and $n = 1$. We expect $K_a \approx 10^{-7}$ or $pK_a \approx 7$, which is in good agreement with the accepted $pK_a = 7.52$. HOClO or ClO(OH) has $m = 1$ and $n = 1$. We expect $K_a \approx 10^{-2}$ or $pK_a \approx 2$, in good agreement with the $pK_a = 1.92$. $HOClO_2$ or $ClO_2(OH)$ has $m = 2$ and $n = 1$. We expect K_a to be large and in good agreement with the accepted value of $pK_a = -3$, $K_a = 10^{-pK_a} = 10^3$. $HOClO_3$ or $ClO_3(OH)$ has $m = 3$ and $n = 1$. We expect K_a to be very large and in good agreement with the accepted $K_a = -8$, $pK_a = -8$, $K_a = 10^{-pK_a} = 10^8$ which turns out to be the case.

   (b) The formula H_3AsO_4 can be rewritten as $AsO(OH)_3$, which has $m = 1$ and $n = 3$. The expected value is $K_a = 10^{-2}$.

   (c) The value of $pK_a = 1.1$ corresponds to $K_a = 10^{-pK_a} = 10^{-1.1} = 0.08$, which indicates that $m = 1$. The following Lewis structure is consistent with this value of m.

EXERCISES

Brønsted-Lowry Theory of Acids and Bases

1.   **(E)**

   (a) HNO_2 is an acid, a proton donor. Its conjugate base is NO_2^-.

   (b) OCl^- is a base, a proton acceptor. Its conjugate acid is HOCl.

   (c) NH_2^- is a base, a proton acceptor. Its conjugate acid is NH_3.

   (d) NH_4^+ is an acid, a proton donor. It's conjugate base is NH_3.

   (e) $CH_3NH_3^+$ is an acid, a proton donor. It's conjugate base is CH_3NH_2.

2.   **(E)** We write the conjugate base as the first product of the equilibrium for which the acid is the first reactant.

   (a) $HIO_3(aq) + H_2O(l) \rightleftharpoons IO_3^-(aq) + H_3O^+(aq)$

   (b) $C_6H_5COOH(aq) + H_2O(l) \rightleftharpoons C_6H_5COO^-(aq) + H_3O^+(aq)$

   (c) $HPO_4^{2-}(aq) + H_2O(l) \rightleftharpoons PO_4^{3-}(aq) + H_3O^+(aq)$

   (d) $C_2H_5NH_3^+(aq) + H_2O(l) \rightleftharpoons C_2H_5NH_2(aq) + H_3O^+(aq)$

3. **(E)** The acids (proton donors) and bases (proton acceptors) are labeled below their formulas. Remember that a proton, in Brønsted-Lowry acid-base theory, is H^+.

    (a) $HOBr(aq)$ + $H_2O(l) \rightleftharpoons H_3O^+(aq)$ + $OBr^-(aq)$
                  acid   base   acid   base

    (b) $HSO_4^-(aq)$ + $H_2O(l) \rightleftharpoons H_3O^+(aq)$ + $SO_4^{2-}(aq)$
                  acid   base   acid   base

    (c) $HS^-(aq)$ + $H_2O(l) \rightleftharpoons H_2S(aq)$ + $OH^-(aq)$
                  base   acid   acid   base

    (d) $C_6H_5NH_3^+(aq)$ + $OH^-(aq) \rightleftharpoons C_6H_5NH_2(aq)$ + $H_2O(l)$
                  acid   base   base   acid

4. **(E)** For each amphiprotic substance, we write both its acid and base hydrolysis reaction. Even for the substances that are not usually considered amphiprotic, both reactions are written, but one of them is labeled as unlikely. In some instances we have written an oxygen as $\varnothing$ to keep track of it through the reaction.

$\varnothing H^- + H_2O \rightleftharpoons \varnothing^{2-} + H_3O^+$ (unlikely) $\varnothing H^- + H_2O \rightleftharpoons H_2\varnothing + OH^-$

$NH_4^+ + H_2O \rightleftharpoons NH_3 + H_3O^+$ NH_4^+ has no e^- pairs that can be donated

$H_2\varnothing + H_2O \rightleftharpoons \varnothing H^- + H_3O^+$ $H_2\varnothing + H_2O \rightleftharpoons H_3\varnothing^+ + OH^-$

$HS^- + H_2O \rightleftharpoons S^{2-} + H_3O^+$ $HS^- + H_2O \rightleftharpoons H_2S + OH^-$

NO_2^- cannot act as an acid, (no protons) $NO_2^- + H_2O \rightleftharpoons HNO_2 + OH^-$

$HCO_3^- + H_2O \rightleftharpoons CO_3^{2-} + H_3O^+$ $HCO_3^- + H_2O \rightleftharpoons H_2CO_3 + OH^-$

$HBr + H_2O \rightleftharpoons H_3O^+ + Br^-$ $HBr + H_2O \rightleftharpoons H_2Br^+ + OH^-$ (unlikely)

5. **(E)** Answer (b), NH_3, is correct. CH_3COOH will react most completely with the strongest base. NO_3^- and Cl^- are very weak bases. H_2O is a weak base, but it is amphiprotic, acting as an acid (donating protons), as in the presence of NH_3. Thus, NH_3 must be the strongest base and the most effective in deprotonating CH_3COOH.

6. **(M)** Lewis structures are given below each equation.
    (a) $2NH_3(l) \rightleftharpoons NH_4^+ + NH_2^-$

(b) $2HF(l) \rightleftharpoons H_2F^+ + F^-$

(c) $2CH_3OH(l) \rightleftharpoons CH_3OH_2^+ + CH_3O^-$

(d) $2HC_2H_3O_2(l) \rightleftharpoons H_2C_2H_3O_2^+ + CH_3COO^-$

(e) $2H_2SO_4(l) \rightleftharpoons 2H_3SO_4^+ + HSO_4^-$

7. **(E)** The principle we will follow here is that, in terms of their concentrations, the weaker acid and the weaker base will predominate at equilibrium. The reason for this is that a strong acid will do a good job of donating its protons and, having done so, its conjugate base will be left behind. The preferred direction is:

strong acid + strong base → weak (conjugate) base + weak (conjugate) acid

(a) The reaction will favor the forward direction because OH^- (a strong base) $> NH_3$ (a weak base) and NH_4^+ (relatively strong weak acid) $> H_2O$ (very weak acid).

(b) The reaction will favor the reverse direction because $HNO_3 > HSO_4^-$ (a weak acid in the second ionization) (acting as acids), and $SO_4^{2-} > NO_3^-$ (acting as bases).

(c) The reaction will favor the reverse direction because $CH_3COOH > CH_3OH$ (not usually thought of as an acid) (acting as acids), and $CH_3O^- > CH_3COO^-$ (acting as bases).

8. **(M)** The principle we follow here is that, in terms of their concentrations, the weaker acid and the weaker base predominate at equilibrium. This is because a strong acid will do a good job of donating its protons and, having done so, its conjugate base will remain in solution. The preferred direction is:

strong acid + strong base $\rightarrow$ weak (conjugate) base + weak (conjugate) acid

(a) The reaction will favor the forward direction because CH_3COOH (a moderate acid) $> HCO_3^-$ (a rather weak acid) (acting as acids) and $CO_3^{2-} > CH_3COO^-$ (acting as bases).

(b) The reaction will favor the reverse direction because $HClO_4$ (a strong acid) $> HNO_2$ (acting as acids), and $NO_2^- > ClO_4^-$ (acting as bases).

(c) The reaction will favor the forward direction, because $H_2CO_3 > HCO_3^-$ (acting as acids) (because $K_1 > K_2$) and $CO_3^{2-} > HCO_3^-$ (acting as bases).

Strong Acids, Strong Bases, and pH

9. **(M)** All of the solutes are strong acids or strong bases.

(a) $\left[H_3O^+\right] = 0.00165 \text{ M HNO}_3 \times \dfrac{1 \text{ mol } H_3O^+}{1 \text{ mol HNO}_3} = 0.00165 \text{ M}$

$\left[OH^-\right] = \dfrac{K_w}{\left[H_3O^+\right]} = \dfrac{1.0 \times 10^{-14}}{0.00165 \text{M}} = 6.1 \times 10^{-12} \text{ M}$

(b) $\left[OH^-\right] = 0.0087 \text{ M KOH} \times \dfrac{1 \text{ mol } OH^-}{1 \text{ mol KOH}} = 0.0087 \text{ M}$

$\left[H_3O^+\right] = \dfrac{K_w}{\left[OH^-\right]} = \dfrac{1.0 \times 10^{-14}}{0.0087 \text{M}} = 1.1 \times 10^{-12} \text{ M}$

(c) $\left[OH^-\right] = 0.00213 \text{ M Sr(OH)}_2 \times \dfrac{2 \text{ mol } OH^-}{1 \text{ mol Sr(OH)}_2} = 0.00426 \text{ M}$

$\left[H_3O^+\right] = \dfrac{K_w}{\left[OH^-\right]} = \dfrac{1.0 \times 10^{-14}}{0.00426 \text{ M}} = 2.3 \times 10^{-12} \text{ M}$

(d) $\left[H_3O^+\right] = 5.8 \times 10^{-4} \text{ M HI} \times \dfrac{1 \text{mol } H_3O^+}{1 \text{mol HI}} = 5.8 \times 10^{-4} \text{ M}$

$\left[OH^-\right] = \dfrac{K_w}{\left[H_3O^+\right]} = \dfrac{1.0 \times 10^{-14}}{5.8 \times 10^{-4} \text{ M}} = 1.7 \times 10^{-11} \text{ M}$

10. **(M)** Again, all of the solutes are strong acids or strong bases.

    (a) $\left[H_3O^+\right] = 0.0045 \text{ M HCl} \times \dfrac{1 \text{ mol } H_3O^+}{1 \text{ mol HCl}} = 0.0045 \text{ M}$

    $pH = -\log(0.0045) = 2.35$

    (b) $\left[H_3O^+\right] = 6.14 \times 10^{-4} \text{ M HNO}_3 \times \dfrac{1 \text{ mol } H_3O^+}{1 \text{ mol HNO}_3} = 6.14 \times 10^{-4} \text{ M}$

    $pH = -\log(6.14 \times 10^{-4}) = 3.21$

    (c) $\left[OH^-\right] = 0.00683 \text{ M NaOH} \times \dfrac{1 \text{ mol } OH^-}{1 \text{ mol NaOH}} = 0.00683 \text{M}$

    $pOH = -\log(0.00683) = 2.166 \text{ and } pH = 14.000 - pOH = 14.000 - 2.166 = 11.83$

    (d) $\left[OH^-\right] = 4.8 \times 10^{-3} \text{ M Ba}(OH)_2 \times \dfrac{2 \text{ mol } OH^-}{1 \text{ mol Ba}(OH)_2} = 9.6 \times 10^{-3} \text{ M}$

    $pOH = -\log(9.6 \times 10^{-3}) = 2.02 \qquad pH = 14.00 - 2.02 = 11.98$

11. **(E)**

    $\left[OH^-\right] = \dfrac{3.9 \text{ g Ba}(OH)_2 \cdot 8H_2O}{100 \text{ mL soln}} \times \dfrac{1000 \text{ mL}}{1 \text{ L}} \times \dfrac{1 \text{ mol Ba}(OH)_2 \cdot 8H_2O}{315.5 \text{ g Ba}(OH)_2 \cdot 8H_2O} \times \dfrac{2 \text{ mol } OH^-}{1 \text{ mol Ba}(OH)_2 \cdot 8H_2O}$

    $= 0.25 \text{ M}$

    $\left[H_3O^+\right] = \dfrac{K_w}{\left[OH^-\right]} = \dfrac{1.0 \times 10^{-14}}{0.25 \text{ M } OH^-} = 4.0 \times 10^{-14} \text{ M} \qquad pH = -\log(4.0 \times 10^{-14}) = 13.40$

12. **(M)** The dissolved $Ca(OH)_2$ is completely dissociated into ions.

    $pOH = 14.00 - pH = 14.00 - 12.35 = 1.65$

    $\left[OH^-\right] = 10^{-pOH} = 10^{-1.65} = 2.2 \times 10^{-2} \text{ M } OH^- = 0.022 \text{ M } OH^-$

    $\text{solubility} = \dfrac{0.022 \text{ mol } OH^-}{1 \text{ L soln}} \times \dfrac{1 \text{ mol Ca}(OH)_2}{2 \text{ mol } OH^-} \times \dfrac{74.09 \text{ g Ca}(OH)_2}{1 \text{ mol Ca}(OH)_2} \times \dfrac{1000 \text{ mg Ca}(OH)_2}{1 \text{ g Ca}(OH)_2}$

    $= \dfrac{8.1 \times 10^2 \text{ mg Ca}(OH)_2}{1 \text{ L soln}}$

    In 100 mL the solubility is $100 \text{ mL} \times \dfrac{1 \text{ L}}{1000 \text{ mL}} \times \dfrac{8.1 \times 10^2 \text{ mg Ca}(OH)_2}{1 \text{ L soln}} = 81 \text{ mg Ca}(OH)_2$

13. (M) First we determine the moles of HCl, and then its concentration.

$$\text{moles HCl} = \frac{PV}{RT} = \frac{\left(751 \text{ mmHg} \times \dfrac{1 \text{ atm}}{760 \text{ mmHg}}\right) \times 0.205 \text{ L}}{0.08206 \text{ L atm mol}^{-1} \text{ K}^{-1} \times 296 \text{ K}} = 8.34 \times 10^{-3} \text{ mol HCl}$$

$$\left[H_3O^+\right] = \frac{8.34 \times 10^{-3} \text{ mol HCl}}{4.25 \text{ L soln}} \times \frac{1 \text{ mol } H_3O^+}{1 \text{ mol HCl}} = 1.96 \times 10^{-3} \text{ M}$$

14. (E) First determine the concentration of NaOH, then of OH^-.

$$\left[OH^-\right] = \frac{0.125 \text{ L} \times \dfrac{0.606 \text{ mol NaOH}}{1 \text{ L}} \times \dfrac{1 \text{ mol } OH^-}{1 \text{ mol NaOH}}}{15.0 \text{ L final solution}} = 0.00505 \text{ M}$$

$$pOH = -\log(0.00505 \text{ M}) = 2.297 \qquad pH = 14.00 - 2.297 = 11.703$$

15. (E) First determine the amount of HCl, and then the volume of the concentrated solution required.

$$\text{amount HCl} = 12.5 \text{ L} \times \frac{10^{-2.10} \text{ mol } H_3O^+}{1 \text{ L soln}} \times \frac{1 \text{ mol HCl}}{1 \text{ mol } H_3O^+} = 0.099 \text{ mol HCl}$$

$$V_{\text{solution}} = 0.099 \text{ mol HCl} \times \frac{36.46 \text{ g HCl}}{1 \text{ mol HCl}} \times \frac{100.0 \text{ g soln}}{36.0 \text{ g HCl}} \times \frac{1 \text{ mL soln}}{1.18 \text{ g soln}} = 8.5 \text{ mL soln}$$

16. (E) First we determine the amount of KOH, and then the volume of the concentrated solution required.

$$pOH = 14.00 - pH = 14.00 - 11.55 = 2.45 \qquad \left[OH^-\right] = 10^{-pOH} = 10^{-2.45} = 0.0035 \text{ M}$$

$$\text{amount KOH} = 25.0 \text{ L} \times \frac{0.0035 \text{ M mol } OH^-}{1 \text{ L soln}} \times \frac{1 \text{ mol KOH}}{1 \text{ mol } OH^-} = 0.088 \text{ mol KOH}$$

$$V_{\text{solution}} = 0.088 \text{ mol KOH} \times \frac{56.11 \text{ g KOH}}{1 \text{ mol KOH}} \times \frac{100.0 \text{ g soln}}{15.0 \text{ g KOH}} \times \frac{1 \text{ mL soln}}{1.14 \text{ g soln}} = 29 \text{ mL soln}$$

17. (E) The volume of HCl(aq) needed is determined by first finding the amount of NH_3(aq) present, and then realizing that acid and base react in a 1:1 molar ratio.

$$V_{HCl} = 1.25 \text{ L base} \times \frac{0.265 \text{ mol } NH_3}{1 \text{ L base}} \times \frac{1 \text{ mol } H_3O^+}{1 \text{ mol } NH_3} \times \frac{1 \text{ mol HCl}}{1 \text{ mol } H_3O^+} \times \frac{1 \text{ L acid}}{6.15 \text{ mol HCl}}$$

$$= 0.0539 \text{ L acid or } 53.9 \text{ mL acid.}$$

18. **(M)** NH_3 and HCl react in a 1:1 molar ratio. According to Avogadro's hypothesis, equal volumes of gases at the same temperature and pressure contain equal numbers of moles. Thus, the volume of $H_2(g)$ at 762 mmHg and $21.0°C$ that is equivalent to 28.2 L of $H_2(g)$ at 742 mmHg and 25.0 °C will be equal to the volume of $NH_3(g)$ needed for stoichiometric neutralization.

$$V_{NH_3(g)} = 28.2 \text{ L HCl}(g) \times \frac{742 \text{ mmHg}}{762 \text{ mmHg}} \times \frac{(273.2+21.0) \text{ K}}{(273.2+25.0) \text{ K}} \times \frac{1 \text{ L NH}_3(g)}{1 \text{ L HCl}(g)} = 27.1 \text{ L NH}_3(g)$$

Alternatively, we can solve the ideal gas equation for the amount of each gas, and then, by equating these two expressions, we can find the volume of NH_3 needed.

$$n\{HCl\} = \frac{742 \text{ mmHg } 28.2 \text{ L}}{R \, 298.2 \text{ K}} \qquad n\{NH_3\} = \frac{762 \text{ mmHg } V\{NH_3\}}{R \, 294.2 \text{ K}}$$

$$\frac{742 \text{ mmHg } 28.2 \text{ L}}{R \, 298.2 \text{ K}} = \frac{762 \text{ mmHg } V\{NH_3\}}{R \, 294.2 \text{ K}} \qquad \text{This yields } V\{NH_3\} = 27.1 \text{ L NH}_3(g)$$

19. **(M)** Here we determine the amounts of H_3O^+ and OH^- and then the amount of the one that is in excess. We express molar concentration in millimoles/milliliter, equivalent to mol/L.

$$50.00 \text{ mL} \times \frac{0.0155 \text{ mmol HI}}{1 \text{ mL soln}} \times \frac{1 \text{ mmol H}_3O^+}{1 \text{ mmol HI}} = 0.775 \text{ mmol H}_3O^+$$

$$75.00 \text{ mL} \times \frac{0.0106 \text{ mmol KOH}}{1 \text{ mL soln}} \times \frac{1 \text{ mmol OH}^-}{1 \text{ mmol KOH}} = 0.795 \text{ mmol OH}^-$$

The net reaction is $H_3O^+(aq) + OH^-(aq) \rightarrow 2 H_2O(l)$.

There is an excess of OH^- of $(0.795 - 0.775 =)\, 0.020$ mmol OH^-.
Thus, this is a basic solution. The total solution volume is $(50.00 + 75.00 =)\, 125.00$ mL.

$$[OH^-] = \frac{0.020 \text{ mmol OH}^-}{125.00 \text{ mL}} = 1.6 \times 10^{-4} \text{ M}, \quad pOH = -\log(1.6 \times 10^{-4}) = 3.80, \quad pH = 10.20$$

20. **(M)** In each case, we need to determine the $[H_3O^+]$ or $[OH^-]$ of each solution being mixed, and then the amount of H_3O^+ or OH^-, so that we can determine the amount in excess. We express molar concentration in millimoles/milliliter, equivalent to mol/L.

$$[H_3O^+] = 10^{-2.12} = 7.6 \times 10^{-3} \text{ M} \qquad \text{moles } H_3O^+ = 25.00 \text{ mL} \times 7.6 \times 10^{-3} \text{ M} = 0.19 \text{ mmol H}_3O^+$$

$$pOH = 14.00 - 12.65 = 1.35 \qquad [OH^-] = 10^{-1.35} = 4.5 \times 10^{-2} \text{ M}$$

$$\text{amount } OH^- = 25.00 \text{ mL} \times 4.5 \times 10^{-2} \text{ M} = 1.13 \text{ mmol OH}^-$$

There is excess OH^- in the amount of 0.94 mmol $(= 1.13$ mmol $OH^- - 0.19$ mmol $H_3O^+)$.

$$[OH^-] = \frac{0.94 \text{ mmol OH}^-}{25.00 \text{ mL} + 25.00 \text{ mL}} = 1.8\underline{8} \times 10^{-2} \text{ M} \qquad pOH = -\log(1.8\underline{8} \times 10^{-2}) = 1.73 \quad pH = 12.27$$

Weak Acids, Weak Bases, and pH

21. **(M)** We organize the solution around the balanced chemical equation.

Equation: $HNO_2(aq)$ + $H_2O(l)$ $\rightleftharpoons$ $H_3O^+(aq)$ + $NO_2^-(aq)$
Initial: 0.143 M — ≈ 0 M 0 M
Changes: $-x$ M — $+x$ M $+x$ M
Equil: $(0.143-x)$ M — x M x M

$$K_a = \frac{[H_3O^+][NO_2^-]}{[HNO_2]} = \frac{x^2}{0.143-x} = 7.2\times10^{-4} \gg \frac{x^2}{0.143} \text{ (if } x \ll 0.143)$$

$$x = \sqrt{0.143\times7.2\times10^{-4}} = 0.010 \text{ M}$$

We have assumed that $x \ll 0.143$ M, an almost acceptable assumption. Another cycle of approximations yields:

$$x = \sqrt{(0.143-0.010)\times7.2\times10^{-4}} = 0.0098 \text{ M} = [H_3O^+] \qquad pH = -\log(0.0098) = 2.01$$

This is the same result as is determined with the quadratic formula roots equation.

22. **(M)** We organize the solution around the balanced chemical equation, and solve first for $\left[OH^-\right]$

Equation: $C_2H_5NH_2(aq)$ + $H_2O(l)$ $\rightleftharpoons$ $OH^-(aq)$ + $C_2H_5NH_3^+(aq)$

Initial: 0.085 M — ≈ 0 M 0 M

Changes: $-x$ M — $+x$ M $+x$ M

Equil: $(0.085-x)$ M — x M x M

$$K_b = \frac{[OH^-][C_2H_5NH_3^+]}{[C_2H_5NH_2]} = \frac{x^2}{0.085-x} = 4.3\times10^{-4} \approx \frac{x^2}{0.085} \text{ assuming } x \ll 0.085$$

$$x = \sqrt{0.085\times4.3\times10^{-4}} = 0.0060 \text{ M}$$

We have assumed that $x \ll 0.085$ M, an almost acceptable assumption. Another cycle of approximations yields:

$$x = \sqrt{(0.085-0.0060)\times4.3\times10^{-4}} = 0.0058 \text{ M} = [OH^-] \qquad \text{Yet another cycle produces:}$$

$$x = \sqrt{(0.085-0.0058)\times4.3\times10^{-4}} = 0.0058 \text{ M} = [OH^-] \qquad pOH = -\log(0.0058) = 2.24$$

$$pH = 14.00 - 2.24 = 11.76 \qquad \left[H_3O^+\right] = 10^{-pH} = 10^{-11.76} = 1.7\times10^{-12} \text{M}$$

This is the same result as determined with the quadratic formula roots equation.

23. **(M)**

(a) The set-up is based on the balanced chemical equation.

Equation: $C_6H_5CH_2CO_2H(aq)$ + $H_2O(l)$ $\rightleftharpoons$ $H_3O^+(aq)$ + $C_6H_5CH_2CO_2^-(aq)$
Initial: 0.186 M — ≈ 0 M 0 M
Changes: $-x$ M — $+x$ M $+x$ M
Equil: $(0.186-x)$ M — x M x M

$$K_a = 4.9 \times 10^{-5} = \frac{[H_3O^+][C_6H_5CH_2CO_2^-]}{[C_6H_5CH_2CO_2H]} = \frac{x \cdot x}{0.186-x} \approx \frac{x^2}{0.186}$$

$$x = \sqrt{0.186 \times 4.9 \times 10^{-5}} = 0.0030 \text{ M} = [H_3O^+] = [C_6H_5CH_2CO_2^-]$$

0.0030 M is less than 5 % OF 0.186 M, thus, the approximation is valid.

(b) The set-up is based on the balanced chemical equation.

Equation: $C_6H_5CH_2CO_2H(aq)$ + $H_2O(l)$ $\rightleftharpoons$ $H_3O^+(aq)$ + $C_6H_5CH_2CO_2^-(aq)$
Initial: 0.121 M — ≈ 0 M 0 M
Changes: $-x$ M — $+x$ M $+x$ M
Equil: $(0.121-x)$ M — x M x M

$$K_a = 4.9 \times 10^{-5} = \frac{[H_3O^+][C_6H_5CH_2CO_2^-]}{[C_6H_5CH_2CO_2H]} = \frac{x^2}{0.121-x} \approx \frac{x^2}{0.121} \quad x = 0.0024 \text{ M} = [H_3O^+]$$

Assumption $x \ll 0.121$, is correct. $pH = -\log(0.0024) = 2.62$

24. **(E)**

$$[CH_3CH_2CO_2H]_{initial} = \left(\frac{0.275 \text{ mol}}{625 \text{ mL}}\right)\left(\frac{1000 \text{ mL}}{1 \text{ L}}\right) = 0.440 \text{ M}$$

$$[CH_3CH_2CO_2H]_{equilibrium} = 0.440 \text{ M} - 0.00239 \text{ M} = 0.438 \text{ M}$$

$$K_a = \frac{[H_3O^+][CH_3CH_2CO_2^-]}{[CH_3CH_2CO_2H]} = \frac{(0.00239)^2}{0.438} = 1.30 \times 10^{-5}$$

25. **(M)** We base our solution on the balanced chemical equation.

$$[H_3O^+] = 10^{-1.56} = 2.8 \times 10^{-2} \text{ M}$$

Equation: $CH_2FCOOH(aq)$ + $H_2O(l)$ $\rightleftharpoons$ $CH_2FCOO^-(aq)$ + $H_3O^+(aq)$
Initial: 0.318 M – 0 M ≈ 0 M
Changes: -0.028 M – $+0.028$ M $+0.028$ M
Equil: 0.290 M – 0.028 M ≈ 0.028 M

$$K_a = \frac{[H_3O^+][CH_2FCOO^-]}{[CH_2FCOOH]} = \frac{(0.028)(0.028)}{0.290} = 2.7 \times 10^{-3}$$

26. **(M)** $\left[HC_6H_{11}O_2\right] = \dfrac{11\,g}{1\,L} \times \dfrac{1\,mol\ HC_6H_{11}O_2}{116.2\,g\ HC_6H_{11}O_2} = 9.5 \times 10^{-2}\,M = 0.095\,M$

$\left[H_3O^+\right]_{equil} = 10^{-2.94} = 1.1 \times 10^{-3}\,M = 0.0011\,M$

The stoichiometry of the reaction, written below, indicates that $\left[H_3O^+\right] = \left[C_6H_{11}O_2^-\right]$

Equation:	$HC_6H_{11}O_2(aq)$	$+$	$H_2O(l)$	$\rightleftharpoons$	$C_6H_{11}O_2^-(aq)$	$+$	$H_3O^+(aq)$
Initial:	0.095 M		–		0 M		≈ 0 M
Changes:	-0.0011 M		–		$+0.0011$ M		$+0.0011$ M
Equil:	0.094 M		–		0.0011 M		0.0011 M

$K_a = \dfrac{\left[C_6H_{11}O_2^-\right]\left[H_3O^+\right]}{\left[HC_6H_{11}O_2\right]} = \dfrac{(0.0011)^2}{0.094} = 1.3 \times 10^{-5}$

27. **(M)** Here we need to find the molarity S of the acid needed that yields
$\left[H_3O^+\right] = 10^{-2.85} = 1.4 \times 10^{-3}\,M$

Equation:	$C_6H_5COOH\,(aq)$	$+$	$H_2O(l)$	$\rightleftharpoons$	$H_3O^+(aq)$	$+$	$C_6H_5COO^-(aq)$
Initial:	S		–		0 M		0 M
Changes:	-0.0014 M		–		$+0.0014$M		$+0.0014$M
Equil:	$S-0.0014$M		–		0.0014 M		0.0014 M

$K_a = \dfrac{\left[H_3O^+\right]\left[C_6H_5COO^-\right]}{\left[C_6H_5COOH\right]} = \dfrac{(0.0014)^2}{S-0.0014} = 6.3 \times 10^{-5}\quad S-0.0014 = \dfrac{(0.0014)^2}{6.3 \times 10^{-5}} = 0.031$

$S = 0.031 + 0.0014 = 0.032\,M = \left[C_6H_5COOH\right]$

$350.0\,mL \times \dfrac{1\,L}{1000\,mL} \times \dfrac{0.032\,mol\ C_6H_5COOH}{1\,L\ soln} \times \dfrac{122.1\,g\ C_6H_5COOH}{1\,mol\ C_6H_5COOH} = 1.4\,g\ C_6H_5COOH$

28. **(M)** First we find $\left[OH^-\right]$ and then use the K_b expression to find $\left[(CH_3)_3N\right]$

$pOH = 14.00 - pH = 14.00 - 11.12 = 2.88 \qquad \left[OH^-\right] = 10^{-pOH} = 10^{-2.88} = 0.0013\,M$

$K_b = 6.3 \times 10^{-5} = \dfrac{\left[(CH_3)_3NH^+\right]\left[OH^-\right]}{\left[(CH_3)_3N\right]_{equil}} = \dfrac{(0.0013)^2}{\left[(CH_3)_3N\right]_{equil}} \qquad \left[(CH_3)_3N\right]_{equil} = 0.027\,M\ (CH_3)_3N$

$\left[(CH_3)_3N\right]_{initial} = 0.027\,M\text{(equil. concentration)} + 0.0013\,M\text{(concentration ionized)}$

$\left[(CH_3)_3N\right]_{initial} = 0.028\,M$

29. **(M)** We use the balanced chemical equation, then solve using the quadratic formula.

Equation :	$HClO_2(aq)$	+	$H_2O(l)$	$\rightleftharpoons$	$H_3O^+(aq)$	+	$ClO_2^-(aq)$
Initial :	0.55 M		–		$\approx 0 M$		0 M
Changes :	$-x$ M		–		$+x$ M		$+x$ M
Equil :	$(0.55 - x)$ M		–		x M		x M

$$K_a = \frac{[H_3O^+][ClO_2^-]}{[HClO_2]} = \frac{x^2}{0.55 - x} = 1.1 \times 10^{-2} = 0.011 \qquad x^2 = 0.0061 - 0.011x$$

$$x^2 + 0.011x - 0.0061 = 0$$

$$x = \frac{-b \pm \sqrt{b^2 - 4ac}}{2a} = \frac{-0.011 \pm \sqrt{0.000121 + 0.0244}}{2} = 0.073 \ M = [H_3O^+]$$

The method of successive approximations converges to the same answer in four cycles.

$$pH = -\log[H_3O^+] = -\log(0.073) = 1.14 \qquad pOH = 14.00 - pH = 14.00 - 1.14 = 12.86$$

$$[OH^-] = 10^{-pOH} = 10^{-12.86} = 1.4 \times 10^{-13} \ M$$

30. **(M)** Organize the solution around the balanced chemical equation, and solve first for $[OH^-]$.

Equation :	$CH_3NH_2(aq)$	+	$H_2O(l)$	$\rightleftharpoons$	$OH^-(aq)$	+	$CH_3NH_3^+(aq)$
Initial :	0.386 M		–		≈ 0 M		0 M
Changes :	$-x$ M		–		$+x$ M		$+x$ M
Equil :	$(0.386 - x)$ M		–		x M		x M

$$K_b = \frac{[OH^-][CH_3NH_3^+]}{[CH_3NH_2]} = \frac{x^2}{0.386 - x} = 4.2 \times 10^{-4} \approx \frac{x^2}{0.386} \qquad \text{assuming } x \ll 0.386$$

$$x = \sqrt{0.386 \times 4.2 \times 10^{-4}} = 0.013 \ M = [OH^-] \qquad pOH = -\log(0.013) = 1.89$$

$$pH = 14.00 - 1.89 = 12.11 \qquad [H_3O^+] = 10^{-pH} = 10^{-12.11} = 7.8 \times 10^{-13} \ M$$

This is the same result as is determined with the quadratic equation roots formula.

31. **(M)**

$$[C_{10}H_7NH_2] = \frac{1 \ g \ C_{10}H_7NH_2}{590 \ g \ H_2O} \times \frac{1.00 \ g \ H_2O}{1 \ mL} \times \frac{1000 \ mL}{1 \ L} \times \frac{1 \ mol \ C_{10}H_7NH_2}{143.2 \ g \ C_{10}H_7NH_2}$$

$$= 0.012 \ M \ C_{10}H_7NH_2$$

$$K_b = 10^{-pK_b} = 10^{-3.92} = 1.2 \times 10^{-4}$$

Equation:	$C_{10}H_7NH_2(aq)$	+	$H_2O(l)$	$\rightleftharpoons$	$OH^-(aq)$	+	$C_{10}H_7NH_3^+(aq)$
Initial:	0.012 M		–		≈ 0 M		0 M
Changes:	$-x$ M		–		$+x$ M		$+x$ M
Equil:	$(0.012 - x)$ M		–		x M		x M

$$K_b = \frac{\left[OH^-\right]\left[C_{10}H_7NH_3^+\right]}{\left[C_{10}H_7NH_2\right]} = \frac{x^2}{0.012 - x} = 1.2 \times 10^{-4} \approx \frac{x^2}{0.012} \qquad \text{assuming } x \ll 0.012$$

$x = \sqrt{0.012 \times 1.2 \times 10^{-4}} = 0.0012$ This is an almost acceptable assumption. Another approximation cycle gives:

$x = \sqrt{(0.012 - 0.0012) \times 1.2 \times 10^{-4}} = 0.0011$ Yet another cycle seems necessary.

$x = \sqrt{(0.012 - 0.0011) \times 1.2 \times 10^{-4}} = 0.0011 \, M = [OH^-]$

The quadratic equation roots formula provides the same answer.

$pOH = -\log\left[OH^-\right] = -\log(0.0011) = 2.96 \quad pH = 14.00 - pOH = 11.04$

$H_3O^+ = 10^{-pH} = 10^{-11.04} = 9.1 \times 10^{-12} \, M$

32. **(M)** The stoichiometry of the ionization reaction indicates that

$\left[H_3O^+\right] = \left[OC_6H_4NO_2^-\right], K_a = 10^{-pK_b} = 10^{-7.23} = 5.9 \times 10^{-8}$ and

$\left[H_3O^+\right] = 10^{-4.53} = 3.0 \times 10^{-5} \, M$. We let S = the molar solubility of o–nitrophenol.

Equation:	$HOC_6H_4NO_2(aq) +$	$H_2O(l)$	$\rightleftharpoons$	$^-OC_6H_4NO_2(aq) +$	$H_3O^+(aq)$
Initial:	S	—		$0 \, M$	$\approx 0 \, M$
Changes:	$-3.0 \times 10^{-5} \, M$	—		$+3.0 \times 10^{-5} \, M$	$+3.0 \times 10^{-5} \, M$
Equil:	$(S - 3.0 \times 10^{-5}) \, M$	—		$3.0 \times 10^{-5} \, M$	$3.0 \times 10^{-5} \, M$

$$K_a = 5.9 \times 10^{-8} = \frac{\left[^-OC_6H_4NO_2\right]\left[H_3O^+\right]}{[HOC_6H_5NO_2]} = \frac{\left(3.0 \times 10^{-5}\right)^2}{S - 3.0 \times 10^{-5}}$$

$$S - 3.0 \times 10^{-5} = \frac{\left(3.0 \times 10^{-5}\right)^2}{5.9 \times 10^{-8}} = 1.5 \times 10^{-2} \, M \quad S = 1.5 \times 10^{-2} \, M + 3.0 \times 10^{-5} \, M = 1.5 \times 10^{-2} \, M$$

Hence,

$$\text{solubility} = \frac{1.5 \times 10^{-2} \, mol \, HOC_6H_4NO_2}{1 \, L \, soln} \times \frac{139.1 \, g \, HOC_6H_4NO_2}{1 \, mol \, HOC_6H_4NO_2} = 2.1 \, g \, HOC_6H_4NO_2 \, / \, L \, soln$$

33. **(M)** Here we determine $\left[H_3O^+\right]$ which, because of the stoichiometry of the reaction, equals $\left[CH_3COO^-\right]$. $\left[H_3O^+\right] = 10^{-pH} = 10^{-4.52} = 3.0 \times 10^{-5} \, M = \left[CH_3COO^-\right]$

We solve for S, the concentration of $HC_2H_3O_2$ in the 0.750 L solution before it dissociates.

Equation:	$CH_3COOH \, (aq) \, +$	$H_2O(l)$	$\rightleftharpoons$	$CH_3COO^-(aq) \, +$	$H_3O^+(aq)$
Initial:	$S \, M$	—		$0 \, M$	$\approx 0 M$
Changes:	$-3.0 \times 10^{-5} M$	—		$+3.0 \times 10^{-5} M$	$+3.0 \times 10^{-5} M$
Equil:	$\left(S - 3.0 \times 10^{-5}\right) M$	—		$3.0 \times 10^{-5} M$	$3.0 \times 10^{-5} M$

$$K_a = \frac{[H_3O^+][CH_3COO^-]}{[CH_3COOH]} = 1.8 \times 10^{-5} = \frac{(3.0 \times 10^{-5})^2}{(S - 3.0 \times 10^{-5})}$$

$$(3.0 \times 10^{-5})^2 = 1.8 \times 10^{-5}(S - 3.0 \times 10^{-5}) = 9.0 \times 10^{-10} = 1.8 \times 10^{-5}S - 5.4 \times 10^{-10}$$

$$S = \frac{9.0 \times 10^{-10} + 5.4 \times 10^{-10}}{1.8 \times 10^{-5}} = 8.0 \times 10^{-5}\,M \quad \text{Now we determine the mass of vinegar needed.}$$

$$\text{mass vinegar} = 0.750\ L \times \frac{8.0 \times 10^{-5}\,\text{mol } CH_3COOH}{1\ L\ \text{soln}} \times \frac{60.05\ g\ CH_3COOH}{1\ \text{mol } CH_3COOH} \times \frac{100.0\ g\ \text{vinegar}}{5.7\ g\ CH_3COO^-}$$

$$CH_3COO^- = 0.063\ g\ \text{vinegar}$$

34. **(M)** First we determine $[OH^-]$ which, because of the stoichiometry of the reaction, equals $[NH_4^+]$.

$$pOH = 14.00 - pH = 14.00 - 11.55 = 2.45 \quad [OH^-] = 10^{-pOH} = 10^{-2.45} = 3.5 \times 10^{-3}\,M = [NH_4^+]$$

We solve for S, the concentration of NH_3 in the 0.625 L solution prior to dissociation.

Equation:	$NH_3(aq)$	+	$H_2O(l)$	$\rightleftharpoons$	$NH_4^+(aq)$	+	$OH^-(aq)$
Initial:	S M		—		0 M		$\approx$ 0 M
Changes:	−0.0035 M		—		+0.0035 M		+0.0035 M
Equil:	$(S - 0.0035)$ M		—		0.0035 M		0.0035 M

$$K_b = \frac{[NH_4^+][OH^-]}{[NH_3]} = 1.8 \times 10^{-5} = \frac{(0.0035)^2}{(S - 0.0035)}$$

$$(0.0035)^2 = 1.8 \times 10^{-5}(S - 0.0035) = 1.225 \times 10^{-5} = 1.8 \times 10^{-5}S - 6.3 \times 10^{-8}$$

$$S = \frac{1.225 \times 10^{-5} + 6.3 \times 10^{-8}}{1.8 \times 10^{-5}} = 0.68\ M$$

Now we determine the volume of household ammonia needed

$$V_{\text{ammonia}} = 0.625\ L\ \text{soln} \times \frac{0.68\ \text{mol } NH_3}{1\ L\ \text{soln}} \times \frac{17.03\ g\ NH_3}{1\ \text{mol } NH_3} \times \frac{100.0\ g\ \text{soln}}{6.8\ g\ NH_3} \times \frac{1\ \text{mL soln}}{0.97\ g\ \text{soln}}$$

$$= 1.1 \times 10^2\ \text{mL household ammonia solution}$$

35. **(D)**

(a) $n_{\text{proplyamine}} = \dfrac{PV}{RT} = \dfrac{\left(316\ \text{Torr} \times \dfrac{1\ \text{atm}}{760\ \text{Torr}}\right)(0.275\ L)}{(0.08206\ \text{atm L K}^{-1}\ \text{mol}^{-1})(298.15\ K)} = 4.67 \times 10^{-3}\ \text{mol propylamine}$

$$[\text{propylamine}] = \frac{n}{V} = \frac{4.67 \times 10^{-3}\ \text{moles}}{0.500\ L} = 9.35 \times 10^{-3}\ M$$

$$K_b = 10^{-pK_b} = 10^{-3.43} = 3.7 \times 10^{-4}$$

$$CH_3CH_2CH_2NH_2(aq) + H_2O(l) \rightleftharpoons CH_3CH_2CH_2NH_3^+(aq) + OH^-(aq)$$

Initial	9.35×10^{-3} M	—	0 M	≈ 0 M
Change	$-x$ M	—	$+x$ M	$+x$ M
Equil.	$(9.35 \times 10^{-3} - x)$ M	—	x M	x M

$$K_b = 3.7 \times 10^{-4} = \frac{x^2}{9.35 \times 10^{-3} - x} \quad \text{or } 3.5 \times 10^{-6} - 3.7 \times 10^{-4}(x) = x^2$$

$$x^2 + 3.7 \times 10^{-4}x - 3.5 \times 10^{-6} = 0$$

Find x with the roots formula:

$$x = \frac{-3.7 \times 10^{-4} \pm \sqrt{(3.7 \times 10^{-4})^2 - 4(1)(-3.5 \times 10^{-6})}}{2(1)}$$

Therefore $x = 1.6\underline{9}5 \times 10^{-3}$ M $= [OH^-]$ pOH $= 2.77$ and pH $= 11.23$

(b) $[OH^-] = 1.7 \times 10^{-3}$ M $= [NaOH]$ $\quad$ $(MM_{NaOH} = 39.997$ g mol$^{-1})$

$n_{NaOH} = (C)(V) = 1.7 \times 10^{-3}$ M $\times 0.500$ L $= 8.5 \times 10^{-4}$ moles NaOH

mass of NaOH $= (n)(MM_{NaOH}) = 8.5 \times 10^{-4}$ mol NaOH $\times 39.997$ g NaOH/mol NaOH

mass of NaOH $= 0.034$ g NaOH (34 mg of NaOH)

36. **(M)** $K_b = 10^{-pK_b} = 10^{-9.5} = 3.\underline{2} \times 10^{-10}$ $\quad$ $MM_{quinoline} = 129.16$ g mol^{-1}

$$\text{Solubility}(25\,°C) = \frac{0.6 \text{ g}}{100 \text{ mL}}$$

$$\text{Molar solubility}(25\,°C) = \frac{0.6 \text{ g}}{100 \text{ mL}} \times \frac{1 \text{ mol}}{129.16 \text{ g}} \times \frac{1000 \text{ mL}}{1 \text{ L}} = 0.04\underline{6} \text{ M (note: only 1 sig fig)}$$

$$C_9H_7N(aq) + H_2O(l) \rightleftharpoons C_9H_7NH^+(aq) + OH^-(aq)$$

Initial	0.046 M	—	0 M	≈ 0 M
Change	$-x$ M	—	$+x$ M	$+x$ M
Equil.	$(0.046 - x)$ M	—	x M	x M

$$3.\underline{2} \times 10^{-10} = \frac{x^2}{0.046 - x} \approx \frac{x^2}{0.046}, \quad x = 3.\underline{8} \times 10^{-6} \text{ M } (x \ll 0.04\underline{6}, \text{ valid assumption})$$

Therefore, $[OH^-] = 4 \times 10^{-6}$ M $\quad$ pOH $= 5.4$ and pH $= 8.6$

37. **(M)** If the molarity of acetic acid is doubled, we expect a lower initial pH (more H_3O^+(aq) in solution) and a lower percent ionization as a result of the increase in concentration. The ratio between $[H_3O^+]$ of concentration, c, and concentration $2c$ is $\sqrt{2} \approx 1.4$. Therefore, (b), containing 14 H_3O^+ symbols best represents the conditions (~1.4 times greater).

38. **(M)** If NH_3 is diluted to half its original molarity, we expect a lower pH (a lower $[OH^-]$) and a higher percent ionization in the diluted sample. The ratio between $[OH^-]$ of concentration, c, and concentration $0.5c$ is $\sqrt{0.5} \approx 0.71$. Since the diagram representing the solution of concentration c has 24 OH^- symbols, then diagram (c), containing 17 OH^- symbols would be the correct choice.

Percent Ionization

39. **(M)** Let us first compute the $[H_3O^+]$ in this solution.

Equation: $CH_3CH_2COOH(aq) + H_2O(l) \rightleftharpoons H_3O^+(aq) + CH_3CH_2COO^-(aq)$

Initial: 0.45 M — ≈ 0 M ≈ 0 M
Changes: $-x$ M — $+x$ M $+x$ M
Equil: $(0.45-x)$ M — x M x M

$$K_a = \frac{[H_3O^+][CH_3CH_2COO^-]}{[CH_3CH_2COOH]} = \frac{x^2}{0.45-x} = 10^{-4.89} = 1.3 \times 10^{-5} \approx \frac{x^2}{0.45}$$

$x = 2.4 \times 10^{-3}$ M; We have assumed that $x \ll 0.45$ M, an assumption that clearly is correct.

(a) $\alpha = \dfrac{[H_3O^+]_{equil}}{[CH_3CH_2COOH]_{initial}} = \dfrac{2.4 \times 10^{-3} \text{ M}}{0.45 \text{ M}} = 0.0053 = $ degree of ionization

(b) % ionization $= \alpha \times 100\% = 0.0053 \times 100\% = 0.53\%$

40. **(M)** For $C_2H_5NH_2$ (ethylamine), $K_b = 4.3 \times 10^{-4}$

$C_2H_5NH_2(aq) + H_2O(l) \rightleftharpoons C_2H_5NH_3^+(aq) + OH^-(aq)$

Initial 0.85 M — 0 M ≈ 0 M
Change $-x$ M — $+x$ M $+x$ M
Equil. $(0.85-x)$ M — x M x M

$$4.3 \times 10^{-4} = \frac{x^2}{(0.85-x) \text{ M}} \approx \frac{x^2}{0.85 \text{ M}} \quad x = 0.019 \text{ M } (x \ll 0.85, \text{ thus a valid assumption})$$

Degree of ionization $\alpha = \dfrac{0.019 \text{ M}}{0.85 \text{ M}} = 0.022$ Percent ionization $= \alpha \times 100\% = 2.2\%$

41. **(M)** Let x be the initial concentration of NH_3, hence, the amount dissociated is $0.042x$

$NH_3(aq) + H_2O(l) \xrightarrow{K_a = 1.8 \times 10^{-5}} NH_4^+(aq) + OH^-(aq)$

Initial x M — 0 M ≈ 0 M
Change $-0.042x$ M — $+0.042x$ M $+0.042x$ M
Equil. $(1x - 0.042x)$ M — $0.042x$ M $0.042x$ M
$= 0.958 x$

$$K_b = 1.8 \times 10^{-5} = \frac{[NH_4^+][OH^-]}{[NH_3]_{equil}} = \frac{[0.042x]^2}{[0.958x]} = 0.00184\underline{x}$$

$$[NH_3]_{initial} = x = \frac{1.8 \times 10^{-5}}{0.00184} = 0.00978 \, M = 0.0098 \, M$$

42. (M)

$$CH_3CH_2COOH + H_2O(l) \xrightarrow{K_a=1.3\times10^{-5}} CH_3CH_2COO^-(aq) + H_3O^+(aq)$$

Initial	0.100 M	—	0 M	≈ 0 M
Change	$-x$ M	—	$+x$ M	$+x$ M
Equil.	$(0.100 - x)$ M	—	x M	x M

$$1.3 \times 10^{-5} = \frac{x^2}{0.100\ M - x} \approx \frac{x^2}{0.100}\quad x = 1.1 \times 10^{-3}\ (x << 0.100,\ \text{thus a valid assumption})$$

Percent ionization $= \dfrac{0.0011}{0.100} \times 100\% = 1.1\underline{4}\ \%$

Next we need to find molarity of acetic acid that is 1.1% ionized

$$CH_3COOH(aq) + H_2O(l) \xrightarrow{K_a=1.8\times10^{-5}} CH_3COO^-(aq) + H_3O^+(aq)$$

Initial	X M	—	0 M	≈ 0 M
Change	$-\dfrac{1.1\underline{4}}{100} X$ M	—	$+\dfrac{1.1\underline{4}}{100} X$ M	$+\dfrac{1.1\underline{4}}{100} X$ M
Equil.	$X - \dfrac{1.1\underline{4}}{100} X$	—	$\dfrac{1.1\underline{4}}{100} X$ M	$\dfrac{1.1\underline{4}}{100} X$ M
	$= 0.98\underline{86}\ X$ M		$= 0.011\underline{4}$ M	$= 0.011\underline{4}$ M

$$1.8 \times 10^{-5} = \frac{\left(\dfrac{1.1\underline{4}}{100} X\right)^2}{0.9886\ X} = 1.3 \times 10^{-4}(X);\qquad X = 0.13\underline{8}\ M$$

Consequently, approximately 0.14 moles of acetic acid must be dissolved in one liter of water in order to have the same percent ionization as 0.100 M propionic acid.

43. **(E)** We would not expect these ionizations to be correct because the calculated degree of ionization is based on the assumption that the $[CH_3COOH]_{initial} \approx [CH_3COOH]_{initial} - [CH_3COOH]_{equil.}$ which is invalid at the 13 and 42 percent levels of ionization seen here.

44. **(M)** CCl_3COOH (trichloroacetic acid) $pK_a = 0.52$ $K_a = 10^{-0.52} = 0.30$
For a 0.035 M solution, the assumption will not work (the concentration is too small and K_a is too large) Thus, we must solve the problem using the quadratic equation.

$$CCl_3COOH(aq) + H_2O(l) \rightleftharpoons CCl_3COO^-(aq) + H_3O^+(aq)$$

Initial	0.035 M	—	0 M	≈ 0 M
Change	$-x$ M	—	$+x$ M	$+x$ M
Equil.	$(0.035 - x)$ M	—	x M	x M

$$0.30 = \frac{x^2}{0.035 - x}\ \text{ or } 0.010\underline{5} - 0.30(x) = x^2 \text{ or } x^2 + 0.30x - 0.010\underline{5} = 0;\text{ solve quadratic:}$$

$$x = \frac{-0.30 \pm \sqrt{(0.30)^2 - 4(1)(0.010\underline{5})}}{2(1)}\qquad \text{Therefore } x = 0.032\ M = [H_3O^+]$$

Degree of ionization $\alpha = \dfrac{0.032\ M}{0.035\ M} = 0.91$ Percent ionization $= \alpha \times 100\% = 91.\ \%$

Polyprotic Acids

45. **(E)** Because H_3PO_4 is a weak acid, there is little HPO_4^{2-} (produced in the 2nd ionization) compared to the H_3O^+ (produced in the 1st ionization). In turn, there is little PO_4^{3-} (produced in the 3rd ionization) compared to the HPO_4^{2-}, and very little compared to the H_3O^+.

46. **(E)** The main estimate involves assuming that the mass percents can be expressed as 0.057 g of 75% H_3PO_4 per 100. mL of solution and 0.084 g of 75% H_3PO_4 per 100. mL of solution. That is, that the density of the aqueous solution is essentially 1.00 g/mL. Based on this assumption, the initial minimum and maximum concentrations of H_3PO_4 is:

$$[H_3PO_4] = \frac{0.057\,g\,impure\,H_3PO_4 \times \dfrac{75\,g\,H_3PO_4}{100\,g\,impure\,H_3PO_4} \times \dfrac{1\,mol\,H_3PO_4}{98.00\ g\,H_3PO_4}}{100\,mL\,soln \times \dfrac{1L}{1000\,mL}} = 0.0044\,M$$

$$[H_3PO_4] = \frac{0.084\,g\,impure\,H_3PO_4 \times \dfrac{75\,g\,H_3PO_4}{100\,g\,impure\,H_3PO_4} \times \dfrac{1\,mol\,H_3PO_4}{98.00\ g\,H_3PO_4}}{100\,mL\,soln \times \dfrac{1L}{1000\,mL}} = 0.0064\,M$$

Equation:	$H_3PO_4(aq)$	+	$H_2O(l)$	$\rightleftharpoons$	$H_2PO_4^-(aq)$	+	$H_3O^+(aq)$
Initial:	0.0044 M		–		0 M		≈ 0 M
Changes:	$-x$ M		–		$+x$ M		$+x$ M
Equil:	$(0.0044-x)$ M		–		x M		x M

$$K_{a_1} = \frac{[H_2PO_4^-][H_3O^+]}{[H_3PO_4]} = \frac{x^2}{0.0044-x} = 7.1\times10^{-3} \qquad x^2 + 0.0071x - 3.1\times10^{-5} = 0$$

$$x = \frac{-b\pm\sqrt{b^2-4ac}}{2a} = \frac{-0.0071\pm\sqrt{5.0\times10^{-5}+1.2\times10^{-4}}}{2} = 3.0\times10^{-3}\,M = [H_3O^+]$$

The set-up for the second concentration is the same as for the first, with the exception that 0.0044 M is replaced by 0.0064 M.

$$K_{a_1} = \frac{[H_2PO_4^-][H_3O^+]}{[H_3PO_4]} = \frac{x^2}{0.0064-x} = 7.1\times10^{-3} \qquad x^2 + 0.0071x - 4.5\times10^{-5} = 0$$

$$x = \frac{-b\pm\sqrt{b^2-4ac}}{2a} = \frac{-0.0071\pm\sqrt{5.0\times10^{-5}+1.8\times10^{-4}}}{2} = 4.0\times10^{-3}\,M = [H_3O^+]$$

The two values of pH now are determined, representing the pH range in a cola drink.

$$pH = -\log(3.0\times10^{-3}) = 2.52 \qquad pH = -\log(4.\times10^{-3}) = 2.40$$

47. (D)

(a) Equation: $H_2S(aq)$ + $H_2O(l)$ $\rightleftharpoons$ $HS^-(aq)$ + $H_3O^+(aq)$

Initial:	0.075 M	—	0 M	≈ 0 M
Changes:	$-x$ M	—	$+x$ M	$+x$ M
Equil:	$(0.075-x)$ M	—	x M	$+x$ M

$$K_{a_1} = \frac{[HS^-][H_3O^+]}{[H_2S]} = 1.0\times10^{-7} = \frac{x^2}{0.075-x} \approx \frac{x^2}{0.075} \quad x = 8.7\times10^{-5}M = [H_3O^+]$$

$$[HS^-] = 8.7\times10^{-5}M \text{ and } [S^{2-}] = K_{a_2} = 1\times10^{-19}M$$

(b) The set-up for this problem is the same as for part (a), with 0.0050 M replacing 0.075 M as the initial value of $[H_2S]$.

$$K_{a_1} = \frac{[HS^-][H_3O^+]}{[H_2S]} = 1.0\times10^{-7} = \frac{x^2}{0.0050-x} \approx \frac{x^2}{0.0050} \quad x = 2.2\times10^{-5}M = [H_3O^+]$$

$$[HS^-] = 2.2\times10^{-5}M \text{ and } [S^{2-}] = K_{a_2} = 1\times10^{-19}M$$

(c) The set-up for this part is the same as for part (a), with 1.0×10^{-5} M replacing 0.075 M as the initial value of $[H_2S]$. The solution differs in that we cannot assume $x \ll 1.0\times10^{-5}$. Solve the quadratic equation to find the desired equilibrium concentrations.

$$K_{a_1} = \frac{[HS^-][H_3O^+]}{[H_2S]} = 1.0\times10^{-7} = \frac{x^2}{1.0\times10^{-5}-x}$$

$$x^2 + 1.0\times10^{-7}x - 1.0\times10^{-12} = 0$$

$$x = \frac{-1.0\times10^{-7} \pm \sqrt{1.0\times10^{-14} + \left(4\times 1.0\times10^{-12}\right)}}{2 \times (1)}$$

$$x = 9.5\times10^{-7}M = [H_3O^+] \quad [HS^-] = 9.5\times10^{-7}M \quad [S^{2-}] = K_{a_2} = 1\times10^{-19}M$$

48. (M) For H_2CO_3, $K_1 = 4.4\times10^{-7}$ and $K_2 = 4.7\times10^{-11}$

(a) The first acid ionization proceeds to a far greater extent than does the second and determines the value of $[H_3O^+]$.

Equation: $H_2CO_3(aq)$ + $H_2O(l)$ $\rightleftharpoons$ $H_3O^+(aq)$ + $HCO_3^-(aq)$

Initial:	0.045 M	—	≈ 0 M	0 M
Changes:	$-x$ M	—	$+x$ M	$+x$ M
Equil:	$(0.045-x)$ M	—	x M	x M

$$K_1 = \frac{[H_3O^+][HCO_3^-]}{[H_2CO_3]} = \frac{x^2}{0.045-x} = 4.4\times10^{-7} \approx \frac{x^2}{0.045} \quad x = 1.4\times10^{-4}M = [H_3O^+]$$

(b) Since the second ionization occurs to only a limited extent,

$$\left[HCO_3^- \right] = 1.4 \times 10^{-4} \text{ M} = 0.00014 \text{ M}$$

(c) We use the second ionization to determine $\left[CO_3^{2-} \right]$.

Equation:	$HCO_3^-(aq)$	$+$	$H_2O(l)$	$\rightleftharpoons$	$H_3O^+(aq)$	$+$	$CO_3^{2-}(aq)$
Initial:	0.00014 M		$-$		0.00014 M		0 M
Changes:	$-x$ M		$-$		$+x$ M		$+x$ M
Equil:	$(0.00014 - x)$ M		$-$		$(0.00014 + x)$ M		x M

$$K_2 = \frac{\left[H_3O^+ \right]\left[CO_3^{2-} \right]}{\left[HCO_3^- \right]} = \frac{(0.00014 + x)x}{0.00014 - x} = 4.7 \times 10^{-11} \approx \frac{(0.00014)\,x}{0.00014}$$

$$x = 4.7 \times 10^{-11} \text{M} = \left[CO_3^{2-} \right]$$

Again we assumed that $x \ll 0.00014$ M, which clearly is the case. We also note that our original assumption, that the second ionization is much less significant than the first, also is a valid one. As an alternative to all of this, we could have recognized that the concentration of the divalent anion equals the second ionization constant:

$$\left[CO_3^{2-} \right] = K_2.$$

49. **(D)** In all cases, of course, the first ionization of H_2SO_4 is complete, and establishes the initial values of $\left[H_3O^+ \right]$ and $\left[HSO_4^- \right]$. Thus, we need only deal with the second ionization in each case.

(a)

Equation:	$HSO_4^-(aq)$	$+$	$H_2O(l)$	$\rightleftharpoons$	$SO_4^{2-}(aq)$	$+$	$H_3O^+(aq)$
Initial:	0.75 M		$-$		0 M		0.75 M
Changes:	$-x$ M		$-$		$+x$ M		$+x$ M
Equil:	$(0.75 - x)$ M		$-$		x M		$(0.75 + x)$ M

$$K_{a_2} = \frac{\left[SO_4^{2-} \right]\left[H_3O^+ \right]}{\left[HSO_4^- \right]} = 0.011 = \frac{x(0.75 + x)}{0.75 - x} \approx \frac{0.75x}{0.75} \qquad x = 0.011 \text{ M} = \left[SO_4^{2-} \right]$$

We have assumed that $x \ll 0.75$ M, an assumption that clearly is correct.

$$\left[HSO_4^- \right] = 0.75 - 0.011 = 0.74 \text{M} \qquad \left[H_3O^+ \right] = 0.75 + 0.011 = 0.76 \text{M}$$

(b) The set-up for this part is similar to part (a), with the exception that 0.75 M is replaced by 0.075 M.

$$K_{a_2} = \frac{\left[SO_4^{2-} \right]\left[H_3O^+ \right]}{\left[HSO_4^- \right]} = 0.011 = \frac{x(0.075 + x)}{0.075 - x} \qquad 0.011(0.075 - x) = 0.075x + x^2$$

$$x^2 + 0.086x - 8.3 \times 10^{-4} = 0$$

$$x = \frac{-b \pm \sqrt{b^2 - 4ac}}{2a} = \frac{-0.086 \pm \sqrt{0.0074 + 0.0033}}{2} = 0.0087\,M$$

$$x = 0.0087\,M = \left[SO_4^{2-}\right]$$

$$\left[HSO_4^-\right] = 0.075 - 0.0087 = 0.066M \quad \left[H_3O^+\right] = 0.075 + 0.0088M = 0.084\,M$$

(c) Again, the set-up is the same as for part (a), with the exception that 0.75 M is replaced by 0.00075 M

$$K_{a_2} = \frac{[SO_4^{2-}][H_3O^+]}{[HSO_4^-]} = 0.011 = \frac{x(0.00075 + x)}{0.00075 - x} \quad 0.011(0.00075 - x) = 0.00075\,x + x^2$$

$$x^2 + 0.0118x - 8.3 \times 10^{-6} = 0$$

$$x = \frac{-b \pm \sqrt{b^2 - 4ac}}{2a} = \frac{-0.0118 \pm \sqrt{1.39 \times 10^{-4} + 3.3 \times 10^{-5}}}{2} = 6.6 \times 10^{-4}$$

$$x = 6.6 \times 10^{-4}\,M = \left[SO_4^{2-}\right] \quad \left[HSO_4^-\right] = 0.00075 - 0.00066 = 9 \times 10^{-5}\,M$$

$$\left[H_3O^+\right] = 0.00075 + 0.00066M = 1.41 \times 10^{-3}\,M \quad \left[H_3O^+\right] \text{ is almost twice the initial}$$

value of $[H_2SO_4]$. Thus, the second ionization of H_2SO_4 is nearly complete in this dilute solution.

50. (D) First we determine $\left[H_3O^+\right]$, with the calculation based on the balanced chemical equation.

Equation: $HOOC(CH_2)_4COOH\,(aq) + H_2O(l) \rightleftharpoons HOOC(CH_2)_4COO^-\,(aq) + H_3O^+\,(aq)$

Initial:	0.10 M	–	0 M	≈ 0 M
Changes:	$-x$ M	–	$+x$ M	$+x$ M
Equil:	$(0.10-x)$ M	–	x M	x M

$$K_{a_1} = \frac{\left[H_3O^+\right]\left[HOOC(CH_2)_4COO^-\right]}{\left[HOOC(CH_2)_4COOH\right]} = 3.9 \times 10^{-5} = \frac{x \cdot x}{0.10 - x} \approx \frac{x^2}{0.10}$$

$$x = \sqrt{0.10 \times 3.9 \times 10^{-5}} = 2.0 \times 10^{-3}\,M = [H_3O^+]$$

We see that our simplifying assumption, that $x \ll 0.10$ M, is indeed valid. Now we consider the second ionization. We shall see that very little H_3O^+ is produced in this ionization because of the small size of two numbers: K_{a_2} and $\left[HOOC(CH_2)_4COO^-\right]$. Again we base our calculation on the balanced chemical equation.

Equation: $HOOC(CH_2)_4COO^-\,(aq) + H_2O(l) \rightleftharpoons {}^-OOC(CH_2)_4COO^-\,(aq) + H_3O^+\,(aq)$

Initial:	2.0×10^{-3} M	–	0 M	2.0×10^{-3} M
Changes:	$-y$ M	–	$+y$ M	$+y$ M
Equil:	$(0.0020-y)$ M	–	y M	$(0.0020+y)$ M

$$K_{a_2} = \frac{[H_3O^+][^-OOC(CH_2)_4COO^-]}{[HOOC(CH_2)_4COO^-]} = 3.9 \times 10^{-6} = \frac{y(0.0020+y)}{0.0020-y} \approx \frac{0.0020\,y}{0.0020}$$

$$y = 3.9 \times 10^{-6}\,M = [^-OOC(CH_2)_4COO^-]$$

Again, we see that our assumption, that $y \ll 0.0020$ M, is valid. In addition, we also note that virtually no H_3O^+ is created in this second ionization. The concentrations of all species have been calculated above, with the exception of $[OH^-]$.

$$[OH^-] = \frac{K_w}{[H_3O^+]} = \frac{1.0 \times 10^{-14}}{2.0 \times 10^{-3}} = 5.0 \times 10^{-12}\,M; \qquad [HOOC(CH_2)_4COOH] = 0.10\,M$$

$$[H_3O^+] = [HOOC(CH_2)_4COO^-] = 2.0 \times 10^{-3}\,M; \qquad [^-OOC(CH_2)_4COO^-] = 3.9 \times 10^{-6}\,M$$

51. (M)

(a) Recall that a base is a proton acceptor, in this case, accepting H^+ from H_2O.

First ionization: $C_{20}H_{24}O_2N_2 + H_2O \rightleftharpoons C_{20}H_{24}O_2N_2H^+ + OH^- \qquad pK_{b_1} = 6.0$

Second ionization: $C_{20}H_{24}O_2N_2H^+ + H_2O \rightleftharpoons C_{20}H_{24}O_2N_2H_2^{2+} + OH^- \quad pK_{b_2} = 9.8$

(b) $[C_{20}H_{24}O_2N_2] = \dfrac{1.00\,g\,quinine \times \dfrac{1\,mol\,quinine}{324.4\,g\,quinine}}{1900\ mL \times \dfrac{1\,L}{1000\,mL}} = 1.62 \times 10^{-3}\,M$

$$K_{b_1} = 10^{-6.0} = 1 \times 10^{-6}$$

Because the OH^- produced in (a) suppresses the reaction in (b) and since $K_{b1} \gg K_{b2}$, the solution's pH is determined almost entirely by the first base hydrolysis of the first reaction. Once again, we set-up the I.C.E. table and solve for the $[OH^-]$ in this case:

Equation: $C_{20}H_{24}O_2N_2(aq) + H_2O(l) \rightleftharpoons C_{20}H_{24}O_2N_2H^+(aq) + OH^-(aq)$

Initial:	0.00162 M	–	0 M	≈ 0 M
Changes:	–x M	–	+x M	+x M
Equil:	(0.00162 – x) M	–	x M	x M

$$K_{b_1} = \frac{[C_{20}H_{24}O_2N_2H^+][OH^-]}{[C_{20}H_{24}O_2N_2]} = 1 \times 10^{-6} = \frac{x^2}{0.00162-x} \approx \frac{x^2}{0.00162} \qquad x \approx 4 \times 10^{-5}\,M$$

The assumption $x \ll 0.00162$, is valid. $pOH = -\log(4 \times 10^{-5}) = 4.4 \quad pH = 9.6$

52. **(M)** Hydrazine is made up of two NH_2 units held together by a nitrogen–nitrogen single bond:

$$
\begin{array}{ccc}
H & & H \\
\backslash & & / \\
:N & - & N: \\
/ & & \backslash \\
H & & H
\end{array}
$$

(a) $N_2H_4(aq) + H_2O(l) \rightleftharpoons N_2H_5^+(aq) + OH^-(aq)$ $K_{b1} = 10^{-6.07} = 8.5 \times 10^{-7}$

(b) $N_2H_5^+(aq) + H_2O(l) \rightleftharpoons N_2H_6^{2+}(aq) + OH^-(aq)$ $K_{b2} = 10^{-15.05} = 8.9 \times 10^{-16}$

Because the OH^- produced in (a) suppresses the reaction in (b) and since $K_{b1} \gg K_{b2}$, the solution's pH is determined almost entirely by the first base hydrolysis reaction (a). Thus we need only solve the I.C.E. table for the hydrolysis of N_2H_4 in order to find the $[OH^-]_{equil}$, which will ultimately provide us with the pH via the relationship $[OH^-] \times [H_3O^+] = 1.00 \times 10^{-14}$.

Reaction:	$N_2H_4(aq) +$	$H_2O(l) \rightleftharpoons$	$N_2H_5^+(aq) +$	$OH^-(aq)$
Initial:	0.245 M	—	0 M	≈ 0 M
Changes:	$-x$ M	—	$+x$ M	$+x$ M
Equil:	$(0.245 - x)$ M	—	x M	x M

$$
K_{b_1} = \frac{\left[N_2H_5^+\right]\left[OH^-\right]}{\left[N_2H_4\right]} = 8.5 \times 10^{-7} = \frac{x^2}{0.245 - x} = \frac{x^2}{0.245} \qquad x = 4.56 \times 10^{-4} \text{ M} = [OH^-]_{equil}
$$

Thus, $[H_3O^+] = \dfrac{1.0 \times 10^{-14}}{4.56 \times 10^{-4}} = 2.19 \times 10^{-11} \text{M}$ $pH = -\log(2.19 \times 10^{-11}) = 10.66$

53. **(E)** Protonated codeine hydrolyzes water according to the following reaction:

$C_{18}H_{21}O_3NH^+ + H_2O \rightleftharpoons C_{18}H_{21}O_3N + H_3O^+$

$pK_a = 6.05$

$pK_b = 14 - pK_a = 7.95$

54. **(E)** Protonated quinoline is, of course, an acid, which hydrolyzes water to give a hydronium ion. The reaction is as follows:

$C_9H_7NH^+ + H_2O \rightleftharpoons C_9H_7N + H_3O^+$

$K_b = \dfrac{K_w}{K_a} = \dfrac{1 \times 10^{-14}}{6.3 \times 10^{-10}} = 1.6 \times 10^{-5}$

$pK_b = -\log\left(1.6 \times 10^{-5}\right) = 4.8$

55. **(E)** The species that hydrolyze are the cations of weak bases, namely, NH_4^+ and $C_6H_5NH_3^+$, and the anions of weak acids, namely, NO_2^- and $C_7H_5O_2^-$.

(a) $NH_4^+(aq) + NO_3^-(aq) + H_2O(l) \rightleftharpoons NH_3(aq) + NO_3^-(aq) + H_3O^+(aq)$

(b) $Na^+(aq) + NO_2^-(aq) + H_2O(l) \rightleftharpoons Na^+(aq) + HNO_2(aq) + OH^-(aq)$

(c) $K^+(aq) + C_6H_5COO^-(aq) + H_2O(l) \Longleftrightarrow K^+(aq) + C_6H_5COOH(aq) + OH^-(aq)$

(d) $K^+(aq) + Cl^-(aq) + Na^+(aq) + I^-(aq) + H_2O(l) \rightarrow$ no reaction

(e) $C_6H_5NH_3^+(aq) + Cl^-(aq) + H_2O(l) \Longleftrightarrow C_6H_5NH_2(aq) + Cl^-(aq) + H_3O^+(aq)$

56. **(E)** Recall that, for a conjugate weak acid–weak base pair, $K_a \times K_b = K_w$

(a) $K_a = \dfrac{K_w}{K_b} = \dfrac{1.0 \times 10^{-14}}{1.5 \times 10^{-9}} = 6.7 \times 10^{-6}$ for $C_5H_5NH^+$

(b) $K_b = \dfrac{K_w}{K_a} = \dfrac{1.0 \times 10^{-14}}{1.8 \times 10^{-4}} = 5.6 \times 10^{-11}$ for $HCOO^-$

(c) $K_b = \dfrac{K_w}{K_a} = \dfrac{1.0 \times 10^{-14}}{1.0 \times 10^{-10}} = 1.0 \times 10^{-4}$ for $C_6H_5O^-$

57. **(E)**

(a) Because it is composed of the cation of a strong base, and the anion of a strong acid, KCl forms a neutral solution (i.e., no hydrolysis occurs).

(b) KF forms an alkaline (basic) solution. The fluoride ion, being the conjugate base of a relatively strong weak acid, undergoes hydrolysis, while potassium ion, the weakly polarizing cation of a strong base, does not react with water.

$F^-(aq) + H_2O(l) \Longleftrightarrow HF(aq) + OH^-(aq)$

(c) $NaNO_3$ forms a neutral solution, being composed of a weakly polarizing cation and anionic conjugate base of a strong acid. No hydrolysis occurs.

(d) $Ca(OCl)_2$ forms an alkaline (basic) solution, being composed of a weakly polarizing cation and the anion of a weak acid Thus, only the hypochlorite ion hydrolyzes.

$OCl^-(aq) + H_2O(l) \Longleftrightarrow HOCl(aq) + OH^-(aq)$

(e) NH_4NO_2 forms an acidic solution. The salt is composed of the cation of a weak base and the anion of a weak acid. The ammonium ion hydrolyzes:

$NH_4^+(aq) + H_2O(l) \Longleftrightarrow NH_3(aq) + H_3O^+(aq)$ $\qquad K_a = 5.6 \times 10^{-10}$

as does the nitrite ion:

$NO_2^-(aq) + H_2O(l) \Longleftrightarrow HNO_2(aq) + OH^-(aq)$ $\qquad K_b = 1.4 \times 10^{-11}$

Since NH_4^+ is a stronger acid than NO_2^- is a base (as shown by the relative sizes of the K values), the solution will be acidic. The ionization constants were computed using the relationship $K_w = K_a \times K_b$ with data from Table 16-3: $K_b = 1.8 \times 10^{-5}$ for NH_3 and $K_a = 7.2 \times 10^{-4}$ for HNO_2.

For NH_4^+, $K_a = \dfrac{1.0 \times 10^{-14}}{1.8 \times 10^{-5}} = 5.6 \times 10^{-10}$ For NO_2^-, $K_b = \dfrac{1.0 \times 10^{-14}}{7.2 \times 10^{-4}} = 1.4 \times 10^{-11}$

58. **(E)** Our list in order of increasing pH is also in order of decreasing acidity. First we look for the strong acids; there is just HNO_3. Next we look for the weak acids; there is only one, CH_3COOH. Next in order of decreasing acidity come salts with cations from weak bases and anions from strong acids; NH_4ClO_4 is in this category. Then come salts in which both ions hydrolyze to the same degree; $NH_4CH_3COO^-$ is an example, forming a pH-neutral solution. Next are salts that have the cation of a strong base and the anion of a weak acid; $NaNO_2$ is in this category. Then come weak bases, of which $NH_3(aq)$ is an example. And finally, we terminate the list with strong bases: NaOH is the only one. Thus, in order of increasing pH of their 0.010 M aqueous solutions, the solutes are:
$$HNO_3 < CH_3COOH < NH_4ClO_4 < NH_4CH_3COO^- < NaNO_2 < NH_3 < NaOH$$

59. **(M)** NaOCl dissociates completely in aqueous solution into $Na^+(aq)$, which does not hydrolyze, and $OCl^-(aq)$, which undergoes base hydrolysis. We determine $[OH^-]$ in a 0.089 M solution of OCl^-, finding the value of the hydrolysis constant from the ionization constant of HOCl, $K_a = 2.9 \times 10^{-8}$.

Equation :	$OCl^-(aq)$	+	$H_2O(l)$	$\rightleftharpoons$	$HOCl(aq)$	+	$OH^-(aq)$
Initial :	0.089 M		—		0 M		≈ 0 M
Changes :	$-x$ M		—		$+x$ M		$+x$ M
Equil :	$(0.089 - x)$ M		—		x M		x M

$$K_b = \frac{K_w}{K_a} = \frac{1.0 \times 10^{-14}}{2.9 \times 10^{-8}} = 3.4 \times 10^{-7} = \frac{[HOCl][OH^-]}{[OCl^-]} = \frac{x^2}{0.089 - x} \approx \frac{x^2}{0.089}$$

1.7×10^{-4} M $\ll$ 0.089, the assumption is valid.

$x = 1.7 \times 10^{-4}$ M $= [OH^-]$; $pOH = -\log(1.7 \times 10^{-4}) = 3.77$, $pH = 14.00 - 3.77 = 10.23$

60. **(M)** dissociates completely in aqueous solution into $NH_4^+(aq)$, which hydrolyzes, and $Cl^-(aq)$, which does not. We determine $[H_3O^+]$ in a 0.123 M solution of NH_4^+, finding the value of the hydrolysis constant from the ionization constant of NH_3, $K_b = 1.8 \times 10^{-5}$.

Equation :	$NH_4^+(aq)$	+	$H_2O(l)$	$\rightleftharpoons$	$NH_3(aq)$	+	$H_3O^+(aq)$
Initial :	0.123 M		—		0 M		≈ 0 M
Changes :	$-x$ M		—		$+x$ M		$+x$ M
Equil :	$(0.123 - x)$ M		—		x M		x M

$$K_b = \frac{K_w}{K_a} = \frac{1.0 \times 10^{-14}}{1.8 \times 10^{-5}} = 5.6 \times 10^{-10} = \frac{[NH_3][H_3O^+]}{[NH_4^+]} = \frac{x^2}{0.123 - x} \approx \frac{x^2}{0.123}$$

8.3×10^{-6} M $\ll$ 0.123, the assumption is valid

$x = 8.3 \times 10^{-6}$ M $= [H_3O^+]$; $pH = -\log(8.3 \times 10^{-6}) = 5.08$

61. **(M)** $KCH_2CH=CH=CHCH_2CO_2$ dissociates completely in aqueous solution into $K^+(aq)$, which does not hydrolyze, and the ion $CH_2CH=CH=CHCH_2CO_2^-(aq)$, which undergoes base hydrolysis. We determine $\left[OH^-\right]$ in 0.37 M $KCH_2CH=CH=CHCH_2CO_2$ solution using an I.C.E. table. Note: $K_a = 10^{-pK} = 10^{-4.77} = 1.7\times10^{-5}$

Equation:

$$CH_2CH=CH=CHCH_2CO_2^-(aq)+H_2O(l)\rightleftharpoons CH_2CH=CH=CHCH_2CO_2H(aq)+OH^-(aq)$$

Initial:	0.37 M	–	0 M	≈ 0 M
Changes:	$-x$ M	–	$+x$ M	$+x$ M
Equil:	$(0.37-x)$ M	–	x M	x M

$$K_b = \frac{K_w}{K_a} = \frac{1.0\times10^{-14}}{1.7\times10^{-5}} = 5.9\times10^{-10} = \frac{[CH_2CH=CH=CHCH_2CO_2H][OH^-]}{[CH_2CH=CH=CHCH_2CO_2^-]}$$

$$= \frac{x^2}{0.37-x} \approx \frac{x^2}{0.37}$$

$$x = 1.5\times10^{-5} M = \left[OH^-\right], \quad pOH = -\log\left(1.5\times10^{-5}\right) = 4.82, \quad pH = 14.00-4.82 = 9.18$$

62. **(M)**

Equation:	$C_5H_5NH^+(aq) +$	$H_2O(l)$	$\rightleftharpoons C_5H_5N(aq)$	$+$	$H_3O^+(aq)$
Initial:	0.0482 M	–	0 M		≈ 0 M
Changes:	$-x$ M	–	$+x$ M		$+x$ M
Equil:	$(0.0482-x)$ M	–	x M		x M

$$K_a = \frac{K_w}{K_b} = \frac{1.0\times10^{-14}}{1.5\times10^{-9}} = 6.7\times10^{-6} = \frac{[C_5H_5N][H_3O^+]}{[C_5H_5NH^+]} = \frac{x^2}{0.0482-x} \approx \frac{x^2}{0.0482}$$

5.7×10^{-4} M $\ll 0.0482$ M, the assumption is valid

$$x = 5.7\times10^{-4} M = \left[H_3O^+\right], \quad pH = -\log\left(5.7\times10^{-4}\right) = 3.24$$

63. **(M)**

(a) $HSO_3^- + H_2O \rightleftharpoons H_3O^+ + SO_3^{2-}$ $K_a = K_{a_2,\text{Sulfurous}} = 6.2\times10^{-8}$

$HSO_3^- + H_2O \rightleftharpoons OH^- + H_2SO_3$ $K_b = \dfrac{K_w}{K_{a_1,\text{Sulfurous}}} = \dfrac{1.0\times10^{-14}}{1.3\times10^{-2}} = 7.7\times10^{-13}$

Since $K_a > K_b$, solutions of HSO_3^- are acidic.

(b) $HS^- + H_2O \rightleftharpoons H_3O^+ + S^{2-}$ $K_a = K_{a_2,\text{Hydrosulfuric}} = 1\times10^{-19}$

$HS^- + H_2O \rightleftharpoons OH^- + H_2S$ $K_b = \dfrac{K_w}{K_{a_1,\text{Hydrosulfuric}}} = \dfrac{1.0\times10^{-14}}{1.0\times10^{-7}} = 1.0\times10^{-7}$

Since $K_a < K_b$, solutions of HS^- are alkaline, or basic.

(c) $HPO_4^{2-} + H_2O \rightleftharpoons H_3O^+ + PO_4^{3-}$ $K_a = K_{a_3, Phosphoric} = 4.2 \times 10^{-13}$

$HPO_4^{2-} + H_2O \rightleftharpoons OH^- + H_2PO_4^-$ $K_b = \dfrac{K_w}{K_{a_2, Phosphoric}} = \dfrac{1.0 \times 10^{-14}}{6.3 \times 10^{-8}} = 1.6 \times 10^{-7}$

Since $K_a < K_b$, solutions of HPO_4^{2-} are alkaline, or basic.

64. **(M)** pH $= 8.65$ (basic). We need a salt made up of a weakly polarizing cation and an anion of a weak acid, which will hydrolyze to produce a basic solution. The salt (c) KNO_2 satisfies these requirements. (a) NH_4Cl is the salt of the cation of a weak base and the anion of a strong acid, and should form an acidic solution. (b) $KHSO_4$ and (d) $NaNO_3$ have weakly polarizing cations and anions of strong acids; they form pH-neutral solutions.

pOH $= 14.00 - 8.65 = 5.35$ $[OH^-] = 10^{-5.35} = 4.5 \times 10^{-6}$ M

Equation:	NO_2^-(aq)	$+$	H_2O(l)	$\rightleftharpoons$	HNO_2(aq)	$+$	OH^-(aq)
Initial:	S		$-$		0 M		≈ 0 M
Changes:	-4.5×10^{-6} M		$-$		$+4.5 \times 10^{-6}$ M		$+4.5 \times 10^{-6}$ M
Equil:	$(S - 4.5 \times 10^{-6}$ M$)$		$-$		4.5×10^{-6} M		4.5×10^{-6} M

$K_b = \dfrac{K_w}{K_a} = \dfrac{1.0 \times 10^{-14}}{7.2 \times 10^{-4}} = 1.4 \times 10^{-11} = \dfrac{[HNO_2][OH^-]}{[NO_2^-]} = \dfrac{(4.5 \times 10^{-6})^2}{S - 4.5 \times 10^{-6}}$

$S - 4.5 \times 10^{-6} = \dfrac{(4.5 \times 10^{-6})^2}{1.4 \times 10^{-11}} = 1.4$ M $S = 1.4$ M $+ 4.5 \times 10^{-6} = 1.4$ M $= [KNO_2]$

Molecular Structure and Acid-Base Behavior

65. **(M)**

(a) $HClO_3$ should be a stronger acid than is $HClO_2$. In each acid there is an $H-O-Cl$ grouping. The remaining oxygen atoms are bonded directly to Cl as terminal O atoms. Thus, there are two terminal O atoms in $HClO_3$ and only one in $HClO_2$. For oxoacids of the same element, the one with the higher number of terminal oxygen atoms is the stronger. With more oxygen atoms, the negative charge on the conjugate base is more effectively spread out, which affords greater stability. $HClO_3 : K_{a_1} = 5 \times 10^2$ and $HClO_2 : K_a = 1.1 \times 10^{-2}$.

(b) HNO_2 and H_2CO_3 each have one terminal oxygen atom. The difference? N is more electronegative than C, which makes $HNO_2 \left(K_a = 7.2 \times 10^{-4}\right)$, a stronger acid than $H_2CO_3 \left(K_{a_1} = 4.4 \times 10^{-7}\right)$.

(c) H_3PO_4 and H_2SiO_3 have the same number (one) of terminal oxygen atoms. They differ in P being more electronegative than Si, which makes H_3PO_4 $\left(K_{a_1} = 7.1 \times 10^{-3}\right)$ a stronger acid than $H_2SiO_3\left(K_{a_1} = 1.7 \times 10^{-10}\right)$.

66. **(E)** CCl_3COOH is a stronger acid than CH_3COOH because in CCl_3COOH there are electronegative (electro-withdrawing) Cl atoms bonded to the carbon atom adjacent to the COOH group. The electron-withdrawing Cl atoms further polarize the OH bond and enhance the stability of the conjugate base, resulting in a stronger acid.

67. **(E)**

(a) HI is the stronger acid because the $H-I$ bond length is longer than the $H-Br$ bond length and, as a result, $H-I$ is easier to cleave.

(b) HOClO is a stronger acid than HOBr because
(i) there is a terminal O in HOClO but not in HOBr
(ii) Cl is more electronegative than Br.

(c) $H_3CCH_2CCl_2COOH$ is a stronger acid than $I_3CCH_2CH_2COOH$ both because Cl is more electronegative than is I and because the Cl atoms are closer to the acidic hydrogen in the COOH group and thus can exert a stronger e^- withdrawing effect on the O–H bond than can the more distant I atoms.

68. **(M)** The weakest of the five acids is CH_3CH_2COOH. The reasoning is as follows. HBr is a strong acid, stronger than the carboxylic acids. A carboxylic acid—such as $CH_2ClCOOH$ and CH_2FCH_2COOH—with a strongly electronegative atom attached to the hydrocarbon chain will be stronger than one in which no such group is present. But the I atom is so weakly electronegative that it barely influences the acid strength. Acid strengths of some of these acids (as values of pK_a) follow. (Larger values of pK_a indicate weaker acids.)
Strength: $CH_3CH_2COOH(4.89) < CI_3COOH < CH_2FCH_2COOH < CH_2ClCOOH < HBr(-8.72)$

69. **(E)** The largest K_b (most basic) belongs to (c) $CH_3CH_2CH_2NH_2$ (hydrocarbon chains have the lowest electronegativity). The smallest K_b (least basic) is that of (a) o-chloroaniline (the nitrogen lone pair is delocalized (spread out over the ring), hence, less available to accept a proton (i.e., it is a poorer Brønsted base)).

70. **(E)** The most basic species is (c) CH_3O^- (methoxide ion). Methanol is the weakest acid, thus its anion is the strongest base. Most acidic: (b) ortho-chlorophenol. In fact, it is the only acidic compound shown.

Lewis Theory of Acids and Bases

71. **(E)**
(a) acid is CO_2 and base is H_2O

(b) acid is BF_3 and base is H_2O

(c) acid is H_2O and base is O^{2-}

(d) acid is SO_3 and base is S^{2-}

72. **(E)**
(a) SOI_2 is the acid, and $BaSO_3$ the base.
(b) $HgCl_3^-$ is the acid, Cl^- the base.

73. **(E)** A Lewis base is an electron pair donor, while a Lewis acid is an electron pair acceptor. We draw Lewis structures to assist our interpretation.

(a) $\left[:\ddot{O}-H\right]^-$
The lone pairs on oxygen can readily be donated; this is a Lewis base.

(b)
The incomplete octet of B provides a site for acceptance of an electron pair, this is a Lewis acid.

(c)

$$H-\overset{\overset{\displaystyle H}{|}}{\underset{\cdot\cdot}{N}}-\overset{\overset{\displaystyle H}{|}}{\underset{\underset{\displaystyle H}{|}}{C}}-H$$

The incomplete octet of B provides a site for acceptance of an electron pair, this is a Lewis acid.

74. **(M)** A Lewis base is an electron pair donor, while a Lewis acid is an electron pair acceptor. We draw Lewis structures to assist our interpretation.

   (a) According to the following Lewis structures, SO_3 appears to be the electron pair acceptor (the Lewis acid), and H_2O is the electron pair donor (the Lewis base). (Note that an additional sulfur-to-oxygen bond is formed upon successful attachment of water to SO_3.)

$$H-\ddot{\underset{\cdot\cdot}{O}}-H \;+\; :\ddot{\underset{\cdot\cdot}{O}}-\overset{\overset{\displaystyle :O:}{||}}{\underset{\underset{\displaystyle :\underset{\cdot\cdot}{O}:}{|}}{S}} \;\longrightarrow\; H-\ddot{\underset{\cdot\cdot}{O}}-\overset{\overset{\displaystyle :O:}{||}}{\underset{\underset{\displaystyle :\underset{\cdot\cdot}{O}:}{|}}{S}}-\ddot{\underset{\cdot\cdot}{O}}-H$$

   (b) The Zn metal center in $Zn(OH)_2$ accepts a pair of electrons. Thus, $Zn(OH)_2$ is a Lewis acid. OH^- donates the pair of electrons that form the covalent bond. Therefore, OH^- is a Lewis base. We have assumed here that Zn has sufficient covalent character to form coordinate covalent bonds with hydroxide ions.

$$2\;{}^{\ominus}:\ddot{\underset{\cdot\cdot}{O}}-H \;\;+\;\; H-\ddot{\underset{\cdot\cdot}{O}}-Zn-\ddot{\underset{\cdot\cdot}{O}}-H \;\longrightarrow\; \left[H-\ddot{\underset{\cdot\cdot}{O}}-\overset{\overset{\displaystyle H}{|}}{\underset{\underset{\displaystyle :O:}{|}}{\overset{\displaystyle :O:}{\underset{\underset{\displaystyle H}{|}}{Zn}}}}-\ddot{\underset{\cdot\cdot}{O}}-H\right]^{2-}$$

   Base: e^- pair donor   Acid: e^- pair acceptor

75. **(M) (a)**

$${}^{\ominus}:\ddot{\underset{\cdot\cdot}{O}}-H \;\;+\;\; H-\ddot{\underset{\cdot\cdot}{O}}-\overset{}{\underset{\underset{\displaystyle :O:}{|}}{\underset{\underset{\displaystyle H}{|}}{B}}}-\ddot{\underset{\cdot\cdot}{O}}-H \;\longrightarrow\; \left[H-\ddot{\underset{\cdot\cdot}{O}}-\overset{\overset{\displaystyle H}{|}}{\underset{\underset{\displaystyle :O:}{|}}{\overset{\displaystyle :O:}{\underset{\underset{\displaystyle H}{|}}{B}}}}{}^{\ominus}-\ddot{\underset{\cdot\cdot}{O}}-H\right]^{-}$$

   Base: e^- pair donor   Acid: e^- pair acceptor

(b)

The actual Lewis acid is H⁺, which is supplied by H_3O^+

(c)

Base: electron pair donor   Acid: electron pair acceptor

76. **(E)** The C in a CO_2 molecule can accept a pair of electrons. Thus, CO_2 is the Lewis acid. The hydroxide anion is the Lewis base as it has pairs of electrons it can donate.

77. **(E)** $I_2(aq) + I^-(aq) \rightleftharpoons I_3^-(aq)$ Lewis acid   Lewis base
(e⁻ pair acceptor)   (e⁻ pair donor)

78. **(E)**

(a)

Lewis base   Lewis acid
(e⁻ pair donor)   (e⁻ pair acceptor)

(b)

Lewis base   Lewis acid
(e⁻ pair donor)   (e⁻ pair acceptor)

79. (E)

80. (E)

INTEGRATIVE AND ADVANCED EXERCISES

81. (E) We use (ac) to represent the fact that a species is dissolved in acetic acid.

(a) $CH_3COO^-(ac) + CH_3COOH(l) \rightleftharpoons CH_3COOH(l) + CH_3COO^-(ac)$

CH_3COO^- is a base in acetic acid.

(b) $H_2O(ac) + CH_3COOH(l) \rightleftharpoons H_3O^+(ac) + CH_3COO^-(ac)$

Since H_2O is a weaker acid than CH_3COOH in aqueous solution, it will also be weaker in acetic acid. Thus H_2O will accept a proton from the solvent acetic acid, making H_2O a base in acetic acid.

(c) $CH_3COOH(l) + CH_3COOH(l) \rightleftharpoons CH_3COOH_2^+(ac) + CH_3COO^-(aq)$

Acetic acid can act as an acid or a base in acetic acid.

(d) $HClO_4(ac) + CH_3COOH(l) \rightleftharpoons ClO_4^-(ac) + CH_3COOH_2^+(ac)$

Since $HClO_4$ is a stronger acid than CH_3COOH in aqueous solution, it will also be stronger in acetic acid. Thus, $HClO_4$ will donate a proton to the solvent acetic acid, making $HClO_4$ an acid in acetic acid.

82. (E) $Sr(OH)_2 \text{ (sat'd)} \rightleftharpoons Sr^{2+}(aq) + 2\ OH^-(aq)$

$pOH = 14 - pH = 14 - 13.12 = 0.88$

$[OH^-] = 10^{-0.88} = 0.132\ M$

$[OH^-]_{dilute} = 0.132M \times (\dfrac{10.0\ ml\ concentrate}{250.0\ mL\ total}) = 5.28 \times 10^{-3}\ M$

$[HCl] = \dfrac{(10.0\ ml) \times (5.28 \times 10^{-3}\ M)}{25.1\ mL} = 2.10 \times 10^{-3} M$

83. (M)

(a) H_2SO_4 is a diprotic acid. A pH of 2 assumes no second ionization step and the second ionization step alone would produce a pH of less than 2, so it is not matched.

(b) pH 4.6 matched; ammonium salts hydrolyze to form solutions with pH < 7.

(c) KI should be nearly neutral (pH 7.0) in solution since it is the salt of a strong acid (HI) and a strong base (KOH). Thus it is not matched.

(d) pH of this solution is not matched as it's a weak base. A 0.002 M solution of KOH has a pH of about 11.3. A 0.0020 M methylamine solution would be lower (~10.9).

(e) pH of this solution is matched, since a 1.0 M hypochlorite salt hydrolyzes to form a solution of ~ pH 10.8.

(f) pH of this solution is not matched. Phenol is a very weak acid (pH >5).

(g) pH of this solution is 4.3. It is close, but not matched.

(h) pH of this solution is 2.1, matched as it's a strong organic acid.

(i) pH of this solution is 2.5, it is close, but not matched.

84. (M) We let $[H_3O^+]_a = 0.500\,[H_3O^+]_i$ $pH = -\log[H_3O^+]_i$

$pH_a = -\log[H_3O^+]_a = -\log(0.500\,[H_3O^+]_i) = -\log[H_3O^+]_i - \log(0.500) = pH_i + 0.301$

The truth of the statement has been demonstrated. Remember, however, that the extent of ionization of weak acids and weak bases in water increases as these solutions become more and more dilute. Finally, there are some solutions whose pH doesn't change with dilution, such as NaCl(aq), which has pH = 7.0 at all concentrations.

85. (M) Since a strong acid is completely ionized, increasing its concentration has the effect of increasing $[H_3O^+]$ by an equal degree. In the case of a weak acid, however, the solution of the K_a expression gives the following equation (if we can assume that $[H_3O^+]$ is negligible compared to the original concentration of the undissociated acid, [HA]). $x^2 = K_a[HA]$ (where $x = [H_3O^+]$), or $x = \sqrt{K_a[HA]}$. Thus, if [HA] is doubled, $[H_3O^+]$ increases by $\sqrt{2}$.

86. (E) $H_2O(l) + H_2O(l) \rightleftharpoons H_3O^+(aq) + OH^-(aq)$ $\Delta H° = (-230.0\ \text{kJ mol}) - (-285.8\ \text{kJ mol}^{-1})$ = 55.8 kJ

Since $\Delta H°$ is positive, the value of K_{eq} is larger at higher temperatures. Therefore, the ionic products increase with increasing temperature. Le Châtelier's principle or the van't Hoff equation would show this to be true.

87. (M) First we assume that molarity and molality are numerically equal in this dilute aqueous solution. Then compute the molality that creates the observed freezing point, with $K_f = 1.86$ °C/m for water.

$$m = \frac{\Delta T_f}{K_f} = \frac{0.096\ °C}{1.86\ °C/m} = 0.052\ m \qquad \text{concentration} = 0.052\ M$$

This is the total concentration of all species in solution, ions as well as molecules. We base our remaining calculation on the balanced chemical equation.

Equation: $CH_2=CHCH_2CO_2H(aq) + H_2O \rightleftharpoons CH_2=CHCH_2CO_2^-(aq) + H_3O^+(aq)$

Initial: 0.0500 M   0 M   0 M

Changes: $-x$ M $+x$ M $+x$ M

Equil: $(0.0500-x)$ M x M x M

Total conc. $= 0.051_6$ M $= (0.0500-x)$ M $+ x$ M $+ x$ M $= 0.0500$ M $+ xM$ $x = 0.001_6$ M

$$K_a = \frac{[CH_2=CHCH_2CO_2^-][H_3O^+]}{[CH_2=CHCH_2CO_2H]} = \frac{x \cdot x}{0.0500-x} = \frac{(0.001_6)^2}{0.0500-0.001_6} = 5 \times 10^{-5}$$

88. **(D)** $[H_3O^+] = 10^{-pH} = 10^{-5.50} = 3.2 \times 10^{-6}$ M

(a) To produce this acidic solution we could not use 15 M $NH_3(aq)$, because aqueous solutions of NH_3 have pH values greater than 7 owing to the fact that NH_3 is a weak base.

(b) $V_{HCl} = 100.0 \text{ mL} \times \dfrac{3.2 \times 10^{-6} \text{mol } H_3O^+}{1 \text{ L}} \times \dfrac{1 \text{ mol HCl}}{1 \text{ mol } H_3O^+} \times \dfrac{1 \text{ L soln}}{12 \text{ mol HCl}}$

$= 2.7 \times 10^{-5}$ mL 12 M HCl soln

(very unlikely, since this small a volume is hard to measure)

(c) $K_a = 5.6 \times 10^{-10}$ for $NH_4^+(aq)$

Equation: $NH_4^+(aq) + H_2O(l) \rightleftharpoons NH_3(aq) + H_3O^+(aq)$

Initial: c M   –   0 M ≈ 0 M

Changes: -3.2×10^{-6} M   – $+3.2 \times 10^{-6}$ M $+3.2 \times 10^{-6}$ M

Equil: $(c-3.2 \times 10^{-6})$ M   – 3.2×10^{-6} M 3.2×10^{-6} M

$$K_a = 5.6 \times 10^{-10} = \frac{[NH_3][H_3O^+]}{[NH_4^+]} = \frac{(3.2 \times 10^{-6})(3.2 \times 10^{-6})}{(c-3.2 \times 10^{-6})}$$

$$c - 3.2 \times 10^{-6} = \frac{(3.2 \times 10^{-6})^2}{5.6 \times 10^{-10}} = 1.8 \times 10^{-2} \text{ M} \qquad [NH_4^+] = 0.018 \text{ M}$$

$$NH_4Cl \text{ mass} = 100.0 \text{ mL} \times \frac{0.018 \text{ mol } NH_4^+}{1000 \text{ mL}} \times \frac{1 \text{ mol } NH_4Cl}{1 \text{ mol } NH_4^+} \times \frac{53.49 \text{ g } NH_4Cl}{1 \text{ mol } NH_4Cl} = 0.096 \text{ g } NH_4Cl$$

This would be an easy mass to measure on a laboratory three decimal place balance.

(d) The set-up is similar to that for NH_4Cl.

Equation: $\quad CH_3COOH\ (aq)\ +\ H_2O\ (l)\ \rightleftharpoons\ CH_3COO^-\ (aq)\ +\ H_3O^+\ (aq)$

Initial: $\quad c$ M $\qquad\qquad\qquad\qquad - \qquad\qquad\quad$ 0 M $\qquad\qquad \approx 0$ M

Changes: $\quad -3.2\times10^{-6}$ M $\qquad\qquad - \qquad\ +3.2\times10^{-6}$ M $\qquad +3.2\times10^{-6}$ M

Equil: $\quad (c-3.2\times10^{-6})$ M $\qquad - \qquad\quad 3.2\times10^{-6}$ M $\qquad 3.2\times10^{-6}$ M

$$K_a = 1.8\times10^{-5} = \frac{[CH_3COO^-][H_3O^+]}{[CH_3COOH]} = \frac{(3.2\times10^{-6})(3.2\times10^{-6})}{c-3.2\times10^{-6}}$$

$$c-3.2\times10^{-6} = \frac{(3.2\times10^{-6})^2}{1.8\times10^{-5}} = 5.7\times10^{-7} \quad c = [CH_3COOH] = 3.8\times10^{-6}$$

$$CH_3COOH\ \text{mass} = 100.0\ \text{mL} \times \frac{3.8\times10^{-6}\ \text{mol}\ CH_3COOH}{1000\ \text{mL}} \times \frac{60.05\ \text{g}\ CH_3COOH}{1\ \text{mol}\ CH_3COOH}$$

$$= 2.3\times10^{-5}\ \text{g}\ CH_3COOH\ \text{(an almost impossibly small mass to measure}$$

using conventional laboratory scales)

89. (D)

(a) 1.0×10^{-5} M HCN

For a solution of acid (HA), there are, in principle, two contributions to the $[H_3O^+]$: (1) the ionization of the acid and (2) the self-ionization of water. The contribution from the ionization of HA is equal to $[A^-]$ because the ionization of HA produces equal amounts of H_3O^+ and A^-. Similarly, the contribution from the self-ionization of water is equal to $[OH^-]$ because the self-ionization of water produces equal amounts of H_3O^+ and OH^-. Therefore, we can write:

$[H_3O^+] = [H_3O^+]_{acid} + [H_3O^+]_{water}$
$\qquad\ = [A^-] + [OH^-]$

The equation $[H_3O^+] = [A^-] + [OH^-]$ is simply the electroneutrality condition for an aqueous solution of HA.

In most solutions of acid we've considered, the acid is the only important source of H_3O^+ in solution. In other words, $[H_3O^+]_{acid} >> [H_3O^+]_{water}$ and $[H_3O^+] \approx [H_3O^+]_{acid} = [A^-]$.

However, in this case, K_a for HCN is rather small (6.2×10^{-10}) and the solution is also very dilute (1.0×10^{-5}). As a result, the ionization of HCN will not generate much H_3O^+. Therefore, we cannot assume that $[H_3O^+]_{acid} >> [H_3O^+]_{water}$.

We use the general approach for solving this problem by writing all the equilibrium constant expressions, a material balance equation, and an electroneutrality condition.

Equilibrium constant expressions: $\quad K_a = [H_3O^+]\,[CN^-]\,/\,[HCN]$

$$K_w = [H_3O^+]\,[OH^-]$$

Material balance equation: $\quad 1.0\times10^{-5}$ M $= [HCN] + [CN^-]$

Electroneutrality condition: $[H_3O^+] = [CN^-] + [OH^-]$

We can express K_a in terms of only $[H_3O^+]$ by using the equations above to express all the other concentrations in terms of $[H_3O^+]$.

$[OH^-] = K_w/[H_3O^+]$

$[CN^-] = [H_3O^+] - [OH^-] = [H_3O^+] - K_w/[H_3O^+]$

$[HCN] = 1.0 \times 10^{-5} - [CN^-] = 1.0 \times 10^{-5} - ([H_3O^+] - K_w/[H_3O^+])$

Therefore,

$$K_a = \underbrace{\frac{[H_3O^+][CN^-]}{[HCN]}}_{\text{equation 1}} = \underbrace{\frac{[H_3O^+][CN^-]}{1.0 \times 10^{-5} - [CN^-]}}_{\text{equation 2}} = \underbrace{\frac{[H_3O^+]([H_3O^+] - K_w/[H_3O^+])}{1.0 \times 10^{-5} - ([H_3O^+] - K_w/[H_3O^+])}}_{\text{equation 3}}$$

Because HCN is a very weak acid ($K_a = 6.2 \times 10^{-10}$), we expect that a very small fraction of the HCN will ionize, even in this very dilute solution. If we assume that $[CN^-] = [H_3O^+] - K_w/[H_3O^+] \ll 1.0 \times 10^{-5}$ M, then we can simplify and rearrange equation 3 as follows.

$$K_a \approx \frac{[H_3O^+]([H_3O^+] - K_w/[H_3O^+])}{1.0 \times 10^{-5}} = \frac{[H_3O^+]^2 - K_w}{1.0 \times 10^{-5}}$$

$$\Rightarrow [H_3O^+]^2 = (1.0 \times 10^{-5})K_a + K_w$$

$$\Rightarrow [H_3O^+] = \sqrt{(1.0 \times 10^{-5})K_a + K_w}$$

Using $K_a = 6.2 \times 10^{-10}$ and $K_w = 1.0 \times 10^{-14}$, we obtain $[H_3O^+] = 1.273 \times 10^{-7}$ mol/L. We can now use this value of $[H_3O^+]$ in the expression $[CN^-] = [H_3O^+] - K_w/[H_3O^+]$ to estimate $[CN^-]$:

$[CN^-] = 1.273 \times 10^{-7} - 1.0 \times 10^{-14}/1.273 \times 10^{-7} = 4.87 \times 10^{-8}$ M

As the calculation below illustrates, only a small percentage of the HCN ionizes, and, therefore, the assumption that $[CN^-] \ll 1.0 \times 10^{-5}$ M is indeed valid.

$$\text{percent ionization} = \frac{[CN^-]}{[HCN]_{\text{initial}}} \times 100 = \frac{4.87 \times 10^{-8} \text{ M}}{1.0 \times 10^{-5} \text{ M}} \times 100 = 0.49$$

Using $[H_3O^+] = 1.27 \times 10^{-7}$ M, we obtain:

$pH = -\log_{10}(1.27 \times 10^{-7}) = 6.90$

$[OH^-] = K_w/[H_3O^+] = 7.9 \times 10^{-8}$ M

$[CN^-] = [H_3O^+] - K_w/[H_3O^+] = 4.9 \times 10^{-8}$ M

$[HCN] = 1.0 \times 10^{-5} - ([H_3O^+] - K_w/[H_3O^+]) = 0.995 \times 10^{-5}$ M $\approx 1.0 \times 10^{-5}$ M

Notice that the pH is just below 7.00, which is what we'd expect for a very dilute solution of a very weak acid.

As a final note, we can demonstrate that most of the H_3O^+ in solution (about 61%) comes from the self-ionization of water.

$[H_3O^+]_{water} = [OH^-] = 7.86 \times 10^{-8}$ M

Percentage of H_3O^+ that comes from the self-ionization of water

$\quad = ([H_3O^+]_{water}/[H_3O^+]\,) \times 100$

$\quad = 61$

Most of the H_3O^+ in solution comes from the self-ionization of water, not from the ionization of HCN. Still, the contribution from the self-ionization of water is less than 1.00×10^{-7} M. This result makes sense because the ionization of HCN generates a small amount of H_3O^+, which in turn suppresses the self-ionization of water to some extent.

(b) 1.0×10^{-5} $C_6H_5NH_2$ (aniline)

To determine the pH of a dilute solution of aniline, a weak base with $K_b = 7.4 \times 10^{-10}$, we can proceed as we did in (a) for HCN, a weak acid with $K_a = 6.2 \times 10^{-10}$. The obvious difference is that all equations are expressed in terms of $[OH^-]$, which is used to calculate pOH. The pH of the solution can then be determined from the pOH. As before, the general approach is used by writing the equilibrium constant expressions, a material balance equation, and an electroneutrality condition. In the equations below, B represents $C_6H_5NH_2$ and BH^+ represents $C_6H_5NH_3^+$.

Equilibrium constant expressions: $\quad K_b = [OH^-][BH^+]/[B]$

$$K_w = [H_3O^+][OH^-]$$

Material balance equation: 1.0×10^{-5} M $= [B] + [BH^+]$

Electroneutrality condition: $[OH^-] = [BH^+] + [H_3O^+]$

We can express K_b in terms of only $[OH^-]$ by using the equations above by expressing all the other concentrations also in terms of $[OH-]$.

$[H_3O^+] = K_w/[OH^-]$

$[BH^+] = [OH^-] - [H_3O^+] = [OH^-] - K_w/[OH^-]$

$[B] = 1.0 \times 10^{-5} - [BH^+] = 1.0 \times 10^{-5} - ([OH^-] - K_w/[OH^-])$

$$K_b = \underbrace{\frac{[HB^+][OH^-]}{[B]}}_{\text{equation 1}} = \underbrace{\frac{[BH^+][OH^-]}{1.0 \times 10^{-5} - [B]}}_{\text{equation 2}} = \underbrace{\frac{[OH^-]\left([OH^-] - K_w/[OH^-]\right)}{1.0 \times 10^{-5} - \left([OH^-] - K_w/[OH^-]\right)}}_{\text{equation 3}}$$

Because aniline is a very weak base ($K_b = 7.4 \times 10^{-10}$), we expect that a very small fraction of the base will ionize, even in this very dilute solution. If we assume $[HB^+] = [OH^-] - K_w/[OH^-] \ll 1.0 \times 10^{-5}$ M, then we can simplify and rearrange equation 3 as follows.

$$K_b = \frac{[OH^-]([OH^-] - K_w/[OH^-])}{1.0 \times 10^{-5}} = \frac{[OH^-]^2 - K_w}{1.0 \times 10^{-5}}$$

$$\Rightarrow [OH^-]^2 = (1.0 \times 10^{-5})K_b + K_w$$

$$\Rightarrow [OH^-] = \sqrt{(1.0 \times 10^{-5})K_b + K_w}$$

Using $K_b = 7.4 \times 10^{-10}$ and $K_w = 1.0 \times 10^{-14}$, we obtain

$[OH^-] = 1.3 \times 10^{-7}$ mol/L

pOH = 6.88

pH = 7.12

$[BH^+] = [C_6H_5NH_3^+] = [OH^-] - K_w/[OH^-] = 5.6 \times 10^{-8}$ M

$[B] = [C_6H_5NH_2] = 1.0 \times 10^{-5} - ([OH^-] - K_w/[OH^-]) = 9.9 \times 10^{-6}$ M

Notice that only a very small percentage (0.56%) of the base exists in ionized form. Also, the pH is just slightly above 7, which is expected for a dilute solution of a very weak base.

90. (D)

(a) For a weak acid, we begin with the ionization constant expression for the weak acid, HA.

$$K_a = \frac{[H_3O^+][A^-]}{[HA]} = \frac{[H^+]^2}{[HA]} = \frac{[H^+]^2}{c - [H^+]} \approx \frac{[H^+]^2}{c}$$

The first modification results from realizing that $[H^+] = [A^-]$. The second modification is based on the fact that the equilibrium [HA] equals the initial [HA] minus the amount that ionizes. And the third modification is an approximation, assuming that the amount of ionized weak acid is small compared to the original amount of HA in solution. Now we take the logarithm of both sides of the equation.

$$\log K_a = \log \frac{[H^+]^2}{c} = \log [H^+]^2 - \log c = 2 \log [H^+] - \log c$$

$-2 \log [H^+] = -\log K_a - \log c \qquad 2 \text{ pH} = pK_a - \log c \qquad pH = \tfrac{1}{2}pK_a - \tfrac{1}{2} \log c$

For a weak base, we begin with the ionization constant expression for a weak base, B.

$$K_b = \frac{[BH^+][OH^-]}{[B]} = \frac{[OH^-]^2}{[B]} = \frac{[OH^-]^2}{c - [OH^-]} \approx \frac{[OH^-]^2}{c}$$

The first modification results from realizing that $[OH^-] = [BH^+]$. The second modification is based on the fact that the equilibrium [B] equals the initial [B] minus the amount that ionizes. And the third modification is an approximation, assuming that the amount of ionized weak base is small compared to the original amount of B in solution. Now we take the logarithm of both sides of the equation.

$$\log K_b = \log \frac{[OH^-]^2}{c} = \log [OH^-]^2 - \log c = 2 \log [OH^-] - \log c$$

$-2 \log [OH^-] = -\log K_b - \log c \qquad 2 \text{ pOH} = pK_b - \log c \qquad pOH = \tfrac{1}{2} pK_b - \tfrac{1}{2} \log c$

$pH = 14.00 - pOH = 14.00 - \tfrac{1}{2}pK_b + \tfrac{1}{2} \log c$

The anion of a relatively strong weak acid is a weak base. Thus, the derivation is the same as that for a weak base, immediately above, with the exception of the value for K_b. We now obtain an expression for pK_b.

$$K_b = \frac{K_w}{K_a} \qquad \log K_b = \log \frac{K_w}{K_a} = \log K_w - \log K_a$$

$$-\log K_b = -\log K_w + \log K_a = pK_b = pK_w - pK_a$$

Substitution of this expression for pK_b into the expression above gives the following result.

$$pH = 14.00 - \tfrac{1}{2}pK_w + \tfrac{1}{2}pK_a + \tfrac{1}{2}\log c$$

(b) 0.10 M CH₃COOH $\qquad pH = 0.500 \times 4.74 - 0.500 \log 0.10 = 2.87$

Equation: $CH_3COOH(aq) + H_2O(l) \rightleftharpoons CH_3COO^-(aq) + H_3O^+(aq)$

Initial: 0.10 M — 0 M ≈ 0 M

Changes: $-x$ M — $+x$ M $+x$ M

Equil: $(0.10-x)$ M — x M x M

$$K_a = \frac{[H_3O^+][CH_3COO^-]}{[CH_3COOH]} = 1.8 \times 10^{-5} = \frac{x \cdot x}{0.10 - x} \approx \frac{x^2}{0.10}$$

$$x = \sqrt{0.10 \times 1.8 \times 10^{-5}} = 1.3 \times 10^{-3} \text{ M}, \; pH = -\log(1.3 \times 10^{-3}) = 2.89$$

0.10 M NH₃ $pH = 14.00 - 0.500 \times 4.74 + 0.500 \log 0.10 = 11.13$

Equation: $NH_3(aq) + H_2O(l) \rightleftharpoons NH_4^+(aq) + OH^-(aq)$

Initial: 0.10 M — 0 M ≈ 0 M

Changes: $-x$ M — $+x$ M $+x$ M

Equil: $(0.10-x)$ M — x M x M

$$K_b = \frac{[NH_4^+][OH^-]}{[NH_3]} = 1.8 \times 10^{-5} = \frac{x \cdot x}{0.10 - x} \approx \frac{x^2}{0.10} \quad x = \sqrt{0.10 \times 1.8 \times 10^{-5}} = 1.3 \times 10^{-3} \text{ M}$$

$pOH = -\log(1.3 \times 10^{-3}) = 2.89 \qquad pH = 14.00 - 2.89 = 11.11$

0.10 M Na CH₃COO⁻ $\qquad pH = 14.00 - 0.500 \times 14.00 + 0.500 \times 4.74 + 0.500 \log 0.10 = 8.87$

Equation: $CH_3COO^-(aq) + H_2O(l) \rightleftharpoons CH_3COOH(aq) + OH^-(aq)$

Initial: 0.10 M — 0 M ≈ 0 M

Changes: $-x$ M — $+x$ M $+x$ M

Equil: $(0.10-x)$ M — x M x M

$$K_a = \frac{[OH^-][CH_3COOH]}{[CH_3COO^-]} = \frac{1.0 \times 10^{-14}}{1.8 \times 10^{-5}} = \frac{x \cdot x}{0.10 - x} \approx \frac{x^2}{0.10}$$

$$x = \sqrt{\frac{0.10 \times 1.0 \times 10^{-14}}{1.8 \times 10^{-5}}} = 7.5 \times 10^{-6} \text{ M} \qquad pOH = -\log(7.5 \times 10^{-6}) = 5.12$$

$pH = 14.00 - 5.12 = 8.88$

91. (D)

(a) We know $K_a = \dfrac{[H_3O^+]_{eq}[A^-]_{eq}}{[HA]_{eq}}$, $\alpha = \dfrac{[A^-]_{eq}}{[HA]_i}$ and finally % ionized $= \alpha \times 100\%$.

Let us see how far we can get with no assumptions. Recall first what we mean by $[HA]_{eq}$.

$[HA]_{eq} = [HA]_i - [A^-]_{eq}$ or $[HA]_i = [HA]_{eq} + [A^-]_{eq}$

We substitute this expression into the expression for α. $\alpha = \dfrac{[A^-]_{eq}}{[HA]_{eq} + [A^-]_{eq}}$

We solve both the α and the K expressions for $[HA]_{eq}$, equate the results, and solve for α.

$$[HA]_{eq} = \frac{[H_3O^+][A^-]}{K_a} \quad [A^-] = \alpha[HA]_{eq} + \alpha[A^-] \quad [HA]_{eq} = \frac{[A^-] - \alpha[A^-]}{\alpha}$$

$$\frac{[H_3O^+][A^-]}{K_a} = \frac{[A^-](1-\alpha)}{\alpha} = R$$

$$R\alpha = 1 - \alpha \quad R\alpha + \alpha = 1 = \alpha(1+R) \quad \alpha = \frac{1}{1+R}$$

Momentarily, for ease in writing, we have let $R = \dfrac{[H_3O]^+}{K_a} = \dfrac{10^{-pH}}{10^{-pK}} = 10^{(pK-pH)}$

Once we realize that $100\alpha = \%$ ionized, we note that we have proven the cited formula. Notice that no approximations were made during the course of this derivation.

(b) Formic acid has $pK_a = 3.74$. Thus $10^{(pK-pH)} = 10^{(3.74-2.50)} = 10^{1.24} = 17.4$

$$\% \text{ ionization} = \frac{100}{1+17.4} = 5.43\%$$

(c) $[H_3O^+] = 10^{-2.85} = 1.4 \times 10^{-3}$ M $\quad \% \text{ ionization} = \dfrac{1.4 \times 10^{-3} \text{ M}}{0.150 \text{ M}} \times 100\% = 0.93\%$

$$0.93 = \frac{100}{1+10^{(pK-pH)}} \quad 1+10^{(pK-pH)} = \frac{100}{0.93} = 108 \quad 10^{(pK-pH)} = 107$$

$$2.03 = pK - pH \quad pK = pH + 2.03 = 2.85 + 2.03 = 4.88 \quad K_a = 10^{-4.88} = 1.3 \times 10^{-5}$$

92. (M) We note that, as the hydrocarbon chain between the two COOH groups increases in length, the two values of pK_a get closer together. The reason for this is that the ionized COOH group, COO⁻, is negatively charged. When the two COOH groups are close together, the negative charge on the molecule, arising from the first ionization, inhibits the second ionization, producing a large difference between the two ionization constants. But as the hydrocarbon chain lengthens, the effect of this negative —COO⁻ group on the second ionization becomes less pronounced, due to the increasing separation between the two carbonyl groups, and the values of the two ionization constants are more alike.

93. (M) Consider only the 1st dissociation.

Equation: $H_2C_4H_4O_4(aq) + H_2O(l) \xrightleftharpoons{6.2\times10^{-5}} H_3O^+(aq) + HC_4H_4O_4^-(aq)$

Initial: 0.100 M   — ≈ 0 M   0 M

Changes: $-x$ M   — $+x$ M $+x$ M

Equil: $(0.100-x)$ M   — x M x M

$K_a = \dfrac{x^2}{0.100-x} = 6.2\times10^{-5}$ $x = 0.0024\underline{6}$ M

Solve using the quadratic equation. Hence pH $= -\log(0.00246) = 2.61$

Consider only the 2nd dissociation.

Equation: $HC_4H_4O_4^-(aq) + H_2O(l) \xrightleftharpoons{2.3\times10^{-5}} H_3O^+(aq) + C_4H_4O_4^{2-}(aq)$

Initial: 0.0975 M   —   0.0024\underline{6} M   0 M

Changes: $-x$ M   — $+x$ M $+x$ M

Equil: $(0.0975-x)$ M   — $0.0024\underline{6}+x$ M x M

$K_a = \dfrac{x(0.00246+x)}{0.0975-x} = 2.3\times10^{-6} = \dfrac{x(0.00246)}{0.0975}$

$x = 0.000091$ M or $x = 0.000088$ M (solve quadratic)   Hence pH ≈ 2.59

Thus, the pH is virually identical, hence, we need only consider the 1st ionization.

94. (M) To have the same freezing point, the two solutions must have the same total concentration of all particles of solute—ions and molecules. We first determine the concentrations of all solute species in 0.150 M $ClCH_2COOH$, $K_a = 1.4\times10^{-3}$

Equation: $ClCH_2COOH_2(aq) + H_2O(l) \rightleftharpoons H_3O^+(aq) + ClCH_2COO^-(aq)$

Initial: 0.150 M   — ≈ 0 M   0 M

Changes: $-x$ M   — $+x$ M $+x$ M

Equil: $(0.150-x)$ M   — $+x$ M x M

$K_a = \dfrac{[H_3O^+][ClCH_2COO^-]}{[ClCH_2COOH]} = \dfrac{x\cdot x}{0.150-x} = 1.4\times10^{-3}$

$x^2 = 2.1\times10^{-4} - 1.4\times10^{-3}x$ $x^2 + 1.4\times10^{-3}x - 2.1\times10^{-4} = 0$

$x = \dfrac{-b\pm\sqrt{b^2-4ac}}{2a} = \dfrac{-1.4\times10^{-3}\pm\sqrt{2.0\times10^{-6}+8.4\times10^{-4}}}{2} = 0.014$ M

total concentration $= (0.150-x) + x + x = 0.150 + x = 0.150 + 0.014 = 0.164$ M

Now we determine the [CH₃COOH] that has this total concentration.

Equation: $CH_3COOH(aq) + H_2O(l) \rightleftharpoons H_3O^+(aq) + CH_3COO^-(aq)$

Initial: z M — ≈ 0 M 0 M

Changes: $-y$ M — $+y$ M $+y$ M

Equil: $(z-y)$ M — y M y M

$$K_a = \frac{[H_3O^+][CH_3COO^-]}{[CH_3COOH]} = 1.8\times10^{-5} = \frac{y \cdot y}{z - y}$$

We also know that the total concentration of all solute species is 0.164 M.

$$z - y + y + y = z + y = 0.164 \qquad z = 0.164 - y \qquad \frac{y^2}{0.164 - 2y} = 1.8\times10^{-5}$$

We assume that $2y \ll 0.164$ $\quad y^2 = 0.164\times1.8\times10^{-5} = 3.0\times10^{-6}$ $\quad y = 1.7\times10^{-3}$

The assumption is valid: $2y = 0.0034 \ll 0.164$

Thus, $[CH_3COOH] = z = 0.164 - y = 0.164 - 0.0017 = 0.162$ M

$$\text{mass } CH_3COOH = 1.000\ L \times \frac{0.162\ mol\ CH_3COOH}{1\ L\ soln} \times \frac{60.05\ g\ CH_3COOH}{1\ mol\ CH_3COOH} = 9.73\ g\ CH_3COOH$$

95. **(M)** The first ionization of H_2SO_4 makes the major contribution to the acidity of the solution. Then the following two ionizations, both of which are repressed because of the presence of H_3O^+ in the solution, must be solved simultaneously.

Equation: $HSO_4^-(aq) + H_2O(l) \rightleftharpoons SO_4^{2-}(aq) + H_3O^+(aq)$

Initial: 0.68 M — 0 M 0.68 M

Changes: $-x$ M — $+x$ M $+x$ M

Equil: $(0.68-x)$ M — x M $(0.68+x)$ M

$$K_2 = \frac{[H_3O^+][SO_4^{2-}]}{[HSO_4^-]} = 0.011 = \frac{x(0.68+x)}{0.68-x}$$

Let us solve this expression for x. $0.011(0.68-x) = 0.68x + x^2 = 0.0075 - 0.011x$

$$x^2 + 0.69x - 0.0075 = 0 \qquad x = \frac{-b\pm\sqrt{b^2-4ac}}{2a} = \frac{-0.69\pm\sqrt{0.48+0.030}}{2} = 0.01\ M$$

This gives $[H_3O^+] = 0.68 + 0.01 = 0.69$ M. Now we solve the second equilibrium.

Equation: $HCOOH(aq) + H_2O(l) \rightleftharpoons HCOO^-(aq) + H_3O^+(aq)$

Initial: 1.5 M — 0 M 0.69 M

Changes: $-x$ M — $+x$ M $+x$ M

Equil: $(1.5-x)$ M — x M $(0.69+x)$ M

$$K_a = \frac{[H_3O^+][HCOO^-]}{[HCOOH]} = 1.8\times10^{-4} = \frac{x(0.69+x)}{1.5-x} \approx \frac{0.69x}{1.5} \qquad x = 3.9\times10^{-4}\ M$$

We see that the second acid does not significantly affect the $[H_3O^+]$, for which a final value is now obtained. $[H_3O^+] = 0.69$ M, pH $= -\log(0.69) = 0.16$

96. (D)

Let the two acids be represented by HA and HB, with ionization constants $K_a^{HA} = K_a$ and $K_a^{HB} = 2 \times K_a$. If the total stoichiometric concentration of both acids is c, we can write:

$$K_a^{HA} = K_a = \frac{[H^+][A^-]}{[HA]} \qquad \text{and} \qquad K_a^{HB} = 2 \times K_a = \frac{[H^+][B^-]}{[HB]}$$

Material balance for A: $\qquad c = [HA] + [A^-]$

Material balance for B: $\qquad c = [HB] + [B^-]$

Electroneutrality condition: $\quad [H^+] = [A^-] + [B^-] + [OH^-]$

If we assume that only a very small fraction of each acid ionizes, then $[HA] \approx c$ and $[HB] \approx c$. Therefore:

$$K_a \approx \frac{[H^+][A^-]}{c} \qquad \text{and} \qquad 2K_a \approx \frac{[H^+][B^-]}{c}$$

We can re-arrange the expressions above for $[A^-]$ and $[B^-]$.

$$[A^-] \approx \frac{cK_a}{[H^+]} \qquad \text{and} \qquad [B^-] \approx \frac{2cK_a}{[H^+]}$$

We can now substitute these expressions, along with $[OH^-] = K_w / [H^+]$, into the electroneutrality condition. We obtain the following result.

$$[H^+] = \frac{cK_a}{[H^+]} + \frac{2cK_a}{[H^+]} + \frac{K_w}{[H^+]}$$

$$[H^+]^2 = cK_a + 2cK_a + K_w = 3cK_a + K_w \approx 3cK_a \text{ (assuming } 3cK_a \gg K_w = 1.0 \times 10^{-14})$$

$$[H^+] \approx \sqrt{3cK_a}$$

Therefore:

$$pH = -\log_{10}[H^+] \approx -\log_{10}\sqrt{3cK_a} = -\log_{10}(3cK_a)^{\frac{1}{2}} = -\tfrac{1}{2}\log_{10}(3cK_a)$$

97. **(M)** $HSbF_6 \rightarrow H^+ + SbF_6^-$

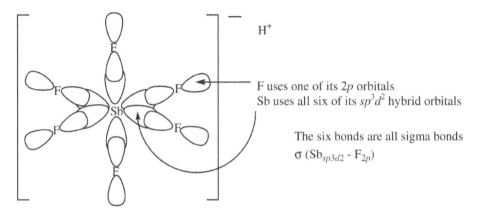

F uses one of its $2p$ orbitals
Sb uses all six of its sp^3d^2 hybrid orbitals

The six bonds are all sigma bonds
$\sigma\ (Sb_{sp3d2} - F_{2p})$

$HBF_4 \rightarrow H^+ + BF_4^-$

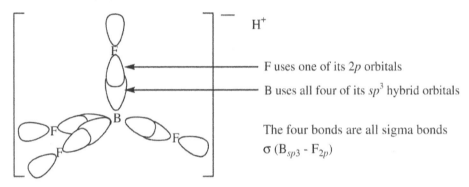

F uses one of its $2p$ orbitals

B uses all four of its sp^3 hybrid orbitals

The four bonds are all sigma bonds
$\sigma\ (B_{sp3} - F_{2p})$

98. **(M)** The structure of H_3PO_3 is shown on the right.

The two ionizable protons are bound to oxygen.

99. **(M)**
(a) $H_2SO_3 > HF > N_2H_5^+ > CH_3NH_3^+ > H_2O$
(b) $OH^- > CH_3NH_2 > N_2H_4 > F^- > HSO_3^-$
(c) (i) to the right and (ii) to the left.

100. **(M)**
(a) Because $K_a \gg 1$, the following equilibrium summary is appropriate.

	$HI(aq)$	$+$	$H_2O(l)$	$\rightleftharpoons$	$I^-(aq)$	$+$	$H_3O^+(aq)$
initial concns:	1.00 M						
to completion:	0 M				1.00 M		1.00 M
to the left:	$+x$ M				$-x$ M		$-x$ M
equil concns:	x M				$(1.00 - x)$ M $\approx$ 1.00 M		$(1.00 - x)$ M $\approx$ 1.00 M

The equilibrium condition is $K_a = (1.00)(1.00)/x$. When this expression is solved for x, we get $x = 1.00/K_a = 10^{-9}$ M.

Therefore, $[HI] \approx 10^{-9}$ M and $[I^-] \approx 1.0$ M

(b) Because K_b (I^-) is so small, we expect very little I^- to react. Therefore, $[I^-] \approx 1.0$ M and the $[H_3O^+]$ and $[OH^-]$ in 1.0 M NaI(aq) will be no different than they are in pure water. Use these values in the K_a expression and solve for [HI].

$K_a = [H_3O^+]\,[I^-]/[HI] \approx (10^{-7})(1.0)/[HI]$

$[HI] = 10^{-7}/K_a = 10^{-7}/10^9 = 10^{-16}$ M

101. (M)

(a) $[HCl]_{total} = [HCl]_{eq} + [Cl^-]_{eq}$. Since $[HCl]_{total} = 1.0 \times 10^{-7}$ M and $[HCl]_{eq} \approx 0$ M, we have 1.0×10^{-7} M $= [Cl^-]_{eq}$. We usually write this expression as $[Cl^-] = 1.0 \times 10^{-7}$ M, for which the equilibrium concentration of Cl^- is implied.

(b) The charge balance equation (electroneutrality condition) is $[H_3O^+] = [Cl^-] + [OH^-]$.

(c) Let $C_o = 1.0 \times 10^{-7}$ M. We have $[Cl^-] = C_o = 1.0 \times 10^{-7}$ M (material balance) and $[H_3O^+] = [Cl^-] + [OH^-]$ (charge balance). We can rewrite the charge balance equation as

$[H_3O^+] = C_o + K_w/[H_3O^+]$

Multiplying both sides of this equation by $[H_3O^+]$ and rearranging, we obtain

$[H_3O^+]^2 - C_o[H_3O^+] - K_w = 0$

(d) The equation in (c) is of the form $ax^2 + bx + c = 0$, with $x = [H_3O^+]$, $a = 1$, $b = -C_o$, and $c = -K_w$, for which the solutions are $x = \dfrac{-b \pm \sqrt{b^2 - 4ac}}{2a}$. Therefore, the solutions to the equation in (c) are

$$[H_3O^+] = \frac{C_o \pm \sqrt{C_o^2 - 4(1)(-K_w)}}{2} = \frac{1.0 \times 10^{-7} \pm \sqrt{5.0 \times 10^{-14}}}{2} = \frac{1.0 \times 10^{-7} \pm 2.2 \times 10^{-7}}{2}$$

Since $[H_3O^+]$ must be a positive quantity, we are interested only in the solution obtained by using the + sign. Therefore,

$$[H_3O^+] = \frac{1.0 \times 10^{-7} + 2.2 \times 10^{-7}}{2} = 1.6 \times 10^{-7} \quad \Rightarrow \quad pH = 6.79$$

The pH is slightly below 7 (slightly acidic), which is what we would expect for a very dilute solution of a strong acid.

(e) To calculate [OH⁻], we use $[H_3O^+] = 1.6 \times 10^{-7}$ M in the equation $[OH^-] = K_w/[H_3O^+]$. We obtain

$$[OH^-] = 1.0 \times 10^{-14}/1.6 \times 10^{-7} = 6.3 \times 10^{-8} \text{ M} = [H_3O^+]_{water}$$

$$[Cl^-] = 1.0 \times 10^{-7} \text{ M} = [H_3O^+]_{HCl}$$

By comparing [OH⁻] and [Cl⁻], we can see that the self-ionization of water contributes slightly less than HCl to the total amount of H_3O^+ in solution (0.63×10^{-7} M from the self-ionization of water versus 1.0×10^{-7} M from the ionization of HCl).

102. **(M)** In the solution to Exercise 101, we developed the following equations for $[H_3O^+]$ and $[H_3O^+]_{water}$ in C_o M HCl(aq).

$$[H_3O^+] = \frac{C_o + \sqrt{C_o^2 - 4(1)(-K_w)}}{2} \qquad \text{and} \qquad [H_3O^+]_{water} = [OH^-] = K_w/[H_3O^+]$$

Using $C_o = 1.0 \times 10^{-6}$ M, we obtain

$$[H_3O^+] = \frac{1.0 \times 10^{-6} + \sqrt{1.04 \times 10^{-12}}}{2} = \frac{1.0 \times 10^{-6} + 1.02 \times 10^{-6}}{2} = 1.01 \times 10^{-6} \text{ M}$$

$$[H_3O^+]_{water} = 1.0 \times 10^{-14}/1.01 \times 10^{-6} = 9.9 \times 10^{-9} \text{ M}$$

% H_3O^+ from water

$= ([H_3O^+]_{water}/[H_3O^+]) \times 100$

$= (9.9 \times 10^{-9} \text{ M}/1.01 \times 10^{-6} \text{ M}) \times 100$

$= 0.98$

Therefore, in 1.0×10^{-6} M HCl(aq), less than 1% of the H_3O^+ in solution comes from the self-ionization of water.

103. **(M)** In general, the stronger the acid, the more stable its conjugate base. Therefore, we can rank a series of compounds in order of increasing acid strength by focusing on the relative stabilities of the anions formed on ionization. When comparing the stabilities of various anions, we consider the sizes and electronegativities of the atoms bearing the negative charge. The greater the electronegativity and the larger the atom, the more stable it is with a negative charge.

(a) The anions formed on ionization are CH_3COO^-, CH_3O^-, and $C_6H_5O^-$. For CH_3O^-, the negative charge is localized on the O atom (no resonance structures can be drawn). For CH_3COO^-, the negative charge is shared equally by the two O atoms.

For $C_6H_5O^-$, we can draw several resonance structures.

Although we can draw a greater number of resonance structures for $C_6H_5O^-$ than for CH_3COO^-, the CH_3COO^- ion is more stable than $C_6H_5O^-$ because in CH_3COO^-, the negative charge is shared equally by two electronegative atoms. Most of the resonance structures we can draw for $C_6H_5O^-$ place the negative charge on a C atom, which is much less electronegative (and therefore less stable with a negative charge) than an O atom.

Therefore,

increasing stability of anion
————————————————————————————————→

CH_3O^-	$C_6H_5O^-$	CH_3COO^-
CH_3OH	C_6H_5OH	CH_3COOH

————————————————————————————————→
increasing acid strength

(b) The anions formed upon ionization are ^-CN, ^-OCN, ^-CCH, and ^-OClO. The Lewis structures are as follows.

The ^-OClO ion is the most stable because the negative charge is shared equally by two O atoms, and O is very electronegative. The next most stable anion is the ^-OCN ion, with the negative charge shared by O and N. In the ^-CN and ^-CCH ions, the negative charge is localized on C. However, the ^-CN ion is more stable than the ^-CCH ion because the N atom is more electronegative than C and draws some electron density away from the C atom toward itself, which helps to stabilize the anion.

Therefore,

increasing stability of anion

————————————————————————————→

| ⁻CCH | ⁻CN | ⁻OCN | ⁻OClO |

| HCCH | HCN | HOCN | HOClO |

————————————————————————————→

increasing acid strength

104. **(M)** K_a for an acid is defined as $K_a = [H_3O^+][A^-]/[HA]$. We may write $[H_3O^+] = 10^{-pH}$ and $[HA] = C_0 - [A^-] = C_0 - \alpha C_0 = C_0(1 - \alpha)$, where α is the fraction of HA that ionizes. Therefore,

$$K_a = \frac{10^{-pH}(\alpha C_0)}{(1-\alpha)C_0} = \frac{10^{-pH}\alpha}{(1-\alpha)} \implies K_a - \alpha K_a = 10^{-pH}\alpha \implies K_a = \alpha(K_a + 10^{-pH})$$

$$\implies \alpha = \frac{K_a}{K_a + 10^{-pH}}$$

For an extremely dilute solution, pH = 7 and $\alpha = \frac{K_a}{K_a + 10^{-7}}$. Thus, for an extremely dilute solution of an acid with $K_a = 10^{-5}$, α will be equal to $10^{-5}/(10^{-5} + 10^{-7}) = 1/1.01 = 0.99$. If $K_a = 10^{-7}$, then α will be equal to $10^{-7}/(10^{-7} + 10^{-7}) = 1/2 = 0.50$. Thus, weak acids are usually very highly ionized in an extremely dilute solution.

FEATURE PROBLEMS

105. **(D)**

(a) From the combustion analysis we can determine the empirical formula. Note that the mass of oxygen is determined by difference.

$$\text{amount C} = 1.599 \text{ g CO}_2 \times \frac{1 \text{ mol CO}_2}{44.01 \text{ g CO}_2} \times \frac{1 \text{ mol C}}{1 \text{ mol CO}_2} = 0.03633 \text{ mol C}$$

$$\text{mass of C} = 0.03633 \text{ mol C} \times \frac{12.011 \text{ g C}}{1 \text{ mol C}} = 0.4364 \text{ g C}$$

$$\text{amount H} = 0.327 \text{ g H}_2\text{O} \times \frac{1 \text{ mol H}_2\text{O}}{18.02 \text{ g H}_2\text{O}} \times \frac{2 \text{ mol H}}{1 \text{ mol H}_2\text{O}} = 0.03629 \text{ mol H}$$

$$\text{mass of H} = 0.03629 \text{ mol H} \times \frac{1.008 \text{ g H}}{1 \text{ mol H}} = 0.03658 \text{ g H}$$

$$\text{amount O} = \left(1.054 \text{ g sample} - 0.4364 \text{ g C} - 0.03568 \text{ g H}\right) \times \frac{1 \text{ mol O}}{16.00 \text{ g O}} = 0.0364 \text{ mol O}$$

There are equal moles of the three elements. The empirical formula is CHO.

The freezing-point depression data are used to determine the molar mass.

$$\Delta T_f = -K_f m \quad m = \frac{\Delta T_f}{-K_f} = \frac{-0.82\,^\circ C}{-3.90\,^\circ C/m} = 0.21\ m$$

$$\text{amount of solute} = 25.10\ g\ \text{solvent} \times \frac{1\ kg}{1000\ g} \times \frac{0.21\ mol\ solute}{1\ kg\ solvent} = 0.0053\ mol$$

$$M = \frac{0.615\ g\ solute}{0.0053\ mol\ solute} = 1.2 \times 10^2\ g/mol$$

The formula mass of the empirical formula is: $(12.0 + 1.0 + 16.0)$ g/mol = 29.0 g/mol Thus, there are four empirical units in a molecule, the molecular formula is $C_4H_4O_4$, and the molar mass is 116.1 g/mol.

(b) Here we determine the mass of maleic acid that reacts with one $mol\ OH^-$,

$$\frac{mass}{mol\ OH^-} = \frac{0.4250\ g\ maleic\ acid}{34.03\ mL\ base \times \frac{1\ L}{1000\ mL} \times \frac{0.2152\ mol\ KOH}{1\ L\ base}} = 58.03\ g/mol\ OH^-$$

This means that one mole of maleic acid (116.1 g/mol) reacts with two moles of hydroxide ion. Maleic acid is a diprotic acid: $H_2C_4H_2O_4$.

(c) Maleic acid has two—COOH groups joined together by a bridging C_2H_2 group. A plausible Lewis structure is shown below:

$$H—\overline{O}—\overset{\overset{|O|}{\|}}{C}—\overset{\overset{H}{|}}{C}=\overset{\overset{H}{|}}{C}—\overset{\overset{|O|}{\|}}{C}—\overline{O}—H$$

(d) We first determine $[H_3O^+] = 10^{-pH} = 10^{-1.80} = 0.016\ M$ and then the initial concentration of acid.

$$\left[(CHCOOH)_2\right]_{initial} = \frac{0.215\ g}{50.00\ mL} \times \frac{1000\ mL}{1L} \times \frac{1\ mol}{116.1\ g} = 0.0370\ M$$

We use the first ionization to determine the value of K_{a_1}

Equation: $(CHCOOH)_2\ (aq) + H_2O(l) \rightleftharpoons H(CHCOO)_2^-\ (aq) + H_3O^+(aq)$

Initial:	0.0370 M	—	0 M	≈0 M
Changes:	−0.016 M	—	+0.016 M	+0.016 M
Equil:	0.021 M	—	0.016 M	0.016 M

$$K_a = \frac{\left[H(CHCOO)_2^-\right]\left[H_3O^+\right]}{\left[(CHCOOH)_2\right]} = \frac{(0.016)(0.016)}{0.021} = 1.2 \times 10^{-2}$$

K_{a_2} could be determined if we had some way to measure the total concentration of all ions in solution, or if we could determine $\left[(CHCOO)_2^{2-}\right] = K_{a_2}$

(e) Practically all the $\left[H_3O^+\right]$ arises from the first ionization.

Equation: $(CHCOOH)_2\,(aq)+ H_2O(l) \;\rightleftharpoons\; H(CHCOO)_2^-\,(aq)+ H_3O^+(aq)$

Initial:	0.0500 M	–	0 M	≈ 0 M
Changes:	$-x$ M	–	$+x$ M	$+x$ M
Equil:	$(0.0500-x)$ M	–	x M	x M

$$K_a = \frac{[H(CHCOO)_2^-][H_3O^+]}{[(CHCOOH)_2]} = \frac{x^2}{0.0500-x} = 1.2\times10^{-2}$$

$$x^2 = 0.00060 - 0.012\,x \qquad x^2 + 0.012\,x - 0.00060 = 0$$

$$x = \frac{-b\pm\sqrt{b^2-4ac}}{2a} = \frac{-0.012\pm\sqrt{0.00014+0.0024}}{2} = 0.019\ M = \left[H_3O^+\right]$$

$$pH = -\log(0.019) = 1.72$$

106. (D)

(a)

$$\frac{x^2}{0.00250-x} \simeq \frac{x^2}{0.00250} \simeq 4.2\times10^{-4} \qquad x_1 \simeq 0.00102$$

$$\frac{x^2}{0.00250-0.00102} = \frac{x^2}{0.00148} \simeq 4.2\times10^{-4} \qquad x_2 \simeq 0.000788$$

$$\frac{x^2}{0.00250-0.000788} = \frac{x^2}{0.00171} \simeq 4.2\times10^{-4} \qquad x_3 \simeq 0.000848$$

$$\frac{x^2}{0.00250-0.000848} = \frac{x^2}{0.00165} \simeq 4.2\times10^{-4} \qquad x_4 \simeq 0.000833$$

$$\frac{x^2}{0.00250-0.000833} = \frac{x^2}{0.00167} \simeq 4.2\times10^{-4} \qquad x_5 \simeq 0.000837$$

$$\frac{x^2}{0.00250-0.000837} = \frac{x^2}{0.00166} \simeq 4.2\times10^{-4} \qquad x_6 \simeq 0.000836$$

$$x_6 \simeq 0.000836 \qquad \text{or} \simeq 8.4\times10^{-4},$$

which is the same as the value obtained using the quadratic equation.

(b) We organize the solution around the balanced chemical equation, as we have done before.

Equation: $HClO_2(aq)+ H_2O(l) \;\rightleftharpoons\; ClO_2^-(aq) + H_3O^+(aq)$

Initial:	0.500 M	–	0 M	≈ 0 M
Changes:	$-x$ M	–	$+x$ M	$+x$ M
Equil:	x M	–	x M	x M

$$K_a = \frac{\left[ClO_2^-\right]\left[H_3O^+\right]}{\left[HClO_2\right]} = \frac{x^2}{0.500-x} = 1.1\times10^{-2} \approx \frac{x^2}{0.500} \quad \text{Assuming } x \ll 0.500\ M,$$

$x = \sqrt{x^2} = \sqrt{0.500 \times 1.1 \times 10^{-2}} = 0.074\,M$ Not significantly smaller than 0.500 M.

Assume $x = 0.074$ $x = \sqrt{(0.500 - 0.0774) \times 1.1 \times 10^{-2}} = 0.068\,M$ Try once more.

Assume $x = 0.068$ $x = \sqrt{(0.500 - 0.068) \times 1.1 \times 10^{-2}} = 0.069\,M$ One more time.

Assume $x = 0.069$ $x = \sqrt{(0.500 - 0.069) \times 1.1 \times 10^{-2}} = 0.069\,M$ Final result!

$\left[H_3O^+ \right] = 0.069$ M, $pH = -\log\left[H_3O^+ \right] = -\log(0.069) = 1.16$

107. (D)

(a) Here, two equilibria must be satisfied simultaneously. The common variable, $\left[H_3O^+ \right] = z$.

Equation: $CH_3COOH(aq)$	+	$H_2O(l)$	$\rightleftharpoons$	$CH_3COO^-(aq)$	+	$H_3O^+(aq)$
Initial:	0.315 M		$-$	0 M		≈ 0 M
Changes:	$+x$ M		$-$	$+x$ M		$+z$ M
Equil:	$(0.315 - x)$ M		$-$	x M		z M

$$K_a = \frac{\left[H_3O^+ \right]\left[CH_3COO^- \right]}{\left[CH_3COOH \right]} = \frac{xz}{0.315 - x} = 1.8 \times 10^{-5}$$

Equation:	$HCOOH(aq)$	+	$H_2O(l)$ $\rightleftharpoons$	$HCOO^-(aq)$	+	$H_3O^+(aq)$
Initial:	0.250 M		$-$	0 M		0 M
Changes:	$-y$ M		$-$	$+y$ M		$+z$ M
Equil:	$(0.250 - y)$ M		$-$	y M		z M

$$K_a = \frac{\left[H_3O^+ \right]\left[HCOO^- \right]}{\left[HCOOH \right]} = \frac{yz}{0.250 - y} = 1.8 \times 10^{-4}$$

In this system, there are three variables, $x = \left[CH_3COO^- \right]$, $y = \left[HCOO^- \right]$, and $z = \left[H_3O^+ \right]$. These three variables also represent the concentrations of the only charged species in the reaction, and thus $x + y = z$. We solve the two K_a expressions for x and y. (Before we do so, however, we take advantage of the fact that x and y are quite small: $x \ll 0.315$ and $y \ll 0.250$.) Then we substitute these results into the expression for z, and solve to obtain a value of that variable.

$xz = 1.8 \times 10^{-5}(0.315) = 5.7 \times 10^{-6}$ $yz = 1.8 \times 10^{-4}(0.250) = 4.5 \times 10^{-5}$

$$x = \frac{5.7 \times 10^{-6}}{z}$$ $$y = \frac{4.5 \times 10^{-5}}{z}$$

$z = x + y = \dfrac{5.7 \times 10^{-6}}{z} + \dfrac{4.5 \times 10^{-5}}{z} = \dfrac{5.07 \times 10^{-5}}{z}$ $z = \sqrt{5.07 \times 10^{-5}} = 7.1 \times 10^{-3}\,M = [H_3O^+]$

$pH = -\log(7.1 \times 10^{-3}) = 2.15$ We see that our assumptions about the sizes of x and y must be valid, since each of them is smaller than z. (Remember that $x + y = z$.)

(b) We first determine the initial concentration of each solute.

$$[NH_3] = \frac{12.5g\ NH_2}{0.375L\ soln} \times \frac{1\ mol\ NH_3}{17.03g\ NH_3} = 1.96M \qquad\qquad K_b = 1.8\times10^{-5}$$

$$[CH_3NH_2] = \frac{1.55\ g\ CH_3NH_2}{0.375L\ soln} \times \frac{1\ mol\ CH_3NH_2}{31.06\ g\ CH_3NH_2} = 0.133M \qquad K_b = 4.2\times10^{-4}$$

Now we solve simultaneously two equilibria, which have a common variable, $\left[OH^-\right] = z$.

Equation:	$NH_3(aq)$	$+$	H_2O	$\rightleftharpoons$	$NH_4^+(aq)$	$+$	$OH^-(aq)$
Initial:	1.96 M		–		0 M		$\approx 0\,M$
Changes:	$-x\,M$		–		$+x\,M$		$+z\,M$
Equil:	$(1.96-x)M$		–		$x\,M$		$z\,M$

$$K_b = \frac{\left[NH_4^+\right]\left[OH^-\right]}{\left[NH_3\right]} = 1.8\times10^{-5} = \frac{xz}{1.96-x} \approx \frac{xz}{1.96}$$

Eqn:	$CH_3NH_2(aq)$	$+$	$H_2O(l)$	$\rightleftharpoons$	$CH_3NH_3^+(aq)$	$+$	$OH^-(aq)$
Initial:	0.133 M		–		0 M		$\approx 0\,M$
Changes:	$-y\,M$		–		$+y\,M$		$+z\,M$
Equil:	$(0.133-y)M$		–		$y\,M$		$z\,M$

$$K_b = \frac{\left[CH_3NH_3^+\right]\left[OH^-\right]}{\left[CH_3NH_2\right]} = 4.2\times10^{-4} = \frac{yz}{0.133-y} = \frac{yz}{0.133}$$

In this system, there are three variables, $x = \left[NH_4^+\right]$, $y = \left[CH_3NH_3^+\right]$, and $z = \left[OH^-\right]$.
These three variables also represent the concentrations of the only charged species in solution in substantial concentration, and thus $x + y = z$. We solve the two K_b expressions for x and y. Then we substitute these results into the expression for z, and solve to obtain the value of that variable.

$$xz = 1.96\times1.8\times10^{-5} = 3.53\times10^{-5} \qquad\qquad yz = 0.133\times4.2\times10^{-5} = 5.59\times10^{-5}$$

$$x = \frac{3.53\times10^{-5}}{z} \qquad\qquad\qquad y = \frac{5.59\times10^{-5}}{z}$$

$$z = x+y = \frac{3.53\times10^{-5}}{z} + \frac{5.59\times10^{-5}}{z} = \frac{9.12\times10^{-5}}{z} \qquad z^2 = 9.12\times10^{-5}$$

$$z = 9.5\times10^{-3}M = \left[OH^-\right] \quad pOH = -\log\left(9.5\times10^{-3}\right) = 2.02 \quad pH = 14.00 - 2.02 = 11.98$$

We see that our assumptions about x and y (that $x \ll 1.96$ M and $y \ll 0.133$ M) must be valid, since each of them is smaller than z. (Remember that $x + y = z$.)

(c) In 1.0 M NH_4CN there are the following species: $NH_4^+(aq)$, $NH_3(aq)$, $CN^-(aq)$, $HCN(aq)$, $H_3O^+(aq)$, and $OH^-(aq)$. These species are related by the following six equations.

(1) $K_w = 1.0 \times 10^{-14} = [H_3O^+][OH^-]$ $\qquad$ $[OH^-] = \dfrac{1.0 \times 10^{-14}}{[H_3O^+]}$

(2) $K_a = 6.2 \times 10^{-10} = \dfrac{[H_3O^+][CN^-]}{[HCN]}$ $\qquad$ (3) $K_b = 1.8 \times 10^{-5} = \dfrac{[NH_4^+][OH^-]}{[NH_3]}$

(4) $[NH_3] + [NH_4^+] = 1.0$ M $\qquad$ $[NH_3] = 1.0 - [NH_4^+]$

(5) $[HCN] + [CN^-] = 1.0$ M $\qquad$ $[HCN] = 1.0 - [CN^-]$

(6) $[NH_4^+] + [H_3O^+] = [CN^-] + [OH^-]$ or $[NH_4^+] \approx [CN^-]$

Equation (6) is the result of charge balance, that there must be the same quantity of positive and negative charge in the solution. The approximation is the result of remembering that not much H_3O^+ or OH^- will be formed as the result of hydrolysis of ions. Substitute equation (4) into equation (3), and equation (5) into equation (2).

(3') $K_b = 1.8 \times 10^{-5} = \dfrac{[NH_4^+][OH^-]}{1.0 - [NH_4^+]}$ $\qquad$ (2') $K_a = 4.0 \times 10^{-10} = \dfrac{[H_3O^+][CN^-]}{1.0 - [CN^-]}$

Now substitute equation (6) into equation (2'), and equation (1) into equation (3').

(2'') $K_a = 6.2 \times 10^{-10} = \dfrac{[H_3O^+][NH_4^+]}{1.0 - [NH_4^+]}$ $\qquad$ (3'') $\dfrac{1.8 \times 10^{-5}}{1.0 \times 10^{-14}} = \dfrac{[NH_4^+]}{[H_3O^+](1.0 - [NH_4^+])}$

Now we solve both of these equations for $[NH_4^+]$.

(2'): $6.2 \times 10^{-10} - 6.2 \times 10^{-10}[NH_4^+] = [H_3O^+][NH_4^+]$ $\qquad$ $[NH_4^+] = \dfrac{6.2 \times 10^{-10}}{6.2 \times 10^{-10} + [H_3O^+]}$

(3'): $1.8 \times 10^9[H_3O^+] - 1.8 \times 10^9[H_3O^+][NH_4^+] = [NH_4^+]$ $\qquad$ $[NH_4^+] = \dfrac{1.8 \times 10^9[H_3O^+]}{1.00 + 1.8 \times 10^9[H_3O^+]}$

We equate the two results and solve for $[H_3O^+]$.

$$\dfrac{6.2 \times 10^{-10}}{6.2 \times 10^{-10} + [H_3O^+]} = \dfrac{1.8 \times 10^9[H_3O^+]}{1.00 + 1.8 \times 10^9[H_3O^+]}$$

$6.2 \times 10^{-10} + 1.1[H_3O^+] = 1.1[H_3O^+] + 1.8 \times 10^9[H_3O^+]^2$ $\qquad$ $6.2 \times 10^{-10} = 1.8 \times 10^9[H_3O^+]^2$

$[H_3O^+] = \sqrt{\dfrac{6.2 \times 10^{-10}}{1.8 \times 10^9}} = 5.9 \times 10^{-10}$ M $\quad$ pH $= -\log(5.9 \times 10^{-10}) = 9.23$

Note that $[H_3O^+] = \sqrt{\dfrac{K_a \times K_w}{K_b}}$ $\qquad$ or $\qquad$ pH $= 0.500(pK_a + pK_w - pK_b)$

SELF-ASSESSMENT EXERCISES

108. (E)

    (a) K_w: Dissociation constant of water, which is defined as $[H_3O^+][OH^-]$

    (b) pH: A logarithmic scale of expressing acidity of a solution (H_3O^+); it is defined as $-\log [H_3O^+]$

    (c) pKa: A logarithmic scale expressing the strength of an acid (which is how much an acid dissociates in water at equilibrium); it is defined as $-\log K_a$

    (d) Hydrolysis: A reaction involving ionization of water

    (e) Lewis acid: A compound or species that accepts electrons

109. (E)

    (a) Conjugate base: A base that is derived by removing an abstractable proton from the acid

    (b) Percent ionization of acid/base: The ratio between the conjugate of the acid or base under study and the acid/base itself times 100

    (c) Self-ionization: A reaction involving ionization of two molecules of water to give $[H_3O^+]$ and $[OH^-]$

    (d) Amphiprotic behavior: A substance acting as either an acid or a base

110. (E)

    (a) Brønstead–Lowry acid and base: A Brønsted–Lowry acid is a substance that when placed in water will cause the formation of hydronium ion by donating a proton to water. The base is one that abstracts a proton from water and results in a hydroxyl ion.

    (b) $[H_3O^+]$ and pH: $[H_3O^+]$ is the molar concentration of hydronium ion in water, whereas pH is the $-\log [H_3O^+]$

    (c) K_a for NH_4^+ and K_b for NH_3: K_b of NH_3 is the equilibrium constant for hydrolysis of water with NH_3 to generate NH_4^+ and OH^-. K_a of NH_4^+ is for deprotonation of NH_4^+ with water to give NH_3 and OH^-.

    (d) Leveling effect and electron-withdrawing effect: The leveling effect is the result of reaction of water with any acid or base such that no acid or base can exist in water that are more acidic than H_3O^+ or more basic than OH^-. The electron-withdrawing effect is the tendency for a central atom with high electronegativity in an oxoacid to withdraw electrons from the O–H bond.

111. (E) The answer is (a), HCO_3^-, because it can donate a proton to water to become CO_3^{2-}, or it can be protonated to give H_2CO_3 (i.e., CO_2(aq)).

112. (E) The answer is (c). CH_3CH_2COOH is a weak acid, so the concentration of H_3O^+ ions it will generate upon dissociation in water will be significantly less than 0.1 M. Therefore, its pH will be higher the 0.10 M HBr, which dissociates completely in water to give 0.10 M H_3O^+.

113. (E) The answer is (d). CH_3NH_2 is a weak base.

114. (M) The answer is (e) because CO_3^{2-} is the strongest base and it drives the dissociation of acetic acid furthest.

115. (M) The answer is (c). H_2SO_4 dissociation is nearly complete for the first proton, giving a $[H_3O^+] = 0.10$ M (pH = 1). The second dissociation is not complete. Therefore, (c) is the only choice that makes sense.

116. (M) The answer is (b). You can write down the stepwise equations for dissociation of H_2SO_3 and then the dissociation of HSO_3^- and calculate the equilibrium concentration of each species. However, you can determine the answer without detailed calculations. The two dissociation equations are given below:

Eq.1 $\quad H_2SO_3 + H_2O \rightleftharpoons HSO_3^- + H_3O^+ \qquad\qquad K_{a1} = 1.3\times10^{-2}$

Eq.2 $\quad HSO_3^- + H_2O \rightleftharpoons SO_3^{2-} + H_3O^+ \qquad\qquad K_{a2} = 6.3\times10^{-8}$

For the first equation, the equilibrium concentrations, of HSO_3^- and H_3O^+ are the same. They become the initial concentration values for the second dissociation reaction. Since K_{a2} is 6.3×10^{-8} (which is small), the equilibrium concentrations of HSO_3^- and H_3O^+ won't change significantly. So, the equation simplifies as follows:

$$K_{a2} = 6.8\times10^{-8} = \frac{\left[SO_3^{2-}\right]\left(\left[H_3O^+\right]+x\right)}{\left[HSO_3^-\right]-x} = \frac{\left[SO_3^{2-}\right]\left[\cancel{H_3O^+}\right]}{\cancel{\left[HSO_3^-\right]}}$$

$$K_{a2} = 6.8\times10^{-8} = \left[SO_3^{2-}\right]$$

117. (E) Since both the acid and the base in this reaction are strong, they dissociate completely. The pH is determined as follows:

mol H_3O^+: 0.248 M HNO_3 × 0.02480 L = 0.00615 mol
mol OH^-: 0.394 M KOH × 0.01540 L = 0.00607 mol
Final: 0.00615 − 0.00607 = 8.00×10^{-5} mol H_3O^+

$$\left[H_3O^+\right] = \frac{8.00\times10^{-5}\,mol}{\left(0.02480\,L + 0.01540\,L\right)} = 0.00200\,M$$

$$pH = -\log\left(0.00200\right) = 2.70$$

118. (M) Since pH = 3.25, the $[H_3O^+] = 10^{-3.25} = 5.62\times10^{-4}$ M. Using the reaction below, we can determine the equilibrium concentrations of other species

$$CH_3COOH + H_2O \rightleftharpoons CH_3COO^- + H_3O^+$$

Initial	c	0	0
Change	$-x$	$+x$	$+x$
Equil.	$c-x$	x	x

Since $x = 5.62\times10^{-4}$ M, the equilibrium expression becomes

$$K_a = \frac{\left[H_3O^+\right]\left[CH_3COO^-\right]}{[CH_3COOH]} = \frac{\left(5.62\times10^{-4}M\right)\left(5.62\times10^{-4}M\right)}{\left(c-5.62\times10^{-4}M\right)} = 1.8\times10^{-5}$$

Solving c gives a concentration of 0.0181 M.
Since concentrated acetic acid is 35% by weight and the density is 1.044 g/mL, the concentration of acetic acid is:

$$\frac{35\text{ g }CH_3COOH}{100\text{ g Conc. }CH_3COOH\text{ sol'n}}\times\frac{1.044\text{ g Conc. }CH_3COOH}{0.001\text{ L sol'n}}\times\frac{1\text{ mol }CH_3COOH}{60.06\text{ g }CH_3COOH} = 6.084\text{ M }CH_3COOH$$

Therefore, volume of concentrated solution required to make 12.5 L of 0.0181 M HAc solution is:

$$(c \cdot V)_{\text{dilute}} = (c \cdot V)_{\text{conc.}}$$

$$V_{\text{conc}} = \frac{(0.0181 \text{ M})(12500 \text{ mL})}{6.084 \text{ M}} = 37.2 \text{ mL}$$

119. **(M)** Table 16.3 has the K_a value for chloroacetic acid, $CH_2ClCOOH$. $K_a = 1.4 \times 10^{-3}$. The solution is made of the chloroacetate salt, which hydrolyzes water according to the following reaction:

	CH_2ClCOO^-	$+$ H_2O	$\rightleftharpoons$	$CH_2ClCOOH$	$+$ OH^-
Initial	2.05			0	0
Change	$-x$			$+x$	$+x$
Equil.	$2.05 - x$			x	x

$$K_b = \frac{K_W}{K_a} = \frac{1.0 \times 10^{-14}}{1.4 \times 10^{-3}} = 7.14 \times 10^{-12}$$

$$K_b = \frac{[CH_2ClCOOH][OH^-]}{[CH_2ClCOO^-]}$$

$$7.14 \times 10^{-12} = \frac{x \cdot x}{2.05 - \cancel{x}}$$

Solving the above simplified expression for x, we get $x = [OH^-] = 3.826 \times 10^{-6}$

$$pH = 14 - pOH = 14 - \left[-\log(3.826 \times 10^{-6}) \right] = 8.58$$

120. **(M)** 0.10 M HI < 0.05 M H_2SO_4 < 0.05 M $CH_2ClCOOH$ < 0.50 M CH_3COOH < 0.50 M NH_4Cl < 1.0 M NaBr < 0.05 M KCH_3COO < 0.05 M NH_3 < 0.06 M NaOH < 0.05 M $Ba(OH)_2$

121. **(M)** Since pH = 5 pOH, pH must be significantly larger than pOH, which means that the solution is basic. The pH can be determined by solving two simultaneous equations:

pH $-$ 5 pOH $= 0$

pH $+$ pOH $= 14$

pOH $= 2.333$

pH $= 14 - 2.33 = 11.67$.

Therefore, $[H_3O^+] = 2.14 \times 10^{-12}$ M (and $[OH^-] = 4.67 \times 10^{-3}$ M)

The solute must be NH_3, because it is the only basic species (the other two are acidic and neutral, respectively). Since the K_b of NH_3 is 1.8×10^{-5}, the concentration of NH_3 can be determined as follows:

$$K_b = \frac{[OH^-][NH_4^+]}{[NH_3]} = \frac{(4.67 \times 10^{-3})(4.67 \times 10^{-3})}{x} = 1.8 \times 10^{-5}$$

$$x = 1.2 \text{ M}$$

122. **(M)** The answer is (a). If CH_3CH_2COOH is 0.42% ionized for a 0.80 M solution, then the concentration of the acid at equilibrium is $(0.80 \times 0.0042) = 0.00336$. The equilibrium expression for the dissociation of CH_3CH_2COOH is:

$$K_a = \frac{\left[H_3O^+\right]\left[CH_3CH_2COO^-\right]}{\left[CH_3CH_2COOH\right]} = \frac{(0.00336)(0.00336)}{(0.800 - 0.00336)} = 1.42 \times 10^{-5}$$

123. **(E)** The answer is (b), because $H_2PO_4^-$ is a result of addition of one proton to the base HPO_4^{2-}.

124. **(M)** The answer is (d). This is because, in the second equation, HNO_2 will give its proton to ClO^- (rather than $HClO$ giving its proton to NO_2^-), which means that HNO_2 is a stronger acid than $HClO$. Also, in the first equation, ClO^- is not a strong enough base to abstract a proton from water, which means that $HClO$ is in turn a stronger acid than H_2O.

125. **(M)** The dominant species in the solution is ClO_2^-. Therefore, determine its concentration and ionization constant first:

$$\left[ClO_2^-\right] = \frac{3.00 \text{ mol } CaClO_2}{2.50 \text{ L}} \times \frac{2 \text{ mol } ClO_2^-}{1 \text{ mol } CaClO_2} = 2.40 \text{ M}$$

$$K_b = \frac{K_w}{K_a} = \frac{1.0 \times 10^{-14}}{1.1 \times 10^{-2}} = 9.1 \times 10^{-13}$$

The reaction and the dissociation of ClO_2^- is as follows:

	ClO_2^-	+ H_2O	$\rightleftharpoons$	$HClO_2$	+ OH^-
Initial	2.40			0	0
Change	$-x$			$+x$	$+x$
Equil.	$2.40 - x$			x	x

$$K_b = \frac{\left[HClO_2\right]\left[OH^-\right]}{\left[ClO_2^-\right]}$$

$$9.1 \times 10^{-13} = \frac{x \cdot x}{2.40 - \cancel{x}}$$

Solving the above simplified expression for x, we get $x = \left[OH^-\right] = 1.478 \times 10^{-6}$.

$$pH = 14 - pOH = 14 - \left[-\log\left(1.478 \times 10^{-6}\right)\right] = 8.2$$

126. **(M)** Section 16-8 discusses the effects of structure on acid/base behavior. The major subtopics are effects of structure on binary acids, oxo acids, organic acids, and amine bases. For binary acids, acidity can be discussed in terms of electronegativity of the main atom, bond length, and heterolytic bond dissociation energy. For oxo acids, the main things affecting acidity are the electronegativity of the central atom and number of oxygen atoms surrounding the central atom. For organic acids, the main topic is the electron-withdrawing capability of constituent groups attached to the carboxyl unit. For amines, the basicity is discussed in terms of electron withdrawing or donating groups attached to the nitrogen in the amine, and the number of resonance structures possible for the base molecule.

CHAPTER 17
ADDITIONAL ASPECTS OF ACID–BASE EQUILIBRIA
PRACTICE EXAMPLES

1A **(D)** Organize the solution around the balanced chemical equation, as we have done before.

Equation:	$HF(aq)$	$+ H_2O(l)$	$\rightleftharpoons$	$H_3O^+(aq)$	$+ F^-(aq)$
Initial:	$0.500\,M$	$-$		$\approx 0\,M$	$0\,M$
Changes:	$-x\,M$	$-$		$+x\,M$	$+x\,M$
Equil:	$(0.500-x)\,M$	$-$		$x\,M$	$x\,M$

$$K_a = \frac{[H_3O^+][F^-]}{[HF]} = \frac{(x)(x)}{0.500-x} = 6.6\times10^{-4} \approx \frac{x^2}{0.500} \qquad \text{assuming } x \ll 0.500$$

$$x = \sqrt{0.500 \times 6.6\times10^{-4}} = 0.018\,M \qquad \text{One further cycle of approximations gives:}$$

$$x = \sqrt{(0.500-0.018)\times 6.6\times10^{-4}} = 0.018\,M = [H_3O^+]$$

Thus, $[HF] = 0.500\,M - 0.018\,M = 0.482\,M$

Recognize that 0.100 M HCl means $\left[H_3O^+\right]_{\text{initial}} = 0.100\,M$, since HCl is a strong acid.

Equation:	$HF(aq)$	$+ H_2O(l)$	$\rightleftharpoons$	$H_3O^+(aq)$	$+ F^-(aq)$
Initial:	$0.500\,M$	$-$		$0.100\,M$	$0\,M$
Changes:	$-x\,M$	$-$		$+x\,M$	$+x\,M$
Equil:	$(0.500-x)\,M$	$-$		$(0.100+x)\,M$	$x\,M$

$$K_a = \frac{[H_3O^+][F^-]}{[HF]} = \frac{(x)(0.100+x)}{0.500-x} = 6.6\times10^{-4} \approx \frac{0.100\,x}{0.500} \quad \text{assuming } x \ll 0.100$$

$$x = \frac{6.6\times10^{-4}\times 0.500}{0.100} = 3.3\times10^{-3}\,M = \left[F^-\right] \qquad \text{The assumption is valid.}$$

$\left[HF\right] = 0.500\,M - 0.003\,M = 0.497\,M$

$[H_3O^+] = 0.100\,M + x = 0.100\,M + 0.003\,M = 0.103\,M$

1B **(M)** From Example 17-6 *in the text*, we know that $[H_3O^+] = [CH_3COO^-] = 1.3 \times 10^{-3}$ M in 0.100 M CH_3COOH. We base our calculation, as usual, on the balanced chemical equation. The concentration of H_3O^+ from the added HCl is represented by x.

Equation: $CH_3COOH(aq) + H_2O(l) \rightleftharpoons H_3O^+(aq) + CH_3COO^-(aq)$

Initial:	0.100 M	–	≈ 0 M	0 M
Changes:	-0.00010 M	–	$+0.00010$ M	$+0.00010$ M
From HCl:			$+x$ M	
Equil:	0.100 M	–	$(0.00010 + x)$ M	0.00010 M

$$K_a = \frac{[H_3O^+][CH_3COO^-]}{[CH_3COOH]} = \frac{(0.00010+x)\,0.00010}{0.100} = 1.8 \times 10^{-5}$$

$$0.00010 + x = \frac{1.8 \times 10^{-5} \times 0.100}{0.00010} = 0.018 \, M \qquad x = 0.018 \, M - 0.00010 \, M = 0.018 \, M$$

$$V_{12\,M\,HCl} = 1.00 \, L \times \frac{0.018 \, mol \, H_3O^+}{1 \, L} \times \frac{1 \, mol \, HCl}{1 \, mol \, H_3O^+} \times \frac{1 \, L \, soln}{12 \, mol \, HCl} \times \frac{1000 \, mL}{1 \, L} \times \frac{1 \, drop}{0.050 \, mL} = 30. \, drops$$

Since 30. drops corresponds to 1.5 mL of 12 M solution, we see that the volume of solution does indeed remain approximately 1.00 L after addition of the 12 M HCl.

2A **(M)** We again organize the solution around the balanced chemical equation.

Equation: $HCOOH(aq) + H_2O(l) \rightleftharpoons HCOO^-(aq) + H_3O^+(aq)$

Initial:	0.100 M	–	0.150 M	≈ 0 M
Changes:	$-x$ M	–	$+x$ M	$+x$ M
Equil:	$(0.100 - x)$ M	–	$(0.150 + x)$ M	x M

$$K_a = \frac{[HCOO^-][H_3O^+]}{[HCOOH]} = \frac{(0.150 + x)(x)}{0.100 - x} = 1.8 \times 10^{-4} \approx \frac{0.150\,x}{0.100} \qquad \text{assuming } x \ll 0.100$$

$$x = \frac{0.100 \times 1.8 \times 10^{-4}}{0.150} = 1.2 \times 10^{-4} \, M = \left[H_3O^+\right], \; x << 0.100, \text{ thus our assumption is valid}$$

$$\left[HCOO^-\right] = 0.150 \, M + 0.00012 \, M = 0.150 \, M$$

2B **(M)** This time, a solid sample of a weak base is being added to a solution of its conjugate acid. We let x represent the concentration of acetate ion from the added sodium acetate. Notice that sodium acetate is a strong electrolyte, thus, it completely dissociates in aqueous solution. $\left[H_3O^+\right] = 10^{-pH} = 10^{-5.00} = 1.0 \times 10^{-5}\,M = 0.000010\,M$

Equation: $CH_3COOH(aq) + H_2O(l) \rightleftharpoons CH_3COO^-(aq) + H_3O^+(aq)$

Initial:	0.100 M	–	0 M	$\approx 0\,M$
Changes:	– 0.000010 M	–	+0.000010 M	+0.000010 M
From NaAc:			+x M	
Equil:	0.100 M	–	$(0.000010 + x)\,M$	0.000010 M

$$K_a = \frac{\left[H_3O^+\right]\left[CH_3COO^-\right]}{\left[CH_3COOH\right]} = \frac{0.000010(0.000010 + x)}{0.100} = 1.8 \times 10^{-5}$$

$$0.000010 + x = \frac{1.8 \times 10^{-5} \times 0.100}{0.000010} = 0.18\,M \qquad x = 0.18\,M - 0.000010\,M = 0.18\,M$$

$$\text{mass of } NaCH_3COO = 1.00\,L \times \frac{0.18\text{ mol } CH_3COO^-}{1\,L} \times \frac{1\,mol\ NaCH_3COO}{1\,mol\ CH_3COO^-} \times \frac{82.03\,g\ NaCH_3COO}{1\,mol\ NaCH_3COO}$$

$$= 15\,g\ NaCH_3COO$$

3A **(M)** A strong acid dissociates essentially completely, and effectively is a source of H_3O^+. $NaCH_3COO$ also dissociates completely in solution. The hydronium ion and the acetate ion react to form acetic acid: $H_3O^+(aq) + CH_3COO^-(aq) \rightleftharpoons CH_3COOH(aq) + H_2O(l)$

All that is necessary to form a buffer is to have approximately equal amounts of a weak acid and its conjugate base together in solution. This will be achieved if we add an amount of HCl equal to approximately half the original amount of acetate ion.

3B **(M)** HCl dissociates essentially completely in water and serves as a source of hydronium ion. This reacts with ammonia to form ammonium ion:

$NH_3(aq) + H_3O^+(aq) \rightleftharpoons NH_4^+(aq) + H_2O(l)$.

Because a buffer contains approximately equal amounts of a weak base (NH_3) and its conjugate acid (NH_4^+), to prepare a buffer we simply add an amount of HCl equal to approximately half the amount of $NH_3(aq)$ initially present.

4A **(M)** We first find the formate ion concentration, remembering that NaCOO is a strong electrolyte, existing in solution as $Na^+(aq)$ and $HCOO^-(aq)$.

$$[HCOO^-] = \frac{23.1g\ NaCOO}{500.0\ mL\ soln} \times \frac{1000\ mL}{1L} \times \frac{1\ mol\ NaCOO}{68.01g\ NaCOO} \times \frac{1\ mol\ HCOO^-}{1\ mol\ NaCOO} = 0.679\,M$$

As usual, the solution to the problem is organized around the balanced chemical equation.

Equation: $HCOOH(aq) + H_2O(l) \rightleftharpoons HCOO^-(aq) + H_3O^+(aq)$

Initial: 0.432 M   –   0.679 M $\approx 0\,M$

Changes: $-x$ M   – $+x$ M $+x$ M

Equil: $(0.432-x)$ M   – $(0.679+x)$ M x M

$$K_a = \frac{[H_3O^+][HCOO^-]}{[HCOOH]} = \frac{x(0.679+x)}{0.432-x} = 1.8\times10^{-4} \approx \frac{0.679x}{0.432} \qquad x = \frac{0.432\times1.8\times10^{-4}}{0.679}$$

This gives $[H_3O^+] = 1.14\times10^{-4}$ M. The assumption that $x \ll 0.432$ is clearly correct.

$pH = -\log[H_3O^+] = -\log(1.14\times10^{-4}) = 3.94 \approx 3.9$

4B **(M)** The concentrations of the components in the 100.0 mL of buffer solution are found via the dilution factor. Remember that $NaC_2H_3O_2$ is a strong electrolyte, existing in solution as

$Na^+(aq)$ and $CH_3COO^-(aq)$.

$$[CH_3COOH] = 0.200\ M \times \frac{63.0\ mL}{100.0\ mL} = 0.126\ M \qquad [CH_3COO^-] = 0.200\ M \times \frac{37.0\ mL}{100.0\ mL} = 0.0740\,M$$

As usual, the solution to the problem is organized around the balanced chemical equation.

Equation: $CH_3COOH(aq) + H_2O(l) \rightleftharpoons CH_3COO^-(aq) + H_3O^+(aq)$

Initial: 0.126 M   –   0.0740 M ≈ 0 M

Changes: $-x$ M   – $+x$ M $+x$ M

Equil: $(0.126-x)$ M   – $(0.0740+x)$ M x M

$$K_a = \frac{[H_3O^+][CH_3COO^-]}{[CH_3COOH]} = \frac{x(0.0740+x)}{0.126-x} = 1.8\times10^{-5} \approx \frac{0.0740x}{0.126}$$

$$x = \frac{1.8\times10^{-5}\times0.126}{0.0740} = 3.1\times10^{-5}\ [H_3O^+] = 3.1\times10^{-5}\ M;$$

$pH = -\log[H_3O^+] = -\log 3.1\times10^{-5} = 4.51$

Note that the assumption is valid: $x \ll 0.0740 < 0.126$.
Thus, x is neglected when added or subtracted

5A **(M)** We know the initial concentration of NH_3 in the buffer solution and can use the pH to find the equilibrium $[OH^-]$. The rest of the solution is organized around the balanced chemical equation. Our first goal is to determine the initial concentration of NH_4^+.

$$pOH = 14.00 - pH = 14.00 - 9.00 = 5.00 \qquad [OH^-] = 10^{-pOH} = 10^{-5.00} = 1.0 \times 10^{-5} \text{ M}$$

Equation:	$NH_3(aq)$	+	$H_2O(l)$	$\rightleftharpoons$	$NH_4^+(aq)$	+	$OH^-(aq)$
Initial:	0.35 M		–		x M		≈ 0 M
Changes:	-1.0×10^{-5} M		–		$+1.0 \times 10^{-5}$ M		$+1.0 \times 10^{-5}$ M
Equil:	$(0.35 - 1.0 \times 10^{-5})$ M		–		$(x + 1.0 \times 10^{-5})$ M		1.0×10^{-5} M

$$K_b = \frac{[NH_4^+][OH^-]}{[NH_3]} = 1.8 \times 10^{-5} = \frac{(x + 1.0 \times 10^{-5})(1.0 \times 10^{-5})}{0.35 - 1.0 \times 10^{-5}} = \frac{1.0 \times 10^{-5} \times x}{0.35}$$

Assume $x \gg 1.0 \times 10^{-5}$ $\qquad x = \dfrac{0.35 \times 1.8 \times 10^{-5}}{1.0 \times 10^{-5}} = 0.63$ M $=$ initial NH_4^+ concentration

$$mass(NH_4)_2 SO_4 = 0.500 \text{ L} \times \frac{0.63 \text{ mol } NH_4^+}{1 \text{ L soln}} \times \frac{1 \text{ mol } (NH_4)_2 SO_4}{2 \text{ mol } NH_4^+} \times \frac{132.1 \text{ g } (NH_4)_2 SO_4}{1 \text{ mol } (NH_4)_2 SO_4}$$

Mass of $(NH_4)_2SO_4$ = 21 g

5B **(M)** The solution is composed of 33.05 g $NaCH_3COO \cdot 3 H_2O$ dissolved in 300.0 mL of 0.250 M HCl. $NaCH_3COO \cdot 3 H_2O$, a strong electrolyte, exists in solution as Na^+(aq) and CH_3COO^- (aq) ions. First we calculate the number of moles of $NaCH_3COO \cdot 3 H_2O$, which, based on the 1:1 stoichiometry, is also equal to the number of moles of CH_3COO^- that are released into solution. From this we can calculate the initial $[CH_3COO^-]$ assuming the solution's volume remains at 300. mL.

moles of $NaCH_3COO \cdot 3 H_2O$ (and moles of CH_3COO^-)

$$= \frac{33.05 \text{ g } NaCH_3COO \cdot 3 H_2O}{\dfrac{1 \text{ mole } NaCH_3COO \cdot 3 H_2O}{136.08 \text{ g } NaCH_3COO \cdot 3 H_2O}} = 0.243 \text{ moles } NaCH_3COO \cdot 3 H_2O = \text{moles } CH_3COO^-$$

$$[CH_3COO^-] = \frac{0.243 \text{ mol } C_2H_3O_2^-}{0.300 \text{ L soln}} = 0.810 \text{ M}$$

However, we must recognize that the H_3O^+ produced by the ionization of HCl will react with some of the CH_3COO^- to produce CH_3COOH. We can organize this information as follows.

Equation:	$CH_3COOH(aq) + H_2O(l) \rightleftharpoons$		$CH_3COO^-(aq)$	$+ H_3O^+(aq)$
Initial:	0 M	–	0.810 M	0.250 M
Form HAc:	+0.250 M	–	–0.250 M	–0.250 M
	0.250 M	–	0.560 M	$\approx$ 0 M
Changes:	$-x$ M	–	$+x$ M	$+x$ M
Equil:	$(0.250 - x)$ M	–	$(0.560 + x)$ M	$+x$ M

$$K_a = \frac{[H_3O^+][CH_3COO^-]}{[CH_3COOH]} = \frac{x(0.560 + x)}{0.250 - x} = 1.8 \times 10^{-5} \approx \frac{0.560\,x}{0.250}$$

$$x = \frac{1.8 \times 10^{-5} \times 0.250}{0.560} = 8.0 \times 10^{-6} \; [H_3O^+] = 8.0 \times 10^{-6} \text{ M}$$

(The approximation was valid since $x \ll$ both 0.250 and 0.560)

$$pH = -\log [H_3O^+] = -\log 8.0 \times 10^{-6} = 5.09 \approx 5.1$$

6A **(D)**

(a) For formic acid, $pK_a = -\log(1.8 \times 10^{-4}) = 3.74$. The Henderson-Hasselbalch equation provides the pH of the original buffer solution:

$$pH = pK_a + \log \frac{[HCOO^-]}{[HCOOH]} = 3.74 + \log \frac{0.350}{0.550} = 3.54$$

(b) The added acid can be considered completely reacted with the formate ion to produce formic acid. Each mole/L of added acid consumes 1 M of formate ion and forms 1 M of formic acid: $HCOO^-(aq) + H_3O^+(aq) \longrightarrow HCOOH(aq) + H_2O(l)$.

$K_{neut} = K_b/K_w \approx 5600$. Thus, $\left[HCOO^-\right] = 0.350 \text{ M} - 0.0050 \text{ M} = 0.345 \text{ M}$

and $[HCOOH] = 0.550 \text{ M} + 0.0050 \text{ M} = 0.555 \text{ M}$. By using the Henderson-Hasselbalch equation

$$pH = pK_a + \log \frac{[HCOO^-]}{[HCOOH]} = 3.74 + \log \frac{0.345}{0.555} = 3.53$$

(c) Added base reacts completely with formic acid producing, an equivalent amount of formate ion. This continues until all of the formic acid is consumed. Each 1 mole of added base consumes 1 mol of formic acid and forms 1 mol of formate ion: $HCOOH + OH^- \longrightarrow HCOO^- + H_2O$. $K_{neut} = K_a/K_w \approx 1.8 \times 10^{10}$.

Thus, $\left[HCOO^-\right] = 0.350 \text{ M} + 0.0050 \text{ M} = 0.355 \text{ M}$

$[HCOOH] = (0.550 - 0.0050) \text{ M} = 0.545 \text{ M}$. With the Henderson-Hasselbalch equation

we find $pH = pK_a + \log \dfrac{\left[HCOO^-\right]}{\left[HCOOH\right]} = 3.74 + \log \dfrac{0.355}{0.545} = 3.55$

6B **(D)** The buffer cited has the same concentration as weak acid and its anion, as does the buffer of Example 17-6. Our goal is to reach $pH = 5.03$ or

$\left[H_3O^+\right] = 10^{-pH} = 10^{-5.03} = 9.3 \times 10^{-6}$ M. Adding strong acid $\left(H_3O^+\right)$, of course,

produces $HC_2H_3O_2$ at the expense of $C_2H_3O_2^-$. Thus, adding H^+ drives the reaction to the left. Again, we use the data around the balanced chemical equation.

Equation: $CH_3COOH(aq) + H_2O(l) \rightleftharpoons CH_3COO^-(aq) + H_3O^+(aq)$

Initial:	0.250 M	–	0.560 M	8.0×10^{-6} M
Add acid:				$+y$ M
Form HAc:	$+y$ M	–	$-y$ M	$-y$ M
	$(0.250 + y)$ M	–	$(0.560 - y)$ M	≈ 0 M
Changes:	$-x$ M	–	$+x$ M	$+x$ M
Equil:	$(0.250 + y - x)$ M	–	$(0.560 - y + x)$ M	9.3×10^{-6} M

$K_a = \dfrac{[H_3O^+][CH_3COO^-]}{[CH_3COOH]} = \dfrac{9.3 \times 10^{-6}(0.560 - y + x)}{0.250 + y - x} = 1.8 \times 10^{-5} \approx \dfrac{9.3 \times 10^{-6}(0.560 - y)}{0.250 + y}$

(Assume that x is negligible compared to y)

$\dfrac{1.8 \times 10^{-5} \times (0.250 + y)}{9.3 \times 10^{-6}} = 0.484 + 1.94 \ y = 0.560 - y$ $y = \dfrac{0.560 - 0.484}{1.94 + 1.00} = 0.026$ M

Notice that our assumption is valid: $x \ll 0.250 + y \ (= 0.276) < 0.560 - y \ (= 0.534)$.

$V_{HNO_3} = 300.0$ mL buffer $\times \dfrac{0.026 \text{ mmol } H_3O^+}{1 \text{ mL buffer}} \times \dfrac{1 \text{ mL HNO}_3 \text{ (aq)}}{6.0 \text{ mmol } H_3O^+} = 1.3$ mL of 6.0 M HNO_3

Instead of the algebraic solution, we could have used the Henderson-Hasselbalch equation, since the final pH falls within one pH unit of the pK_a of acetic acid. We let z indicate the increase in $[CH_3COOH]$, and also the decrease in $\left[CH_3COO^-\right]$

$pH = pK_a + \log \dfrac{\left[CH_3COO^-\right]}{\left[CH_3COOH\right]} = 4.74 + \log \dfrac{0.560 - z}{0.250 + z} = 5.03$ $\dfrac{0.560 - z}{0.250 + z} = 10^{5.03 - 4.74} = 1.95$

$0.560 - z = 1.95 \ (0.250 + z) = 0.488 + 1.95 \ z$ $z = \dfrac{0.560 - 0.488}{1.95 + 1.00} = 0.024$ M

This is, and should be, almost exactly the same as the value of y we obtained by the I.C.E. table method. The slight difference is due to imprecision arising from rounding errors.

7A **(D)**

(a)   The initial pH is the pH of 0.150 M HCl, which we obtain from $\left[H_3O^+\right]$ of that strong acid solution.

$[H_3O^+] = \dfrac{0.150 \text{ mol HCl}}{1 \text{ L soln}} \times \dfrac{1 \text{ mol } H_3O^+}{1 \text{ mol HCl}} = 0.150$ M,

$pH = -\log [H_3O^+] = -\log (0.150) = 0.824$

(b) To determine $\left[H_3O^+\right]$ and then pH at the 50.0% point, we need the volume of the solution and the amount of H_3O^+ left unreacted. First we calculate the amount of hydronium ion present and then the volume of base solution needed for its complete neutralization.

$$\text{amount } H_3O^+ = 25.00 \text{ mL} \times \frac{0.150 \text{ mmol HCl}}{1 \text{ mL soln}} \times \frac{1 \text{ mmol } H_3O^+}{1 \text{ mmol HCl}} = 3.75 \text{ mmol } H_3O^+$$

$$V_{acid} = 3.75 \text{ mmol } H_3O^+ \times \frac{1 \text{ mmol } OH^-}{1 \text{ mmol } H_3O^+} \times \frac{1 \text{ mmol NaOH}}{1 \text{ mmol } OH^-} \times \frac{1 \text{ mL titrant}}{0.250 \text{ mmol NaOH}}$$
$$= 15.0 \text{ mL titrant}$$

At the 50.0% point, half of the H_3O^+ (1.88 mmol H_3O^+) will remain unreacted and only half (7.50 mL titrant) of the titrant solution will be added. From this information, and the original 25.00-mL volume of the solution, we calculate $\left[H_3O^+\right]$ and then pH.

$$\left[H_3O^+\right] = \frac{1.88 \text{ mmol } H_3O^+ \text{ left}}{25.00 \text{ mL original} + 7.50 \text{ mL titrant}} = 0.0578 \text{ M}$$
$$pH = -\log(0.0578) = 1.238$$

(c) Since this is the titration of a strong acid by a strong base, at the equivalence point, the pH = 7.00. This is because the only ions of appreciable concentration in the equivalence point solution are Na^+(aq) and Cl^-(aq), and neither of these species undergoes detectable hydrolysis reactions.

(d) Beyond the equivalence point, the solution pH is determined almost entirely by the concentration of excess OH^-(aq) ions. The volume of the solution is $40.00 \text{ mL} + 1.00 \text{ mL} = 41.00 \text{ mL}$. The amount of hydroxide ion in the excess titrant is calculated and used to determine $\left[OH^-\right]$, from which pH is computed.

$$\text{amount of } OH^- = 1.00 \text{ mL} \times \frac{0.250 \text{ mmol NaOH}}{1 \text{ mL}} = 0.250 \text{ mmol } OH^-$$

$$\left[OH^-\right] = \frac{0.250 \text{ mmol } OH^-}{41.00 \text{ mL}} = 0.006098 \text{ M}$$
$$pOH = -\log(0.006098) = 2.215; \quad pH = 14.00 - 2.215 = 11.785$$

7B (D)

(a) The initial pH is simply the pH of 0.00812 M $Ba(OH)_2$, which we obtain from $\left[OH^-\right]$ for the solution.

$$\left[OH^-\right] = \frac{0.00812 \text{ mol } Ba(OH)_2}{1 \text{ L soln}} \times \frac{2 \text{ mol } OH^-}{1 \text{ mol } Ba(OH)_2} = 0.01624 \text{ M}$$

$$pOH = -\log\left[OH^-\right] = -\log(0.0162) = 1.790; \quad pH = 14.00 - pOH = 14.00 - 1.790 = 12.21$$

(b) To determine $\left[OH^-\right]$ and then pH at the 50.0% point, we need the volume of the solution and the amount of OH^- unreacted. First we calculate the amount of hydroxide ion present and then the volume of acid solution needed for its complete neutralization.

$$\text{amount } OH^- = 50.00\,mL \times \frac{0.00812\,mmol\,Ba\left(OH\right)_2}{1\,mL\,soln} \times \frac{2\,mmol\,OH^-}{1\,mmol\,Ba\left(OH\right)_2} = 0.812\,mmol\,OH^-$$

$$V_{acid} = 0.812\,mmol\,OH^- \times \frac{1\,mmol\,H_3O^+}{1\,mmol\,OH^-} \times \frac{1\,mmol\,HCl}{1\,mmol\,H_3O^+} \times \frac{1\,mL\,titrant}{0.0250\,mmol\,HCl} = 32.48\,mL\,titrant$$

At the 50.0 % point, half (0.406 mmol OH^-) will remain unreacted and only half (16.24 mL titrant) of the titrant solution will be added. From this information, and the original 50.00 mL volume of the solution, we calculate $\left[OH^-\right]$ and then pH.

$$\left[OH^-\right] = \frac{0.406\,mmol\,OH^-\,left}{50.00\,mL\,original + 16.24\,mL\,titrant} = 0.00613\,M$$

$$pOH = -\log\left(0.00613\right) = 2.213; \quad pH = 14.00 - pOH = 11.79$$

(c) Since this is the titration of a strong base by a strong acid, at the equivalence point, pH = 7.00. The solution at this point is neutral because the dominant ionic species in solution, namely Ba^{2+}(aq) and Cl^-(aq), do not react with water to a detectable extent.

8A **(D)**

(a) Initial pH is just that of 0.150 M HF $(pK_a = -\log\left(6.6 \times 10^{-4}\right) = 3.18)$.

[Initial solution contains $20.00\,mL \times \dfrac{0.150\,mmol\,HF}{1\,mL} = 3.00\,mmol\,HF$]

Equation: $HF\left(aq\right) \quad + \quad H_2O(l) \rightleftharpoons H_3O^+\left(aq\right) \quad + \quad F^-\left(aq\right)$

Initial:	0.150 M	–	$\approx 0\,M$	0 M
Changes:	$-x\,M$	–	$+x$ M	$+x$ M
Equil:	$(0.150 - x)$ M	–	x M	x M

$$K_a = \frac{\left[H_3O^+\right]\left[F^-\right]}{\left[HF\right]} = \frac{x \cdot x}{0.150 - x} \approx \frac{x^2}{0.150} = 6.6 \times 10^{-4}$$

$$x = \sqrt{0.150 \times 6.6 \times 10^{-4}} = 9.9 \times 10^{-3}$$

$x > 0.05\left(0.150\right)$. The assumption is invalid. After a second cycle of approximation, $\left[H_3O^+\right] = 9.6 \times 10^{-3}\,M$; $pH = -\log\left(9.6 \times 10^{-3}\right) = 2.02$

(b) When the titration is 25.0% complete, there are $(0.25 \times 3.00 =)$ 0.75 mmol F^- for every 3.00 mmol HF that were present initially. Therefore, $(3.00 - 0.75 =)$ 2.25 mmol HF remain untitrated. We designate the solution volume (the volume holding these 3.00 mmol total) as V and use the Henderson-Hasselbalch equation to find the pH.

$$pH = pK_a + \log \frac{\left[F^-\right]}{\left[HF\right]} = 3.18 + \log \frac{0.75 \text{ mmol}/V}{2.25 \text{ mmol}/V} = 2.70$$

(c) At the midpoint of the titration of a weak base, $pH = pK_a = 3.18$.

(d) At the endpoint of the titration, the pH of the solution is determined by the conjugate base hydrolysis reaction. We calculate the amount of anion and the volume of solution in order to calculate its initial concentration.

$$\text{amount } F^- = 20.00 \text{ mL} \times \frac{0.150 \text{ mmol HF}}{1 \text{ mL soln}} \times \frac{1 \text{ mmol } F^-}{1 \text{ mmol HF}} = 3.00 \text{ mmol } F^-$$

$$\text{volume titrant} = 3.00 \text{ mmol HF} \times \frac{1 \text{ mmol OH}^-}{1 \text{ mmol HF}} \times \frac{1 \text{ mL titrant}}{0.250 \text{ mmol OH}^-} = 12.0 \text{ mL titrant}$$

$$\left[F^-\right] = \frac{3.00 \text{ mmol } F^-}{20.00 \text{ mL original volume} + 12.0 \text{ mL titrant}} = 0.0938 \text{ M}$$

We organize the solution of the hydrolysis problem around its balanced equation.

Equation:	$F^-(aq)$	$+$	$H_2O(l)$	$\rightleftharpoons$	$HF(aq)$	$+$	$OH^-(aq)$
Initial:	0.0938 M		–		0 M		≈ 0 M
Changes:	$-x$ M		–		$+x$ M		$+x$ M
Equil:	$(0.0938 - x)$ M		–		x M		x M

$$K_b = \frac{\left[HF\right]\left[OH^-\right]}{\left[F^-\right]} = \frac{K_w}{K_a} = \frac{1.0 \times 10^{-14}}{6.6 \times 10^{-4}} = 1.5 \times 10^{-11} = \frac{x \cdot x}{0.0938 - x} \approx \frac{x^2}{0.0938}$$

$$x = \sqrt{0.0934 \times 1.5 \times 10^{-11}} = 1.2 \times 10^{-6} = [OH^-] = 1.2 \times 10^{-6} \text{ M}$$

The assumption is valid ($x \ll 0.0934$).

$$pOH = -\log\left(1.2 \times 10^{-6}\right) = 5.92; \quad pH = 14.00 - pOH = 14.00 - 5.92 = 8.08$$

8B **(D)**

(a) The initial pH is simply that of 0.106 M NH_3.

Equation: $NH_3(aq) + H_2O(l) \rightleftharpoons NH_4^+(aq) + OH^-(aq)$

Initial:	0.106 M	–	0 M	≈ 0 M
Changes:	$-x$ M	–	$+x$ M	$+x$ M
Equil:	$(0.106 - x)$ M	–	x M	x M

$$K_b = \frac{\left[NH_4^+ \right]\left[OH^- \right]}{\left[NH_3 \right]} = \frac{x \cdot x}{0.106 - x} \approx \frac{x^2}{0.106} = 1.8 \times 10^{-5}$$

$x = \sqrt{0.106 \times 1.8 \times 10^{-4}} = 1.4 \times 10^{-3}$ $[OH^-] = 1.4 \times 10^{-3}$ M

The assumption is valid ($x \ll 0.106$).

$pOH = -\log(0.0014) = 2.85$ $pH = 14.00 - pOH = 14.00 - 2.85 = 11.15$

(b) When the titration is 25.0% complete, there are 25.0 mmol NH_4^+ for every 100.0 mmol of NH_3 that were present initially (i.e., there are 1.33 mmol of NH_4^+ in solution), 3.98 mmol NH_3 remain untitrated. We designate the solution volume (the volume holding these 5.30 mmol total) as V and use the basic version of the Henderson-Hasselbalch equation to find the pH.

$$pOH = pK_b + \log\frac{\left[NH_4^+ \right]}{\left[NH_3 \right]} = 4.74 + \log\frac{\dfrac{1.33 \text{ mmol}}{V}}{\dfrac{3.98 \text{ mmol}}{V}} = 4.26$$

$pH = 14.00 - 4.26 = 9.74$

(c) At the midpoint of the titration of a weak base, $pOH = pK_b = 4.74$ and $pH = 9.26$

(d) At the endpoint of the titration, the pH is determined by the conjugate acid hydrolysis reaction. We calculate the amount of that cation and the volume of the solution in order to determine its initial concentration.

$$\text{amount } NH_4^+ = 50.00 \text{ mL} \times \frac{0.106 \text{ mmol } NH_3}{1 \text{ mL soln}} \times \frac{1 \text{ mmol } NH_4^+}{1 \text{ mmol } NH_3}$$

$\text{amount } NH_4^+ = 5.30 \text{ mmol } NH_4^+$

$$V_{\text{titrant}} = 5.30 \text{ mmol } NH_3 \times \frac{1 \text{ mmol } H_3O^+}{1 \text{ mmol } NH_3} \times \frac{1 \text{ mL titrant}}{0.225 \text{ mmol } H_3O^+} = 23.6 \text{ mL titrant}$$

$$\left[NH_4^+ \right] = \frac{5.30 \text{ mmol } NH_4^+}{50.00 \text{ mL original volume} + 23.6 \text{ mL titrant}} = 0.0720 \text{ M}$$

We organize the solution of the hydrolysis problem around its balanced chemical equation.

Equation: $NH_4^+ (aq) + H_2O(l) \rightleftharpoons NH_3 (aq) + H_3O^+ (aq)$

Initial:	0.0720 M	–	0 M	≈ 0 M
Changes:	$-x$ M	–	$+x$ M	$+x$ M
Equil:	$(0.0720 - x)$ M	–	x M	x M

$$K_b = \frac{[NH_3][H_3O^+]}{[NH_4^+]} = \frac{K_w}{K_b} = \frac{1.0 \times 10^{-14}}{1.8 \times 10^{-5}} = 5.6 \times 10^{-10} = \frac{x \cdot x}{0.0720 - x} \approx \frac{x^2}{0.0720}$$

$$x = \sqrt{0.0720 \times 5.6 \times 10^{-10}} = 6.3 \times 10^{-6} \; [H_3O^+] = 6.3 \times 10^{-6} \text{ M}$$

The assumption is valid ($x \ll 0.0720$).

$$pH = -\log(6.3 \times 10^{-6}) = 5.20$$

9A   **(M)** The acidity of the solution is principally the result of the hydrolysis of the carbonate ion, which is considered first.

Equation:	CO_3^{2-} (aq)	+ H_2O(l)	$\rightleftharpoons$ HCO_3^- (aq)	+ OH^- (aq)
Initial:	1.0 M	–	0 M	≈ 0 M
Changes:	$-x$ M	–	$+x$ M	$+x$ M
Equil:	$(1.0-x)$ M	–	x M	x M

$$K_b = \frac{K_w}{K_a(HCO_3^-)} = \frac{1.0 \times 10^{-14}}{4.7 \times 10^{-11}} = 2.1 \times 10^{-4} = \frac{[HCO_3^-][OH^-]}{[CO_3^{2-}]} = \frac{x \cdot x}{1.0-x} \approx \frac{x^2}{1.0}$$

$x = \sqrt{1.0 \times 2.1 \times 10^{-4}} = 0.015 \; [OH^-] = 1.5 \times 10^{-2}$ M. The assumption is valid ($x \ll 1.0M$).
Now we consider the hydrolysis of the bicarbonate ion.

Equation:	HCO_3^- (aq)	+ H_2O(l)	$\rightleftharpoons$ H_2CO_3 (aq)	+ OH^- (aq)
Initial:	0.015 M	–	0 M	0.015 M
Changes:	$-y$ M	–	$+y$ M	$+y$ M
Equil:	$(0.015-y)$ M	–	y M	$(0.015+y)$ M

$$K_b = \frac{K_w}{K_a(H_2CO_3)} = \frac{1.0 \times 10^{-14}}{4.4 \times 10^{-7}} = 2.3 \times 10^{-8} = \frac{[H_2CO_3][OH^-]}{[HCO_3^-]} = \frac{y(0.015+y)}{0.015-x} \approx \frac{0.015y}{0.015} = y$$

The assumption is valid ($y \ll 0.015$) and $[H_2CO_3] = 2.3 \times 10^{-8}$ M. Clearly, the second hydrolysis makes a negligible contribution to the acidity of the solution. For the entire solution, then

$$pOH = -\log[OH^-] = -\log(0.015) = 1.82 \qquad pH = 14.00 - 1.82 = 12.18$$

9B   **(M)** The acidity of the solution is principally the result of hydrolysis of the sulfite ion.

Equation:	SO_3^{2-} (aq)	+ H_2O(l)	$\rightleftharpoons$ HSO_3^- (aq)	+ OH^- (aq)
Initial:	0.500 M	–	0 M	≈ 0 M
Changes:	$-x$ M	–	$+x$ M	$+x$ M
Equil:	$(0.500-x)$ M	–	x M	x M

$$K_b = \frac{K_w}{K_a HSO_3^-} = \frac{1.0 \times 10^{-14}}{6.2 \times 10^{-8}} = 1.6 \times 10^{-7} = \frac{[HSO_3^-][OH^-]}{[SO_3^{2-}]} = \frac{x \cdot x}{0.500 - x} \approx \frac{x^2}{0.500}$$

$$x = \sqrt{0.500 \times 1.6 \times 10^{-7}} = 2.8 \times 10^{-4} \quad [OH^-] = 2.8 \times 10^{-4} \text{ M}$$

The assumption is valid ($x \ll 0.500$).

Next we consider the hydrolysis of the bisulfite ion.

Equation: $HSO_3^-(aq) + H_2O(l) \rightleftharpoons H_2SO_3(aq) + OH^-(aq)$

Initial:	0.00028 M	–	0 M	0.00028 M
Changes:	$-y$ M	–	$+y$ M	$+y$ M
Equil:	$(0.00028 - y)$ M	–	y M	$(0.00028 + y)$ M

$$K_b = \frac{K_w}{K_{a_1}(H_2SO_3)} = \frac{1.0 \times 10^{-14}}{1.3 \times 10^{-2}} = 7.7 \times 10^{-13}$$

$$K_b = 7.7 \times 10^{-13} = \frac{[H_2SO_3][OH^-]}{[HSO_3^-]} = \frac{y(0.00028 + y)}{0.00028 - y} \approx \frac{0.00028\,y}{0.00028} = y$$

The assumption is valid ($y \ll 0.00028$) and $y = [H_2SO_3] = 7.7 \times 10^{-13}$ M.

Clearly, the second hydrolysis makes a negligible contribution to the acidity of the solution. For the entire solution, then

$$pOH = -\log[OH^-] = -\log(0.00028) = 3.55 \qquad pH = 14.00 - 3.55 = 10.45$$

INTEGRATIVE EXAMPLE

A. (D)

From the given information, the following can be calculated:

pH of the solution $= 2.716$ therefore, $[H^+] = 1.92 \times 10^{-3}$

pH at the halfway point $= pK_a$
pH $= 4.602 = pK_a$
$pK_a = -\log K_a$ therefore $Ka = 2.50 \times 10^{-5}$

$$FP = 0\,°C + \Delta T_f$$

$$\Delta T_f = -i \times K_f \times m$$

$$\Delta T_f = -1 \times 1.86\,°C/m \times \text{molality}$$

$$\text{molality} = \frac{\# \text{ moles solute}}{\text{kg solvent}} = \frac{\# \text{ moles solute}}{0.500\,\text{kg} - 0.00750\,\text{kg}}$$

To determine the number of moles of solute, convert 7.50 g of unknown acid to moles by using its molar mass. The molar mass can be calculated as follows:

$$\text{pH} = 2.716 \qquad\qquad [H^+] = 1.92 \times 10^{-3}$$

	HA	$\rightleftharpoons$	H^+	$+$	A^-
Initial	$\dfrac{7.50\text{ g}/\text{MM}}{0.500\text{ L}}$		0		0
Change	$-x$		x		x
Equilibrium	$\left(\dfrac{7.50\text{ g}/\text{MM}}{0.500\text{ L}}\right)-1.92\times10^{-3}$		1.92×10^{-3}		1.92×10^{-3}

$$2.50\times10^{-5} = \frac{[H^+][A^-]}{[HA]}$$

$$2.50\times10^{-5} = \frac{(1.92\times10^{-3})^2}{\left(\dfrac{7.50/\text{MM}}{0.500}-1.92\times10^{-3}\right)}$$

$$\text{MM} = 100.4 \text{ g/mol}$$

$$\#\text{moles of solute} = 7.50\text{ g}\times\frac{1\text{ mol}}{100.4\text{ g}} = 0.0747\text{ mol}$$

$$\text{Molality} = \frac{\#\text{ moles solute}}{\text{kg solvent}} = \frac{0.0747\text{ mol}}{0.500\text{ kg} - 0.00750\text{ kg}} = 0.152\text{ m}$$

$$\Delta T_f = -i \times K_f \times m$$
$$\Delta T_f = -1 \times 1.86\,^\circ\text{C/m} \times 0.152\text{ m}$$
$$\Delta T_f = -0.283\,^\circ\text{C}$$

$$\text{FP} = 0\,^\circ\text{C} + \Delta T_f = 0\,^\circ\text{C} - 0.283\,^\circ\text{C} = -0.283\,^\circ\text{C}$$

B. (M) By looking at the titration curve provided, one can deduce that the titrant was a strong acid. The pH before titrant was added was basic, which means that the substance that was titrated was a base. The pH at the end of the titration after excess titrant was added was acidic, which means that the titrant was an acid.

Based on the titration curve provided, the equivalence point is at approximately 50 mL of titrant added. At the halfway point, of approximately 25 mL, the pH = pK_a. A pH ~8 is obtained by extrapolation a the halfway point.

$$pH = 8 = pK_a$$
$$K_a = 10^{-8} = 1 \times 10^{-8}$$
$$K_b = K_w/K_a = 1 \times 10^{-6}$$

~50 mL of 0.2 M strong acid (1×10^{-2} mol) was needed to reach the equivalence point. This means that the unknown contained 1×10^{-2} mol of weak base. The molar mass of the unknown can be determined as follows:

$$\frac{0.800 \text{ g}}{1 \times 10^{-2} \text{ mol}} = 80 \text{ g/mol}$$

EXERCISES

The Common-Ion Effect

1. **(M)**

(a) Note that HI is a strong acid and thus the initial $\left[H_3O^+ \right] = \left[HI \right] = 0.0892 M$

Equation :	CH_3CH_2COOH	+	H_2O	$\rightleftharpoons$	$CH_2CH_2COO^-$	+	H_3O^+
Initial :	0.275 M		–		0M		0.0892M
Changes :	$-x$ M		–		$+x$ M		$+x$ M
Equil :	$(0.275 - x)$ M		–		x M		$(0.0892 + x)$ M

$$K_a = \frac{\left[CH_2CH_2COO^- \right]\left[H_3O^+ \right]}{\left[CH_3CH_2COOH \right]} = 1.3 \times 10^{-5} = \frac{x(0.0892 + x)}{0.275 - x} \approx \frac{0.0892x}{0.275}$$

$$x = 4.0 \times 10^{-5} \text{ M}$$

The assumption that $x \ll 0.0892$ M is correct. $\left[H_3O^+ \right] = 0.0892 M$

(b) $\left[OH^- \right] = \dfrac{K_w}{\left[H_3O^+ \right]} = \dfrac{1.0 \times 10^{-14}}{0.0892} = 1.1 \times 10^{-13}$ M

(c) $\left[CH_2CH_2COO^- \right] = x = 4.0 \times 10^{-5}$ M

(d) $\left[I^- \right] = \left[HI \right]_{intial} = 0.0892$ M

2. (M)

(a) The NH_4Cl dissociates completely, and thus, $\left[NH_4^+\right]_{intial} = \left[Cl^-\right]_{intial} = 0.102\,M$

Equation:	$NH_3(aq)$	$+$	$H_2O(l)$	$\rightleftharpoons$	$NH_4^+(aq)$	$+$	$OH^-(aq)$
Initial:	0.164 M		–		0.102 M		≈ 0 M
Changes:	$-x$ M		–		$+x$ M		$+x$ M
Equil:	$(0.164 - x)$M		–		$(0.102 + x)$M		x M

$$K_b = \frac{\left[NH_4^+\right]\left[OH^-\right]}{\left[NH_3\right]} = \frac{(0.102 + x)x}{0.164 - x} = 1.8 \times 10^{-5} \approx \frac{0.102x}{0.164}; \quad x = 2.9 \times 10^{-5}$$

Assumed $x \ll 0.102$ M, a clearly valid assumption. $\left[OH^-\right] = x = 2.9 \times 10^{-5}$ M

(b) $\left[NH_4^+\right] = 0.102 + x = 0.102\,M$

(c) $\left[Cl^-\right] = 0.102\,M$

(d) $\left[H_3O^+\right] = \dfrac{1.0 \times 10^{-14}}{2.9 \times 10^{-5}} = 3.4 \times 10^{-10}\,M$

3. (M)

(a) We first determine the pH of 0.100 M HNO_2.

Equation	$HNO_2(aq)$	$+$	$H_2O(l)$	$\rightleftharpoons$	$NO_2^-(aq)$	$+$	$H_3O^+(aq)$
Initial:	0.100 M		–		0 M		≈ 0 M
Changes:	$-x$ M		–		$+x$ M		$+x$ M
Equil:	$(0.100 - x)$ M		–		x M		x M

$$K_a = \frac{\left[NO_2^-\right]\left[H_3O^+\right]}{\left[HNO_2\right]} = 7.2 \times 10^{-4} = \frac{x^2}{0.100 - x}$$

Via the quadratic equation roots formula or via successive approximations,

$x = 8.1 \times 10^{-3}$ $\left[H_3O^+\right] = 8.1 \times 10^{-3}$ M

Thus pH $= -\log\left(8.1 \times 10^{-3}\right) = 2.09$

When 0.100 mol $NaNO_2$ is added to 1.00 L of a 0.100 M HNO_2, a solution with $\left[NO_2^-\right] = 0.100M = \left[HNO_2\right]$ is produced. The answer obtained with the Henderson-Hasselbalch equation, is pH $= pK_a = -\log\left(7.2 \times 10^{-4}\right) = 3.14$. Thus, the addition has caused a pH change of 1.05 units.

(b) $NaNO_3$ contributes nitrate ion, NO_3^-, to the solution. Since, however, there is no molecular $HNO_3(aq)$ in equilibrium with hydrogen and nitrate ions, there is no equilibrium to be shifted by the addition of nitrate ions. The $[H_3O^+]$ and the pH are thus unaffected by the addition of $NaNO_3$ to a solution of nitric acid. The pH changes are not the same because there is an equilibrium system to be shifted in the first solution, whereas there is no equilibrium, just a change in total ionic strength, for the second solution.

4. **(M)** The explanation for the different result is that each of these solutions has acetate ion present, CH_3COO^-, which is produced in the ionization of acetic acid. The presence of this ion suppresses the ionization of acetic acid, thus minimizing the increase in $[H_3O^+]$. All three solutions are buffer solutions and their pH can be found with the aid of the Henderson-Hasselbalch equation.

(a) $$pH = pK_a + \log\frac{[CH_3COO^-]}{[CH_3COOH]} = 4.74 + \log\frac{0.10}{1.0} = 3.74 \; [H_3O^+]$$

$$= 10^{-3.74} = 1.8 \times 10^{-4} M$$

$$\% \text{ ionization} = \frac{[H_3O^+]}{[CH_3COOH]} \times 100\% = \frac{1.8 \times 10^{-4} M}{1.0 M} \times 100\% = 0.018\%$$

(b) $$pH = pK_a + \log\frac{[CH_3COO^-]}{[CH_3COOH]} = 4.74 + \log\frac{0.10}{0.10} = 4.74$$

$$[H_3O^+] = 10^{-4.74} = 1.8 \times 10^{-5} M$$

$$\% \text{ ionization} = \frac{[H_3O^+]}{[CH_3COOH]} \times 100\% = \frac{1.8 \times 10^{-5} M}{0.10 M} \times 100\% = 0.018\%$$

(c) $$pH = pK_a + \log\frac{[CH_3COO^-]}{[CH_3COOH]} = 4.74 + \log\frac{0.10}{0.010} = 5.74$$

$$[H_3O^+] = 10^{-5.74} = 1.8 \times 10^{-6} M$$

$$\% \text{ ionization} = \frac{[H_3O^+]}{[CH_3COOH]} \times 100\% = \frac{1.8 \times 10^{-6} M}{0.10 M} \times 100\% = 0.018\%$$

5. **(M)**

(a) The strong acid HCl suppresses the ionization of the weak acid HOCl to such an extent that a negligible concentration of H_3O^+ is contributed to the solution by HOCl. Thus, $[H_3O^+] = [HCl]_{initial} = 0.035 \; M$

(b) This is a buffer solution. Consequently, we can use the Henderson-Hasselbalch equation to determine its pH. $pK_a = -\log(7.2 \times 10^{-4}) = 3.14$;

$$pH = pK_a + \log\frac{\left[NO_2^-\right]}{\left[HNO_2\right]} = 3.14 + \log\frac{0.100\,M}{0.0550\,M} = 3.40$$

$$\left[H_3O^+\right] = 10^{-3.40} = 4.0 \times 10^{-4}\,M$$

(c) As summarized below, the components react to form a buffer solution.

Equation: $H_3O^+\left(aq, \text{ from HCl}\right) + CH_3COO^-\left(aq, \text{ from NaCH}_3COO\right) \rightarrow CH_3COOH(aq) + H_2O(l)$

initially present:	0.0525 M	0.0768 M	0 M	–
changes:	−0.0525 M	−0.0525 M	+0.0525 M	–
after reaction:	≈ 0M	0.0243 M	0.0525 M	–

Now the Henderson-Hasselbalch equation can be used to find the pH.

$$pK_a = -\log(1.8 \times 10^{-5}) = 4.74$$

$$pH = pK_a + \log\frac{\left[CH_3COO^-\right]}{\left[CH_3COO\right]} = 4.74 + \log\frac{0.0243\,M}{0.0525\,M} = 4.41$$

$$\left[H_3O^+\right] = 10^{-4.41} = 3.9 \times 10^{-5}\,M$$

6. **(M)**

(a) Neither $Ba^{2+}(aq)$ nor $Cl^-(aq)$ hydrolyzes to a measurable extent and hence they have no effect on the solution pH. Consequently, $\left[OH^-\right]$ is determined entirely by the $Ba(OH)_2$ solute.

$$\left[OH^-\right] = \frac{0.0062\,\text{mol Ba}(OH)_2}{1\,L\,\text{soln}} \times \frac{2\,\text{mol OH}^-}{1\,\text{mol Ba}(OH)_2} = 0.012\,M$$

(b) We use the Henderson-Hasselbalch equation to find the pH for this buffer solution.

$$\left[NH_4^+\right] = 0.315\,M\,(NH_4)_2\,SO_4 \times \frac{2\,\text{mol NH}_4^+}{1\,\text{mol }(NH_4)_2\,SO_4} = 0.630\,M \quad pK_a = 9.26 \text{ for } NH_4^+.$$

$$pH = pK_a + \log\frac{\left[NH_3\right]}{\left[NH_4^+\right]} = 9.26 + \log\frac{0.486\,M}{0.630\,M} = 9.15 \quad pOH = 14.00 - 9.15 = 4.85$$

$$\left[OH^-\right] = 10^{-4.85} = 1.4 \times 10^{-5}\,M$$

(c)   As summarized below, the components react to form a buffer solution.

Equation: NH_4^+ (aq, from NH_4Cl) + OH^- (aq, from NaOH) $\rightarrow$ NH_3 (aq) + $H_2O(l)$

initially present:	0.264 M	0.196 M	0 M	–
changes:	−0.196 M	−0.196 M	+0.196 M	–
after reaction:	0.068 M	≈ 0M	0.196 M	–

$$pH = pK_a + \log \frac{[NH_3]}{[NH_4^+]} = 9.26 + \log \frac{0.196\,M}{0.068\,M} = 9.72 \qquad pOH = 14.00 - 9.72 = 4.28$$

Buffer Solutions

7.   (M) $[H_3O^+] = 10^{-4.06} = 8.7 \times 10^{-5}\,M$. We let $S = [HCOO^-]_{int}$

Equation:	HCOOH (aq)	+ $H_2O(l)$	$\rightleftharpoons$	$HCOO^-$ (aq)	+	H_3O^+ (aq)
Initial:	0.366 M	–		S M		≈ 0M
Changes:	$-8.7 \times 10^{-5}\,M$	–		$+8.7 \times 10^{-5}\,M$		$+8.7 \times 10^{-5}\,M$
Equil:	0.366 M	–		$(S + 8.7 \times 10^{-5})\,M$		$8.7 \times 10^{-5}\,M$

$$K_a = \frac{[H_3O^+][HCOO^-]}{[HCOOH]} = 1.8 \times 10^{-4} = \frac{(S + 8.7 \times 10^{-5})8.7 \times 10^{-5}}{0.366} \approx \frac{8.7 \times 10^{-5}\,S}{0.366}; \quad S = 0.76$$

To determine S, we assumed $S \gg 8.7 \times 10^{-5}$, which is clearly a valid assumption. Or, we could have used the Henderson-Hasselbalch equation (see below).

$pK_a = -\log(1.8 \times 10^{-4}) = 3.74$

$$4.06 = 3.74 + \log \frac{[HCOO^-]}{[HCOOH]}; \qquad \frac{[HCOO^-]}{[HCOOH]} = 2.1; \qquad [HCOO^-] = 2.1 \times 0.366 = 0.77\,M$$

The difference in the two answers is due simply to rounding.

8.   (E) We use the Henderson-Hasselbalch equation to find the required $[NH_3]$.

$pK_b = -\log(1.8 \times 10^{-5}) = 4.74$

$$pK_a = 14.00 - pK_b = 14.00 - 4.74 = 9.26 \qquad\qquad pH = 9.12 = 9.26 + \log \frac{[NH_3]}{[NH_4^+]}$$

$$\frac{[NH_3]}{[NH_4^+]} = 10^{-0.14} = 0.72 \qquad\qquad [NH_3] = 0.72 \times [NH_4^+] = 0.72 \times 0.732\,M = 0.53\,M$$

9. **(M)**

(a) Equation: $\quad C_6H_5COOH(aq) + H_2O(l) \rightleftharpoons C_6H_5COO^-(aq) + H_3O^+(aq)$

Initial:	0.012 M	–	0.033 M	≈ 0 M
Changes:	$-x$ M	–	$+x$ M	$+x$ M
Equil:	$(0.012-x)$ M	–	$(0.033+x)$ M	x M

$$K_a = \frac{[H_3O^+][C_6H_5COO^-]}{[C_6H_5COOH]} = 6.3\times10^{-5} = \frac{x(0.033+x)}{0.012-x} \approx \frac{0.033x}{0.012} \quad x = 2.3\times10^{-5}$$

To determine the value of x, we assumed $x \ll 0.012$, which is an assumption that clearly is correct. $[H_3O^+] = 2.3\times10^{-5}$ M $\qquad$ pH $= -\log(2.3\times10^{-5}) = 4.64$

(b) Equation: $\quad NH_3(aq) + H_2O(l) \rightleftharpoons NH_4^+(aq) + OH^-(aq)$

Initial:	0.408 M	–	0.153 M	≈ 0 M
Changes:	$-x$ M	–	$+x$ M	$+x$ M
Equil:	$(0.408-x)$ M	–	$(0.153+x)$ M	x M

$$K_b = \frac{[NH_4^+][OH^-]}{[NH_3]} = 1.8\times10^{-5} = \frac{x(0.153+x)}{0.408-x} \approx \frac{0.153x}{0.408} \quad x = 4.8\times10^{-5}$$

To determine the value of x, we assumed $x \ll 0.153$, which clearly is a valid assumption.

$[OH^-] = 4.8\times10^{-5}$ M; $\quad$ pOH $= -\log(4.8\times10^{-5}) = 4.32$; $\quad$ pH $= 14.00 - 4.32 = 9.68$

10. **(M)** Since the mixture is a buffer, we can use the Henderson-Hasselbalch equation to determine K_a of lactic acid.

$$CH_3CH(OH)COO^- = \frac{1.00 \text{ g } NaCH_3CH(OH)COO}{100.0 \text{ mL soln}} \times \frac{1000 \text{ mL}}{1 \text{ L soln}} \times \frac{1 \text{ mol } NaCH_3CH(OH)COO}{112.1 \text{ g } NaCH_3CH(OH)COO}$$

$$\times \frac{1 \text{ mol } CH_3CH(OH)COO^-}{1 \text{ mol } NaCH_3CH(OH)COO} = 0.0892 \text{ M}$$

$$pH = 4.11 = pK_a + \log\frac{[CH_3CH(OH)COO^-]}{[CH_3CH(OH)COOH]} = pK_a + \log\frac{0.0892 \text{ M}}{0.0500 \text{ M}} = pK_a + 0.251$$

$pK_a = 4.11 - 0.251 = 3.86; \quad K_a = 10^{-3.86} = 1.4\times10^{-4}$

11. **(M)**

(a) 0.100 M NaCl is not a buffer solution. Neither ion reacts with water to a detectable extent.

(b) 0.100 M NaCl—0.100 M NH_4Cl is not a buffer solution. Although a weak acid, NH_4^+, is present, its conjugate base, NH_3, is not.

(c) 0.100 M CH_3NH_2 and 0.150 M $CH_3NH_3^+Cl^-$ is a buffer solution. Both the weak base, CH_3NH_2, and its conjugate acid, $CH_3NH_3^+$, are present in approximately equal concentrations.

(d) 0.100 M HCl—0.050 M $NaNO_2$ is not a buffer solution. All the NO_2^- has converted to HNO_2 and thus the solution is a mixture of a strong acid and a weak acid.

(e) 0.100 M HCl—0.200 M $NaCH_3COO$ is a buffer solution. All of the HCl reacts with half of the CH_3COO^- to form a solution with $0.100\,M\,CH_3COOH$, a weak acid, and $0.100\,M\,CH_3COO^-$, its conjugate base.

(f) 0.100 M CH_3COOH and 0.125 M $NaCH_3CH_2COO$ is not a buffer in the strict sense because it does not contain a weak acid and its conjugate base, but rather the conjugate base of another weak acid. These two weak acids (acetic, $K_a = 1.8 \times 10^{-5}$, and propionic, $K_a = 1.35 \times 10^{-5}$) have approximately the same strength, however, this solution would resist changes in its pH on the addition of strong acid or strong base, consequently, it could be argued that this system should also be called a buffer.

12. **(M)**

(a) Reaction with added acid: $HPO_4^{2-} + H_3O^+ \rightarrow H_2PO_4^- + H_2O$

Reaction with added base: $H_2PO_4^- + OH^- \longrightarrow HPO_4^{2-} + H_2O$

(b) We assume initially that the buffer has equal concentrations of the two ions, $\left[H_2PO_4^-\right] = \left[HPO_4^{2-}\right]$

$$pH = pK_{a_2} + \log \frac{\left[HPO_4^{2-}\right]}{\left[H_2PO_4^-\right]} = 7.20 + 0.00 = 7.20 \text{ (pH at which the buffer is most effective).}$$

(c) $pH = 7.20 + \log \dfrac{\left[HPO_4^{2-}\right]}{\left[H_2PO_4^-\right]} = 7.20 + \log \dfrac{0.150\ M}{0.050\ M} = 7.20 + 0.48 = 7.68$

13. **(M)** moles of solute $= 1.15\ \text{mg} \times \dfrac{1\ \text{g}}{1000\ \text{mg}} \times \dfrac{1\ \text{mol}\ C_6H_5NH_3^+Cl^-}{129.6\ \text{g}} \times \dfrac{1\ \text{mol}\ C_6H_5NH_3^+}{1\ \text{mol}\ C_6H_5NH_3^+Cl^-}$

$$= 8.87 \times 10^{-6}\ \text{mol}\ C_6H_5NH_3^+$$

$$\left[C_6H_5NH_3^+\right] = \frac{8.87 \times 10^{-6}\ \text{mol}\ C_6H_5NH_3^+}{3.18\ \text{L soln}} = 2.79 \times 10^{-6}\ \text{M}$$

Equation: $\quad C_6H_5NH_2\ (aq)\ +\ H_2O(l) \rightleftharpoons C_6H_5NH_3^+\ (aq)\ +\ OH^-\ (aq)$

Initial:	0.105 M	–	2.79×10^{-6} M	≈ 0 M
Changes:	$-x$ M	–	$+x$ M	$+x$ M
Equil:	$(0.105 - x)$M	–	$(2.79 \times 10^{-6} + x)$M	x M

$$K_b = \frac{\left[C_6H_5NH_3^+\right]\left[OH^-\right]}{\left[C_6H_5NH_2\right]} = 7.4 \times 10^{-10} = \frac{\left(2.79 \times 10^{-6} + x\right)x}{0.105 - x}$$

$$7.4 \times 10^{-10}\left(0.105 - x\right) = \left(2.79 \times 10^{-6} + x\right)x; \quad 7.8 \times 10^{-11} - 7.4 \times 10^{-10}x = 2.79 \times 10^{-6}x + x^2$$

$$x^2 + \left(2.79 \times 10^{-6} + 7.4 \times 10^{-10}\right)x - 7.8 \times 10^{-11} = 0; \quad x^2 + 2.79 \times 10^{-6}x - 7.8 \times 10^{-11} = 0$$

$$x = \frac{-b \pm \sqrt{b^2 - 4ac}}{2a} = \frac{-2.79 \times 10^{-6} \pm \sqrt{7.78 \times 10^{-12} + 3.1 \times 10^{-10}}}{2} = 7.5 \times 10^{-6}$$

$$pOH = -\log\left(7.5 \times 10^{-6}\right) = 5.12 \qquad pH = 14.00 - 5.12 = 8.88$$

14. **(M)** We determine the concentration of the cation of the weak base.

$$[C_6H_5NH_3^+] = \frac{8.50\text{ g} \times \dfrac{1\text{ mmol }C_6H_5NH_3^+Cl^-}{129.6\text{ g}} \times \dfrac{1\text{ mmol }C_6H_5NH_3^+}{1\text{ mmol }C_6H_5NH_3^+Cl^-}}{750\text{ mL} \times \dfrac{1\text{ L}}{1000\text{ mL}}} = 0.0874\text{ M}$$

In order to be an effective buffer, each concentration must exceed the ionization constant $\left(K_b = 7.4 \times 10^{-10}\right)$ by a factor of at least 100, which clearly is true. Also, the ratio of the two concentrations must fall between 0.1 and 10: $\dfrac{\left[C_6H_5NH_3^+\right]}{\left[C_6H_5NH_2\right]} = \dfrac{0.0874\text{M}}{0.215\text{M}} = 0.407$.

Since both criteria are met, this solution will be an effective buffer.

15. **(M)**

(a) First use the Henderson-Hasselbalch equation. $pK_b = -\log\left(1.8 \times 10^{-5}\right) = 4.74$, $pK_a = 14.00 - 4.74 = 9.26$ to determine $\left[NH_4^+\right]$ in the buffer solution.

$$pH = 9.45 = pK_a + \log\frac{\left[NH_3\right]}{\left[NH_4^+\right]} = 9.26 + \log\frac{\left[NH_3\right]}{\left[NH_4^+\right]}; \quad \log\frac{\left[NH_3\right]}{\left[NH_4^+\right]} = 9.45 - 9.26 = +0.19$$

$$\frac{\left[NH_3\right]}{\left[NH_4^+\right]} = 10^{0.19} = 1.5\underline{5} \quad \left[NH_4^+\right] = \frac{\left[NH_3\right]}{1.5\underline{5}} = \frac{0.258\text{M}}{1.5\underline{5}} = 0.17\text{M}$$

We now assume that the volume of the solution does not change significantly when the solid is added.

$$\text{mass}(NH_4)_2SO_4 = 425\text{ mL} \times \frac{1\text{ L soln}}{1000\text{ mL}} \times \frac{0.17\text{ mol }NH_4^+}{1\text{ L soln}} \times \frac{1\text{ mol}(NH_4)_2SO_4}{2\text{ mol }NH_4^+}$$

$$\times \frac{132.1\text{ g}(NH_4)_2SO_4}{1\text{ mol}(NH_4)_2SO_4} = 4.8\text{ g }(NH_4)_2SO_4$$

(b) We can use the Henderson-Hasselbalch equation to determine the ratio of concentrations of cation and weak base in the altered solution.

$$pH = 9.30 = pK_a + \log\frac{[NH_3]}{[NH_4^+]} = 9.26 + \log\frac{[NH_3]}{[NH_4^+]} \qquad \log\frac{[NH_3]}{[NH_4^+]} = 9.30 - 9.26 = +0.04$$

$$\frac{[NH_3]}{[NH_4^+]} = 10^{0.04} = 1.1 = \frac{0.258}{0.17\,M + x\,M} \qquad 0.19 + 1.1\,x = 0.258 \qquad x = 0.062$$

The reason we decided to add x to the denominator follows. (Notice we cannot remove a component.) A pH of 9.30 is more acidic than a pH of 9.45 and therefore the conjugate acid's (NH_4^+) concentration must increase. Additionally, mathematics tells us that for the concentration ratio to decrease from 1.5$\underline{5}$ to 1.1, its denominator must increase. We solve this expression for x to find a value of 0.062 M. We need to add NH_4^+ to increase its concentration by 0.062 M in 100 mL of solution.

$$(NH_4)_2\,SO_4 \text{ mass} = 0.100\,L \times \frac{0.062\,mol\,NH_4^+}{1\,L} \times \frac{1\,mol\,(NH_4)_2\,SO_4}{2\,mol\,NH_4^+} \times \frac{132.1\,g\,\,(NH_4)_2\,SO_4}{1\,mol\,\,(NH_4)_2\,SO_4}$$

$$= 0.41\,g\,\,(NH_4)_2\,SO_4 \qquad \text{Hence, we need to add} \approx 0.4\,g$$

16. (M)

(a) $$n_{C_6H_5COOH} = 2.00\,g\,C_6H_5COOH \times \frac{1\,mol\,C_6H_5COOH}{122.1\,g\,C_6H_5COOH} = 0.0164\,mol\,C_6H_5COOH$$

$$n_{C_6H_5COO^-} = 2.00\,g\,NaC_6H_5COO \times \frac{1\,mol\,NaC_6H_5COO}{144.1\,g\,NaC_6H_5COO} \times \frac{1\,mol\,C_6H_5COO^-}{1\,mol\,NaC_6H_5COO}$$

$$= 0.0139\,mol\,C_6H_5COO^-$$

$$pH = pK_a + \log\frac{[C_6H_5COO^-]}{[C_6H_5COOH]} = -\log(6.3\times10^{-5}) + \log\frac{0.0139\,mol/0.7500\,L}{0.0164\,mol/0.7500\,L}$$

$$= 4.20 - 0.0718 = 4.13$$

(b) To lower the pH of this buffer solution, that is, to make it more acidic, benzoic acid must be added. The quantity is determined as follows. We use moles rather than concentrations because all components are present in the same volume of solution.

$$4.00 = 4.20 + \log\frac{0.0139\,mol\,C_6H_5COO^-}{x\,mol\,C_6H_5COOH} \qquad \log\frac{0.0139\,mol\,C_6H_5COO^-}{x\,mol\,C_6H_5COOH} = -0.20$$

$$\frac{0.0139\,mol\,C_6H_5COO^-}{x\,mol\,C_6H_5COOH} = 10^{-0.20} = 0.63 \qquad x = \frac{0.0139}{0.63} = 0.022$$

C_6H_5COOH that must be added = amount required − amount already in solution

C_6H_5COOH that must be added = 0.022 mol C_6H_5COOH − 0.0164 mol C_6H_5COOH

C_6H_5COOH that must be added = 0.006 mol C_6H_5COOH

added mass C_6H_5COOH = 0.006 mol $C_6H_5COOH \times \dfrac{122.1 \text{ g } C_6H_5COOH}{1 \text{ mol } C_6H_5COOH}$

$= 0.7 \text{ g } C_6H_5COOH$

17. **(M)** The added HCl will react with the ammonia, and the pH of the buffer solution will decrease. The original buffer solution has $[NH_3] = 0.258$ M and $[NH_4^+] = 0.17$ M. We first calculate the [HCl] in solution, reduced from 12 M because of dilution. [HCl] added $= 12 \text{ M} \times \dfrac{0.55 \text{ mL}}{100.6 \text{ mL}} = 0.066 \text{ M}$ We then determine pK_a for ammonium ion:

$pK_b = -\log(1.8 \times 10^{-5}) = 4.74 \quad pK_a = 14.00 - 4.74 = 9.26$

Equation:	$NH_3(aq)$	+	$H_3O^+(aq)$	$\rightleftharpoons$	$NH_4^+(aq)$	+	$H_2O(l)$
Buffer:	0.258 M		≈ 0 M		0.17 M		–
Added:			+0.066 M				
Changes:	−0.066 M		−0.066 M		+0.066 M		–
Final:	0.192 M		0 M		0.24 M		–

$pH = pK_a + \log \dfrac{[NH_3]}{[NH_4^+]} = 9.26 + \log \dfrac{0.192}{0.24} = 9.16$

18. **(M)** The added NH_3 will react with the benzoic acid, and the pH of the buffer solution will increase. Original buffer solution has $[C_6H_5COO^-] = 0.0139$ mol $C_6H_5COO^-/0.750$ L = 0.0185 M and $[C_6H_5COOH] = 0.0164$ mol $C_6H_5COOH/0.7500$ L = 0.0219 M. We first calculate the $[NH_3]$ in solution, reduced from 15 M because of dilution.

$[NH_3]$ added $= 15 \text{ M} \times \dfrac{0.35 \text{ mL}}{750.35 \text{ mL}} = 0.0070 \text{ M}$

For benzoic acid, $pK_a = -\log(6.3 \times 10^{-5}) = 4.20$

Equation:	$NH_3(aq)$	+	$C_6H_5COOH(aq)$	$\rightleftharpoons$	$NH_4^+(aq)$	+	$C_6H_5COO^-(aq)$
Buffer:	0 M		0.0219 M		0 M		0.0185 M
Added:	0.0070 M						
Changes:	−0.0070 M		−0.0070 M		+0.0070 M		+0.0070 M
Final:	0.000 M		0.0149 M		0.0070 M		0.0255 M

$pH = pK_a + \log \dfrac{[C_6H_5COO^-]}{[C_6H_5COOH]} = 4.20 + \log \dfrac{0.0255}{0.0149} = 4.43$

19. **(M)** The pK_a's of the acids help us choose the one to be used in the buffer. It is the acid with a pK_a within 1.00 pH unit of 3.50 that will do the trick. $pK_a = 3.74$ for HCOOH, $pK_a = 4.74$ for CH_3COOH, and $pK_{a1} = 2.15$ for H_3PO_4. Thus, we choose HCOOH and NaCOO to prepare a buffer with pH = 3.50. The Henderson-Hasselbalch equation is used to determine the relative amount of each component present in the buffer solution.

$$pH = 3.50 = 3.74 + \log\frac{[HCOO^-]}{[HCOOH]} \qquad \log\frac{[HCOO^-]}{[HCOOH]} = 3.50 - 3.74 = -0.24$$

$$\frac{[HCOO^-]}{[HCOOH]} = 10^{-0.24} = 0.58$$

This ratio of concentrations is also the ratio of the number of moles of each component in the buffer solution, since both concentrations are a number of moles in a certain volume, and the volumes are the same (the two solutes are in the same solution). This ratio also is the ratio of the volumes of the two solutions, since both solutions being mixed contain the same concentration of solute. If we assume 100. mL of acid solution, $V_{acid} = 100.$ mL. Then the volume of salt solution is $V_{salt} = 0.58 \times 100.$ mL $= 58$ mL 0.100 M NaHCOO

20. **(D)** We can lower the pH of the 0.250 M CH_3COOH — 0.560 M CH_3COO^- buffer solution by increasing $[CH_3COOH]$ or lowering $[CH_3COO^-]$. Small volumes of NaCl solutions will have no effect, and the addition of NaOH(aq) or $NaCH_3COO$ (aq) will raise the pH. The addition of 0.150 M HCl will raise $[CH_3COOH]$ and lower $[CH_3COO^-]$ through the reaction $H_3O^+ (aq) + CH_3COO^- (aq) \rightleftharpoons CH_3COOH(aq) + H_2O(l)$ and bring about the desired lowering of the pH. We first use the Henderson-Hasselbalch equation to determine the ratio of the concentrations of acetate ion and acetic acid.

$$pH = 5.00 = 4.74 + \log\frac{[CH_3COO^-]}{[CH_3COOH]}$$

$$\log\frac{[CH_3COO^-]}{[CH_3COOH]} = 5.00 - 4.74 = 0.26; \qquad \frac{[CH_3COO^-]}{[CH_3COOH]} = 10^{0.26} = 1.8$$

Now we compute the amount of each component in the original buffer solution.

$$\text{amount of } CH_3COO^- = 300. \text{ mL} \times \frac{0.560 \text{ mmol } CH_3COO^-}{1 \text{ mL soln}} = 168 \text{ mmol } CH_3COO^-$$

$$\text{amount of } CH_3COOH = 300. \text{ mL} \times \frac{0.250 \text{ mmol } CH_3COOH}{1 \text{ mL soln}} = 75.0 \text{ mmol } CH_3COOH$$

Now let x represent the amount of H_3O^+ added in mmol.

$$1.8 = \frac{168-x}{75.0+x}; \quad 168-x = 1.8(75+x) = 135+1.8x \quad 168-135 = 2.8x$$

$$x = \frac{168-135}{2.7} = 12\,mmol\,H_3O^+$$

Volume of 0.150 M HCl $= 12\,mmol\,H_3O^+ \times \dfrac{1\,mmol\,HCl}{1\,mmol\,H_3O^+} \times \dfrac{1\,mL\,soln}{0.150\,mmol\,HCl}$

$$= 80\,mL\,0.150\,M\,HCl\,solution$$

21. (M)

(a) The pH of the buffer is determined via the Henderson-Hasselbalch equation.

$$pH = pK_a + \log\frac{\left[CH_3CH_2COO^-\right]}{\left[CH_3CH_2COOH\right]} = 4.89 + \log\frac{0.100M}{0.100M} = 4.89$$

The effective pH range is the same for every propionate buffer: from $pH = 3.89$ to $pH = 5.89$, one pH unit on either side of pK_a for propionic acid, which is 4.89.

(b) To each liter of 0.100 M CH_3CH_2COOH — $0.100M$ $NaCH_3CH_2COO$ we can add 0.100 mol OH^- before all of the CH_3CH_2COOH is consumed, and we can add 0.100 mol H_3O^+ before all of the $CH_3CH_2COO^-$ is consumed. The buffer capacity thus is 100. millimoles (0.100 mol) of acid or base per liter of buffer solution.

22. (M)

(a) The solution will be an effective buffer one pH uniton either side of the pK_a of methylammonium ion, $CH_3NH_3^+$, $K_b = 4.2 \times 10^{-4}$ for methylamine, $pK_b = -\log(4.2 \times 10^{-4}) = 3.38$. For methylammonium cation, $pK_a = 14.00 - 3.38 = 10.62$. Thus, this buffer will be effective from a pH of 9.62 to a pH of 11.62.

(b) The capacity of the buffer is reached when all of the weak base or all of the conjugate acid has been neutralized by the added strong acid or strong base. Because their concentrations are the same, the number of moles of base is equal to the number of moles of conjugate acid in the same volume of solution.

amount of weak base $= 125\ mL \times \dfrac{0.0500\ mmol}{1\ mL} = 6.25\ mmol\ CH_3NH_2\ or\ CH_3NH_3^+$

Thus, the buffer capacity is 6.25 millimoles of acid or base per 125 mL buffer solution.

23. **(M)**

(a) The pH of this buffer solution is determined with the Henderson-Hasselbalch equation.

$$\text{pH} = \text{p}K_a + \log\frac{\left[\text{HCOO}^-\right]}{\left[\text{HCOOH}\right]} = -\log\left(1.8\times10^{-4}\right) + \log\frac{8.5\,\text{mmol}/75.0\,\text{mL}}{15.5\,\text{mmol}/75.0\,\text{mL}}$$

$$= 3.74 - 0.26 = 3.48$$

[Note: the solution is not a good buffer, as $\left[\text{HCOO}^-\right] = 1.1\times10^{-1}$, which is only ~ 600 times K_a]

(b) Amount of added $\text{OH}^- = 0.25\,\text{mmol Ba(OH)}_2 \times \dfrac{2\,\text{mmol OH}^-}{1\,\text{mmol Ba(OH)}_2} = 0.50\,\text{mmol OH}^-$

The OH^- added reacts with the formic acid and produces formate ion.

Equation:	HCOOH(aq)	+	OH⁻(aq)	⇌	HCOO⁻(aq)	+	H₂O(l)
Buffer:	15.5 mmol		≈ 0 M		8.5 mmol		—
Add base:			+0.50 mmol				
React:	−0.50 mmol		−0.50 mmol		+0.50 mmol		—
Final:	15.0 mmol		0 mmol		9.0 mmol		—

$$\text{pH} = \text{p}K_a + \log\frac{\left[\text{HCOO}^-\right]}{\left[\text{HCOOH}\right]} = -\log\left(1.8\times10^{-4}\right) + \log\frac{9.0\,\text{mmol}/75.0\,\text{mL}}{15.0\,\text{mmol}/75.0\,\text{mL}}$$

$$= 3.74 - 0.22 = 3.52$$

(c) Amount of added $\text{H}_3\text{O}^+ = 1.05\,\text{mL acid} \times \dfrac{12\,\text{mmol HCl}}{1\,\text{mL acid}} \times \dfrac{1\,\text{mmol H}_3\text{O}^+}{1\,\text{mmol HCl}} = 13\,\text{mmol H}_3\text{O}^+$

The H_3O^+ added reacts with the formate ion and produces formic acid.

Equation:	HCOO⁻(aq)	+	H₃O⁺(aq)	⇌	HCOOH(aq)	+	H₂O(l)
Buffer :	8.5 mmol		≈ 0 mmol		15.5 mmol		—
Add acid :			+13 mmol				
React :	−8.5 mmol		−8.5 mmol		+8.5 mmol		—
Final :	0 mmol		4.5 mmol		24.0 mmol		—

The buffer's capacity has been exceeded. The pH of the solution is determined by the excess strong acid present.

$$\left[\text{H}_3\text{O}^+\right] = \frac{4.5\,\text{mmol}}{75.0\,\text{mL} + 1.05\,\text{mL}} = 0.059\,\text{M}; \quad \text{pH} = -\log\left(0.059\right) = 1.23$$

24. (D) For NH_3, $pK_b = -\log(1.8 \times 10^{-5})$ For NH_4^+, $pK_a = 14.00 - pK_b = 14.00 - 4.74 = 9.26$

(a) $[NH_3] = \dfrac{1.68 \text{ g } NH_3}{0.500 \text{ L}} \times \dfrac{1 \text{ mol } NH_3}{17.03 \text{ g } NH_3} = 0.197 \text{ M}$

$[NH_4^+] = \dfrac{4.05 \text{ g } (NH_4)_2 SO_4}{0.500 \text{ L}} \times \dfrac{1 \text{ mol} (NH_4)_2 SO_4}{132.1 \text{ g } (NH_4)_2 SO_4} \times \dfrac{2 \text{ mol } NH_4^+}{1 \text{ mol} (NH_4)_2 SO_4} = 0.123 \text{ M}$

$pH = pK_a + \log \dfrac{[NH_3]}{[NH_4^+]} = 9.26 + \log \dfrac{0.197 \text{ M}}{0.123 \text{ M}} = 9.46$

(b) The $OH^-(aq)$ reacts with the $NH_4^+(aq)$ to produce an equivalent amount of $NH_3(aq)$.

$[OH^-]_i = \dfrac{0.88 \text{ g NaOH}}{0.500 \text{ L}} \times \dfrac{1 \text{ mol NaOH}}{40.00 \text{ g NaOH}} \times \dfrac{1 \text{ mol } OH^-}{1 \text{ mol NaOH}} = 0.044 \text{ M}$

Equation:	$NH_4^+(aq)\ +$	$OH^-(aq)$	$\rightleftharpoons$	$NH_3(aq)\ +$	$H_2O(l)$
Initial:	0.123 M	≈ 0 M		0.197 M	–
Add NaOH:		+0.044 M			
React:	−0.044 M	−0.044 M		+0.044 M	–
Final:	0.079 M	0.0000 M		0.241 M	–

$pH = pK_a + \log \dfrac{[NH_3]}{[NH_4^+]} = 9.26 + \log \dfrac{0.241 \text{ M}}{0.079 \text{ M}} = 9.74$

(c)

Equation:	$NH_3(aq)\ +$	$H_3O^+(aq)$	$\rightleftharpoons$	$NH_4^+(aq)\ +$	$H_2O(l)$
Initial:	0.197 M	≈ 0 M		0.123 M	–
Add HCl:		$+x$ M			
React:	$-x$ M	$-x$ M		$+x$ M	–
Final:	$(0.197 - x)$ M	1×10^{-9} M ≈ 0		$(0.123 + x)$ M	–

$pH = 9.00 = pK_a + \log \dfrac{[NH_3]}{[NH_4^+]} = 9.26 + \log \dfrac{(0.197 - x) \text{ M}}{(0.123 + x) \text{ M}}$

$\log \dfrac{(0.197 - x) \text{ M}}{(0.123 + x) \text{ M}} = 9.00 - 9.26 = -0.26 \qquad \dfrac{(0.197 - x) \text{ M}}{(0.123 + x) \text{ M}} = 10^{-0.26} = 0.55$

$0.197 - x = 0.55(0.123 + x) = 0.068 + 0.55 x \quad 1.55 x = 0.197 - 0.068 = 0.129$

$x = \dfrac{0.129}{1.55} = 0.0832 \text{ M}$

$\text{volume HCl} = 0.500 \text{ L} \times \dfrac{0.0832 \text{ mol } H_3O^+}{1 \text{ L soln}} \times \dfrac{1 \text{ mol HCl}}{1 \text{ mol } H_3O^+} \times \dfrac{1000 \text{ mL HCl}}{12 \text{ mol HCl}} = 3.5 \text{ mL}$

25. (D)

(a) We use the Henderson-Hasselbalch equation to determine the pH of the solution. The total solution volume is

$$36.00\,\text{mL} + 64.00\,\text{mL} = 100.00\,\text{mL}. \quad pK_a = 14.00 - pK_b = 14.00 + \log\left(1.8 \times 10^{-5}\right) = 9.26$$

$$[\text{NH}_3] = \frac{36.00\,\text{mL} \times 0.200\,\text{M NH}_3}{100.00\,\text{mL}} = \frac{7.20\,\text{mmol NH}_3}{100.0\,\text{mL}} = 0.0720\,\text{M}$$

$$[\text{NH}_4^+] = \frac{64.00\,\text{mL} \times 0.200\,\text{M NH}_4^+}{100.00\,\text{mL}} = \frac{12.8\,\text{mmol NH}_4^+}{100.0\,\text{mL}} = 0.128\,\text{M}$$

$$pH = pK_a + \log\frac{[\text{NH}_3]}{[\text{NH}_4^+]} = 9.26 + \log\frac{0.0720\,\text{M}}{0.128\,\text{M}} = 9.01 \approx 9.00$$

(b) The solution has $[\text{OH}^-] = 10^{-4.99} = 1.0 \times 10^{-5}\,\text{M}$

The Henderson-Hasselbalch equation depends on the assumption that:

$$[\text{NH}_3] \gg 1.8 \times 10^{-5}\,\text{M} \ll [\text{NH}_4^+]$$

If the solution is diluted to 1.00 L, $[\text{NH}_3] = 7.20 \times 10^{-3}\,\text{M}$, and

$[\text{NH}_4^+] = 1.28 \times 10^{-2}\,\text{M}$. These concentrations are consistent with the assumption.

However, if the solution is diluted to 1000. L, $[\text{NH}_3] = 7.2 \times 10^{-6}\,\text{M}$, and

$[\text{NH}_3] = 1.28 \times 10^{-5}\,\text{M}$, and these two concentrations are not consistent with the assumption. Thus, in 1000. L of solution, the given quantities of NH_3 and NH_4^+ will not produce a solution with pH = 9.00. With sufficient dilution, the solution will become indistinguishable from pure water (i.e.; its pH will equal 7.00).

(c) The 0.20 mL of added 1.00 M HCl does not significantly affect the volume of the solution, but it does add $0.20\,\text{mL} \times 1.00\,\text{M HCl} = 0.20\,\text{mmol H}_3\text{O}^+$. This added H_3O^+ reacts with NH_3, decreasing its amount from 7.20 mmol NH_3 to 7.00 mmol NH_3, and increasing the amount of NH_4^+ from 12.8 mmol NH_4^+ to 13.0 mmol NH_4^+, as the reaction: $\text{NH}_3 + \text{H}_3\text{O}^+ \rightarrow \text{NH}_4^+ + \text{H}_2\text{O}$

$$pH = 9.26 + \log\frac{7.00\,\text{mmol NH}_3 / 100.20\,\text{mL}}{13.0\,\text{mmol NH}_4^+ / 100.20\,\text{mL}} = 8.99$$

(d) We see in the calculation of part (c) that the total volume of the solution does not affect the pOH of the solution, at least as long as the Henderson-Hasselbalch equation is obeyed. We let x represent the number of millimoles of H_3O^+ added, through 1.00 M HCl. This increases the amount of NH_4^+ and decreases the amount of NH_3, through the reaction $NH_3 + H_3O^+ \rightarrow NH_4^+ + H_2O$

$$pH = 8.90 = 9.26 + \log\frac{7.20 - x}{12.8 + x}; \quad \log\frac{7.20 - x}{12.8 + x} = 8.90 - 9.26 = -0.36$$

Inverting, we have:

$$\frac{12.8 + x}{7.20 - x} = 10^{0.36} = 2.29; \quad 12.8 + x = 2.29(7.20 - x) = 16.5 - 2.29x$$

$$x = \frac{16.5 - 12.8}{1.00 + 2.29} = 1.1 \text{ mmol } H_3O^+$$

$$\text{vol } 1.00 \text{ M HCl} = 1.1 \text{ mmol } H_3O^+ \times \frac{1 \text{ mmol HCl}}{1 \text{ mmol } H_3O^+} \times \frac{1 \text{ mL soln}}{1.00 \text{ mmol HCl}} = 1.1 \text{ mL } 1.00 \text{ M HCl}$$

26. (D)

(a) $$\left[CH_3COO^-\right] = \frac{12.0 \text{ g NaCH}_3COO}{0.300 \text{ L soln}} \times \frac{1 \text{ mol NaCH}_3COO}{82.03 \text{ g NaCH}_3COO} \times \frac{1 \text{ mol CH}_3COO^-}{1 \text{ mol NaCH}_3COO}$$

$$= 0.488 \text{ M CH}_3COO^-$$

Equation :	$CH_3COOH + H_2O \rightleftharpoons$		CH_3COO^- +	H_3O^+
Initial :	0 M	–	0 M	0.200 M
Add CH_3COO^-	0 M	–	+0.488 M	0 M
Consume H_3O^+	+0.200 M	–	−0.200 M	−0.200 M
Buffer :	0.200 M	–	0.288 M	≈ 0 M

Then use the Henderson-Hasselbalch equation to find the pH.

$$pH = pK_a + \log\frac{\left[CH_3COO^-\right]}{\left[CH_3COOH\right]} = 4.74 + \log\frac{0.288 \text{ M}}{0.200 \text{ M}} = 4.74 + 0.16 = 4.90$$

(b) We first calculate the initial $\left[OH^-\right]$ due to the added $Ba(OH)_2$.

$$\left[OH^-\right] = \frac{1.00 \text{ g Ba}(OH)_2}{0.300 \text{ L}} \times \frac{1 \text{ mol Ba}(OH)_2}{171.3 \text{ g Ba}(OH)_2} \times \frac{2 \text{ mol OH}^-}{1 \text{ mol Ba}(OH)_2} = 0.0389 \text{ M}$$

Then CH_3COOH is consumed in the neutralization reaction shown directly below.

Equation:	CH_3COOH +	$OH^- \rightleftharpoons$	CH_3COO^- +	H_2O
Initial:	0.200 M	0.0389 M	0.288 M	—
Consume OH^-:	−0.0389 M	−0.0389 M	+0.0389 M	—
Buffer:	0.161 M	~ 0M	0.327 M	—

Then use the Henderson-Hasselbalch equation.

$$pH = pK_a + \log\frac{\left[CH_3COO^-\right]}{\left[CH_3COOH\right]} = 4.74 + \log\frac{0.327\,M}{0.161\,M} = 4.74 + 0.31 = 5.05$$

(c) $Ba(OH)_2$ can be added up until all of the CH_3COOH is consumed.

$$Ba(OH)_2 + 2CH_3COOH \longrightarrow Ba(CH_3COO^-)_2 + 2H_2O$$

$$\text{moles of } Ba(OH)_2 = 0.300\,L \times \frac{0.200\,mol\,CH_3COOH}{1\,L\,soln} \times \frac{1\,mol\,Ba(OH)_2}{2\,mol\,CH_3COOH} = 0.0300\,mol\,Ba(OH)_2$$

$$\text{mass of } Ba(OH)_2 = 0.0300\,mol\,Ba(OH)_2 \times \frac{171.3\,g\,Ba(OH)_2}{1\,mol\,Ba(OH)_2} = 5.14\,g\,Ba(OH)_2$$

(d) 0.36 g $Ba(OH)_2$ is too much for the buffer to handle and it is the excess of OH^- originating from the $Ba(OH)_2$ that determines the pOH of the solution.

$$\left[OH^-\right] = \frac{0.36\,g\,Ba(OH)_2}{0.300\,L\,soln} \times \frac{1\,mol\,Ba(OH)_2}{171.3\,g\,Ba(OH)_2} \times \frac{2\,mol\,OH^-}{1\,mol\,Ba(OH)_2} = 1.4\times10^{-2}\,M\,OH^-$$

$$pOH = -\log(1.4\times10^{-2}) = 1.85 \qquad pH = 14.00 - 1.85 = 12.15$$

Acid–Base Indicators

27. (E)

(a) The pH color change range is 1.00 pH unit on either side of pK_{HIn}. If the pH color change range is below pH = 7.00, the indicator changes color in acidic solution. If it is above pH = 7.00, the indicator changes color in alkaline solution. If pH = 7.00 falls within the pH color change range, the indicator changes color near the neutral point.

Indicator	K_{HIn}	pK_{HIn}	pH Color Change Range	Changes Color in?
Bromphenol blue	1.4×10^{-4}	3.85	2.9 (yellow) to 4.9 (blue)	acidic solution
Bromcresol green	2.1×10^{-5}	4.68	3.7 (yellow) to 5.7 (blue)	acidic solution
Bromthymol blue	7.9×10^{-8}	7.10	6.1 (yellow) to 8.1 (blue)	neutral solution
2,4-Dinitrophenol	1.3×10^{-4}	3.89	2.9 (colorless) to 4.9 (yellow)	acidic solution
Chlorophenol red	1.0×10^{-6}	6.00	5.0 (yellow) to 7.0 (red)	acidic solution
Thymolphthalein	1.0×10^{-10}	10.00	9.0 (colorless) to 11.0 (blue)	basic solution

(b) If bromcresol green is green, the pH is between 3.7 and 5.7, probably about pH = 4.7. If chlorophenol red is orange, the pH is between 5.0 and 7.0, probably about pH = 6.0.

28. **(M)** We first determine the pH of each solution, and then use the answer in Exercise 27 (a) to predict the color of the indicator. (The weakly acidic or basic character of the indicator does not affect the pH of the solution, since very little indicator is added.)

(a) $\left[H_3O^+\right] = 0.100\ \text{M HCl} \times \dfrac{1\ \text{mol}\ H_3O^+}{1\ \text{mol HCl}} = 0.100\ \text{M};\quad pH = -\log(0.100) = 1.000$

2,4-dinitrophenol is colorless.

(b) Solutions of NaCl(aq) are pH neutral, with $pH = 7.000$. Chlorphenol red assumes its neutral color in such a solution; the solution is red/orange.

(c) Equation: $NH_3(aq)\ +\ H_2O(l)\ \rightleftharpoons\ NH_4^+(aq)\ +\ OH^-(aq)$

	$NH_3(aq)$	$H_2O(l)$	$NH_4^+(aq)$	$OH^-(aq)$
Initial:	1.00 M	—	0 M	≈ 0 M
Changes:	$-x$ M	—	$+x$ M	$+x$ M
Equil:	$(1.00-x)$ M	—	x M	x M

$K_b = \dfrac{\left[NH_4^+\right]\left[OH^-\right]}{\left[NH_3\right]} = 1.8\times10^{-5} = \dfrac{x^2}{1.00-x} \approx \dfrac{x^2}{1.00}\quad x = 4.2\times10^{-3}$

($x \ll 1.00$, thus the approximation was valid).

$pOH = -\log\left(4.2\times10^{-3}\right) = 2.38 \qquad\qquad pH = 14.00 - 2.38 = 11.62$

Thus, thymolphthalein assumes its blue color in solutions with $pH > 11.62$.

(d) From Figure 17-8, seawater has $pH = 7.00$ to 8.50. Bromcresol green solution is blue.

29. **(M)**

(a) In an acid–base titration, the pH of the solution changes sharply at a definite pH that is known prior to titration. (This pH change occurs during the addition of a very small volume of titrant.) Determining the pH of a solution, on the other hand, is more difficult because the pH of the solution is not known precisely in advance. Since each indicator only serves to fix the pH over a quite small region, often less than 2.0 pH units, several indicators—carefully chosen to span the entire range of 14 pH units—must be employed to narrow the pH to ±1 pH unit or possibly lower.

(b) An indicator is, after all, a weak acid. Its addition to a solution will affect the acidity of that solution. Thus, one adds only enough indicator to show a color change and not enough to affect solution acidity.

30. (E)

(a) We use an equation similar to the Henderson-Hasselbalch equation to determine the relative concentrations of HIn, and its anion, In^-, in this solution.

$$pH = pK_{HIn} + \log\frac{\left[In^-\right]}{\left[HIn\right]}; \quad 4.55 = 4.95 + \log\frac{\left[In^-\right]}{\left[HIn\right]}; \quad \log\frac{\left[In^-\right]}{\left[HIn\right]} = 4.55 - 4.95 = -0.40$$

$$\frac{\left[In^-\right]}{\left[HIn\right]} = 10^{-0.40} = 0.40 = \frac{x}{100 - x} \quad x = 40 - 0.40x \quad x = \frac{40}{1.40} = 29\% \ In^- \ \text{and} \ 71\% \ HIn$$

(b) When the indicator is in a solution whose pH equals its pK_a (4.95), the ratio $\left[In^-\right]/\left[HIn\right] = 1.00$. And yet, at the midpoint of its color change range (about $pH = 5.3$), the ratio $\left[In^-\right]/[HIn]$ is greater than 1.00. Even though $\left[HIn\right] < \left[In^-\right]$ at this midpoint, the contribution of HIn to establishing the color of the solution is about the same as the contribution of In^-. This must mean that HIn (red) is more strongly colored than In^- (yellow).

31. (E)

(a) 0.10 M KOH is an alkaline solution and phenol red will display its basic color in such a solution; the solution will be red.

(b) 0.10 M CH_3COOH is an acidic solution, although that of a weak acid, and phenol red will display its acidic color in such a solution; the solution will be yellow.

(c) 0.10 M NH_4NO_3 is an acidic solution due to the hydrolysis of the ammonium ion. Phenol red will display its acidic color, that is, yellow, in this solution.

(d) 0.10 M HBr is an acidic solution, the aqueous solution of a strong acid. Phenol red will display its acidic color in this solution; the solution will be yellow.

(e) 0.10 M NaCN is an alkaline solution because of the hydrolysis of the cyanide ion. Phenol red will display its basic color, red, in this solution.

(f) An equimolar acetic acid–potassium acetate buffer has $pH = pK_a = 4.74$ for acetic acid. In this solution phenol red will display its acid color, namely, yellow.

32. (M)

(a) $pH = -\log(0.205) = 0.688$ The indicator is red in this solution.

(b) The total volume of the solution is 600.0 mL. We compute the amount of each solute.

amount $H_3O^+ = 350.0 \ \text{mL} \times 0.205 \ \text{M} = 71.8 \ \text{mmol} \ H_3O^+$

amount $NO_2^- = 250.0 \ \text{mL} \times 0.500 \ \text{M} = 125 \ \text{mmol} \ NO_2^-$

$$\left[H_3O^+\right] = \frac{71.8 \ \text{mmol}}{600.0 \ \text{mL}} = 0.120 \ \text{M} \qquad \left[NO_2^-\right] = \frac{125 \ \text{mmol}}{600.0 \ \text{mL}} = 0.208 \ \text{M}$$

The H_3O^+ and NO_2^- react to produce a buffer solution in which $[HNO_2] = 0.120\,M$ and $[NO_2^-] = 0.208 - 0.120 = 0.088\,M$. We use the Henderson-Hasselbalch equation to determine the pH of this solution. $pK_a = -\log(7.2 \times 10^{-4}) = 3.14$

$$pH = pK_a + \log\frac{[NO_2^-]}{[HNO_2]} = 3.14 + \log\frac{0.088\,M}{0.120\,M} = 3.01 \quad \text{The indicator is yellow in this}$$

solution.

(c) The total volume of the solution is 750. mL. We compute the amount and then the concentration of each solute. Amount $OH^- = 150\,mL \times 0.100\,M = 15.0\,mmol\ OH^-$ This OH^- reacts with HNO_2 in the buffer solution to neutralize some of it and leave 56.8 mmol $(= 71.8 - 15.0)$ unneutralized.

$$[HNO_2] = \frac{56.8\,mmol}{750.\,mL} = 0.0757\,M \qquad [NO_2^-] = \frac{(125+15)\,mmol}{750.\,mL} = 0.187\,M$$

We use the Henderson-Hasselbalch equation to determine the pH of this solution.

$$pH = pK_a + \log\frac{[NO_2^-]}{[HNO_2]} = 3.14 + \log\frac{0.187\,M}{0.0757\,M} = 3.53$$

The indicator is yellow in this solution.

(d) We determine the $[OH^-]$ due to the added $Ba(OH)_2$.

$$[OH^-] = \frac{5.00\,g\ Ba(OH)_2}{0.750\,L} \times \frac{1\,mol\ Ba(OH)_2}{171.34\,g\ Ba(OH)_2} \times \frac{2\,mol\ OH^-}{1\,mol\ Ba(OH)_2} = 0.0778\,M$$

This is sufficient $[OH^-]$ to react with the existing $[HNO_2]$ and leave an excess $[OH^-] = 0.0778\,M - 0.0757\,M = 0.0021\,M.$ $pOH = -\log(0.0021) = 2.68.$

$pH = 14.00 - 2.68 = 11.32$ The indicator is blue in this solution.

33. **(M)** Moles of $HCl = C \times V = 0.04050\,M \times 0.01000\,L = 4.050 \times 10^{-4}$ moles
Moles of $Ba(OH)_2$ at endpoint $= C \times V = 0.01120\,M \times 0.01790\,L = 2.005 \times 10^{-4}$ moles.
Moles of HCl that react with $Ba(OH)_2 = 2 \times$ moles $Ba(OH)_2$
Moles of HCl in excess 4.050×10^{-4} moles $- 4.010 \times 10^{-4}$ moles $= 4.0\underline{5} \times 10^{-6}$ moles
Total volume at the equivalence point $= (10.00\,mL + 17.90\,mL) = 27.90\,mL$

$$[HCl]_{excess} = \frac{4.05 \times 10^{-6}\ mole\ HCl}{0.02790\ L} = 1.45 \times 10^{-4}\,M; \ pH = -\log(1.45 \times 10^{-4}) = 3.84$$

(a) The approximate $pK_{HIn} = 3.84$ (generally ± 1 pH unit)

(b) This is a relatively good indicator (with $\approx 1\,\%$ of the equivalence point volume), however, pK_{Hin} is not very close to the theoretical pH at the equivalence point (pH = 7.000) For very accurate work, a better indicator is needed (i.e., bromthymol blue ($pK_{Hin} = 7.1$). Note: 2,4-dinitrophenol works relatively well here because the pH near the equivalence point of a strong acid/strong base titration rises very sharply ($\approx$ 6 pH units for an addition of only 2 drops (0.10 mL)).

34. Solution (a): 100.0 mL of 0.100 M HCl, $[H_3O^+] = 0.100$ M and pH = 1.000 (yellow)
Solution (b): 150 mL of 0.100 M NaCH$_3$COO
K_a of CH$_3$COOH = 1.8×10^{-5} $\qquad$ K_b of CH$_3$COO$^-$ = 5.6×10^{-10}

$$CH_3COO^-(aq) \;+\; H_2O(l) \quad \underrightarrow{K_b = 5.6\times10^{-10}} \quad CH_3COOH(aq) \;+\; OH^-(aq)$$

Initial	0.100 M	—	0 M	~0 M
Change	$-x$	—	$+x$	$+x$
Equil.	$0.100 - x$	—	x	x

Assume x is small: $5.6 \times 10^{-11} = x^2$; $x = 7.4\underline{8} \times 10^{-6}$ (assumption valid by inspection)
$[OH^-] = 7.4\underline{8} \times 10^{-6}$ M, pOH = 5.13 and pH = 8.87 (green-blue)
Mixture of solution (a) and (b). Total volume = 250.0 mL
$n_{HCl} = C \times V = 0.1000$ L $\times$ 0.100 M = 0.0100 mol HCl
$n_{CH_3COO^-} = C \times V = 0.1500$ L $\times$ 0.100 M = 0.0150 mol CH$_3$COO$^-$
HCl is the limiting reagent. Assume 100% reaction.
Therefore, 0.0050 moles CH$_3$COO$^-$ are left unreacted, and 0.0100 moles of CH$_3$COOH form.

$$[CH_3COO^-] = \frac{n}{V} = \frac{0.0050 \text{ mol}}{0.250 \text{ L}} = 0.020 \text{ M} \quad [CH_3COOH] = \frac{n}{V} = \frac{0.0100 \text{ mol}}{0.250 \text{ L}} = 0.0400 \text{ M}$$

$$CH_3COOH(aq) \;+\; H_2O(l) \quad \underrightarrow{K_a = 1.8\times10^{-5}} \quad CH_3COO^-(aq) \;+\; H_3O^+(aq)$$

Initial	0.0400 M	—	0.020 M	~0 M
Change	$-x$	—	$+x$	$+x$
Equil.	$0.0400 - x$	—	$0.020 + x$	x

$$1.8 \times 10^{-5} = \frac{x(0.020 + x)}{0.0400 - x} \approx \frac{x(0.020)}{0.0400} \qquad x = 3.6 \times 10^{-5}$$

(x is only 0.18% of 0.020, so the assumption was valid.)
$[H_3O^+] = 3.6 \times 10^{-5}$ pH = 4.44 Color of thymol blue at various pHs:

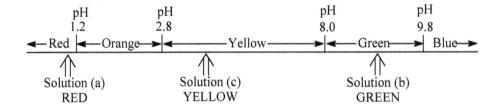

Neutralization Reactions

35. **(E)** The reaction (to second equiv. pt.) is:

$$H_3PO_4(aq) + 2\,KOH(aq) \longrightarrow K_2HPO_4(aq) + 2\,H_2O(l).$$

The molarity of the H_3PO_4 solution is determined in the following manner.

$$H_3PO_4 \text{ molarity} = \dfrac{31.15\,mL\,KOH\,soln \times \dfrac{0.2420\,mmol\,KOH}{1\,mL\,KOH\,soln} \times \dfrac{1\,mmol\,H_3PO_4}{2\,mmol\,KOH}}{25.00\,mL\,H_3PO_4\,soln} = 0.1508\,M$$

36. **(E)** The reaction (first to second equiv. pt.) is:

$$NaH_2PO_4(aq) + NaOH(aq) \longrightarrow Na_2HPO_4(aq) + H_2O(l).$$ The molarity of the H_3PO_4

solution is determined in the following manner.

$$H_3PO_4 \text{ molarity} = \dfrac{18.67\,mL\,NaOH\,soln \times \dfrac{0.1885\,mmol\,NaOH}{1\,mL\,NaOH\,soln} \times \dfrac{1\,mmol\,H_3PO_4}{1\,mmol\,NaOH}}{20.00\,mL\,H_3PO_4\,soln} = 0.1760\,M$$

37. **(M)** Here we must determine the amount of H_3O^+ or OH^- in each solution, and the amount of excess reagent.

$$\text{amount } H_3O^+ = 50.00\,mL \times \dfrac{0.0150\,mmol\,H_2SO_4}{1\,mL\,soln} \times \dfrac{2\,mmol\,H_3O^+}{1\,mmol\,H_2SO_4} = 1.50\,mmol\,H_3O^+$$

(assuming complete ionization of H_2SO_4 and HSO_4^- in the presence of OH^-)

$$\text{amount } OH^- = 50.00\,mL \times \dfrac{0.0385\,mmol\,NaOH}{1\,mL\,soln} \times \dfrac{1\,mmol\,OH^-}{1\,mmol\,NaOH} = 1.93\,mmol\,OH^-$$

Result:

	Titration reaction :	$OH^-(aq)$	$+$	$H_3O^+(aq)$	$\rightleftharpoons$	$2\,H_2O(l)$
	Initial amounts :	1.93 mmol		1.50 mmol		
	After reaction :	0.43 mmol		≈ 0 mmol		

$$\left[OH^-\right] = \dfrac{0.43\,mmol\,OH^-}{100.0\,mL\,soln} = 4.3 \times 10^{-3}\,M$$

$$pOH = -\log\left(4.3 \times 10^{-3}\right) = 2.37 \qquad\qquad pH = 14.00 - 2.37 = 11.63$$

38. **(M)** Here we must determine the amount of solute in each solution, followed by the amount of excess reagent.

$$\left[H_3O^+\right] = 10^{-2.50} = 0.0032 \, M$$

$$\text{mmol HCl} = 100.0 \, mL \times \frac{0.0032 \, \text{mmol } H_3O^+}{1 \, mL \, soln} \times \frac{1 \, \text{mmol HCl}}{1 \, \text{mmol } H_3O^+} = 0.32 \, \text{mmol HCl}$$

$$pOH = 14.00 - 11.00 = 3.00 \quad \left[OH^-\right] = 10^{-3.00} = 1.0 \times 10^{-3} \, M$$

$$\text{mmol NaOH} = 100.0 \, mL \times \frac{0.0010 \, \text{mmol } OH^-}{1 \, mL \, soln} \times \frac{1 \, \text{mmol NaOH}}{1 \, \text{mmol } OH^-} = 0.10 \, \text{mmol NaOH}$$

Result:

Titration reaction :	$NaOH(aq)$	$+$	$HCl(aq)$	$\longrightarrow$	$NaCl(aq)$	$+$	$H_2O(l)$
Initial amounts :	0.10 mmol		0.32 mmol		0 mmol		–
After reaction :	0.00 mmol		0.22 mmol		0.10 mmol		–

$$\left[H_3O^+\right] = \frac{0.22 \, \text{mmol HCl}}{200.0 \, mL \, soln} \times \frac{1 \, \text{mmol } H_3O^+}{1 \, \text{mmol HCl}} = 1.1 \times 10^{-3} \, M \quad pH = -\log\left(1.1 \times 10^{-3}\right) = 2.96$$

Titration Curves

39. **(M)** First we calculate the amount of HCl. The relevant titration reaction is

$$HCl(aq) + KOH(aq) \rightarrow KCl(aq) + H_2O(l)$$

$$\text{amount HCl} = 25.00 \, mL \times \frac{0.160 \, \text{mmol HCl}}{1 \, mL \, soln} = 4.00 \, \text{mmol HCl} = 4.00 \, \text{mmol } H_3O^+ \text{present}$$

Then, in each case, we calculate the amount of OH^- that has been added, determine which ion, $OH^-(aq)$ or $H_3O^+(aq)$, is in excess, compute the concentration of that ion, and determine the pH.

(a) $\quad \text{amount } OH^- = 10.00 \, mL \times \frac{0.242 \, \text{mmol } OH^-}{1 \, mL \, soln} = 2.42 \, \text{mmol } OH^-; \quad H_3O^+ \text{ is in excess.}$

$$[H_3O^+] = \frac{4.00 \, \text{mmol } H_3O^+ - \left(2.42 \, \text{mmol } OH^- \times \dfrac{1 \, \text{mmol } H_3O^+}{1 \, \text{mmol } OH^-}\right)}{25.00 \, mL \, \text{originally} + 10.00 \, mL \, \text{titrant}} = 0.0451 \, M$$

$$pH = -\log(0.0451) = 1.346$$

(b) amount $OH^- = 15.00 \text{ mL} \times \dfrac{0.242 \text{ mmol } OH^-}{1 \text{ mL soln}} = 3.63 \text{ mmol } OH^-$; H_3O^+ is in excess.

$$[H_3O^+] = \dfrac{4.00 \text{ mmol } H_3O^+ - \left(3.63 \text{ mmol } OH^- \times \dfrac{1 \text{ mmol } H_3O^+}{1 \text{ mmol } OH^-}\right)}{25.00 \text{ mL originally} + 15.00 \text{ mL titrant}} = 0.00925 \text{ M}$$

$pH = -\log(0.00925) = 2.034$

40. **(M)** The titration reaction is $KOH(aq) + HCl(aq) \rightarrow KCl(aq) + H_2O(l)$

mmol of $KOH = 20.00 \text{ mL} \times \dfrac{0.275 \text{ mmol KOH}}{1 \text{ mL soln}} = 5.50 \text{ mmol KOH}$

(a) The total volume of the solution is $V = 20.00 \text{ mL} + 15.00 \text{ mL} = 35.00 \text{ mL}$

mmol $HCl = 15.00 \text{ mL} \times \dfrac{0.350 \text{ mmol HCl}}{1 \text{ mL soln}} = 5.25 \text{ mmol HCl}$

mmol excess $OH^- = (5.50 \text{ mmol KOH} - 5.25 \text{ mmol HCl}) \times \dfrac{1 \text{ mmol } OH^-}{1 \text{ mmol KOH}} = 0.25 \text{ mmol } OH^-$

$\left[OH^-\right] = \dfrac{0.25 \text{ mmol } OH^-}{35.00 \text{ mL soln}} = 0.0071 \text{M}$ $\qquad pOH = -\log(0.0071) = 2.15$

$pH = 14.00 - 2.15 = 11.85$

(b) The total volume of solution is $V = 20.00 \text{ mL} + 20.00 \text{ mL} = 40.00 \text{ mL}$

mmol $HCl = 20.00 \text{ mL} \times \dfrac{0.350 \text{ mmol HCl}}{1 \text{ mL soln}} = 7.00 \text{ mmol HCl}$

mmol excess $H_3O^+ = (7.00 \text{ mmol HCl} - 5.50 \text{ mmol KOH}) \times \dfrac{1 \text{ mmol } H_3O^+}{1 \text{ mmol HCl}}$

$= 1.50 \text{ mmol } H_3O^+$

$\left[H_3O^+\right] = \dfrac{1.50 \text{ mmol } H_3O^+}{40.00 \text{ mL}} = 0.0375 \text{ M}$ $\qquad pH = -\log(0.0375) = 1.426$

41. **(M)** The titration reaction is $HNO_2(aq) + NaOH(aq) \rightarrow NaNO_2(aq) + H_2O(l)$

amount $HNO_2 = 25.00 \text{ mL} \times \dfrac{0.132 \text{ mmol } HNO_2}{1 \text{ mL soln}} = 3.30 \text{ mmol } HNO_2$

(a) The volume of the solution is $25.00 \text{ mL} + 10.00 \text{ mL} = 35.00 \text{ mL}$

$$\text{amount NaOH} = 10.00 \text{ mL} \times \frac{0.116 \text{ mmol NaOH}}{1 \text{ mL soln}} = 1.16 \text{ mmol NaOH}$$

1.16 mmol $NaNO_2$ are formed in this reaction and there is an excess of
$(3.30 \text{ mmol HNO}_2 - 1.16 \text{ mmol NaOH}) = 2.14 \text{ mmol HNO}_2$. We can use the Henderson-Hasselbalch equation to determine the pH of the solution.

$$pK_a = -\log\left(7.2 \times 10^{-4}\right) = 3.14$$

$$pH = pK_a + \log\frac{\left[NO_2^-\right]}{\left[HNO_2\right]} = 3.14 + \log\frac{1.16 \text{ mmol NO}_2^-/35.00 \text{ mL}}{2.14 \text{ mmol HNO}_2/35.00 \text{ mL}} = 2.87$$

(b) The volume of the solution is $25.00 \text{ mL} + 20.00 \text{ mL} = 45.00 \text{ mL}$

$$\text{amount NaOH} = 20.00 \text{ mL} \times \frac{0.116 \text{ mmol NaOH}}{1 \text{ mL soln}} = 2.32 \text{ mmol NaOH}$$

2.32 mmol $NaNO_2$ are formed in this reaction and there is an excess of
$(3.30 \text{ mmol HNO}_2 - 2.32 \text{ mmol NaOH} =) 0.98 \text{ mmol HNO}_2$.

$$pH = pK_a + \log\frac{\left[NO_2^-\right]}{\left[HNO_2\right]} = 3.14 + \log\frac{2.32 \text{ mmol NO}_2^-/45.00 \text{ mL}}{0.98 \text{ mmol HNO}_2/45.00 \text{ mL}} = 3.51$$

42. **(M)** The titration reaction is $NH_3(aq) + HCl(aq) \rightarrow NH_4Cl(aq) + H_2O(l)$.

$$\text{amount NH}_3 = 20.00 \text{ mL} \times \frac{0.318 \text{ mmol NH}_3}{1 \text{ mL soln}} = 6.36 \text{ mmol NH}_3$$

(a) The volume of the solution is $20.00 \text{ mL} + 10.00 \text{ mL} = 30.00 \text{ mL}$

$$\text{amount HCl} = 10.00 \text{ mL} \times \frac{0.475 \text{ mmol NaOH}}{1 \text{ mL soln}} = 4.75 \text{ mmol HCl}$$

4.75 mmol NH_4Cl is formed in this reaction and there is an excess of
$(6.36 \text{ mmol NH}_3 - 4.75 \text{ mmol HCl} =) 1.61 \text{ mmol NH}_3$. We can use the Henderson-Hasselbalch equation to determine the pH of the solution.

$$pK_b = -\log\left(1.8 \times 10^{-5}\right) = 4.74; \quad pK_a = 14.00 - pK_b = 14.00 - 4.74 = 9.26$$

$$pH = pK_a + \log\frac{\left[NH_3\right]}{\left[NH_4^+\right]} = 9.26 + \log\frac{1.61 \text{ mmol NH}_3/30.00 \text{ mL}}{4.75 \text{ mmol NH}_4^+/30.00 \text{ mL}} = 8.79$$

(b) The volume of the solution is $20.00 \text{ mL} + 15.00 \text{ mL} = 35.00 \text{ mL}$

$$\text{amount HCl} = 15.00 \text{ mL} \times \frac{0.475 \text{ mmol NaOH}}{1 \text{ mL soln}} = 7.13 \text{ mmol HCl}$$

6.36 mmol NH_4Cl is formed in this reaction and there is an excess of (7.13 mmol HCl – 6.36 mmol NH_3 =) 0.77 mmol HCl; this excess HCl determines the pH of the solution.

$$\left[H_3O^+\right] = \frac{0.77\,\text{mmol HCl}}{35.00\,\text{mL soln}} \times \frac{1\,\text{mmol}\,H_3O^+}{1\,\text{mmol HCl}} = 0.022\,M \quad pH = -\log(0.022) = 1.66$$

43. **(E)** The titration reaction is $HA(aq) + NaOH(aq) \rightarrow NaA(aq) + H_2O(l)$. The volume of titrant needed to reach the equivalence point is determined by the volume and concentration of the HA solution and the concentration of the NaOH solution, irrespective of whether HA is a strong acid or a weak acid. The volume of NaOH(aq) required to reach the equivalence point is

$$V_{NaOH} = 25.00\,\text{mL} \times \frac{0.100\,\text{mmol HA}}{1\,\text{mL}} \times \frac{1\,\text{mmol NaOH}}{1\,\text{mmol HA}} \times \frac{1\,\text{mL}}{0.100\,\text{mmol NaOH}} = 25.00\,\text{mL}$$

The pH at the equivalence point, however, is determined by the nature of the salt NaA, and especially by the nature of A^-. If HA is a strong acid, then A^- is a very weak base that will not hydrolyze in water. Consequently, for the titration of a strong acid with NaOH, the solution will be neutral at the equivalence point. If HA is a weak acid, then A^- is a weak base that will hydrolyze to produce OH^- ions: $A^- + H_2O \rightleftharpoons HA + OH^-$. Therefore, for the titration of a weak acid with NaOH, the solution will be basic at the equivalence point.

44. **(E)**

(a) This equivalence point solution is the result of the titration of a weak acid with a strong base. The CO_3^{2-} in this solution, through its hydrolysis, will form an alkaline, or basic solution. The other ionic species in solution, Na^+, will not hydrolyze. Thus, pH > 7.0.

(b) This is the titration of a strong acid with a weak base. The NH_4^+ present in the equivalence point solution hydrolyzes to form an acidic solution. Cl^- does not hydrolyze. Thus, pH < 7.0.

(c) This is the titration of a strong acid with a strong base. Two ions are present in the solution at the equivalence point, namely, K^+ and Cl^-, neither of which hydrolyzes. Thus the solution will have a pH of 7.00.

45. **(D)**

(a) Initial $\left[OH^-\right] = 0.100\,M\,OH^-$ $\quad$ pOH $= -\log(0.100) = 1.000$ $\quad$ pH $= 13.00$

Since this is the titration of a strong base with a strong acid, KI is the solute present at the equivalence point, and since KI is a neutral salt, the pH = 7.00. The titration reaction is:

$$KOH(aq) + HI(aq) \longrightarrow KI(aq) + H_2O(l)$$

$$V_{HI} = 25.0\,\text{mL KOH soln} \times \frac{0.100\,\text{mmol KOH}}{1\,\text{mL soln}} \times \frac{1\,\text{mmol HI}}{1\,\text{mmol KOH}} \times \frac{1\,\text{mL HI soln}}{0.200\,\text{mmol HI}}$$

$$= 12.5\,\text{mL HI soln}$$

Initial amount of KOH present $= 25.0\,\text{mL KOH soln} \times 0.100\,\text{M} = 2.50\,\text{mmol KOH}$

At the 40% titration point: $5.00\,\text{mL HI soln} \times 0.200\,\text{M HI} = 1.00\,\text{mmol HI}$

excess KOH $= 2.50\,\text{mmol KOH} - 1.00\,\text{mmol HI} = 1.50\,\text{mmol KOH}$

$$\left[\text{OH}^-\right] = \frac{1.50\,\text{mmol KOH}}{30.0\,\text{mL total}} \times \frac{1\,\text{mmol OH}^-}{1\,\text{mmol KOH}} = 0.0500\,\text{M} \quad \text{pOH} = -\log(0.0500) = 1.30$$
$$\text{pH} = 14.00 - 1.30 = 12.70$$

At the 80% titration point: $10.00\,\text{mL HI soln} \times 0.200\,\text{M HI} = 2.00\,\text{mmol HI}$

excess KOH $= 2.50\,\text{mmol KOH} - 2.00\,\text{mmol HI} = 0.50\,\text{mmol KOH}$

$$\left[\text{OH}^-\right] = \frac{0.50\,\text{mmol KOH}}{35.0\,\text{mL total}} \times \frac{1\,\text{mmol OH}^-}{1\,\text{mmol KOH}} = 0.0143\,\text{M} \quad \text{pOH} = -\log(0.0143) = 1.84$$
$$\text{pH} = 14.00 - 1.84 = 12.16$$

At the 110% titration point: $13.75\,\text{mL HI soln} \times 0.200\,\text{M HI} = 2.75\,\text{mmol HI}$

excess HI $= 2.75\,\text{mmol HI} - 2.50\,\text{mmol HI} = 0.25\,\text{mmol HI}$

$$\left[\text{H}_3\text{O}^+\right] = \frac{0.25\,\text{mmol HI}}{38.8\,\text{mL total}} \times \frac{1\,\text{mmol H}_3\text{O}^+}{1\,\text{mmol HI}} = 0.0064\,\text{M}; \quad \text{pH} = -\log(0.0064) = 2.19$$

Since the pH changes very rapidly at the equivalence point, from about $\text{pH} = 10$ to about $\text{pH} = 4$, most of the indicators in Figure 17-8 can be used. The main exceptions are alizarin yellow R, bromphenol blue, thymol blue (in its acid range), and methyl violet.

(b) *Initial pH*:

Since this is the titration of a weak base with a strong acid, NH_4Cl is the solute present at the equivalence point, and since NH_4^+ is a weakly acidic cation, the pH should be slightly lower than 7. The titration reaction is:

Equation:	$\text{NH}_3\,(\text{aq})$	$+\,\text{H}_2\text{O}(\text{l})$	$\rightleftharpoons$	$\text{NH}_4^+\,(\text{aq})$	$+\quad\text{OH}^-\,(\text{aq})$
Initial:	$1.00\,\text{M}$	—		$0\,\text{M}$	$\approx 0\,\text{M}$
Changes:	$-x\,\text{M}$	—		$+x\,\text{M}$	$+x\,\text{M}$
Equil:	$(1.00-x)\,\text{M}$	—		$x\,\text{M}$	$x\,\text{M}$

$$K_b = \frac{\left[\text{NH}_4^+\right]\left[\text{OH}^-\right]}{\left[\text{NH}_3\right]} = 1.8\times10^{-5} = \frac{x^2}{1.00-x} \approx \frac{x^2}{1.00}$$

($x \ll 1.0$, thus the approximation is valid)

$x = 4.2\times10^{-3} \left[\text{OH}^-\right] = 4.2\times10^{-3}\,\text{M}, \quad \text{pOH} = -\log(4.2\times10^{-3}) = 2.38,$

$\text{pH} = 14.00 - 2.38 = 11.62 = \text{initial pH}$

Volume of titrant : $\quad NH_3 + HCl \longrightarrow NH_4Cl + H_2O$

$$V_{HCl} = 10.0\,mL \times \frac{1.00\,mmol\,NH_3}{1\,mL\,soln} \times \frac{1\,mmol\,HCl}{1\,mmol\,NH_3} \times \frac{1\,mL}{0.250\,mmol\,HCl} = 40.0\,mL$$

pH at equivalence point: The total solution volume at the equivalence point is $(10.0 + 40.0)\,mL = 50.0\,mL$

Also at the equivalence point, all of the NH_3 has reacted to form NH_4^+. It is this NH_4^+ that hydrolyzes to determine the pH of the solution.

$$[NH_4^+] = \frac{10.0\,mL \times \dfrac{1.00\,mmol\,NH_3}{1\,mL\,soln} \times \dfrac{1\,mmol\,NH_4^+}{1\,mmol\,NH_3}}{50.0\,mL\ total\ solution} = 0.200\,M$$

Equation : $\quad NH_4^+(aq) \quad + \quad H_2O(l) \rightleftharpoons NH_3(aq) + H_3O^+(aq)$

Initial : $\quad\quad$ 0.200 M $\quad\quad\quad$ — $\quad\quad\quad$ 0M $\quad\quad \approx 0M$

Changes : $\quad -x\,M \quad\quad\quad$ — $\quad\quad\quad +x\,M \quad\quad +x\,M$

Equil : $\quad (0.200-x)M \quad$ — $\quad\quad\quad x\,M \quad\quad\quad x\,M$

$$K_a = \frac{K_w}{K_b} = \frac{1.0\times10^{-14}}{1.8\times10^{-5}} = \frac{[NH_3][H_3O^+]}{[NH_3]} = \frac{x^2}{0.200-x} \approx \frac{x^2}{0.200}$$

($x \ll 0.200$, thus the approximation is valid)

$$x = 1.1\times10^{-5}; \quad [H_3O^+] = 1.1\times10^{-5}\,M; \quad pH = -\log(1.1\times10^{-5}) = 4.96$$

Of the indicators in Figure 17-8, one that has the pH of the equivalence point within its pH color change range is methyl red (yellow at $pH = 6.2$ and red at $pH = 4.5$); Bromcresol green would be another choice. At the 50% titration point, $[NH_3] = [NH_4^+]$ and $pOH = pK_b = 4.74 \quad pH = 14.00 - 4.74 = 9.26$

The titration curves for parts **(a)** and **(b)** follow.

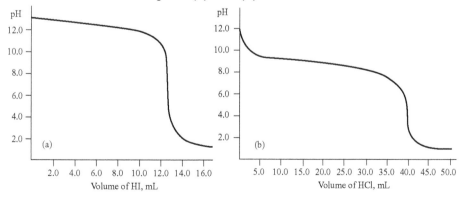

46. (M)

(a) This part simply involves calculating the pH of a $0.275\,M\,NH_3$ solution.

Equation: $NH_3(aq) + H_2O(l) \rightleftharpoons NH_4^+(aq) + OH^-(aq)$

Initial:	$0.275\,M$	—	$0\,M$	$\approx 0\,M$
Changes:	$-x\,M$	—	$+x\,M$	$+x\,M$
Equil:	$(0.275-x)\,M$	—	$x\,M$	$x\,M$

$$K_b = \frac{\left[NH_4^+\right]\left[OH^-\right]}{\left[NH_3\right]} = 1.8\times10^{-5} = \frac{x^2}{0.275-x} \approx \frac{x^2}{0.275} \quad x = 2.2\times10^{-3}\left[OH^-\right] = 2.2\times10^{-3}\,M$$

($x \ll 0.275$, thus the approximation is valid)

$pOH = -\log\left(2.2\times10^{-3}\right) = 2.66 \qquad pH = 11.34$

(b) This is the volume of titrant needed to reach the equivalence point.
The relevant titration reaction is $NH_3(aq) + HI(aq) \longrightarrow NH_4I(aq)$

$$V_{HI} = 20.00\text{ mL }NH_3\text{ soln} \times \frac{0.275\text{ mmol }NH_3}{1\text{ mL }NH_3\text{ soln}} \times \frac{1\text{ mmol }HI}{1\text{ mmol }NH_3} \times \frac{1\text{ mL }HI\text{ soln}}{0.325\text{ mmol }HI}$$

$V_{HI} = 16.9\text{ mL }HI\text{ soln}$

(c) The pOH at the half-equivalence point of the titration of a weak base with a strong acid is equal to the pK_b of the weak base.

$pOH = pK_b = 4.74; \quad pH = 14.00 - 4.74 = 9.26$

(d) NH_4^+ is formed during the titration, and its hydrolysis determines the pH of the solution. Total volume of solution $= 20.00\,mL + 16.9\,mL = 36.9\,mL$

$$\text{mmol }NH_4^+ = 20.00\,mL\,NH_3(aq) \times \frac{0.275\text{ mmol }NH_3}{1\text{ mL }NH_3\text{ soln}} \times \frac{1\text{ mmol }NH_4^+}{1\text{ mmol }NH_3} = 5.50\text{ mmol }NH_4^+$$

$$\left[NH_4^+\right] = \frac{5.50\text{ mmol }NH_4^+}{36.9\,mL\text{ soln}} = 0.149\,M$$

Equation: $NH_4^+(aq) + H_2O(l) \rightleftharpoons NH_3(aq) + H_3O^+(aq)$

Initial:	$0.149\,M$	—	$0\,M$	$\approx 0\,M$
Changes:	$-x\,M$	—	$+x\,M$	$+x\,M$
Equil:	$(0.149-x)\,M$	—	$x\,M$	$x\,M$

$$K_a = \frac{K_w}{K_b} = \frac{1.0\times10^{-14}}{1.8\times10^{-5}} = \frac{\left[NH_3\right]\left[H_3O^+\right]}{\left[NH_4^+\right]} = \frac{x^2}{0.149-x} \approx \frac{x^2}{0.149}$$

($x \ll 0.149$, thus the approximation is valid)

$x = 9.1\times10^{-6}\left[H_3O^+\right] = 9.1\times10^{-6}\,M \quad pH = -\log\left(9.1\times10^{-6}\right) = 5.04$

47. **(M)** A pH greater than 7.00 in the titration of a strong base with a strong acid means that the base is not completely titrated. A pH less than 7.00 means that excess acid has been added.

(a) We can determine $[OH^-]$ of the solution from the pH. $[OH^-]$ is also the quotient of the amount of hydroxide ion in excess divided by the volume of the solution: 20.00 mL base $+x$ mL added acid.

$$pOH = 14.00 - pH = 14.00 - 12.55 = 1.45 \qquad [OH^-] = 10^{-pOH} = 10^{-1.45} = 0.035\,M$$

$$[OH^-] = \frac{\left(20.00\,mL\,base \times \dfrac{0.175\,mmol\,OH^-}{1\,mL\,base}\right) - \left(x\,mL\,acid \times \dfrac{0.200\,mmol\,H_3O^+}{1\,mL\,acid}\right)}{20.00\,mL + x\,mL} = 0.035\,M$$

$$3.50 - 0.200x = 0.70 + 0.035x; \quad 3.50 - 0.70 = 0.035x + 0.200x; \quad 2.80 = 0.235x$$

$$x = \frac{2.80}{0.235} = 11.9\,mL\,acid\,added.$$

(b) The set-up here is the same as for part (a).

$$pOH = 14.00 - pH = 14.00 - 10.80 = 3.20 \qquad [OH^-] = 10^{-pOH} = 10^{-3.20} = 0.00063\,M$$

$$[OH^-] = \frac{\left(20.00\,mL\,base \times \dfrac{0.175\,mmol\,OH^-}{1\,mL\,base}\right) - \left(x\,mL\,acid \times \dfrac{0.200\,mmol\,H_3O^+}{1\,mL\,acid}\right)}{20.00\,mL + x\,mL}$$

$$[OH^-] = 0.00063\,\frac{mmol}{mL} = 0.00063\,M$$

$$3.50 - 0.200x = 0.0126 + 0.00063x; \quad 3.50 - 0.0126 = 0.00063x + 0.200x; \quad 3.49 = 0.201x$$

$$x = \frac{3.49}{0.201} = 17.4\,mL\,acid\,added.\ This\ is\ close\ to\ the\ equivalence\ point\ at\ 17.5\,mL.$$

(c) Here the acid is in excess, so we reverse the set-up of part (a). We are just slightly beyond the equivalence point. This is close to the "mirror image" of part (b).

$$[H_3O^+] = 10^{-pH} = 10^{-4.25} = 0.000056\,M$$

$$[H_3O^+] = \frac{\left(x\,mL\,acid \times \dfrac{0.200\,mmol\,H_3O^+}{1\,mL\,acid}\right) - \left(20.00\,mL\,base \times \dfrac{0.175\,mmol\,OH^-}{1\,mL\,base}\right)}{20.00\,mL + x\,mL}$$

$$= 5.6 \times 10^{-5}\,M$$

$$0.200x - 3.50 = 0.0011 + 5.6 \times 10^{-5}x; \quad 3.50 + 0.0011 = -5.6 \times 10^{-5}x + 0.200x;$$

$$3.50 = 0.200x$$

$$x = \frac{3.50}{0.200} = 17.5\,mL\,acid\,added,\ which\ is\ the\ equivalence\ point\ for\ this\ titration.$$

48. **(D)** In the titration of a weak acid with a strong base, the middle range of the titration, with the pH within one unit of pK_a $(= 4.74$ for acetic acid), is known as the buffer region. The Henderson-Hasselbalch equation can be used to determine the ratio of weak acid and anion concentrations. The amount of weak acid then is used in these calculations to determine the amount of base to be added.

(a)

$$pH = pK_a + \log \frac{\left[CH_3COO^-\right]}{\left[CH_3COOH\right]} = 3.85 = 4.74 + \log \frac{\left[CH_3COO^-\right]}{\left[CH_3COOH\right]}$$

$$\log \frac{\left[CH_3COO^-\right]}{\left[CH_3COOH\right]} = 3.85 - 4.74 \qquad \frac{\left[CH_3COO^-\right]}{\left[CH_3COOH\right]} = 10^{-0.89} = 0.13;$$

$$n_{CH_3COOH} = 25.00\,mL \times \frac{0.100\,mmol\ CH_3COOH}{1\,mL\ acid} = 2.50\,mmol$$

Since acetate ion and acetic acid are in the same solution, we can use their amounts in millimoles in place of their concentrations. The amount of acetate ion is the amount created by the addition of strong base, one millimole of acetate ion for each millimole of strong based added. The amount of acetic acid is reduced by the same number of millimoles. $CH_3COOH + OH^- \rightarrow CH_3COO^- + H_2O$

$$0.13 = \frac{x\,mL\ base \times \dfrac{0.200\,mmol\,OH^-}{mL\ base} \times \dfrac{1\,mmol\,CH_3COO^-}{1\,mmol\,OH^-}}{2.50\,mmol\,CH_3COOH - \left(x\,mL\ base \times \dfrac{0.200\,mmol\,OH^-}{mL\ base}\right)} = \frac{0.200\,x}{2.50 - 0.200\,x}$$

$$0.200\,x = 0.13(2.50 - 0.200\,x) = 0.33 - 0.026x \qquad 0.33 = 0.200\,x + 0.026\,x = 0.226\,x$$

$$x = \frac{0.33}{0.226} = 1.5\ mL\ of\ base$$

(b) This is the same set-up as part (a), except for a different ratio of concentrations.

$$pH = 5.25 = 4.74 + \log \frac{\left[CH_3COO^-\right]}{\left[CH_3COOH\right]} \qquad \log \frac{\left[CH_3COO^-\right]}{\left[CH_3COOH\right]} = 5.25 - 4.74 = 0.51$$

$$\frac{\left[CH_3COO^-\right]}{\left[CH_3COOH\right]} = 10^{0.51} = 3.2 \qquad 3.2 = \frac{0.200x}{2.50 - 0.200x}$$

$$0.200\,x = 3.2(2.50 - 0.200\,x) = 8.0 - 0.64\,x \qquad 8.0 = 0.200\,x + 0.64\,x = 0.84\,x$$

$$x = \frac{8.0}{0.84} = 9.5\,mL\ base.$$ This is close to the equivalence point, which is reached by adding 12.5 mL of base.

(c) This is after the equivalence point, where the pH is determined by the excess added base.

$$pOH = 14.00 - pH = 14.00 - 11.10 = 2.90 \qquad \left[OH^-\right] = 10^{-pOH} = 10^{-2.90} = 0.0013\,M$$

$$\left[OH^-\right] = 0.0013\ M = \frac{x\,mL \times \dfrac{0.200\,mmol\,OH^-}{1\,mL\ base}}{x\,mL + (12.50\,mL + 25.00\,mL)} = \frac{0.200\,x}{37.50 + x}$$

$$0.200\,x = 0.0013(37.50 + x) = 0.049 + 0.0013\,x \qquad x = \frac{0.049}{0.200 - 0.0013} = 0.25\,mL\ \text{excess}$$

Total base added $= 12.5$ mL to equivalence point $+ 0.25$ mL excess $= 12.8$ mL

49. **(D)** For each of the titrations, the pH at the half-equivalence point equals the pK_a of the acid.

The initial pH is that of 0.1000 M weak acid: $K_a = \dfrac{x^2}{0.1000 - x}$ $\qquad x = [H_3O^+]$

x must be found using the quadratic formula roots equation unless the approximation is valid.

One method of determining if the approximation will be valid is to consider the ratio C_a/K_a. If the value of C_a/K_a is greater than 1000, the assumption should be valid, however, if the value of C_a/K_a is less than 1000, the quadratic should be solved exactly (i.e., the 5% rule will not be satisfied).

The pH at the equivalence point is that of 0.05000 M anion of the weak acid, for which the $\left[OH^-\right]$ is determined as follows.

$$K_b = \frac{K_w}{K_a} \approx \frac{x^2}{0.05000} \qquad x = \sqrt{\frac{K_w}{K_a} 0.05000} = [OH^-]$$

We can determine the pH at the quarter and three quarter of the equivalence point by using the Henderson-Hasselbalch equation (effectively ± 0.48 pH unit added to the pK_a).

And finally, when 0.100 mL of base has been added beyond the equivalence point, the pH is determined by the excess added base, as follows (for all three titrations).

$$\left[OH^-\right] = \frac{0.100\,mL \times \dfrac{0.1000\,mmol\,NaOH}{1\,mL\ NaOH\ soln} \times \dfrac{1\,mmol\,OH^-}{1\,mmol\,NaOH}}{20.1\ mL\ soln\ total} = 4.98 \times 10^{-4}\ M$$

$$pOH = -\log(4.98 \times 10^{-4}) = 3.303 \qquad pH = 14.000 - 3.303 = 10.697$$

(a) $C_a/K_a = 14.3$; thus, the approximation is <u>not</u> valid and the full quadratic equation must be solved.

Initial: From the roots equation $x = [H_3O^+] = 0.023\,M \qquad pH = 1.63$
Half equivalence point: $pH = pK_a = 2.15$
pH at quarter equivalence point $= 2.15 - 0.48 = 1.67$
pH at three quarter equivalence point $= 2.15 + 0.48 = 2.63$

Equiv: $x = \left[OH^-\right] = \sqrt{\dfrac{1.0 \times 10^{-14}}{7.0 \times 10^{-3}} \times 0.05000} = 2.7 \times 10^{-7}$ $\quad$ pOH = 6.57

$\qquad\qquad\qquad\qquad\qquad\qquad\qquad\qquad\qquad\qquad\qquad$ pH = 14.00 − 6.57 = 7.43

Indicator: bromthymol blue, yellow at pH = 6.2 and blue at pH = 7.8

(b) $C_a/K_a = 333$; thus, the approximation is <u>not</u> valid and the full quadratic equation must be solved.

Initial: From the roots equation $x = [H_3O^+] = 0.0053\,M$ $\quad$ pH=2.28

Half equivalence point: pH = pK_a = 3.52

pH at quarter equivalence point = 3.52 − 0.48 = 3.04

pH at three quarter equivalence point = 3.52 + 0.48 = 4.00

Equiv: $x = \left[OH^-\right] = \sqrt{\dfrac{1.0 \times 10^{-14}}{3.0 \times 10^{-4}} \times 0.05000} = 1.3 \times 10^{-6}$

$\qquad$ pOH = 5.89

$\qquad$ pH = 14.00 − 5.89 = 8.11

Indicator: thymol blue, yellow at pH = 8.0 and blue at pH = 9.6

(c) $C_a/K_a = 5 \times 10^6$; thus, the approximation <u>is</u> valid.

Initial: $[H_3O^+] = \sqrt{0.1000 \times 2.0 \times 10^{-8}} = 0.000045\,M$ pH = 4.35

pH at quarter equivalence point = 4.35 − 0.48 = 3.87

pH at three quarter equivalence point = 4.35 + 0.48 = 4.83

Half equivalence point: pH = pK_a = 7.70

Equiv: $x = \left[OH^-\right] = \sqrt{\dfrac{1.0 \times 10^{-14}}{2.0 \times 10^{-8}} \times 0.0500} = 1.6 \times 10^{-4}$

$\qquad$ pOH = 3.80

$\qquad$ pH = 14.00 − 3.80 = 10.20

Indicator: alizarin yellow R, yellow at pH = 10.0 and violet at pH = 12.0

The three titration curves are drawn with respect to the same axes in the diagram below.

50. **(D)** For each of the titrations, the pOH at the half-equivalence point equals the pK_b of the base. The initial pOH is that of 0.1000 M weak base, determined as follows.

$$K_b = \frac{x^2}{0.1000 - x}; \qquad x \approx \sqrt{0.1000 \times K_a} = [OH^-] \text{ if } C_b/K_b > 1000. \text{ For those cases where}$$

this is not the case, the approximation is invalid and the complete quadratic equation must be solved. The pH at the equivalence point is that of 0.05000 M cation of the weak base, for which the $[H_3O^+]$ is determined as follows.

$$K_a = \frac{K_w}{K_b} = \frac{x^2}{0.05000} \qquad\qquad x = \sqrt{\frac{K_w}{K_b}0.05000} = [H_3O^+]$$

And finally, when 0.100 mL of acid has been added beyond the equivalence point, the pH for all three titrations is determined by the excess added acid, as follows.

$$[H_3O^+] = \frac{0.100 \text{ mL HCl} \times \dfrac{0.1000 \text{ mmol HCl}}{1 \text{ mL HCl soln}} \times \dfrac{1 \text{ mmol H}_3O^+}{1 \text{ mmol HCl}}}{20.1 \text{ mL soln total}} = 4.98 \times 10^{-4} \text{ M}$$

$$pH = -\log(4.98 \times 10^{-4}) = 3.303$$

(a) $C_b/K_b = 100$; thus, the approximation is <u>not</u> valid and the full quadratic equation must be solved.

Initial: From the roots equation $x = 0.0095$. Therefore,
$[OH^-] = 0.0095 \text{ M} \qquad pOH = 2.02 \qquad pH = 11.98$

Half-equiv: $\qquad pOH = -\log(1 \times 10^{-3}) = 3.0 \qquad\qquad\qquad pH = 11.0$

Equiv: $\qquad x = [H_3O^+] = \sqrt{\dfrac{1.0 \times 10^{-14}}{1 \times 10^{-3}} \times 0.05000} = 7 \times 10^{-7} \quad pH = 6.2$

Indicator: methyl red, yellow at $pH = 6.3$ and red at $pH = 4.5$

(b) $C_b/K_b = 33,000$; thus, the approximation <u>is</u> valid.

Initial: $\qquad [OH^-] = \sqrt{0.1000 \times 3 \times 10^{-6}} = 5.5 \times 10^{-4} \text{ M} \quad pOH = 3.3 \qquad pH = 10.7$

Half-equiv: $pOH = -\log(3 \times 10^{-6}) = 5.5 \qquad\qquad pH = 14 - pOH \qquad pH = 8.5$

Equiv: $\quad x = [H_3O^+] = \sqrt{\dfrac{1.0 \times 10^{-14}}{3 \times 10^{-6}} \times 0.05000} = 1 \times 10^{-5} \qquad pH - \log(1 \times 10^{-5}) = 5.0$

Indicator: methyl red, yellow at $pH = 6.3$ and red at $pH = 4.5$

(c) $C_b/K_b = 1.4 \times 10^6$; thus, the approximation is valid.

Initial: $[OH^-] = \sqrt{0.1000 \times 7 \times 10^{-8}} = 8 \times 10^{-5}$ M   pOH = 4.1   pH = 9.9

Half-equiv: pOH = $-\log(7 \times 10^{-8}) = 7.2$ pH = 14 − pOH   pH = 6.8

Equiv: $x = [H_3O^+] = \sqrt{\dfrac{1.0 \times 10^{-14}}{7 \times 10^{-8}} \times 0.05000} = 8.5 \times 10^{-5}$ pH = 4.1

Indicator: bromcresol green, blue at pH = 5.5 and yellow at pH = 4.0
The titration curves are drawn with respect to the same axes in the diagram below.

51.   **(D)** 25.00 mL of 0.100 M NaOH is titrated with 0.100 M HCl

(i) Initial pOH for 0.100 M NaOH: $[OH^-]$ = 0.100 M, pOH = 1.000 or pH = 13.000

(ii) After addition of 24 mL: $[NaOH] = 0.100 \text{ M} \times \dfrac{25.00 \text{ mL}}{49.00 \text{ mL}} = 0.0510$ M

$[HCl] = 0.100 \text{ M} \times \dfrac{24.00 \text{ mL}}{49.00 \text{ mL}} = 0.0490$ M

NaOH is in excess by 0.0020 M = $[OH^-]$ pOH = 2.70

(iii) At the equivalence point (25.00 mL), the pOH should be 7.000 and pH = 7.000

(iv) After addition of 26 mL: $[NaOH] = 0.100 \text{M} \times \dfrac{25.00}{51.00} = 0.0490$ M

$[HCl] = 0.100 \text{ M} \times \dfrac{26.00 \text{ mL}}{51.00 \text{ mL}} = 0.0510$ M

HCl is in excess by 0.0020 M = $[H_3O^+]$ pH = 2.70 or pOH = 11.30

(v) After addition of 33.00 mL HCl(xs) $[NaOH] = 0.100 \text{ M} \times \dfrac{25.00 \text{ mL}}{58.00 \text{ mL}} = 0.0431 \text{ M}$

$[HCl] = 0.100 \text{ M} \times \dfrac{33.00 \text{ mL}}{58.00 \text{ mL}} = 0.0569 \text{ M}$ $[HCl]_{excess} = 0.0138 \text{ M}$ pH = 1.860, pOH = 12.140

The graphs look to be mirror images of one another. In reality, one must reflect about a horizontal line centered at pH or pOH = 7 to obtain the other curve.

52. **(D)** 25.00 mL of 0.100 M NH_3 is titrated with 0.100 M HCl $K_a = \dfrac{K_w}{K_b} = \dfrac{1\times10^{-14}}{1.8\times10^{-5}} = 5.6 \times 10^{-10}$

(i) For initial pOH, use I.C.E.(initial, change, equilibrium) table.

	$NH_3(aq)$	+	$H_2O(l)$	$\xrightarrow{K_b = 1.8 \times 10^{-5}}$	$NH_4^+(aq)$	+	$OH^-(aq)$
Initial	0.100 M				0 M		≈ 0 M
Change	$-x$				$+x$		$+x$
Equil.	$0.100 - x$				x		x

$1.8 \times 10^{-5} = \dfrac{x^2}{0.100 - x} \approx \dfrac{x^2}{0.100}$ (Assume $x \sim 0$) $x = 1.3 \times 10^{-3}$

($x < 5\%$ of 0.100, thus, the assumption is valid).
Hence, $[OH^-] = 1.3 \times 10^{-3}$ M pOH = 2.89, pH = 11.11

(ii) After 2 mL of HCl is added: $[HCl] = 0.100 \text{ M} \times \dfrac{2.00 \text{ mL}}{27.00 \text{ mL}} = 0.00741 \text{ M}$ (after dilution)

$[NH_3] = 0.100 \text{ M} \times \dfrac{25.00 \text{ mL}}{27.00 \text{ mL}} = 0.0926 \text{ M}$ (after dilution)

The equilibrium constant for the neutralization reaction is large ($K_{neut} = K_b/K_w = 1.9\times10^5$) and thus the reaction goes to nearly 100% completion. Assume that the limiting reagent is used up (100% reaction in the reverse direction) and re-establish the equilibrium by a shift in the forward direction. Here H_3O^+ (HCl) is the limiting reagent.

	$NH_4^+(aq)$	+	$H_2O(l)$	$\xrightarrow{K_a = 5.6 \times 10^{-10}}$	$NH_3(aq)$	+	$H_3O^+(aq)$
Initial	0 M		–		0.0926 M		0.00741 M
Change	$+x$		–	$x = 0.00741$	$-x$		$-x$
100% rxn	0.00741		–		0.0852		0
Change	$-y$		–	re-establish equilibrium	$+y$		$+y$
Equil	$0.00741-y$		–		$0.0852 + y$		y

$$5.6 \times 10^{-10} = \frac{y(0.0852 + y)}{(0.00741 - y)} = \frac{y(0.0852)}{(0.00741)} \quad (\text{set } y \sim 0) \, y = 4.8 \times 10^{-11}$$

(the approximation is clearly valid)

$y = [H_3O^+] = 4.8 \times 10^{-11}$; pH = 10.32 and pOH = 3.68

(iii) pH at 1/2 equivalence point = pK_a = $-\log 5.6 \times 10^{-10}$ = 9.25 and pOH = 4.75

(iv) After addition of 24 mL of HCl:

$$[HCl] = 0.100 \, M \times \frac{24.00 \, mL}{49.00 \, mL} = 0.0490 \, M; \, [NH_3] = 0.100 \, M \times \frac{25.00 \, mL}{49.00 \, mL} = 0.0510 \, M$$

The equilibrium constant for the neutralization reaction is large (see above), and thus the reaction goes to nearly 100% completion. Assume that the limiting reagent is used up (100% reaction in the reverse direction) and re-establish the equilibrium in the reverse direction. Here H_3O^+ (HCl) is the limiting reagent.

	$NH_4^+(aq)$	+ $H_2O(l)$	$K_a = 5.6 \times 10^{-10}$	$NH_3(aq)$	+ $H_3O^+(aq)$
Initial	0 M	–		0.0541 M	0.0490 M
Change	+x	–	**x = 0.0490**	−x	−x
100% rxn	0.0490	–		0.0020	0
Change	−y	–	**re-establish equilibrium**	+y	+y
Equil	0.0490−y	–		0.0020 + y	y

$$5.6 \times 10^{-10} = \frac{y(0.0020 + y)}{(0.0490 - y)} = \frac{y(0.0020)}{(0.0490)} \quad (\text{Assume } y \sim 0) \, y = 1.3 \times 10^{-8} \text{ (valid)}$$

$y = [H_3O^+] = 1.3 \times 10^{-8}$; pH = 7.89 and pOH = 6.11

(v) Equiv. point: 100% reaction of $NH_3 \rightarrow NH_4^+$: $[NH_4^+] = 0.100 \times \frac{25.00 \, mL}{50.00 \, mL} = 0.0500 \, M$

	$NH_4^+(aq)$	+ $H_2O(l)$	$K_a = 5.6 \times 10^{-10}$	$NH_3(aq)$	+ $H_3O^+(aq)$
Initial	0.0500 M	–		0 M	∼ 0 M
Change	−x	–		+x	+x
Equil	0.0500−x	–		x	x

$$5.6 \times 10^{-10} = \frac{x^2}{(0.0500 - x)} = \frac{x^2}{0.0500} \quad (\text{Assume } x \sim 0) \, x = 5.3 \times 10^{-6}$$

(the approximation is clearly valid)

$x = [H_3O^+] = 5.3 \times 10^{-6}$; pH = 5.28 and pOH = 8.72

(vi) After addition of 26 mL of HCl, HCl is in excess. The pH and pOH should be the same as those in Exercise 51. pH = 2.70 and pOH = 11.30

(vii) After addition of 33 mL of HCl, HCl is in excess. The pH and pOH should be the same as those in Exercise 51. pH = 1.860 and pOH = 12.140. This time the curves are not mirror images of one another, but rather they are related through a reflection in a horizontal line centered at pH or pOH = 7.

Salts of Polyprotic Acids

53. (E) We expect a solution of Na_2S to be alkaline, or basic. This alkalinity is created by the hydrolysis of the sulfide ion, the anion of a very weak acid ($K_2 = 1 \times 10^{-19}$ for H_2S).

$$S^{2-}(aq) + H_2O(l) \Longrightarrow HS^-(aq) + OH^-(aq)$$

54. (E) We expect the pH of a solution of sodium dihydrogen citrate, $NaH_2Cit,$ to be acidic because the pK_a values of first and second ionization constants of polyprotic acids are reasonably large. The pH of a solution of the salt is the average of pK_1 and pK_2. For citric acid, in fact, this average is $(3.13 + 4.77) \div 2 = 3.95$. Thus, NaH_2Cit affords acidic solutions.

55. (M)

(a) $H_3PO_4(aq) + CO_3^{2-}(aq) \Longrightarrow H_2PO_4^-(aq) + HCO_3^-(aq)$

$H_2PO_4^-(aq) + CO_3^{2-}(aq) \Longrightarrow HPO_4^{2-}(aq) + HCO_3^-(aq)$

$HPO_4^{2-}(aq) + OH^-(aq) \Longrightarrow PO_4^{3-}(aq) + H_2O(l)$

(b)   The pH values of 1.00 M solutions of the three ions are;

1.0 M $OH^- \rightarrow$ pH = 14.00   1.0 M $CO_3^{2-} \rightarrow$ pH = 12.16   1.0 M $PO_4^{3-} \rightarrow$ pH = 13.15

Thus, we see that CO_3^{2-} is not a strong enough base to remove the third proton from H_3PO_4. As an alternative method of solving this problem, we can compute the equilibrium constants of the reactions of carbonate ion with $H_3PO_4,$ $H_2PO_4^-$ and HPO_4^{2-}.

$$H_3PO_4 + CO_3^{2-} \Longrightarrow H_2PO_4^- + HCO_3^- \quad K = \frac{K_{a1}\{H_3PO_4\}}{K_{a2}\{H_2CO_3\}} = \frac{7.1 \times 10^{-3}}{4.7 \times 10^{-11}} = 1.5 \times 10^8$$

$$H_2PO_4^- + CO_3^{2-} \Longrightarrow HPO_4^{2-} + HCO_3^- \quad K = \frac{K_{a2}\{H_3PO_4\}}{K_{a2}\{H_2CO_3\}} = \frac{6.3 \times 10^{-8}}{4.7 \times 10^{-11}} = 1.3 \times 10^3$$

$$HPO_4^{2-} + CO_3^{2-} \Longrightarrow PO_4^{3-} + HCO_3^- \quad K = \frac{K_{a3}\{H_3PO_4\}}{K_{a2}\{H_2CO_3\}} = \frac{4.2 \times 10^{-13}}{4.7 \times 10^{-11}} = 8.9 \times 10^{-3}$$

Since the equilibrium constant for the third reaction is much smaller than 1.00, we conclude that it proceeds to the right to only a negligible extent and thus is not a practical method of producing PO_4^{3-}. The other two reactions have large equilibrium constants, and products are expected to strongly predominate. They have the advantage of involving an inexpensive base and, even if they do not go to completion, they will be drawn to completion by reaction with OH^- in the last step of the process.

56. **(M)** We expect CO_3^{2-} to hydrolyze and the hydrolysis products to determine the pH of the solution.

Equation:	$HCO_3^-(aq)$	+	$H_2O(l)$	$\rightleftharpoons$	"H_2CO_3" (aq)	+	$OH^-(aq)$
Initial	1.00 M		–		0 M		≈ 0 M
Changes:	$-x$ M		–		$+x$ M		$+x$ M
Equil:	$(1.00 - x)$ M		–		x M		x M

$$K_b = \frac{K_w}{K_1} = \frac{1.00\times10^{-14}}{4.4\times10^{-7}} = 2.3\times10^{-8} = \frac{[H_2CO_3][OH^-]}{[HCO_3^-]} = \frac{(x)(x)}{1.00-x} \approx \frac{x^2}{1.00}$$

(C_b/K_b = a very large number; thus, the approximation is valid).

$x = \sqrt{1.00\times2.3\times10^{-8}} = 1.5\times10^{-4}$ $[OH^-] = 1.5\times10^{-4}$ M; $pOH = -\log(1.5\times10^{-4}) = 3.82$
$pH = 10.18$

For 1.00 M NaOH, $[OH^-] = 1.00$ $pOH = -\log(1.00) = 0.00$ $pH = 14.00$

Both 1.00 M $NaHCO_3$ and 1.00 M NaOH have an equal capacity to neutralize acids since one mole of each neutralizes one mole of strong acid.

$$NaOH(aq) + H_3O^+(aq) \rightarrow Na^+(aq) + 2H_2O(l)$$

$$NaHCO_3(aq) + H_3O^+(aq) \rightarrow Na^+(aq) + CO_2(g) + 2H_2O(l).$$

But on a per gram basis, the one with the smaller molar mass is the more effective. Because the molar mass of NaOH is 40.0 g/mol, while that of $NaHCO_3$ is 84.0 g/mol, NaOH(s) is more than twice as effective as $NaHCO_3$(s) on a per gram basis. $NaHCO_3$ is preferred in laboratories for safety and expense reasons. NaOH is not a good choice because it can cause severe burns. $NaHCO_3$, baking soda, by comparison, is relatively non-hazardous. It also is much cheaper than NaOH.

57. **(M)** Malonic acid has the formula $H_2C_3H_2O_4$ MM = 104.06 g/mol

Moles of $H_2C_3H_2O_4 = 19.5$ g $\times \dfrac{1\ mol}{104.06\ g} = 0.187$ mol

Concentration of $H_2C_3H_2O_4 = \dfrac{moles}{V} = \dfrac{0.187\ moles}{0.250\ L} = 0.748$ M

The second proton that can dissociate has a negligible effect on pH (K_{a_2} is very small). Thus the pH is determined almost entirely by the first proton loss.

$$\begin{array}{lcccc}
 & \text{H}_2\text{A(aq)} & + \ \text{H}_2\text{O(l)} & \rightleftharpoons \ \text{HA}^-\text{(aq)} & + \ \text{H}_3\text{O}^+\text{(aq)} \\
\text{Initial} & 0.748 \text{ M} & - & 0 \text{ M} & \approx 0 \text{ M} \\
\text{Change} & -x & - & +x & +x \\
\text{Equil} & 0.748-x & - & x & x
\end{array}$$

So, $x = \dfrac{x^2}{0.748-x} = K_a$; pH = 1.47, therefore, $[\text{H}_3\text{O}^+] = 0.034$ M $= x$,

$K_{a_1} = \dfrac{(0.034)^2}{0.748-0.034} = 1.6 \times 10^{-3}$

$(1.5 \times 10^{-3}$ in tables, difference owing to ionization of the second proton)

$$\begin{array}{lcccc}
 & \text{HA}^-\text{(aq)} & + \ \text{H}_2\text{O(l)} & \rightleftharpoons \ \text{A}^{2-}\text{(aq)} & + \ \text{H}_3\text{O}^+\text{(aq)} \\
\text{Initial} & 0.300 \text{ M} & - & 0 \text{ M} & \approx 0 \text{ M} \\
\text{Change} & -x & - & +x & +x \\
\text{Equil} & 0.300-x & - & x & x
\end{array}$$

pH = 4.26, therefore, $[\text{H}_3\text{O}^+] = 5.5 \times 10^{-5}$ M $= x$, $K_{a_2} = \dfrac{(5.5\times10^{-5})^2}{0.300-5.5\times10^{-5}} = 1.0 \times 10^{-8}$

58. **(M)** *Ortho*-phthalic acid. $K_{a_1} = 1.1 \times 10^{-3}$, $K_{a_2} = 3.9 \times 10^{-6}$

(a) We have a solution of HA.

$$\begin{array}{lcccc}
 & \text{HA}^-\text{(aq)} & + \ \text{H}_2\text{O(l)} & \rightleftharpoons \ \text{A}^{2-}\text{(aq)} & + \ \text{H}_3\text{O}^+\text{(aq)} \\
\text{Initial} & 0.350 \text{ M} & - & 0 \text{ M} & \sim 0 \text{ M} \\
\text{Change} & -x & - & +x & +x \\
\text{Equil} & 0.350-x & - & x & x
\end{array}$$

$3.9 \times 10^{-6} = \dfrac{x^2}{0.350-x} \simeq \dfrac{x^2}{0.350}$, $x = 1.2 \times 10^{-3}$

$(x \ll 0.350$, thus, the approximation is valid)
$x = [\text{H}_3\text{O}^+] = 1.2 \times 10^{-3}$, pH = 2.92

(b) 36.35 g of potassium *ortho*-phthalate (MM = 242.314 g mol^{-1})

moles of potassium *ortho*-phthalate = 36.35 g $\times \dfrac{1 \text{ mol}}{242.314 \text{ g}} = 0.150$ mol in 1 L

$$\begin{array}{lcccc}
 & \text{A}^{2-}\text{(aq)} & + \ \text{H}_2\text{O(l)} & \rightleftharpoons \ \text{HA}^-\text{(aq)} & + \ \text{OH}^-\text{(aq)} \\
\text{Initial} & 0.150 \text{ M} & - & 0 \text{ M} & \approx 0 \text{ M} \\
\text{Change} & -x & - & +x & +x \\
\text{Equil} & 0.150-x & - & x & x
\end{array}$$

$K_{b,\text{A}^{2-}} = \dfrac{K_w}{K_{a_2}} = \dfrac{1.0\times10^{-14}}{3.9\times10^{-6}} = 2.6\times10^{-9} = \dfrac{x^2}{0.150-x} \approx \dfrac{x^2}{0.150}$

$x = 2.0\times10^{-5}$ $(x \ll 0.150$, so the approximation is valid) = $[\text{OH}^-]$
pOH $= -\log 2.0 \times 10^{-5} = 4.70$; pH = 9.30

General Acid–Base Equilibria

59. **(E)**

    (a) $Ba(OH)_2$ is a strong base.

$$pOH = 14.00 - 11.88 = 2.12 \quad \left[OH^-\right] = 10^{-2.12} = 0.0076 \text{ M}$$

$$\left[Ba(OH)_2\right]_{initial} = \frac{0.0076 \text{ mol OH}^-}{1 \text{ L}} \times \frac{1 \text{ mol Ba}(OH)_2}{2 \text{ mol OH}^-} = 0.0038 \text{ M}$$

    (b) $pH = 4.52 = pK_a + \log\dfrac{\left[CH_3COO^-\right]}{\left[CH_3COOH\right]} = 4.74 + \log\dfrac{0.294 \text{ M}}{\left[CH_3COOH\right]}$

$$\log\frac{0.294 \text{ M}}{\left[CH_3COOH\right]} = 4.52 - 4.74 \qquad \frac{0.294 \text{ M}}{\left[CH_3COOH\right]} = 10^{-0.22} = 0.60$$

$$\left[CH_3COOH\right] = \frac{0.294 \text{ M}}{0.60} = 0.49 \text{ M}$$

60. **(M)**

    (a) $pOH = 14.00 - 8.95 = 5.05 \qquad \left[OH^-\right] = 10^{-5.05} = 8.9 \times 10^{-6} \text{ M}$

Equation:	$C_6H_5NH_2(aq)$	+	$H_2O(l)$	$\rightleftharpoons$	$C_6H_5NH_3^+(aq)$	+	$OH^-(aq)$
Initial	x M		–		0 M		≈ 0 M
Changes:	-8.9×10^{-6} M		–		$+8.9 \times 10^{-6}$ M		$+8.9 \times 10^{-6}$ M
Equil:	$(x - 8.9 \times 10^{-6})$ M		–		8.9×10^{-6} M		8.9×10^{-6} M

$$K_b = \frac{\left[C_6H_5NH_3^+\right]\left[OH^-\right]}{\left[C_6H_5NH_2\right]} = 7.4 \times 10^{-10} = \frac{\left(8.9 \times 10^{-6}\right)^2}{x - 8.9 \times 10^{-6}}$$

$$x - 8.9 \times 10^{-6} = \frac{\left(8.9 \times 10^{-6}\right)^2}{7.4 \times 10^{-10}} = 0.11 \quad \text{molarity of aniline} = 0.11 \text{ M}$$

    (b) $\left[H_3O^+\right] = 10^{-5.12} = 7.6 \times 10^{-6} \text{ M}$

Equation:	$NH_4^+(aq)$	+	$H_2O(l)$	$\rightleftharpoons$	$NH_3(aq)$	+	$H_3O^+(aq)$
Initial	x M		–		0 M		≈ 0 M
Changes:	-7.6×10^{-6} M		–		$+7.6 \times 10^{-6}$ M		$+7.6 \times 10^{-6}$ M
Equil:	$(x - 7.6 \times 10^{-6})$ M		–		7.6×10^{-6} M		7.6×10^{-6} M

$$K_a = \frac{\left[NH_3\right]\left[H_3O^+\right]}{\left[NH_4^+\right]} = \frac{K_w}{K_b \text{ for } NH_3} = \frac{1.0 \times 10^{-14}}{1.8 \times 10^{-5}} = 5.6 \times 10^{-10} = \frac{\left(7.6 \times 10^{-6}\right)^2}{x - 7.6 \times 10^{-6}}$$

$$x - 7.6 \times 10^{-6} = \frac{\left(7.6 \times 10^{-6}\right)^2}{5.6 \times 10^{-10}} = 0.10 \quad \left[NH_4^+\right] = \left[NH_4Cl\right] = 0.10 \text{ M}$$

61. (M)

(a) A solution can be prepared with equal concentrations of weak acid and conjugate base (it would be a buffer, with a buffer ratio of 1.00, where the $pH = pK_a = 9.26$). Clearly, this solution can be prepared, however, it would not have a pH of 6.07.

(b) These solutes can be added to the same solution, but the final solution will have an appreciable $[CH_3COOH]$ because of the reaction of $H_3O^+(aq)$ with $CH_3COO^-(aq)$

Equation: $\qquad H_3O^+(aq) \quad + \quad CH_3COO^-(aq) \quad \rightleftharpoons CH_3COOH(aq) + H_2O(l)$

Initial	0.058 M	0.10 M	0 M	–
Changes:	–0.058 M	–0.058 M	+0.058 M	–
Equil:	≈0.000 M	0.04 M	0.058 M	–

Of course, some H_3O^+ will exist in the final solution, but not equivalent to 0.058 M HI.

(c) Both 0.10 M KNO_2 and 0.25 M KNO_3 can exist together. Some hydrolysis of the $NO_2^-(aq)$ ion will occur, forming $HNO_2(aq)$ and $OH^-(aq)$.

(d) $Ba(OH)_2$ is a strong base and will react as much as possible with the weak conjugate acid NH_4^+, to form $NH_3(aq)$. We will end up with a solution of $BaCl_2(aq)$, $NH_3(aq)$, and unreacted $NH_4Cl(aq)$.

(e) This will be a benzoic acid–benzoate ion buffer solution. Since the two components have the same concentration, the buffer solution will have $pH = pK_a = -\log(6.3 \times 10^{-5}) = 4.20$. This solution can indeed exist.

(f) The first three components contain no ions that will hydrolyze. But CH_3COO^- is the anion of a weak acid and will hydrolyze to form a slightly basic solution. Since $pH = 6.4$ is an acidic solution, the solution described cannot exist.

62. (M)

(a) When $[H_3O^+]$ and $[CH_3COOH]$ are high and $[CH_3COO^-]$ is very low, a common ion H_3O^+ has been added to a solution of acetic acid, suppressing its ionization.

(b) When $[CH_3COO^-]$ is high and $[H_3O^+]$ and $[CH_3COOH]$ are very low, we are dealing with a solution of acetate ion, which hydrolyzes to produce a small concentration of $HC_2H_3O_2$.

(c) When $[CH_3COOH]$ is high and both $[H_3O^+]$ and $[CH_3COO^-]$ are low, the solution is an acetic acid solution, in which the solute is partially ionized.

(d) When both $[CH_3COOH]$ and $[CH_3COO^-]$ are high while $[H_3O^+]$ is low, the solution is a buffer solution, in which the presence of acetate ion suppresses the ionization of acetic acid.

INTEGRATIVE AND ADVANCED EXERCISES

63. (M)

(a) $NaHSO_4(aq) + NaOH(aq) \longrightarrow Na_2SO_4(aq) + H_2O(l)$

$HSO_4^-(aq) + OH^-(aq) \longrightarrow SO_4^{2-}(aq) + H_2O(l)$

(b) We first determine the mass of $NaHSO_4$.

$$\text{mass } NaHSO_4 = 36.56 \text{ mL} \times \frac{1 \text{ L}}{1000 \text{ mL}} \times \frac{0.225 \text{ mol NaOH}}{1 \text{ L}} \times \frac{1 \text{ mol NaHSO}_4}{1 \text{ mol NaOH}}$$

$$\times \frac{120.06 \text{ g NaHSO}_4}{1 \text{ mol NaHSO}_4} = 0.988 \text{ g NaHSO}_4$$

$$\% \text{ NaCl} = \frac{1.016 \text{ g sample} - 0.988 \text{ g NaHSO}_4}{1.016 \text{ g sample}} \times 100\% = 2.8\% \text{ NaCl}$$

(c) At the endpoint of this titration the solution is one of predominantly SO_4^{2-}, from which the pH is determined by hydrolysis. Since K_a for HSO_4^- is relatively large (1.1×10^{-2}), base hydrolysis of SO_4^{2-} should not occur to a very great extent. The pH of a neutralized solution should be very nearly 7, and most of the indicators represented in Figure 17-8 would be suitable. A more exact solution follows.

$$[SO_4^{2-}] = \frac{0.988 \text{ g NaHSO}_4}{0.03656 \text{ L}} \times \frac{1 \text{ mol NaHSO}_4}{120.06 \text{ g NaHSO}_4} \times \frac{1 \text{ mol SO}_4^{2-}}{1 \text{ mol NaHSO}_4} = 0.225 \text{ M}$$

Equation:	$SO_4^{2-}(aq)$	$+$	$H_2O(l)$	$\rightleftharpoons$	$HSO_4^-(aq)$	$+$	$OH^-(aq)$
Initial:	0.225 M		–		0 M		≈ 0 M
Changes:	$-x$ M		–		$+x$ M		$+x$ M
Equil:	$(0.225 - x)$ M		–		x M		x M

$$K_b = \frac{[HSO_4^-][OH^-]}{[SO_4^{2-}]} = \frac{K_w}{K_{a_2}} = \frac{1.0 \times 10^{-14}}{1.1 \times 10^{-2}} = 9.1 \times 10^{-13} = \frac{x \cdot x}{0.225 - x} \approx \frac{x^2}{0.225}$$

$$[OH^-] = \sqrt{9.1 \times 10^{-13} \times 0.225} = 4.5 \times 10^{-7} \text{ M}$$

(the approximation was valid since $x \ll 0.225$ M)

$$pOH = -\log(4.5 \times 10^{-7}) = 6.35 \qquad pH = 14.00 - 6.35 = 7.65$$

Thus, either bromthymol blue (pH color change range from pH = 6.1 to pH = 7.9) or phenol red (pH color change range from pH = 6.4 to pH = 8.0) would be a suitable indicator, since either changes color at pH = 7.65.

64. (D) The original solution contains

$$250.0 \text{ mL} \times \frac{0.100 \text{ mmol CH}_3CH_2COOH}{1 \text{ mL soln}} = 25.0 \text{ mmol CH}_3CH_2COOH$$

$pK_a = -\log(1.35 \times 10^{-5}) = 4.87$ We let V be the volume added to the solution, in mL.

(a) Since we add V mL of HCl solution (and each mL adds 1.00 mmol H_3O^+ to the solution), we have added V mmol H_3O^+ to the solution. Now the final $[H_3O^+] = 10^{-1.00} = 0.100$ M.

$$[H_3O^+] = \frac{V \text{ mmol } H_3O^+}{(250.0 + V) \text{ mL}} = 0.100 \text{ M}$$

$V = 25.0 + 0.100 \; V$, therefore, $V = \dfrac{25.0}{0.900} = 27.8$ mL added

Now, we check our assumptions. The total solution volume is 250.0 mL + 27.8 mL = 277.8 mL There are 25.0 mmol CH_3CH_2COOH present before equilibrium is established,
and 27.8 mmol H_3O^+ also.

$$[CH_3COOH] = \frac{25.0 \text{ mmol}}{277.8 \text{ mL}} = 0.0900 \text{ M} \qquad [H_3O^+] = \frac{27.8 \text{ mmol}}{277.8 \text{ mL}} = 0.100 \text{ M}$$

Equation: $\quad CH_3CH_2COOH(aq) + H_2O(l) \rightleftharpoons CH_3CH_2COO^-(aq) + H_3O^+(aq)$

Initial:	0.0900 M	—	0 M	0.100 M
Changes:	$-x$ M	—	$+x$ M	$+x$ M
Equil:	$(0.08999 - x)$ M	—	x M	$(0.100 + x)$ M

$$K_a = \frac{[H_3O^+][CH_3CH_2COO^-]}{[CH_3CH_2COOH]} = 1.35 \times 10^{-5} = \frac{x(0.100 + x)}{0.0900 - x} \approx \frac{0.100 \; x}{0.0900} \quad x = 1.22 \times 10^{-5} \text{ M}$$

The assumption used in solving this equilibrium situation, that $x \ll 0.0900$ clearly is correct. In addition, the tacit assumption that virtually all of the H_3O^+ comes from the HCl also is correct.

(b) Let V_{soln} be the volume of 1.00 M $NaCH_3CH_2COO$ required. Since the pH desired is within 1.00 pH unit of the pK_a, we can use the Henderson-Hasselbalch equation to find the required buffer ratio.

$$pH = pK_a + \frac{[A^-]}{[HA]} = pK_a + \log \frac{n_{A^-}/V}{n_{HA}/V} = pK_a + \log \frac{n_{A^-}}{n_{HA}} = 4.00 = 4.87 + \log \frac{n_{A^-}}{n_{HA}}$$

$$\log \frac{n_{A^-}}{n_{HA}} = -0.87 \qquad \frac{n_{A^-}}{n_{HA}} = 10^{-0.87} = 0.13 = \frac{n_{A^-}}{25.00} \qquad n_{A^-} = 3.3$$

$$V = 3.3 \text{ mmol } CH_3CH_2COO^- \times \frac{1 \text{ mmol } NaCH_3CH_2COO}{1 \text{ mmol } CH_3CH_2COO^-} \times \frac{1 \text{ mL soln}}{1.00 \text{ mmol } NaCH_3CH_2COO}$$

$$= 3.3 \text{ mL added}$$

We have assumed that all of the $CH_3CH_2COO^-$ is obtained from the $NaCH_3CH_2COO$ solution, since the addition of that ion in the solution should suppress the ionization of CH_3CH_2COOH.

(c) We let V be the final volume of the solution.

Equation: $\quad CH_3CH_2COOH(aq) + H_2O(l) \rightleftharpoons CH_3CH_2COO^-(aq) + H_3O^+(aq)$

Initial:	$25.0/V$	—	$0\ M$	$\approx 0\ M$
Changes:	$-x/V\ M$	—	$+x/V\ M$	$+x/V\ M$
Equil:	$(25.0/V - x/V)\ M$	—	$x/V\ M$	$x/V\ M$

$$K_a = \frac{[H_3O^+]\,[CH_3CH_2COO^-]}{[CH_3CH_2COOH]} = 1.35 \times 10^{-5} = \frac{(x/V)^2}{25.0/V - x/V} \approx \frac{x^2/V}{25.0}$$

When $V = 250.0$ mL, $x = 0.29$ mmol H_3O^+ $\qquad [H_3O^+] = \dfrac{0.29\ \text{mmol}}{250.0\ \text{mL}} = 1.2 \times 10^{-3}\ M$

$pH = -\log(1.2 \times 10^{-3}) = 2.92$
An increase of 0.15 pH unit gives $pH = 2.92 + 0.15 = 3.07$
$[H_3O^+] = 10^{-3.07} = 8.5 \times 10^{-4}\ M \qquad$ This is the value of x/V. Now solve for V.

$$1.3 \times 10^{-5} = \frac{(8.5 \times 10^{-4})^2}{25.0/V - 8.5 \times 10^{-4}} \qquad\qquad 25.0/V - 8.5 \times 10^{-4} = \frac{(8.5 \times 10^{-4})^2}{1.3 \times 10^{-5}} = 0.056$$

$$25.0/V = 0.056 + 0.00085 = 0.057 \qquad\qquad V = \frac{25.0}{0.057} = 4.4 \times 10^2\ \text{mL}$$

On the other hand, if we had used $[H_3O^+] = 1.16 \times 10^{-3}$ M (rather than 1.2×10^{-3} M), we would obtain $V = 4.8 \times 10^2$ mL. The answer to the problem thus is sensitive to the last significant figure that is retained. We obtain $V = 4.6 \times 10^2$ mL, requiring the addition of 2.1×10^2 mL of H_2O.

Another possibility is to recognize that $[H_3O^+] = \sqrt{K_a C_a}$ for a weak acid with ionization constant K_a and initial concentration C_a if the approximation is valid.

If C_a is changed to $C_a/2$, $[H_3O^+] = \sqrt{K_a/C_a} \times \sqrt{2/2}$. Since, $pH = -\log[H_3O^+]$, the change in pH given by: $\Delta pH = -\log\sqrt{2} = -\log 2^{1/2} = -0.5\log 2 = -0.5 \times 0.30103 = -0.15$. This corresponds to doubling the solution volume, that is, to adding 250 mL water. Diluted by half with water, $[H_3O^+]$ goes down and pH rises, then $(pH_1 - pH_2) < 0$.

65. **(E)** Carbonic acid is unstable in aqueous solution, decomposing to $CO_2(aq)$ and H_2O. The $CO_2(aq)$, in turn, escapes from the solution, to a degree determined in large part by the partial pressure of $CO_2(g)$ in the atmosphere.

Thus, a solution of carbonic acid in the laboratory soon will reach a low $[H_2CO_3]$, since the partial pressure of $CO_2(g)$ in the atmosphere is quite low. Thus, such a solution would be unreliable as a buffer. In the body, however, the $[H_2CO_3]$ is regulated in part by the process of respiration. Respiration rates increase when it is necessary to decrease $[H_2CO_3]$ and respiration rates decrease when it is necessary to increase $[H_2CO_3]$.

66. (E)

(a) At a pH = 2.00, in Figure 17-8 the pH is changing gradually with added NaOH. There would be no sudden change in color with the addition of a small volume of NaOH.

(b) At pH = 2.0 in Figure 17-8, approximately 20.5 mL have been added. Since, equivalence required the addition of 25.0 mL, there are 4.5 mL left to add.

Therefore,

$$\% \text{ HCl unneutralized} = \frac{4.5}{25.0} \times 100\% = 18\%$$

67. (D) Let us begin the derivation with the definition of $[H_3O^+]$.

$$[H_3O^+] = \frac{\text{amount of excess } H_3O^+}{\text{volume of titrant} + \text{volume of solution being titrated}}$$

Let V_a = volume of acid (solution being titrated) V_b = volume of base (titrant)

c_a = molarity of acid c_b = molarity of base

$$[H_3O^+] = \frac{V_a \times c_a - V_b \times c_b}{V_a + V_b}$$

Now we solve this equation for V_b

$$V_a \times c_a - V_b \times c_b = [H_3O^+](V_a + V_b) \qquad V_b([H_3O^+] + c_b) = V_a(c_a - [H_3O^+])$$

$$V_b = \frac{V_a(c_a - [H_3O^+])}{[H_3O^+] + c_b} \qquad\qquad V_b = \frac{V_a(c_a - 10^{-pH})}{10^{-pH} + c_b}$$

(a) $10^{-pH} = 10^{-2.00} = 1.0 \times 10^{-2} M$ $V_b = \dfrac{20.00 \text{ mL } (0.1500 - 0.010)}{0.010 + 0.1000} = 25.4\underline{5} \text{ mL}$

(b) $10^{-pH} = 10^{-3.50} = 3.2 \times 10^{-4} M$ $V_b = \dfrac{20.00 \text{ mL } (0.1500 - 0.0003)}{0.0003 + 0.1000} = 29.85 \text{ mL}$

(c) $10^{-pH} = 10^{-5.00} = 1.0 \times 10^{-5} M$ $V_b = \dfrac{20.00 \text{ mL } (0.1500 - 0.00001)}{0.00001 + 0.1000} = 30.00 \text{ mL}$

Beyond the equivalence point, the situation is different.

$$[OH^-] = \frac{\text{amount of excess } OH^-}{\text{total solution volume}} = \frac{V_b \times c_b - V_a \times c_a}{V_a + V_b}$$

Solve this equation for V_b. $[OH^-](V_a + V_b) = V_b \times c_b - V_a \times c_a$

$$V_a([OH^-] + c_a) = V_b(c_b - [OH^-]) \qquad V_b = \frac{V_a([OH^-] + c_a)}{c_b - [OH^-]}$$

(d) $[OH^-] = 10^{-pOH} = 10^{-14.00+pH} = 10^{-3.50} = 0.00032 \text{ M};$

$$V_b = 20.00 \text{ mL} \left(\frac{0.00032 + 0.1500}{0.1000 - 0.00032} \right) = 30.16 \text{ mL}$$

(e) $[OH^-] = 10^{-pOH} = 10^{-14.00+pH} = 10^{-2.00} = 0.010$ M;

$$V_b = 20.00 \text{ mL} \left(\frac{0.010 + 0.1500}{0.1000 - 0.010} \right) = 35.5\underline{6} \text{ mL}$$

The initial pH = –log(0.150) = 0.824. The titration curve is sketched below.

68. (D)

(a) The expressions that we obtained in Exercise 67 were for an acid being titrated by a base. For this titration, we need to switch the *a* and *b* subscripts and exchange $[OH^-]$ and $[H_3O^+]$.

Before the equivalence point: $V_a = V_b \dfrac{c_b - [OH^-]}{[OH^-] + c_a}$

After the equivalence point: $V_a = V_b \dfrac{[H_3O^+] + c_b}{c_a - [H_3O^+]}$

pH = 13.00   pOH = 14.00 – 13.00 = 1.00 $[OH^-] = 10^{-1.00} = 1.0 \times 10^{-1} = 0.10$ M

$$V_a = 25.00 \text{ mL} \frac{0.250 - 0.10}{0.10 + 0.300} = 9.38 \text{ mL}$$

pH = 12.00   pOH = 14.00 – 12.00 = 2.00 $[OH^-] = 10^{-2.00} = 1.0 \times 10^{-2} = 0.010$ M

$$V_a = 25.00 \text{ mL} \frac{0.250 - 0.010}{0.010 + 0.300} = 19.4 \text{ mL}$$

pH = 10.00   pOH = 14.00 – 10.00 = 4.00 $[OH^-] = 10^{-4.00} = 1.0 \times 10^{-4} = 0.00010$ M

$$V_a = 25.00 \text{ mL} \frac{0.250 - 0.00010}{0.00010 + 0.300} = 20.8 \text{ mL}$$

pH = 4.00 $[H_3O^+] = 10^{-4.00} = 1.0 \times 10^{-4} = 0.00010$ M

$$V_a = 25.00 \frac{0.00010 + 0.250}{0.300 - 0.00010} = 20.8 \text{ mL}$$

$$pH = 3.00 \quad [H_3O^+] = 10^{-3.00} = 1.0 \times 10^{-3} = 0.0010 \text{ M}$$

$$V_a = 25.00 \frac{0.0010 + 0.250}{0.300 - 0.0010} = 21.0 \text{ mL}$$

(b) Our expression does not include the equilibrium constant, K_a. But K_a is not needed after the equivalence point. $pOH = 14.00 - 11.50 = 2.50$ $[OH^-] = 10^{-2.50} = 3.2 \times 10^{-3} = 0.0032 \text{ M}$

$$V_b = \frac{V_a(c_a + [OH^-])}{c_b - [OH^-]} = \frac{50.00 \text{ mL} \ (0.0100 + 0.0032)}{0.0500 - 0.0032} = 14.1 \text{ mL}$$

Let us use the Henderson-Hasselbalch equation as a basis to derive an expression that incorporates K_a. Note that because the numerator and denominator of that expression are concentrations of substances present in the same volume of solution, those concentrations can be replaced by numbers of moles.
Amount of anion = $V_b c_b$ since the added OH⁻ reacts 1:1 with the weak acid.
Amount of acid = $V_a c_a - V_b c_b$ the acid left unreacted

$$pH = pK_a + \log \frac{[A^-]}{[HA]} = pK_a + \log \frac{V_b c_b}{V_a c_a - V_b c_b}$$

Rearrange and solve for V_b $\qquad 10^{pH-pK} = \dfrac{V_b c_b}{V_a c_a - V_b c_b}$

$$(V_a c_a - V_b c_b) \ 10^{pH-pK} = V_b c_b \qquad V_b = \frac{V_a c_a \ 10^{pH-pK}}{c_b(1 + 10^{pH-pK})}$$

$$pH = 4.50, \ 10^{pH-pK} = 10^{4.50-4.20} = 2.0 \quad V_b = \frac{50.00 \text{ mL} \times 0.0100 \text{ M} \times 2.0}{0.0500(1 + 2.0)} = 6.7 \text{ mL}$$

$$pH = 5.50, \ 10^{pH-pK} = 10^{5.50-4.20} = 20. \quad V_b = \frac{50.00 \text{ mL} \times 0.0100 \text{ M} \ 20}{0.0500(1 + 20.)} = 9.5 \text{ mL}$$

69. (M)

(a) We concentrate on the ratio of concentrations of which the logarithm is taken.

$$\frac{[\text{conjugate base}]_{eq}}{[\text{weak acid}]_{eq}} = \frac{\text{equil. amount conj. base}}{\text{equil. amount weak acid}} = \frac{f \times \text{initial amt. weak acid}}{(1 - f) \times \text{initial amt. weak acid}} = \frac{f}{1 - f}$$

The first transformation is the result of realizing that the volume in which the weak acid and its conjugate base are dissolved is the same volume, and therefore the ratio of equilibrium amounts is the same as the ratio of concentrations. The second transformation is the result of realizing, for instance, that if 0.40 of the weak acid has been titrated, 0.40 of the original amount of weak acid now is in the form of its conjugate base, and 0.60 of that amount remains as weak acid. Equation 17.2 then is: $pH = pK_a + \log (f/(1 - f))$

(b) We use the equation just derived. $pH = 10.00 + \log \dfrac{0.27}{(1 - 0.23)} = 9.56$

70. **(M)**

(a) $pH = pK_{a2} + \log\dfrac{[HPO_4^{2-}]}{[H_2PO_4^-]} = 7.20 + \log\dfrac{[HPO_4^{2-}]}{[H_2PO_4^-]} = 7.40 \quad \dfrac{[HPO_4^{2-}]}{[H_2PO_4^-]} = 10^{+0.20} = 1.6$

(b) In order for the solution to be isotonic, it must have the same concentration of ions as does the isotonic NaCl solution.

$$[ions] = \frac{9.2\ g\ NaCl}{1\ L\ soln} \times \frac{1\ mol\ NaCl}{58.44\ g\ NaCl} \times \frac{2\ mol\ ions}{1\ mol\ NaCl} = 0.31\ M$$

Thus, 1.00 L of the buffer must contain 0.31 moles of ions. The two solutes that are used to formulate the buffer both ionize: KH_2PO_4 produces 2 mol of ions (K^+ and $H_2PO_4^-$) per mole of solute, while $Na_2HPO_4 \cdot 12\,H_2O$ produces 3 mol of ions ($2\ Na^+$ and HPO_4^{2-}) per mole of solute. We let x = amount of KH_2PO_4 and y = amount of $Na_2HPO_4 \cdot 12\,H_2O$.

$$\frac{y}{x} = 1.6 \quad \text{or} \quad y = 1.6x \qquad 2x + 3y = 0.31 = 2x + 3(1.6x) = 6.8x$$

$$x = \frac{0.31}{6.8} = 0.046\ mol\ KH_2PO_4 \qquad y = 1.6 \times 0.046 = 0.074\ mol\ Na_2HPO_4 \cdot 12\,H_2O$$

$$mass\ KH_2PO_4 = 0.046\ mol\ KH_2PO_4 \times \frac{136.08\ g\ KH_2PO_4}{1\ mol\ KH_2PO_4} = 6.3\ g\ KH_2PO_4$$

$$mass\ of\ Na_2HPO_4 \cdot 12H_2O = 0.074\ mol\ Na_2HPO_4 \cdot 12H_2O \times \frac{358.1\ g\ Na_2HPO_4 \cdot 12H_2O}{1\ mol\ Na_2HPO_4 \cdot 12H_2O}$$

$$= 26\ g\ Na_2HPO_4 \cdot 12H_2O$$

71. **(M)** A solution of NH_4Cl should be acidic, hence, we should add an alkaline solution to make it pH neutral. We base our calculation on the ionization equation for $NH_3(aq)$, and assume that little $NH_4^+(aq)$ is transformed to $NH_3(aq)$ because of the inhibition of that reaction by the added $NH_3(aq)$, and because the added volume of $NH_3(aq)$ does not significantly alter the V_{total}.

Equation: $\qquad NH_3(aq) + H_2O(l) \rightleftharpoons NH_4^+(aq) + OH^-(aq)$

Initial: $\qquad\qquad x\,M \qquad\qquad\qquad\qquad 0.500\ M \qquad 1.0 \times 10^{-7}\,M$

$$K_b = \frac{[NH_4^+][OH^-]}{[NH_3]} = \frac{(0.500\ M)(1.0 \times 10^{-7}\ M)}{x\ M} = 1.8 \times 10^{-5}$$

$$x\ M = \frac{(0.500\ M)(1.0 \times 10^{-7}\ M)}{1.8 \times 10^{-5}\ M} = 2.8 \times 10^{-3}\ M = [NH_3]$$

$$V = 500\ mL \times \frac{2.8 \times 10^{-3}\,mol\ NH_3}{1\ L\ final\ soln} \times \frac{1\ L\ conc.\ soln}{10.0\ mol\ NH_3} \times \frac{1\ drop}{0.05\ mL} = 2.8\ drops \approx 3\ drops$$

72. (D)

(a) In order to sketch the titration curve, we need the pH at the following points.

i) Initial point. That is the pH of 0.0100 M *p*-nitrophenol, which we represent by the general formula for an indicator that also is a weak acid, HIn.

Equation:	HIn(aq)	+	$H_2O(l)$	$\rightleftharpoons$	H_3O^+(aq)	+	In^-(aq)
Initial:	0.0100 M		–		≈ 0 M		0 M
Changes:	$-x$ M		–		$+x$ M		$+x$ M
Equil:	(0.0100–x) M		–		x M		x M

$$K_{HIn} = 10^{-7.15} = 7.1\times10^{-8} = \frac{[H_3O^+]\ [In^-]}{[HIn]} = \frac{x\cdot x}{0.0100-x} \approx \frac{x^2}{0.0100}$$

$C_a/K_a = 1\times10^5$; thus, the approximation is valid

$$[H_3O^+] = \sqrt{0.0100\times7.1\times10^{-8}} = 2.7\times10^{-5}\ M \qquad pH = -\log(2.7\times10^{-5}) = 4.57$$

ii) At the half-equivalence point, the pH = pK_{HIn} = 7.15

iii) At the equiv point, pH is that of In^-. n_{In-} = 25.00 mL × 0.0100 M = 0.250 mmol In^-

$$V_{titrant} = 0.25\ \text{mmol HIn}\times\frac{1\ \text{mmol NaOH}}{1\ \text{mmol HIn}}\times\frac{1\ \text{mL titrant}}{0.0200\ \text{mmol NaOH}} = 12.5\ \text{mL titrant}$$

$$[In^-] = \frac{0.25\ \text{mmol }In^-}{25.00\ \text{mL}+12.5\ \text{mL}} = 6.67\times10^{-3}\ M = 0.00667\ M$$

Equation:	In^-(aq)	+	$H_2O(l)$	$\rightleftharpoons$	HIn(aq)	+	OH^-(aq)
Initial:	0.00667 M		–		0 M		≈ 0 M
Changes:	$-x$ M		–		$+x$ M		$+x$ M
Equil:	(0.00667 $-x$) M		–		x M		x M

$$K_b = \frac{[HIn][OH^-]}{[In^-]} = \frac{K_w}{K_a} = \frac{1.0\times10^{-4}}{7.1\times10^{-8}} = 1.4\times10^{-7} \approx \frac{x\cdot x}{0.00667-x} = \frac{x\cdot x}{0.00667}$$

($C_a/K_a = 1.4\times10^5$; thus, the approximation is valid)

$$[OH^-] = \sqrt{0.00667\times1.4\times10^{-7}} = 3.1\times10^{-5}$$

$pOH = -\log(3.1\times10^{-5}) = 4.51$; therefore, pH = 14.00 − pOH = 9.49

iv) Beyond the equivalence point, the pH is determined by the amount of excess OH^- in solution. After 13.0 mL of 0.0200 M NaOH is added, 0.50 mL is in excess, and the total volume is 38.0 mL.

$$[OH^-] = \frac{0.50\ \text{mL}\times0.0200\ M}{38.0\ \text{mL}} = 2.63\times10^{-4}\ M \quad pOH = 3.58 \quad pH = 10.42$$

After 14.0 mL of 0.0200 M NaOH is added, 1.50 mL is in excess, and Vtotal = 39.0 mL.

$$[OH^-] = \frac{1.50\ \text{mL}\times0.0200\ M}{39.0\ \text{mL}} = 7.69\times10^{-4}\ M \quad pOH = 3.11 \quad pH = 10.89$$

v) In the buffer region, the pH is determined with the use of the Henderson-Hasselbalch equation.

$$\text{At } f = 0.10, \text{ pH} = 7.15 + \log\frac{0.10}{0.90} = 6.20 \quad \text{At } f = 0.90, \text{ pH} = 7.15 + \log\frac{0.90}{0.10} = 8.10$$

$f = 0.10$ occurs with 0.10×12.5 mL $= 1.25$ mL added titrant; $f = 0.90$ with 11.25 mL added. The titration curve plotted from these points follows.

(b) The pH color change range of the indicator is shown on the titration curve.

(c) The equivalence point of the titration occurs at a pH of 9.49, far above the pH at which *p*-nitrophenol has turned yellow. In fact, the color of the indicator changes gradually during the course of the titration, making it unsuitable as an indicator for this titration. Possible indicators are as follows.

Phenolphthalein: pH color change range from colorless at pH = 8.0 to red at pH = 10.0
Thymol blue: pH color change range from yellow at pH = 8.0 to blue at pH = 9.8
Thymolphthalein: pH color change range from colorless at $\text{pH} \approx 9$ to blue at $\text{pH} \approx 11$

The red tint of phenolphthalein will appear orange in the titrated *p*-nitrophenol solution. The blue of thymol blue or thymolphthalein will appear green in the titrated *p*-nitrophenol solution, producing a somewhat better yellow end point than the orange phenolphthalein endpoint.

73. (M)

(a) Equation (1) is the reverse of the equation for the self-ionization of water. Thus, its equilibrium constant is simply the inverse of K_w.

$$K = \frac{1}{K_\text{w}} = \frac{1}{1.0 \times 10^{-14}} = 1.00 \times 10^{14}$$

Equation (2) is the reverse of the hydrolysis reaction for NH^{4+}. Thus, its equilibrium constant is simply the inverse of the acid ionization constant for NH^{4+}, $K_\text{a} = 5.6 \times 10 - 10$

$$K' = \frac{1}{K_\text{a}} = \frac{1}{5.6 \times 10^{-10}} = 1.8 \times 10^9$$

(b) The extremely large size of each equilibrium constant indicates that each reaction goes essentially to completion. In fact, a general rule of thumb suggests that a reaction is considered essentially complete if $K > 1000$ for the reaction.

74. (D) The initial pH is that of 0.100 M CH₃COOH.

Equation: $\quad$ $CH_3COOH(aq)$ $\quad + \quad$ $H_2O(l) \rightleftharpoons$ $CH_3COO^-(aq)$ $\quad + \quad$ $H_3O^+(aq)$

Initial: $\qquad$ 0.100 M $\qquad\qquad\qquad$ – $\qquad\qquad$ 0 M $\qquad\qquad$ ≈ 0 M

Changes: $\qquad$ $-x$ M $\qquad\qquad\qquad$ – $\qquad\qquad$ $+x$ M $\qquad\qquad$ $+x$ M

Equil: $\qquad$ $(0.100 - x)$ M $\qquad\qquad$ – $\qquad\qquad$ x M $\qquad\qquad$ x M

$$K_a = \frac{[H_3O^+][CH_3COO^-]}{[CH_3COOH]} = 1.8 \times 10^{-5} = \frac{x \cdot x}{0.100 - x} \approx \frac{x^2}{0.100}$$

$(C_a/K_a = 5.5 \times 10^3$; thus, the approximation is valid)

$$[H_3O^+] = \sqrt{0.100 \times 1.8 \times 10^{-5}} = 1.3 \times 10^{-3} \text{ M} \qquad pH = -\log(1.3 \times 10^{-3}) = 2.89$$

At the equivalence point, we have a solution of $NH_4C_2H_3O_2$ which has a pH = 7.00, because both NH_4^+ and CH_3COO^- hydrolyze to an equivalent extent, since $K_a(CH_3COOH) \approx K_b(NH_3)$ and their hydrolysis constants also are virtually equal.
Total volume of titrant = 10.00 mL, since both acid and base have the same concentrations.

At the half equivalence point, which occurs when 5.00 mL of titrant have been added, pH = pK_a = 4.74. *When the solution has been 90% titrated,* 9.00 mL of 0.100 M NH₃ has been added. We use the Henderson-Hasselbalch equation to find the pH after 90% of the acid has been titrated

$$pH = pK_a + \log\frac{[CH_3COO^-]}{[CH_3COOH]} = 4.74 + \log\frac{9}{1} = 5.69$$

When the solution is 110% titrated, 11.00 mL of 0.100 M NH₃ have been added.
amount NH₃ added = 11.00 mL × 0.100 M = 1.10 mmol NH₃
amount NH_4^+ produced = amount CH₃COOH consumed = 1.00 mmol NH_4^+
amount NH₃ unreacted = 1.10 mmol NH₃ – 1.00 mmol NH_4^+ = 0.10 mmol NH₃
We use the Henderson-Hasselbalch equation to determine the pH of the solution.

$$pOH = pK_b + \log\frac{[NH_4^+]}{[NH_3]} = 4.74 + \log\frac{1.00 \text{ mmol NH}_4^+}{0.10 \text{ mmol NH}_3} = 5.74 \quad pH = 8.26$$

When the solution is 150% titrated, 15.00 mL of 0.100 M NH₃ have been added.
amount NH₃ added = 15.00 mL × 0.100 M = 1.50 mmol NH₃
amount NH_4^+ produced = amount CH₃COOH consumed = 1.00 mmol NH_4^+
amount NH₃ unreacted = 1.50 mmol NH₃ – 1.00 mmol NH_4^+ = 0.50 mmol NH₃

$$pOH = pK_b + \log\frac{[NH_4^+]}{[NH_3]} = 4.74 + \log\frac{1.00 \text{ mmol NH}_4^+}{0.50 \text{ mmol NH}_3} = 5.04 \quad pH = 8.96$$

The titration curve based on these points is sketched next. We note that the equivalence point is not particularly sharp and thus, satisfactory results are not obtained from acetic acid–ammonia titrations.

75. (D) $C_6H_5NH_3^+$ is a weak acid, whose acid ionization constant is determined from $K_b(C_6H_5NH_2) = 7.4 \times 10^{-10}$.

$$K_a = \frac{1.0 \times 10^{-14}}{7.4 \times 10^{-10}} = 1.4 \times 10^{-5} \text{ and } pK_a = 4.85. \text{ We first determine the } \textit{initial pH}.$$

Equation:	$C_6H_5NH_3^+(aq)$	$+$ $H_2O(l)$	$\rightleftharpoons$	$C_6H_5NH_2(aq) +$	$H_3O^+(aq)$
Initial:	0.0500 M	–		0 M	≈ 0 M
Changes:	$-x$ M	–		$+x$ M	$+x$ M
Equil:	$(0.0500 - x)$ M	–		x M	x M

$$K_a = 1.4 \times 10^{-5} = \frac{[C_6H_5NH_2]\ [H_3O^+]}{[C_6H_5NH_3^+]} = \frac{x \cdot x}{0.0500 - x} \approx \frac{x^2}{0.0500}$$

(Since $C_a/K_a = 3.6 \times 10^3$; thus, the approximation is valid)

$$[H_3O^+] = \sqrt{0.0500 \times 1.4 \times 10^{-5}} = 8.4 \times 10^{-4} \text{ M} \qquad pH = -\log\ (8.4 \times 10^{-4}) = 3.08$$

At the equivalence point, we have a solution of $C_6H_5NH_2(aq)$. Now find the volume of titrant needed to reach the equivalence point.

$$V = 10.00 \text{ mL} \times \frac{0.0500 \text{ mmol } C_6H_5NH_3^+}{1 \text{ mL}} \times \frac{1 \text{ mmol NaOH}}{1 \text{ mmol } C_6H_5NH_3^+} \times \frac{1 \text{ mL titrant}}{0.100 \text{ mmol NaOH}} = 5.00 \text{ mL}$$

amount $C_6H_5NH_2 = 10.00 \text{ mL} \times 0.0500 \text{ M} = 0.500 \text{ mmol } C_6H_5NH_2$

$$[C_6H_5NH_2] = \frac{0.500 \text{ mmol } C_6H_5NH_2}{10.00 \text{ mL} + 5.00 \text{ mL}} = 0.0333 \text{ M}$$

Equation:	$C_6H_5NH_2(aq)$	$+$	$H_2O(l)$	$\rightleftharpoons$	$C_6H_5NH_3^+(aq)$	$+$	$OH^-(aq)$
Initial:	0.0333 M		–		0 M		≈ 0 M
Changes:	$-x$ M		–		$+x$ M		$+x$ M
Equil:	$(0.0333 - x)$ M		–		x M		x M

$$K_b = 7.4 \times 10^{-10} = \frac{[C_6H_5NH_3^+][OH^-]}{[C_6H_5NH_2]} = \frac{x \cdot x}{0.0333 - x} \approx \frac{x^2}{0.0333}$$

(C_b/K_b = very large number; thus, the approximation is valid)

$$[OH^-] = \sqrt{0.0333 \times 7.4 \times 10^{-10}} = 5.0 \times 10^{-6} \qquad pOH = 5.30 \qquad pH = 8.70$$

At the half equivalence point, when 5.00 mL of 0.1000 M NaOH has been added, pH = pKa = 4.85. At points in the buffer region, we use the expression derived in Exercise 69.

After 4.50 mL of titrant has been added, f = 0.90, pH = 4.85 + log $\dfrac{0.90}{0.10}$ = 5.80

After 4.75 mL of titrant has been added, f = 0.95, pH = 4.85 + log $\dfrac{0.95}{0.05}$ = 6.13

After the equivalence point has been reached, with 5.00 mL of titrant added, the pH of the solution is determined by the amount of excess OH⁻ that has been added.

For 0.25 mL excess of NaOH:
$$[OH^-] = \frac{0.25 \text{ mL} \times 0.100 \text{ M}}{15.25 \text{ mL}} = 0.0016 \text{ M} \qquad pOH = 2.80 \quad pH = 11.20$$

For 1.00 mL excess of NaOH:
$$[OH^-] = \frac{1.00 \text{ mL} \times 0.100 \text{ M}}{16.00 \text{ mL}} = 0.00625 \text{ M} \qquad pOH = 2.20 \quad pH = 11.80$$

Of course, one could sketch a suitable titration curve by calculating fewer points. Below is the titration curve.

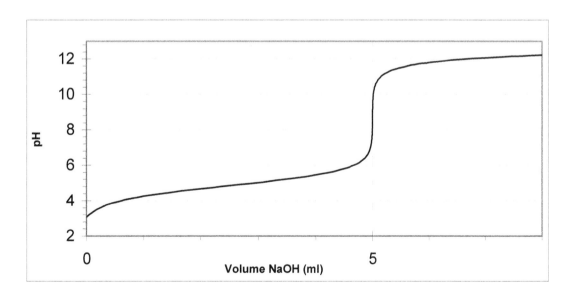

76. In order for a diprotic acid to be titrated to two distinct equivalence points, the acid must initially start out with two undissociated protons and the K_a values for the first and second protons must differ by >1000. This certainly is not the case for H_2SO_4, which is a strong acid (first proton is 100% dissociated). Effectively, this situation is very similar to the titration of a monoprotic acid that has added strong acid (i.e., HCl or HNO_3). With the leveling effect of water, $K_{a1} = 1$ and $K_{a2} = 0.011$, there is a difference of only 100 between K_{a1} and K_{a2} for H_2SO_4.

77. (D)

(a) The *initial pH* is that of a solution of HCO_3^-(aq). This is an anion that can ionize to CO_3^{2-} (aq) or be hydrolyzed to H_2CO_3(aq). Thus,

$$pH = \tfrac{1}{2}(pK_{a_1} + pK_{a_2}) = \tfrac{1}{2}(6.35 + 10.33) = 8.34$$

The *pH at the equivalence point* is that of 0.500 M H_2CO_3(aq). All of the NaOH(aq) has been neutralized, as well as all of the HCO_3^-(aq), by the added HCl(aq).

Equation:	$H_2CO_3(aq)$	$+ H_2O(l)$	$\rightleftharpoons$	$HCO_3^-(aq)$	$+ H_3O^+(aq)$
Initial:	0.500 M	–		0 M	≈ 0 M
Changes:	$-x$ M	–		$+x$ M	$+x$ M
Equil:	$(0.500 - x)$ M	–		x M	x M

$$K_b = \frac{[HCO_3^-][H_3O^+]}{[H_2CO_3]} = 4.43 \times 10^{-7} = \frac{x \cdot x}{0.500 - x} \approx \frac{x^2}{0.500}$$

$(c_a/K_a = 1.1 \times 10^6$; thus, the approximation is valid)

$$[H_3O^+] = \sqrt{0.500 \times 4.4 \times 10^{-7}} = 4.7 \times 10^{-4} \, M \qquad pH = 3.33$$

During the course of the titration, the pH is determined by the Henderson-Hasselbalch equation, with the numerator being the percent of bicarbonate ion remaining, and as the denominator being the percent of bicarbonate ion that has been transformed to H_2CO_3.

90% titrated: $pH = 6.35 + \log\dfrac{10\%}{90\%} = 5.40$ 10% titrated: $pH = 6.35 + \log\dfrac{90\%}{10\%} = 7.30$

95% titrated: $pH = 6.35 + \log\dfrac{5\%}{95\%} = 5.07$ 5% titrated: $pH = 6.35 + \log\dfrac{95\%}{5\%} = 7.63$

After the equivalence point, the pH is determined by the excess H_3O^+.

For 0.5 mL excess of HCl: $[H_3O^+] = \dfrac{0.50 \text{ mL} \times 1.00 \text{ M}}{20.5 \text{ mL}} = 0.024$ \qquad $pH = 1.61$

For 2.00 mL excess of HCl: $[H_3O^+] = \dfrac{2.00 \text{ mL} \times 1.00 \text{ M}}{22.0 \text{ mL}} = 0.091 \text{ M}$ \qquad $pH = 1.04$

The titration curve derived from these data is sketched below.

(b) In the titration of Na_2CO_3 with HCl, the pH at the first equivalence point is that of a solution of $HCO_3^-(aq)$. This is an anion that can be ionized to $CO_3^{2-}(aq)$ or hydrolyzed to $H_2CO_3(aq)$. Thus, $pH = \frac{1}{2}(pK_{a_1} + pK_{a_2}) = \frac{1}{2}(6.35 + 10.33) = 8.34$. The *initial pH* is that of 1.000 M $CO_3^{2-}(aq)$, which is determined by considering the hydrolysis of the anion.

Equation:	$CO_3^{2-}(aq)$	$+$	$H_2O(l)$	$\rightleftharpoons$	$HCO_3^-(aq)$	$+$	$OH^-(aq)$
Initial:	1.000 M		$-$		0 M		≈ 0 M
Changes:	$-x$ M		$-$		$+x$ M		$+x$ M
Equil:	$(1.000 - x)$ M		$-$		x M		x M

$$K_b = \frac{[HCO_3^-][OH^-]}{[CO_3^{2-}]} = \frac{K_w}{K_{a_2}} = \frac{1.0 \times 10^{-14}}{4.7 \times 10^{-11}} = 2.1 \times 10^{-4} = \frac{x \cdot x}{1.000 - x} \approx \frac{x^2}{1.000}$$

$$[OH^-] = \sqrt{1.000 \times 2.1 \times 10^{-4}} = 1.4 \times 10^{-2} \text{ M} \qquad pOH = 1.85 \qquad pH = 12.15$$

Before the first equivalence point is reached, the pH is determined by the Henderson-Hasselbalch equation, modified as in Exercise 69, but using as the numerator the percent of carbonate ion remaining, and as the denominator the percent of carbonate ion that has been transformed to HCO_3^-.

90% titrated: $pH = 10.33 + \log\dfrac{10\%}{90\%} = 9.38$ 10% titrated: $pH = 10.33 + \log\dfrac{90\%}{10\%} = 11.28$

95% titrated: $pH = 10.33 + \log\dfrac{5\%}{95\%} = 9.05$ 5% titrated: $pH = 10.33 + \log\dfrac{95\%}{5\%} = 11.61$

During the course of the second step of the titration, the values of pH are precisely as they are for the titration of $NaHCO_3$, except the titrant volume is 10.00 mL more (the volume needed to reach the first equivalence point). The solution *at the second equivalence* point is 0.333 M H_2CO_3, for which the set-up is similar to that for 0.500 M H_2CO_3.

$$[H_3O^+] = \sqrt{0.333 \times 4.4 \times 10^{-7}} = 3.8 \times 10^{-4} \text{ M} \qquad pH = 3.42$$

After the equivalence point, the pH is determined by the excess H_3O^+.

For 0.5 mL excess of HCl: $[H_3O^+] = \dfrac{0.50 \text{ mL} \times 1.00 \text{ M}}{30.5 \text{ mL}} = 0.0164 \text{ M} \quad pH = 1.8$

For 2.00 mL excess of HCl: $[H_3O^+] = \dfrac{2.00 \text{ mL} \times 1.00 \text{ M}}{32.0 \text{ mL}} = 0.0625 \text{ M} \quad pH = 1.20$

The titration curve from these data is sketched below.

(c) $V_{HCl} = 1.00 \text{ g NaHCO}_3 \times \dfrac{1 \text{ mol NaHCO}_3}{84.01 \text{ g NaHCO}_3} \times \dfrac{1 \text{ mol HCl}}{1 \text{ mol NaHCO}_3} \times \dfrac{1000 \text{ mL}}{0.100 \text{ mol HCl}}$

$\qquad = 119 \text{ mL } 0.100 \text{ M HCl}$

(d) $V_{HCl} = 1.00 \text{ g Na}_2\text{CO}_3 \times \dfrac{1 \text{ mol Na}_2\text{CO}_3}{105.99 \text{ g Na}_2\text{CO}_3} \times \dfrac{2 \text{ mol HCl}}{1 \text{ mol Na}_2\text{CO}_3} \times \dfrac{1000 \text{ mL}}{0.100 \text{ mol HCl}}$

$\qquad = 189 \text{ mL } 0.100 \text{ M HCl}$

(e) The phenolphthalein endpoint occurs at pH = 8.00 and signifies that the NaOH has been neutralized, and that Na_2CO_3 has been half neutralized. The methyl orange endpoint occurs at about pH = 3.3 and is the result of the second equivalence point of Na_2CO_3. The mass of Na_2CO_3 can be determined as follows:

$$\text{mass Na}_2\text{CO}_3 = 0.78 \text{ mL} \times \dfrac{1 \text{ L}}{1000 \text{ mL}} \times \dfrac{0.1000 \text{ mol HCl}}{1 \text{ L soln}} \times \dfrac{1 \text{ mol HCO}_3^-}{1 \text{ mol HCl}} \dfrac{1 \text{ mol Na}_2\text{CO}_3}{1 \text{ mol HCO}_3^-}$$

$$\times \dfrac{105.99 \text{ g Na}_2\text{CO}_3}{1 \text{ mol Na}_2\text{CO}_3} = 0.0083 \text{ g Na}_2\text{CO}_3$$

$$\% \text{ Na}_2\text{CO}_3 = \dfrac{0.0083 \text{g}}{0.1000 \text{g}} \times 100 = 8.3\% \text{ Na}_2\text{CO}_3 \text{ by mass}$$

78. (M) We shall represent piperazine as Pip in what follows. The cation resulting from the first ionization is $HPiP^+$, and that resulting from the second ionization is H_2Pip^{2+}.

(a) $[Pip] = \dfrac{1.00\,g\ C_4H_{10}N_2 \cdot 6H_2O}{0.100\,L} \times \dfrac{1\,mol\ C_4H_{10}N_2 \cdot 6H_2O}{194.22\,g\ C_4H_{10}N_2 \cdot 6H_2O} = 0.0515\ M$

Equation:	Pip(aq)	+	$H_2O(l)$	$\rightleftharpoons$	$HPip^+$(aq)	+	OH^-(aq)
Initial:	0.0515 M		—		0 M		≈ 0 M
Changes:	$-x$ M		—		$+x$ M		$+x$ M
Equil:	$(0.0515 - x)$ M		—		x M		x M

$c_a/K_a = 858$; thus, the approximation is <u>not</u> valid. The full quadratic equation must be solved.

$$K_{b_1} = 10^{-4.22} = 6.0 \times 10^{-5} = \frac{[HPip^+][OH^-]}{[Pip]} = \frac{x \cdot x}{0.0515 - x}$$

From the roots of the equation, $x = [OH^-] = 1.7 \times 10^{-3}$ M $\quad$ pOH = 2.77 $\quad$ pH = 11.23

(b) At the half-equivalence point of the first step in the titration, pOH = pK_{b1} = 4.22
pH = 14.00 − pOH = 14.00 − 4.22 = 9.78

(c) Volume of HCl = 100. mL $\times \dfrac{0.0515\,mmol\ Pip}{1\,mL} \times \dfrac{1\,mmol\ HCl}{1\,mmol\ Pip} \times \dfrac{1\,mL\ titrant}{0.500\ mmol\ HCl} = 10.3\,mL$

(d) At the first equivalence point we have a solution of $HPip^+$. This ion can react as a base with H_2O to form H_2Pip^{2+} or it can react as an acid with water, forming Pip (i.e. $HPip^+$ is amphoteric). The solution's pH is determined as follows (base hydrolysis predominates):
pOH = ½ (pK_{b1} + pK_{b2}) = ½ (4.22 + 8.67) = 6.45, hence pH = 14.00 − 6.45 = 7.55

(e) The pOH at the half-equivalence point in the second step of the titration equals pK_{b2}.
pOH = pK_{b2} = 8.67 $\qquad$ pH = 14.00 − 8.67 = 5.33

(f) The volume needed to reach the second equivalence point is twice the volume needed to reach the first equivalence point, that is 2 × 10.3 mL = 20.6 mL.

(g) The pH at the second equivalence point is determined by the hydrolysis of the H_2Pip^{2+} cation, of which there is 5.15 mmol in solution, resulting from the reaction of $HPip^+$ with HCl. The total solution volume is 100. mL + 20.6 mL = 120.6 mL

$[H_2Pip^{2+}] = \dfrac{5.15\ mmol}{120.6\ mL} = 0.0427$ M $\qquad K_{b_2} = 10^{-8.67} = 2.1 \times 10^{-9}$

Equation:	H_2Pip^{2+}(aq)	+	$H_2O(l)$	$\rightleftharpoons$	$HPip^+$(aq)	+	H_3O^+(aq)
Initial:	0.0427 M		—		0 M		≈ 0 M
Changes:	$-x$ M		—		$+x$ M		$+x$ M
Equil:	$(0.0427 - x)$ M		—		x M		x M

$$K_a = \frac{K_w}{K_{b_2}} = \frac{1.00 \times 10^{-14}}{2.1 \times 10^{-9}} = \frac{[HPip^+][H_3O^+]}{[H_2Pip^{2+}]} = 4.8 \times 10^{-6} = \frac{x \cdot x}{0.0427 - x} \approx \frac{x^2}{0.0427}$$

$x = \sqrt{0.0427 \times 4.8 \times 10^{-6}} = 4.5 \times 10^{-4}$ $\qquad [H_3O^+] = 4.5 \times 10^{-4}$ M $\quad$ pH = 3.34$\underline{7}$
($x \ll 0.0427$; thus, the approximation is valid).

79. (M) Consider the two equilibria shown below.

$$H_2PO_4^-(aq) + H_2O(l) \rightleftharpoons HPO_4^{2-}(aq) + H_3O^+(aq) \qquad K_{a_2} = \frac{[HPO_4^{2-}][H_3O^+]}{[H_2PO_4^-]}$$

$$H_2PO_4^-(aq) + H_2O(l) \rightleftharpoons H_3PO_4(aq) + OH^-(aq) \qquad K_b = K_w/K_{a_1} = \frac{[H_3PO_4][OH^-]}{[H_2PO_4^-]}$$

All of the phosphorus containing species must add up to the initial molarity c.
Hence,   mass balance: $[HPO_4^{2-}] + [H_2PO_4^-] + [H_3PO_4] = c$
           charge balance: $[H_3O^+] + [Na^+] = [H_2PO_4^-] + 2\times[HPO_4^{2-}]$
           Note: $[Na^+]$ for a solution of $NaH_2PO_4 = c$
Thus, $[H_3O^+] + [Na^+] = [H_2PO_4^-] + 2\times[HPO_4^{2-}] = [H_3O^+] + c$ (substitute mass balance equation)
           $[H_3O^+] + [HPO_4^{2-}] + [H_2PO_4^-] + [H_3PO_4] = [H_2PO_4^-] + 2\times[HPO_4^{2-}]$ (cancel terms)
           $[H_3O^+] = [HPO_4^{2-}] - [H_3PO_4]$
           (Note: $[HPO_4^{2-}] =$ initial $[H_3O^+]$ and $[H_3PO_4] =$ initial $[OH^-]$)
           Thus: $[H_3O^+]_{equil} = [H_3O^+]_{initial} - [OH^-]_{initial}$ (excess H_3O^+ reacts with OH^- to form H_2O)
Rearrange the expression for K_{a_2} to solve for $[HPO_4^{2-}]$, and the expression for K_b
to solve for $[H_3PO_4]$.

$$[H_3O^+] = [HPO_4^{2-}] - [H_3PO_4] = \frac{K_{a_2}[H_2PO_4^-]}{[H_3O^+]} - \frac{K_b[H_2PO_4^-]}{[OH^-]}$$

$$[H_3O^+] = \frac{K_{a_2}[H_2PO_4^-]}{[H_3O^+]} - \frac{\dfrac{K_w}{K_{a_1}}[H_2PO_4^-]}{\dfrac{K_w}{[H_3O^+]}} = \frac{K_{a_2}[H_2PO_4^-]}{[H_3O^+]} - \frac{[H_3O^+][H_2PO_4^-]}{K_{a_1}}$$

Multiply through by $[H_3O^+]K_{a_1}$ and solve for $[H_3O^+]$.

$$K_{a_1}[H_3O^+][H_3O^+] = K_{a_1}K_{a_2}[H_2PO_4^-] - [H_3O^+][H_3O^+][H_2PO_4^-]$$

$$K_{a_1}[H_3O^+]^2 = K_{a_1}K_{a_2}[H_2PO_4^-] - [H_3O^+]^2[H_2PO_4^-]$$

$$K_{a_1}[H_3O^+]^2 + [H_3O^+]^2[H_2PO_4^-] = K_{a_1}K_{a_2}[H_2PO_4^-] = [H_3O^+]^2(K_{a_1} + [H_2PO_4^-])$$

$$K_{a_1}[H_3O^+]^2 + [H_3O^+]^2[H_2PO_4^-] = K_{a_1}K_{a_2}[H_2PO_4^-] = [H_3O^+]^2(K_{a_1} + [H_2PO_4^-])$$

$$[H_3O^+]^2 = \frac{K_{a_1}K_{a_2}[H_2PO_4^-]}{(K_{a_1} + [H_2PO_4^-])} \quad \text{For moderate concentrations of } [H_2PO_4^-],\ K_{a_1} \ll [H_2PO_4^-]$$

This simplifies our expression to: $[H_3O^+]^2 = \dfrac{K_{a_1}K_{a_2}[H_2PO_4^-]}{[H_2PO_4^-]} = K_{a_1}K_{a_2}$

Take the square root of both sides: $[H_3O^+]^2 = K_{a_1}K_{a_2} \longrightarrow [H_3O^+] = \sqrt{K_{a_1}K_{a_2}} = (K_{a_1}K_{a_2})^{1/2}$

Take the $-\log$ of both sides and simplify:

$$-\log[H_3O^+] = -\log(K_{a_1}K_{a_2})^{1/2} = -1/2\left(\log(K_{a_1}K_{a_2})\right) = -1/2(\log K_{a_1} + \log K_{a_2})$$

$-\log[H_3O^+] = 1/2(-\log K_{a_1} - \log K_{a_2})$ Use $-\log[H_3O^+] = pH$ and $-\log K_{a_1} = pK_{a_2} - \log K_{a_2} = pK_{a_2}$

Hence, $-\log[H_3O^+] = +1/2(-\log K_{a_1} - \log K_{a_2})$ becomes $pH = 1/2(pK_{a_1} + pK_{a_2})$ (Equation 17.10)
Equation 17.11 can be similarly derived.

80. **(D)** $H_2PO_4^-$ can react with H_2O by both ionization and hydrolysis.

$$H_2PO_4^-\ (aq) + H_2O(l) \rightleftharpoons HPO_4^{2-}(aq) + H_3O^+(aq)$$

$$HPO_4^{2-}(aq) + H_2O(l) \rightleftharpoons PO_4^{3-}(aq) + H_3O^+(aq)$$

The solution cannot have a large concentration of both H_3O^+ and OH^- (cannot be simultaneously an acidic and a basic solution). Since the solution **is** acidic, some of the H_3O^+ produced in the first reaction reacts with virtually all of the OH^- produced in the second. In the first reaction $[H_3O^+] = [HPO_4^{2-}]$ and in the second reaction $[OH^-] = [H_3PO_4]$. Thus, following the neutralization of OH^- by H_3O^+, we have the following.

$$[H_3O^+] = [HPO_4^{2-}] - [H_2PO_4^-] = \frac{K_{a_2}[H_2PO_4^-]}{[H_3O^+]} - \frac{K_b[H_2PO_4^-]}{[OH^-]} = \frac{K_{a_2}[H_2PO_4^-]}{[H_3O^+]} - \frac{\dfrac{K_w}{K_{a_1}}[H_2PO_4^-]}{\dfrac{K_w}{[H_3O^+]}}$$

$$= \frac{K_{a_2}[H_2PO_4^-]}{[H_3O^+]} - \frac{[H_3O^+][H_2PO_4^-]}{K_{a_1}} \qquad \text{Then multiply through by } [H_3O^+]K_{a_1} \text{ and solve for } [H_3O^+].$$

$$[H_3O^+]^2 K_{a_1} = K_{a_1}K_{a_2}[H_2PO_4^-] - [H_3O^+]^2[H_2PO_4^-] \qquad [H_3O^+] = \sqrt{\frac{K_{a_1}K_{a_2}[H_2PO_4^-]}{[K_{a_1}+[H_2PO_4^-]]}}$$

But, for a moderate $[H_2PO_4^-]$, from Table 16-6, $K_{a_1} = 7.1 \times 10^{-3} < [H_2PO_4^-]$ and thus $K_{a_1} + [H_2PO_4^-] \approx [H_2PO_4^-]$. Then we have the following expressions for $[H_3O^+]$ and pH.

$$[H_3O^+] = \sqrt{K_{a_1} \times K_{a_2}}$$

$$pH = -\log[H_3O^+] = -\log(K_{a_1} \times K_{a_2})^{1/2} = \tfrac{1}{2}[-\log(K_{a_1} \times K_{a_2})] = \tfrac{1}{2}(-\log K_{a_1} - \log K_{a_2})$$

$$pH = \tfrac{1}{2}(pK_{a_1} + pK_{a_2})$$

Notice that we assumed $K_a < [H_2PO_4^-]$. This assumption is not valid in quite dilute solutions because $K_a = 0.0071$.

81. **(D)**
   (a) A buffer solution is able to react with small amounts of added acid or base. When strong acid is added, it reacts with formate ion.

   $$HCOO^-(aq) + H_3O^+(aq) \longrightarrow HCOOH(aq) + H_2O$$

   Added strong base reacts with acetic acid.

   $$CH_3COOH(aq) + OH^-(aq) \longrightarrow H_2O(l) + CH_3COO^-(aq)$$

   Therefore neither added strong acid nor added strong base alters the pH of the solution very much. Mixtures of this type are referred to as buffer solutions.

(b) We begin with the two ionization reactions.

$$HCOOH(aq) + H_2O(l) \rightleftharpoons HCOO^-(aq) + H_3O^+(aq)$$

$$CH_3COOH(aq) + H_2O(l) \rightleftharpoons CH_3COO^-(aq) + H_3O^+(aq)$$

$[Na^+] = 0.250 \quad [OH^-] \approx 0 \quad\quad [H_3O^+] = x \quad [CH_3COO^-] = y \quad [HCOO^-] = z$

$0.150 = [CH_3COOH] + [CH_3COO^-] \quad [CH_3COOH] = 0.150 - [CH_3COO^-] = 0.150 - y$

$0.250 = [HCOOH] + [HCOO^-] \quad\quad [HCOOH] = 0.250 - [HCOO^-] = 0.250 - z$

$[Na^+] + [H_3O^+] = [CH_3COO^-] + [HCOO^-] + [OH^-] \text{ (electroneutrality)}$

$$0.250 + x = [CH_3COO^-] + [HCOO^-] = y + z \tag{1}$$

$$\frac{[H_3O^+][CH_3COO^-]}{[CH_3COOH]} = K_A = 1.8 \times 10^{-5} = \frac{x \cdot y}{0.150 - y} \tag{2}$$

$$\frac{[H_3O^+][HCOO^-]}{[HCOOH]} = K_F = 1.8 \times 10^{-4} = \frac{x \cdot z}{0.250 - z} \tag{3}$$

There now are three equations—(1), (2), and (3)—in three unknowns—x, y, and z. We solve equations (2) and (3), respectively, for y and z in terms of x.

$$0.150\,K_A - y\,K_A = xy \quad\quad\quad y = \frac{0.150\,K_A}{K_A + x}$$

$$0.250\,K_F - z\,K_F = xz \quad\quad\quad z = \frac{0.250\,K_F}{K_F + x}$$

Then we substitute these expressions into equation (1) and solve for x.

$$0.250 + x = \frac{0.150\,K_A}{K_A + x} + \frac{0.250\,K_F}{K_F + x} \approx 0.250 \quad\quad \text{since } x \ll 0.250$$

$$0.250\,(K_F + x)(K_A + x) = 0.150\,K_A\,(K_F + x) + 0.250\,K_F\,(K_A + x)$$

$$K_A K_F + (K_A + K_F)x + x^2 = 1.60\,K_A K_F + x(0.600\,K_A + 1.00\,K_F)$$

$$x^2 + 0.400\,K_A x - 0.600\,K_A K_F = 0 = x^2 + 7.2 \times 10^{-6} x - 1.9 \times 10^{-9}$$

$$x = \frac{-7.2 \times 10^{-6} \pm \sqrt{5.2 \times 10^{-11} + 7.6 \times 10^{-9}}}{2} = 4.0 \times 10^{-5} \text{ M} = [H_3O^+]$$

pH = 4.40

(c) Adding 1.00 L of 0.100 M HCl to 1.00 L of buffer of course dilutes the concentrations of all components by a factor of 2. Thus, $[Na^+] = 0.125$ M; total acetate concentration = 0.0750 M; total formate concentration = 0.125 M. Also, a new ion is added to the solution, namely, $[Cl^-] = 0.0500$ M.

$[Na^+] = 0.125 \quad [OH^-] \approx 0 \quad [H_3O^+] = x \quad [Cl^-] = 0.0500 \text{ M} \quad [CH_3COO^-] = y \quad [HCOO^-] = z$

$0.0750 = [CH_3COOH] + [CH_3COO^-] \quad [CH_3COOH] = 0.0750 - [CH_3COO^-] = 0.0750 - y$

$0.125 = [HCOOH] + [HCOO^-] \qquad [HCOOH] = 0.125 - [HCOO^-] = 0.125 - z$

$[Na^+] + [H_3O^+] = [CH_3COO^-] + [OH^-] + [HCOO^-] + [Cl^-] \text{ (electroneutrality)}$

$0.125 + x = [CH_3COO^-] + [HCOO^-] + [Cl^-] = y + z + 0 + 0.0500 \qquad 0.075 + x = y + z$

$$\frac{[H_3O^+][CH_3COO^-]}{[CH_3COOH]} = K_A = 1.8 \times 10^{-5} = \frac{x \cdot y}{0.0750 - y}$$

$$\frac{[H_3O^+][HCOO^-]}{[HCOOH]} = K_F = 1.8 \times 10^{-4} = \frac{x \cdot z}{0.125 - z}$$

Again, we solve the last two equations for y and z in terms of x.

$$0.0750\, K_A - y\, K_A = xy \qquad y = \frac{0.0750\, K_A}{K_A + x}$$

$$0.125\, K_F - z\, K_F = xz \qquad z = \frac{0.125\, K_F}{K_F + x}$$

Then we substitute these expressions into equation (1) and solve for x.

$$0.0750 + x = \frac{0.0750\, K_A}{K_A + x} + \frac{0.125\, K_F}{K_F + x} \approx 0.0750 \qquad \text{since } x \ll 0.0750$$

$0.0750\, (K_F + x)\, (K_A + x) = 0.0750\, K_A\, (K_F + x) + 0.125\, K_F\, (K_A + x)$

$K_A K_F + (K_A + K_F)x + x^2 = 2.67\, K_A K_F + x(1.67\, K_F + 1.00\, K_A)$

$x^2 - 0.67\, K_F x - 1.67\, K_A K_F = 0 = x^2 - 1.2 \times 10^{-4} x - 5.4 \times 10^{-9}$

$$x = \frac{1.2 \times 10^{-4} \pm \sqrt{1.4 \times 10^{-8} + 2.2 \times 10^{-8}}}{2} = 1.55 \times 10^{-4}\ M = [H_3O^+]$$

$pH = 3.81 \approx 3.8$

As expected, the addition of HCl(aq), a strong acid, caused the pH to drop. The decrease in pH was relatively small, nonetheless, because the H_3O^+(aq) was converted to the much weaker acid HCOOH via the neutralization reaction:

$HCOO^-$(aq) + H_3O^+(aq) $\rightarrow$ HCOOH(aq) + H_2O(l)   (buffering action)

82. **(M)** First we find the pH at the equivalence point:

$$CH_3CH(OH)COOH(aq) + OH^-(aq) \rightleftharpoons CH_3CH(OH)COO^-(aq) + H_2O(l)$$

$$\text{1 mmol} \qquad\qquad \text{1 mmol} \qquad\qquad \text{1 mmol}$$

The concentration of the salt is 1×10^{-3} mol/0.1 L = 0.01 M

The lactate anion undergoes hydrolysis thus:

$$CH_3CH(OH)COO^-(aq) + H_2O(l) \rightleftharpoons CH_3CH(OH)COOH(aq) + OH^-(aq)$$

Initial	0.01 M	–	0 M	≈ 0 M
Change	$-x$	–	$+x$	$+x$
Equilibrium	$(0.01 - x)$ M	–	x	x

Where x is the [hydrolyzed lactate ion], as well as that of the [OH$^-$] produced by hydrolysis

$$K \text{ for the above reaction} = \frac{[CH_3CH(OH)COOH][OH^-]}{[CH_3CH(OH)COO^-]} = \frac{K_w}{K_a} = \frac{1.0 \times 10^{-14}}{10^{-3.86}} = 7.2 \times 10^{-11}$$

so $\dfrac{x^2}{0.01-x} \approx \dfrac{x^2}{0.01} = 7.2 \times 10^{-11}$ and $x = 8.49 \times 10^{-7}$; $[OH^-] = 8.49 \times 10^{-7}$ M

$x \ll 0.01$, thus, the assumption is valid

$$pOH = -\log(8.49 \times 10^{-7}) = 6.07 \qquad pH = 14 - pOH = 14.00 - 6.07 = 7.93$$

(a) Bromthymol blue or phenol red would be good indicators for this titration since they change color over this pH range.

(b) The $H_2PO_4^-/HPO_4^{2-}$ system would be suitable because the pK_a for the acid (namely, $H_2PO_4^-$) is close to the equivalence point pH of 7.93. An acetate buffer would be too acidic, an ammonia buffer too basic.

(c) $H_2PO_4^- + H_2O \rightleftharpoons H_3O^+ + HPO_4^{2-}$ $K_{a2} = 6.3 \times 10^{-8}$

Solving for $\dfrac{[HPO_4^{2-}]}{[H_2PO_4^-]} = \dfrac{K_{a2}}{[H_3O^+]} = \dfrac{6.3 \times 10^{-8}}{10^{-7.93}} = 5.4$ (buffer ratio required)

83. **(M)**

$$H_2O_2(aq) + H_2O(l) \rightleftharpoons H_3O^+(aq) + HO_2^-(aq) \qquad K_a = \frac{[H_3O^+][HO_2^-]}{[H_2O_2]}$$

Data taken from experiments 1 and 2:

$[H_2O_2] + [HO_2^-] = 0.259$ M $\qquad (6.78) \times (0.00357$ M$) + [HO_2^-] = 0.259$ M

$[HO_2^-] = 0.235$ M $\qquad [H_2O_2] = (6.78)(0.00357$ M$) = 0.0242$ M

$[H_3O^+] = 10^{-(pKw - pOH)}$

$-\log(0.250 - 0.235)$ M NaOH$) = -\log(0.015$ M NaOH$) = 1.82\underline{4}$

$[H_3O^+] = 10^{-(14.94 - 1.82\underline{4})} = 7.7 \times 10^{-14}$

$$K_a = \frac{[H_3O^+][HO_2^-]}{[H_2O_2]} = \frac{(7.7\times10^{-14})(0.235)}{(0.0242)} = 7.4\times10^{-13}$$

$$pK_a = 12.14$$

From data taken from experiments 1 and 3:

$[H_2O_2]+[HO_2^-]=0.123 \text{ M}$ $\qquad$ $(6.78)(0.00198 \text{ M})+[HO_2^-]=0.123 \text{ M}$

$[HO_2^-]=0.109\underline{6} \text{ M}$

$[H_2O_2]=(6.78)(0.00198 \text{ M})=0.0134 \text{ M}$

$[H_3O^+]=10^{-(pK_w-pOH)}$, $\quad pOH=-\log[(0.125-0.109\underline{6}) \text{ M NaOH}]=1.81$

$[H_3O^+]=10^{-(14.94-1.81)}=7.41\times10^{-14}$

$$K_a = \frac{[H_3O^+][HO_2^-]}{[H_2O_2]} = \frac{(7.41\times10^{-14})(0.1096)}{(0.0134)} = 6.06\times10^{-13}$$

$$pK_a = -\log(6.06\times10^{-13})=12.22$$

Average value for $pK_a = 12.17$

84. **(D)** Let's consider some of the important processes occurring in the solution.

(1) $HPO_4^{2-}(aq)+H_2O(l)\rightleftharpoons H_2PO_4^-(aq)+OH^-(aq)$ $\quad K_{(1)}=K_{a_2}=4.2\times10^{-13}$

(2) $HPO_4^{2-}(aq)+H_2O(l)\rightleftharpoons H_3O^+(aq)+PO_4^{3-}(aq)$ $\quad K_{(2)}=K_b=\dfrac{1.0\times10^{-14}}{6.3\times10^{-8}}=1.6\times10^{-7}$

(3) $NH_4^+(aq)+H_2O(l)\rightleftharpoons H_3O^+(aq)+NH_3(aq)$ $\quad K_{(3)}=K_a=\dfrac{1.0\times10^{-14}}{1.8\times10^{-5}}=5.6\times10^{-10}$

(4) $NH_4^+(aq)+OH^-(aq)\rightleftharpoons H_2O(l)+NH_3(aq)$ $\quad K_{(4)}=\dfrac{1}{1.8\times10^{-5}}=5.6\times10^4$

May have interaction between NH_4^+ and OH^- formed from the hydrolysis of HPO_4^{2-}.

$\qquad NH_4^+(aq) \;+\; HPO_4^{2-}(aq) \;\rightleftharpoons\; H_2PO_4^-(aq)+NH_3(aq)$

Initial $\quad$ 0.10M $\qquad$ 0.10M $\qquad\qquad$ 0 M $\qquad$ 0 M

Change $\quad -x \qquad\qquad -x \qquad\qquad +x \qquad +x$

Equil. $\quad 0.100-x \quad 0.100-x \qquad\quad x \qquad\quad x$

(where x is the molar concentration of NH_4^+ that hydrolyzes)

$$K = K_{(2)}\times K_{(4)} = (1.6\times10^{-7})\times(5.6\times10^4)= 9.0\times10^{-3}$$

$$K=\frac{[H_2PO_4^-][NH_3]}{[NH_4^+][HPO_4^{2-}]}=\frac{[x]^2}{[0.10-x]^2}=9.0\times10^{-3}\text{ and } x=8.7\times10^{-3}$$

Finding the pH of this buffer system:

$$pH = pK_a + \log\frac{[HPO_4{}^{2-}]}{[H_2PO_4{}^-]} = -\log(6.3\times10^{-8}) + \log\left(\frac{0.100 - 8.7\times10^{-3}\,M}{8.7\times10^{-3}\,M}\right) = 8.2$$

As expected, we get the same result using the $NH_3/NH_4{}^+$ buffer system.

85. Consider the two weak acids and the equilibrium for water (autodissociation)

$$HA(aq) + H_2O(l) \rightleftharpoons H_3O^+(aq) + A^-(aq) \quad K_{HA} = \frac{[H_3O^+][A^-]}{[HA]} \quad [HA] = \frac{[H_3O^+][A^-]}{K_{HA}}$$

$$HB(aq) + H_2O(l) \rightleftharpoons H_3O^+(aq) + B^-(aq) \quad K_{HB} = \frac{[H_3O^+][B^-]}{[HB]} \quad [HB] = \frac{[H_3O^+][B^-]}{K_{HB}}$$

$$H_2O(l) + H_2O(l) \rightleftharpoons H_3O^+(aq) + OH^-(aq) \quad K_w = [H_3O^+][OH^-] \quad [OH^-] = \frac{K_w}{[H_3O^+]}$$

Mass Balance: $[HA]_{initial} = [HA]+[A^-] = \dfrac{[H_3O^+][A^-]}{K_{HA}} + [A^-] = [A^-]\left(\dfrac{[H_3O^+]}{K_{HA}} + 1\right)$

From which: $[A^-] = \dfrac{[HA]_{initial}}{\left(\dfrac{[H_3O^+]}{K_{HA}} + 1\right)}$

$[HB]_{initial} = [HB]+[B^-] = \dfrac{[H_3O^+][B^-]}{K_{HB}} + [B^-] = [B^-]\left(\dfrac{[H_3O^+]}{K_{HB}} + 1\right)$

From which: $[B^-] = \dfrac{[HB]_{initial}}{\left(\dfrac{[H_3O^+]}{K_{HB}} + 1\right)}$

Charge Balance: $[H_3O^+] = [A^-]+[B^-]+[OH^-]$ (substitute above expressions)

$$[H_3O^+] = \frac{[HA]_{initial}}{\left(\dfrac{[H_3O^+]}{K_{HA}}+1\right)} + \frac{[HB]_{initial}}{\left(\dfrac{[H_3O^+]}{K_{HB}}+1\right)} + \frac{K_w}{[H_3O^+]}$$

86. (D) We are told that the solution is 0.050 M in acetic acid ($K_a = 1.8\times10^{-5}$) and 0.010 M in phenyl acetic acid ($K_a = 4.9\times10^{-5}$). Because the K_a values are close, both equilibria must be satisfied simultaneously. Note: $[H_3O^+]$ is common to both equilibria (assume z is the concentration of $[H_3O^+]$).

Reaction:	$CH_3COOH(aq) + H_2O(l)$	$\rightleftharpoons$	$CH_3COO^-(aq)$	$+ H_3O^+(aq)$
Initial:	0.050 M	—	0 M	≈ 0 M
Change:	$-x$ M	—	$+x$ M	$+z$ M
Equilibrium	$(0.050 - x)$M	—	x M	z M

864

For acetic acid: $K_a = \dfrac{[H_3O^+][CH_3COO^-]}{[CH_3COOH]} = \dfrac{xz}{(0.050-x)} = 1.8\times10^{-5}$ or $x = \dfrac{1.8\times10^{-5}(0.050-x)}{z}$

Reaction: $\quad$ C$_6$H$_5$CH$_2$COOH (aq) $\quad$ + H$_2$O(l) $\quad\rightleftharpoons\quad$ C$_6$H$_5$CH$_2$COO$^-$ (aq) $\quad$ + H$_3$O$^+$ (aq)

Initial: $\qquad$ 0.010 M $\qquad\qquad$ — $\qquad\qquad\qquad\qquad$ 0 M $\qquad\qquad$ ≈ 0 M

Change: $\qquad\quad$ –y M $\qquad\qquad$ — $\qquad\qquad\qquad\qquad$ + y M $\qquad\qquad$ + z M

Equilibrium $\quad$ (0.010 – y)M $\qquad$ — $\qquad\qquad\qquad\qquad\quad$ y M $\qquad\qquad\quad$ z M

For phenylacetic acid: $K_a = \dfrac{[H_3O^+][C_6H_5CH_2COO^-]}{[C_6H_5CH_2COOH]} = \dfrac{yz}{(0.010-y)} = 4.9\times10^{-5}$

or $y = \dfrac{4.9\times10^{-5}(0.010-y)}{z}$

There are now three variables: $x = [CH_3COO^-]$, $y = [C_6H_5CH_2COO^-]$, and $z = [H_3O^+]$
These are the only charged species, hence, $x + y = z$.
(This equation neglects contribution from the $[H_3O^+]$ from water.)
Next we substitute in the values of x and y from the rearranged K_a expressions above.

$$x + y = z = \frac{1.8\times10^{-5}(0.050-x)}{z} + \frac{4.9\times10^{-5}(0.010-y)}{z}$$

Since these are weak acids, we can simplify this expression by assuming that $x \ll 0.050$ and $y \ll 0.010$.

$$z = \frac{1.8\times10^{-5}(0.050)}{z} + \frac{4.9\times10^{-5}(0.010)}{z}$$ Simplify even further by multiplying through by z.

$z_2 = 9.0 \times 10^{-7} + 4.9 \times 10^{-7} = 1.4 \times 10^{-6}$

$z = 1.18 \times 10^{-3} = [H_3O^+]$ $\qquad$ From which we find that $x = 7.6 \times 10^{-4}$ and $y = 4.2 \times 10^{-4}$
(as a quick check, we do see that $x + y = z$).

We finish up by checking to see if the approximation is valid (5% rule).

For x : $\dfrac{7.6\times10^{-4}}{0.050}\times100\% = 1.5\%$ $\qquad$ For y : $\dfrac{4.2\times10^{-4}}{0.010}\times100\% = 4.2\%$

Since both are less than 5%, we can be assured that the assumption is valid.
The pH of the solution = $-\log(1.18 \times 10^{-3}) = 2.93$.
(If we simply plug the appropriate values into the equation developed in the previous question we get the exact answer 2.933715 (via the method of successive approximations), but the final answers can only be reported to 2 significant figures. Hence the best we can do is say that the pH is expected to be 2.93 (which is the same level of precision as that for the result obtained following the 5% rule).

87. (D)

(a) By using dilution, there are an infinite number of ways of preparing the pH = 7.79 buffer. We will consider a method that does not use dilution.

Let TRIS = weak base and $TRISH^+$ be the conjugate acid.

$pK_b = 5.91$, $pK_a = 14 - pK_b = 8.09$ Use the Henderson Hasselbalch equation.

$pH = pK_a + \log (TRIS/TRISH^+) = 7.79 = 8.09 + \log (TRIS/TRISH^+)$

$\log (TRIS/TRISH^+) = 7.79 - 8.09 = -0.30$ Take antilog of both sides

$(TRIS/TRISH^+) = 10^{-0.30} = 0.50$; Therefore, $nTRIS = 0.50(nTRISH^+)$

Since there is no guidance given on the capacity of the buffer, we will choose an arbitrary starting point. We start with 1.00 L of 0.200 M TRIS (0.200 moles). We need to convert 2/3 of this to the corresponding acid ($TRISH^+$) using 10.0 M HCl, in order for the TRIS/$TRISH^+$ ratio to be 0.5. In all, we need (2/3) × 0.200 mol of HCl, or a total of 0.133 moles of HCl.

Volume of HCl required = 0.133 mol ÷ 10.0 mol/L = 0.0133 L or 13.3 mL.

This would give a total volume of 1013.3 mL, which is almost a liter (within 1.3%). If we wish to make up exactly one liter, we should only use 987 mL of 0.200 M TRIS. This would require 13.2 mL of HCl, resulting in a final volume of 1.0002 L.

Let's do a quick double check of our calculations.
$nHCl = 0.0132 \text{ L} \times 10.0 \text{ M} = 0.132 \text{ mol} = nTRISH^+$
$nTRIS = n\text{initial} - n\text{reacted} = 0.200 \text{ M} \times 0.987 \text{ L} - 0.132 \text{ mol} = 0.0654 \text{ mol}$
$pH = pK_a + \log (TRIS/TRISH^+) = 8.09 + \log (0.0654 \text{ mol}/0.132 \text{ mol}) = 7.785$

We have prepared the desired buffer (realize that this is just one way of preparing the buffer).

(b) To 500 mL of the buffer prepared above, is added 0.030 mol H_3O^+.
In the 500 mL of solution we have 0.132 mol ÷ 2 mol $TRISH^+$ = 0.0660 mol $TRISH^+$ and 0.0654 mol ÷ 2 mol TRIS = 0.032$\underline{7}$ mol TRIS (we will assume no change in volume).

HCl will completely react (≈ 100%) with TRIS, converting it to $TRISH^+$.
After complete reaction, there will be no excess HCl, 0.0327 mol – 0.0300 mol = 0.0027 mol TRIS and 0.0660 mol + 0.0300 mol = 0.0960 mol $TRISH^+$.

By employing the Henderson Hasselbalch equation, we can estimate the pH of the resulting solution:

$pH = pK_a + \log (TRIS/TRISH^+) = 8.09 + \log (0.0027 \text{ mol}/0.0960 \text{ mol}) = 6.54$
This represents a pH change of 1.25 units. The buffer is nearly exhausted owing to the fact that almost all of the TRIS has been converted to $TRISH^+$. Generally, a pH change of 1 unit suggests that the capacity of the buffer has been pretty much completely expended. This is the case here.

(Alternatively, you may solve this question using an ICE table).

(c) Addition of 20.0 mL of 10.0 M HCl will complete exhaust the buffer (in part (b) we saw that addition of 3 mL of HCl used up most of the TRIS in solution). The buffer may be regenerated by adding 20.0 mL of 10.0 M NaOH. The buffer will be only slightly diluted after the addition of HCl and NaOH (500 mL → 540 mL). Through the slow and careful addition of NaOH, one can regenerate the pH = 7.79 buffer in this way (if a pH meter is used to monitor the addition).

88. (M)

(a) The formula given needs to be rearranged to isolate α, as shown below.

$$pH = pK_a - \log\left(\frac{1}{\alpha} - 1\right)$$

$$pH - pK_a = -\log\left(\frac{\left[H_3O^+\right]}{K_a}\right) = -\log\left(\frac{1}{\alpha} - 1\right)$$

$$\frac{\left[H_3O^+\right]}{K_a} = \frac{1}{\alpha} - 1$$

$$\alpha = \frac{K_a}{\left[H_3O^+\right] + K_a} = \frac{K_a}{10^{-pH} + K_a}$$

Now, use the given K_a (6.3×10^{-8}) and calculate α for a range of pH values.

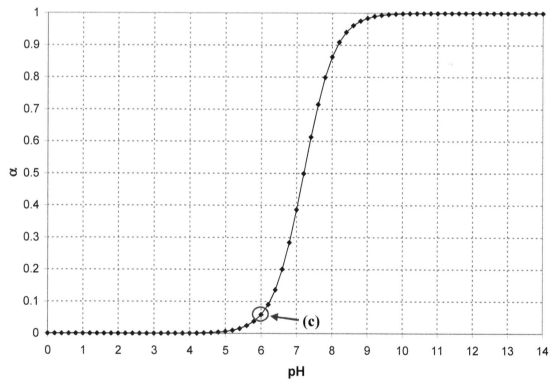

(b) When $pH = pK_a$, $\alpha = 0.5$ or 50%.

(c) At a pH of 6.0, $\alpha = \dfrac{K_a}{10^{-pH} + K_a} = \dfrac{6.3 \times 10^{-8}}{10^{-6.0} + 6.3 \times 10^{-8}} = 0.059$ or 5.9%.

89. **(D)**

(a) We start by writing the equilibrium expression for all reactions:

$$K_1 = \frac{\left[CO_2\left(aq\right)\right]}{\left[CO_2\left(g\right)\right]} \qquad\qquad K_2 = \left[Ca^{2+}\right]\left[CO_3^{2-}\right]$$

$$K_3 = \frac{\left[HCO_3^-\right]}{\left[H_3O^+\right]\left[CO_3^{2-}\right]} \qquad\qquad K_4 = \frac{\left[CO_2\left(aq\right)\right]}{\left[HCO_3^-\right]\left[H_3O^+\right]}$$

First, we have to express $[H_3O^+]$ using the available expressions:

$$\left[H_3O^+\right] = \frac{\left[HCO_3^-\right]}{K_3\left[CO_3^{2-}\right]}$$

$$\left[H_3O^+\right] = \frac{\left[CO_2\left(aq\right)\right]}{K_4\left[HCO_3^-\right]}$$

$$\left[H_3O^+\right]^2 = \frac{\left[HCO_3^-\right]}{K_3\left[CO_3^{2-}\right]} \times \frac{\left[CO_2\left(aq\right)\right]}{K_4\left[HCO_3^-\right]} = \frac{\left[CO_2\left(aq\right)\right]}{K_3 \cdot K_4\left[CO_3^{2-}\right]}$$

From the expression for K_1, we know that $[CO_2(aq)] = K_1[CO_2(g)]$. Therefore,

$$\left[H_3O^+\right]^2 = \frac{K_1\left[CO_2\left(g\right)\right]}{K_3 \cdot K_4\left[CO_3^{2-}\right]}$$

Now, the expression for K_2 can be plugged into the above expression as follows:

$$\left[H_3O^+\right]^2 = \frac{K_1\left[CO_2\left(g\right)\right]}{K_3 \cdot K_4\left[CO_3^{2-}\right]} = \frac{K_1\left[CO_2\left(g\right)\right]\left[Ca^{2+}\right]}{K_2 \cdot K_3 \cdot K_4}$$

$$\left[H_3O^+\right] = \sqrt{\frac{K_1\left[CO_2\left(g\right)\right]\left[Ca^{2+}\right]}{K_2 \cdot K_3 \cdot K_4}}$$

(b) The K values for the reactions are as follows:

$K_1 = 0.8317$ (given in the problem)

$K_2 = 2.8 \times 10^{-9}$ (given in the problem)

$K_3 = 1/K_a$ of $HCO_3^- = 1/(4.7 \times 10^{-11}) = 2.13 \times 10^{10}$

$K_4 = 1/K_a$ of $H_2CO_3 = 1/(4.4 \times 10^{-7}) = 2.27 \times 10^6$

$$[CO_2(g)] = \frac{280 \times 10^{-6} \text{ L } CO_2}{\text{L air}} \times \frac{1 \text{ mol } CO_2}{24.45 \text{ L } CO_2} = 1.145 \times 10^{-5} \frac{\text{mol } CO_2}{\text{L air}}$$

$$[H_3O^+] = \sqrt{\frac{K_1[CO_2(g)][Ca^{2+}]}{K_2 \cdot K_3 \cdot K_4}} = \sqrt{\frac{(0.8317)(1.145 \times 10^{-5})(10.24 \times 10^{-3})}{(2.8 \times 10^{-9})(2.13 \times 10^{10})(2.27 \times 10^6)}}$$

$$= 2.684 \times 10^{-8} \text{ M}$$

$$pH = -\log(2.684 \times 10^{-8}) = 7.57$$

90. **(M)** To determine pH, we must first determine what is the final charge balance of the solution *without* adding any H_3O^+ or OH^- ions. As such, we have to calculate the number of moles of each ion (assume 1 L):

Moles of Na^+: 23.0 g Na^+ × (1 mol/23.0 g) = 1.00 mol Na^+
Moles of Ca^{2+}: 10.0 g Ca^{2+} × (1 mol/40.0 g) = 0.250 mol Ca^{2+}
Moles of CO_3^{2-}: 40.02 g CO_3^{2-} × (1 mol/60.01 g) = 0.670 mol CO_3^{2-}
Moles of SO_4^{2-}: 9.6 g SO_4^{2-} × (1 mol/96.056 g) = 0.100 mol

Looking at the list of ions and consulting the solubility guide, we note that Ca^{2+} will precipitate with both SO_4^{2-} and CO_3^{2-}. Since both of these anions have a 2− charge, it doesn't matter with which anion the precipitation occurs (in reality, it does a little, but the effects are small compared to the effects of adding H_3O^+ or OH^- ions).

Moles of anions left = (0.670 + 0.100) − 0.250 = 0.520 moles

Since we have 0.520 moles of 2− ions, we must have 1.04 moles of 1+ ions to balance. However, we only have 1 mole of Na^+. The difference in charge is:
1.04(−) − 1.0(+) = 0.04(−) moles of ions

To balance, we need 0.04 moles of H_3O^+. The pH = −log (0.04) = 1.40.

91. **(M)**
(a) We note that the pH is 5.0. Therefore, $[H_3O^+] = 10^{-5.0} = 1.0 \times 10^{-5}$ M

$$\beta = \frac{C \cdot K_a \cdot [H_3O^+]}{(K_a + [H_3O^+])^2} = \frac{(2.0 \times 10^{-2})(1.8 \times 10^{-5})(1.0 \times 10^{-5})}{(1.8 \times 10^{-5} + 1.0 \times 10^{-5})^2} = 4.6 \times 10^{-3}$$

(b) $\beta \approx -dC_A / d(pH) \Rightarrow d(pH) \approx -dC_A / \beta$

$$d(pH) = -(1.0 \times 10^{-3}) / 4.6 \times 10^{-3} = -0.22$$

$$pH = 5 - 0.22 = 4.78$$

(c) At an acetic acid concentration of 0.1 M, C is also 0.1, because C is the total concentration of the acetic acid and acetate. The maximum buffer index β (2.50×10^{-2}) happens at a pH of 4.75, where [HAc] = [Ac⁻]. The minima are located at pH values of 8.87 (which correspond to pH of a solution of 0.1 M acetic acid and 0.1 M acetate, respectively).

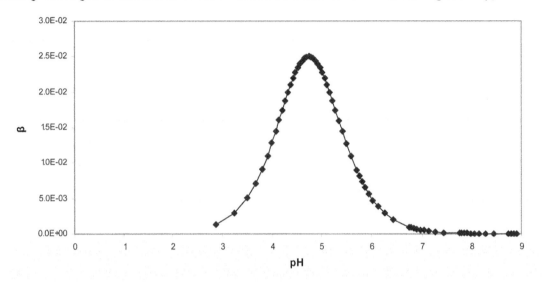

FEATURE PROBLEMS

92. **(D)**

(a) The two curves cross the point at which half of the total acetate is present as acetic acid and half is present as acetate ion. This is the half equivalence point in a titration, where pH = pK_a = 4.74.

(b) For carbonic acid, there are three carbonate containing species: "H_2CO_3" which predominates at low pH, HCO_3^-, and CO_3^{2-}, which predominates in alkaline solution. The points of intersection should occur at the half-equivalence points in each step-wise titration: at pH = pK_{a_1} = $-\log(4.4 \times 10^{-7})$ = 6.36 and at

pH = pK_{a_2} = $-\log(4.7 \times 10^{-11})$ = 10.33. The following graph was computer-calculated (and then drawn) from these equations. f in each instance represents the fraction of the species whose formula is in parentheses.

$$\frac{1}{f(H_2A)} = 1 + \frac{K_1}{[H^+]} + \frac{K_1 K_2}{[H^+]^2}$$

$$\frac{1}{f(HA^-)} = \frac{[H^+]}{K_1} + 1 + \frac{K_2}{[H^+]}$$

$$\frac{1}{f(A^{2-})} = \frac{[H^+]^2}{K_1 K_2} + \frac{[H^+]}{K_2} + 1$$

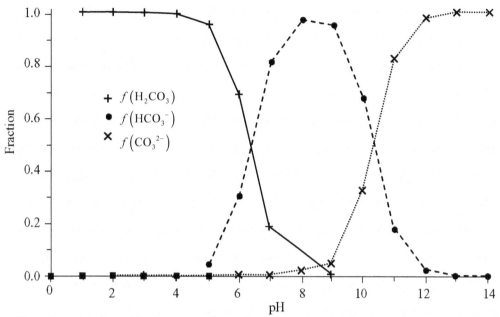

(c) For phosphoric acid, there are four phosphate containing species: H_3PO_4 under acidic conditions, $H_2PO_4^-$, HPO_4^{2-}, and PO_4^{3-}, which predominates in alkaline solution. The points of intersection should occur at $pH = pK_{a_1} = -\log(7.1 \times 10^{-3}) = 2.15$, $pH = pK_{a_2} = -\log(6.3 \times 10^{-8}) = 7.20$, and $pH = pK_{a_3} = -\log(4.2 \times 10^{-13}) = 12.38$, a quite alkaline solution. The graph that follows was computer-calculated and drawn.

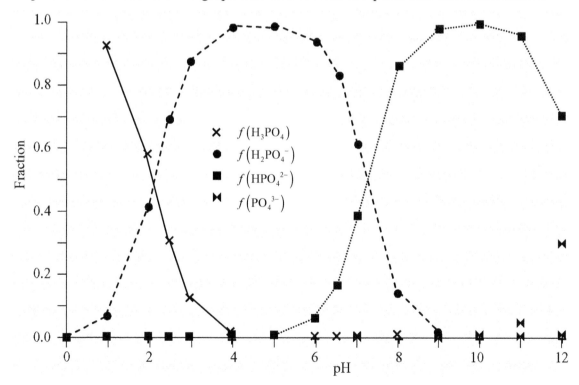

93. (D)

(a) This is exactly the same titration curve we would obtain for the titration of 25.00 mL of 0.200 M HCl with 0.200 M NaOH, because the acid species being titrated is H_3O^+. Both acids are strong acids and have ionized completely before titration begins. For a solution that is simultaneously 0.100 M HCl (a strong acid) and 0.100 M HNO₃ (a strong acid), $[H_3O^+] = (0.100 + 0.100)$ M $= 0.200$ M. Therefore, $pH = -\log(0.200) = 0.70$. At the equivalence point, pH = 7.000. We treat this problem as we would for the titration of a single strong acid with a strong base.

(b) In Figure 17-8, we note that the equivalence point of the titration of a strong acid occurs at pH = 7.00, but that the strong acid is essentially completely neutralized at pH = 4. In Figure 17-12, we see that the first equivalence point of H_3PO_4 occurs at about pH = 4.6. Thus, the first equivalence point represents the complete neutralization of HCl and the neutralization of H_3PO_4 to $H_2PO_4^-$. Then, the second equivalence point represents the neutralization of $H_2PO_4^-$ to HPO_4^{2-}. To reach the first equivalence point requires about 20.0 mL of 0.216 M NaOH, while to reach the second one requires a total of 30.0 mL of 0.216 M NaOH, or an additional 10.0 mL of base beyond the first equivalence point. The equations for the two titration reactions are as follows.

To the first equivalence point: $\quad NaOH + H_3PO_4 \longrightarrow NaH_2PO_4 + H_2O$

$$NaOH + HCl \longrightarrow NaCl + H_2O$$

To the second equivalence point: $NaOH + NaH_2PO_4 \longrightarrow Na_2HPO_4 + H_2O$

There is a third equivalence point, not shown in the figure, which would require an additional 10.0 mL of base to reach. Its titration reaction is represented by the following equation.

To the third equivalence point: $NaOH + Na_2HPO_4 \longrightarrow Na_3PO_4 + H_2O$

We determine the molar concentration of H_3PO_4 and then of HCl. Notice that only 10.0 mL of the NaOH needed to reach the first equivalence point reacts with the HCl(aq); the rest reacts with H_3PO_4.

$$\frac{(30.0-20.0)\ \text{mL NaOH(aq)} \times \dfrac{0.216\ \text{mmol NaOH}}{1\ \text{mL NaOH soln}} \times \dfrac{1\ \text{mmol } H_3PO_4}{1\ \text{mmol NaOH}}}{10.00\ \text{mL acid soln}} = 0.216\ \text{M } H_3PO_4$$

$$\frac{(20.0-10.0)\ \text{mL NaOH(aq)} \times \dfrac{0.216\ \text{mmol NaOH}}{1\ \text{mL NaOH soln}} \times \dfrac{1\ \text{mmol HCl}}{1\ \text{mmol NaOH}}}{10.00\ \text{mL acid soln}} = 0.216\ \text{M HCl}$$

(c) We start with a phosphoric acid-dihydrogen phosphate buffer solution and titrate until all of the H_3PO_4 is consumed. We begin with

$$10.00\ \text{mL} \times \frac{0.0400\ \text{mmol } H_3PO_4}{1\ \text{mL}} = 0.400\ \text{mmol } H_3PO_4 \text{ and the diprotic anion,}$$

$$10.00\ \text{mL} \times \frac{0.0150\ \text{mmol } H_2PO_4^{-}}{1\ \text{mL}} = 0.150\ \text{mmol } H_2PO_4^{2-}. \text{ The volume of } 0.0200\ \text{M}$$

NaOH needed is: $0.400\ \text{mmol } H_3PO_4 \times \dfrac{1\ \text{mmol NaOH}}{1\ \text{mmol } H_3PO_4} \times \dfrac{1\ \text{mL NaOH}}{0.0200\ \text{mmol NaOH}} = 20.00\ \text{mL}$

To reach the first equivalence point. The pH value of points during this titration are computed with the Henderson-Hasselbalch equation.

$$\text{Initially}: \text{pH} = pK_1 + \log \frac{\left[H_2PO_4^{-} \right]}{\left[H_3PO_4 \right]} = -\log\left(7.1 \times 10^{-3}\right) + \log\frac{0.0150}{0.0400}$$

$$= 2.15 - 0.43 = 1.72$$

$$\text{At } 5.00\ \text{mL}: \text{pH} = 2.15 + \log\frac{0.150 + 0.100}{0.400 - 0.100} = 2.15 - 0.08 = 2.07$$

$$\text{At } 10.0\ \text{mL}, \text{pH} = 2.15 + \log\frac{0.150 + 0.200}{0.400 - 0.200} = 2.15 + 0.24 = 2.39$$

$$\text{At } 15.0\ \text{mL}, \text{pH} = 2.15 + \log\frac{0.150 + 0.300}{0.400 - 0.300} = 2.15 + 0.65 = 2.80$$

This is the first equivalence point, a solution of 30.00 mL (= 10.00 mL originally + 20.00 mL titrant), containing 0.400 mmol $H_2PO_4^{-}$ from the titration and the 0.150 mmol $H_2PO_4^{2-}$ originally present.

This is a solution with

$$\left[H_2PO_4^{-}\right] = \frac{(0.400 + 0.150) \text{ mmol } H_2PO_4^{-}}{30.00 \text{ mL}} = 0.0183 \text{ M, which has}$$

$$pH = \frac{1}{2}(pK_1 + pK_2) = 0.50\left(2.15 - \log\left(6.3 \times 10^{-8}\right)\right) = 0.50(2.15 + 7.20) = 4.68$$

To reach the second equivalence point means titrating 0.550 mmol $H_2PO_4^{-}$, which requires an additional volume of titrant given by

$$0.550 \text{ mmol } H_2PO_4^{-} \times \frac{1 \text{ mmol NaOH}}{1 \text{ mmol } H_2PO_4^{-}} \times \frac{1 \text{ mL NaOH}}{0.0200 \text{ mmol NaOH}} = 27.5 \text{ mL.}$$

To determine pH during this titration, we divide the region into five equal portions of 5.5 mL and use the Henderson-Hasselbalch equation.

At $(20.0 + 5.5)$ mL,

$$pH = pK_2 + \log\frac{\left[HPO_4^{2-}\right]}{\left[H_2PO_4^{-}\right]} = 7.20 + \log\frac{(0.20 \times 0.550) \text{ mmol } HPO_4^{2-} \text{ formed}}{(0.80 \times 0.550) \text{ mmol } H_2PO_4^{-} \text{ remaining}}$$

$$pH = 7.20 - 0.60 = 6.60$$

At $(20.0 + 11.0)$ mL $= 31.0$ mL, $pH = 7.20 + \log\dfrac{0.40 \times 0.550}{0.60 \times 0.550} = 7.02$

At 36.5 mL, $pH = 7.38$ At 42.0 mL, $pH = 7.80$

The pH at the second equivalence point is given by

$$pH = \frac{1}{2}(pK_2 + pK_3) = 0.50\left(7.20 - \log\left(4.2 \times 10^{-13}\right)\right) = 0.50\,(7.20 + 12.38) = 9.79.$$

Another 27.50 mL of 0.020 M NaOH would be required to reach the third equivalence point. pH values at each of four equally spaced volumes of 5.50 mL additional 0.0200 M NaOH are computed as before, assuming the Henderson-Hasselbalch equation is valid.

At $(47.50 + 5.50)$ mL $= 53.00$ mL, $pH = pK_3 + \log\dfrac{\left[PO_4^{3-}\right]}{\left[HPO_4^{2-}\right]} = 12.38 + \log\dfrac{0.20 \times 0.550}{0.80 \times 0.550}$

$$= 12.38 - 0.60 = 11.78$$

At 58.50 mL, pH = 12.20   At 64.50 mL, pH = 12.56   At 70.00 mL, pH = 12.98
But at infinite dilution with 0.0200 M NaOH, the pH = 12.30, so this point can't be reached.

At the last equivalence point, the solution will contain 0.550 mmol PO_4^{3-} in a total of $10.00 + 20.00 + 27.50 + 27.50$ mL = 85.00 mL of solution, with

$$\left[PO_4^{3-}\right] = \frac{0.550 \text{ mmol}}{85.00 \text{ mL}} = 0.00647 \text{ M. But we can never reach this point, because the}$$

pH of the 0.0200 M NaOH titrant is 12.30. Moreover, the titrant is diluted by its addition to the solution. Thus, our titration will cease sometime shortly after the second equivalence point. We never will see the third equivalence point, largely because the titrant is too dilute. Our results are plotted below.

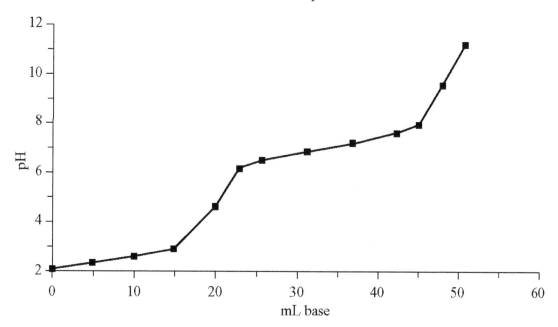

94. **(D)** $pK_{a_1} = 2.34$; $K_{a_1} = 4.6 \times 10^{-3}$ and $pK_{a_2} = 9.69$; $K_{a_2} = 2.0 \times 10^{-10}$

(a) Since the K_a values are so different, we can treat alanine (H_2A^+) as a monoprotic acid with $K_{a_1} = 4.6 \times 10^{-3}$. Hence:

	H_2A^+(aq)	+ H_2O(l)	⇌	HA(aq)	+ H_3O^+(aq)
Initial	0.500 M	—		0 M	≈ 0 M
Change	−x M	—		+x M	+x M
Equilibrium	(0.500 −x) M	—		x M	x M

$$K_{a_1} = \frac{[HA][H_3O^+]}{[H_2A^+]} = \frac{(x)(x)}{(0.500 - x)} = 4.6 \times 10^{-3} \approx \frac{x^2}{0.500}$$

$x = 0.048$ ($x = 0.0457$, solving the quadratic equation)
pH = $-\log[H_3O^+] = -\log(0.046) = 1.34$

(b) At the first half-neutralization point a buffer made up of H_2A^+/HA is formed, where $[H_2A^+] = [HA]$. The Henderson-Hasselbalch equation gives $pH = pK_a = 2.34$.

(c) At the first equivalence point, all of the $H_2A^+(aq)$ is converted to $HA(aq)$. $HA(aq)$ is involved in both K_{a_1} and K_{a_2}, so both ionizations must be considered.

If we assume that the solution is converted to 100% HA, we must consider two reactions. HA may act as a weak acid ($HA \rightarrow A^- + H^+$) or HA may act as a base ($HA + H^+ \rightarrow H_2A^+$). See the following diagram.

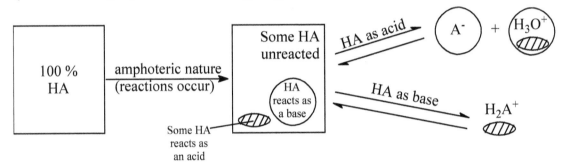

Using the diagram above, we see that the following relations must hold true.
$[A^-] = [H_3O^+] + [H_2A^+]$

$$K_{a_2} = \frac{[A^-][H_3O^+]}{[HA]} \text{ or } [A^-] = \frac{K_{a_2}[HA]}{[H_3O^+]} \ \& \ K_{a_1} = \frac{[HA][H_3O^+]}{[H_2A^+]} \text{ or } [H_2A^+] = \frac{[H_3O^+][HA]}{K_{a_1}}$$

Substitute for $[A^-]$ and $[H_2A^+]$ in $[A^-] = [H_3O^+] + [H_2A^+]$

$$\frac{K_{a_2}[HA]}{[H_3O^+]} = [H_3O^+] + \frac{[H_3O^+][HA]}{K_{a_1}} \text{ (multiply both sides by } K_{a_1}[H_3O^+])$$

$$K_{a_1}K_{a_2}[HA] = K_{a_1}[H_3O^+][H_3O^+] + [H_3O^+][H_3O^+][HA]$$

$$K_{a_1}K_{a_2}[HA] = [H_3O^+]^2(K_{a_1} + [HA])$$

$$[H_3O^+]^2 = \frac{K_{a_1}K_{a_2}[HA]}{(K_{a_1} + [HA])} \text{ Usually, } [HA] \gg K_{a_1} \text{ (Here, } 0.500 \gg 4.6 \times 10^{-3})$$

Make the assumption that $K_{a_1} + [HA] \approx [HA]$

$$[H_3O^+]^2 = \frac{K_{a_1}K_{a_2}[HA]}{[HA]} = K_{a_1}K_{a_2} \qquad \text{Take } -\log \text{ of both sides}$$

$$-\log[H_3O^+]^2 = -2\log[H_3O^+] = 2(pH) = -\log K_{a_1}K_{a_2} = -\log K_{a_1} - \log K_{a_2} = pK_{a_1} + pK_{a_2}$$

$$2(pH) = pK_{a_1} + pK_{a_2}$$

$$pH = \frac{pK_{a_1} + pK_{a_2}}{2} = \frac{2.34 + 9.69}{2} = 6.02$$

(d) Half-way between the first and second equivalence points, half of the HA(aq) is converted to A⁻(aq). We have a HA/A⁻ buffer solution where $[HA] = [A^-]$. The Henderson-Hasselbalch equation yields pH = pK_{a_2} = 9.69.

(e) At the second equivalence point, all of the H_2A^+(aq) is converted to A⁻(aq). We can treat this simply as a weak base in water having:

$$K_b = \frac{K_w}{K_{a_2}} = \frac{1\times10^{-14}}{2.0\times10^{-10}} = 5.0 \times 10^{-5}$$

Note: There has been a 1:3 dilution, hence the $[A^-]$ = 0.500 M × $\frac{1\ V}{3\ V}$ = 0.167 M

	A⁻(aq)	+	H₂O(l)	⇌	HA(aq)	+	OH⁻(aq)
Initial	0.167 M		—		0 M		≈ 0 M
Change	−x M		—		+x M		+x M
Equilibrium	(0.167 −x) M		—		x M		x M

$$K_b = \frac{[HA][OH^-]}{[A^-]} = \frac{(x)(x)}{(0.167-x)} = 5.0 \times 10^{-5} \approx \frac{x^2}{0.167}$$

$x = 0.0029$ M = $[OH^-]$; pOH = $-\log[OH^-]$ = 2.54;

pH = 14.00 − pOH = 14.00 − 2.54 = 11.46

(f) All of the points required in (f) can be obtained using the Henderson-Hasselbalch equation (the chart below shows that the buffer ratio for each point is within the acceptable range (0.25 to 4.0))

(i) After 10.0 mL

Here we will show how to obtain the answer using both the Henderson-Hasselbalch equation and setting up the I. C. E. (Initial, Change, Equilibrium) table. The results will differ within accepted experimental limitation of the experiment ($\pm$ 0.01 pH units)

$n_{H_2A^+}$ = (C × V) = (0.500 M)(0.0500 L) = 0.0250 moles H₂A⁻

n_{OH^-} = (C × V) = (0.500 M)(0.0100 L) = 0.00500 moles OH⁻
V_{total} = (50.0 + 10.0) mL = 60.0 mL or 0.0600 L

$$[H_2A^+] = \frac{n_{H_2A^+}}{V_{total}} = \frac{0.0250\,mol}{0.0600\,L} = 0.417\,M$$

$$[OH^-] = \frac{n_{OH^-}}{V_{total}} = \frac{0.00500\,mol}{0.0600\,L} = 0.0833\,M$$

For the titration reaction, $K = \dfrac{1}{K_{b(HA)}} = \dfrac{1}{\left(\dfrac{K_w}{K_{a_1}}\right)} = \dfrac{K_{a_1}}{K_w} = \dfrac{4.6\times10^{-3}}{1.00\times10^{-14}} = 4.6\times10^{11}$

	$H_2A^+(aq)$	+	$OH^-(aq)$	$\rightleftharpoons$	$HA(aq)$	+	$H_2O(l)$
Initial:	0.417 M		0.0833 M		0 M		—
100% rxn:	−0.0833		−0.0833 M		+0.0833 M		—
New initial:	0.334 M		0 M		0.0833 M		—
Change:	+x M		+x M		−x M		—
Equilibrium:	≈0.334 M		x M		≈0.0833 M		—

$$4.6\times10^{11} = \frac{(0.0833)}{(0.334)(x)} \;;\; x = \frac{(0.0833)}{(0.334)(4.6\times10^{11})} = 5.4\times10^{-13} \text{ (valid assumption)}$$

$x = 5.4\times10^{-13} = [OH^-]$; $pOH = -\log(5.4\times10^{-13}) = 12.27$;
$pH = 14.00 - pOH = 14.00 - 12.27 = 1.73$
Alternative method using the Henderson-Hasselbalch equation:

(i) After 10.0 mL, 20% of H_2A^+ reacts, forming the conjugate base HA.
Hence the buffer solution is 80% H_2A^+ (acid) and 20% HA (base).

$$pH = pK_{a_1} + \log\frac{base}{acid} = 2.34 + \log\frac{20.0}{80.0} = 2.34 + (-0.602) = 1.74(\text{within } +0.01)$$

For the remainder of the calculations we will employ the Henderson-Hasselbalch equation with the understanding that using the method that employs the I.C.E. table gives the same result within the limitation of the data.

(ii) After 20.0 mL, 40% of H_2A^+ reacts, forming the conjugate base HA.
Hence the buffer solution is 60% H_2A^+ (acid) and 40% HA (base).

$$pH = pK_{a_1} + \log\frac{base}{acid} = 2.34 + \log\frac{40.0}{60.0} = 2.34 + (-0.176) = 2.16$$

(iii) After 30.0 mL, 60% of H_2A^+ reacts, forming the conjugate base HA.
Hence the buffer solution is 40% H_2A^+ (acid) and 60% HA (base).

$$pH = pK_{a_1} + \log\frac{base}{acid} = 2.34 + \log\frac{60.0}{40.0} = 2.34 + (+0.176) = 2.52$$

(iv) After 40.0 mL, 80% of H_2A^+ reacts, forming the conjugate base HA.
Hence the buffer solution is 20% H_2A^+ (acid) and 80% HA (base).

$$pH = pK_{a_1} + \log \frac{\text{base}}{\text{acid}} = 2.34 + \log \frac{80.0}{20.0} = 2.34 + (0.602) = 2.94$$

(v) After 50 mL, all of the $H_2A^+(aq)$ has reacted, and we begin with essentially 100% HA(aq), which is a weak acid. Addition of base results in the formation of the conjugate base (buffer system) $A^-(aq)$. We employ a similar solution, however, now we must use $pK_{a_2} = 9.69$.

(vi) After 60.0 mL, 20% of HA reacts, forming the conjugate base A^-.
Hence the buffer solution is 80% HA (acid) and 20% A^- (base)

$$pH = pK_{a_2} + \log \frac{\text{base}}{\text{acid}} = 9.69 + \log \frac{20.0}{80.0} = 9.69 + (-0.602) = 9.09$$

(vii) After 70.0 mL, 40% of HA reacts, forming the conjugate base A^-.
Hence the buffer solution is 60% HA (acid) and 40% A^- (base).

$$pH = pK_{a_2} + \log \frac{\text{base}}{\text{acid}} = 9.69 + \log \frac{40.0}{60.0} = 9.69 + (-0.176) = 9.51$$

(viii) After 80.0 mL, 60% of HA reacts, forming the conjugate base A^-.
Hence the buffer solution is 40% HA (acid) and 60% A^- (base).

$$pH = pK_{a_2} + \log \frac{\text{base}}{\text{acid}} = 9.69 + \log \frac{60.0}{40.0} = 9.69 + (+0.176) = 9.87$$

(ix) After 90.0 mL, 80% of HA reacts, forming the conjugate base A^-.
Hence the buffer solution is 20% HA (acid) and 80% A^- (base).

$$pH = pK_{a_2} + \log \frac{\text{base}}{\text{acid}} = 9.69 + \log \frac{80.0}{20.0} = 9.69 + (0.602) = 10.29$$

(x) After the addition of 110.0 mL, NaOH is in excess. (10.0 mL of 0.500 M NaOH is in excess, or, 0.00500 moles of NaOH remains unreacted). The pH of a solution that has NaOH in excess is determined by the $[OH^-]$ that is in excess.
(For a diprotic acid, this occurs after the second equivalence point.)

$$[OH^-]_{\text{excess}} = \frac{n_{OH^-}}{V_{\text{total}}} = \frac{0.00500 \, \text{mol}}{0.1600 \, \text{L}} = 0.03125 \, \text{M} \; ; pOH = -\log(0.03125) = 1.51$$

$$pH = 14.00 - pOH = 14.00 - 1.51 = 12.49$$

(g) A sketch of the titration curve for the 0.500 M solution of alanine hydrochloride, with some significant points labeled on the plot, is shown below.

SELF-ASSESSMENT EXERCISES

95. (E)
   (a) mmol: millimoles, or 1×10^{-3} mol
   (b) HIn: An indicator, which is a weak acid
   (c) Equivalence point of a titration: When the moles of titrant equals the moles of the substance being titrated
   (d) Titration curve: A curve of pH of the solution being titrated versus the pH of the titrating solution

96. (E)
   (a) The common-ion effect: A process by which ionization of a compound is suppressed by having present one of the product ions (from another source) in the solution
   (b) use of buffer to maintain constant pH: A buffer is a solution of a weak acid and its conjugate base, and it resists large changes in pH when small amounts of an acid or base are added.
   (c) determination of pK_a from titration curve: At the half-way point (when half of the species being titrated is consumed, the concentration of that species and its conjugate is the same, and the equilibrium expression simplifies to $pK_a = pH$
   (d) measurement of pH with an indicator: An approximate method of measuring the pH, where the color of an ionizable organic dye changes based on the pH

97. (E)

(a) Buffer capacity and buffer range: Buffer capacity is a measure of how much acid or base can be added to the buffer without an appreciable change in the pH, and is determined by the concentration of the weak acid and conjugate base in the buffer solution. The buffer range, however, refers to the range over which a buffer effectively neutralizes added acids and bases and maintains a fairly constant pH.

(b) Hydrolysis and neutralization: Hydrolysis is reaction of an acid or base with water molecules, which causes water to split into hydronium and hydroxide ions. Neutralization is the reaction of H_3O^+ and OH^- together to make water.

(c) First and second equivalence points in the titration of a weak diprotic acid: First equivalence point is when the first proton of a weak diprotic acid is completely abstracted and the resulting acid salt and base have been consumed and neither is in excess. Second equivalence point is the equivalence point at which all protons are abstracted from the acid and what remains is the (2–) anion.

(d) Equivalence point of a titration and end point of an indicator: Equivalence point of a titration is when the moles of titrant added are the same as the moles of acid or base in the solution being titrated. The endpoint of an indicator is when the indicator changes color because of abstraction or gain of a proton, and is ideally as close as possible to the pH of the equivalence point.

98. (E)

(a) $HCOOH + OH^- \rightarrow HCOO^- + H_2O$
$HCOO^- + H_3O^+ \rightarrow HCOOH + H_2O$

(b) $C_6H_5NH_3^+ + OH^- \rightarrow C_6H_5NH_2 + H_2O$
$C_6H_5NH_2 + H_3O^+ \rightarrow C_6H_5NH_3^+ + H_2O$

(c) $H_2PO_4^- + OH^- \rightarrow HPO_4^{2-} + H_2O$
$HPO_4^{2-} + H_3O^+ \rightarrow H_2PO_4^- + H_2O$

99. (M)

(a) The pH at the equivalence point is 7. Use bromthymol blue.

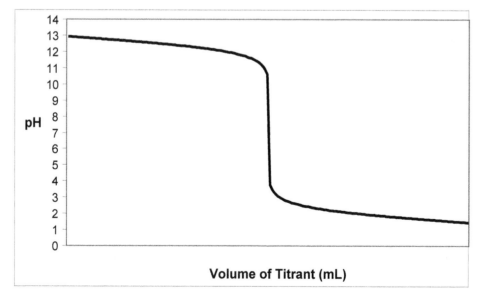

(b) The pH at the equivalence point is ~5.3 for a 0.1 M solution. Use methyl red.

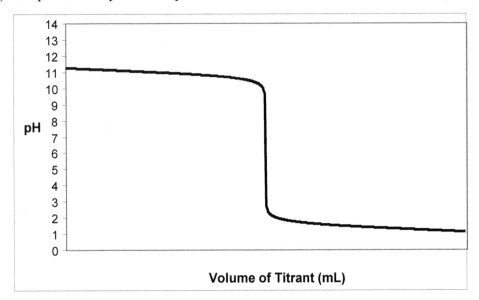

(c) The pH at the equivalence point is ~8.7 for a 0.1 M solution. Use phenolphthalein, because it just begins to get from clear to pink around the equivalence point.

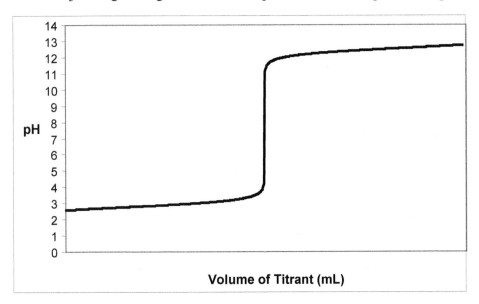

(d) The pH for the first equivalence point ($NaH_2PO_4^-$ to $Na_2HPO_4^{2-}$) for a 0.1 M solution is right around ~7, so use bromthymol blue.

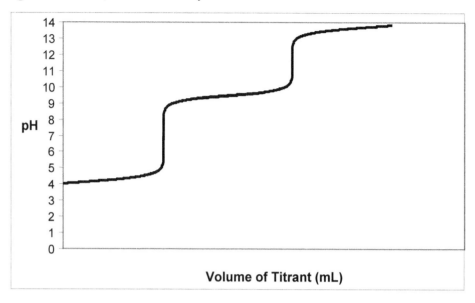

100. (D)

(a) This is the initial equilibrium before any base has reacted with the acid. The reaction that dominates, along with changes in concentration, is shown below:

$$C_6H_5COOH \; + \; H_2O \; \rightleftharpoons \; C_6H_5COO^- \; + \; H_3O^+$$

0.0100	0	0
$-x$	$+x$	$+x$
$0.0100 - x$	x	x

$$K_a = \frac{[H_3O^+][C_6H_5COO^-]}{[C_6H_5COOH]}$$

$$6.3\times10^{-5} = \frac{(x)(x)}{0.0100 - x}$$

Solving for x using the quadratic formula, $x = 7.63\times10^{-4}$.

$$pH = -\log[H_3O^+] = -\log(7.63\times10^{-4}) = 3.12$$

(b) In this case, we titrate the base with 0.00625 L of $Ba(OH)_2$. Therefore, we have to calculate the final moles of the base and the total volume to determine the concentration.

$$\text{mol } C_6H_5COOH = 0.02500 \text{ L} \times 0.0100 \text{ M } C_6H_5COOH = 2.5\times10^{-4} \text{ mol}$$

$$\text{mol OH}^- = 0.00625 \text{ L} \times 0.0100 \text{ M } Ba(OH)_2 \times \frac{2 \text{ mol OH}^-}{1 \text{ mol } Ba(OH)_2} = 1.25\times10^{-4} \text{ mol}$$

Since the amount of OH^- is half of the initial amount of C_6H_5COOH, the moles of C_6H_5COOH and $C_6H_5COO^-$ are equal. Therefore, $K_a = [H_3O^+]$, and $pH = -\log(6.3 \times 10^{-5}) = 4.20$.

(c) At the equivalence point, there is initially no C_6H_5COOH. The equilibrium is dominated by $C_6H_5COO^-$ hydrolyzing water. The concentration of $C_6H_5COO^-$ is:
Total moles of $C_6H_5COOH = 2.5 \times 10^{-4}$ mol as shown previously. At the equivalence point, the moles of acid equal moles of OH^-.

$$\text{mol } Ba(OH)_2 = 2.5 \times 10^{-4} \text{ mol } OH^- \times \frac{1 \text{ mol } Ba(OH)_2}{2 \text{ mol } OH^-} = 1.25 \times 10^{-4} \text{ mol}$$

Vol of $Ba(OH)_2 = 1.25 \times 10^{-4}$ mol / 0.0100 M = 0.0125 L

Total volume of the solution at the equivalence point is the sum of the initial volume plus the volume of $Ba(OH)_2$ added. That is,

$$V_{TOT} = 0.02500 \text{ L} + 0.0125 \text{ L} = 0.0375 \text{ L}$$

Therefore, the concentration of $C_6H_5COO^- = 2.5 \times 10^{-4}/0.0375$ L = 0.00667 M.

$C_6H_5COO^-$	$+ \ H_2O$	$\rightleftharpoons$	C_6H_5COOH	$+ \ OH^-$
0.00667			0	0
$-x$			$+x$	$+x$
$0.00667 - x$			x	x

Since this is a base reaction, $K_b = K_w/K_a = (1.00 \times 10^{-4})/6.3 \times 10^{-5} = 1.587 \times 10^{-10}$.

$$K_b = \frac{\left[OH^-\right]\left[C_6H_5COOH\right]}{\left[C_6H_5COO^-\right]}$$

$$1.59 \times 10^{-10} = \frac{(x)(x)}{0.00667 - \cancel{x}}$$

solving for x (by simplifying the formula above) yields $x = 1.03 \times 10^{-6}$ M.

$$pH = 14 - pOH = 14 - \left[-\log\left(1.03 \times 10^{-6}\right)\right] = 14 - 6.00 = 8.00$$

(d) In this part, we have an excess of a strong base. As such, we have to determine how much excess base there is and what is the final volume of the solution.

$$\text{mol}\left(OH^-\right) = 0.01500 \text{ L} \times 0.0100 \ \frac{\text{mol } Ba(OH)_2}{L} \times \frac{2 \text{ mol } OH^-}{1 \text{ mol } Ba(OH)_2}$$

$$= 3.000 \times 10^{-4} \text{ mol } OH^-$$

Excess mol $OH^- = $ mol $HC_7H_5O_2 - $ mol $OH^- = 3.000 \times 10^{-4} - 2.500 \times 10^{-4}$

$$= 5.000 \times 10^{-5} \text{ mol}$$

$$\left[OH^-\right] = \frac{5.0 \times 10^{-5} \text{ mol}}{(0.02500 \text{ L} + 0.01500 \text{ L})} = 0.00125 \text{ M}$$

$$pH = 14 - pOH = 14 - \left[-\log\left(0.00125\right)\right] = 14 - 2.903 = 11.1$$

101. (E) The answer is (c); because of the common ion-effect, the presence of HCOO⁻ will repress ionization of formic acid.

102. (E) The answer is (d), because $NaHCO_3$ is a weak base and will react with protons in water, shifting the formic acid ionization equilibrium to the right.

103. (E) The answer is (b), raise the pH. NH_4^+ is an acid, and to be converted to its conjugate base, it must react with a base to abstract its proton.

104. (E) The answer is (b), because at that point, the number of moles of weak base remaining is the same as its conjugate acid, and the equilibrium expression simplifies to $K_a = [H_3O^+]$.

105. (M) The base, $C_2H_5NH_2$, reacts with $HClO_4$. The reaction is:

$$C_2H_5NH_2 + HClO_4 \rightarrow C_2H_5NH_3^+ + ClO_4^-$$

Assuming a volume of 1 L for each solution,

$$[C_2H_5NH_2] = \frac{1.49 \text{ mol} - 1.001 \text{ mol}}{2 \text{ L}} = \frac{0.489 \text{ mol}}{2 \text{ L}} = 0.2445 \text{ M}$$

$$[C_2H_5NH_3^+] = \frac{1.001 \text{ mol}}{2 \text{ L}} = 0.5005 \text{ M}$$

$$4.3 \times 10^{-4} = \frac{[C_2H_5NH_3^+][OH^-]}{[C_2H_5NH_2]} = \frac{(0.5005 + x)(x)}{(0.2445 - x)}$$

$$x = 2.10 \times 10^{-4}$$

$$pOH = -\log(2.10 \times 10^{-4}) = 3.68$$

$$pH = 14 - 3.68 = 10.32$$

106. (D) We assume that all of $Ca(HSe)_2$ dissociates in water. The concentration of HSe^- is therefore:

$$0.5 \text{ M } Ca(HSe)_2 \times \frac{2 \text{ mol } HSe^-}{1 \text{ mol } Ca(HSe)_2} = 1.0 \text{ M } HSe^-$$

We note that HSe^- is amphoteric; that is, it can act either as an acid or a base. The acid reaction of HSe^- and the concentration of $[H_3O^+]$ generated, are as follows:

$$HSe^- + H_2O \rightleftharpoons Se^{2-} + H_3O^+$$

$$1.00 \times 10^{-11} = \frac{[Se^{2-}][H_3O^+]}{[HSe^-]} = \frac{(x)(x)}{(1.00 - x)}$$

$$x = \sqrt{1.00 \times 10^{-11}} = 3.16 \times 10^{-6}$$

The basic reaction of HSe^- and the concentration of $[OH^-]$ generated, are as follows:

$$HSe^- + H_2O \rightleftharpoons H_2Se + OH^-$$

$$K_b = 1.00 \times 10^{-14}/1.3 \times 10^{-4} = 7.69 \times 10^{-11}$$

$$7.69 \times 10^{-11} = \frac{[H_2Se][OH^-]}{[HSe^-]} = \frac{(x)(x)}{(1.00-x)}$$

$$x = \sqrt{7.69 \times 10^{-11}} = 8.77 \times 10^{-6}$$

Therefore, we have $[H_3O^+] = 3.16 \times 10^{-6}$ and $[OH^-] = 8.77 \times 10^{-6}$. Since these two react to give H_2O, the result is $8.77 \times 10^{-6} - 3.16 \times 10^{-6} = 5.61 \times 10^{-6}$ M $[OH^-]$. The pH of the solution is:

$$pH = 14 - pOH = 14 - 5.25 = 8.75$$

107. **(E)** The answer is (a). The solution system described is a buffer, and will resist large changes in pH. Adding KOH should raise the pH slightly.

108. **(E)** The answer is (b), because HSO_3^- is a much stronger acid ($K_a = 1.3 \times 10^{-2}$) than $H_2PO_4^-$ ($K_a = 6.3 \times 10^{-8}$).

109. **(E)** The answer is (b). The pK_a of the acid is 9, which puts it squarely in the middle of the 8–10 pH range for the equivalence point.

110. **(E)**
  (a) $NaHCO_3$ titrated with NaOH: pH > 7, because HCO_3^- is itself slightly basic, and is being titrated with NaOH to yield CO_3^{2-} at the equivalence point, which is even more basic.
  (b) HCl titrated with NH_3: pH < 7, because the resulting NH_4^+ at the equivalence point is acidic.
  (c) KOH titrated with HI: pH = 7, because a strong base is being titrated by a strong acid, and the resulting anions and cations are all non-basic and non-acidic.

111. **(M)** The concepts that define Sections 17-2, 17-3, and 17-4 are buffers, indicators, and titrations. For buffers, after definition, there are a number of concepts, such as composition, application, the equilibrium expression (the Henderson-Hasselbalch equation is a subtopic of the equilibrium expression). Under composition, there are other subtopics such as buffer range and capacity. For indicators, after defining it, there are subtopics such as equilibrium expression and usage. With titration, topics such as form (weak acid titrated by strong base, and weak base titrated by strong acid), the titration curve, and the equivalence point. Look at these sections to find inter-related terminology and other concepts.

CHAPTER 18
SOLUBILITY AND COMPLEX-ION EQUILIBRIA
PRACTICE EXAMPLES

1A **(E)** In each case, we first write the balanced equation for the solubility equilibrium and then the equilibrium constant expression for that equilibrium, the K_{sp} expression:

    (a) $MgCO_3(s) \rightleftharpoons Mg^{2+}(aq) + CO_3^{2-}(aq)$ $K_{sp} = [Mg^{2+}][CO_3^{2-}]$

    (b) $Ag_3PO_4(s) \rightleftharpoons 3Ag^+(aq) + PO_4^{3-}(aq)$ $K_{sp} = [Ag^+]^3[PO_4^{3-}]$

1B **(E)**

    (a)   Provided the $[OH^-]$ is not too high, the hydrogen phosphate ion is not expected to ionize in aqueous solution to a significant extent because of the quite small values for the second and third ionization constants of phosphoric acid.

         $CaHPO_4(s) \rightleftharpoons Ca^{2+}(aq) + HPO_4^{2-}(aq)$

    (b)   The solubility product constant is written in the manner of a K_c expression:

         $K_{sp} = [Ca^{2+}][HPO_4^{2-}] = 1. \times 10^{-7}$

2A **(M)** We calculate the solubility of silver cyanate, s, as a molarity. We then use the solubility equation to (1) relate the concentrations of the ions and (2) write the K_{sp} expression.

$$s = \frac{7 \text{ mg AgOCN}}{100 \text{ mL}} \times \frac{1000 \text{ mL}}{1 \text{ L}} \times \frac{1 \text{ g}}{1000 \text{ mg}} \times \frac{1 \text{ mol AgOCN}}{149.9 \text{ g AgOCN}} = 5 \times 10^{-4} \text{ mol/L}$$

Equation : $AgOCN(s) \rightleftharpoons Ag^+(aq) + OCN^-(aq)$

Solubility Product : s s

$$K_{sp} = \left[Ag^+\right]\left[OCN^-\right] = (s) \times (s) = s^2 = \left(5 \times 10^{-4}\right)^2 = 3 \times 10^{-7}$$

2B **(E)** We calculate the solubility of lithium phosphate, s, as a molarity. We then use the solubility equation to (1) relate the concentrations of the ions and (2) write the K_{sp} expression.

$$s = \frac{0.034 \text{ g Li}_3PO_4}{100 \text{ mL soln}} \times \frac{1000 \text{ mL}}{1 \text{ L}} \times \frac{1 \text{ mol Li}_3PO_4}{115.79 \text{ g Li}_3PO_4} = 0.0029 \text{ mol/L}$$

Equation: $Li_3PO_4(s) \rightleftharpoons 3Li^+(aq) + PO_4^{3-}(aq)$

Solubility Product: $(3s)^3$ s

$$K_{sp} = \left[Li^+\right]^3\left[PO_4^{3-}\right] = (3s)^3 \cdot (s) = 27s^4 = 27(0.0029)^4 = 1.9 \times 10^{-9}$$

3A **(E)** We use the solubility equilibrium to write the K_{sp} expression, which we then solve to obtain the molar solubility, s, of $Cu_3(AsO_4)_2$.

$$Cu_3(AsO_4)_2(s) \rightleftharpoons 3\,Cu^{2+}(aq) + 2\,AsO_4^-(aq)$$

$$K_{sp} = \left[Cu^{2+}\right]^3\left[AsO_4^-\right]^2 = (3s)^3(2s)^2 = 108s^5 = 7.6\times10^{-36}$$

Solubility : $\quad s = \sqrt[5]{\dfrac{7.6\times10^{-36}}{108}} = 3.7\times10^{-8}\,M$

3B **(E)** First we determine the solubility of $BaSO_4$, and then find the mass dissolved.

$$BaSO_4(aq) \rightleftharpoons Ba^{2+}(aq) + SO_4^{2-}(aq) \qquad\qquad K_{sp} = \left[Ba^{2+}\right]\left[SO_4^{2-}\right] = s^2$$

The last relationship is true because $\left[Ba^{2+}\right] = \left[SO_4^{2-}\right]$ in a solution produced by dissolving $BaSO_4$ in pure water. Thus, $s = \sqrt{K_{sp}} = \sqrt{1.1\times10^{-10}} = 1.05\times10^{-5}\,M$.

$$\text{mass } BaSO_4 = 225\ mL \times \frac{1.05\times10^{-5}\,mmol\ BaSO_4}{1\ mL\ \text{sat'd soln}} \times \frac{233.39\,mg\ BaSO_4}{1\,mmol\ BaSO_4} = 0.55\,mg\ BaSO_4$$

4A **(M)** For PbI_2, $K_{sp} = \left[Pb^{2+}\right]\left[I^-\right]^2 = 7.1\times10^{-9}$. The solubility equilibrium is the basis of the calculation.

Equation:	$PbI_2(s)$	$\rightleftharpoons$	$Pb^{2+}(aq)$	$+$	$2I^-(aq)$
Initial:	—		0.10 M		0 M
Changes:	—		$+s$ M		$+2s$ M
Equil:	—		$(0.10 + s)$ M		$2s$ M

$$K_{sp} = \left[Pb^{2+}\right]\left[I^-\right]^2 = 7.1\times10^{-9} = (0.10+s)(2s)^2 \approx 0.40\,s^2 \qquad s = \sqrt{\frac{7.1\times10^{-9}}{0.40}} = 1.3\times10^{-4}\,M$$

(assumption $0.10 \gg s$ is valid)

This value of s is the solubility of PbI_2 in $0.10\ M\ Pb(NO_3)_2\,(aq)$.

4B **(E)** We find pOH from the given pH:

pOH = 14.00 − 8.20 = 5.80; $[OH^-] = 10^{-pOH} = 10^{-5.80} = 1.6\times10^{-6}$ M.

We assume that pOH remains constant, and use the K_{sp} expression for $Fe(OH)_3$.

$$K_{sp} = \left[Fe^{3+}\right]\left[OH^-\right]^3 = 4\times10^{-38} = \left[Fe^{3+}\right](1.6\times10^{-6})^3 \qquad \left[Fe^{3+}\right] = \frac{4\times10^{-38}}{(1.6\times10^{-6})^3} = 9.8\times10^{-21}\,M$$

Therefore, the molar solubility of $Fe(OH)_3$ is 9.8×10^{-21} M.

The dissolved $Fe(OH)_3$ does not significantly affect $\left[OH^-\right]$.

5A **(M)** First determine $\left[I^-\right]$ as altered by dilution. We then compute Q_{sp} and compare it with K_{sp}.

$$\left[I^-\right] = \frac{3\,\text{drops} \times \dfrac{0.05\,\text{mL}}{1\,\text{drop}} \times \dfrac{0.20\,\text{mmol KI}}{1\,\text{mL}} \times \dfrac{1\,\text{mmol I}^-}{1\,\text{mmol KI}}}{100.0\,\text{mL soln}} = 3 \times 10^{-4}\,\text{M}$$

$$Q_{sp} = \left[Ag^+\right]\left[I^-\right] = (0.010)(3 \times 10^{-4}) = 3 \times 10^{-6}$$

$Q_{sp} > 8.5 \times 10^{-17} = K_{sp}$ Thus, precipitation should occur.

5B **(M)** We first use the solubility product constant expression for PbI_2 to determine the $\left[I^-\right]$ needed in solution to just form a precipitate when $\left[Pb^{2+}\right] = 0.010$ M. We assume that the volume of solution added is small and that $\left[Pb^{2+}\right]$ remains at 0.010 M throughout.

$$K_{sp} = \left[Pb^{2+}\right]\left[I^-\right]^2 = 7.1 \times 10^{-9} = (0.010)\left[I^-\right]^2 \qquad \left[I^-\right] = \sqrt{\frac{7.1 \times 10^{-9}}{0.010}} = 8.4 \times 10^{-4}\,\text{M}$$

We determine the volume of 0.20 M KI needed.

$$\text{volume of KI(aq)} = 100.0\,\text{mL} \times \frac{8.4 \times 10^{-4}\,\text{mmol I}^-}{1\,\text{mL}} \times \frac{1\,\text{mmol KI}}{1\,\text{mmol I}^-} \times \frac{1\,\text{mL KI(aq)}}{0.20\,\text{mmol KI}} \times \frac{1\,\text{drop}}{0.050\,\text{mL}}$$

$$= 8.4\,\text{drops} = 9\,\text{drops}$$

Since one additional drop is needed, 10 drops will be required. This is an insignificant volume compared to the original solution, so $\left[Pb^{2+}\right]$ remains constant.

6A **(E)** Here we must find the maximum $\left[Ca^{2+}\right]$ that can coexist with $\left[OH^-\right] = 0.040$ M.

$$K_{sp} = 5.5 \times 10^{-6} = \left[Ca^{2+}\right]\left[OH^-\right]^2 = \left[Ca^{2+}\right](0.040)^2; \quad \left[Ca^{2+}\right] = \frac{5.5 \times 10^{-6}}{(0.040)^2} = 3.4 \times 10^{-3}\,\text{M}$$

For precipitation to be considered complete, $\left[Ca^{2+}\right]$ should be less than 0.1% of its original value. 3.4×10^{-3} M is 34% of 0.010 M and therefore precipitation of $Ca(OH)_2$ is not complete under these conditions.

6B **(E)** We begin by finding $\left[Mg^{2+}\right]$ that corresponds to $1\,\mu g\ Mg^{2+}\,/\,L$.

$$\left[Mg^{2+}\right] = \frac{1\,\mu g\ Mg^{2+}}{1\,\text{L soln}} \times \frac{1\,\text{g}}{10^6\,\mu g} \times \frac{1\,\text{mol Mg}^{2+}}{24.3\,\text{g Mg}^{2+}} = 4 \times 10^{-8}\,\text{M}$$

Now we use the K_{sp} expression for $Mg(OH)_2$ to determine $\left[OH^-\right]$.

$$K_{sp} = 1.8 \times 10^{-11} = \left[Mg^{2+}\right]\left[OH^-\right]^2 = \left(4 \times 10^{-8}\right)\left[OH^-\right]^2 \qquad \left[OH^-\right] = \sqrt{\frac{1.8 \times 10^{-11}}{4 \times 10^{-8}}} = 0.02\,\text{M}$$

7A **(M)** Let us first determine $\left[Ag^+\right]$ when AgCl(s) just begins to precipitate. At this point, Q_{sp} and K_{sp} are equal.

$$K_{sp} = 1.8 \times 10^{-10} = \left[Ag^+\right]\left[Cl^-\right] = Q_{sp} = \left[Ag^+\right] \times 0.115 M \quad \left[Ag^+\right] = \frac{1.8 \times 10^{-10}}{0.115} = 1.6 \times 10^{-9} M$$

Now let us determine the maximum $\left[Br^-\right]$ that can coexist with this $\left[Ag^+\right]$.

$$K_{sp} = 5.0 \times 10^{-13} = \left[Ag^+\right]\left[Br^-\right] = 1.6 \times 10^{-9} M \times \left[Br^-\right]; \quad \left[Br^-\right] = \frac{5.0 \times 10^{-13}}{1.6 \times 10^{-9}} = 3.1 \times 10^{-4} M$$

The remaining bromide ion has precipitated as AgBr(s) with the addition of $AgNO_3(aq)$.

$$\text{Percent of } Br^- \text{ remaining} = \frac{[Br^-]_{final}}{[Br^-]_{initial}} \times 100\% = \frac{3.1 \times 10^{-4} M}{0.264 M} \times 100\% = 0.12\%$$

7B **(M)** Since the ions have the same charge and the same concentrations, we look for two K_{sp} values for the salt with the same anion that are as far apart as possible. The K_{sp} values for the carbonates are very close, while those for the sulfates and fluorides are quite different. However, the difference in the K_{sp} values is greatest for the chromates; K_{sp} for $BaCrO_4 \left(1.2 \times 10^{-10}\right)$ is so much smaller than K_{sp} for $SrCrO_4 \left(2.2 \times 10^{-5}\right)$, $BaCrO_4$ will precipitate first and $SrCrO_4$ will begin to precipitate when $\left[CrO_4^{2-}\right]$ has the value:

$$\left[CrO_4^{2-}\right] = \frac{K_{sp}}{\left[Sr^{2+}\right]} = \frac{2.2 \times 10^{-5}}{0.10} = 2.2 \times 10^{-4} \text{ M.}$$

At this point $\left[Ba^{2+}\right]$ is found as follows.

$$\left[Ba^{2+}\right] = \frac{K_{sp}}{\left[CrO_4^{2-}\right]} = \frac{1.2 \times 10^{-10}}{2.2 \times 10^{-4}} = 5.5 \times 10^{-7} \text{ M};$$

[Ba^{2+}] has dropped to 0.00055% of its initial value and therefore is considered to be completely precipitated, before $SrCrO_4$ begins to precipitate. The two ions are thus effectively separated as chromates. The best precipitating agent is a group 1 chromate salt.

8A **(M)** First determine [OH$^-$] resulting from the hydrolysis of acetate ion.

Equation: $CH_3COO^-(aq) + H_2O(l) \rightleftharpoons CH_3COOH(aq) + OH^-(aq)$

Initial:	0.10 M	—	0 M	≈ 0 M
Changes:	$-x$ M	—	$+x$ M	$+x$ M
Equil:	$(0.10-x)$ M	—	x M	x M

$$K_b = \frac{1.0 \times 10^{-14}}{1.8 \times 10^{-5}} = 5.6 \times 10^{-10} = \frac{[CH_3COOH][OH^-]}{[CH_3COO^-]} = \frac{x \cdot x}{0.10 - x} \approx \frac{x^2}{0.10}$$

$x = [OH^-] = \sqrt{0.10 \times 5.6 \times 10^{-10}} = 7.5 \times 10^{-6} \, M$ (the assumption $x \ll 0.10$ was valid)

Now compute the value of the ion product in this solution and compare it with the value of K_{sp} for $Mg(OH)_2$.

$$Q_{sp} = [Mg^{2+}][OH^-]^2 = (0.010M)(7.5 \times 10^{-6} M)^2 = 5.6 \times 10^{-13} < 1.8 \times 10^{-11} = K_{sp}[Mg(OH)_2]$$

Because Q_{sp} is smaller than K_{sp}, this solution is unsaturated and precipitation of $Mg(OH)_2(s)$ will not occur.

8B **(M)** Here we can use the Henderson–Hasselbalch equation to determine the pH of the buffer.

$$pH = pK_a + \log\frac{[CH_3COO^-]}{[CH_3COOH]} = -\log(1.8 \times 10^{-5}) + \log\frac{0.250M}{0.150M} = 4.74 + 0.22 = 4.96$$

$pOH = 14.00 - pH = 14.00 - 4.96 = 9.04 \qquad [OH^-] = 10^{-pOH} = 10^{-9.04} = 9.1 \times 10^{-10} \, M$

Now we determine Q_{sp} to see if precipitation will occur.

$$Q_{sp} = [Fe^{3+}][OH^-]^3 = (0.013M)(9.1 \times 10^{-10})^3 = 9.8 \times 10^{-30}$$

$Q_{sp} > 4 \times 10^{-38} = K_{sp}$; Thus, $Fe(OH)_3$ precipitation should occur.

9A **(M)** Determine $[OH^-]$, and then the pH necessary to prevent the precipitation of $Mn(OH)_2$.

$$K_{sp} = 1.9 \times 10^{-13} = [Mn^{2+}][OH^-]^2 = (0.0050M)[OH^-]^2$$

$$[OH^-] = \sqrt{\frac{1.9 \times 10^{-13}}{0.0050}} = 6.2 \times 10^{-6} \, M$$

$pOH = -\log(6.2 \times 10^{-6}) = 5.21 \qquad pH = 14.00 - 5.21 = 8.79$

We will use this pH in the Henderson–Hasselbalch equation to determine $[NH_4^+]$.

$pK_b = 4.74$ for NH_3.

$$pH = pK_a + \log\frac{[NH_3]}{[NH_4^+]} = 8.79 = (14.00 - 4.74) + \log\frac{0.025M}{[NH_4^+]}$$

$$\log\frac{0.025M}{[NH_4^+]} = 8.79 - (14.00 - 4.74) = -0.47 \qquad \frac{0.025}{[NH_4^+]} = 10^{-0.47} = 0.34$$

$$[NH_4^+] = \frac{0.025}{0.34} = 0.074M$$

9B **(M)** First we must calculate the $[H_3O^+]$ in the buffer solution that is being employed to dissolve the magnesium hydroxide:

$$NH_3(aq) + H_2O(l) \rightleftharpoons NH_4^+(aq) + OH^-(aq) ; \quad K_b = 1.8 \times 10^{-5}$$

$$K_b = \frac{[NH_4^+][OH^-]}{[NH_3]} = \frac{[0.100M][OH^-]}{[0.250M]} = 1.8 \times 10^{-5}$$

$$[OH^-] = 4.5 \times 10^{-5}\,M; \quad [H_3O^+] = \frac{1.00 \times 10^{-14}\,M^2}{4.5 \times 10^{-5}\,M} = 2.2_2 \times 10^{-10}\,M$$

Now we can employ Equation 18.4 to calculate the molar solubility of $Mg(OH)_2$ in the buffer solution; molar solubility $Mg(OH)_2 = [Mg^{2+}]_{equil}$

$$Mg(OH)_2(s) + 2H_3O^+(aq) \xrightleftharpoons{K=1.8\times10^{17}} Mg^{2+}(aq) + 4H_2O(l) ;$$

Equilibrium $\quad - \quad 2.2 \times 10^{-10} \quad\quad x \quad -$

$$K = \frac{[Mg^{2+}]}{[H_3O^+]^2} = \frac{x}{[2.2\times10^{-10}\,M]^2} = 1.8 \times 10^{17} \qquad x = 8.7\times10^{-3}\,M = [Mg^{2+}]_{equil}$$

So, the molar solubility for $Mg(OH)_2 = 8.7\times10^{-3}M$.

10A **(M)**

(a) In solution are $Cu^{2+}(aq)$, $SO_4^{2-}(aq)$, $Na^+(aq)$, and $OH^-(aq)$.

$$Cu^{2+}(aq) + 2OH^-(aq) \rightarrow Cu(OH)_2(s)$$

(b) In the solution above, $Cu(OH)_2(s)$ is $Cu^{2+}(aq)$:

$$Cu(OH)_2(s) \rightleftharpoons Cu^{2+}(aq) + 2OH^-(aq)$$

This $Cu^{2+}(aq)$ reacts with the added $NH_3(aq)$:

$$Cu^{2+}(aq) + 4NH_3(aq) \rightleftharpoons [Cu(NH_3)_4]^{2+}(aq)$$

The overall result is: $Cu(OH)_2(s) + 4NH_3(aq) \rightleftharpoons [Cu(NH_3)_4]^{2+}(aq) + 2OH^-(aq)$

(c) $HNO_3(aq)$ (a strong acid), forms $H_3O^+(aq)$, which reacts with $OH^-(aq)$ and $NH_3(aq)$.

$$OH^-(aq) + H_3O^+(aq) \rightarrow 2H_2O(l); \quad NH_3(aq) + H_3O^+(aq) \rightarrow NH_4^+(aq) + H_2O(l)$$

As $NH_3(aq)$ is consumed, the reaction below shifts to the left.

$$Cu(OH)_2(s) + 4NH_3(aq) \rightleftharpoons [Cu(NH_3)_4]^{2+}(aq) + 2OH^-(aq)$$

But as $OH^-(aq)$ is consumed, the dissociation reactions shift to the side with the dissolved ions: $Cu(OH)_2(s) \rightleftharpoons Cu^{2+}(aq) + 2OH^-(aq)$

The species in solution at the end of all this are $Cu^{2+}(aq)$, $NO_3^-(aq)$, $NH_4^+(aq)$, excess $H_3O^+(aq)$, $Na^+(aq)$, and $SO_4^{2-}(aq)$ (probably $HSO_4^-(aq)$ as well).

10B **(M)**

(a) In solution are $Zn^{2+}(aq)$, $SO_4^{2-}(aq)$, and $NH_3(aq)$,

$$Zn^{2+}(aq) + 4NH_3(aq) \rightleftharpoons [Zn(NH_3)_4]^{2+}(aq)$$

(b) $HNO_3(aq)$, a strong acid, produces $H_3O^+(aq)$, which reacts with $NH_3(aq)$.

$NH_3(aq) + H_3O^+(aq) \rightarrow NH_4^+(aq) + H_2O(l)$ As $NH_3(aq)$ is consumed, the tetrammine complex ion is destroyed.

$$[Zn(NH_3)_4]^{2+}(aq) + 4H_3O^+(aq) \rightleftharpoons [Zn(H_2O)_4]^{2+}(aq) + 4NH_4^+(aq)$$

(c) $NaOH(aq)$ is a strong base that produces $OH^-(aq)$, forming a hydroxide precipitate.

$$[Zn(H_2O)_4]^{2+}(aq) + 2OH^-(aq) \rightleftharpoons Zn(OH)_2(s) + 4H_2O(l)$$

Another possibility is a reversal of the reaction of part **(b)**.

$$[Zn(H_2O)_4]^{2+}(aq) + 4NH_4^+(aq) + 4OH^-(aq) \rightleftharpoons [Zn(NH_3)_4]^{2+}(aq) + 8H_2O(l)$$

(d) The precipitate dissolves in excess base.

$$Zn(OH)_2(s) + 2OH^-(aq) \rightleftharpoons [Zn(OH)_4]^{2-}(aq)$$

11A **(M)** We first determine $[Ag^+]$ in a solution that is 0.100 M $Ag^+(aq)$ (from $AgNO_3$) and 0.225 M $NH_3(aq)$. Because of the large value of $K_f = 1.6 \times 10^7$, we start by having the reagents form as much complex ion as possible, and approach equilibrium from this point.

Equation:	$Ag^+(aq)$	$+$	$2NH_3(aq)$	$\rightleftharpoons$	$[Ag(NH_3)_2]^+(aq)$
In soln	0.100 M		0.225 M		0 M
Form complex	−0.100 M		−0.200 M		+0.100 M
Initial	0 M		0.025 M		0.100 M
Changes	+x M		+2x M		−x M
Equil	x M		(0.025 + x) M		(0.100 − x) M

$$K_f = 1.6 \times 10^7 = \frac{\left[[Ag(NH_3)_2]^+\right]}{[Ag^+][NH_3]^2} = \frac{0.100 - x}{x(0.025 + 2x)^2} \approx \frac{0.100}{x(0.025)^2}$$

$$x = \frac{0.100}{(0.025)^2 1.6 \times 10^7} = 1.0 \times 10^{-5} M = [Ag^+] = \text{concentration of free silver ion}$$

($x \ll 0.025$ M, so the approximation was valid)

The $[Cl^-]$ is diluted: $[Cl^-]_{final} = [Cl^-]_{initial} \times \frac{1.00\,mL_{initial}}{1,500\,mL_{final}} = 3.50\,M \div 1500 = 0.00233\,M$

Finally we compare Q_{sp} with K_{sp} to determine if precipitation of $AgCl(s)$ will occur.

$$Q_{sp} = [Ag^+][Cl^-] = (1.0 \times 10^{-5}\,M)(0.00233\,M) = 2.3 \times 10^{-8} > 1.8 \times 10^{-10} = K_{sp}$$

Because the value of the Q_{sp} is larger than the value of the K_{sp}, precipitation of $AgCl(s)$ should occur.

11B (M) We organize the solution around the balanced equation of the formation reaction.

Equation: $Pb^{2+}(aq)$ + $EDTA^{4-}(aq)$ $\rightleftharpoons$ $[PbEDTA]^{2-}(aq)$

Initial	0.100 M	0.250 M	0 M
Form Complex:	–0.100 M	(0.250 – 0.100) M	0.100 M
Equil	x M	$(0.150+x)$ M	$(0.100-x)$ M

$$K_f = \frac{\left[[PbEDTA]^{2-}\right]}{\left[Pb^{2+}\right]\left[EDTA^{4-}\right]} = 2\times10^{18} = \frac{0.100-x}{x(0.150+x)} \approx \frac{0.100}{0.150\,x}$$

$$x = \frac{0.100}{0.150\times2\times10^{18}} = 3\times10^{-19}\ M \qquad (x \ll 0.100\ M, \text{ thus the approximation was valid.})$$

We calculate Q_{sp} and compare it to K_{sp} to determine if precipitation will occur.

$$Q_{sp} = \left[Pb^{2+}\right]\left[I^-\right]^2 = (3\times10^{-19}M)(0.10M)^2 = 3\times10^{-21}.$$

$Q_{sp} < 7.1\times10^{-9} = K_{sp}$ Thus precipitation will not occur.

12A (M) We first determine the maximum concentration of free Ag^+.

$$K_{sp} = \left[Ag^+\right]\left[Cl^-\right] = 1.8\times10^{-10} \qquad \left[Ag^+\right] = \frac{1.8\times10^{-10}}{0.0075} = 2.4\times10^{-8}\ M.$$

This is so small that we assume that all the Ag^+ in solution is present as complex ion:

$\left[\left[Ag(NH_3)_2\right]^+\right] = 0.13\ M$. We use K_f to determine the concentration of free NH_3.

$$K_f = \frac{\left[\left[Ag(NH_3)_2\right]^+\right]}{\left[Ag^+\right]\left[NH_3\right]^2} = 1.6\times10^7 = \frac{0.13M}{2.4\times10^{-8}\left[NH_3\right]^2}$$

$$[NH_3] = \sqrt{\frac{0.13}{2.4\times10^{-8}\times1.6\times10^7}} = 0.58\ M.$$

If we combine this with the ammonia present in the complex ion, the total ammonia concentration is $0.58M+(2\times0.13M) = 0.84M$. Thus, the <u>minimum</u> concentration of ammonia necessary to keep AgCl(s) from forming is 0.84 M.

12B **(M)** We use the solubility product constant expression to determine the maximum $[Ag^+]$ that can be present in 0.010 M Cl^- without precipitation occurring.

$$K_{sp} = 1.8 \times 10^{-10} = [Ag^+][Cl^-] = [Ag^+](0.010\,M) \qquad [Ag^+] = \frac{1.8 \times 10^{-10}}{0.010} = 1.8 \times 10^{-8}\,M$$

This is also the concentration of free silver ion in the K_f expression. Because of the large value of K_f, practically all of the silver ion in solution is present as the complex ion, $[Ag(S_2O_3)_2]^{3-}$. We solve the expression for $[S_2O_3^{2-}]$ and then add the $[S_2O_3^{2-}]$ "tied up" in the complex ion.

$$K_f = 1.7 \times 10^{13} = \frac{\left[[Ag(S_2O_3)_2]^{3-}\right]}{[Ag^+][S_2O_3^{2-}]^2} = \frac{0.10\,M}{1.8 \times 10^{-8}\,M\,[S_2O_3^{2-}]^2}$$

$$[S_2O_3^{2-}] = \sqrt{\frac{0.10}{1.8 \times 10^{-8} \times 1.7 \times 10^{13}}} = 5.7 \times 10^{-4}\,M = \text{concentration of free } S_2O_3^{2-}$$

$$\text{total } [S_2O_3^{2-}] = 5.7 \times 10^{-4}\,M + 0.10\,M\,[Ag(S_2O_3)_2]^{3-} \times \frac{2\,mol\,S_2O_3^{2-}}{1\,mol\,[Ag(S_2O_3)_2]^{3-}}$$

$$= 0.20\,M + 0.00057\,M = 0.20\,M$$

13A **(M)** We must combine the two equilibrium expressions, for K_f and for K_{sp}, to find $K_{overall}$.

$$Fe(OH)_3(s) \rightleftharpoons Fe^{3+}(aq) + 3\,OH^-(aq) \qquad\qquad K_{sp} = 4 \times 10^{-38}$$

$$Fe^{3+}(aq) + 3\,C_2O_4^{2-}(aq) \rightleftharpoons [Fe(C_2O_4)_3]^{3-}(aq) \qquad\qquad K_f = 2 \times 10^{20}$$

$$Fe(OH)_3(s) + 3\,C_2O_4^{2-}(aq) \rightleftharpoons [Fe(C_2O_4)_3]^{3-}(aq) + 3\,OH^-(aq) \qquad K_{overall} = 8 \times 10^{-18}$$

Initial	0.100 M	0 M	$\approx 0\,M$
Changes	$-3x\,M$	$+x\,M$	$+3x\,M$
Equil	$(0.100 - 3x)\,M$	$x\,M$	$3x\,M$

$$K_{overall} = \frac{\left[[Fe(C_2O_4)_3]^{3-}\right][OH^-]^3}{[C_2O_4^{2-}]^3} = \frac{(x)(3x)^3}{(0.100 - 3x)^3} = 8 \times 10^{-18} \approx \frac{27x^4}{(0.100)^3}$$

($3x << 0.100$ M, thus the approximation was valid.)

$$x = \sqrt[4]{\frac{(0.100)^3\,8 \times 10^{-18}}{27}} = 4 \times 10^{-6}\,M \quad \text{The assumption is valid.}$$

Thus the solubility of $Fe(OH)_3$ in 0.100 M $C_2O_4^{2-}$ is $4 \times 10^{-6}\,M$.

13B **(M)** In Example 18-13 we saw that the expression for the solubility, s, of a silver halide in an aqueous ammonia solution, where $[NH_3]$ is the concentration of aqueous ammonia, is given by:

$$K_{sp} \times K_f = \left(\frac{s}{[NH_3] - 2s} \right)^2 \quad or \quad \sqrt{K_{sp} \times K_f} = \frac{s}{[NH_3] - 2s}$$

For all scenarios, the $[NH_3]$ stays fixed at 0.1000 M and K_f is always 1.6×10^7. We see that s will decrease as does K_{sp}. The relevant values are:

$$K_{sp}(AgCl) = 1.8 \times 10^{-10}, \quad K_{sp}(AgBr) = 5.0 \times 10^{-13}, \quad K_{sp}(AgI) = 8.5 \times 10^{-17}.$$

Thus, the order of decreasing solubility must be: AgI > AgBr > AgCl.

14A **(M)** For FeS, we know that $K_{spa} = 6 \times 10^2$; for Ag_2S, $K_{spa} = 6 \times 10^{-30}$.

We compute the value of Q_{spa} in each case, with $[H_2S] = 0.10\,M$ and $[H_3O^+] = 0.30\,M$.

For FeS, $Q_{spa} = \dfrac{0.020 \times 0.10}{(0.30)^2} = 0.022 < 6 \times 10^2 = K_{spa}$

Thus, precipitation of FeS should not occur.

For Ag_2S, $Q_{spa} = \dfrac{(0.010)^2 \times 0.10}{(0.30)^2} = 1.1 \times 10^{-4}$

$Q_{spa} > 6 \times 10^{-30} = K_{spa}$; thus, precipitation of Ag_2S should occur.

14B **(M)** The $[H_3O^+]$ needed to just form a precipitate can be obtained by direct substitution of the provided concentrations into the K_{spa} expression. When that expression is satisfied, a precipitate will just form.

$$K_{spa} = \frac{[Fe^{2+}][H_2S]}{[H_3O^+]^2} = 6 \times 10^2 = \frac{(0.015\,M\,Fe^{2+})(0.10\,M\,H_2S)}{[H_3O^+]^2}, \quad [H_3O^+] = \sqrt{\frac{0.015 \times 0.10}{6 \times 10^2}} = 0.002\,M$$

$$pH = -\log[H_3O^+] = -\log(0.002) = 2.7$$

INTEGRATIVE EXAMPLES

A. **(D)** To determine the amount of $Ca(NO_3)_2$ needed, one has to calculate the amount of Ca^{2+} that will result in only 1.00×10^{-12} M of PO_4^{3-}

$$Ca_3(PO_4)_2 \rightleftharpoons 3\,Ca^{2+} + 2\,PO_4^{3-}$$

$$K_{sp} = (3s)^3 (2s)^2$$

Using the common–ion effect, we will try to determine what concentration of Ca^{2+} ions forces the equilibrium in the lake to have only 1.00×10^{-12} M of phosphate, noting that $(2s)$ is the equilibrium concentration of phosphate.

$$1.30 \times 10^{-32} = \left[Ca^{2+}\right]^3 \left(1.00 \times 10^{-12}\right)^2$$

Solving for $[Ca^{2+}]$ yields a concentration of 0.00235 M.

The volume of the lake: $V = 300\ m \times 150\ m \times 5\ m = 225000\ m^3$ or 2.25×10^8 L.

Mass of $Ca(NO_3)_2$ is determined as follows:

$$\text{mass } Ca(NO_3)_2 = 2.25 \times 10^8\ L \times \frac{0.00235\ mol\ Ca^{2+}}{L} \times \frac{1\ mol\ Ca(NO_3)_2}{1\ mol\ Ca^{2+}} \times \frac{164.1\ g\ Ca(NO_3)_2}{1\ mol\ Ca(NO_3)_2}$$

$$= 87 \times 10^6\ g\ Ca(NO_3)_2$$

B. **(M)** The reaction of $AgNO_3$ and Na_2SO_4 is as follows:

$$2AgNO_3 + Na_2SO_4 \rightarrow 2NaNO_3 + Ag_2SO_4$$

$$\text{mol } Ag_2SO_4 = (0.350\ L \times 0.200\ M)\ AgNO_3 \times \frac{1\ mol\ Ag_2SO_4}{2\ mol\ AgNO_3} = 3.5 \times 10^{-2}\ mol$$

$$\text{mol } NaNO_3 = (0.250\ L \times 0.240\ M)\ Na_2SO_4 \times \frac{2\ mol\ NaNO_3}{1\ mol\ Na_2SO_4} = 0.12\ mol$$

Ag_2SO_4 is the precipitate. Since it is also the limiting reagent, there are 3.5×10^{-2} moles of Ag_2SO_4 produced.

The reaction of Ag_2SO_4 with $Na_2S_2O_3$ is as follows:

$$Na_2S_2O_3 + Ag_2SO_4 \rightarrow Na_2SO_4 + Ag_2S_2O_3$$

$$\text{mol } Na_2S_2O_3 = (0.400\ L \times 0.500\ M)\ Na_2S_2O_3 = 0.200\ mol$$

Ag_2SO_4 is the limiting reagent, so no Ag_2SO_4 precipitate is left.

EXERCISES

K_{sp} and Solubility

1. **(E)**

   (a) $Ag_2SO_4(s) \rightleftharpoons 2Ag^+(aq) + SO_4^{2-}(aq)$ $K_{sp} = \left[Ag^+\right]^2\left[SO_4^{2-}\right]$

   (b) $Ra(IO_3)_2(s) \rightleftharpoons Ra^{2+}(aq) + 2IO_3^-(aq)$ $K_{sp} = \left[Ra^{2+}\right]\left[IO_3^-\right]^2$

   (c) $Ni_3(PO_4)_2(s) \rightleftharpoons 3Ni^{2+}(aq) + 2PO_4^{3-}(aq)$ $K_{sp} = \left[Ni^{2+}\right]^3\left[PO_4^{3-}\right]^2$

   (d) $PuO_2CO_3(s) \rightleftharpoons PuO_2^{2+}(aq) + CO_3^{2-}(aq)$ $K_{sp} = \left[PuO_2^{2+}\right]\left[CO_3^{2-}\right]$

2. **(E)**

   (a) $K_{sp} = \left[Fe^{3+}\right]\left[OH^-\right]^3$ $Fe(OH)_3(s) \rightleftharpoons Fe^{3+}(aq) + 3OH^-(aq)$

   (b) $K_{sp} = \left[BiO^+\right]\left[OH^-\right]$ $BiOOH(s) \rightleftharpoons BiO^+(aq) + OH^-(aq)$

   (c) $K_{sp} = \left[Hg_2^{2+}\right]\left[I^-\right]^2$ $Hg_2I_2(s) \rightleftharpoons Hg_2^{2+}(aq) + 2I^-(aq)$

   (d) $K_{sp} = \left[Pb^{2+}\right]^3\left[AsO_4^{3-}\right]^2$ $Pb_3(AsO_4)_2(s) \rightleftharpoons 3Pb^{2+}(aq) + 2AsO_4^{3-}(aq)$

3. **(E)**

   (a) $CrF_3(s) \rightleftharpoons Cr^{3+}(aq) + 3F^-(aq)$ $K_{sp} = \left[Cr^{3+}\right]\left[F^-\right]^3 = 6.6 \times 10^{-11}$

   (b) $Au_2(C_2O_4)_3(s) \rightleftharpoons 2Au^{3+}(aq) + 3C_2O_4^{2-}(aq)$ $K_{sp} = \left[Au^{3+}\right]^2\left[C_2O_4^{2-}\right]^3 = 1 \times 10^{-10}$

   (c) $Cd_3(PO_4)_2(s) \rightleftharpoons 3Cd^{2+}(aq) + 2PO_4^{3-}(aq)$ $K_{sp} = \left[Cd^{2+}\right]^3\left[PO_4^{3-}\right]^2 = 2.1 \times 10^{-33}$

   (d) $SrF_2(s) \rightleftharpoons Sr^{2+}(aq) + 2F^-(aq)$ $K_{sp} = \left[Sr^{2+}\right]\left[F^-\right]^2 = 2.5 \times 10^{-9}$

4. **(E)** Let s = solubility of each compound in moles of compound per liter of solution.

   (a) $K_{sp} = \left[Ba^{2+}\right]\left[CrO_4^{2-}\right] = (s)(s) = s^2 = 1.2 \times 10^{-10}$ $s = 1.1 \times 10^{-5}$ M

   (b) $K_{sp} = \left[Pb^{2+}\right]\left[Br^-\right]^2 = (s)(2s)^2 = 4s^3 = 4.0 \times 10^{-5}$ $s = 2.2 \times 10^{-2}$ M

   (c) $K_{sp} = \left[Ce^{3+}\right]\left[F^-\right]^3 = (s)(3s)^3 = 27s^4 = 8 \times 10^{-16}$ $s = 7 \times 10^{-5}$ M

   (d) $K_{sp} = \left[Mg^{2+}\right]^3\left[AsO_4^{3-}\right]^2 = (3s)^3(2s)^2 = 108s^5 = 2.1 \times 10^{-20}$ $s = 4.5 \times 10^{-5}$ M

5. **(E)** We use the value of K_{sp} for each compound in determining the molar solubility in a saturated solution. In each case, s represents the molar solubility of the compound.

$AgCN$ $\quad K_{sp} = \left[Ag^+\right]\left[CN^-\right] = (s)(s) = s^2 = 1.2\times10^{-16} \quad s = 1.1\times10^{-8}\,M$

$AgIO_3$ $\quad K_{sp} = \left[Ag^+\right]\left[IO_3^-\right] = (s)(s) = s^2 = 3.0\times10^{-8} \quad s = 1.7\times10^{-4}\,M$

AgI $\quad K_{sp} = \left[Ag^+\right]\left[I^-\right] \quad = (s)(s) = s^2 = 8.5\times10^{-17} \quad s = 9.2\times10^{-9}\,M$

$AgNO_2$ $\quad K_{sp} = \left[Ag^+\right]\left[NO_2^-\right] = (s)(s) = s^2 = 6.0\times10^{-4} \quad s = 2.4\times10^{-2}\,M$

Ag_2SO_4 $\quad K_{sp} = \left[Ag^+\right]^2\left[SO_4^{2-}\right] = (2s)^2(s) = 4s^3 = 1.4\times10^{-5} \;\; s = 1.5\times10^{-2}\,M$

Thus, in order of increasing molar solubility, from smallest to largest:

$AgI < AgCN < AgIO_3 < Ag_2SO_4 < AgNO_2$

6. **(E)** We use the value of K_{sp} for each compound in determining $\left[Mg^{2+}\right]$ in its saturated solution. In each case, s represents the molar solubility of the compound.

(a) $MgCO_3$ $\qquad K_{sp} = \left[Mg^{2+}\right]\left[CO_3^{2-}\right] = (s)(s) = s^2 = 3.5\times10^{-8}$

$\qquad\qquad s = 1.9\times10^{-4}\,M\left[Mg^{2+}\right] = 1.9\times10^{-4}\,M$

(b) MgF_2 $\qquad K_{sp} = \left[Mg^{2+}\right]\left[F^-\right]^2 = (s)(2s)^2 = 4s^3 = 3.7\times10^{-8}$

$\qquad\qquad s = 2.1\times10^{-3}\,M\left[Mg^{2+}\right] = 2.1\times10^{-3}\,M$

(c) $Mg_3(PO_4)_2$ $\qquad K_{sp} = \left[Mg^{2+}\right]^3\left[PO_4^{3-}\right]^2 = (3s)^3(2s)^2 = 108s^5 = 2.1\times10^{-25}$

$\qquad\qquad s = 4.5\times10^{-6}\,M \qquad\qquad \left[Mg^{2+}\right] = 1.4\times10^{-5}\,M$

Thus a saturated solution of MgF_2 has the highest $\left[Mg^{2+}\right]$.

7. **(M)** We determine $[F^-]$ in saturated CaF_2, and from that value the concentration of F^- in ppm.

For CaF_2 $\quad K_{sp} = \left[Ca^{2+}\right]\left[F^-\right]^2 = (s)(2s)^2 = 4s^3 = 5.3\times10^{-9} \quad s = 1.1\times10^{-3}\,M$

The solubility in ppm is the number of grams of CaF_2 in 10^6 g of solution. We assume a solution density of $1.00\,g/mL$.

$$\text{mass of } F^- = 10^6\,g\,\text{soln}\times\frac{1\,mL}{1.00\,g\,\text{soln}}\times\frac{1\,L\,\text{soln}}{1000\,mL}\times\frac{1.1\times10^{-3}\,mol\,CaF_2}{1\,L\,\text{soln}}$$

$$\times\frac{2\,mol\,F^-}{1\,mol\,CaF_2}\times\frac{19.0\,g\,F^-}{1\,mol\,F^-} = 42\,g\,F^-$$

This is 42 times more concentrated than the optimum concentration of fluoride ion for fluoridation. CaF_2 is, in fact, more soluble than is necessary. Its uncontrolled use might lead to excessive F^- in solution.

8. **(E)** We determine $\left[OH^-\right]$ in a saturated solution. From this $\left[OH^-\right]$ we determine the pH.

$$K_{sp} = \left[BiO^+\right]\left[OH^-\right] = 4\times10^{-10} = s^2 \qquad s = 2\times10^{-5}\,M = \left[OH^-\right] = \left[BiO^+\right]$$

$$pOH = -\log\left(2\times10^{-5}\right) = 4.7 \qquad pH = 9.3$$

9. **(M)** We first assume that the volume of the solution does not change appreciably when its temperature is lowered. Then we determine the mass of $Mg\left(CH_3(CH_2)_{14}COO\right)_2$ dissolved in each solution, recognizing that the molar solubility of $Mg\left(CH_3(CH_2)_{14}COO\right)_2$ equals the cube root of one fourth of its solubility product constant, since it is the only solute in the solution.

$$K_{sp} = 4s^3 \qquad s = \sqrt[3]{K_{sp}/4}$$

At $50\,^\circ C$: $\; s = \sqrt[3]{4.8\times10^{-12}/4} = 1.1\times10^{-4}$ M; At $25\,^\circ C$: $s = \sqrt[3]{3.3\times10^{-12}/4} = 9.4\times10^{-5}$ M

amount of $Mg\left(CH_3(CH_2)_{14}COO\right)_2$ (50°C)

$$= 0.965\,L \times \frac{1.1\times10^{-4}\,\text{mol } Mg\left(CH_3(CH_2)_{14}COO\right)_2}{1\,L\ \text{soln}} = 1.1\times10^{-4}\,\text{mol}$$

amount of $Mg\left(CH_3(CH_2)_{14}COO\right)_2$ (25°C)

$$= 0.965\,L \times \frac{9.4\times10^{-5}\,\text{mol } Mg\left(CH_3(CH_2)_{14}COO\right)_2}{1\,L\ \text{soln}} = 0.91\times10^{-4}\,\text{mol}$$

mass of $Mg\left(CH_3(CH_2)_{14}COO\right)_2$ precipitated:

$$= (1.1-0.91)\times10^{-4}\,\text{mol} \times \frac{535.15\,\text{g } Mg\left(CH_3(CH_2)_{14}COO\right)_2}{1\,\text{mol } Mg\left(CH_3(CH_2)_{14}COO\right)_2} \times \frac{1000\,\text{mg}}{1\,\text{g}} = 11\,\text{mg}$$

10. **(M)** We first assume that the volume of the solution does not change appreciably when its temperature is lowered. Then we determine the mass of CaC_2O_4 dissolved in each solution, recognizing that the molar solubility of CaC_2O_4 equals the square root of its solubility product constant, since it is the only solute in the solution.

At $95\,^\circ C$ $\; s = \sqrt{1.2\times10^{-8}} = 1.1\times10^{-4}$ M; At $13\,^\circ C$: $\qquad s = \sqrt{2.7\times10^{-9}} = 5.2\times10^{-5}$ M

$$\text{mass of } CaC_2O_4\ (95\ ^\circ C) = 0.725\ L \times \frac{1.1\times10^{-4}\,\text{mol } CaC_2O_4}{1\ L\ \text{soln}} \times \frac{128.1\,\text{g } CaC_2O_4}{1\ \text{mol } CaC_2O_4} = 0.010\,\text{g } CaC_2O_4$$

$$\text{mass of } CaC_2O_4\ (13\ ^\circ C) = 0.725\ L \times \frac{5.2\times10^{-5}\,\text{mol } PbSO_4}{1\ L\ \text{soln}} \times \frac{128.1\,\text{g } CaC_2O_4}{1\ \text{mol } CaC_2O_4} = 0.0048\,\text{g } CaC_2O_4$$

$$\text{mass of } CaC_2O_4\ \text{precipitated} = (0.010\ \text{g} - 0.0048\ \text{g}) \times \frac{1000\ \text{mg}}{1\ \text{g}} = 5.2\,\text{mg}$$

11. **(M)** First we determine $\left[I^-\right]$ in the saturated solution.

$$K_{sp} = \left[Pb^{2+}\right]\left[I^-\right]^2 = 7.1\times10^{-9} = (s)(2s)^2 = 4s^3 \qquad\qquad s = 1.2\times10^{-3}\,M$$

The $AgNO_3$ reacts with the I^- in this saturated solution in the titration.

$Ag^+(aq) + I^-(aq) \rightarrow AgI(s)$ We determine the amount of Ag^+ needed for this titration, and then $\left[AgNO_3\right]$ in the titrant.

$$\text{moles }Ag^+ = 0.02500\,L \times \frac{1.2\times10^{-3}\,\text{mol }PbI_2}{1\,L\,\text{soln}} \times \frac{2\,\text{mol }I^-}{1\,\text{mol }PbI_2} \times \frac{1\,\text{mol }Ag^+}{1\,\text{mol }I^-} = 6.0\times10^{-5}\,\text{mol }Ag^+$$

$$AgNO_3\text{ molarity} = \frac{6.0\times10^{-5}\,\text{mol }Ag^+}{0.0133\,L\,\text{soln}} \times \frac{1\,\text{mol }AgNO_3}{1\,\text{mol }Ag^+} = 4.5\times10^{-3}\,M$$

12. **(M)** We first determine $\left[C_2O_4^{2-}\right] = s$, the solubility of the saturated solution.

$$\left[C_2O_4^{2-}\right] = \frac{4.8\,mL \times \dfrac{0.00134\,\text{mmol }KMnO_4}{1\,mL\,\text{soln}} \times \dfrac{5\,\text{mmol }C_2O_4^{2-}}{2\,\text{mmol }MnO_4^-}}{250.0\,mL} = 6.4\times10^{-5}\,M = s = \left[Ca^{2+}\right]$$

$$K_{sp} = \left[Ca^{2+}\right]\left[C_2O_4^{2-}\right] = (s)(s) = s^2 = \left(6.4\times10^{-5}\right)^2 = 4.1\times10^{-9}$$

13. **(M)** We first use the ideal gas law to determine the moles of H_2S gas used.

$$n = \frac{PV}{RT} = \frac{\left(748\text{ mmHg} \times \dfrac{1\,atm}{760\text{ mmHg}}\right) \times \left(30.4\text{ mL} \times \dfrac{1\,L}{1000\text{ mL}}\right)}{0.08206\text{ L atm mol}^{-1}\,K^{-1} \times (23+273)\,K} = 1.23\times10^{-3}\text{ moles}$$

If we assume that all the H_2S is consumed in forming Ag_2S, we can compute the $[Ag^+]$ in the $AgBrO_3$ solution. This assumption is valid if the equilibrium constant for the cited reaction is large, which is the case, as shown below:

$$2Ag^+(aq) + HS^-(aq) + OH^-(aq) \rightleftharpoons Ag_2S(s) + H_2O(l) \qquad K_{a_2}/K_{sp} = \frac{1.0\times10^{-19}}{2.6\times10^{-51}} = 3.8\times10^{31}$$

$$H_2S(aq) + H_2O(l) \rightleftharpoons HS^-(aq) + H_3O^+(aq) \qquad\qquad K_1 = 1.0\times10^{-7}$$

$$2H_2O(l) \rightleftharpoons H_3O^+(aq) + OH^-(aq) \qquad\qquad K_w = 1.0\times10^{-14}$$

$$\overline{2Ag^+(aq) + H_2S(aq) + 2H_2O(l) \rightleftharpoons Ag_2S(s) + 2H_3O^+(aq)}$$

$$K_{\text{overall}} = (K_{a_2}/K_{sp})(K_1)(K_w) = (3.8\times10^{31})(1.0\times10^{-7})(1.0\times10^{-14}) = 3.8\times10^{10}$$

$$\left[Ag^+\right] = \frac{1.23\times10^{-3}\,\text{mol }H_2S}{338\text{ mL soln}} \times \frac{1000\text{ mL}}{1\,L\,\text{soln}} \times \frac{2\,\text{mol }Ag^+}{1\,\text{mol }H_2S} = 7.28\times10^{-3}\,M$$

Then, for $AgBrO_3$, $K_{sp} = \left[Ag^+\right]\left[BrO_3^-\right] = \left(7.28\times10^{-3}\right)^2 = 5.30\times10^{-5}$

14. **(M)** The titration reaction is $Ca(OH)_2(aq) + 2HCl(aq) \longrightarrow CaCl_2(aq) + 2H_2O(l)$

$$\left[OH^-\right] = \frac{10.7 \text{ mL HCl} \times \dfrac{1 \text{ L}}{1000 \text{ mL}} \times \dfrac{0.1032 \text{ mol HCl}}{1 \text{ L}} \times \dfrac{1 \text{ mol OH}^-}{1 \text{ mol HCl}}}{50.00 \text{ mL Ca(OH)}_2 \text{ soln} \times \dfrac{1 \text{ L}}{1000 \text{ mL}}} = 0.0221 \text{ M}$$

In a saturated solution of $Ca(OH)_2$, $\left[Ca^{2+}\right] = \left[OH^-\right] \div 2$

$K_{sp} = \left[Ca^{2+}\right]\left[OH^-\right]^2 = (0.0221 \div 2)(0.0221)^2 = 5.40 \times 10^{-6}$ (5.5×10^{-6} in Appendix D).

The Common-Ion Effect

15. **(E)** We let $s =$ molar solubility of $Mg(OH)_2$ in moles solute per liter of solution.

(a) $K_{sp} = \left[Mg^{2+}\right]\left[OH^-\right]^2 = (s)(2s)^2 = 4s^3 = 1.8 \times 10^{-11}$ $s = 1.7 \times 10^{-4} \text{ M}$

(b) Equation: $\quad Mg(OH)_2(s) \rightleftharpoons Mg^{2+}(aq) \quad + \quad 2OH^-(aq)$

Initial:	–	0.0862 M	≈ 0 M
Changes:	–	+s M	+2s M
Equil:	–	(0.0862 + s) M	2s M

$K_{sp} = (0.0862 + s) \times (2s)^2 = 1.8 \times 10^{-11} \approx (0.0862) \times (2s)^2 = 0.34 s^2$ $s = 7.3 \times 10^{-6} \text{ M}$
($s \ll 0.0802$ M, thus, the approximation was valid.)

(c) $\left[OH^-\right] = [KOH] = 0.0355 \text{ M}$

Equation: $\quad Mg(OH)_2(s) \rightleftharpoons Mg^{2+}(aq) \quad + \quad 2OH^-(aq)$

Initial:	–	0 M	0.0355 M
Changes:	–	+ s M	+ 2s M
Equil:	–	s M	(0.0355 + 2s) M

$K_{sp} = (s)(0.0355 + 2s)^2 = 1.8 \times 10^{-11} \approx (s)(0.0355)^2 = 0.0013 s$ $s = 1.4 \times 10^{-8} \text{ M}$

16. **(E)** The solubility equilibrium is $\quad CaCO_3(s) \rightleftharpoons Ca^{2+}(aq) + CO_3^{2-}(aq)$

(a) The addition of $Na_2CO_3(aq)$ produces $CO_3^{2-}(aq)$ in solution. This common ion suppresses the dissolution of $CaCO_3(s)$.

(b) HCl(aq) is a strong acid that reacts with carbonate ion:
$CO_3^{2-}(aq) + 2H_3O^+(aq) \rightarrow CO_2(g) + 3H_2O(l)$.
This decreases $\left[CO_3^{2-}\right]$ in the solution, allowing more $CaCO_3(s)$ to dissolve.

(c) HSO_4^- (aq) is a moderately weak acid. It is strong enough to protonate appreciable concentrations of carbonate ion, thereby decreasing $\left[CO_3^{2-}\right]$ and enhancing the solubility of $CaCO_3$ (s), as the value of K_c indicates.

$$HSO_4^-\text{(aq)} + CO_3^{2-}\text{(aq)} \rightleftharpoons SO_4^{2-}\text{(aq)} + HCO_3^-\text{(aq)}$$

$$K_c = \frac{K_a(HSO_4^-)}{K_a(HCO_3^-)} = \frac{0.011}{4.7\times10^{-11}} = 2.3\times10^8$$

17. **(E)** The presence of KI in a solution produces a significant $\left[I^-\right]$ in the solution. Not as much AgI can dissolve in such a solution as in pure water, since the ion product, $\left[Ag^+\right]\left[I^-\right]$, cannot exceed the value of K_{sp} (i.e., the I^- from the KI that dissolves represses the dissociation of AgI(s)). In similar fashion, $AgNO_3$ produces a significant $\left[Ag^+\right]$ in solution, again influencing the value of the ion product; not as much AgI can dissolve as in pure water.

18. **(E)** If the solution contains KNO_3, more AgI will end up dissolving than in pure water, because the activity of each ion will be less than its molarity. On an ionic level, the reason is that ion pairs, such as $Ag^+NO_3^-$ (aq) and K^+I^- (aq) form in the solution, preventing Ag^+ and I^- ions from coming together and precipitating.

19. **(E)** Equation: Ag_2SO_4 (s) $\rightleftharpoons$ $2Ag^+$ (aq) $+$ SO_4^{2-} (aq)

Original:	—	0 M	0.150 M
Add solid:	—	$+2x$ M	$+x$ M
Equil:	—	$2x$ M	$(0.150+x)$ M

$$2x = \left[Ag^+\right] = 9.7\times10^{-3}\,M;\quad x = 0.0048\underline{5}\,M$$

$$K_{sp} = \left[Ag^+\right]^2\left[SO_4^{2-}\right] = (2x)^2(0.150+x) = \left(9.7\times10^{-3}\right)^2(0.150+0.0048\underline{5}) = 1.5\times10^{-5}$$

20. **(M)** Equation: $CaSO_4$ (s) $\rightleftharpoons$ Ca^{2+} (aq) $+$ SO_4^{2-} (aq).

Soln:	—	0 M	0.0025 M
Add $CaSO_4$ (s)	—	$+x$ M	$+x$ M
Equil:	—	x M	$(0.0025+x)$ M

If we use the approximation that $x \ll 0.0025$, we find $x = 0.0036$. Clearly, x is larger than 0.0025 and thus the approximation is not valid. The quadratic equation must be solved.

$$K_{sp} = \left[Ca^{2+}\right]\left[SO_4^{2-}\right] = 9.1\times10^{-6} = x(0.0025+x) = 0.0025x + x^2$$

$$x^2 + 0.0025x - 9.1\times10^{-6} = 0$$

$$x = \frac{-b \pm \sqrt{b^2 - 4ac}}{2a} = \frac{-0.0025 \pm \sqrt{6.3 \times 10^{-6} + 3.6 \times 10^{-5}}}{2} = 2.0 \times 10^{-3} \text{M} = [\text{CaSO}_4]$$

$$\text{mass CaSO}_4 = 0.1000 \,\text{L} \times \frac{2.0 \times 10^{-3} \text{ mol CaSO}_4}{1 \text{ L soln}} \times \frac{136.1 \text{ g CaSO}_4}{1 \text{ mol CaSO}_4} = 0.027 \text{ g CaSO}_4$$

21. **(M)** For PbI_2, $K_{sp} = 7.1 \times 10^{-9} = [\text{Pb}^{2+}][\text{I}^-]^2$

In a solution where 1.5×10^{-4} mol PbI_2 is dissolved, $[\text{Pb}^{2+}] = 1.5 \times 10^{-4}$ M, and

$[\text{I}^-] = 2[\text{Pb}^{2+}] = 3.0 \times 10^{-4}$ M

Equation: $\text{PbI}_2(s) \rightleftharpoons \text{Pb}^{2+}(aq) + 2\text{I}^-(aq)$

Initial:	—	1.5×10^{-4} M	3.0×10^{-4} M
Add lead(II):	—	$+x$ M	
Equil:	—	$(0.00015 + x)$ M	0.00030 M

$K_{sp} = 7.1 \times 10^{-9} = (0.00015 + x)(0.00030)^2$; $(0.00015 + x) = 0.079$; $x = 0.079$ M $= [\text{Pb}^{2+}]$

22. **(M)** For PbI_2, $K_{sp} = 7.1 \times 10^{-9} = [\text{Pb}^{2+}][\text{I}^-]^2$

In a solution where 1.5×10^{-5} mol PbI_2/L is dissolved, $[\text{Pb}^{2+}] = 1.5 \times 10^{-5}$ M, and

$[\text{I}^-] = 2[\text{Pb}^{2+}] = 3.0 \times 10^{-5}$ M

Equation: $\text{PbI}_2(s) \rightleftharpoons \text{Pb}^{2+}(aq) + 2\text{I}^-(aq)$

Initial:	—	1.5×10^{-5} M	3.0×10^{-5} M
Add KI:	—		$+x$ M
Equil:	—	1.5×10^{-5} M	$(3.0 \times 10^{-5} + x)$ M

$K_{sp} = 7.1 \times 10^{-9} = (1.5 \times 10^{-5}) \times (3.0 \times 10^{-5} + x)^2$
$(3.0 \times 10^{-5} + x) = (7.1 \times 10^{-9} \div 1.5 \times 10^{-5})^{1/2}$
$x = (2.2 \times 10^{-2}) - (3.0 \times 10^{-5}) = 2.1 \times 10^{-2}$ M $= [\text{I}^-]$

23. **(D)** For Ag_2CrO_4, $K_{sp} = 1.1 \times 10^{-12} = [\text{Ag}^+]^2[\text{CrO}_4^{2-}]$

In a 5.0×10^{-8} M solution of Ag_2CrO_4, $[\text{CrO}_4^{2-}] = 5.0 \times 10^{-8}$ M and $[\text{Ag}^+] = 1.0 \times 10^{-7}$ M

Equation: $\text{Ag}_2\text{CrO}_4(s) \rightleftharpoons 2\text{Ag}^+(aq) + \text{CrO}_4^{2-}(aq)$

Initial:	—	1.0×10^{-7} M	5.0×10^{-8} M
Add chromate:	—		$+x$ M
Equil:	—	1.0×10^{-7} M	$(5.0 \times 10^{-8} + x)$ M

$K_{sp} = 1.1 \times 10^{-12} = (1.0 \times 10^{-7})^2 (5.0 \times 10^{-8} + x)$; $(5.0 \times 10^{-8} + x) = 1.1 \times 10^2 = [\text{CrO}_4^{2-}]$.

This is an impossibly high concentration to reach. Thus, we cannot lower the solubility of Ag_2CrO_4 to 5.0×10^{-8} M with CrO_4^{2-} as the common ion. Let's consider using Ag^+ as the common ion.

Equation: $\qquad Ag_2CrO_4(s) \rightleftharpoons 2Ag^+(aq) + CrO_4^{2-}(aq)$

Initial:	—	1.0×10^{-7} M	5.0×10^{-8} M
Add silver(I) ion:	—	$+x$ M	
Equil:	—	$(1.0\times10^{-7}+x)$ M	5.0×10^{-8} M

$$K_{sp} = 1.1\times10^{-12} = (1.0+x)^2 (5.0\times10^{-8}) \qquad (1.0\times10^{-7}+x) = \sqrt{\frac{1.1\times10^{-12}}{5.0\times10^{-8}}} = 4.7\times10^{-3}$$

$x = 4.7\times10^{-3} - 1.0\times10^{-7} = 4.7\times10^{-3}\,M = [I^-]$; this is an easy-to-reach concentration. Thus, the solubility can be lowered to 5.0×10^{-8} M by carefully adding $Ag^+(aq)$.

24. **(M)** Even though $BaCO_3$ is more soluble than $BaSO_4$, it will still precipitate when 0.50 M $Na_2CO_3(aq)$ is added to a saturated solution of $BaSO_4$ because there is a sufficient $[Ba^{2+}]$ in such a solution for the ion product $[Ba^{2+}][CO_3^{2-}]$ to exceed the value of K_{sp} for the compound. An example will demonstrate this phenomenon. Let us assume that the two solutions being mixed are of equal volume and, to make the situation even more unfavorable, that the saturated $BaSO_4$ solution is not in contact with solid $BaSO_4$, meaning that it does not maintain its saturation when it is diluted. First we determine $[Ba^{2+}]$ in saturated $BaSO_4(aq)$.

$$K_{sp} = [Ba^{2+}][SO_4^{2-}] = 1.1\times10^{-10} = s^2 \qquad s = \sqrt{1.1\times10^{-10}} = 1.0\times10^{-5}\,M$$

Mixing solutions of equal volumes means that the concentrations of solutes not common to the two solutions are halved by dilution.

$$[Ba^{2+}] = \frac{1}{2}\times\frac{1.0\times10^{-5}\,mol\ BaSO_4}{1\ L}\times\frac{1\ mol\ Ba^{2+}}{1\ mol\ BaSO_4} = 5.0\times10^{-6}\,M$$

$$[CO_3^{2-}] = \frac{1}{2}\times\frac{0.50\ mol\ Na_2CO_3}{1\ L}\times\frac{1\ mol\ CO_3^{2-}}{1\ mol\ Na_2CO_3} = 0.25\,M$$

$$Q_{sp}\{BaCO_3\} = [Ba^{2+}][CO_3^{2-}] = (5.0\times10^{-6})(0.25) = 1.3\times10^{-6} > 5.0\times10^{-9} = K_{sp}\{BaCO_3\}$$

Thus, precipitation of $BaCO_3$ indeed should occur under the conditions described.

25. **(E)** $[Ca^{2+}] = \dfrac{115g\ Ca^{2+}}{10^6 g\ soln}\times\dfrac{1\ mol\ Ca^{2+}}{40.08\ g\ Ca^{2+}}\times\dfrac{1000\ g\ soln}{1\ L\ soln} = 2.87\times10^{-3}\,M$

$[Ca^{2+}][F^-]^2 = K_{sp} = 5.3\times10^{-9} = (2.87\times10^{-3})[F^-]^2 \qquad [F^-] = 1.4\times10^{-3}\,M$

ppm $F^- = \dfrac{1.4\times10^{-3}\,mol\ F^-}{1\ L\ soln}\times\dfrac{19.00\ g\ F^-}{1\ mol\ F^-}\times\dfrac{1\ L\ soln}{1000\ g}\times10^6 g\ soln = 27$ ppm

26. **(M)** We first calculate the $[Ag^+]$ and the $[Cl^-]$ in the saturated solution.

$$K_{sp} = [Ag^+][Cl^-] = 1.8 \times 10^{-10} = (s)(s) = s^2 \qquad s = 1.3 \times 10^{-5}\,M = [Ag^+] = [Cl^-]$$

Both of these concentrations are marginally diluted by the addition of 1 mL of NaCl(aq)

$$[Ag^+] = [Cl^-] = 1.3 \times 10^{-5}\,M \times \frac{100.0\ mL}{100.0\ mL + 1.0\ mL} = 1.3 \times 10^{-5}\,M$$

The $[Cl^-]$ in the NaCl(aq) also is diluted. $[Cl^-] = 1.0\ M \times \dfrac{1.0\ mL}{100.0\ mL + 1.0\ mL} = 9.9 \times 10^{-3}\ M$

Let us use this $[Cl^-]$ to determine the $[Ag^+]$ that can exist in this solution.

$$[Ag^+][Cl^-] = 1.8 \times 10^{-10} = [Ag^+](9.9 \times 10^{-3}\ M) \qquad [Ag^+] = \frac{1.8 \times 10^{-10}}{9.9 \times 10^{-3}} = 1.8 \times 10^{-8}\ M$$

We compute the amount of AgCl in this final solution, and in the initial solution.

$$\text{mmol AgCl final} = 101.0\ mL \times \frac{1.8 \times 10^{-8}\,mol\ Ag^+}{1\ L\ soln} \times \frac{1\ mmol\ AgCl}{1\ mmol\ Ag^+} = 1.8 \times 10^{-6}\,mmol\ AgCl$$

$$\text{mmol AgCl initial} = 100.0\ mL \times \frac{1.3 \times 10^{-5}\,mol\ Ag^+}{1\ L\ soln} \times \frac{1\ mmol\ AgCl}{1\ mmol\ Ag^+} = 1.3 \times 10^{-3}\,mmol\ AgCl$$

The difference between these two amounts is the amount of AgCl that precipitates. Next we compute its mass.

$$\text{mass AgCl} = (1.3 \times 10^{-3} - 1.8 \times 10^{-6})\ mmol\ AgCl \times \frac{143.3\ mg\ AgCl}{1\ mmol\ AgCl} = 0.19\ mg$$

We conclude that the precipitate will not be visible to the unaided eye, since its mass is less than 1 mg.

Criteria for Precipitation from Solution

27. **(E)** We first determine $[Mg^{2+}]$, and then the value of Q_{sp} in order to compare it to the value of K_{sp}. We express molarity in millimoles per milliliter, entirely equivalent to moles per liter.

$$[Mg^{2+}] = \frac{22.5\ mg\ MgCl_2}{325\ mL\ soln} \times \frac{1\ mmol\ MgCl_2 \cdot 6H_2O}{203.3\ mg\ MgCl_2 \cdot 6H_2O} \times \frac{1\ mmol\ Mg^{2+}}{1\ mmol\ MgCl_2} = 3.41 \times 10^{-4}\ M$$

$$Q_{sp} = [Mg^{2+}][F^-]^2 = (3.41 \times 10^{-4})(0.035)^2 = 4.2 \times 10^{-7} > 3.7 \times 10^{-8} = K_{sp}$$

Thus, precipitation of $MgF_2(s)$ should occur from this solution.

28. **(E)** The solutions mutually dilute each other.

$$[Cl^-] = 0.016\ M \times \frac{155\ mL}{155\ mL + 245\ mL} = 6.2 \times 10^{-3}\ M$$

$$[Pb^{2+}] = 0.175\ M \times \frac{245\ mL}{245\ mL + 155\ mL} = 0.107\ M$$

Then we compute the value of the ion product and compare it to the solubility product constant value.

$$Q_{sp} = \left[Pb^{2+} \right]\left[Cl^- \right]^2 = (0.107)(6.2\times10^{-3})^2 = 4.1\times10^{-6} < 1.6\times10^{-5} = K_{sp}$$

Thus, precipitation of $PbCl_2(s)$ will not occur from these mixed solutions.

29. **(E)** We determine the $\left[OH^- \right]$ needed to just initiate precipitation of $Cd(OH)_2$.

$$K_{sp} = \left[Cd^{2+} \right]\left[OH^- \right]^2 = 2.5\times10^{-14} = (0.0055\ M)\left[OH^- \right]^2 \qquad \left[OH^- \right] = \sqrt{\frac{2.5\times10^{-14}}{0.0055}} = 2.1\times10^{-6}\ M$$

$$pOH = -\log(2.1\times10^{-6}) = 5.68 \qquad pH = 14.00 - 5.68 = 8.32$$

Thus, $Cd(OH)_2$ will precipitate from a solution with $pH > 8.32$.

30. **(E)** We determine the $\left[OH^- \right]$ needed to just initiate precipitation of $Cr(OH)_3$.

$$K_{sp} = [Cr^{3+}][OH^-]^3 = 6.3\times10^{-31} = (0.086\ M)\ [OH^-]^3; \quad [OH^-] = \sqrt[3]{\frac{6.3\times10^{-31}}{0.086}} = 1.9\times10^{-10}\ M$$

$$pOH = -\log(1.9\times10^{-10}) = 9.72 \qquad pH = 14.00 - 9.72 = 4.28$$

Thus, $Cr(OH)_3$ will precipitate from a solution with $pH > 4.28$.

31. **(D)**

(a) First we determine $\left[Cl^- \right]$ due to the added NaCl.

$$\left[Cl^- \right] = \frac{0.10\ mg\ NaCl}{1.0\ L\ soln} \times \frac{1\ g}{1000\ mg} \times \frac{1\ mol\ NaCl}{58.4\ g\ NaCl} \times \frac{1\ mol\ Cl^-}{1\ mol\ NaCl} = 1.7\times10^{-6}\ M$$

Then we determine the value of the ion product and compare it to the solubility product constant value.

$$Q_{sp} = \left[Ag^+ \right]\left[Cl^- \right] = (0.10)(1.7\times10^{-6}) = 1.7\times10^{-7} > 1.8\times10^{-10} = K_{sp}\ \text{for AgCl}$$

Thus, precipitation of AgCl(s) should occur.

(b) The KBr(aq) is diluted on mixing, but the $\left[Ag^+ \right]$ and $\left[Cl^- \right]$ are barely affected by dilution.

$$\left[Br^- \right] = 0.10\ M \times \frac{0.05\ mL}{0.05\ mL + 250\ mL} = 2\times10^{-5}\ M$$

Now we determine $\left[Ag^+ \right]$ in a saturated AgCl solution.

$$K_{sp} = \left[Ag^+ \right]\left[Cl^- \right] = (s)(s) = s^2 = 1.8\times10^{-10} \qquad s = 1.3\times10^{-5}\ M$$

Then we determine the value of the ion product for AgBr and compare it to the solubility product constant value.

$$Q_{sp} = \left[Ag^+\right]\left[Br^-\right] = \left(1.3\times10^{-5}\right)\left(2\times10^{-5}\right) = 3\times10^{-10} > 5.0\times10^{-13} = K_{sp} \text{ for AgBr}$$

Thus, precipitation of AgBr(s) should occur.

(c) The hydroxide ion is diluted by mixing the two solutions.

$$\left[OH^-\right] = 0.0150 \text{ M}\times\frac{0.05 \text{ mL}}{0.05 \text{ mL}+3000 \text{ mL}} = 2.5\times10^{-7}\text{ M}$$

But the $\left[Mg^{2+}\right]$ does not change significantly.

$$\left[Mg^{2+}\right] = \frac{2.0 \text{ mg Mg}^{2+}}{1.0 \text{ L soln}}\times\frac{1 \text{ g}}{1000 \text{ mg}}\times\frac{1 \text{ mol Mg}^{2+}}{24.3 \text{ g Mg}} = 8.2\times10^{-5} \text{ M}$$

Then we determine the value of the ion product and compare it to the solubility product constant value.

$$Q_{sp} = \left[Mg^{2+}\right]\left[OH^-\right]^2 = \left(2.5\times10^{-7}\right)^2\left(8.2\times10^{-5}\right) = 5.1\times10^{-18}$$

$$Q_{sp} < 1.8\times10^{-11} = K_{sp} \text{ for Mg(OH)}_2 \quad \text{Thus, no precipitate forms.}$$

32. First we determine the moles of H_2 produced during the electrolysis, then determine [OH⁻].

$$\text{moles } H_2 = \frac{PV}{RT} = \frac{752 \text{ mmHg}\times\dfrac{1 \text{ atm}}{760 \text{ mmHg}}\times0.652 \text{ L}}{0.08206 \text{ L atm mol}^{-1}\text{ K}^{-1}\times295 \text{ K}} = 0.0267 \text{ mol } H_2$$

$$\left[OH^-\right] = \frac{0.0267 \text{ mol } H_2\times\dfrac{2 \text{ mol OH}^-}{1 \text{ mol } H_2}}{0.315 \text{ L sample}} = 0.170 \text{ M}$$

$$Q_{sp} = \left[Mg^{2+}\right]\left[OH^-\right]^2 = \left(0.185\right)\left(0.170\right)^2 = 5.35\times10^{-3} > 1.8\times10^{-11} = K_{sp}$$

Thus, yes, precipitation of Mg(OH)$_2$(s) should occur during the electrolysis.

33. **(D)** First we must calculate the initial [H$_2$C$_2$O$_4$] upon dissolution of the solid acid:

$$[H_2C_2O_4]_{initial} = 1.50 \text{ g } H_2C_2O_4\times\frac{1 \text{ mol } H_2C_2O_4}{90.036 \text{ g } H_2C_2O_4}\times\frac{1}{0.200 \text{ L}} = 0.0833 \text{ M}$$

(We assume the volume of the solution stays at 0.200 L.)
Next we need to determine the [C$_2$O$_4$$^{2-}$] in solution after the hydrolysis reaction between oxalic acid and water reaches equilibrium. To accomplish this we will need to solve two ICE tables:

Table 1: $H_2C_2O_4(aq) + H_2O(l) \xrightleftharpoons{K_{a1}=5.2 \times 10^{-2}} HC_2O_4^-(aq) + H_3O^+(aq)$

Initial:	0.0833 M	—	0 M $\qquad$ 0 M
Change:	$-x$	—	$+x$ M $\qquad$ $+x$ M
Equilibrium:	$0.0833 - x$ M	—	x M $\qquad$ x M

Since $C_a/K_a = 1.6$, the approximation cannot be used, and thus the full quadratic equation must be solved: $x^2/(0.0833 - x) = 5.2 \times 10^{-2}$; $\quad x^2 + 5.2 \times 10^{-2}x - 4.3\underline{3} \times 10^{-3}$

$$x = \frac{-5.2 \times 10^{-2} \pm \sqrt{2.7 \times 10^{-3} + 0.0173}}{2} \qquad x = 0.045 \text{ M} = [HC_2O_4^-] \approx [H_3O^+]$$

Now we can solve the ICE table for the second proton loss:

Table 2: $HC_2O_4^-(aq) + H_2O(l) \xrightleftharpoons{K_{a1}=5.4 \times 10^{-5}} C_2O_4^{2-}(aq) + H_3O^+(aq)$

Initial:	0.045 M	—	0 M $\qquad$ ≈ 0.045 M
Change:	$-y$	—	$+y$ M $\qquad$ $+y$ M
Equilibrium:	$(0.045 - y)$ M	—	y M $\qquad$ $\approx (0.045 + y)$ M

Since $C_a/K_a = 833$, the approximation may not be valid and we yet again should solve the full quadratic equation:

$$\frac{y \times (0.045 + y)}{(0.045 - y)} = 5.4 \times 10^{-5}; \qquad y^2 + 0.045y = 2.4\underline{3} \times 10^{-6} - 5.4 \times 10^{-5}y$$

$$y = \frac{-0.045 \pm \sqrt{2.0\underline{3} \times 10^{-3} + 9.7\underline{2} \times 10^{-6}}}{2} \qquad y = 8.2 \times 10^{-5} \text{ M} = [C_2O_4^{2-}]$$

Now we can calculate the Q_{sp} for the calcium oxalate system:
$Q_{sp} = [Ca^{2+}]_{initial} \times [C_2O_4^{2-}]_{initial} = (0.150)(8.2 \times 10^{-5}) = 1.2 \times 10^{-5} > 1.3 \times 10^{-9}$ (K_{sp} for CaC_2O_4)
Thus, CaC_2O_4 should precipitate from this solution.

34. **(D)** The solutions mutually dilute each other. We first determine the solubility of each compound in its saturated solution and then its concentration after dilution.

$$K_{sp} = \left[Ag^+\right]^2 \left[SO_4^{2-}\right] = 1.4 \times 10^{-5} = (2s)^2 s = 4s^3 \qquad s = \sqrt[3]{\frac{1.4 \times 10^{-5}}{4}} = 1.5 \times 10^{-2} \text{ M}$$

$$\left[SO_4^{2-}\right] = 0.015 \text{ M} \times \frac{100.0 \text{ mL}}{100.0 \text{ mL} + 250.0 \text{ mL}} = 0.0043 \text{ M} \qquad \left[Ag^+\right] = 0.0086 \text{ M}$$

$$K_{sp} = [Pb^{2+}][CrO_4^{2-}] = 2.8 \times 10^{-13} = (s)(s) = s^2 \qquad s = \sqrt{2.8 \times 10^{-13}} = 5.3 \times 10^{-7} \text{ M}$$

$$\left[Pb^{2+}\right] = \left[CrO_4^{2-}\right] = 5.3 \times 10^{-7} \times \frac{250.0 \text{ mL}}{250.0 \text{ mL} + 100.0 \text{ mL}} = 3.8 \times 10^{-7} \text{ M}$$

From the balanced chemical equation, we see that the two possible precipitates are $PbSO_4$ and Ag_2CrO_4. (Neither $PbCrO_4$ nor Ag_2SO_4 can precipitate because they have been diluted below their saturated concentrations.) $PbCrO_4 + Ag_2SO_4 \rightleftharpoons PbSO_4 + Ag_2CrO_4$ Thus, we compute the value of Q_{sp} for each of these compounds and compare those values with the solubility constant product value.

$$Q_{sp} = \left[Pb^{2+} \right]\left[SO_4^{2-} \right] = \left(3.8\times10^{-7} \right)\left(0.0043 \right) = 1.6\times10^{-9} < 1.6\times10^{-8} = K_{sp} \text{ for } PbSO_4$$

Thus, $PbSO_4(s)$ will not precipitate.

$$Q_{sp} = \left[Ag^+ \right]^2 \left[CrO_4^{2-} \right] = \left(0.0086 \right)^2 \left(3.8\times10^{-7} \right) = 2.8\times10^{-11} > 1.1\times10^{-12} = K_{sp} \text{ for } Ag_2CrO_4$$

Thus, $Ag_2CrO_4(s)$ should precipitate.

Completeness of Precipitation

35. **(M)** First determine that a precipitate forms. The solutions mutually dilute each other.

$$\left[CrO_4^{2-} \right] = 0.350 \text{ M} \times \frac{200.0 \text{ mL}}{200.0 \text{ mL} + 200.0 \text{ mL}} = 0.175 \text{ M}$$

$$\left[Ag^+ \right] = 0.0100 \text{ M} \times \frac{200.0 \text{ mL}}{200.0 \text{ mL} + 200.0 \text{ mL}} = 0.00500 \text{ M}$$

We determine the value of the ion product and compare it to the solubility product constant value.

$$Q_{sp} = \left[Ag^+ \right]^2 \left[CrO_4^{2-} \right] = \left(0.00500 \right)^2 \left(0.175 \right) = 4.4\times10^{-6} > 1.1\times10^{-12} = K_{sp} \text{ for } Ag_2CrO_4$$

Ag_2CrO_4 should precipitate.

Now, we assume that as much solid forms as possible, and then we approach equilibrium by dissolving that solid in a solution that contains the ion in excess.

Equation:	$Ag_2CrO_4(s)$ $\xrightleftharpoons{1.1\times10^{-12}}$	$2Ag^+(aq)$	$+$	$CrO_4^{2-}(aq)$
Orig. soln :	–	0.00500 M		0.175 M
Form solid :	–	−0.00500 M		−0.00250 M
Not at equilibrium	–	0 M		0.173 M
Changes :	–	$+2x$ M		$+x$ M
Equil :	–	$2x$ M		$(0.173+x)$ M

$$K_{sp} = \left[Ag^+ \right]^2 \left[CrO_4^{2-} \right] = 1.1\times10^{-12} = \left(2x \right)^2 \left(0.173 + x \right) \approx \left(4x^2 \right)\left(0.173 \right)$$

$$x = \sqrt{1.1\times10^{-12}/\left(4\times0.173 \right)} = 1.3\times10^{-6} \text{ M} \qquad \left[Ag^+ \right] = 2x = 2.6\times10^{-6} \text{ M}$$

$$\% \text{ Ag}^+ \text{ unprecipitated} = \frac{2.6\times10^{-6} \text{ M final}}{0.00500 \text{ M initial}} \times 100\% = 0.052\% \text{ unprecipitated}$$

36. **(M)** $[Ag^+]_{diluted} = 0.0208 \text{ M} \times \dfrac{175 \text{ mL}}{425 \text{ mL}} = 0.008565 \text{ M}$

$[CrO_4^{2-}]_{diluted} = 0.0380 \text{ M} \times \dfrac{250 \text{ mL}}{425 \text{ mL}} = 0.02235 \text{ M}$

$$Q_{sp} = \left[Ag^+ \right]^2 \left[CrO_4^{2-} \right] = 1.6\times10^{-6} > K_{sp}$$

Because $Q_{sp} > K_{sp}$, then more $Ag_2Cr_2O_4$ precipitates out. Assume that the limiting reagent is used up (100% reaction in the reverse direction) and re-establish the equilibrium in the reverse direction. Here Ag^+ is the limiting reagent.

$$Ag_2CrO_4(s) \xrightleftharpoons{K_{sp(Ag_2CrO_4)} = 1.1 \times 10^{-12}} 2\,Ag^+(aq) \quad + \quad CrO_4^{2-}(aq)$$

Initial	–		0.008565 M	0.02235 M
Change	–	$x = 0.00428$ M	$-2x$	$-x$
100% rxn	–		0	0.0181
Change	–	re-establish equil	$+2y$	$+y$
Equil	–	(assume $y \sim 0$)	$2y$	$0.0181 + y$

$1.1 \times 10^{-12} = (2y)^2(0.0181 + y) \approx (2y)^2(0.0181)$ $\qquad y = 3.9 \times 10^{-6}$ M

$y << 0.0181$, so this assumption is valid.

$2y = [Ag^+] = 7.8 \times 10^{-6}$ M after precipitation is complete.

$\% \, [Ag^+]_{unprecipitated} = \dfrac{7.8 \times 10^{-6}}{0.00856} \times 100\% = 0.091\%$ (precipitation is essentially quantitative)

37. **(M)** We first use the solubility product constant expression to determine $\left[Pb^{2+}\right]$ in a solution with 0.100 M Cl^-.

$K_{sp} = \left[Pb^{2+}\right]\left[Cl^-\right]^2 = 1.6 \times 10^{-5} = \left[Pb^{2+}\right](0.100)^2$ $\quad \left[Pb^{2+}\right] = \dfrac{1.6 \times 10^{-5}}{(0.100)^2} = 1.6 \times 10^{-3}$ M

Thus, % unprecipitated $= \dfrac{1.6 \times 10^{-3} \text{ M}}{0.065 \text{ M}} \times 100\% = 2.5\%$

Now, we want to determine what $[Cl^-]$ must be maintained to keep $[Pb^{2+}]_{final} = 1\%$;

$[Pb^{2+}]_{initial} = 0.010 \times 0.065 \text{ M} = 6.5 \times 10^{-4}$ M

$K_{sp} = \left[Pb^{2+}\right]\left[Cl^-\right]^2 = 1.6 \times 10^{-5} = \left(6.5 \times 10^{-4}\right)\left[Cl^-\right]^2$ $\qquad \left[Cl^-\right]\sqrt{\dfrac{6 \times 10^{-5}}{6.5 \times 10^{-4}}} = 0.16$ M

38. **(M)** Let's start by assuming that the concentration of Pb^{2+} in the untreated wine is no higher than 1.5×10^{-4} M (this assumption is not unreasonable.) As long as the Pb^{2+} concentration is less than 1.5×10^{-4} M, then the final sulfate ion concentration in the $CaSO_4$ treated wine should be virtually the same as the sulfate ion concentration in a saturated solution of $CaSO_4$ formed by dissolving solid $CaSO_4$ in pure water (i.e., with $[Pb^{2+}]$ less than or equal to 1.5×10^{-4} M, the $[SO_4^{2-}]$ will not drop significantly below that for a saturated solution, $\approx 3.0 \times 10^{-3}$ M.) Thus, the addition of $CaSO_4$ to the wine would result in the precipitation of solid $PbSO_4$, which would continue until the concentration of Pb^{2+} was equal to the K_{sp} for $PbSO_4$ divided by the concentration of dissolved sulfate ion, i.e., $[Pb^{2+}]_{max} = 1.6 \times 10^{-8} \text{M}^2 / 3.0 \times 10^{-3} \text{ M} = 5.3 \times 10^{-6}$ M.

Fractional Precipitation

39. **(M)** First, assemble all of the data. K_{sp} for $Ca(OH)_2 = 5.5 \times 10^{-6}$, K_{sp} for $Mg(OH)_2 = 1.8 \times 10^{-11}$

$$[Ca^{2+}] = \frac{440 \text{ g } Ca^{2+}}{1000 \text{ kg seawater}} \times \frac{1 \text{ mol } Ca^{2+}}{40.078 \text{ g } Ca^{2+}} \times \frac{1 \text{ kg seawater}}{1000 \text{ g seawater}} \times \frac{1.03 \text{ kg seawater}}{1 \text{ L seawater}} = 0.0113 \text{ M}$$

$[Mg^{2+}] = 0.059$ M, obtained from Example 18-6. $[OH^-] = 0.0020$ M (maintained)

(a) $Q_{sp} = [Ca^{2+}] \times [OH^-]^2 = (0.0113)(0.0020)^2 = 4.5 \times 10^{-8}$ $Q_{sp} < K_{sp}$ ∴ no precipitate forms.

(b) For the separation to be complete, >>99.9% of the Mg^{2+} must be removed before Ca^{2+} begins to precipitate. We have already shown that Ca^{2+} will not precipitate if the $[OH^-] = 0.0020$ M and is maintained at this level. Let us determine how much of the 0.059 M Mg^{2+} will still be in solution when $[OH^-] = 0.0020$ M.
$K_{sp} = [Mg^{2+}] \times [OH^-]^2 = (x)(0.0020)^2 = 1.8 \times 10^{-11}$ $x = 4.5 \times 10^{-6}$ M

The percent Mg^{2+} ion left in solution = $\dfrac{4.5 \times 10^{-6}}{0.059} \times 100\% = 0.0076\%$

This means that $100\% - 0.0076\%$ Mg = 99.992% has precipitated.
Clearly, the magnesium ion has been separated from the calcium ion (i.e., >> 99.9% of the Mg^{2+} ions have precipitated and virtually all of the Ca^{2+} ions are still in solution.)

40. **(D)**

(a) 0.10 M NaCl will not work at all, since both $BaCl_2$ and $CaCl_2$ are soluble in water.

(b) $K_{sp} = 1.1 \times 10^{-10}$ for $BaSO_4$ and $K_{sp} = 9.1 \times 10^{-6}$ for $CaSO_4$. Since these values differ by more than 1000, 0.05 M Na_2SO_4 would effectively separate Ba^{2+} from Ca^{2+}.

We first compute $\left[SO_4^{2-} \right]$ when $BaSO_4$ begins to precipitate.

$$\left[Ba^{2+} \right]\left[SO_4^{2-} \right] = (0.050)\left[SO_4^{2-} \right] = 1.1 \times 10^{-10}; \quad \left[SO_4^{2-} \right] = \frac{1.1 \times 10^{-10}}{0.050} = 2.2 \times 10^{-9} \text{ M}$$

And then we calculate $\left[SO_4^{2-} \right]$ when $\left[Ba^{2+} \right]$ has decreased to 0.1% of its initial value, that is, to 5.0×10^{-5} M.

$$\left[Ba^{2+} \right]\left[SO_4^{2-} \right] = (5.0 \times 10^{-5})\left[SO_4^{2-} \right] = 1.1 \times 10^{-10}; \quad \left[SO_4^{2-} \right] = \frac{1.1 \times 10^{-10}}{5.0 \times 10^{-5}} = 2.2 \times 10^{-6} \text{ M}$$

And finally, $\left[SO_4^{2-} \right]$ when $CaSO_4$ begins to precipitate.

$$\left[Ca^{2+} \right]\left[SO_4^{2-} \right] = (0.050)\left[SO_4^{2-} \right] = 9.1 \times 10^{-6}; \quad \left[SO_4^{2-} \right] = \frac{9.1 \times 10^{-6}}{0.050} = 1.8 \times 10^{-4} \text{ M}$$

(c) Now, $K_{sp} = 5 \times 10^{-3}$ for $Ba(OH)_2$ and $K_{sp} = 5.5 \times 10^{-6}$ for $Ca(OH)_2$. The fact that these two K_{sp} values differ by almost a factor of 1000 does not tell the entire story, because $\left[OH^-\right]$ is squared in both K_{sp} expressions. We compute $\left[OH^-\right]$ when $Ca(OH)_2$ begins to precipitate.

$$\left[Ca^{2+}\right]\left[OH^-\right]^2 = 5.5 \times 10^{-6} = (0.050)\left[OH^-\right]^2 \quad \left[OH^-\right] = \sqrt{\frac{5.5 \times 10^{-6}}{0.050}} = 1.0 \times 10^{-2} \text{ M}$$

Precipitation will not proceed, as we only have 0.001 M NaOH, which has $\left[OH^-\right] = 1 \times 10^{-3}$ M.

(d) $K_{sp} = 5.1 \times 10^{-9}$ for $BaCO_3$ and $K_{sp} = 2.8 \times 10^{-9}$ for $CaCO_3$. Since these two values differ by less than a factor of 2, 0.50 M Na_2CO_3 would not effectively separate Ba^{2+} from Ca^{2+}.

41. **(M)**

(a) Here we need to determine $\left[I^-\right]$ when AgI just begins to precipitate, and $\left[I^-\right]$ when PbI_2 just begins to precipitate.

$$K_{sp} = \left[Ag^+\right]\left[I^-\right] = 8.5 \times 10^{-17} = (0.10)\left[I^-\right] \qquad \left[I^-\right] = 8.5 \times 10^{-16} \text{ M}$$

$$K_{sp} = \left[Pb^{2+}\right]\left[I^-\right]^2 = 7.1 \times 10^{-9} = (0.10)\left[I^-\right]^2 \qquad \left[I^-\right] = \sqrt{\frac{7.1 \times 10^{-9}}{0.10}} = 2.7 \times 10^{-4} \text{ M}$$

Since 8.5×10^{-16} M is less than 2.7×10^{-4} M, AgI will precipitate before PbI_2.

(b) $\left[I^-\right]$ must be equal to 2.7×10^{-4} M before the second cation, Pb^{2+}, begins to precipitate.

(c) $K_{sp} = \left[Ag^+\right]\left[I^-\right] = 8.5 \times 10^{-17} = \left[Ag^+\right](2.7 \times 10^{-4}) \quad \left[Ag^+\right] = 3.1 \times 10^{-13}$ M

(d) Since $\left[Ag^+\right]$ has decreased to much less than 0.1% of its initial value before any PbI_2 begins to precipitate, we conclude that Ag^+ and Pb^{2+} can be separated by precipitation with iodide ion.

42. **(D)** Normally we would worry about the mutual dilution of the two solutions, but the values of the solubility product constants are so small that only a very small volume of 0.50 M $Pb(NO_3)_2$ solution needs to be added, as we shall see.

(a) Since the two anions are present at the same concentration and they have the same type of formula (one anion per cation), the one forming the compound with the smallest K_{sp} value will precipitate first. Thus, CrO_4^{2-} is the first anion to precipitate.

(b) At the point where $SO_4{}^{2-}$ begins to precipitate, we have

$$K_{sp} = \left[Pb^{2+}\right]\left[SO_4{}^{2-}\right] = 1.6 \times 10^{-8} = \left[Pb^{2+}\right](0.010M); \left[Pb^{2+}\right] = \frac{1.6 \times 10^{-8}}{0.010} = 1.6 \times 10^{-6} \, M$$

Now we can test our original assumption, that only a very small volume of 0.50 M $Pb(NO_3)_2$ solution has been added. We assume that we have 1.00 L of the original solution, the one with the two anions dissolved in it, and compute the volume of 0.50 M $Pb(NO_3)_2$ that has to be added to achieve $\left[Pb^{2+}\right] = 1.6 \times 10^{-6}$ M.

$$V_{added} = 1.00 \, L \times \frac{1.6 \times 10^{-6} \, mol \, Pb^{2+}}{1 \, L \, soln} \times \frac{1 \, mol \, Pb(NO_3)_2}{1 \, mol \, Pb^{2+}} \times \frac{1 \, L \, Pb^{2+} soln}{0.50 \, mol \, Pb(NO_3)_2}$$

$$V_{added} = 3.2 \times 10^{-5} \, L \, Pb^{2+} soln = 0.0032 mL \, Pb^{2+} soln$$

This is less than one drop (0.05 mL) of the Pb^{2+} solution, clearly a very small volume.

(c) The two anions are effectively separated if $\left[Pb^{2+}\right]$ has not reached 1.6×10^{-6} M when $\left[CrO_4{}^{2-}\right]$ is reduced to 0.1% of its original value, that is, to

$$0.010 \times 10^{-3} \, M = 1.0 \times 10^{-5} \, M = \left[CrO_4{}^{2-}\right]$$

$$K_{sp} = \left[Pb^{2+}\right]\left[CrO_4{}^{2-}\right] = 2.8 \times 10^{-13} = \left[Pb^{2+}\right]\left(1.0 \times 10^{-5}\right)$$

$$\left[Pb^{2+}\right] = \frac{2.8 \times 10^{-13}}{1.0 \times 10^{-5}} = 2.8 \times 10^{-8} \, M$$

Thus, the two anions can be effectively separated by fractional precipitation.

43. **(M)** First, let's assemble all of the data. K_{sp} for AgCl = 1.8×10^{-10} K_{sp} for AgI = 8.5×10^{-17}

$[Ag^+]$ = 2.00 M $[Cl^-]$ = 0.0100 M $[I^-]$ = 0.250 M

(a) AgI(s) will be the first to precipitate by virtue of the fact that the K_{sp} value for AgI is about 2 million times smaller than that for AgCl.

(b) AgCl(s) will begin to precipitate when the Q_{sp} for AgCl(s) > K_{sp} for AgCl(s). The concentration of Ag^+ required is: $K_{sp} = [Ag^+][Cl^-] = 1.8 \times 10^{-10} = (0.0100) \times (x)$
$x = 1.8 \times 10^{-8}$ M
Using this data, we can determine the remaining concentration of I^- using the K_{sp}.
$K_{sp} = [Ag^+][I^-] = 8.5 \times 10^{-17} = (x) \times (1.8 \times 10^{-8})$ $x = 4.7 \times 10^{-9}$ M

(c) In part (b) we saw that the $[I^-]$ drops from 0.250 M $\rightarrow$ 4.7×10^{-9} M. Only a small percentage of the ion remains in solution. $\dfrac{4.7 \times 10^{-9}}{0.250} \times 100\% = 0.0000019 \, \%$

This means that 99.999998% of the I^- ion has been precipitated before any of the Cl^- ion has precipitated. Clearly, the fractional separation of Cl^- from I^- is feasible.

44. (M)

(a) We first determine the $\left[Ag^+\right]$ needed to initiate precipitation of each compound.

$$AgCl:\ K_{sp} = \left[Ag^+\right]\left[Cl^-\right] = 1.8\times10^{-10} = \left[Ag^+\right](0.250);\quad \left[Ag^+\right] = \frac{1.8\times10^{-10}}{0.250} = 7.2\times10^{-10}\ M$$

$$AgBr:\ K_{sp} = \left[Ag^+\right]\left[Br^-\right] = 5.0\times10^{-13} = \left[Ag^+\right](0.0022);\quad \left[Ag^+\right] = \frac{5.0\times10^{-13}}{0.0022} = 2.3\times10^{-10}\ M$$

Thus, Br^- precipitates first, as AgBr, because it requires a lower $\left[Ag^+\right]$.

(b) $\left[Ag^+\right] = 7.2\times10^{-10}\ M$ when chloride ion, the second anion, begins to precipitate.

(c) Cl^- and Br^- cannot be separated by this fractional precipitation. $\left[Ag^+\right]$ will have to rise to 1000 times its initial value, to $2.3\times10^{-7}\ M$, before AgBr is completely precipitated. But as soon as $\left[Ag^+\right]$ reaches $7.2\times10^{-10}\ M$, AgCl will begin to precipitate.

Solubility and pH

45. (E) In each case we indicate whether the compound is more soluble in water. We write the net ionic equation for the reaction in which the solid dissolves in acid. Substances are more soluble in acid if either (1) an acid-base reaction occurs or (2) a gas is produced, since escape of the gas from the reaction mixture causes the reaction to shift to the right.

Same: KCl (K^+ and Cl^- do not react appreciably with H_2O)

Acid: $MgCO_3(s) + 2H^+(aq) \longrightarrow Mg^{2+}(aq) + H_2O(l) + CO_2(g)$

Acid: $FeS(s) + 2H^+(aq) \longrightarrow Fe^{2+}(aq) + H_2S(g)$

Acid: $Ca(OH)_2(s) + 2H^+(aq) \longrightarrow Ca^{2+}(aq) + 2H_2O(l)$

Water: C_6H_5COOH is less soluble in acid, because of the H_3O^+ common ion.

46. (E) In each case we indicate whether the compound is more soluble in base than in water. We write the net ionic equation for the reaction in which the solid dissolves in base. Substances are soluble in base if either (1) acid-base reaction occurs [as in (b)] or (2) a gas is produced, since escape of the gas from the reaction mixture causes the reaction to shift to the right.

Water: $BaSO_4$ is less soluble in base, hydrolysis of SO_4^{2-} will be repressed.

Base: $H_2C_2O_4(s) + 2OH^-(aq) \longrightarrow C_2O_4^{2-}(aq) + 2H_2O(l)$

Water: $Fe(OH)_3$ is less soluble in base because of the OH^- common ion.

Same: $NaNO_3$ (neither Na^+ nor NO_3^- react with H_2O to a measurable extent).

Water: MnS is less soluble in base because hydrolysis of S^{2-} will be repressed.

47. **(E)** We determine $\left[Mg^{2+}\right]$ in the solution.

$$\left[Mg^{2+}\right] = \frac{0.65 \text{ g Mg}(OH)_2}{1 \text{ L soln}} \times \frac{1 \text{ mol Mg}(OH)_2}{58.3 \text{ g Mg}(OH)_2} \times \frac{1 \text{ mol Mg}^{2+}}{1 \text{ mol Mg}(OH)_2} = 0.011 \text{ M}$$

Then we determine $\left[OH^-\right]$ in the solution, and its pH.

$$K_{sp} = \left[Mg^{2+}\right]\left[OH^-\right]^2 = 1.8 \times 10^{-11} = (0.011)\left[OH^-\right]^2; \left[OH^-\right] = \sqrt{\frac{1.8 \times 10^{-11}}{0.011}} = 4.0 \times 10^{-5} \text{ M}$$

$$pOH = -\log\left(4.0 \times 10^{-5}\right) = 4.40 \qquad\qquad pH = 14.00 - 4.40 = 9.60$$

48. **(M)** First we determine the $[Mg^{2+}]$ and $[NH_3]$ that result from dilution to a total volume of 0.500 L.

$$\left[Mg^{2+}\right] = 0.100 \text{ M} \times \frac{0.150 \text{ L}_{initial}}{0.500 \text{ L}_{final}} = 0.0300 \text{ M}; \quad \left[NH_3\right] = 0.150 \text{ M} \times \frac{0.350 \text{ L}_{initial}}{0.500 \text{ L}_{final}} = 0.105 \text{ M}$$

Then determine the $\left[OH^-\right]$ that will allow $\left[Mg^{2+}\right] = 0.0300$ M in this solution.

$$K_{sp} = 1.8 \times 10^{-11} = \left[Mg^{2+}\right]\left[OH^-\right]^2 = (0.0300)\left[OH^-\right]^2; \left[OH^-\right] = \sqrt{\frac{1.8 \times 10^{-11}}{0.0300}} = 2.4 \times 10^{-5} \text{ M}$$

This $\left[OH^-\right]$ is maintained by the NH_3 / NH_4^+ buffer; since it is a buffer, we can use the Henderson–Hasselbalch equation to find the $[NH_4^+]$.

$$pH = 14.00 - pOH = 14.00 + \log\left(2.4 \times 10^{-5}\right) = 9.38 = pK_a + \log\frac{\left[NH_3\right]}{\left[NH_4^+\right]} = 9.26 + \log\frac{\left[NH_3\right]}{\left[NH_4^+\right]}$$

$$\log\frac{\left[NH_3\right]}{\left[NH_4^+\right]} = 9.38 - 9.26 = +0.12; \quad \frac{\left[NH_3\right]}{\left[NH_4^+\right]} = 10^{+0.12} = 1.3; \quad \left[NH_4^+\right] = \frac{0.105 \text{ M NH}_3}{1.3} = 0.081 \text{ M}$$

$$\text{mass } (NH_4)_2 SO_4 = 0.500 \text{ L} \times \frac{0.081 \text{ mol NH}_4^+}{\text{L soln}} \times \frac{1 \text{ mol }(NH_4)_2 SO_4}{2 \text{ mol NH}_4^+} \times \frac{132.1 \text{ g }(NH_4)_2 SO_4}{1 \text{ mol }(NH_4)_2 SO_4} = 2.7 \text{ g}$$

49. **(M)**

(a) Here we calculate $\left[OH^-\right]$ needed for precipitation.

$$K_{sp} = [Al^{3+}][OH^-]^3 = 1.3 \times 10^{-33} = (0.075 \text{ M})[OH^-]^3$$

$$[OH^-] = \sqrt[3]{\frac{1.3 \times 10^{-33}}{0.075}} = 2.6 \times 10^{-11} \quad pOH = -\log\left(2.6 \times 10^{-11}\right) = 10.59$$

$$pH = 14.00 - 10.59 = 3.41$$

(b) We can use the Henderson–Hasselbalch equation to determine $\left[CH_3COO^-\right]$.

$$pH = 3.41 = pK_a + \log\frac{\left[CH_3COO^-\right]}{\left[CH_3COOH\right]} = 4.74 + \log\frac{\left[CH_3COO^-\right]}{1.00\ M}$$

$$\log\frac{\left[CH_3COO^-\right]}{1.00\ M} = 3.41 - 4.74 = -1.33;\quad \frac{\left[CH_3COO^-\right]}{1.00\ M} = 10^{-1.33} = 0.047;\quad \left[CH_3COO^-\right] = 0.047\ M$$

This situation does not quite obey the guideline that the ratio of concentrations must fall in the range 0.10 to 10.0, but the resulting error is a small one in this circumstance.

$$mass\ NaCH_3COO = 0.2500\ L \times \frac{0.047\ mol\ CH_3COO^-}{1\ L\ soln} \times \frac{1\ mol\ NaCH_3COO}{1\ mol\ CH_3COO^-} \times \frac{82.03\ g\ NaCH_3COO}{1\ mol\ NaCH_3COO}$$

$$= 0.96\ g\ NaCH_3COO$$

50. (D)

(a) Since HI is a strong acid, $\left[I^-\right] = 1.05 \times 10^{-3}\ M + 1.05 \times 10^{-3}\ M = 2.10 \times 10^{-3}\ M$.

We determine the value of the ion product and compare it to the solubility product constant value.

$$Q_{sp} = \left[Pb^{2+}\right]\left[I^-\right]^2 = \left(1.1 \times 10^{-3}\right)\left(2.10 \times 10^{-3}\right)^2 = 4.9 \times 10^{-9} < 7.1 \times 10^{-9} = K_{sp}\ for\ PbI_2$$

Thus a precipitate of PbI_2 will not form under these conditions.

(b) We compute the $\left[OH^-\right]$ needed for precipitation.

$$K_{sp} = \left[Mg^{2+}\right]\left[OH^-\right]^2 = 1.8 \times 10^{-11} = (0.0150)\left[OH^-\right]^2;\quad \left[OH^-\right] = \sqrt{\frac{1.8 \times 10^{-11}}{0.0150}} = 3.5 \times 10^{-5}\ M$$

Then we compute $\left[OH^-\right]$ in this solution, resulting from the ionization of NH_3.

$$\left[NH_3\right] = 6.00\ M \times \frac{0.05 \times 10^{-3}\ L}{2.50\ L} = 1.2 \times 10^{-4}\ M$$

Even though NH_3 is a weak base, the $\left[OH^-\right]$ produced from the NH_3 hydrolysis reaction will approximate 4×10^{-5} M (3.85 if you solve the quadratic) in this very dilute solution. (Recall that degree of ionization is high in dilute solution.) And since $\left[OH^-\right] = 3.5 \times 10^{-5}$ M is needed for precipitation to occur, we conclude that $Mg(OH)_2$ will precipitate from this solution (note: not much of a precipitate is expected).

(c) 0.010 M CH_3COOH and 0.010 M $NaCH_3COO$ is a buffer solution with $pH = pK_a$ of acetic acid (the acid and its anion are present in equal concentrations.) From this, we determine the $\left[OH^-\right]$.

$$pH = 4.74 \qquad pOH = 14.00 - 4.74 = 9.26 \qquad \left[OH^- \right] = 10^{-9.26} = 5.5 \times 10^{-10}$$

$$Q = \left[Al^{3+} \right] \left[OH^- \right]^3 = (0.010)(5.5 \times 10^{-10})^3 = 1.7 \times 10^{-30} > 1.3 \times 10^{-33} = K_{sp} \text{ of } Al(OH)_3$$

Thus, $Al(OH)_3(s)$ should precipitate from this solution.

Complex-Ion Equilibria

51. **(E)** Lead(II) ion forms a complex ion with chloride ion. It forms no such complex ion with nitrate ion. The formation of this complex ion decreases the concentrations of free $Pb^{2+}(aq)$ and free $Cl^-(aq)$. Thus, $PbCl_2$ will dissolve in the HCl(aq) up until the value of the solubility product is exceeded. $Pb^{2+}(aq) + 3Cl^-(aq) \rightleftharpoons [PbCl_3]^-(aq)$

52. **(E)** $Zn^{2+}(aq) + 4NH_3(aq) \rightleftharpoons \left[Zn(NH_3)_4 \right]^{2+}(aq) \qquad K_f = 4.1 \times 10^8$

$NH_3(aq)$ will be least effective in reducing the concentration of the complex ion. In fact, the addition of $NH_3(aq)$ will increase the concentration of the complex ion by favoring a shift of the equilibrium to the right. $NH_4^+(aq)$ will have a similar effect, but not as direct. $NH_3(aq)$ is formed by the hydrolysis of $NH_4^+(aq)$ and, thus, increasing $\left[NH_4^+ \right]$ will eventually increase $NH_3(aq)$: $NH_4^+(aq) + H_2O(l) \rightleftharpoons NH_3(aq) + H_3O^+(aq)$. The addition of HCl(aq) will cause the greatest decrease in the concentration of the complex ion. HCl(aq) will react with $NH_3(aq)$ to decrease its concentration (by forming NH_4^+) and this will cause the complex ion equilibrium reaction to shift left toward free aqueous ammonia and $Zn^{2+}(aq)$.

53. **(E)** We substitute the given concentrations directly into the K_f expression to calculate K_f.

$$K_f = \frac{[[Cu(CN)_4^{3-}]]}{[Cu^+][CN^-]^4} = \frac{0.0500}{(6.1 \times 10^{-32})(0.80)^4} = 2.0 \times 10^{30}$$

54. **(M)** The solution to this problem is organized around the balanced chemical equation. Free $\left[NH_3 \right]$ is 6.0 M at equilibrium. The size of the equilibrium constant indicates that most copper(II) is present as the complex ion at equilibrium.

Equation:	$Cu^{2+}(aq)$	$+ 4NH_3(aq)$	$\rightleftharpoons$	$\left[Cu(NH_3)_4 \right]^{2+}(aq)$
Initial:	0.10 M	6.00 M		0 M
Change(100 % rxn):	−0.10 M	−0.40 M		+0.10 M
Completion:	0 M	5.60 M		0.10 M
Changes:	+x M	+4x M		−x M
Equil:	x M	5.60 + 4x M		$(0.10 - x)$ M

Let's assume $(5.60 + 4x)$ M ≈ 5.60 M and $(0.10 - x)$ M ≈ 0.10 M

$$K_f = \frac{\left[\left[Cu(NH_3)_4\right]^{2+}\right]}{\left[Cu^{2+}\right]\left[NH_3\right]^4} = 1.1 \times 10^{13} = \frac{0.10 - x}{x(5.60 - 4x)^4} \approx \frac{0.10}{(5.60)^4 x} \approx \frac{0.10}{983.4x}$$

$$x = \frac{0.10}{983.4 \times (1.1 \times 10^{13})} = 9.2 \times 10^{-18} \text{ M} = \left[Cu^{2+}\right] \quad (x \ll 0.10, \text{ thus the approximation was valid})$$

55. **(M)** We first find the concentration of free metal ion. Then we determine the value of Q_{sp} for the precipitation reaction, and compare its value with the value of K_{sp} to determine whether precipitation should occur.

Equation:	$Ag^+(aq) +$	$2\,S_2O_3^{2-}(aq)$	$\rightleftharpoons$	$\left[Ag(S_2O_3)_2\right]^{3-}(aq)$
Initial:	0 M	0.76 M		0.048 M
Changes:	$+x$ M	$+2x$ M		$-x$ M
Equil:	x M	$(0.76 + 2x)$ M		$(0.048 - x)$ M

$$K_f = \frac{\left[\left[Ag(S_2O_3)_2\right]^{3-}\right]}{\left[Ag^+\right]\left[S_2O_3^{2-}\right]^2} = 1.7 \times 10^{13} = \frac{0.048 - x}{x(0.76 + 2x)^2} \approx \frac{0.048}{(0.76)^2 x}; x = 4.9 \times 10^{-15} \text{M} = \left[Ag^+\right]$$

$(x \ll 0.048$ M, thus the approximation was valid.)

$Q_{sp} = \left[Ag^+\right]\left[I^-\right] = (4.9 \times 10^{-15})(2.0) = 9.8 \times 10^{-15} > 8.5 \times 10^{-17} = K_{sp}$.

Because $Q_{sp} > K_{sp}$, precipitation of AgI(s) should occur.

56. **(M)** We need to determine $\left[OH^-\right]$ in this solution, and also the free $\left[Cu^{2+}\right]$.

$$pH = pK_a + \log\frac{\left[NH_3\right]}{\left[NH_4^+\right]} = 9.26 + \log\frac{0.10 \text{ M}}{0.10 \text{ M}} = 9.26 \quad pOH = 14.00 - 9.26 = 4.74$$

$\left[OH^-\right] = 10^{-4.74} = 1.8 \times 10^{-5}$ M $\qquad Cu^{2+}(aq) + 4NH_3(aq) \rightleftharpoons \left[Cu(NH_3)_4\right]^{2+}(aq)$

$$K_f = \frac{\left[\left[Cu(NH_3)_4\right]^{2+}\right]}{\left[Cu^{2+}\right]\left[NH_3\right]^4} = 1.1 \times 10^{13} = \frac{0.015}{\left[Cu^{2+}\right] 0.10^4}; \left[Cu^{2+}\right] = \frac{0.015}{1.1 \times 10^{13} \times 0.10^4} = 1.4 \times 10^{-11} \text{M}$$

Now we determine the value of Q_{sp} and compare it with the value of K_{sp} for $Cu(OH)_2$.

$$Q_{sp} = \left[Cu^{2+}\right]\left[OH^-\right]^2 = (1.4 \times 10^{-11}) \times (1.8 \times 10^{-5})^2 = 4.5 \times 10^{-21} < 2.2 \times 10^{-20}(K_{sp} \text{ for } Cu(OH)_2)$$

Precipitation of $Cu(OH)_2(s)$ from this solution should not occur.

57. **(M)** We first compute the free $\left[Ag^+\right]$ in the original solution. The size of the complex ion formation equilibrium constant indicates that the reaction lies far to the right, so we form as much complex ion as possible stoichiometrically.

Equation:	$Ag^+(aq)+$	$2NH_3(aq)$	$\rightleftharpoons$	$\left[Ag(NH_3)_2\right]^+(aq)$
In soln:	0.10 M	1.00 M		0 M
Form complex:	−0.10 M	−0.20 M		+0.10 M
	0 M	0.80 M		0.10 M
Changes:	$+x$ M	$+2x$ M		$-x$ M
Equil:	x M	$(0.80+2x)$ M		$(0.10-x)$ M

$$K_f = 1.6\times10^7 = \frac{\left[\left[Ag(NH_3)_2\right]^+\right]}{\left[Ag^+\right]\left[NH_3\right]^2} = \frac{0.10-x}{x(0.80+2x)^2} \approx \frac{0.10}{x(0.80)^2} \quad x = \frac{0.10}{1.6\times10^7(0.80)^2} = 9.8\times10^{-9}\ M.$$

($x \ll 0.80$ M, thus the approximation was valid.)

Thus, $\left[Ag^+\right] = 9.8\times10^{-9}$ M. We next determine the $\left[I^-\right]$ that can coexist in this solution without precipitation.

$$K_{sp} = \left[Ag^+\right]\left[I^-\right] = 8.5\times10^{-17} = \left(9.8\times10^{-9}\right)\left[I^-\right]; \quad \left[I^-\right] = \frac{8.5\times10^{-17}}{9.8\times10^{-9}} = 8.7\times10^{-9}\ M$$

Finally, we determine the mass of KI needed to produce this $\left[I^-\right]$

$$\text{mass KI} = 1.00\ L\ soln \times \frac{8.7\times10^{-9}\ mol\ I^-}{1\ L\ soln} \times \frac{1\ mol\ KI}{1\ mol\ I^-} \times \frac{166.0\ g\ KI}{1\ mol\ KI} = 1.4\times10^{-6}\ g\ KI$$

58. **(M)** First we determine $\left[Ag^+\right]$ that can exist with this $\left[Cl^-\right]$. We know that $\left[Cl^-\right]$ will be unchanged because precipitation will not be allowed to occur.

$$K_{sp} = \left[Ag^+\right]\left[Cl^-\right] = 1.8\times10^{-10} = \left[Ag^+\right]0.100\ M; \quad \left[Ag^+\right] = \frac{1.8\times10^{-10}}{0.100} = 1.8\times10^{-9}\ M$$

We now consider the complex ion equilibrium. If the complex ion's final concentration is x, then the decrease in $\left[NH_3\right]$ is $2x$, because 2 mol NH_3 react to form each mole of complex ion, as follows. $Ag^+(aq)+2NH_3(aq)\rightleftharpoons\left[Ag(NH_3)_2\right]^+(aq)$ We can solve the K_f expression for x.

$$K_f = 1.6\times10^7 = \frac{\left[\left[Ag(NH_3)_2\right]^+\right]}{\left[Ag^+\right]\left[NH_3\right]^2} = \frac{x}{1.8\times10^{-9}(1.00-2x)^2}$$

$$x = \left(1.6\times10^7\right)\left(1.8\times10^{-9}\right)(1.00-2x)^2 = 0.029(1.00-4.00x+4.00x^2) = 0.029 - 0.12x + 0.12x^2$$

$$0 = 0.029 - 1.12x + 0.12x^2 \quad \text{We use the quadratic formula roots equation to solve for } x.$$

$$x = \frac{-b\pm\sqrt{b^2-4ac}}{2a} = \frac{1.12\pm\sqrt{(1.12)^2-4\times0.029\times0.12}}{2\times0.12} = \frac{1.12\pm1.11\underline{4}}{0.24} = 9.3,\ 0.025$$

Thus, we can add 0.025 mol $AgNO_3$ (~ 4.4 g $AgNO_3$) to this solution before we see a precipitate of AgCl(s) form.

Precipitation and Solubilities of Metal Sulfides

59. **(M)** We know that $K_{spa} = 3 \times 10^7$ for MnS and $K_{spa} = 6 \times 10^2$ for FeS. The metal sulfide will begin to precipitate when $Q_{spa} = K_{spa}$. Let us determine the $\left[H_3O^+\right]$ just necessary to form each precipitate. We assume that the solution is saturated with H_2S, $[H_2S] = 0.10$ M.

$$K_{spa} = \frac{[M^{2+}][H_2S]}{[H_3O^+]^2} \quad [H_3O^+] = \sqrt{\frac{[M^{2+}][H_2S]}{K_{spa}}} = \sqrt{\frac{(0.10)(0.10)}{3 \times 10^7}} = 1.8 \times 10^{-5} \text{ M for MnS}$$

$$\left[H_3O^+\right] = \sqrt{\frac{(0.10)(0.10)}{6 \times 10^2}} = 4.1 \times 10^{-3} \text{ M for FeS}$$

Thus, if the $[H_3O^+]$ is maintained just a bit higher than 1.8×10^{-5} M, FeS will precipitate and Mn^{2+}(aq) will remain in solution. To determine if the separation is complete, we see whether $\left[Fe^{2+}\right]$ has decreased to 0.1% or less of its original value when the solution is held at the aforementioned acidity. Let $\left[H_3O^+\right] = 2.0 \times 10^{-5}$ M and calculate $\left[Fe^{2+}\right]$.

$$K_{spa} = \frac{\left[Fe^{2+}\right][H_2S]}{\left[H_3O^+\right]^2} = 6 \times 10^2 = \frac{\left[Fe^{2+}\right](0.10)}{\left(2.0 \times 10^{-5}\right)^2}; \quad \left[Fe^{2+}\right] = \frac{\left(6 \times 10^2\right)\left(2.0 \times 10^{-5}\right)^2}{0.10} = 2.4 \times 10^{-6} \text{ M}$$

$$\% Fe^{2+} \text{(aq) remaining} = \frac{2.4 \times 10^{-6} \text{ M}}{0.10 \text{ M}} \times 100\% = 0.0024\% \quad \therefore \text{Separation is complete.}$$

60. **(M)** Since the cation concentrations are identical, the value of Q_{spa} is the same for each one. It is this value of Q_{spa} that we compare with K_{spa} to determine if precipitation occurs.

$$Q_{spa} = \frac{\left[M^{2+}\right][H_2S]}{\left[H_3O^+\right]^2} = \frac{0.05 \times 0.10}{\left(0.010\right)^2} = 5 \times 10^1$$

If $Q_{spa} > K_{spa}$, precipitation of the metal sulfide should occur. But, if $Q_{spa} < K_{spa}$, precipitation will not occur.

For CuS, $K_{spa} = 6 \times 10^{-16} < Q_{spa} = 5 \times 10^1$ Precipitation of CuS(s) should occur.

For HgS, $K_{spa} = 2 \times 10^{-32} < Q_{spa} = 5 \times 10^1$ Precipitation of HgS(s) should occur.

For MnS, $K_{spa} = 3 \times 10^7 > Q_{spa} = 5 \times 10^1$ Precipitation of MnS(s) will not occur.

61. **(M)**

(a) We can calculate $[H_3O^+]$ in the buffer with the Henderson–Hasselbalch equation.

$$pH = pK_a + \log\frac{[CH_3COO^-]}{[CH_3COOH]} = 4.74 + \log\frac{0.15\,M}{0.25\,M} = 4.52 \quad [H_3O^+] = 10^{-4.52} = 3.0\times10^{-5}\,M$$

We use this information to calculate a value of Q_{spa} for MnS in this solution and then comparison of Q_{spa} with K_{spa} will allow us to decide if a precipitate will form.

$$Q_{spa} = \frac{[Mn^{2+}][H_2S]}{[H_3O^+]^2} = \frac{(0.15)(0.10)}{(3.0\times10^{-5})^2} = 1.7\times10^7 < 3\times10^7 = K_{spa} \text{ for MnS}$$

Thus, precipitation of MnS(s) will not occur.

(b) We need to change $[H_3O^+]$ so that

$$Q_{spa} = 3\times10^7 = \frac{(0.15)(0.10)}{[H_3O^+]^2}; \quad [H_3O^+] = \sqrt{\frac{(0.15)(0.10)}{3\times10^7}} \quad [H_3O^+] = 2.2\times10^{-5}\,M \quad pH = 4.66$$

This is a more basic solution, which we can produce by increasing the basic component of the buffer solution, namely, the acetate ion. We can find out the necessary acetate ion concentration with the Henderson–Hasselbalch equation.

$$pH = pK_a + \log\frac{[CH_3COO^-]}{[CH_3COOH]} = 4.66 = 4.74 + \log\frac{[CH_3COO^-]}{0.25\,M}$$

$$\log\frac{[CH_3COO^-]}{0.25\,M} = 4.66 - 4.74 = -0.08$$

$$\frac{[CH_3COO^-]}{0.25\,M} = 10^{-0.08} = 0.83 \quad [CH_3COO^-] = 0.83\times0.25\,M = 0.21\,M$$

62. **(M)**

(a) CuS is in the hydrogen sulfide group of qualitative analysis. Its precipitation occurs when 0.3 M HCl is saturated with H_2S. It will certainly precipitate from a (non-acidic) saturated solution of H_2S which has a much higher $[S^{2-}]$.

$$Cu^{2+}(aq) + H_2S(\text{satd aq}) \longrightarrow CuS(s) + 2\,H^+(aq)$$

This reaction proceeds to an essentially quantitative extent in the forward direction.

(b) MgS is soluble, according to the solubility rules listed in Chapter 5.

$$Mg^{2+}(aq) + H_2S(\text{satd aq}) \xrightarrow{\text{0.3 M HCl}} \text{no reaction}$$

(c) As in part (a), PbS is in the qualitative analysis hydrogen sulfide group, which precipitates from a 0.3 M HCl solution saturated with H_2S. Therefore, PbS does not dissolve appreciably in 0.3 M HCl. $PbS(s) + HCl(0.3\,M) \longrightarrow$ no reaction

(d) Since ZnS(s) does not precipitate in the hydrogen sulfide group, we conclude that it is soluble in acidic solution.

$$ZnS(s) + 2\,HNO_3(aq) \longrightarrow Zn(NO_3)_2(aq) + H_2S(g)$$

Qualitative Cation Analysis

63. **(E)** The purpose of adding hot water is to separate Pb^{2+} from AgCl and Hg_2Cl_2. Thus, the most important consequence would be the absence of a valid test for the presence or absence of Pb^{2+}. In addition, if we add NH_3 first, $PbCl_2$ may form $Pb(OH)_2$. If $Pb(OH)_2$ does form, it will be present with Hg_2Cl_2 in the solid, although $Pb(OH)_2$ will not darken with added NH_3. Thus, we might falsely conclude that Ag^+ is present.

64. **(M)** For $PbCl_2(aq)$, $2[Pb^{2+}]=[Cl^-]$ where $s=$ molar solubility of $PbCl_2$. Thus $s=[Pb^{2+}]$.

$$K_{sp} = [Pb^{2+}][Cl^-]^2 = (s)(2s)^2 = 4s^3 = 1.6\times10^{-5}; \quad s=\sqrt[3]{1.6\times10^{-5}\div4}=1.6\times10^{-2}\ M=[Pb^{2+}]$$

Both $[Pb^{2+}]$ and $[CrO_4^{2-}]$ are diluted by mixing the two solutions.

$$[Pb^{2+}]=0.016\ M\times\frac{1.00\ mL}{1.05\ mL}=0.015\ M \qquad [CrO_4^{2-}]=1.0\ M\times\frac{0.05\ mL}{1.05\ mL}=0.048\ M$$

$$Q_{sp}=[Pb^{2+}][CrO_4^{2-}]=(0.015\ M)(0.048\ M)=7.2\times10^{-4}>2.8\times10^{-13}=K_{sp}$$

Thus, precipitation should occur from the solution described.

65. **(E)**

(a) Ag^+ and/or Hg_2^{2+} are probably present. Both of these cations form chloride precipitates from acidic solutions of chloride ion.

(b) We cannot tell whether Mg^{2+} is present or not. Both MgS and $MgCl_2$ are water soluble.

(c) Pb^{2+} possibly is absent; it is the only cation of those given which forms a precipitate in an acidic solution that is treated with H_2S, and no sulfide precipitate was formed.

(d) We cannot tell whether Fe^{2+} is present. FeS will not precipitate from an acidic solution that is treated with H_2S; the solution must be alkaline for a FeS precipitate to form.

(a) and (c) are the valid conclusions.

66. **(E)**

(a) $Pb^{2+}(aq)+2\ Cl^-(aq)\longrightarrow PbCl_2(s)$

(b) $Zn(OH)_2(s)+2\ OH^-(aq)\longrightarrow[Zn(OH)_4]^{2-}(aq)$

(c) $Fe(OH)_3(s)+3\ H_3O^+(aq)\longrightarrow Fe^{3+}(aq)+6\ H_2O(l)$ or $[Fe(H_2O)_6]^{3+}(aq)$

(d) $Cu^{2+}(aq)+H_2S(aq)\longrightarrow CuS(s)+2\ H^+(aq)$

INTEGRATIVE AND ADVANCED EXERCISES

67. (M) We determine s, the solubility of $CaSO_4$ in a saturated solution, and then the concentration of $CaSO_4$ in ppm in this saturated solution, assuming that the solution's density is 1.00 g/mL.

$$K_{sp} = [Ca^{2+}][SO_4^{2-}] = (s)(s) = s^2 = 9.1 \times 10^{-6} \qquad s = 3.0 \times 10^{-3} \text{ M}$$

$$\text{ppm } CaSO_4 = 10^6 \text{g soln} \times \frac{1 \text{ mL}}{1.00 \text{ g}} \times \frac{1 \text{ L soln}}{1000 \text{ mL}} \times \frac{0.0030 \text{ mol } CaSO_4}{1 \text{ L soln}} \times \frac{136.1 \text{ g } CaSO_4}{1 \text{ mol } CaSO_4} = 4.1 \times 10^2 \text{ ppm}$$

Now we determine the volume of solution remaining after we evaporate the 131 ppm $CaSO_4$ down to a saturated solution (assuming that both solutions have a density of 1.00 g/mL.)

$$\text{volume sat'd soln} = 131 \text{ g } CaSO_4 \times \frac{10^6 \text{ g sat'd soln}}{4.1 \times 10^2 \text{ g } CaSO_4} \times \frac{1 \text{ mL}}{1.00 \text{ g}} = 3.2 \times 10^5 \text{ mL}$$

Thus, we must evaporate 6.8×10^5 mL of the original 1.000×10^6 mL of solution, or 68% of the water sample.

68. (M)

(a) First we compute the molar solubility, s, of $CaHPO_4 \cdot 2H_2O$.

$$s = \frac{0.32 \text{ g } CaHPO_4 \cdot 2H_2O}{1 \text{ L soln}} \times \frac{1 \text{ mol } CaHPO_4 \cdot 2H_2O}{172.1 \text{ g } CaHPO_4 \cdot 2H_2O} = 1.9 \times 10^{-3} \text{ M}$$

$$K_{sp} = [Ca^{2+}][HPO_4^{2-}] = (s)(s) = s^2 = (1.9 \times 10^{-3})^2 = 3.6 \times 10^{-6}$$

Thus the values are not quite consistent.

(b) The value of K_{sp} given in the problem is consistent with a smaller value of the molar solubility. The reason is that not all of the solute ends up in solution as HPO_4^{2-} ions. HPO_4^{2-} can act as either an acid or a base in water (see below), but it is base hydrolysis that predominates.

$$HPO_4^{2-}(aq) + H_2O(l) \rightleftharpoons H_3O^+(aq) + PO_4^{3-}(aq) \qquad K_{a3} = 4.2 \times 10^{-13}$$

$$HPO_4^{2-}(aq) + H_2O(l) \rightleftharpoons OH^-(aq) + H_2PO_4^-(aq) \qquad K_b = \frac{K_w}{K_2} = 1.6 \times 10^{-7}$$

69. (M) The solutions mutually dilute each other and, because the volumes are equal, the concentrations are halved in the final solution: $[Ca^{2+}] = 0.00625$ M, $[SO_4^{2-}] = 0.00760$ M. We cannot assume that either concentration remains constant during the precipitation. Instead, we assume that precipitation proceeds until all of one reagent is used up. Equilibrium is reached from that point.

Equation: $CaSO_4(s) \rightleftharpoons$ $Ca^{2+}(aq)$ + $SO_4^{2-}(aq) K_{sp} = 9.1 \times 10^{-6}$

In soln	–	0.00625 M	0.00760 M	$K_{sp} = [Ca^{2+}][SO_4^{2-}]$
Form ppt	–	−0.00625 M	−0.00625 M	$K_{sp} = (x)(0.00135 + x)$
Not at equil	–	0 M	0.00135 M	$K_{sp} \approx 0.00135\,x$
Changes	–	+x M	+x M	$x = \dfrac{9.1 \times 10^{-6}}{0.00135} = 6.7 \times 10^{-3}\,M$
Equil:	–	x M	(0.00135 + x) M	{not a reasonable assumption!}

Solving the quadratic $0 = x^2 + (1.35 \times 10^{-2})x - 9.1 \times 10^{-6}$ yields $x = 2.4 \times 10^{-3}$.

$$\% \text{ unprecipitated } Ca^{2+} = \frac{2.4 \times 10^{-3}\ M_{final}}{0.00625\ M_{initial}} \times 100\% = 38\% \text{ unprecipitated}$$

70. (M) If equal volumes are mixed, each concentration is reduced to one-half of its initial value. We assume that all of the limiting ion forms a precipitate, and then equilibrium is achieved by the reaction proceeding in the forward direction to a small extent.

Equation: $BaCO_3(s) \rightleftharpoons$ $Ba^{2+}(aq)$ + $CO_3^{2-}(aq)$

Orig. soln:	–	0.00050 M	0.0010 M
Form ppt:	–	0 M	0.0005 M
Changes:	–	+x M	+x M
Equil:	–	x M	(0.0005 + x)M

$$K_{sp} = [Ba^{2+}][CO_3^{2-}] = 5.1 \times 10^{-9} = (x)(0.0005 + x) \approx 0.0005\,x$$

$x = \dfrac{5.1 \times 10^{-9}}{0.0005} = 1 \times 10^{-5}\ M$ The $[Ba^{2+}]$ decreases from 5×10^{-4} M to 1×10^{-5} M.

($x < 0.0005$ M, thus the approximation was valid.)

$$\% \text{ unprecipitated} = \frac{1 \times 10^{-5} M}{5 \times 10^{-4} M} \times 100\% = 2\% \text{ Thus, } 98\% \text{ of the } Ba^{2+} \text{ is precipitated as } BaCO_3(s).$$

71. (M) The pH of the buffer establishes $[H_3O^+] = 10^{-pH} = 10^{-3.00} = 1.0 \times 10^{-3}$ M.

Now we combine the two equilibrium expressions, and solve the resulting expression for the molar solubility of $Pb(N_3)_2$ in the buffer solution.

$Pb(N_3)_2(s) \rightleftharpoons Pb^{2+}(aq) + 2\,N_3^-(aq)$ $\qquad\qquad\qquad\qquad K_{sp} = 2.5 \times 10^{-9}$

$\underline{2\,H_3O^+(aq) + 2\,N_3^-(aq) \rightleftharpoons 2\,HN_3(aq) + 2\,H_2O(l)} \qquad 1/K_a^2 = \dfrac{1}{(1.9 \times 10^{-5})^2} = 2.8 \times 10^9$

$Pb(N_3)_2(s) + 2\,H_3O^+(aq) \rightleftharpoons Pb^{2+}(aq) + 2\,HN_3(aq) + 2\,H_2O(l) \qquad K = K_{sp} \times (1/K_a^2) = 7.0$

$$Pb(N_3)_2(s) + 2\,H_3O^+(aq) \rightleftharpoons Pb^{2+}(aq) + 2\,HN_3(aq) + 2\,H_2O\,(l)$$

Buffer:	–	0.0010 M	0 M	0 M	–
Dissolving:	–	(buffer)	+x M	+2x M	–
Equilibrium:	–	0.0010 M	x M	2x M	–

$$K = \frac{[Pb^{2+}][HN_3]^2}{[H_3O^+]^2} = 7.0 = \frac{(x)\,(2x)^2}{(0.0010)^2} \qquad 4x^3 = 7.0\,(0.0010)^2 \qquad x = \sqrt[3]{\frac{7.0(0.0010)^2}{4}} = 0.012\ M$$

Thus, the molar solubility of $Pb(N_3)_2$ in a pH = 3.00 buffer is 0.012 M.

72. **(M)** We first determine the equilibrium constant of the suggested reaction.

$$Mg(OH)_2(s) \rightleftharpoons Mg^{2+}(aq) + 2\,OH^-(aq) \qquad\qquad K_{sp} = 1.8 \times 10^{-11}$$

$$2\,NH_4^+(aq) + 2\,OH^-(aq) \rightleftharpoons 2\,NH_3(aq) + 2\,H_2O(l) \quad 1/K_b^{\,2} = 1/(1.8 \times 10^{-5})^2$$

$$Mg(OH)_2(s) + 2\,NH_4^+(aq) \rightleftharpoons Mg^{2+}(aq) + 2\,NH_3(aq) + 2\,H_2O(l)$$

Initial:	–	1.00 M	0 M	0 M	–
Changes:	–	–2x M	+x M	+2x M	–
Equil:	–	(1.00 – 2x) M	x M	2x M	–

$$K = \frac{K_{sp}}{K_b^{\,2}} = \frac{1.8 \times 10^{-11}}{(1.8 \times 10^{-5})^2} = \frac{[Mg^{2+}][NH_3]^2}{[NH_4^+]^2} = 0.056 = \frac{x(2x)^2}{(1.00 - 2x)^2} \approx \frac{4x^3}{1.00^2}$$

$$x = \sqrt[3]{\frac{0.056}{4}} = 0.24\ M$$

Take this as a first approximation and cycle through again. $2x = 0.48$

$$K \approx \frac{4x^3}{(1.00 - 0.48)^2} = 0.056 \qquad\qquad x = \sqrt[3]{\frac{0.056\,(1.00 - 0.48)^2}{4}} = 0.16\ M$$

Yet another cycle gives a somewhat more consistent value. $2x = 0.32$

$$K \approx \frac{4x^3}{(1.00 - 0.32)^2} = 0.056 \qquad\qquad x = \sqrt[3]{\frac{0.056\,(1.00 - 0.38)^2}{4}} = 0.19\ M$$

Another cycle gives more consistency. $2x = 0.38$

$$K \approx \frac{4x^3}{(1.00 - 0.38)^2} = 0.056 \qquad\qquad x = \sqrt[3]{\frac{0.056\,(1.00 - 0.38)^2}{4}} = 0.18\ M = [Mg^{2+}]$$

The molar solubility of $Mg(OH)_2$ in a 1.00 M NH_4Cl solution is 0.18 M.

73. (D) First we determine the value of the equilibrium constant for the cited reaction.

$$CaCO_3(s) \rightleftharpoons Ca^{2+}(aq) + CO_3^{2-}(aq) \qquad\qquad K_{sp} = 2.8\times10^{-9}$$

$$\underline{H_3O^+(aq) + CO_3^{2-}(aq) \rightleftharpoons H_2O(l) + HCO_3^-(aq) \qquad\qquad 1/K_{a2} = 1/4.7\times10^{-11}}$$

$$CaCO_3(aq) + H_3O^+(aq) \rightleftharpoons Ca^{2+}(aq) + HCO_3^-(aq) + H_2O(l) \qquad K_{overall} = K_{sp}\times(1/K_{a2})$$

$$K_{overall} = \frac{2.8\times10^{-9}}{4.7\times10^{-11}} = 60$$

Equation: $CaCO_3(s) + H_3O^+(aq) \rightleftharpoons Ca^{2+}(aq) + HCO_3^-(aq) + H_2O(l)$

	Equation	H_3O^+	Ca^{2+}	HCO_3^-	H_2O
Initial:	–	10^{-pH}	0 M	0 M	–
Change:	–	(*buffer*)	+x M	+x M	–
Equil:	–	10^{-pH}	x M	x M	–

In the above set-up, we have assumed that the pH of the solution did not change because of the dissolving of the $CaCO_3(s)$. That is, we have treated the rainwater as if it were a buffer solution.

(a) $K = \dfrac{[Ca^{2+}][HCO_3^-]}{[H_3O^+]} = 60. = \dfrac{x^2}{3\times10^{-6}}$ $x = \sqrt{60\times3\times10^{-6}} = 1\times10^{-2}\,M = [Ca^{2+}]$

(b) $K = \dfrac{[Ca^{2+}][HCO_3^-]}{[H_3O^+]} = 60. = \dfrac{x^2}{6.3\times10^{-5}}$ $x = \sqrt{60\times6.3\times10^{-5}} = 6.1\times10^{-2}\,M = [Ca^{2+}]$

74. We use the Henderson-Hasselbalch equation to determine $[H_3O^+]$ in this solution, and then use the K_{sp} expression for MnS to determine $[Mn^{2+}]$ that can exist in this solution without precipitation occurring.

$$pH = pK_a + \log\frac{[CH_3COO^-]}{[CH_3COOH]} = 4.74 + \log\frac{0.500\,M}{0.100\,M} = 4.74 + 0.70 = 5.44$$

$$[H_3O^+] = 10^{-5.44} = 3.6\times10^{-6}\,M$$

$$MnS(s) + 2\,H_3O^+(aq) \rightleftharpoons Mn^{2+}(aq) + H_2S(aq) + 2\,H_2O(l) \qquad K_{spa} = 3\times10^7$$

Note that $[H_2S] = [Mn^{2+}] = s$, the molar solubility of MnS.

$$K_{spa} = \frac{[Mn^{2+}][H_2S]}{[H_3O^+]^2} = 3\times10^7 = \frac{s^2}{(3.6\times10^{-6}\,M)^2} \qquad s = 0.02\,M$$

$$\text{mass MnS/L} = \frac{0.02\,\text{mol Mn}^{2+}}{1\,\text{L soln}} \times \frac{1\,\text{mol MnS}}{1\,\text{mol Mn}^{2+}} \times \frac{87\,\text{g MnS}}{1\,\text{mol MnS}} = 2\,\text{g MnS/L}$$

75. (M)

(a) The precipitate is likely $Ca_3(PO_4)_2$. Let us determine the %Ca of this compound (by mass)

$$\%Ca = \frac{3 \times 40.078\ g\ Ca}{310.18\ g\ Ca_3(PO_4)_2} \times 100\% = 38.763\%\ Ca$$

$$3\ Ca^{2+}(aq) + 2\ HPO_4^{2-}(aq) \longrightarrow Ca_3(PO_4)_2(s) + 2\ H^+(aq)$$

(b) The bubbles are $CO_2(g)$: $\qquad CO_2(g) + H_2O(l) \longrightarrow \text{``}H_2CO_3(aq)\text{''}$

$$Ca^{2+}(aq) + H_2CO_3(aq) \longrightarrow CaCO_3(s) + 2\ H^+(aq) \qquad \text{precipitation}$$

$$CaCO_3(s) + H_2CO_3(aq) \longrightarrow Ca^{2+}(aq) + 2\ HCO_3^-(aq) \qquad \text{redissolving}$$

76. (D)

(a) A solution of $CO_2(aq)$ has $[CO_3^{2-}] = K_a[H_2CO_3] = 5.6 \times 10^{-11}$. Since $K_{sp} = 2.8 \times 10^{-9}$ for $CaCO_3$, the $[Ca^{2+}]$ needed to form a precipitate from this solution can be computed.

$$[Ca^{2+}] = \frac{K_{sp}}{[CO_3^{2-}]} = \frac{2.8 \times 10^{-9}}{5.6 \times 10^{-11}} = 50.\ M$$

This is too high to reach by dissolving $CaCl_2$ in solution. The reason why the technique works is because the $OH^-(aq)$ produced by $Ca(OH)_2$ neutralizes some of the $HCO_3^-(aq)$ from the ionization of $CO_2(aq)$, thereby increasing the $[CO_3^{2-}]$ above a value of 5.6×10^{-11}.

(b) The equation for redissolving can be obtained by combining several equations.

$$CaCO_3(s) \rightleftharpoons Ca^{2+}(aq) + CO_3^{2-}(aq) \qquad\qquad K_{sp} = 2.8 \times 10^{-9}$$

$$CO_3^{2-}(aq) + H_3O^+(aq) \rightleftharpoons HCO_3^-(aq) + H_2O(l) \qquad \frac{1}{K_{a2}} = \frac{1}{5.6 \times 10^{-11}}$$

$$CO_2(aq) + 2\ H_2O(l) \rightleftharpoons HCO_3^-(aq) + H_3O^+(aq) \qquad K_{a1} = 4.2 \times 10^{-7}$$

$$CaCO_3(s) + CO_2(aq) + H_2O(l) \rightleftharpoons Ca^{2+}(aq) + 2\ HCO_3^-(aq) \qquad K = \frac{K_{sp} \times K_{a1}}{K_{a2}}$$

$$K = \frac{(2.8 \times 10^{-9})(4.2 \times 10^{-7})}{5.6 \times 10^{-11}} = 2.1 \times 10^{-5} = \frac{[Ca^{2+}][HCO_3^-]^2}{[CO_2]}$$

If $CaCO_3$ is precipitated from 0.005 M $Ca^{2+}(aq)$ and then redissolved, $[Ca^{2+}] = 0.005$ M and $[HCO_3^{2-}] = 2 \times 0.005$ M = 0.010 M. We use these values in the above expression to compute $[CO_2]$.

$$[CO_2] = \frac{[Ca^{2+}][HCO_3^-]^2}{2.1 \times 10^{-5}} = \frac{(0.005)(0.010)^2}{2.1 \times 10^{-5}} = 0.02\ M$$

We repeat the calculation for saturated $Ca(OH)_2$, in which $[OH^-] = 2\,[Ca^{2+}]$, after first determining $[Ca^{2+}]$ in this solution.

$$K_{sp} = [Ca^{2+}][OH^-]^2 = 4\,[Ca^{2+}] = 5.5 \times 10^{-6} \quad [Ca^{2+}] \sqrt[3]{\frac{5.5 \times 10^{-6}}{4}} = 0.011$$

$$M[CO_2] = \frac{[Ca^{2+}][HCO_3^-]^2}{2.1 \times 10^{-5}} = \frac{(0.011)(0.022)^2}{2.1 \times 10^{-5}} = 0.25 \text{ M}$$

Thus, to redissolve the $CaCO_3$ requires that $[CO_2] = 0.25$ M if the solution initially is saturated $Ca(OH)_2$, but only 0.02 M CO_2 if the solution initially is 0.005 M $Ca(OH)_2(aq)$. A handbook lists the solubility of CO_2 as 0.034 M. Clearly the $CaCO_3$ produced cannot redissolve if the solution was initially saturated with $Ca(OH)_2(aq)$.

77. **(M)**

(a)

$$BaSO_4(s) \rightleftharpoons Ba^{2+}(aq) + SO_4^{2-}(aq) \qquad K_{sp} = 1.1 \times 10^{-10}$$

$$\underline{Ba^{2+}(aq) + CO_3^{2-}(aq) \rightleftharpoons BaCO_3(s) \qquad \frac{1}{K_{sp}} = \frac{1}{5.1 \times 10^{-9}}}$$

$$\text{Sum} \quad BaSO_4(s) + CO_3^{2-}(aq) \rightleftharpoons BaCO_3(s) + SO_4^{2-}(aq) \qquad K_{overall} = \frac{1.1 \times 10^{-10}}{5.1 \times 10^{-9}} = 0.0216$$

Initial   –   3 M   – ≈ 0

Equil.   – $(3-x)$M   – x

(where x is the carbonate used up in the reaction)

$$K = \frac{[SO_4^{2-}]}{[CO_3^{2-}]} = \frac{x}{3-x} = 0.0216 \text{ and } x = 0.063 \quad \text{Since } 0.063 \text{ M} > 0.050 \text{ M, the response is yes.}$$

(b)

$$2\,AgCl(s) \rightleftharpoons 2\,Ag^+(aq) + 2\,Cl^-(aq) \qquad K_{sp} = (1.8 \times 10^{-10})^2$$

$$2\,Ag^+(aq) + CO_3^{2-}(aq) \rightleftharpoons Ag_2CO_3(s) \qquad 1/K_{sp} = \frac{1}{8.5 \times 10^{-12}}$$

$$\text{Sum} \quad 2\,AgCl(s) + CO_3^{2-}(aq) \rightleftharpoons Ag_2CO_3(s) + 2\,Cl^-(aq) \qquad K_{overall} = \frac{(1.8 \times 10^{-10})^2}{8.5 \times 10^{-12}} = 3.8 \times 10^{-9}$$

Initial   –   3 M   – ≈ 0 M

Equil.   – $(3-x)$M   – $2x$

(where x is the carbonate used up in the reaction)

$$K_{overall} = \frac{[Cl^-]^2}{[CO_3^{2-}]} = \frac{(2x)^2}{3-x} = 3.8 \times 10^{-9} \text{ and } x = 5.3 \times 10^{-5} \text{ M}$$

Since $2x$, $(2(5.35 \times 10^{-5}M))$, $\ll 0.050$ M, the response is no.

(c)

$$MgF_2(s) \rightleftharpoons Mg^{2+}(aq) + 2\,F^-(aq) \qquad K_{sp} = 3.7 \times 10^{-8}$$

$$Mg^{2+}(aq) + CO_3^{2-}(aq) \rightleftharpoons MgCO_3(s) \qquad 1/K_{sp} = \dfrac{1}{3.5 \times 10^{-8}}$$

sum $MgF_2(s) + CO_3^{2-}(aq) \rightleftharpoons MgCO_3(s) + 2\,F^-(aq) \qquad K_{overall} = \dfrac{3.7 \times 10^{-8}}{3.5 \times 10^{-8}} = 1.1$

initial   –   3 M   –   0 M

equil.   – $(3-x)$M   – $2x$

(where x is the carbonate used up in the reaction)

$$K_{overall} = \dfrac{[F^-]^2}{[CO_3^{2-}]} = \dfrac{(2x)^2}{3-x} = 1.1 \text{ and } x = 0.769M$$

Since $2x$, $(2(0.769M)) > 0.050$ M, the response is yes.

---

78. (D) For ease of calculation, let us assume that 100 mL, that is, 0.100 L of solution, is to be titrated. We also assume that $[Ag^+] = 0.10$ M in the titrant. In order to precipitate 99.9% of the Br^- as AgBr, the following volume of titrant must be added.

$$\text{volume titrant } = 0.999 \times 100 \text{ mL} \times \dfrac{0.010 \text{ mmol } Br^-}{1 \text{ mL sample}} \times \dfrac{1 \text{ mmol } Ag^+}{1 \text{ mmol } Br^-} \times \dfrac{1 \text{ mL titrant}}{0.10 \text{ mmol } Ag^+} = 9.99 \text{ mL}$$

We compute $[Ag^+]$ when precipitation is complete.

$$[Ag^+] = \dfrac{K_{sp}}{[Br^-]_f} = \dfrac{5.0 \times 10^{-13}}{0.001 \times 0.01 \text{ M}} = 5.0 \times 10^{-8} M$$

Thus, during the course of the precipitation of AgBr, while 9.99 mL of titrant is added, $[Ag^+]$ increases from *zero* to 5.0×10^{-8} M. $[Ag^+]$ increases from 5.0×10^{-8} M to 1.0×10^{-5} M from the point where AgBr is completely precipitated to the point where Ag_2CrO_4 begins to precipitate. Let us assume, for the purpose of making an initial estimate, that this increase in $[Ag^+]$ occurs while the total volume of the solution is 110 mL (the original 100 mL plus 10 mL of titrant needed to precipitate all the AgBr.) The amount of Ag^+ added during this increase is the difference between the amount present just after AgBr is completely precipitated and the amount present when Ag_2CrO_4 begins to precipitate.

$$\text{amount } Ag^+ \text{ added} = 110 \text{ mL} \times \dfrac{1.0 \times 10^{-5} \text{mmol } Ag^+}{1 \text{ mL soln}} - 110 \text{ mL} \times \dfrac{5.0 \times 10^{-8} \text{mmol } Ag^+}{1 \text{ mL soln}}$$

$$= 1.1 \times 10^{-3} \text{ mmol } Ag^+$$

$$\text{volume added titrant} = 1.1 \times 10^{-3} \text{ mmol } Ag^+ \times \dfrac{1 \text{ mL titrant}}{0.10 \text{ mmol } Ag^+} = 1.1 \times 10^{-2} \text{mL titrant}$$

We see that the total volume of solution remains essentially constant. Note that $[Ag^+]$ has increased by more than two powers of ten while the volume of solution increased a very small degree; this is indeed a very rapid rise in $[Ag^+]$, as stated.

79. (D) The chemistry of aluminum is complex, however, we can make the following assumptions. Consider the following reactions at various pH:

$$\text{pH} > 7 \quad Al(OH)_3(s) + OH^- \xrightarrow{K_{overall} = K_f K_{sp} = 1.43} Al(OH)_4^-(aq)$$

$$\text{pH} < 7 \quad Al(OH)_3(s) \xrightarrow{K_{sp} = 1.3 \times 10^{-33}} Al^{3+}(aq) + 3\,OH^-$$

For the solubilities in basic solutions, consider the following equilibrium at pH = 13.00 and 11.00.

At pH = 13.00:

	$Al(OH)_3(s) +$	$OH^- \xrightarrow{K_{overall} = K_f K_{sp} = 1.43}$	$Al(OH)_4^-(aq)$
Initial :	–	0.10	0
Change:	–	$-x$	$+x$
Equilibrium:	–	$0.10 - x$	x

$$K_f = 1.4\underline{3} = \frac{x}{0.10 - x} \approx \frac{x}{0.10} \quad \text{(buffered at pH = 13.00)} \quad x = 0.14\underline{3}\ M$$

At pH = 11.00: $\quad K_f = 1.4\underline{3} = \dfrac{x}{0.0010 - x} \approx \dfrac{x}{0.0010} \quad$ (buffered at pH = 11) $\quad x = 0.0014\underline{3}\ M$

Thus, in these two calculations we see that the formation of the aluminate ion $[Al(OH)_4^-]$ is favored at high pH values. Note that the concentration of aluminum(III) increases by a factor of one-hundred when the pH is increased from 11.00 to 13.00, and it will increase further still above pH 13. Now consider the solubility equilibrium established at pH = 3.00, 4.00, and 5.00. These correspond to $[OH^-] = 1.0 \times 10^{-11}\ M$, $1.0 \times 10^{-10}\ M$, and $1.0 \times 10^{-9}\ M$, respectively.

$$Al(OH)_3(s) \xrightarrow{K_{sp} = 1.3 \times 10^{-33}} Al^{3+}(aq) + 3\,OH^-(aq)$$

At these pH values, $[Al^{3+}]$ in saturated aqueous solutions of $Al(OH)_3$ are

$$[Al^{3+}] = 1.3 \times 10^{-33} / (1.0 \times 10^{-11})^3 = 1.3\ M \text{ at pH} = 3.00$$

$$[Al^{3+}] = 1.3 \times 10^{-33} / (1.0 \times 10^{-10})^3 = 1.3 \times 10^{-3}\ M \text{ at pH} = 4.00$$

$$[Al^{3+}] = 1.3 \times 10^{-33} / (1.0 \times 10^{-9})^3 = 1.3 \times 10^{-6}\ M \text{ at pH} = 5.00$$

These three calculations show that in strongly acidic solutions the concentration of aluminum(III) can be very high and is certainly not limited by the precipitation of $Al(OH)_3(s)$. However, this solubility decreases rapidly as the pH increases beyond pH 4.

At neutral pH 7, a number of equilibria would need to be considered simultaneously, including the self-ionization of water itself. However, the results of just these five calculations do indicate that concentration of aluminum(III) increases at both low and high pH values, with a very low concentration at intermediate pH values around pH 7, thus aluminum(III) concentration as a function of pH is a U-shaped (or V-shaped) curve.

80. (M) We combine the solubility product expression for AgCN(s) with the formation expression for $[Ag(NH_3)_2]^+(aq)$.

Solubility: $\qquad AgCN(s) \rightleftharpoons Ag^+(aq) + CN^-(aq) \qquad K_{sp} = ?$

Formation: $\quad Ag^+(aq) + 2NH_3(aq) \rightleftharpoons [Ag(NH_3)_2]^+(aq) \qquad K_f = 1.6 \times 10^{+7}$

Net reaction: $\quad AgCN(s) + 2\,NH_3(aq) \rightleftharpoons [Ag(NH_3)_2]^+ + CN^-(aq)\; K_{overall} = K_{sp} \times K_f$

$$K_{overall} = \frac{[[Ag(NH_3)_2]^+][CN^-]}{[NH_3]^2} = \frac{(8.8 \times 10^{-6})^2}{(0.200)^2} = 1.9 \times 10^{-9} = K_{sp} \times 1.6 \times 10^{+7}$$

$$K_{sp} = \frac{1.9 \times 10^{-9}}{1.6 \times 10^{+7}} = 1.2 \times 10^{-16}$$

Because of the extremely low solubility of AgCN in the solution, we assumed that $[NH_3]$ was not altered by the formation of the complex ion.

81. We combine the solubility product constant expression for $CdCO_3(s)$ with the formation expression for $[CdI_4]^{2-}(aq)$.

Solubility: $\qquad CdCO_3(s) \rightleftharpoons Cd^{2+}(aq) + CO_3^{2-}(aq) \qquad K_{sp} = 5.2 \times 10^{-12}$

Formation: $\quad Cd^{2+}(aq) + 4\,I^-(aq) \rightleftharpoons [CdI_4]^{2-}(aq) \qquad K_f = ?$

Net reaction: $CdCO_3(s) + 4\,I^-(aq) \rightleftharpoons [CdI_4]^{2-}(aq) + CO_3^{2-}(aq) \qquad K_{overall} = K_{sp} \times K_f$

$$K_{overall} = \frac{[[CdI_4]^{2-}][CO_3^{2-}]}{[I^-]^4} = \frac{(1.2 \times 10^{-3})^2}{(1.00)^4} = 1.4 \times 10^{-6} = 5.2 \times 10^{-12}\, K_f$$

$$K_f = \frac{1.4 \times 10^{-6}}{5.2 \times 10^{-12}} = 2.7 \times 10^5$$

Because of the low solubility of $CdCO_3$ in this solution, we assumed that $[I^-]$ was not appreciably lowered by the formation of the complex ion.

82. (M) We first determine $[Pb^{2+}]$ in this solution, which has $[Cl^-] = 0.10$ M.

$$K_{sp} = 1.6 \times 10^{-5} = [Pb^{2+}][Cl^-]^2 \qquad [Pb^{2+}] = \frac{K_{sp}}{[Cl^-]^2} = \frac{1.6 \times 10^{-5}}{(0.10)^2} = 1.6 \times 10^{-3}\,M$$

Then we use this value of $[Pb^{2+}]$ in the K_f expression to determine $[[PbCl_3]^-]$.

$$K_f = \frac{[[PbCl_3]^-]}{[Pb^{2+}][Cl^-]^3} = 24 = \frac{[[PbCl_3]^-]}{(1.6 \times 10^{-3})(0.10)^3} = \frac{[[PbCl_3]^-]}{1.6 \times 10^{-6}}$$

$$[[PbCl_3]^-] = 24 \times 1.6 \times 10^{-6} = 3.8 \times 10^{-5}\,M$$

The solubility of $PbCl_2$ in 0.10 M HCl is the following sum.

solubility $= [Pb^{2+}] + [[PbCl_3]^-] = 1.6 \times 10^{-3}\,M + 3.8 \times 10^{-5}\,M = 1.6 \times 10^{-3}\,M$

83. (M) Two of the three relationships needed to answer this question are the two solubility product expressions. $1.6 \times 10^{-8} = [Pb^{2+}][SO_4^{2-}]$ $4.0 \times 10^{-7} = [Pb^{2+}][S_2O_3^{2-}]$

The third expression required is the electroneutrality equation, which states that the total positive charge concentration must equal the total negative charge concentration: $[Pb^{2+}] = [SO_4^{2-}] + [S_2O_3^{2-}]$, provided $[H_3O^+] = [OH^-]$.

Or, put another way, there is one Pb^{2+} ion in solution for each SO_4^{2-} ion *and* for each $S_2O_3^{2-}$ ion. We solve each of the first two expressions for the concentration of each anion, substitute these expressions into the electroneutrality expression, and then solve for $[Pb^{2+}]$.

$$[SO_4^{2-}] = \frac{1.6 \times 10^{-8}}{[Pb^{2+}]} \qquad [S_2O_3^{2-}] = \frac{4.0 \times 10^{-7}}{[Pb^{2+}]} \qquad [Pb^{2+}] = \frac{1.6 \times 10^{-8}}{[Pb^{2+}]} + \frac{4.0 \times 10^{-7}}{[Pb^{2+}]}$$

$$[Pb^{2+}]^2 = 1.6 \times 10^{-8} + 4.0 \times 10^{-7} = 4.2 \times 10^{-7} \qquad [Pb^{2+}] = \sqrt{4.2 \times 10^{-7}} = 6.5 \times 10^{-4} \text{ M}$$

84. (D) The chemical equations are:

$$PbCl_2(s) \rightleftharpoons Pb^{2+}(aq) + 2\,Cl^-(aq) \quad \text{and} \quad PbBr_2(s) \rightleftharpoons Pb^{2+}(aq) + 2\,Br^-(aq)$$

The two solubility constant expressions, $[Pb^{2+}][Cl^-]^2 = 1.6 \times 10^{-5}$, $[Pb^{2+}][Br^-]^2 = 4.0 \times 10^{-5}$ and the condition of electroneutrality, $2[Pb^{2+}] = [Cl^-] + [Br^-]$, must be solved simultaneously to determine $[Pb^{2+}]$. (Rearranging the electroneutrality relationship, one obtains: $[Pb^{2+}] = \frac{1}{2}[Cl^-] + \frac{1}{2}[Br^-]$.) First we solve each of the solubility constant expressions for the concentration of the anion. Then we substitute these values into the electroneutrality expression and solve the resulting equation for $[Pb^{2+}]$.

$$[Cl^-] = \sqrt{\frac{1.6 \times 10^{-5}}{[Pb^{2+}]}} \qquad [Br^-] = \sqrt{\frac{4.0 \times 10^{-5}}{[Pb^{2+}]}} \qquad 2[Pb^{2+}] = \sqrt{\frac{1.6 \times 10^{-5}}{[Pb^{2+}]}} + \sqrt{\frac{4.0 \times 10^{-5}}{[Pb^{2+}]}}$$

$$2\sqrt{[Pb^{2+}]^3} = \sqrt{1.6 \times 10^{-5}} + \sqrt{4.0 \times 10^{-5}} = 4.0 \times 10^{-3} + 6.3 \times 10^{-3} = 1.03 \times 10^{-2}$$

$$\sqrt{[Pb^{2+}]^3} = 5.2 \times 10^{-3} \qquad [Pb^{2+}]^3 = 2.7 \times 10^{-5} \qquad [Pb^{2+}] = 3.0 \times 10^{-2}\,M$$

85. (D) (a)   First let us determine if there is sufficient Ag_2SO_4 to produce a saturated solution, in which $[Ag^+] = 2\,[SO_4^{2-}]$.

$$K_{sp} = 1.4 \times 10^{-5} = [Ag^+]^2[SO_4^{2-}] = 4[SO_4^{2-}]^3 \qquad [SO_4^{2-}] = \sqrt[3]{\frac{1.4 \times 10^{-5}}{4}} = 0.015\,M$$

$$[SO_4^{2-}] = \frac{2.50\,g\,Ag_2SO_4}{0.150\,L} \times \frac{1\,mol\,Ag_2SO_4}{311.8\,g\,Ag_2SO_4} \times \frac{1\,mol\,SO_4^{2-}}{1\,mol\,Ag_2SO_4} = 0.0535\,M$$

Thus, there is more than enough Ag_2SO_4 present to form a saturated solution. Let us now see if AgCl or $BaSO_4$ will precipitate under these circumstances. $[SO_4^{2-}] = 0.015$ M and $[Ag^+] = 0.030$ M.

$Q = [Ag^+][Cl^-] = 0.030 \times 0.050 = 1.5 \times 10^{-3} > 1.8 \times 10^{-10} = K_{sp}$, thus AgCl should precipitate.

$Q = [Ba^{2+}][SO_4^{2-}] = 0.025 \times 0.015 = 3.8 \times 10^{-4} > 1.1 \times 10^{-10} = K_{sp}$, thus $BaSO_4$ should precipitate.

Thus, the net ionic equation for the reaction that will occur is as follows.

$Ag_2SO_4(s) + Ba^{2+}(aq) + 2Cl^-(aq) \longrightarrow BaSO_4(s) + 2AgCl(s)$

(b) Let us first determine if any $Ag_2SO_4(s)$ remains or if it is all converted to $BaSO_4(s)$ and $AgCl(s)$. Thus, we have to solve a limiting reagent problem.

$$\text{amount } Ag_2SO_4 = 2.50\,g\ Ag_2SO_4 \times \frac{1\,mol\ Ag_2SO_4}{311.8\,g\ Ag_2SO_4} = 8.02 \times 10^{-3}\ mol\ Ag_2SO_4$$

$$\text{amount } BaCl_2 = 0.150\,L \times \frac{0.025\,mol\ BaCl_2}{1\,L\ soln} = 3.75 \times 10^{-3}\ mol\ BaCl_2$$

Since the two reactants combine in a 1 mole to 1 mole stoichiometric ratio, $BaCl_2$ is the limiting reagent. Since there must be some Ag_2SO_4 present and because Ag_2SO_4 is so much more soluble than either $BaSO_4$ or AgCl, we assume that $[Ag^+]$ and $[SO_4^{2-}]$ are determined by the solubility of Ag_2SO_4. They will have the same values as in a saturated solution of Ag_2SO_4.

$[SO_4^{2-}] = 0.015\ M$ $\qquad\qquad$ $[Ag^+] = 0.030\ M$

We use these values and the appropriate K_{sp} values to determine $[Ba^{2+}]$ and $[Cl^-]$.

$$[Ba^{2+}] = \frac{1.1 \times 10^{-10}}{0.015} = 7.3 \times 10^{-9}\ M \qquad [Cl^-] = \frac{1.8 \times 10^{-10}}{0.030} = 6.0 \times 10^{-9}\ M$$

Since $BaCl_2$ is the limiting reagent, we can use its amount to determine the masses of $BaSO_4$ and AgCl.

$$\text{mass } BaSO_4 = 0.00375\,mol\ BaCl_2 \times \frac{1\,mol\ BaSO_4}{1\,mol\ BaCl_2} \times \frac{233.4\,g\ BaSO_4}{1\,mol\ BaSO_4} = 0.875\,g\ BaSO_4$$

$$\text{mass } AgCl = 0.00375\,mol\ BaCl_2 \times \frac{2\,mol\ AgCl}{1\,mol\ BaCl_2} \times \frac{143.3\,g\ AgCl}{1\,mol\ AgCl} = 1.07\,g\ AgCl$$

The mass of unreacted Ag_2SO_4 is determined from the initial amount and the amount that reacts with $BaCl_2$.

$$\text{mass } Ag_2SO_4 = \left(0.00802\,mol\ Ag_2SO_4 - 0.00375\,mol\ BaCl_2 \times \frac{1\,mol\ Ag_2SO_4}{1\,mol\ BaCl_2}\right) \times \frac{311.8\,g\ Ag_2SO_4}{1\,mol\ Ag_2SO_4}$$

$\text{mass } Ag_2SO_4 = 1.33\,g\ Ag_2SO_4$ unreacted

Of course, there is some Ag_2SO_4 dissolved in solution. We compute its mass.

$$\text{mass dissolved Ag}_2\text{SO}_4 = 0.150\,\text{L} \times \frac{0.0150\,\text{mol Ag}_2\text{SO}_4}{1\,\text{L soln}} \times \frac{311.8\,\text{g Ag}_2\text{SO}_4}{1\,\text{mol Ag}_2\text{SO}_4}$$

$$= 0.702\,\text{g dissolved}$$

$$\text{mass Ag}_2\text{SO}_4(\text{s}) = 1.33\,\text{g} - 0.702\,\text{g} = 0.63\,\text{g Ag}_2\text{SO}_4(\text{s})$$

86. **(M)** To determine how much NaF must be added, determine what the solubility of BaF_2 is considering that the final concentration of F^- must be 0.030 M. $K_{sp} = 1 \times 10^{-6}$.

BaF_2 (s)	$\rightleftharpoons$	Ba^{2+} (aq)	$+$	$2F^-$ (aq)
		0		0
		$+s$		$+2s$
		s		$2s = 0.030$

$$K_{sp} = 1 \times 10^{-6} = (s)(0.030)^2 = s(9.0 \times 10^{-4}); \text{ Therefore, } s = 0.0011\,\text{M}.$$

Since s is 0.0011 M, the F^- contribution from BaF_2 considering the common ion effect exerted by NaF is 0.0022 M. Therefore, the total number of moles of NaF in a 1 L solution required is therefore 0.0278 moles.

To determine how much BaF_2 precipitates, we must first determine what the value of s is for a saturated solution in absence of the common ion effect. That is,

$$K_{sp} = 1 \times 10^{-6} = (s)(2s)^2 = 4s^3; \text{ Therefore, } s = 0.0063\,\text{M}.$$

Since in absence of the common ion effect from NaF the solubility of BaF_2 is 0.0063 M, and with NaF the solubility is 0.0011, the difference between the two (0.0063 – 0.0011 = 0.0052 M) has to be precipitated. The mass of the precipitate is therefore:

$$\text{mass of BaF}_2 = \frac{0.0052\,\text{mol BaF}_2}{1\,\text{L solution}} \times \frac{175.3\,\text{g BaF}_2}{1\,\text{mol BaF}_2} = 0.91\,\text{g}$$

FEATURE PROBLEMS

87. **(M)** $\left[Ca^{2+}\right]=\left[SO_4^{2-}\right]$ in the saturated solution. Let us first determine the amount of H_3O^+ in the 100.0 mL diluted effluent. $H_3O^+(aq)+NaOH(aq)\longrightarrow 2H_2O(l)+Na^+(aq)$

$$\text{mmol } H_3O^+ =100.0 \text{ mL}\times\frac{8.25 \text{ mL base}}{10.00 \text{ mL sample}}\times\frac{0.0105 \text{ mmol NaOH}}{1 \text{ mL base}}\times\frac{1 \text{ mmol } H_3O^+}{1 \text{ mmol NaOH}}$$

$$= 0.866 \text{ mmol } H_3O^+(aq)$$

Now we determine $\left[Ca^{2+}\right]$ in the original 25.00 mL sample, remembering that $2H_3O^+$ were produced for each Ca^{2+}.

$$\left[Ca^{2+}\right]=\frac{0.866 \text{ mmol } H_3O^+(aq)\times\dfrac{1 \text{ mmol } Ca^{2+}}{2 \text{ mmol } H_3O^+}}{25.00 \text{ mL}}=0.0173 \text{ M}$$

$K_{sp}=\left[Ca^{2+}\right]\left[SO_4^{2-}\right]=(0.0173)^2=3.0\times10^{-4}$; the K_{sp} for $CaSO_4$ is 9.1×10^{-6} in Appendix D.

88. **(D)**

(a) We assume that there is little of each ion present in solution at equilibrium (that this is a simple stoichiometric calculation). This is true because the K value for the titration reaction is very large. $K_{titration} = 1/K_{sp(AgCl)} = 5.6\times10^9$. We stop the titration when just enough silver ion has been added. $Ag^+(aq)+Cl^-(aq)\longrightarrow AgCl(s)$

$$V=100.0 \text{ mL}\times\frac{29.5 \text{ mg Cl}^-}{1000 \text{ mL}}\times\frac{1 \text{ mmol Cl}^-}{35.45 \text{ mg Cl}^-}\times\frac{1 \text{ mmol Ag}^+}{1 \text{ mmol Cl}^-}\times\frac{1 \text{ mL}}{0.01000 \text{ mmol AgNO}_3}$$

$$= 8.32 \text{ mL}$$

(b) We first calculate the concentration of each ion as the consequence of dilution. Then we determine the $[Ag^+]$ from the value of K_{sp}.

$$\text{initial }\left[Ag^+\right]= 0.01000 \text{ M}\times\frac{8.32 \text{ mL added}}{108.3 \text{ mL final volume}}=7.68\times10^{-4} \text{ M}$$

$$\text{initial }\left[Cl^-\right]=\frac{29.5 \text{ mg Cl}^-\times\dfrac{1 \text{ mmol Cl}^-}{35.45 \text{ mg Cl}^-}}{1000 \text{ mL}}\times\frac{100.0 \text{ mL taken}}{108.3 \text{ mL final volume}}=7.68\times10^{-4}\text{M}$$

The slight excess of each ion will precipitate until the solubility constant is satisfied.

$$\left[Ag^+\right]=\left[Cl^-\right]=\sqrt{K_{sp}}=\sqrt{1.8\times10^{-10}}=1.3\times10^{-5} \text{ M}$$

(c) If we want Ag_2CrO_4 to appear just when AgCl has completed precipitation,

$\left[Ag^+\right]=1.3\times10^{-5}$ M. We determine $\left[CrO_4^{2-}\right]$ from the K_{sp} expression.

$$K_{sp}=\left[Ag^+\right]^2\left[CrO_4^{2-}\right]=1.1\times10^{-12}=\left(1.3\times10^{-5}\right)^2\left[CrO_4^{2-}\right];\ \left[CrO_4^{2-}\right]=\frac{1.1\times10^{-12}}{\left(1.3\times10^{-5}\right)^2}=0.0065 \text{ M}$$

(d) If $\left[CrO_4^{\,2-}\right]$ were greater than the answer just computed for part (c), Ag_2CrO_4 would appear before all Cl^- had precipitated, leading to a false early endpoint. We would calculate a falsely low $\left[Cl^-\right]$ for the original solution.

If $\left[CrO_4^{\,2-}\right]$ were less than computed in part 3, Ag_2CrO_4 would appear somewhat after all Cl^- had precipitated, leading one to conclude there was more Cl^- in solution than actually was the case.

(e) If it was Ag^+ that was being titrated, it would react immediately with the $CrO_4^{\,2-}$ in the sample, forming a red-orange precipitate. This precipitate would not likely dissolve, and thus, very little if any $AgCl$ would form. There would be no visual indication of the endpoint.

89. (D)

(a) We need to calculate the $\left[Mg^{2+}\right]$ in a solution that is saturated with $Mg(OH)_2$.

$$K_{sp} = 1.8 \times 10^{-11} = \left[Mg^{2+}\right]\left[OH^-\right]^2 = (s)(2s)^2 = 4s^3$$

$$s = \sqrt[3]{\frac{1.8 \times 10^{-11}}{4}} = 1.7 \times 10^{-4}\ M = [Mg^{2+}]$$

(b) Even though water has been added to the original solution, it remains saturated (it is in equilibrium with the undissolved solid $Mg(OH)_2$). $\left[Mg^{2+}\right] = 1.7 \times 10^{-4}\ M$.

(c) Although $HCl(aq)$ reacts with OH^-, it will not react with Mg^{2+}. The solution is simply a more dilute solution of Mg^{2+}.

$$\left[Mg^{2+}\right] = 1.7 \times 10^{-4}\ M \times \frac{100.0\ \text{mL initial volume}}{(100.0 + 500.)\ \text{mL final volume}} = 2.8 \times 10^{-5}\ M$$

(d) In this instance, we have a dual dilution to a 275.0 mL total volume, followed by a common-ion scenario.

$$\text{initial}\left[Mg^{2+}\right] = \frac{\left(25.00\ \text{mL} \times \dfrac{1.7 \times 10^{-4}\ \text{mmol}\,Mg^{2+}}{1\ \text{mL}}\right) + \left(250.0\ \text{mL} \times \dfrac{0.065\ \text{mmol}\,Mg^{2+}}{1\ \text{mL}}\right)}{275.0\ \text{mL total volume}}$$

$$= 0.059\ M$$

$$\text{initial}\left[OH^-\right] = \frac{25.00\ \text{mL} \times \dfrac{1.7 \times 10^{-4}\ \text{mmol}\,Mg^{2+}}{1\ \text{mL}} \times \dfrac{2\ \text{mmol}\,OH^-}{1\ \text{mmol}\,Mg^{2+}}}{275.0\ \text{mL total volume}} = 3.1 \times 10^{-5}\ M$$

Let's see if precipitation occurs.

$$Q_{sp} = \left[Mg^{2+}\right]\left[OH^-\right]^2 = (0.059)(3.1 \times 10^{-5})^2 = 5.7 \times 10^{-11} > 1.8 \times 10^{-11} = K_{sp}$$

Thus, precipitation does occur, but very little precipitate forms. If $\left[OH^-\right]$ goes down by 1.4×10^{-5} M (which means that $\left[Mg^{2+}\right]$ drops by 0.7×10^{-5} M), then $\left[OH^-\right] = 1.7 \times 10^{-5}$ M and

$$\left[Mg^{2+}\right] = \left(0.059 \text{ M} - 0.7 \times 10^{-5} \text{ M} =\right) 0.059 \text{ M, then } Q_{sp} < K_{sp} \text{ and precipitation will}$$

stop. Thus, $\left[Mg^{2+}\right] = 0.059$ M.

(e) Again we have a dual dilution, now to a 200.0 mL final volume, followed by a common-ion scenario.

$$\text{initial }\left[Mg^{2+}\right] = \frac{50.00 \text{ mL} \times \dfrac{1.7 \times 10^{-4} \text{ mmol Mg}^{2+}}{1 \text{ mL}}}{200.0 \text{ mL total volume}} = 4.3 \times 10^{-5} \text{ M}$$

$$\text{initial }\left[OH^-\right] = 0.150 \text{ M} \times \frac{150.0 \text{ mL initial volume}}{200.0 \text{ mL total volume}} = 0.113 \text{ M}$$

Now it is evident that precipitation will occur. Next we determine the $\left[Mg^{2+}\right]$ that can exist in solution with 0.113 M OH$^-$. It is clear that $\left[Mg^{2+}\right]$ will drop dramatically to satisfy the K_{sp} expression but the larger value of $\left[OH^-\right]$ will scarcely be affected.

$$K_{sp} = \left[Mg^{2+}\right]\left[OH^-\right]^2 = 1.8 \times 10^{-11} = \left[Mg^{2+}\right](0.0113 \text{ M})^2$$

$$\left[Mg^{2+}\right] = \frac{1.8 \times 10^{-11}}{(0.113)^2} = 1.4 \times 10^{-9} \text{ M}$$

SELF-ASSESSMENT EXERCISES

90. (E)

    (a) K_{sp}: The solubility product constant, which is the constant for the equilibrium established between a solid solute and its ions in a saturated solution

    (b) K_f: The formation constant of a complex ion, which is the equilibrium constant describing the formation of a complex ion from a central ion (typically a metal cation) and the ligands that attach to it

    (c) Q_{sp}: The ion product, which is the product of concentrations of the constituent ions of a compound, and is used to determine if they meet the precipitation criteria or not.

    (d) Complex ion: A polyatomic cation or anion composed of a central metal ion to which other groups (molecules or ions) called ligands are coordinated/attached to.

91. (E)

    (a) Common-ion effect in solubility equilibrium: Where the solubility of a sparingly soluble compound is suppressed by the presence of a quantity (often large) of one of the compound's ions from another source

    (b) Fractional precipitation: A technique in which two or more ions in solution, each capable of being precipitated by the same reagent, are separated by the proper use of that reagent: One ion is precipitated, while the other(s) remains in solution.

    (c) Ion-pair formation: Pair of ions held loosely together by electrostatic interactions in water

    (d) Qualitative cation analysis: A qualitative method that is used to identify various the cations present in a solution by stepwise addition of various anions in order to selectively precipitate out various cations in steps.

92. (E)

    (a) Solubility and solubility product constant: Solubility is the number of moles of a precipitate dissolved in a certain mass of water (or some other solvent.) The solubility product constant is the constant for the equilibrium established between a solid solute and its ions in a saturated solution.

    (b) Common–ion effect and salt effect: The common ion effect is a consequence of Le Châtelier's principle, where the equilibrium concentration of all ions resulting from the dissolution of a sparingly soluble precipitate is reduced because a large amount of one (or more) of the ions from another source is present. The salt effect is the presence of a large quantity of ions from a very soluble salt which slightly increases the solubility of a sparingly soluble precipitate.

    (c) Ion pair and ion product: An ion pair comprises two oppositely charged ions held together by electrostatic forces. The ion product (Q_{sp}) is the product of concentrations of the constituent ions of a compound, and is used to determine if they meet the precipitation criteria or not.

93. **(E)** The answer is (d). See the reasoning below.
(a) Wrong, because the stoichiometry is wrong
(b) Wrong, because $K_{sp} = [Pb^{2+}] \cdot [I^-]^2$
(c) Wrong, because $[Pb^{2+}] = K_{sp}/[I^-]^2$
(d) Correct because of the $[Pb^{2+}]{:}2[I^-]$ stoichiometry

94. **(E)** The answer is (a). $BaSO_4(s) \rightleftharpoons Ba^{2+} + SO_4^{2-}$. If Na_2SO_4 is added, the common–ion effect forces the equilibrium to the left and reduces $[Ba^{2+}]$.

95. **(E)** The answer is (c). Choices (b) and (d) reduce solubility because of the common–ion effect. In the case of choice (c), the diverse non-common–ion effect or the "salt effect" causes more Ag_2CrO_4 to dissolve.

96. **(E)** The answer is (b). The sulfate salt of Cu is soluble, whereas the Pb salt is insoluble.

97. **(M)** The answers are (c) and (d). Adding NH_3 causes the solution to become basic (adding OH^-). Mg, Fe, Cu, and Al all have insoluble hydroxides. However, only Cu can form a complex ion with NH_3, which is soluble. In the case of $(NH_4)_2SO_4$, it is slightly acidic and dissolved readily in a base.

98. **(M)** The answer is (a). $CaCO_3$ is slightly basic, so it is more soluble in an acid. The only option for an acid given is NH_4Cl.

99. **(M)** The answer is (c). Referring to Figure 18-7, it is seen that ammonia is added to an aqueous H_2S solution to precipitate more metal ions. Since ammonia is a base, increasing the pH should cause more precipitation.

100. **(M)**
(a) $H_2C_2O_4$ is a moderately strong acid, so it is more soluble in a basic solution.
(b) $MgCO_3$ is slightly basic, so it is more soluble in an acidic solution.
(c) CdS is more soluble in acidic solutions, but the solubility is still so small that it is essentially insoluble even in acidic solutions.
(d) KCl is a neutral salt, and therefore its solubility is independent of pH.
(e) $NaNO_3$ is a neutral salt, and therefore its solubility is independent of pH.
(f) $Ca(OH)_2$, a strong base, is more soluble in an acidic solution.

101. **(E)** The answer is NH_3. NaOH(aq) precipitates both, and HCl(aq) precipitates neither. $Mg(OH)_2$ precipitates from an NH_3(aq) solution but forms the soluble complex $Cu(NH_3)_4(OH)_2$.

102. **(D)** $Al(OH)_3$ will precipitate. To demonstrate this, the pH of the acetate buffer needs to be determined first, from which the OH^- can be determined. The OH^- concentration can be used to calculate Q_{sp}, which can then be compared to K_{sp} to see if any $Al(OH)_3$ will precipitate. This is shown below:

$$pH = pK_a + \log\frac{\left[CH_3COO^-\right]}{\left[CH_3COOH\right]} = -\log\left(1.8\times10^{-5}\right) + \log\frac{0.35\ M}{0.45\ M} = 4.65$$

$$[OH^-] = 10^{-(14-pH)} = 4.467\times10^{-10}\ M$$

$$Al(OH)_3 \rightleftharpoons Al^{3+} + 3\ OH^-$$

$$Q_{sp} = (s)(3s)^3$$

$$Q_{sp} = (0.275)\left(4.467\times10^{-10}\right)^3 = 2.45\times10^{-29}$$

$Q_{sp} > K_{sp}$, therefore there will be precipitation.

103. **(E)** The answer is (b). Based on solubility rules, $Cu_3(PO_4)_2$ is the only species that is sparingly soluble in water.

104. **(M)** The answer is (d). The abbreviated work shown for each part calculates the molar solubility (s) for all the salts. They all follow the basic outlined below:

$$M_xA_y(s) \rightleftharpoons xM + yA(aq)$$

$$K_{sp} = (x\cdot s)^x \cdot (y\cdot s)^y$$

and we solve for s.

(a) $MgF_2(s) \rightleftharpoons Mg^{2+}(aq) + 2\ F^-(aq)$

$3.7\times10^{-8} = s\cdot(2s)^2 = 4s^3$

$s = 2.1\times10^{-3}\ M$

(c) $Mg_3(PO_4)_2(s) \rightleftharpoons 3\ Mg^{2+}(aq) + 2\ PO_4{}^{3-}(aq)$

$1\times10^{-25} = (3s)^3 \cdot (2s)^2 = 108\,s^5$

$s = 3.9\times10^{-6}\ M$

(b) $MgCO_3(s) \rightleftharpoons Mg^{2+}(aq) + CO_3^{2-}(aq)$

$3.5\times10^{-8} = s\cdot s$

$s = 1.9\times10^{-4}\ M$

(d) $Li_3PO_4(s) \rightleftharpoons 3\ Li^+(aq) + PO_4{}^{3-}(aq)$

$3.2\times10^{-9} = (3s)^3 \cdot s = 27\,s^4$

$s = 3.3\times10^{-3}\ M$

105. **(E)** The answer is (b). This is due to the "salt effect." The more moles of salt there are available, the greater the solubility. For (b), there are 0.300 moles of ions (3×0.100 M $Na_2S_2O_3$).

106. **(E)** It will decrease the amount of precipitate. Since all salts of $NO_3{}^-$ are highly soluble and Ag^+ and Hg^{2+} salts of I^- are not, anything that forms a soluble complex ion with Ag^+ and Hg^{2+} will reduce the amount of those ions available for precipitation with I^- and therefore will reduce the amount of precipitate.

107. (M) No precipitate will form. To demonstrate this, one has to calculate $[Ag^+]$, and then, using $[I^-]$, determine the Q_{sp} and compare it to K_{sp} of AgI.

Since K_f is for the formation of the complex ion $Ag(CN)_2^-$, its inverse is for the dissociation of $Ag(CN)_2^-$ to Ag^+ and CN^-.
$$K_{dis} = 1/K_f = 1/5.6 \times 10^{18} = 1.786 \times 10^{-19}$$

The dissociation of $Ag(CN)_2^-$ is as follows:
$$Ag(CN)_2^-(aq) \rightleftharpoons Ag^+ + 2CN^-$$

$$K_{dis} = \frac{x(1.05 + \cancel{x})}{(0.012 - \cancel{x})} = 1.786 \times 10^{-19}$$

We can simplify the calculations by noting that x is very small in relation to $[Ag^+]$ and $[CN^-]$. Therefore, $x = 1.70 \times 10^{-19}$ M.

Dissociation of AgI is as follows:
$$AgI \rightleftharpoons Ag^+ + I^-$$
$$Q_{sp} = (1.7 \times 10^{-19})(2.0) = 3.4 \times 10^{-19}$$

Since $Q_{sp} < K_{sp}$, no precipitate will form.

108. (M) In both cases, the dissolution reaction is similar to reaction (18.5), for which $K = K_f \times K_{sp}$. This is an exceedingly small quantity for (a) but large for (b). $CuCO_3$ is soluble in $NH_3(aq)$ and $CuS(s)$ is not.

109. (M) In this chapter, the concept of solubility of sparingly soluble precipitates is the overarching concept. Deriving from this overall concept is the dissociation constant for the precipitate, K_{sp} and molar solubility. Also emanating from the solubility concept are factors that affect solubility: the common ion–effect, the salt effect, the effects of pH on solubility, and formation of complex ions. Take a look at the subsection headings and problems for more refining of the general and specific concepts.

CHAPTER 19

ELECTROCHEMISTRY

PRACTICE EXAMPLES

1A **(E)** The conventions state that the anode material is written first, and the cathode material is written last.

Anode, oxidation: $Sc(s) \rightarrow Sc^{3+}(aq) + 3\,e^-$

Cathode, reduction: $\{Ag^+(aq) + e^- \rightarrow Ag(s)\} \times 3$

Net reaction $\quad Sc(s) + 3\,Ag^+(aq) \rightarrow Sc^{3+}(aq) + 3\,Ag(s)$

1B **(E)** Oxidation of Al(s) at the anode: $\quad Al(s) \rightarrow Al^{3+}(aq) + 3\,e^-$

Reduction of $Ag^+(aq)$ at the cathode: $Ag^+(aq) + e^- \rightarrow Ag(s)$

Overall reaction in cell: $Al(s) + 3\,Ag^+(aq) \rightarrow Al^{3+}(aq) + 3\,Ag(s)$

Diagram: $Al(s)|Al^{3+}(aq)\|Ag^+(aq)|Ag(s)$

2A **(E)** Anode, oxidation: $\quad Sn(s) \rightarrow Sn^{2+}(aq) + 2\,e^-$

Cathode, reduction: $\quad \{Ag^+(aq) + 1\,e^- \rightarrow Ag(s)\} \times 2$

Overall reaction in cell: $Sn(s) + 2\,Ag^+(aq) \rightarrow Sn^{2+}(aq) + 2\,Ag(s)$

2B **(E)** Anode, oxidation: $\quad \{In(s) \rightarrow In^{3+}(aq) + 3\,e^-\} \times 2$

Cathode, reduction: $\quad \{Cd^{2+}(aq) + 2\,e^- \rightarrow Cd(s)\} \times 3$

Overall reaction in cell: $2\,In(s) + 3\,Cd^{2+}(aq) \rightarrow 2\,In^{3+}(aq) + 3\,Cd(s)$

3A **(M)** We obtain the two balanced half-equations and the half-cell potentials from Table 19.1.

Oxidation: $\{Fe^{2+}(aq) \rightarrow Fe^{3+}(aq) + e^-\} \times 2 \qquad -E^\circ = -0.771\,V$

Reduction: $Cl_2(g) + 2\,e^- \rightarrow 2\,Cl^-(aq) \qquad\qquad E^\circ = +1.358\,V$

Net: $2\,Fe^{2+}(aq) + Cl_2(g) \rightarrow 2\,Fe^{3+}(aq) + 2\,Cl^-(aq); \quad E^\circ_{cell} = +1.358\,V - 0.771\,V = +0.587\,V$

3B **(M)** Since we need to refer to Table 19.1, in any event, it is perhaps a bit easier to locate the two balanced half-equations in the table. There is only one half-equation involving both $Fe^{2+}(aq)$ and $Fe^{3+}(aq)$ ions. It is reversed and written as an oxidation below. The half-equation involving $MnO_4^-(aq)$ is also written below. [Actually, we need to know that in acidic solution $Mn^{2+}(aq)$ is the principal reduction product of $MnO_4^-(aq)$.]

Oxidation: $\{Fe^{2+}(aq) \rightarrow Fe^{3+}(aq) + e^-\} \times 5$ $\quad -E^\circ = -0.771V$

Reduction: $MnO_4^-(aq) + 8H^+(aq) + 5e^- \rightarrow Mn^{2+}(aq) + 4H_2O(l)$ $\quad E^\circ = +1.51V$

Net: $MnO_4^-(aq) + 5Fe^{2+}(aq) + 8H^+(aq) \rightarrow Mn^{2+}(aq) + 5Fe^{3+}(aq) + 4H_2O(l)$

$E^\circ_{cell} = +1.51V - 0.771V = +0.74V$

4A **(M)** We write down the oxidation half-equation following the method of Chapter 5, and obtain the reduction half-equation from Table 19.1, along with the reduction half-cell potential.

Oxidation: $\{H_2C_2O_4(aq) \longrightarrow 2CO_2(aq) + 2H^+(aq) + 2e^-\} \times 3$ $\quad -E^\circ\{CO_2/H_2C_2O_4\}$

Reduction: $Cr_2O_7^{2-}(aq) + 14H^+(aq) + 6e^- \rightarrow 2Cr^{3+}(aq) + 7H_2O(l)$ $\quad E^\circ = +1.33V$

Net: $Cr_2O_7^{2-}(aq) + 8H^+(aq) + 3H_2C_2O_4(aq) \rightarrow 2Cr^{3+}(aq) + 7H_2O(l) + 6CO_2(g)$

$E^\circ_{cell} = +1.81V = +1.33V - E^\circ\{CO_2/H_2C_2O_4\}; \quad E^\circ\{CO_2/H_2C_2O_4\} = 1.33V - 1.81V = -0.48V$

4B **(M)** The 2nd half-reaction must have $O_2(g)$ as reactant and $H_2O(l)$ as product.

Oxidation: $\{Cr^{2+} + (aq) \longrightarrow Cr^{3+}(aq) + e^-\} \times 4$ $\quad -E^\circ\{Cr^{3+}/Cr^{2+}\}$

Reduction: $O_2(g) + 4H^+(aq) + 4e^- \rightarrow 2H_2O(l)$ $\quad E^\circ = +1.229V$

Net: $O_2(g) + 4H^+(aq) + 4Cr^{2+}(aq) \rightarrow 2H_2O(l) + 4Cr^{3+}(aq)$

$E^\circ_{cell} = +1.653V = +1.229V - E^\circ\{Cr^{3+}/Cr^{2+}\}; \quad E^\circ\{Cr^{3+}/Cr^{2+}\} = 1.229V - 1.653V = -0.424V$

5A **(M)** First we write down the two half-equations, obtain the half-cell potential for each, and then calculate E°_{cell}. From that value, we determine $\Delta_r G^\circ$

Oxidation: $\{Al(s) \rightarrow Al^{3+}(aq) + 3e^-\} \times 2$ $\quad -E^\circ = +1.676V$

Reduction: $\{Br_2(l) + 2e^- \rightarrow 2Br^-(aq)\} \times 3$ $\quad E^\circ = +1.065V$

Net: $2Al(s) + 3Br_2(l) \rightarrow 2Al^{3+}(aq) + 6Br^-(aq)$ $\quad E^\circ_{cell} = 1.676V + 1.065V = 2.741V$

$\Delta_r G^\circ = -zFE^\circ_{cell} = -6 \text{ mol } e^- \times \dfrac{96,485 \text{ C}}{1 \text{ mol } e^-} \times 2.741 \text{ V} = -1.587 \times 10^6 \text{ J} = -1587 \text{ kJ}$

5B **(M)** First we write down the two half-equations, one of which is the reduction equation from the previous example. The other is the oxidation that occurs in the standard hydrogen electrode.

Oxidation: $2H_2(g) \rightarrow 4H^+(aq) + 4e^-$

Reduction: $O_2(g) + 4H^+(aq) + 4e^- \rightarrow 2H_2O(l)$

Net: $\quad 2H_2(g) + O_2(g) \rightarrow 2H_2O(l)$ $\quad z = 4$ in this reaction.

This net reaction is simply twice the formation reaction for $H_2O(l)$ and, therefore,

$$\Delta_r G^\circ = 2\Delta_f G^\circ \left[H_2O(l) \right] = 2 \times \left(-237.1 \text{ kJ mol}^{-1} \right) = -474.2 \times 10^3 \text{ J mol}^{-1} = -zFE^\circ_{\text{cell}}$$

$$E^\circ_{\text{cell}} = \frac{-\Delta_r G^\circ}{zF} = \frac{-\left(-474.2 \times 10^3 \text{ J mol}^{-1} \right)}{4 \times \dfrac{96{,}485 \text{ C}}{\text{mol}}} = +1.229 \text{ V} = E^\circ, \text{ as we might expect.}$$

6A **(M)** Cu(s) will displace metal ions of a metal less active than copper. Silver ion is one example.

Oxidation: $Cu(s) \rightarrow Cu^{2+}(aq) + 2e^-$ $-E^\circ = -0.340 \text{V}$ (from Table 19.1)

Reduction: $\{Ag^+(aq) + e^- \rightarrow Ag(s)\} \times 2$ $E^\circ = +0.800 \text{V}$

Net: $2 Ag^+(aq) + Cu(s) \rightarrow Cu^{2+}(aq) + 2 Ag(s)$ $E^\circ_{\text{cell}} = -0.340 \text{ V} + 0.800 \text{ V} = +0.460 \text{ V}$

6B **(M)** We determine the value for the hypothetical reaction's cell potential.

Oxidation: $\{Na(s) \rightarrow Na^+(aq) + e^-\} \times 2$ $-E^\circ = +2.713 \text{ V}$

Reduction: $Mg^{2+}(aq) + 2 e^- \rightarrow Mg(s)$ $E^\circ = -2.356 \text{ V}$

Net: $2 Na(s) + Mg^{2+}(aq) \rightarrow 2 Na^+(aq) + Mg(s)$ $E^\circ_{\text{cell}} = 2.713 \text{ V} - 2.356 \text{ V} = +0.357 \text{ V}$

The method is not feasible because another reaction occurs that has a more positive cell potential, i.e., Na(s) reacts with water to form $H_2(g)$ and NaOH(aq):

Oxidation: $\{Na(s) \rightarrow Na^+(aq) + e^-\} \times 2$ $-E^\circ = +2.713 \text{ V}$

Reduction: $2 H_2O + 2 e^- \rightarrow H_2(g) + 2 OH^-(aq)$ $E^\circ = -0.828 \text{ V}$

$E^\circ_{\text{cell}} = 2.713 \text{ V} - 0.828 \text{ V} = +1.885 \text{ V}.$

7A **(M)** The oxidation is that of SO_4^{2-} to $S_2O_8^{2-}$, the reduction is that of O_2 to H_2O.

Oxidation: $\{2 SO_4^{2-}(aq) \rightarrow S_2O_8^{2-}(aq) + 2 e^-\} \times 2$ $-E^\circ = -2.01 \text{ V}$

Reduction: $O_2(g) + 4 H^+(aq) + 4 e^- \rightarrow 2 H_2O(l)$ $E^\circ = +1.229 \text{ V}$

Net: $O_2(g) + 4 H^+(aq) + 2 SO_4^{2-}(aq) \rightarrow S_2O_8^{2-}(aq) + 2 H_2O(l)$ $E^\circ_{\text{cell}} = -0.78 \text{ V}$

Because the standard cell potential is negative, we conclude that this cell reaction is nonspontaneous under standard conditions. This would not be a feasible method of producing peroxodisulfate ion.

7B **(M)**

(1) The oxidation is that of $Sn^{2+}(aq)$ to $Sn^{4+}(aq)$; the reduction is that of O_2 to H_2O.

Oxidation: $\{Sn^{2+}(aq) \rightarrow Sn^{4+}(aq) + 2 e^-\} \times 2$ $-E^\circ = -0.154 \text{ V}$

Reduction: $O_2(g) + 4 H^+(aq) + 4 e^- \rightarrow 2 H_2O(l)$ $E^\circ = +1.229 \text{ V}$

Net: $O_2(g) + 4 H^+(aq) + 2 Sn^{2+}(aq) \rightarrow 2 Sn^{4+}(aq) + 2 H_2O(l)$ $E^\circ_{\text{cell}} = +1.075 \text{ V}$

Since the standard cell potential is positive, this cell reaction is spontaneous under standard conditions.

(2) The oxidation is that of Sn(s) to $Sn^{2+}(aq)$; the reduction is still that of O_2 to H_2O.

Oxidation: $\{Sn(s) \rightarrow Sn^{2+}(aq) + 2\,e^-\} \times 2$ $\qquad -E^\circ = +0.137\ V$

Reduction: $O_2(g) + 4\,H^+(aq) + 4\,e^- \rightarrow 2\,H_2O(l)$ $\quad E^\circ = +1.229\ V$

Net: $\qquad O_2(g) + 4\,H^+(aq) + 2\,Sn(s) \rightarrow 2\,Sn^{2+}(aq) + 2\,H_2O(l)$

$E^\circ_{cell} = 0.137\ V + 1.229\ V = +1.366\ V$

The standard cell potential for this reaction is more positive than that for situation (1). Thus, reaction (2) should occur preferentially. Also, if $Sn^{4+}(aq)$ is formed, it should react with Sn(s) to form $Sn^{2+}(aq)$.

Oxidation: $Sn(s) \rightarrow Sn^{2+}(aq) + 2\,e^-$ $\qquad -E^\circ = +0.137\ V$

Reduction: $Sn^{4+}(aq) + 2\,e^- \rightarrow Sn^{2+}(aq)$ $\quad E^\circ = +0.154\ V$

Net: $Sn^{4+}(aq) + Sn(s) \rightarrow 2\,Sn^{2+}(aq)$ $\qquad E^\circ_{cell} = +0.137\ V + 0.154\ V = +0.291\ V$

8A **(M)** For the reaction $2\,Al(s) + 3\,Cu^{2+}(aq) \rightarrow 2\,Al^{3+}(aq) + 3\,Cu(s)$ we know $z = 6$ and $E^\circ_{cell} = +2.013\ V$. We calculate the value of K_{eq}.

$E^\circ_{cell} = \dfrac{0.0257\ V}{z} \ln K; \quad \ln K = \dfrac{zE^\circ_{cell}}{0.0257\ V} = \dfrac{6 \times (+2.013\ V)}{0.0257\ V} = 470; \quad K = e^{470} = 10^{204}$

The huge size of the equilibrium constant indicates that this reaction indeed will go to essentially 100% to completion.

8B **(M)** We first determine the value of E°_{cell} from the half-cell potentials.

Oxidation: $Sn(s) \rightarrow Sn^{2+}(aq) + 2\,e^-$ $\qquad\qquad -E^\circ = +0.137\ V$

Reduction: $Pb^{2+}(aq) + 2\,e^- \rightarrow Pb(s)$ $\qquad\qquad E^\circ = -0.125\ V$

Net: $Pb^{2+}(aq) + Sn(s) \rightarrow Pb(s) + Sn^{2+}(aq)$ $\qquad E^\circ_{cell} = +0.137\ V - 0.125\ V = +0.012\ V$

$E^\circ_{cell} = \dfrac{0.0257\ V}{z} \ln K \qquad \ln K = \dfrac{zE^\circ_{cell}}{0.0257\ V} = \dfrac{2 \times (+0.012\ V)}{0.0257\ V} = 0.93 \qquad K = e^{0.93} = 2.5$

The equilibrium constant's small size $(0.001 < K < 1000)$ indicates that this reaction will not go to completion.

9A **(M)** We first need to determine the standard cell voltage and the cell reaction.

Oxidation: $\{Al(s) \rightarrow Al^{3+}(aq) + 3\,e^-\} \times 2$ $\qquad\qquad -E^\circ = +1.676\ V$

Reduction: $\{Sn^{4+}(aq) + 2\,e^- \rightarrow Sn^{2+}(aq)\} \times 3$ $\qquad\qquad E^\circ = +0.154\ V$

Net: $2\,Al(s) + 3\,Sn^{4+}(aq) \rightarrow 2\,Al^{3+}(aq) + 3\,Sn^{2+}(aq)$ $\quad E^\circ_{cell} = +1.676\ V + 0.154\ V = +1.830\ V$

Note that $z = 6$. We now set up and substitute into the Nernst equation.

$$E_{cell} = E_{cell}^o - \frac{0.0257\,V}{z}\ln\frac{\left[Al^{3+}\right]^2\left[Sn^{2+}\right]^3}{\left[Sn^{4+}\right]^3} = +1.830\,V - \frac{0.0257\,V}{6}\ln\frac{(0.36)^2(0.54)^3}{(0.086)^3}$$

$$= +1.830\,V - 0.0149\,V = +1.815\,V$$

9B **(M)** We first need to determine the standard cell voltage and the cell reaction.

Oxidation: $2\,Cl^- (1.0\,M) \rightarrow Cl_2\,(1\,bar) + 2\,e^-$ $\qquad -E^o = -1.358\,V$

Reduction: $PbO_2\,(s) + 4\,H^+\,(aq) + 2\,e^- \rightarrow Pb^{2+}\,(aq) + 2\,H_2O(l)$ $\qquad E^o = +1.455\,V$

Net: $PbO_2\,(s) + 4\,H^+\,(0.10\,M) + 2\,Cl^-\,(1.0\,M) \rightarrow Cl_2\,(1\,atm) + Pb^{2+}\,(0.050\,M) + 2\,H_2O(l)$

$E_{cell}^o = -1.358\,V + 1.455\,V = +0.097\,V$ $\qquad$ Note that $z = 2$. Substitute values into the Nernst equation.

$$E_{cell} = E_{cell}^o - \frac{0.0257\,V}{z}\ln\frac{P\{Cl_2\}\left[Pb^{2+}\right]}{\left[H^+\right]^4\left[Cl^-\right]^2} = +0.097\,V - \frac{0.0257\,V}{2}\ln\frac{(1.0)(0.050)}{(0.10)^4(1.0)^2}$$

$$= +0.097\,V - 0.080\,V = +0.017\,V$$

10A **(M)** The cell reaction is $2\,Fe^{3+}\,(0.35\,M) + Cu(s) \rightarrow 2\,Fe^{2+}\,(0.25\,M) + Cu^{2+}\,(0.15\,M)$ with $z = 2$ and $E_{cell}^o = -0.337\,V + 0.771\,V = 0.434\,V$ $\qquad$ Next, substitute this voltage and the concentrations into the Nernst equation.

$$E_{cell} = E_{cell}^o - \frac{0.0257\,V}{z}\ln\frac{\left[Fe^{2+}\right]^2\left[Cu^{2+}\right]}{\left[Fe^{3+}\right]^2} = 0.434\,V - \frac{0.0257\,V}{2}\ln\frac{(0.25)^2(0.15)}{(0.35)^2} = 0.434 + 0.033$$

$E_{cell} = +0.467\,V$ $\quad$ Thus the reaction is spontaneous under standard conditions as written.

10B **(M)** The reaction is not spontaneous under standard conditions in either direction when $E_{cell} = 0.000\,V$. We use the standard cell potential from Example 19-10.

$$E_{cell} = E_{cell}^o - \frac{0.0257\,V}{z}\ln\frac{\left[Ag^+\right]^2}{\left[Hg^{2+}\right]}; \quad 0.000\,V = -0.054\,V - \frac{0.0257\,V}{2}\ln\frac{\left[Ag^+\right]^2}{\left[Hg^{2+}\right]}$$

$$\ln\frac{\left[Ag^+\right]^2}{\left[Hg^{2+}\right]} = \frac{-0.054\,V \times 2}{0.0257\,V} = -1.82; \quad \frac{\left[Ag^+\right]^2}{\left[Hg^{2+}\right]} = 10^{-1.82} = 0.0150$$

11A **(M)** In this concentration cell $E_{cell}^o = 0.000\,V$ because the same reaction occurs at anode and cathode, only the concentrations of the ions differ. $\left[Ag^+\right] = 0.100\,M$ in the cathode compartment. The anode compartment contains a saturated solution of AgCl(aq).

$$K_{sp} = 1.8 \times 10^{-10} = \left[Ag^+\right]\left[Cl^-\right] = s^2; \quad s = \sqrt{1.8 \times 10^{-10}} = 1.3 \times 10^{-5}\ M$$

Now we apply the Nernst equation. The cell reaction is

$$Ag^+(0.100\,M) \rightarrow Ag^+\left(1.3 \times 10^{-5}\,M\right)$$

$$E_{cell} = 0.000\ V - \frac{0.0257\ V}{1} \ln \frac{1.3 \times 10^{-5}\ M}{0.100\ M} = +0.23\ V$$

11B **(D)** Because the electrodes in this cell are identical, the standard electrode potentials are numerically equal and subtracting one from the other leads to the value $E^\circ_{cell} = 0.000\,V$. However, because the ion concentrations differ, there is a potential difference between the two half cells (non-zero nonstandard voltage for the cell). $\left[Pb^{2+}\right] = 0.100\ M$ in the cathode compartment, while the anode compartment contains a saturated solution of PbI_2.

We use the Nernst equation (with $n = 2$) to determine $\left[Pb^{2+}\right]$ in the saturated solution.

$$E_{cell} = +0.0567\ V = 0.000\ V - \frac{0.0257\ V}{2} \ln \frac{x\,M}{0.100\,M}; \quad \ln \frac{x\,M}{0.100\,M} = \frac{2 \times 0.0567\ V}{-0.0257\ V} = -1.92$$

$$\frac{x\,M}{0.100\,M} = e^{-4.41} = 0.012; \quad \left[Pb^{2+}\right]_{anode} = x\ M = 0.012 \times 0.100\ M = 0.0012\ M;$$

$$\left[I^-\right] = 2 \times 0.0012\ M = 0.0024\ M$$

$$K_{sp} = \left[Pb^{2+}\right]\left[I^-\right]^2 = (0.0012)(0.0024)^2 = 6.9 \times 10^{-9}\ \text{compared with}\ 7.1 \times 10^{-9}\ \text{in Appendix D}$$

12A **(M)** From Table 19.1 we choose one oxidations and one reductions reaction so as to get the least negative cell voltage. This will be the most likely pair of ½ -reactions to occur.

Oxidation: $2I^-(aq) \rightarrow I_2(s) + 2\ e^-$ $\qquad\qquad -E^\circ = -0.535\ V$

$\qquad\qquad 2H_2O(l) \rightarrow O_2(g) + 4H^+(aq) + 4e^-$ $\qquad -E^\circ = -1.229\,V$

Reduction: $K^+(aq) + e^- \rightarrow K(s)$ $\qquad\qquad\qquad E^\circ = -2.924\ V$

$\qquad\qquad 2H_2O(l) + 2e^- \rightarrow H_2(g) + 2OH^-(aq)$ $\qquad E^\circ = -0.828\ V$

The least negative standard cell potential $(-0.535\,V - 0.828\,V = -1.363\,V)$ occurs when $I_2(s)$ is produced by oxidation at the anode, and $H_2(g)$ is produced by reduction at the cathode.

12B **(M)** We obtain from Table 19.1 all the possible oxidations and reductions and choose one of each to get the least negative cell voltage. That pair is the most likely pair of half-reactions to occur.

Oxidation: $2H_2O(l) \rightarrow O_2(g) + 4H^+(aq) + 4e^-$ $\qquad -E^\circ = -1.229\,V$

$\qquad\qquad Ag(s) \rightarrow Ag^+(aq) + e^-$ $\qquad\qquad\qquad -E^\circ = -0.800\,V$

[We cannot further oxidize $NO_3^-(aq)$ or $Ag^+(aq)$.]

Reduction: $Ag^+(aq) + e^- \rightarrow Ag(s)$ $\qquad\qquad E^\circ = +0.800 V$

$\qquad\qquad 2H_2O(l) + 2e^- \rightarrow H_2(g) + 2OH^-(aq)$ $\qquad E^\circ = -0.828 V$

Thus, we expect to form silver metal at the cathode and $Ag^+(aq)$ at the anode.

13A (M) The half-cell equation is $Cu^{2+}(aq) + 2e^- \rightarrow Cu(s)$, indicating that two moles of electrons are required for each mole of copper deposited. Current is measured in amperes, or coulombs per second. We convert the mass of copper to coulombs of electrons needed for the reduction and the time in hours to seconds.

$$\text{Current} = \frac{12.3 \text{ g Cu} \times \dfrac{1 \text{ mol Cu}}{63.6463 \text{ g Cu}} \times \dfrac{2 \text{ mol e}^-}{1 \text{ mol Cu}} \times \dfrac{96,485 \text{ C}}{1 \text{ mol e}^-}}{5.50 \text{ h} \times \dfrac{60 \text{ min}}{1 \text{ h}} \times \dfrac{60 \text{ s}}{1 \text{ min}}} = \frac{3.735 \times 10^4 \text{ C}}{1.98 \times 10^4 \text{ s}} = 1.89 \text{ amperes}$$

13B (D) We first determine the moles of $O_2(g)$ produced with the ideal gas equation.

$$\text{moles } O_2(g) = \frac{\left(738 \text{ mmHg} \times \dfrac{1.01325 \text{ atm}}{760 \text{ mmHg}}\right) \times 2.62 \text{ L}}{0.08314 \text{ L atm mol}^{-1} \text{ K}^{-1} \times (26.2 + 273.15) \text{ K}} = 0.104 \text{ mol } O_2$$

Then we determine the time needed to produce this amount of O_2.

$$\text{elapsed time} = 0.104 \text{ mol } O_2 \times \frac{4 \text{ mol e}^-}{1 \text{ mol } O_2} \times \frac{96,485 \text{ C}}{1 \text{ mol e}^-} \times \frac{1 \text{ s}}{2.13 \text{ C}} \times \frac{1 \text{ h}}{3600 \text{ s}} = 5.23 \text{ h}$$

INTEGRATIVE EXAMPLES

14A (D) In this problem we are asked to determine E° for the reduction of $CO_2(g)$ to $C_3H_8(g)$ in an acidic solution. We proceed by first determining $\Delta_r G^\circ$ for the reaction using tabulated values for $\Delta_f G^\circ$ in Appendix D. Next, E°_{cell} for the reaction can be determined using $\Delta G^\circ = -zFE^\circ_{cell}$. Given reaction can be separated into reduction and oxidation. Since we are in acidic medium, the reduction half-cell potential can be found in Table 19.1. Lastly, the oxidation half-cell potential can be calculated using $E^\circ_{cell} = E^\circ(\text{reduction half-cell}) - E^\circ(\text{oxidation half-cell})$.

Stepwise approach

First determine $\Delta_r G^\circ$ for the reaction using tabulated values for $\Delta_f G^\circ$ in Appendix D:

$\qquad\qquad$ $C_3H_8(g)$ $\quad + \quad$ $5O_2(g)$ $\quad \rightarrow \quad$ $3CO_2(g)$ $\quad + \quad$ $4H_2O(l)$

$\Delta_f G^\circ$ $\quad$ -23.3 kJ/mol $\qquad$ 0 kJ/mol $\qquad$ -394.4 kJ/mol $\quad$ -237.1 kJ/mol

$\Delta_r G^\circ = 3 \times \Delta_f G^\circ(CO_2(g)) + 4 \times \Delta_f G^\circ(H_2O(l)) - [\Delta_f G^\circ(C_3H_8(g)) + 5 \times \Delta_f G^\circ(O_2(g))]$

$\Delta_r G^\circ = [3 \times (-394.4) + 4 \times (-237.1) - (-23.3 + 5 \times 0)]$ kJ/mol

$\Delta_r G^\circ = -2108$ kJ/mol

In order to calculate $E°_{cell}$ for the reaction using $\Delta_r G° = -zFE°_{cell}$, z must be first determined. We proceed by separating the given reaction into oxidation and reduction:

Reduction: $5 \times \{O_2(g) + 4\,H^+(aq) + 4\,e^- \rightarrow 2\,H_2O(l)\}$ $E° = +1.229$ V

Oxidation: $C_3H_8(g) + 6\,H_2O(l) \rightarrow 3\,CO_2(g) + 20\,H^+ + 20\,e^-$ $E° = x$V

Overall: $C_3H_8(g) + 5\,O_2(g) \rightarrow 3\,CO_2(g) + 4\,H_2O(l)$ $E° = +1.229$ V$-x$V

Since $z = 20$, $E°_{cell}$ can now be calculated using $\Delta_r G° = -zFE°_{cell}$:

$$\Delta_r G° = -zFE°_{cell}$$

$$-2108 \times 1000 \text{ J/mol} = -20 \times \frac{96,485 \text{ C}}{1 \text{ mol}} \times E°_{cell}$$

$$E°_{cell} = \frac{-2108 \times 1000}{-20 \times 96485} \text{ V} = 1.092 \text{ V}$$

Finally, $E°$ (reduction half-cell) can be calculated using

$E°_{cell} = E°$(reduction half-cell) $- E°$(oxidation half-cell) :

1.092 V $= 1.229$ V $- E°$(oxidation half-cell) V

$E°$(oxidation half-cell) $= 1.229$ V $- 1.092$ V $= 0.137$ V

Therefore, $E°$ for the reduction of $CO_2(g)$ to $C_3H_8(g)$ in an acidic medium is 0.137 V.

14B **(D)** This is a multi component problem dealing with a flow battery in which oxidation occurs at an aluminum anode and reduction at a carbon-air cathode. Al^{3+} produced at the anode is complexed with OH^- anions from $NaOH(aq)$ to form $[Al(OH)_4]^-$.

Stepwise approach:

Part (a): The flow battery consists of aluminum anode where oxidation occurs and the formed Al^{3+} cations are complexes with OH^- anions to form $[Al(OH)_4]^-$. The plausible half-reaction for the oxidation is:

Oxidation: $Al(s) + 4\,OH^-(aq) \rightarrow [Al(OH)_4]^- + 3\,e^-$

The cathode, on the other hand consists of carbon and air. The plausible half-reaction for the reduction involves the conversion of O_2 and water to form OH^- anions (basic medium):

Reduction: $O_2(g) + 2\,H_2O(l) + 4\,e^- \rightarrow 4\,OH^-(aq)$

Combining the oxidation and reduction half-reactions we obtain overall reaction for the process:

Oxidation: $\{Al(s) + 4\,OH^-(aq) \rightarrow [Al(OH)_4]^- + 3\,e^-\} \times 4$

Reduction: $\{O_2(g) + 2\,H_2O(l) + 4\,e^- \rightarrow 4\,OH^-(aq)\} \times 3$

Overall: $4\,Al(s) + 4\,OH^-(aq) + 3\,O_2(g) + 6\,H_2O(l) \rightarrow 4[Al(OH)_4]^-(aq)$

<u>Part(b):</u> In order to find $E°$ for the reduction, use the known value for $E°_{cell}$ as well as E° for the reduction half-reaction from Table 19.1:

$E°_{cell} = E°(\text{reduction half-cell}) - E°(\text{oxidation half-cell})$

$E°_{cell} = +0.401 \text{ V} - E°(\text{oxidation half-cell}) = +2.73 \text{ V}$

$E°(\text{oxidation half-cell}) = +0.401 \text{ V} - 2.73 \text{ V} = -2.329 \text{ V}$

<u>Part (c):</u> From the given value for $E°_{cell}$ (+2.73V) first calculate $\Delta_r G°$ using $\Delta_r G° = -zFE°_{cell}$ (notice that $z = 12$ from part (a) above):

$$\Delta_r G° = -zFE°_{cell} = -12 \text{ mol e}^- \times \frac{96,485 \text{ C}}{1 \text{ mol e}^-} \times 2.73 \text{ V}$$

$\Delta_r G° = -3161 \text{ kJ/mol}$

Given the overall reaction (part (a)) and $\Delta_f G°$ for OH$^-$(aq) anions and H$_2$O(l), we can calculate the Gibbs energy of formation of the aluminate ion, $[Al(OH)_4]^-$:

Overall reaction: 4 Al(s) + 4 OH$^-$(aq) + 3 O$_2$(g) + 6 H$_2$O(l) $\rightarrow$ 4[Al(OH)$_4$]$^-$(aq)

          $\Delta_f G°$ 0 kJ/mol -157 kJ/mol   0 kJ/mol -237.2 kJ/mol x

$\Delta_r G° = \{4 \times x - [4 \times 0 + 4 \times (-157) + 3 \times 0 + 6 \times (-237.2)]\} \text{ kJ/mol} = -3161 \text{ kJ/mol}$

$4x = -3161 - 2051.2 = -5212.2 \text{ kJ/mol}$

$x = -1303 \text{ kJ/mol}$

Therefore, $\Delta_f G°([Al(OH)_4]^-) = -1303 \text{ kJ/mol}$

<u>Part (d):</u> First calculate the number of moles of electrons:

$$\text{number of mol e}^- = \text{current(C/s)} \times \text{time(s)} \times \frac{1 \text{ mol e}^-}{96,485 \text{ C}}$$

$$\text{number of mol e}^- = 4.00 \text{ h} \times \frac{60 \text{ min}}{1 \text{ h}} \times \frac{60 \text{ s}}{1 \text{ min}} \times 10.0 \frac{\text{C}}{\text{s}} \times \frac{1 \text{ mol e}^-}{96,485 \text{ C}}$$

$\text{number of mol e}^- = 1.49 \text{ mol e}^-$

Now, use the oxidation half-reaction to determine the mass of Al(s) consumed:

$$\text{mass (Al)} = 1.49 \text{ mol e}^- \times \frac{1 \text{ mol Al}}{3 \text{ mol e}^-} \times \frac{26.9815 \text{ g Al}}{1 \text{ mol Al}} = 13.4 \text{ g}$$

EXERCISES

Standard Electrode Potential

<u>**1.**</u> **(E)**

(a) If the metal dissolves in HNO_3, it has a reduction potential that is smaller than $E°\{NO_3^-(aq)/NO(g)\} = 0.956\,V$. If it also does not dissolve in HCl, it has a reduction potential that is larger than $E°\{H^+(aq)/H_2(g)\} = 0.000\,V$. If it displaces $Ag^+(aq)$ from solution, then it has a reduction potential that is smaller than $E°\{Ag^+(aq)/Ag(s)\} = 0.800\,V$. But if it does not displace $Cu^{2+}(aq)$ from solution, then its reduction potential is larger than $E°\{Cu^{2+}(aq)/Cu(s)\} = 0.340\,V$ Thus, $0.340\,V < E° < 0.800\,V$

(b) If the metal dissolves in HCl, it has a reduction potential that is smaller than $E°\{H^+(aq)/H_2(g)\} = 0.000\,V$. If it does not displace $Zn^{2+}(aq)$ from solution, its reduction potential is larger than $E°\{Zn^{2+}(aq)/Zn(s)\} = -0.763\,V$. If it also does not displace $Fe^{2+}(aq)$ from solution, its reduction potential is larger than $E°\{Fe^{2+}(aq)/Fe(s)\} = -0.440\,V$. $-0.440\,V < E° < 0.000\,V$

2. **(E)** We would place a strip of solid indium metal into each of the metal ion solutions and see if the dissolved metal plates out on the indium strip. Similarly, strips of all the other metals would be immersed in a solution of In^{3+} to see if indium metal plates out. Eventually, we will find one metal whose ions are displaced by indium and another metal that displaces indium from solution, which are adjacent to each other in Table 19.1. The standard electrode potential for the $In/In^{3+}(aq)$ pair will lie between the standard reduction potentials for these two metals. This technique will work only if indium metal does not react with water, that is, if the standard reduction potential of $In^{3+}(aq)/In(s)$ is greater than about $-1.8\,V$. The inaccuracy inherent in this technique is due to overpotentials, which can be as much as $0.200\,V$. Its imprecision is limited by the closeness of the reduction potentials for the two bracketing metals

<u>**3.**</u> **(M)** We separate the given equation into its two half-equations. One of them is the reduction of nitrate ion in acidic solution, whose standard half-cell potential we retrieve from Table 19.1 and use to solve the problem.

Oxidation: $\{Pt(s) + 4\,Cl^-(aq) \longrightarrow [PtCl_4]^{2-}(aq) + 2\,e^-\} \times 3$; $-E°\{[PtCl_4]^{2-}(aq)/Pt(s)\}$

Reduction: $\{NO_3^-(aq) + 4\,H^+(aq) + 3\,e^- \rightarrow NO(g) + 2\,H_2O(l)\} \times 2$; $E° = +0.956\,V$

Net: $3\,Pt(s) + 2\,NO_3^-(aq) + 8\,H^+(aq) + 12\,Cl^-(aq) \rightarrow 3[PtCl_4]^{2-}(aq) + 2\,NO(g) + 6\,H_2O(l)$

$E°_{cell} = 0.201\,V = +0.956\,V - E°\{[PtCl_4]^{2-}(aq)/Pt(s)\}$

$E°\{[PtCl_4]^{2-}(aq)/Pt(s)\} = 0.956\,V - 0.201\,V = +0.755\,V$

4. **(M)** In this problem, we are dealing with the electrochemical reaction involving the reduction of Fe^{3+}(aq) to Fe^{2+}(aq) ions and the oxidation of ascorbic acid (Vitamin C, $C_6H_6O_6H_2$(aq)) to dehydroascorbic acid ($C_6H_6O_6$(aq)). Given that $E°_{cell} = 0.71$ V, we are asked to find $E°$ for the reduction of dehydroascorbic acid to ascorbic acid. We proceed by separating the given equation into its two half-equations. One of them is the reduction of Fe^{3+}(aq) to Fe^{2+}(aq), whose standard half-cell potential can be obtained from Table 19.1.

Separate the given equation into two half-equations:

Oxidation: $C_6H_6O_6H_2$(aq) $\rightarrow$ $C_6H_6O_6$(aq) + 2 H^+ + 2 e^- $-E°\{C_6H_6O_6$(aq)$/C_6H_6O_6$(aq)$\}$

Reduction: $\{Fe^{3+}$(aq) + $e^- \rightarrow Fe^{2+}$(aq)$\} \times 2$ $E° = +0.771$ V

Net: $C_6H_6O_6H_2$(aq) + 2 Fe^{3+}(aq) $\rightarrow C_6H_6O_6$(aq) + 2 Fe^{2+}(aq) $E°_{cell} = 0.71$ V
$+ 2 H^+$(aq)

Use $E°_{cell} = E°$(reduction half-cell) $- E°$(oxidation half-cell) to solve for $E°$(oxidation half-cell):

$E°$ (oxidation half-cell) :

$E°_{cell} = 0.71$ V $= +0.771$ V $- E°\{C_6H_6O_6$(aq)$/C_6H_6O_6$(aq)$\}$

$E°\{C_6H_6O_6$(aq)$/C_6H_6O_6$(aq)$\} = +0.771$ V $- 0.71$ V $= 0.061$ V

5. **(M)** We divide the net cell equation into two half-equations.

Oxidation: $\{Al(s) + 4 OH^-$(aq)$ \rightarrow [Al(OH)_4]^-(aq) + 3 e^-\} \times 4$; $-E°\{[Al(OH)_4]^-$(aq)$/Al(s)\}$

Reduction: $\{O_2(g) + 2 H_2O(l) + 4e^- \rightarrow 4 OH^-(aq)\} \times 3$; $E° = +0.401$ V

Net: $4 Al(s) + 3 O_2(g) + 6 H_2O(l) + 4 OH^-(aq) \rightarrow 4[Al(OH)_4]^-$(aq) $E°_{cell} = 2.71$ V

$E°_{cell} = 2.71$ V $= +0.401$ V $- E°\{[Al(OH)_4]^-$(aq)$/Al(s)\}$

$E°\{[Al(OH)_4]^-$(aq)$/Al(s)\} = 0.401$ V $- 2.71$ V $= -2.31$ V

6. **(M)** We divide the net cell equation into two half-equations.

Oxidation: $CH_4(g) + 2 H_2O(l) \rightarrow CO_2(g) + 8 H^+(aq) + 8 e^-$ $-E°\{CO_2(g)/CH_4(g)\}$

Reduction: $\{O_2(g) + 4 H^+$(aq)$ + 4 e^- \rightarrow 2 H_2O(l)\} \times 2$ $E° = +1.229$ V

Net: $CH_4(g) + 2 O_2(g) \rightarrow CO_2(g) + 2 H_2O(l)$ $E°_{cell} = 1.06$ V

$E°_{cell} = 1.06$ V $= +1.229$ V $- E°\{CO_2(g)/CH_4(g)\}$

$E°\{CO_2(g)/CH_4(g)\} = 1.229$ V $- 1.06$ V $= +0.17$ V

7. **(M)**
   (a) We need standard reduction potentials for the given half-reactions from Table 19.1:
   Ag^+(aq) + $e^- \rightarrow Ag(s)$ $E° = +0.800$ V
   Zn^{2+}(aq) + 2 $e^- \rightarrow Zn(s)$ $E° = -0.763$ V
   Cu^{2+}(aq) + 2 $e^- \rightarrow Cu(s)$ $E° = +0.340$ V
   Al^{3+}(aq) + 3 $e^- \rightarrow Al(s)$ $E° = -1.676$ V

Therefore, the largest positive cell potential will be obtained for the reaction involving the oxidation of Al(s) to Al^{3+}(aq) and the reduction of Ag^+(aq) to Ag(s):

$$Al(s) + 3\ Ag^+(aq) \rightarrow 3\ Ag(s) + Al^{3+}(aq) \qquad E°_{cell} = +1.676\ V + 0.800\ V = 2.476\ V$$

Ag is the anode and Al is the cathode.

(b) Reverse to the above, the cell with the smallest positive cell potential will be obtained for the reaction involving the oxidation of Zn(s) to Zn^{2+}(aq) (anode) and the reduction of Cu^{+2}(aq) to Cu(s) (cathode):

$$Zn(s) + Cu^{2+}(aq) \rightarrow Cu(s) + Zn^{2+}(aq) \qquad E°_{cell} = 0.763\ V + 0.340\ V = 1.103\ V$$

8. **(M)**

(a) The largest positive cell potential will be obtained for the reaction:

$$Zn(s) + 4\ NH_3(aq) + 2\ VO^{2+}(aq) + 4\ H^+(aq) \rightarrow [Zn(NH_3)_4]^{2+}(aq) + 2\ V^{3+}(aq) + 2\ H_2O(l)$$

$$E°_{cell} = E°(\text{reduction half-cell}) - E°(\text{oxidation half-cell}) = 0.340\ V - (-1.015\ V) = 1.355\ V$$

Zn is the anode and VO^{2+} is the cathode.

(b) Reverse to the above, the cell with the smallest positive cell potential will be obtained for the reaction involving the oxidation of Ti^{2+}(aq) to Ti^{3+}(aq) (anode) and the reduction of Sn^{+2}(aq) to Sn(s) (cathode):

$$2\ Ti^{2+}(aq) + Sn^{2+}(aq) \rightarrow 2\ Ti^{3+}(aq) + Sn(aq)$$

$$E°_{cell} = E°(\text{reduction half-cell}) - E°(\text{oxidation half-cell}) = -0.14\ V - (-0.37\ V) = 0.23\ V$$

Predicting Oxidation-Reduction Reactions

9. **(E) (a)** Ni^{2+}, **(b)** Cd.

10. **(E)** The metal with a lower standard reduction potential will be the stronger reducing agent. **(a)** magnesium $(E° = -2.372\ V)$, **(b)** sodium $(E° = -2.714\ V)$.

11. **(M)**

(a) Oxidation: $Sn(s) \rightarrow Sn^{2+}(aq) + 2\,e^-$ $-E° = +0.137\ V$

Reduction: $Pb^{2+}(aq) + 2\,e^- \rightarrow Pb(s)$ $E° = -0.125\ V$

Net: $Sn(s) + Pb^{2+}(aq) \rightarrow Sn^{2+}(aq) + Pb(s)$ $E°_{cell} = +0.012\ V$ Spontaneous

(b) Oxidation: $2\ I^-(aq) \rightarrow I_2(s) + 2\,e^-$ $-E° = -0.535\ V$

Reduction: $Cu^{2+}(aq) + 2\,e^- \rightarrow Cu(s)$ $E° = +0.340\ V$

Net: $2\ I^-(aq) + Cu^{2+}(aq) \rightarrow Cu(s) + I_2(s)$ $E°_{cell} = -0.195\ V$ Nonspontaneous

(c) Oxidation: $\{2\ H_2O(l) \rightarrow O_2(g) + 4\ H^+(aq) + 4\,e^-\} \times 3$ $-E° = -1.229\ V$

Reduction: $\{NO_3^-(aq) + 4\ H^+(aq) + 3\,e^- \rightarrow NO(g) + 2\ H_2O(l)\} \times 4$ $E° = +0.956\ V$

Net: $4\ NO_3^-(aq) + 4\ H^+(aq) \rightarrow 3\ O_2(g) + 4\ NO(g) + 2\ H_2O(l)$ $E°_{cell} = -0.273\ V$

Nonspontaneous

(d) Oxidation: $Cl^-(aq) + 2\,OH^-(aq) \rightarrow OCl^-(aq) + H_2O(l) + 2\,e^-$ $-E^\circ = -0.890\text{ V}$

Reduction: $O_3(g) + H_2O(l) + 2\,e^- \rightarrow O_2(g) + 2\,OH^-(aq)$ $E^\circ = +1.246\text{ V}$

Net: $Cl^-(aq) + O_3(g) \rightarrow OCl^-(aq) + O_2(g)$ (basic solution) $E^\circ_{cell} = +0.356\text{ V}$

Spontaneous

12. **(M)** It is more difficult to oxidize $Hg(l)$ to $Hg_2^{2+}\,(-0.797\,\text{V})$ than it is to reduce H^+ to H_2 (0.000 V); $Hg(l)$ will not dissolve in 1 M HCl. The standard reduction of nitrate ion to $NO(g)$ in acidic solution is strongly spontaneous in acidic media ($+0.956\,\text{V}$). This can help overcome the reluctance of Hg to be oxidized. $Hg(l)$ will react with and dissolve in the $HNO_3(aq)$.

13. <u>**13.**</u> **(M)**

(a) Oxidation: $Mg(s) \rightarrow Mg^{2+}(aq) + 2\,e^-$ $-E^\circ = +2.356\text{ V}$

Reduction: $Pb^{2+}(aq) + 2\,e^- \rightarrow Pb(s)$ $E^\circ = -0.125\text{ V}$

Net: $Mg(s) + Pb^{2+}(aq) \rightarrow Mg^{2+}(aq) + Pb(s)$ $E^\circ_{cell} = +2.231\text{ V}$

This reaction occurs to a significant extent.

(b) Oxidation: $Sn(s) \rightarrow Sn^{2+}(aq) + 2\,e^-$ $-E^\circ = +0.137\text{ V}$

Reduction: $2\,H^+(aq) \rightarrow H_2(g)$ $E^\circ = 0.000\text{ V}$

Net: $Sn(s) + 2\,H^+(aq) \rightarrow Sn^{2+}(aq) + H_2(g)$ $E^\circ_{cell} = +0.137\text{ V}$

This reaction will occur to a significant extent.

(c) Oxidation: $Sn^{2+}(aq) \rightarrow Sn^{4+}(aq) + 2\,e^-$ $-E^\circ = -0.154\text{ V}$

Reduction: $SO_4^{2-}(aq) + 4\,H^+(aq) + 2\,e^- \rightarrow SO_2(g) + 2\,H_2O(l)$ $E^\circ = +0.17\text{ V}$

Net: $Sn^{2+}(aq) + SO_4^{2-}(aq) + 4\,H^+(aq) \rightarrow Sn^{4+}(aq) + SO_2(g) + 2\,H_2O(l)$ $E^\circ_{cell} = +0.02\text{ V}$

This reaction will occur, but not to a large extent.

(d) Oxidation: $\{H_2O_2(aq) \rightarrow O_2(g) + 2\,H^+(aq) + 2\,e^-\} \times 5$ $-E^\circ = -0.695\text{ V}$

Reduction: $\{MnO_4^-(aq) + 8\,H^+(aq) + 5\,e^- \rightarrow Mn^{2+}(aq) + 4\,H_2O(l)\} \times 2$ $E^\circ = +1.51\text{ V}$

Net: $5\,H_2O_2(aq) + 2\,MnO_4^-(aq) + 6\,H^+(aq) \rightarrow 5\,O_2(g) + 2\,Mn^{2+}(aq) + 8\,H_2O(l)$ $E^\circ_{cell} = +0.82\text{ V}$

This reaction will occur to a significant extent.

(e) Oxidation: $2\,Br^-(aq) \rightarrow Br_2(aq) + 2\,e^-$ $-E^\circ = -1.065\text{ V}$

Reduction: $I_2(s) + 2\,e^- \rightarrow 2\,I^-(aq)$ $E^\circ = +0.535\text{ V}$

Net: $2\,Br^-(aq) + I_2(s) \rightarrow Br_2(aq) + 2\,I^-(aq)$ $E^\circ_{cell} = -0.530\text{ V}$

This reaction will not occur to a significant extent.

14. **(M)** In this problem we are asked to determine whether the electrochemical reaction between $Co(s)$ and $Ni^{2+}(aq)$ to yield $Co^{2+}(aq) + Ni(s)$ will proceed to completion based on the known $E°_{cell}$ value. This question can be answered by simply determining the equilibrium constant.

First comment on the value of $E°_{cell}$:

The relatively small positive value of $E°_{cell}$ for the reaction indicates that the reaction will proceed in the forward direction, but will stop short of completion. A much larger positive value of $E°_{cell}$ would be necessary before we would conclude that the reaction goes to completion.

Calculate the equilibrium constant for the reaction using $E°_{cell} = \dfrac{0.0257}{z} \ln K_{eq}$:

$$E°_{cell} = \frac{0.0257}{z} \ln K \qquad \ln K = \frac{z \times E°_{cell}}{0.0257} = \frac{2 \times 0.02}{0.0257} = 2$$

$$K_{eq} = e^2 = 7$$

Comment on the value of K:

K is small. A value of 1000 or more is needed before we can describe the reaction as one that goes to completion.

15. **(M)** If $E°_{cell}$ is positive, the reaction will occur. For the reduction of $Cr_2O_7^{2-}$ to $Cr^{3+}(aq)$:

$$Cr_2O_7^{2-}(aq) + 14 H^+(aq) + 6 e^- \rightarrow 2 Cr^{3+}(aq) + 7 H_2O(l) \qquad E° = +1.33\,V$$

If the oxidation has $-E°$ smaller (more negative) than $-1.33\,V$, the oxidation will not occur.

(a) $\quad Sn^{2+}(aq) \rightarrow Sn^{4+}(aq) + 2 e^- \hspace{4cm} -E° = -0.154\,V$

Hence, $Sn^{2+}(aq)$ can be oxidized to $Sn^{4+}(aq)$ by $Cr_2O_7^{2-}(aq)$.

(b) $\quad I_2(s) + 6 H_2O(l) \rightarrow 2 IO_3^-(aq) + 12 H^+(aq) + 10 e^- \hspace{1.5cm} -E° = -1.20\,V$

$I_2(s)$ can be oxidized to $IO_3^-(aq)$ by $Cr_2O_7^{2-}(aq)$.

(c) $\quad Mn^{2+}(aq) + 4 H_2O(l) \rightarrow MnO_4^-(aq) + 8 H^+(aq) + 5 e^- \hspace{0.8cm} -E° = -1.51\,V$

$Mn^{2+}(aq)$ cannot be oxidized to $MnO_4^-(aq)$ by $Cr_2O_7^{2-}(aq)$.

16. **(M)** In order to reduce Eu^{3+} to Eu^{2+}, a stronger reducing agent than Eu^{2+} is required. From the list given, $Al(s)$ and $H_2C_2O_4(aq)$ are stronger reducing agents. This is determined by looking at the reduction potentials ($-1.676\,V$ for $Al^{3+}/Al(s)$ and $-0.49\,V$ for CO_2, $H^+/H_2C_2O_4(aq)$), are more negative than $-0.43\,V$). $Co(s)$, H_2O_2 and $Ag(s)$ are not strong enough reducing agents for this process. A quick look at their reduction potentials shows that they all have more positive reduction potentials than that for Eu^{3+} to Eu^{2+} ($-0.277\,V$ for $Co^{2+}/Co(s)$, $+0.695\,V$ for O_2, $H^+/H_2O_2(aq)$ and $+0.800\,V$ for $Ag^+/Ag(s)$).

17. **(M)**

(a) Oxidation: $\{Ag(s) \rightarrow Ag^+(aq) + e^-\} \times 3$ $\qquad -E° = -0.800\,\text{V}$

Reduction: $NO_3^-(aq) + 4\,H^+(aq) + 3\,e^- \rightarrow NO(g) + 2\,H_2O(l)$ $\qquad E° = +0.956\,\text{V}$

Net: $3\,Ag(s) + NO_3^-(aq) + 4\,H^+(aq) \rightarrow 3\,Ag^+(aq) + NO(g) + 2\,H_2O(l)$ $\quad E°_{cell} = +0.156\,\text{V}$

Ag(s) reacts with $HNO_3(aq)$ to form a solution of $AgNO_3(aq)$.

(b) Oxidation: $Zn(s) \rightarrow Zn^{2+}(aq) + 2\,e^-$ $\qquad -E° = +0.763\,\text{V}$

Reduction: $2\,H^+(aq) + 2\,e^- \rightarrow H_2(g)$ $\qquad E° = 0.000\,\text{V}$

Net: $Zn(s) + 2\,H^+(aq) \rightarrow Zn^{2+}(aq) + H_2(g)$ $\qquad E°_{cell} = +0.763\,\text{V}$

Zn(s) reacts with HI(aq) to form a solution of $ZnI_2(aq)$.

(c) Oxidation: $Au(s) \rightarrow Au^{3+}(aq) + 3\,e^-$ $\qquad -E° = -1.52\,\text{V}$

Reduction: $NO_3^-(aq) + 4\,H^+(aq) + 3\,e^- \rightarrow NO(g) + 2\,H_2O(l)$ $\qquad E° = +0.956\,\text{V}$

Net: $Au(s) + NO_3^-(aq) + 4\,H^+(aq) \rightarrow Au^{3+}(aq) + NO(g) + 2\,H_2O(l)$; $E°_{cell} = -0.56\,\text{V}$

Au(s) does not react with 1.00 M $HNO_3(aq)$.

18. **(M)** In each case, we determine whether $E°_{cell}$ is greater than zero; if so, the reaction will occur.

(a) Oxidation: $Fe(s) \rightarrow Fe^{2+}(aq) + 2\,e^-$ $\qquad -E° = 0.440\,\text{V}$

Reduction: $Zn^{2+}(aq) + 2\,e^- \rightarrow Zn(s)$ $\qquad E° = -0.763\,\text{V}$

Net: $Fe(s) + Zn^{2+}(aq) \rightarrow Fe^{2+}(aq) + Zn(s)$ $\qquad E°_{cell} = -0.323\,\text{V}$

The reaction is not spontaneous under standard conditions as written

(b) Oxidation: $\{2\,Cl^-(aq) \rightarrow Cl_2(g) + 2\,e^-\} \times 5$ $\qquad -E° = -1.358\,\text{V}$

Reduction: $\{MnO_4^-(aq) + 8\,H^+(aq) + 5\,e^- \rightarrow Mn^{2+}(aq) + 4\,H_2O(l)\} \times 2$; $E° = 1.51\,\text{V}$

Net: $10\,Cl^-(aq) + 2\,MnO_4^-(aq) + 16\,H^+(aq) \rightarrow 5\,Cl_2(g) + 2\,Mn^{2+}(aq) + 8\,H_2O(l)$

$E°_{cell} = +0.15\,\text{V}$. The reaction is spontaneous under standard conditions as written.

(c) Oxidation: $\{Ag(s) \rightarrow Ag^+(aq) + e^-\} \times 2$ $\qquad -E° = -0.800\,\text{V}$

Reduction: $2\,H^+(aq) + 2\,e^- \rightarrow H_2(g)$ $\qquad E° = +0.000\,\text{V}$

Net: $2\,Ag(s) + 2\,H^+(aq) \rightarrow 2\,Ag^+(aq) + H_2(g)$ $\qquad E°_{cell} = -0.800\,\text{V}$

The reaction is not spontaneous under standard conditions as written.

(d) Oxidation: $\{2\,Cl^-(aq) \rightarrow Cl_2(g) + 2\,e^-\} \times 2$ $\qquad -E° = -1.358\,\text{V}$

Reduction: $O_2(g) + 4\,H^+(aq) + 4\,e^- \rightarrow 2\,H_2O(l)$ $\qquad E° = +1.229\,\text{V}$

Net: $4\,Cl^-(aq) + 4\,H^+(aq) + O_2(g) \rightarrow 2\,Cl_2(g) + 2\,H_2O(l)$ $\qquad E°_{cell} = -0.129\,\text{V}$

The reaction is not spontaneous under standard conditions as written.

Galvanic Cells

19. **(M)**

(a) Oxidation: $\{Al(s) \rightarrow Al^{3+}(aq) + 3e^-\} \times 2$ $\qquad -E^\circ = +1.676$ V

Reduction: $\{Sn^{2+}(aq) + 2e^- \rightarrow Sn(s)\} \times 3$ $\qquad E^\circ = -0.137$ V

Net: $\quad 2\,Al(s) + 3\,Sn^{2+}(aq) \rightarrow 2\,Al^{3+}(aq) + 3\,Sn(s)$ $\quad E^\circ_{cell} = +1.539$ V

(b) Oxidation: $Fe^{2+}(aq) \rightarrow Fe^{3+}(aq) + e^-$ $\qquad -E^\circ = -0.771$ V

Reduction: $Ag^+(aq) + e^- \rightarrow Ag(s)$ $\qquad E^\circ = +0.800$ V

Net: $\quad Fe^{2+}(aq) + Ag^+(aq) \rightarrow Fe^{3+}(aq) + Ag(s)$ $\quad E^\circ_{cell} = +0.029$ V

(c) Oxidation: $\{Cr(s) \rightarrow Cr^{2+}(aq) + 2e^-\} \times 3$ $\qquad -E^\circ = +0.90$ V

Reduction: $\{Au^{3+}(aq) + 3e^- \rightarrow Au(s)\} \times 2$ $\qquad E^\circ = 1.52$ V

Net: $\quad 3\,Cr(s) + 2\,Au^{3+}(aq) \rightarrow 3\,Cr^{2+}(aq) + 2\,Au(s)$ $\quad E^\circ_{cell} = 2.42$ V

(d) Oxidation: $2\,H_2O(l) \rightarrow O_2(g) + 4\,H^+(aq) + 4\,e^-$ $\qquad -E^\circ = -1.229$ V

Reduction: $O_2(g) + 2\,H_2O(l) + 4\,e^- \rightarrow 4\,OH^-(aq)$ $\qquad E^\circ = +0.401$ V

Net: $\quad H_2O(l) \rightarrow H^+(aq) + OH^-(aq)$ $\quad E^\circ_{cell} = -0.828$ V

20. **(M)** In this problem we are asked to write the half-reactions, balanced chemical equation and determine E°_{cell} for a series of electrochemical cells.

(a) Oxidation: $Cu(s) \rightarrow Cu^{2+}(aq) + 2\,e^-$ $\qquad -E^\circ = -0.340$ V

Reduction: $\{Cu^+(aq) + e^- \rightarrow Cu(s)\} \times 2$ $\qquad E^\circ = +0.520$ V

Net: $\quad 2\,Cu^+(aq) \rightarrow Cu^{2+}(aq) + Cu(s)$ $\quad E^\circ_{cell} = +0.18$ V

Follow the same methodology for parts (b), (c), and (d).

(b) Oxidation: $Ag(s) + I^-(aq) \rightarrow AgI(s) + e^-$ $\qquad -E^\circ = +0.152$ V

Reduction: $AgCl(s) + e^- \rightarrow Ag(s) + Cl^-(aq)$ $\qquad E^\circ = +0.2223$ V

Net: $\quad AgCl(s) + I^-(aq) \rightarrow AgI(s) + Cl^-(aq)$ $\quad E^\circ_{cell} = +0.3743$ V

(c) Oxidation: $\{Ce^{3+}(aq) \rightarrow Ce^{4+}(aq) + e^-\} \times 2$ $\qquad -E^\circ = -1.76$ V

Reduction: $I_2(s) + 2\,e^- \rightarrow 2\,I^-(aq)$ $\qquad E^\circ = +0.535$ V

Net: $\quad 2\,Ce^{3+}(aq) + I_2(s) \rightarrow 2\,Ce^{4+}(aq) + 2\,I^-(aq)$ $\quad E^\circ_{cell} = -1.225$ V

(d) Oxidation: $\{U(s) \rightarrow U^{3+}(aq) + 3\,e^-\} \times 2$ $\qquad -E^\circ = +1.66$ V

Reduction: $\{V^{2+}(aq) + 2\,e^- \rightarrow V(s)\} \times 3$ $\qquad E^\circ = -1.13$ V

Net: $\quad 2\,U(s) + 3\,V^{2+}(aq) \rightarrow 2\,U^{3+}(aq) + 3\,V(s)$ $\quad E^\circ_{cell} = +0.53$ V

21. **(M)** In each case, we determine whether $E°_{cell}$ is greater than zero; if so, the reaction will occur.

(a) Oxidation: $H_2(g) \rightarrow 2H^+ + 2e^-(aq)$ $\qquad -E° = 0.000$ V

Reduction: $F_2(g) + 2e^- \rightarrow 2F^-(aq)$ $\qquad E° = 2.866$ V

Net: $H_2(g) + F_2(g) \rightarrow 2H^+(aq) + 2F^-(aq)$ $\quad E°_{cell} = +2.866$ V

The reaction is spontaneous under standard conditions as written

(b) Oxidation: $Cu(s) \rightarrow Cu^{2+}(aq) + 2e^-$ $\qquad -E° = -0.340$ V

Reduction: $Ba^{2+}(aq) + 2e^- \rightarrow Ba(s)$; $\qquad E° = -2.92$ V

Net: $Cu(s) + Ba^{2+}(aq) \rightarrow Cu^{2+}(aq) + Ba(s)$ $\quad E°_{cell} = -3.26$ V.

The reaction is not spontaneous under standard conditions as written.

(c) Oxidation: $\{Fe^{2+}(aq) \rightarrow Fe^{3+}(aq) + e^-\} \times 2$ $\qquad -E° = -0.771$ V

Reduction: $Fe^{2+}(aq) + 2e^- \rightarrow Fe(s)$ $\qquad E° = -0.440$ V

Net: $3Fe^{2+}(aq) \rightarrow Fe(s) + 2Fe^{3+}(aq)$ $\qquad E°_{cell} = -1.211$ V

The reaction is not spontaneous as written.

(d) Oxidation: $2Hg(l) + 2Cl^- \rightarrow Hg_2Cl_2(s) + 2e^-$ $\qquad -E° = -(0.2676)$ V

Reduction: $2HgCl_2(aq) + 2e^- \rightarrow Hg_2Cl_2(s) + 2Cl^-(aq)$ $\quad E° = +0.63$ V

Net: $2Hg(l) + 2HgCl_2(aq) \rightarrow 2Hg_2Cl_2(s)$ $\qquad E°_{cell} = +0.36$ V

(divide by 2 to get $Hg(l) + HgCl_2(aq) \rightarrow Hg_2Cl_2(s)$)

The reaction is spontaneous under standard conditions as written.

22. **(M) (a)**

Anode, oxidation: $Cu(s) \rightarrow Cu^{2+}(aq) + 2e^-$ $\qquad -E° = -0.340$ V

Cathode, reduction: $\{Fe^{3+}(aq) + e^- \rightarrow Fe^{2+}(aq)\} \times 2$; $\qquad E° = +0.771$ V

Net: $Cu(s) + 2Fe^{3+}(aq) \rightarrow Cu^{2+}(aq) + 2Fe^{2+}(aq)$ $\qquad E°_{cell} = +0.431$ V

(b)

Anode, oxidation: $\{Al(s) \rightarrow Al^{3+}(aq) + 3e^-\} \times 2$ $-E° = +1.676$ V

Cathode, reduction: $\{Pb^{2+}(aq) + 2e^- \rightarrow Pb(s)\} \times 3$; $E° = -0.125$ V

Net: $2\,Al(s) + 3\,Pb^{2+}(aq) \rightarrow 2\,Al^{3+}(aq) + 3\,Pb(s)$ $E°_{cell} = +1.551$ V

(c)

Anode, oxidation: $2\,H_2O(l) \rightarrow O_2(g) + 4\,H^+(aq) + 4e^-$ $-E° = -1.229$ V

Cathode, reduction: $\{Cl_2(g) + 2e^- \rightarrow 2\,Cl^-(aq)\} \times 2$ $E° = +1.358$ V

Net: $2\,H_2O(l) + 2\,Cl_2(g) \rightarrow O_2(g) + 4\,H^+(aq) + 4\,Cl^-(aq)$ $E°_{cell} = +0.129$ V

(d)

Anode, oxidation: $\{Zn(s) \rightarrow Zn^{2+}(aq) + 2\,e^-\} \times 3$ $-E° = +0.763$ V

Cathode, reduction: $\{NO_3^-(aq) + 4\,H^+(aq) + 3e^- \rightarrow NO(g) + 2\,H_2O(l)\} \times 2$; $E° = +0.956$ V

Net: $3\,Zn(s) + 2\,NO_3^-(aq) + 8\,H^+(aq) \rightarrow 3\,Zn^{2+}(aq) + 2\,NO(g) + 4\,H_2O(l)$ $E°_{cell} = +1.719$ V

23. **(M)** In each case, we determine whether E°_{cell} is greater than zero; if so, the reaction will occur.

(a) Oxidation: $Ag(s) \rightarrow Ag^+(aq) + e^-$ $-E^\circ = -0.800$ V

Reduction: $Fe^{3+}(aq) + e^- \rightarrow Fe^{2+}(aq)$ $E^\circ = +0.771$ V

Net: $Ag(s) + Fe^{3+}(aq) \rightarrow Ag^+(aq) + Fe^{2+}(aq)$ $E^\circ_{cell} = -0.029$ V

The reaction is not spontaneous under standard conditions as written.

(b) Oxidation: $Sn(s) \rightarrow Sn^{2+}(aq) + 2\,e^-$ $-E^\circ = +0.137$ V

Reduction: $Sn^{4+}(aq) + 2\,e^- \rightarrow Sn^{+2}(aq)$ $E^\circ = +0.154$ V

Net: $Sn(s) + Sn^{4+}(aq) \rightarrow 2\,Sn^{2+}(aq)$ $E^\circ_{cell} = +0.291$ V

The reaction is spontaneous under standard conditions as written.

(c) Oxidation: $2\,Br^-(aq) \rightarrow Br_2(l) + 2\,e^-$ $-E^\circ = -1.065$ V

Reduction: $2\,Hg^{2+}(aq) + 2\,e^- \rightarrow Hg_2^+(aq)$ $E^\circ = +0.630$ V

Net: $2\,Br^-(aq) + 2\,Hg^{2+}(aq) \rightarrow Br_2(l) + Hg_2^+$ $E^\circ_{cell} = -0.435$ V

The reaction is not spontaneous under standard conditions as written.

(d) Oxidation: $\{NO_3^-(aq) + 2\,H^+(aq) + e^- \rightarrow NO_2(g) + H_2O(l)\} \times 2$ $-E^\circ = -2.326$ V

Reduction: $Zn(s) \rightarrow Zn^{2+}(aq) + 2e^-$ $E^\circ = +1.563$ V

Net: $2\,NO_3^-(aq) + 4\,H^+(aq) + Zn(s) \rightarrow 2\,NO_2(g) + 2\,H_2O(l) + Zn^{2+}(aq)$ $E^\circ_{cell} = -0.435$ V

The reaction is not spontaneous under standard conditions as written.

24. **(M)**

(a) $Fe(s)|Fe^{2+}(aq)\| Cl^-(aq)Cl_2(g)|Pt(s)$

Oxidation: $Fe(s) \rightarrow Fe^{2+}(aq) + 2e^-$ $-E^\circ = +0.440$ V

Reduction: $Cl_2(g) + 2e^- \rightarrow 2Cl^-(aq)$ $E^\circ = +1.358$ V

Net: $Fe(s) + Cl_2(g) \rightarrow Fe^{2+}(aq) + 2Cl^-(aq)$ $E^\circ_{cell} = +1.798$ V

(b) $Zn(s)|Zn^{2+}(aq)\| Ag^+(aq)|Ag(s)$

Oxidation: $Zn(s) \rightarrow Zn^{2+}(aq) + 2e^-$ $-E^\circ = +0.763$ V

Reduction: $\{Ag^+(aq) + e^- \rightarrow Ag(s)\} \times 2$ $E^\circ = +0.800$ V

Net: $Zn(s) + 2Ag^+(aq) \rightarrow Zn^{2+}(aq) + 2Ag(s)$ $E^\circ_{cell} = +1.563$ V

(c) $Pt(s)|Cu^+(aq), Cu^{2+}(aq)\| Cu^+(aq)|Cu(s)$

Oxidation: $Cu^+(aq) \rightarrow Cu^{2+}(aq) + e^-$ $-E^\circ = -0.159$ V

Reduction: $Cu^+(aq) + e^- \rightarrow Cu(s)$ $E^\circ = +0.520$ V

Net: $2Cu^+(aq) \rightarrow Cu^{2+}(aq) + Cu(s)$ $E^\circ_{cell} = +0.361$ V

(d) $Mg(s)|Mg^{2+}(aq)||Br^-(aq)Br_2(l)|Pt(s)$

Oxidation: $Mg(s) \rightarrow Mg^{2+}(aq) + 2e^-$ $\qquad -E^\circ = +2.356\ V$

Reduction: $Br_2(l) + 2e^- \rightarrow 2Br^-(aq)$ $\qquad E^\circ = +1.065\ V$

Net: $Mg(s) + Br_2(l) \rightarrow Mg^{2+}(aq) + 2Br^-(aq)$ $\qquad E^\circ_{cell} = +3.421\ V$

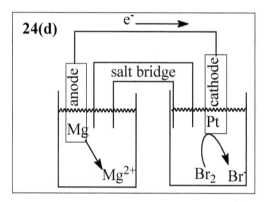

$\Delta_r G^\circ$, E°_{cell}, and K

25. **(M)**

(a) Oxidation: $\{Al(s) \rightarrow Al^{3+}(aq) + 3e^-\} \times 2$ $\qquad -E^\circ = +1.676\ V$

Reduction: $\{Cu^{2+}(aq) + 2e^- \rightarrow Cu(s)\} \times 3$ $\qquad E^\circ = +0.337\ V$

Net: $2Al(s) + 3Cu^{2+}(aq) \rightarrow 2Al^{3+}(aq) + 3Cu(s)$ $\qquad E^\circ_{cell} = +2.013\ V$

$\Delta_r G^\circ = -zFE^\circ_{cell} = -(6)(96,485\ C/mol)(2.013\ V)$

$\Delta_r G^\circ = -1.165 \times 10^6\ J\ mol^{-1} = -1.165 \times 10^3\ kJ\ mol^{-1}$

(b) Oxidation: $\{2I^-(aq) \rightarrow I_2(s) + 2e^-\} \times 2$ $\qquad -E^\circ = -0.535\ V$

Reduction: $O_2(g) + 4H^+(aq) + 4e^- \rightarrow 2H_2O(l)$ $\qquad E^\circ = +1.229\ V$

Net: $4I^-(aq) + O_2(g) + 4H^+(aq) \rightarrow 2I_2(s) + 2H_2O(l)$ $\qquad E^\circ_{cell} = +0.694\ V$

$\Delta_r G^\circ = -zFE^\circ_{cell} = -(4)(96,485\ C/mol)(0.694\ V) = -2.68 \times 10^5\ J\ mol^{-1} = -268\ kJ\ mol^{-1}$

(c) Oxidation: $\{Ag(s) \rightarrow Ag^+(aq) + e^-\} \times 6$ $\hspace{2cm}$ $-E° = -0.800\ V$

Reduction: $Cr_2O_7^{2-}(aq) + 14\ H^+(aq) + 6\ e^- \rightarrow 2\ Cr^{3+}(aq) + 7\ H_2O(l)$ $\hspace{0.5cm}$ $E° = +1.33\ V$

Net: $6\ Ag(s) + Cr_2O_7^{2-}(aq) + 14 H^+(aq) \rightarrow 6 Ag^+(aq) + 2 Cr^{3+}(aq) + 7 H_2O(l)$

$E°_{cell} = -0.800\ V + 1.33\ V = +0.53\ V$

$\Delta_r G° = -zFE°_{cell} = -(6)(96,485\ C/mol)(0.53\ V) = -3.1 \times 10^5\ J\ mol^{-1} = -3.1 \times 10^2\ kJ\ mol^{-1}$

26. **(M)** In this problem we need to write the equilibrium constant expression for a set of redox reactions and determine the value of K at 25 °C. We proceed by calculating $E°_{cell}$ from standard electrode reduction potentials (Table 19.1). Then we use the expression $\Delta_r G° = -zFE°_{cell} = -RT \ln K$ to calculate K.

Determine $E°_{cell}$ from standard electrode reduction potentials (Table 19.1):

Oxidation: $Ni(s) \rightarrow Ni^{2+}(aq) + 2\ e^-$ $\hspace{2cm}$ $-E° = 0.257\ V$

Reduction: $\{V^{3+}(aq) + e^- \rightarrow V^{2+}(aq)\} \times 2$ $\hspace{1.5cm}$ $E° = -0.255\ V$

Net: $Ni(s) + 2\ V^{3+}(aq) \rightarrow Ni^{2+}(aq) + 2\ V^{2+}(aq)$ $\hspace{1cm}$ $E°_{cell} = 0.003\ V$

$\Delta_r G° = -zFE°_{cell} = -RT \ln K \Rightarrow \ln K = \dfrac{zFE°_{cell}}{RT} = \dfrac{z \times 96,485\ C\ mol^{-1}}{8.314\ JK^{-1}mol^{-1} \times 298.15\ K} E°_{cell}$

$\ln K = \dfrac{z}{0.0257\ V} E°_{cell} = \dfrac{2 \times 0.003\ V}{0.0257\ V} = 0.233$

$K = e^{0.233} = 1.26 = \dfrac{[Ni^{2+}][V^{2+}]^2}{[V^{3+}]^2}$

Similar methodology can be used for parts (b) and (c)

(b) Oxidation: $2\ Cl^-(aq) \rightarrow Cl_2(g) + 2\ e^-$ $\hspace{2cm}$ $-E° = -1.358\ V$

Reduction: $MnO_2(s) + 4\ H^+(aq) + 2\ e^- \rightarrow Mn^{2+}(aq) + 2\ H_2O(l)$ $\hspace{0.3cm}$ $E° = +1.23\ V$

Net: $2\ Cl^-(aq) + MnO_2(s) + 4\ H^+(aq) \rightarrow Mn^{2+}(aq) + Cl_2(g) + 2\ H_2O(l)$ $\hspace{0.3cm}$ $E°_{cell} = -0.13\ V$

$\ln K = \dfrac{2 \times (-0.13\ V)}{0.0257\ V} = -10.1;\ \ K = e^{-10.1} = 4 \times 10^{-5} = \dfrac{[Mn^{2+}]P\{Cl_2(g)\}}{[Cl^-]^2[H^+]^4}$

(c) Oxidation: $4\ OH^-(aq) \rightarrow O_2(g) + 2\ H_2O(l) + 4\ e^-$ $\hspace{1.5cm}$ $-E° = -0.401\ V$

Reduction: $\{OCl^-(aq) + H_2O(l) + 2\ e^- \rightarrow Cl^-(aq) + 2\ OH^-\} \times 2$ $\hspace{0.3cm}$ $E° = +0.890\ V$

Net: $2\ OCl^-(aq) \longrightarrow 2\ Cl^-(aq) + O_2(g)$ $\hspace{2cm}$ $E°_{cell} = +0.489\ V$

$\ln K = \dfrac{4(0.489\ V)}{0.0257\ V} = 76.1$ $\hspace{1cm}$ $K = e^{76.1} = 1 \times 10^{33} = \dfrac{[Cl^-]^2\ P\{O_2(g)\}}{[OCl^-]^2}$

27. **(M)** First calculate $E°_{cell}$ from standard electrode reduction potentials (Table 19.1). Then use $\Delta_r G° = -zFE°_{cell} = -RT \ln K$ to determine $\Delta_r G°$ and K.

(a)

Oxidation: $\{Ce^{3+}(aq) \rightarrow Ce^{4+}(aq) + e^-\} \times 5$	$-E° = -1.61$ V
Reduction: $MnO_4^-(aq) + 8H^+(aq) + 5e^- \rightarrow Mn^{2+}(aq) + 4H_2O(l)$	$E° = +1.51$ V

Net: $MnO_4^-(aq) + 8H^+(aq) + 5Ce^{3+}(aq) \rightarrow Mn^{2+}(aq) + 4H_2O(l) + 5Ce^{4+}(aq)$ $E°_{cell} = -0.100$ V

(b) $\Delta_r G° = -zFE°_{cell} = -RT \ln K;$

$$\Delta_r G° = -5 \times 96,485 \frac{C}{mol} \times (-0.100 \text{ V}) = 48.24 \text{ kJ mol}^{-1}$$

(c) $\Delta_r G° = -RT \ln K \Rightarrow 48.24 \times 1000 \text{ J mol}^{-1} = -8.314 \text{ J K}^{-1}\text{mol}^{-1} \times 298.15 \text{ K} \ln K$

$\ln K = -19.46 \Rightarrow K = e^{-19.46} = 3.5 \times 10^{-9}$

(d) Since K is very small the reaction will not go to completion.

28. **(M)** First calculate $E°_{cell}$ from standard electrode reduction potentials (Table 19.1). Then use $\Delta_r G° = -zFE°_{cell} = -RT \ln K$ to determine $\Delta_r G°$ and K.

(a)

Oxidation: $Cr^{2+}(aq) \rightarrow Cr^{3+}(aq) + e^-$	$-E° = 0.424$ V
Reduction: $V^{3+}(aq) + e^- \rightarrow V^{2+}(aq)$	$E° = -0.255$ V

Net: $Cr^{2+}(aq) + V^{3+}(aq) \rightarrow Cr^{3+}(aq) + V^{2+}(aq)$ $E°_{cell} = +0.169$ V

(b) $\Delta_r G° = -zFE°_{cell} = -RT \ln K \Rightarrow \Delta_r G° = -1 \times 96485 \frac{C}{mol} \times (0.169 \text{ V}) = -16306 \text{ J mol}^{-1}$

(c) $\Delta_r G° = -RT \ln K \Rightarrow -16306 \text{ J mol}^{-1} = -8.314 \text{ J K}^{-1} \text{ mol}^{-1} \times 298.15 \text{ K} \ln K$

$\ln K = 6.58 \Rightarrow K = e^{6.58} = 721$

(d) The value of K is relatively large and the reaction will be shifted toward the products.

29. **(M)**

(a) A negative value of $E°_{cell}$ (-0.0050 V) indicates that $\Delta_r G° = -zFE°_{cell}$ is positive which in turn indicates that K is less than one $(K < 1.00)$; $\Delta_r G° = -RT \ln K$.

$$K = \frac{\left[Cu^{2+}\right]^2 \left[Sn^{2+}\right]}{\left[Cu^+\right]^2 \left[Sn^{4+}\right]}$$

Thus, when all concentrations are the same, the ion product, Q, equals 1.00. From the negative standard cell potential, it is clear that K must be (slightly) less than one. Therefore, all the concentrations cannot be 0.500 M at the same time.

(b) In order to establish equilibrium, that is, to have the ion product become less than 1.00, and equal the equilibrium constant, the concentrations of the products must decrease and those of the reactants must increase. A net reaction to the left (towards the reactants) will occur.

30. **(D)**

(a) First we must calculate the value of the equilibrium constant from the standard cell potential.

$$E^{\circ}_{\text{cell}} = \frac{0.0257}{n}\ln K; \quad \ln K = \frac{zE^{\circ}_{\text{cell}}}{0.0257\text{ V}} = \frac{2\times(-0.017)\text{ V}}{0.0257\text{ V}} = -1.32$$

$$K = e^{-1.32} = 0.266$$

To determine if the described solution is possible, we compare

K with Q. Now $K = \dfrac{\left[\text{BrO}_3^-\right]\left[\text{Ce}^{4+}\right]^2}{\left[\text{H}^+\right]^2\left[\text{BrO}_4^-\right]\left[\text{Ce}^{3+}\right]^2}$. Thus, when

$$\left[\text{BrO}_4^-\right]=\left[\text{Ce}^{4+}\right]=0.675\text{ M}, \quad \left[\text{BrO}_3^-\right]=\left[\text{Ce}^{3+}\right]=0.600\text{ M} \text{ and pH}=1\ \left(\left[\text{H}^+\right]=0.1\text{M}\right)$$

the ion product, $Q = \dfrac{0.600\times0.675^2}{0.1^2\times0.675\times0.600^2} = 112.5 > 0.266 = K$. Therefore, the

described situation can occur

(b) In order to establish equilibrium, that is, to have the ion product (112.5) become equal to 0.266, the equilibrium constant, the concentrations of the reactants must increase and those of the products must decrease. Thus, a net reaction to the left (formation of reactants) will occur.

31. **(M)** Cell reaction: $\text{Zn}(s)+\text{Ag}_2\text{O}(s)\rightarrow\text{ZnO}(s)+2\text{Ag}(s)$. We assume that the cell operates at 298 K.

$$\Delta_r G^{\circ} = \Delta_f G^{\circ}\left[\text{ZnO}(s)\right]+2\,\Delta_f G^{\circ}\left[\text{Ag}(s)\right]-\Delta_f G^{\circ}\left[\text{Zn}(s)\right]-\Delta_f G^{\circ}\left[\text{Ag}_2\text{O}(s)\right]$$

$$= -318.3\text{ kJ/mol}+2\left(0.00\text{ kJ/mol}\right)-0.00\text{ kJ/mol}-\left(-11.20\text{ kJ/mol}\right)$$

$$= -307.1\text{ kJ/mol} = -zFE^{\circ}_{\text{cell}}$$

$$E^{\circ}_{\text{cell}} = -\frac{\Delta_r G^{\circ}}{zF} = -\frac{-307.1\times10^3\text{ J/mol}}{2\times96,485\text{ C/mol}} = 1.591\text{ V}$$

32. **(M)** From equation (19.15) we know $z=12$ and the overall cell reaction. First we must compute value of $\Delta_r G^{\circ}$.

$$\Delta_r G^{\circ} = -z\,FE^{\circ}_{\text{cell}} = -12\times\frac{96,485\text{ C}}{1\text{ mol}}\times2.71\text{ V} = -3.14\times10^6\text{ J mol}^{-1} = -3.14\times10^3\text{ kJ mol}^{-1}$$

Then we will use this value, the balanced equation and values of $\Delta_f G^{\circ}$ to calculate

$\Delta_f G^{\circ}\left[\text{Al}(\text{OH})_4^-\right]$.

$$4\text{ Al}(s)+3\text{ O}_2(g)+6\text{ H}_2\text{O}(l)+4\text{ OH}^-(aq)\rightarrow4\left[\text{Al}(\text{OH})_4\right]^-(aq)$$

$$\Delta_r G^{\circ} = 4\,\Delta_f G^{\circ}\left[\text{Al}(\text{OH})_4\right]^- -4\,\Delta_f G^{\circ}[\text{Al}(s)]-3\,\Delta_f G^{\circ}[\text{O}_2(g)]-6\,\Delta_f G^{\circ}[\text{H}_2\text{O}(l)]-4\,\Delta_f G^{\circ}[\text{OH}^-(aq)]$$

$$-3.14\times10^3\text{ kJ/mol} = 4\,\Delta_f G^{\circ}\left[\text{Al}(\text{OH})_4\right]^- -4\times0.00\text{ kJ/mol}-3\times0.00\text{ kJ/mol}-6\times(-237.1\text{ kJ/mol})$$

$$-4\times(-157.2\text{ kJ/mol})$$

$$= 4\Delta_f G^{\circ}\left[\text{Al}(\text{OH})_4\right]^- +2051.4\text{ kJ/mol}$$

$$\Delta_f G^{\circ}\left[\text{Al}(\text{OH})_4\right]^- = \left(-3.14\times10^3\text{ kJ/mol}-2051.4\text{ kJ/mol}\right)\div4 = -1.30\times10^3\text{ kJ/mol}$$

33. **(D)** From the data provided we can construct the following Latimer diagram.

$$IrO_2 \xrightarrow{\ 0.223\ V\ } Ir^{3+} \xrightarrow{\ 1.156\ V\ } Ir \quad \text{(Acidic conditions)}$$
$$\text{(IV)} \qquad\qquad \text{(III)} \qquad\qquad \text{(0)}$$

Latimer diagrams are used to calculate the standard potentials of non-adjacent half-cell couples. Our objective in this question is to calculate the voltage differential between IrO_2 and iridium metal (Ir), which are separated in the diagram by Ir^{3+}. The process basically involves adding two half-reactions to obtain a third half-reaction. The potentials for the two half-reactions cannot, however, simply be added to get the target half-cell voltage because the electrons are not cancelled in the process of adding the two half-reactions. Instead, to find $E°_{1/2\ cell}$ for the target half-reaction, we must use free energy changes, which are additive. To begin, we will balance the relevant half-reactions in acidic solution:

$$4\ H^+(aq) + IrO_2(s) + e^- \rightarrow Ir^{3+}(aq) + 2\ H_2O(l) \qquad E°_{1/2red(a)} = 0.223\ V$$
$$Ir^{3+}(aq) + 3\ e^- \rightarrow Ir(s) \qquad E°_{1/2red(b)} = 1.156V$$

$$\overline{4\ H^+(aq) + IrO_2(s) + 4\ e^- \rightarrow 2\ H_2O(l) + Ir(s) \qquad E°_{1/2red(c)} = ?}$$

$E°_{1/2red(c)} \neq E°_{1/2red(a)} + E°_{1/2red(b)}$ but $\Delta_r G°_{(a)} + \Delta_r G°_{(b)} = \Delta_r G°_{(c)}$ and $\Delta_r G° = -zFE°$

$$-4F(E°_{1/2red(c)}) = -1F(E°_{1/2red(a)}) + -3F(E°_{1/2red(b)})$$
$$-4F(E°_{1/2red(c)}) = -1F(0.223) + -3F(1.156)$$

$$E°_{1/2red(c)} = \frac{-1F(0.223) + -3F(1.156)}{-4F} = \frac{-1(0.223) + -3(1.156)}{-4} = 0.923\ V$$

In other words, $E°_{(c)}$ is the weighted average of $E°_{(a)}$ and $E°_{(b)}$

34. **(D)** This question will be answered in a manner similar to that used to solve 31. Let's get underway by writing down the appropriate Latimer diagram:

$$H_2MoO_4 \xrightarrow{\ 0.646\ V\ } MoO_2 \xrightarrow{\ ?\ V\ } Mo^{3+} \quad \text{(Acidic conditions)}$$
$$\text{(VI)} \qquad\qquad \text{(IV)} \qquad\qquad \text{(III)}$$
$$\underset{0.428\ V}{\longmapsto\hspace{3cm}\longrightarrow}$$

This time we want to calculate the standard voltage change for the 1 e^- reduction of MoO_2 to Mo^{3+}. Once again, we must balance the half-cell reactions in acidic solution:

$$H_2MoO_4(aq) + 2\ e^- + 2\ H^+(aq) \rightarrow MoO_2(s) + 2\ H_2O(l) \qquad E°_{1/2red(a)} = 0.646\ V$$
$$MoO_2(s) + 4\ H^+(aq) + 1\ e^- \rightarrow Mo^{3+}(aq) + 2\ H_2O(l) \qquad E°_{1/2red(b)} = ?\ V$$

$$\overline{H_2MoO_4(aq) + 3\ e^- + 6\ H^+(aq) \rightarrow Mo^{3+}(aq) + 4\ H_2O(l) \qquad E°_{1/2red(c)} = 0.428\ V}$$

So, $-3F(E°_{1/2red(c)}) = -2F(E°_{1/2red(a)}) + -1F(E°_{1/2red(b)})$

$$-3F(0.428\ V) = -2F(0.646) + -1F(E°_{1/2red(b)})$$
$$-1FE°_{1/2red(b)} = -3F(0.428\ V) + 2F(0.646)$$

$$E°_{1/2red(c)} = \frac{-3F(0.428\ V) + 2F(0.646)}{-1F} = 1.284\ V - 1.292\ V = -0.008\ V$$

Concentration Dependence of E_{cell}—the Nernst Equation

35. **(M)** In this problem we are asked to determine the concentration of $[Ag^+]$ ions in electrochemical cell that is under nonstandard conditions. We proceed by first determining $E°_{cell}$. Using the Nerst equation and the known value of E, we can then calculate the concentration of $[Ag^+]$.

Oxidation: $Zn(s) \rightarrow Zn^{2+}(aq) + 2e^-$ $\qquad\qquad -E° = +0.763$ V

Reduction: $\{Ag^+(aq) + e^- \rightarrow Ag(s)\} \times 2$ $\qquad\qquad E° = +0.800$ V

Net: $Zn(s) + 2 Ag^+(aq) \rightarrow Zn^{2+}(aq) + 2 Ag(s)$ $\qquad E°_{cell} = +1.563$ V

Use the Nerst equation and the known value of E to solve for $[Ag]^+$:

$$E = E°_{cell} - \frac{0.0257 \text{ V}}{z} \ln \frac{[Zn^{2+}]}{[Ag^+]^2} = +1.563 \text{ V} - \frac{0.0257 \text{ V}}{2} \ln \frac{1.00}{x^2} = +1.250 \text{ V}$$

$$\ln \frac{1.00}{x^2} = \frac{-2 \times (1.250 - 1.563) \text{ V}}{0.0257 \text{ V}} = 10.6; \quad x = \sqrt{2.5 \times 10^{-11}} = 5 \times 10^{-6}$$

Therefore, $[Ag^+] = 5 \times 10^{-6}$ M

36. **(M)** In each case, we employ the equation $E_{cell} = 0.0592 \text{ V} \times pH$.

(a) $E_{cell} = 0.0592 \text{ V} \times pH = 0.0592 \text{ V} \times 5.25 = 0.311$ V

(b) $pH = -\ln(0.0103) = 1.987$ $\qquad E_{cell} = 0.0592 \text{ V} \times pH = 0.0592 \text{ V} \times 1.987 = 0.118$ V

(c) $K_a = \dfrac{[H^+][C_2H_3O_2^-]}{[HC_2H_3O_2]} = 1.8 \times 10^{-5} = \dfrac{x^2}{0.158 - x} \approx \dfrac{x^2}{0.158}$

$x = \sqrt{0.158 \times 1.8 \times 10^{-5}} = 1.7 \times 10^{-3}$ and $[H^+] = 1.7 \times 10^{-3}$ M

$pH = -\log(1.7 \times 10^{-3}) = 2.77$

$E_{cell} = 0.0592 \text{ V} \times pH = 0.0592 \text{ V} \times 2.77 = 0.164$ V

37. **(M)** We first calculate $E°_{cell}$ for each reaction and then use the Nernst equation to calculate E_{cell}.

(a) Oxidation: $\{Al(s) \rightarrow Al^{3+}(0.18 \text{ M}) + 3 e^-\} \times 2$ $\qquad\qquad -E° = +1.676$ V

Reduction: $\{Fe^{2+}(0.85 \text{ M}) + 2 e^- \rightarrow Fe(s)\} \times 3$ $\qquad\qquad E° = -0.440$ V

Net: $2 Al(s) + 3 Fe^{2+}(0.85 \text{ M}) \rightarrow 2 Al^{3+}(0.18 \text{ M}) + 3 Fe(s)$ $\qquad E°_{cell} = +1.236$ V

$$E_{cell} = E°_{cell} - \frac{0.0257 \text{ V}}{z} \ln \frac{[Al^{3+}]^2}{[Fe^{2+}]^3} = 1.236 \text{ V} - \frac{0.0257 \text{ V}}{6} \ln \frac{(0.18)^2}{(0.85)^3} = 1.249 \text{ V}$$

(b) Oxidation: $\{Ag(s) \rightarrow Ag^+ (0.34\ M) + e^-\} \times 2$ $\qquad\qquad -E° = -0.800\ V$

Reduction: $Cl_2 (0.55\ bar) + 2\ e^- \rightarrow 2\ Cl^- (0.098\ M)$ $\qquad\qquad E° = +1.358\ V$

Net: $Cl_2 (0.55\ bar) + 2\ Ag(s) \rightarrow 2\ Cl^- (0.098\ M) + 2\ Ag^+ (0.34\ M);\ E°_{cell} = +0.558\ V$

$$E_{cell} = E°_{cell} - \frac{0.0257\ V}{z} \ln \frac{\left[Cl^-\right]^2 \left[Ag^+\right]^2}{P\{Cl_2(g)\}} = +0.558\ V - \frac{0.0257\ V}{2} \ln \frac{(0.34)^2 (0.098)^2}{0.55} = +0.638\ V$$

38. (M)

(a) Oxidation: $Mn(s) \rightarrow Mn^{2+} (0.40\ M) + 2\ e^-$ $\qquad\qquad -E° = +1.18\ V$

Reduction: $\{Cr^{3+} (0.35\ M) + 1\ e^- \rightarrow Cr^{2+} (0.25\ M)\} \times 2$ $\qquad\qquad E° = -0.424\ V$

Net: $2\ Cr^{3+} (0.35\ M) + Mn(s) \rightarrow 2\ Cr^{2+} (0.25\ M) + Mn^{2+} (0.40\ M)$ $\qquad E°_{cell} = +0.76\ V$

$$E_{cell} = E°_{cell} - \frac{0.0257\ V}{z} \ln \frac{\left[Cr^{2+}\right]^2 \left[Mn^{2+}\right]}{\left[Cr^{3+}\right]^2} = +0.76\ V - \frac{0.0257\ V}{2} \ln \frac{(0.25)^2 (0.40)}{(0.35)^2} = +0.78\ V$$

(b) Oxidation: $\{Mg(s) \rightarrow Mg^{2+} (0.016\ M) + 2\ e^-\} \times 3$ $\qquad\qquad -E° = +2.356\ V$

Reduction: $\{\left[Al(OH)_4\right]^- (0.25\ M) + 3\ e^- \rightarrow 4\ OH^- (0.042\ M) + Al(s)\} \times 2;\ E° = -2.310\ V$

Net: $3\ Mg(s) + 2[Al(OH)_4]^- (0.25\ M) \rightarrow 3\ Mg^{2+} (0.016\ M) + 8\ OH^- (0.042\ M) + 2\ Al(s);$

$$E°_{cell} = +0.046\ V$$

$$E_{cell} = E°_{cell} - \frac{0.0257\ V}{6} \ln \frac{\left[Mg^{2+}\right]^3 \left[OH^-\right]^8}{\left[\left[Al(OH)_4\right]^-\right]^2} = +0.046\ V - \frac{0.0257\ V}{6} \ln \frac{(0.016)^3 (0.042)^8}{(0.25)^2}$$

$$= 0.046\ V + 0.150\ V = 0.196\ V$$

39. (M) All these observations can be understood in terms of the procedure we use to balance half-equations: the ion—electron method.

(a) The reactions for which E depends on pH are those that contain either $H^+ (aq)$ or $OH^- (aq)$ in the balanced half-equation. These reactions involve oxoacids and oxoanions whose central atom changes oxidation state.

(b) $H^+ (aq)$ will inevitably be on the left side of the reduction of an oxoanion because reduction is accompanied by not only a decrease in oxidation state, but also by the loss of oxygen atoms, as in $ClO_3^- \rightarrow ClO_2^-$, $SO_4^{2-} \rightarrow SO_2$, and $NO_3^- \rightarrow NO$. These oxygen atoms appear on the right-hand side as H_2O molecules. The hydrogens that are added to the right-hand side with the water molecules are then balanced with $H^+ (aq)$ on the left-hand side.

(c) If a half-reaction with $H^+(aq)$ ions present is transferred to basic solution, it may be re-balanced by adding to each side $OH^-(aq)$ ions equal in number to the $H^+(aq)$ originally present. This results in $H_2O(l)$ on the side that had $H^+(aq)$ ions (the left side in this case) and $OH^-(aq)$ ions on the other side (the right side.)

40. **(M)** Oxidation: $2\,Cl^-(aq) \rightarrow Cl_2(g) + 2\,e^-$ $\qquad -E° = -1.358\ V$

Reduction: $PbO_2(s) + 4\,H^+(aq) + 2\,e^- \rightarrow Pb^{2+}(aq) + 2\,H_2O(l)$ $\qquad E° = +1.455\ V$

Net: $PbO_2(s) + 4\,H^+(aq) + 2\,Cl^-(aq) \rightarrow Pb^{2+}(aq) + 2\,H_2O(l) + Cl_2(g); \qquad E°_{cell} = +0.097\ V$

We derive an expression for E_{cell} that depends on just the changing $[H^+]$.

$$E_{cell} = E°_{cell} - \frac{0.0257\ V}{2} \ln \frac{P\{Cl_2\}[Pb^{2+}]}{[H^+]^4[Cl^-]^2} = +0.097\ V - 0.0129\ V \ln \frac{(1.00)(1.00)}{[H^+]^4(1.00)^2}$$

$$= +0.097\ V + 4 \times 0.0129\ V \ln[H^+] = +0.097\ V + 0.0516\ V \ln[H^+]$$

$$= +0.097\ V - (0.0516\ V)\,pH$$

(a) $E_{cell} = +0.097\ V + 0.0516\ V \ln(6.0) = +0.189\ V$

∴ Forward reaction is spontaneous under standard conditions

(b) $E_{cell} = +0.097\ V + 0.0516\ V \ln(1.2) = +0.106\ V$

∴ Forward reaction is spontaneous under standard conditions

(c) $E_{cell} = +0.097\ V - 0.0516\ V \times 9.73 = -0.405\ V$

∴ Forward reaction is nonspontaneous under standard conditions

The reaction is spontaneous in strongly acidic solutions (very low pH), but is nonspontaneous under standard conditions in basic, neutral, and weakly acidic solutions.

41. **(M)** Oxidation: $Zn(s) \rightarrow Zn^{2+}(aq) + 2\,e^-$ $\qquad -E° = +0.763\ V$

Reduction: $Cu^{2+}(aq) + 2\,e^- \rightarrow Cu(s)$ $\qquad E° = +0.337\ V$

Net: $Zn(s) + Cu^{2+}(aq) \rightarrow Cu(s) + Zn^{2+}(aq)$ $\qquad E°_{cell} = +1.100\ V$

(a) We set $E = 0.000\ V$, $[Zn^{2+}] = 1.00\ M$, and solve for $[Cu^{2+}]$ in the Nernst equation.

$$E_{cell} = E°_{cell} - \frac{0.0257\ V}{2} \ln \frac{[Zn^{2+}]}{[Cu^{2+}]}; \quad 0.000 = 1.100 - 0.0129\ V \ln \frac{1.0\ M}{[Cu^{2+}]}$$

$$\ln \frac{1.0\ M}{[Cu^{2+}]} = \frac{0.000 - 1.100}{-0.0129\ V} = 85.3; \quad [Cu^{2+}] = e^{-85.3} = 9 \times 10^{-38}\ M$$

(b) If we work the problem the other way, by assuming initial concentrations of $[Cu^{2+}]_{initial} = 1.0\ M$ and $[Zn^{2+}]_{initial} = 0.0\ M$, we obtain $[Cu^{2+}]_{final} = 6 \times 10^{-38}\ M$ and $[Zn^{2+}]_{final} = 1.0\ M$. Thus, we would conclude that this reaction goes to completion.

42. **(M)** Oxidation: $Sn(s) \rightarrow Sn^{2+}(aq) + 2\,e^-$ $\quad\quad\quad -E° = +0.137\,V$

Reduction: $Pb^{2+}(aq) + 2\,e^- \rightarrow Pb(s)$ $\quad\quad\quad\quad E° = -0.125\,V$

Net: $\quad\quad Sn(s) + Pb^{2+}(aq) \rightarrow Sn^{2+}(aq) + Pb(s) \quad E°_{cell} = +0.012\,V$

Now we wish to find out if $Pb^{2+}(aq)$ will be completely displaced, that is, will $\left[Pb^{2+}\right]$ reach 0.0010 M, if $\left[Sn^{2+}\right]$ is fixed at 1.00 M? We use the Nernst equation to determine if the cell voltage still is positive under these conditions.

$$E_{cell} = E°_{cell} - \frac{0.0257\,V}{2} \ln\frac{\left[Sn^{2+}\right]}{\left[Pb^{2+}\right]} = +0.012\,V - \frac{0.0257\,V}{2} \ln\frac{1.00}{0.0010} = +0.012\,V - 0.089\,V = -0.077\,V$$

The negative cell potential tells us that this reaction will not go to completion under the conditions stated. The reaction stops being spontaneous when $E_{cell} = 0$. We can work this the another way as well: assume that $\left[Pb^{2+}\right] = (1.0 - x)$ M and calculate $\left[Sn^{2+}\right] = x$ M at equilibrium, that is, where $E_{cell} = 0\,V$.

$$E_{cell} = 0.00\,V = E°_{cell} - \frac{0.0257\,V}{2} \ln\frac{\left[Sn^{2+}\right]}{\left[Pb^{2+}\right]} = +0.012\,V - \frac{0.0257\,V}{2} \ln\frac{x}{1.0 - x}$$

$$\ln\frac{x}{1.0 - x} = \frac{2 \times 0.012}{0.0257\,V} = 0.47 \quad x = e^{0.47}(1.0 - x) = 1.6 - 1.6x \quad x = \frac{1.6}{2.2} = 0.72\,M$$

We would expect the final $\left[Sn^{2+}\right]$ to equal 1.0 M (or at least 0.999 M) if the reaction went to completion. Instead it equals 0.72 M and consequently, the reaction fails to go to completion.

43. **(M)**

(a) The two half-equations and the cell equation are given below. $E°_{cell} = 0.000\,V$

Oxidation: $\quad H_2(g) \rightarrow 2\,H^+(0.65\,M\,KOH) + 2\,e^-$

Reduction: $\quad 2\,H^+(1.0\,M) + 2\,e^- \rightarrow H_2(g)$

Net: $\quad\quad\quad 2\,H^+(1.0\,M) \rightarrow 2\,H^+(0.65\,M\,KOH)$

$$\left[H^+\right]_{base} = \frac{K_w}{\left[OH^-\right]} = \frac{1.00 \times 10^{-14}}{0.65} = 1.5 \times 10^{-14}\,M$$

$$E_{cell} = E°_{cell} - \frac{0.0257\,V}{2} \ln\frac{\left[H^+\right]_{base}^2}{\left[H^+\right]_{acid}^2} = 0.000\,V - \frac{0.0257\,V}{2} \ln\frac{\left(1.5 \times 10^{-14}\right)^2}{\left(1.0\right)^2} = +0.818\,V$$

(b) For the reduction of $H_2O(l)$ to $H_2(g)$ in basic solution, $2\,H_2O(l) + 2\,e^- \rightarrow 2\,H_2(g) + 2\,OH^-(aq)$, $E° = -0.828$ V. This reduction is the reverse of the reaction that occurs in the anode of the cell described, with one small difference: in the standard half-cell, $[OH^-] = 1.00$ M, while in the anode half-cell in the case at hand, $[OH^-] = 0.65$ M. Or, viewed in another way, in 1.00 M KOH, $[H^+]$ is smaller still than in 0.65 M KOH. The forward reaction (dilution of H^+) should be even more spontaneous, (i.e. a more positive voltage will be created), with 1.00 M KOH than with 0.65 M KOH. We expect that $E°_{cell}$ (1.000 M NaOH) should be a little larger than E_{cell} (0.65 M NaOH), which, is in fact, the case.

44. (M)

(a) Because $NH_3(aq)$ is a weaker base than KOH(aq), $[OH^-]$ will be smaller than in the previous problem. Therefore the $[H^+]$ will be higher. Its logarithm will be less negative, and the cell voltage will be less positive. Or, viewed as in Exercise 41(b), the difference in $[H^+]$ between 1.0 M H^+ and 0.65 M KOH is greater than the difference in $[H^+]$ between 1.0 M H^+ and 0.65 M NH_3. The forward reaction is "less spontaneous" and E_{cell} is less positive.

(b) Reaction:

	$NH_3(aq) + H_2O(l)$	$\rightleftharpoons$	$NH_4^+(aq) +$	$OH^-(aq)$
Initial:	0.65 M		0 M	≈ 0 M
Changes:	$-x$ M		$+x$ M	$+x$ M
Equil:	$(0.65-x)$ M		x M	x M

$$K_b = \frac{[NH_4^+][OH^-]}{[NH_3]} = 1.8\times10^{-5} = \frac{x\cdot x}{0.65-x} \approx \frac{x^2}{0.65}$$

$$x = [OH^-] = \sqrt{0.65\times1.8\times10^{-5}} = 3.4\times10^{-3}\ M; \quad [H_3O^+] = \frac{1.00\times10^{-14}}{3.4\times10^{-3}} = 2.9\times10^{-12}\ M$$

$$E_{cell} = E°_{cell} - \frac{0.0257\ V}{2}\ln\frac{[H^+]^2_{base}}{[H^+]^2_{acid}} = 0.000\ V - \frac{0.0257\ V}{2}\ln\frac{(2.9\times10^{-12})^2}{(1.0)^2} = +0.683\ V$$

45. (M) First we need to find $[Mg^{2+}]$ in a saturated solution of $Mg_3(PO_4)_2$.

$Mg_3(PO_4)_2(s) \rightarrow 3\,Mg^{2+}(aq) + 2\,PO_4^{3-}(aq)$

$$K_{sp} = [mg^{2+}]^3[PO_4^{3-}]^2 = (3s)^3(2s)^2 = 108s^5 = 1.0\times10^{-25} \qquad s = \sqrt[5]{\frac{1.0\times10^{-25}}{108}} = 3.9\times10^{-6}\ M$$

The cell diagrammed is a concentration cell, for which $E°_{cell} = 0.000$ V, $z = 2$, and

$$[Mg^{2+}]_{anode} = 3s = 3\times3.9\times10^{-6}\ M = 1.17\times10^{-5}\ M$$

Cell reaction: $Mg(s) + Mg^{2+}(0.125\ M) \rightarrow Mg(s) + Mg^{2+}(1.17\times10^{-5}M)$

$$E_{cell} = E°_{cell} - \frac{0.0257}{2}\ln\frac{1.17\times10^{-5}M}{0.125\ M} = 0.000 + 0.119\ V = 0.119\ V$$

46. **(M)** First we need to determine $\left[Ag^+\right]$ in the saturated solution of Ag_3PO_4.

The cell diagrammed is a concentration cell, for which $E^{\circ}_{cell} = 0.000\ V,\ z = 1$.

Cell reaction: $Ag(s) + Ag^+(0.140\ M) \rightarrow Ag(s) + Ag^+(x\ M)$

$E_{cell} = 0.180\ V = E^{\circ}_{cell} - \dfrac{0.0257\ V}{1} \log \dfrac{x\ M}{0.140\ M};\quad \log \dfrac{x\ M}{0.140\ M} = \dfrac{0.180\ V}{-0.0257\ V} = -7.00$

$x\ M = 0.140\ M \times e^{-7.00} = 0.140\ M \times 9.1 \times 10^{-4} = 1.3 \times 10^{-4}\ M = \left[Ag^+\right]_{anode}$

$K_{sp} = \left[Ag^+\right]^3\left[PO_4^{3-}\right] = (3s)^3(s) = \left(1.3 \times 10^{-4}\right)^3\left(1.3 \times 10^{-4} \div 3\right) = 9.5 \times 10^{-17}$

47. **(D)**

(a) Oxidation: $Sn(s) \rightarrow Sn^{2+}(0.075\ M) + 2\ e^-$ $\qquad\qquad -E^{\circ} = +0.137\ V$

Reduction: $Pb^{2+}(0.600\ M) + 2\ e^- \rightarrow Pb(s)$ $\qquad\qquad E^{\circ} = -0.125\ V$

Net: $Sn(s) + Pb^{2+}(0.600\ M) \rightarrow Pb(s) + Sn^{2+}(0.075\ M); E^{\circ}_{cell} = +0.012\ V$

$E_{cell} = E^{\circ}_{cell} - \dfrac{0.0257\ V}{2} \ln \dfrac{\left[Sn^{2+}\right]}{\left[Pb^{2+}\right]} = 0.012\ V - 0.0129\ V \ln \dfrac{0.075}{0.600} = 0.012\ V + 0.027\ V = 0.039\ V$

(b) As the reaction proceeds, $[Sn^{2+}]$ increases while $[Pb^{2+}]$ decreases. These changes cause the driving force behind the reaction to steadily decrease with the passage of time. This decline in driving force is manifested as a decrease in E_{cell} with time.

(c) When $\left[Pb^{2+}\right] = 0.500\ M = 0.600\ M - 0.100\ M$, $\left[Sn^{2+}\right] = 0.075\ M + 0.100\ M$, because the stoichiometry of the reaction is 1:1 for Sn^{2+} and Pb^{2+}.

$E_{cell} = E^{\circ}_{cell} - \dfrac{0.0257\ V}{2} \ln \dfrac{\left[Sn^{2+}\right]}{\left[Pb^{2+}\right]} = 0.012\ V - 0.0129\ V \ln \dfrac{0.175}{0.500} = (0.012 + 0.013)V = 0.025\ V$

(d) Reaction:

	$Sn(s) +$	$Pb^{2+}(aq)$	$\rightarrow$	$Pb(s)$	$+$	$Sn^{2+}(aq)$
Initial:	—	0.600 M		—		0.075 M
Changes:	—	$-x$ M		—		$+x$ M
Final:	—	$(0.600 - x)$ M		—		$(0.075 + x)$ M

$E_{cell} = E^{\circ}_{cell} - \dfrac{0.0257\ V}{2} \ln \dfrac{\left[Sn^{2+}\right]}{\left[Pb^{2+}\right]}$, so $0.020\ V = 0.012\ V - 0.0129\ V \ln \dfrac{0.075 + x}{0.600 - x}$

$\ln \dfrac{0.075 + x}{0.600 - x} = \dfrac{E_{cell} - 0.012\ V}{-0.0129\ V} = \dfrac{0.020 - 0.012}{-0.0129\ V} = -0.27;\ \dfrac{0.075 + x}{0.600 - x} = e^{-0.62} = 0.54$

$0.075 + x = 0.54(0.600 - x) = 0.324 - 0.54x;\ x = \dfrac{0.324 - 0.075}{1.54} = 0.162$

$\left[Sn^{2+}\right] = (0.075 + 0.162)\ M = 0.237\ M$

(e) Here we use the expression developed in part (d).

$$\ln\frac{0.075+x}{0.600-x}=\frac{E_{cell}-0.012\text{ V}}{-0.0129\text{ V}}=\frac{(0.000-0.012)\text{ V}}{-0.0129\text{ V}}=+0.93$$

$$\frac{0.075+x}{0.600-x}=e^{+0.93}=2.6;\quad 0.075+x=2.6(0.600-x)=1.6-2.6x$$

$$x=\frac{1.6-0.075}{3.6}=0.42\text{ M}$$

$$\left[Sn^{2+}\right]=(0.075+0.42)\text{M}=0.50\text{ M};\qquad \left[Pb^{2+}\right]=(0.600-0.42)\text{M}=0.18\text{ M}$$

48. (D)

(a) Oxidation: $Ag(s)\rightarrow Ag^+(0.015\text{ M})+e^-$ $\qquad\qquad -E^\circ=-0.800\text{ V}$

Reduction: $Fe^{3+}(0.055\text{ M})+e^-\rightarrow Fe^{2+}(0.045\text{ M})$ $\qquad E^\circ=+0.771\text{ V}$

Net: $Ag(s)+Fe^{3+}(0.055\text{ M})\rightarrow Ag^+(0.015\text{ M})+Fe^{2+}(0.045\text{ M})$ $\;E^\circ_{cell}=-0.029\text{ V}$

$$E_{cell}=E^\circ_{cell}-\frac{0.0257\text{ V}}{1}\ln\frac{\left[Ag^+\right]\left[Fe^{2+}\right]}{\left[Fe^{3+}\right]}=-0.029\text{ V}-0.0257\text{ V}\ln\frac{0.015\times0.045}{0.055}$$

$$=-0.029\text{ V}+0.113\text{ V}=+0.084\text{ V}$$

(b) As the reaction proceeds, $\left[Ag^+\right]$ and $\left[Fe^{2+}\right]$ will increase, while $\left[Fe^{3+}\right]$ decrease. These changes cause the driving force behind the reaction to steadily decrease with the passage of time. This decline in driving force is manifested as a decrease in E_{cell} with time.

(c) When $\left[Ag^+\right]=0.020\text{ M}=0.015\text{ M}+0.005\text{ M},\;\left[Fe^{2+}\right]=0.045\text{ M}+0.005\text{ M}=0.050\text{ M}$ and $\left[Fe^{3+}\right]=0.055\text{ M}-0.005\text{ M}=0.500\text{ M}$, because, by the stoichiometry of the reaction, a mole of Fe^{2+} is produced and a mole of Fe^{3+} is consumed for every mole of Ag^+ produced.

$$E_{cell}=E^\circ_{cell}-\frac{0.0257\text{ V}}{1}\ln\frac{\left[Ag^+\right]\left[Fe^{2+}\right]}{\left[Fe^{3+}\right]}=-0.029\text{ V}-0.0257\text{ V}\ln\frac{0.020\times0.050}{0.050}$$

$$=-0.029\text{ V}+0.101\text{ V}=+0.072\text{ V}$$

(d) Reaction: $Ag(s)+\;\;Fe^{3+}(0.055\text{M})\;\rightleftharpoons\;Ag^+(0.015\text{ M})+\;Fe^{2+}(0.045\text{ M})$

Initial: $\qquad\qquad 0.055$ M $\qquad\qquad 0.015$ M $\qquad 0.045$ M

Changes: $\qquad\qquad -x$ M $\qquad\qquad +x$ M $\qquad +x$ M

Final: $\qquad\qquad (0.055-x)$ M $\qquad (0.015+x)$ M $\quad (0.045+x)$ M

$$E_{cell}=E^\circ_{cell}-\frac{0.0257\text{ V}}{1}\ln\frac{\left[Ag^+\right]\left[Fe^{2+}\right]}{\left[Fe^{3+}\right]}=-0.029\text{ V}-0.0257\text{ V}\ln\frac{(0.015+x)(0.045+x)}{(0.055-x)}$$

$$\ln \frac{(0.015+x)(0.045+x)}{(0.055-x)} = \frac{E_{cell}+0.029 \text{ V}}{-0.0257 \text{ V}} = \frac{(0.010+0.029) \text{ V}}{-0.0257 \text{ V}} = -1.52$$

$$\frac{(0.015+x)(0.045+x)}{(0.055-x)} = e^{-1.52} = 0.22$$

$$0.00068+0.060x+x^2 = 0.22(0.055-x) = 0.012-0.22x \quad x^2+0.28x-0.011=0$$

$$x = \frac{-b \pm \sqrt{b^2-4ac}}{2a} = \frac{-0.28 \pm \sqrt{(0.28)^2+4 \times 0.011}}{2} = 0.035 \text{ M}$$

$$[Ag^+] = 0.015 \text{ M} + 0.035 \text{ M} = 0.050 \text{ M}$$

$$[Fe^{2+}] = 0.045 \text{ M} + 0.035 \text{ M} = 0.080 \text{ M}$$

$$[Fe^{3+}] = 0.055 \text{ M} - 0.035 \text{ M} = 0.020 \text{ M}$$

(e) We use the expression that was developed in part (d).

$$\ln \frac{(0.015+x)(0.045+x)}{(0.055-x)} = \frac{E_{cell}+0.029 \text{ V}}{-0.0257 \text{ V}} = \frac{(0.000+0.029) \text{ V}}{-0.0257 \text{ V}} = -1.13$$

$$\frac{(0.015+x)(0.045+x)}{(0.055-x)} = e^{-1.13} = 0.32$$

$$0.00068+0.060x+x^2 = 0.32(0.055-x) = 0.018-0.32x \quad x^2+0.38x-0.017=0$$

$$x = \frac{-b \pm \sqrt{b^2-4ac}}{2a} = \frac{-0.38 \pm \sqrt{(0.38)^2+4 \times 0.017}}{2} = 0.040 \text{ M}$$

$$[Ag^+] = 0.015 \text{ M} + 0.040 \text{ M} = 0.055 \text{ M}$$

$$[Fe^{2+}] = 0.045 \text{ M} + 0.040 \text{ M} = 0.085 \text{ M}$$

$$[Fe^{3+}] = 0.055 \text{ M} - 0.040 \text{ M} = 0.015 \text{ M}$$

49. **(M)** First we will need to come up with a balanced equation for the overall redox reaction. Clearly, the reaction must involve the oxidation of $Cl^-(aq)$ and the reduction of $Cr_2O_7^{2-}(aq)$:

$14 \text{ H}^+(aq) + Cr_2O_7^{2-}(aq) + 6 \text{ e}^- \rightarrow 2 \text{ Cr}^{3+}(aq) + 7 \text{ H}_2O(l)$	$E°_{red} = 1.33 \text{ V}$
$\{Cl^-(aq) \rightarrow 1/2 \text{ Cl}_2(g) + 1 \text{ e}^-\} \times 6$	$E°_{ox} = -1.358 \text{ V}$

$$14 \text{ H}^+(aq) + Cr_2O_7^{2-}(aq) + 6 \text{ Cl}^-(aq) \rightarrow 2 \text{ Cr}^{3+}(aq) + 7 \text{ H}_2O(l) + 3 \text{ Cl}_2(g) \quad E°_{cell} = -0.03 \text{ V}$$

A <u>negative</u> cell potential means, the oxidation of $Cl^-(aq)$ to $Cl_2(g)$ by $Cr_2O_7^{2-}(aq)$ at standard conditions will <u>not</u> occur spontaneously. We could obtain some $Cl_2(g)$ from this reaction by driving it to the product side with an external voltage. In other words, the reverse reaction is the spontaneous reaction at standard conditions and if we want to produce some $Cl_2(g)$ from the system, we must push the non-spontaneous reaction in its forward direction with an external voltage, (i.e., a DC power source). Since $E°_{cell}$ is only slightly negative, we could also drive the reaction by removing products as they are formed and replenishing reactants as they are consumed.

50. (D) We proceed by first deriving a balanced equation for the reaction occurring in the cell:

Oxidation: $Fe(s) \rightarrow Fe^{2+}(aq) + 2e^-$

Reduction: $\{Fe^{3+}(aq) + e^- \rightarrow Fe^{2+}(aq)\} \times 2$

Net: $\quad Fe(s) + 2Fe^{3+}(aq) \rightarrow 3Fe^{2+}(aq)$

(a) $\Delta_r G°$ and the equilibrium constant K can be calculated using

$\Delta_r G° = -zFE°_{cell} = -RT \ln K$:

$\Delta_r G° = -zFE°_{cell} = -2 \times 96485 \text{ C mol}^{-1} \times 1.21 \text{ V} = -233.5 \text{ kJ mol}^{-1}$

$\Delta_r G° = -RT \ln K = -8.314 \text{ J K}^{-1}\text{mol}^{-1} \times 298.15 \text{ K} \times \ln K = -233.5 \times 1000 \text{ J mol}^{-1}$

$\ln K = 94.2 \Rightarrow K = e^{94.2} = 8.1 \times 10^{40}$

(b) Before calculating voltage using the Nernst equation, we need to re-write the net reaction to take into account concentration gradient for $Fe^{2+}(aq)$:

Oxidation: $Fe(s) \rightarrow Fe^{2+}(aq, 1.0 \times 10^{-3} \text{ M}) + 2e^-$

Reduction: $\{Fe^{3+}(aq, 1.0 \times 10^{-3} \text{ M}) + e^- \rightarrow Fe^{2+}(aq, 0.10 \text{ M})\} \times 2$

Net: $Fe(s) + 2Fe^{3+}(aq, 1.0 \times 10^{-3} \text{ M}) \rightarrow Fe^{2+}(aq, 1.0 \times 10^{-3} \text{ M}) + 2Fe^{2+}(aq, 0.10 \text{ M})$

Therefore,

$$Q = \frac{1.0 \times 10^{-3} \times (0.10)^2}{(1.0 \times 10^{-3})^2} = 10$$

Now, we can apply the Nerst equation to calculate the voltage:

$$E_{cell} = E°_{cell} - \frac{0.0257 \text{ V}}{z} \ln Q = 1.21 \text{ V} - \frac{0.0257}{2} \ln 10 = 1.18 \text{ V}$$

(c) From parts (a) and (b) we can conclude that the reaction between $Fe(s)$ and $Fe^{3+}(aq)$ is spontaneous. The reverse reaction (i.e. disproportionation of $Fe^{2+}(aq)$) must therefore be nonspontaneous.

Batteries and Fuel Cells

51. (M)

(a) The cell diagram begins with the anode and ends with the cathode.

Cell diagram: $Cr(s)|Cr^{2+}(aq), Cr^{3+}(aq)||Fe^{2+}(aq), Fe^{3+}(aq)|Fe(s)$

(b) Oxidation: $Cr^{2+}(aq) \rightarrow Cr^{3+}(aq) + e^- \qquad\qquad -E° = +0.424 \text{ V}$

Reduction: $Fe^{3+}(aq) + e^- \rightarrow Fe^{2+}(aq) \qquad\qquad E° = +0.771 \text{ V}$

Net: $Cr^{2+}(aq) + Fe^{3+}(aq) \rightarrow Cr^{3+}(aq) + Fe^{2+}(aq) \quad E°_{cell} = +1.195 \text{ V}$

52. (M)

(a) Oxidation: $Zn(s) \rightarrow Zn^{2+}(aq) + 2 e^-$ $\qquad -E° = +0.763$ V

Reduction: $2 MnO_2(s) + H_2O(l) + 2 e^- \rightarrow Mn_2O_3(s) + 2 OH^-(aq)$

Acid-base: $\{NH_4^+(aq) + OH^-(aq) \rightarrow NH_3(g) + H_2O(l)\} \times 2$

Complex: $Zn^{2+}(aq) + 2 NH_3(aq) + 2 Cl^-(aq) \rightarrow [Zn(NH_3)_2]Cl_2(s)$

Net: $Zn(s) + 2 MnO_2(s) + 2 NH_4^+(aq) + 2 Cl^-(aq) \rightarrow Mn_2O_3(s) + H_2O(l) + [Zn(NH_3)_2]Cl_2(s)$

(b) $\Delta_r G° = -zFE°_{cell} = -(2)(96,485 \text{ C/mol})(1.55 \text{ V}) = -2.99 \times 10^5$ J/mol

This is the standard free energy change for the entire reaction, which is composed of the four reactions in part (a). We can determine the values of $\Delta_r G°$ for the acid-base and complex formation reactions by employing the appropriate data from Appendix D and $pK_f = -4.81$ (the negative log of the K_f for $[Zn(NH_3)_2]^{2+}$).

$\Delta G°_{a-b} = -RT\ln K_b^2 = -(8.3145 \text{ J mol}^{-1} \text{ K}^{-1})(298.15 \text{ K})\ln(1.8 \times 10^{-5})^2 = 5.417 \times 10^4$ J/mol

$\Delta G°_{cmplx} = -RT \ln K_f = -(8.3145 \text{ J mol}^{-1} \text{ K}^-)(298.15 \text{ K})\ln(10^{4.81}) = -2.746 \times 10^4$ J/mol

Then $\Delta G°_{total} = \Delta G°_{redox} + \Delta G°_{a-b} + \Delta G°_{cmplx}$ $\qquad \Delta G°_{redox} = \Delta G°_{total} - \Delta G°_{a-b} - \Delta G°_{complx}$

$= (-2.99 \times 10^5 - 5.417 \times 10^4 + 2.746 \times 10^4) \text{ J/mol} = -3.26 \times 10^5$ J/mol

Thus, the voltage of the redox reactions alone is

$E° = \dfrac{-3.26 \times 10^5 \text{ J mol}^{-1}}{-2 \times 96,485 \text{ C/mol}} = 1.69$ V $\qquad 1.69\text{V} = +0.763\text{V} + E°\{MnO_2/Mn_2O_3\}$

$E°\{MnO_2/Mn_2O_3\} = 1.69 \text{ V} - 0.763 \text{ V} = +0.93$ V

The electrode potentials were calculated by using equilibrium constants from Appendix D. These calculations do not take into account the cell's own internal resistance to the flow of electrons, which makes the actual voltage developed by the electrodes less than the theoretical values derived from equilibrium constants. Also because the solid species (other than Zn) do not appear as compact rods, but rather are dispersed in a paste, and since very little water is present in the cell, the activities for the various species involved in the electrochemical reactions will deviate markedly from unity. As a result, the equilibrium constants for the reactions taking place in the cell will be substantially different from those provided in Appendix D, which apply only to dilute solutions and reactions involving solid reactants and products that posses small surface areas. The actual electrode voltages, therefore, will end up being different from those calculated here.

53. (M)

(a) Cell reaction: $2 H_2(g) + O_2(g) \rightarrow 2 H_2O(l)$

$\Delta_r G° = 2\Delta_f G°[H_2O(l)] = 2(-237.1 \text{ kJ/mol}) = -474.2$ kJ/mol

$E°_{cell} = -\dfrac{\Delta_r G°}{zF} = -\dfrac{-474.2 \times 10^3 \text{ J/mol}}{4 \times 96,485 \text{ C/mol}} = 1.229$ V

(b) Anode, oxidation: $\{Zn(s) \rightarrow Zn^{2+}(aq) + 2\,e^-\} \times 2$ $\qquad -E° = +0.763$ V

Cathode, reduction: $O_2(g) + 4\,H^+(aq) + 4\,e^- \rightarrow 2\,H_2O(l)$ $\qquad E° = +1.229$ V

Net: $2\,Zn(s) + O_2(g) + 4\,H^+(aq) \rightarrow 2\,Zn^{2+}(aq) + 2\,H_2O(l)$ $\quad E°_{cell} = +1.992$ V

(c) Anode, oxidation: $Mg(s) \rightarrow Mg^{2+}(aq) + 2\,e^-$ $\qquad -E° = +2.356$ V

Cathode, reduction: $I_2(s) + 2\,e^- \rightarrow 2\,I^-(aq)$ $\qquad E° = +0.535$ V

Net: $Mg(s) + I_2(s) \rightarrow Mg^{2+}(aq) + 2\,I^-(aq)$ $\qquad E°_{cell} = +2.891$ V

54. (M)

(a) Oxidation: $\qquad\qquad\qquad\qquad Zn(s) \rightleftharpoons Zn^{2+}(aq) + 2\,e^-$

Precipitation: $\qquad Zn^{2+}(aq) + 2\,OH^-(aq) \rightleftharpoons Zn(OH)_2(s)$

Reduction: $\qquad 2\,MnO_2(s) + H_2)(l) + 2\,e^- \rightleftharpoons Mn_2O_3(s) + 2\,OH^-(aq)$

Net : $Zn(s) + 2\,MnO_2(s) + H_2O(l) + 2\,OH^-(aq) \rightleftharpoons Mn_2O_3(s) + Zn(OH)_2(s)$

(b) In 50, we determined that the standard voltage for the reduction reaction is $+0.93$ V ($z = 2\,e^-$). To convert this voltage to an equilibrium constant (at 25 °C) use:

$$\log K_{red} = \frac{zE°}{0.0257\text{ V}} = \frac{2(0.93)}{0.0257\text{ V}} = 72.\underline{4}; \qquad K_{red} = e^{72.4} = 3 \times 10^{31}$$

and for $Zn(s) \rightleftharpoons Zn^{2+}(aq) + 2\,e^-$ ($E° = 0.763$ V and $z = 2\,e^-$)

$$\log K_{ox} = \frac{zE°}{0.0257\text{ V}} = \frac{2(0.763)}{0.0257\text{ V}} = 59.\underline{4}; \qquad K_{ox} = e^{59.4} = 6 \times 10^{25}$$

$$\Delta_r G°_{total} = \Delta_r G°_{precipitation} + \Delta_r G°_{oxidation} + \Delta_r G°_{reduction}$$

$$\Delta_r G°_{total} = -RT\ln\frac{1}{K_{sp,\,Zn(OH)_2}} + (-RT\ln K_{ox}) + (-RT\ln K_{red})$$

$$\Delta_r G°_{total} = -RT\,(\ln\frac{1}{K_{sp,\,Zn(OH)_2}} + \ln K_{ox} + \ln K_{red})$$

$$\Delta_r G°_{total} = -0.0083145\,\frac{\text{kJ}}{\text{K mol}}\,(298\text{ K})\,(\ln\frac{1}{1.2 \times 10^{-17}} + \ln(6.0 \times 10^{25}) + \ln(2.6 \times 10^{31}))$$

$$\Delta_r G°_{total} = -423\text{ kJ mol}^{-1} = -zFE°_{total}$$

Hence, $E°_{total} = E°_{cell} = \dfrac{-423 \times 10^3\text{ J mol}^{-1}}{-(2)(96{,}485\text{ C mol}^{-1})} = 2.19$ V

55. (M) Aluminum-Air Battery: $2\,Al(s) + 3/2\,O_2(g) \rightarrow Al_2O_3(s)$

Zinc-Air Battery: $\qquad Zn(s) + ½\,O_2(g) \rightarrow ZnO(s)$

Iron-Air Battery $\qquad Fe(s) + ½\,O_2(g) \rightarrow FeO(s)$

Calculate the quantity of charge transferred when 1.00 g of metal is consumed in each cell.

Aluminum-Air Cell:

$$1.00 \text{ g Al(s)} \times \frac{1 \text{ mol Al(s)}}{26.98 \text{ g Al(s)}} \times \frac{3 \text{ mol e}^-}{1 \text{ mol Al(s)}} \times \frac{96,485 \text{C}}{1 \text{ mol e}^-} = 1.07 \times 10^4 \text{ C}$$

Zinc-Air Cell:

$$1.00 \text{ g Zn(s)} \times \frac{1 \text{ mol Zn(s)}}{65.38 \text{ g Zn(s)}} \times \frac{2 \text{ mol e}^-}{1 \text{ mol Zn(s)}} \times \frac{96,485 \text{ C}}{1 \text{ mol e}^-} = 2.95 \times 10^3 \text{ C}$$

Iron-Air Cell:

$$1.00 \text{ g Fe(s)} \times \frac{1 \text{ mol Fe(s)}}{55.845 \text{ g Fe(s)}} \times \frac{2 \text{ mol e}^-}{1 \text{ mol Fe(s)}} \times \frac{96,485 \text{ C}}{1 \text{ mol e}^-} = 3.46 \times 10^3 \text{ C}$$

As expected, aluminum has the greatest quantity of charge transferred per unit mass (1.00 g) of metal oxidized. This is because aluminum has the smallest molar mass and forms the most highly charged cation (3+ for aluminum vs 2+ for Zn and Fe).

56. (M)

(a) A voltaic cell with a voltage of 0.1000 V would be possible by using two half-cells whose standard reduction potentials differ by approximately 0.10 V, such as the following pair.

Oxidation: $2 \text{ Cr}^{3+}(aq) + 7 \text{ H}_2\text{O}(l) \rightarrow \text{Cr}_2\text{O}_7^{2-}(aq) + 14 \text{ H}^+(aq) + 6 \text{ e}^- \qquad -E° = -1.33 \text{ V}$

Reduction: $\{\text{PbO}_2(s) + 4 \text{ H}^+(aq) + 2\text{e}^- \rightarrow \text{Pb}^{2+}(aq) + 2 \text{ H}_2\text{O}(l)\} \times 3 \qquad E° = +1.455 \text{ V}$

Net: $2 \text{ Cr}^{3+}(aq) + 3 \text{ PbO}_2(s) + \text{H}_2\text{O}(l) \rightarrow \text{Cr}_2\text{O}_7^{2-}(aq) + 3 \text{ Pb}^{2+}(aq) + 2 \text{ H}^+(aq) \quad E°_{cell} = 0.12\underline{5} \text{ V}$

The voltage can be adjusted to 0.1000 V by a suitable alteration of the concentrations. $\left[\text{Pb}^{2+}\right]$ or $\left[\text{H}^+\right]$ could be increased or $\left[\text{Cr}^{3+}\right]$ could be decreased, or any combination of the three of these.

(b) To produce a cell with a voltage of 2.500 V requires that one start with two half-cells whose reduction potentials differ by about that much. An interesting pair follows.

Oxidation: $\text{Al}(s) \rightarrow \text{Al}^{3+}(aq) + 3 \text{ e}^- \qquad\qquad -E° = +1.676 \text{ V}$

Reduction: $\{\text{Ag}^+(aq) + \text{e}^- \rightarrow \text{Ag}(s)\} \times 3 \qquad\qquad E° = +0.800 \text{ V}$

Net: $\qquad \text{Al}(s) + 3 \text{ Ag}^+(aq) \rightarrow \text{Al}^{3+}(aq) + 3 \text{ Ag}(s) \qquad E°_{cell} = +2.476 \text{ V}$

Again, the desired voltage can be obtained by adjusting the concentrations. In this case increasing $\left[\text{Ag}^+\right]$ and/or decreasing $\left[\text{Al}^{3+}\right]$ would do the trick.

(c) Since no known pair of half-cells has a potential difference larger than about 6 volts, we conclude that producing a single cell with a potential of 10.00 V is currently impossible. It is possible, however, to join several cells together into a battery that delivers a voltage of 10.00 V. For instance, four of the cells from part (b) would deliver ~10.0 V at the instant of hook-up.

57. **(M)**

Oxidation (anode): $Li(s) \rightarrow Li^+(aq) + e^-$ $\qquad$ $-E° = +3.040$ V

Reduction (cathode): $MnO_2(s) + 2H_2O(l) + e^- \rightarrow Mn(OH)_3(s) + OH^-(aq)$ $\qquad$ $E° = -0.20$ V

Net: $MnO_2(s) + 2H_2O(l) + Li(s) \rightarrow Mn(OH)_3(s) + OH^-(aq) + Li^+(aq)$ $\qquad$ $E°_{cell} = 2.84$ V

Cell diagram: $Li(s), Li^+(aq) | KOH(satd) | MnO_2(s), Mn(OH)_3(s) |$

58. **(M)**

(a)

Oxidation (anode):	$Zn(s) \rightarrow Zn^{+2}(aq) + 2e^-$	$-E° = +0.763$ V
Reduction (cathode):	$Br_2(l) + 2e^- \rightarrow 2Br^-(aq)$	$E° = +1.065$ V
Net:	$Zn(s) + Br_2(l) \rightarrow Zn^{2+}(aq) + 2Br^-(aq)$	$E°_{cell} = 1.828$ V

(b)

Oxidation (anode):	$\{Li(s) \rightarrow Li^+(aq) + e^-\} \times 2$	$-E° = +3.040$ V
Reduction (cathode):	$F_2(g) + 2e^- \rightarrow 2F^-(aq)$	$E° = +2.866$ V
Net:	$2Li(s) + F_2(g) \rightarrow 2Li^+(aq) + 2F^-(aq)$	$E°_{cell} = 4.868$ V

Electrochemical Mechanism of Corrosion

59. **(M)**

(a) Because copper is a less active metal than is iron (i.e. a weaker reducing agent), this situation would be similar to that of an iron or steel can plated with a tin coating that has been scratched. Oxidation of iron metal to $Fe^{2+}(aq)$ should be enhanced in the body of the nail (blue precipitate), and hydroxide ion should be produced in the vicinity of the copper wire (pink color), which serves as the cathode.

(b) Because a scratch tears the iron and exposes "fresh" metal, it is more susceptible to corrosion. We expect blue precipitate in the vicinity of the scratch.

(c) Zinc should protect the iron nail from corrosion. There should be almost no blue precipitate; the zinc corrodes instead. The pink color of OH^- should continue to form.

60. **(M)** The oxidation process involved at the anode reaction, is the formation of $Fe^{2+}(aq)$. This occurs far below the water line. The reduction process involved at the cathode, is the formation of $OH^-(aq)$ from $O_2(g)$. It is logical that this reaction would occur at or near the water line close to the atmosphere (which contains O_2). This reduction reaction requires $O_2(g)$ from the atmosphere and $H_2O(l)$ from the water. The oxidation reaction, on the other hand simply requires iron from the pipe together with an aqueous solution into which the $Fe^{2+}(aq)$ can disperse and not build up to such a high concentration that corrosion is inhibited.

Anode, oxidation: $\qquad$ $Fe(s) \rightarrow Fe^{2+}(aq) + 2e^-$

Cathode, reduction: $\qquad$ $O_2(g) + 2H_2O(l) + 4e^- \rightarrow 4OH^-(aq)$

61. **(M)** During the process of corrosion, the metal that corrodes loses electrons. Thus, the metal in these instances behaves as an anode and, hence, can be viewed as bearing a latent negative polarity. One way in which we could retard oxidation of the metal would be to convert it into a cathode. Once transformed into a cathode, the metal would develop a positive charge and no longer release electrons (or oxidize). This change in polarity can be accomplished by hooking up the metal to an inert electrode in the ground and then applying a voltage across the two metals in such a way that the inert electrode becomes the anode and the metal that needs protecting becomes the cathode. This way, any oxidation that occurs will take place at the negatively charged inert electrode rather than the positively charged metal electrode.

62. **(M)** As soon as the iron and copper came into direct contact, an electrochemical cell was created, in which the more powerfully reducing metal (Fe) was oxidized. In this way, the iron behaved as a sacrificial anode, protecting the copper from corrosion. The two half-reactions and the net cell reaction are shown below:

Anode (oxidation)	$Fe(s) \rightarrow Fe^{2+}(aq) + 2\ e^-$	$-E° = 0.440$ V
Cathode (reduction)	$Cu^{2+}(aq) + 2\ e^- \rightarrow Cu(s)$	$E° = 0.337$ V
Net:	$Fe(s) + Cu^{2+}(aq) \rightarrow Fe^{2+}(aq) + Cu(s)$	$E°_{cell} = 0.777$ V

Note that because of the presence of iron and its electrical contact with the copper, any copper that does corrode is reduced back to the metal.

Electrolysis Reactions

63. **(M)** Here we start by calculating the total amount of charge passed and the number of moles of electrons transferred.

$$\text{mol } e^- = 75\ \text{min} \times \frac{60\ \text{s}}{1\ \text{min}} \times \frac{2.15\ \text{C}}{1\ \text{s}} \times \frac{1\ \text{mol } e^-}{96,485\ \text{C}} = 0.10\ \text{mol } e^-$$

(a) $\quad \text{mass Zn} = 0.10\ \text{mol } e^- \times \dfrac{1\ \text{mol Zn}^{2+}}{2\ \text{mol } e^-} \times \dfrac{1\ \text{mol Zn}}{1\ \text{mol Zn}^{2+}} \times \dfrac{65.38\ \text{g Zn}}{1\ \text{mol Zn}} = 3.3\ \text{g Zn}$

(b) $\quad \text{mass Al} = 0.10\ \text{mol } e^- \times \dfrac{1\ \text{mol Al}^{3+}}{3\ \text{mol } e^-} \times \dfrac{1\ \text{mol Al}}{1\ \text{mol Al}^{3+}} \times \dfrac{26.9815\ \text{g Al}}{1\ \text{mol Al}} = 0.90\ \text{g Al}$

(c) $\quad \text{mass Ag} = 0.10\ \text{mol } e^- \times \dfrac{1\ \text{mol Ag}^+}{1\ \text{mol } e^-} \times \dfrac{1\ \text{mol Ag}}{1\ \text{mol Ag}^+} \times \dfrac{107.8682\ \text{g Ag}}{1\ \text{mol Ag}} = 11\ \text{g Ag}$

(d) $\quad \text{mass Ni} = 0.10\ \text{mol } e^- \times \dfrac{1\ \text{mol Ni}^{2+}}{2\ \text{mol } e^-} \times \dfrac{1\ \text{mol Ni}}{1\ \text{mol Ni}^{2+}} \times \dfrac{58.6934\ \text{g Ni}}{1\ \text{mol Ni}} = 2.9\ \text{g Ni}$

64. **(M)** We proceed by first writing down the net electrochemical reaction. The number of moles of hydrogen produced in the reaction can be calculated from the reaction stoichiometry. Lastly, the volume of hydrogen can be determined using ideal gas law. The two half reactions follow: $Cu^{2+}(aq) + 2 e^- \rightarrow Cu(s)$ and $2 H^+(aq) + 2 e^- \rightarrow H_2(g)$ Thus, two moles of electrons are needed to produce each mole of $Cu(s)$ and two moles of electrons are needed to produce each mole of $H_2(g)$. With this information, we can compute the moles of $H_2(g)$ that will be produced.

$$\text{mol } H_2(g) = 3.28 \text{ g Cu} \times \frac{1 \text{ mol Cu}}{63.5463 \text{ g Cu}} \times \frac{2 \text{ mol } e^-}{1 \text{ mol Cu}} \times \frac{1 \text{ mol } H_2(g)}{2 \text{ mol } e^-} = 0.0516 \text{ mol } H_2(g)$$

Then we use the ideal gas equation to find the volume of $H_2(g)$.

$$\text{Volume of } H_2(g) = \frac{0.0516 \text{ mol } H_2 \times 0.08314 \text{ L bar mol}^{-1} \text{ K}^{-1} \times (28.2 + 273.15) \text{ K}}{763 \text{ mmHg} \times \dfrac{1.01325 \text{ bar}}{760 \text{ mmHg}}} = 1.27 \text{ L}$$

This answer assumes the $H_2(g)$ is not collected over water, and that the $H_2(g)$ formed is the only gas present in the container (i.e. no water vapor present)

65. **(M)** Here we must determine the standard cell voltage of each chemical reaction. Those chemical reactions that have a negative voltage are the ones that require electrolysis.

(a) Oxidation: $2 H_2O(l) \rightarrow 4 H^+(aq) + O_2(g) + 4 e^-$ $-E° = -1.229 \text{ V}$

Reduction: $\{2 H^+(aq) + 2 e^- \rightarrow H_2(g)\} \times 2$ $E° = 0.000 \text{ V}$

Net: $2 H_2O(l) \rightarrow 2 H_2(g) + O_2(g)$ $E°_{cell} = -1.229 \text{ V}$

This reaction requires electrolysis, with an applied voltage greater than $+1.229 \text{V}$.

(b) Oxidation: $Zn(s) \rightarrow Zn^{2+}(aq) + 2 e^-$ $-E° = +0.763 \text{ V}$

Reduction: $Fe^{2+}(aq) + 2 e^- \rightarrow Fe(s)$ $E° = -0.440 \text{ V}$

Net: $Zn(s) + Fe^{2+}(aq) \rightarrow Fe(s) + Zn^{2+}(aq)$ $E°_{cell} = +0.323 \text{ V}$

This is a spontaneous reaction under standard conditions.

(c) Oxidation: $\{Fe^{2+}(aq) \rightarrow Fe^{3+}(aq) + e^-\} \times 2$ $-E° = -0.771 \text{ V}$

Reduction: $I_2(s) + 2 e^- \rightarrow 2 I^-(aq)$ $E° = +0.535 \text{ V}$

Net: $2 Fe^{2+}(aq) + I_2(s) \rightarrow 2 Fe^{3+}(aq) + 2 I^-(aq)$ $E°_{cell} = -0.236 \text{ V}$

This reaction requires electrolysis, with an applied voltage greater than $+0.236 \text{ V}$.

(d) Oxidation: $Cu(s) \rightarrow Cu^{2+}(aq) + 2 e^-$ $-E° = -0.337 \text{ V}$

Reduction: $\{Sn^{4+}(aq) + 2 e^- \rightarrow Sn^{2+}(aq)\} \times 2$ $E° = +0.154 \text{ V}$

Net: $Cu(s) + Sn^{4+}(aq) \rightarrow Cu^{2+}(aq) + Sn^{2+}(aq)$ $E°_{cell} = -0.183 \text{ V}$

This reaction requires electrolysis, with an applied voltage greater than $+0.183 \text{ V}$.

66. (M)

(a) Because oxidation occurs at the anode, we know that the product cannot be H_2 (H_2 is produced from the reduction of H_2O), SO_2, (which is a reduction product of SO_4^{2-}), or SO_3 (which is produced from SO_4^{2-} without a change of oxidation state; it is the dehydration product of H_2SO_4). It is, in fact O_2 that forms at the anode. The oxidation of water at the anode produces the $O_2(g)$.

(b) Reduction should occur at the cathode. The possible species that can be reduced are H_2O to $H_2(g)$, $K^+(aq)$ to $K(s)$, and $SO_4^{2-}(aq)$ to perhaps $SO_2(g)$. Because potassium is a highly active metal, it will not be produced in aqueous solution. In order for $SO_4^{2-}(aq)$ to be reduced, it would have to migrate to the negatively charged cathode, which is not very probable since like charges repel each other. Thus, $H_2(g)$ is produced at the cathode.

(c) At the anode: $\quad 2\,H_2O(l) \rightarrow 4\,H^+(aq) + O_2(g) + 4\,e^- \qquad -E° = -1.229\ \text{V}$

At the cathode: $\quad \{2\,H^+(aq) + 2\,e^- \rightarrow H_2(g)\} \times 2 \qquad E° = 0.000\ \text{V}$

Net cell reaction: $2\,H_2O(l) \rightarrow 2\,H_2(g) + O_2(g) \qquad E°_{cell} = -1.229\ \text{V}$

A voltage greater than 1.229 V is required. Because of the high overpotential required for the formation of gases, we expect that a higher voltage will be necessary.

67. (M)

(a) The two gases that are produced are $H_2(g)$ and $O_2(g)$.

(b) At the anode: $2\,H_2O(l) \rightarrow 4\,H^+(aq) + O_2(g) + 4\,e^- \qquad -E° = -1.229\ \text{V}$

At the cathode: $\{2\,H^+(aq) + 2\,e^- \rightarrow H_2(g)\} \times 2 \qquad E° = 0.000\ \text{V}$

Net cell reaction: $2\,H_2O(l) \rightarrow 2\,H_2(g) + O_2(g) \qquad E°_{cell} = -1.229\ \text{V}$

68. (M) The electrolysis of $Na_2SO_4(aq)$ produces molecular oxygen at the anode. $-E°\{O_2(g)/H_2O\} = -1.229$ V. The other possible product is $S_2O_8^{2-}(aq)$. It is however, unlikely to form because it has a considerably less favorable half-cell potential. $-E°\{S_2O_8^{2-}(aq)/SO_4^{2-}(aq)\} = -2.01$ V.

$H_2(g)$ is formed at the cathode.

$$\text{mol } O_2 = 3.75\,\text{h} \times \frac{3600\,\text{s}}{1\,\text{h}} \times \frac{2.83\,\text{C}}{1\,\text{s}} \times \frac{1\,\text{mol } e^-}{96,485\,\text{C}} \times \frac{1\,\text{mol } O_2}{4\,\text{mol } e^-} = 0.0990\,\text{mol } O_2$$

The vapor pressure of water at 25°C, from Table 12.3, is 23.8 mmHg.

$$V = \frac{nRT}{p} = \frac{0.0990\,\text{mol} \times 0.08314\,\text{L bar mol}^{-1}\,\text{K}^{-1} \times 298\,\text{K}}{(742 - 23.8)\,\text{mmHg} \times \dfrac{1.01325\,\text{bar}}{760\,\text{mmHg}}} = 2.56\,\text{L } O_2(g)$$

69. (M)

(a) $Zn^{2+}(aq) + 2e^- \rightarrow Zn(s)$

mass of Zn $= 42.5 \text{ min} \times \dfrac{60 \text{ s}}{1 \text{ min}} \times \dfrac{1.87 \text{ C}}{1 \text{ s}} \times \dfrac{1 \text{ mol e}^-}{96,485 \text{ C}} \times \dfrac{1 \text{ mol Zn}}{2 \text{ mol e}^-} \times \dfrac{65.38 \text{g Zn}}{1 \text{ mol Zn}} = 1.62 \text{ g Zn}$

(b) $2I^-(aq) \rightarrow I_2(s) + 2e^-$

time needed $= 2.79 \text{ g I}_2 \times \dfrac{1 \text{mol I}_2}{253.8090 \text{ g I}_2} \times \dfrac{2 \text{ mol e}^-}{1 \text{mol I}_2} \times \dfrac{96,485 \text{ C}}{1 \text{ mol e}^-} \times \dfrac{1 \text{ s}}{1.75 \text{C}} \times \dfrac{1 \text{ min}}{60 \text{ s}} = 20.2 \text{ min}$

70. (M) (a) $Cu^{2+}(aq) + 2e^- \rightarrow Cu(s)$

mmol Cu^{2+} consumed $= 282 \text{ s} \times \dfrac{2.68 \text{ C}}{1 \text{ s}} \times \dfrac{1 \text{ mol e}^-}{96,485 \text{ C}} \times \dfrac{1 \text{ mol Cu}^{2+}}{2 \text{ mol e}^-} \times \dfrac{1000 \text{ mmol}}{1 \text{mol}}$

$= 3.92 \text{ mmol Cu}^{2+}$

decrease in $[Cu^{2+}] = \dfrac{3.92 \text{ mmol Cu}^{2+}}{425 \text{ mL}} = 0.00922 \text{ M}$

final $[Cu^{2+}] = 0.366 \text{ M} - 0.00922 \text{ M} = 0.357 \text{ M}$

(b) mmol Ag^+ consumed $= 255 \text{ mL}(0.196 \text{ M} - 0.175 \text{ M}) = 5.3\underline{6} \text{ mmol Ag}^+$

time needed $= 5.36 \text{ mmol Ag}^+ \times \dfrac{1 \text{ mol Ag}^+}{1000 \text{ mmol Ag}^+} \times \dfrac{1 \text{ mol e}^-}{1 \text{ mol Ag}^+} \times \dfrac{96,485 \text{ C}}{1 \text{ mol e}^-} \times \dfrac{1 \text{ s}}{1.84 \text{ C}}$

$= 28\underline{1} \text{ s} \approx 2.8 \times 10^2 \text{ s}$

71. (M)

(a) charge $= 1.206 \text{ g Ag} \times \dfrac{1 \text{ mol Ag}}{107.8682 \text{ g Ag}} \times \dfrac{1 \text{ mol e}^-}{1 \text{ mol Ag}} \times \dfrac{96,485 \text{ C}}{1 \text{ mol e}^-} = 1079 \text{ C}$

(b) current $= \dfrac{1079 \text{ C}}{1412 \text{ s}} = 0.7642 \text{ A}$

72. (D)

(a) Anode, oxidation: $2 H_2O(l) \rightarrow 4 H^+(aq) + 4 e^- + O_2(g)$ $\qquad -E° = -1.229 \text{ V}$

Cathode, reduction: $\{Ag^+(aq) + e^- \rightarrow Ag(s)\} \times 4$ $\qquad E° = +0.800 \text{ V}$

Net: $2 H_2O(l) + 4 Ag^+(aq) \rightarrow 4 H^+(aq) + O_2(g) + 4 Ag(s)$ $\qquad E°_{cell} = -0.429 \text{ V}$

(b) charge $= (25.8639 - 25.0782) \text{ g Ag} \times \dfrac{1 \text{ mol Ag}}{107.8682 \text{ g Ag}} \times \dfrac{1 \text{ mol e}^-}{1 \text{ mol Ag}} \times \dfrac{96,485 \text{ C}}{1 \text{ mol e}^-} = 702.8 \text{ C}$

current $= \dfrac{702.8 \text{ C}}{2.00 \text{ h}} \times \dfrac{1 \text{h}}{3600 \text{ s}} = 0.0976 \text{ A}$

(c) The gas is molecular oxygen.

$$V = \frac{nRT}{p} = \frac{\left(702.8 \text{ C} \times \dfrac{1 \text{ mol e}^-}{96{,}485 \text{ C}} \times \dfrac{1 \text{ mol O}_2}{4 \text{ mol e}^-}\right) \times 0.08314 \text{ L bar mol}^{-1} \text{ K}^{-1} \times (23 + 273.15) \text{ K}}{755 \text{ mmHg} \times \dfrac{1.01325 \text{ bar}}{760 \text{ mmHg}}}$$

$$= 0.0445 \text{ L O}_2 \times \frac{1000 \text{ mL}}{1 \text{ L}} = 44.5 \text{ mL of O}_2$$

<u>**73.**</u> **(D)**

(a) The electrochemical reaction is:

Anode (oxidation): $\{\text{Ag(s)} \rightarrow \text{Ag}^+(\text{aq}) + \text{e}^-(\text{aq})\} \times 2$ $-E° = -0.800 \text{ V}$

Cathode (reduction): $\text{Cu}^{2+}(\text{aq}) + 2\text{ e}^- \rightarrow \text{Cu(s)}$ $E° = +0.340 \text{ V}$

Net: $2\text{ Ag(s)} + \text{Cu}^{2+}(\text{aq}) \rightarrow \text{Cu(s)} + 2\text{ Ag}^+(\text{aq})$ $E°_{\text{cell}} = -0.46 \text{ V}$

Therefore, copper should plate out first.

(b) $\text{current} = \dfrac{\text{charge}}{2.50 \text{ h min}} \times \dfrac{1 \text{ h}}{3600 \text{ s}} = 0.75 \text{ A} \Rightarrow \text{charge} = 6750 \text{ C}$

$$\text{mass} = 6750 \text{ C} \times \frac{1 \text{ mole}^-}{96{,}485 \text{ C}} \times \frac{1 \text{ mol Cu}}{2 \text{ mol e}^-} \times \frac{63.5463 \text{ g Cu}}{1 \text{ mol Cu}} = 2.22 \text{ g Cu}$$

(c) The total mass of the metal is 3.50 g out of which 2.22 g is copper. Therefore, the mass of silver in the sample is 3.50 g – 2.22 g = 1.28 g or (1.28/3.50) × 100 = 37%.

74. **(D)** First, calculate the number of moles of electrons involved in the electrolysis:

$$1.20 \text{ C/s} \times 32.0 \text{ min} \times \frac{60 \text{ sec}}{1 \text{ min}} \times \frac{1 \text{ mole e}^-}{96{,}485 \text{ C}} = 0.0239 \text{ mol e}^-$$

From the known mass of platinum, determine the number of moles:

$$2.12 \text{ gPt} \times \frac{1 \text{ mol Pt}}{195.08 \text{ g Pt}} = 0.0109 \text{ mol Pt}$$

Determine the number of electrons transferred:

$$\frac{0.0239 \text{ mol e}^-}{0.0109 \text{ mol Pt}} = 2.19$$

Therefore, 2.19 is shared between Pt^{2+} and Pt^{x+}. Since we know the mole ratio between Pt^{2+} and Pt^{x+}, we can calculate x:

2.19 = 0.90 × (+2) + 0.10 × (x).

$2.19 = 1.80 + 0.10 \times x \Rightarrow x \approx 4$

(a) The oxidation state of the contaminant is +4.

INTEGRATIVE AND ADVANCED EXERCISES

75. (M) Oxidation: $V^{3+} + H_2O \longrightarrow VO^{2+} + 2\,H^+ + e^-$ $-E^{\circ}{}_a$

Reduction: $Ag^+ + e^- \longrightarrow Ag(s)$ $E^{\circ} = +0.800\ \text{V}$

Net: $V^{3+} + H_2O + Ag^+ \longrightarrow VO^{2+} + 2\,H^+ + Ag(s)$ $E^{\circ}_{cell} = 0.439\ \text{V}$

$0.439\ \text{V} = -E^{\circ}{}_a + 0.800\ \text{V}$ $E^{\circ}{}_a = 0.800\ \text{V} - 0.439\ \text{V} = 0.361\ \text{V}$

Oxidation: $V^{2+} \longrightarrow V^{3+} + e^-$ $-E^{\circ}{}_b$

Reduction: $VO^{2+} + 2\,H^+ + e^- \longrightarrow V^{3+} + H_2O$ $E^{\circ} = +0.361\ \text{V}$

Net: $V^{2+} + VO^{2+} + 2\,H^+ \longrightarrow 2\,V^{3+} + H_2O$ $E^{\circ}_{cell} = +0.616\ \text{V}$

$0.616\ \text{V} = -E^{\circ}{}_b + 0.361\ \text{V}$ $E^{\circ}{}_b = 0.361\ \text{V} - 0.616\ \text{V} = -0.255\ \text{V}$

Thus, for the cited reaction: $V^{3+} + e^- \longrightarrow V^{2+}$ $E^{\circ} = -0.255\ \text{V}$

76. (M) The cell reaction for discharging a lead storage battery is equation (19.24).

$$Pb(s) + PbO_2(s) + 2\,H^+(aq) + 2\,HSO_4{}^-(aq) \longrightarrow PbSO_4(s) + 2\,H_2O(l)$$

The half-reactions with which this equation was derived indicates that two moles of electrons are transferred for every two moles of sulfate ion consumed. We first compute the amount of H_2SO_4 initially present and then the amount of H_2SO_4 consumed.

$$\text{initial amount } H_2SO_4 = 1.50\ \text{L} \times \frac{5.00\ \text{mol } H_2SO_4}{1\ \text{L soln}} = 7.50\ \text{mol } H_2SO_4$$

$$\text{amount } H_2SO_4 \text{ consumed} = 6.0\ \text{h} \times \frac{3600\ \text{s}}{1\ \text{h}} \times \frac{2.50\ \text{C}}{1\ \text{s}} \times \frac{1\ \text{mol } e^-}{96485\ \text{C}} \times \frac{2\ \text{mol } SO_4{}^{2-}}{2\ \text{mol } e^-} \times \frac{1\ \text{mol } H_2SO_4}{1\ \text{mol } SO_4{}^{2-}}$$

$$= 0.56\ \text{mol } H_2SO_4$$

$$\text{final}\,[H_2SO_4] = \frac{7.50\ \text{mol} - 0.56\ \text{mol}}{1.50\ \text{L}} = 4.63\ \text{M}$$

77. (M) The cell reaction is $2\,Cl^-(aq) + 2\,H_2O(l) \longrightarrow 2\,OH^-(aq) + H_2(g) + Cl_2(g)$

We first determine the charge transferred per 1000 kg Cl_2.

$$\text{charge} = 1000\ \text{kg } Cl_2 \times \frac{1000\ \text{g}}{1\ \text{kg}} \times \frac{1\ \text{mol } Cl_2}{70.8920\ \text{g } Cl_2} \times \frac{2\ \text{mol } e^-}{1\ \text{mol } Cl_2} \times \frac{96{,}485\ \text{C}}{1\ \text{mol } e^-} = 2.72 \times 10^9\ \text{C}$$

(a) $\text{energy} = 3.45\ \text{V} \times 2.72 \times 10^9\ \text{C} \times \dfrac{1\ \text{J}}{1\ \text{V} \cdot \text{C}} \times \dfrac{1\ \text{kJ}}{1000\ \text{J}} = 9.38 \times 10^6\ \text{kJ}$

(b) $\text{energy} = 9.38 \times 10^9\ \text{J} \times \dfrac{1\ \text{W} \cdot \text{s}}{1\ \text{J}} \times \dfrac{1\ \text{h}}{3600\ \text{s}} \times \dfrac{1\ \text{kWh}}{1000\ \text{W} \cdot \text{h}} = 2.61 \times 10^3\ \text{kWh}$

78. (D) Separate the given equation into two half-equations:

Oxidation: $\text{Ni(s)} \rightarrow \text{Ni}^{2+}\text{(aq)} + 2\,e^-$ $-E° = 0.257$ V

Reduction: $\{\text{V}^{3+}\text{(aq)} + e^- \rightarrow \text{V}^{2+}\text{(aq)}\} \times 2$ $E° = -0.255$ V

Net: $\text{Ni(s)} + 2\,\text{V}^{3+}\text{(aq)} \rightleftharpoons \text{Ni}^{2+}\text{(aq)} + 2\,\text{V}^{2+}\text{(aq)}$ $E°_{\text{cell}} = 0.002$ V

Next, determine the equilibrium constant for the reaction:

$$\Delta_r G° = -zFE°_{\text{cell}} = -RT \ln K \Rightarrow \ln K = \frac{zFE°_{\text{cell}}}{RT}$$

$$\ln K = \frac{2 \text{ mol} \times 96485 \text{ C/mol} \times 0.002 \text{ V}}{8.3145 \text{ J mol}^{-1} \text{ K}^{-1} \times 298 \text{ K}} = 0.156 \quad K = e^{0.156} = 1.17$$

Reaction:	Ni(s)	+	$2\,\text{V}^{3+}\text{(aq)}$	$\rightleftharpoons$	$\text{Ni}^{2+}\text{(aq)}$	+	$2\,\text{V}^{2+}\text{(aq)}$
Initial:			0.500 M		0 M		0 M
Changes:			$-2x$ M		$+x$ M		$+2x$ M
Equil.:			$(0.500 - 2x)$ M		x M		$2x$ M

$$K = \frac{[\text{Ni}^{2+}][\text{V}^{2+}]^2}{[\text{V}^{3+}]^2} = 1.17 = \frac{x\,(2x)^2}{(0.500 - 2x)^2}$$

We can either directly solve this cubic equation or use the method of successive approximations to find a solution for x. Note that x cannot be larger than 0.25 (values > 0.25 will result in a negative value for the denominator).

Trial 1 ($x = 0.20$)

$$K = \frac{0.20(2 \times 0.20)^2}{(0.50 - 2 \times 0.20)^2} = 3.2 > 1.17$$

Trial 2 ($x = 0.15$)

$$K = \frac{0.15(2 \times 0.15)^2}{(0.50 - 2 \times 0.15)^2} = 0.338 < 1.17$$

Trial 3 ($x = 0.17$)

$$K = \frac{0.17(2 \times 0.17)^2}{(0.50 - 2 \times 0.17)^2} = 0.768 < 1.17$$

Therefore, we conclude that $x \approx 0.18$ $[\text{Ni}^{2+}] = 0.18$ M.

79. (D) First we calculate the standard cell potential.

Oxidation: $\text{Fe}^{2+}\text{(aq)} \longrightarrow \text{Fe}^{3+}\text{(aq)} + e^-$ $-E° = -0.771$ V

Reduction: $\text{Ag}^+\text{(aq)} + e^- \longrightarrow \text{Ag(s)}$ $E° = +0.800$ V

Net: $\text{Fe}^{2+}\text{(aq)} + \text{Ag}^+\text{(aq)} \longrightarrow \text{Fe}^{3+}\text{(aq)} + \text{Ag(s)}$ $E°_{\text{cell}} = 0.029$ V

Next, we use the given concentrations to calculate the cell voltage with the Nernst equation.

$$E_{cell} = E^\circ{}_{cell} - \frac{0.0257\ V}{1} \ln \frac{[Fe^{3+}]}{[Fe^{2+}][Ag^+]} = 0.029\ V - 0.0257\ V \ln \frac{0.0050}{0.0050 \times 2.0} = (0.029 + 0.018)\ V = 0.047\ V$$

The reaction will continue to move in the forward direction until concentrations of reactants decrease and those of products increase a bit more. At equilibrium, $E_{cell} = 0$, and we have the following.

$$E^\circ{}_{cell} = \frac{0.0257\ V}{1} \ln \frac{[Fe^{3+}]}{[Fe^{2+}][Ag^+]} = 0.029\ V \quad \ln \frac{[Fe^{3+}]}{[Fe^{2+}][Ag^+]} = \frac{0.029\ V}{0.0257\ V} = 1.13$$

Reaction:	$Fe^{2+}(aq)$	$+$	$Ag^+(aq)$	$\rightleftharpoons$	$Fe^{3+}(aq)$	$+$	$Ag(s)$	
Initial:	0.0050 M		2.0 M		0.0050 M			–
Changes:	$-x$ M		$-x$ M		$+x$ M			–
Equil:	$(0.0050 - x)$ M		$(2.0 - x)$ M		$(0.0050 + x)$ M			–

$$\frac{[Fe^{3+}]}{[Fe^{2+}][Ag^+]} = e^{1.13} = 3.1 = \frac{0.0050 + x}{(0.0050 - x)(2.0 - x)} \approx \frac{0.0050 + x}{2.0(0.0050 - x)}$$

$$6.2(0.0050 - x) = 0.0050 + x = 0.031 - 6.2\ x \quad 7.2\ x = 0.026 \quad x = \frac{0.026}{7.2} = 0.0036$$

Note that the assumption that $x \ll 2.0$ is valid. $[Fe^{2+}] = 0.0050\ M - 0.0036\ M = 0.0014\ M$

80. (D) We first note that we are dealing with a concentration cell, one in which the standard oxidation reaction is the reverse of the standard reduction reaction, and consequently its standard cell potential is precisely zero volts. For this cell, the Nernst equation permits us to determine the ratio of the two silver ion concentrations.

$$E_{cell} = 0.000\ V - \frac{0.0257\ V}{1} \ln \frac{[Ag^+(\text{satd AgI})]}{[Ag^+(\text{satd AgCl},\ x\ M\ Cl^-)]} = 0.0860\ V$$

$$\ln \frac{[Ag^+(\text{satd AgI})]}{[Ag^+(\text{satd AgCl},\ x\ M\ Cl^-)]} = \frac{-0.0860\ V}{0.0257\ V} = -3.35 \quad \frac{[Ag^+(\text{satd AgI})]}{[Ag^+(\text{satd AgCl},\ x\ M\ Cl^-)]} = e^{-3.35} = 0.035$$

We can determine the numerator concentration from the solubility product expression for AgI(s)

$$K_{sp} = [Ag^+][I^-] = 8.5 \times 10^{-17} = s^2 \quad s = \sqrt{8.5 \times 10^{-17}} = 9.2 \times 10^{-9}\ M$$

This permits the determination of the concentration in the denominator.

$$[Ag^+(\text{satd AgCl},\ x\ M\ Cl^-)] = \frac{9.2 \times 10^{-9}}{0.035} = 2.6 \times 10^{-7}\ M$$

We now can determine the value of x. Note: Cl^- arises from two sources, one being the dissolved AgCl.

$$K_{sp} = [Ag^+][Cl^-] = 1.8 \times 10^{-10} = (2.6 \times 10^{-7})(2.6 \times 10^{-7} + x) = 6.8 \times 10^{-14} + 2.6 \times 10^{-7}\ x$$

$$x = \frac{1.8 \times 10^{-10} - 6.8 \times 10^{-14}}{2.6 \times 10^{-7}} = 6.9 \times 10^{-4}\ M = [Cl^-]$$

81. **(M)** The Faraday constant can be evaluated by measuring the electric charge needed to produce a certain quantity of chemical change. For instance, let's imagine that an electric circuit contains the half-reaction $Cu^{2+}(aq) + 2\ e^- \rightleftharpoons Cu(s)$. The electrode on which the solid copper plates out is weighed before and after the passage of electric current. The mass gain is the mass of copper reduced, which then is converted into the moles of copper reduced. The number of moles of electrons involved in the reduction then is computed from the stoichiometry for the reduction half-reaction. In addition, the amperage is measured during the reduction, and the time is recorded. For simplicity, we assume the amperage is constant. Then the total charge (in coulombs) equals the current (in amperes, that is, coulombs per second) multiplied by the time (in seconds). The ratio of the total charge (in coulombs) required by the reduction divided by the amount (in moles) of electrons is the Faraday constant. To determine the Avogadro constant, one uses the charge of the electron, 1.602×10^{-19} C and the Faraday constant in the following calculation.

$$N_A = \frac{96,485\ C}{1\ mol\ electrons} \times \frac{1\ electron}{1.602 \times 10^{-19}\ C} = 6.023 \times 10^{23}\ \frac{electrons}{mole}$$

82. **(M)** In this problem we are asked to determine ΔG_f° for $N_2H_4(aq)$ using the electrochemical data for hydrazine fuel cell. We first determine the value of ΔG° for the cell reaction, a reaction in which $z = 4$. $\Delta_f G^\circ$ can then be determined using data in Appendix D.

Stewise approach:

Calculate ΔG° for the cell reaction (n=4):

$$\Delta_r G^\circ = -zFE^\circ_{cell} - 4\ mol\ e^- \times \frac{96,485\ C}{1\ mol} \times 1.559\ V = -6.017 \times 10^5\ J\ mol^{-1} = -601.7\ kJ\ mol^{-1}$$

Using the data in Appendix D, determine $\Delta_f G^\circ$ for hydrazine (N_2H_4):

$$-601.7\ kJ/mol = \Delta_f G^\circ[N_2(g)] + 2\ \Delta_f G^\circ[H_2O(l)] - \Delta_f G^\circ[N_2H_4(aq)] - \Delta_f G^\circ[O_2(g)]$$
$$= 0.00\ kJ/mol + 2 \times (-237.2\ kJ/mol) - \Delta_f G^\circ[N_2H_4(aq)] - 0.00\ kJ/mol$$

$$\Delta_f G^\circ[N_2H_4(aq)] = 2 \times (-237.2\ kJ/mol) + 601.7\ kJ/mol = +127.3\ kJ/mol$$

83. **(M)** In general, we shall assume that both ions are present initially at concentrations of 1.00 M. Then we shall compute the concentration of the more easily reduced ion when its reduction potential has reached the point at which the other cation starts being reduced by electrolysis. In performing this calculation we use the Nernst equation, but modified for use with a half-reaction. We find that, in general, the greater the difference in E° values for two reduction half-reactions, the more effective the separation.

(a) In this case, no calculation is necessary. If the electrolysis takes place in aqueous solution, $H_2(g)$ rather than $K(s)$ will be produced at the cathode. Cu^{2+} can be separated from K^+ by electrolysis.

(b) $Cu^{2+}(aq) + 2\,e^- \rightarrow Cu(s)$ $E° = +0.340$ V $\qquad$ $Ag^+(aq) + e^- \rightarrow Ag(s)$ $\quad$ $E° = +0.800$ V

Ag^+ will be reduced first. Now we ask what $[Ag^+]$ will be when $E = +0.337$ V.

$$0.337\ \text{V} = 0.800\ \text{V} - \frac{0.0257\ \text{V}}{1}\ \ln\frac{1}{[Ag^+]} \qquad \ln\frac{1}{[Ag^+]} = \frac{(0.800 - 0.340)\ \text{V}}{0.0257\ \text{V}} = +17.9$$

$[Ag^+] = 1.7 \times 10^{-8}$ M. Separation of the two cations is essentially complete.

(c) $Pb^{2+}(aq) + 2\,e^- \rightarrow Pb(s)$ $E° = -0.125$ V $\qquad$ $Sn^{2+}(aq) + 2\,e^- \rightarrow Sn(s)$ $\quad$ $E° = -0.137$ V

Pb^{2+} will be reduced first. We now ask what $[Pb^{2+}]$ will be when $E° = -0.137$ V.

$$-0.137\ \text{V} = -0.125\ \text{V} - \frac{0.0257\ \text{V}}{2}\ \ln\frac{1}{[Pb^{2+}]} \qquad \ln\frac{1}{[Pb^{2+}]} = \frac{2(0.137\ \text{V} - 0.125\ \text{V})}{0.0257\ \text{V}} = 0.93$$

$[Pb^{2+}] = e^{-0.93} = 0.39$ M $\quad$ Separation of Pb^{2+} from Sn^{2+} is not complete.

84. (D) The efficiency value for a fuel cell will be greater than 1.00 for any exothermic reaction ($\Delta_r H° < 0$) that has $\Delta_r G°$ that is more negative than its $\Delta_r H°$ value. Since $\Delta_r G° = \Delta_r H° - T\,\Delta_r S°$, this means that the value of $\Delta_r S°$ must be positive. Moreover, for this to be the case, Δn_{gas} is usually greater than zero. Let us consider the situation that might lead to this type of reaction. The combustion of carbon-hydrogen-oxygen compounds leads to the formation of $H_2O(l)$ and $CO_2(g)$. Since most of the oxygen in these compounds comes from $O_2(g)$ (some is present in the C—H—O compound), there is a balance in the number of moles of gas produced—$CO_2(g)$—and those consumed—$O_2(g)$—which is offset in a negative direction by the $H_2O(l)$ produced. Thus, the combustion of these types of compounds will only have a positive value of Δn_{gas} if the number of oxygens in the formula of the compound is more than twice the number of hydrogens. By comparison, the decomposition of NOCl(g), an oxychloride of nitrogen, does produce more moles of gas than it consumes. Let us investigate this decomposition reaction.

$NOCl(g) \longrightarrow \tfrac{1}{2}N_2(g) + \tfrac{1}{2}\,O_2(g) + \tfrac{1}{2}\,Cl_2(g)$

$\Delta_r H° = \tfrac{1}{2}\Delta_f H°[N_2(g)] + \tfrac{1}{2}\Delta_f H°[O_2(g)] + \tfrac{1}{2}\Delta_f H°[Cl_2(g)] - \Delta_f H°[NOCl(g)]$

$\quad = 0.500\,(0.00\ \text{kJ/mol} + 0.00\ \text{kJ/mol} + 0.00\ \text{kJ/mol}) - 51.71\ \text{kJ/mol} = -51.71\ \text{kJ/mol}$

$\Delta_r G° = \tfrac{1}{2}\Delta_f G°[N_2(g)] + \tfrac{1}{2}\Delta_f G°[O_2(g)] + \tfrac{1}{2}\Delta_f G°[Cl_2(g)] - \Delta_f G°[NOCl(g)]$

$\quad = 0.500\,(0.00\ \text{kJ/mol} + 0.00\ \text{kJ/mol} + 0.00\ \text{kJ/mol}) - 66.08\ \text{kJ/mol} = -66.08\ \text{kJ/mol}$

$$\varepsilon = \frac{\Delta_r G°}{\Delta_r H°} = \frac{-66.08\ \text{kJ/mol}}{-51.71\ \text{kJ/mol}} = 1.278$$

Yet another simple reaction that meets the requirement that $\Delta_r G° < \Delta_r H°$ is the combustion of graphite: $C(graphite) + O_2(g) \longrightarrow CO_2(g)$ We see from Appendix D that $\Delta_f G°[CO_2(g)] = -394.4$ kJ/mol is more negative than $\Delta_f H°[CO_2(g)] = -393.5$ kJ/mol. (This reaction is accompanied by an increase in entropy; $\Delta_r S = 213.7 - 5.74 - 205.1 = 2.86$ J/K, $\varepsilon = 1.002$.)

$\Delta_r G° < \Delta_r H°$ is true of the reaction in which CO(g) is formed from the elements. From Appendix D, $\Delta_f H°\{CO(g)\} = -110.5$ kJ/mol, and $\Delta_f G°\{CO(g)\} = -137.2$ kJ/mol, producing $\varepsilon = (-137.2/-110.5) = 1.242$.

Note that any reaction that has $\varepsilon > 1.00$ will be spontaneous under standard conditions at all temperatures. (There, of course, is another category, namely, an endothermic reaction that has $\Delta_r S° < 0$. This type of reaction is nonspontaneous under standard conditions at all temperatures. As such it consumes energy while it is running, which is clearly not a desirable result for a fuel cell.)

85. (M) We first write the two half-equations and then calculate a value of $\Delta_r G°$ from thermochemical data. This value then is used to determine the standard cell potential.

Oxidation: $CH_3CH_2OH(g) + 3\ H_2O(l) \longrightarrow 2\ CO_2(g) + 12\ H^+(aq) + 12\ e^-$

Reduction: $\{O_2(g) + 4\ H^+(aq) + 4e^- \longrightarrow 2\ H_2O(l)\} \times 3$

Overall: $CH_3CH_2OH(g) + 3\ O_2(g) \longrightarrow 3\ H_2O(l) + 2\ CO_2(g)$

Thus, $z = 12$

(a) $\Delta_r G° = 2\Delta_f G°[CO_2(g)] + 3\Delta_f G°[H_2O(l)] - \Delta_f G°[CH_3CH_2OH(g)] - 3\Delta_f G°[O_2(g)]$

$= 2(-394.4\text{ kJ/mol}) + 3(-237.1\text{ kJ/mol}) - (-168.5\text{ kJ/mol}) - 3(0.00\text{ kJ/mol})$

$= -1331.6\text{ kJ/mol}$

$E°_{cell} = -\dfrac{\Delta_r G°}{z\ F} = -\dfrac{-1331.6 \times 10^3\text{ J/mol}}{12 \times 96,485\text{ C/mol}} = +1.1501\text{ V}$

(b) $E°_{cell} = E°[O_2(g)/H_2O] - E°[CO_2(g)/CH_3CH_2OH(g)] = 1.1501\text{ V}$

$= 1.229\text{ V} - E°[CO_2(g)/CH_3CH_2OH(g)]$

$E°[CO_2(g)/CH_3CH_2OH(g)] = (1.229 - 1.1501)\text{ V} = +0.079\text{ V}$

86. (M) First we determine the change in the amount of H^+ in each compartment.

Oxidation: $2\ H_2O(l) \rightarrow O_2(g) + 4\ H^+(aq) + 4\ e^-$ Reduction: $2\ H^+(aq) + 2\ e^- \rightarrow H_2(g)$

Change in amount of $H^+ = 212\text{ min} \times \dfrac{60\text{ s}}{1\text{ min}} \times \dfrac{1.25\text{ C}}{1\text{ s}} \times \dfrac{1\text{ mol e}^-}{96,485\text{ C}} \times \dfrac{1\text{ mol H}^+}{1\text{ mol e}^-} = 0.165\text{ mol H}^+$

Before electrolysis, there is 0.500 mol $H_2PO_4^-$ and 0.500 mol HPO_4^{2-} in each compartment. The electrolysis adds 0.165 mol H^+ to the anode compartment, which has the effect of transforming 0.165 mol HPO_4^{2-} into 0.165 mol $H_2PO_4^-$, giving a total of 0.335 mol HPO_4^{2-} (0.500 mol − 0.165 mol) and 0.665 mol $H_2PO_4^-$ (0.500 mol + 0.165 mol). We can use the Henderson-Hasselbalch equation to determine the pH of the solution in the anode compartment.

$pH = pK_{a_2} + \log \dfrac{[HPO_4^{2-}]}{[H_2PO_4^-]} = 7.20 + \log \dfrac{0.335\text{ mol}/0.500\text{ L}}{0.665\text{ mol}/0.500\text{ L}} = 6.90$

Again we use the Henderson-Hasselbalch equation in the cathode compartment. After electrolysis there is 0.665 mol HPO_4^{2-} and 0.335 mol $H_2PO_4^-$. Again we use the Henderson-Hasselbalch equation.

$$pH = pK_{a_2} + \log\frac{[HPO_4^{2-}]}{[H_2PO_4^-]} = 7.20 + \log\frac{0.665 \text{ mol}/0.500 \text{ L}}{0.335 \text{ mol}/0.500 \text{ L}} = 7.50$$

87. (M) We first determine the change in the amount of M^{2+} ion in each compartment.

$$\text{Change in amount of } M^{2+} = 10.00 \text{ h} \times \frac{3600 \text{ s}}{1 \text{ h}} \times \frac{0.500 \text{ C}}{1 \text{ s}} \times \frac{1 \text{ mol e}^-}{96,485 \text{ C}} \times \frac{1 \text{ mol } M^{2+}}{2 \text{ mol e}^-} = 0.0933 \text{ mol } M^{2+}$$

This change in amount is the increase in the amount of Cu^{2+} and the decrease in the amount of Zn^{2+}. We can also calculate the change in each of the concentrations.

$$\Delta[Cu^{2+}] = \frac{+0.0933 \text{ mol } Cu^{2+}}{0.1000 \text{ L}} = +0.933 \text{ M} \quad \Delta[Zn^{2+}] = \frac{-0.0933 \text{ mol } Zn^{2+}}{0.1000 \text{ L}} = -0.933 \text{ M}$$

Then the concentrations of the two ions are determined.

$[Cu^{2+}] = 1.000 \text{ M} + 0.933 \text{ M} = 1.933 \text{ M} \quad [Zn^{2+}] = 1.000 \text{ M} - 0.933 \text{ M} = 0.067 \text{ M}$

Now we run the cell as a voltaic cell, first determining the value of $E°_{cell}$.

Oxidation: $Zn(s) \longrightarrow Zn^{2+}(aq) + 2e^- \qquad -E° = +0.763 \text{ V}$

Reduction: $Cu^{2+}(aq) + 2e^- \quad Cu(s) \qquad E° = +0.340 \text{ V}$

Net: $Zn(s) + Cu^{2+}(aq) \longrightarrow Cu(s) \qquad E°_{cell} = +1.103 \text{ V}$

Then we use the Nernst equation to determine the voltage of this cell.

$$E_{cell} = E°_{cell} - \frac{0.0257 \text{ V}}{2} \ln\frac{[Zn^{2+}]}{[Cu^{2+}]} = 1.103 - \frac{0.0257 \text{ V}}{2} \ln\frac{0.067 \text{ M}}{1.933 \text{ M}} = (1.103 + 0.043) \text{ V} = 1.146 \text{ V}$$

88. (M)

(a)

Anode: $Zn(s) \longrightarrow Zn^{2+}(aq) + 2e^- \qquad -E° = +0.763 \text{ V}$

Cathode: $\{AgCl(s) + e^-(aq) \longrightarrow Ag(s) + Cl^-(1 \text{ M})\} \times 2 \qquad E° = +0.2223 \text{ V}$

Net: $Zn(s) + 2AgCl(s) \longrightarrow Zn^{2+}(aq) + 2Ag(s) + 2Cl^-(1 \text{ M}) \quad E°_{cell} = +0.985 \text{ V}$

(b) The major reason why this electrode is easier to use than the standard hydrogen electrode is that it does not involve a gas. Thus there are not the practical difficulties involved in handling gases. Another reason is that it yields a higher value of $E°_{cell}$, thus, this is a more spontaneous system.

(c) Oxidation: $Ag(s) \longrightarrow Ag^+(aq) + e^- \qquad -E° = -0.800 \text{ V}$

Reduction: $AgCl(s) + e^- \longrightarrow Ag(s) + Cl^-(aq) \qquad E = +0.2223 \text{ V}$

Net: $AgCl(s) \longrightarrow Ag^+(aq) + Cl^-(aq) \qquad E°_{cell} = -0.578 \text{ V}$

The net reaction is the solubility reaction, for which the equilibrium constant is K_{sp}.

$$\Delta_r G^\circ = -zFE^\circ = -RT \ln K_{sp}$$

$$\ln K_{sp} = \frac{zFE^\circ}{RT} = \frac{1 \times \dfrac{96,485\ C}{1\ mol} \times (-0.578\ V) \times \dfrac{1\ J\ C^{-1}}{1\ V}}{8.3145\ J\ mol^{-1}\ K^{-1} \times 298.15\ K} = -22.5$$

$$K_{sp} = e^{-22.5} = 1.7 \times 10^{-10}$$

This value is in good agreement with the value of 1.8×10^{-10} given in Table 18-1.

89. (D)

(a)

$$\begin{array}{lll} Ag(s) & \rightarrow & Ag^+(aq) + e^- & -E^\circ = -0.800\ V \\ AgCl(s) + e^- & \rightarrow & Ag(s) + Cl^-(aq) & E^\circ = 0.2223\ V \\ \hline AgCl(s) & \rightarrow & Ag^+(aq) + Cl^-(aq) & E^\circ_{cell} = -0.577\underline{7}\ V \end{array}$$

$$E_{cell} = E^\circ_{cell} - \frac{0.0257\ V}{1}\left(\ln \frac{[Ag^+][Cl^-]}{1}\right) = -0.577\underline{7}\ V - \frac{0.0257\ V}{1}\ln\left(\frac{[1.00][1.00 \times 10^{-3}]}{1}\right) = -0.400\ V$$

(b) 10.00 mL of 0.0100 M CrO_4^{2-} + 100.0 mL of 1.00×10^{-3} M Ag^+ (V_{total} = 110.0 mL)

Concentration of CrO_4^{2-} after dilution: 0.0100 M × 10.00 mL/110.00 mL = 0.000909 M

Concentration of Ag^+ after dilution: 0.00100 M × 100.0 mL/110.00 mL = 0.000909 M

$Ag_2CrO_4(s)$ $\xrightleftharpoons{K_{sp}=1.1\times10^{-12}}$	$2Ag^+(aq)$ +	$CrO_4^{2-}(aq)$
Initial	0.000909 M	0.000909 M
Change(100% rxn)	–0.000909 M	–0.000455 M
New initial	0 M	0.000455 M
Change	+2x	+x
Equilibrium	2x	0.000455 M+x ≈ 0.000455 M

$1.1 \times 10^{-12} = (2x)^2(0.000454)$

$x = 0.0000246$ M Note: 5.4% of 0.000455 M (assumption may be considered valid)

(Answer would be $x = 0.0000253$ using method of successive approx.)

$[Ag^+] = 2x = 0.0000492$ M (0.0000506 M using method of successive approx.)

$$E_{cell} = E^\circ_{cell} - \frac{0.0257\ V}{1}\ln [Ag^+][Cl^-] = -0.577\underline{7}\ V - \frac{0.0257\ V}{1}\ln [1.00][4.92 \times 10^{-4}]$$

$$= -0.323\ V\ (-0.306\ V\ \text{for method of successive approximations})$$

(c) 10.00 mL 0.0100 M NH_3 + 10.00 mL 0.0100 M CrO_4^{2-} + 100.0 mL 1.00×10^{-3} M Ag^+ (V_{total} = 120.0 mL)

Concentration of NH_3 after dilution: 10.0 M × 10.00 mL /120.00 mL = 0.833 M

Concentration of CrO_4^{2-} after dilution: 0.0100 M × 10.00 mL /110.00 mL = 0.000833 M

Concentration of Ag^+ after dilution: 0.00100 M × 100.0 mL /110.00 mL = 0.000833 M

In order to determine the equilibrium concentration of free $Ag^+(aq)$, we first consider complexation of $Ag^+(aq)$ by $NH_3(aq)$ and then check to see if precipitation occurs.

	$Ag^+(aq)$	+	$2NH_3(aq)$ $\xrightarrow{K_f=1.6\times10^7}$	$Ag(NH_3)_2^+(aq)$
Initial	0.000833 M		0.833 M	0 M
Change(100% rxn)	−0.000833 M		−0.00167 M	+0.000833 M
New initial	0 M		0.831 M	0.000833 M
Change	+x		+2x	−x
Equilibrium	x		(0.831+2x) M	(0.000833 −x) M
Equilibrium (x ≈0)	x		0.831 M	0.000833 M

$1.6 \times 10^7 = 0.000833/x(0.831)^2$ $\qquad x = 7.5\underline{4}\times10^{-11}$ M $= [Ag^+]$

Note: The assumption is valid

Now we look to see if a precipitate forms: $Q_{sp} = (7.5\underline{4}\times10^{-11})^2(0.000833) = 4.7 \times10^{-24}$

Since $Q_{sp} < K_{sp}$ (1.1×10^{-12}), no precipitate forms and $[Ag^+] = 7.5\underline{4} \times 10^{-11}$ M

$$E_{cell} = E°_{cell} - \frac{0.0257\text{ V}}{1}\ln[Ag^+][Cl^-] = -0.577\underline{7}\text{ V} - \frac{0.0257\text{ V}}{1}\ln[1.00][7.5\underline{4}\times10^{-11}]$$

$$E_{cell} = 0.021\underline{5}\text{ V}$$

90. **(M)** We assume that the $Pb^{2+}(aq)$ is "ignored" by the silver electrode, that is, the silver electrode detects only silver ion in solution.

Oxidation : $H_2(g) \longrightarrow 2H^+(aq) + 2e^-$ $\qquad -E° = 0.000$ V

Reduction: $\{Ag^+(aq) + e^- \longrightarrow Ag(s)\}\times2$ $\qquad E° = 0.800$ V

Net: $\quad H_2(g) + 2Ag^+ \longrightarrow 2H^+(aq) + 2Ag(s)$ $\quad E°_{cell} = 0.800$ V

$$E_{cell} = E°_{cell} - \frac{0.0257\text{ V}}{2}\ln\frac{[H^+]^2}{[Ag^+]^2} 0.503\text{ V} = 0.800\text{ V} - \frac{0.0257\text{ V}}{2}\ln\frac{1.00^2}{[Ag^+]^2}$$

$$\log\frac{1.00^2}{[Ag^+]^2} = \frac{2(0.800-0.503)}{0.0257\text{ V}} = 23.1 \qquad \frac{1.00^2}{[Ag^+]^2} = e^{+23.1} = 1.0\times10^{10}$$

$[Ag^+]^2 = 1.0\times10^{-10}M^2 \Rightarrow [Ag^+] = 1.0\times10^{-5}$ M

$$\text{mass Ag} = 0.500\text{ L}\times\frac{1.0\times10^{-5}\text{ mol }Ag^+}{1\text{ L soln}}\times\frac{1\text{ mol Ag}}{1\text{ mol }Ag^+}\times\frac{107.87\text{ g Ag}}{1\text{ mol Ag}} = 5.4\times10^{-4}\text{ g Ag}$$

$$\%\text{ Ag} = \frac{5.4\times10^{-4}\text{ g Ag}}{1.050\text{ g sample}}\times100\% = 0.051\%\text{ Ag (by mass)}$$

91. **(M)** 250.0 mL of 0.1000 M $CuSO_4$ = 0.02500 moles Cu^{2+} initially.

$$\text{moles of }Cu^{2+}\text{ plated out} = \frac{3.512\text{ C}}{s}\times1368\text{ s}\times\frac{1\text{ mol }e^-}{96,485\text{ C}}\times\frac{1\text{ mol }Cu^{2+}}{2\text{ mol }e^-} = 0.02490\text{ mol }Cu^{2+}$$

moles of Cu^{2+} in solution = 0.02500 mol – 0.02490 mol = 0.00010 mol Cu^{2+}

$[Cu^{2+}]$ = 0.00010 mol Cu^{2+}/0.250 L = 4.0×10^{-4} M

	Cu^{2+}(aq)	+ 4NH$_3$(aq) $\xrightarrow{K_f=1.1\times10^{13}}$	$Cu(NH_3)_4{}^{2+}$(aq)
Initial	0.00040 M	0.10 M	0 M
Change(100% rxn)	–0.00040M	maintained	+0.00040 M
New initial	0 M	0.10 M	0.00040 M
Change	+x	maintained	–x
Equilibrium	x	0.10 M	(0.00040 –x) M ≈ 0.00040 M

$$K_f = \frac{[Cu(NH_3)_4{}^{2+}]}{[Cu^{2+}][NH_3]^4} = \frac{0.00040}{[Cu^{2+}](0.10)^4} = 1.1\times10^{13} \qquad [Cu^{2+}] = 3.6\times10^{-13}\,M$$

Hence, the assumption is valid. The concentration of $Cu(NH_3)_4{}^{2+}$(aq) = 0.00040 M which is 40 times greater than the 1×10^{-5} detection limit. Thus, the blue color should appear.

92. **(M)** First we determine the molar solubility of AgBr in 1 M NH$_3$.

Sum	AgBr(s) + 2 NH$_3$(aq) $\rightleftharpoons$	Ag(NH$_3$)$_2{}^{+}$(aq) + Br$^-$(aq)	$K = K_{sp} \times K_f = 8.0\times10^{-6}$
Initial	1.00 M	0 M 0 M	
Equil.	1.00 – 2 s	s s	{s = AgBr molar solubility}

$$K = \frac{[Ag(NH_3)_2{}^{+}][Br^-]}{[NH_3(aq)]} = \frac{s^2}{(1-2s)^2} = 8.0\times10^{-6} \qquad s = 2.8\underline{1}\times10^{-3}\,M \text{ (also [Br}^-])$$

So $[Ag^+] = \dfrac{K_{sp}}{[Br^-]} = \dfrac{5.0\times10^{-13}}{2.8\underline{1}\times10^{-3}} = 1.8\times10^{-10}\,M$

$$AgBr(s) \rightleftharpoons Ag^+ + Br^- \qquad\qquad K_{sp} = 5.0\times10^{-13}$$

$$\underline{Ag^+ + 2\,NH_3 \rightleftharpoons Ag(NH_3)_2{}^{+}} \qquad\qquad K_f = 1.6\times10^{7}$$

(sum) AgBr(s) + 2 NH$_3$(aq) $\rightleftharpoons$ Ag(NH$_3$)$_2{}^{+}$ + Br$^-$ $K = K_{sp} \times K_f = 8.0\times10^{-6}$

Now, let's construct the cell, guessing that the standard hydrogen electrode is the anode.

Oxidation:	H_2(g) $\longrightarrow$ 2 H$^+$ + 2 e$^-$	$E° = -0.000$ V
Reduction:	{Ag$^+$(aq) + e$^-$ $\longrightarrow$ Ag(s) }×2	$E° = +0.800$ V
Net:	2 Ag$^+$(aq) + H$_2$(g) $\longrightarrow$ 2 Ag(s) + 2 H$^+$(aq)	$E°_{cell} = +0.800$ V

From the Nernst equation:

$$E = E° - \frac{0.0257\,V}{z}\ln Q = E° - \frac{0.0257\,V}{z}\ln\frac{[H^+]^2}{[Ag^+]^2} = 0.800\,V - \frac{0.0257\,V}{2}\ln\frac{1^2}{(1.7\underline{8}\times10^{-10})^2}$$

and $E = 0.22\underline{3}$ V. Since the voltage is positive, our guess is correct and the standard hydrogen electrode is the anode (oxidizing ele*ctrode*).

93. (M)

(a) Anode: $\qquad\qquad 2H_2O(l) \rightarrow 4e^- + 4H^+(aq) + O_2(g)$

Cathode: $\qquad \underline{2H_2O(l) + 2e^- \rightarrow 2OH^-(aq) + H_2(g)}$

Overall: $\qquad 2H_2O(l) + 4\,\cancel{H_2O(l)} \rightarrow 4\,\cancel{H^+(aq)} + 4\,\cancel{OH^-(aq)} + 2H_2(g) + O_2(g)$

$\qquad\qquad\qquad 2H_2O(l) \rightarrow 2H_2(g) + O_2(g)$

(b) 21.5 mA = 0.0215 A or 0.0215 C s^{-1} for 683 s

$$\text{mol H}_2\text{SO}_4 = \frac{0.0215 \text{ C}}{\text{s}} \times 683\,\text{s} \times \frac{1 \text{ mol e}^-}{96485 \text{ C}} \times \frac{1 \text{ mol H}^+}{1 \text{ mol e}^-} \times \frac{1 \text{ mol H}_2\text{SO}_4}{2 \text{ mol H}^+} = 7.61 \times 10^{-5} \text{ mol H}_2\text{SO}_4$$

7.61×10^{-5} mol H$_2$SO$_4$ in 10.00 mL. Hence [H$_2$SO$_4$] = 7.61×10^{-5} mol/0.01000 L = 7.61×10^{-3} M

94. (D) First we need to find the total surface area

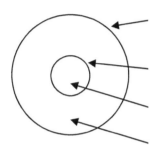

Outer circumference = $2\pi r = 2\pi(2.50 \text{ cm}) = 15.7$ cm
Surface area = circumference × thickness = 15.7 cm × 0.50 cm = 7.8$\underline{5}$ cm^2

Inner circumference = $2\pi r = 2\pi(1.00 \text{ cm}) = 6.28$ cm
Surface area = circumference × thickness = 6.28 cm × 0.50 cm = 3.1$\underline{4}$ cm^2

Area of small circle = $\pi r^2 = \pi(1.00 \text{ cm})^2 = 3.14$ cm^2

Area of large circle = $\pi r^2 = \pi(2.50 \text{ cm})^2 = 19.6$ cm^2

Total area = 7.85 cm^2 + 3.14 cm^2 + 2 × (19.6 cm^2) − 2 × (3.1$\underline{4}$ cm^2) = 43.9$\underline{1}$ cm^2

Volume of metal needed = surface area × thickness of plating = 43.9$\underline{1}$ cm^2 × 0.0050 cm = 0.22 cm^3

Charge required = $0.22 \text{ cm}^3 \times \dfrac{8.90 \text{ g}}{\text{cm}^3} \times \dfrac{1 \text{ mol Ni}}{58.693 \text{ g Ni}} \times \dfrac{2 \text{ mol e}^-}{1 \text{ mol Ni}} \times \dfrac{96{,}485 \text{ C}}{1 \text{ mol e}^-} = 6437.5$ C

Time = charge/time = 6437.5 C / 1.50 C/s = 4291.7 s or 71.5 min

95. (M) The overall reaction for the electrolytic cell is:

$\text{Cu(s)} + \text{Zn}^{2+}(aq) \rightarrow \text{Cu}^{2+}(aq) + \text{Zn(s)} \qquad E^\circ_{\text{cell}} = -1.103$ V

Next, we calculate the number of moles of Zn^{2+}(aq) plated out and number of moles of Cu^{2+}(aq) formed:

$$n(\text{Cu}^{2+}) = \frac{0.500 \text{ C}}{\text{s}} \times 10 \text{ h} \times \frac{60 \text{ min}}{1 \text{ h}} \times \frac{60 \text{ s}}{1 \text{ min}} \times \frac{1 \text{ mol e}^-}{96{,}485 \text{ C}} \times \frac{1 \text{ mol Cu}^{2+}}{2 \text{ mol e}^-} = 0.0935 \text{ mol Cu}^{2+}$$

$n(\text{Zn}^{2+}) = n(\text{Cu}^{2+}) = 0.0935$ mol

Initially, solution contained 1.00 mol L^{-1} × 0.100 L = 0.100 mol Zn^{2+}(aq). Therefore, at the end of electrolysis we are left with:

$$n(\text{Zn}^{2+})_{\text{LEFT}} = (0.100 - 0.0935) \text{ mol} = 6.5 \times 10^{-3} \text{ mol} \Rightarrow [\text{Zn}^{2+}] = \frac{6.5 \times 10^{-3} \text{ mol}}{0.1 \text{ L}} = 6.5 \times 10^{-2} \text{ M}$$

$$n(\text{Cu}^{2+})_{\text{FORMED}} = 0.0935 \text{ mol} \Rightarrow [\text{Cu}^{2+}] = \frac{0.0935 \text{ mol}}{0.1 \text{ L}} = 0.936 \text{ M}$$

The new potential after the cell was switched to a voltaic one can be calculated using Nernst equation:

$$E_{cell} = E°_{cell} - \frac{0.0257 \text{ V}}{2} \ln \frac{[Zn^{2+}]}{[Cu^{2+}]} = 1.103 - \frac{0.0257 \text{ V}}{2} \ln \frac{6.5 \times 10^{-3} \text{ M}}{0.935 \text{ M}} = (1.103 + 0.064) \text{ V} = 1.167 \text{ V}$$

96. (M)

(a) The metal has to have a reduction potential more negative than –0.691 V, so that its oxidation can reverse the tarnishing reaction's –0.691 V reduction potential. Aluminum is a good candidate, because it is inexpensive, readily available, will not react with water and has an $E°$ of –1.676 V. Zinc is also a possibility with an $E°$ of –0.763 V, but we don't choose it because there may be an overpotential associated with the tarnishing reaction.

(b) Oxidation: $\{Al(s) \longrightarrow Al^{3+}(aq) + 3 \text{ e}^-\} \times 2$

Reduction: $\{Ag_2S(s) + 2 \text{ e}^- \longrightarrow Ag(s) + S^{2-}(aq) \} \times 3$

Net: $2 \text{ Al}(s) + 3 \text{ Ag}_2S(s) \longrightarrow 6 \text{ Ag}(s) + 2 \text{ Al}^{3+}(aq) + 3 \text{ S}^{2-}(aq)$

(c) The dissolved $NaHCO_3(s)$ serves as an electrolyte. It would also enhance the electrical contact between the two objects.

(d) There are several chemicals involved: Al, H_2O, and $NaHCO_3$. Although the aluminum plate will be consumed very slowly because silver tarnish is very thin, it will, nonetheless, eventually erode away. We should be able to detect loss of mass after many uses.

97. (M)

(a) Overall: $C_3H_8(g) + 5 \text{ O}_2(g) \rightarrow 3 \text{ CO}_2(g) + 4 \text{ H}_2O(l)$
Anode: $6 \text{ H}_2O(l) + C_3H_8(g) \rightarrow 3 \text{ CO}_2(g) + 20 \text{ H}^+(g) + 20 \text{ e}^-$
Cathode: $20 \text{ e}^- + 20 \text{ H}^+(g) + 5 \text{ O}_2(g) \rightarrow 10 \text{ H}_2O(l)$

$\Delta_r G° = 3(-394.4 \text{ kJ/mol}) + 4(-237.1 \text{ kJ/mol}) - 1(-23.3 \text{ kJ/mol}) = -2108.3 \text{ kJ/mol}$

$\Delta_r G° = -2108.3 \text{ kJ/mol} = -2,108,300 \text{ J/mol}$
$\Delta_r G° = -zFE°_{cell} = -20 \text{ mol e}^- \times (96485 \text{ C/mol e}^-) \times E°_{cell}$
$E°_{cell} = +1.0926 \text{ V}$

$20 \text{ e}^- + 20 \text{ H}^+(g) + 5 \text{ O}_2(g) \rightarrow 10 \text{ H}_2O(l) \quad E°_{cathode} = +1.229 \text{ V}$

Hence $E°_{cell} = E°_{cathode} - E°_{anode} \qquad +1.0926 \text{ V} = +1.229 \text{ V} - E°_{anode}$

$E°_{anode} = +0.136 \text{ V}$ (reduction potential for $3 \text{ CO}_2(g) + 20 \text{ H}^+(g) + 20 \text{ e}^- \rightarrow 6 \text{ H}_2O(l) + C_3H_8(g)$)

(b) Use thermodynamic tables for $3 \text{ CO}_2(g) + 20 \text{ H}^+(g) + 20 \text{ e}^- \rightarrow 6 \text{ H}_2O(l) + C_3H_8(g)$

$\Delta_r G° = 6(-237.1 \text{ kJ/mol}) + 1(-23.3 \text{ kJ/mol}) - [(-394.4 \text{ kJ/mol}) + 20(0 \text{kJ/mol})]$
$= -262.7 \text{ kJ/mol}$
$\Delta_r G°_{red} = -262.7 \text{ kJ/mol} = -262,700 \text{ J/mol} = -zFE°_{red} = -20 \text{ mol e}^- \times (96,485 \text{ C/mol e}^-) \times E°_{red}$
$E°_{red} = 0.136 \text{ V}$ (Same value, as found in (a))

98. (D)

(a) Equation 19.15 ($\Delta_r G° = -zFE°_{cell}$) gives the relationship between the standard Gibbs energy of a reaction and the standard cell potential. Gibbs free energy also varies with temperature ($\Delta_r G° = \Delta_r H° - T\Delta_r S°$). If we assume that $\Delta_r H°$ and $\Delta_r S°$ do not vary significantly over a small temperature range, we can derive an equation for the temperature variation of $E°_{cell}$:

$$\Delta_r G° = \Delta_r H° - T\Delta_r S° = zFE°_{cell} \Rightarrow E°_{cell} = \frac{\Delta_r H° - T\Delta_r S°}{zF}$$

Considering two different temperatures one can write:

$$E°_{cell}(T_1) = \frac{\Delta_r H° - T_1\Delta_r S°}{zF} \text{ and } E°_{cell}(T_2) = \frac{\Delta_r H° - T_2\Delta_r S°}{zF}$$

$$E°_{cell}(T_1) - E°_{cell}(T_2) = \frac{\Delta_r H° - T_1\Delta_r S°}{zF} - \frac{\Delta_r H° - T_2\Delta_r S°}{zF}$$

$$E°_{cell}(T_1) - E°_{cell}(T_2) = \frac{-T_1\Delta_r S° + T_2\Delta_r S°}{zF} = \frac{\Delta_r S°}{zF}(T_2 - T_1)$$

(b) Using this equation, we can now calculate the cell potential of a Daniel cell at 50 °C:

$$E°_{cell}(25 °C) - E°_{cell}(50 °C) = \frac{-10.4 \text{ J K}^{-1} \text{ mol}^{-1}}{2 \times 96485 \text{ C mol}^{-1}}(50 - 25)\text{ K} = -0.00135$$

$$E°_{cell}(50 °C) = 1.103 \text{ V} + 0.00135 = 1.104 \text{ V}$$

99. (D) Recall that under non-standard conditions $\Delta_r G = \Delta_r G° + RT \ln K$. Substituting $\Delta_r G° = \Delta_r H° - T\Delta_r S°$ and $\Delta_r G = -zFE_{cell}$ one obtains:

$$-zFE_{cell} = \Delta_r H° - T\Delta_r S° + RT \ln Q$$

For two different temperatures (T_1 and T_2) we can write:

$$-zFE_{cell}(T_1) = \Delta_r H° - T_1\Delta_r S° + RT_1 \ln Q$$

$$-zFE_{cell}(T_2) = \Delta_r H° - T_2\Delta_r S° + RT_2 \ln Q$$

$$-E_{cell}(T_1) + E_{cell}(T_2) = \frac{\Delta_r H° - T_1\Delta_r S° + RT_1 \ln Q - \Delta_r H° + T_2\Delta_r S° - RT_2 \ln Q}{zF}$$

$$-E_{cell}(T_1) + E_{cell}(T_2) = \frac{-T_1\Delta_r S° + RT_1 \ln Q + T_2\Delta_r S° - RT_2 \ln Q}{zF}$$

$$E_{cell}(T_1) - E_{cell}(T_2) = \frac{T_1\Delta_r S° - RT_1 \ln Q}{zF} - \frac{T_2\Delta_r S° + RT_2 \ln Q}{zF}$$

$$E_{cell}(T_1) - E_{cell}(T_2) = T_1\left(\frac{\Delta_r S° - R \ln Q}{zF}\right) - T_2\left(\frac{\Delta_r S° - R \ln Q}{zF}\right)$$

$$E_{cell}(T_1) - E_{cell}(T_2) = (T_1 - T_2)\left(\frac{\Delta_r S° - R \ln Q}{zF}\right)$$

The value of Q at 25 °C can be calculated from $E°_{cell}$ and E_{cell}. First calculate $E°_{cell}$:

Oxidation:	$Cu(s) \rightarrow Cu^{2+}(aq) + 2\,e^-$	$-E° = -0.340$ V
Reduction:	$2\,Fe^{3+}(aq) + 2\,e^- \rightarrow 2\,Fe^{2+}(aq)$	$-E° = +0.771$ V
Overall:	$Cu(s) + 2\,Fe^{3+} \rightarrow Cu^{2+}(aq) + 2\,Fe^{2+}$	$E°_{cell} = 0.431$ V

$$0.370 = 0.431 - \frac{0.0257\,V}{2} \ln Q \Rightarrow 0.0129\,V \ln Q = 0.431 - 0.370 = 0.061$$

$$\ln Q = 4.73 \Rightarrow Q = e^{4.73} = 83.9$$

Now, use the above derived equation and solve for $\Delta_r S°$:

$$0.394 - 0.370 = (50 - 25)\left(\frac{\Delta_r S° - 8.314 \times \ln 83.9}{2 \times 96,485} \right)$$

$$0.024 = 25 \times (\frac{\Delta_r S° - 3.96}{192,970}) \Rightarrow \Delta_r S° - 3.96 = 185.3 \Rightarrow \Delta_r S° = 189.2\,J\,K^{-1}$$

Since $\Delta_r G° = \Delta_r H° - T\Delta_r S° = -zFE°_{cell}$ we can calculate $\Delta_r G°$, K (at 25 °C) and $\Delta_r H°$:

$$\Delta_r G° = -zFE°_{cell} = -2 \times 96,485 \times 0.431 = -83.2\,kJ$$

$$\Delta_r G° = -RT \ln K \Rightarrow -83.2 \times 1000 = -8.314 \times 298.1 \times \ln K$$

$$\ln K = 33.56 \Rightarrow K = e^{33.56} = 3.77 \times 10^{14}$$

$$-83.2\,kJ = \Delta_r H° - 298.15 \times \frac{189.2}{1000}\,kJ \Rightarrow \Delta_r H° = -83.2 + 56.4 = -26.8\,kJ$$

Since we have $\Delta_r H°$ and $\Delta_r S°$ we can calculate the value of the equilibrium constant at 50 °C:

$$\Delta_r G° = \Delta_r H° - T\Delta_r S° = -26.8\,kJ - (273.15 + 50)K \times \frac{189.2}{1000}\,kJ\,K^{-1} = -87.9\,kJ$$

$$-87.9 \times 1000\,J = -8.314\,J\,K^{-1}\,mol^{-1} \times (273.15 + 50)K \times \ln K$$

$$\ln K = 32.7 \Rightarrow K = e^{32.7} = 1.59 \times 10^{14}$$

Choose the values for the concentrations of Fe^{2+}, Cu^{2+} and Fe^{3+} that will give the value of the above calculated Q. For example:

$$Q = \frac{\left[Fe^{2+}\right]^2 \left[Cu^{2+}\right]}{\left[Fe^{3+}\right]^2} = 1.61$$

$$\frac{0.1^2 \times 1.61}{0.1^2} = 1.61$$

Determine the equilibrium concentrations at 50 °C. Notice that since $Q < K$, a net change occurs from left to right (the direction of the forward reaction):

$$Cu(s) + 2\,Fe^{3+} \rightarrow Cu^{2+}(aq) + 2\,Fe^{2+}$$

Initial:	0.1	1.61	0.1
Change:	$0.1 - x$	$1.61 + x$	$0.1 + x$

$$K = \frac{\left[Fe^{2+}\right]^2_{eq}\left[Cu^{2+}\right]_{eq}}{\left[Fe^{3+}\right]^2_{eq}} = 1.59 \times 10^{14} = \frac{(0.1+x)^2 \times (1.61+x)}{(0.1-x)^2}$$

Obviously, the reaction is almost completely shifted towards products. First assume that the reaction goes to completion, and then let the equilibrium be shifted towards reactants:

$$Cu(s) + 2\,Fe^{3+} \rightarrow Cu^{2+}(aq) + 2\,Fe^{2+}$$

Initial:	0.1	1.61	0.1
Final	0	1.71	0.2
Equilibrium	$0+x$	$1.71-x$	$0.2-x$

$$K = \frac{\left[Fe^{2+}\right]^2_{eq}\left[Cu^{2+}\right]_{eq}}{\left[Fe^{3+}\right]^2_{eq}} = 1.59 \times 10^{14} = \frac{(0.2-x)^2 \times (1.71-x)}{(x)^2} \approx \frac{0.2^2 \times 1.71}{x^2}$$

$$x^2 \approx \frac{0.2^2 \times 1.71}{1.59 \times 10^{14}} \approx 4.3 \times 10^{-16}$$

$$x \approx 2.1 \times 10^{-8}\,M$$

Therefore, $[Cu^{2+}] \approx 1.7$ M, $[Fe^{2+}] \approx 0.2$ M and $[Fe^{3+}] \approx 2.1 \times 10^{-8}$ M

100. **(D)** This problem can be solved by utilizing the relationship between $\Delta_r G°$ and $E°_{cell}$ $(\Delta_r G° = -zFE°_{cell})$:

Consider a hypothetical set of the following reactions:

$$A + ne^- \rightarrow A^{n-} \quad E°_1 \text{ and } \Delta_r G°_1$$

$$B + me^- \rightarrow B^{m-} \quad E°_2 \text{ and } \Delta_r G°_2$$

Overall: $\quad A + B + ne^- + me^- \rightarrow A^{n-} + B^{m-} \quad E°_r = ? \text{ and } \Delta_r G°_{rxn} = \Delta_r G°_1 + \Delta_r G°_2$

$$\Delta_r G° = \Delta_r G°_1 + \Delta_r G°_2 = -nFE°_1 - mFE°_2$$

$$-(n+m)FE° = -nFE°_1 - mFE°_2$$

$$(n+m)FE° = nFE°_1 + mFE°_2 \Rightarrow E° = \frac{nFE°_1 + mFE°_2}{n+m}$$

Therefore, for n-sets of half-reactions:

$$E° = \frac{\sum n_i E°_i}{\sum n_i}$$

The $E°$ for the given half-reaction can be determined by combining four half-reactions:

$$H_6IO_6 + H^+ + 2\,e^- \rightarrow IO_3^- + 3\,H_2O \Rightarrow E° = 1.60 \text{ V}$$

$$IO_3^- + 6\,H^+ + 5\,e^- \rightarrow \frac{1}{2}I_2 + 3\,H_2O \Rightarrow E° = 1.19 \text{ V}$$

$$I_2 + 2\,H_2O \rightarrow 2\,HIO + 2\,H^+ + 2\,e^- \Rightarrow E° = -1.45 \text{ V}$$

$$2\,I^- \rightarrow I_2 + 2\,e^- \Rightarrow E° = -0.535 \text{ V}$$

Overall :

$$H_6IO_6 + H^+ + 2\,e^- + IO_3^- + 6\,H^+ + 5\,e^- + I_2 + 2\,H_2O + 2\,I^- \rightarrow$$

$$IO_3^- + 3\,H_2O + \frac{1}{2}I_2 + 3\,H_2O + 2\,HIO + 2\,H^+ + 2\,e^- + I_2 + 2\,e^-$$

$$H_6IO_6 + 5\,H^+ + 2\,I^- + 3\,e^- \rightarrow \frac{1}{2}I_2 + 4\,H_2O + 2\,HIO$$

$$E° = \frac{1.60 \times 3 + 1.19 \times 5 - 1.45 \times 2 - 0.535 \times 2}{2 + 5 - 2 - 2} = 2.26\ V$$

FEATURE PROBLEMS

101. (D) (a)   Anode: $H_2\,(g, 1\ bar) \rightarrow 2\,H^+\,(1\,M) + 2\,e^-$ $-E° = -0.0000\ V$

Cathode: $\{Ag^+\,(x\,M) + e^- \rightarrow Ag(s)\} \times 2$ $E° = 0.800\ V$

Net: $H_2\,(g, 1\ atm) + 2\,Ag^+\,(aq) \rightarrow 2\,H^+\,(1\,M) + 2\,Ag(s)$ $E°_{cell} = 0.800$

(b)   Since the voltage in the anode half-cell remains constant, we use the Nernst equation to calculate the half-cell voltage in the cathode half-cell, with two moles of electrons. This is then added to $-E$ for the anode half-cell. Because $-E° = 0.000$ for the anode half cell, $E_{cell} = E_{cathode}$

$$E = E° - \frac{0.0257\ V}{2}\ln\frac{1}{\left[Ag^+\right]^2} = 0.800\ V + 0.0257\ V\,\ln\left[Ag^+\right] = 0.800\ V + 0.0257\ V\,\ln x$$

(c)   (i)   Initially $\left[Ag^+\right] = 0.0100;$ $E = 0.800 + 0.0257\ln 0.0100 = 0.682\ V = E_{cell}$

Note that 50.0 mL of titrant is required for the titration, since both $AgNO_3$ and KI have the same concentrations and they react in equimolar ratios.

(ii)   After 20.0 mL of titrant is added, the total volume of solution is 70.0 mL and the unreacted Ag^+ is that in the untitrated 30.0 mL of 0.0100 M $AgNO_3\,(aq)$.

$$\left[Ag^+\right] = \frac{30.0\ mL \times 0.0100\ M}{70.0\ mL} = 0.00429\ M$$

$$E = 0.800\ V + 0.0257\ V\,\ln(0.00429) = 0.660\ V = E_{cell}$$

(iii)   After 49.0 mL of titrant is added, the total volume of solution is 99.0 mL and the unreacted Ag^+ is that in the untitrated 1.0 mL of 0.0100 M $AgNO_3\,(aq)$.

$$\left[Ag^+\right] = \frac{1.0\ mL \times 0.0100\ M}{99.0\ mL} = 0.00010\ M$$

$$E = 0.800\ V + 0.0257\ V\,\ln(0.00010) = 0.563\ V = E_{cell}$$

(iv) At the equivalence point, we have a saturated solution of AgI, for which

$$\left[Ag^+\right] = \sqrt{K_{sp}(AgI)} = \sqrt{8.5\times10^{-17}} = 9.2\times10^{-9}$$

$$E = 0.800\ \text{V} + 0.0257\ \text{V}\ \ln\left(9.2\times10^{-9}\right) = 0.324\ \text{V} = E_{cell}.$$

After the equivalence point, the $[Ag^+]$ is determined by the $[I^-]$ resulting from the excess KI(aq).

(v) When 51.0 mL of titrant is added, the total volume of solution is 101.0 mL and the excess I^- is that in 1.0 mL of 0.0100 M KI(aq).

$$\left[I^-\right] = \frac{1.0\ \text{mL}\times0.0100\ \text{M}\ I^-}{101.0\ \text{mL}} = 9.9\times10^{-5}\ \text{M} \qquad \left[Ag^+\right] = \frac{K_{sp}}{\left[I^-\right]} = \frac{8.5\times10^{-17}}{0.000099} = 8.6\times10^{-13}\ \text{M}$$

$$E = 0.800\ \text{V} + 0.0257\ \text{V}\ \ln\left(8.6\times10^{-13}\right) = 0.086\ \text{V} = E_{cell}$$

(vi) When 60.0 mL of titrant is added, the total volume of solution is 110.0 mL and the excess I^- is that in 10.0 mL of 0.0100 M KI(aq).

$$\left[I^-\right] = \frac{10.0\ \text{mL}\times0.0100\ \text{M}}{110.0\ \text{mL}} = 0.00091\ \text{M}$$

$$\left[Ag^+\right] = \frac{K_{sp}}{\left[I^-\right]} = \frac{8.5\times10^{-17}}{0.00091} = 9.3\times10^{-14}\ \text{M}$$

$$E = 0.800\ \text{V} + 0.0257\ \text{V}\ \ln\left(9.3\times10^{-14}\right) = 0.029\ \text{V} = E_{cell}$$

(d) The titration curve is presented below.

102. (D)

(a) (1) anode: $Na(s) \rightarrow Na^+\,(\text{in ethylamine}) + e^-$

cathode: $Na^+\,(\text{in ethylamine}) \rightarrow Na(\text{amalgam, 0.206 \%})$

Net: $Na(s) \rightarrow Na(\text{amalgam, 0.206\%})$

(2)   anode: $2\,Na\,(amalgam,\,0.206\%) \rightarrow 2\,Na^+\,(1\,M) + 2\,e^-$

cathode: $2\,H^+\,(aq,\,1\,M) + 2\,e^- \rightarrow H_2\,(g,\,1\,atm)$

Net: $2\,Na\,(amalgam,\,0.206\%) + 2\,H^+\,(aq,\,1\,M) \rightarrow 2\,Na^+\,(1\,M) + H_2\,(g,\,1\,atm)$

(b) (1) $\Delta_r G = -1 \times \dfrac{96,485\,C}{1\,mol} \times 0.8453\,V = -8.156 \times 10^4\,J\,mol^{-1}$ or $-81.56\,kJ\,mol^{-1}$

(2) $\Delta_r G = -2 \times \dfrac{96,485\,C}{1\,mol} \times 1.8673\,V = -36.033 \times 10^4\,J\,mol^{-1}$ or $-360.33\,kJ\,mol^{-1}$

(c) (1) $2\,Na(s) \rightarrow 2\,Na(amalgam,\,0.206\%)$ $\Delta_r G_1 = -2 \times 8.156 \times 10^4\,J\,mol^{-1}$

(2) $2\,Na\,(amalg,\,0.206\%) + 2\,H^+\,(aq,\,1\,M) \rightarrow 2\,Na^+\,(1\,M) + H_2\,(g,\,1\,atm)$

$\Delta_r G_2 = -36.033 \times 10^4\,J\,mol^{-1}$

Overall: $2\,Na(s) + 2\,H^+\,(aq) \rightarrow 2\,Na^+\,(1\,M) + H_2\,(g,\,1\,atm)$

$\Delta_r G = \Delta_r G_1 + \Delta_r G_2 = -16.312 \times 10^4\,J\,mol^{-1} - 36.033 \times 10^4\,J\,mol^{-1} = -52.345 \times 10^4\,J\,mol^{-1}$
or $-523.45\,kJ\,mol^{-1}$

Since standard conditions are implied in the overall reaction, $\Delta_r G = \Delta_r G°$.

(d) $E°_{cell} = -\dfrac{-52.345 \times 10^4\,J\,mol^{-1}}{2 \times \dfrac{96,485\,C}{1\,mol} \times \dfrac{1\,J\,C^{-1}}{1\,V}} = E°\{H^+\,(1\,M)/H_2\,(1\,atm)\} - E°\{Na^+\,(1\,M)/Na\,(s)\}$

$E°\{Na^+\,(1\,M)/Na\,(s)\} = -2.713\,V$. This is precisely the same as the value in Appendix D.

103. (D) The question marks in the original Latimer diagram have been replaced with letters in the diagram below to make the solution easier to follow:

By referring to Appendix D and by employing the correct procedure for adding together half-reactions of the same type we obtain:

(c) $Br_2\,(l) + 2\,e^- \rightarrow 2\,Br^-\,(aq)$ $E_c° = 1.065\,V$ (Appendix D)

(d) $BrO^-\,(aq) + H_2O(l) + 2\,e^- \rightarrow Br^-\,(aq) + 2\,OH^-\,(aq)$ $E_d° = 0.766\,V$ (Appendix D)

(b) $2\,BrO^-\,(aq) + 2\,H_2O(l) + 2\,e^- \rightarrow Br_2\,(l) + 4\,OH^-\,(aq)$ $E_b° = 0.455\,V$ (Appendix D)

(a) $\{BrO_3^-\,(aq) + 2\,H_2O(l) + 4\,e^- \rightarrow BrO^-\,(aq) + 4\,OH^-\,(aq)\} \times 2$ $E_a° = ?$

(b) $2\,BrO^-\,(aq) + 2\,H_2O(l) + 2\,e^- \rightarrow Br_2\,(l) + 4\,OH^-\,(aq)$ $E_b° = 0.455\,V$

(c) $\quad Br_2(l) + 2\,e^- \rightarrow 2\,Br^-(aq)$ $\hspace{4cm}$ $E_c^\circ = 1.065\ V$

(e) $\quad 2\,BrO_3^-(aq) + 6\,H_2O(l) + 12\,e^- \rightarrow 12\,OH^-(aq) + 2\,Br^-(aq)$ $\hspace{1cm}$ $E_e^\circ = 0.584\ V$

$$\Delta_r G^\circ_{Total} = \Delta_r G^\circ_{(a)} + \Delta_r G^\circ_{(b)} + \Delta_r G^\circ_{(c)}$$

$$-12F\left(E_e^\circ\right) = -8F\left(E_a^\circ\right) + -2F\left(E_b^\circ\right) + -2F\left(E_c^\circ\right)$$

$$-12F\left(0.584\ V\right) = -8F\left(E_a^\circ\right) + -2F\left(0.455\ V\right) + -2F\left(1.065\ V\right)$$

$$E_a^\circ = \frac{-12F\left(0.584\ V\right) + 2F\left(0.455\ V\right) + 2F\left(1.065\ V\right)}{-8F} = 0.496\ V$$

104. (D)

(a) The capacitance of the cell membrane is given by the following equation,

$$C = \frac{\varepsilon_0 \varepsilon A}{l}$$

where $\varepsilon_0 \varepsilon = 3 \times 8.854 \times 10^{-12}\ C^2\ N^{-1}\ m^{-2}$; $A = 1 \times 10^{-6}\ cm^2$; and $l = 1 \times 10^{-6}\ cm$. Together with the factors necessary to convert from cm to m and from cm^2 to m^2, these data yield

$$C = \frac{(3)\left(8.854 \times 10^{-12}\ \dfrac{C^2}{N^1\ m^2}\right)(1 \times 10^{-6}\ cm^2)\left(\dfrac{1\ m}{100\ cm}\right)^2}{(1 \times 10^{-6}\,cm)\left(\dfrac{1\ m}{100\ cm}\right)} = 2.66 \times 10^{-13}\ \frac{C^2}{N\,m}$$

$$C = \left(2.66 \times 10^{-13}\ \frac{C^2}{N\,m}\right)\left(\frac{1\ F}{1\,\dfrac{C^2}{N\,m}}\right) = 2.66 \times 10^{-13}\ F$$

(b) Since the capacitance C is the charge in coulombs per volt, the charge on the membrane, Q, is given by the product of the capacitance and the potential across the cell membrane.

$$Q = 2.66 \times 10^{-13}\ \frac{C}{V} \times 0.085\ V = 2.26 \times 10^{-14}\ C$$

(c) The number of K^+ ions required to produce this charge is

$$\frac{Q}{e} = \frac{2.26 \times 10^{-14}\ C}{1.602 \times 10^{-19}\ C/ion} = 1.41 \times 10^5\ K^+\ ions$$

(d) The number of K^+ ions in a typical cell is

$$\left(6.022 \times 10^{23}\ \frac{ions}{mol}\right)\left(155 \times 10^{-3}\ \frac{mol}{L}\right)\left(\frac{1\,L}{1000\ cm^3}\right)(1 \times 10^{-8}\ cm^3) = 9.3 \times 10^{11}\ ions$$

(e) The fraction of the ions involved in establishing the charge on the cell membrane is

$$\frac{1.4 \times 10^5\ ions}{9.3 \times 10^{11}\ ions} = 1.5 \times 10^{-7}\ (\sim 0.000015\ \%)$$

Thus, the concentration of K^+ ions in the cell remains constant at 155 mM.

105. (M) Reactions with a positive cell potential are reactions for which $\Delta_r G° < 0$, or reactions for which $K > 1$. $\Delta_r S°$, $\Delta_r H°$ and $\Delta_r U°$ cannot be used alone to determine whether a particular electrochemical reaction will have a positive or negative value.

106. (M) The half-reactions for the first cell are:

Anode (oxidation): $\quad X(s) \rightarrow X^+(aq) + e^- \qquad -E°_{X^+/X}$

Cathode (reduction): $\quad 2H^+(aq) + 2e^- \rightarrow H_2(g) \qquad E° = 0\ V$

Since the electrons are flowing from metal X to the standard hydrogen electrode, $E°_{X^+/X} < 0\ V$.

The half-reactions for the second cell are:

Anode (oxidation): $\quad X(s) \rightarrow X^+(aq) + e^- \qquad -E°_{X^+/X}$

Cathode (reduction): $\quad Y^{2+} + 2e^- \rightarrow Y(s) \qquad E°_{Y^{2+}/Y}$

Since the electrons are flowing from metal X to metal Y, $-E°_{X^+/X} + E°_{Y^{2+}/Y} > 0$.

From the first cell we know that $E°_{X^+/X} < 0\ V$. Therefore, $E°_{X^+/X} > E°_{Y^{2+}/Y}$.

107. (M) The standard reduction potential of the $Fe^{2+}(aq)/Fe(s)$ couple can be determined from:

$Fe^{2+}(aq) \rightarrow Fe^{3+}(aq) + e^-\ E° = -0.771\ V$

$Fe^{3+}(aq) + 3e^- \rightarrow Fe(s)\ \ E° = -0.04\ V$

Overall:

$Fe^{2+}(aq) + 2e^- \rightarrow Fe(s)$

We proceed similarly to the solution for 100:

$$E° = \frac{\sum n_i E°_i}{\sum n_i} = \frac{-0.771 \times (1) - 0.04 \times 3}{3 - 1} = -0.445\ V$$

108. (D)

(a) For the reaction $\frac{3}{2} H_2(g) + NO_3^-(aq) + H^+(aq) \rightarrow NO(g) + 2\ H_2O(l)$, we have:

$$\Delta_r G° = [(1)\mu°_{NO(g)} + (2)\mu°_{H_2O(l)}] - [(\frac{3}{2})\mu°_{H_2(g)} + (1)\mu°_{NO_3^-(aq)} + (1)\mu°_{H^+(aq)}]$$

$$= [(1)\mu^*_{NO(g)} + (1)RT\ln(P°/P^*) + (2)\mu^*_{H_2O(l)}]$$

$$\quad - [(\frac{3}{2})\mu^*_{H_2(g)} + (\frac{3}{2})RT\ln\ln(P°/P^*) + (1)\mu^*_{NO_3^-(aq)} + (1)\mu^*_{H^+(aq)}]$$

$$= [(1)\mu^*_{NO(g)} + (2)\mu^*_{H_2O(l)}] - [(\frac{3}{2})\mu^*_{H_2(g)} + (1)\mu^*_{NO_3^-(aq)} + (1)\mu^*_{H^+(aq)}] + (1 - \frac{3}{2})RT\ln(P°/P^*)$$

$$= \Delta_r G^* + \Delta v_{gas} RT\ln(P°/P^*)$$

(b) Since $\Delta_r G = -zFE_{cell}$, then $E_{cell} = -\Delta_r G/(zF)$. Multiplying the expression for $\Delta_r G^\circ$ from (a) by $[-1/(zF)]$, we obtain

$$\left(-\frac{1}{zF}\right) \times \Delta_r G^\circ = \left(-\frac{1}{zF}\right) \times \Delta_r G^* + \left(-\frac{1}{zF}\right) \times \Delta v_{gas} RT \ln(P^\circ / P^*)$$

$$E_{cell}^\circ = E_{cell}^* - \frac{\Delta v_{gas}}{z} \times \frac{RT \ln(P^\circ / P^*)}{F}$$

Using $P^\circ = 1$ bar, $P^* = 1$ atm $= 1.01325$ bar, $T = 298.15$ K, $R = 8.3145$ J K^{-1} mol^{-1} and $F = 96{,}485$ C mol^{-1}, we obtain

$$E_{cell}^\circ = E_{cell}^* - \frac{\Delta v_{gas}}{z} \times \frac{(8.3145 \text{ J K}^{-1} \text{ mol}^{-1})(298.15 \text{ K}) \ln(1.0 \text{ bar} / 1.01325 \text{ bar})}{96{,}485 \text{ C mol}^{-1}}$$

$$= E_{cell}^* - \frac{\Delta v_{gas}}{z} \times (3.382 \times 10^{-4} \text{ J C}^{-1}) = E_{cell}^* - \frac{\Delta v_{gas}}{z} \times (3.382 \times 10^{-4} \text{ V})$$

(c) For the overall reaction we are considering in this problem, $\Delta v_{gas} = [1 - \frac{3}{2}] = -\frac{1}{2}$ and

$z = 3$. Therefore, $E_{cell}^\circ = E_{cell}^* + \frac{\left(-\frac{1}{2}\right)}{3} \times 3.382 \times 10^{-4}$ V $= E_{cell}^* + 2.8 \times 10^{-5}$ V. Therefore,

$E_{cell}^\circ - E_{cell}^* = 2.8 \times 10^{-5}$ V $= 0.028$ mV

(d) Using $E_{cell}^* = 0.956$ V in the expression $E_{cell}^\circ - E_{cell}^* = 2.8 \times 10^{-5}$ V, we find that $E_{cell}^\circ = 0.956$ V $+ 0.000028$ V $= 0.956$ V. Therefore, changing the standard state pressure from 1 atm to 1 bar has essentially no effect on the value of the standard reduction potential.

109. (M)

(a) $2 \text{ C}_6\text{H}_{12}\text{O}_6(aq) + \text{O}_2(g) \rightleftharpoons 2 \text{ H}_2\text{O}(l) + 2 \text{ C}_6\text{H}_{10}\text{O}_6(aq)$

(b) $\text{Pt}(s)|\text{C}_6\text{H}_{12}\text{O}_6(aq), \text{C}_6\text{H}_{10}\text{O}_6(aq)||\text{H}^+(aq)|\text{O}_2(g)|\text{Pt}(s)$

(c) $E_{cell}^\circ = E_R^\circ - E_L^\circ = 0.82 \text{ V} - (-0.3583 \text{ V}) = 1.18 \text{ V}$

110. (M)

(a) $2 \text{ CO}_2 + 7 \text{ H}^+ + 8 \text{ e}^- \rightleftharpoons \text{CH}_3\text{COO}^- + 2 \text{ H}_2\text{O} \quad E^\circ = -0.29 \text{ V}$

(b) $\text{O}_2 + 4 \text{ H}^+ + 4 \text{ e}^- \rightleftharpoons 2 \text{ H}_2\text{O}, \quad E^\circ = 0.82 \text{ V}$

(c) $4 \text{ CH}_3\text{COO}^- + 8 \text{ O}_2 + 4 \text{ H}^+ \rightleftharpoons 8 \text{ CO}_2 + 8 \text{ H}_2\text{O}, \quad E^\circ = 1.11 \text{ V}$

(d) The microbe contains the enzyme that carries out the oxidation reaction and provides electrons to the process.

SELF-ASSESSMENT EXERCISES

111. (E)

    (a) A standard electrode potential $E°$ measures the tendency for a reduction process to occur at an electrode.

    (b) F is the Faraday constant, or the electric charge per mole of electrons (96485 C/mol).

    (c) The anode is the electrode at which oxidation occurs.

    (d) The cathode is the electrode at which reduction occurs.

112. (E)

    (a) A salt bridge is a devise used to connect the oxidation and reduction half-cells of a galvanic (voltaic) cell.

    (b) The standard hydrogen electrode (abbreviated SHE), also called normal hydrogen electrode (NHE), is a redox electrode which forms the basis of the thermodynamic scale of oxidation-reduction potentials. By definition electrode potential for SHE is 0.

    (c) Cathodic protection is a technique commonly used to control the corrosion of a metal surface by making it work as a cathode of an electrochemical cell. This is achieved by placing in contact with the metal to be protected another more easily corroded metal to act as the anode of the electrochemical cell.

    (d) A fuel cell is an electrochemical cell that produces electricity from fuels. The essential process in a fuel cell is fuel+oxygen→ oxidation products.

113. (E)

    (a) An overall cell reaction is a combination of oxidation and reduction half-reactions.

    (b) In a galvanic (voltaic) cell, chemical change is used to produce electricity. In an electrolytic cell, electricity is used to produce a nonspontaneous rection.

    (c) In a primary cell, the cell reaction is not reversible. In a secondary cell, the cell reaction can be reversed by passing electricity through the cell (charging).

    (d) $E°_{cell}$ refers to the standard cell potential (the ionic species are present in aqueous solution at unit activity (approximately 1M), and gases are at 1 bar pressure (approximately 1 atm).

114. (M)

    (a) False. The cathode is the positive electrode in a voltaic cell and negative in electrolytic cell.

    (b) False. The function of the salt bridge is to permit the migration of the ions not electrons.

(c) True. The anode is the negative electrode in a voltaic cell.

(d) True.

(e) True. Reduction always occurs at the cathode of an electrochemical cell. Because of the removal of electrons by the reduction half-reaction, the cathode of a voltaic cell is positive. Because of the electrons forced onto it, the cathode of an electrolytic cell is negative. For both types, the cathode is the electrode at which electrons enter the cell.

(f) False. Reversing the direction of the electron flow changes the voltaic cell into an electrolytic cell.

(g) True. The cell reaction is an oxidation-reduction reaction.

115. (M) The correct answer is (b), $Hg^{2+}(aq)$ is more readily reduced than $H^+(aq)$.

116. (M) Under non-standard conditions, apply the Nernst equation to calculate E_{cell}:

$$E_{cell} = E^{\circ}_{cell} - \frac{0.0257 \text{ V}}{z} \ln Q$$

$$E_{cell} = 0.66 \text{ V} - \frac{0.0257 \text{ V}}{2} \ln \frac{0.10}{0.01} = 0.63 \text{ V}$$

The correct answer is (d).

117. (E) **(c)** The displacement of $Ni(s)$ from the solution will proceed to a considerable extent, but the reaction will not go to completion.

118. (E) The gas evolved at the anode when $K_2SO_4(aq)$ is electrolyzed between Pt electrodes is most likely oxygen.

119. (M) The electrochemical reaction in the cell is:

Anode (oxidation): $\{Al(s) \rightarrow Al^{3+}(aq) + 3\,e^-\} \times 2$

Cathode (reduction): $\{H_2(g) + 2\,e^- \rightarrow 2\,H^+(aq)\} \times 3$

Overall: $2\,Al(s) + 3\,H_2(g) \rightarrow 2\,Al^{3+}(aq) + 6\,H^+(aq)$

$$4.5 \text{ g Al} \times \frac{1 \text{ mol Al}}{26.98 \text{ g Al}} \times \frac{3 \text{ mol } H_2}{2 \text{ mol Al}} = 0.250 \text{ mol } H_2$$

$$0.250 \text{ mol } H_2 \times \frac{22.4 \text{ L } H_2}{1 \text{ mol } H_2} = 5.6 \text{ L } H_2$$

120. (E) The correct answer is (a) $\Delta_r G$.

121. (M)

Anode (oxidation): $\{Zn(s) \rightarrow Zn^{2+}(aq) + 2\,e^-\} \times 3$ $\hspace{2cm}$ $-E° = 0.763$ V

Cathode (reduction): $\{NO_3^-(aq) + 4\,H^+(aq) + 3\,e^- \rightarrow NO(g) + 2\,H_2O(l)\} \times 2$ $\hspace{0.5cm}$ $E° = +0.956$ V

Overall: $3\,Zn(s) + 2\,NO_3^-(aq) + 8\,H^+(aq) \rightarrow 3\,Zn^{2+}(aq) + 2\,NO(g) + 4\,H_2O(l)$ $\hspace{0.3cm}$ $E_{cell}^o = 1.719$ V

Cell diagram: $Zn(s)\left|Zn^{2+}(1\,M)\right\|H^+(1\,M),\,NO_3^-(1\,M)\left|NO(g,\,1\,atm)\right|Pt(s)$

122. (M) Apply the Nernst equation:

$$E_{cell} = E_{cell}^o - \frac{0.0257\text{ V}}{z}\ln Q$$

$$0.108\text{ V} = 0\text{ V} - \frac{0.0257\text{ V}}{2}\ln x^2 \Rightarrow \ln x^2 = -8.40$$

$$x^2 = e^{-8.40} \Rightarrow x = 0.0150$$

$$pH = -\log(0.0150) = 1.82$$

123. (M)

(a) Since we are given E_{cell}^o, we can calculate K for the given reaction:

$$E_{cell}^o = \frac{RT}{zF}\ln K$$

$$-0.0050\text{ V} = \frac{8.314\text{ J K}^{-1}\text{mol}^{-1} \times 298\text{ K}}{2 \times 96,485\text{ C mol}^{-1}}\ln K \Rightarrow \ln K = -0.389$$

$$K = e^{-0.389} = 0.68$$

Since for the given conditions $Q = 1$, the system is not at equilibrium.

(b) Because $Q > K$, a net reaction occurs to the left.

124. (M)

(a) $Fe(s) + Cu^{2+}(1\,M) \rightarrow Fe^{2+}(1\,M) + Cu(s),\ E_{cell}^o = -0.780$ V, electrons flow from B to A

(b) $Sn^{2+}(1\,M) + 2\,Ag^+(1\,M) \rightarrow Sn^{4+}(aq) + 2\,Ag(s),\ E_{cell}^o = +0.646$ V, electrons flow from A to B.

(c) $Zn(s) + Fe^{2+}(0.0010\,M) \rightarrow Zn^{2+}(0.10\,M) + Fe(s),\ E_{cell}^o = +0.264$ V, electrons flow from A to B.

125. (M)

(a) $Cl_2(g)$ at anode and $Cu(s)$ at cathode.

(b) $O_2(g)$ at anode and $H_2(g)$ and $OH^-(aq)$ at cathode.

(c) $Cl_2(g)$ at anode and $Ba(l)$ at cathode.

(d) $O_2(g)$ at anode and $H_2(g)$ and $OH^-(aq)$ at cathode.

126. **(E)** One possibility for the concept map showing the relationship between electrochemical cells and thermodynamic properties is illustrated in Figure 19-8.

127. **(E)** One possibility for the concept map illustrating the relationship between batteries and electrochemical ideas is shown below:

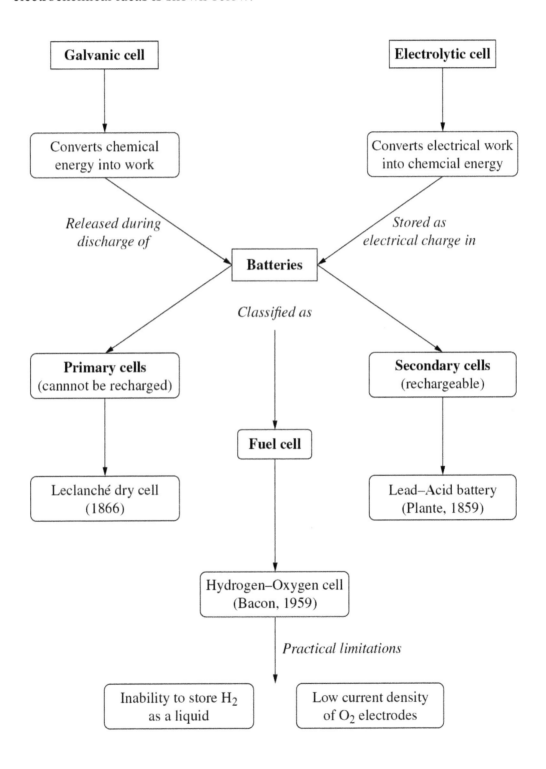

128. **(E)** One possibility for the concept map illustrating the principles of electrolysis and its industrial applications is shown below:

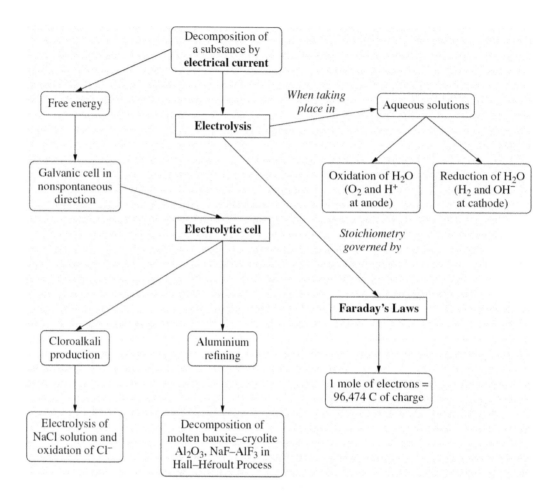

CHAPTER 20
CHEMICAL KINETICS

PRACTICE EXAMPLES

1A **(E)** The rate of consumption for a reactant is expressed as the negative of the change in molarity divided by the time interval. The rate of reaction is expressed as the rate of consumption of a reactant or production of a product divided by its stoichiometric coefficient.

$$\text{rate of consumption of A} = \frac{-\Delta[A]}{\Delta t} = \frac{-(0.3187\ M - 0.3629\ M)}{8.25\ min} \times \frac{1\ min}{60\ s} = 8.93 \times 10^{-5}\ M\ s^{-1}$$

$$\text{rate of reaction} = \text{rate of consumption of A} \div 2 = \frac{8.93 \times 10^{-5}\ M\ s^{-1}}{2} = 4.46 \times 10^{-5}\ M\ s^{-1}$$

1B **(E)** We use the rate of reaction of A to determine the rate of formation of B, noting from the balanced equation that 3 moles of B form (+3 moles B) when 2 moles of A react (–2 moles A). (Recall that "M" means "moles per liter.")

$$\text{rate of B formation} = \frac{0.5522\ M\ A - 0.5684\ M\ A}{2.50\ min \times \dfrac{60\ s}{1\ min}} \times \frac{+3\ moles\ B}{-2\ moles\ A} = 1.62 \times 10^{-4}\ M\ s^{-1}$$

2A **(M)**

(a) The 2400-s tangent line intersects the 1200-s vertical line at 0.75 M and reaches 0 M at 3500 s. The slope of that tangent line is thus

$$\text{slope} = \frac{0\ M - 0.75\ M}{3500\ s - 1200\ s} = -3.3 \times 10^{-4}\ M\ s^{-1} = -\text{instantaneous rate of reaction}$$

The instantaneous rate of reaction $= 3.3 \times 10^{-4}\ M\ s^{-1}$.

(b) At 2400 s, $[H_2O_2] = 0.39\ M$. At 2450 s, $[H_2O_2] = 0.39\ M + \text{rate} \times \Delta t$

$$\text{At 2450 s,}\ [H_2O_2] = 0.39\ M + \left[-3.3 \times 10^{-4} mol\ H_2O_2\ L^{-1}s^{-1} \times 50s \right]$$

$$= 0.39\ M - 0.017\ M = 0.37\ M$$

2B **(M)** With only the data of Table 20.2 we can use only the reaction rate during the first 400 s, $-\Delta[H_2O_2]/\Delta t = 15.0 \times 10^{-4}\ M\ s^{-1}$, and the initial concentration, $[H_2O_2]_o = 2.32\ M$. We calculate the change in $[H_2O_2]$ and add it to $[H_2O_2]_o$ to determine $[H_2O_2]_{100}$.

$$\Delta[H_2O_2] = \text{rate of reaction of } H_2O_2 \times \Delta t = -15.0 \times 10^{-4}\ M\ s^{-1} \times 100\ s = -0.15\ M$$

$$[H_2O_2]_{100} = [H_2O_2]_o + \Delta[H_2O_2] = 2.32\ M + (-0.15\ M) = 2.17\ M$$

This value differs from the value of 2.15 M determined in *text* Example 20-2b because the *text* used the initial rate of reaction $(17.1 \times 10^{-4}\ M\ s^{-1})$, which is a bit faster than the average rate over the first 400 seconds.

3A **(M)** We write the equation for each rate, divide them into each other, and solve for n.

$$R_1 = k \times [N_2O_5]_1^n = 5.45 \times 10^{-5} \text{ M s}^{-1} = k(3.15 \text{ M})^n$$

$$R_2 = k \times [N_2O_5]_2^n = 1.35 \times 10^{-5} \text{ M s}^{-1} = k(0.78 \text{ M})^n$$

$$\frac{R_1}{R_2} = \frac{5.45 \times 10^{-5} \text{ M s}^{-1}}{1.35 \times 10^{-5} \text{ M s}^{-1}} = 4.04 = \frac{k \times [N_2O_5]_1^n}{k \times [N_2O_5]_2^n} = \frac{k(3.15 \text{ M})^n}{k(0.78 \text{ M})^n} = \left(\frac{3.15}{0.78}\right)^n = (4.0\underline{4})^n$$

We kept an extra significant figure (4) to emphasize that the value of $n = 1$. Thus, the reaction is first-order in N_2O_5.

3B **(E)** For the reaction, we know that rate $= k[HgCl_2]^1[C_2O_4^{2-}]^2$. Here we will compare Expt. 4 to Expt. 1 to find the rate.

$$\frac{\text{rate}_4}{\text{rate}_1} = \frac{k[HgCl_2]^1[C_2O_4^{2-}]^2}{k[HgCl_2]^1[C_2O_4^{2-}]^2} = \frac{0.025 \text{ M} \times (0.045 \text{ M})^2}{0.105 \text{ M} \times (0.150 \text{ M})^2} = 0.0214 = \frac{\text{rate}_4}{1.8 \times 10^{-5} \text{ M min}^{-1}}$$

The desired rate is $\text{rate}_4 = 0.0214 \times 1.8 \times 10^{-5} \text{ M min}^{-1} = 3.9 \times 10^{-7} \text{ M min}^{-1}$.

4A **(E)** We place the initial concentrations and the initial rates into the rate law and solve for k.

$$\text{rate} = k[A]^2[B] = 4.78 \times 10^{-2} \text{ M s}^{-1} = k(1.12 \text{ M})^2(0.87 \text{ M})$$

$$k = \frac{4.78 \times 10^{-2} \text{ M s}^{-1}}{(1.12 \text{ M})^2 \, 0.87 \text{ M}} = 4.4 \times 10^{-2} \text{ M}^{-2} \text{ s}^{-1}$$

4B **(E)** We know that rate $= k[HgCl_2]^1[C_2O_4^{2-}]^2$ and $k = 7.6 \times 10^{-3} \text{ M}^{-2} \text{min}^{-1}$.

Thus, insertion of the starting concentrations and the k value into the rate law yields:

$$\text{Rate} = 7.6 \times 10^{-3} \text{ M}^{-2} \text{ min}^{-1} (0.050 \text{ M})^1 (0.025 \text{ M})^2 = 2.4 \times 10^{-7} \text{ M min}^{-1}$$

5A **(E)** Here we substitute directly into the integrated rate law equation.

$$\ln [A]_t = -kt + \ln [A]_o = -3.02 \times 10^{-3} \text{ s}^{-1} \times 325 \text{ s} + \ln(2.80) = -0.982 + 1.030 = 0.048$$

$$[A]_t = e^{0.048} = 1.0 \text{ M}$$

5B **(M)** This time we substitute the provided values into text Equation 20.13.

$$\ln \frac{[H_2O_2]_t}{[H_2O_2]_o} = -kt = -k \times 600 \text{ s} = \ln \frac{1.49 \text{ M}}{2.32 \text{ M}} = -0.443 \qquad k = \frac{-0.443}{-600 \text{ s}} = 7.38 \times 10^{-4} \text{ s}^{-1}$$

Now we choose $[H_2O_2]_o = 1.49 \text{ M}$, $[H_2O_2]_t = 0.62$, $\qquad t = 1800 \text{ s} - 600 \text{ s} = 1200 \text{ s}$

$$\ln \frac{[H_2O_2]_t}{[H_2O_2]_o} = -kt = -k \times 1200 \text{ s} = \ln \frac{0.62 \text{ M}}{1.49 \text{ M}} = -0.88 \qquad k = \frac{-0.88}{-1200 \text{ s}} = 7.3 \times 10^{-4} \text{ s}^{-1}$$

These two values agree within the limits of the experimental error and thus, the reaction is first-order in $[H_2O_2]$.

6A **(M)** We can use the integrated rate equation to find the ratio of the final and initial concentrations. This ratio equals the fraction of the initial concentration that remains at time t.

$$\ln\frac{[A]_t}{[A]_o} = -kt = -2.95\times10^{-3}\text{ s}^{-1}\times150\text{ s} = -0.443$$

$$\frac{[A]_t}{[A]_o} = e^{-0.443} = 0.642; \quad 64.2\% \text{ of } [A]_o \text{ remains.}$$

6B **(M)** After two-thirds of the sample has decomposed, one-third of the sample remains. Thus $[H_2O_2]_t = [H_2O_2]_o \div 3$, and we have

$$\ln\frac{[H_2O_2]_t}{[H_2O_2]_o} = -kt = \ln\frac{[H_2O_2]_o \div 3}{[H_2O_2]_o} = \ln(1/3) = -1.099 = -7.30\times10^{-4}\text{ s}^{-1}t$$

$$t = \frac{-1.099}{-7.30\times10^{-4}\text{ s}^{-1}} = 1.51\times10^3\text{ s}\times\frac{1\text{ min}}{60\text{ s}} = 25.1\text{ min}$$

7A **(M)** At the end of one half-life the pressure of DTBP will have been halved, to 400 mmHg. At the end of another half-life, at 160 min, the pressure of DTBP will have halved again, to 200 mmHg. Thus, the pressure of DTBP at 125 min will be intermediate between the pressure at 80.0 min (400 mmHg) and that at 160 min (200 mmHg). To obtain an exact answer, first we determine the value of the rate constant from the half-life.

$$k = \frac{0.693}{t_{1/2}} = \frac{0.693}{80.0\text{ min}} = 0.00866\text{ min}^{-1}$$

$$\ln\frac{(P_{DTBP})_t}{(P_{DTBP})_o} = -kt = -0.00866\text{ min}^{-1}\times125\text{ min} = -1.08$$

$$\frac{(P_{DTBP})_t}{(P_{DTBP})_o} = e^{-1.08} = 0.340$$

$$(P_{DTBP})_t = 0.340\times(P_{DTBP})_o = 0.340\times800\text{ mmHg} = 272\text{ mmHg}$$

7B **(M)**

(a) We use partial pressures in place of concentrations in the integrated first-order rate equation. Notice first that more than 30 half-lives have elapsed, and thus the ethylene oxide pressure has declined to at most $(0.5)^{30} = 9\times10^{-10}$ of its initial value.

$$\ln\frac{P_{30}}{P_o} = -kt = -2.05\times10^{-4}\text{ s}^{-1}\times30.0\text{ h}\times\frac{3600\text{ s}}{1\text{ h}} = -22.1 \quad \frac{P_{30}}{P_o} = e^{-22.1} = 2.4\times10^{-10}$$

$$P_{30} = 2.4\times10^{-10}\times P_o = 2.4\times10^{-10}\times782\text{ mmHg} = 1.9\times10^{-7}\text{ mmHg}$$

(b) $P_{\text{ethylene oxide}}$ initially 782 mmHg $\rightarrow 1.9 \times 10^{-7}$ mmHg (~ 0). Essentially all of the ethylene oxide is converted to CH_4 and CO. Since pressure is proportional to moles, the final pressure will be twice the initial pressure (1 mole gas $\rightarrow$ 2 moles gas; 782 mmHg $\rightarrow$ 1564 mmHg). The final pressure will be 1.56×10^3 mmHg.

8A **(D)** We first begin by looking for a constant rate, indicative of a zero-order reaction. If the rate is constant, the concentration will decrease by the same quantity during the same time period. If we choose a 25-s time period, we note that the concentration decreases $(0.88\ \text{M} - 0.74\ \text{M} =)\ 0.14\ \text{M}$ during the first 25 s, $(0.74\ \text{M} - 0.62\ \text{M} =)\ 0.12\ \text{M}$ during the second 25 s, $(0.62\ \text{M} - 0.52\ \text{M} =)\ 0.10\ \text{M}$ during the third 25 s, and $(0.52\ \text{M} - 0.44\ \text{M} =)\ 0.08\ \text{M}$ during the fourth 25-s period. This is hardly a constant rate and we thus conclude that the reaction is not zero-order.

We next look for a constant half-life, indicative of a first-order reaction. The initial concentration of 0.88 M decreases to one half of that value, 0.44 M, during the first 100 s, indicating a 100-s half-life. The concentration halves again to 0.22 M in the second 100 s, another 100-s half-life. Finally, we note that the concentration halves also from 0.62 M at 50 s to 0.31 M at 150 s, yet another 100-s half-life. The rate is established as first-order. The rate constant is $k = \dfrac{0.693}{t_{1/2}} = \dfrac{0.693}{100\ \text{s}} = 6.93 \times 10^{-3}\ \text{s}^{-1}$.

That the reaction is first-order is made apparent by the fact that the ln[B] vs time plot is a straight line with slope $= -k$ ($k = 6.85 \times 10^{-3}\ \text{s}^{-1}$).

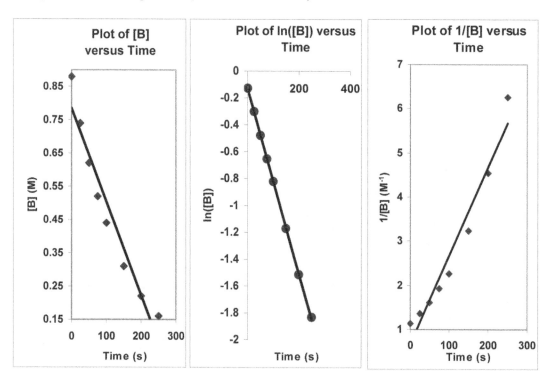

8B **(D)** We plot the data in three ways to determine the order. (1) A plot of [A] vs. time is linear if the reaction is zero-order. (2) A plot of ln [A] vs. time will be linear if the reaction is first-order. (3) A plot of 1/[A] vs. time will be linear if the reaction is second-order. It is obvious from the plots below that the reaction is zero-order. The negative of the slope of the line equals $k = -(0.083 \text{ M} - 0.250 \text{ M}) \div 18.00 \text{ min} = 9.28 \times 10^{-3}$ M/min ($k = 9.30 \times 10^{-3}$ M/min using a graphical approach).

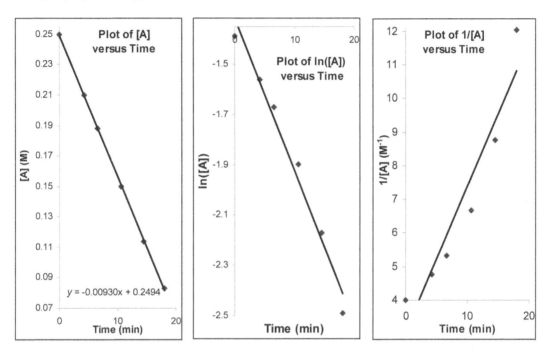

9A **(M)** First we compute the value of the rate constant at $75.0 \,^\circ\text{C}$ with the Arrhenius equation. We know that the activation energy is $E_a = 1.06 \times 10^5$ J/mol, and that $k = 3.46 \times 10^{-5} \text{ s}^{-1}$ at 298 K. The temperature of $75.0 \,^\circ\text{C} = 348.2$ K.

$$\ln \frac{k_2}{k_1} = \ln \frac{k_2}{3.46 \times 10^{-5} \text{ s}^{-1}} = -\frac{E_a}{R}\left(\frac{1}{T_2} - \frac{1}{T_1}\right) = -\frac{1.06 \times 10^5 \text{ J/mol}}{8.3145 \text{ J mol}^{-1} \text{ K}^{-1}}\left(\frac{1}{348.2 \text{ K}} - \frac{1}{298.2 \text{ K}}\right) = 6.14$$

$$k_2 = 3.46 \times 10^{-5} \text{ s}^{-1} \times e^{+6.14} = 3.46 \times 10^{-5} \text{ s}^{-1} \times 4.6 \times 10^2 = 0.016 \text{ s}^{-1}$$

$$t_{1/2} = \frac{0.693}{k} = \frac{0.693}{0.016 \text{ s}^{-1}} = 43 \text{ s at } 75 \,^\circ\text{C}$$

9B **(M)** We use the integrated rate equation to determine the rate constant, realizing that one-third remains when two-thirds have decomposed.

$$\ln \frac{[N_2O_5]_t}{[N_2O_5]_o} = \ln \frac{[N_2O_5]_o \div 3}{[N_2O_5]_o} = \ln \frac{1}{3} = -kt = -k(1.50 \text{ h}) = -1.099$$

$$k = \frac{1.099}{1.50 \text{ h}} \times \frac{1 \text{ h}}{3600 \text{ s}} = 2.03 \times 10^{-4} \text{ s}^{-1}$$

Now use the Arrhenius equation to determine the temperature at which the rate constant is $2.04 \times 10^{-4}\ \text{s}^{-1}$.

$$\ln\frac{k_2}{k_1} = \ln\frac{2.04\times10^{-4}\ \text{s}^{-1}}{3.46\times10^{-5}\ \text{s}^{-1}} = 1.77 = -\frac{E_a}{R}\left(\frac{1}{T_2} - \frac{1}{T_1}\right) = -\frac{1.06\times10^5\ \text{J/mol}}{8.3145\ \text{J mol}^{-1}\ \text{K}^{-1}}\left(\frac{1}{T_2} - \frac{1}{298\ \text{K}}\right)$$

$$\frac{1}{T_2} = \frac{1}{298\ \text{K}} + \frac{1.77\times8.3145\ \text{K}^{-1}}{-1.06\times10^5} = 3.22\times10^{-3}\ \text{K}^{-1} \qquad T_2 = 311\ \text{K}$$

10A **(M)** The two steps of the mechanism must add, in a Hess's law fashion, to produce the overall reaction.

Overall reaction: $CO + NO_2 \longrightarrow CO_2 + NO$ or $CO + NO_2 \longrightarrow CO_2 + NO$

Second step: $-\left(NO_3 + CO \longrightarrow NO_2 + CO_2\right)$ or $+\left(NO_2 + CO_2 \longrightarrow NO_3 + CO\right)$

First step: $\qquad\qquad\qquad\qquad\qquad\qquad\qquad\qquad 2\ NO_2 \longrightarrow NO + NO_3$

If the first step is the slow step, then it will be the rate-determining step, and the rate of that step will be the rate of the reaction, namely, rate of reaction $= k_1[NO_2]^2$.

10B **(M)**

(1) The steps of the mechanism must add, in a Hess's law fashion, to produce the overall reaction. This is done below. The two intermediates, $NO_2F_2(g)$ and $F(g)$, are each produced in one step and consumed in the next one.

Fast: $\quad NO_2(g) + F_2(g) \rightleftharpoons NO_2F_2(g)$

Slow: $\quad NO_2F_2(g) \rightarrow NO_2F(g) + F(g)$

Fast: $\quad F(g) + NO_2(g) \rightarrow NO_2F(g)$

Net: $\quad 2\ NO_2(g) + F_2(g) \rightarrow 2\ NO_2F(g)$

(2) The proposed mechanism must agree with the rate law. We expect the rate-determining step to determine the reaction rate: Rate $= k_3[NO_2F_2]$. To eliminate $[NO_2F_2]$, we recognize that the first elementary reaction is very fast and will have the same rate forward as reverse: $R_f = k_1[NO_2][F_2] = k_2[NO_2F_2] = R_r$. We solve for the concentration of intermediate: $[NO_2F_2] = k_1[NO_2][F_2]/k_2$. We now substitute this expression for $[NO_2F_2]$ into the rate equation: Rate $= (k_1 k_3/k_2)[NO_2][F_2]$. Thus the predicted rate law agrees with the experimental rate law.

INTEGRATIVE EXAMPLE

A. **(M)**

(a) The time required for the fixed (c) process of souring is three times as long at 3 °C refrigerator temperature (276 K) as at 20 °C room temperature (293 K).

$$\ln\frac{c/t_2}{c/t_1} = \ln\frac{t_1}{t_2} = \ln\frac{64\ \text{h}}{3\times 64\ \text{h}} = -1.10 = -\frac{E_a}{R}\left(\frac{1}{T_2}-\frac{1}{T_1}\right) = -\frac{E_a}{R}\left(\frac{1}{276\ \text{K}}-\frac{1}{293\ \text{K}}\right) = -\frac{E_a}{R}(2.10\times10^{-4})$$

$$E_a = \frac{1.10\ R}{2.10\times10^{-4}\ \text{K}^{-1}} = \frac{1.10\times8.3145\ \text{J mol}^{-1}\ \text{K}^{-1}}{2.10\times10^{-4}\ \text{K}^{-1}} = 4.4\times10^4\ \text{J/mol} = 44\ \text{kJ/mol}$$

(b) Use the E_a determined in part **(a)** to calculate the souring time at 40 °C = 313 K.

$$\ln\frac{t_1}{t_2} = -\frac{E_a}{R}\left(\frac{1}{T_2}-\frac{1}{T_1}\right) = -\frac{4.4\times10^4\ \text{J/mol}}{8.3145\ \text{J mol}^{-1}\ \text{K}^{-1}}\left(\frac{1}{293\ \text{K}}-\frac{1}{313\ \text{K}}\right) = -1.15 = \ln\frac{t_1}{64\ \text{h}}$$

$$\frac{t_1}{64\ \text{h}} = e^{-1.15} = 0.317 \quad t_1 = 0.317\times64\ \text{h} = 20.\ \text{h}$$

B. **(M)** The species A^* is a reactive intermediate. Let's deal with this species by using a steady state approximation.

$d[A^*]/dt = 0 = k_1[A]^2 - k_{-1}[A^*][A] - k_2[A^*]$. Solve for $[A^*]$. $k_{-1}[A^*][A] + k_2[A^*] = k_1[A]^2$

$$[A^*] = \frac{k_1[A]^2}{k_{-1}[A] + k_2} \qquad \text{The rate of reaction is: Rate} = k_2[A^*] = \frac{k_2 k_1[A]^2}{k_{-1}[A] + k_2}$$

At low pressures ($[A] \sim 0$ and hence $k_2 \gg k_{-1}[A]$), the denominator becomes $\sim k_2$ and the rate law is

$$\text{Rate} = \frac{k_2 k_1[A]^2}{k_2} = k_1[A]^2 \quad \text{Second-order with respect to } [A]$$

At high pressures ($[A]$ is large and $k_{-1}[A] \gg K_2$), the denominator becomes $\sim k_{-1}[A]$ and the rate law is

$$\text{Rate} = \frac{k_2 k_1[A]^2}{k_{-1}[A]} = \frac{k_2 k_1[A]}{k_{-1}} \quad \text{First-order with respect to } [A]$$

EXERCISES

Rates of Reactions

1. **(M)** $2A + B \rightarrow C + 3D \qquad -\dfrac{\Delta[A]}{\Delta t} = 6.2\times10^{-4}\ \text{M s}^{-1}$

(a) $\text{Rate} = -\dfrac{1}{2}\dfrac{\Delta[A]}{\Delta t} = 1/2(6.2\times10^{-4}\ \text{M s}^{-1}) = 3.1\times10^{-4}\ \text{M s}^{-1}$

(b) Rate of disappearance of B $= -\dfrac{1}{2}\dfrac{\Delta[A]}{\Delta t} = 1/2(6.2\times10^{-4}\ \text{M s}^{-1}) = 3.1\times10^{-4}\ \text{M s}^{-1}$

(c) Rate of appearance of D $= -\dfrac{3}{2}\dfrac{\Delta[A]}{\Delta t} = 3(6.2\times10^{-4}\ \text{M s}^{-1}) = 9.3\times10^{-4}\ \text{M s}^{-1}$

2. **(M)** In each case, we draw the tangent line to the plotted curve.

    (a) The slope of the line is $\dfrac{\Delta[H_2O_2]}{\Delta t} = \dfrac{1.7\ M - 0.6\ M}{400\ s - 1600\ s} = -9.2 \times 10^{-4}\ M\ s^{-1}$

    reaction rate $= -\dfrac{\Delta[H_2O_2]}{\Delta t} = 9.2 \times 10^{-4}\ M\ s^{-1}$

    (b) Read the value where the horizontal line $[H_2O_2] = 0.50$ M intersects the curve, $\approx 21\underline{5}0$ s or ≈ 36 minutes

3. **(E)** Rate $= -\dfrac{\Delta[A]}{\Delta t} = -\dfrac{(0.474\ M - 0.485\ M)}{82.4\ s - 71.5\ s} = 1.0 \times 10^{-3}\ M\ s^{-1}$

4. **(M)**

    (a) Rate $= -\dfrac{\Delta[A]}{\Delta t} = -\dfrac{0.1498\ M - 0.1565\ M}{1.00\ min - 0.00\ min} = 0.0067\ M\ min^{-1}$

    Rate $= -\dfrac{\Delta[A]}{\Delta t} = -\dfrac{0.1433\ M - 0.1498\ M}{2.00\ min - 1.00\ min} = 0.0065\ M\ min^{-1}$

    (b) The rates are not equal because, in all except zero-order reactions, the rate depends on the concentration of reactant. And, of course, as the reaction proceeds, reactant is consumed and its concentration decreases, so the rate of the reaction decreases.

5. **(M)**

    (a) $[A] = [A]_i + \Delta[A] = 0.588\ M - 0.013\ M = 0.575\ M$

    (b) $\Delta[A] = 0.565\ M - 0.588\ M = -0.023\ M$

    $\Delta t = \Delta[A] \dfrac{\Delta t}{\Delta[A]} = \dfrac{-0.023\ M}{-2.2 \times 10^{-2}\ M/min} = 1.0\ min$

    $time = t + \Delta t = (4.40 + 1.0)\ min = 5.4\ min$

6. **(M)** Initial concentrations are $[HgCl_2] = 0.105$ M and $[C_2O_4{}^{2-}] = 0.300$ M.

The initial rate of the reaction is $7.1 \times 10^{-5}\ M\ min^{-1}$. Recall that the reaction is:

$2\ HgCl_2(aq) + C_2O_4^{2-}(aq) \rightarrow 2\ Cl^-(aq) + 2\ CO_2(g) + Hg_2Cl_2(aq)$.

The rate of reaction equals the rate of disappearance of $C_2O_4^{2-}$. Then, after 1 hour, assuming that the rate is the same as the initial rate,

    (a) $[HgCl_2] = 0.105\ M - \left(7.1 \times 10^{-5}\ \dfrac{mol\ C_2O_4^{2-}}{L \cdot s} \times \dfrac{2\ mol\ HgCl_2}{1\ mol\ C_2O_4^{2-}} \times 1\ h \times \dfrac{60\ min}{1\ h}\right) = 0.096\ M$

    (b) $[C_2O_4^{2-}] = 0.300\ M - \left(7.1 \times 10^{-5}\ \dfrac{mol}{L \cdot min} \times 1\ h \times \dfrac{60\ min}{1\ h}\right) = 0.296\ M$

7. **(M)**

(a) $\text{Rate} = \dfrac{-\Delta[A]}{\Delta t} = \dfrac{\Delta[C]}{2\Delta t} = 1.76 \times 10^{-5} \text{ M s}^{-1}$

$\dfrac{\Delta[C]}{\Delta t} = 2 \times 1.76 \times 10^{-5} \text{ M s}^{-1} = 3.52 \times 10^{-5} \text{ M/s}$

(b) $\dfrac{\Delta[A]}{\Delta t} = -\dfrac{\Delta[C]}{2\Delta t} = -1.76 \times 10^{-5} \text{ M s}^{-1}$ Assume this rate is constant.

$[A] = 0.3580 \text{ M} + \left(-1.76 \times 10^{-5} \text{ M s}^{-1} \times 1.00 \min \times \dfrac{60 \text{ s}}{1 \min} \right) = 0.357 \text{ M}$

(c) $\dfrac{\Delta[A]}{\Delta t} = -1.76 \times 10^{-5} \text{ M s}^{-1}$

$\Delta t = \dfrac{\Delta[A]}{-1.76 \times 10^{-5} \text{ M/s}} = \dfrac{0.3500 \text{ M} - 0.3580 \text{ M}}{-1.76 \times 10^{-5} \text{ M/s}} = 4.5 \times 10^{2} \text{ s}$

8. **(M)**

(a) $\dfrac{\Delta n[O_2]}{\Delta t} = 1.00 \text{ L soln} \times \dfrac{5.7 \times 10^{-4} \text{ mol } H_2O_2}{1 \text{ L soln} \cdot \text{s}} \times \dfrac{1 \text{ mol } O_2}{2 \text{ mol } H_2O_2} = 2.9 \times 10^{-4} \text{ mol } O_2/\text{s}$

(b) $\dfrac{\Delta n[O_2]}{\Delta t} = 2.9 \times 10^{-4} \dfrac{\text{mol } O_2}{\text{s}} \times \dfrac{60 \text{ s}}{1 \min} = 1.7 \times 10^{-2} \text{ mol } O_2 \text{ / min}$

(c) $\dfrac{\Delta V[O_2]}{\Delta t} = 1.7 \times 10^{-2} \dfrac{\text{mol } O_2}{\min} \times \dfrac{22,711 \text{ mL } O_2 \text{ at STP}}{1 \text{ mol } O_2} = \dfrac{3.8 \times 10^{2} \text{ mL } O_2 \text{ at STP}}{\min}$

9. **(M)** Notice that, for every 1000 mmHg drop in the pressure of A(g), there will be a corresponding 2000 mmHg rise in the pressure of B(g) plus a 1000 mmHg rise in the pressure of C(g).

(a) We set up the calculation with three lines of information below the balanced equation: (1) the initial conditions, (2) the changes that occur, which are related to each other by reaction stoichiometry, and (3) the final conditions, which simply are initial conditions + changes.

	A(g)	→	2B(g)	+	C(g)
Initial	1000. mmHg		0. mmHg		0. mmHg
Changes	−1000. mmHg		+2000. mmHg		+1000. mmHg
Final	0. mmHg		2000. MmHg		1000. mmHg

Total final pressure = 0. mmHg + 2000. mmHg + 1000. mmHg = 3000. mmHg

(b)

	A(g)	→	2B(g)	+	C(g)
Initial	1000. mmHg		0. mmHg		0. mmHg
Changes	−200. mmHg		+400. mmHg		+200. mmHg
Final	800 mmHg		400. mmHg		200. mmHg

Total pressure = 800. mmHg + 400. mmHg + 200. mmHg = 1400. mmHg

10. (M)

(a) We will use the ideal gas law to determine N_2O_5 pressure

$$P\{N_2O_5\} = \frac{nRT}{V} = \frac{\left(1.00\,g \times \dfrac{1\,mol\,N_2O_5}{108.0\,g}\right) \times 0.08206\,\dfrac{L\,atm}{mol\,K} \times (273+65)\,K}{15\,L} \times \frac{760\,mmHg}{1\,atm} = 13\,mmHg$$

(b) After 2.38 min, one half-life passes. The initial pressure of N_2O_5 decreases by half to 6.5 mmHg.

(c) From the balanced chemical equation, the reaction of 2 mol $N_2O_5(g)$ produces 4 mol $NO_2(g)$ and 1 mol $O_2(g)$. That is, the consumption of 2 mol of reactant gas produces 5 mol of product gases. When measured at the same temperature and confined to the same volume, pressures will behave as amounts: the reaction of 2 mmHg of reactant produces 5 mmHg of product.

$$P_{total} = 13\,mmHg\,N_2O_5\,(\text{initially}) - 6.5\,mmHg\,N_2O_5\,(\text{reactant}) + \left(6.5\,mmHg_{(\text{reactant})} \times \frac{5\,mmHg_{(\text{product})}}{2\,mmHg_{(\text{reactant})}}\right)$$

$$= (13 - 6.5 + 16)\,mmHg = 23\,mmHg$$

Method of Initial Rates

11. (M)

(a) From Expt. 1 to Expt. 3, [A] is doubled, while [B] remains fixed. This causes the rate to increases by a factor of $\dfrac{6.75 \times 10^{-4}\,M\,s^{-1}}{3.35 \times 10^{-4}\,M\,s^{-1}} = 2.01 \approx 2$.

Thus, the reaction is first-order with respect to A.
From Expt. 1 to Expt. 2, [B] doubles, while [A] remains fixed. This causes the rate to increases by a factor of $\dfrac{1.35 \times 10^{-3}\,M\,s^{-1}}{3.35 \times 10^{-4}\,M\,s^{-1}} = 4.03 \approx 4$.

Thus, the reaction is second-order with respect to B.

(b) Overall reaction order = order with respect to A + order with respect to B = $1 + 2 = 3$. The reaction is third-order overall.

(c) Rate $= 3.35 \times 10^{-4}\,M\,s^{-1} = k(0.185\,M)(0.133\,M)^2$

$$k = \frac{3.35 \times 10^{-4}\,M\,s^{-1}}{(0.185\,M)(0.133\,M)^2} = 0.102\,M^{-2}\,s^{-1}$$

12. (M) From Expt. 1 and Expt. 2 we see that [B] remains fixed while [A] triples. As a result, the initial rate increases from 4.2×10^{-3} M/min to 1.3×10^{-2} M/min, that is, the initial reaction rate triples. Therefore, the reaction is first-order in [A]. Between Expt. 2 and Expt. 3, we see that [A] doubles, which would double the rate, and [B] doubles. As a consequence, the initial rate goes from 1.3×10^{-2} M/min to 5.2×10^{-2} M/min, that is, the rate quadruples. Since an additional doubling of the rate is due to the change in [B], the reaction is first-order in [B]. Now we determine the value of the rate constant.

$$\text{Rate} = k[A]^1[B]^1 \qquad k = \frac{\text{Rate}}{[A][B]} = \frac{5.2 \times 10^{-2} \text{ M/min}}{3.00 \text{ M} \times 3.00 \text{ M}} = 5.8 \times 10^{-3} \text{ L mol}^{-1}\text{min}^{-1}$$

The rate law is $\text{Rate} = \left(5.8 \times 10^{-3} \text{ L mol}^{-1}\text{min}^{-1}\right)[A]^1[B]^1$.

13. **(M)** From Experiment 1 to 2, [NO] remains constant while $[Cl_2]$ is doubled. At the same time the initial rate of reaction is found to double. Thus, the reaction is first-order with respect to $[Cl_2]$, since dividing reaction 2 by reaction 1 gives $2 = 2^x$ when $x = 1$. From Experiment 1 to 3, $[Cl_2]$ remains constant, while [NO] is doubled, resulting in a quadrupling of the initial rate of reaction. Thus, the reaction must be second-order in [NO], since dividing reaction 3 by reaction 1 gives $4 = 2^x$ when $x = 2$. Overall the reaction is third-order: $\text{Rate} = k[NO]^2[Cl_2]$. The rate constant may be calculated from any one of the experiments. Using data from Exp. 1,

$$k = \frac{\text{Rate}}{[NO]^2[Cl_2]} = \frac{2.27 \times 10^{-5} \text{ M s}^{-1}}{(0.0125 \text{ M})^2(0.0255 \text{ M})} = 5.70 \text{ M}^{-2}\text{ s}^{-1}$$

14. **(M)**

(a) From Expt. 1 to Expt. 2, [B] remains constant at 1.40 M and [C] remains constant at 1.00 M, but [A] is halved $(\times 0.50)$. At the same time the rate is halved $(\times 0.50)$.

Thus, the reaction is first-order with respect to A, since $0.50^x = 0.50$ when $x = 1$. From Expt. 2 to Expt. 3, [A] remains constant at 0.70 M and [C] remains constant at 1.00 M, but [B] is halved $(\times 0.50)$, from 1.40 M to 0.70 M. At the same time, the rate is quartered $(\times 0.25)$. Thus, the reaction is second-order with respect to B, since $0.50^y = 0.25$ when $y = 2$.

From Expt. 1 to Expt. 4, [A] remains constant at 1.40 M and [B] remains constant at 1.40 M, but [C] is halved $(\times 0.50)$, from 1.00 M to 0.50 M. At the same time, the rate is increased by a factor of 2.0.

$$\left[\text{Rate}_4 = 16 \text{ Rate}_3 = 16 \times \frac{1}{4}\text{Rate}_2 = 4 \text{ Rate}_2 = 4 \times \frac{1}{2}\text{Rate}_1 = 2 \times \text{Rate}_1.\right]$$

Thus, the order of the reaction with respect to C is -1, since $0.5^z = 2.0$ when $z = -1$.

(b) $\text{rate}_5 = k(0.70 \text{ M})^1(0.70 \text{ M})^2(0.50 \text{ M})^{-1} = k\left(\frac{1.40 \text{ M}}{2}\right)^1\left(\frac{1.40 \text{ M}}{2}\right)^2\left(\frac{1.00 \text{ M}}{2}\right)^{-1}$

$= k\frac{1}{2}^1(1.40 \text{ M})^1 \frac{1}{2}^2(1.40 \text{ M})^2 \frac{1}{2}^{-1}(1.00 \text{ M})^{-1} = \text{rate}_1\left(\frac{1}{2}\right)^{1+2-1} = \text{rate}_1\left(\frac{1}{2}\right)^2 = \frac{1}{4}\text{rate}_1$

This is based on $\text{rate}_1 = k(1.40 \text{ M})^1(1.40 \text{ M})^2(1.00 \text{ M})^{-1}$

First-Order Reactions

15. **(E)**

 (a) TRUE   The rate of the reaction does decrease as more and more of B and C are formed, but not because more and more of B and C are formed. Rather, the rate decreases because the concentration of A must decrease to form more and more of B and C.

 (b) FALSE   The time required for one half of substance A to react—the half-life—is independent of the quantity of A present.

16. **(E)**

 (a) FALSE   For first-order reactions, a plot of ln [A] or log [A] vs. time yields a straight line. A graph of [A] vs. time yields a curved line.

 (b) TRUE   The rate of formation of C is related to the rate of disappearance of A by the stoichiometry of the reaction.

17. **(M)**

 (a) Since the half-life is 180 s, after 900 s five half-lives have elapsed, and the original quantity of A has been cut in half five times.

 final quantity of A $= (0.5)^5 \times$ initial quantity of A $= 0.03125 \times$ initial quantity of A

 About 3.13% of the original quantity of A remains unreacted after 900 s.

 or

 More generally, we would calculate the value of the rate constant, k, using

 $k = \dfrac{\ln 2}{t_{1/2}} = \dfrac{0.693}{180 \text{ s}} = 0.00385 \text{ s}^{-1}$ Now ln (% unreacted) $= -kt = -0.00385 \text{ s}^{-1} \times (900\text{s})$

 $= -3.46\underline{5}$

 (% unreacted) $= 0.0313 \times 100\% = 3.13\%$ of the original quantity.

 (b) Rate $= k[\text{A}] = 0.00385 \text{ s}^{-1} \times 0.50 \text{ M} = 0.00193 \text{ M/s}$

18. **(M)**

 (a) The reaction is first-order, thus

 $\ln \dfrac{[\text{A}]_t}{[\text{A}]_0} = -kt = \ln \dfrac{0.100 \text{ M}}{0.800 \text{ M}} = -54 \min(k)$ $k = -\dfrac{-2.08}{54 \text{ min}} = 0.038\underline{5} \text{ min}^{-1}$

 We may now determine the time required to achieve a concentration of 0.025 M

 $\ln \dfrac{[\text{A}]_t}{[\text{A}]_0} = -kt = \ln \dfrac{0.025 \text{ M}}{0.800 \text{ M}} = -0.038\underline{5} \text{ min}^{-1}(t)$ $t = \dfrac{-3.4\underline{7}}{-0.038\underline{5} \text{ min}^{-1}} = 90. \text{ min}$

 (b) Since we know the rate constant for this reaction (see above),

 Rate $= k[\text{A}]^1 = 0.038\underline{5} \text{ min}^{-1} \times 0.025 \text{ M} = 9.6 \times 10^{-4} \text{ M/min}$

19. (M)

(a) The mass of A has decreased to one fourth of its original value, from 1.60 g to 0.40 g. Since $\frac{1}{4} = \frac{1}{2} \times \frac{1}{2}$, we see that two half-lives have elapsed.

Thus, $2 \times t_{1/2} = 38$ min, or $t_{1/2} = 19$ min.

(b) $k = 0.693 / t_{1/2} = \dfrac{0.693}{19\,\text{min}} = 0.036\,\text{min}^{-1}$ $\quad \ln\dfrac{[A]_t}{[A]_o} = -kt = -0.036\,\text{min}^{-1} \times 60\,\text{min} = -2.2$

$\dfrac{[A]_t}{[A]_o} = e^{-2.2} = 0.1\underline{1}$ or $[A]_t = [A]_o\, e^{-kt} = 1.60\,\text{g A} \times 0.1\underline{1} = 0.1\underline{8}\,\text{g A}$

20. (M)

(a) $\ln\dfrac{[A]_t}{[A]_o} = -kt = \ln\dfrac{0.632\,\text{M}}{0.816\,\text{M}} = -0.256 \quad k = -\dfrac{-0.256}{16.0\,\text{min}} = 0.0160\,\text{min}^{-1}$

(b) $t_{1/2} = \dfrac{0.693}{k} = \dfrac{0.693}{0.0160\,\text{min}^{-1}} = 43.3\,\text{min}$

(c) We need to solve the integrated rate equation to find the elapsed time.

$\ln\dfrac{[A]_t}{[A]_o} = -kt = \ln\dfrac{0.235\,\text{M}}{0.816\,\text{M}} = -1.245 = -0.0160\,\text{min}^{-1} \times t \quad t = \dfrac{-1.245}{-0.0160\,\text{min}^{-1}} = 77.8\,\text{min}$

(d) $\ln\dfrac{[A]}{[A]_o} = -kt$ becomes $\dfrac{[A]}{[A]_o} = e^{-kt}$ which in turn becomes

$[A] = [A]_o\, e^{-kt} = 0.816\,\text{M} \exp\left(-0.0160\,\text{min}^{-1} \times 2.5\,\text{h} \times \dfrac{60\,\text{min}}{1\,\text{h}}\right) = 0.816 \times 0.0907 = 0.074\,\text{M}$

21. **(M)** We determine the value of the first-order rate constant and from that we can calculate the half-life. If the reactant is 99% decomposed in 137 min, then only 1% (0.010) of the initial concentration remains.

$\ln\dfrac{[A]_t}{[A]_o} = -kt = \ln\dfrac{0.010}{1.000} = -4.61 = -k \times 137\,\text{min} \qquad k = \dfrac{-4.61}{-137\,\text{min}} = 0.0336\,\text{min}^{-1}$

$t_{1/2} = \dfrac{0.0693}{k} = \dfrac{0.693}{0.0336\,\text{min}^{-1}} = 20.6\,\text{min}$

22. **(E)** If 99% of the radioactivity of ^{32}P is lost, 1% (0.010) of that radioactivity remains. First we compute the value of the rate constant from the half-life.

$k = \dfrac{0.693}{t_{1/2}} = \dfrac{0.693}{14.3\,\text{d}} = 0.0485\,\text{d}^{-1}$

Then we use the integrated rate equation to determine the elapsed time.

$\ln\dfrac{[A]_t}{[A]_o} = -kt \quad t = -\dfrac{1}{k}\ln\dfrac{[A]_t}{[A]_o} = -\dfrac{1}{0.0485\,\text{d}^{-1}}\ln\dfrac{0.010}{1.000} = 95\,\text{days}$

23. **(D)**

(a) $\ln\left(\dfrac{\dfrac{35}{100}[A]_o}{[A]_o}\right) = \ln(0.35) = -kt = (-4.81 \times 10^{-3}\ \text{min}^{-1})t$ $\qquad t = 218$ min.

Note: We did not need to know the initial concentration of acetoacetic acid to answer the question.

(b) Let's assume that the reaction takes place in a 1.00L container.

10.0 g acetoacetic acid $\times \dfrac{1\ \text{mol acetoacetic acid}}{102.090\ \text{g acetoacetic acid}} = 0.09795$ mol acetoacetic acid.

After 575 min. (~ 4 half lives, hence, we expect $\sim 6.25\%$ remains as a rough approximation), use integrated form of the rate law to find $[A]_t = 575$ min.

$\ln\left(\dfrac{[A]_t}{[A]_o}\right) = -kt = (-4.81 \times 10^{-3}\ \text{min}^{-1})(575\ \text{min}) = -2.766$

$\dfrac{[A]_t}{[A]_o} = e^{-2.766} = 0.06293\ (\sim 6.3\%\ \text{remains})\qquad \dfrac{[A]_t}{0.09795\ \text{moles}} = 0.063\ [A]_t = 6.2 \times 10^{-3}$

moles.

$[A]_{\text{reacted}} = [A]_o - [A]_t = (0.098 - 6.2 \times 10^{-3})$ moles $= 0.092$ moles acetoacetic acid. The stoichiometry is such that for every mole of acetoacetic acid consumed, one mole of CO_2 forms. Hence, we need to determine the volume of 0.0918 moles CO_2 at 24.5 °C (297.65 K) and 748 torr (0.984 atm) by using the Ideal Gas law.

$V = \dfrac{nRT}{P} = \dfrac{0.0918\ \text{mol}\left(0.08206\ \dfrac{\text{L atm}}{\text{K mol}}\right)297.65\ \text{K}}{0.984\ \text{atm}} = 2.3\ \text{L}\ CO_2$

24. **(M)**

(a) $\ln\dfrac{[A]_t}{[A]_o} = -kt = \ln\dfrac{2.5\ \text{g}}{80.0\ \text{g}} = -3.47 = -6.2 \times 10^{-4}\ \text{s}^{-1}t$

$t = \dfrac{3.47}{6.2 \times 10^{-4}\ \text{s}^{-1}} = 5.6 \times 10^3\ \text{s} \approx 93\ \text{min}$

We substituted masses for concentrations, because the same substance (with the same molar mass) is present initially at time t, and because it is a closed system.

(b) amount $O_2 = 77.5$ g $N_2O_5 \times \dfrac{1\ \text{mol}\ N_2O_5}{108.0\ \text{g}\ N_2O_5} \times \dfrac{1\ \text{mol}\ O_2}{2\ \text{mol}\ N_2O_5} = 0.359$ mol O_2

$V = \dfrac{nRT}{P} = \dfrac{0.359\ \text{mol}\ O_2 \times 0.08206\ \dfrac{\text{L atm}}{\text{mol K}} \times (45+273)\ \text{K}}{745\ \text{mmHg} \times \dfrac{1\ \text{atm}}{760\ \text{mmHg}}} = 9.56\ \text{L}\ O_2$

25. **(D)**

(a) If the reaction is first-order, we will obtain the same value of the rate constant from several sets of data.

$$\ln\frac{[A]_t}{[A]_o} = -kt = \ln\frac{0.497\text{ M}}{0.600\text{ M}} = -k\times100\text{ s} = -0.188, \quad k = \frac{0.188}{100\text{ s}} = 1.88\times10^{-3}\text{ s}^{-1}$$

$$\ln\frac{[A]_t}{[A]_o} = -kt = \ln\frac{0.344\text{ M}}{0.600\text{ M}} = -k\times300\text{ s} = -0.556, \quad k = \frac{0.556}{300\text{ s}} = 1.85\times10^{-3}\text{ s}^{-1}$$

$$\ln\frac{[A]_t}{[A]_o} = -kt = \ln\frac{0.285\text{ M}}{0.600\text{ M}} = -k\times400\text{ s} = -0.744, \quad k = \frac{0.744}{400\text{ s}} = 1.86\times10^{-3}\text{ s}^{-1}$$

$$\ln\frac{[A]_t}{[A]_o} = -kt = \ln\frac{0.198\text{ M}}{0.600\text{ M}} = -k\times600\text{ s} = -1.109, \quad k = \frac{1.109}{600\text{ s}} = 1.85\times10^{-3}\text{ s}^{-1}$$

$$\ln\frac{[A]_t}{[A]_o} = -kt = \ln\frac{0.094\text{ M}}{0.600\text{ M}} = -k\times1000\text{ s} = -1.854, \quad k = \frac{1.854}{1000\text{ s}} = 1.85\times10^{-3}\text{ s}^{-1}$$

The virtual constancy of the rate constant throughout the time of the reaction confirms that the reaction is first-order.

(b) For this part, we assume that the rate constant equals the average of the values obtained in part (a).

$$k = \frac{1.88+1.85+1.86+1.85}{4}\times10^{-3}\text{ s}^{-1} = 1.86\times10^{-3}\text{ s}^{-1}$$

(c) We use the integrated first-order rate equation:

$$[A]_{750} = [A]_o\exp(-kt) = 0.600\text{ M}\exp(-1.86\times10^{-3}\text{ s}^{-1}\times750\text{ s})$$

$$[A]_{750} = 0.600\text{ M e}^{-1.40} = 0.148\text{ M}$$

26. **(D)**

(a) If the reaction is first-order, we will obtain the same value of the rate constant from several sets of data.

$$\ln\frac{P_t}{P_o} = -kt = \ln\frac{264\text{ mmHg}}{312\text{ mmHg}} = -k\times390\text{ s} = -0.167, \quad k = \frac{0.167}{390\text{ s}} = 4.28\times10^{-4}\text{ s}^{-1}$$

$$\ln\frac{P_t}{P_o} = -kt = \ln\frac{224\text{ mmHg}}{312\text{ mmHg}} = -k\times777\text{ s} = -0.331, \quad k = \frac{0.331}{777\text{ s}} = 4.26\times10^{-4}\text{ s}^{-1}$$

$$\ln\frac{P_t}{P_o} = -kt = \ln\frac{187\text{ mmHg}}{312\text{ mmHg}} = -k\times1195\text{ s} = -0.512, \quad k = \frac{0.512}{1195\text{ s}} = 4.28\times10^{-4}\text{ s}^{-1}$$

$$\ln\frac{P_t}{P_o} = -kt = \ln\frac{78.5\text{ mmHg}}{312\text{ mmHg}} = -k\times3155\text{ s} = -1.38, \quad k = \frac{1.38}{3155\text{ s}} = 4.37\times10^{-4}\text{ s}^{-1}$$

The virtual constancy of the rate constant confirms that the reaction is first-order.

(b) For this part we assume the rate constant is the average of the values in part (a): $4.3\times10^{-4}\text{ s}^{-1}$.

(c) At 390 s, the pressure of dimethyl ether has dropped to 264 mmHg. Thus, an amount of dimethyl ether equivalent to a pressure of $(312 \text{ mmHg} - 264 \text{ mmHg} =)$ 48 mmHg has decomposed. For each 1 mmHg pressure of dimethyl ether that decomposes, 3 mmHg of pressure from the products is produced. Thus, the increase in the pressure of the products is $3 \times 48 = 144$ mmHg. The total pressure at this point is 264 mmHg $+144$ mmHg $= 408$ mmHg. Below, this calculation is done in a more systematic fashion:

	$(CH_3)_2O(g)$	$\rightarrow$	$CH_4(g)$	$+$	$H_2(g)$ $+$	$CO(g)$
Initial	312 mmHg		0 mmHg		0 mmHg	0 mmHg
Changes	-48 mmHg		$+48$ mmHg		$+48$ mmHg	$+48$ mmHg
Final	264 mmHg		48 mmHg		48 mmHg	48 mmHg

$$P_{total} = P_{DME} + P_{methane} + P_{hydrogen} + P_{CO}$$
$$= 264 \text{ mmHg} + 48 \text{ mmHg} + 48 \text{ mmHg} + 48 \text{ mmHg} = 408 \text{ mmHg}$$

(d) This question is solved in the same manner as part (c). The results are summarized below.

	$(CH_3)_2O(g)$	$\rightarrow$	$CH_4(g)$	$+$	$H_2(g)$	$+$	$CO(g)$
Initial	312 mmHg		0 mmHg		0 mmHg		0 mmHg
Changes	-312 mmHg		$+312$ mmHg		$+312$ mmHg		$+312$ mmHg
Final	0 mmHg		312 mmHg		312 mmHg		312 mmHg

$$P_{total} = P_{DME} + P_{methane} + P_{hydrogen} + P_{CO}$$
$$= 0 \text{ mmHg} + 312 \text{ mmHg} + 312 \text{ mmHg} + 312 \text{ mmHg} = 936 \text{ mmHg}$$

(e) We first determine P_{DME} at 1000 s. $\ln\dfrac{P_{1000}}{P_0} = -kt = -4.3 \times 10^{-4} \text{ s}^{-1} \times 1000 \text{ s} = -0.43$

$$\frac{P_{1000}}{P_0} = e^{-0.43} = 0.65 \qquad P_{1000} = 312 \text{ mmHg} \times 0.65 = 203 \text{ mmHg}$$

Then we use the same approach as was used for parts (c) and (d)

	$(CH_3)_2O(g)$	$\rightarrow$	$CH_4(g)$	$+$	$H_2(g)$	$+$	$CO(g)$
Initial	312 mmHg		0 mmHg		0 mmHg		0 mmHg
Changes	-109 mmHg		$+109$ mmHg		$+109$ mmHg		$+109$ mmHg
Final	203 mmHg		109 mmHg		109 mmHg		109 mmHg

$$P_{total} = P_{DME} + P_{methane} + P_{hydrogen} + P_{CO}$$
$$= 203 \text{ mmHg} + 109 \text{ mmHg} + 109 \text{ mmHg} + 109 \text{ mmHg} = 530. \text{ mmHg}$$

Reactions of Various Orders

27. **(M)**

(a) Set II is data from a zero-order reaction. We know this because the rate of set II is constant.

0.25 M/25 s = 0.010 M s^{-1}. Zero-order reactions have constant rates of reaction.

(b) A first-order reaction has a constant half-life. In set I, the first half-life is slightly less than 75 sec, since the concentration decreases by slightly more than half (from 1.00 M to 0.47 M) in 75 s. Again, from 75 s to 150 s the concentration decreases from 0.47 M to 0.22 M, again by slightly more than half, in a time of 75 s. Finally, two half-lives should see the concentration decrease to one-fourth of its initial value. This, in fact, is what we see. From 100 s to 250 s, 150 s of elapsed time, the concentration decreases from 0.37 M to 0.08 M, i.e., to slightly less than one-fourth of its initial value. Notice that we cannot make the same statement of constancy of half-life for set III. The first half-life is 100 s, but it takes more than 150 s (from 100 s to 250 s) for [A] to again decrease by half.

(c) For a second-order reaction, $1/[A]_t - 1/[A]_o = kt$. For the initial 100 s in set III, we have

$$\frac{1}{0.50\ M} - \frac{1}{1.00\ M} = 1.0\ L\ mol^{-1} = k\,100\ s, \qquad k = 0.010\ L\ mol^{-1}\ s^{-1}$$

For the initial 200 s, we have

$$\frac{1}{0.33\ M} - \frac{1}{1.00\ M} = 2.0\ L\ mol^{-1} = k\,200\ s, \qquad k = 0.010\ L\ mol^{-1}\ s^{-1}$$

Since we obtain the same value of the rate constant using the equation for second-order kinetics, set III must be second-order.

28. **(E)** For a zero-order reaction (set II), the slope equals the rate constant:

$k = -\Delta[A]/\Delta t = 1.00\ M/100\ s = 0.0100\ M/s$

29. **(M)** Set I is the data for a first-order reaction; we can analyze those items of data to determine the half-life. In the first 75 s, the concentration decreases by a bit more than half. This implies a half-life slightly less than 75 s, perhaps 70 s. This is consistent with the other time periods noted in the answer to Review Question 18 (b) and also to the fact that in the 150-s interval from 50 s to 200 s, the concentration decreases from 0.61 M to 0.14 M, which is a bit more than a factor-of-four decrease. The factor-of-four decrease, to one-fourth of the initial value, is what we would expect for two successive half-lives. We can determine the half-life more accurately, by obtaining a value of k from the relation $\ln([A]_t/[A]_o) = -kt$ followed by $t_{1/2} = 0.693/k$ For instance, $\ln(0.78/1.00) = -k\,(25\ s)$; $k = 9.9\underline{4} \times 10^{-3}\ s^{-1}$. Thus, $t_{1/2} = 0.693/9.9\underline{4} \times 10^{-3}\ s^{-1} = 70\ s$.

30. **(E)** We can determine an approximate initial rate by using data from the first 25 s.

$$Rate = -\frac{\Delta[A]}{\Delta t} = -\frac{0.80\ M - 1.00\ M}{25\ s - 0\ s} = 0.0080\ M\ s^{-1}$$

31. (M) The approximate rate at 75 s can be taken as the rate over the time period from 50 s to 100 s.

(a) $\text{Rate}_{\text{II}} = -\dfrac{\Delta[A]}{\Delta t} = -\dfrac{0.00\ \text{M} - 0.50\ \text{M}}{100\ \text{s} - 50\ \text{s}} = 0.010\ \text{M s}^{-1}$

(b) $\text{Rate}_{\text{I}} = -\dfrac{\Delta[A]}{\Delta t} = -\dfrac{0.37\ \text{M} - 0.61\ \text{M}}{100\ \text{s} - 50\ \text{s}} = 0.0048\ \text{M s}^{-1}$

(c) $\text{Rate}_{\text{III}} = -\dfrac{\Delta[A]}{\Delta t} = -\dfrac{0.50\ \text{M} - 0.67\ \text{M}}{100\ \text{s} - 50\ \text{s}} = 0.0034\ \text{M s}^{-1}$

Alternatively we can use [A] at 75 s (the values given in the table) in the relationship $\text{Rate} = k[A]^m$, where $m = 0,\ 1,$ or 2.

(a) $\text{Rate}_{\text{II}} = 0.010\ \text{M s}^{-1} \times (0.25\ \text{mol/L})^0 = 0.010\ \text{M s}^{-1}$

(b) Since $t_{1/2} = 70\,\text{s}$, $k = 0.693 / 70\,\text{s} = 0.0099\,\text{s}^{-1}$

$\text{Rate}_{\text{I}} = 0.0099\,s^{-1} \times (0.47\,\text{mol/L})^1 = 0.0047\,\text{M s}^{-1}$

(c) $\text{Rate}_{\text{III}} = 0.010\ \text{L mol}^{-1}\ \text{s}^{-1} \times (0.57\ \text{mol/L})^2 = 0.0032\ \text{M s}^{-1}$

32. (M) We can combine the approximate rates from Exercise 31, with the fact that 10 s have elapsed, and the concentration at 100 s.

(a) $[A]_{\text{II}} = 0.00\ \text{M}$ There is no reactant left after 100 s.

(b) $[A]_{\text{I}} = [A]_{100} - (10\ \text{s} \times \text{rate}) = 0.37\ \text{M} - (10\ \text{s} \times 0.0047\ \text{M s}^{-1}) = 0.32\ \text{M}$

(c) $[A]_{\text{III}} = [A]_{100} - (10\ \text{s} \times \text{rate}) = 0.50\ \text{M} - (10\ \text{s} \times 0.0032\ \text{M s}^{-1}) = 0.47\ \text{M}$

33. (E) Substitute the given values into the rate equation to obtain the rate of reaction.

$\text{Rate} = k[A]^2[B]^0 = (0.0103\ \text{M}^{-1}\text{min}^{-1})(0.116\ \text{M})^2(3.83\ \text{M})^0 = 1.39 \times 10^{-4}\ \text{M / min}$

34. (M)

(a) A first-order reaction has a constant half-life. Thus, half of the initial concentration remains after 30.0 minutes, and at the end of another half-life—60.0 minutes total— half of the concentration present at 30.0 minutes will have reacted: the concentration has decreased to one-quarter of its initial value. Or, we could say that the reaction is 75% complete after two half-lives—60.0 minutes.

(b) A zero-order reaction proceeds at a constant rate. Thus, if the reaction is 50% complete in 30.0 minutes, in twice the time—60.0 minutes—the reaction will be 100% complete. (And in one-fifth the time—6.0 minutes—the reaction will be 10% complete. Alternatively, we can say that the rate of reaction is 10%/6.0 min.) Therefore, the time required for the reaction to be 75%

$\text{complete} = 75\% \times \dfrac{60.0\ \text{min}}{100\%} = 45\ \text{min.}$

35. (M) For reaction: $HI(g) \rightarrow 1/2\ H_2(g) + 1/2\ I_2(g)$ (700 K)

Plot of 1/[HI] vs time

$y = 0.00118x + 0.997$

Time (s)	[HI] (M)	ln[HI]	1/[HI](M^{-1})
0	1.00	0	1.00
100	0.90	−0.105	1.11
200	0.81	−0.211	1.23$\underline{5}$
300	0.74	−0.301	1.35
400	0.68	−0.386	1.47

From data above, a plot of 1/[HI] vs. t yields a straight line. The reaction is second-order in HI at 700 K. Rate = $k[HI]^2$. The slope of the line = $k = 0.00118\ M^{-1}s^{-1}$

36. (D)

(a) We can graph 1/[ArSO$_2$H] vs. time and obtain a straight line. We can also graph [ArSO$_2$H] vs. time and ln([ArSO$_2$H]) vs. time to demonstrate that they do not yield a straight line. Only the plot of 1/[ArSO$_2$H] versus time is shown.

Plot of 1/[ArSO$_2$H] versus Time

$y = 0.137x + 9.464$

The linearity of the line indicates that the reaction is second-order.

(b) We solve the rearranged integrated second-order rate law for the rate constant, using

the longest time interval. $\dfrac{1}{[A]_t} - \dfrac{1}{[A]_o} = kt$ $\qquad \dfrac{1}{t}\left(\dfrac{1}{[A]_t} - \dfrac{1}{[A]_o}\right) = k$

$k = \dfrac{1}{300\ \text{min}}\left(\dfrac{1}{0.0196\ \text{M}} - \dfrac{1}{0.100\ \text{M}}\right) = 0.137\ \text{L mol}^{-1}\text{min}^{-1}$

(c) We use the same equation as in part (b), but solved for t, rather than k.

$t = \dfrac{1}{k}\left(\dfrac{1}{[A]_t} - \dfrac{1}{[A]_o}\right) = \dfrac{1}{0.137\ \text{L mol}^{-1}\text{min}^{-1}}\left(\dfrac{1}{0.0500\ \text{M}} - \dfrac{1}{0.100\ \text{M}}\right) = 73.0\ \text{min}$

(d) We use the same equation as in part (b), but solve for t, rather than k.

$$t = \frac{1}{k}\left(\frac{1}{[A]_t} - \frac{1}{[A]_0}\right) = \frac{1}{0.137 \text{ L mol}^{-1}\text{min}^{-1}}\left(\frac{1}{0.0250 \text{ M}} - \frac{1}{0.100 \text{ M}}\right) = 219 \text{ min}$$

(e) We use the same equation as in part (b), but solve for t, rather than k.

$$t = \frac{1}{k}\left(\frac{1}{[A]_t} - \frac{1}{[A]_0}\right) = \frac{1}{0.137 \text{ L mol}^{-1}\text{min}^{-1}}\left(\frac{1}{0.0350 \text{ M}} - \frac{1}{0.100 \text{ M}}\right) = 136 \text{ min}$$

37. **(M)**

(a) Plot [A] vs t, ln[A] vs t, and 1/[A] vs t and see which yields a straight line.

Clearly we can see that the reaction is zero-order in reactant A with a rate constant of 5.0×10^{-3}.

(b) The half-life of this reaction is the time needed for one half of the initial [A] to react.

Thus, $\Delta[A] = 0.715 \text{ M} \div 2 = 0.358 \text{ M}$ and $t_{1/2} = \dfrac{0.358 \text{ M}}{5.0 \times 10^{-3} \text{ M/s}} = 72 \text{ s}$.

38. (D)

(a) We can either graph $1/[C_4H_6]$ vs. time and obtain a straight line, or we can determine the second-order rate constant from several data points. Then, if k indeed is a constant, the reaction is demonstrated to be second-order. We shall use the second technique in this case. First we do a bit of algebra.

$$\frac{1}{[A]_t} - \frac{1}{[A]_o} = kt \qquad\qquad \frac{1}{t}\left(\frac{1}{[A]_t} - \frac{1}{[A]_o}\right) = k$$

$$k = \frac{1}{12.18 \text{ min}}\left(\frac{1}{0.0144 \text{ M}} - \frac{1}{0.0169 \text{ M}}\right) = 0.843 \text{ L mol}^{-1}\text{min}^{-1}$$

$$k = \frac{1}{24.55 \text{ min}}\left(\frac{1}{0.0124 \text{ M}} - \frac{1}{0.0169 \text{ M}}\right) = 0.875 \text{ L mol}^{-1}\text{min}^{-1}$$

$$k = \frac{1}{42.50 \text{ min}}\left(\frac{1}{0.0103 \text{ M}} - \frac{1}{0.0169 \text{ M}}\right) = 0.892 \text{ L mol}^{-1}\text{min}^{-1}$$

$$k = \frac{1}{68.05 \text{ min}}\left(\frac{1}{0.00845 \text{ M}} - \frac{1}{0.0169 \text{ M}}\right) = 0.870 \text{ L mol}^{-1}\text{min}^{-1}$$

The fact that each calculation generates similar values for the rate constant indicates that the reaction is second-order.

(b) The rate constant is the average of the values obtained in part (a).

$$k = \frac{0.843 + 0.875 + 0.892 + 0.870}{4} \text{ L mol}^{-1}\text{min}^{-1} = 0.87 \text{ L mol}^{-1}\text{min}^{-1}$$

(c) We use the same equation as in part (a), but solve for t, rather than k.

$$t = \frac{1}{k}\left(\frac{1}{[A]_t} - \frac{1}{[A]_o}\right) = \frac{1}{0.870 \text{ L mol}^{-1}\text{min}^{-1}}\left(\frac{1}{0.00423 \text{ M}} - \frac{1}{0.0169 \text{ M}}\right) = 2.0 \times 10^2 \text{ min}$$

(d) We use the same equation as in part (a), but solve for t, rather than k.

$$t = \frac{1}{k}\left(\frac{1}{[A]_t} - \frac{1}{[A]_o}\right) = \frac{1}{0.870 \text{ L mol}^{-1}\text{min}^{-1}}\left(\frac{1}{0.0050 \text{ M}} - \frac{1}{0.0169 \text{ M}}\right) = 1.6 \times 10^2 \text{ min}$$

39. (E)

(a) $\text{initial rate} = -\dfrac{\Delta[A]}{\Delta t} = -\dfrac{1.490 \text{ M} - 1.512 \text{ M}}{1.0 \text{ min} - 0.0 \text{ min}} = +0.022 \text{ M / min}$

$\text{initial rate} = -\dfrac{\Delta[A]}{\Delta t} = -\dfrac{2.935 \text{ M} - 3.024 \text{ M}}{1.0 \text{ min} - 0.0 \text{ min}} = +0.089 \text{ M / min}$

(b) When the initial concentration is doubled $(\times 2.0)$, from 1.512 M to 3.024 M, the initial rate quadruples $(\times 4.0)$. Thus, the reaction is second-order in A (since $2.0^x = 4.0$ when $x = 2$).

40. **(M)**

(a) Let us assess the possibilities. If the reaction is zero-order, its rate will be constant. During the first 8 min, the rate is $-(0.60\ M - 0.80\ M)/8\ min = 0.03\ M/min$. Then, during the first 24 min, the rate is $-(0.35\ M - 0.80\ M)/24\ min = 0.019\ M/min$. Thus, the reaction is not zero-order. If the reaction is first-order, it will have a constant half-life that is consistent with its rate constant. The half-life can be assessed from the fact that 40 min elapse while the concentration drops from 0.80 M to 0.20 M, that is, to one-fourth of its initial value. Thus, 40 min equals two half-lives and $t_{1/2} = 20$ min. This gives $k = 0.693/t_{1/2} = 0.693/20\ min = 0.035\ min^{-1}$. Also

$$kt = -\ln\frac{[A]_t}{[A]_o} = -\ln\frac{0.35\ M}{0.80\ M} = 0.827 = k \times 24\ min \qquad k = \frac{0.827}{24\ min} = 0.034\ min^{-1}$$

The constancy of the value of k indicates that the reaction is first-order.

(b) The value of the rate constant is $k = 0.034\ min^{-1}$.

(c) Reaction rate $= \frac{1}{2}$ (rate of formation of B) $= k[A]^1$ First we need [A] at $t = 30$. min

$$\ln\frac{[A]}{[A]_o} = -kt = -0.034\ min^{-1} \times 30.\ min = -1.0_2 \qquad \frac{[A]}{[A]_0} = e^{-1.02} = 0.36$$

$$[A] = 0.36 \times 0.80\ M = 0.29\ M$$

rate of formation of B $= 2 \times 0.034\ min^{-1} \times 0.29\ M = 2.0 \times 10^{-2}\ M\ min^{-1}$

41. **(M)** The half-life of the reaction depends on the concentration of A and, thus, this reaction cannot be first-order. For a second-order reaction, the half-life varies inversely with the reaction rate: $t_{1/2} = 1/\left(k[A]_o\right)$ or $k = 1/\left(t_{1/2}[A]_o\right)$. Let us attempt to verify the second-order nature of this reaction by seeing if the rate constant is fixed.

$$k = \frac{1}{1.00\ M \times 50\ min} = 0.020\ L\ mol^{-1}min^{-1}$$

$$k = \frac{1}{2.00\ M \times 25\ min} = 0.020\ L\ mol^{-1}min^{-1}$$

$$k = \frac{1}{0.50\ M \times 100\ min} = 0.020\ L\ mol^{-1}\ min^{-1}$$

The constancy of the rate constant demonstrates that this reaction indeed is second-order. The rate equation is Rate $= k[A]^2$ and $k = 0.020\ L\ mol^{-1}min^{-1}$.

42. (M)

(a) The half-life depends on the initial $[NH_3]$ and, thus, the reaction cannot be first-order. Let us attempt to verify second-order kinetics.

$$k = \frac{1}{[NH_3]_o \, t_{1/2}} \text{ for a second-order reaction} \quad k = \frac{1}{0.0031 \text{ M} \times 7.6 \text{ min}} = 42 \text{ M}^{-1}\text{min}^{-1}$$

$$k = \frac{1}{0.0015 \text{ M} \times 3.7 \text{ min}} = 180 \text{ M}^{-1}\text{min}^{-1} \quad k = \frac{1}{0.00068 \text{ M} \times 1.7 \text{min}} = 865 \text{ M}^{-1}\text{min}^{-1}$$

The reaction is not second-order. But, if the reaction is zero-order, its rate will be constant.

$$\text{Rate} = \frac{[A]_o /2}{t_{1/2}} = \frac{0.0031 \text{ M} \div 2}{7.6 \text{ min}} = 2.0 \times 10^{-4} \text{ M/min}$$

$$\text{Rate} = \frac{0.0015 \text{ M} \div 2}{3.7 \text{ min}} = 2.0 \times 10^{-4} \text{ M/min}$$

$$\text{Rate} = \frac{0.00068 \text{ M} \div 2}{1.7 \text{ min}} = 2.0 \times 10^{-4} \text{ M/min} \qquad \text{Zero-order reaction}$$

(b) The constancy of the rate indicates that the decomposition of ammonia under these conditions is zero-order, and the rate constant is $k = 2.0 \times 10^{-4}$ M/min.

43. (M) Zero-order: $t_{1/2} = \dfrac{[A]_o}{2k}$ \qquad Second-order: $t_{1/2} = \dfrac{1}{k[A]_o}$

A zero-order reaction has a half life that varies proportionally to $[A]_o$, therefore, increasing $[A]_o$ increases the half-life for the reaction. A second-order reaction's half-life varies inversely proportional to $[A]_o$, that is, as $[A]_o$ increases, the half-life decreases. The reason for the difference is that a zero-order reaction has a constant rate of reaction (independent of $[A]_o$). The larger the value of $[A]_o$, the longer it will take to react. In a second-order reaction, the rate of reaction increases as the square of the $[A]_o$, hence, for high $[A]_o$, the rate of reaction is large and for very low $[A]_o$, the rate of reaction is very slow. If we consider a bimolecular elementary reaction, we can easily see that a reaction will not take place unless two molecules of reactants collide. This is more likely when the $[A]_o$ is large than when it is small.

44. (M)

(a) $\dfrac{[A]_o}{2k} = \dfrac{0.693}{k}$ \qquad Hence, $\dfrac{[A]_o}{2} = 0.693$ or $[A]_o = 1.39$ M

(b) $\dfrac{[A]_o}{2k} = \dfrac{1}{k[A]_o},$ \qquad Hence, $\dfrac{[A]_o^2}{2} = 1$ or $[A]_o^2 = 2.00$ M \qquad $[A]_o = 1.41\underline{4}$ M

(c) $\dfrac{0.693}{k} = \dfrac{1}{k[A]_o},$ \qquad Hence, $0.693 = \dfrac{1}{[A]_o}$ or $[A]_o = 1.44$ M

Collision Theory; Activation Energy

45. **(M)**

    (a) The rate of a reaction depends on at least two factors other than the frequency of collisions. The first of these is whether each collision possesses sufficient energy to get over the energy barrier to products. This depends on the activation energy of the reaction; the higher it is, the smaller will be the fraction of successful collisions. The second factor is whether the molecules in a given collision are properly oriented for a successful reaction. The more complex the molecules are, or the more freedom of motion the molecules have, the smaller will be the fraction of collisions that are correctly oriented.

    (b) Although the collision frequency increases relatively slowly with temperature, the fraction of those collisions that have sufficient energy to overcome the activation energy increases much more rapidly. Therefore, the rate of reaction will increase dramatically with temperature.

    (c) The addition of a catalyst has the net effect of decreasing the activation energy of the overall reaction, by enabling an alternative mechanism. The lower activation energy of the alternative mechanism, (compared to the uncatalyzed mechanism), means that a larger fraction of molecules have sufficient energy to react. Thus the rate increases, even though the temperature does not.

46. **(M)**

    (a) The activation energy for the reaction of hydrogen with oxygen is quite high, too high, in fact, to be supplied by the energy ordinarily available in a mixture of the two gases at ambient temperatures. However, the spark supplies a suitably concentrated form of energy to initiate the reaction of at least a few molecules. Since the reaction is highly exothermic, the reaction of these first few molecules supplies sufficient energy for yet other molecules to react and the reaction proceeds to completion or to the elimination of the limiting reactant.

    (b) A larger spark simply means that a larger number of molecules react initially. But the eventual course of the reaction remains the same, with the initial reaction producing enough energy to initiate still more molecules, and so on.

47. **(M)**

    (a) The products are 21 kJ/mol closer in energy to the energy activated complex than are the reactants. Thus, the activation energy for the reverse reaction is
84 kJ/mol − 21 kJ/mol = 63 kJ/mol.

(b) The reaction profile for the reaction in Figure 20-10 is sketched below.

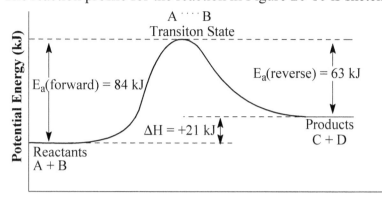

Progress of Reaction

48. **(M)** In an endothermic reaction (right), E_a must be larger than the ΔH for the reaction. For an exothermic reaction (left), the magnitude of E_a may be either larger or smaller than that of ΔH. In other words, a small activation energy can be associated with a large decrease in the enthalpy, or a large E_a can be connected to a small decrease in enthalpy.

49. **(E)**
    (a) There are two intermediates (B and C).

    (b) There are three transition states (peaks/maxima) in the energy diagram.

    (c) The fastest step has the smallest E_a, hence, step 3 is the fastest step in the reaction with step 2 a close second.

    (d) Reactant A (step 1) has the highest E_a, and therefore the slowest smallest constant

    (e) Endothermic; energy is needed to go from A to B.

    (f) Exothermic; energy is released moving from A to D.

50. **(E)**
    (a) There are two intermediates (B and C).

    (b) There are three transition states (peaks/maxima) in the energy diagram.

    (c) The fastest step has the smallest E_a, hence, step 2 is the fastest step in the reaction.

    (d) Reactant A (step 1) has the highest E_a, and therefore the slowest smallest constant

(e) Endothermic; energy is needed to go from A to B.

(f) Endothermic, energy is needed to go from A to D.

Effect of Temperature on Rates of Reaction

51. (M)

$$\ln\frac{k_2}{k_1} = -\frac{E_a}{R}\left(\frac{1}{T_2}-\frac{1}{T_1}\right) = \ln\frac{2.8\times10^{-2}\ \text{L mol}^{-1}\ \text{s}^{-1}}{5.4\times10^{-4}\ \text{L mol}^{-1}\ \text{s}^{-1}} = -\frac{E_a}{R}\left(\frac{1}{683\ \text{K}}-\frac{1}{599\ \text{K}}\right)$$

$$3.95R = E_a \times 2.05\times10^{-4}$$

$$E_a = \frac{3.95\ R}{2.05\times10^{-4}} = 1.93\times10^4\ \text{K}^{-1}\times 8.3145\ \text{J mol}^{-1}\ \text{K}^{-1} = 1.60\times10^5\ \text{J / mol} = 160\ \text{kJ / mol}$$

52. (M)

$$\ln\frac{k_2}{k_1} = -\frac{E_a}{R}\left(\frac{1}{T_2}-\frac{1}{T_1}\right) = \ln\frac{5.0\times10^{-3}\ \text{L mol}^{-1}\ \text{s}^{-1}}{2.8\times10^{-2}\ \text{L mol}^{-1}\ \text{s}^{-1}} = -\frac{1.60\times10^5\ \text{J/mol}}{8.3145\ \text{J mol}^{-1}\ \text{K}^{-1}}\left(\frac{1}{683\ \text{K}}-\frac{1}{T}\right)$$

$$-1.72 = -1.92\times10^4\left(\frac{1}{683\ \text{K}}-\frac{1}{T}\right) \qquad \left(\frac{1}{683\ \text{K}}-\frac{1}{T}\right) = \frac{1.72}{1.92\times10^4} = 8.96\times10^{-5}$$

$$\frac{1}{T} = 8.96\times10^{-5} + 1.46\times10^{-3} = 1.55\times10^{-3} \qquad T = 645\ \text{K}$$

53. (D)

(a) First we need to compute values of $\ln k$ and $1/T$. Then we plot the graph of $\ln k$ versus 1/T.

T,°C	0 °C	10 °C	20 °C	30 °C
T, K	273 K	283 K	293 K	303 K
$1/T$, K^{-1}	0.00366	0.00353	0.00341	0.00330
k, s^{-1}	5.6×10^{-6}	3.2×10^{-5}	1.6×10^{-4}	7.6×10^{-4}
$\ln k$	−12.09	−10.35	−8.74	−7.18

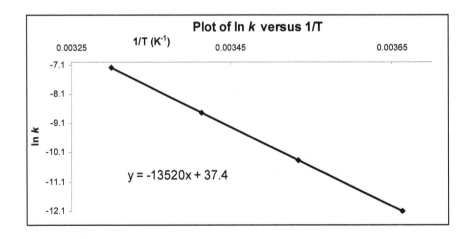

(b) The slope $= -E_a/R.$

$$E_a = -R \times \text{slope} = -8.3145 \frac{J}{\text{mol K}} \times -1.35_2 \times 10^4 \text{ K} \times \frac{1 \text{ kJ}}{1000 \text{ J}} = 112 \frac{\text{kJ}}{\text{mol}}$$

(c) We apply the Arrhenius equation, with $k = 5.6 \times 10^{-6} \text{ s}^{-1}$ at $0\,^{\circ}\text{C}$ (273 K), $k = ?$ at $40\,^{\circ}\text{C}$ (313 K), and $E_a = 113 \times 10^3$ J/mol.

$$\ln \frac{k}{5.6 \times 10^{-6} \text{ s}^{-1}} = -\frac{E_a}{R}\left(\frac{1}{T_2} - \frac{1}{T_1}\right) = -\frac{112 \times 10^3 \text{ J/mol}}{8.3145 \text{ J mol}^{-1} \text{ K}^{-1}}\left(\frac{1}{313 \text{ K}} - \frac{1}{273 \text{ K}}\right) = 6.30\underline{6}$$

$$e^{6.30\underline{6}} = 548 = \frac{k}{5.6 \times 10^{-6} \text{ s}^{-1}} \qquad k = 548 \times 5.6 \times 10^{-6} \text{ s}^{-1} = 3.0\underline{7} \times 10^{-3} \text{ s}^{-1}$$

$$t_{1/2} = \frac{0.693}{k} = \frac{0.693}{3.0\underline{7} \times 10^{-3} \text{ s}^{-1}} = 2.3 \times 10^2 \text{ s}$$

54. (D)

(a) Here we plot $\ln k$ vs. $1/T$. The slope of the straight line equals $-E_a / R$. First we tabulate the data to plot. (the plot is shown below).

$T,\,^{\circ}C$		15.83	32.02	59.75	90.61
$T,\,K$	288.98	305.17		332.90	363.76
$1/T,\,K^{-1}$	0.0034604	0.0032769		0.0030039	0.0027491
$k,\,M^{-1}s^{-1}$	5.03×10^{-5}	3.68×10^{-4}		6.71×10^{-3}	0.119
$\ln k$	-9.898	-7.907		-5.004	-2.129

The slope of this graph $= -1.09 \times 10^4 \text{ K} = E_a/R$

$$E_a = -\left(-1.089 \times 10^4 \text{ K}\right) \times 8.3145 \frac{J}{\text{mol K}} = 9.054 \times 10^4 \frac{J}{\text{mol}} \times \frac{1 \text{ kJ}}{1000 \text{ J}} = 90.5 \frac{\text{kJ}}{\text{mol}}$$

(b) We calculate the activation energy with the Arrhenius equation using the two extreme data points.

$$\ln\frac{k_2}{k_1} = \ln\frac{0.119}{5.03\times10^{-5}} = +7.77 = -\frac{E_a}{R}\left(\frac{1}{T_2}-\frac{1}{T_1}\right) = -\frac{E_a}{R}\left(\frac{1}{363.76\text{ K}}-\frac{1}{288.98\text{ K}}\right)$$

$$= 7.1138\times10^{-4}\text{ K}^{-1}\frac{E_a}{R} \qquad E_a = \frac{7.769\times8.3145\text{ J mol}^{-1}\text{ K}^{-1}}{7.1138\times10^{-4}\text{ K}^{-1}} = 9.0\underline{8}\times10^4\text{ J/mol}$$

$E_a = 91\,\text{kJ/mol}$. The two E_a values are in quite good agreement, within experimental limits.

(c) We apply the Arrhenius equation, with $E_a = 9.080\times10^4$ J/mol,
$k = 5.03\times10^{-5}$ M^{-1} s^{-1} at 15.83 °C (288.98 K), and $k = ?$ at 100.0 °C (373.2 K).

$$\ln\frac{k}{5.03\times10^{-5}\text{ M}^{-1}\text{ s}^{-1}} = -\frac{E_a}{R}\left(\frac{1}{T_2}-\frac{1}{T_1}\right) = -\frac{90.80\times10^3\text{ J/mol}}{8.3145\text{ J mol}^{-1}\text{ K}^{-1}}\left(\frac{1}{373.2\text{ K}}-\frac{1}{288.98\text{ K}}\right)$$

$$\ln\frac{k}{5.03\times10^{-5}\text{ M}^{-1}\text{ s}^{-1}} = 8.528 \qquad e^{8.528} = 5.05\times10^3 = \frac{k}{5.03\times10^{-5}\text{ M}^{-1}\text{ s}^{-1}}$$

$$k = 5.05\times10^3\times5.03\times10^{-5}\text{ M}^{-1}\text{ s}^{-1} = 0.254\text{ M}^{-1}\text{ s}^{-1}$$

55. **(M)** The half-life of a first-order reaction is inversely proportional to its rate constant: $k = 0.693/t_{1/2}$. Thus we can apply a modified version of the Arrhenius equation to find E_a.

(a) $\displaystyle \ln\frac{k_2}{k_1} = \ln\frac{(t_{1/2})_1}{(t_{1/2})_2} = -\frac{E_a}{R}\left(\frac{1}{T_2}-\frac{1}{T_1}\right) = \ln\frac{46.2\text{ min}}{2.6\text{ min}} = -\frac{E_a}{R}\left(\frac{1}{(102+273)\text{ K}}-\frac{1}{298\text{ K}}\right)$

$$2.88 = \frac{E_a}{R}6.89\times10^{-4} \qquad E_a = \frac{2.88\times8.3145\text{ J mol}^{-1}\text{ K}^{-1}}{6.89\times10^{-4}\text{ K}^{-1}}\times\frac{1\text{ kJ}}{1000\text{ J}} = 34.8\text{ kJ/mol}$$

(b) $\displaystyle \ln\frac{10.0\text{ min}}{46.2\text{ min}} = -\frac{34.8\times10^3\text{ J/mol}}{8.3145\text{ J mol}^{-1}\text{ K}^{-1}}\left(\frac{1}{298}-\frac{1}{T}\right) = -1.53 = -4.19\times10^3\left(\frac{1}{298}-\frac{1}{T}\right)$

$$\left(\frac{1}{298}-\frac{1}{T}\right) = \frac{-1.53}{-4.19\times10^3} = -3.65\times10^{-4} \qquad \frac{1}{T} = 2.99\times10^{-3} \qquad T = 334\text{ K} = 61\text{ °C}$$

56. **(M)** The half-life of a first-order reaction is inversely proportional to its rate constant: $k = 0.693/t_{1/2}$. Thus, we can apply a modified version of the Arrhenius equation.

(a) $\displaystyle \ln\frac{k_2}{k_1} = \ln\frac{(t_{1/2})_1}{(t_{1/2})_2} = -\frac{E_a}{R}\left(\frac{1}{T_2}-\frac{1}{T_1}\right) = \ln\frac{22.5\text{ h}}{1.5\text{ h}} = -\frac{E_a}{R}\left(\frac{1}{(40+273)\text{ K}}-\frac{1}{293\text{ K}}\right)$

$$2.71 = \frac{E_a}{R}2.18\times10^{-4}, \qquad E_a = \frac{2.71\times8.3145\text{ J mol}^{-1}\text{ K}^{-1}}{2.18\times10^{-4}\text{ K}^{-1}}\times\frac{1\text{ kJ}}{1000\text{ J}} = 103\text{ kJ/mol}$$

(b) The relationship is $k = A\,\exp(-E_a/RT)$

$$k = 2.05\times10^{13}\text{ s}^{-1}\exp\left(\frac{-103\times10^3\text{ J mol}^{-1}}{8.3145\text{ J mol}^{-1}\text{ K}^{-1}\times(273+30)\text{ K}}\right) = 2.05\times10^{13}\text{ s}^{-1}\times e^{-40.9} = 3.5\times10^{-5}\text{ s}^{-1}$$

57. **(M)**

(a) It is the change in the value of the rate constant that causes the reaction to go faster. Let k_1 be the rate constant at room temperature, 20 °C (293 K). Then, ten degrees higher (30 °C or 303 K), the rate constant $k_2 = 2 \times k_1$.

$$\ln \frac{k_2}{k_1} = \ln \frac{2 \times k_1}{k_1} = 0.693 = -\frac{E_a}{R}\left(\frac{1}{T_2} - \frac{1}{T_1}\right) = -\frac{E_a}{R}\left(\frac{1}{303} - \frac{1}{293 \text{ K}}\right) = 1.13 \times 10^{-4} \text{ K}^{-1} \frac{E_a}{R}$$

$$E_a = \frac{0.693 \times 8.3145 \text{ J mol}^{-1} \text{ K}^{-1}}{1.13 \times 10^{-4} \text{ K}^{-1}} = 5.1 \times 10^4 \text{ J / mol} = 51 \text{ kJ / mol}$$

(b) Since the activation energy for the depicted reaction (i.e., $N_2O + NO \rightarrow N_2 + NO_2$) is 209 kJ/mol, we would not expect this reaction to follow the rule of thumb.

58. **(M)** Under a pressure of 2.00 atm, the boiling point of water is approximately 121 °C or 394 K. Under a pressure of 1 atm, the boiling point of water is 100 °C or 373 K. We assume an activation energy of 5.1×10^4 J / mol and compute the ratio of the two rates.

$$\ln \frac{\text{Rate}_2}{\text{Rate}_1} = -\frac{E_a}{R}\left(\frac{1}{T_2} - \frac{1}{T_1}\right) = -\frac{5.1 \times 10^4 \text{ J/mol}}{8.3145 \text{ J mol}^{-1} \text{ K}^{-1}}\left(\frac{1}{394} - \frac{1}{373 \text{ K}}\right) = 0.88$$

$\text{Rate}_2 = e^{0.88} \text{ Rate}_1 = 2.4 \text{ Rate}_1$. Cooking will occur 2.4 times faster in the pressure cooker.

Catalysis

59. **(E)**

(a) Although a catalyst is *recovered unchanged from the reaction mixture*, it does "take part in the reaction." Some catalysts actually slow down the rate of a reaction. Usually, however, these negative catalysts are called inhibitors.

(b) The function of a catalyst is to *change the mechanism of a reaction*. The new mechanism is one that has a different (lower) activation energy (and frequently a different A value), than the original reaction.

60. **(M)** If the reaction is first-order, its half-life is 100 min, for in this time period [S] decreases from 1.00 M to 0.50 M, that is, by one half. This gives a rate constant of $k = 0.693/t_{1/2} = 0.693 / 100 \text{ min} = 0.00693 \text{ min}^{-1}$.

The rate constant also can be determined from any two of the other sets of data.

$$kt = \ln \frac{[A]_o}{[A]_t} = \ln \frac{1.00 \text{ M}}{0.70 \text{ M}} = 0.357 = k \times 60 \text{ min} \qquad k = \frac{0.357}{60 \text{ min}} = 0.00595 \text{ min}^{-1}$$

This is not a very good agreement between the two k values, so the reaction is probably not first-order in [A]. Let's try zero-order, where the rate should be constant.

$$\text{Rate} = -\frac{0.90 \text{ M} - 1.00 \text{ M}}{20 \text{ min}} = 0.0050 \text{ M/min} \qquad \text{Rate} = -\frac{0.50 \text{ M} - 1.00 \text{ M}}{100 \text{ min}} = 0.0050 \text{ M/min}$$

$$\text{Rate} = -\frac{0.20 \text{ M} - 0.90 \text{ M}}{160 \text{ min} - 20 \text{ min}} = 0.0050 \text{ M/min} \qquad \text{Rate} = -\frac{0.50 \text{ M} - 0.90 \text{ M}}{100 \text{ min} - 20 \text{ min}} = 0.0050 \text{ M/min}$$

Thus, this reaction is zero-order with respect to [S].

61. **(E)** Both platinum and an enzyme have a metal center that acts as the active site. Generally speaking, platinum is not dissolved in the reaction solution (heterogeneous), whereas enzymes are generally soluble in the reaction media (homogeneous). The most important difference, however, is one of specificity. Platinum is rather nonspecific, catalyzing many different reactions. An enzyme, however, is quite specific, usually catalyzing only one reaction rather than all reactions of a given class.

62. **(E)** In both the enzyme and the metal surface cases, the reaction occurs in a specialized location: either within the enzyme pocket or on the surface of the catalyst. At high concentrations of reactant, the limiting factor in determining the rate is not the concentration of reactant present but how rapidly active sites become available for reaction to occur. Thus, the rate of the reaction depends on either the quantity of enzyme present or the surface area of the catalyst, rather than on how much reactant is present (i.e., the reaction is zero-order). At low concentrations or gas pressures the reaction rate depends on how rapidly molecules can reach the available active sites. Thus, the rate depends on concentration or pressure of reactant and is first-order.

63. **(E)** For the straight-line graph of Rate versus [Enzyme], an excess of substrate must be present.

64. **(E)** For human enzymes, we would expect the maximum in the curve to appear around 37 °C, i.e., normal body temperature (or possibly at slightly elevated temperatures to aid in the control of diseases (37 – 41 °C). At lower temperatures, the reaction rate of enzyme-activated reactions decreases with decreasing temperature, following the Arrhenius equation. However, at higher temperatures, these temperature sensitive biochemical processes become inhibited, probably by temperature-induced structural modifications to the enzyme or the substrate, which prevent formation of the enzyme-substrate complex.

Reaction Mechanisms

65. **(E)** The molecularity of an elementary process is the number of reactant molecules in the process. This molecularity is equal to the order of the overall reaction only if the elementary process in question is the slowest and, thus, the rate-determining step of the overall reaction. In addition, the elementary process in question should be the only elementary step that influences the rate of the reaction.

66. **(E)** If the type of molecule that is expressed in the rate law as being first-order collides with other molecules that are present in much larger concentrations, the reaction will seem to depend only on the amount of those types of molecules present in smaller concentration, since the larger concentration will be essentially unchanged during the course of the reaction. Such a situation is quite common, and has been given the name pseudo first-order. It is also possible to have molecules which, do not participate directly in the reaction— including product molecules—strike the reactant molecules and impart to them sufficient energy to react. Finally, collisions of the reactant molecules with the container walls may also impart adequate energy for reaction to occur.

67. **(M)** The three elementary steps must sum to give the overall reaction. That is, the overall reaction is the sum of step 1 + step 2 + step 3. Hence, step 2 = overall reaction −step 1 −step 3. Note that all species in the equations below are gases.

Overall: $2\,NO + 2\,H_2 \rightarrow N_2 + 2\,H_2O$ $2\,NO + 2\,H_2 \rightarrow N_2 + 2\,H_2O$

−First: $-(2\,NO \rightleftharpoons N_2O_2)$ $N_2O_2 \rightleftharpoons 2NO$

−Third $-(N_2O + H_2 \rightarrow N_2 + H_2O)$ or $N_2 + H_2O \rightarrow N_2O + H_2$

The result is the second step, which is slow: $H_2 + N_2O_2 \rightarrow H_2O + N_2O$

The rate of this rate-determining step is: Rate $= k_2[H_2][N_2O_2]$

Since N_2O_2 does not appear in the overall reaction, we need to replace its concentration with the concentrations of species that do appear in the overall reaction. To do this, recall that the first step is rapid, with the forward reaction occurring at the same rate as the reverse reaction. $k_1[NO]^2 =$ forward rate $=$ reverse rate $= k_{-1}[N_2O_2]$. This expression is solved for $[N_2O_2]$, which then is substituted into the rate equation for the overall reaction.

$$[N_2O_2] = \frac{k_1[NO]^2}{k_{-1}} \qquad\qquad Rate = \frac{k_2 k_1}{k_{-1}}[H_2][NO]^2$$

The reaction is first-order in $[H_2]$ and second-order in $[NO]$. This result conforms to the experimentally determined reaction order.

68. **(M)** Proposed mechanism: $I_2(g) \underset{k_{-1}}{\overset{k_1}{\rightleftharpoons}} 2I(g)$ Observed rate law:

$$\frac{2\,I(g) + H_2(g) \xrightarrow{\ k_2\ } 2\,HI(g)}{I_2(g) + H_2(g) \rightarrow 2\,HI(g)} \qquad Rate = k[I_2][H_2]$$

The first step is a fast equilibrium reaction and step 2 is slow. Thus, the predicted rate law is Rate $= k_2[I]^2[H_2]$. In the first step, set the rate in the forward direction for the equilibrium equal to the rate in the reverse direction. Then solve for $[I]^2$.

Rate$_{forward}$ = Rate$_{reverse}$ Use: Rate$_{forward}$ = $k_1[I_2]$ and Rate$_{reverse}$ = $k_{-1}[I]^2$

From this we see: $k_1[I_2] = k_{-1}[I]^2$. Rearranging (solving for $[I]^2$)

$[I]^2 = \dfrac{k_1[I_2]}{k_{-1}}$ Substitute into Rate $= k_2[I]^2[H_2] = k_2 \dfrac{k_1[I_2]}{k_{-1}}[H_2] = k_{obs}[I_2][H_2]$

Since the predicted rate law is the same as the experimental rate law, this mechanism is plausible.

69. **(M)** Proposed mechanism:

$$Cl_2(g) \underset{k_{-1}}{\overset{k_1}{\rightleftharpoons}} 2\,Cl(g)$$

Observed rate law:

$$2\,Cl(g) + 2\,NO(g) \xrightarrow{k_2} 2\,NOCl(g)$$

$$Rate = k[Cl_2][NO]^2$$

$$\overline{Cl_2(g) + 2NO(g) \rightarrow 2\,NOCl(g)}$$

The first step is a fast equilibrium reaction and step 2 is slow. Thus, the predicted rate law is Rate = $k_2[Cl]^2[NO]^2$ In the first step, set the rate in the forward direction for the equilibrium equal to the rate in the reverse direction. Then express $[Cl]^2$ in terms of k_1, k_{-1} and $[Cl_2]$. This mechanism is almost certainly not correct because it involves a tetra molecular second step.

$Rate_{forward} = Rate_{reverse}$ Use: $Rate_{forward} = k_1[Cl_2]$ and $Rate_{reverse} = k_{-1}[Cl]^2$
From this we see: $k_1[Cl_2] = k_{-1}[Cl]^2$. Rearranging (solving for $[Cl]^2$)

$[Cl]^2 = \dfrac{k_1[Cl_2]}{k_{-1}}$ Substitute into Rate = $k_2[Cl]^2[NO]^2 = k_2\dfrac{k_1[Cl_2]}{k_{-1}}[NO]^2 = k_{obs}[Cl_2][NO_2]^2$

There is another plausible mechanism. $Cl_2(g) + NO(g) \underset{k_{-1}}{\overset{k_1}{\rightleftharpoons}} NOCl(g) + Cl(g)$

$$Cl(g) + NO(g) \underset{k_{-1}}{\overset{k_1}{\rightleftharpoons}} NOCl(g)$$

$$\overline{Cl_2(g) + 2NO(g) \rightarrow 2\,NOCl(g)}$$

$Rate_{forward} = Rate_{reverse}$ Use: $Rate_{forward} = k_1[Cl_2][NO]$ and $Rate_{reverse} = k_{-1}[Cl][NOCl]$

From this we see: $k_1[Cl_2][NO] = k_{-1}[Cl][NOCl]$. Rearranging (solving for $[Cl]$)

$[Cl] = \dfrac{k_1[Cl_2][NO]}{k_{-1}[NOCl]}$ Substitute into Rate = $k_2[Cl][NO] = \dfrac{k_2 k_1[Cl_2][NO]^2}{k_{-1}[NOCl]}$

If [NOCl], the product is assumed to be constant (~ 0 M using method of initial rates), then

$\dfrac{k_2 k_1}{k_{-1}[NOCl]}$ = constant = k_{obs} Hence, the predicted rate law is $k_{obs}[Cl_2][NO]^2$ which agrees

with the experimental rate law. Since the predicted rate law agrees with the experimental rate law, both this and the previous mechanism are plausible, however, the first is dismissed as it has a tetramolecular elementary reaction (extremely unlikely to have four molecules simultaneously collide).

70. **(M)** A possible mechanism is: Step 1: $O_3 \rightleftharpoons O_2 + O\,(fast)$

Step 2: $O + O_3 \xrightarrow{k_3} 2\,O_2\,(slow)$

The overall rate is that of the slow step: Rate = $k_3[O][O_3]$. But O is a reaction intermediate, whose concentration is difficult to determine. An expression for [O] can be found by assuming that the forward and reverse "fast" steps proceed with equal speed.

$Rate_1 = Rate_2$ $k_1[O_3] = k_2[O_2][O]$ $[O] = \dfrac{k_1[O_3]}{k_2[O_2]}$ Rate = $k_3\dfrac{k_1[O_3]}{k_2[O_2]}[O_3] = \dfrac{k_3 k_1}{k_2}\dfrac{[O_3]^2}{[O_2]}$

Then substitute this expression into the rate law for the reaction. This rate equation has the same form as the experimentally determined rate law and thus the proposed mechanism is plausible.

71. **(M)**

$$S_1 + S_2 \underset{k_{-1}}{\overset{k_1}{\rightleftharpoons}} (S_1 : S_2)^* \quad \text{(fast)}$$

$$(S_1 : S_2)^* \xrightarrow{k_2} S_1 : S_2 \quad \text{(slow)}$$

The first step is a fast equilibrium, so the rate of the forward reaction is equal to the rate of the reverse reaction.

$$k_1 [S_1][S_2] = k_{-1} \left[(S_1 : S_2) \right]^*$$

$$\left[(S_1 : S_2) \right]^* = \frac{k_1}{k_{-1}} [S_1][S_2]$$

$$\frac{d[S_1 : S_2]}{dt} = k_2 \left[(S_1 : S_2) \right]^* = \frac{k_2 \cdot k_1 [S_1][S_2]}{k_{-1}}$$

72. **(M)**

$$(CH_3)_2 CO \,(aq) + OH^- \underset{k_{-1}}{\overset{k_1}{\rightleftharpoons}} CH_3C(O)CH_2^- \,(aq) + H_2O \,(l)$$

$$CH_3C(O)CH_2^- \,(aq) + (CH_3)_2 CO \,(aq) \xrightarrow{k_2} Prod$$

We note that $CH_3C(O)CH_2^-$ is an intermediate species. Using the steady state approximation, while its concentration is not known during the reaction, the rate of change of its concentration is zero, except for the very beginning and towards the end of the reaction. Therefore,

$$\frac{d\left[CH_3C(O)CH_2^- \right]}{dt} = k_1 \left[(CH_3)_2 CO \right]\left[OH^- \right] - k_{-1} \left[CH_3C(O)CH_2^- \right][H_2O]$$

$$- k_2 \left[CH_3C(O)CH_2^- \right]\left[(CH_3)_2 CO \right] = 0$$

Rearranging the above expression to solve for $CH_3C(O)CH_2^-$ gives the following expression

$$\left[CH_3C(O)CH_2^- \right] = \frac{k_1 \left[(CH_3)_2 CO \right]\left[OH^- \right]}{k_{-1}[H_2O] + k_2 \left[(CH_3)_2 CO \right]}$$

The rate of formation of product, therefore, is:

$$\frac{d[Prod]}{dt} = k_2 \left[CH_3C(O)CH_2^- \right]\left[(CH_3)_2 CO \right]$$

$$= k_2 \left[(CH_3)_2 CO \right] \cdot \frac{k_1 \left[(CH_3)_2 CO \right]\left[OH^- \right]}{k_{-1}[H_2O] + k_2 \left[(CH_3)_2 CO \right]}$$

$$= \frac{k_2 k_1 \left[(CH_3)_2 CO \right]^2 \left[OH^- \right]}{k_{-1}[H_2O] + k_2 \left[(CH_3)_2 CO \right]}$$

INTEGRATIVE AND ADVANCED EXERCISES

73. **(M)** The data for the reaction starting with 1.00 M being first-order or second-order as well as that for the first-order reaction using 2.00 M is shown below

Time (min)	$[A]_o = 1.00$ M (second order)	$[A]_o = 1.00$ M (first order)	$[A]_o = 2.00$ M (second order)	$[A]_o = 2.00$ M (first order)
0	1.00	1.00	2.00	2.00
5	0.63	0.55	0.91	1.10
10	0.46	0.30	0.59	0.60
15	0.36	0.16<u>5</u>	0.43<u>5</u>	0.33
25	0.25	0.05	0.28<u>6</u>	0.10

Clearly we can see that when $[A]_o = 1.00$ M, the first-order reaction concentrations will always be lower than that for the second-order case (assumes magnitude of the rate constant is the same). If, on the other hand, the concentration is above 1.00 M, the second-order reaction decreases faster than the first-order reaction (remember that the half-life shortens for a second-order reaction as the concentration increases, whereas for a first-order reaction, the half-life is constant).

From the data, it appears that the crossover occurs in the case where $[A]_o = 2.00$ M at just over 10 minutes.

Second-order at 11 minutes: $\dfrac{1}{[A]} = \dfrac{1}{2} + \left(\dfrac{0.12}{\text{M min}}\right) \times (11 \text{ min})$ $[A] = 0.549$ M

First-order at 11 minutes: $\ln[A] = \ln(2) - \left(\dfrac{0.12}{\text{min}}\right) \times (11 \text{ min})$ $[A] = 0.534$ M

A quick check at 10.5 minutes reveals,

Second-order at 10.5 minutes: $\dfrac{1}{[A]} = \dfrac{1}{2} + \dfrac{0.12(10.5 \text{ min})}{\text{M min}}$ $[A] = 0.568$ M

First-order at 10.5 minutes: $\ln[A] = \ln(2) - \dfrac{0.12(10.5 \text{ min})}{\text{M min}}$ $[A] = 0.567$ M

Hence, at approximately 10.5 minutes, these two plots will share a common point (point at which the concentration versus time curves overlap).

74. **(M)**

   (a) The concentration vs. time graph is not linear. Thus, the reaction is obviously not zero-order (the rate is not constant with time). A quick look at various half lives for this reaction shows the ~2.37 min (1.000 M to 0.5 M), ~2.32 min (0.800 M to 0.400 M), and ~2.38 min (0.400 M to 0.200 M). Since the half-life is constant, the reaction is probably first-order.

   (b) average $t_{1/2} = \dfrac{(2.37 + 2.32 + 2.38)}{3} = 2.36$ min $k = \dfrac{0.693}{t_{1/2}} = \dfrac{0.693}{2.36 \text{ min}} = 0.294 \text{ min}^{-1}$

      or perhaps better expressed as $k = 0.29 \text{ min}^{-1}$ due to imprecision.

(c) When $t = 3.5$ min, $[A] = 0.352$ M.

Then, rate $= k[A] = 0.294$ min$^{-1} \times 0.352$ M $= 0.103$ M/min.

(d) Slope $= \dfrac{\Delta[A]}{\Delta t} = -\text{Rate} = \dfrac{0.1480 \text{ M} - 0.339 \text{ M}}{6.00 \text{ min} - 3.00 \text{ min}} = -0.0637$ M / min   Rate $= 0.064$ M/min.

(e) Rate $= k[A] = 0.294$ min$^{-1} \times 1.000$ M $= 0.294$ M/min.

75. (M) The reaction being investigated is:

$$2 \text{ MnO}_4^-(aq) + 5 \text{ H}_2\text{O}_2(aq) + 6 \text{ H}^+(aq) \longrightarrow 2 \text{ Mn}^{2+}(aq) + 8 \text{ H}_2\text{O}(l) + 5 \text{ O}_2(g)$$

We use the stoichiometric coefficients in this balanced reaction to determine $[H_2O_2]$.

$$[\text{H}_2\text{O}_2] = \dfrac{37.1 \text{ mL titrant} \times \dfrac{0.1000 \text{ mmol MnO}_4^-}{1 \text{ mL titrant}} \times \dfrac{5 \text{ mmol H}_2\text{O}_2}{2 \text{ mmol MnO}_4^-}}{5.00 \text{ mL}} = 1.86 \text{ M}$$

76. (D) We assume in each case that 5.00 mL of reacting solution is titrated.

$$\text{volume MnO}_4^- = 5.00 \text{ mL} \times \dfrac{2.32 \text{ mmol H}_2\text{O}_2}{1 \text{ mL}} \times \dfrac{2 \text{ mmol MnO}_4^-}{5 \text{ mmol H}_2\text{O}_2} \times \dfrac{1 \text{ mL titrant}}{0.1000 \text{ mmol MnO}_4^-}$$

$$= 20.0 \times 2.32 \text{ M H}_2\text{O}_2 = 46.4 \text{ mL } 0.1000 \text{ M MnO}_4^- \text{ titrant at 0 s}$$

At 200 s $V_{\text{titrant}} = 20.0 \times 2.01$ M H$_2$O$_2 = 40.2$ mL
At 400 s $V_{\text{titrant}} = 20.0 \times 1.72$ M H$_2$O$_2 = 34.4$ mL
At 600 s $V_{\text{titrant}} = 20.0 \times 1.49$ M H$_2$O$_2 = 29.8$ mL
At 1200 s $V_{\text{titrant}} = 20.0 \times 0.98$ M H$_2$O$_2 = 19.6$ mL
At 1800 s $V_{\text{titrant}} = 20.0 \times 0.62$ M H$_2$O$_2 = 12.4$ mL
At 3000 s $V_{\text{titrant}} = 20.0 \times 0.25$ M H$_2$O$_2 = 5.0_0$ mL

The graph of volume of titrant vs. elapsed time is given above. This graph is of approximately the same shape as Figure 20-2, in which $[H_2O_2]$ is plotted against time. In order to determine the rate, the tangent line at 1400 s has been drawn on the graph. The intercepts of the tangent line are at 34 mL of titrant and 2800 s. From this information we determine the rate of the reaction.

$$\text{Rate} = \dfrac{\dfrac{34 \text{ mL}}{2800 \text{ s}} \times \dfrac{1 \text{ L}}{1000 \text{ mL}} \times \dfrac{0.1000 \text{ mol MnO}_4^-}{1 \text{ L titrant}} \times \dfrac{5 \text{ mol H}_2\text{O}_2}{2 \text{ mol MnO}_4^-}}{0.00500 \text{ L sample}} = 6.1 \times 10^{-4} \text{ M/s}$$

This is the same as the value of 6.1×10^{-4} obtained in Figure 20-2 for 1400 s. The discrepancy is due, no doubt, to the coarse nature of our plot.

77. **(M)** First we compute the change in $[H_2O_2]$. This is then used to determine the amount, and ultimately the volume, of oxygen evolved from the given quantity of solution. Assume the $O_2(g)$ is dry.

$$\Delta[H_2O_2] = -\frac{\Delta[H_2O_2]}{\Delta t}\Delta t = -\left(-1.7\times10^{-3}\ M/s\times1.00\ \text{min}\times\frac{60\ s}{1\ \text{min}}\right) = 0.102\ M$$

$$\text{amount O}_2 = 0.175\ \text{L soln}\times\frac{0.102\ \text{mol H}_2O_2}{1\ L}\times\frac{1\ \text{mol O}_2}{2\ \text{mol H}_2O_2} = 0.00892\ \text{mol O}_2$$

$$\text{Volume O}_2 = \frac{nRT}{P} = \frac{0.00892\ \text{mol O}_2\times0.08206\dfrac{L\cdot atm}{mol\cdot K}\times(273+24)\ K}{757\ \text{mmHg}\times\dfrac{1\ atm}{760\ \text{mmHg}}} = 0.22\ L\ O_2$$

<u>78.</u> **(M)** We know that rate has the units of M/s, and also that concentration has the units of M. The generalized rate equation is $\text{Rate} = k[A]_o$. In terms of units, this becomes

$\text{M/s} = \{\text{units of }k\}\ M_o$. Therefore $\{\text{Units of }k\} = \dfrac{M/s}{M_o} = M_{1-o}\ s^{-1}$

79. **(M)**

   (a) Comparing the third and the first lines of data, $[I^-]$ and $[OH^-]$ stay fixed, while $[OCl^-]$ doubles. Also the rate for the third kinetics run is one half of the rate found for the first run. Thus, the reaction is <u>first-order</u> in $[OCl^-]$. Comparing the fourth and fifth lines, $[OCl^-]$ and $[I^-]$ stay fixed, while $[OH^-]$ is halved. Also, the fifth run has a reaction rate that is twice that of the fourth run. Thus, the reaction is *minus* <u>first-order</u> in $[OH^-]$. Comparing the third and second lines of data, $[OCl^-]$ and $[OH^-]$ stay fixed, while the $[I^-]$ doubles. Also, the second run has a reaction rate that is double that found for the third run. Thus, the reaction is <u>first-order</u> in $[I^-]$.

   (b) The reaction is first-order in $[OCl^-]$ and $[I^-]$ and minus first-order in $[OH^-]$. Thus, the overall order $= 1 + 1 - 1 = 1$. The reaction is first-order overall.

   (c) $\text{Rate} = k\dfrac{[OCl^-][I^-]}{[OH^-]}$

   using data from first run: $\dfrac{\text{Rate}\ [OH^-]}{[OCl^-][I^-]} = \dfrac{4.8\times10^{-4}\ M/s\times1.00\ M}{0.0040\ M\times0.0020\ M} = 60.\ s^{-1}$

80. **(M)** We first determine the number of moles of N_2O produced. The partial pressure of $N_2O(g)$ in the "wet" N_2O is 756 mmHg − 12.8 mmHg = 743 mmHg.

$$\text{amount N}_2O = \frac{PV}{RT} = \frac{743\ \text{mmHg}\times\dfrac{1\ atm}{760\ \text{mmHg}}\times0.0500\ L}{0.08206\ L\ atm\ mol^{-1}\ K^{-1}\times(273+15)\ K} = 0.00207\ \text{mol N}_2O$$

Now we determine the change in $[NH_2NO_2]$.

$$\Delta[NH_2NO_2] = \frac{0.00207 \text{ mol N}_2O \times \dfrac{1 \text{ mol NH}_2NO_2}{1 \text{ mol N}_2O}}{0.165 \text{ L soln}} = 0.0125 \text{ M}$$

$$[NH_2NO_2]_{final} = 0.105 \text{ M} - 0.0125 \text{ M} = 0.093 \text{ M} \qquad k = \frac{0.693}{123 \text{ min}} = 0.00563 \text{ min}^{-1}$$

$$t = -\frac{1}{k} \ln\frac{[A]_t}{[A]_o} = -\frac{1}{0.00563 \text{ min}^{-1}} \ln\frac{0.093 \text{ M}}{0.105 \text{ M}} = 22 \text{ min} = \text{elapsed time}$$

81. (D) We need to determine the partial pressure of ethylene oxide at each time in order to determine the order of the reaction. First, we need the initial pressure of ethylene oxide. The pressure at infinite time is the pressure that results when all of the ethylene oxide has decomposed. Because two moles of product gas are produced for every mole of reactant gas, this infinite pressure is twice the initial pressure of ethylene oxide. $P_{initial} = 249.88$ mmHg ÷ 2 = 124.94 mmHg. Now, at each time we have the following.

$$(CH_2)_2O(g) \longrightarrow CH_4(g) + CO(g)$$

Initial: 124.94 mmHg Changes: $-x$ mmHg $+x$ mmHg $+x$ mmHg Final: $124.94 + x$ mmHg
Thus, $x = P_{tot} - 124.94$ and $P_{EtO} = 124.94 - x = 124.94 - (P_{tot} - 124.94) = 249.88 - P_{tot}$
Hence, we have, the following values for the partial pressure of ethylene oxide.

t, min	0	10	20	40	60	100	200
P_{EtO}, mmHg	124.94	110.74	98.21	77.23	60.73	37.54	11.22

For the reaction to be zero-order, its rate will be constant.

The rate in the first 10 min is: $\text{Rate} = \dfrac{-(110.74 - 124.94) \text{ mmHg}}{10 \text{ min}} = 1.42 \text{ mmHg/min}$

The rate in the first 40 min is: $\text{Rate} = \dfrac{-(77.23 - 124.94) \text{ mmHg}}{40 \text{ min}} = 1.19 \text{ mmHg/min}$

We conclude from the non-constant rate that the reaction is not zero-order. For the reaction to be first-order, its half-life must be constant. From 40 min to 100 min—a period of 60 min—the partial pressure of ethylene oxide is approximately halved, giving an approximate half-life of 60 min. And, in the first 60 min, the partial pressure of ethylene oxide is approximately halved. Thus, the reaction appears to be first-order. To verify this tentative conclusion, we use the integrated first-order rate equation to calculate some values of the rate constant.

$$k = -\frac{1}{t} \ln\frac{P}{P_0} = -\frac{1}{10 \text{ min}} \ln\frac{110.74 \text{ mmHg}}{124.94 \text{ mmHg}} = 0.0121 \text{ min}^{-1}$$

$$k = -\frac{1}{100 \text{ min}} \ln\frac{37.54 \text{ mmHg}}{124.94 \text{ mmHg}} = 0.0120 \text{ min}^{-1} \qquad k = -\frac{1}{60 \text{ min}} \ln\frac{60.73 \text{ mmHg}}{124.94 \text{ mmHg}} = 0.0120 \text{ min}^{-1}$$

The constancy of the first-order rate constant suggests that the reaction is first-order.

82. (M) For this first-order reaction $\ln\dfrac{P_t}{P_o} = -kt$ Elapsed time is computed as: $t = -\dfrac{1}{k}\ln\dfrac{P_t}{P_o}$

We first determine the pressure of DTBP when the total pressure equals 2100 mmHg.

Reaction: $\quad C_8H_{18}O_2(g) \longrightarrow 2C_3H_6O(g) + C_2H_6(g)$ [Equation 15.17]

Initial: $\quad\quad$ 800.0 mmHg

Changes: $\quad -x$ mmHg $\quad\quad\quad\quad +2x$ mmHg $\quad +x$ mmHg

Final: $\quad\quad (800.0 - x)$ mmHg $\quad\quad 2x$ mmHg $\quad\quad x$ mmHg

Total pressure $= (800.0 - x) + 2x + x = 800.0 + 2x = 2100.$

$x = 650.$ mmHg $\quad P\{C_8H_{18}O_2(g)\} = 800.$ mmHg $- 650.$ mmHg $= 150.$ mmHg

$t = -\dfrac{1}{k}\ln\dfrac{P_t}{P_o} = -\dfrac{1}{8.7\times10^{-3}\ \text{min}^{-1}}\ln\dfrac{150.\ \text{mmHg}}{800.\ \text{mmHg}} = 19_2\ \text{min} = 1.9\times10^2\ \text{min}$

83. (D) If we compare Experiment 1 with Experiment 2, we notice that [B] has been halved, and also that the rate, expressed as $\Delta[A]/\Delta t$, has been halved. This is most evident for the times 5 min, 10 min, and 20 min. In Experiment 1, [A] decreases from 1.000×10^{-3} M to 0.779×10^{-3} M in 5 min, while in Experiment 2 this same decrease in [A] requires 10 min. Likewise in Experiment 1, [A] decreases from 1.000×10^{-3} M to 0.607 M $\times 10^{-3}$ in 10 min, while in Experiment 2 the same decrease in [A] requires 20 min. This dependence of rate on the first power of concentration is characteristic of a first-order reaction. This reaction is first-order in [B]. We now turn to the order of the reaction with respect to [A]. A zero-order reaction will have a constant rate. Determine the rate

After over the first minute: $\quad\quad$ Rate $= \dfrac{-(0.951 - 1.000)\times10^{-3}\ \text{M}}{1\ \text{min}} = 4.9\times10^{-5}$ M/min

After over the first five minutes: $\quad\quad$ Rate $= \dfrac{-(0.779 - 1.000)\times10^{-3}\ \text{M}}{5\ \text{min}} = 4.4\times10^{-5}$ M/min

After over the first twenty minutes: $\quad\quad$ Rate $= \dfrac{-(0.368 - 1.000)\times10^{-3}\ \text{M}}{20\ \text{min}} = 3.2\times10^{-5}$ M/min

This is not a very constant rate; we conclude that the reaction is not zero-order. There are no clear half-lives in the data with which we could judge the reaction to be first-order. But we can determine the value of the first-order rate constant for a few data.

$k = -\dfrac{1}{t}\ln\dfrac{[A]}{[A]_0} = -\dfrac{1}{1\ \text{min}}\ln\dfrac{0.951\ \text{mM}}{1.000\ \text{mM}} = 0.0502\ \text{min}^{-1}$

$k = -\dfrac{1}{10\ \text{min}}\ln\dfrac{0.607\ \text{mM}}{1.000\ \text{mM}} = 0.0499\ \text{min}^{-1} \quad\quad k = -\dfrac{1}{20\ \text{min}}\ln\dfrac{0.368\ \text{mM}}{1.000\ \text{mM}} = 0.0500\ \text{min}^{-1}$

The constancy of the first-order rate constant indicates that the reaction indeed is first-order in [A]. (As a point of interest, notice that the concentrations chosen in this experiment are such that the reaction is pseudo-zero-order in [B]. Here, then it is not necessary to consider the variation of [B] with time as the reaction proceeds when determining the kinetic dependence on [A].)

84. **(M)** In Exercise 79 we established the rate law for the iodine-hypochlorite ion reaction: Rate $= k[OCl^-][I^-][OH^-]^{-1}$. In the mechanism, the slow step gives the rate law; Rate $= k_3\ [I^-][HOCl]$. We use the initial fast equilibrium step to substitute for [HOCl] in this rate equation. We assume in this fast step that the forward rate equals the reverse rate.

$$k_1[OCl^-][H_2O] = k_{-1}[HOCl][OH^-] \qquad [HOCl] = \frac{k_1[OCl^-][H_2O]}{k_{-1}[OH^-]}$$

$$\text{Rate} = k_2\ [I^-]\frac{k_1[OCl^-][H_2O]}{k_{-1}[OH^-]} = \frac{k_2 k_1[H_2O]}{k_{-1}}\frac{[OCl^-][I^-]}{[OH^-]} = k\frac{[OCl^-][I^-]}{[OH^-]}$$

This is the same rate law that we established in Exercise 79. We have incorporated [H$_2$O] in the rate constant for the reaction because, in an aqueous solution, [H$_2$O] remains effectively constant during the course of the reaction. (The final fast step simply involves the neutralization of the acid HOI by the base hydroxide ion, OH$^-$.)

85. **(M)** It is more likely that the *cis*-isomer, compound (I), would be formed than the *trans*-isomer, compound (II). The reason for this is that the reaction will involve the adsorption of both CH$_3$—C≡C—CH$_3$ and H$_2$ onto the surface of the catalyst. These two molecules will eventually be adjacent to each other. At some point, one of the π bonds in the C≡C bond will break, the H–H bond will break, and two C–H bonds will form. Since these two C–H bonds form on the same side of the carbon chain, compound (I) will be produced. In the sketches below, dotted lines (…) indicate bonds forming or breaking.

$$\begin{array}{ccc} \text{H}-\text{H} & \text{H}\cdots\text{H} & \text{H}\ \ \text{H} \\ \text{CH}_3-\text{C}{\equiv}\text{C}-\text{CH}_3 \longrightarrow & \text{CH}_3-\overset{\vdots}{\text{C}}{\equiv}\overset{\vdots}{\text{C}}-\text{CH}_3 \longrightarrow & \text{CH}_3-\text{C}{=}\text{C}-\text{CH}_3 \end{array}$$

86. **(D)** $Hg_2^{2+} + Tl^{3+} \rightarrow 2\ Hg^{2+} + Tl^+$ Experimental rate law $= k\dfrac{[Hg_2^{2+}][Tl^{3+}]}{[Hg^{2+}]}$

Possible mechanism:

$$Hg_2^{2+} + Tl^{3+} \underset{k_{-1}}{\overset{k_1}{\rightleftharpoons}} Hg^{2+} + HgTl^{3+} \qquad (\text{fast})$$
$$\underline{HgTl^{3+} \overset{k_2}{\longrightarrow} Hg^{2+} + Tl^{3+} \qquad\qquad (\text{slow})}$$
$$Hg_2^{2+} + Tl^{3+} \rightarrow 2\ Hg^{2+} + Tl^+ \qquad \text{Rate} = k_2[HgTl^{3+}]$$

$$k_1[Hg_2^{2+}][Tl^{3+}] = k_{-1}\ [Hg^{2+}][HgTl^{3+}] \quad \text{—rearrange}\rightarrow\ [HgTl^{3+}] = \frac{k_1}{k_{-1}}\frac{[Hg_2^{2+}][Tl^{3+}]}{[Hg^{2+}]}$$

$$\text{Rate} = k_2[HgTl^{3+}] = \frac{k_2 k_1}{k_{-1}}\frac{[Hg_2^{2+}][Tl^{3+}]}{[Hg^{2+}]} = k_{obs}\frac{[Hg_2^{2+}][Tl^{3+}]}{[Hg^{2+}]}$$

87. (M)

$$\frac{\Delta CCl_3}{\Delta t} = rate_{formation} + rate_{disappearance} = 0 \qquad \text{so } rate_{formation} = rate_{decomposition}$$

$$k_2[Cl(g)][CHCl_3] = k_3[CCl_3][[Cl(g)] \text{ and, simplifying, } [CCl_3] = \frac{k_2}{k_3}[CHCl_3]$$

since $rate = k_3[CCl_3][Cl(g)] = k_3\left(\frac{k_2}{k_3}[CHCl_3]\right)[Cl(g)] = k_2[CHCl_3][Cl(g)]$

We know: $[Cl(g)] = \left(\frac{k_1}{k_{-1}}[Cl_2(g)]\right)^{1/2}$ then $rate_{overall} = k_2[CHCl_3]\left(\frac{k_1}{k_{-1}}[Cl_2(g)]\right)^{1/2}$

and the rate constant k will be: $k = k_2\left(\frac{k_1}{k_{-1}}\right)^{1/2} = (1.3 \times 10^{-2})\left(\frac{4.8 \times 10^3}{3.6 \times 10^3}\right)^{1/2} = 0.015$

88. (D)

$$Rate = k[A]^3 - \frac{d[A]}{dt} \qquad \text{Rearrange:} \qquad -kt = \frac{d[A]}{[A]^3}$$

Integrate using the limits $\rightarrow$ time (0 to t) and concentration ($[A]_o$ to $[A]_t$)

$$-k\int_0^t t = \int_{[A]_o}^{[A]_t} \frac{d[A]}{[A]^3} \qquad \Rightarrow \qquad -kt - (-k(0)) = -\frac{1}{2}\frac{1}{[A]_t^2} - \left(-\frac{1}{2}\frac{1}{[A]_o^2}\right)$$

Simplify: $-kt = -\frac{1}{2[A]_t^2} + \frac{1}{2[A]_o^2}$ \qquad Rearrange: $\frac{1}{2[A]_t^2} = kt + \frac{1}{2[A]_o^2}$

Multiply through by 2 to give the integrated rate law: $\frac{1}{[A]_t^2} = 2kt + \frac{1}{[A]_o^2}$

To derive the half life($t_{1/2}$) substitute $t = t_{1/2}$ and $[A]_t = \frac{[A]_o}{2}$

$$\frac{1}{\left(\frac{[A]_o}{2}\right)^2} = 2kt_{1/2} + \frac{1}{[A]_o^2} = \frac{1}{\frac{[A]_o^2}{4}} = \frac{4}{[A]_o^2} \qquad \text{Collect terms}$$

$$2kt_{1/2} = \frac{4}{[A]_o^2} - \frac{1}{[A]_o^2} = \frac{3}{[A]_o^2} \qquad \text{Solve for } t_{1/2} \qquad t_{1/2} = \frac{3}{2k[A]_o^2}$$

89. (D) Consider the reaction: A + B $\rightarrow$ products (first-order in A, first-order in B). The initial concentration of each reactant can be defined as $[A]_o$ and $[B]_o$ Since the stoichiometry is 1:1, we can define x as the concentration of reactant A and reactant B that is removed (a variable that changes with time).

The $[A]_t = ([A]_o - x)$ and $[B]_t = ([B]_o - x)$.

Algebra note: $[A]_o - x = -(x - [A]_o)$ and $[B]_o - x = -(x - [B]_o)$.

As well, the calculus requires that we use the absolute value of $|x - [A]_o|$ and $|x - [B]_o|$ when taking the integral of the reciprocal of $|x - [A]_o|$ and $|x - [B]_o|$

$$\text{Rate} = -\frac{d[A]}{dt} = -\frac{d[B]}{dt} = \frac{dx}{dt} = k[A]_t[B]_t = k([A]_o - x)([B]_o - x) \quad \text{or} \quad \frac{dx}{([A]_o - x)([B]_o - x)} = kdt$$

In order to solve this, partial fraction decomposition is required to further ease integration:

$$dx \left(\underbrace{\frac{1}{([B]_o - [A]_o)}}_{\text{Note: this is a constant}} \right) \left(\frac{1}{([A]_o - x)} - \frac{1}{([B]_o - x)} \right) = kdt$$

From the point of view of integration, a further rearrangement is desirable (See algebra note above).

$$dx \left(\frac{1}{([B]_o - [A]_o)}_t \right) \left(\frac{-1}{|x - [A]_o|} - \frac{-1}{|x - [B]_o|} \right) = kdt$$

Integrate both sides $\left(\frac{1}{([B]_o - [A]_o)} \right) \left[-\ln|x - [A]_o| - (-\ln|x - [B]_o|) \right] = kt + C$

$|x - [A]_o| = [A]_o - x$ and $|x - [B]_o| = [B]_o - x$ \qquad Substitute and simplify

$$\left(\frac{1}{([B]_o - [A]_o)} \right) \ln \left(\frac{([B]_o - x)}{[A]_o - x} \right) = kt + C \qquad \text{Determine C by setting } x = 0 \text{ at t} = 0$$

$$C = \left(\frac{1}{([B]_o - [A]_o)} \right) \ln \frac{[B]_o}{[A]_o} \quad \text{Hence:} \left(\frac{1}{([B]_o - [A]_o)} \right) \ln \left(\frac{([B]_o - x)}{([A]_o - x)} \right) = kt + \left(\frac{1}{([B]_o - [A]_o)} \right) \ln \frac{[B]_o}{[A]_o}$$

Multiply both sides by $([B]_o - [A]_o)$, hence, $\ln \left(\frac{([B]_o - x)}{([A]_o - x)} \right) = ([B]_o - [A]_o) \times kt + \ln \frac{[B]_o}{[A]_o}$

$$\ln \left(\frac{([B]_o - x)}{([A]_o - x)} \right) - \ln \frac{[B]_o}{[A]_o} = ([B]_o - [A]_o) \times kt = \ln \frac{\left(\frac{([B]_o - x)}{([A]_o - x)} \right)}{\frac{[B]_o}{[A]_o}} = \ln \left(\frac{[A]_o([B]_o - x)}{[B]_o([A]_o - x)} \right)$$

Set $([A]_o - x) = [A]_t$ and $([B]_o - x) = [B]_t$ to give $\ln \left(\frac{[A]_o \times [B]_t}{[B]_o \times [A]_t} \right) = ([B]_o - [A]_o) \times kt$

90. **(D)** Let 250-2x equal the partial pressure of $CO(g)$ and x be the partial pressure of $CO_2(g)$.

$$2CO \rightarrow CO_2 + C(s)$$

$$P_{tot} = P_{CO} + P_{CO2} = 250 - 2x + x = 250 - x$$

$$250 - 2x \quad\quad x \quad\quad -$$

P_{tot} [torr]	Time [sec]	P_{CO2}	P_{CO} [torr]
250	0	0	250
238	398	12	226
224	1002	26	198
210	1801	40	170

The plots that follow show that the reaction appears to obey a second-order rate law.
Rate = $k[CO]^2$

ZERO ORDER PLOT

T	P_{CO}
0	250
398	226
1002	198
1801	170

1ˢᵗ ORDER PLOT

T	lnP_{CO}
0	5.521461
398	5.420535
1002	5.288267
1801	5.135798

2ⁿᵈ ORDER PLOT

T	1/CO
0	0.004
398	0.004425
1002	0.005051
1801	0.005882

(Best correlation coefficient)

91. **(D)** Let 100-4x equal the partial pressure of $PH_3(g)$, x be the partial pressure of $P_4(g)$ and 6x be the partial pressure of $H_2(g)$

$$4\,PH_3(g) \rightarrow P_4(g) + 6\,H_2(g)$$

$$100 - 4x \qquad x \qquad\qquad 6x$$

$$P_{tot} = P_{PH_3} + P_{P_4} + P_{H_2} = 100 - 4x + x + 6x = 100 + 3x$$

P_{tot} [torr]	Time [sec]	P_{P_4} [torr]	P_{PH_3} [torr]
100	0	0	100
150	40	50/3	100 − (4)(50/3)
167	80	67/3	100 − (4)(67/3)
172	120	72/3	100 − (4)(72/3)

The plots to follow show that the reaction appears to obey a first-order rate law.
Rate = k[PH₃]

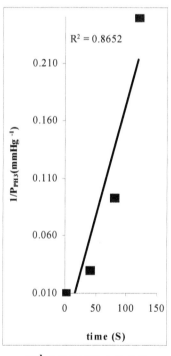

ZERO ORDER PLOT

T	P_{PH3}
0	100
40	33.3
80	10.7
120	4

1ˢᵗ ORDER PLOT

T	lnP_{PH3}
0	4.61
40	3.51
80	2.37
120	1.39

2ⁿᵈ ORDER PLOT

T	$1/P_{PH3}$
0	0.010
40	0.030
80	0.093
120	0.250

92. **(D)** Consider the following equilibria.

$$E + S \underset{k_{-1}}{\overset{k_1}{\rightleftharpoons}} ES \xrightarrow{k_2} E + P \qquad\qquad E + I \underset{}{\overset{K_I}{\rightleftharpoons}} EI$$

Product production $\dfrac{d[P]}{dt} = k_2[ES]$ Use the steady state approximation for [ES]

$$\frac{d[ES]}{dt} = k_1[E][S] - k_{-1}[ES] - k_2[ES] = k_1[E][S] - [ES](k_{-1} + k_2) = 0$$

solve for [ES] $\left(\text{Keep in mind } K_M = \dfrac{k_{-1} + k_2}{k_1} \right)$ $\qquad [ES] = \dfrac{k_1[E][S]}{k_{-1} + k_2} = \dfrac{[E][S]}{K_M}$

Formation of EI: $K_I = \dfrac{[E][I]}{[EI]} \qquad [EI] = \dfrac{[E][I]}{K_I}$

$$[E_o] = [E] + [ES] + [EI] = [E] + \frac{[E][S]}{K_M} + \frac{[E][I]}{K_I}$$

$$[E_o] = [E]\left(1 + \frac{[S]}{K_M} + \frac{[I]}{K_I} \right) \quad \text{Solve for [E]} \qquad [E] = \frac{[E_o]}{\left(1 + \dfrac{[S]}{K_M} + \dfrac{[I]}{K_I} \right)}$$

From above: $[ES] = \dfrac{[E][S]}{K_M} \qquad [ES] = \dfrac{[E_o]\left(\dfrac{[S]}{K_M} \right)}{\left(1 + \dfrac{[S]}{K_M} + \dfrac{[I]}{K_I} \right)}$ $\qquad$ multiplication by $\dfrac{K_M}{K_M}$ affords

$$[ES] = \frac{[E_o][S]}{\left(K_M + [S] + \dfrac{[I]K_M}{K_I} \right)} = \frac{[E_o][S]}{K_M\left(1 + \dfrac{[I]}{K_I} \right) + [S]}$$

Remember $\dfrac{d[P]}{dt} = k_2[ES] = \dfrac{k_2[E_o][S]}{K_M\left(1 + \dfrac{[I]}{K_I} \right) + [S]}$

If we substitute $k_2[E_o] = V_{max}$ then $\dfrac{d[P]}{dt} = \dfrac{V_{max}[S]}{K_M\left(1 + \dfrac{[I]}{K_I} \right) + [S]}$

Thus, as [I] increases, the ratio $\dfrac{V_{max}[S]}{K_M\left(1 + \dfrac{[I]}{K_I} \right) + [S]}$ decreases;

i.e., the rate of product formation decreases as [I] increases.

93. **(D)** In order to determine a value for K_M, we need to rearrange the equation so that we may obtain a linear plot and extract parameters from the slope and intercepts.

$$V = \frac{k_2[E_o][S]}{K_M+[S]} \qquad \frac{1}{V} = \frac{K_M+[S]}{k_2[E_o][S]} = \frac{K_M}{k_2[E_o][S]} + \frac{[S]}{k_2[E_o][S]}$$

$$\frac{1}{V} = \frac{K_M}{k_2[E_o][S]} + \frac{1}{k_2[E_o]} \qquad \text{We need to have this in the form of } y = mx+b$$

Plot $\dfrac{1}{V}$ on the y-axis and $\dfrac{1}{[S]}$ on the x-axis. See result below:

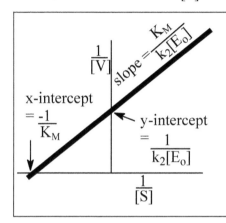

The plot of 1/V vs 1/[S] should yield a slope of $\dfrac{K_M}{k_2[E_o]}$ and a y-intercept of $\dfrac{1}{k_2[E_o]}$. The x-intercept $= -1/K_M$

$$0 = \frac{K_M}{k_2[E_o]}\left(\frac{1}{[S]}\right) - \frac{1}{k_2[E_o]} \qquad \frac{1}{[S]} = \frac{-k_2[E_o]}{k_2[E_o] \times K_M} = \frac{-1}{K_M}$$

To find the value of K_M take the negative inverse of x-intercept. To find k_2, invert the y-intercept and divide by the $[E_o]$.

94. **(M)**

(a) The first elementary step $HBr + O_2 \xrightarrow{k1} HOOBr$ is rate-determining if the reaction obeys reaction rate $= k\,[HBr][O_2]$ since the rate of this step is identical to that of the experimental rate law.

(b) No, mechanisms cannot be shown to be absolutely correct, only consistent with experimental observations.

(c) Yes; the sum of the elementary steps ($3\,HBr + O_2 \rightarrow HOBr + Br_2 + H_2O$) is not consistent with the overall stoichiometry (since HOBr is not detected as a product) of the reaction and therefore cannot be considered a valid mechanism.

95. **(M)**
(a) Both reactions are first-order, because the units on the rate constants are s^{-1}.
(b) k_2 is the slow reaction.
(c) To determine the concentration of the product, N_2, we must first determine how much reactant remains at the end of the given time period, from which we can calculate the amount of reactant consumed and therefore the amount of product produced. Since this is a first-order reaction, the concentration of the reactant, N_2O after time t is determined as follows:

$$[A]_t = [A]_o e^{-kt}$$

$$[N_2O]_{0.1} = (2.0\,M)\cdot \exp\left(-(25.7\,s^{-1})(0.1\,s)\right) = 0.153\,M\,N_2O \text{ remaining}$$

The amount of N_2O consumed = 2.0 M − 0.153 M = 1.847 M

$$[N_2] = 1.847 \text{ M NO} \times \frac{1 \text{ M } N_2}{2 \text{ M NO}} = 0.9235 \text{ M } N_2$$

(d) The process is identical to step (c).

$$[N_2O]_{0.1} = (4.0 \text{ M}) \cdot \exp\left(-(18.2 \text{ s}^{-1})(0.025 \text{ s})\right) = 2.538 \text{ M } N_2O \text{ remaining}$$

The amount of N_2O consumed = 4.0 M − 2.538 M = 1.462 M

$$[N_2O] = 1.462 \text{ M NO} \times \frac{1 \text{ M } N_2O}{2 \text{ M NO}} = 0.731 \text{ M } N_2O$$

FEATURE PROBLEMS

96. **(D)**

(a) To determine the order of the reaction, we need $[C_6H_5N_2Cl]$ at each time. To determine this value, note that 58.3 mL $N_2(g)$ evolved corresponds to total depletion of $C_6H_5N_2Cl$, to $[C_6H_5N_2Cl] = 0.000$ M.

Thus, at any point in time, $[C_6H_5N_2Cl] = 0.071 \text{ M} - \left(\text{volume } N_2(g) \times \dfrac{0.071 \text{ M } C_6H_5N_2Cl}{58.3 \text{ mL } N_2(g)}\right)$

Consider 21 min: $[C_6H_5N_2Cl] = 0.071 \text{ M} - \left(44.3 \text{ mL } N_2 \times \dfrac{0.071 \text{ M } C_6H_5N_2Cl}{58.3 \text{ mL } N_2(g)}\right) = 0.017 \text{ M}$

The numbers in the following table are determined with this method.

Time, min	0	3	6	9	12	15	18	21	24	27	30	∞
V_{N_2}, mL	0	10.8	19.3	26.3	32.4	37.3	41.3	44.3	46.5	48.4	50.4	58.3
$[C_6H_5N_2Cl]$, mM	71	58	47	39	32	26	21	17	14	12	10	0

[The concentration is given in thousandths of a mole per liter (mM).]

(b)

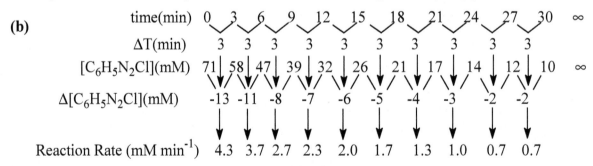

(c) The two graphs are drawn on the same axes.

(d) The rate of the reaction at $t = 21$ min is the slope of the tangent line to the $[C_6H_5N_2Cl]$ curve. The tangent line intercepts the vertical axis at about $[C_6H_5N_2Cl] = 39$ mM and the horizontal axis at about 37 min

$$\text{Reaction rate} = \frac{39 \times 10^{-3} \text{ M}}{37 \text{ min}} = 1.0_5 \times 10^{-3} \text{ M min}^{-1} = 1.1 \times 10^{-3} \text{ M min}^{-1}$$

The agreement with the reported value is very good.

(e) The initial rate is the slope of the tangent line to the $[C_6H_5N_2Cl]$ curve at $t = 0$. The intercept with the vertical axis is 71 mM, of course. That with the horizontal axis is about 13 min.

$$\text{Rate} = \frac{71 \times 10^{-3} \text{ M}}{13 \text{ min}} = 5.5 \times 10^{-3} \text{ M min}^{-1}$$

(f) The first-order rate law is $\text{Rate} = k[C_6H_5N_2Cl]$, which we solve for k:

$$k = \frac{\text{Rate}}{[C_6H_5N_2Cl]} \qquad k_0 = \frac{5.5 \times 10^{-3} \text{ M min}^{-1}}{71 \times 10^{-3} \text{ M}} = 0.077 \text{ min}^{-1}$$

$$k_{21} = \frac{1.1 \times 10^{-3} \text{ M min}^{-1}}{17 \times 10^{-3} \text{ M}} = 0.065 \text{ min}^{-1}$$

An average value would be a reasonable estimate: $k_{avg} = 0.071 \text{ min}^{-1}$

(g) The estimated rate constant gives one value of the half-life:

$$t_{1/2} = \frac{0.693}{k} = \frac{0.693}{0.071 \text{ min}^{-1}} = 9.8 \text{ min}$$

The first half-life occurs when $[C_6H_5N_2Cl]$ drops from 0.071 M to 0.0355 M. This occurs at about 10.5 min.

(h) The reaction should be three-fourths complete in two half-lives, or about 20 minutes.

(i) The graph plots $\ln[C_6H_5N_2Cl]$ (in millimoles/L) vs. time in minutes.

Plot of ln[C₆H₅N₂Cl] versus time

The linearity of the graph demonstrates that the reaction is first-order.

(j) $k = -\text{ slope} = -\left(-6.61\times10^{-2}\right) \text{ min}^{-1} = 0.0661 \text{ min}^{-1}$

$t_{1/2} = \dfrac{0.693}{0.0661 \text{ min}^{-1}} = 10.5 \text{ min}$, in good agreement with our previously determined values.

97. **(D)**

(a) In Experiments 1 & 2, [KI] is the same (0.20 M), while $\left[(NH_4)_2 S_2O_8\right]$ is halved, from 0.20 M to 0.10 M. As a consequence, the time to produce a color change doubles (i.e., the rate is halved). This indicates that reaction (a) is first-order in $S_2O_8^{2-}$. Experiments 2 and 3 produce a similar conclusion. In Experiments 4 and 5, $\left[(NH_4)_2 S_2O_8\right]$ is the same (0.20 M) while [KI] is halved, from 0.10 to 0.050 M. As a consequence, the time to produce a color change nearly doubles, that is, the rate is halved. This indicates that reaction (a) is also first-order in I^-. Reaction (a) is (1 + 1) second-order overall.

(b) The blue color appears when all the $S_2O_3^{2-}$ has been consumed, for only then does reaction (b) cease. The same amount of $S_2O_3^{2-}$ is placed in each reaction mixture.

$\text{amount } S_2O_3^{2-} = 10.0 \text{ mL} \times \dfrac{1 \text{ L}}{1000 \text{ mL}} \times \dfrac{0.010 \text{ mol Na}_2S_2O_3}{1 \text{ L}} \times \dfrac{1 \text{ mol } S_2O_3^{2-}}{1 \text{ mol Na}_2S_2O_3} = 1.0\times10^{-4} \text{mol}$

Through stoichiometry, we determine the amount of each reactant that reacts before this amount of $S_2O_3^{2-}$ will be consumed.

$\text{amount } S_2O_8^{2-} = 1.0\times10^{-4} \text{ mol } S_2O_3^{2-} \times \dfrac{1 \text{ mol } I_3^-}{2 \text{ mol } S_2O_3^{2-}} \times \dfrac{1 \text{ mol } S_2O_8^{2-}}{1 \text{ mol } I_3^-}$

$= 5.0\times10^{-5} \text{ mol } S_2O_8^{2-}$

$\text{amount } I^- = 5.0\times10^{-5} \text{ mol } S_2O_8^{2-} \times \dfrac{2 \text{ mol } I^-}{1 \text{ mol } S_2O_8^{2-}} = 1.0\times10^{-4} \text{ mol } I^-$

Note that we do not use "3 mol I⁻" from equation (a) since one mole has not been oxidized; it simply complexes with the product I_2. The total volume of each solution is $(25.0 \text{ mL} + 25.0 \text{ mL} + 10.0 \text{ mL} + 5.0 \text{ mL} =) 65.0 \text{ mL}$, or 0.0650 L.

The amount of $S_2O_8^{2-}$ that reacts in each case is 5.0×10^{-5} mol and thus

$$\Delta\left[S_2O_8^{2-}\right] = \frac{-5.0 \times 10^{-5} \text{ mol}}{0.0650 \text{ L}} = -7.7 \times 10^{-4} \text{ M}$$

Thus, $\text{Rate}_1 = \dfrac{-\Delta\left[S_2O_8^{2-}\right]}{\Delta t} = \dfrac{+7.7 \times 10^{-4} \text{ M}}{21 \text{ s}} = 3.7 \times 10^{-5} \text{ M s}^{-1}$

(c) For Experiment 2, $\text{Rate}_2 = \dfrac{-\Delta\left[S_2O_8^{2-}\right]}{\Delta t} = \dfrac{+7.7 \times 10^{-4} \text{ M}}{42 \text{ s}} = 1.8 \times 10^{-5} \text{ M s}^{-1}$

To determine the value of k, we need initial concentrations, as altered by dilution.

$\left[S_2O_8^{2-}\right]_1 = 0.20 \text{ M} \times \dfrac{25.0 \text{ mL}}{65.0 \text{ mL total}} = 0.077 \text{ M}$ $\qquad \left[I^-\right]_1 = 0.20 \text{ M} \times \dfrac{25.0 \text{ mL}}{65.0 \text{ mL}} = 0.077 \text{ M}$

$\text{Rate}_1 = 3.7 \times 10^{-5} \text{ M s}^{-1} = k\left[S_2O_8^{2-}\right]_1^1\left[I^-\right]_1^1 = k(0.077 \text{ M})^1(0.077 \text{ M})^1$

$k = \dfrac{3.7 \times 10^{-5} \text{ M s}^{-1}}{0.077 \text{ M} \times 0.077 \text{ M}} = 6.2 \times 10^{-3} \text{ M}^{-1} \text{ s}^{-1}$

$\left[S_2O_8^{2-}\right]_2 = 0.10 \text{ M} \times \dfrac{25.0 \text{ mL}}{65.0 \text{ mL total}} = 0.038 \text{ M}$ $\qquad \left[I^-\right]_2 = 0.20 \text{ M} \times \dfrac{25.0 \text{ mL}}{65.0 \text{ mL}} = 0.077 \text{ M}$

$\text{Rate}_2 = 1.8 \times 10^{-5} \text{ M s}^{-1} = k\left[S_2O_8^{2-}\right]^1\left[I^-\right]^1 = k(0.038 \text{ M})^1(0.077 \text{ M})^1$

$k = \dfrac{1.8 \times 10^{-5} \text{ M s}^{-1}}{0.038 \text{ M} \times 0.077 \text{ M}} = 6.2 \times 10^{-3} \text{ M}^{-1} \text{ s}^{-1}$

(d) First we determine concentrations for Experiment 4.

$\left[S_2O_8^{2-}\right]_4 = 0.20 \text{ M} \times \dfrac{25.0 \text{ mL}}{65.0 \text{ mL total}} = 0.077 \text{ M}$ $\qquad \left[I^-\right]_4 = 0.10 \times \dfrac{25.0 \text{ mL}}{65.0 \text{ mL}} = 0.038 \text{ M}$

We have two expressions for Rate; let us equate them and solve for the rate constant.

$\text{Rate}_4 = \dfrac{-\Delta\left[S_2O_8^{2-}\right]}{\Delta t} = \dfrac{+7.7 \times 10^{-4} \text{ M}}{\Delta t} = k\left[S_2O_8^{2-}\right]_4^1\left[I^-\right]_4^1 = k(0.077 \text{ M})(0.038 \text{ M})$

$k = \dfrac{7.7 \times 10^{-4} \text{ M}}{\Delta t \times 0.077 \text{ M} \times 0.038 \text{ M}} = \dfrac{0.26 \text{ M}^{-1}}{\Delta t}$ $\qquad k_3 = \dfrac{0.26 \text{ M}^{-1}}{189 \text{ s}} = 0.0014 \text{ M}^{-1} \text{ s}^{-1}$

$k_{13} = \dfrac{0.26 \text{ M}^{-1}}{88 \text{ s}} = 0.0030 \text{ M}^{-1} \text{ s}^{-1}$ $\qquad\qquad k_{24} = \dfrac{0.26 \text{ M}^{-1}}{42 \text{ s}} = 0.0062 \text{ M}^{-1} \text{ s}^{-1}$

$k_{33} = \dfrac{0.26 \text{ M}^{-1}}{21 \text{ s}} = 0.012 \text{ M}^{-1} \text{ s}^{-1}$

(e) We plot $\ln k$ vs. $1/T$ The slope of the line $= -E_a / R$.

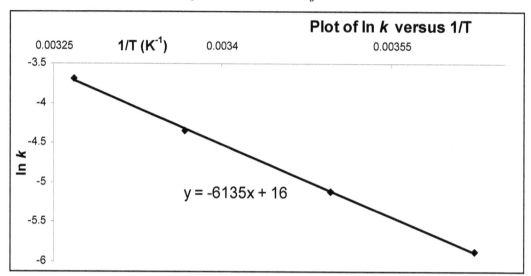

$E_a = +6135\ \text{K} \times 8.3145\ \text{J mol}^{-1}\ \text{K}^{-1} = 51.0 \times 10^3\ \text{J/mol} = 51.0\ \text{kJ/mol}$

The scatter of the data permits only a two significant figure result: 51 kJ/mol

(f) For the mechanism to agree with the reaction stoichiometry, the steps of the mechanism must sum to the overall reaction, in the manner of Hess's law.

(slow) $I^- + S_2O_8^{2-} \rightarrow IS_2O_8^{3-}$

(fast) $IS_2O_8^{3-} \rightarrow 2\ SO_4^{2-} + I^+$

(fast) $I^+ + I^- \rightarrow I_2$

(fast) $I_2 + I^- \rightarrow I_3^-$

(net) $3\ I^- + S_2O_8^{2-} \rightarrow 2\ SO_4^{2-} + I_3^-$

Each of the intermediates cancels: $IS_2O_8^{3-}$ is produced in the first step and consumed in the second, I^+ is produced in the second step and consumed in the third, I_2 is produced in the third step and consumed in the fourth. The mechanism is consistent with the stoichiometry. The rate of the slow step of the mechanism is

$\text{Rate}_1 = k_1 \left[S_2O_8^{2-} \right]^1 \left[I^- \right]^1$

This is exactly the same as the experimental rate law. It is reasonable that the first step be slow since it involves two negatively charged species coming together. We know that like charges repel, and thus this should not be an easy or rapid process.

SELF-ASSESSMENT EXERCISES

98. **(E)**

(a) $[A]_0$: Initial concentration of reactant A

(b) k: Reaction rate constant, which is the proportionality constant between reaction rate and reactant concentration

(c) $t_{1/2}$: Half-life of the reaction, the amount of time that the concentration of a certain reactant is reduced by half

(d) Zero-order reaction: A reaction in which the rate is not dependent on the concentration of the reactant

(e) Catalyst: A substance which speeds up the reaction by lowering the activation energy, but it does not itself get consumed

99. **(E)**

(a) Method of initial rates: A study of the kinetics of the reaction by measuring the initial reaction rates, used to determine the reaction order

(b) Activated complex: Species that exist in a transitory state between the reactants and the products

(c) Reaction mechanism: Sequential elementary steps that show the conversion of reactant(s) to final product(s)

(d) Heterogeneous Catalyst: A catalyst which is in a different physical phase than the reaction medium

(e) Rate-determining step: A reaction which occurs more slowly than other reactions in a mechanism and therefore usually controls the overall rate of the reaction

100. **(E)**

(a) First-order and second-order reactions: In a first-order reaction, the rate of the reaction depends on the concentration of only one substrate and in a 1-to-1 manner (doubling the concentration of the reactant doubles the rate of the reaction). In a second-order reaction, the rate depends on two molecules reacting with each other at the elementary level.

(b) Rate law and integrated rate law: Rate law describes how the rate relates to the concentration of the reactants and the overall rate of a reaction, whereas the integrated rate law expresses the concentration of a reactant as a function of time

(c) Activation energy and enthalpy of reaction: Activation energy is the minimum energy required for a particular reaction to take place, whereas enthalpy of reaction is the amount of heat generated (or consumed) by a reaction when it happens

(d) Elementary process and overall reaction: Individual steps of a reaction mechanism, which describes any molecular event that significantly alters a molecule's energy or geometry or produces a new molecule

(e) Enzyme and substrate: An enzyme is a protein that acts as a catalyst for a biological reaction. A substrate is the reactant that is transformed in the reaction (in this context, by the enzyme).

101. **(E)** The answer is (c). The rate constant k is only dependent on temperature, not on the concentration of the reactants

102. **(E)** The answers are (b) and (e). Because half-life is 75 seconds, the quantity of reactant left at two half-lives (75 + 75 = 150) equals one-half of the level at 75 seconds. Also, if the initial concentration is doubled, after one half-life the remaining concentration would have to be twice as much as the original concentration.

103. **(E)** The answer is (a). Half-life $t_{1/2} = 13.9$ min, $k = \ln 2/t_{1/2} = 0.050$ min^{-1}. Rate of a first-order reaction is as follows:

$$\frac{d[A]}{dt} = k[A] = (0.050 \text{ min}^{-1})(0.40 \text{ M}) = 0.020 \text{ M min}^{-1}$$

104. **(E)** The answer is (d). A second-order reaction is expressed as follows:

$$\frac{d[A]}{dt} = k[A]^2$$

If the rate of the reaction when $[A] = 0.50$ is $k(0.50)^2 = k(0.25)$. If $[A] = 0.25$ M, then the rate is $k(0.0625)$, which is ¼ of the rate at $[A] = 0.50$.

105. **(M)** The answer is (b). Going to slightly higher temperatures broadens the molecular speed distribution, which in turn increases the fraction of molecules at the high kinetic energy range (which are those sufficiently energetic to make a reaction happen).

106. **(E)** The answer is (c). Since the reaction at hand is described as an elementary one, the rate of the reaction is $k[A][B]$.

107. **(E)** We note that from the given data, the half-life of the reaction is 100 seconds (at t = 0, $[A] = 0.88$ M/s, whereas at t = 100, $[A] = 0.44$ M/s). Therefore, the rate constant k is: $k = \ln 2/100$ s $= 0.00693$ s^{-1}. We can now calculate instantaneous rate of the reaction: $d[A]/dt = (0.00693 \text{ s}^{-1})(0.44 \text{ M}) = 3.0 \times 10^{-3}$ M·s^{-1}

108. **(M)**

(a) For a first-order reaction,

$$k = \frac{\ln 2}{t_{1/2}} = \frac{0.693}{30} = 0.0231 \text{ min}^{-1}$$

$$\ln[A]_t - \ln[A]_o = -kt$$

$$t = \frac{\ln[A]_t - \ln[A]_o}{-k} = \frac{\ln(0.25) - 0}{-0.0231 \text{ min}^{-1}} = 60.0 \text{ min}$$

(b) For a zero-order reaction,

$$k = \frac{0.5}{t_{1/2}} = \frac{0.5}{30} = 0.0167 \text{ min}^{-1}$$

$$[A]_t - [A]_o = -kt$$

$$t = \frac{[A]_t - [A]_o}{-k} = \frac{0.25 - 1.00}{-0.0167 \text{ min}^{-1}} = 45.0 \text{ min}$$

109. **(M)** The reaction is second-order, because the half-life doubles with each successive half-life period.

110. (M)

(a) The initial rate $= \Delta M / \Delta t = (1.204\ M - 1.180\ M)/(1.0\ \text{min}) = 0.024\ M/\text{min}$

(b) In experiment 2, the initial concentration is twice that of experiment A. For a second-order reaction:

$$\text{Rate} = k\ [A_{\exp 2}]^2 = k\ [2 \times A_{\exp 1}]^2 = 4\ k\ [A_{\exp 1}]^2$$

This means that if the reaction is second order, its initial rate of experiment 2 will be 4 times that of experiment 1 (that is, 4 times as many moles of A will be consumed in a given amount of time). The initial rate is $4 \times 0.024\ M/\text{min} = 0.096\ M/s$. Therefore, at 1 minute, $[A] = 2.408 - 0.0960 = 2.312\ M$.

(c) The half-life of the reaction, obtained from experiment 1, is 35 minutes. If the reaction is first-order, then $k = \ln 2/35\ \text{min} = 0.0198\ \text{min}^{-1}$.

For a first-order reaction,

$$[A]_t = [A]_o\ e^{-kt}$$

$$[A]_{35\,\text{min}} = (2.408)\exp\left(-0.0198\ \text{min}^{-1} \cdot 30\ \text{min}\right) = 1.33\ M$$

111. (D) The overall stoichiometry of the reaction is determined by adding the two reactions with each other: $A + 2B \rightleftharpoons C + D$

(a) Since I is made slowly but is used very quickly, its rate of formation is essentially zero. The amount of I at any given time during the reaction can be expressed as follows:

$$\frac{d[I]}{dt} = 0 = k_1[A][B] - k_2[B][I]$$

$$[I] = \frac{k_1}{k_2}[A]$$

Using the above expression for [I], we can now determine the overall reaction rate law:

$$\frac{d[C]}{dt} = k_2[I][B] = k_2 \cdot \frac{k_1}{k_2}[A]\cdot[B] = k_1[A][B]$$

(b) Adding the two reactions given, we still get the same overall stoichiometry as part (a). However, with the given proposed reaction mechanisms, the rate law for the product(s) is given as follows:

$$\frac{d[B_2]}{dt} = k_1[B]^2 - k_{-1}[B_2] - k_2[A][B] = 0$$

$$[B_2] = \frac{k_1[B]^2}{k_{-1} + k_2[A]}$$

Therefore,

$$\frac{d[C]}{dt} = k_2[A][B_2] = \frac{k_2 k_1[A][B]^2}{k_{-1} + k_2[A]}$$

which does not agree with the observed reaction rate law.

112. **(M)** The answer is (b), first-order, because only in a first-order reaction is the half-life independent of the concentration of the reacting species.

113. **(E)** The answer is (a), zero-order, because in a zero-order reaction the relationship between concentration and time is: $[A]_t = kt + [A]_o$

114. **(E)** The answer is (c), remain the same. This is because for a zero-order reaction,

$d[A]/dt = k[A]^0 = k$. Therefore, the reaction rate is independent of the concentration of the reactant.

115. **(M)** The overarching concept for this concept map is kinetics as a result of successful collision. The subtopics are collision theory, molecular transition theory. Molecular speed and orientation derive from collision theory. Transition complexes and partial bonds fall under the molecular transition theory heading. Deriving from the collision theory is another major topic, the Arrhenius relationship. The Arrhenius relationship encompasses the ideas of activation energy, Arrhenius collision factor, and exponential relationship between temperature and rate constant.

CHAPTER 21
CHEMISTRY OF THE MAIN-GROUP ELEMENTS I: GROUPS 1, 2, 13, AND 14

PRACTICE EXAMPLES

1A **(E)** From Figure 21-2, the route from sodium chloride to sodium nitrate begins with electrolysis of NaCl(aq) to form NaOH(aq).

$2 NaCl(aq) + 2 H_2O(l) \xrightarrow{\text{electrolysis}} 2 NaOH(aq) + H_2(g) + Cl_2(g)$ followed by addition of $NO_2(g)$ to NaOH(aq). $2 NaOH(aq) + 3 NO_2(g) \rightarrow 2 NaNO_3(aq) + NO(g) + H_2O(l)$

1B **(E)** From Figure 21-2, we see that the route from sodium chloride to sodium thiosulfate begins with the electrolysis of NaCl(aq) to produce NaOH(aq),

$2 NaCl(aq) + 2 H_2O(l) \xrightarrow{\text{electrolysis}} 2 NaOH(aq) + H_2(g) + Cl_2(g)$

and continues through the reaction of $SO_2(g)$ with the NaOH(aq) in an acid-base reaction $[SO_2(g)$ is an acid anhydride] to produce

$Na_2SO_3(aq)$: $2 NaOH(aq) + SO_2(g) \rightarrow Na_2SO_3(aq) + H_2O(l)$ and (3) concludes with the addition of S to the boiling solution: $Na_2SO_3(aq) + S(s) \xrightarrow{\text{boil}} Na_2S_2O_3(aq)$.

2A **(M)** The first reaction indicates that 0.1 mol of $NaNO_2$ reacts with 0.3 mol of Na to yield 0.2 mol of compound X and 0.05 mol of N_2. Since this reaction liberates nitrogen gas, it is very likely that compound X is an oxide of sodium. The two possibilities include Na_2O and Na_2O2. Na_2O_2 will not react with oxygen, but Na_2O will. Therefore, compound X is most likely Na_2O and compound Y is Na_2O_2. The balanced chemical equations for two processes are:

$$NaNO_2(s) + 3 Na(s) \rightarrow 2 Na_2O(s) + \frac{1}{2}N_2(g)$$

$$Na_2O(s) + \frac{1}{2}O_2(g) \rightarrow Na_2O_2(s)$$

2B **(M)** Since compound X is used in plaster of Paris it must contain calcium. Calcium reacts with carbon to form calcium carbide, according to the following chemical equation:
$Ca(s) + 2C(s) \rightarrow CaC_2(s)$

Furthermore, compound X or calcium carbide reacts with nitrogen gas to form compound Y or calcium cyanamide:
$CaC_2(s) + N_2(g) \rightarrow CaCN_2(s) + C(s)$

CN_2^{2-} anion is isoelectronic with CO_2 and it therefore contains 16 electrons. The structure of this anion is:

$$\ddot{N} = C = \ddot{N}$$

3A **(M)** The first two reactions, are those from Example 21-3, used to produce B_2O_3.

$$Na_2B_4O_7 \cdot 10\,H_2O(s) + H_2SO_4(l) \longrightarrow 4\,B(OH)_3(s) + Na_2SO_4(s) + 5\,H_2O(l)$$

$$2\,B(OH)_3(s) \xrightarrow{\Delta} B_2O_3(s) + 3\,H_2O(g)$$

The next reaction is conversion to BCl_3 with heat, carbon, and chlorine.

$$2\,B_2O_3(s) + 3\,C(s) + 6\,Cl_2(g) \xrightarrow{\Delta} 4\,BCl_3(g) + 3\,CO_2(g)$$

$LiAlH_4$ is used as a reducing agent to produce diborane.

$$4\,BCl_3(g) + 3\,LiAlH_4(s) \rightarrow 2\,B_2H_6(g) + 3\,LiCl(s) + 3\,AlCl_3(s)$$

3B **(M)** $Na_2B_4O_7 \cdot 10\,H_2O(s) + H_2SO_4(aq) \rightarrow 4\,B(OH)_3(s) + Na_2SO_4(aq) + 5\,H_2O(l)$
$2\,B(OH)_3(s) \xrightarrow{\Delta} B_2O_3(s) + 3\,H_2O(l)$
$B_2O_3(s) + 3\,CaF_2(s) + 3\,H_2SO_4(l) \xrightarrow{\Delta} 2\,BF_3(g) + 3\,CaSO_4(s) + 3\,H_2O(g)$

INTEGRATIVE EXAMPLES

A **(M)** $NaCN$ and $Al(NO_3)_3$ dissociate in water according to the following equations:

$$NaCN(aq) \rightarrow Na^+(aq) + CN^-(aq)$$

$$Al(NO_3)_3(aq) \rightarrow Al^{3+}(aq) + 3\,NO_3^-(aq)$$

$NaCN$ is a salt of strong base ($NaOH$) and weak acid (HCN) and its solution is therefore basic.

We proceed by first determining the $[OH]^-$ concentration in a solution which is 1.0M in $NaCN$:

$$CN^- + H_2O \rightleftharpoons HCN + OH^-$$

1.0		/	/
$1.0 - x$		x	x

$$K_b = \frac{K_w}{K_a(HCN)} = \frac{1.0 \times 10^{-14}}{6.2 \times 10^{-10}} = 1.6 \times 10^{-5}$$

$$K_b = \frac{[HCN][OH^-]}{[CN^-]} = \frac{x \times x}{1.0 - x} = \frac{x^2}{1.0 - x} = 1.6 \times 10^{-5}$$

Assume, $x \ll 1$ and $1.0 - x \approx 1.0$

$$x^2 = 1.6 \times 10^{-5} \Rightarrow x = \sqrt{1.6 \times 10^{-5}} = 4.0 \times 10^{-3}$$

$$[OH^-] = 4.0 \times 10^{-3}$$

On mixing, $[OH^-] = 2.0 \times 10^{-3}$ M and $[Al^{3+}] = 0.50$ M. The precipitation will occur according to the following equation:

$$Al^{3+}(aq) + 3\,OH^-(aq) \rightleftharpoons Al(OH)_3(s)$$

The product $[Al^{3+}][OH^-]^3 = 0.50 \times (2.0 \times 10^{-3})^3 = 4.0 \times 10^{-9}$ is much greater than K_{sp} for $Al(OH)_3$ (1.3×10^{-33}) and therefore precipitation will occur.

__B__ **(M)** When $BeCl_2 \cdot 4\,H_2O$ is heated, it decomposes to $Be(OH)_2(s)$, $H_2O(g)$, and $HCl(g)$, as discussed in Section 21-3. $BeCl_2 \cdot 4\,H_2O$ comprises $[Be(H_2O)_4]^{2+}$ and Cl^- ions. Because of the high polarizing power of Be^{2+}, it is difficult to remove the coordinated water molecules by heating the solid and the acidity of the coordinated H_2O molecules is enhanced. When $BeCl_2 \cdot 4\,H_2O$ is dissolved in water, $[Be(H_2O)_4]^{2+}$ ions react with water, and $[Be(H_2O)_3(OH)]^+$ and H_3O^+ ions are produced. Hence, a solution of $BeCl_2 \cdot 4\,H_2O$ is expected to be acidic.

When $CaCl_2 \cdot 6\,H_2O$ is heated, $CaCl_2(s)$ and $H_2O(g)$ are produced. Because the charge density and polarizing power of Ca^{2+} is much less than that of Be^{2+}, it is much easier to drive off the coordinated water molecules by heating the solid. When $CaCl_2 \cdot 6\,H_2O$ is dissolved in water, $Ca^{2+}(aq)$ and $Cl^-(aq)$ are produced. However, the charge density of the Ca^{2+} ion is too low to affect the acidity of water molecules in the hydration sphere of the Ca^{2+} ion. Hence, a solution of $CaCl_2 \cdot 6\,H_2O$ has a neutral pH.

EXERCISES

Group 1: The Alkali Metals

__1.__ **(E)** **(a)** $2\,Cs(s) + Cl_2(g) \longrightarrow 2\,CsCl(s)$

(b) $2\,Na(s) + O_2(g) \longrightarrow Na_2O_2(s)$

(c) $Li_2CO_3(s) \xrightarrow{\Delta} Li_2O(s) + CO_2(g)$

(d) $Na_2SO_4(s) + 4\,C(s) \rightarrow Na_2S(s) + 4\,CO(g)$

(e) $K(s) + O_2(g) \longrightarrow KO_2(s)$

__2.__ **(a)** $2\,Rb(s) + 2\,H_2O(l) \longrightarrow 2RbOH(aq) + H_2(g)$

(b) $2\,KHCO_3(s) \xrightarrow{\Delta} K_2CO_3(aq) + H_2O(l) + CO_2(g)$

(c) $2\,Li(s) + 1/2\,O_2(g) \longrightarrow Li_2O(s)$

(d) $2\,KCl(s) + H_2SO_4(aq) \longrightarrow K_2SO_4(aq) + 2\,HCl(g)$

(e) $LiH(s) + H_2O(l) \longrightarrow LiOH(aq) + H_2(g)$

__3.__ **(E)** Both LiCl and KCl are soluble in water, but Li_3PO_4 is not very soluble. Hence the addition of $K_3PO_4(aq)$ to a solution of the white solid will produce a precipitate if the white solid is LiCl, but no precipitate if the white solid is KCl. The best method is a flame test; lithium gives a red color to a flame, while the potassium flame test is violet.

4. **(E)** When heated, Li_2CO_3 decomposes to $CO_2(g)$ and $Li_2O(l)$. $K_2CO_3(s)$ simply melts when heated. The evolution of $CO_2(g)$ bubbles should be sufficient indication of the difference in behavior. The flame test affords a violet flame if K^+ is present, and a red flame if Li^+ is present.

5. **(M)** First we note that sodium carbonate ionizes virtually completely when dissolved in H_2O and thus is described as highly soluble in water. This is made evident by the fact that there is no K_{sp} value for Na_2CO_3. By contrast, the existence of K_{sp} values for $MgCO_3$ and Li_2CO_3 shows that these compounds have lower solubilities in water than Na_2CO_3. To decide whether $MgCO_3$ is more or less soluble than Li_2CO_3, we must calculate the molar solubility for each salt and then compare the two values. Clearly, the salt that has the larger molar solubility will be more soluble in water. The molar solubilities can be found using the respective K_{sp} expressions for the two salts.

1. $$MgCO_3 \underset{MgCO_3\ excess - s}{\overset{K_{sp}\ =\ 3.5\times 10^{-8}}{\rightleftharpoons}} \underset{s}{Mg^{2+}(aq)} + \underset{s}{CO_3^{2-}(aq)} \quad \text{Let "}s\text{"} = \text{molar solubility of}$$
   $s^2 = 3.5\times 10^{-8} \qquad s = 1.9 \times 10^{-4}\ M$

2. $$Li_2CO_3 \underset{Li_2CO_3\ excess - s}{\overset{K_{sp}=\ 2.5\times 10^{-2}}{\rightleftharpoons}} \underset{2s}{2\ Li^+(aq)} + \underset{s}{CO_3^{2-}(aq)} \quad \text{Let "}s\text{"} = \text{molar solubility of}$$
   $$(2\ s)^2 \times (s) = 2.5 \times 10^{-8}\ \ 4s^3 = 2.5 \times 10^{-8} \quad s = \sqrt[3]{\frac{2.5\times 10^{-8}}{4}} = 0.18\ M$$

We can conclude that Li_2CO_3 is more soluble than $MgCO_3$. Thus, the expected order of increasing solubility in water is: $MgCO_3 < Li_2CO_3 < Na_2CO_3$.

6. **(M)** We know sodium metal was produced at the cathode from the reduction of sodium ion, Na^+. Thus, hydroxide must have been involved in oxidation at the anode. The hydrogen in hydroxide ion already is in its highest oxidation state and thus cannot be oxidized. This leaves oxidation of the hydroxide ion to elemental oxygen as the remaining reaction.

Cathode, reduction : $\quad \{Na^+ + e^- \longrightarrow Na(l)\} \ \times 4$

Anode, oxidation : $\quad 4\ OH^- \longrightarrow O_2(g) + 2\ H_2O(g) + 4\ e^-$

$\qquad$ Net : $\quad 4\ Na^+ + 4\ OH^- \longrightarrow 4\ Na(l) + O_2(g) + 2\ H_2O(g)$

7. **(M)**
   (a) $H_2(g)$ and $Cl_2(g)$ are produced during the electrolysis of $KCl(aq)$.
   The electrode reactions are:
   Anode, oxidation: $\quad 2\ Cl^-(aq) \rightarrow Cl_2(g) + 2\ e^-$
   Cathode, reduction: $\quad 2\ H_2O(l) + 2\ e^- \rightarrow H_2(g) + 2\ OH^-(aq)$
   We can compute the amount of OH^- produced at the cathode.

   $$\text{mol}\ OH^- = 3.50\ \text{min} \times \frac{60\ s}{1\ \text{min}} \times \frac{0.910\ C}{1s} \times \frac{1\text{mol}\ e^-}{96485\ C} \times \frac{2\ \text{mol}\ OH^-}{2\ \text{mol}\ e^-} = 1.98\times 10^{-3}\ \text{mol}$$

Now, we can calculate the [OH⁻]and, from that, the pH of the solution:

$$[OH^-] = \frac{1.98 \times 10^{-3} \text{ mol OH}^-}{1.26 \text{ L soln}} = 1.57 \times 10^{-3} \text{ M}$$

$$pOH = -\log(1.57 \times 10^{-3}) = 2.80$$
$$pH = 14.000 - 2.80 = 11.2$$

(b) As long as KCl is in excess and the volume of the solution is nearly constant, the solution pH only depends on the number of electrons transferred.

8. **(M)**

(a) total energy $= 3.0 \text{ V} \times 0.50 \text{ A h} \times \dfrac{3600 \text{ s}}{1 \text{h}} \times \dfrac{1 \text{ C/s}}{1 \text{ A}} \times \dfrac{1 \text{ J}}{1 \text{ V} \cdot \text{C}} = 5.4 \times 10^3 \text{ J}$

We obtained the first conversion factor for time as follows.

$$5.0 \, \mu W \times \frac{1 \times 10^{-6} \text{ W}}{1 \, \mu W} \times \frac{1 \text{ J/s}}{1 \text{ W}} = \frac{5.0 \times 10^{-6} \text{ J}}{1 \text{ s}}$$

time $= 5.4 \times 10^3 \text{ J} \times \dfrac{1 \text{ s}}{5 \times 10^{-6} \text{ J}} = 1.1 \times 10^9 \text{ s} \times \dfrac{1 \text{h}}{3600 \text{ s}} \times \dfrac{1 \text{ day}}{24 \text{h}} \times \dfrac{1 \text{ y}}{365 \text{ days}} = 34 \text{ y}$

(b) The capacity of the battery is determined by the mass of Li present.

mass Li $= 0.50 \text{ A h} \times \dfrac{1 \text{ C/s}}{1 \text{ A}} \times \dfrac{3600 \text{ s}}{1 \text{h}} \times \dfrac{1 \text{ mol e}^-}{96485 \text{ C}} \times \dfrac{1 \text{ mol Li}}{1 \text{ mol e}^-} \times \dfrac{6.941 \text{ g Li}}{1 \text{ mol Li}} = 0.13 \text{ g Li}$

9. **(M)**

(a) We first compute the mass of $NaHCO_3$ that should be produced from 1.00 ton NaCl, assuming that all of the Na in the NaCl ends up in the $NaHCO_3$. We use the unit, ton-mole, to simplify the calculations.

mass $NaHCO_3 = 1.00 \text{ ton NaCl} \times \dfrac{1 \text{ ton-mol NaCl}}{58.4 \text{ ton NaCl}} \times \dfrac{1 \text{ ton-mol Na}}{1 \text{ ton-mol NaCl}}$

$\times \dfrac{1 \text{ tol-mol } NaHCO_3}{1 \text{ ton-mol Na}} \times \dfrac{84.0 \text{ ton } NaHCO_3}{1 \text{ ton mol } NaHCO_3} = 1.44 \text{ ton } NaHCO_3$

% yield $= \dfrac{1.03 \text{ ton } NaHCO_3 \text{ produced}}{1.44 \text{ ton } NaHCO_3 \text{ expected}} \times 100\% = 71.5\% \text{ yield}$

(b) NH_3 is used in the principal step of the Solvay process to produce a solution in which $NaHCO_3$ is formed and from which it will precipitate. The filtrate contains NH_4Cl, from which NH_3 is recovered by treatment with $Ca(OH)_2$. Thus, NH_3 is simply used during the Solvay process to produce the proper conditions for the desired reactions. Any net consumption of NH_3 is the result of unavoidable losses during production.

10. **(M)**

(a) $Ca(OH)_2(s) + SO_4^{2-}(aq) \rightleftharpoons CaSO_4(s) + 2OH^-(aq)$

(b) We sum two solubility reactions and combine their values of K_{sp}

$Ca(OH)_2(s) \rightleftharpoons Ca^{2+}(aq) + 2OH^-(aq)$ $\qquad\qquad K_{sp} = 5.5 \times 10^{-6}$

$Ca^{2+}(aq) + SO_4^{2-}(aq) \rightleftharpoons CaSO_4(s)$ $\qquad\qquad 1/K_{sp} = 1/9.1 \times 10^{-6}$

$Ca(OH)_2(s) + SO_4^{2-}(aq) \rightleftharpoons CaSO_4(s) + 2OH^-(aq)$ $\qquad K = \dfrac{5.5 \times 10^{-6}}{9.1 \times 10^{-6}} = 0.60$

Because K is close to 1.00, we conclude that the reaction lies neither very far to the right (it does not go to completion) nor to the left.

(c) Reaction: $Ca(OH)_2(s) + SO_4^{2-}(aq) \rightleftharpoons CaSO_4(s) + 2OH^-(aq)$

Initial:	—	1.00 M	—	≈ 0 M
Changes:	—	-x M	—	+2x M
Equil:	—	(1.00–x) M	—	2x M

$$K = \frac{\left[OH^-\right]^2}{\left[SO_4^{2-}\right]} = 0.60 = \frac{4x^2}{1.00 - x} \qquad 4x^2 = 0.60 - 0.60x \qquad 4x^2 + 0.60x - 0.60 = 0$$

$$x = \frac{-b \pm \sqrt{b^2 - 4ac}}{2a} = \frac{-0.60 \pm \sqrt{0.36 + 9.60}}{8} = 0.32 \text{ M}$$

$$\left[SO_4^{2-}\right] = 1.00 - x = 0.68 \text{ M} \qquad \left[OH^-\right] = 2x = 0.64 \text{ M}$$

11. **(M)** Use $\Delta_f G°$ values to calculate $\Delta_r G°$ for the reaction and then the equilibrium constant K at 298 K.

$$Na_2O_2(s) \rightleftharpoons Na_2O(s) + \frac{1}{2}O_2(g)$$

$\Delta_f G°(\text{kJ mol}^{-1}) -449.63 - 379.09$

$\Delta_r G° = -379.09 - (-449.63) = 70.54 \text{ kJ mol}^{-1}$

$\Delta_r G° = -RT \ln K$

$-8.314 \text{ JK}^{-1}\text{mol}^{-1} \times 298 \text{ K} \times \ln K = 70.54 \times 1000 \text{ Jmol}^{-1}$

$$\ln K = \frac{70.54 \times 1000 \text{ Jmol}^{-1}}{-8.314 \text{ JK}^{-1}\text{mol}^{-1} \times 298 \text{ K}} = -28.47 \Rightarrow K = e^{-28.47} = 4.32 \times 10^{-13}$$

Since $K = p_{O_2}^{\frac{1}{2}} \Rightarrow p_{O_2} = K^2 = 1.87 \times 10^{-25}$. The equilibrium constant and partial pressure of oxygen are both very small at 298 K. Therefore, $Na_2O_2(s)$ is thermodynamically stable with respect to $Na_2O(s)$ and $O_2(g)$ at 298 K.

12. **(M)** Use $\Delta_f G°$ values to calculate $\Delta_r G°$ for the reaction and then the equilibrium constant K at 298 K.

$$2\,KO_2(s) \rightleftharpoons K_2O(s) + \frac{3}{2}O_2(g)$$

$\Delta_f G°(kJmol^{-1})$ -240.59 -322.09

$\Delta_r G° = -322.09 - (-2 \times 240.59) = 159.1\ kJ\ mol^{-1}$

$\Delta_r G° = -RT \ln K$

$-8.314\ JK^{-1}mol^{-1} \times 298\ K \times \ln K = 159.1 \times 1000\ Jmol^{-1}$

$\ln K = \dfrac{159.1 \times 1000\ Jmol^{-1}}{-8.314\ JK^{-1}mol^{-1} \times 298\ K} = -64 \Rightarrow K = e^{-64} = 1.604 \times 10^{-28}$

Since $K = p_{O_2}^{\frac{3}{2}} \Rightarrow p_{O_2} = K^{\frac{2}{3}} = 2.952 \times 10^{-19}$. The equilibrium constant and partial pressure of oxygen are both very small at 298 K. Therefore, $KO_2(s)$ is thermodynamically stable with respect to $K_2O(s)$ and $O_2(g)$ at 298 K.

Group 2: The Alkaline Earth Metals

13. **(M)** $CaO \xleftarrow{\ \Delta\ } CaCO_3 \xleftarrow{\ CO_2\ } Ca(OH)_2 \xrightarrow{\ HCl\ } CaCl_2 \xrightarrow{\ electrolysis\ } Ca$

$CaHPO_4 \xleftarrow{\ H_3PO_4\ } \ \Big|\ \xrightarrow[\ ]{H_2SO_4} CaSO_4$

The reactions are as follows. $Ca(OH)_2(s) + 2\,HCl(aq) \rightarrow CaCl_2(aq) + 2\,H_2O(l)$

$CaCl_2(l) \xrightarrow{\ \Delta,electrolysis\ } Ca(l) + Cl_2(g)$ $Ca(OH)_2(s) + CO_2(g) \rightarrow CaCO_3(s) + H_2O(g)$

$CaCO_3(s) \xrightarrow{\ \Delta\ } CaO(s) + CO_2(g)$ $Ca(OH)_2(s) + H_2SO_4(aq) \rightarrow CaSO_4(s) + 2\,H_2O(l)$

$Ca(OH)_2(s) + H_3PO_4(aq) \rightarrow CaHPO_4(aq) + 2\,H_2O(l)$. Actually $CaO(s)$ is the industrial starting material from which $Ca(OH)_2$ is made. $CaO(s) + H_2O(l) \longrightarrow Ca(OH)_2(s)$

14. **(M)** $MgO \xleftarrow{\ \Delta\ } MgCO_3 \xleftarrow{\ CO_2\ } Mg(OH)_2 \xrightarrow{\ HCl\ } MgCl_2 \xrightarrow{\ electrolysis\ } Mg \xrightarrow{\ N_2\ } Mg_3N_2$

$MgHPO_4 \xleftarrow{\ H_3PO_4\ } \ \Big|\ \xrightarrow[\ ]{H_2SO_4} MgSO_4$

Once we return to $Mg(OH)_2$ from $MgSO_4$, the other substances can be made by the indicated pathways. The return reaction is: $MgSO_4(aq) + 2\,NaOH(aq) \rightarrow Mg(OH)_2(s) + Na_2SO_4(aq)$. Then the other reactions are

$Mg(OH)_2(s) + 2\,HCl(aq) \rightarrow MgCl_2(aq) + 2\,H_2O(l)$

$MgCl_2(l) \xrightarrow{\ \Delta,\ electrolysis\ } Mg(l) + Cl_2(g)$; $Mg(OH)_2(s) + CO_2(g) \rightarrow MgCO_3(s) + H_2O(g)$

$MgCO_3(s) \xrightarrow{\ \Delta\ } MgO(s) + CO_2(g)$; $Mg(OH)_2(s) + H_2SO_4(aq) \rightarrow MgSO_4(s) + 2\,H_2O(l)$

$Mg(OH)_2(s) + H_3PO_4(aq) \rightarrow MgHPO_4(aq) + 2\,H_2O(l)$

15. **(M)** The reactions involved are:

$Mg^{2+}(aq) + Ca^{2+}(aq) + 2\ OH^-(aq) \rightarrow Mg(OH)_2(s) + Ca^{2+}(aq)$

$Mg(OH)_2(s) + 2\ H^+(aq) + 2\ Cl^-(aq) \rightarrow Mg^{2+}(aq) + 2\ H_2O(l) + 2\ Cl^-(aq)$

$Mg^{2+}(aq) + 2\ Cl^-(aq) \xrightarrow{\Delta} MgCl_2(s)$

$MgCl_2(s) \overset{\text{(electrolysis)}}{-\!\!-\!\!-\!\!\longrightarrow} Mg(l) + Cl_2(g)$

$\underline{Mg(l) \rightarrow Mg(s)}$

$Mg^{2+} + 2\ Cl^-(aq) \rightarrow Mg(s) + Cl_2(g)$ (Overall reaction)

As can be seen, the process does not violate the principle of conservation of charge.

16. **(M)**

    (a) MgO vs. BaO: MgO would have the higher melting point because, although Mg^{2+} and Ba^{2+} have the same charge, Mg^{2+} is a smaller ion. Smaller ions have a larger electrostatic attraction to anions (here, in both cases, the anion is O^{2-}), which is due to the smaller charge separation (Coulomb's law).

    (b) MgF_2 vs. $MgCl_2$ solubility in water. F^- is smaller than Cl^-, hence, electrostatic attraction between Mg^{2+} and the halide is greater in F^- than Cl^-. If we assume that hydration of the ions is similar, we expect that MgF_2 is less soluble than $MgCl_2$. (Note: K_{sp} given for MgF_2, which is sparingly soluble, while no K_{sp} value is given for readily soluble $MgCl_2$.)

17. **(M) (a)** $BeF_2(s) + Mg(s) \xrightarrow{\Delta} Be(s) + MgF_2(s)$

    (b) $Ba(s) + Br_2(l) \longrightarrow BaBr_2(s)$

    (c) $UO_2(s) + 2\ Ca(s) \longrightarrow U(s) + 2\ CaO(s)$

    (d) $MgCO_3 \cdot CaCO_3(s) \xrightarrow{\Delta} MgO(s) + CaO(s) + 2\ CO_2(g)$

    (e) $2\ H_3PO_4(aq) + 3\ CaO(s) \longrightarrow Ca_3(PO_4)_2(s) + 3\ H_2O(l)$

18. **(M) (a)** $Mg(HCO_3)_2(s) \xrightarrow{\text{heat}} MgO(s) + 2\ CO_2(g) + H_2O(l)$

    (b) $BaCl_2(l) \xrightarrow{\text{electrolysis}} Ba(l) + Cl_2(g)$

    (c) $Sr(s) + 2\ HBr(aq) \longrightarrow SrBr_2(aq) + H_2(g)$

    (d) $H_2SO_4(aq) + Ca(OH)_2(aq) \longrightarrow CaSO_4(s) + 2\ H_2O(l)$

    (e) $CaSO_4 \cdot 2\ H_2O(s) \xrightarrow{\Delta} CaSO_4 \cdot \frac{1}{2}H_2O(s) + \frac{3}{2}\ H_2O(g)$

19. **(D)** Let us compute the value of the equilibrium constant for each reaction by combining the two solubility product constants. Large values of equilibrium constants indicate that the reaction is displaced far to the right. Values of K that are much smaller than 1 indicate that the reaction is displaced far to the left.

    (a) $BaSO_4(s) \rightleftharpoons Ba^{2+}(aq) + SO_4^{2-}(aq)$ $K_{sp} = 1.1 \times 10^{-10}$

         $Ba^{2+}(aq) + CO_3^{2-}(aq) \rightleftharpoons BaCO_3(s)$ $1/K_{sp} = 1/(5.1 \times 10^{-9})$

$$BaSO_4(s) + CO_3^{2-}(aq) \rightleftharpoons BaCO_3(s) + SO_4^{2-}(aq) \qquad K = \frac{1.1 \times 10^{-10}}{5.1 \times 10^{-9}} = 2.2 \times 10^{-2}$$

    Thus, the equilibrium lies slightly to the left.

(b) $Mg_3(PO_4)_2(s) \rightleftharpoons 3\,Mg^{2+}(aq) + 2\,PO_4^{3-}(aq)$ $\qquad K_{sp} = 2.1 \times 10^{-25}$

$3\{Mg^{2+}(aq) + CO_3^{2-}(aq) \rightleftharpoons MgCO_3(s)\}$ $\qquad 1/(K_{sp})^3 = 1/(3.5 \times 10^{-8})^3$

$\overline{Mg_3(PO_4)_2(s) + 3\,CO_3^{2-}(aq) \rightleftharpoons 3\,MgCO_3(s) + 2\,PO_4^{3-}(aq)}$

$K = \dfrac{2.1 \times 10^{-25}}{(3.5 \times 10^{-8})^3} = 4.9 \times 10^{-3}$ Thus, the equilibrium lies to the left.

(c) $Ca(OH)_2(s) \rightleftharpoons Ca^{2+}(aq) + 2\,OH^-(aq)$ $\qquad K_{sp} = 5.5 \times 10^{-6}$

$Ca^{2+}(aq) + 2\,F^-(aq) \rightleftharpoons CaF_2(s)$ $\qquad 1/K_{sp} = 1/(5.3 \times 10^{-9})$

$\overline{Ca(OH)_2(s) + 2\,F^-(aq) \rightleftharpoons CaF_2(s) + 2\,OH^-(aq)} \quad K = \dfrac{5.5 \times 10^{-6}}{5.3 \times 10^{-9}} = 1.0 \times 10^3$

Thus, the equilibrium lies to the right.

20. **(M)** We expect the reaction to occur to a significant extent in the forward direction if its equilibrium constant is >> 1.

(a) $BaCO_3(s) \rightleftharpoons Ba^{2+}(aq) + CO_3^{2-}(aq)$ $\qquad K_{sp} = 5.1 \times 10^{-9}$

$2\,HC_2H_3O_2(aq) \rightleftharpoons 2\,H^+(aq) + 2\,C_2H_3O_2^-(aq) \quad K_a^2 = (1.8 \times 10^{-5})^2$

$H^+(aq) + CO_3^{2-}(aq) \rightleftharpoons HCO_3^-(aq)$ $\qquad 1/K_{a_2} = 1/(4.7 \times 10^{-11})$

$H^+(aq) + HCO_3^-(aq) \rightleftharpoons H_2CO_3(aq)$ $\qquad 1/K_{a_1} = 1/(4.2 \times 10^{-7})$

$\overline{BaCO_3(s) + 2\,HC_2H_3O_2(aq) \rightleftharpoons Ba(C_2H_3O_2)_2(aq) + H_2CO_3(aq)}$

$K = \dfrac{5.1 \times 10^{-9} \times (1.8 \times 10^{-5})^2}{4.7 \times 10^{-11} \times 4.2 \times 10^{-7}} = 8.4 \times 10^{-2}$

Thus, no significant reaction occurs (the equilibrium mixture contains appreciable amounts of all four species involved in the reaction.

(b) $Ca(OH)_2(s) \rightleftharpoons Ca^{2+}(aq) + 2\,OH^-(aq)$ $\qquad K_{sp} = 5.5 \times 10^{-6}$

$2\,NH_4^+(aq) + 2\,OH^-(aq) \rightleftharpoons 2\,NH_3(aq) + 2\,H_2O(l)$ $\qquad 1/K_b^2 = 1/(1.8 \times 10^{-5})^2$

$\overline{Ca(OH)_2(s) + 2\,NH_4^+(aq) \rightleftharpoons Ca^{2+}(aq) + 2\,NH_3(aq) + 2\,H_2O(l)}$

$K = \dfrac{5.5 \times 10^{-6}}{(1.8 \times 10^{-5})^2} = 1.7 \times 10^4$ Thus, this reaction would occur to a significant extent.

(c) $BaF_2(s) \rightleftharpoons Ba^{2+}(aq) + 2\,F^-(aq)$ $\qquad K_{sp} = 1.0 \times 10^{-6}$

$2\,H_3O^+(aq) + 2\,F^-(aq) \rightleftharpoons 2\,HF(aq) + 2\,H_2O(l)$ $\qquad 1/K_a^2 = 1/(6.6 \times 10^{-4})^2$

$\overline{BaF_2(s) + 2\,H_3O^+(aq) \rightleftharpoons Ba^{2+}(aq) + 2\,HF(aq) + 2\,H_2O(l)}; \ K = \dfrac{1.0 \times 10^{-6}}{(6.6 \times 10^{-4})^2} = 2.3$

This reaction would occur to some extent, but certainly not to completion.

21. **(M)** The SO_4^{2-} ion is a large polarizable ion. A cation with a high polarizing power will polarize the SO_4^{2-} ion and kinetically assist the decomposition to SO_3. Because Be^{2+} has the largest charge density of the group 2 cations, we expect Be^{2+} to be the most polarizing and thus, $BeSO_4$ will be the least stable with respect to decomposition.

22. **(M)** The CO_3^{2-} ion is a large polarizable ion. A cation with a high polarizing power will polarize the CO_3^{2-} ion and kinetically assist the decomposition to CO_2. A cation with a low polarizing power will not polarize the anion as much; thus, the decomposition of CO_3^{2-} to CO_2 will not occur as readily in the presence of such a cation. Because Ba^{2+} has the smallest charge density of the group 2 cations, we expect Ba^{2+} to be the least polarizing; thus, $BaSO_3$ will be the most stable with respect to decomposition.

Group 13: The Boron Family

23. **(M)**

(a) B_4H_{10} contains a total of $4 \times 3 + 10 \times 1 = 22$ valence electrons or 11 pairs. Ten of these pairs could be allocated to form 10 B—H bonds, leaving but one pair to bond the four B atoms together, which is clearly an electron deficient situation.

(b) In our analysis in part (a), we noted that the four B atoms had but one electron pair to bond them together. To bond these four atoms into a chain requires three electron pairs. Since each electron pair in a bridging bond replaces two "normal" bonds, there must be at least two bridging bonds in the B_4H_{10} molecules. By analogy with B_2H_6, we might write the structure below left. But this structure uses only a total of 20 electrons. (The bridge bonds are shown as dots, normal bonds—electron pairs—as dashes.) In the structure at right below, we have retained some of the form of B_2H_6, and produced a compound with the formula B_4H_{10} and 11 electron pairs. (The experimentally determined structure of B_4H_{10} consists of a four-membered ring of alternating B and H atoms, held together by bridging bonds. Two of the B atoms have two H atoms bonded to each of them by normal covalent bonds. The other two B atoms have one H atom covalently bonded to each. One final B—B bond joins these last two B atoms, across the diameter of the ring.). See the diagram that follows:

$$\begin{array}{ccccc}
H & H & H & H & H \\
\backslash & \cdot\cdot & \cdot\cdot & \cdot\cdot & / \\
& B & B & B & B \\
/ & \cdot\cdot & \cdot\cdot & \cdot\cdot & \backslash \\
H & H & H & H & H
\end{array}
\qquad
\begin{array}{ccccc}
H\,H & & H & H & H \\
| & \backslash & \cdot\cdot & \cdot\cdot & / \\
H{-}B{-}B & & B & B \\
| & & \cdot\cdot & \cdot\cdot & \backslash \\
H & & H & H & H
\end{array}$$

(c) C_4H_{10} contains a total of $4 \times 4 + 10 \times 1 = 26$ valence electrons or 13 pairs. A plausible Lewis structure follows. (Note that each atom possess an octet of electrons.)

$$\begin{array}{cccc}
H & H & H & H \\
| & | & | & | \\
H{-}C{-}C{-}C{-}C{-}H \\
| & | & | & | \\
H & H & H & H
\end{array}$$

24. (E)

(a)

$$\left(\begin{array}{c} |\overline{F}| \\ | \\ |\overline{F}-B-\overline{F}| \\ | \\ |\overline{F}| \end{array}\right)^{-}$$

(b)

$$:\overset{..}{\underset{..}{F}}: \quad H \quad H \quad H$$
$$:\overset{..}{F}-\overset{+}{\underset{..}{B}}\overset{|}{\underset{:F:}{}}-\overset{|}{\underset{|}{N}}-\overset{|}{\underset{|}{C}}-\overset{|}{\underset{|}{C}}-H$$
$$:\overset{..}{\underset{..}{F}}: \quad H \quad H \quad H$$

25. (M)

(a) $2\,BBr_3(l) + 3\,H_2(g) \longrightarrow 2\,B(s) + 6\,HBr(g)$

(b) i) $B_2O_3(s) + 3\,C(s) \overset{\Delta}{\longrightarrow} 3\,CO(g) + 2\,B(s)$

ii) $2\,B(s) + 3\,F_2(g) \overset{\Delta}{\longrightarrow} 2\,BF_3(g)$

(c) $2\,B(s) + 3\,N_2O(g) \overset{\Delta}{\longrightarrow} 3\,N_2(g) + B_2O_3(s)$

26. (M) Each boron atom has an oxidation number of +3. The hydroxyl oxygens are each –2, while the bridging oxygens are each –1. Finally, the hydroxyl H atoms are all in the +1 oxidation state. The oxidation numbers for the all the constituent atoms add up to the charge on the perborate ion, namely, 2–.

27. (M) (a) $2\,Al(s) + 6\,HCl(aq) \rightarrow 2\,AlCl_3(aq) + 3\,H_2(g)$

(b) $2\,NaOH(aq) + 2\,Al(s) + 6\,H_2O(l) \rightarrow 2\,Na^+(aq) + 2\left[Al(OH)_4\right]^-(aq) + 3\,H_2(g)$

(c) Oxidation: $\{Al(s) \longrightarrow Al^{3+}(aq) + 3\,e^-\}$ $\qquad\qquad \times 2$

Reduction: $\{SO_4^{2-}(aq) + 4\,H^+(aq) + 2e^- \longrightarrow SO_2(g) + 2\,H_2O(l)\}$ $\quad \times 3$

Net: $2\,Al(s) + 3\,SO_4^{2-}(aq) + 12\,H^+(aq) \longrightarrow 2\,Al^{3+}(aq) + 3\,SO_2(aq) + 6\,H_2O(l)$

28. (M)

(a) $2\,Al(s) + 3\,Br_2(l) \longrightarrow 2\,AlBr_3(s)$

(b) $2\,Al(s) + Cr_2O_3(s) \overset{heat}{\longrightarrow} 2\,Cr(l) + Al_2O_3(s)$

(c) $Fe_2O_3(s) + OH^-(aq) \longrightarrow$ no reaction

$Al_2O_3(s) + 2\,OH^-(aq) + 3\,H_2O(l) \longrightarrow 2\left[Al(OH)_4\right]^-(aq)$

29. (M) One method of analyzing this reaction is to envision the HCO_3^- ion as a combination of CO_2 and OH^-. Then the OH^- reacts with Al^{3+} and forms $Al(OH)_3$. This method of envisioning HCO_3^- does have its basis in reality. After all,

$H_2CO_3(= H_2O + CO_2) + OH^- \longrightarrow HCO_3^- + H_2O$

$Al^{3+}(aq) + 3\,HCO_3^-(aq) \longrightarrow Al(OH)_3(s) + 3\,CO_2(g)$

Another method is to consider the reaction as, first, the hydrolysis of hydrated aluminum ion to produce $Al(OH)_3 (s)$ and an acidic solution, followed by the reaction of the acid with bicarbonate ion.

$$\left[Al(H_2O)_6\right]^{3+}(aq) + 3 H_2O(l) \longrightarrow Al(OH)_3(H_2O)_3(s) + 3 H_3O^+(aq)$$

$$3 H_3O^+(aq) + 3 HCO_3^-(aq) \longrightarrow 6 H_2O(l) + 3 CO_2(g)$$

This gives the same net reaction:

$$\left[Al(H_2O)_6\right]^{3+}(aq) + 3 HCO_3^-(aq) \longrightarrow Al(OH)_3(H_2O)_3(s) + 3 CO_2(g) + 3 H_2O(l)$$

30. **(E)** The $Al^{3+}(aq)$ ion hydrolyzes. $Al^{3+}(aq) + 3 H_2O(l) \longrightarrow Al(OH)_3(s) + 3 H^+(aq)$

Subsequently, the hydrogen ion that is produced reacts with bicarbonate ion to liberate $CO_2(g)$.

$$H^+(aq) + HCO_3^-(aq) \longrightarrow H_2O(l) + CO_2(g)$$

31. **(M)** Aluminum and its oxide are soluble in both acid and base.

$2 Al(s) + 6 H^+(aq) \longrightarrow 2 Al^{3+}(aq) + 3 H_2(g)$

$Al_2O_3(s) + 6 H^+(aq) \longrightarrow 2 Al^{3+}(aq) + 3 H_2O(l)$

$2 Al(s) + 2 OH^-(aq) + 6 H_2O(l) \longrightarrow 2\left[Al(OH)_4\right]^-(aq) + 3 H_2(g)$

$Al_2O_3(s) + 2 OH^-(aq) + 3 H_2O(l) \longrightarrow 2\left[Al(OH)_4\right]^-(aq)$

$Al(s)$ is resistant to corrosion only over the pH range 4.5 to 8.5. Thus, aluminum is inert only when the medium to which it is exposed is neither highly acidic nor highly basic.

32. **(M)** Both Al and Mg are attacked by acid and their ions are both precipitated by hydroxide ion.

$2 Al(s) + 6 H^+(aq) \longrightarrow 2 Al^{3+}(aq) + 3 H_2(g) \quad Mg(s) + 2 H^+(aq) \longrightarrow Mg^{2+}(aq) + H_2(g)$

$Al^{3+}(aq) + 3 OH^-(aq) \longrightarrow Al(OH)_3(s) \qquad Mg^{2+}(aq) + 2 OH^- \longrightarrow Mg(OH)_2(s)$

But, of these two solid hydroxides, only $Al(OH)_3(s)$ redissolves in excess $OH^-(aq)$.

$$Al(OH)_3(s) + OH^-(aq) \longrightarrow \left[Al(OH)_4\right]^-(aq)$$

Thus, the analytical procedure consists of dissolving the sample in HCl(aq) and then treating the resulting solution with NaOH(aq) until a precipitate forms. If this precipitate dissolves completely in excess NaOH(aq), the sample is aluminum 2S. If at least some of the precipitate does not dissolve, the sample was magnesium.

33. **(M)** $CO_2(g)$ is, of course, the anhydride of an acid. The reaction here is an acid-base reaction.

$$\left[Al(OH)_4\right]^-(aq) + CO_2(aq) \longrightarrow Al(OH)_3(s) + HCO_3^-(aq)$$

HCl(aq), being a strong acid, can't be used because it will dissolve the $Al(OH)_3(s)$.

34. (M)

(a) Oersted: $2 \, Al_2O_3(s) + 3 \, C(s) + 6 \, Cl_2(g) \xrightarrow{\Delta} 4 \, AlCl_3(s) + 3 \, CO_2(g)$

(b) Wöhler: $AlCl_3(s) + 3 \, K(s) \xrightarrow{\Delta} Al(s) + 3 \, KCl(s)$

35. (M) $2 \, KOH(aq) + 2 \, Al(s) + 6 \, H_2O(l) \rightarrow 2 \, K[Al(OH)_4](aq) + 3 \, H_2(g)$

$2 \, K[Al(OH)_4](aq) + 4 \, H_2SO_4(aq) \rightarrow K_2SO_4(aq) + Al_2(SO_4)_3(aq) + 8 \, H_2O(l)$
— crystallize$\rightarrow 2 \, KAl(SO_4)_2(s)$

36. (E) HCO_3^- and CO_3^{2-} solutions are basic (they produce an excess of OH^-). $Al^{3+}(aq)$ in the presence of $OH^-(aq)$ will precipitate as the hydroxide $Al(OH)_3(s)$.

37. (M) The chemical reaction for the disproportionation of $FB(BF_2)_2$ is
$3 \, FB(BF_2)_2 \rightarrow BF_3 + B_8F_{12}$
The structure of B_8F_{12} is

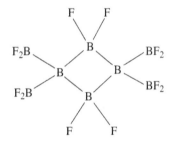

38. (E) The structure and bonding in Ga_2Cl_6 is similar to the structure of and bonding in Al_2Cl_6.

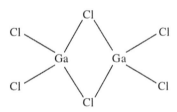

Group 14: The Carbon Family

39. (E) In the sense that diamonds react imperceptibly slowly at room temperature (either with oxygen to form carbon dioxide, or in its transformation to the more stable graphite), it is essentially true that "diamonds last forever." However, at elevated temperatures, diamond will burn to form $CO_2(g)$ and thus the statement is false. Also, the transformation C(diamond) $\rightarrow$ C(graphite) might occur more rapidly under other conditions. Eventually, of course, the conversion to graphite occurs.

40. **(E)** The graphite in the pencil "lead" is a good dry lubricant that will make slippery the stickiness (or reluctance) in the lock and enable it to work smoothly. The key carries the graphite to the site that needs to be lubricated within the lock mechanism.

<u>41.</u> **(M)**

(a) $3 \text{ SiO}_2(s) + 4 \text{ Al}(s) \xrightarrow{\Delta} 2 \text{ Al}_2\text{O}_3(s) + 3 \text{ Si}(s)$

(b) $\text{K}_2\text{CO}_3(s) + \text{SiO}_2(s) \xrightarrow{\Delta} \text{CO}_2(g) + \text{K}_2\text{SiO}_3(s)$

(c) $\text{Al}_4\text{C}_3(s) + 12 \text{ H}_2\text{O}(l) \longrightarrow 3 \text{ CH}_4(g) + 4\text{Al(OH)}_3(s)$

42. **(M)**

(a) $2 \text{ KCN}(aq) + \text{AgNO}_3(aq) \longrightarrow \text{KAg(CN)}_2(aq) + \text{KNO}_3(aq)$
    or $\text{KCN}(aq) + \text{AgNO}_3(aq) \longrightarrow \text{Ag(CN)}(s) + \text{KNO}_3(aq)$

(b) $\text{Si}_3\text{H}_8(l) + 5 \text{ O}_2(g) \longrightarrow 3 \text{ SiO}_2(s) + 4 \text{ H}_2\text{O}(l)$

(c) $\text{N}_2(g) + \text{CaC}_2(s) \xrightarrow{\Delta} \text{CaNCN}(s) + \text{C}(s)$

<u>43.</u> **(M)** A silane is a silicon-hydrogen compound, with the general formula $\text{Si}_n\text{H}_{2n+2}$. A silanol is a compound in which one or more of the hydrogens of silane is replaced by an —OH group. Then, the general formula becomes $\text{Si}_n\text{H}_{2n+1}(\text{OH})$. In both of these classes of compounds, the number of silicon atoms, n, ranges from 1 to 6. Silicones are produced when silanols condense into chains, with the elimination of a water molecule between every two silanol molecules.

$$\text{HO—Si}_n\text{H}_{2n}\text{—OH} + \text{HO—Si}_n\text{H}_{2n}\text{—OH} \longrightarrow \text{HO—Si}_n\text{H}_{2n}\text{—O—Si}_n\text{H}_{2n}\text{—OH} + \text{H}_2\text{O}$$

44. **(M)** Both the alkali metal carbonates and the alkali metal silicates are soluble in water. Hence, they also are soluble in acids. However, the carbonates will produce gaseous carbon dioxide— CO_2 —on reaction with acid,

$$\left(\text{CO}_3{}^{2-}(aq) + 2 \text{ H}^+(aq) \longrightarrow \text{"H}_2\text{CO}_3\text{"} \longrightarrow \text{H}_2\text{O}(l) + \text{CO}_2(g)\right), \text{ while the silicates will}$$

produce silica— SiO_2 — in an analogous reaction

$$\left(\text{SiO}_4{}^{4-}(aq) + 4\text{H}^+(aq) \longrightarrow \text{"H}_4\text{SiO}_4\text{"} \longrightarrow 2 \text{ H}_2\text{O}(l) + \text{SiO}_2(s)\right). \text{ The silica is produced in}$$

many forms depending on reaction conditions: a colloidal dispersion, a gelatinous precipitate, or a semisolid gel. Silicates of cations other than those of alkali metals are insoluble in water, as are the analogous carbonates. However, the carbonates will dissolve in acids (witness the reaction of acid rain on limestone carvings and marble statues, both forms of CaCO_3), while the silicates will not. (Silicate rocks are not significantly affected by acid rain.)

<u>45.</u> **(M)**

(1) $2 \text{ CH}_4(g) + \text{S}_8(g) \longrightarrow 2 \text{ CS}_2(g) + 4 \text{ H}_2\text{S}(g)$

(2) $\text{CS}_2(g) + 3 \text{ Cl}_2(g) \longrightarrow \text{CCl}_4(l) + \text{S}_2\text{Cl}_2(l)$

(3) $4 \text{ CS}_2(g) + 8 \text{ S}_2\text{Cl}_2(g) \longrightarrow 4 \text{ CCl}_4(l) + 3 \text{ S}_8(s)$

46. **(M)**

(a) $(CH_3)_3 SiCl(l) + H_2O(l) \longrightarrow (CH_3)_3 Si—OH(aq) + HCl(aq)$

$2 (CH_3)_3 Si—OH(aq) \longrightarrow (CH_3)_3 Si—O—Si(CH_3)_3 (s) + H_2O(l)$

(b) A silicone polymer does not form from $(CH_3)_3 Si—Cl$. Only a dimer is produced.

(c) The product that results from the treatment of CH_3SiCl_3 is two long Si—O—Si chains, with CH_3 groups on the outside, linked by Si—O—Si bridges. Part of one of these chains and the beginnings of the bridges are shown below.

47. **(D)** Muscovite or white mica has the formula $KAl_2(OH)_2(AlSi_3O_{10})$. Since they are not segregated into O_2 units in the formula, all of the oxygen atoms in the mineral must be in the −2 oxidation state. Potassium is obviously in the +1 oxidation state, as are the hydrogen atoms in the hydroxyl groups. Up to this point, we have -24 from the twelve oxygen atoms and +3 from the potassium and hydrogen atoms for a net number of -21 for the oxidation state. We still have three aluminum atoms and three silicon atoms to account for. In oxygen-rich salts such as mica, we would expect that the silicon and the aluminum atoms would be in their highest possible oxidation states, namely +4 and +3, respectively. Since the salt is neutral, the oxidation numbers for the silicon and aluminum atoms must add up to +21. This is precisely the total that is obtained if the silicon and aluminum atoms are in their highest possible oxidation states: $(3 \times (+3) + 3 \times (+4) = +21)$. Consequently, the empirical formula for white muscovite is consistent with the expected oxidation state for each element present.

48. **(D)** Crysotile asbestos has the formula $[Mg_3Si_2O_5(OH)_4]$. Since they are not segregated to O_2 units in the formula, all of the oxygen atoms in the mineral must be in the −2 oxidation state. The three magnesium atoms are obviously in the +2 oxidation state, while hydrogen atoms in the hydroxyl groups have an oxidation state of +1. Up to this point, then, the sum of the oxidation numbers equals −8 (−18 from O-atoms, +6 from Mg-atoms, and + 4 from H-atoms). Since the mineral is neutral, the two silicon atoms must have oxidation states that sum to +8 (−8 + 8 = neutral mineral), therefore, each silicon would need to be in the +4 oxidation state. In oxygen−rich salts such as asbestos, we would expect that the silicon atoms would be in their highest possible oxidation state, namely +4. Thus, the oxidation states for the element, in this mineral are precisely consistent with expectations.

49. **(M)**

(a) $PbO(s) + 2 HNO_3(aq) \longrightarrow Pb(NO_3)_2(s) + H_2O(l)$

(b) $SnCO_3(s) \overset{\Delta}{\longrightarrow} SnO(s) + CO_2(g)$

(c) $PbO(s) + C(s) \overset{\Delta}{\longrightarrow} Pb(l) + CO(g)$

(d) $2 \text{ Fe}^{3+}(\text{aq}) + \text{Sn}^{2+}(\text{aq}) \longrightarrow 2 \text{ Fe}^{2+}(\text{aq}) + \text{Sn}^{4+}(\text{aq})$

(e) $2 \text{ PbS}(\text{s}) + 3 \text{ O}_2(\text{g}) \xrightarrow{\Delta} 2 \text{ PbO}(\text{s}) + 2 \text{ SO}_2(\text{g})$

$2 \text{ SO}_2(\text{g}) + \text{O}_2(\text{g}) \longrightarrow 2 \text{ SO}_3(\text{g})$

$\text{SO}_3(\text{g}) + \text{PbO}(\text{s}) \longrightarrow \text{PbSO}_4(\text{s})$

Or perhaps simply: $\text{PbS}(\text{s}) + 2 \text{O}_2(\text{g}) \longrightarrow \text{PbSO}_4(\text{s})$

Yet a third possibility:

$\text{PbO}(\text{s}) + \text{SO}_2(\text{s}) \longrightarrow \text{PbSO}_3(\text{s})$, followed by $2 \text{ PbSO}_3(\text{s}) + \text{O}_2(\text{s}) \longrightarrow 2\text{PbSO}_4(\text{s})$

50. (M)

(a) Treat tin(II) oxide with hydrochloric acid.

$\text{SnO}(\text{s}) + 2 \text{ HCl}(\text{aq}) \longrightarrow \text{SnCl}_2(\text{aq}) + \text{H}_2\text{O}(\text{l})$

(b) Attack tin with chlorine. $\text{Sn}(\text{s}) + 2 \text{ Cl}_2(\text{g}) \longrightarrow \text{SnCl}_4(\text{s})$

(c) First we dissolve $\text{PbO}_2(\text{s})$ in $\text{HNO}_3(\text{aq})$ and then treat the resulting solution with $\text{K}_2\text{CrO}_4(\text{aq})$ to precipitate $\text{PbCrO}_4(\text{s})$

$2 \text{ PbO}_2(\text{s}) + 4 \text{ HNO}_3(\text{aq}) \longrightarrow 2 \text{ Pb}(\text{NO}_3)_2(\text{aq}) + \text{O}_2(\text{g}) + 2 \text{ H}_2\text{O}(\text{l})$

$\text{Pb}(\text{NO}_3)_2(\text{aq}) + \text{K}_2\text{CrO}_4(\text{aq}) \longrightarrow \text{PbCrO}_4(\text{s}) + 2 \text{ KNO}_3(\text{aq})$

51. **(M)** We start by using the Nernst equation to determine whether the cell voltage still is positive when the reaction has gone to completion.

(a) Oxidation: $\text{Fe}^{2+}(\text{aq}) \rightarrow \text{Fe}^{3+}(\text{aq}) + \text{e}^-\} \times 2$ $\qquad\qquad -E° = -0.771 \text{ V}$

Reduction: $\text{PbO}_2(\text{s}) + 4 \text{ H}^+(\text{aq}) + 2 \text{ e}^- \longrightarrow \text{Pb}^{2+}(\text{aq}) + 2 \text{ H}_2\text{O}(\text{l})$ $\quad E° = +1.455 \text{ V}$

Net: $2 \text{ Fe}^{2+}(\text{aq}) + \text{PbO}_2(\text{s}) + 4 \text{ H}^+(\text{aq}) \longrightarrow 2 \text{ Fe}^{3+}(\text{aq}) + \text{Pb}^{2+}(\text{aq}) + 2 \text{ H}_2\text{O}(\text{l})$

$E°_{\text{cell}} = -0.771 \text{ V} + 1.455 \text{ V} = +0.684 \text{ V}$

In this case, when the reaction has gone to completion,

$\left[\text{Fe}^{2+}\right] = 0.001 \text{ M,} \left[\text{Fe}^{3+}\right] = 0.999 \text{ M, and } \left[\text{Pb}^{2+}\right] = 0.500 \text{ M.}$

$E_{\text{cell}} = E°_{\text{cell}} - \dfrac{0.0257}{2} \ln \dfrac{[\text{Fe}^{3+}]^2[\text{Pb}^{2+}]}{[\text{Fe}^{2+}]^2} = 0.684 \ V - \dfrac{0.0257}{2} \ln \dfrac{[0.999]^2[0.500]}{[0.001]^2} = 0.515 \ V.$

Thus, this reaction will go to completion.

(b) Oxidation: $2 \text{ SO}_4{}^{2-}(\text{aq}) \longrightarrow \text{S}_2\text{O}_8{}^{2-}(\text{aq}) + 2 \text{ e}^-$ $\qquad\qquad -E° = -2.01 \text{ V}$

Reduction: $\text{PbO}_2(\text{s}) + 4 \text{ H}^+(\text{aq}) + 2 \text{ e}^- \longrightarrow \text{Pb}^{2+}(\text{aq}) + 2 \text{ H}_2\text{O}(\text{l})$ $\quad E° = +1.455 \text{ V}$

$2 \text{ SO}_4{}^{2-}(\text{aq}) + \text{PbO}_2(\text{s}) + 4 \text{ H}^+(\text{aq}) \longrightarrow \text{S}_2\text{O}_8{}^{2-}(\text{aq}) + \text{Pb}^{2+}(\text{aq}) + 2 \text{ H}_2\text{O}(\text{l})$

$E°_{\text{cell}} = -2.01 + 1.455 = -0.56 \text{ V}$ This reaction is not even spontaneous initially.

(c) Oxidation: $\{Mn^{2+}(1\times10^{-4}M)+4\,H_2O(l)\longrightarrow MnO_4^-(aq)+8\,H^+(aq)+5\,e^-\}\times2;\;-E°=-1.51\,V$

Reduction: $\{PbO_2(s)+4\,H^+(aq)+2\,e^-\longrightarrow Pb^{2+}(aq)+2\,H_2O(l)\}\times5 \qquad E°=+1.455\,V$

Net: $2\,Mn^{2+}(1\times10^{-4}M)+5\,PbO_2(s)+4\,H^+\longrightarrow 2\,MnO_4^-(aq)+5\,Pb^{2+}(aq)+2\,H_2O(l)$

$E°_{cell}=-1.51+1.455=-0.06\,V$. The standard cell potential indicates that this reaction is not spontaneous when all concentrations are 1 M. Since the concentration of a reactant $\left(Mn^{2+}\right)$ is lower than 1.00 M, this reaction is even less spontaneous than the standard cell potential indicates.

52. **(M)** A positive value of $E°_{cell}$ indicates that an electrochemical reaction should occur spontaneously under standard conditions.

(a) Oxidation: $Sn^{2+}(aq)\qquad\rightarrow Sn^{4+}(aq)+2\,e^- \qquad\qquad E°=-0.154\,V$

Reduction: $I_2(s)+2\,e^-\rightarrow 2\,I^-(aq) \qquad\qquad\qquad\qquad E°=+0.535\,V$

Overall: $Sn^{2+}(aq)+I_2(s)\rightarrow Sn^{4+}(aq)+2\,I^-(aq) \qquad E°_{cell}=+0.381\,V$

Yes, $Sn^{2+}(aq)$ will reduce $I_2(s)$ to $I^-(aq)$.

(b) Oxidation: $Sn^{2+}(aq)\qquad\qquad\rightarrow Sn^{4+}(aq)+2\,e^- \qquad\qquad E°=-0.154\,V$

Reduction: $\{Fe^{3+}(aq)+e^-\qquad\rightarrow Fe^{2+}(aq)\}\times2 \qquad\qquad E°=+0.771\,V$

Overall: $Sn^{2+}(aq)+2\,Fe^{3+}(s)\rightarrow Sn^{4+}(aq)+2\,Fe^{2+}(aq) \qquad E°_{cell}=+0.617\,V$

Yes, $Sn^{2+}(aq)$ will reduce $Fe^{3+}(aq)$ to $Fe^{2+}(aq)$.

(c) Oxidation: $Sn^{2+}(aq)\qquad\qquad\rightarrow Sn^{4+}(aq)+2\,e^- \qquad\qquad E°=-0.154\,V$

Reduction: $Zn^{2+}(aq)+2\,e^-\rightarrow Zn(s) \qquad\qquad\qquad\qquad E°=-0.763\,V$

Overall: $Sn^{2+}(aq)+Zn^{2+}(s)\rightarrow Sn^{4+}(aq)+Zn(s) \qquad E°_{cell}=-0.917\,V$

No, $Sn^{2+}(aq)$ will not reduce $Zn^{2+}(aq)$ to $Zn(s)$.

(d) Oxidation: $Sn^{2+}(aq)\qquad\qquad\rightarrow Sn^{4+}(aq)+2\,e^- \qquad\qquad E°=-0.154\,V$

Reduction: $Pb^{2+}(aq)+2\,e^-\rightarrow Pb(s) \qquad\qquad\qquad\qquad E°=-0.125\,V$

Overall: $Sn^{2+}(aq)+Pb^{2+}(s)\rightarrow Sn^{4+}(aq)+Pb(s) \qquad E°_{cell}=-0.279\,V$

No, $Sn^{2+}(aq)$ will not reduce $Pb^{2+}(aq)$ to $Pb(s)$.

53. **(E)** As we move down a group, the lower oxidation state is generally favored. Thus, we expect $SnCl_2$, with tin in the +2 oxidation state, to be the product.

54. **(M)** As we move down a group, the lower oxidation state is generally favored. The higher oxidation state is favored for elements higher in the group. Thus, we expect GeF_4, with germanium in the +4 oxidation state, to be the product.

INTEGRATIVE AND ADVANCED EXERCISES

55. **(M)** What most likely happened is that a deliquescent solid has absorbed water vapor from the air over time and formed a saturated solution. This saturated solution can be used in any circumstance where the solid would be used to prepared an aqueous solution. Of course, the concentration will have to be determined by some means other than weighing, such as a gravimetric analysis or using a standard to react with the substance in a titration. Alternatively, the saturated solution can be heated in a drying oven to drive off the water and the solid may be recovered. Often, unfortunately, a solid with an unknown percent of water results from this treatment.

56. **(D)**

(a) A solution of $CO_2(aq)$ has $[CO_3^{2-}] = K_{a2}[H_2CO_3] = 5.6 \times 10^{-11}$ M. Since the $K_{sp} = 2.8 \times 10^{-9}$ for $CaCO_3$, the $[Ca^{2+}]$ needed to form a precipitate from this solution can be computed.

$$[Ca^{2+}] = \frac{K_{sp}}{[Ca^{2+}]} = \frac{2.8 \times 10^{-9}}{5.6 \times 10^{-11}} = 50. \text{ M}$$

This is too high to reach by dissolving $CaCl_2$ in solution. The reason a solid forms is that the OH^- produced by the $Ca(OH)_2$ neutralized some of the HCO_3^- from the ionization of $CO_2(aq)$, thereby increasing the $[CO_3^{2-}]$ above a value of 5.6×10^{-11} M.

(b) The equation for redissolving can be obtained by combining several equations.

$$
\begin{array}{ll}
CaCO_3(s) \rightleftharpoons Ca^{2+}(aq) + CO_3^{2-}(aq) & K_{sp} = 2.8 \times 10^{-9} \\
CO_3^{2-}(aq) + H_3O^+(aq) \rightleftharpoons HCO_3^-(aq) + H_2O(l) & 1/K_{a2} = 1/(5.6 \times 10^{-11}) \\
CO_2(aq) + 2\,H_2O(l) \rightleftharpoons HCO_3^-(aq) + H_3O^+(aq) & K_{a1} = 4.2 \times 10^{-7}
\end{array}
$$

$$CaCO_3(s) + CO_2(aq) + H_2O(l) \rightleftharpoons Ca^{2+}(aq) + 2\,HCO_3^-(aq) \qquad K = \frac{K_{sp} \times K_{a1}}{K_{a2}}$$

$$K = \frac{(2.8 \times 10^{-9}) \times (4.2 \times 10^{-7})}{(5.6 \times 10^{-11})} = 2.1 \times 10^{-5} = \frac{[Ca^{2+}][HCO_3^-]^2}{[CO_2]}$$

If $CaCO_3(s)$ is precipitated from 0.005 M $Ca^{2+}(aq)$ and then redissolved, $[Ca^{2+}] = 0.005$ M and $[HCO_3^-] = 2 \times 0.005$ M $= 0.010$ M. We use these values in the above expression to compute the $[CO_2]$.

$$[CO_2] = \frac{[Ca^{2+}][HCO_3^-]^2}{(2.1 \times 10^{-5})} = 0.002 \text{ M}$$

We repeat the calculation for saturated $Ca(OH)_2$, in which $[OH^-] = 2 \times [OH^-]$, after first determining $[Ca^{2+}]$ in this solution.

$$K_{sp} = [Ca^{2+}][OH^-]^2 = 4 \times [Ca^{2+}] = 5.5 \times 10^{-6} \qquad [Ca^{2+}] = \sqrt[3]{\frac{5.5 \times 10^{-6}}{4}} = 0.011 \text{ M}$$

$$[CO_2] = \frac{[Ca^{2+}][HCO_3^-]^2}{(2.1 \times 10^{-5})} = \frac{(0.011)(0.022)^2}{2.1 \times 10^{-5}} = 0.25 \text{ M}$$

Thus, to redissolve the $CaCO_3$ requires that the $[CO_2] = 0.25$ M, assuming the solution is initially saturated with $Ca(OH)_2(aq)$.

(c) follow the solution for (b) above.

1082

57. (M) There are two principal reasons why the electrolysis of NaCl(l) is used to produce sodium commercially rather than the electrolysis of NaOH(l). First, NaCl is readily available whereas NaOH is produced from the electrolysis of NaCl(aq). Thus the raw material NaCl is much cheaper than is NaOH. Second, but less important, when sodium is produced from the electrolysis of NaCl(l), a by-product is $Cl_2(g)$, whereas $O_2(g)$ is a by-product of the production of NaOH(l). Since $O_2(g)$ can be produced more cheaply by the fractional distillation of liquid air, $Cl_2(g)$ can be sold for a higher price than $O_2(g)$. Thus, the two reasons for producing sodium from NaCl(l) rather than NaOH(l) are a much cheaper raw material and a more profitable by-product.

<u>58.</u> (M) The triiodide ion is linear (AX_2E_3). The Li^+ ion has a high charge density and significant polarizing power. The Li^+ ion will polarize the I_3^- to a significant extent and presumably assists the decomposition of I_3^- to I_2 and I^-.

$$: \ddot{I} \!-\! \ddot{I} \!-\! \ddot{I} :$$

<u>59.</u> (M) Use $\Delta_f G°$ values to calculate $\Delta_r G°$ for the reaction and then K. Because $K = P_{O_2}^{\frac{1}{2}}$, the value of K can then be used to calculate P_{O_2}.

$$Li_2O_2(s) \rightleftharpoons Li_2O(s) + \frac{1}{2}O_2(g)$$

$$\Delta_f G°[kJ/mol] \quad -419.02 \quad -466.40$$

$\Delta_r G° = -466.40 - (-419.02) = -47.38 \, kJ\,mol^{-1}$

$\Delta_r G° = -RT \ln K$

$-8.314 \, JK^{-1}mol^{-1} \times 1000 \, K \times \ln K = -47.38 \times 1000 \, Jmol^{-1}$

$\ln K = \dfrac{-47.38 \times 1000 \, Jmol^{-1}}{-8.314 \, JK^{-1}mol^{-1} \times 1000 \, K} = 5.70 \Rightarrow K = e^{5.70} = 298$

$K = P_{O_2}^{\frac{1}{2}} \Rightarrow P_{O_2} = K^2 = 298^2 = 8.8 \times 10^4$

60. (M) Use $\Delta_{hydr.}S° = \frac{1}{T}\left(\Delta_{hydr.}H° - \Delta_{hydr.}G°\right)$ to calculate $\Delta_{hydr.}S°$ values:

$\Delta_{hydr.}S°(Li^+) = \frac{1}{298}\left(-522 - (-481)\right) = -0.14 \, J/Kmol$

$\Delta_{hydr.}S°(Na^+) = \frac{1}{298}\left(-407 - (-375)\right) = -0.11 \, J/Kmol$

$\Delta_{hydr.}S°(K^+) = \frac{1}{298}\left(-324 - (-304)\right) = -0.07 \, J/Kmol$

$\Delta_{hydr.}S°(Rb^+) = \frac{1}{298}\left(-299 - (-281)\right) = -0.06 \, J/Kmol$

$\Delta_{hydr.}S°(Cs^+) = \frac{1}{298}\left(-274 - (-258)\right) = -0.05 \, J/Kmol$

All the $\Delta_{hydr.}S°$ values are negative because, in the process, a gas is being converted into a liquid solution. However, $\Delta_{hydr.}S°$ is most negative for Li^+. The $\Delta_{hydr.}S°$ values increase as we move down the group from Li^+ to Cs^+. As the charge density and polarizing power of the metal cation decreases, so too does the degree of order (or organization) in the hydration sphere. Thus, the entropy change should be most negative for Li^+ and least negative for Cs^+.

61. **(M)**

(a) Use the Kapustinskii equation in the form $U = \dfrac{120,200z_+z_-v}{r_+ + r_-}\left(1 - \dfrac{34.5}{r_+ + r_-}\right)$, with r_+ and r_- in picometers, to calculate U in kJ mol^{-1}. For LiO$_2$, $z_+ = +1$, $z_- = -1$, and $v = 2$.

(b) When we apply the Born–Fajans–Haber cycle to the reaction $Li(s) + O_2(g) \rightarrow LiO_2(s)$, we get $\Delta_f H° = \Delta H°_{Li(g)} + IE(1)_{Li} - 43 + U$. Values of $\Delta_f H°_{Li(g)}$ and $IE(1)_{Li}$ are given in Appendix D and in Table 21.2, respectively.

(c) For the reaction $2\ LiO_2(s) \rightarrow Li_2O(s) + \frac{3}{2}O_2(g)$, $\Delta_r H° = \Delta_f H°_{Li_2O(s)} - 2\ \Delta_f H°_{LiO_2(s)}$.

(d) The decomposition reaction is exothermic ($\Delta_r H° < 0$) and, with the assumption that entropy effects are not important, the decomposition of $LiO_2(s)$ to $Li_2O(s)$ and $O_2(g)$ is thermodynamically favorable.

<u>62.</u> **(D)**

(a) The mass of CaO(s) that would be produced can be determined with information from the balanced chemical equation for the oxidation of Ca(s).

$2\ Ca(s) + O_2(g) \longrightarrow 2\ CaO(s)$

$\text{mass CaO} = 0.250\ \text{g Ca} \times \dfrac{1\ \text{mol Ca}}{40.0784\ \text{g Ca}} \times \dfrac{2\ \text{mol CaO}}{2\ \text{mol Ca}} \times \dfrac{56.0774\ \text{g CaO}}{1\ \text{mol CaO}}$

$= 0.350\ \text{g CaO}$

(b) If the mass of product formed from the starting Ca differs from the 0.350 g CaO predicted, then the product could be a mixture of calcium nitride and calcium oxide. This scenario is not implausible since molecular nitrogen is readily available in the atmosphere. $3\ Ca(s) + N_2(g) \longrightarrow Ca_3N_2(s)$

$\text{mass Ca}_3\text{N}_2 = 0.250\ \text{g Ca} \times \dfrac{1\ \text{mol Ca}}{40.0784\ \text{g Ca}} \times \dfrac{1\ \text{mol Ca}_3\text{N}_2}{3\ \text{mol Ca}} \times \dfrac{148.2480\ \text{g Ca}_3\text{N}_2}{1\ \text{mol Ca}_3\text{N}_2}$

$= 0.308\ \text{g Ca}_3\text{N}_2$

We can use a technique similar to determining the percent abundance of an isotope to find the mass fraction of CaO in the product. Let $f =$ the mass fraction of CaO in the product. Then, $(1.000 - f)$ is the mass fraction of Ca$_3$N$_2$ in the product. Finally, product mass = mass CaO $\times f$ + mass Ca$_3$N$_2 \times (1.000 - f)$

$0.325\ \text{g product} = 0.350 \times f + 0.308 \times (1.000 - f)] = 0.308 + f(0.350 - 0.308)$

$f = \dfrac{0.325 - 0.308}{0.350 - 0.308} = 0.40$

Therefore, the product is 40% by mass CaO.

63. (M) Reaction (21.4) is $KCl(l) + Na(l) \xrightarrow{850\,°C} NaCl(l) + K(g)$ It is practical when the reactant element is a liquid and the product element is a gas at the same temperature.

(a) Since Li has a higher boiling point (1347 °C) than K (773.9 °C), a reaction similar to (21.4) is not a feasible way of producing Li metal from LiCl.

(b) On one hand, Cs has a lower boiling point (678.5 °C) than K (773.9 °C), and thus a reaction similar to (21.4) is a feasible method of producing Cs metal from CsCl. However, the ionization energy of Na is considerably larger than that of Cs, making it difficult to transfer an electron from Na to Cs^+.

64. (M)

(a) $2\,Al(s) + Fe_2O_3(s) \rightarrow 2\,Fe(s) + Al_2O_3(s)$ $\qquad \Delta_r H° = -852$ kJ mol^{-1}

(b) $4\,Al(s) + 3\,MnO_2(s) \rightarrow 2\,Al_2O_3(s) + 3\,Mn(s)$ $\qquad \Delta_r H° = -1792$ kJ mol^{-1}

(c) $2\,Al(s) + 3\,MgO(s) \rightarrow Al_2O_3(s) + 3\,Mg(s)$ $\qquad \Delta_r H° = +129$ kJ mol^{-1}

65. (M) $Li^+(aq) + e^- \rightarrow Li(s)$ $\Delta G° = -293.3$ kJ $= -zFE° = -1$ mol e^- (96,485 C/mol e^-)$E°$

$E° = -3.040$ V (this value is the same as the one that appears in Table 21.2.)

66. (M) The partial pressure of H_2 is 748 mmHg − 21 mmHg = 727 mmHg

$$\text{amount } H_2 = \frac{PV}{RT} = \frac{(727 \text{ mm Hg} \times (1 \text{ atm/760 mmHg})) \times 0.104 \text{ L}}{0.08206 \text{ L atm K}^{-1} \text{ mol}^{-1} \times 296 \text{ K}} = 4.10 \times 10^{-3} \text{ mol } H_2$$

The electrode reactions are the following.

Anode: $2\,Cl^-(aq) \longrightarrow Cl_2(g) + 2\,e^-$ Cathode: $2\,H_2O(l) + 2\,e^- \longrightarrow 2\,OH^-(aq) + H_2(g)$
Thus 2 mol $OH^-(aq)$ are produced per mole of $H_2(g)$; 8.20×10^{-3} mol $OH^-(aq)$ are produced.

$$[OH^-] = \frac{8.20 \times 10^{-3} \text{ mol OH}^-}{0.250 \text{ L soln}} = 3.28 \times 10^{-2} \text{ M} = 0.0328 \text{ M}$$

Then we compute the ion product and compare its value to the value of K_{sp} for $Mg(OH)_2$.
$Q_{sp} = [Mg^{2+}][OH^-]^2 = (0.220)(0.0328)^2 = 2.37 \times 10^{-4} > 1.8 \times 10^{-11} = K_{sp}$ for $Mg(OH)_2$
Thus, $Mg(OH)_2$ should precipitate.

67. (D)

(a) We determine the amount of Ca^{2+} associated with each anion in 10^6 g of the water.

$$\text{amount } Ca^{2+} (SO_4^{2-}) = 56.9 \text{ g SO}_4^{2-} \times \frac{1 \text{ mol SO}_4^{2-}}{96.06 \text{ g SO}_4^{2-}} \times \frac{1 \text{ mol Ca}^{2+}}{1 \text{ mol SO}_4^{2-}} = 0.592 \text{ mol}$$

$$\text{amount } Ca^{2+} (HCO_3^-) = 176 \text{ g HCO}_3^- \times \frac{1 \text{ mol HCO}_3^-}{61.02 \text{ g HCO}_3^-} \times \frac{1 \text{ mol Ca}^{2+}}{2 \text{ mol HCO}_3^-} = 1.44 \text{ mol}$$

Then we determine the total mass of Ca^{2+}, numerically equal to the ppm Ca^{2+}.

$$\text{mass Ca}^{2+} = (0.592 + 1.44) \text{ mol Ca}^{2+} \times \frac{40.08 \text{ g Ca}^{2+}}{1 \text{ mol Ca}^{2+}} = 81.4 \text{ g Ca}^{2+} \longrightarrow 81.4 \text{ ppm Ca}^{2+}$$

(b) The reactions for the removal of HCO_3^-(aq) begin with the formation of hydroxide ion resulting from dissolving CaO(s). Hydroxide ion reacts with bicarbonate ion to form carbonate ion, which then combines with calcium ion to form the $CaCO_3$(s) precipitate.

$$CaO(s) + H_2O(l) \longrightarrow Ca^{2+}(aq) + 2 OH^-(aq)$$

$$OH^-(aq) + HCO_3^-(aq) \longrightarrow H_2O(l) + CO_3^{2-}(aq)$$

$$Ca^{2+}(aq) + CO_3^{2-}(aq) \longrightarrow CaCO_3(s)$$

For each 1.000×10^6 g of water, we need to remove 176 g HCO_3^-(aq) with the added CaO(s).

$$\text{mass CaO} = 602 \times 10^3 \text{ g water} \times \frac{176 \text{ g HCO}_3^-}{1.000 \times 10^6 \text{ g water}} \times \frac{1 \text{ mol HCO}_3^-}{61.02 \text{ g HCO}_3^-} \times \frac{1 \text{ mol OH}^-}{1 \text{ mol HCO}_3^-}$$

$$\times \frac{1 \text{ mol CaO}}{2 \text{ mol OH}^-} \times \frac{56.08 \text{ g CaO}}{1 \text{ mol CaO}} = 48.7 \text{ g CaO}$$

(c) Here we determine the total amount of Ca^{2+} in 602 kg of water, <u>and</u> that added as CaO.

$$Ca^{2+} = \left(\frac{602 \text{ kg}}{1 \times 10^6 \text{ kg}}\right)(0.592 + 1.44) \text{ mol Ca}^{2+} + \left(48.7 \text{ g CaO} \times \frac{1 \text{ mol CaO}}{56.08 \text{ g CaO}} \times \frac{1 \text{ mol Ca}^{2+}}{1 \text{ mol CaO}}\right) = 2.09 \text{ mol Ca}^{2+}$$

The amount of Ca^{2+} that has precipitated equals the amount of HCO_3^- in solution, since each mole of HCO_3^- is transformed into 1 mole of CO_3^{2-}, which reacts with and then precipitates one mole of Ca^{2+}. Thus the amount of Ca^{2+} that has precipitated is $(0.602)(1.44) = 0.867$ mol Ca^{2+} as $CaCO_3$(s). Then we can determine the concentration of Ca^{2+} remaining in solution.

$$[Ca^{2+}] = \frac{2.09 \text{ mol Ca}^{2+} \text{ total} - 0.867 \text{ mol Ca}^{2+}}{10^6 \text{ g water}} \times \frac{10^3 \text{ g water}}{1 \text{ L water}} = 2.03 \times 10^{-3} \text{ M}$$

To consider the Ca^{2+} "removed", its concentration should be decreased to 0.1% (0.001) of its initial value, or 2.03×10^{-6} M. We use the K_{sp} expression for $CaCO_3$ to determine the needed $[CO_3^{2-}]$

$$K_{sp} = [Ca^{2+}][CO_3^{2-}] = 2.8 \times 10^{-9} = 1.46 \times 10^{-6} \text{ M}$$

$$[CO_3^{2-}] = \frac{2.8 \times 10^{-9}}{2.03 \times 10^{-6}} = 0.0014 \text{ M}$$

This carbonate ion concentration can readily be achieved by adding solid Na_2CO_3.

(d) The amount of CO_3^{2-} needed is that which ends up in the precipitate plus that needed to attain the 0.0014 M concentration in the 602 kg = 602 L of water.

$$n_{CO_3^{-2}} = 602 \text{ L} \times \left(\left(\frac{0.00203 \text{ mol Ca}^{2+}}{1 \text{ L water}} \times \frac{1 \text{ mol CO}_3^{2-}}{1 \text{ mol Ca}^{2+}} \right) + \frac{0.0014 \text{ mol CO}_3^{2-}}{1 \text{ L water}} \right) = 2.1 \text{ mol CO}_3^{2-}$$

This CO_3^{2-} comes from the added $Na_2CO_3(s)$.

$$\text{mass Na}_2CO_3 = 2.0 \text{ mol CO}_3^{2-} \times \frac{1 \text{ mol Na}_2CO_3}{1 \text{ mol CO}_{3^{2-}}} \times \frac{105.99 \text{ g Na}_2CO_3}{1 \text{ mol Na}_2CO_3} = 2.2 \times 10^2 \text{ g Na}_2CO_3$$

68. (M)

(a) In the cell reaction, three moles of electrons are required to reduce each mole of Al^{3+}.

$$\text{mass Al} = 8.00 \text{ h} \times \frac{3600 \text{ s}}{1 \text{ h}} \times \frac{1.00 \times 10^5 \text{ C}}{1 \text{ s}} \times \frac{1 \text{ mol e}^-}{96,485 \text{ C}} \times \frac{1 \text{ mol Al}}{3 \text{ mol e}^-} \times \frac{26.98 \text{ g Al}}{1 \text{ mol Al}} = 2.68 \times 10^5 \text{ g Al}$$

The 38% efficiency is not considered in this calculation. All of the electrons produced must pass through the electrolytic cell; they simply require a higher than optimum voltage to do so, leading to resistance heating (which consumes some of the electrical energy).

(b) total energy = $4.5 \text{ V} \times 8.00 \text{ h} \times \frac{3600 \text{ s}}{1 \text{ h}} \times \frac{1.00 \times 10^5 \text{ C}}{1 \text{ s}} \times \frac{1 \text{ J}}{1 \text{ V} \cdot \text{C}} \times \frac{1 \text{ kJ}}{1000 \text{ J}} = 1.3 \times 10^7 \text{ kJ}$

$$\text{mass coal} = 1.3 \times 10^7 \text{ kJ electricity} \times \frac{1 \text{ kJ heat}}{0.35 \text{ kJ electricity}} \times \frac{1 \text{ g C}}{32.8 \text{ kJ}} \times \frac{1 \text{ g coal}}{0.85 \text{ g C}} \times \frac{1 \text{ metric ton}}{10^6 \text{g}}$$

mass coal = 1.3 metric tons of coal

69. (M) We begin by rewriting Equation 21.25 for the electrolysis of $Al_2O_3(s)$ with $z = 12$ e$^-$.

$3 \text{ C(s)} + 2 \text{ Al}_2O_3(s) \rightarrow 4 \text{ Al(s)} + 3 \text{ CO}_2(g)$

$\Delta_r G° = 4(0 \text{ kJ mol}^{-1}) + 3(-394 \text{ kJ mol}^{-1}) - [3(0 \text{ kJ mol}^{-1}) + 2(-1520 \text{ kJ mol}^{-1})] = +1858 \text{ kJ mol}^{-1}$

$\Delta_r G° = 1.858 \times 10^6 \text{ J} = -zFE° = -12(96,485 \text{ C/mol})E°$

$E° = -1.605$ V Note: this is just an estimate because $\Delta G°$ values are at 298 K, whereas the reaction occurs at a temperature that is much higher than 298 K.

If the oxidation of C(s) to $CO_2(g)$ did not occur, then the cell reaction would just be the reverse of the formation reaction of Al_2O_3 with n = 6 e$^-$.

$$E° = \Delta E° = \frac{-\Delta G°}{zF} = \frac{1.520 \times 10^6 \text{ J}}{6 \text{ mol e}^- \times 96485 \text{ C/mol e}^-} = -2.626 \text{ V}$$

70. (M) It would not be unreasonable to predict that Raoult's law holds under these circumstances. This is predicated on the assumption, of course, that $Pb(NO_3)_2$ is completely ionized in aqueous solution.

$$P_{water} = x_{water} P°_{water} \qquad x_{water} = \frac{P_{water}}{P°_{water}} = 97\% = 0.97$$

Thus, there are 97 mol H_2O in every 100 mol solution. The remaining 3 moles are 1 mol Pb^{2+} and 2 mol NO_3^-. Thus there is 1 mol $Pb(NO_3)_2$ for every 97 mol H_2O. Compute the mass of $Pb(NO_3)_2$ in 100 g H_2O.

$$\text{mass}_{Pb(NO_3)_2} = 100.0 \text{ g } H_2O \times \frac{1 \text{ mol } H_2O}{18.02 \text{ g } H_2O} \times \frac{1 \text{ mol } Pb(NO_3)_2}{97 \text{ mol } H_2O} \times \frac{331.21 \text{ g } Pb(NO_3)_2}{1 \text{ mol } Pb(NO_3)_2} = 19 \text{ g } Pb(NO_3)_2$$

If we did not assume complete ionization of $Pb(NO_3)_2$, we would obtain 3 moles of un-ionized $Pb(NO_3)_2$ in solution for every 97 moles of H_2O. Then there would be 57 g $Pb(NO_3)_2$ dissolved in 100 g H_2O. A handbook gives the solubility as 56 g $Pb(NO_3)_2$/100 g H_2O, indicating only partial dissociation or, more probably, extensive re-association into ion pairs, triplets, quadruplets, etc.

71. **(M)** Considerable energy is required to produce the Pb^{4+} cation—four ionization steps, one for the removal of each electron. It therefore needs quite a large lattice energy to compensate for its energy of production. Both Br^- and I^- are large anions, and therefore the Pb^{4+}—Br^- and Pb^{4+}—I^- interionic distances are long. But lattice energy depends on the charge of the cation (which is quite large) multiplied by the charge of the anion (which is reasonably small) divided by the square of the interionic distance (long, as we have said). Thus, we predict a small lattice energy that is insufficient to stabilize the Pb^{4+} cation. We would predict, however, that PbF_4 and $PbCl_4$ (both with small anions) and PbO_2 and PbS_2 (both with small, highly charged anions) would be stable compounds. In addition, notice that $E^\circ \{Pb^{4+}|Pb^{2+}\}$ = 1.5 V (from Table 21-6) is sufficient to oxidize Br^- to Br_2 and I^- to I_2, since $E^\circ \{Br_2|Br^-\}$ = +1.065 V and $E^\circ \{I_2|I^-\}$ = +0.535 V. Thus, even if PbI_4 or $PbBr_4$ could be prepared they would be thermodynamically unstable.

72. **(M)** $Na_2B_4O_7 \cdot 10 H_2O(s) + 6 CaF_2(s) + 8 H_2SO_4(aq) \rightarrow 4 BF_3(aq) + 6 CaSO_4(aq) + 17 H_2O(l) + 2 NaHSO_4(aq)$

73. **(D)** **(a)** 1.00 M NH_4Cl is a somewhat acidic solution due to hydrolysis of $NH_4^+(aq)$; $MgCO_3$ should be most soluble in this solution. The remaining two solutions are buffer solutions, and the 0.100 M NH_3–1.00 M NH_4Cl buffer is more acidic of the two. In this solution, $MgCO_3$ has intermediate solubility. $MgCO_3$ is least soluble in the most alkaline solution, namely, 1.00 M NH_3–1.00 M NH_4Cl.

$$MgCO_3(s) \rightleftharpoons Mg^{2+}(aq) + CO_3^{2-}(aq) \qquad K_{sp} = 3.5 \times 10^{-8}$$
$$NH_4^+(aq) + OH^-(aq) \rightleftharpoons NH_3(aq) + H_2O(l) \qquad 1/K_b = 1/1.8 \times 10^{-5}$$
$$CO_3^{2-}(aq) + H_3O^+(aq) \rightleftharpoons HCO_3^-(aq) + H_2O(l) \qquad 1/K_2 = 1/4.7 \times 10^{-11}$$
$$\underline{2 H_2O(l) \rightleftharpoons H_3O^+(aq) + OH^-(aq) \qquad K_w = 1.0 \times 10^{-14}}$$
$$MgCO_3(s) + NH_4^+(aq) \rightleftharpoons Mg^{2+} + HCO_3^-(aq) + NH_3(aq)$$

$$K = \frac{K_{sp} \times K_w}{K_b \times K_2} = \frac{3.5 \times 10^{-8} \times 1.0 \times 10^{-14}}{1.8 \times 10^{-5} \times 4.7 \times 10^{-11}} = 4.1 \times 10^{-7}$$

In 1.00 M NH₄Cl

Reaction: $MgCO_3(s)$ + $NH_4^+(aq)$ ⇌ $Mg^{2+}(aq)$ + $HCO_3^-(aq)$ + $NH_3(aq)$

Initial: —   1.00 M   0 M   0 M   0 M
Changes: — $-x$ M $+x$ M $+x$ M $+x$ M
Equil: — $(1.00-x)$M x M x M x M

$$K = \frac{[Mg^{2+}][HCO_3^-][NH_3]}{[NH_4^+]} = \frac{x \cdot x \cdot x}{1.00-x} \approx \frac{x^3}{1.00}$$

$x = \sqrt[3]{4.1 \times 10^{-7}} = 7.4 \times 10^{-3}$ M = molar solubility of $MgCO_3$ in 1.00 M NH_4Cl

($x \ll 1.00$ M, thus the approximation was valid)

(b) In 1.00 M NH₃–1.00 M NH₄Cl

Reaction: $MgCO_3(s)$ + $NH_4^+(aq)$ ⇌ $Mg^{2+}(aq)$ + $HCO_3^-(aq)$ + $NH_3(aq)$

Initial: —   1.00 M   0 M   0 M   1.00 M
Changes: — $-x$ M $+x$ M $+x$ M $+x$ M
Equil: — $(1.00-x)$M x M $+x$M $(1.00+x)$M

$$K = \frac{[Mg^{2+}][HCO_3^-][NH_3]}{[NH_4^+]} = \frac{x \cdot x \cdot (1.00+x)}{1.00-x} \approx \frac{x^2 \cdot 1.00}{1.00}$$

$x = \sqrt{4.1 \times 10^{-7}} = 6.4 \times 10^{-4}$ M = molar solubility of $MgCO_3$ in 1.00 M NH_3 –1.00 M NH_4Cl

($x \ll 1.00$ M, thus the approximation was valid)

(c) In 0.100 M NH₃–1.00 M NH₄Cl

Reaction: $MgCO_3(s)$ + $NH_4^+(aq)$ ⇌ $Mg^{2+}(aq)$ + $HCO_3^-(aq)$ + $NH_3(aq)$

Initial: —   1.00 M   0 M   0 M   0.100 M
Changes: — $-x$ M $+x$ M $+x$ M $+x$ M
Equil: — $(1.00-x)$M xM $+x$M $(0.100+x)$M

$$K = \frac{[Mg^{2+}][HCO_3^-][NH_3]}{[NH_4^+]} = \frac{x \cdot x \cdot (0.100+x)}{1.00-x} \approx \frac{x^2 \times 0.100}{1.00}$$

$x = \sqrt{\dfrac{4.1 \times 10^{-7}}{0.100}} = 2.0 \times 10^{-3}$ M = solubility of $MgCO_3$ in 0.100 M NH_3 –1.00 M NH_4Cl

(x is 2 % of 0.100 M, so the approximation was valid)

74. **(M)** If the value of the equilibrium constant for the reaction is quite large, then the conversion will be almost complete. We write the net ionic equation and then add the two solubility reactions to obtain the net ionic equation for the conversion. The equilibrium constants are multiplied together to give the equilibrium constant for the conversion.

Net ionic equation: $Ca(OH)_2(s) + CO_3^{2-}(aq) \rightleftharpoons CaCO_3(s) + 2\ OH^-(aq)$

$Ca(OH)_2(s) \rightleftharpoons Ca^{2+}(aq) + 2\ OH^-(aq)$ $\qquad\qquad K_{sp} = 5.5 \times 10^{-6}$

$Ca^{2+}(aq) + CO_3^{2-}(aq) \rightleftharpoons CaCO_3(s)$ $\qquad\qquad 1/K_{sp} = 1/2.8 \times 10^{-9}$

$Ca(OH)_2(s) + CO_3^{2-}(aq) \rightleftharpoons CaCO_3(s) + 2\ OH^-(aq)$ $\quad K_{overall} = \dfrac{5.5 \times 10^{-6}}{2.8 \times 10^{-9}} = 2.0 \times 10^3$

Because $K_{overall} > 1000$, the conversion is substantially complete.

75. **(M)** The density of each metal depends on two factors: its atomic size and the masses of the individual atoms. Density is thus, proportional to the atomic mass divided by the cube of the atomic radius. We calculate this ratio for each of the elements.

Li: $\dfrac{\text{atomic mass}}{(\text{atomic radius})^3}$ $\qquad$ Na: $\dfrac{\text{atomic mass}}{(\text{atomic radius})^3}$ $\qquad$ K: $\dfrac{\text{atomic mass}}{(\text{atomic radius})^3}$

$= \dfrac{6.941\ (\text{g/mol})}{[1.52\ (\text{Å})]^3} = 1.98$ $\qquad = \dfrac{22.99\ (\text{g/mol})}{[1.86\ (\text{Å})]^3} = 3.57$ $\qquad = \dfrac{39.10\ (\text{g/mol})}{[2.27\ (\text{Å})]^3} = 3.34$

We see that the calculated ratios follow the same pattern as the densities: Na > K > Li, thus explaining why Na has a higher density than both Li and K.

76. **(M)** We would expect MgO(s) to have a larger value of lattice energy than MgS(s) because of the smaller interionic distance in MgO(s).

Lattice energy of MgO:

Enthalpy of formation:	$Mg(s) + O_2(g) \longrightarrow MgO(s)$	$\Delta_f H° = -6.02 \times 10^2\ kJ\ mol^{-1}$
Sublimation of Mg(s):	$Mg(s) \longrightarrow Mg(g)$	$\Delta_{sub} H° = +146\ kJ\ mol^{-1}$
Ionization of Mg(g)	$Mg(g) \longrightarrow Mg^+(g) + e^-$	$\Delta I_1 = +737.7\ kJ\ mol^{-1}$
Ionization of Mg(g):	$Mg^+(g) \longrightarrow Mg^{2+}(g) + e^-$	$\Delta I_2 = +1451\ kJ\ mol^{-1}$
$\frac{1}{2}$ Dissociation $O_2(g)$:	$\frac{1}{2} O_2(g) \longrightarrow O(g)$	$DE = \frac{1}{2} \times 497.4 = 248.7\ kJ\ mol^{-1}$
O(g) electron affinity:	$O(g) + e^- \longrightarrow O^-(g)$	$EA_1 = -141\ kJ\ mol^{-1}$
O(g) electron affinity:	$O^-(g) + e^- \longrightarrow O^{2-}(g)$	$EA_2 = +744\ kJ\ mol^{-1}$
Lattice energy:	$Mg^{2+}(g) + O^{2-}(g) \rightarrow MgO(s)$	L.E $= -3789\ kJ\ mol^{-1}$ (see below)

L.E $= -602\ kJ\ mol^{-1} - 146\ kJ\ mol^{-1} - 737.7\ kJ\ mol^{-1} - 1451\ kJ\ mol^{-1} - 248.7\ kJ\ mol^{-1} + 141\ kJ\ mol^{-1} - 744\ kJ\ mol^{-1} = -3789\ kJ\ mol^{-1}$

Lattice energy of MgS:

Enthalpy of formation:	$Mg(s) + S(g) \longrightarrow MgS(s)$	$\Delta_f H° = -3.46 \times 10^2$ kJ mol^{-1}
Sublimation of Mg(s):	$Mg(s) \longrightarrow Mg(g)$	$\Delta_{sub} H = +146$ kJ mol^{-1}
Ionization of Mg(g)	$Mg(g) \longrightarrow Mg^+(g) + e^-$	$\Delta I_1 = +737.7$ kJ mol^{-1}
Ionization of Mg(g):	$Mg^+(g) \longrightarrow Mg^{2+}(g) + e^-$	$\Delta I_2 = +1451$ kJ mol^{-1}
$\frac{1}{2}$ Dissociation of S_2(g):	$\frac{1}{2} S_{rhombic}(g) \longrightarrow S(g)$	$DE = \frac{1}{2} \times 557.6 = 278.8$ kJ mol^{-1}
S(g) electron affinity:	$S(g) + e^- \longrightarrow S^-(g)$	$EA_1 = -200.4$ kJ mol^{-1}
S(g) electron affinity:	$S^-(g) + e^- \longrightarrow S^{2-}(g)$	$EA_2 = +456$ kJ mol^{-1}
Lattice energy:	$Mg^{2+}(g) + S^{2-}(g) \rightarrow MgS(s)$	L.E = -3215 kJ mol^{-1}

L.E = -346 kJ mol^{-1} − 146 kJ mol^{-1} − 737.7 kJ mol^{-1} − 1451 kJ mol^{-1} − 278.8 kJ mol^{-1} + 200.4 kJ mol^{-1} − 456 kJ mol^{-1} = −3215 kJ mol^{-1}

77. (M) In one unit cell, there are $\frac{1}{8} \times 8 + \frac{1}{2} \times 6 = 4$ fulleride ions and $\frac{1}{4} \times 12 + 1 + 8 = 12$ alkali metal ions. The ratio of cations to anions is 12:4 = 3:1, and so the fulleride ion is C_{60}^{3-} and the empirical formula is M_3C_{60}.

FEATURE PROBLEMS

78. (D) Li(s) → Li(g) 159.4 kJ mol^{-1}; (Using $\Delta_r H° = \Sigma\Delta_f H°_{products} - \Sigma\Delta_f H°_{reactants}$ in Appendix D)
Li(g) → Li$^+$(g) + e$^-$ 520.2 kJ mol^{-1}; (Data given in Table 21.2, Chapter 21)
$\underline{Li^+(g) \rightarrow Li^+(aq) \quad -506 \text{ kJ mol}^{-1}; \quad}$ (Provided in the question)
Li(s) → Li$^+$(aq) + e$^-$ 174 kJ mol^{-1}

1/2 H$_2$(g) → H(g) 218.0 kJ mol^{-1} (Using $\Delta_r H° = \Sigma\Delta_f H°_{products} - \Sigma\Delta_f H°_{reactants}$ in Appendix D)
H(g) → H$^+$(g) + e$^-$ 1312 kJ mol^{-1} (Use $R_H(N_A)$Bohr theory = 2.179×10^{-18} J(6.022×10^{23}))
$\underline{H^+(g) \rightarrow H^+(aq) \quad -1079 \text{ kJ mol}^{-1}}$ (Provided in the question)
1/2 H$_2$(g) → H$^+$(aq) + e$^-$ 451 kJ mol^{-1}

(a) Li(s) + H$^+$(aq) → Li$^+$(aq) + 1/2 H$_2$(g)
$\Delta_r H° = 174$ kJ mol^{-1} − 451 kJ mol^{-1} = −277 kJ mol^{-1} ≈ $\Delta_r G°$

$$E_{ox}° = \frac{\Delta_r G°}{-zF} = \frac{-277 \times 10^3 \text{ J mol}^{-1}}{-1\left(96{,}485 \dfrac{C}{mol}\right)} = 2.87 \frac{J}{C} = 2.87 \text{ V}$$

In this reaction, Li(s) is being oxidized to $Li^+(aq)$. If we wish to compare this to the reduction potential for $Li^+(aq)$ being reduced to Li(s), we would have to reverse the reaction, which would result in the same answer only as a negative value. Alternatively, we can change the sign of the oxidation potential ($Li \rightarrow Li^+$) to -2.87 V for the reduction potential for $Li^+ \rightarrow Li$.

(it apears as -3.040 V in Appendix D; here, we see much better agreement.)

(b) $\Delta_r S = \Sigma S^\circ_{products} - \Sigma S^\circ_{reactants}$

$$= [1\left(13.4\frac{J}{K\,mol}\right) + 0.5\left(130.7\frac{J}{K\,mol}\right)] -$$

$$[1\left(29.12\frac{J}{K\,mol}\right) + 1\left(0\frac{J}{K\,mol}\right)] = 49.6\frac{J}{K\,mol}$$

$$\Delta_r G^\circ = \Delta_r H^\circ - T\Delta_r S^\circ = -277 \text{ kJ mol}^{-1} - 298.15 \text{ K}\left(49.6\frac{J}{K\,mol}\right) \times \frac{1\,kJ}{1000\,J} =$$

$$-292 \times 10^3 \text{ J mol}^{-1}$$

$$E_{ox}^\circ = \frac{\Delta_r G^\circ}{-zF} = \frac{-292 \times 10^3 \text{ J mol}^{-1}}{-1\left(96,485\frac{C}{mol}\right)} = 3.03\frac{J}{C} = 3.03 \text{ V}$$

As mentioned in part (a) of this question, we have calculated the oxidation potential for the half reaction $Li(s) \rightarrow Li^+(aq) + e^-$. The reduction potential is the reverse half-reaction and has a potential of -3.03 V. This is in excellent agreement with -3.040 V given in Appendix D.

79. (D) (a)

$$\frac{0.438 \text{ mol NaCl}}{L} \times \frac{58.4428 \text{ g NaCl}}{1 \text{ mol NaCl}} = 25.6 \text{ g NaCl}$$

$$\frac{0.0512 \text{ mol MgCl}_2}{L} \times \frac{95.211 \text{ g MgCl}_2}{1 \text{ mol MgCl}_2} = 4.87 \text{ g MgCl}_2$$

30.5 g of salt per liter of seawater

$$18 \text{ tbs NaHCO}_3 \times \frac{10 \text{ g NaHCO}_3}{1 \text{ tbs NaHCO}_3} = 180 \text{ g NaHCO}_3$$

$$10 \text{ tbs NaCl} \times \frac{10 \text{ g NaCl}}{1 \text{ tbs NaCl}} = 100 \text{ g NaCl}$$

$$8 \text{ tsp MgSO}_4 \cdot 7 \text{ H}_2\text{O} \times \frac{1 \text{ tbs}}{3 \text{ tsp}} \times \frac{10 \text{ g MgSO}_4 \cdot 7 \text{ H}_2\text{O}}{1 \text{ tbs MgSO}_4 \cdot 7 \text{ H}_2\text{O}} = 27 \text{ g MgSO}_4 \cdot 7 \text{ H}_2\text{O}$$

307 g of salt per gal. of lake water (3.7854 L/gal)

(b) The pH of the lake will be determined by the amphiprotic bicarbonate ion, (HCO_3^-), which hydrolyzes in water ($K_{a_1} = 4.4 \times 10^{-7}$ or $pK_{a_1} = 6.36$ and $K_{a_2} = 4.7 \times 10^{-11}$ or $pK_{a_2} = 10.33$). We saw earlier (Chapter 18, Exercise 100) that the pH of a solution of alanine, a diprotic species is independent of concentration (as long as it is relatively concentrated). The $pH = \dfrac{(pK_{a_1} + pK_{a_2})}{2} = \dfrac{(6.36 + 10.33)}{2} = 8.35$

This is not as basic as the actual pH of the lake. Addition of borax (sodium salt of boric acid) would aid in increasing the pH of the solution (since borax contains an anion that is the conjugate base of a weak acid). The lake may be more basic due to the presence of other basic anions, namely carbonate ion (CO_3^{2-}).

(c) Tufa are mostly made of calcium carbonate ($CaCO_3(s)$). Since they form near underwater springs, one must assume that the springs have a high concentration of calcium ion ($Ca^{2+}(aq)$). We then couple this with the fact that the lake has a high salinity (high carbonate and bicarbonate ion content). We can thus conclude that two major reactions are most likely responsible for the formation of a tufa (see below):

$$Ca^{2+}(aq) + CO_3^{2-}(aq) \rightarrow CaCO_3(s)$$
$$Ca^{2+}(aq) + 2\ HCO_3^-(aq) \rightarrow Ca(HCO_3)_2(aq) \rightarrow CaCO_3(s) + H_2O(l) + CO_2(g)$$

SELF-ASSESSMENT EXERCISES

80. (E)
(a) A dimer is a chemical or biological entity consisting of two structurally similar subunits called monomers, which are joined by bonds, which can be strong or weak.
(b) An adduct is a product of a direct addition of two or more distinct molecules, resulting in a single reaction product containing all atoms of all components.
(c) Calcination is a thermal treatment process applied to ores and other solid materials in order to bring about a thermal decomposition, phase transition, or removal of a volatile fraction.
(d) An amphoteric oxide is an oxide that can act both as an acid and as a base. An example is aluminum oxide, Al_2O_3.
(e) A three-center two-electron bond is an electron deficient chemical bond where three atoms share two electrons. The combination of three atomic orbitals form three molecular orbitals: one bonding, one non-bonding, and one anti-bonding. The two electrons go into the bonding orbital, resulting in a net bonding effect and constituting a chemical bond among all three atoms.

81. **(E)**

    (a) A diagonal relationship exists between certain pairs of diagonally adjacent elements in the second and third periods of the periodic table. These pairs (Li and Mg, Be and Al, B and Si, etc.) exhibit similar properties. For example boron and silicon are both semiconductors.

    (b) One way to prepare deionized water is by passing it through an ion exchange column. The latter is composed of insoluble chemicals which remove both positive and negative ions from water.

    (c) Thermite is a pyrotechnic composition of a metal powder and a metal oxide, which produces an aluminothermic reaction known as a thermite reaction.

    (d) The inert pair effect is the tendency of the outermost s electrons to remain un-ionized or unshared in post-transition compounds.

82. **(E)**

    (a) A peroxide is a compound containing an oxygen-oxygen single bond. A superoxide contains the O_2^- anion.

    (b) Calcium oxide (CaO) is commonly known as burnt lime, lime or quicklime. Calcium hydroxide ($Ca(OH)_2$) on the other hand is commonly known as slaked lime, hydrated lime, or slack lime.

    (c) Soap is an anionic surfactant used in conjunction with water for washing and cleaning. Soap consists of sodium or potassium salts of fatty acids and is obtained by reacting common oils or fats with a strong alkaline solution in a process known as saponification. Detergents, on the other hand, are prepared synthetically.

    (d) A silicate is a compound containing an ion in which one or more central silicon atoms are surrounded by electronegative ligands. Silicones are compounds containing silicon-oxygen and silicon-carbon bonds that have the capability to act as bonding intermediates between glass and organic compounds, and to form polymers with useful properties such as impermeability to water, flexibility and resistance to chemical attack.

    (e) The sol-gel process is a chemical solution deposition technique widely used in the fields of materials science and ceramic engineering. Typical precursors are metal alkoxides and metal chlorides, which undergo various forms of hydrolysis and polycondensation reactions.

83. **(E) (c)** MgO The reason for MgO having the highest melting point is that MgO is ionic with a +2 on magnesium and a −2 on the oxygen.

84. **(E) (f)** PbO$_2$ Lead(IV) easily undergoes reduction to lead(II). Much more so than the reduction of the other elements, e.g., Li^+, Mg^{2+}, Al^{3+}, C^{4+}, and Sn^{4+}.

85. **(M) (a)** BCl$_3$NH$_3$(g) (an adduct); **(b)** KO$_2$(s); **(c)** Li$_2$O(s); **(d)** Ba(OH)$_2$(aq) and H$_2$O$_2$(aq); H$_2$O$_2$(aq) slowly disproportionates into H$_2$O(l) and O$_2$(g).

86. **(M)** The thermite reaction is evidence that aluminum will readily extract oxygen from Fe$_2$O$_3$. Aluminum can be used for making products that last and for structural purposes, because aluminum develops a coating of Al$_2$O$_3$ that protects the metal beneath it.

87. **(M) (b)** $Ca(s)$ and $CaH_2(s)$

88. **(M)**

(a) $Li_2CO_3(s) \xrightarrow{\Delta} Li_2O(s) + CO_2(g)$

(b) $CaCO_3(s) + 2\ HCl(aq) \longrightarrow CaCl_2(aq) + H_2O(l) + CO_2(g)$

(c) $2\ Al(s) + 2\ NaOH(aq) + 6 H_2O(l) \longrightarrow 2\ Na[Al(OH)_4](aq) + 2\ H_2(g)$

(d) $BaO(s) + H_2O(l) \longrightarrow Ba(OH)_2(aq,\ limited\ solubility)$

(e) $2\ Na_2O_2(s) + 2\ CO_2(g) \longrightarrow 2\ Na_2CO_3(s) + O_2(g)$

89. **(M)**

(a) $MgCO_3(s) + 2\ HCl(aq) \longrightarrow MgCl_2(aq) + H_2O(l) + CO_2(g)$

(b) $2\ Na(s) + 2\ H_2O(l) \longrightarrow 2\ NaOH(aq) + H_2(g)$ followed by the reaction in Exercise 82(c)

(c) $2\ NaCl(s) + H_2SO_4(concd.,\ aq) \xrightarrow{\Delta} Na_2SO_4(s) + 2\ HCl(g)$

90. **(M)**

(a) $K_2CO_3(aq) + Ba(OH)_2(aq) \longrightarrow BaCO_3(s) + 2\ KOH(aq)$

(b) $Mg(HCO_3)_2(aq) \xrightarrow{\Delta} MgCO_3(s) + H_2O(l) + CO_2(g)$

(c) $SnO(s) + C(s) \xrightarrow{\Delta} Sn(l) + CO(g)$

(d) $CaF_2(s) + H_2SO_4(concd.\ aq) \xrightarrow{\Delta} CaSO_4(s) + 2\ HF(g)$

(e) $NaHCO_3(s) + HCl(aq) \longrightarrow NaCl(aq) + H_2O(l) + CO_2(g)$

(f) $PbO_2(s) + 4\ HBr(aq) \longrightarrow PbBr_2(s) + Br_2(l) + 2\ H_2O(l)$

(g) $SiF_4(g) + 4\ Na(l) \longrightarrow Si(s) + 4\ NaF(s)$

91. **(M)** $CaSO_4 \cdot 2\ H_2O(s) + (NH_4)_2CO_3(aq) \longrightarrow CaCO_3(s) + (NH_4)_2SO_4(aq) + 2\ H_2O(l)$.
The reaction proceeds to the right because K_{sp} for $CaCO_3 < K_{sp}$ for $CaSO_4$

92. **(M)**

(a) $2\ B(OH)_3(s) \longrightarrow B_2O_3(s) + 3\ H_2O(g)$

(b) no reaction

(c) $CaSO_4 \cdot 2\ H_2O(s)[gypsum] \xrightarrow{\Delta} CaSO_4 \times \frac{1}{2} H_2O(s)[plaster\ of\ Paris] + \frac{3}{2} H_2O(g)$

93. **(M)**

(a) $Pb(NO_3)_2(aq) + 2\,NaHCO_3(aq) \longrightarrow PbCO_3(s) + 2\,NaNO_3(aq) + H_2O(l) + CO_2(g)$

In $NaHCO_3(aq)$ the concentration of $CO_3{}^{2-}(aq)$ is high enough that K_{sp} of $PbCO_3$ is exceeded.

(b) $Li_2O(s) + (NH_4)_2CO_3(aq) \longrightarrow Li_2CO_3(s) + 2\,NH_3(g) + H_2O(l)$. $Li_2O(s)$ is the anhydride of the strong base LiOH, which reacts with acidic $NH_4{}^+(aq)$ to liberate $NH_3(g)$. $Li_2CO_3(s)$ is only slightly soluble, so most of it precipitates.

(c) $H_2SO_4(aq) + BaO_2(aq) \longrightarrow H_2O_2(aq) + BaSO_4(s)$. The forward reaction is favored by the formation of a precipitate, $BaSO_4(s)$.

(d) $2\,PbO(s) + Ca(OCl)_2(aq) \longrightarrow CaCl_2(aq) + 2\,PbO_2(s)$. Hypochlorite ion oxidizes lead(II) oxide to lead(IV) oxide.

94. **(M)**

(a) Stalactites are primarily $CaCO_3(s)$.

(b) Gypsum is $CaSO_4 \cdot 2\,H_2O(s)$.

(c) Suspension of $BaSO_4(s)$ in water.

(d) $Al_2O_3(s)$ with Fe^{3+} and Ti^{4+} replacing some Al^{3+} in the crystal structure.

95. **(M)** Dolomite, molar mass of 184.4 g/mol yields 2 mol $CO_2(g)$ per mol of dolomite on decomposition. The 5.00×10^3 kg sample yields 5.42×10^4 mol CO_2 which, under the stated conditions occupies a volume of 1.27×10^3 m^3.

CHAPTER 22
CHEMISTRY OF THE MAIN GROUP ELEMENTS II: GROUPS 18, 17, 16, 15 AND HYDROGEN

PRACTICE EXAMPLES

1A **(D)** This question involves calculating $E°$ for the reduction half-reaction:

$$ClO_3^-(aq) + 3\ H_2O(l) + 6\ e^- \rightarrow Cl^-(aq) + 6\ OH^-(aq)$$

Here we will consider just one of the several approaches available to solve this problem. The four half-reactions (and their associated $E°$ values) that are used in this method to come up with the "missing $E°$ value" are given below. (Note: the $E°$ for the first reaction was determined in Example 22-1)

1) $ClO_3^-(aq) + H_2O(l) + 2\ e^- \rightarrow ClO_2^-(aq) + 2\ OH^-(aq)$ $E° = 0.295$ V $\Delta_r G°_1 = -2FE°$

2) $ClO_2^-(aq) + H_2O(l) + 2\ e^- \rightarrow OCl^-(aq) + 2\ OH^-(aq)$ $E° = 0.681$ V $\Delta_r G°_2 = -2FE°$

3) $OCl^-(aq) + H_2O(l) + 1\ e^- \rightarrow 1/2\ Cl_2(aq) + 2\ OH^-(aq)$ $E° = 0.421$ V $\Delta_r G°_3 = -1FE°$

4) $1/2\ Cl_2(aq) + 1\ e^- \rightarrow Cl^-(aq)$ $E° = 1.358$ V $\Delta_r G°_4 = -1FE°$

Although the reactions themselves may be added to obtain the desired equation, the $E°$ for this equation is not the sum of the $E°$ values for the above four reactions. The $E°$ value for the desired equation is actually the weighted average of the $E°$ values for reactions (1) to (4). It can be calculated by summing up the free energy changes for the four reactions. (The standard voltages for half-reactions of the same type are not additive. The $\Delta_r G°$ values for these reactions can, however, be summed together.)

When (1), (2), (3) and (4) are added together we obtain

     1) $ClO_3^-(aq) + H_2O(l) + 2\ e^- \rightarrow ClO_2^-(aq) + 2\ OH^-(aq)$ $E°_1 = 0.295$ V

+ 2) $ClO_2^-(aq) + H_2O(l) + 2\ e^- \rightarrow OCl^-(aq) + 2\ OH^-(aq)$ $E°_2 = 0.681$ V

+ 3) $OCl^-(aq) + H_2O(l) + 1\ e^- \rightarrow 1/2\ Cl_2(aq) + 2\ OH^-(aq)$ $E°_3 = 0.421$ V

+ 4) $1/2\ Cl_2(aq) + 1\ e^- \rightarrow Cl^-(aq)$ $E°_4 = 1.358$ V

            $ClO_3^-(aq) + 3\ H_2O(l) + 6\ e^- \rightarrow Cl^-(aq) + 6\ OH^-(aq)$ $E°_5 = ?$

and $\Delta G°_5 = \Delta G°_1 + \Delta G°_2 + \Delta G°_3 + \Delta G°_4$

so, $-6FE°_5 = -2F(0.295\ \text{V}) + -2F(0.681\text{V}) + -1F(0.421\ \text{V}) + -1F(1.358\ \text{V})$

Hence, $E°_5 = \dfrac{-2F(0.295\ \text{V}) + -2F(0.681\text{V}) + -1F(0.421\ \text{V}) + -1F(1.358\ \text{V})}{-6\,F} = 0.622$ V

1B. **(D)** This question involves calculating $E°$ for the reduction half-reaction:

$$2\ ClO_3^-(aq)\ +\ 12\ H^+(aq)\ +\ 10\ e^-\ \rightarrow\ Cl_2(aq)\ +\ 6\ H_2O(l)$$

The three half-reactions (and their associated $E°$ values) are given below:

(1) $ClO_3^-(aq) + 3\ H^+(aq) + 2\ e^- \rightarrow HClO_2(aq) + H_2O(l)$ $E° = 1.181$ V

(2) $HClO_2(aq) + 2\ H^+(aq) + 2\ e^- \rightarrow HClO(aq) + H_2O(l)$ $E° = 1.645$ V

(3) $2\ HClO\ (aq) + 2\ H^+(aq) + 2\ e^- \rightarrow Cl_2(aq) + 2\ H_2O(l)$ $E° = 1.611$ V
(remember that $\Delta_r G° = -zFE°$)

Although the reactions themselves can be added to obtain the desired equation, the $E°$ for this equation is not the sum of the $E°$ values for the above three reactions. The $E°$ for the desired equation is actually the weighted average of the $E°$ values for reactions (1) to (3). It can be obtained by summing up the free energy changes for the three reactions. (For reactions of the same type, standard voltages are not additive; $\Delta G°$ values are additive, however.) When (1) and (2) (each multiplied by two) are added to (3) we obtain:

$2 \times$ (1) $2\ ClO_3^-(aq) + 6\ H^+(aq) + 4\ e^- \rightarrow 2\ HClO_2(aq) + 2\ H_2O(l)$ $E°_1 = 1.181$ V
$2 \times$ (2) $2\ HClO_2(aq) + 4\ H^+(aq) + 4\ e^- \rightarrow 2\ HClO(aq) + 2\ H_2O(l)$ $E°_2 = 1.645$ V
(3) $2\ HClO\ (aq) + 2\ H^+(aq) + 2\ e^- \rightarrow Cl_2(aq) + 2\ H_2O(l)$ $E°_3 = 1.611$ V

$$2\ ClO_3^-(aq)\ +\ 12\ H^+(aq)\ +\ 10\ e^-\ \rightarrow\ Cl_2(aq)\ +\ 6\ H_2O(l)\quad E°_4 = ?$$

and $\Delta G°_4 = \Delta G°_1 + \Delta G°_2 + \Delta G°_3$

so, $-10FE°_4 = -4F(1.181\ \text{V}) + -4F(1.645\ \text{V}) + -2F(1.611\ \text{V})$

Hence, $E°_4 = \dfrac{-4F(1.181\ \text{V}) + -4F(1.645\ \text{V}) + -2F(1.611\ \text{V})}{-10\ F} = 1.453$ V

2A **(M)** The dissociation reaction is the reverse of the formation reaction, and thus $\Delta_r G°$ for the dissociation reaction is the negative of $\Delta_f G°$

$$HF(g) \longrightarrow \tfrac{1}{2} H_2(g) + \tfrac{1}{2} F_2(g) \quad \Delta_r G° = -\Delta_f G° = -(-273.2\ \text{kJ/mol})$$

We know that

$$\Delta_r G° = -RT \ln K_p \qquad +273.2 \times 10^3\ \text{J/mol} = -8.3145\ \text{J mol}^{-1}\ \text{K}^{-1} \times 298\ \text{K} \times \ln K_p$$

$$\ln K_p = \frac{273.2 \times 10^3\ \text{J mol}^{-1}}{-8.3145\ \text{J mol}^{-1}\ \text{K}^{-1} \times 298\ \text{K}} = -110 \quad K_p = e^{-110} = 1.7 \times 10^{-48} \approx 2 \times 10^{-48}$$

Virtually no dissociation of HF(g) into its elements occurs.

2B **(M)** The dissociation reaction with all integer coefficients is twice the reverse of the formation reaction.

$$2\,HCl(g) \rightleftharpoons H_2(g) + Cl_2(g) \qquad \Delta_r G^\circ = -2 \times (-95.30\;\text{kJ/mol}) = +190.6\;\text{kJ/mol} = -RT\ln K_p$$

$$\ln K_p = \frac{-\Delta_r G^\circ}{RT} = \frac{-190.6 \times 10^3\;\text{J/mol}}{8.3145\;\text{J mol}^{-1}\,\text{K}^{-1} \times 298\;\text{K}} = -76.9 \qquad K_p = e^{-76.9} = 4 \times 10^{-34}$$

We assume an initial HCl(g) pressure of P atm, and calculate the final pressure of $Cl_2(g)$ and $H_2(g)$, x atm.

Reaction:	$2\,HCl(g)$	$\rightleftharpoons$	$H_2(g)$	$+$	$Cl_2(g)$
Initial:	P atm		0 atm		0 atm
Changes:	$-2x$ atm		$+x$ atm		$+x$ atm
Equil:	$(P-2x)$ atm		x atm		x atm

$$K_p = \frac{P\{H_2(g)\}P\{Cl_2(g)\}}{P\{HCl(g)\}^2} = \frac{x \cdot x}{(P-2x)^2} = \left(\frac{x}{P-2x}\right)^2 \qquad \frac{x}{P-2x} = \sqrt{4 \times 10^{-34}} = 2 \times 10^{-17}$$

$$x = 2 \times 10^{-17}\,(P-2x) \approx 2 \times 10^{-17}\,P$$

$$\%\;\text{decomposition} = \frac{2x}{P} \times 100\% = 2 \times 2 \times 10^{-17} \times 100\% = 4 \times 10^{-15}\;\%\;\text{decomposed}$$

INTEGRATIVE EXAMPLES

A **(M)** The half-reactions are:

$NO_2^- + 2\,OH^- \rightarrow NO_3^- + H_2O + 2\,e^-$	$-E^\circ = 0.04\;V$
$\{NO_2^- + H_2O + e^- \rightarrow NO + 2\,OH^-\} \times 2$	$E^\circ = -0.46\;V$

$3\,NO_2^- + H_2O \rightarrow NO_3^- + 2\,NO + 2\,OH^-$	$E^\circ_{cell} = -0.42\;V$

E° for the first reaction (oxidation) can be calculated by using the approach in Example 22-1. The calculated value is very small, and so the E° for the disproportionation reaction is negative. The disproportionation of NO_2^- to NO_3^- and NO is therefore not spontaneous.

B **(M)** The half-reactions are:

$HNO_2 + H_2O \rightarrow NO_3^- + 3\,H^+ + 2\,e^-$	$-E^\circ = -0.934\;V$
$\{HNO_2 + H^+ + e^- \rightarrow NO + H_2O\} \times 2$	$E^\circ = 0.996\;V$

$3\,HNO_2 \rightarrow NO_3^- + H^+ + H_2O + 2\,NO$	$E^\circ_{cell} = 0.062\;V$

E° for the first reaction (oxidation) can be calculated by using the approach in Example 22-1. E°_{cell} for the reaction is positive and therefore disproportionation of HNO_2 to NO_3^- and NO is spontaneous under standard conditions.

EXERCISES

Periodic Trends in Bonding and Acid-Base Character of Oxides

1. (E) LiF, BeF_2, BF_3, CF_4, NF_3, OF_2. LiF is an ionic compound, BeF_2 is a network covalent compound, and the others are molecular covalent compounds.

2. (E) NaF, MgF_2, AlF_3, SiF_4, PF_5, SF_6, and ClF_5. NaF and MgF_2 are ionic compounds, AlF_3 is a network covalent compound, and the others are molecular covalent compounds.

3. (E) The metallic character of the elements increases as we move down a group, and so too does the basic character of the oxides. Bi_2O_3 is most basic, P_4O_6 is least basic (and is actually acidic), and Sb_4O_6 is amphoteric.

4. (M) The metallic character of the elements increases as we move down a group, and so too does the basic character of the oxides. Stated another way, the acidic character of the oxides decreases as we move down a group. On this basis, we expect SeO_2 to be the acidic oxide and TeO_2 to be the amphoteric oxide.

The Noble Gases

5. (M) First we use the ideal gas law to determine the amount in moles of argon.

$$n = \frac{PV}{RT} = \frac{145 \text{ atm} \times 55 \text{ L}}{0.08206 \text{ L atm mol}^{-1} \text{ K}^{-1} \times 299 \text{ K}} = 3.2\underline{5} \times 10^2 \text{ mol Ar}$$

$$\text{L air} = 3.2\underline{5} \times 10^2 \text{ mol Ar} \times \frac{22.711 \text{ L Ar STP}}{1 \text{ mol Ar}} \times \frac{100.000 \text{ L air}}{0.934 \text{ L Ar}} = 7.9 \times 10^5 \text{ L air}$$

6. (M) First we compute the volume occupied by 5.00 g of He at STP, and then the volume of natural gas. From Chapter 6 we saw that 1 mol of gas at STP occupied 22.711 L.

$$\text{natural gas volume} = 5.00 \text{ g He} \times \frac{1 \text{ mol He}}{4.003 \text{ g He}} \times \frac{22.711 \text{ L He}}{1 \text{ mol He}} \times \frac{100 \text{ L air}}{8 \text{ L He}}$$

$$\text{natural gas volume} = 3.\underline{5} \times 10^2 \text{ L air at STP} \cong 350 \text{ L}$$

7. (M) (a) $|\overline{\underline{O}}-\overline{X}e-\overline{\underline{O}}|$ with $|\underline{O}|$ below

(b) $|\overline{\underline{O}}|$ above, $|\overline{\underline{O}}-Xe-\overline{\underline{O}}|$ with $|\underline{O}|$ below

(c) $\left[\begin{array}{c} |\overline{F}| \\ \langle F \rangle \\ |Xe-\overline{F}| \\ \langle F \rangle \\ |\underline{F}| \end{array} \right]^+$

(a) The Lewis structure has three ligands and one lone pair on Xe. XeO_3 has a trigonal pyramidal shape.

(b)   The Lewis structure has four ligands on Xe. XeO_4 has a tetrahedral shape.

(c)   There are five ligands and one lone pair on Xe in XeF_5^+. Its shape is square pyramidal.

8.   **(M)** We use VSEPR theory to predict the shapes of the species involved.

(a) O_2XeF_2 has a total of $2\times6+8+2\times7 = 34$ valence electrons $= 17$ pairs.

(b) O_3XeF_2 has a total of $3\times6+8+2\times7 = 40$ valence electrons $= 20$ pairs.

(c) $OXeF_4$ has a total of $6+8+4\times7 = 42$ valence electrons $= 21$ pairs.

We draw a plausible Lewis structure for each species below.

(a)

$$
\begin{array}{c}
|\overline{O}| \\
| \quad \backslash \\
|\overline{F}-Xe-\overline{F}| \\
| \\
|\underline{O}|
\end{array}
$$

(b)

$$
\begin{array}{c}
|\overline{\overline{F}} \quad \overline{\overline{F}}| \\
|\overline{O}-Xe-\overline{O}| \\
| \\
|\underline{O}|
\end{array}
$$

(c)

$$
\begin{array}{c}
|\overline{\overline{F}} \quad \overline{\overline{F}}| \\
|\overline{F}-Xe-\overline{F}| \\
| \\
|\underline{O}|
\end{array}
$$

(a)   There are four ligands and one lone pair on Xe in O_2XeF_2. Its shape is a see-saw.

(b)   There are five ligands and no lone pairs on Xe in O_3XeF_2. Its shape is trigonal bipyramidal.

(c)   The Lewis structure has five ligands and one lone pair on Xe. $OXeF_4$ has a square pyramidal shape.

<u>9.</u>   **(E)** $3 \ XeF_4(aq) \ + \ 6 \ H_2O(l) \ \rightarrow \ 2 \ Xe(g) + \ 3/2 \ O_2(g) + 12 \ HF(g) + XeO_3(s)$

10.   **(E)** $2 \ XeF_6(aq) + 16 \ OH^-(aq) \rightarrow \ Xe(g) + XeO_6^{4-}(aq) + O_2(g) + 8 \ H_2O(l) + 12 \ F^-(aq)$

<u>11.</u>   **(E)** For these noble gases, the bond energy of the noble gas fluorine is too small to offset the energy required to break the F—F bond.

12.   **(E)** The bond energy of the $Xe = O$ bond is too small to offset the energy required to break the $O = O$ bond.

The Halogens

13. **(M)** Iodide ion is slowly oxidized to iodine, which is yellow-brown in aqueous solution, by oxygen in the air.

Oxidation: $\{2\,I^-(aq) \longrightarrow I_2(aq) + 2\,e^-\} \times 2$ $-E° = -0.535\,V$

Reduction: $O_2(g) + 4\,H^+(aq) + 4\,e^- \longrightarrow 2\,H_2O(l)$ $E° = +1.229\,V$

Net: $4\,I^-(aq) + O_2(g) + 4\,H^+(aq) \longrightarrow 2\,I_2(aq) + 2\,H_2O(l)$ $E°_{cell} = +0.694\,V$

Possibly followed by: $I_2(aq) + I^-(aq) \longrightarrow I_3^-(aq)$

14. **(E)** $MnF_6^{2-} + 2\,SbF_5 \longrightarrow MnF_4 + 2\,SbF_6^-$; $2\,MnF_4 \longrightarrow 2\,MnF_3 + F_2(g)$

15. **(M)** Displacement reactions involve one element displacing another element from solution. The element that dissolves in the solution is more *"active"* than the element supplanted from solution. Within the halogen group, the activity decreases from top to bottom. Thus, each halogen is able to displace the members of the group below it, but not those above it. For instance, molecular bromine can oxidize aqueous iodide ion but molecular iodine is incapable of oxidizing bromide ion:

$Br_2(aq) + 2\,I^-(aq) \rightarrow 2\,Br^-(aq) + I_2(aq)$ however, $I_2(aq) + 2\,Br^-(aq) \rightarrow$ NO RXN

The only halogen with sufficient oxidizing power to displace $O_2(g)$ from water is $F_2(g)$:

$2\,H_2O(l) \rightarrow 4\,H^+ + O_2(g) + 4\,e^-$ $E°_{ox} = -1.229\,V$

$\{F_2(g) + 2\,e^- \rightarrow 2\,F^-(aq)\} \times 2$ $E°_{red} = 2.866\,V$

$2\,F_2(g) + 2\,H_2O(l) \rightarrow 4\,H^+ + O_2(g) + 4\,F^-(aq)$ $E°_{cell} = 1.637\,V$

The large positive standard reduction potential for this reaction indicates that the reaction will occur spontaneously, with products being strongly preferred under standard state conditions. None of the halogens reacts with water to form $H_2(g)$. In order to displace molecular hydrogen from water, one must add a strong reducing agent, such as sodium metal.

16. **(M)** We first list the relevant values of halogen properties.

		F	Cl	Br	I
(a)	Covalent radius (pm):	71	99	114	133
(b)	Ionic radius(pm):	133	181	196	220
(c)	First ionization energy (kJ/mol):	1681	1251	1140	1008
(d)	Electron affinity(kJ/mol):	−328.0	−349.0	−324.6	−295.2
(e)	Electronegativity:	4.0	3.0	2.8	2.5
(f)	Standard reduction potential:	+2.886 V	+1.358 V	+1.065 V	+0.535 V

We can do a reasonably good job of predicting the properties of astatine by simply looking at the difference between Br and I and assuming that the same difference exists between I and At.

(a)   Covalent radius: ≈ 152 pm   (b) Ionic radius: 244 pm

(c)   1st ionization energy: 876 kJ/mol   (d) Electron affinity: ≈ -265 kJ/mol

(e)   Electronegativity: ≈ 2.2 (f) $E° \approx 0.005$ V to 0.010 V

Depending on the technique that you use, you will arrive at different answers. For example, -260 kJ/mol is a reasonable estimation of the electron affinity by the following reasoning. The difference between the value for Cl and Br is 24 kJ/mol, the difference between the values for Br and I is 29 kJ/mol, so the difference between I and At should be about 35 kJ/mol.

17. **(M)**

(a) $$\text{mass } F_2 = 1 \text{ km}^3 \times \left(\frac{1000 \text{ m}}{1 \text{ km}} \times \frac{100 \text{ cm}}{1 \text{ m}}\right)^3 \times \frac{1.03 \text{ g}}{1 \text{ cm}^3} \times \frac{1 \text{ lb}}{454 \text{ g}} \times \frac{1 \text{ ton}}{2000 \text{ lb}} \times \frac{1 \text{ g F}^-}{1 \text{ ton}} \times \frac{37.996 \text{ g F}_2}{18.998 \text{ g F}^-}$$

$$= 2 \times 10^9 \text{ g F}_2 = 2 \times 10^6 \text{ kg F}_2$$

(b)   Bromine can be extracted by displacing it from solution with $Cl_2(g)$. Since there is no chemical oxidizing agent that is stronger than $F_2(g)$, this method of displacement would not work for $F_2(g)$. Even if there were a chemical oxidizing agent stronger than $F_2(g)$, it would displace $O_2(g)$ before it displaced $F_2(g)$. Obtaining $F_2(g)$ would require electrolysis of one of its molten salts, obtained from seawater evaporate.

18. **(E)** $\text{Mass } F_2 = 1.00 \times 10^3 \text{ kg rock} \times \dfrac{1000 \text{ g}}{1 \text{ kg}} \times \dfrac{1 \text{ mol } 3 \text{ Ca}_3(\text{PO}_4)_2 \cdot \text{CaF}_2}{1009 \text{ g}} \times \dfrac{2 \text{ mol F}}{1 \text{ mol } 3 \text{ Ca}_3(\text{PO}_4)_2 \cdot \text{CaF}_2}$

$\times \dfrac{19.00 \text{ g F}}{1 \text{ mol F}} \times \dfrac{1 \text{ kg}}{1000 \text{ g}} = 37.7 \text{ kg fluorine}$

19. **(M)** In order for the disproportionation reaction to occur under standard conditions, the $E°$ for the overall reaction must be greater than zero. To answer this question, we must refer to the Standard Electrode Potential Diagrams (also known as Latimer diagrams) provided in Figure 22-4 and the answer to Practice Example 22-1B.

(i)   Reduction half reaction (acidic solution)
       $Cl_2(aq) + 2 e^- \rightarrow 2 Cl^-(aq)$ $E°_{red} = 1.358$ V

(ii)   Oxidation half reaction (acidic solution)
       $Cl_2(aq) + 6 H_2O(l) \rightarrow 2 ClO_3^-(aq) + 12 H^+(aq) + 10 e^-$ $E°_{ox} = -1.453$ V

Combining (i) $\times$ 5 with (ii) $\times$ 1, we obtain the desired disproportionation reaction:
$6 Cl_2(aq) + 6 H_2O(l) \rightarrow 2 ClO_3^-(aq) + 12 H^+(aq) + 10 Cl^-(aq)$ $E°_{cell} = -0.095$ V

Since the final cell voltage is negative, the disproportionation reaction will not occur spontaneously under standard conditions. Alternatively, we can calculate K by using $\ln K = -\Delta_r G°/RT$ and $\Delta_r G° = -zFE°$. This method gives a $K = 8.6 \times 10^{-17}$. Clearly, the reaction will not go to completion under standard conditions.

20. **(D)** To find out whether the reaction will go to completion, we must first calculate the standard potential for the disproportionation of hypochlorous acid (HOCl). As was the case for Exercise 15, we will use information contained in Fig. 22.4 to answer this question.

(i) $2 \text{ HOCl(aq)} + 2 \text{ H}_2\text{O(l)} \rightarrow 2 \text{ HClO}_2\text{(aq)} + 4 \text{ H}^+\text{(aq)} + 4 \text{ e}^-$ $-E°_{(i)} = -(1.645 \text{ V})$ (oxidation)

(ii) $2 \text{ HOCl(aq)} + 2 \text{ H}^+\text{(aq)} + 2 \text{ e}^- \rightarrow \text{Cl}_2\text{(aq)} + 2 \text{ H}_2\text{O(l)}$ $E°_{(ii)} = +1.611 \text{ V}$

(iii) $\text{Cl}_2\text{(aq)} + 2 \text{ e}^- \rightarrow 2 \text{ Cl}^-\text{(aq)}$ $E°_{(iii)} = +1.358 \text{ V}$

Next we need to determine the potential of the following half reaction using the relationship between standard free energies and standard potential

(iv) $2 \text{ HOCl(aq)} + 2 \text{ H}^+\text{(aq)} + 4 \text{ e}^- \rightarrow 2 \text{ Cl}^-\text{(aq)} + 2 \text{ H}_2\text{O(l)}$ $E°_{(iv)}$

We can determine this using half reaction (ii) and (iii) since adding (ii) and (iii) give (iv). Hence,

$$-4FE°_{(iv)} = -2F(1.611 \text{ V}) + -2F(1.358 \text{ V}) \qquad \text{So, } E°_{(iv)} = 1.485 \text{ V}$$

Therefore, by adding equation (i) to equation (iv), we can obtain the standard cell voltage for the disproportionation of HOCl. We divide by 2 to give the target

(i) $\div 2$ $\text{HOCl(aq)} + \text{H}_2\text{O(l)} \rightarrow \text{HClO}_2\text{(aq)} + 2 \text{ H}^+\text{(aq)} + 2 \text{ e}^-$ $-E°_{(i)} = -(1.645 \text{ V})$

(iv) $\div 2$ $\text{HOCl(aq)} + \text{H}^+\text{(aq)} + 2 \text{ e}^- \rightarrow \text{Cl}^-\text{(aq)} + \text{H}_2\text{O(l)}$ $E°_{red} = 1.485 \text{ V}$

$$\overline{\qquad \qquad 2 \text{ HOCl(aq)} \rightarrow \text{HClO}_2\text{(aq)} + \text{Cl}^-\text{(aq)} + \text{H}^+\text{(aq)} \qquad E°_{cell} = -0.160 \text{ V}}$$
(disproportionation reaction of HOCl(aq))

Since the standard cell potential is negative, the equilibrium will favor the reactants and thus the reaction will not go to completion as written (i.e., reactants will predominate at equilibrium and thus the reaction will be far from complete). Alternatively, we can calculate K from the reaction by using $\ln K = -\Delta_r G°/RT$ and $\Delta_r G° = -zFE°$. This gives $K = 3.9 \times 10^{-6}$. Clearly, the reaction will not go to completion because K is very small (reactants strongly predominate at equilibrium, not products).

21. **(M)** First we must draw the Lewis structures for all of the species listed. Following this, we will deduce their electron-group geometries and molecular shapes following the VSEPR approach.

(a) BrF$_3$: 28 valence electrons
VSEPR class: AX$_3$E$_2$
Thus BrF$_3$ is T-shaped

(b) IF$_5$ 42 valence electrons
VSEPR class: AX$_5$E
Thus IF$_5$ is square pyramidal

(c) Cl$_3$IF$^-$ 36 valence electrons
VSEPR class: AX$_4$E$_2$
Thus Cl$_3$IF$^-$ is square planar

22. **(M)** To answer this question we need to apply the VSEPR method to each species:

(i) ClF_2^+ (total number of valence electrons = 20 e$^-$)
Molecular shape: AX_2E_2 angular (<109.5° due to lone pairs on Cl atom)

(ii) $IBrF^-$ (total number of valence electrons = 22 e$^-$)
Molecular shape: AX_2E_3 linear (~180°)

(iii) OCl_2 (total number of valence electrons = 20 e$^-$)
Molecular shape: AX_2E_2 angular (<109.5° due to lone pairs on O or Cl atom)
Note: Cl—O—Cl preferred over Cl—Cl—O because all atoms have a formal charge of zero.

(iv) ClF_3 (total number of valence electrons = 28 e$^-$)
Molecular shape: AX_3E_2 T-shaped molecule

(v) SF_4 (total number of valence electrons = 34 e$^-$)
Molecular shape: AX_4E See-saw molecular geometry (or distorted tetrahedron)

The VSEPR treatment of each species indicates only $IBrF^-$ has a linear structure. Since (i) and (iii) belong to the same VSEPR class (AX_2E_2), it is not unreasonable to assume that they have the same "bent structure".

23. **(M)**

(a) The half-reactions are:

Oxidation: $3\,I^- \rightarrow I_3^- + 2\,e^-$

Reduction: $I_2(aq) + 2\,e^- \rightarrow 2\,I^-(aq)$

Overall: $I_2(aq) + I^-(aq) \rightarrow I_3^-(aq)$

From the known value of the equilibrium constant at 25 °C, we can calculate $\Delta_r G°$ and consequently $E°$:

$\Delta_r G° = -RT \ln K = -zFE°$

$-8.314\ JK^{-1}mol^{-1} \times 298.15\ K \ln K = -2 \times 96485\ Cmol^{-1} \times E°$

$E° = \dfrac{-8.314\ JK^{-1}mol^{-1} \times 298.15\ K \ln 7.7 \times 10^2}{-2 \times 96485\ C\ mol^{-1}} = 0.085\ V$

(b) Set up the ICE table and solve for the equilibrium concentrations:

$I_2(aq)$	+	$I^-(aq)$	$\rightleftharpoons$	$I_3^-(aq)$
0.0010M		0.0050M		0
0.0010 − x		0.0050 − x		x

$$K = 7.7 \times 10^2 = \frac{x}{(0.0010-x)\times(0.0050-x)} = \frac{x}{5.0\times10^{-6} - 0.0060x + x^2}$$

$$7.7 \times 10^2 \times (5.0\times10^{-6} - 0.0060x + x^2) = x$$

$$7.7 \times 10^2 x^2 - 5.62x + 3.85\times10^{-3} = 0$$

Solving the quadratic equation gives $x = 7.65 \times 10^{-3}$ M.

24. **(M)**
    (a) Cl_3^- has the same structure as I_3^-, which is given in Figure 22.7
    (b) Set up the ICE table and solve for the equilibrium concentrations:

$$Cl_3^-(aq) \rightleftharpoons Cl^-(aq) + Cl_2(aq)$$

0	0.0010M	0.0010M
x	0.0010 − x	0.0010 − x

$$K = 5.5 = \frac{(0.0010-x)\times(0.0010-x)}{x} \approx \frac{0.0010^2}{x} = \frac{1.0\times10^{-6}}{x}$$

$$x = \frac{1.0\times10^{-6}}{5.5} = 1.8\times10^{-7}\,M$$

Oxygen

25. **(E)(a)** $2\,HgO(s) \xrightarrow{\Delta} 2\,Hg(l) + O_2(g)$ **(b)** $2\,KClO_4(s) \xrightarrow{\Delta} 2\,KClO_3(s) + O_2(g)$

26. **(E)**
    (a) $Br^-(aq) + O_3(g) \rightarrow BrO^-(aq) + O_2(g)$ [Br is in oxidation state +1 in $BrO^-(aq)$]
    (b) $NO(g) + O_3(g) \rightarrow NO_2(g) + O_2(g)$
    (c) $2\,Fe^{2+}(aq) + 2\,H^+(aq) + O_3(g) \rightarrow 2\,Fe^{3+}(aq) + H_2O + O_2(g)$
    (d) $Ag(s) + O_3(g) \rightarrow AgO(s) + O_2(g)$
    (e) $2[Fe(CN)_6]^{4-}(aq) + O_3(g) + H_2O(l) \rightarrow 2[Fe(CN)_6]^{3-}(aq) + 2\,OH^-(aq) + O_2(g)$

27. **(M)** We first write the formulas of the four substances: N_2O_4, Al_2O_3, P_4O_6, CO_2. The one constant in all these substances is oxygen. If we compare amounts of substance with the same amount (in moles) of oxygen, the one with the smallest mass of the other element will have the highest percent oxygen.

3 mol N_2O_4 contains 12 mol O and 6 mol N: $6\times14.0 = 84.0$ g N
4 mol Al_2O_3 contains 12 mol O and 8 mol Al: $8\times27.0 = 216$ g Al
2 mol P_4O_6 contains 12 mol O and 8 mol P: $8\times31.0 = 248$ g P
6 mol CO_2 contains 12 mol O and 6 mol C: $6\times12.0 = 72.0$ g C

Thus, of the oxides listed, CO_2 contains the largest percent oxygen by mass.

28. (M) $2\,NH_4NO_3(s) \xrightarrow{400\,°C} 2\,N_2(g) + O_2(g) + 4\,H_2O(g)$

$2\,H_2O_2(l) \rightarrow 2\,H_2O(l) + O_2(g)$

$2\,KClO_3(s) \xrightarrow{\Delta} 23\,KCl(s) + 3\,O_2(g)$

(a) All three reactions have two moles of reactant, and the decomposition of potassium chlorate produces three moles of $O_2(g)$, compared to one mole of $O_2(g)$ for each of the others. The potassium chlorate decomposition produces the most oxygen per mole of reactant.

(b) If each reaction produced the same amount of $O_2(g)$, then the one with the lightest mass of reactant would produce the most oxygen per gram of reactant. When the first two reactions are compared, it is clear that 2 mol H_2O_2 have less mass than 2 mol NH_4NO_3. (Notice that each mole of NH_4NO_3 contains the amounts of elements— 2 mol H and 2 mol O—present in each mole H_2O_2 plus some more.) So now we need to compare hydrogen peroxide with potassium chlorate. Notice that 6 H_2O_2 produces the same amount of $O_2(g)$ as 2 $KClO_3$.

6 mol H_2O_2 has a mass of $34.01 \times 6 = 204.1$ g, while 2 mol $KClO_3$ has a mass of $122.2 \times 2 = 244.2$ g. Thus, H_2O_2 produces the most $O_2(g)$ per gram of reactant.

29. (M) Recall that fraction by volume and fraction by pressure are numerically equal. Additionally, one atmosphere pressure is equivalent to 760 mmHg. We combine these two facts.

$$P\{O_3\} = 760\ \text{mmHg} \times \frac{0.04\ \text{mmHg of } O_3}{10^6\ \text{mmHg of atmosphere}} = 3 \times 10^{-5}\ \text{mmHg}$$

30. (M)

$$P = \frac{nRT}{V} = \frac{\left(5 \times 10^{12}\ \text{molecules} \times \dfrac{1\ \text{mol } O_3}{6.022 \times 10^{23}\ \dfrac{\text{molecule}}{\text{mole}}}\right) \times \dfrac{0.08206\ \text{L atm}}{\text{mol K}} \times 220\ \text{K}}{1\ \text{cm}^3 \times \dfrac{1\ \text{L}}{1000\ \text{cm}^3}}$$

$$P = 1.\underline{5} \times 10^{-7}\ \text{atm} \times \frac{760\ \text{mmHg}}{1\ \text{atm}} = 1.\underline{1} \times 10^{-4}\ \text{mmHg}$$

31. (M) The electrolysis reaction is $2\,H_2O(l) \xrightarrow{electrolysis} 2\,H_2(g) + O_2(g)$. In this reaction, 2 moles of $H_2(g)$ are produced for each mole of $O_2(g)$. By the law of combining volumes, we would expect the volume of hydrogen to be twice the volume of oxygen produced. (Actually the volumes are not exactly in the ratio of 2:1 because of the different solubilities of oxygen and hydrogen in water.)

32. **(M)** The electrolysis reaction is $2\,H_2O(l)\xrightarrow{\text{electrolysis}}2\,H_2(g)+O_2(g)$. In this reaction, 2 moles of water are decomposed to produce each mole of $O_2(g)$. We use the data in the problem to determine the amount of $O_2(g)$ produced, which we then convert to the mass of H_2O needed.

$$\text{mass } H_2O(l)=\frac{\left(736.7\text{ mmHg}\times\dfrac{1\text{ atm}}{760\text{ mmHg}}\right)\left(22.83\text{ mL}\times\dfrac{1\text{ L}}{1000\text{ mL}}\right)}{\dfrac{0.08206\text{ L atm}}{\text{mol K}}\times(25.0+273.2)K}\times\frac{2\text{ mol }H_2O}{1\text{ mol }O_2}$$

$$\times\frac{18.02\text{ g }H_2O}{1\text{ mol }H_2O}=0.03259\text{ g }H_2O\text{ decomposed}$$

33. **(D)** Since the pK_a for H_2O_2 had been provided to us, we can find the solution pH simply by solving an I.C.E. table for the hydrolysis of a 3.0 % H_2O_2 solution (by mass). Of course, in order to use this method, the mass percent must first be converted to molarity. We must assume that the density of the solution is 1.0 g mL^{-1}.

$$[H_2O_2]=\frac{3.0\text{ g }H_2O_2}{100\text{ g solution}}\times\frac{1\text{ g solution}}{1\text{ mL solution}}\times\frac{1\text{ mol }H_2O_2}{34.015\text{ g }H_2O_2}\times\frac{1000\text{ mL}}{1L}=0.88\text{ M}$$

The pK_a for H_2O_2 is 11.75. The K_a for H_2O_2 is therefore $10^{-11.75}$ or 1.8×10^{-12}. By comparison with pure water, which has a K_a of 1.8×10^{-16} at 25 °C, one can see that H_2O_2 is indeed a stronger acid than water but the difference in acidity between the two is not that great. Consequently, we cannot ignore the contribution of protons of pure water when we work out the pH of the solution at equilibrium.

Reaction: $\qquad H_2O_2(aq)\;+\;H_2O(l)\;\underset{}{\overset{K_a=1.8\times10^{-12}}{\rightleftharpoons}}\;H_3O^+(aq)\;+\;HO_2^-(aq)$

Initial:	0.88 M	—	1.0×10^{-7} M	0 M
Change:	$-x$ M	—	$+x$ M	$+x$ M
Equilibrium:	$(0.88-x)$ M	—	$(1.0\times10^{-7}+x)$M	x M
	$(\sim0.88$ M$)$			

So, $1.8\times10^{-12}=\dfrac{x(x\;+\;1.0\times10^{-7})}{\sim0.88}\qquad x^2+1.0\times10^{-7}x-1.58\times10^{-12}=0$

$$x=\frac{-\;1.0\times10^{-7}\pm\;\sqrt{1.0\times10^{-14}\;+\;4(1.58\times10^{-12})}}{2}$$

The root that makes sense in this context is $x=1.2\times10^{-6}$ M.
Thus, the $[H_3O^+]=1.2\times10^{-6}$ M $+1.0\times10^{-7}$ M $=1.3\times10^{-6}$ M
Consequently, the pH for the 3.0 % H_2O_2 solution (by mass) should be 5.89
(i.e., the solution is weakly acidic)

34. **(E)** Oxide ion reacts essentially quantitatively with water to form hydroxide ion.

$$K_2O(s) + H_2O(l) \rightarrow 2K^+(aq) + 2OH^-(aq)$$

First we calculate the concentration of $[OH]^-$ and then the solution's pH.

$$[OH]^- = \frac{0.1000 \text{ g K}_2\text{O}}{1.25 \text{ L}} \times \frac{1 \text{ mol K}_2\text{O}}{94.196 \text{ g K}_2\text{O}} \times \frac{2 \text{ mol OH}^-}{1 \text{ mol K}_2\text{O}} = 0.00170 \text{ M}$$

$$\text{pOH} = -\log(0.00170) = 2.77 \quad \text{pH} = 14.00 - \text{pOH} = 14.00 - 2.77 = 11.23$$

35. **(E)** $3 \; \overline{\underline{O}} = \overline{\underline{O}} \longrightarrow 2 \; \overline{\underline{O}} \cdot \cdot \cdot \overline{\underline{O}} \cdot \cdot \cdot \overline{\underline{O}}$

Bonds broken: $3 \times (O=O) = 3 \times 498 \text{ kJ/mol} = 1494 \text{ kJ/mol}$

Bonds formed: $4 \times (O \cdot \cdot \cdot O)$

$$\Delta_r H^\circ = +285 \text{ kJ/mol} = \text{bonds broken} - \text{bonds formed} = 1494 \text{ kJ/mol} - 4 \times (O \cdot \cdot \cdot O)$$

$$4 \times (O \cdot \cdot \cdot O) = 1494 \text{ kJ/mol} - 285 \text{ kJ/mol} = 1209 \text{ kJ/mol}$$

$$O \cdot \cdot \cdot O = 1209 \text{ kJ/mol} + 4 = 302 \text{ kJ/mol}$$

36. **(E)** $3 \; \overset{..}{\underset{..}{O}} = \overset{..}{\underset{..}{O}} \longrightarrow 2 \; :\overset{..}{\underset{..}{O}} - \overset{..}{O} = \overset{..}{\underset{..}{O}}:$ (all gaseous species)

$$\text{Average bond energy} = \frac{O=O + O-O}{2} = \frac{(498 + 142) \frac{\text{kJ}}{\text{mol}}}{2} = 320 \frac{\text{kJ}}{\text{mol}}$$

37. **(E)**

(a) H_2S, while polar, forms only weak hydrogen bonds. H_2O forms much stronger hydrogen bonds, leading to a higher boiling point and thus a liquid at room temperature.

(b) All electrons are paired in O_3, producing a diamagnetic molecule.

38. **(M)**

(a) $\overline{\underline{O}} = \overline{\underline{O}}$ $\quad$ $|\overline{\underline{O}} - \overline{\underline{O}} = \overline{\underline{O}}$ $\quad$ $H - \overline{\underline{O}} - \overline{\underline{O}} - H$

The O—O bond in O_2 is a double bond, which should be short (121 pm). That in O_3 is a "one-and-a-half" bond, of intermediate length (128 pm). And that in H_2O_2 is a longer (148 pm) single bond.

(b) The O_2^+ ion has one less electron than does the O_2 molecule. Based on Lewis structures,

$$\overline{\underline{O}} = \overline{\underline{O}} \quad \overline{\underline{O}} \overset{\cdot}{-} \overline{\underline{O}}$$

one would predict that O_2^+ would have a bond order of 1.5, thereby making its O—O bond weaker than the double bond of O_2, and therefore longer, in contradiction to the experimental evidence. The molecular orbital picture of the two species suggests the opposite. According to this model, O_2 has a bond order of 2.0 while that for O_2^+ is 2.5. Thus MO theory predicts a shorter bond for O_2^+.

$$\sigma_{1s} \quad \sigma*_{1s} \quad \sigma_{2s} \quad \sigma*_{2s} \quad \sigma_{2p} \quad \pi_{2p} \quad \pi*_{2p} \quad \sigma*_{2p}$$

O_2

bond order = (no. bonding electrons – no. antibonding electrons) ÷ 2

bond order = $(10-6) \div 2 = 2.0$

$$\sigma_{1s} \quad \sigma*_{1s} \quad \sigma_{2s} \quad \sigma*_{2s} \quad \sigma_{2p} \quad \pi_{2p} \quad \pi*_{2p} \quad \sigma*_{2p}$$

$O_2{}^+$

bond order = (no. bonding electrons – no. antibonding electrons) ÷ 2 = $(10-5) \div 2 = 2.5$

39. **(M)** Reactions that have K values greater than 1000 are considered to be essentially quantitative (i.e., they go virtually 100% to completion). So to answer this question we need only calculate the equilibrium constant for each reaction using the equation $E°_{cell} = (0.0257/z) \ln K$.

(a) $H_2O_2(aq) + 2\,H^+(aq) + 2\,e^- \rightleftharpoons 2\,H_2O(l)$ $E°_{red} = +1.763$ V

                $2\,I^-(aq) \rightleftharpoons I_2(s) + 2\,e^-$ $E°_{ox} = -0.535$ V

$H_2O_2(aq) + 2\,H^+(aq) + 2\,I^-(aq) \rightleftharpoons I_2(s) + 2\,H_2O(l)$ $E°_{cell} = +1.228$ V $(n = 2\,e^-)$

$$\ln K = \frac{1.228\text{ V} \times 2}{0.0257\text{ V}} = 95.56 \qquad K = 3.2 \times 10^{41}$$

Therefore the reaction goes to completion (or very nearly so).

(b) $O_2(g) + 2\,H_2O(l) + 4\,e^- \rightleftharpoons 4\,OH^-(aq)$ $E°_{red} = +0.401$ V

     $4\,Cl^-(aq) \rightleftharpoons 2\,Cl_2(g) + 4\,e^-$ $E°_{ox} = -1.358$ V

$O_2(g) + 2\,H_2O(l) + 4\,Cl^-(aq) \rightleftharpoons 2\,Cl_2(g) + 4\,OH^-(aq)$ $E°_{cell} = -0.957$ V

                                                             $(z = 4\,e^-)$

$$\ln K = \frac{-0.957\text{ V} \times 4}{0.0257\text{ V}} = -148.95 \qquad K = 2.1 \times 10^{-65}$$

The extremely small value of K indicates that reactants are strongly preferred and thus, the reaction does not even come close to going to completion.

(c) $O_3(g) + 2\,H^+(aq) + 2\,e^- \rightleftharpoons O_2(g) + H_2O(l)$ $E°_{red} = +2.075$ V

$Pb^{2+}(aq) + 2\,H_2O(l) \rightleftharpoons PbO_2(s) + 4H^+(aq) + 2\,e^-$ $E°_{ox} = -1.455$ V

$O_3(g) + Pb^{2+}(aq) + H_2O(l) \rightleftharpoons PbO_2(s) + 2\,H^+(aq) + O_2(g)$ $E°_{cell} = 0.620$ V

$$\ln K = \frac{+0.62\text{ V} \times 2}{0.0257\text{ V}} = 48.25 \qquad K = 9.0 \times 10^{20}$$

Therefore the reaction goes to completion (or very nearly so).

(d)

$$HO_2^-(aq) + H_2O(l) + 2\ e^- \rightleftharpoons 3\ OH^-(aq) \qquad E^\circ_{red} = +0.878\ V$$
$$2\ Br^-(aq) \rightleftharpoons Br_2(l) + 2\ e^- \qquad E^\circ_{ox} = -1.065\ V$$

$$\overline{HO_2^-(aq) + H_2O(l) + 2\ Br^-(aq) \rightleftharpoons Br_2(s) + 3\ OH^-(aq) \qquad E^\circ_{cell} = -0.187\ V}$$

$$\ln K = \frac{-0.187\ V \times 2}{0.0257\ V} = -14.55 \qquad K = 4.8 \times 10^{-7}$$

The extremely small value of K indicates the reaction heavily favors reactants at equilibrium and thus, the reaction does not even come close to going to completion.

40. (M)

(a) $Hg(NO_3)_2(s) \xrightarrow{\Delta} Hg(l) + 2\ NO_2(g) + O_2(g)$

or

$Hg(NO_3)_2(s) \xrightarrow{\Delta} Hg(NO_2)_2(g) + O_2(g)$

$\left. \right\}$ Depending on the temperature

(b) $H_2O_2(l) \xrightarrow{\Delta} H_2O(l) + 1/2\ O_2(g)$

41. **(M)** The reaction is $2\ KClO_3(s) \xrightarrow[MnO_2(s)]{\Delta} 2\ KCl(s) + 3\ O_2(g)$.

$$1.0\ g\ KClO_3 \times \frac{1\ mol}{122.549\ g} \times \frac{3\ mol\ O_2}{2\ mol\ KClO_3} \times \frac{31.998\ g\ O_2}{1\ mol\ O_2} = 0.392\ g\ O_2$$

$$pV = nRT \Rightarrow V = \frac{nRT}{p} = \frac{0.01224 \times 8.314\ J\ K^{-1}mol^{-1} \times 298.15\ K}{101\ kPa \times \dfrac{1\ atm}{101.325\ kPa}} = 30\ L$$

42. **(M)** The reaction is $2\ HgO(s) \xrightarrow{\Delta} 2\ Hg(l) + O_2(g)$.

$$1.0\ g\ HgO \times \frac{1\ mol}{216.589\ g\ HgO} \times \frac{1\ mol\ O_2}{2\ mol\ HgO} = 2.31 \times 10^{-3}\ mol\ O_2$$

$$p_{O_2} = (756 - 23.76) = 752\ mmHg$$

$$pV = nRT \Rightarrow V = \frac{nRT}{p} = \frac{2.31 \times 10^{-3} \times 8.314\ J\ K^{-1}mol^{-1} \times 298.15\ K}{752\ mmHg \times \dfrac{1\ atm}{760\ mmHg}} = 5.8\ L$$

Sulfur

43. **(E)**

    (a)   MgS, magnesium sulfide   **(b)** H_2S, hydrogen sulfide

    (c) $Ca(HSO_3)_2$, calcium hydrogen sulfite   **(d)** $Na_2S_2O_3$, sodium thiosulfate

    (e) S_4N_4, tetrasulfur tetranitride

44. **(E) (a)** $CaSO_4 \cdot 2H_2O$, calcium sulfate dihydrate   **(b)** $H_2S(aq)$, hydrosulfuric acid

    (c) $NaHSO_4$, sodium hydrogen sulfate   **(d)** $H_2S_2O_7 (aq)$, disulfuric acid

45. **(M)**

    (a) $FeS(s) + 2\ HCl(aq) \longrightarrow FeCl_2 (aq) + H_2S(aq)$ MnS(s), ZnS(s), etc. also are possible.

    (b) $CaSO_3 (s) + 2\ HCl(aq) \longrightarrow CaCl_2 (aq) + H_2O(l) + SO_2 (g)$

    (c)   Oxidation: $SO_2 (aq) + 2\ H_2O(l) \longrightarrow SO_4^{2-} (aq) + 4\ H^+ (aq) + 2\ e^-$

            Reduction: $MnO_2 (s) + 4\ H^+ (aq) + 2\ e^- \longrightarrow Mn^{2+} (aq) + 2\ H_2O(l)$

            Net: $SO_2 (aq) + MnO_2 (s) \longrightarrow Mn^{2+} (aq) + SO_4^{2-} (aq)$

    (d)   Oxidation: $S_2O_3^{2-} (aq) + H_2O(l) \longrightarrow 2\ SO_2 (g) + 2\ H^+ (aq) + 4\ e^-$

            Reduction: $S_2O_3^{2-} (aq) + 6\ H^+ (aq) + 4\ e^- \longrightarrow 2\ S(s) + 3\ H_2O(l)$

            Net: $S_2O_3^{2-} (aq) + 2\ H^+ (aq) \longrightarrow S(s) + SO_2 (g) + H_2O(l)$

46. **(M)**

    (a) $S(s) + O_2 (g) \longrightarrow SO_2 (g)$

        $2\ Na(s) + 2\ H_2O(l) \longrightarrow 2\ NaOH(aq) + H_2 (g)$

        $2\ NaOH(aq) + SO_2 (g) \longrightarrow Na_2SO_3 (aq) + H_2O(l)$

    (b) $S(s) + O_2 (g) \longrightarrow SO_2 (g)$

        $SO_2 (g) + 2\ H_2O(l) + Cl_2 (g) \longrightarrow SO_4^{2-} (aq) + 2\ Cl^- (aq) + 4\ H^+ (aq)$ $\left(E_{cell}^{\circ} = +1.19V \right)$

        $2\ Na(s) + 2\ H_2O(l) \longrightarrow 2\ NaOH(aq) + H_2 (g)$

        $2\ NaOH(aq) + 2\ H^+ (aq) + SO_4^{2-} (aq) \longrightarrow Na_2SO_4 (aq) + 2\ H_2O(l)$

    (c) $S(s) + O_2 (g) \longrightarrow SO_2 (g)$

        $2\ Na(s) + 2\ H_2O(l) \longrightarrow 2\ NaOH(aq) + H_2 (g)$

        $2\ NaOH(aq) + SO_2 (g) \longrightarrow Na_2SO_3 (aq) + H_2O(l)$

        $Na_2SO_3 (aq) + S(s) \longrightarrow NaS_2O_3 (aq)$

    (Thus, one must boil the reactants in an alkaline solution.)

47. **(M)** The decomposition of thiosulfate ion is more highly favored in an acidic solution. If the white solid is Na_2SO_4, there will be no reaction with strong acids such as HCl. By contrast, if the white solid is $Na_2S_2O_3$, $SO_2(g)$ will be liberated and a pale yellow precipitate of S(s,rhombic) will form upon addition of HCl(aq).

$$S_2O_3^{2-}(aq) + 2H^+(aq) \longrightarrow S(s) + SO_2(g) + H_2O(l)$$

Consequently, the solid can be identified by adding a strong mineral acid such as HCl(aq).

48. **(M)** Sulfites are easily oxidized to sulfates by, for example, O_2 in the atmosphere. On the other hand, there are no oxidizing agents naturally available in reasonable concentrations that can oxidize SO_4^{2-} to a higher oxidation state, such as in $S_2O_8^{2-}$. Similarly, the atmosphere of Earth is an oxidizing one. Reducing agents are not present to reduce SO_4^{2-} to a species with a lower oxidation state, except in localized areas.

49. **(D)** Mg^{2+}(aq) is only weakly polarizing, and it will not hydrolyze in aqueous medium. But HSO_4^-(aq) will ionize further, $K_{a_2} = 1.1 \times 10^{-2}$ for HSO_4^-(aq). We proceed by setting up the dissociation equilibrium for $[HSO_4^-(aq)]$ and then solving the quadratic equation to obtain $[H_3O^+(aq)]$:

$$Mg(HSO_4)_2(aq) \rightarrow Mg^{2+}(aq) + 2\,HSO_4^-(aq)$$

$$[HSO_4^-(aq)] = \frac{16.5\text{ g Mg(HSO}_4)_2}{250.0\text{ mL soln}} \times \frac{1000\text{ mL}}{1\text{ L soln}} \times \frac{1\text{ mol Mg(HSO}_4)_2}{218.43\text{ g Mg(HSO}_4)_2} \times \frac{2\text{ mol HSO}_4^-}{1\text{ mol Mg(HSO}_4)_2}$$

$$= 0.604\text{ M}$$

Reaction:	HSO_4^-(aq)	+	H_2O(l)	$\rightleftharpoons$	SO_4^{2-}(aq)	+	H_3O+(aq)
Initial:	0.604 M				0 M		0 M
Changes:	$-x$ M				$+x$ M		$+x$ M
Equil:	$(0.604 - x)$ M				x M		x M

Since the value of the equilibrium constant ($K = 0.011$) is moderate, the full quadratic equation must be solved (i.e., no assumptions can be made).

$$K_{a_2} = \frac{[H_3O^+][SO_4^{2-}]}{[HSO_4^-]} = 0.011 = \frac{x^2}{0.604 - x} \qquad x^2 = 0.00664 - 0.011x$$

$$x^2 + 0.011x - 0.00664 = 0$$

$$x = \frac{-b \pm \sqrt{b^2 - 4ac}}{2a} = \frac{-0.011 \pm \sqrt{1.2 \times 10^{-4} + 2.7 \times 10^{-2}}}{2} = 0.077 = [H_3O^+]$$

$$pH = -\log_{10}(0.077) = 1.1$$

50. **(M)** Oxidation: $\{SO_3^{2-}(aq) + H_2O(l) \longrightarrow SO_4^{2-}(aq) + 2\,H^+(aq) + 2\,e^-\} \times 5$

Reduction: $\{MnO_4^-(aq) + 8\,H^+(aq) + 5\,e^- \longrightarrow Mn^{2+}(aq) + 4\,H_2O(l)\} \times 2$

Net: $5\,SO_3^{2-}(aq) + 2\,MnO_4^-(aq) + 6\,H^+(aq) \longrightarrow 5\,SO_4^{2-}(aq) + 2\,Mn^{2+}(aq) + 3\,H_2O(l)$

$$\text{mass Na}_2SO_3 = 26.50\ \text{mL} \times \frac{1\ \text{L}}{1000\ \text{mL}} \times \frac{0.0510\ \text{mol MnO}_4^-}{1\ \text{L soln}} \times \frac{5\ \text{mol SO}_3^{2-}}{2\ \text{mol MnO}_4^-} \times \frac{1\ \text{mol Na}_2SO_3}{1\ \text{mol SO}_3^{2-}}$$

$$\times \frac{126.0\ \text{g Na}_2SO_3}{1\ \text{mol Na}_2SO_3} = 0.426\ \text{g Na}_2SO_3$$

51. **(M)** This question is concerned with assaying for the mass percent of iron in an ore. The assay in this instance involves the quantitative determination of the amount of metal in an ore by chemical analysis. The titration for iron in the sample does not occur directly but rather indirectly via the number of moles of $I_2(aq)$ produced from the reaction of $Fe^{3+}(aq)$ with excess $I^-(aq)$:

$2\,Fe^{3+}(aq) + 2\,I^-(aq) \rightarrow 2\,Fe^{2+}(aq) + I_2(aq)$

The number of moles of $I_2(aq)$ produced is then determined by titrating the iodide-treated sample with sodium thiosulfate. The balanced oxidation reaction that forms the basis for the titration is

$I_2(aq) + 2\,S_2O_3^-(aq) \rightarrow 2\,I^-(aq) + S_4O_6^{2-}(aq)$

The stoichiometric ratio is one $I_2(aq)$ reacting with two $S_2O_3^{2-}(aq)$ in this titration. The number of moles of $I_2(aq)$ formed is therefore

$$0.01525\ \text{L S}_2O_3^-(aq) \times \frac{0.100\ \text{mol S}_2O_3^-(aq)}{1\ \text{L S}_2O_3^-(aq)} \times \frac{1\ \text{mol I}_2(aq)}{2\ \text{mol S}_2O_3^-(aq)} = 7.63 \times 10^{-4}\ \text{mol I}_2(aq)$$

Hence, the number of moles of $Fe^{3+}(aq)$ released when the sample is dissolved is

$$7.63 \times 10^{-4}\ \text{mol I}_2(aq) \times \frac{2\ \text{mol Fe}^{3+}(aq)}{1\ \text{mol I}_2(aq)} = 1.53 \times 10^{-3}\ \text{mol Fe}^{3+}(aq)$$

Consequently, the mass percent of iron in the ore is

$$1.53 \times 10^{-3}\ \text{mol Fe}^{3+}(aq) \times \frac{55.8452\ \text{g Fe}^{3+}(aq)}{1\,\text{mol Fe}^{3+}(aq)} \times \frac{1}{1.500\ \text{g of Fe ore}} \times 100\% = 5.70\%$$

52. **(M)** First you must realize that pressure and temperature are irrelevant, but must be constant when answering this question. The reaction is $Pb^{2+}(aq) + H_2S(aq) \rightarrow 2\,H^+(aq) + PbS(s)\downarrow$ This means that there is a one to one relationship between the moles of PbS and H_2S. If we realize that 1 m^3 is 1000 L (40 times larger than the sample used), then we can calculate the mass of PbS in 1 m^3, namely, 40×0.535 g PbS = 21.4 g PbS.

The mass of sulfur can be calculated using stoichiometry.

$$\text{mass of S} = 21.4 \text{ g PbS} \times \frac{1 \text{ mol PbS}}{239.3 \text{ g PbS}} \times \frac{1 \text{ mol S}}{1 \text{ mol PbS}} \times \frac{32.066 \text{ g S}}{1 \text{ mol S}} = 2.87 \text{ g S (per 1 m}^3)$$

Alternatively, knowing that the mass percent of S in PbS is 13.40 %. We can calculate the mass of sulfur as: $21.4 \text{ g PbS} \times \dfrac{13.40 \text{ g S}}{100 \text{ g PbS}} = 2.87 \text{ g S (per 1 m}^3 \text{ natural gas)}$.

53. **(E)**
(a) $Mg = +2, O = -2, S = -(+2 - 3 \times 2) = +4$;
(b) $Cl = -4, S = +4$;
(c) $Mg = +2, O = -2, S = -(+2 - 4 \times 2) = +6$;
(d) $I = -1, S = -\dfrac{1}{2} \times (-2) = +1$;
(e) $N = -3, S = -1/4 \times (-3 \times 4) = +3$.

54. **(E) (a)** $+1$; **(b)** $+2$; **(c)** $+2$ and **(d)** $+2.5$

Nitrogen Family

55. **(M)**
(a) The Haber-Bosch process is the principal artificial method of fixing atmospheric nitrogen. $N_2(g) + 3 H_2(g) \rightleftharpoons 2 NH_3(g)$

(b) The first step of the Ostwald process: $4 NH_3(g) + 5 O_2(g) \xrightarrow{850\,°C,\,Pt} 4 NO(g) + 6 H_2O(g)$

(c) The second and third steps of the process: $2 NO(g) + O_2(g) \rightarrow 2 NO_2(g)$
$$3 NO_2(g) + H_2O(l) \rightarrow 2 HNO_3(aq) + NO(g)$$

56. **(M)**
(a) $2 NH_4NO_3(s) \xrightarrow{400\,°C} 2 N_2(g) + O_2(g) + 4 H_2O(g)$

The equation was balanced by inspection, by realizing first that each mole of $NH_4NO_3(s)$ would produce 1 mol $N_2(g)$ and 2 mol $H_2O(l)$, with 1 mol O [or 1/2 mol $O_2(g)$] remaining.

(b) $NaNO_3(s) \rightarrow NaNO_2(s) + 1/2 O_2(g)$ or $2 NaNO_3(s) \rightarrow 2 NaNO_2(s) + O_2(g)$
(c) $Pb(NO_3)_2(s) \rightarrow PbO(s) + 2 NO_2(g) + 1/2 O_2(g)$
$2 Pb(NO_3)_2(s) \rightarrow 2 PbO(s) + 4 NO_2(g) + O_2(g)$

57. **(D)** Begin with the chemical formulas of the species involved:

$$Na_2CO_3(aq) + O_2(g) + NO(g) \rightarrow NaNO_2(aq)$$

Oxygen is reduced and nitrogen (in NO) is oxidized. We use the ion-electron method.

Two couples:	$NO(g) \rightarrow NO_2^-(aq)$ and	$O_2 \rightarrow$ products
Balance oxygens:	$H_2O + NO \rightarrow NO_2^-$	$O_2 \rightarrow 2\,H_2O$
Balance hydrogens:	$H_2O + NO \rightarrow NO_2^- + 2\,H^+$	$4\,H^+ + O_2 \rightarrow 2\,H_2O$
Balance charge:	$H_2O + NO \rightarrow NO_2^- + 2\,H^+ + e^-$	$4\,e^- + 4\,H^+ + O_2 \rightarrow 2\,H_2O$
Combine:	$4\,H_2O + 4\,NO + 4\,H^+ + O_2 \rightarrow 2\,H_2O + 4NO_2^- + 8\,H^+$	
Simplify:	$2\,H_2O + 4\,NO + O_2 \rightarrow 4NO_2^- + 4\,H^+$	
Add spectator ions:	$4\,Na^+ + 2CO_3^{2-} \rightarrow 4\,Na^+ + 2CO_3^{2-}$	
	$2\,Na_2CO_3 + 2\,H_2O + 4\,NO + O_2 \rightarrow 4\,NaNO_2 + 2\,H_2O + 2\,CO_2$	
simplify:	$2\,Na_2CO_3(aq) + 4\,NO(g) + O_2(g) \rightarrow 4\,NaNO_2(aq) + 2\,CO_2(g)$	

58. **(E)** mass % $HNO_3 = \dfrac{15\ \text{mol HNO}_3 \times \dfrac{63.01\ \text{g HNO}_3}{1\ \text{mol HNO}_3}}{1\ \text{L soln} \times \dfrac{1000\ \text{mL}}{1\ \text{L}} \times \dfrac{1.41\ \text{g}}{1\ \text{mL soln}}} \times 100\% = 67\%\ HNO_3$

59. **(E)** $75 \times 10^9\ \text{gal} \times \dfrac{15\ \text{miles}}{1\ \text{gal}} \times \dfrac{5\ \text{g}}{1\ \text{mile}} \times \dfrac{1\ \text{kg}}{1000\ \text{g}} = 6 \times 10^9\ \text{kg of nitrogen oxides released.}$

60. **(E)** $2\,NH_{3(g)} + 3\,NO(g) \rightarrow 5/2\,N_2(g) + 3\,H_2O(g)$ (or, dividing by 2):

$NH_{3(g)} + 3/2NO(g) \rightarrow 5/4N_2(g) + 3/2H_2O(g)$

$\Delta_r H^\circ = \Sigma \Delta_f H^\circ_{\text{products}} - \Sigma \Delta_f H^\circ_{\text{reactants}}$

$\Delta_r H^\circ = [5/4(0\ \text{kJ mol}^{-1}) + 3/2(-241.8\ \text{kJ mol}^{-1})]$
$-[3/2(90.25\ \text{kJ mol}^{-1}) + 1(-46.11\ \text{kJ mol}^{-1})] = -452\ \text{kJ mol}^{-1}$

61. **(M)**

(a) $2\,NO_2(g) \rightleftharpoons N_2O_4(g)$

(b)   i) $HNO_2(aq) + N_2H_5^+(aq) \rightarrow HN_3(aq) + 2H_2O(l) + H^+(aq)$
      ii) $HN_3(aq) + HNO_2(aq) \rightarrow N_2(g) + H_2O(l) + N_2O(g)$

(c) $H_3PO_4(aq) + 2\,NH_3(aq) \rightarrow (NH_4)_2HPO_4(aq)$

62. **(M)**

(a) $3\,Ag(s) + 4\,H^+(aq) + 4\,NO_3^-(aq) \longrightarrow 3\,AgNO_3(aq) + NO(g) + 2\,H_2O(l)$

(b) $(CH_3)_2\,NNH_2(l) + 4\,O_2(g) \longrightarrow 2\,CO_2(g) + 4\,H_2O(l) + N_2(g)$

(c) $NaH_2PO_4(s) + 2Na_2HPO_4(s) \xrightarrow{\Delta} 2H_2O(l) + Na_5P_3O_{10}(s)$

63. **(M)**

(a)	$CH_3(NH)NH_2$ has 20 valence electrons.	
(b)	$(CH_3)_2NNH_2$ has 26 valence electrons.	
(c)	N_2O_4 has 34 valence electrons.	
(d)	H_3PO_4 has 32 valence electrons.	
(e)	$ClNO_2$ has 24 valence electrons.	

64. **(M)** Hyponitrous acid is a weak diprotic acid while nitramide has an amide group, $—NH_2$

Both Lewis structures for nitramide are plausible based on the information supplied. To choose between them would require further information about #2 and #3, such as whether the molecule contains a nitrogen-nitrogen bond. Experimental evidence indicates the structure adopted is the one with the nitrogen-nitrogen bond, i.e. structure #3.

65. **(E)**

(a) HPO_4^{2-}, hydrogen phosphate ion

(b) $Ca_2P_2O_7$, calcium pyrophosphate or calcium diphosphate

(c) $H_6P_4O_{13}$, tetrapolyphosphoric acid

66. **(E)**

(a) $HONH_2$, hydroxylamine

(b) $CaHPO_4$, calcium hydrogen phosphate

(c) Li_3N, lithium nitride

67. **(M)**

(i)	$2 H^+(aq) + N_2O_4(aq) + 2 e^- \rightarrow 2 HNO_2(aq)$	$E°_1 = +1.065$ V
(ii)	$2 HNO_2(aq) + 2 H^+(aq) + 2 e^- \rightarrow 2 NO(aq) + 2 H_2O(l)$	$E°_2 = +0.996$ V
(iii)	$N_2O_4(aq) + 4 H^+(aq) + 4 e^- \rightarrow 2 NO(aq) + 2 H_2O(l)$	$E°_3 = ?$ V

Recall that $\Delta_r G° = -zFE°$ and that $\Delta_r G°$ values, not standard voltages are additive for reactions in which the number of electrons do not cancel out.

So, $-4 FE°_3 = -2 F(1.065 \text{ V}) + -2 F(0.996 \text{ V})$ $E°_3 = 1.031$ V (4 sig figs)

68. **(M)**

(i)	$2 NO_3^-(aq) + 2 H_2O(l) + 2 e^- \rightarrow N_2O_4(aq) + 4 OH^-(aq)$	$E°_1 = -0.86$ V
(ii)	$N_2O_4(aq) + 2 e^- \rightarrow 2 NO_2^-(aq)$	$E°_2 = +0.87$ V
(iii)	$2 NO_3^-(aq) + 2 H_2O(l) + 4 e^- \rightarrow 2 NO_2^-(aq) + 4 OH^-(aq)$	$E°_3 = ?$ V

Recall that $\Delta_r G° = -zFE°$ and that $\Delta_r G°$ values, not standard voltages, are additive for reactions in which the numbers of electrons do not cancel out.

So, $-4 FE°_3 = -2 F(-0.86 \text{ V}) + -2 F(0.87 \text{ V})$

$-4 FE°_3 = 1.72 F - 1.74 F = 0.02 F$ (1 sig fig)

$E°_3 = 0.005$ V (1 sig fig)

69. **(M)**

(a) The nitrogen atom cannot bond to five fluorine atoms because, as a second-row element, it cannot accommodate more than four electron pairs.

(b) The NF_3 molecule is trigonal pyramidal. The lone pair on the N atom causes the F—N—F bond angle to decrease from the ideal tetrahedral bond angle of 109° to 102.5°.

70. **(M)** On the basis of electronegativities, the N—H and N—F bonds are both quite polar. However, the polarities of the bonds are opposite. In NH_3, the H atoms are slightly positive and in NF_3, the N atom is slightly positive. The lone pair on N presumably enhances the bond dipoles in NH_3 and diminishes the bond dipoles in NF_3. Consequently, the NH_3 is very polar and NF_3 is less so.

Hydrogen

71. **(M)** The four reactions of interest are: (Note: $\Delta_{comb}H° = \Sigma\Delta_f H°_{products} - \Sigma\Delta_f H°_{reactants}$)

$CH_4(g) + 2 O_{2(g)} \rightarrow CO_2(g) + 2 H_2O(l)$ $\Delta_{comb}H° = -890.3$ kJ mol^{-1}
(Molar mass $CH_4 = 16.0428$ g mol^{-1})

$C_2H_6(g) + 7/2 O_{2(g)} \rightarrow 2 CO_2(g) + 3 HO(l)$ $\Delta_{comb}H° = -1559.7$ kJ mol^{-1}
(Molar mass $C_2H_6 = 30.070$ g mol^{-1})

$C_3H_8(g) + 5 O_{2(g)} \rightarrow 3 CO_2(g) + 4 H_2O(l)$ $\Delta_{comb}H° = -2219.9$ kJ mol^{-1}
(Molar mass $C_3H_8 = 44.097$ g mol^{-1})

$C_4H_{10}(g) + 13/2 O_{2(g)} \rightarrow 4 CO_2(g) + 5 H_2O(l)$ $\Delta_{comb}H° = -2877.4$ kJ mol^{-1}
(Molar mass $C_4H_{10} = 58.123$ g mol^{-1})

72. **(M)** Using the answers obtained in question 71, the per gram energy release is:
$CH_4(g) - 55.5$ kJ; $C_2H_6(g) - 51.9$ kJ; $C_3H_8(g) - 50.3$ kJ; $C_4H_{10}(g) - 49.5$ kJ

    (a) $C_4H_{10}(g)$ evolves the most energy on a per mole basis ($- 2877.4$ kJ).

    (b) $CH_4(g)$ evolves the most energy on a per gram basis ($- 55.5$ kJ).

    (c) $CH_4(g)$ is the most desirable alkane from the standpoint of emission, producing the least quantity of $CO_2(g)$ per mole and/or per gram of fuel burned (as well per kJ of energy produced).

73. **(E)**

    (a) $2\ Al(s) + 6\ HCl(aq) \rightarrow 2\ AlCl_3(aq) + 3\ H_2(g)$

    (b) $3\ CO(g) + 7\ H_2(g) \rightarrow C_3H_8(g) + 3\ H_2O(g)$

    (c) $MnO_2(s) + 2\ H_2(g) \xrightarrow{\Delta} Mn(s) + 2\ H_2O(g)$

74. **(M)**

    (a) $2\ H_2O(l) \xrightarrow{\text{electricity}} O_2(g) + 2\ H_2(g)$

    (b) $2\ HI(aq) + Zn(s) \rightarrow ZnI_2(aq) + H_2(g)$ Any moderately active metal is suitable.

    (c) $Mg(s) + H_2SO_4(aq) \rightarrow MgSO_4(aq) + H_2(g)$ Any strong acid is suitable.

    (d) $CO(g) + H_2O(g) \rightarrow CO_2(g) + H_2(g)$

75. **(M)** $CaH_2(s) + 2\ H_2O(l) \rightarrow Ca(OH)_2(aq) + 2\ H_2(g)$

$$Ca(s) + 2\ H_2O(l) \rightarrow Ca(OH)_2(aq) + H_2(g)$$
$$\overline{2\ Na(s) + 2\ H_2O(l) \rightarrow 2\ NaOH(aq) + H_2(g)}$$

    (a) The reaction that produces the largest volume of $H_2(g)$ per liter of water also produces the largest amount of $H_2(g)$ per mole of water used. All three reactions use two moles of water and the reaction with $CaH_2(s)$ produces the most $H_2(g)$.

    (b) We can compare three reactions that produce the same amount of hydrogen; the one that requires the smallest mass of solid produces the greatest amount of H_2 per gram of solid. The amount of hydrogen we will choose, to simplify matters, is 2 moles, which means that we compare 1 mol CaH_2 (42.09 g) with 2 mol Ca (80.16 g) and with 4 mol Na (91.96 g). Clearly CaH_2 produces the greatest amount of H_2 per gram of solid.

76. **(M)** The balanced equation is $C_{17}H_{33}COOH(l) + H_2(g) \rightarrow C_{17}H_{35}COOH(s)$. One mole of oleic acid requires one mole of $H_2(g)$.

$$V = \frac{nRT}{P} = \frac{1.00\ \text{mol} \times 0.08206\ \dfrac{\text{L atm}}{\text{mol K}} \times 298\ \text{K}}{752\ \text{mm Hg} \times \dfrac{1\ \text{atm}}{760\ \text{mmHg}}} \times \frac{0.95\ \text{L calculated}}{1.0\ \text{L produced}} = 23.5\ \text{L H}_2(g)$$

77. **(M)** Greatest mass percent hydrogen:
The atmosphere is mostly $N_2(g)$ and $O_2(g)$ with only a trace of hydrogen containing gas molecules. Seawater is $H_2O(l)$, natural gas is $CH_4(g)$ and ammonia is $NH_3(g)$. Each of these compounds has one non-hydrogen atom, and the non-hydrogen atoms have approximately the same mass ($\sim 14 \pm 2$ g mol^{-1}). Since CH_4 has the highest hydrogen atom to non-hydrogen atom ratio, this molecule has the greatest mass percent hydrogen.

78. **(M)** The reaction is $CaH_2(s) + 2\, H_2O(l) \rightarrow Ca(OH)_2(aq) + 2\, H_2(g)$

First we calculate the amount of $H_2(g)$ needed and then the mass of $CaH_2(s)$ required.

$$\text{mol } H_2 = \frac{PV}{RT} = \frac{722 \text{ mm Hg} \times \dfrac{1 \text{ atm}}{760 \text{ mmHg}} \times 235 \text{ L}}{0.08206 \text{ L atm mol}^{-1}\text{K}^{-1} \times (273.2 + 19.7)\text{K}} = 9.29 \text{ mol } H_2$$

$$\text{mass } CaH_2 = 9.29 \text{ mol } H_2 \times \frac{1 \text{ mol } CaH_2}{2 \text{ mol } H_2} \times \frac{42.09 \text{ g } CaH_2}{1 \text{ mol } CaH_2} = 196 \text{ g } CaH_2$$

79. **(M)** NH_2^- has 8 valence electrons (and is isoelectronic with H_2O). The first four MO's are fully occupied. Because the $2p_x$ orbital on N is strongly bonding in the bent configuration, as shown in Figure 22-27, the energy of the NH_2^- will be much lower for the bent configuration. (The same argument applies to H_2O.) On the basis of molecular orbital theory, we expect that NH_2^- will be bent.

80. **(M)** NH_2^+ has 6 valence electrons and is isoelectronic with CH_2. On this basis, we anticipate that structure of NH_2^+ will be similar to that of CH_2: a slightly bent molecule with two unpaired electrons.

INTEGRATIVE AND ADVANCED EXERCISES

81. **(M)** In step (1), oxygen is converted to H_2O by the reaction $H_2(g) + \dfrac{1}{2}O_2(g) \rightarrow H_2O(l)$.

Step (2) ensures that unreacted hydrogen from step (1) is also converted to $H_2O(l)$. The dehydrated zeolite has a very strong affinity for water molecules and thus, $H_2O(l)$ is removed from the gas mixture.

82. **(M)** The AsF_6^- is octahedral. The F—AsF bond angles are 90°. The most important Lewis structure for the $HCNKrF^+$ ion is shown below. If we assume that the lone pairs on Kr occupy equatorial positions (to minimize lone pair repulsions), then the $HCNKrF^+$ ion is linear:

$$H\!-\!C \equiv \underset{+1}{N}\!-\!\ddot{K}r\!:\!-\!\ddot{F}\!:$$

83. **(E)** The electrolysis reaction is $2 H_2O(l) \xrightarrow{\text{electroysis}} 2 H_2(g) + O_2(g)$. In this reaction, 2 moles of water are decomposed to produce one mole of oxygen and two moles of hydrogen. We use the data in the exercise to determine the volumes of oxygen and hydrogen produced.

$$n(H_2O) = \frac{m}{M} = \frac{17.3\ g}{18.015\ g/mol} = 0.96\ mol$$

$$V(O_2) = \frac{nRT}{p} = 0.96\ mol\ H_2O \times \frac{1\ mol\ O_2}{2\ mol\ H_2O} \times \frac{0.08206\ L\ atm/mol\ K \times 298.15\ K}{755\ mmHg \times \dfrac{1\ atm}{760\ mmHg}} = 11.8\ L$$

$$V(H_2) = \frac{nRT}{p} = 0.96\ mol\ H_2O \times \frac{2\ mol\ O_2}{2\ mol\ H_2O} \times \frac{0.08206\ L\ atm/mol\ K \times 298.15\ K}{755\ mmHg \times \dfrac{1\ atm}{760\ mmHg}} = 23.6\ L$$

84. **(M)** $NaNO_2$ decolorizes acidic solution of $KMnO_4$ according to the following balanced chemical equation:

$2 KMnO_4 + 3 H_2SO_4 + 5 NaNO_2 \rightarrow 5 NaNO_3 + K_2SO_4 + 2 MnSO_4 + 3 H_2O$

$NaNO_3$ does not react with acidic solution of $KMnO_4$.

85. **(D)** First we balance the equation, then determine the number of millimoles of $NH_3(g)$ that are produced, and finally find the $[NO_3^-]$ in the original solution.

The skeleton half-equations: $NO_3^-(aq) \longrightarrow NH_3(g) \qquad Zn(s) \longrightarrow Zn(OH)_4^{2-}(aq)$

Balance O's and H's: $NO_3^-(aq) \longrightarrow NH_3(g) + 3 H_2O(l)$

$$NO_3^-(aq) + 9 H^+(aq) \longrightarrow NH_3(g) + 3 H_2O(l)$$

Balance charge and add $OH^-(aq)$ $\quad NO_3^-(aq) + 6 H_2O(l) + 8 e^- \longrightarrow NH_3(g) + 9 OH^-(aq)$

Add OH^- (ad)'s and then electrons: $Zn(s) + 4 OH^-(aq) \longrightarrow Zn(OH)_4^{2-}(aq) + 2 e^-$

Oxidation: $\qquad \{ Zn(s) + 4 OH^-(aq) \longrightarrow Zn(OH)_4^{2-}(aq) + 2 e^- \} \quad \times 4$

Reduction: $\qquad NO_3^-(aq) + 6 H_2O(l) + 8 e^- \longrightarrow NH_3(g) + 9 OH^-(aq)$

Net: $NO_3^-(aq) + 4 Zn(s) + 6 H_2O(l) + 7 OH^-(aq) \longrightarrow Zn(OH)_4^{2-}(aq) + NH_3(g)$

The titration reactions are the following.

$HCl(aq) + NaOH(aq) \longrightarrow NaCl(aq) + H_2O(l) \quad NH_3(aq) + HCl(aq) \longrightarrow NH_4Cl(aq)$

$$mmol\ excess\ HCl = 32.10\ mL \times \frac{0.1000\ mmol\ NaOH}{1\ mL\ soln} \times \frac{1\ mmol\ HCl}{1\ mmol\ NaOH} = 3.210\ mmol\ HCl$$

$$mmol\ HCl\ at\ start = 50.00\ mL \times \frac{0.1500\ mmol\ HCl}{1\ mL\ soln} = 7.500\ mmol\ HCl$$

$$mmol\ NH_3\ produced = (7.500 - 3.210) \qquad mmol\ HCl \times \frac{1\ mmol\ NH_3}{1\ mmol\ HCl} = 4.290\ mmol\ NH_3$$

$$[NO_3^-] = \frac{4.290 \text{ mmol } NH_3 \times \dfrac{1 \text{ mmol } NO_3^-}{1 \text{ mmol } NH_3}}{25.00 \text{ mL soln}} = 0.1716 \text{ M}$$

Notice that it was not necessary to balance the equation, since NO_3^- and NH_3 are the only nitrogen-containing species involved, and thus they must be in a one-to-one molar ratio.

86. **(M)** First we compute the root-mean-square speed of O at 1500 K.

$$u_{rms} = \sqrt{\frac{3RT}{M}} = \sqrt{\frac{3 \times 8.314 \text{ J mol}^{-1}\text{K}^{-1} \times 1500 K}{0.0160 \text{ kg/mol}}} = 1.5 \times 10^3 \text{ m/s}$$

Kinetic Energy =

$$KE = \tfrac{1}{2}mu^2 = 0.5 \times \frac{0.0160 \text{ kg/mol}}{6.022 \times 10^{23} \text{ atoms/mol}} \times (1.5 \times 10^3 \text{ m/s})^2 = 3.0 \times 10^{-20} \text{ J/atom}$$

87. **(M)** Reduction: $\{ 2 NO_3^-(aq) + 10 H^+(aq) + 8 e^- \rightarrow N_2O(g) + 5 H_2O(l) \} \times 7$

Oxidation: $\{C_6H_{11}O(aq) + 3 H_2O(l) \rightarrow HOOC(CH_2)_4COOH(aq) + 7 H^+(aq) + 7 e^-\} \times 8$

Net: $14 NO_3^-(aq) + 14 H^+(aq) + 8 C_6H_{11}O(aq) \rightarrow 7 N_2O(g) + 8 HOOC(CH_2)_4COOH(aq) + 11 H_2O(l)$

88. **(D)** The Lewis structures for the two compounds are drawn below. The four bonded groups in XeO_4 and no lone pairs on the central atom give it a tetrahedral shape in which there are four oxygen atoms on the periphery of the molecule. These rounded tetrahedral should not stick well together. In fact, each oxygen is slightly negatively charged and they should repel each other. Thus, we expect weak intermolecular forces between XeO_4 molecules. In XeO_3, on the other hand, the three bonds and one lone pair produces a trigonal pyramidal molecule in which the central Xe (carrying a slight positive charge), is exposed to other molecules. There thus can be strong dipole-dipole forces leading to strong intermolecular forces and a relatively high boiling point vis-à-vis XeO_4.

Note: You can also expand the octets to reduce formal charges. There are a number of resonance forms, however, Lewis structures(octets) are shown.

89. **(E)** The N center in the ammonium ion is the reducing agent, while Cl in the perchlorate anion is the oxidizing agent.

$$2 NH_4ClO_4(s) \longrightarrow N_2(g) + 4 H_2O(g) + Cl_2(g) + 2 O_2(g)$$

90. **(E)** $\Delta_f H° =$ Bonds broken in reactants – Bonds formed in products

(a) $\tfrac{1}{2} Cl_2(g) + \tfrac{1}{2} F_2(g) \rightarrow Cl{-}F(g)$ $\qquad \Delta_f H° = \tfrac{1}{2} (159 \text{ kJ mol}^{-1}) + \tfrac{1}{2} (243 \text{ kJ mol}^{-1}) - 251 \text{ kJ mol}^{-1} = -50 \text{ kJ mol}^{-1}$

(b) $\tfrac{1}{2} O_2(g) + F_2(g) \rightarrow F{-}O{-}F(g)$ $\qquad \Delta_f H° = \tfrac{1}{2} (498 \text{ kJ mol}^{-1}) + (159 \text{ kJ mol}^{-1}) - 2(213 \text{ kJ mol}^{-1}) = -18 \text{ kJ mol}^{-1}$

(c) $\frac{1}{2} O_2(g) + Cl_2(g) \rightarrow Cl—O—Cl(g)$ $\quad \Delta_f H° = \frac{1}{2}(498 \text{ kJ mol}^{-1}) + (243 \text{ kJ mol}^{-1}) - 2(205 \text{ kJ mol}^{-1}) = +82 \text{ kJ mol}^{-1}$

(d) $\frac{1}{2} N_2(g) + 3/2\, F_2(g) \rightarrow NF_3(g)$ $\quad \Delta_f H° = \frac{1}{2}(946 \text{ kJ mol}^{-1}) + 1.5(159 \text{ kJ mol}^{-1}) - 3(280 \text{ kJ mol}^{-1}) = -128.\underline{5} \text{ kJ mol}^{-1}$

91. **(E)** The electrode reaction is: $\quad F_2(g) + 2\, e^- \longrightarrow 2\, F^-(aq)$

$\Delta G° = 2\, \Delta_f G°[F^-(aq)] - \Delta_f G°[F_2(g)] = 2(-278.8 \text{ kJ/mol}) - (0 \text{ kJ/mol})$

$\Delta G° = -557.6 \text{ kJ/mol} = -2\, z\text{FE}°$

$E° = \dfrac{-557.6 \times 10^3 \text{ J/mol}}{2 \times 96,485 \text{ C/mol}} = +2.890 \text{ V}$

This value compares favorably with the value of +2.866 V in Appendix D.

92. **(M)** Each simple cubic unit cell has one Po atom at each of its eight corners, but each corner is shared among eight unit cells. Thus, there is a total of one Po atom per unit cell. The edge of that unit cell is 335 pm. From this information we obtain the density of polonium.

$$\text{density} = \dfrac{1\,\text{Po atom} \times \dfrac{1\,\text{mol Po}}{6.022 \times 10^{23}\,\text{Po atoms}} \times \dfrac{209\,\text{g Po}}{1\,\text{mol Po}}}{\left(335\,\text{pm} \times \dfrac{1\,\text{m}}{10^{12}\,\text{pm}} \times \dfrac{100\,\text{cm}}{1\,\text{m}}\right)^3} = 9.23\,\text{g/cm}^3$$

93. **(M)** First we write the molecular orbital diagram of each of the species. From each molecular orbital diagram we determine the number of bonding electrons and the number of antibonding electrons (*) and thus the bond order [(number of bonding electrons — number of antibonding electrons) $\div 2$]. Species with high bond order have strong bonds, which are short. Those with low bond order have weak bonds, which are long.

Number of e^-	σ_{1s}	σ_{1s}^*	σ_{2s}	σ_{2s}^*	σ_{2p}	π_{2p}	π_{2p}^*	σ_{2p}^*	Antibonding e^-	Bond order
O_2^+ $\quad (2 \times 8) - 1 = 15$	⇅	⇅	⇅	⇅	⇅	⇅ ⇅	↑	□	5	2.5
O_2 $\quad (2 \times 8) = 16$	⇅	⇅	⇅	⇅	⇅	⇅ ⇅	↑ ↑	□	6	2
O_2^- $\quad (2 \times 8) + 1 = 17$	⇅	⇅	⇅	⇅	⇅	⇅ ⇅	⇅ ↑	□	7	1.5
O_2^{2-} $\quad (2 \times 8) + 2 = 18$	⇅	⇅	⇅	⇅	⇅	⇅ ⇅	⇅ ⇅	□	8	1.0

We have only listed the number of antibonding electrons above because, for each species, the number of bonding electrons is the same, namely 10. Recall that the bond order is determined as follows: bond order = (number of bonding electrons — number of antibonding electrons) $\div 2$

(a) In order of increasing bond distance: $O_2^+ < O_2 < O_2^- < O_2^{2-}$

(b) In order of increasing bond strength: $O_2^{2-} < O_2^- < O_2 < O_2^+$

94. (M)

(a)

As shown in the Lewis structures above, the net result of this reaction is breaking a C—Cl bond. From Table 10-3, the energy of this bond is 339 kJ/mol, and this must be the energy of the photons involved in the reaction.

(b) $E = h\nu$ or $\nu = E/h$ on a molecular basis. Thus, we have the following.

$$\nu = \frac{339 \times 10^3 \text{ J/mol}}{6.626 \times 10^{-34} \text{ J} \cdot \text{s} \times 6.022 \times 10^{23} / \text{mol}} = 8.50 \times 10^{14} \text{ s}^{-1}$$

$$\lambda = \frac{c}{\nu} = \frac{3.00 \times 10^8 \text{ m/s}}{8.50 \times 10^{14} / \text{s}} = 3.53 \times 10^{-7} \text{ m} \times \frac{10^9 \text{ nm}}{1 \text{ m}} = 353 \text{ nm}$$

This radiation is in the near ultraviolet region of the electromagnetic spectrum.

95. (M)

(a) % P indicates the number of grams of P per 100 g of material, while % P_4O_{10} indicates the number of grams of P_4O_{10} per 100 g of material.

$$\text{mass P} = 1.000 \text{ g P}_4\text{O}_{10} \times \frac{1 \text{ mol P}_4\text{O}_{10}}{283.89 \text{ g P}_4\text{O}_{10}} \times \frac{4 \text{ mol P}}{1 \text{ mol P}_4\text{O}_{10}} \times \frac{30.974 \text{ g P}}{1 \text{ mol P}} = 0.436 \text{ g P}$$

Thus, multiplying the mass of P_4O_{10} by 0.436 will give the mass (or mass percent) of P. % BPL indicates the number of grams of $Ca_3(PO_4)_2$ per 100 g of material.

$$\text{mass Ca}_3(\text{PO}_4)_2 = 1.000 \text{ g P}_4\text{O}_{10} \times \frac{1 \text{ mol P}_4\text{O}_{10}}{283.89 \text{ g P}_4\text{O}_{10}} \times \frac{4 \text{ mol P}}{1 \text{ mol P}_4\text{O}_{10}}$$

$$\times \frac{1 \text{ mol Ca}_3(\text{PO}_4)_2}{2 \text{ mol P}} \times \frac{310.18 \text{ g Ca}_3(\text{PO}_4)_2}{1 \text{ mol Ca}_3(\text{PO}_4)_2} = 2.185 \text{ g Ca}_3(\text{PO}_4)_2$$

Thus, multiplying the mass of P_4O_{10} (283.88) by 2.185 will give the mass (or mass %) of BPL.

(b) A %BPL greater than 100% means that the material has a larger %P than does pure $Ca_3(PO_4)_2$.

(c) $\%P = \dfrac{6 \text{ mol P}}{1\text{mol 3Ca}_3(\text{PO}_4)_2 \cdot \text{CaF}_2} \times \dfrac{1 \text{ mol 3Ca}_3(\text{PO}_4)_2 \cdot \text{CaF}_2}{1008.6 \text{ g 3Ca}_3(\text{PO}_4)_2 \cdot \text{ CaF}_2} \times \dfrac{30.974 \text{ g P}}{1 \text{ mol P}} \times 100\%$

$$= 18.43\% \text{ P}$$

$$\%\text{P}_4\text{O}_{10} = \frac{\%\text{P}}{0.436} = \frac{18.43}{0.436} = 42.3\% \text{ P}_4\text{O}_{10}$$

$$\%\text{BPL} = 2.185 \times \%\text{P}_4\text{O}_{10} = 2.185 \times 42.3\% \text{ P}_4\text{O}_{10} = 92.4\% \text{ BPL}$$

96. (M) The chemical equation is $Cl_2(g) \rightleftharpoons 2\,Cl(g)$. From Appendix D,
$\Delta_f H°[Cl(g)] = 121.7$ kJ/mol, 243.4 kJ/2 mol Cl or 243.4 kJ/mol Cl_2.
$\Delta_r S° = 2S°[Cl(g)] - S°[Cl_2(g)] = (2 \times 165.2) - 223.1 = 107.3$ J K^{-1} mol^{-1}.

We assume the values of $\Delta_r H°$ and $\Delta_r S°$ are unchanged from 298 K to 1000 K, and we calculate the value of $\Delta_r G°$ at 1000 K.

$\Delta_r G° = \Delta_r H° - T\Delta_r S° = 243.4$ kJ mol^{-1} $- (1000$ K $\times 0.1073$ kJ K^{-1} mol$^{-1}) = 136.1$ kJ
$\Delta_r G° = -RT \ln K_p$

$\ln K_p = \dfrac{-\Delta_r G°}{RT} = \dfrac{-136.1 \times 10^3 \text{ J/mol}}{8.314 \text{ J mol}^{-1}\text{ K}^{-1} \times 1000 \text{ K}} = -16.37 \qquad K_p = e^{-16.37} = 7.8 \times 10^{-8}$

Since the value of K_p is so small, we assume the initial $Cl_2(g)$ pressure is 1.00 atm.

Reaction:	$Cl_2(g) \rightleftharpoons$	$2\,Cl(g)$	$K_p = \dfrac{P_{Cl}^2}{P_{Cl_2}} = 7.8 \times 10^{-8} = \dfrac{(2x)^2}{1.00-x} \approx \dfrac{4x^2}{1.00}$
Initial:	1.00 atm	0 atm	
Changes:	$-x$ atm	$+2x$ atm	$x = \sqrt{\dfrac{7.8 \times 10^{-8}}{4}} = 1.4 \times 10^{-4}$
Equil:	$(1.00 - x)$	$2x$ atm	

Our assumption, that $x \ll 1.00$ atm, obviously is valid. x is the degree of dissociation. The % dissociation now can be calculated. % dissociation $= x \times 100\% = 1.4 \times 10^{-4} \times 100\% = 0.014\%$

97. (E) The *peroxo* prefix of peroxonitrous acid hints at the presence of a $-O-O-$ linkage in the molecule.

nitric acid   H—Ō—N—Ō|
                    ‖
                  |O|

peroxonitrous acid   H—Ō—Ō—N̄=Ō

98. (M) The Lewis structures of these two compounds are similar. If we designate CH_3 as Me and SiH_3 as Sl, the two Lewis structures are   Me—N̄—Me   Sl—N̄—Sl
                                                                                                                                                        | |
                                                                                                                                                      Me   Sl

The pyramidal structure of $N(CH_3)_3$ indicates a tetrahedral electron pair geometry, with sp^3 hybridization for N in $N(CH_3)_3$ and the lone pair of electrons residing in an sp^3 *hybrid* orbital. The N—C bond involves the overlap of $N(sp^3)-C(sp^3)$. The C—H bonds are $C(sp^3)-H(1s)$. The planar arrangement of $N(SiH_3)_3$ indicates that the nitrogen atom is sp^2 hybridized; the lone pair is in a $2p$ atomic orbital on the central N atom, perpendicular to the $N-Si$ plane in the center of the molecule. If we assume that the Si atom is sp^3 hybridized (to account for the four bonds each Si atom forms), the N—Si bond involves the overlap between $N(sp^2)-Si(sp^3)$. Thus, the Si—H bonds are $Si(sp^3)-H(1s)$.

99. **(M)** pH = 3.5 means $[H^+] = 10^{-3.5} = 3 \times 10^{-4}$ M. This is quite a dilute acidic solution, and we expect H_2SO_4 to be completely ionized under these circumstances.

$$\text{mass } H_2SO_4 = 1.00 \times 10^3 \text{ L} \times \frac{3 \times 10^{-4} \text{ mol } H^+}{1 \text{ L}} \times \frac{1 \text{ mol } H_2SO_4}{2 \text{ mol } H^+} \times \frac{98.08 \text{ g } H_2SO_4}{1 \text{ mol } H_2SO_4} = 15 \text{ g } H_2SO_4$$

$$\text{mass } Cl_2 = 1.00 \times 10^3 \text{ L} \times \frac{1000 \text{ cm}^3}{1 \text{ L}} \times \frac{1.03 \text{ g}}{1 \text{ cm}^3} \times \frac{70 \text{ g } Br_2}{10^6 \text{ g seawater}} \times \frac{1 \text{ mol } Br_2}{159.81 \text{ g } Br_2} \times \frac{1 \text{ mol } Cl_2}{1 \text{ mol } Br_2}$$

$$\times \frac{70.91 \text{ g } Cl_2}{1 \text{ mol } Cl_2} \times \frac{115 \text{ g } Cl_2 \text{ used}}{100 \text{ g } Cl_2 \text{ needed}} = 37 \text{ g } Cl_2$$

100. **(M)** $E = E^o - \dfrac{0.0592}{z} \log_{10} Q$;

assuming E = 0 for a process that is no longer spontaneous:

$$\log_{10} Q = \frac{zE^\circ}{0.0592} = \frac{(16)(0.065)}{0.0592} = 17.\underline{6} \qquad\qquad P_{SO_2} = 1 \times 10^{-6}$$

$$Q = 10^{17.\underline{6}} = 3.9 \times 10^{17} = \frac{(P_{SO_2})^8}{1^8 (H^+)^{16}} = \frac{(1 \times 10^{-6})^8}{1^8 (H^+)^{16}}$$

Solving for $[H^+]$ yields a value of 8×10^{-5} M, which corresponds to a pH of 4.1

Thus, the solution is still acidic.

101. **(M)** In the process of forming XeF_2 and $XeCl_2$, either a Cl—Cl bond or a F—F bond is broken. We note that the F—F bond is much weaker than the Cl—Cl bond and thus much less energy is required to break it. Since greater stability indicates that the resulting product is of lower energy, the greater stability for XeF_2 compared to $XeCl_2$ can be partially explained by the need to expend less energy to break the bonds of the reactants. (Another reason, of course, is that the shorter Xe—F bond is stronger, and hence more stable, than the somewhat longer Xe—Cl bond.)

102. **(M)**

Oxidations: $XeF_4(g) + 3 H_2O \longrightarrow XeO_3(g) + 4 HF(aq) + 2 H^+(aq) + 2 e^-$

$\{2 H_2O(l) \longrightarrow O_2(g) + 4 H^+(aq) + 4 e^-\} \times \frac{3}{2}$

Reduction: $\{XeF_4(g) + 4 e^- \longrightarrow Xe(g) + 4 F^-(aq)\} \qquad \times 2$

Net: $3 XeF_4(g) + 6 H_2O(l) \longrightarrow 2 XeO_3(g) + 12 HF(aq) + \frac{3}{2} O_2(g) + 2 Xe(g)$

The fact that O_2 is also produced indicates that there are two oxidation half-reactions. The production ratio of Xe and XeO_3 indicates the amount by which the other two half-reactions must be multiplied before they are added. Then the half-reaction for the production of O_2 is multiplied by $\frac{3}{2}$ to balance charge.

103. (M) $S(s) + 2 H^+(aq) + 2 e^- \rightarrow H_2S(g)$ $E^\circ = 0.174$ V

$S(s) + 2 H^+(aq) + 2 e^- \rightarrow H_2S(aq)$ $E^\circ = 0.144$ V

The difference is that one results in an aqueous solution being formed, while the other gives a gaseous product. They can both be correct because the product has a different phase (the products have different $\Delta_f G^\circ$ values, hence one would expect different E° values).

104. (M) The initial concentration of $Cl_2(aq) = \dfrac{6.4g}{70.91 \text{ g/mol}} = 0.090M$

$$Cl_2(aq) \; + \; H_2O(l) \; \xrightleftharpoons{\;K_c = 4.4 \times 10^{-4}\;} \; HOCl(aq) + \; H^+(aq) \; + \; Cl^-(aq)$$

initial   0.090 M   0 M   0 M   0 M

equil.   (0.090-x) M x M x M x M

{where x is the molar solubility of Cl_2 in water}

$$K = \frac{[HOCl(aq)][\,H^+(aq)]\,[Cl^-(aq)]}{[Cl_2(aq)]} = \frac{x^3}{0.090\text{-}x} = 4.4 \times 10^{-4}$$

By using successive approximations, we find $x = 0.030$ M, so:

$[HOCl(aq)] = [H^+(aq)] \; = \; [Cl^-(aq)] = 0.030$ M and $[Cl_2(aq)] = 0.090 - 0.030 = 0.060$ M

105. (M)

$2e^- + N_2(g) + 4 H^+(aq) + 2H_2O(l) \rightarrow 2 NH_3OH^+(aq)$ $E^\circ = -1.87$ V

$2 NH_3OH^+(aq) + H^+(aq) + 2e^- \rightarrow N_2H_5^+(aq) + 2 H_2O(l)$ $E^\circ = 1.42$ V

$N_2H_5^+(aq) + 3 H^+(aq) + 2e^- \rightarrow 2 NH_4^+(aq)$ $E^\circ = 1.275$ V

$\overline{N_2(g) + 8 H^+(aq) + \; 6e^- \rightarrow 2 NH_4^+(aq)}$ $E^\circ = 0.275$ V (see below)

$\Delta_r G^\circ = \Delta G^\circ_1 + \Delta G^\circ_2 + \Delta G^\circ_3 = -z_{tot} F E^\circ_{tot} = -zFE^\circ_1 - zFE^\circ_2 - zFE^\circ_3$

$E^\circ_{tot} = \dfrac{n_1 E^\circ_1 + n_2 E^\circ_2 + n_3 E^\circ_3}{n_{tot}}$

$E^\circ_{tot} = [2(-1.87) + 2(1.42) + 2(1.275)]/6 = 0.275$ V

moving on...

$2 HN_3(aq) \rightarrow 3 N_2(g) + 2 H^+(aq) + 2 e^-$ $E^\circ = +3.09$ V (oxidation)

$\underline{3 N_2(g) + 24 H^+(aq) + 18e^- \rightarrow 6 NH_4^+(aq)}$ $E^\circ = 0.275$ V (top equation multiplied by 3)

$2 HN_3(aq) \; + \; 22 H^+(aq) \; + \; 16 e^- \; \rightarrow \; 6 NH_4^+(aq)$ [*sum*]

[divide by 2]

$HN_3(aq) + 11 H^+(aq) + 8 e^- \rightarrow 3 NH_4^+(aq)$ $E^\circ = 0.70$ V

since

$\Delta_r G^\circ = \Delta G^\circ_1 + \Delta G^\circ_2 = -zFE^\circ_{tot} = -zFE^\circ_1 - zFE^\circ_2$

$E^\circ_{total} = [2(3.09) + 18(0.275)\,]/16 = 0.70$ V

106. (E) Ignoring distortions arising from different bond lengths and different bond orders, we can say the following:

(a) In $FClO_2$, the Cl atom is bonded to three atoms and a lone pair of electrons. The electron group geometry is tetrahedral. The molecular structure is ammonia-like (trigonal pyramidal).

(b) In $FClO_3$, the Cl atom is bonded to four atoms and has no lone pairs. The electron group geometry is tetrahedral. The molecular structure is methane-like (tetrahedral).

(c) In F_3ClO, the Cl atom is bonded to four atoms and has one lone pair. The electron group geometry is trigonal bipyramidal with the lone pair in an equatorial position. The molecular structure is SF_4-like (seesaw).

107. (E) Both molecules are V shaped, with a lone pair of electrons on the central atom. For O_3, the structure is a hybrid of two equivalent structures. In each of these structures, the central atom has a formal charge of +1. The oxygen–oxygen bond order is between 1 and 2. Although many resonance structures can be drawn for SO_2, in the most important structure, the formal charge on the S atom is zero and the sulfur–oxygen bonds are double bonds.

108. (M)

109. (M) $\Delta_f H^\circ = [\frac{3}{2}(498) - 3(36)] = 639 \text{ kJ mol}^{-1}$

The formation reaction is very endothermic and thus energetically unfavorable. This result supports the observation that Xe(g) does not react directly with $O_2(g)$ to form $XeO_3(g)$. Because the reaction converts 2.5 moles of gas into 1 mole of gas, we expect $\Delta_f S^\circ < 0$; thus, the reaction is also entropically unfavorable.

FEATURE PROBLEMS

110. (D) The goal here is to demonstrate that the three reactions result in the decomposition of water as the net reaction: Net: $2 H_2O \rightarrow 2 H_2 + O_2$ First balance each equation.

(1) $3 FeCl_2 + 4 H_2O \rightarrow Fe_3O_4 + HCl + H_2$ Balance by inspection. Notice that there are 3 Fe and 4 O on the right-hand side. Then balance Cl.

$$3 FeCl_2 + 4 H_2O \rightarrow Fe_3O_4 + 6 HCl + H_2$$

(2) $Fe_3O_4 + HCl + Cl_2 \rightarrow FeCl_3 + H_2O + O_2$ Try the half-equation method.

$Cl_2 + 2 e^- \rightarrow 2 Cl^-$ But realize that $Fe_3O_4 = Fe_2O_3 \cdot FeO$.

$2 FeO \rightarrow 2 Fe^{3+} + O_2 + 6 e^-$ Now combine the two half-equations.

$$2 FeO + 3 Cl_2 \rightarrow 2 Fe^{3+} + O_2 + 6 Cl^-$$

Add in $2 Fe_2O_3 + 12 H^+ \rightarrow 4 Fe^{3+} + 6 H_2O$

$$2 Fe_3O_4 + 3 Cl_2 + 12 H^+ \rightarrow 6 Fe^{3+} + O_2 + 6 Cl^- + 6 H_2O$$

And 12 Cl^- spectators: $2 Fe_3O_4 + 3 Cl_2 + 12 HCl \rightarrow 6 FeCl_3 + O_2 + 6 H_2O$

(3) $FeCl_3 \rightarrow FeCl_2 + Cl_2$ by inspection $2 FeCl_3 \rightarrow 2 FeCl_2 + Cl_2$

One strategy is to consider each of the three equations and the net equation. Only equation (1) produces hydrogen. Thus, we must run it twice. Only equation (2) produces oxygen. Since only one mole of $O_2(g)$ is needed, we only have to run it once. Equation (3) can balance out the Cl_2 required by equation (2), but we have to run it three times to cancel all the $Cl_2(g)$.

$2\times(1)$ $6 FeCl_2(s) + 8 H_2O(l) \rightarrow 2 Fe_3O_4(s) + 12 HCl(l) + 2 H_2(g)$

$1\times(2)$ $2 Fe_3O_4(s) + 3 Cl_2(g) + 12 HCl(g) \rightarrow 6 FeCl_3(s) + O_2(g) + 6 H_2O(l)$

$3\times(3)$ $6 FeCl_3(s) \rightarrow 6 FeCl_2(s) + 3 Cl_2(g)$

Net: $2 H_2O(l) \rightarrow 2 H_2(g) + O_2(g)$

111. (D) We begin by calculating the standard voltages for the two steps in the decomposition mechanism. Step 1 involves the reduction of Fe^{3+} and the oxidation of H_2O_2. The two half-reactions that constitute this step are:

(i) $Fe^{3+}(aq) + e^- \rightleftharpoons Fe^{2+}(aq)$ $\qquad\qquad E^\circ_{i,red} = 0.771$ V

(ii) $H_2O_2(aq) \rightleftharpoons O_2(g) + 2 H^+(aq) + 2 e^-$ $\qquad E^\circ_{ii,ox} = -0.695$ V

The balanced reaction is obtained by combining reaction (i), multiplied by two, with reaction (ii).

2(i) $2(Fe^{3+}(aq) + e^- \rightleftharpoons Fe^{2+}(aq))$

(ii) $H_2O_2(aq) \rightleftharpoons O_2(g) + 2\ H^+(aq) + 2\ e^-$

(iii) $2\ Fe^{3+}(aq) + H_2O_2(aq) \rightleftharpoons 2\ Fe^{2+}(aq) + O_2(g) + 2\ H^+(aq),$

for which $E°_{cell} = E°_{i(red)} + E°_{ii(ox)} = 0.771\ V + (-0.695\ V) = 0.076\ V$

Since the overall cell potential is positive, this step is spontaneous. The next step involves oxidation of $Fe^{2+}(aq)$ back to $Fe^{3+}(aq)$, (i.e. the reverse of reaction (i) and the reduction of $H_2O_2(aq)$ to $H_2O(l)$ in acidic solution, for which the half-reaction is

(iv) $H_2O_2(aq) + 2\ H^+(aq) + 2\ e^- \rightleftharpoons 2\ H_2O(l)$ $E°_{iv(red)} = 1.763\ V$

Combining (iv) with two times the reverse of (i) gives the overall reaction for the second step:

(i) $\{Fe^{2+}(aq) \rightleftharpoons Fe^{3+}(aq) + e^-\} \times 2$

(iv) $H_2O_2(aq) + 2\ H^+(aq) + 2\ e^- \rightleftharpoons 2\ H_2O(l)$

(v) $2\ Fe^{2+}(aq) + H_2O_2(aq) + 2\ H^+(aq) \rightleftharpoons 2\ Fe^{3+}(aq) + 2\ H_2O(l)$

Thus the overall cell potential for the second step in the mechanism, via equation (v) is

$E°_{cell} = -E°_{i(red)} + E°_{iv(red)} = -0.771\ V + (1.763\ V) = 0.992\ V.$

Since the overall standard cell potential is positive, like step 1, this reaction is spontaneous.

The overall reaction arising from the combination of these two steps is:

Step 1 $2\ Fe^{3+}(aq) + H_2O_2(aq) \rightleftharpoons 2\ Fe^{2+} + (aq) + O_2(g) + 2\ H^+(aq)$

Step 2 $2\ Fe^{2+}(aq) + H_2O_2(aq) + 2\ H^+(aq) \rightleftharpoons 2\ Fe^{3+}(aq) + 2\ H_2O(l)$

Overall $2\ H_2O_2(aq) \rightleftharpoons O_2(g) + 2\ H_2O(l)$

The overall potential, $E°_{overall} = E°_{step1} + E°_{step2} = 0.076\ V + 0.992\ V = 1.068\ V$
Therefore, the reaction is spontaneous at standard conditions.

To determine the minimum and maximum $E°$ values necessary for the catalyst, we need to consider each step separately.

In step 1, if $E°_{(1)}$ is less than 0.695 V, the overall voltage for the first step will be negative and hence non-spontaneous. In step 2, if the oxidation half-reaction has a potential that is more negative than -1.763 V, the overall potential for this step will be negative, and hence non-spontaneous. Consequently, $E°_{(1)}$ must fall between 0.695 V and 1.763 V in order for both steps to be spontaneous. On this basis we find that

(a) $Cu^{2+}(aq) + 2\ e^- \rightleftharpoons Cu(s)$ $E°_{red} = 0.337\ V$ cannot catalyze the reaction.

(b) $Br_2(l) + 2\ e^- \rightleftharpoons 2\ Br^-(aq)$ $E°_{red} = 1.065\ V$ may catalyze the reaction.

(c) $Al^{3+}(aq) + 3\ e^- \rightleftharpoons Al(s)$ $E°_{red} = -1.676\ V$ cannot catalyze the reaction.

(d) $Au^{3+}(aq) + 2\ e^- \rightleftharpoons Au^+(s)$ $E°_{red} = 1.36\ V$ may catalyze the reaction.

In the reaction of hydrogen peroxide with iodic acid in acidic solution, the relevant half-reactions are:

$$2 \, IO_3^-(aq) + 12 \, H^+(aq) + 10 \, e^- \rightleftharpoons I_2(s) + 6 \, H_2O(l) \quad E°_{red} = 1.20 \text{ V}$$
$$H_2O_2(aq) \rightleftharpoons O_2(g) + 2 \, H^+(aq) + 2e^- \quad E°_{ox} = -0.695 \text{ V}$$

Thus, both steps in the decomposition of H_2O_2, as described above, are spontaneous if IO_3^- is used as the catalyst. As the iodate gets reduced to I_2, the I_2 forms a highly colored complex with the starch, resulting in the appearance of a deep blue color solution. Some of the H_2O_2 will be simultaneously oxidized to $O_2(g)$ by the iodic acid When sufficient $I_2(s)$ accumulates, the reduction of H_2O_2 by I_2 begins to take place and the deep blue color fades as I_2 is consumed in the reaction. Additional iodate is formed concurrently, and this goes on to oxidize the $H_2O_2(aq)$, thereby causing the cycle to repeat itself. Each cycle results in some H_2O_2 being depleted. Thus, the oscillations of color can continue until the H_2O_2 has been largely consumed.

112. (D)

$$ClO_3^- \xrightarrow{(??)} ClO_2 \xrightarrow{(??)} HClO_2$$
$$\underline{\qquad\qquad 1.181 \text{ V} \qquad\qquad}$$

In order to add ClO_2 to the Standard Electrode Potential Diagrams (also known as Latimer diagram) drawn above, we must calculate the voltages denoted by (?) and (??) . The equation associated with the reduction potential (?) is

(i) $2 \, H^+(aq) + ClO_3^-(aq) + 1 \, e^- \rightarrow ClO_2(g) + H_2O(l)$
The standard voltage for this half-reaction is given in Appendix D:

To finish up this problem, we just need to calculate the standard voltage (??) for the half-reaction (ii):

(ii) $H^+(aq) + ClO_2(aq) + 1 \, e^- \rightarrow HClO_2(g) \quad E° = (??)$

To obtain the voltage for reaction (ii), we need to subtract reaction (i) from reaction (iii) below, which has been taken from Figure 22-2:

(iii) $3 \, H^+(aq) + ClO_3^-(aq) + 2 \, e^- \rightleftharpoons HClO_2(g) + H_2O(l) \quad E° = 1.181 \text{ V}$

Thus,

(iii)	$3 \, H^+(aq) + ClO_3^-(aq) + 2 \, e^- \rightleftharpoons HClO_2(g) + H_2O(l)$	$E°(iii) = 1.181 \text{ V}$
$-1 \times$ (i)	$2 \, H^+(aq) + ClO_3^-(aq) + 1 \, e^- \rightarrow ClO_2(g) + H_2O(l)$	$E°(i) = 1.175 \text{ V}$
Net (ii)	$H^+(aq) + ClO_2(g) + 1 \, e^- \rightarrow HClO_2(g)$	$E°(ii) = (??)$

Since reactions (i) and (iii) are both reduction half reactions, we cannot simply subtract the potential for (i) from the potential for (iii). Instead, we are forced to obtain the voltage for (ii) via the free energy changes for the three half reactions. Thus,

$$\Delta_r G° \, (ii) = \Delta_r G° \, (iii) - \Delta_r G° \, (i) = -1 \, FE°(ii) = -2 \, F(1.181 \text{ V}) + 1 \, F(1.175 \text{ V})$$

Dividing both sides by $-F$ gives

$$E° \, (ii) = 2(1.181 \text{ V}) - 1.175 \text{ V} \qquad \text{So, } E° \, (??) = 1.187 \text{ V}.$$

113. (D)

(a) As before, we can organize a solution around the balanced chemical equation.

Equation:	$I_2(aq)$	$\rightleftharpoons$	$I_2(CCl_4)$
Initial:	1.33×10^{-3} M		0 M
Initial:	0.0133 mmol		0 mmol
Changes:	$-x$ mmol		$+x$ mmol
Equil:	$(0.0133 - x)$ mmol		x mmol

$$K_c = 85.5 = \frac{[I_2(CCl_4)]}{[I_2(aq)]} = \frac{\dfrac{x}{10.0 \text{ mL}}}{\dfrac{0.0133 - x}{10.0 \text{ mL}}}$$

$x = 1.13\underline{7} - 85.5\,x \qquad 86.5x = 1.13\underline{7} \qquad x = \dfrac{1.13\underline{7}}{86.5} = 0.01315$ mmol I_2 in CCl_4

$I_2(aq) = (0.0133 - 0.01315)$ mmol $= 0.00015$ mmol

mass $I_2 = 0.00015$ mmol $\times \dfrac{253.81 \text{ mg } I_2}{1 \text{ mmol } I_2} = 3.8 \times 10^{-2}$ mg $I_2 = 0.038$ mg I_2 remaining

(b) We have the same set-up, except that the initial amount $I_2(aq) = 0.00015$ mmol.

$$K_c = 85.5 = \frac{[I_2(CCl_4)]}{[I_2(aq)]} = \frac{x}{0.00015 - x}$$

$x = 0.0128 - 85.5x \qquad 86.5x = 0.0128$

$x = \dfrac{0.0128}{86.5} = 0.0001480$ mmol $= I_2(CCl_4)$,

$I_2(aq) = 0.00015 - 0.0001480 = 2.0 \times 10^{-6}$ mmol I_2

mass $I_2 = 2.0 \times 10^{-6}$ mmol in $H_2O \times \dfrac{253.81 \text{ mg } I_2}{1 \text{ mol } I_2} = 5.1 \times 10^{-4}$ mg $I_2 = 0.00051$ mg I_2

(c) If twice the volume of CCl_4 were used for the initial extraction, the equilibrium concentrations would have been different from those in part (a).

Equation:	$I_2(aq)$	$\rightleftharpoons$	$I_2(CCl_4)$
Initial:	1.33×10^{-3} M		0 M
Initial:	0.0133 mmol		0 mmol
Changes:	$-x$ mmol		$+x$ mmol
Equil:	$(0.0133 - x)$ mmol		x mmol

$$K_c = 85.5 = \frac{[I_2(CCl_4)]}{[I_2(aq)]} = \frac{\dfrac{x}{20.0 \text{ mL}}}{\dfrac{0.0133 - x}{10.0 \text{ mL}}}$$

$x \div 2 = 1.13\underline{7} - 85.5x \qquad 86.0x = 1.13\underline{7} \qquad x = \dfrac{1.137}{86.0} = 1.32 \times 10^{-2}$ mmo $I_2(CCl_4)$

total mass $I_2 = \dfrac{1.33 \times 10^{-3} \text{ mmol } I_2}{1 \text{ mL}} \times 10.0 \text{ mL soln} \times \dfrac{253.81 \text{ mg } I_2}{1 \text{ mol } I_2} = 3.376$ mg I_2

mass I_2 in $CCl_4 = 1.32\underline{2} \times 10^{-2}$ mmol $\times \dfrac{253.81 \text{ mg } I_2}{1 \text{ mol } I_2} = 3.355$ mg I_2

mass I_2 remaining in water $= 3.376$ mg $- 3.356$ mg $= 0.021$ mg

Thus, two smaller volume extractions are much more efficient than one large volume extraction.

114. (D)

(a) The pyroanions, a series of structurally analogous anions with the general formula $X_2O_7^{n-}$, are known for Si, P and S. The Lewis structures for these three anions are drawn below: (Note: Every member of the series has 56 valence e^-)

$$X = Si : Si_2O_7^{6-}$$
$$X = P_{\oplus}: P_2O_7^{4-}$$
$$X = S_{2\oplus}: S_2O_7^{2-}$$

Based upon a VSEPR approach, we would predict tetrahedral geometry for each X atom (i.e. Si, P^+, S^{2+}) and a bent geometry for each bridging oxygen atom Therefore, a maximum of five atoms in each pyroanion can lie in a plane:

Atoms labeled 1-5 are all in the same plane.

(b) The related *"mononuclear"* acids, which contain just one third-row element are H_4SiO_4, H_3PO_3 and H_2SO_4. A series of pyroacids can be produced by strongly heating the *"mononuclear"* acids in the absence of air. In each case, the reaction proceeds via loss of water:

$$2\ H_4SiO_4 \xrightarrow{\Delta} H_6Si_2O_7(l)\ +\ H_2O(l)$$
$$2\ H_3PO_3 \xrightarrow{\Delta} H_4P_2O_7(l)\ +\ H_2O(l)$$
$$2\ H_2SO_4 \xrightarrow{\Delta} H_2S_2O_7(l)\ +\ H_2O(l)$$

(c) The highest oxidation state that Cl can achieve is VII (+7); consequently, the chlorine containing compound that is analogous to the mononuclear acids mentioned earlier is $HClO_4$. The strong heating of perchloric acid in the absence of air, should, in principle, afford Cl_2O_7, which is the neutral chlorine analogue of the pyroanions. Thus, Cl_2O_7 is the anhydride of perchloric acid.

$$2\ HClO_4 \xrightarrow{\Delta} Cl_2O_7(l) + H_2O(l)$$

When heated to temperatures above 150 °C, perchloric acid becomes a strong oxidizer and eventually becomes unstable.

115. (D)

(a) The bonding in the XeF_2 molecule can be explained quite simply in terms of a 3−center, 4 electron bond that spans all three atoms in the molecule. The bonding in this molecular orbital description involves the filled $5p_z$ orbital of Xe and the half-filled $2p_z$ orbitals of the two F-atoms. The linear combination of these three atomic orbitals affords one bonding, one non-bonding and one anti-bonding orbital, as depicted below:

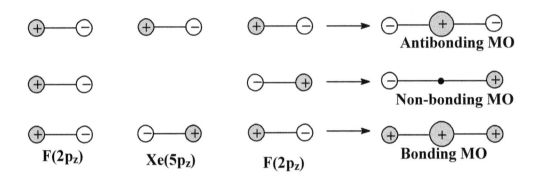

(b) If one assumes that the order of energies for molecular orbitals is:
bonding MO < non-bonding MO < antibonding MO,
the following molecular orbital representation of the bonding can be sketched.

Thus, a single bonding pair of electrons is responsible for holding all three atoms together. The non-bonding pair of electrons is localized primarily on the two F−atoms. This suggests that the bond possesses substantial ionic character. Bond order is defined as one-half the difference between the number of bonding electrons and the number of antibonding electrons. In the case of XeF_2, the overall bond order is

therefore: $\dfrac{2e^- - 0e^-}{2e^-} = 1.0$.

(i.e., each Xe—F bond has a bond order of 0.5)

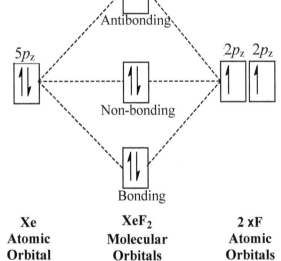

(c) By invoking a molecular orbital description based upon three-center bonding for the three F—Xe—F units in XeF_6, one obtains an octahedral structure in which there are six identical Xe—F bonds. The extra nonbonding pair of electrons is delocalized over the entire structure in this scheme. In spite of its manifest appeal, this explanation of the bonding in XeF_6 is incorrect, or at best a stretch, because the actual structure for this molecule is a distorted octahedron. A more accurate description of the stereochemistry adopted by XeF_6 is provided by VSEPR theory. In this approach, the shape of the molecule is determined by repulsions between bonding and non-bonding electrons in the valence shell of the central Xe atom.

Accordingly, in XeF_6, six bonding pairs and one lone pair of electrons surround the Xe. Having the repulsions of 7 pairs of electrons to cope with, the XeF_6 molecule adopts a distorted structure that approaches either a monocapped octahedron or a pentagonal bipyramidal arrangement of electron pairs, depending on how one chooses to view the structure. In either case, these two shapes are much closer to the true shape for XeF_6 than that predicted by the molecular orbital treatment involving three, three-center bonds. By contrast, the molecular orbital description involving three-center bonds gives far better results when applied to XeF_4. In this instance, with two three-center F—Xe—F bonds in the structure, molecular orbital theory predicts that XeF_4 should adopt a square planar structure.

The result here is quite satisfactory because XeF_4 does in fact exhibit square planar geometry. It is worth noting, however, that a square planar shape for XeF_4 is also predicted by VSEPR theory. Despite the fact that the molecular orbital method has made some inroads as of late, VSEPR is still the best approach available for rationalizing the molecular geometries of noble gas compounds.

116. (D)

(a) In the phase diagram sketched in the problem, extend the liquid-vapor equilibrium curve (the vapor pressure curve) to lower temperatures (supercooled liquid region). Extend the S_α-vapor equilibrium curve (sublimation curve) to the temperature at which it intersects the extended vapor pressure curve. This should come at 113 °C. Draw a line from this point of intersection to the "peak" of the S_β phase region. Erase the three lines that bound the S_β region in the original sketch. The remaining three lines would represent the equilibria, S_α V, S_α L, and L-V, producing the phase diagram if S_α (rhombic) were the only solid form of sulfur.

(b) If rhombic sulfur is heated rapidly, the transition to monoclinic sulfur at 95.3 °C might not occur. (Solid-state transitions are often very slow.) In this case, rhombic sulfur would melt at 113 °C, as described in the modified phase diagram in part (a). If the molten rhombic sulfur is further heated and then cooled, the liquid very likely will freeze at the equilibrium temperature of 119 °C, producing *monoclinic*, not rhombic, sulfur.

SELF-ASSESSMENT EXERCISES

117. (E)
  (a) The halogens can combine with each other to form polyhalide ions.
  (b) Polyphosphates are anionic phosphate polymers linked between hydroxyl groups and hydrogen atoms.
  (c) The halogens react with each other to form interhalogen compounds. The general formula of most interhalogen compounds is XY_n, where n = 1, 3, 5 or 7 (X is the less electronegative of the two halogens).
  (d) Disproportionation is the chemical reaction in which the same element is spontaneously oxidized and reduced.

118. (E)
  (a) The Frasch process is a method to extract sulfur from underground deposits.
  (b) The water-gas shift reaction is a chemical reaction in which carbon monoxide reacts with water vapor to form carbon dioxide and hydrogen: $CO + H_2O \rightarrow CO_2 + H_2$. It is a very important industrial reaction.
  (c) Eutrophication is an increase in the concentration of chemical nutrients in an ecosystem to an extent that increases the primary productivity of the ecosystem.
  (d) Electrode potential diagrams are used to simplify actual electrochemical cells summarize reduction potentials between species of varying oxidation states.

119. (E)
  (a) An acid anhydride is an organic compound that has two acyl groups bound to the same oxygen atom. Acid salt is an anionic compound.
  (b) Azide functionality is $-N_3$. A nitride is a compound of nitrogen with a less electronegative element where nitrogen has an oxidation state of -3.
  (c) Elemental phosphorus exists in two major forms - white phosphorus and red phosphorus, they are structurally different.
  (d) Both terms are similar and represent a class of compounds in which hydrogen is bound to a very electropositive element (such as alkali earth metals).

120. **(E)** **(b)**

121. **(E)** **(d)**

122. **(E)** **(c)**

123. **(E)** **(a)**

124. **(E)** **(d)**

125. **(E)** **(b)**

126. **(E)** **(a)** and **(d)**

127. (M)

(a) $Cl_2(g) + 2\,NaOH(aq) \rightarrow NaCl(aq) + NaOCl(aq) + H_2O(l)$

(b) $2\,NaI(s) + 2\,H_2SO_4(concd\ aq) \rightarrow Na_2SO_4(a) + 2\,H_2O(g) + SO_2(g) + I_2(g)$

(c) $Cl_2(g) + 2\,KI_3(aq) \rightarrow 2\,KCl(aq) + 3\,I_2(s)$

(d) $3\,NaBr(s) + H_3PO_4(concd\ aq) \rightarrow Na_3PO_4 + 3\,HBr(g)$

(e) $5\,HSO_3^-(aq) + 2\,MnO_4^-(aq) + H^+(aq) \rightarrow 5\,SO_4^{2-}(aq) + 2\,Mn^{2+}(aq) + 3\,H_2O(l)$

128. (M)

(a) $2\,KClO_3(s) \rightarrow 2\,KCl(s) + 3\,O_2(g)$ a catalyst such as MnO_2 is required, electrolysis of H_2O is an alternate method.

(b) $3\,Cu(s) + 8\,H + (aq) + 2\,NO_3^-(aq) \rightarrow 3\,Cu^{2+}(aq) + 4\,H_2O(l) + 2\,NO(g)$, difficult to control reaction so that $NO(g)$ is the only reduction product.

(c) $Zn(s) + 2\,H^+(aq) \rightarrow Zn^{2+}(aq) + H_2(g)$, a number of other metals can be used.

(d) $NH_4Cl(aq) + NaOH(aq) \rightarrow NaCl(aq) + H_2O(l) + NH_3(g)$, other ammonium salts and other bases work as well.

(e) $CaCO_3(s) + 2\,HCl(aq) \rightarrow CaCl_2(aq) + H_2O(l) + CO_2(g)$, other carbonates and acids can be used.

129. (M)

(a) $LiH(s) + H_2O(l) \rightarrow LiOH(aq) + H_2(g)$

(b) $C(s) + H_2O(g) \rightarrow CO(g) + H_2(g)$

(c) $3\,NO_2(g) + H_2O(l) \rightarrow 2\,HNO_3(aq) + NO(g)$

130. (M) $3\,Cl_2(g) + I^-(aq) + 3\,H_2O(l) \rightarrow 6\,Cl^-(aq) + IO_3^-(aq) + 6\,H^+(aq)$

$Cl_2(g) + 2\,Br^-(aq) \rightarrow 2\,Cl^-(aq) + Br_2(aq)$ and Br_2 is extracted by CS_2.

131. (M) One conversion pathway is ton $\rightarrow$ lb $\rightarrow$ kg $\rightarrow$ g $H_2SO_4 \rightarrow$ g S $\rightarrow$ mg S $\rightarrow$ L seawater $\rightarrow m^3 \rightarrow km^3$ seawater, leading to about 5.0 km^3 of seawater.

132. (M) (a) AgAt, (b) sodium perxenate, (c) MgPo, (d) tellurous acid, (e) K_2SeSO_3, (f) potassium perastatate

133. (D) Convert the $E°$ values to $\Delta_r G°$ values for the reduction of H_2SeO_3 to Se and from Se to H_2Se. Add those two $\Delta_r G°$ values to obtain $\Delta_r G°$ for the reduction of H_2SeO_3 to H_2Se. Convert this $\Delta_r G°$ value to $E°$, which proves to be 0.38 V.

134. (M) (a) SO_3, (b) SO_2, (c) Cl_2O_7, (d) I_2O_5

135. (M) (a) false, (b) true, (c) true.

CHAPTER 23
THE TRANSITION ELEMENTS
PRACTICE EXAMPLES

1A **(E) (a)** Cu_2O should form. $2\,Cu_2S(s)+3\,O_2(g)\rightarrow 2\,Cu_2O(s)+2\,SO_2(g)$

(b) W(s) is the reduction product. $WO_3(s)+3\,H_2(g)\rightarrow W(s)+3\,H_2O(g)$

(c) Hg(l) forms. $2\,HgO(s)\xrightarrow{\Delta}2\,Hg(l)+O_2(g)$

1B **(E) (a)** $SiO_2(s)$ is the oxidation product of Si.

$$3\,Si(s)+2\,Cr_2O_3(s)\xrightarrow{\Delta}3\,SiO_2(s)+4\,Cr(s)$$

(b) Roasting is simply heating in air. $2\,Co(OH)_3(s)\xrightarrow{\Delta,Air}Co_2O_3(s)+3\,H_2O(g)$

(c) $MnO_2(s)$ forms; (acidic solution). $Mn^{2+}(aq)+2\,H_2O(l)\rightarrow MnO_2(s)+4\,H^+(aq)+2\,e^-$

2A **(M)** We write and combine the half-equations for oxidation and reduction. If $E° > 0$, the reaction is spontaneous.

Oxidation: $\{V^{3+}(aq)+H_2O(l)\rightarrow VO^{2+}(aq)+2\,H^+(aq)+e^-\}\times 3$ $\qquad E°=-0.337\,V$

Reduction: $NO_3^-(aq)+4\,H^+(aq)+3\,e^-\rightarrow NO(g)+2\,H_2O$ $\qquad E°=+0.956\,V$

Net: $NO_3^-(aq)+3\,V^{3+}(aq)+H_2O(l)\rightarrow NO(g)+3\,VO^{2+}(aq)+2\,H^+(aq)$ $\quad E°_{cell}=+0.619\,V$

Because the cell potential is positive, nitric acid can be used to oxidize $V^{3+}(aq)$ to $VO^{2+}(aq)$ under standard conditions.

2B **(M)** The reducing couple must have a half-cell potential of such a size and sign that a positive sum results when this half-cell potential is combined with
$E°\{VO^{2+}(aq)|V^{2+}(aq)\}=0.041\,V$ (this is the weighted average of the $VO^{2+}|V^{3+}$ and $V^{3+}|V^{2+}$ reduction potentials) *and* a negative sum must be produced when this half-cell potential is combined with $E°\{V^{2+}(aq)|V(s)\}=-1.13\,V$.

So, $-E°$ for the couple must be $> -0.041\,V$ and $< +1.13\,V$ (i.e., it cannot be more positive than 1.13V, nor more negative than $-0.041\,V$). Some possible reducing couples from Table 19-1 are:
$-E°\{Cr^{3+}(aq)|Cr^{2+}(aq)\}=+0.42\,V$; $-E°\{Fe^{2+}(aq)|Fe(s)\}=+0.440\,V$
$-E°\{Zn^{2+}(aq)|Zn(s)\}=+0.763\,V$. Thus Fe(s), $Cr^{2+}(aq)$, and Zn(s) will do the job.

INTEGRATIVE EXAMPLE

3A **(M)** Because the reduction potential for $PtCl_6^{2-}$ is more positive than that of V^{3+}, the following half-reactions occur spontaneously in the cell:
Oxidation: $[\,V^{2+}+e^-\rightarrow V^{3+}\,]\times 2$ $\qquad E°=+0.255\,V$
Reduction: $PtCl_6^{2-}+2\,e^-\rightarrow PtCl_4^{2-}+2\,Cl^-$ $\qquad E°=+0.68\,V$
Overall: $2\,V^{2+}+PtCl_6^{2-}\rightarrow 2\,V^{3+}+PtCl_4^{2-}+2\,Cl^-$ $\quad E°=0.94\,V$

The equilibrium constant for the overall reaction is $K = 10^{\frac{2(0.94)}{0.0592}} = 5.7 \times 10^{31}$. For the reverse reaction to be spontaneous, we need $Q > 5.7 \times 10^{31}$. Because $Q = [V^{3+}]^2 [PtCl_4^{2-}]$ $[Cl^-]^2/[V^{2+}] [PtCl_6^{2-}]$, the formation of $PtCl_6^{2-}$ is favored by using a very low concentration of V^{2+} and very high concentrations of V^{3+}, $PtCl_4^{2-}$, and Cl^-. In practical terms, though, the amount of $PtCl_6^{2-}$ that could be formed spontaneously would be small. A quick calculation shows that starting from $[V^{3+}]_o = [PtCl_4^{2-}]_o = [Cl^-]_o = 1.$ M and $[V^{2+}]$ $= [PtCl_6^{2-}]_o = 0$, the equilibrium concentration of PtC_6^{2-} would be about 1.6×10^{-11} M. So, in practical terms, an external voltage source would be required to make a significant amount of $PtCl_6^{2-}$ from V^{3+}, $PtCl_4^{2-}$, and Cl^-.

3B   **(M)** The disproportionation reaction is $3\ Ti^{2+} \rightarrow 2\ Ti^{3+} + Ti$ and $E° = -1.261$ V. Because $E° < 0$, the reaction is not spontaneous under standard conditions.

EXERCISES

Properties of the Transition Elements

1.   **(E)**

(a) V [Ar]

(b) Cr^{3+} [Ar]

(c) Mn^{2+} [Ar]

(d) Fe^{2+} [Ar]

(e) Cu^{2+} [Ar]

(f) Ni^{2+} [Ar]

2.   **(E)** We first give the orbital diagram for each of the species, and then count the number of unpaired electrons.

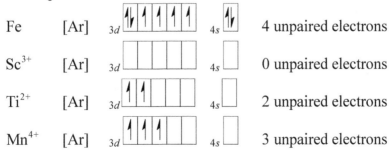

Fe   [Ar] $3d$ $4s$ 4 unpaired electrons

Sc^{3+} [Ar] $3d$ $4s$ 0 unpaired electrons

Ti^{2+} [Ar] $3d$ $4s$ 2 unpaired electrons

Mn^{4+} [Ar] $3d$ $4s$ 3 unpaired electrons

Cr   [Ar] $3d$ | ↑ | ↑ | ↑ | ↑ | ↑ | $4s$ | ↑ | 6 unpaired electrons

Cu²⁺   [Ar] $3d$ | ↑↓ | ↑↓ | ↑↓ | ↑↓ | ↑ | $4s$ | | 1 unpaired electron

Finally, arrange in order of decreasing number of unpaired e^-: $Cr > Fe > Mn^{4+} > Ti^{2+} > Cu^{2+} > Sc^{3+}$

3.   **(M)** A given main-group metal typically displays just one oxidation state, usually equal to its family number in the periodic table. Exceptions are elements such as Tl (+1 and +3), Pb (+2 and +4), and Sn (+2 and +4), for which the lower oxidation state represents a pair of s electrons not being ionized (a so-called "inert pair").

Main group metals do not form a wide variety of complex ions, with Al^{3+}, Sn^{2+}, Sn^{4+}, and Pb^{2+} being major exceptions. On the other hand, most transition metal ions form an extensive variety of complex ions. Most compounds of main group metals are colorless; exceptions occur when the anion is colored. On the other hand, many of the compounds of transition metal cations are colored, due to d-d electron transitions. Virtually every main-group metal cation has no unpaired electrons and hence is diamagnetic. On the other hand, many transition metals cations have one or more unpaired electrons and therefore are paramagnetic.

4.   **(M)** As we proceed from Sc to Cr, the valence electron configuration has an increasing number of unpaired electrons, which are capable of forming bonds to adjacent atoms. As we continue beyond Cr, however, these electrons become paired, and the resulting atoms are less able to form bonds with their neighbors. Also, smaller atoms tend to bond more tightly, making their metallic agglomerations more difficult to melt. (i.e., the smaller the metal atom, the higher the melting point). This trend of increasing melting point with decreasing size is clearly visible for the first transition series from Sc to Zn.

5.   **(M)** When an electron and a proton are added to a main group element to create the element of next highest atomic number, it is the electron that influences the radius. The electron is added to the outermost shell (n value), which is farthest from the nucleus. Moreover, the added electron is well shielded from the nucleus and hence it is only weakly attracted to the nucleus. Thus, this electron billows out and, as a result, has a major influence on the size of the atom. However, when an electron and a proton are added to a transition metal atom to create the atom of next highest atomic number, the electron it is not added to the outermost shell. The electron is added to the d-orbitals, which are one principal quantum number lower than the outermost shell. Also, the electron in the same subshell as the added electron offers little shielding. Thus it has small effect on the size of the atom.

6.   **(M)** The reason why the radii of Pd (138 pm) and Pt (139 pm) are so similar, and yet so different from the radius of Ni (125 pm) is because the lanthanide series intrudes between Pd and Pt. Because of the lanthanide contraction, elements in the second transition row are almost identical in size to their congeners (family members) in the third transition row.

7.   **(M)** Of the first transition series, manganese exhibits the greatest number of different oxidation states in its compounds, namely, every state from +1 to +7. One possible explanation might be its $3d^5 4s^2$ electron configuration. Removing one electron produces an electron configuration ($3d^5 4s^1$) with two half-filled subshells, removing two produces one with a half-filled and an empty subshell. Then there is no point of semistability until the remaining five d electrons are removed. These higher oxidation states all are stabilized by being present in oxides (MnO_2) or oxoanions (e.g., MnO_4^-).

8. **(M)** At the beginning of the series, there are few electrons beyond the last noble gas that can be ionized and thus the maximum oxidation state is limited. Toward the end of the series, many of the electrons are paired up or the d subshell is filled, and thus a somewhat stable situation would be disrupted by ionization.

9. **(M)** The greater ease of forming lanthanide cations compared to forming transition metal cations, is due to the larger size of lanthanide atoms. The valence (outer shell) electrons of these larger atoms are further from the nucleus, less strongly attracted to the positive charge of the nucleus in diffuse f-orbitals that are do not penetrate effectively and are very effectively shielded by the core electrons. As a result, they are removed much more readily.

10. **(M)** This is not a simple straightforward question. There are a number of factors to consider. Proceeding across the first transition series, electrons are added to the $3d$ subshell which is a shell that is beneath the $4s$ subshell, the outer most subshell in the valence shell occupied by one or two electrons. The metallic character of the first transition element, Sc, is rather similar to that of Ca (e.g., $E° = -2.03$ V compared to -2.84 V). Following this, there is a fairly regular rise in $E°$, (e.g., -1.63 V for Ti, -1.13 V for V...), reaching a maximum of $E° = 0.340$ V with Cu. These trends can be related to the regular increase in Z_{eff} and other aspects of electron configurations (half filled shell for Mn^{2+} and loss of half filled shell for Cr^{2+}). Complicating matters is the fact that these ions will have different aqueous coordination numbers and geometries.

In the lanthanide series, it is the $4f$ subshell that fills at the same time that the $5d$ subshell is mostly vacant and the $6s$ subshell is filled. Differences in electron configurations are essentially confined to a subshell two shells removed from the outermost valence shell, which translates into close similarities among all the elements in the series, including $E°$ values.

Recall that the lanthanide series is an *inner* transition series—a transition series within another transition series. This inner transition series runs its course between La ($E° = -2.38$ V) and Hf ($E° = -1.70$ V). The difference between these two $E°$ values is about 0.7 V, which is comparable to the 0.4 V difference between the first (Sc) and second (Ti) members of the first transition series.

Reactions of Transition Metals and Their Compounds

11. **(M)** **(a)** $TiCl_4(g) + 4Na(l) \xrightarrow{\Delta} Ti(s) + 4NaCl(l)$

   (b) $Cr_2O_3(s) + 2Al(s) \xrightarrow{\Delta} 2Cr(l) + Al_2O_3(s)$

   (c) $Ag(s) + HCl(aq) \rightarrow$ no reaction

(d) $K_2Cr_2O_7(aq) + 2KOH(aq) \rightarrow 2\ K_2CrO_4(aq) + H_2O(l)$

(e) $MnO_2(s) + 2\ C(s) \xrightarrow{\Delta} Mn(l) + 2CO(g)$

12. **(M) (a)** $Cr(s) + 2HCl(aq) \rightarrow CrCl_2(aq) + H_2(g)$ Virtually any first period transition metal except Cu can be substituted for Cr.

(b) $Cr_2O_3(s) + 2\ OH^-(aq) + 3\ H_2O(l) \rightarrow 2\ Cr(OH)_4^-(aq)$

The oxide must be amphoteric. Thus, Sc_2O_3, TiO_2, ZrO_2, and ZnO could be substituted for Cr_2O_3.

(c) $2\ La(s) + 6\ HCl(aq) \rightarrow 2\ LaCl_3(aq) + 3\ H_2(g)$

Any lanthanide or actinide element can be substituted for lanthanum.

13. **(M) (a)** $Sc(OH)_3(s) + 3H^+(aq) \rightarrow Sc^{3+}(aq) + 3\ H_2O(l)$

(b) $3\ Fe^{2+}(aq) + MnO_4^-(aq) + 2\ H_2O(l) \rightarrow 3\ Fe^{3+}(aq) + MnO_2(s) + 4\ OH^-(aq)$

(c) $2\ KOH(l) + TiO_2(s) \xrightarrow{\Delta} K_2TiO_3(s) + H_2O(g)$

(d) $Cu(s) + 2\ H_2SO_4(conc, aq) \rightarrow CuSO_4(aq) + SO_2(g) + 2\ H_2O(l)$

14. **(M) (a)** $2\ Sc_2O_3(l, in\ Na_3ScF_6) + 3\ C(s) \xrightarrow{electrolysis} 4\ Sc(l) + 3\ CO_2(g)$

[By analogy with the equation for the electrolytic production of Al]

(b) $Cr(s) + 2\ HCl(aq) \rightarrow Cr^{2+}(aq) + 2\ Cl^-(aq) + H_2(g)$

(c) $4\ Cr^{2+}(aq) + O_2(g) + 4\ H^+(aq) \rightarrow 4\ Cr^{3+}(aq) + 2\ H_2O(l)$

(d) $Ag(s) + 2\ HNO_3(aq) \rightarrow AgNO_3(aq) + NO_2(g) + H_2O(l)$

15. **(M)** We write some of the following reactions as total equations rather than as net ionic equations so that the reagents used are indicated.

(a) $FeS(s) + 2\ HCl(aq) \rightarrow FeCl_2(aq) + H_2S(g)$

$4\ Fe^{2+}(aq) + O_2(g) + 4H^+(aq) \rightarrow 4Fe^{3+}(aq) + 2\ H_2O(l)$

$Fe^{3+}(aq) + 3\ OH^-(aq) \rightarrow Fe(OH)_3(s)$

(b) $BaCO_3(s) + 2\ HCl(aq) \rightarrow BaCl_2(aq) + H_2O(l) + CO_2(g)$

$2\,BaCl_2(aq) + K_2Cr_2O_7(aq) + 2\,NaOH(aq) \rightarrow 2\,BaCrO_4(s) + 2\,KCl(aq) + 2\,NaCl(aq) + H_2O(l)$

16. **(M) (a)** **(i)** $CuO(s) + 2H^+(aq) \longrightarrow Cu^{2+}(aq) + H_2O(l)$

(ii) $Cu^{2+}(aq) + 2OH^-(aq) \longrightarrow Cu(OH)_2(s)$

(b) $(NH_4)_2Cr_2O_7(s) \xrightarrow{\Delta} N_2(g) + 4\ H_2O(g) + Cr_2O_3(s)$

$Cr_2O_3(s) + 6\ HCl(aq) \rightarrow CrCl_3(aq) + 3\ H_2O(l)$

Extractive Metallurgy

17. **(E)** $HgS(s) + O_2(g) \xrightarrow{\Delta} Hg(l) + SO_2(g)$

$4 HgS(s) + 4 CaO(s) \xrightarrow{\Delta} 4 Hg(l) + 3 CaS(s) + CaSO_4(s)$

18. **(E) (a)** $C(s) + O_2(g) \rightarrow CO_2(g)$ $\Delta S° = 213.7 \text{ J mol}^{-1}\text{ K}^{-1}$
$$- (5.74 \text{ J mol}^{-1}\text{ K}^{-1} + 205.1 \text{ J mol}^{-1}\text{ K}^{-1})$$
$$\Delta S° = 2.86 \text{ J mol}^{-1}\text{ K}^{-1}$$

Since $\Delta_r S° \approx 0$, $\Delta_r G°$ will be relatively constant with temperature.

(b) $2 CO(g) + O_2(g) \rightarrow 2 CO_2(g)$
$$\Delta_r S° = (2(213.7 \text{ J mol}^{-1}\text{ K}^{-1}) - (205.1 \text{ J mol}^{-1}\text{ K}^{-1} + 2(197.7 \text{ J mol}^{-1}\text{ K}^{-1}))$$
$$\Delta_r S° = -173.1 \text{ J mol}^{-1}\text{ K}^{-1}$$
Since $\Delta_r S°$ is less than zero, $\Delta_r G°$ will increase (become less negative or more positive) as temperature increases.

19. **(M)** The plot of $\Delta_r G°$ versus T will consist of three lines of increasing positive slope. The first line is joined to the second line at the melting point for Ca(s), while the second line is joined to the third at the boiling point for Ca(l).

$$2 Ca(s) + O_2(g) \rightarrow 2 CaO(s) \qquad \Delta_f H° = -1270.2 \text{ kJ mol}^{-1}$$

$$\Delta_r S° = 2(39.75 \text{ J mol}^{-1}\text{ K}^{-1}) - [2 \times (41.42 \text{ J mol}^{-1}\text{ K}^{-1}) + 205.1 \text{ J mol}^{-1}\text{ K}^{-1}] = -208.4 \text{ J mol}^{-1}\text{ K}^{-1}$$

The graph should be similar to that for $2 Mg(s) + O_2(g) \rightarrow 2 MgO(s)$. We expect a positive slope with slight changes in the slope after the melting point (839 °C) and boiling point (1484 °C), mainly owing to changes in entropy. The plot will be below the $\Delta_r G°$ line for $2 Mg(s) + O_2(g) \rightarrow 2 MgO(s)$ at all temperatures.

20. **(E)** $2 Na_2CrO_4(s) + 3 C(s) + 4 HCl(aq) \rightarrow Cr_2O_3(s) + 2 H_2O(l) + 3 CO(g) + 4 NaCl(aq)$

$2 Cr_2O_3(s) + 3 Si(s) \rightarrow 4 Cr(s) + 3 SiO_2(s)$

Oxidation-Reduction

21. **(E)**

(a) $CuO(s) + 2 H^+(aq) + e^- \rightarrow Cu^+(aq) + H_2O$

(b) $FeO(s) + 2 H^+(aq) \rightarrow Fe^{3+}(aq) + H_2O + e^-$

22. **(E)**

(a) Oxidation: $Fe(OH)_3(s) + 5 OH^-(aq) \rightarrow FeO_4^{2-}(aq) + 4 H_2O(l) + 3 e^-$

(b) Reduction: $\left[Ag(CN)_2\right]^-(aq) + e^- \rightarrow Ag(s) + 2 CN^-(aq)$

23. **(M)**

(a) First we need the reduction potential for the couple $VO_2^+(aq)/V^{2+}(aq)$. We will use the half-cell addition method learned in Chapter 19.

$$VO_2^+(aq)+2\ H^+(aq)+e^- \rightarrow VO^{2+}(aq)+H_2O(l) \qquad \Delta_r G^\circ = -1\ F(+1.000\ V)$$

$$VO^{2+}(aq)+2\ H^+(aq)+e^- \rightarrow V^{3+}(aq)+H_2O(l) \qquad \Delta_r G^\circ = -1\ F(+0.337\ V)$$

$$V^{3+}(aq)+e^- \rightarrow V^{2+}(aq) \qquad \Delta_r G^\circ = -1\ F(-0.255\ V)$$

$$\overline{VO_2^+(aq)+4\ H^+(aq)+3\ e^- \rightarrow V^{2+}(aq)+2\ H_2O \quad \Delta_r G^\circ = -3\ FE^\circ}$$

$$E^\circ = \frac{1.000\ V + 0.337\ V - 0.255\ V}{3} = +0.361\ V$$

We next analyze the oxidation-reduction reaction.

Oxidation: $\{2\ Br^-(aq) \rightarrow Br_2(l)+2e^-\} \times 3$ $\qquad\qquad -E^\circ = -1.065\ V$

Reduction: $\{VO_2^+(aq)+4H^+(aq)+3e^- \rightarrow V^{2+}(aq)+2H_2O(l)\} \times 2 \quad E^\circ = +0.361V$

$$\overline{\text{Net: } 6\ Br^-(aq)+2\ VO_2^+(aq)+8\ H^+(aq) \rightarrow 3\ Br_2(l)+2\ V^{2+}(aq)+4\ H_2O}$$

$E_{cell}^\circ = -0.704V$

Thus, this reaction does not occur to a significant extent as written under standard conditions.

(b) Oxidation: $Fe^{2+}(aq) \rightarrow Fe^{3+}(aq)+e^-$ $\qquad\qquad -E^\circ = -0.771V$

Reduction: $VO_2^+(aq)+2\ H^+(aq)+e^- \rightarrow VO^{2+}(aq)+H_2O(l) \quad E^\circ = +1.000V$

$$\overline{\text{Net: } \quad Fe^{2+}(aq)+VO_2^+(aq)+2\ H^+(aq) \rightarrow Fe^{3+}(aq)+VO^{2+}(aq)+H_2O(l)}$$

$E_{cell}^\circ = +0.229V$

This reaction does occur to a significant extent under standard conditions.

(c) Oxidation: $H_2O_2 \rightarrow 2\ H^+(aq)+2\ e^- +O_2(g)$ $\qquad\qquad -E^\circ = -0.695\ V$

Reduction: $MnO_2(s)+4\ H^+(aq)+2\ e^- \rightarrow Mn^{2+}(aq)+2\ H_2O(l) \quad E^\circ = +1.23V$

$$\overline{\text{Net: } H_2O_2 + MnO_2(s)+2\ H^+(aq) \rightarrow O_2(g)+Mn^{2+}(aq)+2\ H_2O(l) \quad E_{cell}^\circ = +0.54V}$$

Thus, this reaction does occur to a significant extent under standard conditions.

24. **(D)** When a species acts as a reducing agent, it is oxidized. From Appendix D, we obtain the potentials for each of the following couples.

$$-E^0\{Zn^{2+}(aq)/Zn(s)\} = +0.763\ V; \quad -E^0\{Sn^{4+}(aq)/Sn^{2+}(aq)\} = -0.154V$$

$$-E^\circ\{I_2(s)/I^-(aq)\} = -0.535\ V$$

Each of these potentials is combined with the cited reduction potential. If the resulting value of E^o_{cell} is positive, then the reducing agent will be effective in accomplishing the desired reduction, which we indicate with "yes"; if not, we write "no".

(a) $E^o\{Cr_2O_7{}^{2-}(aq)/Cr^{3+}(aq)\} = +1.33 \text{ V}$

$E^o_{cell} = E^o\{Cr_2O_7{}^{2-}(aq)/Cr^{3+}(aq)\} - E^o\{Zn^{2+}(aq)/Zn(s)\}$

$E^o_{cell} = +1.33 \text{ V} - (-0.763)\text{V} = +2.09 \text{ V} \implies$ Yes

$E^o_{cell} = E^o\{Cr_2O_7{}^{2-}(aq)/Cr^{3+}(aq)\} - E^o\{Sn^{4+}(aq)/Sn^{2+}(aq)\}$

$E^o_{cell} = +1.33 \text{ V} - 0.154 \text{ V} = +1.18 \text{ V} \implies$ Yes

$E^o_{cell} = E^o\{Cr_2O_7{}^{2-}(aq)/Cr^{3+}(aq)\} - E^o\{I_2(s)/I^-(aq)\}$

$E^o_{cell} = +1.33 \text{ V} - 0.535 \text{ V} = +0.80 \text{ V} \implies$ Yes

(b) $E^o\{Cr^{3+}(aq)/Cr^{2+}(aq)\} = -0.424 \text{ V}$

$E^o_{cell} = E^o\{Cr^{3+}(aq)/Cr^{2+}(aq)\} - E^o\{Zn^{2+}(aq)/Zn(s)\}$

$E^o_{cell} = -0.424 \text{ V} + 0.763 \text{ V} = +0.339 \text{ V} \implies$ Yes

$E^o_{cell} = E^o\{Cr^{3+}(aq)/Cr^{2+}(aq)\} - E^o\{Sn^{4+}(aq)/Sn^{2+}(aq)\}$

$E^o_{cell} = -0.424 \text{ V} - 0.154 \text{ V} = -0.578 \text{ V} \implies$ No

$E^o_{cell} = E^o\{Cr^{3+}(aq)/Cr^{2+}(aq)\} - E^o\{I_2(s)/I^-(aq)\}$

$E^o_{cell} = -0.424 \text{ V} - 0.535 \text{ V} = -0.959 \text{ V} \implies$ No

(c) $E^o\{SO_4{}^{2-}(aq)/SO_2(g)\} = +0.17 \text{ V}$

$E^o_{cell} = E^o\{SO_4{}^{2-}(aq)/SO_2(g)\} - E^o\{Zn^{2+}(aq)/Zn(s)\}$

$E^o_{cell} == +0.17 \text{ V} + 0.763 \text{ V} = +0.93 \text{ V} \implies$ Yes

$E^o_{cell} = E^o\{SO_4{}^{2-}(aq)/SO_2(g)\} - E^o\{Sn^{4+}(aq)/Sn^{2+}(aq)\}$

$E^o_{cell} = +0.17 \text{ V} - 0.154 \text{ V} = +0.02 \text{ V} \implies$ Yes (barely)

$E^o_{cell} = E^o\{SO_4{}^{2-}(aq)/SO_2(g)\} - E^o\{I_2(s)/I^-(aq)\}$

$E^o_{cell} = +0.17 \text{ V} - 0.535 \text{ V} = -0.37 \text{ V} \implies$ No

25. **(M)** The reducing couple that we seek must have a half-cell potential of such a size and sign that a positive sum results when this half-cell potential is combined with $E^o\{VO^{2+}(aq)|V^{3+}(aq)\} = 0.337 \text{ V}$ *and* a negative sum must be produced when this half-cell potential is combined with $E^o\{V^{3+}(aq)|V^{2+}(aq)\} = -0.255\text{V}$.

So, $-E°$ for the couple must be> -0.337 V and <+ 0.255 V (i.e. it cannot be more positive than 0.255V, or more negative than -0.337 V)

Some possible reducing couples from Table 19.1 are:

$-E°\{Sn^{2+}(aq)|Sn(s)\} = +0.137$ V ; $-E°\{H^+(aq)|H_2(g)] = 0.000$ V
$-E°\{Pb^{2+}(aq)|Pb(s)] = +0.125$ V ; thus Pb(s), Sn(s), H$_2$(g) , to name but a few, will do the job.

26. **(M)** There are two methods that can be used to determine the MnO_4^-/Mn^{2+} reduction potential.
Method 1: $MnO_4^- — 1.70$ V $\rightarrow MnO_2 — 1.23$ V $\rightarrow Mn^{2+}$

$$E°_{MnO_4^-/Mn^{2+}} = \frac{3\,(1.70\text{ V}) + 2\,(1.23\text{ V})}{5} = 1.51\underline{2}\text{ V} \sim 1.51\text{ V}$$

Method 2: $MnO_4^- \rightarrow MnO_4^{2-} \rightarrow MnO_2 \rightarrow Mn^{3+} \rightarrow Mn^{2+}$

$$E°_{MnO_4^-/Mn^{2+}} = \frac{0.56\text{ V} + 2\,(2.27\text{ V}) + 0.95\text{ V} + 1.49\text{ V}}{5} = 1.50\underline{8}\text{ V} \sim 1.51\text{ V}$$

These answers compare favorably to Table 19.1, where $E°_{MnO_4^-/Mn^{2+}} = 1.51$ V

27. **(M)** Table D-4 contains the following data: Cr^{3+}/Cr^{2+} reduction potential = -0.424 V, $Cr_2O_7^{2-}/Cr^{3+}$ reduction potential = 1.33 V and Cr^{2+}/Cr reduction potential = -0.90 V.
By using the additive nature of free energies and the fact that $\Delta G° = -zFE°$, we can determine the two unknown potentials and complete the diagram.

(i) $Cr_2O_7^{2-}/Cr^{2+}$: $E° = \dfrac{3(1.33\text{ V}) - 0.424\text{ V}}{4} = 0.892$ V

(ii) Cr^{3+}/Cr : $E° = \dfrac{-0.424\text{ V} + 2(-0.90)\text{V}}{3} = -0.74$ V

28. **(M)** From Table 23.4 we are given: VO_2^+/VO^{2+} reduction potential = 1.000 V, VO^{2+}/V^{3+} reduction potential = 0.337 V, V^{3+}/V^{2+} reduction potential = -0.255 V and V^{2+}/V reduction potential $= -1.13$ V. By taking advantage of the additive nature of free energies and the fact that $\Delta_r G° = -zFE°$, we can determine the three unknown potentials and complete the diagram.

(i) VO_2^+ / V^{3+} : $E° = \dfrac{1.000\text{ V} + 0.337\text{ V}}{2} = 0.669$ V

(ii) VO_2^+/V^{2+} : $\dfrac{1.000\text{ V} + 0.337\text{ V} + (-0.255\text{ V})}{3} = 0.361$ V

(iii) VO_2^+/V : $\dfrac{1.000\text{ V} + 0.337\text{ V} + (-0.255\text{ V}) + 2(-1.13\text{ V})}{5} = -0.24$ V

Chromium and Chromium Compounds

29. **(M)** Orange dichromate ion is in equilibrium with yellow chromate ion in aqueous solution.

$$Cr_2O_7^{2-}(aq) + H_2O(l) \rightleftharpoons 2\,CrO_4^{2-}(aq) + 2\,H^+(aq)$$

The chromate ion in solution then reacts with lead(II) ion to form a precipitate of yellow lead(II) chromate. $Pb^{2+}(aq) + CrO_4^{2-}(aq) \rightleftharpoons PbCrO_4(s)$

$PbCrO_4(s)$ will form until $\left[H^+\right]$ from the first equilibrium increases to the appropriate level and both equilibria are simultaneously satisfied.

30. **(M)** The initial dissolving reaction forms orange dichromate ion.

$$2\,BaCrO_4(s) + 2\,HCl(aq) \rightleftharpoons 2\,Ba^{2+}(aq) + Cr_2O_7^{2-}(aq) + 2\,Cl^-(aq) + H_2O(l)$$

Dichromate ion is a good oxidizing agent, that is strong enough to oxidize $Cl^-(aq)$ to $Cl_2(g)$ if the concentrations of reactants are high, the solution is acidic, and the product $Cl_2(g)$ is allowed to escape.

$$6\,Cl^-(aq) + Cr_2O_7^{2-}(aq) + 14\,H^+(aq) \rightleftharpoons 3\,Cl_2(g) + 2\,Cr^{3+}(aq) + 7\,H_2O(l)$$

Chromium(III) can hydrolyze in aqueous solution to produce green $\left[Cr(OH)_4\right]^-(aq)$, but the solution needs to be alkaline (pH >7) for this to occur. A more likely source of the green color is a complex ion such as $\left[Cr(H_2O)_4\,Cl_2\right]^+$.

31. **(D)** Oxidation: $\{Zn(s) \rightarrow Zn^{2+}(aq) + 2\,e^-\} \times 3$

Reduction: $Cr_2O_7^{2-}(aq, orange) + 14\,H^+(aq) + 6\,e^- \rightarrow 2\,Cr^{3+}(aq, green) + 7\,H_2O(l)$

Net: $\qquad 3\,Zn(s) + Cr_2O_7^{2-}(aq) + 14\,H^+(aq) \rightarrow 3\,Zn^{2+}(aq) + 2\,Cr^{3+}(aq) + 7\,H_2O(l)$

Oxidation: $\qquad Zn(s) \rightarrow Zn^{2+}(aq) + 2\,e^-$

Reduction: $\qquad \{Cr^{3+}(aq, green) + e^- \rightarrow Cr^{2+}(aq, blue)\} \times 2$

Net: $\qquad Zn(s) + 2\,Cr^{3+}(aq) \rightarrow Zn^{2+}(aq) + 2\,Cr^{2+}(aq)$

The green color is most likely due to a chloro complex of Cr^{3+}, such as $\left[Cr(H_2O)_4\,Cl_2\right]^+$.

Oxidation: $\qquad \{Cr^{2+}(aq, blue) \rightarrow Cr^{3+}(aq, green) + e^-\} \times 4$

Reduction: $\qquad O_2(g) + 4\,H^+(aq) + 4\,e^- \rightarrow 2\,H_2O(l)$

Net: $\qquad 4\,Cr^{2+}(aq) + O_2(g) + 4\,H^+(aq) \rightarrow 4\,Cr^{3+}(aq) + 2\,H_2O(l)$

32. **(M)** $CO_2(g)$, as the oxide of a nonmetal, is an acid anhydride. Its function is to make the solution acidic. A reasonable guess of the reactions that occur follows.

$$2\ CrO_4^{2-}(aq) + 2\ H^+(aq) \Longleftrightarrow Cr_2O_7^{2-}(aq) + H_2O(l)$$

$$2\ H_2O(l) + 2\ CO_2(aq) \Longleftrightarrow 2\ H^+(aq) + 2\ HCO_3^-(aq)$$

$$\overline{2\ CrO_4^{2-}(aq) + 2\ CO_2(aq) + H_2O(l) \Longleftrightarrow Cr_2O_7^{2-}(aq) + 2\ HCO_3^-(aq)}$$

33. **(M)** Simple substitution into equation (23.19) yields $\left[Cr_2O_7^{2-}\right]$ in each case. The expression is readily solved for the desired concentration as follows:

$\left[Cr_2O_7^{2-}\right] = 3.2 \times 10^{14} \times \left[H^+\right]^2 \times \left[CrO_4^{2-}\right]^2$. In each case, we use the value of pH to determine $\left[H^+\right]$ ($\left[H^+\right] = 10^{-pH}$).

(a) $\left[Cr_2O_7^{2-}\right] = 3.2 \times 10^{14} \times (10^{-7.12})^2 \times (0.20)^2 = 0.074$ M

(b) $\left[Cr_2O_7^{2-}\right] = 3.2 \times 10^{14} \times \left(10^{-9.15}\right)^2 \times (0.20)^2 = 6.4 \times 10^{-6}$ M

34. **(M)** We use Equation (23.19) again:

$$\frac{\left[Cr_2O_7^{2-}\right]}{\left[CrO_4^{2-}\right]^2} = 3.2 \times 10^{14} \left[H^+\right]^2 = 3.2 \times 10^{14} \left(10^{-7.55}\right)^2 = 3.2 \times 10^{14} \left(2.8 \times 10^{-8}\right)^2 = 0.254$$

$$\left[CrO_4^{2-}\right]_{initial} = \frac{1.505\ g\ Na_2CrO_4}{0.345\ L\ soln} \times \frac{1\ mol\ Na_2CrO_4}{161.97\ g\ Na_2CrO_4} \times \frac{1\ mol\ CrO_4^{2-}}{1\ mol\ Na_2CrO_4} = 0.0269\ M$$

Reaction:	$2\ CrO_4^{2-}(aq)$	+	$2\ H^+(aq)$	$\Longleftrightarrow$	$Cr_2O_7^{2-}(aq) + H_2O\ (l)$	
Initial:	0.0269 M		2.8×10^{-8} (fixed)		0 M	—
Changes:	$-2x$ M		0		$+x$ M	—
Equil:	$(0.0269 - 2x)$ M		2.8×10^{-8} (fixed)		x M	—

$$\frac{\left[Cr_2O_7^{2-}\right]}{\left[CrO_4^{2-}\right]^2} = 0.254 = \frac{x}{(0.0269 - 2x)^2} \qquad x = 0.254\left(0.000724 - 0.108x + 4x^2\right)$$

$$x = 0.000184 - 0.0274\ x + 1.016\ x^2 \qquad 1.016\ x^2 - 1.0274\ x + 0.000184 = 0$$

$$x = \frac{-b \pm \sqrt{b^2 - 4ac}}{2a} = \frac{1.0274 \pm \sqrt{1.0556 - 0.000736}}{2.032} = 1.0111\ M,\ \ 0.00016\ M$$

We choose the second root because the first root gives a negative $\left[CrO_4^{2-}\right]$.

$\left[Cr_2O_7^{2-}\right] = x = 0.00016$ M $\quad \left[CrO_4^{2-}\right] = 0.0269 - 2x = 0.0266$ M

We carry extra significant figures to avoid a significant rounding error in this problem.

35. **(E)** Each mole of chromium metal plated out from a chrome plating bath (i.e., CrO_3 and H_2SO_4) requires six moles of electrons.

$$\text{mass Cr} = 1.00 \text{ h} \times \frac{3600 \text{ s}}{1 \text{ hr}} \times \frac{3.4 \text{ C}}{1 \text{ s}} \times \frac{1 \text{ mol e}^-}{96485 \text{ C}} \times \frac{1 \text{ mol Cr}}{6 \text{ mol e}^-} \times \frac{52.00 \text{ g Cr}}{1 \text{ mol Cr}} = 1.10 \text{ g Cr}$$

36. **(M)** First we compute the amount of Cr(s) deposited.

$$\text{mol Cr} = \left(0.0010 \text{ mm} \times \frac{1 \text{ cm}}{10 \text{ mm}} \times 0.375 \text{ m}^2 \times \frac{10^4 \text{ cm}^2}{1 \text{ m}^2} \right) \times \frac{7.14 \text{ g Cr}}{1 \text{ cm}^3 \text{ Cr}} \times \frac{1 \text{ mol Cr}}{52.0 \text{ g Cr}} = 5.1 \times 10^{-2} \text{ mol Cr}$$

Recall that the deposition of each mole of chromium requires six moles of electrons. We now compute the time required to deposit the 5.1×10^{-2} mol Cr.

$$\text{time} = 5.1 \times 10^{-2} \text{ mol Cr} \times \frac{6 \text{ mol e}^-}{1 \text{ mol Cr}} \times \frac{96485 \text{ C}}{1 \text{ mol e}^-} \times \frac{1 \text{ s}}{3.5 \text{ C}} \times \frac{1 \text{ h}}{3600 \text{ s}} = 2.3 \text{ h}$$

37. **(M)** Dichromate ion is the prevalent species in acidic solution. Oxoanions are better oxidizing agents in acidic solution because increasing the concentration of hydrogen ion favors formation of product. The half-equation is:
$Cr_2O_7^{2-}(aq) + 14 \, H^+(aq) + 6 \, e^- \longrightarrow 2 \, Cr^{3+}(aq) + 7 \, H_2O(l)$ Note that precipitation occurs most effectively in alkaline solution. In fact, adding an acid to a compound is often an effective way of dissolving a water-insoluble compound. Thus, we expect to see the form that predominates in alkaline solution to be the most effective precipitating agent. Notice also that CrO_4^{2-} is smaller than is $Cr_2O_7^{2-}$, giving it a higher lattice energy in its compounds, which makes these compounds harder to dissolve.

38. **(M)** Both metal ions precipitate as hydroxides when $\left[OH^- \right]$ is moderate.

$Mg^{2+}(aq) + 2 \, OH^-(aq) \rightarrow Mg(OH)_2(s)$ $\qquad$ $Cr^{3+}(aq) + 3 \, OH^-(aq) \rightarrow Cr(OH)_3(s)$

Because chromium(III) oxides and hydroxides are amphoteric (and those of magnesium ion are not), $Cr(OH)_3(s)$ will dissolve in excess base.

$Cr(OH)_3(s) + NaOH(aq) \rightarrow Na^+(aq) + \left[Cr(OH)_4 \right]^-(aq)$

The Iron Triad

39. **(M)** $4 \, Fe^{2+}(aq) + O_2(g) + 4 \, H^+ \rightarrow 4 \, Fe^{3+}(aq) + 2 \, H_2O(l)$ $\qquad$ $E° = 0.44 \text{ V}$

$[Fe^{2+}] = [Fe^{3+}]$; pH = 3.25 or $[H^+] = 5.6 \times 10^{-4}$ and $P_{O_2} = 0.20$ atm

$$E = E° - \frac{0.0592}{z} \log \left(\frac{[Fe^{3+}]^4}{[Fe^{2+}]^4 [H^+]^4 P_{O_2}} \right) = 0.44 \text{ V} - \frac{0.0592}{4} \log \left(\frac{[Fe^{3+}]^4}{[Fe^{2+}]^4 [10^{-3.25}]^4 \, 0.20} \right)$$

$E = 0.24$ V (spontaneous under these conditions)

40. **(M)** $\{NiO(OH)(s) + e^- + H^+(aq) \rightarrow Ni(OH)_2(s) \qquad \}\times 2 \qquad E°_{red}$

$\{Cd(s) + 2\,OH^-(aq) \rightarrow Cd(OH)_2(s) + 2\,e^- \quad \}\times 1 \qquad E°_{ox}$

$\{H_2O(l) \rightarrow H^+(aq) + OH^-(aq)\} \qquad\qquad\qquad \}\times 2$

$\overline{2\,NiO(OH)(s) + Cd(s) + 2\,H_2O(l) \rightarrow Cd(OH)_2(s) + 2\,Ni(OH)_2(s) \quad E°_{cell} \approx 1.50\ V}$

$E°_{ox}$ may be obtained by combining the K_{sp} value for $Cd(OH)_2(s)$

$(K_{sp\,Cd(OH)_2} = 2.5\times 10^{-14})$ and $E°_{red} = -0.403\ V$ for $Cd^{2+}(aq) + 2\,e^- \rightarrow Cd(s)$. Hence,

$Cd(s) \rightarrow Cd^{2+}(aq) + 2\,e^- \qquad\qquad\qquad E°_{ox} = 0.403\ V$

$Cd^{2+}(aq) + 2\,OH^-(aq) \rightarrow Cd(OH)_2(s) \quad E°_{cell} = \dfrac{0.0257}{z}\ln\left(\dfrac{1}{K_{sp}}\right) = \dfrac{0.0257}{2}\ln\left(\dfrac{1}{2.5\times 10^{-14}}\right) = 0.40\underline{3}\ V$

$\overline{Cd(s) + 2\,OH^-(aq) \rightarrow Cd(OH)_2(s) + 2\,e^- \quad E°_{ox} = 0.80\underline{6}\ V}$

Now plug this result back into the first set of redox reactions:

$\{NiO(OH)(s) + e^- + H^+(aq) \rightarrow Ni(OH)_2(s) \qquad \}\times 2 \qquad E°_{red}$

$\{Cd(s) + 2\,OH^-(aq) \rightarrow Cd(OH)_2(s) + 2\,e^- \quad \}\times 1 \qquad E°_{ox} = 0.80\underline{6}\ V$

$\overline{2\,NiO(OH)(s) + Cd(s) + 2\,H_2O(l) \rightarrow Cd(OH)_2(s) + 2\,Ni(OH)_2(s) \quad E°_{cell} \approx 1.50\ V}$

$E°_{red} = 1.50\ V - 0.80\underline{6}\ V = 0.69\ V$

41. **(E)** $Fe^{3+}(aq) + K_4[\overset{[II]}{Fe}(CN)_6](aq) \rightarrow K\overset{[III]}{Fe}\,[\overset{[II]}{Fe}(CN)_6](s) + 3\,K^+(aq)$

Alternate formulation: $4Fe^{3+} + 3[\overset{[II]}{Fe}(CN)_6]^{4-}(aq) + Fe_4[\overset{[II]}{Fe}(CN)_6]_3$

42. **(E)** $K^+(aq) + Fe^{2+}(aq) + K_3[\overset{[III]}{Fe}(CN)_6](aq) \rightarrow Fe^{3+}(aq) + K_4[\overset{[II]}{Fe}(CN)_6](aq)$

$Fe^{3+}(aq) + K_4[\overset{[II]}{Fe}(CN)_6](aq) \rightarrow K\overset{[III]}{Fe}\,[\overset{[II]}{Fe}(CN)_6](s) + 3\,K^+(aq)$

Group 11 Metals

43. **(E) (a)** $Cu^{2+}(aq) + H_2(g) \rightarrow Cu(s) + 2\,H^+(aq)$

(b) $Au^+(aq) + Fe^{2+}(aq) \rightarrow Au(s) + Fe^{3+}(aq)$

(c) $2\,Cu^{2+}(aq) + SO_2(g) + 2\,H_2O(l) \rightarrow 2\,Cu^+(aq) + SO_4^{2-}(aq) + 4\,H^+(aq)$

44. **(M)** In either case, the acid acts as an oxidizing agent and dissolves silver; the gold is unaffected.

Oxidation: $\{Ag(s) \rightarrow Ag^+(aq) + e^-\}\times 3$

Reduction: $NO_3^-(aq) + 4\,H^+(aq) + 3\,e^- \rightarrow NO(g) + 2\,H_2O(l)$

Net: $3\,Ag(s) + NO_3^-(aq) + 4\,H^+(aq) \rightarrow 3\,Ag^+(aq) + NO(g) + 2\,H_2O(l)$

Oxidation: $\{Ag(s) \rightarrow Ag^+(aq) + e^-\}\times 2$

Reduction: $SO_4^{2-}(aq) + 4\,H^+(aq) + 2\,e^- \rightarrow SO_2(g) + 2\,H_2O(l)$

Net: $2\,Ag(s) + SO_4^{2-}(aq) + 4\,H^+(aq) \rightarrow 2\,Ag^+(aq) + SO_2(g) + 2\,H_2O(l)$

45. **(M)** The Integrative Example showed $K_c = 1.2 \times 10^6 = \dfrac{\left[Cu^{2+}\right]}{\left[Cu^+\right]^2}$ or

$$\left[Cu^{2+}\right] = 1.2 \times 10^6 \left[Cu^+\right]^2$$

(a) When $\left[Cu^+\right] = 0.20$ M, $\left[Cu^{2+}\right] = 1.2 \times 10^6 (0.20)^2 = 4.8 \times 10^4$ M. This is an impossibly high concentration. Thus $\left[Cu^+\right] = 0.20$ M can never be achieved.

(b) When $\left[Cu^+\right] = 1.0 \times 10^{-10}$ M, $\left[Cu^{2+}\right] = 1.2 \times 10^6 (1.0 \times 10^{-10})^2 = 1.2 \times 10^{-14}$ M. This is an entirely reasonable (even though small) concentration; $\left[Cu^+\right] = 1.0 \times 10^{-10}$ M can be maintained in solution.

46. **(M)** Oxidation: $\{Cu(s) \rightarrow Cu^{2+} + 2\ e^-$ $\}\times 2$
Reduction: $\{O_2(g) + 2\ H_2O(l) + 4\ e^- \rightarrow 4\ OH^-(aq) \}\times 1$

Overall: $2\ Cu(s) + O_2(g) + 2\ H_2O(l) \rightarrow 2\ Cu^{2+}(aq) + 4\ OH^-(aq)$

Note: This produces an alkaline solution. CO_2 dissolves in this alkaline solution to produce carbonate ion.

Step(a): $CO_2(g) + OH^-(aq) \rightarrow HCO_3^-(aq)$
Step(b): $HCO_3^-(aq) + OH^-(aq) \rightarrow CO_3^{2-}(aq) + H_2O(l)$

Total: $CO_2(g) + 2\ OH^-(aq) \rightarrow CO_3^{2-}(aq) + H_2O(l)$

Combination of the reactions labeled "overall" and "total" gives the following result.

$2\ Cu(s) + O_2(g) + H_2O(l) + CO_2(g) \rightarrow 2\ Cu^{2+}(aq) + 2\ OH^-(aq) + CO_3^{2-}(aq)$

The ionic product of the resultant reaction combine in a precipitation reaction to form

$2\ Cu^{2+}(aq) + 2\ OH^-(aq) + CO_3^{2-}(aq) \rightarrow Cu_2(OH)_2CO_3(s)$

Group 12 Metals

47. **(E)** Given: Hg^{2+}/Hg reduction potential = 0.854 V and Hg_2^{2+}/Hg reduction potential = 0.796 V Using the additive nature of free energies and the fact that $\Delta_r G° = -zFE°$, we can determine the Hg^{2+}/Hg_2^{2+} potential as $\dfrac{2(0.854V) - 0.796V}{1} = 0.912$ V

48. **(M)** $\Delta_r G° = -25,000$ J mol^{-1} = $-RT \ln K$ = $-(8.3145$ J mol^{-1} K$^{-1})(673$ K$)(\ln K)$

$K = K_p = 87$ atm$^{-1} = \dfrac{1}{P_{O_2}}$ Therefore, $P_{O_2} = \dfrac{1}{K_P} = \dfrac{1}{87} = 0.011$ atm

49. **(M) (a)** Estimate K_p for $ZnO(s) + C(s) \rightarrow Zn(l) + CO(g)$ at 800 °C (Note: Zn(l) boils at 907 °C)

$\{2\,C(s) + O_2(g) \rightarrow 2\,CO(g)\} \times 1/2 \qquad \Delta_r G° \approx (-415 \text{ kJ mol}^{-1}) \times (1/2)$

$\{2\,ZnO(s) \rightarrow 2\,Zn(l) + O_2(g)\} \times 1/2 \qquad \Delta_r G° = (+485 \text{ kJ mol}^{-1}) \times (1/2)$

$ZnO(s) + C(s) \rightarrow Zn(l) + CO(g) \qquad \Delta_r G° = 35 \text{ kJ mol}^{-1}$

Use $\Delta_r G° = -RT \ln K$ where $T = 800$ °C, $K = K_p$

$35 \text{ kJ mol}^{-1} = -(8.3145 \times 10^{-3} \text{ kJ mol}^{-1} \text{ K}^{-1})((273.15 + 800) \text{ K})(\ln K_p)$

$\ln K_p = -3.9$ or $K_p = 0.02$

(b) $K_p = P_{CO} = 0.02$ Hence, $P_{CO} = 0.02$ atm

50. **(M)** $T = 298$ K. Hence, $\log (P_{mmHg}) = \dfrac{-0.05223\,(61{,}960)}{298} + 8.118 = -2.742$

$P_{mmHg} = 0.001811$ mmHg

$PV = nRT \rightarrow \dfrac{n}{V} = \dfrac{P}{RT} = [Hg] = \dfrac{(0.001811 \text{ mmHg})(\dfrac{1\,\text{atm}}{760\,\text{mmHg}})}{\left(0.08206\,\dfrac{L\,\text{atm}}{K\,\text{mol}}\right)(298K)} = 9.744 \times 10^{-8} \text{ mol L}^{-1}$

Next, convert to mg Hg m^{-3}:

$[Hg] = \left(9.744 \times 10^{-8}\,\dfrac{\text{mol}}{L}\right)\left(\dfrac{1000\,L}{m^3}\right)\left(\dfrac{200.59\,\text{g Hg}}{1\,\text{mol Hg}}\right)\left(\dfrac{1000\,\text{mg}}{1\,\text{g Hg}}\right) = 19.5$ mg Hg m^{-3}

(This is approximately 400 times greater than the permissible level of 0.05 mg Hg m^{-3})

51. **(M)** We must calculate the wavelength of light absorbed in order to promote an electron across each band gap.

First, a few relationships. $E_{mole} = N_A E_{photon} \qquad E_{photon} = h\nu \qquad c = \nu\lambda$ or $\nu = c/\lambda$

Then, some algebra. $E_{mole} = N_A E_{photon} = N_A h\nu = N_A hc/\lambda \qquad$ or $\qquad \lambda = N_A hc/E_{mole}$

For ZnO, $\lambda = \dfrac{6.022 \times 10^{23} \text{ mol}^{-1} \times 6.626 \times 10^{-34} \text{ J s} \times 2.998 \times 10^{8} \text{ m s}^{-1}}{325 \times 10^3 \text{ J mol}^{-1}} \times \dfrac{10^9 \text{ nm}}{1\,m}$

$= \dfrac{1.196 \times 10^8 \text{ J mol}^{-1} \text{ nm}}{325 \times 10^3 \text{ J mol}^{-1}} = 368$ nm violet light

For CdS, $\lambda = \dfrac{1.196 \times 10^8 \text{ J mol}^{-1} \text{ nm}}{250 \times 10^3 \text{ J mol}^{-1}} = 479$ nm blue light

The blue light absorbed by CdS is subtracted from the white light incident on the surface of the solid. The remaining reflected light is yellow in this case. When the violet light is subtracted from the white light incident on the ZnO surface, the reflected light appears white.

52. **(D)** The color that we see is the complementary color to the color absorbed. The color absorbed, in turn, is determined by the energy separation of the band gap. If the wavelength for the absorbed color is short, the energy separation for the band gap is large.

The yellow color of CdS means that the complementary color, violet, is absorbed. Since violet light has a quite short wavelength (about 479 nm), CdS must have a very large band gap energetically.

HgS is red, meaning that the color absorbed is green, which has a moderate wavelength (about 520 nm). HgS must have a band gap of intermediate energy.

CdSe is black, meaning that visible light of all wavelengths and thus all energies in the visible region are absorbed. This would occur if CdSe has a very small band gap, smaller than that of least energetic red light (about 650 nm).

INTEGRATIVE AND ADVANCED EXERCISES

<u>53.</u> **(M)** There are two reasons why Au is soluble in aqua regia while Ag is not. First, Ag^+, the oxidation product, forms a very insoluble chloride, AgCl, which probably adheres to the surface of the metal and prevents further reaction. $AuCl_3$ is not noted as being an insoluble chloride. Second, gold(III) forms a very stable complex ion with chloride ion, $[AuCl_4]^-$. This complex ion is much more stable than the corresponding dichloroargentate ion, $[AgCl_2]^-$.

54. **(E)** Sc and Ti metals form carbides in the presence of carbon (coke). Thus, reduction of their oxides using carbon is avoided.

55. **(M)** Both tin and zinc are toxic metals in high concentrations. Tin plated iron is more desirable than zinc plated (galvanized) iron. The reason for this is that zinc is a very reactive metal, especially in the presence of acidic foods. Tin, on the other hand, is much less reactive ($E°_{Sn^{2+}/Sn} = -0.137$ V vs. $E°_{Zn^{2+}/Zn} = -0.763$ V). As well, tin is more malleable and more easily prepared in pure form (free of oxide).

56. **(M)**

Oxidation : $\{Cu(s) \longrightarrow Cu^{2+}(aq) + 2\ e^-\} \times 2$

Reduction : $O_2(g) + 2\ H_2O(l) + 4\ e^- \longrightarrow 4\ OH^-(aq)$

Net : $2\ Cu(s) + O_2(g) + 2\ H_2O(l) \longrightarrow 2\ Cu^{2+}(aq) + 4\ OH^-(aq)$

This oxidation-reduction reaction produces an alkaline solution. $SO_3(g)$ dissolves in this alkaline solution to produce hydrogen sulfate ion in an acid-base reaction.

Step (a): $\quad SO_3(g) + OH^-(aq) \longrightarrow HSO_4^-(aq)$

Step (b): $\quad HSO_4^-(aq) + OH^-(aq) \longrightarrow SO_4^{2-}(aq) + H_2O(l)$

Total: $\quad SO_3(g) + 2\ OH^-(aq) \longrightarrow SO_4^{2-}(aq) + H_2O(l)$

The combination of the reactions labeled "Net:" and "Total:" gives the following result.

$$2\ Cu(s) + O_2(g) + H_2O(l) + SO_3(g) \longrightarrow 2\ Cu^{2+}(aq) + 2\ OH^-(aq) + SO_4^{2-}(aq)$$

The ionic products of this resultant reaction combine in a precipitation reaction to form $Cu_2(OH)_2SO_4(s)$. Thus, $2\ Cu^{2+}(aq) + 2\ OH^-(aq) + SO_4^{2-}(aq) \longrightarrow Cu_2(OH)_2SO_4(s)$

57. **(M)** The noble gas formalism requires that the number of valence electrons possessed by the metal atom plus the number of sigma electrons be equal to the number of electrons in the succeeding noble gas atom.

(a) $Mo(CO)_6$; Mo has 42 electrons, 6 CO contribute another 12 for 54, which is the number of electrons in Xe

(b) $Os(CO)_5$; Os has 76 electrons, 5 CO contribute another 10 for 86, which is the number of electrons in Rn

(c) $Re(CO)_5^-$; Re anion has 76 electrons, 5 CO contribute another 10 for 86, which is the number of electrons in Rn

(d) All of the metal carbonyls have zero dipole moments and very weak intermolecular forces. Therefore one would expect these compounds to be liquids or low melting solids at room temperature. Since chromium carbonyls have more electrons than the other compounds it will be more polarizable and therefore have the strongest dispersion force leading to it being a solid while the other metal carbonyls are liquids. Another reason that the nickel and iron carbonyls are liquids and the chromium carbonyl is a solid is due to the differences in their shape. The nickel carbonyl $Ni(CO)_4$ being four-coordinate is tetrahedral while the iron carbonyl $Fe(CO)_5$ being penta-coordinate is trigonal bipyramidal. These two shapes do not lend themselves to forming crystals while the octahedral shape of chromium carbonyl, more spherical in nature, does fit better into a crystal lattice.

(e) This compound would be an ionic, salt-like material consisting of Na^+ and $V(CO)_6^-$ ions.

58. **(M)**

(a) Breaks occur at the melting point and boiling point due to changes in the states of the metals (solid $\rightarrow$ liquid $\rightarrow$ gas).

(b) Slopes of these lines become more positive as the temperature increases due to the sign of ΔS° for these reactions. The slope should be equal to $-\Delta S^\circ$, where ΔS° is a negative number in these cases that becomes more negative with a change in phase (higher temperature).

(c) The break at the boiling point is sharper than the break at the melting point because $\Delta_{fus}S^\circ \ll \Delta_{vap}S^\circ$.

59. (M) Oxidation : $\qquad 2\,I^-(aq) \longrightarrow I_2(s) + 2\ e^- \qquad\qquad -E° = -0.535$ V

Reduction:$\{Cu^{2+}(aq) + e^- \longrightarrow Cu^+(aq)\} \qquad \times 2 \qquad E° = +0.159$ V

Net: $\qquad Cu^{2+}(aq) + 2\ I^-(aq) \longrightarrow 2\ Cu^+(aq) + I_2(s)\ E°_{cell} = -0.376$ V $\quad n = 2$

$\Delta_r G° = -zFE° = -RT \ln K$

$\ln\ K = \dfrac{zFE°}{RT} = \dfrac{2\ e^- \times 96485\ \text{C/mol e}^- \times -0.376\ \text{V}}{8.3145\ \text{J mol}^{-1}\ \text{K}^{-1} \times 298.15\ \text{K}} = -29.3 \qquad K = e^{-29.3} = 2\times10^{-13}$

Redox: $\qquad Cu^{2+}(aq) + 4\,I^-(aq) \longrightarrow 2\ Cu^+(aq) + I_2(s) + 2\,I^-(aq)\quad K_{redox} = 2\times10^{-13}$

Precipitation: $\{Cu^+(aq) + I^-(aq) \longrightarrow CuI(s)\}\times 2\ \ 1/K_{sp}^{\ 2} = 1/(1.1\times10^{-12})^2$

Total: $\qquad Cu^{2+}(aq) + 4\,I^-(aq) \longrightarrow 2\ CuI(s) + I_2(s)\ K$

$K = \dfrac{K_{redox}}{K_{sp}^{\ 2}} = \dfrac{2\times10^{-13}}{(1.1\times10^{-12})^2} = 2\times10^{11}$ Clearly this reaction will occur as written.

I_2 and I^- form I_3^- in aqueous solution. So, adding an additional mole of I^- to the last reaction yields: $\qquad Cu^{2+}(aq) + 5\ I^-(aq) \longrightarrow 2\ CuI(s) + I_3^-(s)$

60. (D) A "detailed calculation" would involve determining the final concentrations of all species. But we can get approximate values of the gold-containing ions by determining values of the equilibrium constants for the reactions involved. First, we determine the value of the equilibrium constant for the disproportionation of $Au^+(aq)$. To accomplish this, find the value of $E°$ for the couple $Au^+(aq)|Au(s)$.

Oxidation $\qquad Au^+(aq) \longrightarrow Au^{3+}(aq) + 2\ e^- \qquad\qquad -E° = -1.36$ V

Reduction: $\qquad \{Au^+(aq) + e^- \longrightarrow Au(s)\}\times 2 \qquad\qquad E° = +1.83$ V

Net: $\qquad 3\ Au^+(aq) \longrightarrow Au^{3+}(aq) + 2\ Au(s)\ E°_{cell} = 0.47$ V

$\ln K = \dfrac{zFE°}{RT} = \dfrac{2\ e^- \times 96485\ \text{C/mol e}^- \times 0.47\ \text{V}}{8.3145\ \text{J mol}^{-1}\ \text{K}^{-1} \times 298.15\ \text{K}} = 36.6 \qquad K = e^{36.6} = 8\times10^{15}$

Then we determine the value of the equilibrium constant for dissolving and disproportionation.

Disproportionation : $\qquad 3\ Au^+(aq) \longrightarrow Au^{3+}(aq) + 2\ Au(s)\ K_{disp} = 8\times10^{15}$

Dissolving : $\qquad \{AuCl(s) \longrightarrow Au^+(aq) + Cl^-(aq)\}\ \ \times 3 \qquad K_{sp}^{\ 3} = (2.0\times10^{-13})^3$

Net : $\qquad 3\ AuCl(s) \longrightarrow Au^{3+}(aq) + 2\ Au(s) + 3\ Cl^-(aq)\quad K$

$K = K_{disp} \times K_{sp}^{\ 3} = 8\times10^{15} \times (2.0\times10^{-13})^3 = 6.4\times10^{-23} = [Au^{3+}][Cl^-]^3 = (x)(3x)^3 = 27\ x^4$

$x = \sqrt[4]{\dfrac{6.4\times10^{-23}}{27}} = 1\times10^{-6}\ \text{M} = [Au^{3+}]$

This is a significant amount of decomposition, particularly when compared with $[Au^+] = 4.5 \times 10^{-7}$ M, which is the concentration present in saturated AuCl, assuming no disproportionation.

61. (M)

(a) Dissolution: $AgO(s) + 2 H^+(aq) \longrightarrow Ag^{2+}(aq) + H_2O(l)$

Oxidation: $2 H_2O(l) \longrightarrow O_2(g) + 4 H^+(aq) + 4 e^- \qquad -E° = -1.229 V$

Reduction: $\{Ag^{2+}(aq) + e^- \longrightarrow Ag^+(aq)\} \qquad \times 4 \qquad E° = 1.98 V$

Net: $2 H_2O(l) + 4 Ag^{2+}(aq) \longrightarrow O_2(g) + 4 H^+(aq) + 4 Ag^+(aq)$

(b) $E°_{cell} = -1.229 V + 1.98 V = +0.75 V \rightarrow$ spontaneous since $E°_{cell} > 0$.

62. (M)

Association: $2 H^+(aq) + 2 CrO_4^{2-}(aq) \rightleftharpoons 2 HCrO_4^-(aq) \qquad 1/K_a^2 = 1/(3.2 \times 10^{-7})^2$

Elimination: $2 HCrO_4^-(aq) \rightleftharpoons Cr_2O_7^{2-}(aq) + H_2O(l) \qquad K$

Eqn. (23.18): $2 H^+(aq) + 2 CrO_4^{2-}(aq) \rightleftharpoons Cr_2O_7^{2-}(aq) + H_2O(l) \quad K_c = 3.2 \times 10^{14}$

$K_c = 3.2 \times 10^{14} = \dfrac{K}{K_a^2} = \dfrac{K}{(3.2 \times 10^{-7})^2} \qquad K = 3.2 \times 10^{14} \times (3.2 \times 10^{-7})^2 = 33$

63. (D) The presence of both acetate ion and acetic acid establishes a buffer and fixes the pH of the solution. This, in turn, fixes $[CrO_4^{2-}]$. We then can determine the concentration of each of the cations that can coexist with this $[CrO_4^{2-}]$ before precipitation occurs. First we determine $[H_3O^+]$, with the aid of the Henderson-Hasselbalch equation.

$$pH = pK_a + \log \frac{[CH_3COO^-]}{[CH_3COOH]} = -\log (1.8 \times 10^{-5}) + \log \frac{1.0 M}{1.0 M} = 4.74$$

$$[H_3O^+] = 10^{-4.74} = 1.8 \times 10^{-5} M$$

$$K_c = 3.2 \times 10^{14} = \frac{[Cr_2O_7^{2-}]}{[CrO_4^{2-}]^2[H_3O^+]^2} = \frac{0.0010 M}{[CrO_4^{2-}]^2 (1.8 \times 10^{-5})^2} = \frac{3.1 \times 10^6}{[CrO_4^{2-}]^2}$$

$$[CrO_4^{2-}] = \sqrt{\frac{3.1 \times 10^6}{3.2 \times 10^{14}}} = 9.8 \times 10^{-5} M$$

$$[Ba^{2+}]_{max} = \frac{K_{sp}}{[CrO_4^{2-}]} = \frac{1.2 \times 10^{-10}}{9.8 \times 10^{-5}} = 1.2 \times 10^{-6} M$$

$$[Sr^{2+}]_{max} = \frac{2.2 \times 10^{-5}}{9.8 \times 10^{-5}} = 0.22 M$$

$$[Ca^{2+}]_{max} = \frac{7.1 \times 10^{-4}}{9.8 \times 10^{-5}} = 7.2 M$$

Each cation is initially present at 0.10 M. Neither strontium ion nor calcium ion will precipitate, while $BaCrO_4$ will precipitate until $[Ba^{2+}]$ has declined to far less than 0.1% of its original value. Thus, barium ion is effectively separated from the other two cations by chromate ion precipitation under these conditions.

64. (D) The equations are first balanced with the ion-electron method. Oxalic acid is oxidized in each case.

Reaction 1:

Oxidation: $H_2C_2O_4(aq) \rightarrow 2\,H^+(aq) + 2e^- + CO_2(g)$

Reduction: $Fe_2O_3(s) + 6\,H^+(aq) + 2e^- \rightarrow 2\,Fe^{2+}(aq) + 3\,H_2O(l)$

Net: $H_2C_2O_4(aq) + Fe_2O_3(s) + 4\,H^+(aq) \rightarrow 2\,CO_2(g) + 2\,Fe^{2+}(aq) + 3\,H_2O(l)$

Reaction 2:

Oxidation: $\{H_2C_2O_4(aq) \rightarrow 2\,H^+(aq) + 2e^- + CO_2(g)\} \times 5$

Reduction: $\{MnO_4^-(aq) + 8\,H^+(aq) + 5e^- \rightarrow Mn^{2+}(aq) + 4\,H_2O(l)\} \times 2$

Net: $5\,H_2C_2O_4(aq) + 8\,H^+(aq) + 2\,MnO_4^-(aq) \rightarrow 2\,Mn^{2+}(aq) + 10\,CO_2(g) + 8\,H_2O(l)$

The mass of excess oxalic acid can be calculated from the second reaction:

$$\text{mass } H_2C_2O_4 \cdot 2\,H_2O = 0.03516\ L \times \frac{0.1000\ \text{mol } MnO_4^-}{1\ L\ \text{soln}} \times \frac{5\ \text{mol } H_2C_2O_4}{2\ \text{mol } MnO_4^-}$$

$$\times \frac{126.07\ g\ H_2C_2O_4 \cdot 2\,H_2O}{1\ \text{mol } H_2C_2O_4 \cdot 2\,H_2O} = 1.108\ g\ H_2C_2O_4 \cdot 2\,H_2O$$

Therefore, the mass of oxalic acid that reacted with Fe_2O_3 is $1.752\ g - 1.108\ g = 0.644\ g$. Finally, using reaction 1, we can calculate the mass and percent of Fe_2O_3 in the impure sample of hematite:

$$\text{mass } Fe_2O_3 = 0.644\ g\ H_2C_2O_4 \cdot 2\,H_2O \times \frac{1\ \text{mol } H_2C_2O_4 \cdot 2\,H_2O}{126.07\ g\ H_2C_2O_4 \cdot 2\,H_2O} \times \frac{1\ \text{mol } Fe_2O_3}{1\ \text{mol } H_2C_2O_4 \cdot 2\,H_2O}$$

$$\times \frac{159.69\ g\ Fe_2O_3}{1\,\text{mol } Fe_2O_3} = 0.816\ g\ Fe_2O_3$$

$$\%\ Fe_2O_3 = \frac{0.816\ g}{0.960\ g} \times 100\% = 85.0\%$$

65. (D)

(a) We consider reaction with 1.00 millimoles of Fe^{2+}. In each case, we need the balanced chemical equation of the redox reaction.

$$Cr_2O_7^{2-}(aq) + 14\,H^+(aq) + 6\,Fe^{2+}(aq) \longrightarrow 2\,Cr^{3+}(aq) + 7\,H_2O(l) + 6\,Fe^{3+}(aq)$$

$$\text{titrant volume} = 1.00\ \text{mmol } Fe^{2+} \times \frac{1\ \text{mmol } Cr_2O_7^{2-}}{6\ \text{mmol } Fe^{2+}} \times \frac{1\ mL\ \text{solution}}{0.1000\ \text{mmol } Cr_2O_7^{2-}} = 1.67\ mL\ \text{soln}$$

$$MnO_4^-(aq) + 8\,H^+(aq) + 5\,Fe^{2+}(aq) \longrightarrow Mn^{2+}(aq) + 4\,H_2O + 5\,Fe^{3+}(aq)$$

$$\text{titrant volume} = 1.00\ \text{mmol } Fe^{3+} \times \frac{1\ \text{mmol } MnO_4^-}{5\ \text{mmol } Fe^{2+}} \times \frac{1\ mL\ \text{solution}}{0.1000\ \text{mmol } MnO_4^-} = 2.00\ mL\ \text{soln}$$

More of the 0.1000 M MnO_4^- solution would be required.

(b) We use the reaction of each with Fe^{2+} to find the equivalence between them.

$$V_{MnO_4^-} = 24.50 \text{ mL} \times \frac{0.1000 \text{ mmol } Cr_2O_7^{2-}}{1 \text{ mL soln}} \times \frac{6 \text{ mmol } Fe^{2+}}{1 \text{ mmol } Cr_2O_7^{2-}} \times \frac{1 \text{ mmol } MnO_4^-}{5 \text{ mmol } Fe^{2+}}$$

$$\times \frac{1 \text{ mL soln}}{0.1000 \text{ mmol } MnO_4^-} = 29.40 \text{ mL of } 0.1000 \text{ mmol } MnO_4^-$$

66. **(M)** A high oxidation state of a metal can only be stabilized by an anion of an element that is highly electronegative. Fluorine and oxygen are the two most electronegative elements in the periodic table and thus should be most effective at stabilizing a high oxidation state of a metal.

67. **(D)** The addition of the first 10.00 mL aliquot to $BaCl_2$ results in the precipitation of $BaCrO_4$. From this we are able to determine the amount of Cr in solution. The titration of the second 10.00 mL aliquot with Fe^{2+} results in the redox reaction between Fe^{2+}, MnO_4^- and $Cr_2O_7^{2-}$. Since we have the amount of Cr from the first titration we can determine the amount of $Cr_2O_7^{2-}$ was present and determine the amount of Fe^{2+} that was needed to reduce the dichromate from which we can determine the amount of Mn that was in solution.

Equation: $MnO_4^-(aq) + 8 H^+(aq) + 5 Fe^{2+}(aq) \longrightarrow Mn^{2+}(aq) + 4 H_2O + 5 Fe^{3+}(aq)$

$$\text{mass of Cr} = 250.0 \text{ mL soln} \times \frac{0.549 \text{ g } BaCrO_4}{10.00 \text{ mL sample}} \times \frac{1 \text{ mol } BaCrO_4}{253.3 \text{ g } BaCrO_4} \times \frac{1 \text{ mol Cr}}{1 \text{ mol } BaCrO_4} \times \frac{52.00 \text{ g Cr}}{1 \text{ mol Cr}}$$

mass of Cr = 2.82 g Cr

equation: $Cr_2O_7^{2-} + 14 H^+ + 6 Fe^{2+} \rightarrow 2Cr^{3+} + 7 H_2O + 6 Fe^{3+}$

$$\text{volume of titrant to reduce } Cr_2O_7^{2-} = 2.82 \text{ g Cr} \times \frac{10 \text{ ml}}{250 \text{ ml}} \times \frac{1 \text{ mol } Cr^{3+}}{52.00 \text{ g Cr}} \times \frac{6 \text{ mol } Fe^{2+}}{1 \text{ mol } Cr_2O_7^{2-}}$$

$$\times \frac{1 \text{ mol } Cr_2O_7^{2-}}{2 \text{ mol } Cr^{3+}} \times \frac{1 \text{ L titrant}}{0.0750 \text{ mol } Fe^{2+}} \times \frac{1000 \text{ mL}}{1 \text{ L}} = 86.78 \text{ ml } Fe^{2+} \text{ titrant}$$

Now the volume of titrant to reduce both MnO_4^- and $Cr_2O_7^{2-}$ must be $(15.95 + 86.78)$ mL

Volume of titrant = 102.73 mL.

Not just 15.95 mL, which must be the volume of titrant required for MnO_4^- *alone*.

$$\text{mass Mn} = 250.0 \text{ mL soln} \times \frac{15.95 \text{ mL titrant}}{10.00 \text{ mL sample}} \times \frac{0.0750 \text{ mmol } Fe^{2+}}{1 \text{ mL titrant}} \times \frac{1 \text{ mmol } MnO_4^-}{5 \text{ mmol } Fe^{2+}}$$

$$\times \frac{1 \text{ mmol Mn}}{1 \text{ mmol } MnO_4^-} \times \frac{54.94 \text{ mg Mn}}{1 \text{ mmol Mn}} \times \frac{1 \text{ g Mn}}{1000 \text{ mg Mn}} = 0.3286 \text{ Mn}$$

$$\%Mn = \frac{0.3286 \text{ g Mn}}{10.000 \text{ g steel}} \times 100\% = 3.286\% \text{ Mn} \qquad \%Cr = \frac{2.82 \text{ g Cr}}{10.000 \text{ g steel}} \times 100\% = 28.2\% \text{ Cr}$$

68. **(M) (a)** We use the technique from Chapter 3 to determine the empirical formula of palladium dimethylglyoximate.

$$31.61 \text{g Pd} \times \frac{1 \text{ mol Pd}}{106.42 \text{ g Pd}} = 0.2970 \text{ mol Pd} \div 0.2970 \rightarrow 1.000 \text{ mol Pd}$$

$$28.54 \text{ g C} \times \frac{1 \text{ mol C}}{12.011 \text{ g C}} = 2.376 \text{ mol C} \div 0.2970 \rightarrow 8.000 \text{ mol C}$$

$$4.19 \text{ g H} \times \frac{1 \text{ mol H}}{1.008 \text{ g H}} = 4.16 \text{ mol H} \div 0.2970 \rightarrow 14.01 \text{ mol H}$$

$$19.01 \text{ g O} \times \frac{1 \text{ mol O}}{15.999 \text{ g O}} = 1.188 \text{ mol O} \div 0.2970 \rightarrow 4.000 \text{ mol O}$$

$$16.64 \text{g N} \times \frac{1 \text{ mol N}}{14.007 \text{ g N}} = 1.188 \text{ mol N} \div 0.2970 \rightarrow 4.000 \text{ mol N}$$

The empirical formula of palladium dimethylglyoximate ($PdDmgH_2$) is $PdC_8H_{14}O_4N_4$, with an empirical molar mass of 336.64 g/mol.

(b) mass of Pd $= 250.0 \text{ mL} \times \dfrac{0.0784 \text{ g PdDmgH}_2}{10.00 \text{ mL}} \times \dfrac{1 \text{ mol PdDmgH}_2}{336.64 \text{ g PdDmgH}_2} \times \dfrac{1 \text{ mol Pd}}{1 \text{ mol PdDmgH}_2}$

$\times \dfrac{106.42 \text{ g Pd}}{1 \text{ mol Pd}} = 0.620 \text{ g Pd}$

% Pd in steel $= \dfrac{0.620 \text{ g Pd}}{16.312 \text{ g steel}} \times 100\% = 3.80\%$

69. **(M)** A look at Appendix D indicates that $Cr(OH)_3$, $K_{sp} = 6.3 \times 10^{-31}$; $Zn(OH)_2$, $K_{sp} = 1.2 \times 10^{-17}$; $Fe(OH)_3$, $K_{sp} = 4 \times 10^{-38}$; and $Ni(OH)_2$, $K_{sp} = 2.0 \times 10^{-15}$; all are expected to form. But in excess NaOH, $[Cr(OH)_4]^-$, $K_f = 8 \times 10^{29}$, which probably is green in color; and $[Zn(OH)_4]^{2-}$, $K_f = 4.6 \times 10^{17}$, also will form. (i.e., their hydroxides will dissolve). The lack of color in the solution indicates that Cr^{3+} is not present. The presence of a hydroxide precipitate indicates that Ni^{2+} and Fe^{3+} may be present. Because Ni^{2+} forms a complex ion with NH_3, $[Ni(NH_3)_6]^{2+}$, $K_f = 5.5 \times 10^8$, and Fe^{3+} does not, the lack of a second precipitate indicates that Fe^{3+} is absent. The fact that there was a hydroxide precipitate indicates that Ni^{2+} is present. We are sure that Ni^{2+} is present and that Fe^{2+} and Cr^{3+} are absent, but we are uncertain about the presence or absence of Zn^{2+}.

70. **(M)** First calculate concentration of $Hg(NO_3)_2$ solution:
? mol NaCl $= 2.00 \times 10^{-3}$ mL $\times 0.0108$ mol $L^{-1} = 2.16 \times 10^{-5}$ mol NaCl

? mol $HgCl_2 = \dfrac{1}{2} \times 2.16 \times 10^{-5}$ mol NaCl $= 1.08 \times 10^{-5}$ mol

$c = 1.08 \times 10^{-5}$ mol$/1.12 \times 10^{-3}$ L $= 9.64 \times 10^{-3}$ mol L^{-1}

Next, calculate amount of Cl^- in the serum sample:

amount of $Cl^- = 1.23 \times 10^{-3}$ L $\times 9.64 \times 10^{-3}$ mol Hg^{2+} $L^{-1} \times 2$ mol $Cl^-/1$ mol Hg^{2+}

$= 2.37 \times 10^{-5}$ mol Cl^-

$= 0.0237$ mmol

This amount of Cl^- came from a 0.500 mL serum sample, so the concentration of Cl^- in mmol L^{-1} is C = 0.0237 mmol/0.500 $\times 10^{-3}$ L = 47 mmol L^{-1}.

The concentration is smaller than the lower limit of the normal range.

71. **(M)**

| **(a)** | **(b)** | **(c)** |

$[Hg\!-\!\!-\!Hg]^{+2}$

72. **(M)** $\rho = \dfrac{(7)(1.60 \times 10^{-19}\ C)}{(4/3)\pi(39 \times 10^{-9}\ mm)^3} = 4500$ C mm^{-3}

This value is more than 4 times the value given in Table 21.4 for Be^{2+} (1108 C mm^{-3}). We know that there is significant covalent bonding in beryllium compounds. We expect the bonding in Mn_2O_7 to be primarily covalent. With such a large charge density, a Mn^{7+} ion would be very strongly polarizing, drawing electron density away from surrounding anions and leading to bonds with primarily covalent character.

73. **(M)** ? Ti per unit cell $= \dfrac{1}{8}$ Ti per corner $\times 8$ corners per cell $= 1$ Ti

? Ni per unit cell = 1

The empirical formula is NiTi. The % Ti by mass is $100 \times 47.88/(47.88 + 63.55) = 45\%$

FEATURE PROBLEMS

74. **(D)**

(a) If $\Delta n_{gas} = 0$, then $\Delta_r S^\circ \sim 0$ and $\Delta_r G^\circ$ is essentially independent of temperature

$(C(s) + O_2(g) \rightarrow CO_2(g))$

If $\Delta n_{gas} > 0$, then $\Delta_r S^\circ > 0$ and $\Delta_r G^\circ$ will become more negative with increasing temperature, hence the graph has a negative slope $(2\ C(s) + O_2(g) \rightarrow 2\ CO\ (g))$.

If $\Delta n_{gas} < 0$, then $\Delta_r S^\circ < 0$ and $\Delta_r G^\circ$ will become more positive with increasing temperature, hence the graph has a positive slope $(2\ CO(g) + O_2(g) \rightarrow 2\ CO_2\ (g))$.

(b) The additional blast furnace reaction, $C(s) + CO_2(g) \rightarrow 2\ CO(g)$, has

$\Delta_r H° = [2 \times -110.5\text{ kJ}] - [-393.5\text{ kJ} + 0\text{ kJ}] = 172.5\text{ kJ mol}^{-1}$ and

$\Delta_r S° = [2 \times 197.7\text{ J K}^{-1}] - [1 \times 5.74\text{ J K}^{-1} + 213.7\text{ J K}^{-1}] = 176.0\text{ J K}^{-1}\text{ mol}^{-1}$

It can be obtained by adding reaction (b) to the reverse of reaction (c) (both appear in the provided figure)

$C(s) + O_2(g) \rightarrow CO_2(g)$ Reaction (b)

$2\ CO_2(s) \rightarrow 2\ CO(g) + O_2(g)$ Reverse of Reaction (c)

Net: $C(s) + CO_2(g) \rightarrow 2\ CO(g)$ (Additional Blast Furnace Reaction)

Consequently, the plot of $\Delta_r G°$ for the *net* reaction as a function of temperature will be a straight line with a slope of $-[\{\Delta_r S° \text{ (Rxn b)}\} - \{\Delta_r S° \text{ (Rxn c)}\}]$ (in kJ mol^{-1} K^{-1}) and a y-intercept of $[\{\Delta_r H° \text{ (Rxn b)}\} - \{\Delta_r H° \text{ (Rxn c)}\}]$ (in kJ mol^{-1}).
Since $\Delta_r H°$ (Rxn b) = -393.5 kJ mol^{-1}, $\Delta_r H°$ (Rxn c) = -566 kJ/mol, $\Delta_r S°$ (Rxn b) = 2.9 J mol^{-1} K^{-1} and $\Delta_r S°$ (Rxn c) = -173.1 J mol^{-1} K^{-1}, the plot of $\Delta_r G°$ vs. T for the reaction $C(s) + CO_2(g) \rightarrow 2\ CO(g)$ will follow the equation $y = -0.176x + 172.5$

From the graph, we can see that the difference in $\Delta_r G°$ (line b – line c at 1000 °C) is ~ -40 kJ mol^{-1}. K_p is readily calculated using this value of $\Delta_r G°$.

$\Delta_r G° = -RT\ln K_p = -40\text{ kJ} = -(8.3145 \times 10^{-3}\text{ kJ K}^{-1}\text{ mol}^{-1})(1273\text{ K})(\ln K_p)$
$\ln K_p = 3.\underline{8}$ Hence, $K_p = 4\underline{4}$

The equilibrium partial pressure for CO(g) is then determined by using the K_p expression:

$K_p = \dfrac{\left(P_{CO}\right)^2}{\left(P_{CO_2}\right)} = 4\underline{4} = \dfrac{\left(P_{CO}\right)^2}{(0.25\text{ atm})}$ Hence, $(P_{CO})^2 = 1\underline{1}$ and $P_{CO} = 3.\underline{3}$ atm or 3 atm.

Alternatively, we can determine the partial pressure for CO_2 at 1000 °C via the calculated $\Delta_r H°$ and $\Delta_r S°$ values for the reaction $C(s) + CO_2(g) \rightarrow 2\ CO(g)$ to find $\Delta_r G°$ at 1000 °C , and ultimately K_p with the relationship $\Delta_r G° = -RT\ln K_p$ (here we are making the assumption that $\Delta_r H°$ and $\Delta_r S°$ are relatively constant over the temperature range 298 K to 1273 K). The calculated values of $\Delta_r H°$ and $\Delta_r S°$ (using Appendix D) are given below:

$\Delta_r H° = [2 \times -110.5\text{ kJ}] - [-393.5\text{ kJ} + 0\text{ kJ}] = 172.5\text{ kJ mol}^{-1}$
$\Delta_r S° = [2 \times 197.7\text{ J K}^{-1}] - [1 \times 5.74\text{ J K}^{-1} + 213.7\text{ J K}^{-1}] = 176.0\text{ J K}^{-1}\text{ mol}^{-1}$

To find $\Delta_r G°$ at 1000°C, we simply plug $x = 1273$ K into the straight-line equation we developed above and solve for y ($\Delta_r G°$).
So, $y = -0.176(1273\text{ K}) + 172.5$; $y = -51.5\text{ kJ mol}^{-1}$
Next we need to calculate the K_p for the reaction at 1000°C.

$\Delta_r G° = -RT\ln K_p = -51.5\text{ kJ mol}^{-1} = -(8.3145 \times 10^{-3}\text{ kJ mol}^{-1}\text{ K}^{-1})(1273\text{ K})(\ln K_p)$
$\ln K_p = 4.87$. Hence, $K_p = 1.3 \times 10^2$

The equilibrium $P_{CO(g)}$ is then determined by using the K_p expression:

$$K_p = \frac{\left(P_{CO}\right)^2}{\left(P_{CO_2}\right)} = 130 = \frac{\left(P_{CO}\right)^2}{(0.25 \text{ atm})} \quad \text{Hence, } (P_{CO})^2 = 32.\underline{5} \text{ atm and } P_{CO} = 5.7 \text{ atm}$$

75. **(M) (a)** The amphoteric cations are Al^{3+}, Cr^{3+}, and Zn^{2+}.

$$Cr^{3+}(aq) + 4OH^-(aq) \rightarrow [Cr(OH)_4]^-(aq)$$

$$Al^{3+}(aq) + 4OH^-(aq) \rightarrow [Al(OH)_4]^-(aq)$$

$$Zn^{2+}(aq) + 4OH^-(aq) \rightarrow [Zn(OH)_4]^{2-}(aq)$$

$$Fe^{3+}(aq) + 3OH^-(aq) \rightarrow Fe(OH)_3(s)$$

$$Ni^{2+}(aq) + 2OH^-(aq) \rightarrow Ni(OH)_2(s)$$

$$Co^{2+}(aq) + 2OH^-(aq) \rightarrow Co(OH)_2(s)$$

(b) Of the three hydroxide precipitates, only Co^{2+} is easily oxidized: (refer to the Standard Reduction Potential table in Appendix D).

$$2\,Co(OH)_2(s) + H_2O_2(aq) \longrightarrow 2\,Co(OH)_3(s)$$

(c) We know that the chromate ion is yellow. Thus,

$$[Cr(OH)_4]^-(aq) + 3/2\,H_2O_2(aq) + OH^-(aq) \longrightarrow CrO_4^{2-}(aq, \text{YELLOW}) + 4\,H_2O(l)$$

(d) Co^{3+} is reduced to Co^{2+} by the HCl in solution. The other hydroxides simply dissolve in strong acid:

(i) $Co(OH)_3(s) + 3H^+(aq) \longrightarrow Co^{3+}(aq) + 3H_2O(l)$

(ii) $\quad 2\,Co^{3+}(aq) + 2\,Cl^-(aq) \longrightarrow 2\,Co^{2+}(aq) + Cl_2(g)$

(iii) $\quad Fe(OH)_3(s) + 3\,H^+(aq) \longrightarrow Fe^{3+}(aq) + 3\,H_2O(l)$

(iv) $\quad Ni(OH)_2(s) + 2\,H^+(aq) \longrightarrow Ni^{2+}(aq) + 2\,H_2O(l)$

(e) The $Fe^{3+}(aq)$ ions in the presence of concentrated ammonia(6 M) form an insoluble precipitate with the hydroxide ions generated by the ammonia hydrolysis reaction:

$$NH_3(aq) + H_2O(l) \rightleftharpoons NH_4^+(aq) + OH^-(aq)$$

$$Fe^{3+}(aq) + 3\,OH^-(aq) \rightleftharpoons Fe(OH)_3(s); \qquad K_{sp}\,Fe(OH)_3 = 4\times10^{-38}$$

Both Co^{3+} and Ni^{2+} form soluble complex ions with ammonia ligands rather than hydroxide precipitates.

SELF-ASSESSMENT EXERCISES

76. **(E)**

(a) A key feature of ferromagnetism is that in the solid state, the metal atoms are thought to be grouped together into small regions— called domains—containing rather large numbers of atoms.

(b) Flotation is a process to separate rock from ore.

(c) Leaching is the process by which metal ions are extracted (leached) from the ore by a liquid. Leaching agents include water, acids, bases, and salt solutions. Oxidation–reduction reactions may also be involved.

(d) Mercury alloys, called amalgams, are commonly made with most metals, and some of these amalgams are of commercial importance.

77. **(E)**

(a) In the series of elements in which the $4f$ subshell is filled, atomic radii decrease somewhat. This phenomenon occurs in the lanthanide series ($Z = 58$ to 71) and is called the lanthanide contraction.

(b) Zone melting (or zone refining or floating zone process) is a group of similar methods of purifying crystals, in which a narrow region of a crystal is molten, and this molten zone is moved along the crystal (in practice, the crystal is pulled through the heater). The molten region melts impure solid at its forward edge and leaves a wake of purer material solidified behind it as it moves through the ingot. The impurities concentrate in the melt, and are moved to one end of the ingot.

(c) Basic oxygen process is a steelmaking method in which pure oxygen is blown into a bath of molten blast-furnace iron and scrap. The oxygen initiates a series of intensively exothermic (heat-releasing) reactions, including the oxidation of such impurities as carbon, silicon, phosphorus, and manganese.

(d) Slag formation is used to remove impurities from ores.

78. **(E)**

(a) Ferromagnetism is the basic mechanism by which certain materials (such as iron) form permanent magnets, or are attracted to magnets. Paramagnetism is a form of magnetism which occurs only in the presence of an externally applied magnetic field. Paramagnetic materials are also attracted to magnetic fields.

(b) An ore is roasted (heated to a high temperature) to convert a metal compound to its oxide, which can then be reduced. The oxidation number of a metal decreases as a result of reduction.

    (c) Hydrometallurgy is part of the field of extractive metallurgy involving the use of aqueous chemistry for the recovery of metals from ores, concentrates, and recycled or residual materials. Pyrometallurgy is a branch of extractive metallurgy. It consists of the thermal treatment of minerals and metallurgical ores and concentrates to bring about physical and chemical transformations in the materials to enable recovery of valuable metals.

    (d) Chromates are the salts that contain CrO_4^{2-} anions. Dichromates, on the other hand, contain $Cr_2O_7^{2-}$ anions. In both compounds chromium is in +6 oxidation state.

79. **(E)**

    (a) Pig iron is impure iron (95% Fe) formed in the reduction of iron ore in a blast furnace.

    (b) Ferromanganese is an iron-manganese alloy formed by the reduction of a mixture of iron and manganese oxides.

    (c) Chromite ore, $Fe(CrO_2)_2$ is the principal chromium ore.

    (d) Brass is an alloy of Zn and Cu with small amounts of Sn, Pb, and Fe.

    (e) Aqua regia is a mixture of HCl(aq) and HNO_3(aq) that dissolves inactive metals by a combination of oxidation and complex ion formation.

    (f) Blister copper, formed in the reduction of a mixture of Cu_2O(s) and Cu_2S(s), is impure Cu(s) containing SO_2(g).

    (g) Stainless steel is an iron alloy with varying quantities of metals such as Cr, Mn, and Ni, and a small and carefully controlled percentage of carbon.

80. **(E)** (c), (f), and (g).

81. **(E)** (b)

82. **(E)** (d)

83. **(E)** (a)

84. **(E)** (d)

85. **(E)** (c) and (e)

86. **(M)** CrO_3(s), **(b)** potassium manganate, **(c)** chromium carbonyl, **(d)** $BaCr_2O_7$, **(e)** lanthanum(III) sulfate nonahydrate, **(f)** $Au(CN)_3 \cdot 3\ H_2O$.

87. **(M)**

    (a) $2\ Fe_2S_3(s) + 3\ O_2(g) + 6\ H_2O(l) \rightarrow 4\ Fe(OH)_3(s) + 6\ S(s)$

    (b) $2\ Mn^{2+}(aq) + 8\ H_2O(l) + 5\ S_2O_8^{2-}(aq) \rightarrow 2\ MnO_4^{-}(aq) + 16\ H^{+}(aq) + 10\ SO_4^{2-}(aq)$

    (c) $4\ Ag(s) + 8\ CN^{-}(aq) + O_2(g) + 2\ H_2O(l) \rightarrow 4[Ag(CN_2]^{-}(aq) + 4\ OH^{-}(aq)$

88. **(M)** Atoms of Zn, Cd and Hg have configurations of $4s^2 3d^{10}$, $5s^2 4d^{10}$, and $6s^2 4f^{14} 5d^{10}$, respectively. The ns^2 electrons participate in bonding, and in this regard Zn, Cd, and Hg resemble the group 2 elements.

89. **(M)** HNO_3 is the oxidizing agent for oxidizing the metal to Au^{3+} but Au^{3+} must be stabilized in solution. In aqua regia, Cl^- ions combine with Au^{3+} to form $[AuCl_4]^-$, which is stable in solution.

90. **(M)** The Fe^{3+} ion forms a complex ion, $Fe(H_2O)_6^{3+}$, in aqueous solution. The complex behaves as a weak monoprotic acid in solution. See Equation (23.26).

CHAPTER 24
COMPLEX IONS AND COORDINATION COMPOUNDS
PRACTICE EXAMPLES

1A (E) There are two different kinds of ligands in this complex ion, I^- and CN^-. Both are monodentate ligands, that is, they each form only one bond to the central atom. Since there are five ligands in total for the complex ion, the coordination number is 5: C.N. = 5. Each CN^- ligand has a charge of −1, as does the I^- ligand. Thus, the O.S. must be such that: $O.S. + \left[(4+1) \times (-1)\right] = -3 = O.S. - 5$. Therefore, O.S. = +2.

1B (E) The ligands are all CN^-. Fe^{3+} is the central metal ion. The complex ion is $\left[Fe(CN)_6\right]^{3-}$.

2A (E) There are six "Cl^-" ligands (chloride), each with a charge of 1−. The platinum metal center has an oxidation state of + 4. Thus, the complex ion is $\left[PtCl_6\right]^{2-}$, and we need two K^+ to balance charge: $K_2\left[PtCl_6\right]$.

2B (E) The "SCN^-" ligand is the thiocyanato-S group, with a charge of 1−, bonding to the central metal ion through the sulfur atom. The "NH_3" ligand is ammonia, a neutral ligand. There are five (penta) ammine ligands bonded to the metal. The oxidation state of the cobalt atom is +3. The complex ion is not negatively charged, so its name does not end with "-ate". The name of the compound is pentaamminethiocyanato-*S*-cobalt(III) chloride.

3A (M) The oxalato ligand must occupy two *cis-* positions. Either the two NH_3 or the two Cl^- ligands can be coplanar with the oxalate ligand, leaving the other two ligands axial. The other isomer has one NH_3 and one Cl^- ligand coplanar with the oxalate ligand. The structures are sketched below.

3B (M) We start out with the two pyridines, C_5H_5N, located *cis* to each other. With this assignment imposed, we can have the two Cl^- ligands *trans* and the two CO ligands *cis*, the two CO ligands *trans* and the two Cl^- ligands *cis*, or both the Cl^- ligands and the two CO ligands *cis*. If we now place the two pyridines *trans*, we can have either both other pairs *trans*, or both other pairs *cis*. There are five geometric isomers. They follow, in the order described.

4A **(M)** The F^- ligand is a weak field ligand. $\left[MnF_6\right]^{2-}$ is an octahedral complex. Mn^{4+} has three $3d$ electrons. The ligand field splitting diagram for $\left[MnF_6\right]^{2-}$ is sketched below. There are three unpaired electrons.

4B **(M)** Co^{2+} has seven $3d$ electrons. Cl^- is a weak field ligand. H_2O is a moderate field ligand. There are three unpaired electrons in each case. The number of unpaired electrons has no dependence on geometry for either metal ion complex.

5A **(M)** CN^- is a strong field ligand. Co^{2+} has seven $3d$ electrons. In the absence of a crystal field, all five d orbitals have the same energy. Three of the seven d electrons in this case will be unpaired. We need an orbital splitting diagram in which there are three orbitals of the same energy at higher energy. This is the case with a tetrahedral orbital diagram.

⇅ ⇅ ↑ ↑ ↑   ↑ ↑ ↑   ↑ —

In absence of a
crystal field   ⇅ ⇅   ⇅ ⇅ ⇅

             Tetrahedral geometry   Octahedral geometry

Thus, $\left[Co(CN)_4\right]^{2-}$ must be tetrahedral (3 unpaired electrons) and not octahedral (1 unpaired electron) because the magnetic behavior of a tetrahedral arrangement would agree with the experimental observations (3 unpaired electrons).

5B **(M)** NH_3 is a strong field ligand. Cu^{2+} has nine $3d$ electrons. There is only one way to arrange nine electrons in five d-orbitals and that is to have four fully occupied orbitals (two electrons in each orbital), and one half-filled orbital. Thus, the complex ion must be paramagnetic to the extent of one unpaired electron, regardless of the geometry the ligands adopt around the central metal ion.

6A **(M)** We are certain that $\left[Co(H_2O)_6\right]^{2+}$ is octahedral with a moderate field ligand. Tetrahedral $\left[CoCl_4\right]^{2-}$ has a weak field ligand. The relative values of ligand field splitting for the same ligand are $\Delta_t = 0.44\,\Delta_o$. Thus, $\left[Co(H_2O)_6\right]^{2+}$ absorbs light of higher energy, blue or green light, leaving a light pink as the complementary color we observe. $\left[CoCl_4\right]^{2-}$ absorbs lower energy red light, leaving blue light to pass through and be seen.

6B **(M)** In order, the two complex ions are $\left[\text{Fe}\left(\text{H}_2\text{O}\right)_6\right]^{2+}$ and $\left[\text{Fe}\left(\text{CN}\right)_6\right]^{4-}$. We know that CN^- is a strong field ligand; it should give rise to a large value of Δ_o and absorb light of the shorter wavelength. We would expect the cyano complex to absorb blue or violet light and thus $\text{K}_4\left[\text{Fe}\left(\text{CN}\right)_6\right]\cdot 3\,\text{H}_2\text{O}$ should appear yellow. The compound $\left[\text{Fe}\left(\text{H}_2\text{O}\right)_6\right]\left(\text{NO}_3\right)_2$, contains the weak field ligand H_2O and thus should be green. (The weak field would result in the absorption of light of long wavelength (namely, red light), which would leave green as the color we observe.)

INTEGRATIVE EXAMPLE

A **(M)**

(a) There is no reaction with AgNO_3 or en, so the compound must be *trans*-chloridobis(ethylenediamine)nitrito-*N*-cobalt(III) nitrite

(b) If the compound reacts with AgNO_3, but not with en, it must be *trans*-bis(ethylenediamine)dinitrito-*N*-cobalt(III) chloride.

(c) If it reacts with AgNO_3 and en and is optically active, it must be *cis*-bis(ethylenediamine)dinitrito-*N*-cobalt(III) chloride.

..

B **(D)** We first need to compute the empirical formula of the complex compound:

$$46.2 \text{ g Pt} \times \frac{1 \text{ mol Pt}}{195.08 \text{ g Pt}} = 0.237 \text{ mol Pt} \Rightarrow \frac{0.237}{0.237} = 1 \text{ mol Pt}$$

$$33.6 \text{ g Cl} \times \frac{1 \text{ mol Cl}}{35.45 \text{ g Cl}} = 0.948 \text{ mol Cl} \Rightarrow \frac{0.948}{0.237} = 4 \text{ mol Cl}$$

$$16.6 \text{ g N} \times \frac{1 \text{ mol N}}{14.01 \text{ g N}} = 1.18 \text{ mol N} \Rightarrow \frac{1.18}{0.237} = 5 \text{ mol N}$$

$$3.6 \text{ g Pt} \times \frac{1 \text{ mol H}}{1.008 \text{ g H}} = 3.6 \text{ mol H} \Rightarrow \frac{3.6}{0.237} = 15 \text{ mol H}$$

The nitrogen ligand is NH_3, apparently, so the empirical formula is $PtCl_4(NH_3)_5$.

The effective molality of the solution is $m = \dfrac{\Delta T}{K_{fp}} = \dfrac{0.74 \,^{\circ}C}{1.86 \,^{\circ}C/(\text{mol kg}^{-1})} = 0.4 \text{ mol kg}^{-1}$.

The effective molality is 4 times the stated molality, so we have 4 particles produced per mole of Pt complex, and therefore 3 ionizable chloride ions. We can write this in the following way:
$[PtCl(NH_3)_5][Cl_3]$. Only one form of the cation (with charge 3+) shown below will exist.

EXERCISES

Nomenclature

1. **(E)**

(a) $\left[CrCl_4(NH_3)_2 \right]^-$ diamminetetrachloridochromate(III) ion

(b) $\left[Fe(CN)_6 \right]^{3-}$ hexacyanidoferrate(III) ion

(c) $\left[Cr(en)_3 \right]_2 \left[Ni(CN)_4 \right]_3$ tris(ethylenediamine)chromium(III) tetracyanidonickelate(II) ion

2. **(E)**

(a) $\left[Co(NH_3)_6 \right]^{2+}$ The coordination number of Co is 6; there are six monodentate NH_3 ligands attached to Co. Since the NH_3 ligand is neutral, the oxidation state of cobalt is $+2$, the same as the charge for the complex ion; hexaamminecobalt(II) ion.

(b) $\left[AlF_6\right]^{3-}$ The coordination number of Al is 6; F^- is monodentate. Each F^- has a 1– charge; thus the oxidation state of Al is +3; hexafluoridoaluminate(III) ion.

(c) $\left[Cu(CN)_4\right]^{2-}$ The coordination number of Cu is 4; CN^- is monodentate. CN^- has a 1– charge; thus the oxidation state of Cu is +2; tetracyanidocuprate(II) ion

(d) $\left[CrBr_2(NH_3)_4\right]^+$ The coordination number of Cr is 6; NH_3 and Br^- are monodentate. NH_3 has no charge; Br^- has a 1– charge. The oxidation state of chromium is +3; tetraamminedibromidochromium(III) ion

(e) $\left[Co(ox)_3\right]^{4-}$ The coordination number of Co is 6; oxalate is bidentate. $C_2O_4^{2-}$ (ox) has a 2– charge; thus the oxidation state of cobalt is +2; trioxalatocobaltate(II) ion.

(f) $\left[Ag(S_2O_3)_2\right]^{3-}$ The coordination number of Ag is 2; $S_2O_3{}^{2-}$ is monodentate. $S_2O_3{}^{2-}$ has a 2– charge; thus the oxidation state of silver is +1; dithiosulfatoargentate(I) ion. (Although +1 is by far the most common oxidation state for silver in its compounds, stable silver(III) complexes are known. Thus, strictly speaking, silver is not a non-variable metal, and hence when naming silver compounds, the oxidation state(s) for the silver atom(s) should be specified).

3. **(M)**
   (a) diamminesilver(I) chloride
   (b) tetraamminediaquacopper(II) sulfate
   (c) dichlorido(1,2-ethanediamine)platinum(II)
   (d) pentaaquabromidochromium(III) ion
   (e) rubidium tetrafluoridoargentate(III)
   (f) sodium pentacyanidooxidonitrogenferrate(III)

4. **(M)**
   (a) $K_3\left[Fe(CN)_6\right]$ potassium hexacyanidoferrate(III)

   (b) $\left[Cu(en)_2\right]^{2+}$ bis(ethylenediamine)copper(II) ion

   (c) $\left[Al(H_2O)_5(OH)\right]Cl_2$ pentaaquahydroxidoaluminum(III) chloride

   (d) $\left[CrCl(en)_2NH_3\right]SO_4$ amminechloridobis(ethylenediammine)chromium(III) sulfate

   (e) $\left[Fe(en)_3\right]_4\left[Fe(CN)_6\right]_3$ tris(ethylenediamine)iron(III) hexacyanidoferrate(II)

Bonding and Structure in Complex Ions

5. **(E)** The Lewis structures are grouped together at the end.

(a) H_2O has $1 \times 2 + 6 = 8$ valence electrons, or 4 pairs.

(b) CH_3NH_2 has $4 + 3 \times 1 + 5 + 2 \times 1 = 14$ valence electrons, or 7 pairs.

(c) ONO^- has $2 \times 6 + 5 + 1 = 18$ valence electrons, or 9 pairs. The structure has a 1– formal charge on the oxygen that is singly bonded to N.

(d) SCN^- has $6 + 4 + 5 + 1 = 16$ valence electrons, or 8 pairs. This structure, appropriately, gives a 1– formal charge to N.

6. **(M)** The Lewis structures are grouped together at the end.

(a) OH^- has $6 + 1 + 1 = 8$ valence electrons, or 4 pairs.

(b) SO_4^{2-} has $6 + 6 \times 4 + 2 = 32$ valence electrons, or 16 pairs.

(c) $C_2O_4^{2-}$ has $2 \times 4 + 6 \times 4 + 2 = 34$ valence electrons, or 17 pairs.

(d) SCN^- has $6 + 4 + 5 + 1 = 16$ valence electrons, or 8 pairs. This structure, appropriately, gives a 1– formal charge to N.

7. **(M)**

(a)

(b)

(c)

(d)

trans *cis*

(e)

8. **(M)** The structures for $\left[\text{Pt}(\text{ox})_2\right]^{2-}$ and $\left[\text{Cr}(\text{ox})_3\right]^{3-}$ are drawn below. The structure of $\left[\text{Fe}(\text{EDTA})\right]^{2-}$ is the same as the generic structure for $\left[\text{M}(\text{EDTA})\right]^{2-}$ drawn in Figure 24-23, with $\text{M}^{n+} = \text{Fe}^{2+}$.

(a)

(b)

9. **(M)**

(a)

trans-NH₃ *cis*-H₂O   *trans*-NH₃ *trans*-H₂O   *cis*-NH₃ *trans*-H₂O   *cis*-NH₃ *cis*-H₂O

(b)

(c)

NH₃ coordination complex (Pt), *trans* and *cis*

(d)

NH₃ coordination complex (Co), *trans* and *cis*

trans   *cis*   *trans*   *cis*

10. (M)

(a) pentaamminenitrito-N-cobalt(III) ion

(b) ethylenediaminedithiocyanato-S-copper(II)

$$\left[\begin{array}{c} NH_3 \\ \quad NH_3 \\ O_2N-Co-NH_3 \\ H_3N \quad NH_3 \end{array} \right]^{2+}$$

Cu complex with ethylenediamine, NCS and SCN

(c) hexaaquanickel(II) ion

$$\left[\begin{array}{c} H_2O \quad OH_2 \\ H_2O-Ni-OH_2 \\ H_2O \quad H_2O \end{array} \right]^{2+}$$

Isomerism

<u>**11.**</u> **(E)**

(a) *cis-trans* isomerism cannot occur with tetrahedral structures because all of the ligands are separated by the same angular distance from each other. One ligand cannot be on the other side of the central atom from another.

(b) Square planar structures can show *cis-trans* isomerism. Examples are drawn following, with the *cis*-isomer drawn on the left, and the *trans*-isomer drawn on the right.

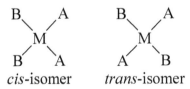

cis-isomer   *trans*-isomer

(c) Linear structures do not display *cis-trans* isomerism; there is only one way to bond the two ligands to the central atom.

12. **(M)**

(a) $\left[Cr(NH_3)_5(OH) \right]^{2+}$ has one isomer.

$$\left[\begin{array}{c} NH_3 \\ \ | \quad \underset{\mathllap{}}{\overset{\mathrlap{NH_3}}{}} \\ HO-Cr-NH_3 \\ H_3N \overset{\diagup}{\ } \ | \\ \quad NH_3 \end{array} \right]^{2+}$$

(b) $\left[CrCl_2(H_2O)(NH_3)_3 \right]^{+}$ has three isomers.

$$\left[\begin{array}{c} Cl \\ | \ NH_3 \\ H_2O-Cr-Cl \\ H_3N \ | \\ NH_3 \end{array} \right]^{+} \quad \left[\begin{array}{c} Cl \\ | \ Cl \\ H_2O-Cr-NH_3 \\ H_3N \ | \\ NH_3 \end{array} \right]^{+} \quad \left[\begin{array}{c} Cl \\ | \ NH_3 \\ H_2O-Cr-NH_3 \\ H_3N \ | \\ Cl \end{array} \right]^{+}$$

(c) $\left[CrCl_2(en)_2 \right]^{+}$ has two geometric isomers, *cis*- and *trans*-.

$$\left[\begin{array}{c} Cl \\ | \ Cl \\ N-Cr-N \\ C \diagdown N \ | \ C \\ C \quad N \quad C \\ \quad C \end{array} \right]^{+} \quad \left[\begin{array}{c} C \diagdown N \\ C \quad | \ Cl \\ N-Cr-N \\ Cl \ | \quad C \\ N \diagdown C \end{array} \right]^{+}$$

(d) $\left[CrCl_4(en) \right]^{-}$ has only one isomer since the ethylenediamine (en) ligand cannot bond *trans* to the central metal atom.

$$\left[\begin{array}{c} Cl \\ | \ Cl \\ Cl-Cr-N \\ Cl \ | \quad C \\ N \diagdown C \end{array} \right]^{-}$$

(e) $\left[Cr(en)_3 \right]^{3+}$ has only one geometric isomer; it has two optical isomers.

$$\left[\begin{array}{c} C \diagdown C \\ N \quad C \\ | \quad N \\ N-Cr-N \\ C \diagup N \ | \quad C \\ C \quad N \quad C \\ \quad C \end{array} \right]^{3+}$$

13. **(M)**

   (a) There are three different square planar isomers, with D, C, and B, respectively, trans to the A ligand. They are drawn below.

   (b) Tetrahedral $[ZnABCD]^{2+}$ does display optical isomerism. The two optical isomers are drawn above.

14. **(M)** There are a total of four coordination isomers. They are listed below. We assume that the oxidation state of each central metal ion is +3.

   $[Co(en)_3][Cr(ox)_3]$ tris(ethylenediamine)cobalt(III) trioxalatochromate(III)

   $[Co(en)_2(ox)][Cr(en)(ox)_2]$ bis(ethylenediamine)oxalatocobalt(III)
   (ethylenediamine)dioxalatochromate(III)

   $[Cr(en)_2(ox)][Co(en)(ox)_2]$ bis(ethylenediamine)oxalatochromium(III)
   (ethylenediamine)dioxalatocobaltate(III)

   $[Cr(en)_3][Co(ox)_3]$ tris(ethylenediamine)chromium(III) trioxalatocobaltate(III)

15. **(M)** The *cis*-dichloridobis(ethylenediamine)cobalt(III) ion is optically active. The two optical isomers are drawn below. The *trans*-isomer is not optically active: the ion and its mirror image are superimposable.

   cis-isomers   *trans*-isomer

16. **(M)** Complex ions (a) and (b) are identical; complex ions (a) and (d) are geometric isomers; complex ions (b) and (d) are geometric isomers; complex ion (c) is distinctly different from the other three complex ions (it has a different chemical formula).

Crystal Field Theory

17. **(E)** In crystal field theory, the five *d* orbitals of a central transition metal ion are split into two (or more) groups of different energies. The energy spacing between these groups often corresponds to the energy of a photon of visible light. Thus, the transition-metal complex will absorb light with energy corresponding to this spacing. If white light is incident on the complex ion, the light remaining after absorption will be missing some of its components. Thus, light of certain wavelengths (corresponding to the energies absorbed) will no longer be present in the formerly white light. The resulting light is colored. For example, if blue light is absorbed from white light, the remaining light will be yellow in color.

18. (E) The difference in color is due to the difference in the value of Δ, which is the ligand field splitting energy. When the value of Δ is large, short wavelength light, which has a blue color, is absorbed, and the substance or its solution appears yellow. On the other hand, when the value of Δ is small, light of long wavelength, which has a red or yellow color, is absorbed, and the substance or its solution appears blue. The cyano ligand is a strong field ligand, producing a large value of Δ, and thus yellow complexes. On the other hand, the aqua ligands are weak field ligands, which produce a small value of Δ, and hence blue complexes.

19. (M) We begin with the 7 electron *d*-orbital diagram for Co^{2+} [Ar]

The strong field and weak field diagrams for octahedral complexes follow, along with the number of unpaired electrons in each case.

Strong Field   *Weak Field*

(1 unpaired electron)   (3 unpaired electrons)

20. (M) We begin with the 8 electron *d*-orbital diagram for Ni^{2+} [Ar]

The strong field and weak field diagrams for octahedral complexes follow, along with the number of unpaired electrons in each case.

Strong Field   *Weak Field*

(2 unpaired electrons)   (2 unpaired electrons)

(2 unpaired electrons)

The number of unpaired electrons is the same in both cases.

21. (M)

(a) Both of the central atoms have the same oxidation state, +3. We give the electron configuration of the central atom to the left, then the completed crystal field diagram in the center, and finally the number of unpaired electrons. The chlorido ligand is a weak field ligand in the spectrochemical series.

Mo^{3+} [Kr] $4d^3$ *weak field*
[Kr]$_{4d}$

3 unpaired electrons; paramagnetic

The ethylenediamine ligand is a strong field ligand in the spectrochemical series.

Co^{3+} $[Ar] 3d^6$

$[Ar]$ ⇅↑↑↑↑↑

strong field   ☐☐ e_g

⇅ ⇅ ⇅ t_{2g}

no unpaired electrons; diamagnetic

(b) In $[CoCl_4]^{2-}$ the oxidation state of cobalt is 2+. Chlorido is a weak field ligand. The electron configuration of Co^{2+} is $[Ar] 3d^7$ or $[Ar]$ ⇅⇅↑↑↑

The tetrahedral ligand field diagram is shown on the right.

weak field ↑ ↑ ↑ t_{2g}
⇅ ⇅ e_g

3 unpaired electrons

22. (M)

(a) In $[Cu(py)_4]^{2+}$ the oxidation state of copper is +2. Pyridine is a strong field ligand. The electron configuration of Cu^{2+} is $[Ar] 3d^9$ or $[Ar]$ ⇅⇅⇅⇅↑

There is no possible way that an odd number of electrons can be paired up, without at least one electron being unpaired. $[Cu(py)_4]^{2+}$ is paramagnetic.

(b) In $[Mn(CN)_6]^{3-}$ the oxidation state of manganese is +3. Cyanido is a strong field ligand. The electron configuration of Mn^{3+} is $[Ar] 3d^4$ or $[Ar]$ ↑↑↑↑☐

The ligand field diagram follows, on the left-hand side. In $[FeCl_4]^-$ the oxidation state of iron is +3. Chlorido is a weak field ligand. The electron configuration of Fe^{3+} is $[Ar] 3d^5$ or $[Ar]$ ↑↑↑↑↑

The ligand field diagram follows, below.

strong field ☐☐ e_g

weak field ↑ ↑ ↑ t_{2g}
↑ ↑ e_g

⇅ ↑ ↑ t_{2g}

2 unpaired electrons   5 unpaired electrons

There are more unpaired electrons in $[FeCl_4]^-$ than in $[Mn(CN)_6]^{3-}$.

23. **(M)** The electron configuration of Ni^{2+} is $[Ar] 3d^8$ or $[Ar]$ ⇅⇅⇅↑↑

Ammonia is a strong field ligand. The ligand field diagrams follow, octahedral at left, tetrahedral in the center and square planar at right.

Octahedral

↑ ↑ e_g
⇅ ⇅ ⇅ t_{2g}

Tetrahedral

⇅ ↑ ↑ t_{2g}
⇅ ⇅ e_g

Square Planar

☐ $d_{x^2-y^2}$
⇅ d_{xy}
⇅ d_{z^2}
⇅ ⇅ d_{xz}, d_{yz}

Since the octahedral and tetrahedral configurations have the same number of unpaired electrons (that is, 2 unpaired electrons), we cannot use magnetic behavior to determine whether the ammine complex of nickel(II) is octahedral or tetrahedral. But we can determine if the complex is square planar, since the square planar complex is diamagnetic with zero unpaired electrons.

24. **(M)** The difference is due to the fact that $\left[Fe(CN_6)\right]^{4-}$ is a strong field complex ion, while $\left[Fe(H_2O)_6\right]^{2+}$ is a weak field complex ion. The electron configurations for an iron atom and an iron(II) ion, and the ligand field diagrams for the two complex ions follow.

iron atom $[Ar]\ _{3d}\boxed{\uparrow\downarrow|\uparrow|\uparrow|\uparrow|\uparrow}\ _{4s}\boxed{\uparrow\downarrow}$

iron(II) ion $[Ar]\ _{3d}\boxed{\uparrow\downarrow|\uparrow|\uparrow|\uparrow|\uparrow}\ _{4s}\boxed{\ }$

$\left[Fe(CN)_6\right]^{4-}$

$\boxed{\ }\boxed{\ }$ e_g

$\boxed{\uparrow\downarrow}\boxed{\uparrow\downarrow}\boxed{\uparrow\downarrow}$ t_{2g}

$[Fe(H_2O)_6]^{2+}$

$\boxed{\uparrow}\boxed{\uparrow}$ e_g

$\boxed{\uparrow\downarrow}\boxed{\uparrow}\boxed{\uparrow}$ t_{2g}

Complex-Ion Equilibria

25. **(E)**

(a) $Zn(OH)_2(s) + 4\ NH_3(aq) \Longrightarrow \left[Zn(NH_3)_4\right]^{2+}(aq) + 2\ OH^-(aq)$

(b) $Cu^{2+}(aq) + 2\ OH^-(aq) \Longrightarrow Cu(OH)_2(s)$

The blue color is most likely due to the presence of some unreacted $[Cu(H_2O)_4]^{2+}$ (pale blue)

$Cu(OH)_2(s) + 4\ NH_3(aq) \Longrightarrow \left[Cu(NH_3)_4\right]^{2+}(aq,\ dark\ blue) + 2\ OH^-(aq)$

$\left[Cu(NH_3)_4\right]^{2+}(aq) + 4\ H_3O^+(aq) \Longrightarrow \left[Cu(H_2O)_4\right]^{2+}(aq) + 4\ NH_4^+(aq)$

26. **(M)**

(a) $CuCl_2(s) + 2\ Cl^-(aq) \Longrightarrow [CuCl_4]^{2-}(aq,\ yellow)$

$2[CuCl_4]^{2-}(aq) + 4H_2O(l)$

$\updownarrow$

$[CuCl_4]^{2-}(aq,\ yellow) + \left[Cu(H_2O)_4\right]^{2+}(aq,\ pale\ blue) + 4\ Cl^-(aq)$

or

$2\left[Cu(H_2O)_2Cl_2\right](aq,\ green) + 4\ Cl^-(aq)$

Either $[CuCl_4]^{2-}(aq) + 4\ H_2O(l) \Longrightarrow \left[Cu(H_2O)_4\right]^{2+}(aq) + 4\ Cl^-(aq)$

Or $[CuCl_2(H_2O)_2](aq) + 2H_2O(l) \Longrightarrow \left[Cu(H_2O)_4\right]^{2+}(aq) + 2\ Cl^-(aq)$

(b) The blue solution is that of $[Cr(H_2O)_6]^{2+}$. This is quickly oxidized to Cr^{3+} by $O_2(g)$ from the atmosphere. The green color is due to $\left[CrCl_2\left(H_2O\right)_4\right]^{3+}$.

$$4\,[Cr(H_2O)_6]^{2+}(aq,\ blue)+4\ H^+(aq)+8\ Cl^-(aq)+O_2(g)$$

$$\downarrow$$

$$4\,[CrCl_2(H_2O)_4]^+(aq,\ green)+10\ H_2O(l)$$

Over a period of time, we might expect volatile HCl(g) to escape, leading to the formation of complex ions with more H_2O and less Cl^-.

$$H^+\left(aq\right)+\ Cl^-\left(aq\right)\rightleftharpoons HCl\left(g\right)$$

$$\left[CrCl_2\left(H_2O\right)_4\right]^+\left(aq,\ green\right)+H_2O(l)\rightleftharpoons\left[CrCl(H_2O)_5\right]^{2+}\left(aq,\ blue\text{-}green\right)+Cl^-\left(aq\right)$$

$$\left[CrCl(H_2O)_5\right]^{2+}\left(aq,\ blue\text{-}green\right)+H_2O(l)\rightleftharpoons\left[Cr\left(H_2O\right)_6\right]^{3+}\left(aq,\ blue\right)+Cl^-\left(aq\right)$$

Actually, to ensure that these final two reactions actually do occur in a timely fashion, it would be helpful to dilute the solution with water after the chromium metal has dissolved.

27. **(M)** $[Cu(en)_3]^{2+}$ should have the largest overall K_f value. Generally, a complex ion containing polydentate ligands, such as 1,2-ethanediamine (en), will have a larger value for the formation constant than a complex ion containing only monodentate ligands. This phenomenon is known as the *chelate effect*. After one end of a polydentate ligand becomes attached to the central metal, the coordination of the remaining electron pairs is relatively easy because they are already in a close proximity (i.e., no migration from a distant point in the solution is required).

28. **(M)**

(a) $\left[Zn\left(NH_3\right)_4\right]^{2+}$

$\beta_4=K_1\times K_2\times K_3\times K_4=3.9\times10^2\times2.1\times10^2\times1.0\times10^2\times50.=4.1\times10^8.$

(b) $\left[Ni\left(H_2O\right)_2\left(NH_3\right)_4\right]^{2+}$

$\beta_4=K_1\times K_2\times K_3\times K_4=6.3\times10^2\times1.7\times10^2\times54\times15=8.7\times10^7$

29. **(M)** First: $\left[Fe\left(H_2O\right)_6\right]^{3+}\left(aq\right)+en\left(aq\right)\rightleftharpoons\left[Fe(en)(H_2O)_4\right]^{3+}\left(aq\right)+2H_2O(l)$ $\qquad K_1=10^{4.34}$

Second: $\left[Fe(en)(H_2O)_4\right]^{3+}\left(aq\right)+\ en\left(aq\right)\rightleftharpoons\left[Fe(en)_2(H_2O)^+\right]^{3+}\left(aq\right)+2H_2O(l)$ $\qquad K_2=10^{3.31}$

Third: $\left[Fe(en)_2(H_2O)_2\right]^{3+}\left(aq\right)+\ en\left(aq\right)\rightleftharpoons\left[Fe\left(en\right)_3\right]^{3+}\left(aq\right)+2H_2O(l)$ $\qquad K_3=10^{2.05}$

Net: $\left[Fe\left(H_2O\right)_6\right]^{3+}\left(aq\right)+3\ en\left(aq\right)\rightleftharpoons\left[Fe\left(en\right)_3\right]^{3+}\left(aq\right)+6H_2O(l)$ $\;K_f=K_1\times K_2\times K_3$

$\log K_f=4.34+3.31+2.05=9.70$ $\qquad\qquad\qquad K_f=10^{9.70}=5.0\times10^9=\beta_3$

30. **(M)** Since the overall formation constant is the product of the individual stepwise formation constants, the logarithm of the overall formation constant is the sum of the logarithms of the individual stepwise formation constants:

$$[Cu(H_2O)_6]^{2+} + NH_3 \rightleftharpoons [Cu(H_2O)_5(NH_3)]^{2+} + H_2O \qquad \log_{10} K_1 = 4.25$$

$$[Cu(H_2O)_5(NH_3)]^{2+} + NH_3 \rightleftharpoons [Cu(H_2O)_4(NH_3)_2]^{2+} + H_2O \qquad \log_{10} K_2 = 3.61$$

$$[Cu(H_2O)_4(NH_3)_2]^{2+} + NH_3 \rightleftharpoons [Cu(H_2O)_3(NH_3)_3]^{2+} + H_2O \qquad \log_{10} K_3 = 2.98$$

$$[Cu(H_2O)_3(NH_3)_3]^{2+} + NH_3 \rightleftharpoons [Cu(H_2O)_2(NH_3)_4]^{2+} + H_2O \qquad \log_{10} K_4 = 2.24$$

Overall:

$$[Cu(H_2O)_6]^{2+} + 4NH_3 \rightleftharpoons [Cu(H_2O)_2(NH_3)_4]^{2+} + 4H_2O$$

$$\log K_f = \log_{10} K_1 + \log_{10} K_2 + \log_{10} K_3 + \log_{10} K_4$$

$$\log K_f = 4.25 + 3.61 + 2.98 + 2.24 = 13.08$$

$$K_f = 10^{13.08} = 1.20 \times 10^{13}$$

31. **(M)**

(a) Aluminum(III) forms a stable (and soluble) hydroxo complex but not a stable ammine complex.

$$\left[Al(H_2O)_3(OH)_3\right](s) + OH^-(aq) \rightleftharpoons \left[Al(H_2O)_2(OH)_4\right]^-(aq) + H_2O(l)$$

(b) Although zinc(II) forms a soluble stable ammine complex ion, its formation constant is not sufficiently large to dissolve highly insoluble ZnS. However, it is sufficiently large to dissolve the moderately insoluble $ZnCO_3$. Said another way, ZnS does not produce sufficient $\left[Zn^{2+}\right]$ to permit the complex ion to form.

$$ZnCO_3(s) + 4\,NH_3(aq) \rightleftharpoons \left[Zn(NH_3)_4\right]^{2+}(aq) + CO_3^{2-}(aq)$$

(c) Chloride ion forms a stable complex ion with silver(I) ion, that dissolves the AgCl(s) that formed when $\left[Cl^-\right]$ is low.

$$AgCl(s) \rightleftharpoons Ag^+(aq) + Cl^-(aq) \qquad \text{and} \qquad Ag^+(aq) + 2\,Cl^-(aq) \rightleftharpoons \left[AgCl_2\right]^-(aq)$$

$$\text{Overall:} \quad AgCl(s) + Cl^-(aq) \rightleftharpoons \left[AgCl_2\right]^-(aq)$$

32. **(M)**

(a) Because of the large value of the formation constant for the complex ion, $\left[Co(NH_3)_6\right]^{3+}(aq)$, the concentration of free $Co^{3+}(aq)$ is too small to enable it to oxidize water to $O_2(g)$. Since there is not a complex ion present, except, of course, $\left[Co(H_2O)_6\right]^{3+}(aq)$, when $CoCl_3$ is dissolved in water, the $\left[Co^{3+}\right]$ is sufficiently high for the oxidation-reduction reaction to be spontaneous.

$$4\,Co^{3+}(aq) + 2\,H_2O(l) \rightarrow 4\,Co^{2+}(aq) + 4\,H^+(aq) + O_2(g)$$

(b) Although AgI(s) is often described as insoluble, there is actually a small concentration of Ag^+ (aq) present because of the solubility equilibrium:

$$2\,AgI(s) \rightleftharpoons Ag^+(aq) + I^-(aq)$$

These silver ions react with thiosulfate ion to form the stable dithiosulfatoargentate(I) complex ion:

$$Ag^+(aq) + 2S_2O_3^{2-}(aq) \rightleftharpoons [Ag(S_2O_3)_2]^-(aq)$$

Acid-Base Properties

33. (E) $\left[Al(H_2O)_6\right]^{3+}$ (aq) is capable of releasing H^+:

$$\left[Al(H_2O)_6\right]^{3+}(aq) + H_2O(l) \rightleftharpoons [Al(H_2O)_5OH]^{2+}(aq) + H_3O^+(aq)$$

The value of its ionization constant ($pK_a = 5.01$) approximates that of acetic acid.

34. (M)

(a) $[Cr(H_2O)_5OH]^{2+}(aq) + OH^-(aq) \rightarrow [Cr(H_2O)_4(OH)_2]^+(aq) + H_2O(l)$

(b) $[Cr(H_2O)_5OH]^{2+}(aq) + H_3O^+(aq) \rightarrow \left[Cr(H_2O)_6\right]^{3+}(aq) + H_2O(l)$

Applications

35. (M)

(a) Solubility: $\qquad AgBr(s) \xrightleftharpoons{K_{sp}=5.0\times10^{-13}} Ag^+(aq) + Br^-(aq)$

Cplx. Ion Formation: $\quad Ag^+(aq) + 2S_2O_3^{2-}(aq) \xrightleftharpoons{K_f=1.7\times10^{13}} [Ag(S_2O_3)_2]^{3-}(aq)$

Net: $AgBr(s) + 2S_2O_3^{2-}(aq) \rightleftharpoons [Ag(S_2O_3)_2]^{3-}(aq) + Br^-(aq) \qquad K_{overall} = K_{sp} \times K_f$

$K_{overall} = 5.0\times10^{-13} \times 1.7\times10^{13} = 8.5$

With a reasonably high $[S_2O_3^{2-}]$, this reaction will go essentially to completion.

(b) NH_3 (aq) cannot be used in the fixing of photographic film because of the relatively small value of K_f for $\left[Ag(NH_3)_2\right]^+$ (aq), $K_f = 1.6\times10^7$. This would produce a value of $K = 8.0\times10^{-6}$ in the expression above, which is nowhere large enough to drive the reaction to completion.

36. (M) Oxidation: $\left\{[Co(NH_3)_6]^{2+}(aq) \rightarrow [Co(NH_3)_6]^{3+}(aq) + e^-\right\}\times 2 \qquad -E^\circ = -0.10\ V$

Reduction: $\left\{H_2O_2(aq) + 2e^- \rightarrow 2OH^-(aq)\right\} \qquad\qquad\qquad E^\circ = 0.88\ V$

Net: $\qquad H_2O_2(aq) + 2\left[Co(NH_3)_6\right]^{2+}(aq) \rightarrow 2\left[Co(NH_3)_6\right]^{3+}(aq) + 2OH^-(aq)$

$E^\circ_{cell} = +0.88\ V + -0.10\ V = +0.78\ V.$

The positive value of the standard cell potential indicates that this is a spontaneous reaction.

37. **(M)** To make the *cis* isomer, we must use ligands that show a strong tendency for directing incoming ligands to positions that are *trans* to themselves. I^- has a stronger tendency than does Cl^- or NH_3 for directing incoming ligands to the *trans* positions, and so it is beneficial to convert $K_2[PtCl_4]$ to $K_2[PtI_4]$ before replacing ligands around Pt with NH_3 molecules.

38. **(M)** Transplatin is more reactive and is involved in more side reactions before it reaches its target inside of cancer cells. Thus, although it is more reactive, it is less effective at killing cancer cells.

$$trans\text{-}Pt(NH_3)_2Cl_2 \qquad cis\text{-}Pt(NH_3)_2Cl_2$$

INTEGRATIVE AND ADVANCED EXERCISES

39. **(M)**
(a) cupric tetraammine ion   tetraamminecopper(II) ion $[Cu(NH_3)_4]^{2+}$
(b) dichloridotetraamminecobaltic chloride   tetraamminedichloridocobalt(III) chloride $[CoCl_2(NH_3)_4]Cl$
(c) platinic(IV) hexachlorido ion   hexachloridoplatinate(IV) ion $[PtCl_6]^{2-}$
(d) disodium copper tetrachloride   sodium tetrachloridocuprate(II) $Na_2[CuCl_4]$
(e) dipotassium antimony(III) pentachloride   potassium pentachloridoantimonate(III) $K_2[SbCl_5]$

40. **(E)** $[Pt(NH_3)_4][PtCl_4]$ tetraammineplatinum(II) tetrachloridoplatinate(II)

41. **(M)** The four possible isomers for $[CoCl_2(en)(NH_3)_2]^+$ are sketched below:

42. **(M)** The color of the green solid, as well as that of the green solution, is produced by the complex ion $[CrCl_2(H_2O)_4]^+$. Over time in solution, the chlorido ligands are replaced by aqua ligands, producing violet $[Cr(H_2O)_6]^{3+}$(aq). When the water is evaporated, the original complex is re-formed as the concentration of chloro ligand, $[Cl^-]$, gets higher and the chloro ligands replace the aqua ligands.

43. **(M)**The chlorido ligand, being lower in the spectrochemical series than the ethylenediamine ligand, is less strongly bonded to the central atom than is the ethylenediamine ligand. Therefore, of the two types of ligands, we expect the chloro ligand to be replaced more readily. In the *cis* isomer, the two chloro ligands are 90° from each other. This is the angular spacing that can be readily spanned by the oxalato ligand, thus we expect reaction with the cis isomer to occur rapidly. On the other hand, in the *trans* isomer, the two chloro ligands are located 180° from each other. After the chloro ligands are removed, at least one end of one ethylenediamine ligand would have to be relocated to allow the oxalato ligand to bond as a bidentate ligand. Consequently, replacement of the two chloro ligands by the oxalato ligand should be much slower for the *trans* isomer than for the *cis* isomer.

44. **(M)** $Cl_2 + 2\,e^- \rightarrow 2\,Cl^-$

$$\frac{[Pt(NH_3)_4]^{2+} \rightarrow [Pt(NH_3)_4]^{4+} + 2\,e^-}{Cl_2 + [Pt(NH_3)_4]^{2+} \rightarrow [PtCl_2(NH_3)_4]^{2+}}$$

45. **(M)** The successive acid ionizations of a complex ion such as $[Fe(OH)_6]^{3+}$ are more nearly equal in magnitude than those of an uncharged polyprotic acid such as H_3PO_4 principally because the complex ion has a positive charge. The second proton is leaving a species which has one fewer positive charge but which is nonetheless positively charged. Since positive charges repel each other, successive ionizations should not show a great decrease in the magnitude of their ionization constants. In the case of polyprotic acids, on the other hand, successive protons are leaving a species whose negative charge is increasingly greater with each step. Since unlike charges attract each other, it becomes increasingly difficult to remove successive protons.

46. **(M)**

47. (M)

(a)
$$\text{Fe(H}_2\text{O)}_6^{3+}(aq) \quad + \quad \text{H}_2\text{O(l)} \xrightarrow{K=9.0\times10^{-4}} \text{Fe(H}_2\text{O)}_5\text{OH}^{2+}(aq) \quad + \quad \text{H}_3\text{O}^+$$

Initial	0.100 M	–	0 M	≈ 0 M
Equil.	$(0.100-x)$ M	–	x	x

{where x is the molar quantity of $\text{Fe(H}_2\text{O)}_6^{3+}(aq)$ hydrolyzed}

$$K = \frac{[[\text{Fe(H}_2\text{O)}_5\text{OH}]^{2+}]\,[\text{H}_3\text{O}^+]}{[[\text{Fe(H}_2\text{O)}_6]^{3+}]} = \frac{x^2}{0.100-x} = 9.0 \times 10^{-4}$$

Solving, we find $x = 9.5\times10^{-3}$ M, which is the $[\text{H}_3\text{O}^+]$ so:

$$\text{pH} = -\log(9.5 \times10^{-3}) = 2.02$$

(b)
$$[\text{Fe(H}_2\text{O)}_6]^{3+}(aq) \quad + \quad \text{H}_2\text{O(l)} \xrightarrow{K = 9.0 \times 10^{-4}} [\text{Fe(H}_2\text{O)}_5\text{OH}]^{2+}(aq) + \text{H}_3\text{O}^+$$

initial	0.100 M	–	0 M	0.100 M
equil.	$(0.100-x)$ M	–	x M	$(0.100+x)$ M

{where x is $[[\text{Fe(H}_2\text{O)}_6]^{3+}]$ reacting}

$$K = \frac{[[\text{Fe(H}_2\text{O)}_5\text{OH}]^{2+}]\,[\text{H}_3\text{O}^+]}{[[\text{Fe(H}_2\text{O)}_6]^{3+}]} = \frac{x\,(0.100+x)}{(0.100-x)} = 9.0 \times 10^{-4}$$

Solving, we find $x = 9.0\times10^{-4}$ M, which is the $[[\text{Fe(H}_2\text{O)}_5\text{OH}]^{2+}]$

(c) We simply substitute $[[\text{Fe(H}_2\text{O)}_5\text{OH}]^{2+} = 1.0 \times 10^{-6}$ M into the K_a expression with $[\text{Fe(H}_2\text{O)}_6]^{3+} = 0.100$ M and determine the concentration of H_3O^+

$$[\text{H}_3\text{O}^+] = \frac{K_a[[\text{Fe(H}_2\text{O)}_6]^{3+}]}{[[\text{Fe(H}_2\text{O)}_5\text{OH}]^{2+}]} = \frac{9.0 \times 10^{-4}(0.100\text{ M})}{[1.0 \times10^{-6}\text{M}]} = 90.\text{ M}$$

To maintain the concentration at this level requires an impossibly high concentration of H_3O^+

48. (D) Let us first determine the concentration of the uncomplexed (free) $\text{Pb}^{2+}(aq)$. Because of the large value of the formation constant, we assume that most of the lead(II) ion is present as the EDTA complex ion ($[\text{Pb(EDTA)}]^{2-}$). Once equilibrium is established, we can see if there is sufficient lead(II) ion present in solution to precipitate with the sulfide ion. (Note: the concentration of EDTA remains constant at 0.20 M)

$$\text{Reaction:} \quad \text{Pb}^{2+}(aq) + \text{EDTA}^{4-}(aq) \xrightarrow{2\times10^{18}} [\text{Pb(EDTA)}]^{2-}(aq)$$

Initial:	0 M	0.20 M	0.010 M
Change:	$+x$ M	constant	$-x$ M
Equilibrium:	x M	0.20 M	$(0.010-x)$ M ≈ 0.010 M

$$K_f = \frac{[\text{Pb(EDTA)}^{2-}]}{[\text{Pb}^{2+}][\text{EDTA}^{4-}]} = 2\times10^{18} = \frac{0.010}{0.20(x)} \quad x = 2.5\times10^{-20}\text{ M} = [\text{Pb}^{2+}]$$

Now determine the $[S^{2-}]$ required to precipitate PbS from this solution.

$$K_{sp} = [Pb^{2+}][S^{2-}] = 8\times10^{-28}$$

$$[S^{2-}] = \frac{8\times10^{-28}}{(2.5\times10^{-20})} = 3.2\times10^{-8}\text{ M}$$

Recall (i) that a saturated H_2S solution is ~0.10 M H_2S and (ii) That the $[S^{2-}] = K_{a2} = 1 \times 10^{-14}$

$Q_{sp} = [Pb^{2+}][S^{2-}] = 2.\underline{5} \times 10^{-20} \times 1 \times 10^{-14} = 2.\underline{5} \times 10^{-34}$ $K_{sp} = 8 \times 10^{-28}$

$Q_{sp} \ll K_{sp}$ Hence, PbS(s) will not precipitate from this solution.

49. **(M)** The formation of $[Cu(NH_3)_4]^{2+}(aq)$ from $[Cu(H_2O)_4]^{2+}(aq)$ has $K_1 = 1.9 \times 10^4$, $K_2 = 3.9 \times 10^3$, $K_3 = 1.0 \times 10^3$, and $K_4 = 1.5 \times 10^2$. Since these equilibrium constants are all considerably larger than 1.00, one expects that the reactions they represent, yielding ultimately the ion $[Cu(NH_3)_4]^{2+}(aq)$, will go essentially to completion. However, if the concentration of NH_3 were limited to less than the stoichiometric amount, that is, to less than 4 mol NH_3 per mol of $Cu^{2+}(aq)$, one would expect that the ammine-aqua complex ions would be present in significantly higher concentrations than the $[Cu(NH_3)_4]^{2+}(aq)$ ions.

50. **(D)** For $[Ca(EDTA)]^{2-}$, $K_f = 4 \times 10^{10}$ and for $[Mg(EDTA)]^{2-}$, $K_f = 4 \times 10^8$. In Table 18-1, the least soluble calcium compound is $CaCO_3$, $K_{sp} = 2.8 \times 10^{-9}$, and the least soluble magnesium compound is $Mg_3(PO_4)_2$, $K_{sp} = 1 \times 10^{-25}$. We can determine the equilibrium constants for adding carbonate ion to $[Ca(EDTA)]^{2-}(aq)$ and for adding phosphate ion to $[Mg(EDTA)]^{2-}(aq)$ as follows:

Instability: $[Ca(EDTA)]^{2-}(aq) \rightleftharpoons Ca^{2+}(aq) + EDTA^{4-}(aq)$ $K_i = 1/(4 \times 10^{10})$

Precipitation: $Ca^{2+}(aq) + CO_3{}^{2-}(aq) + \rightleftharpoons CaCO_3(s)$ $K_{ppt} = 1/2.8 \times 10^{-9}$

Net: $[Ca(EDTA)]^{2-} + CO_3{}^{2-}(aq) \rightleftharpoons CaCO_3(s) + EDTA^{4-}(aq)$ $K = K_i \times K_{ppt}$

$$K = \frac{1}{(4 \times 10^{10})(2.8 \times 10^{-9})} = 9 \times 10^{-3}$$

The small value of the equilibrium constant indicates that this reaction does not proceed very far toward products.

Instability: $\{[Mg(EDTA)]^{2-}(aq) \rightleftharpoons Mg^{2+}(aq) + EDTA^{4-}(aq)\} \times 3$ $K_i^3 = 1/(4 \times 10^8)^3$

Precipitation: $3\,Mg^{2+}(aq) + 2\,PO_4{}^{3-}(aq) \rightleftharpoons Mg_3(PO_4)_2(s)$ $K_{ppt} = 1/1 \times 10^{-25}$

Net : $3\,[Mg(EDTA)]^{2-} + 2\,PO_4{}^{3-}(aq) \rightleftharpoons Mg_3(PO_4)_2(s) + 3\,EDTA^{4-}(aq)$ $K = K_i^3 \times K_{ppt}$

$$K = \frac{1}{(4 \times 10^8)^3(1 \times 10^{-25})} = 0.1_6$$

This is not such a small value, but again we do not expect the formation of much product, particularly if the $[EDTA^{4-}]$ is kept high. We can approximate what the concentration of precipitating anion must be in each case, assuming that the concentration of complex ion is 0.10 M and that of $[EDTA^{4-}]$ also is 0.10 M.

Reaction: $[Ca(EDTA)]^{2-} + CO_3{}^{2-}(aq) \rightleftharpoons CaCO_3(s) + EDTA^{4-}(aq)$

$$K = \frac{[EDTA^{4-}]}{[[Ca(EDTA)]^{2-}][CO_3{}^{2-}]} = 9 \times 10^{-3} = \frac{0.10\ M}{0.10\ M\ [CO_3{}^{2-}]}$$ $[CO_3{}^{2-}] = 1 \times 10^2\ M$

This is an impossibly high $[CO_3^{2-}]$.

Reaction: $\quad 3[Mg(EDTA)]^{2-} + 2\,PO_4^{3-}\,(aq) \rightleftharpoons Mg_3(PO_4)_2\,(s) + 3\,EDTA^{4-}\,(aq)$

$$K = \frac{[EDTA^{4-}]^3}{[[Mg(EDTA)]^{2-}]^3[PO_4^{3-}]^2} = 0.1_6 = \frac{(0.10\ M)^3}{(0.10\ M)^3\ [PO_4^{3-}]^2} \qquad [PO_4^{3-}] = 2._5\ M$$

Although this $[PO_4^{3-}]$ is not impossibly high, it is unlikely that it will occur without the deliberate addition of phosphate ion to the water. *Alternatively,* we can substitute $[[M(EDTA)]^{2-}] = 0.10$ M and $[EDTA^{4-}] = 0.10$ M into the formation constant

expression: $K_f = \dfrac{[[M(EDTA)]^{2-}]}{[M^{2+}][EDTA^{4-}]}$

This substitution gives $[M^{2+}] = \dfrac{1}{K_f}$, hence, $[Ca^{2+}] = 2.5 \times 10^{-11}$ M and $[Mg^{2+}] = 2.5 \times 10^{-9}$ M,

which are concentrations that do not normally lead to the formation of precipitates unless the concentrations of anions are substantial. Specifically, the required anion concentrations are $[CO_3^{2-}] = 1.1 \times 10^2$ M for $CaCO_3$, and $[PO_4^{3-}] = 2.5$ M, just as computed above.

51. **(M)** If a 99% conversion to the chloro complex is achieved, which is the percent conversion necessary to produce a yellow color, $[[CuCl_4]^{2-}] = 0.99 \times 0.10$ M $= 0.099$ M, and $[[Cu(H_2O)_4]^{2+}] = 0.01 \times 0.10$ M $= 0.0010$ M. We substitute these values into the formation constant expression and solve for $[Cl^-]$.

$$K_f = \frac{[[CuCl_4]^{2-}]}{[[Cu(H_2O)_4]^{2+}]\,[Cl^-]^4} = 4.2 \times 10^5 = \frac{0.099\ M}{0.0010\ M\ [Cl^-]^4}$$

$$[Cl^-] = \sqrt[4]{\frac{0.099}{0.0010 \times 4.2 \times 10^5}} = 0.12\ M$$

This is the final concentration of free chloride ion in the solution. If we wish to account for all chloride ion that has been added, we must include the chloride ion present in the complex ion.

total $[Cl^-] = 0.12$ M free Cl^- + $(4 \times 0.099$ M$)$ bound $Cl^- = 0.52$ M

52. **(M)**

(a) Oxidation: $\quad 2H_2O(l) \longrightarrow O_2(g) + 4\,H^+(aq) + 4\,e^- \qquad\qquad -E° = -1.229$ V

$\quad\quad$ Reduction: $\{Co^{3+}((aq) + e^- \longrightarrow Co^{2+}(aq)\} \times 4 \qquad\qquad E° = +1.82$ V

$\quad\quad$ Net: $\quad 4\,Co^{3+}(aq) + 2\,H_2O(l) \longrightarrow 4\,Co^{2+}(aq) + 4\,H^+(aq) + O_2(g)\quad E°_{cell} = +0.59$ V

(b) Reaction: $Co^{3+}(aq) + 6\,NH_3(aq) \rightleftharpoons [Co(NH_3)_6]^{3+}(aq)$

Initial: $\quad$ 0.1 M $\qquad$ 0.10 M $\qquad\qquad$ 0 M

Changes: $\quad -x$M $\qquad$ constant $\qquad\qquad +x$M

Equil: $(0.1 - x)$M $\qquad$ 0.10 M $\qquad\qquad\quad x$M

$$K_f = \frac{[[Co(NH_3)_6]^{3+}]}{[Co^{3+}][NH_3]^6} = 4.5 \times 10^{33} = \frac{x}{(0.1-x)(0.10)^6} \qquad \frac{x}{0.1-x} = 4.5 \times 10^{27}$$

Thus $[[Co(NH_3)_6]^{3+}] = 0.1$ M because K is so large, and $[Co^{3+}] = \dfrac{1}{4.5 \times 10^{27}} = 2.2 \times 10^{-28}$ M

(c) The equilibrium and equilibrium constant for the reaction of NH_3 with water follows.

$$NH_3(aq) + H_2O(l) \rightleftharpoons NH_4^+(aq) + OH^-(aq)$$

$$K_b = 1.8 \times 10^{-5} = \frac{[NH_4^+][OH^-]}{[NH_3]} = \frac{[OH^-]^2}{0.10} \quad [OH^-] = \sqrt{0.10(1.8 \times 10^{-5})} = 0.0013 \text{ M}$$

In determining the $[OH^-]$, we have noted that $[NH_4^+] = [OH^-]$ by stoichiometry, and also that $[NH_3] = 0.10$ M, as we assumed above.

$$[H_3O^+] = \frac{K_w}{[OH^-]} = \frac{1.0 \times 10^{-14}}{0.0013} = 7.7 \times 10^{-12} \text{ M}$$

We use the Nernst equation to determine the potential of reaction (24.12) at the conditions described.

$$E = E^\circ{}_{cell} - \frac{0.0257}{4} \ln \frac{[Co^{2+}]^4 \, [H^+]^4 \, P[O_2]}{[Co^{3+}]^4}$$

$$E = +0.59 - \frac{0.0257}{4} \ln \frac{(1 \times 10^{-4})^4 \, (7.7 \times 10^{-12})^4 \, 0.2}{(2.2 \times 10^{-28})^4}$$

$$= +0.59 \text{ V} - 0.732 \text{ V} = -0.142 \text{ V}$$

The negative cell potential indicates that the reaction indeed does not occur.

53. **(M)** We use the Nernst equation to determine the value of $[Cu^{2+}]$. The cell reaction follows.

$$Cu(s) + 2 H^+(aq) \longrightarrow Cu^{2+}(aq) + H_2(g) \qquad E^\circ{}_{cell} = -0.337 \text{ V}$$

$$E = E^\circ - \frac{0.0257}{2} \ln \frac{[Cu^{2+}]}{[H^+]^2} = 0.08 \text{ V} = -0.337 - \frac{0.0257}{2} \ln \frac{[Cu^{2+}]}{(1.00)^2}$$

$$\ln[Cu^{2+}] = \frac{2(-0.337 - 0.08)}{0.0257} = -32.4 \qquad [Cu^{2+}] = 8 \times 10^{-15} \text{ M}$$

Now we determine the value of K_f.

$$K_f = \frac{[[Cu(NH_3)_4]^{2+}]}{[Cu^{2+}][NH_3]^4} = \frac{1.00}{8 \times 10^{-15}(1.00)^4} = 1 \times 10^{14}$$

This compares favorably with the value of $K_f = 1.1 \times 10^{13}$ given in Table 18-2, especially considering the imprecision with which the data are known. ($E_{cell} = 0.08$ V is known to but one significant figure.)

54. **(M)** We first determine $[Ag^+]$ in the cyanide solution.

$$K_f = \frac{[[Ag(CN)_2]^-]}{[Ag^+][CN^-]^2} = 5.6 \times 10^{18} = \frac{0.10}{[Ag^+](0.10.)^2}$$

$$[Ag^+] = \frac{0.10}{5.6 \times 10^{18} (0.10)^2} = 1.8 \times 10^{-18}$$

The cell reaction is as follows. It has $E^{\circ}_{cell} = 0.000$ V; the same reaction occurs at both anode and cathode and thus the Nernstian voltage is influenced only by the Ag^+ concentration.

$$Ag^+ (0.10\,M) \longrightarrow Ag^+ (0.10\,M\,[Ag(CN)_2]^-,\ 0.10\,M\,KCN)$$

$$E = E^{\circ} - \frac{0.0257}{1} \ln \frac{[Ag^+]_{CN}}{[Ag^+]} = 0.000 - 0.0257 \ln \frac{1.8 \times 10^{-18}}{0.10} = +0.99\ V$$

55. (M)

A 0.10 mol/L solution of these compounds would result in ion concentration of 0.20 mol/L for $[Co\,Cl\,(H_2O(NH_3)_4)]Cl \cdot H_2O$ or 0.30 mol/L for $[Co(H_2O)_2\,(NH_3)_4]Cl_2$.

Observed freezing point depression = –0.56 °C.

$\Delta T = -K_f \times m \times i = -0.56\ \text{deg} = -1.86\ \text{mol}^{-1}\ \text{kg deg}(0.10\ \text{mol/L}) \times i$

Hence, $i = 3.0$. This suggests that the compound is $[Co(H_2O)_2\,(NH_3)_4]Cl_2$.

56. (M) $Sc(H_2O)_6^{3+}$ and $Zn(H_2O)_4^{2+}$ have outer energy shells with 18 electrons, and thus they do not have any electronic transitions in the energy range corresponding to visible light. $Fe(H_2O)_6^{3+}$ has 17 electrons (not 18) in its outer shell; thus, it does have electronic transitions in the energy range corresponding to visible light.

57. (M) The Cr^{3+} ion would have 3 unpaired electrons, each residing in a $3d$ orbital and would be sp^3d^2 hybridized. The hybrid orbitals would be hybrids of $4s$, $4p$, and $3d$ (or $4d$) orbitals. Each Cr–NH$_3$ coordinate covalent bond is a σ bond formed when a lone pair in an sp^3 orbital on N is directed toward an empty sp^3d^2 orbital on Cr^{3+}. The number of unpaired electrons predicted by valence bond theory would be the same as the number of unpaired electrons predicted by crystal field theory.

58. (D) We proceed by first writing the stepwise equilibria:

$$Cu^{2+} + NH_3 \rightleftharpoons [Cu(NH_3)]^{2+} \qquad \log_{10} K_1 = 4.28$$

$$[Cu(NH_3)]^{2+} + NH_3 \rightleftharpoons [Cu(NH_3)_2]^{2+} \qquad \log_{10} K_2 = 3.59$$

$$[Cu(NH_3)_2]^{2+} + NH_3 \rightleftharpoons [Cu(NH_3)_3]^{2+} \qquad \log_{10} K_3 = 3.00$$

$$[Cu(NH_3)_3]^{2+} + NH_3 \rightleftharpoons [Cu(NH_3)_4]^{2+} \qquad \log_{10} K_2 = 2.18$$

Using the concept of the overall cumulative equilibrium constant (β),

$$Cu^{2+} + NH_3 \rightleftharpoons [Cu(NH_3)]^{2+} \qquad \beta_1 = \frac{[Cu(NH_3)^{2+}]}{[Cu^{2+}][NH_3]} \Rightarrow [Cu(NH_3)^{2+}] = \beta_1[Cu^{2+}][NH_3]$$

$$Cu^{2+} + 2NH_3 \rightleftharpoons [Cu(NH_3)_2]^{2+} \qquad \beta_2 = \frac{[Cu(NH_3)_2^{2+}]}{[Cu^{2+}][NH_3]^2} \Rightarrow [Cu(NH_3)_2^{2+}] = \beta_2[Cu^{2+}][NH_3]^2$$

$$Cu^{2+} + 3NH_3 \rightleftharpoons [Cu(NH_3)_3]^{2+} \qquad \beta_3 = \frac{[Cu(NH_3)_3^{2+}]}{[Cu^{2+}][NH_3]^3} \Rightarrow [Cu(NH_3)_3^{2+}] = \beta_3[Cu^{2+}][NH_3]^3$$

$$Cu^{2+} + 4NH_3 \rightleftharpoons [Cu(NH_3)_4]^{2+} \qquad \beta_4 = \frac{[Cu(NH_3)_4^{2+}]}{[Cu^{2+}][NH_3]^4} \Rightarrow [Cu(NH_3)_4^{2+}] = \beta_4[Cu^{2+}][NH_3]^4$$

Recall that β's are related to K (by definition $\beta_0 = 1$):

$$\beta_1 = K_1 = 10^{4.28} = 1.90 \times 10^4$$

$$\beta_2 = K_1 K_2 = 10^{4.28} \times 10^{3.59} = 10^{7.87} = 7.41 \times 10^7$$

$$\beta_3 = K_1 K_2 K_3 = 10^{4.28} \times 10^{3.59} \times 10^{3.00} = 10^{10.9} = 7.41 \times 10^{10}$$

$$\beta_4 = K_1 K_2 K_3 K_4 = 10^{4.28} \times 10^{3.59} \times 10^{3.00} \times 10^{2.18} = 10^{13.1} = 1.12 \times 10^{13}$$

Therefore, the mole fraction (α) of copper in the uncomplexed form (i.e., Cu^{2+}) is

$$\alpha_{Cu^{2+}} = \frac{[Cu^{2+}]}{[Cu^{2+}]+[Cu(NH_3)^{2+}]+[Cu(NH_3)_2^{2+}]+[Cu(NH_3)_3^{2+}]+[Cu(NH_3)_4^{2+}]}$$

$$\alpha_{Cu^{2+}} = \frac{[Cu^{2+}]}{[Cu^{2+}]+\beta_1[Cu^{2+}][NH_3]+\beta_2[Cu^{2+}][NH_3]^2+\beta_3[Cu^{2+}][NH_3]^3+\beta_4[Cu^{2+}][NH_3]^4}$$

$$\alpha_{Cu^{2+}} = \frac{1}{1+\beta_1[NH_3]+\beta_2[NH_3]^2+\beta_3[NH_3]^3+\beta_4[NH_3]^4}$$

Substituting the values for cumulative equilibrium constants (β's) and the equilibrium concentration of [NH$_3$]:

$$\alpha_{Cu^{2+}} = \frac{1}{1+1.90\times10^4\times2.00+7.41\times10^7\times2.00^2+7.41\times10^{10}\times2.00^3+1.12\times10^{11}\times2.00^4}\times100\%$$

$$\alpha_{Cu^{2+}} = 4.20\times10^{-11}\%$$

Essentially, all of Cu^{2+} cations have been complexed with NH$_3$.
Similarly, the mole fraction (α) of $[Cu(NH_3)^{2+}]$ is

$$\alpha_{[Cu(NH_3)^{2+}]} = \frac{\beta_1[NH_3]}{1+\beta_1[NH_3]+\beta_2[NH_3]^2+\beta_3[NH_3]^3+\beta_4[NH_3]^4}$$

$$\alpha_{[Cu(NH_3)^{2+}]} = \frac{1.90\times10^4\times2.00}{1+1.90\times10^4\times2.00+7.41\times10^7\times2.00^2+7.41\times10^{10}\times2.00^3+1.12\times10^{11}\times2.00^4}\times100\%$$

$$\alpha_{[Cu(NH_3)^{2+}]} = 1.59\times10^{-6}\%$$

The mole fractions of the remaining species can be calculated accordingly:

$$\alpha_{[Cu(NH_3)_3^{2+}]} = \frac{\beta_3[NH_3]^3}{1+\beta_1[NH_3]+\beta_2[NH_3]^2+\beta_3[NH_3]^3+\beta_4[NH_3]^4}$$

$$\alpha_{[Cu(NH_3)_3^{2+}]} = \frac{7.41\times10^{10}\times2.00^3}{1+1.90\times10^4\times2.00+7.41\times10^7\times2.00^2+7.41\times10^{10}\times2.00^3+1.12\times10^{11}\times2.00^4}\times100\%$$

$$\alpha_{[Cu(NH_3)_3^{2+}]} = 24.8\%$$

$$\alpha_{[Cu(NH_3)_3^{2+}]} = \frac{\beta_4[NH_3]^4}{1+\beta_1[NH_3]+\beta_2[NH_3]^2+\beta_3[NH_3]^3+\beta_4[NH_3]^4}$$

$$\alpha_{[Cu(NH_3)_3^{2+}]} = \frac{1.12\times10^{11}\times2.00^4}{1+1.90\times10^4\times2.00+7.41\times10^7\times2.00^2+7.41\times10^{10}\times2.00^3+1.12\times10^{11}\times2.00^4}\times100\%$$

$$\alpha_{[Cu(NH_3)_3^{2+}]} = 75.2\%$$

Notice that for a general case, the mole fraction of a particular species in a solution containing metal (M) and n number of ligands (L) can be written as

$$\alpha_{ML_n} = \frac{\beta_n[L]^n}{\displaystyle\sum_{n=0}^{N}\beta_n[L]^n}$$

The corresponding plot of a mole fraction for each species versus the equilibrium concentration of [NH₃] is shown below:

59. (M)

Co(acac)₃

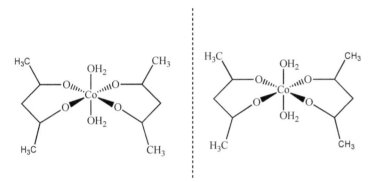

This compound has a non-superimposable mirror image (therefore it is optically active). These are enantiomers. One enantiomer rotates plane polarized light clockwise, while the other rotates plane polarized light counter-clockwise. Polarimetry can be used to determine which isomer rotates plane polarized light in a particular direction.

***trans*-[Co(acac)₂(H₂O)₂]Cl₂**

This compound has a superimposable mirror image (therefore it is optically inactive). These are the same compound. This compound will not rotate plane polarized light (net rotation = 0).

***cis*-[Co(acac)₂(H₂O)₂]Cl₂**

This compound has a non-superimposable mirror image (therefore it is optically active). These are enantiomers. One enantiomer rotates plane polarized light clockwise, while the other rotates plane polarized light counter-clockwise. By using a polarimeter, we can determine which isomer rotates plane polarized light in a particular direction.

60. (D) $[Co(H_2O)_6]^{3+}(aq) + e^- \rightarrow [Co(H_2O)_6]^{2+}(aq)$

$\ln K = zE°/0.0257 = (1)(1.82)/0.0257 = 73.68.$ $K = e^{70.82} \ 10^{30.74}$

$[Co(en)_3]^{3+}(aq) + 6\ H_2O(l)$	$\rightarrow$	$[Co(H_2O)_6]^{3+}(aq) + 3\ en$	$K = 1/10^{47.30}$
$[Co(H_2O)_6]^{2+}(aq) + 3\ en$	$\rightarrow$	$[Co(en)_3]^{2+}(aq) + 6\ H_2O(l)$	$K = 10^{12.18}$
$[Co(H_2O)_6]^{3+}(aq) + e^-$	$\rightarrow$	$[Co(H_2O)_6]^{2+}(aq)$	$K = 10^{30.74}$
$[Co(en)_3]^{3+}(aq) + e^-$	$\rightarrow$	$[Co(en)_3]^{2+}(aq)$	$K_{overall} = ?$

$$K_{overall} = 1/10^{47.30} \times 10^{12.18} \times 10^{30.74} = 10^{-4.38} = 0.0000041\underline{7}$$

$$E° = (0.0257/z)\ln K = (0.0257/1)\ln(0.0000041\underline{7}) = -0.26 \text{ V}$$

$$\begin{array}{ll} 4 \text{ Co}^{3+}(aq) + 4 \text{ e}^- \rightarrow 4 \text{ Co}^{2+}(aq) & E°_{cathode} = 1.82 \text{ V} \\ \underline{2 \text{ H}_2\text{O}(l) \rightarrow 4 \text{ H}^+(aq) + \text{O}_2(g) + 4 \text{ e}^-} & \underline{E°_{anode} = 1.23 \text{ V}} \\ 4 \text{ Co}^{3+}(aq) + 2 \text{ H}_2\text{O}(l) \rightarrow 4 \text{ H}^+(aq) + \text{O}_2(g) + 4 \text{ Co}^{2+}(aq) & \end{array}$$

$$E°_{cell} = E°_{cathode} - E°_{anode} = 1.82\text{V} - 1.23 \text{ V} = +0.59 \text{ V (Spontaneous)}$$

$$\begin{array}{ll} 4 \text{ [Co(en)}_3]^{3+}(aq) + 4 \text{ e}^- \rightarrow 4 \text{ [Co(en)}_3]^{2+}(aq) & E°_{cathode} = -0.26 \text{ V} \\ \underline{2 \text{ H}_2\text{O}(l) \rightarrow 4 \text{ H}^+(aq) + \text{O}_2(g) + 4 \text{ e}^-} & \underline{E°_{anode} = 1.23 \text{ V}} \\ 4 \text{ [Co(en)}_3]^{3+}(aq) + 2 \text{ H}_2\text{O}(l) \rightarrow 4 \text{ H}^+(aq) + \text{O}_2(g) + 4 \text{ [Co(en)}_3]^{2+}(aq) & \end{array}$$

$$E°_{cell} = E°_{cathode} - E° = -0.26 \text{ V} - 1.23 \text{ V} = -1.49 \text{ V (non-spontaneous)}$$

61. **(M)** There are two sets of isomers for Co(gly)$_3$. Each set comprises two enantiomers (non-superimposable mirror images). One rotates plane polarized light clockwise (+), the other counter-clockwise (−). Experiments are needed to determine which enantiomer is (+) and which is (−).

(+)-*fac*-tris(glycinato)cobalt(III)   (+)-*mer*-tris(glycinato)cobalt(III)

(−)-*fac*-tris(glycinato)cobalt(III)   (−)-*mer*-tris(glycinato)cobalt(III)

[Co(gly)$_2$Cl(NH$_3$)] has 10 possible isomer, four pairs of enantiomers and two achiral isomers.

62. (M) The coordination compound is face-centered cubic, K^+ occupies tetrahedral holes, while $PtCl_6^{2-}$ occupies octahedral holes.

63. (M)

# NH_3	0	1	2	3
Formula:	$K_2[PtCl_6]$	$K[PtCl_5(NH_3)]$	$PtCl_4(NH_3)_2$	$[PtCl_3(NH_3)_3]Cl$
Total # ions (per formula unit)	3	2	0	2

# NH_3	4	5	6
Formula:	$[PtCl_2(NH_3)_4]Cl_2$	$[PtCl(NH_3)_5]Cl_3$	$[Pt(NH_3)_6]Cl_4$
Total # ions (per formula unit)	3	4	5

FEATURE PROBLEMS

64. (M)

(a) A trigonal prismatic structure predicts three geometric isomers for $[CoCl_2(NH_3)_4]^+$, which is one more than the actual number of geometric isomers found for this complex ion. All three geometric isomers arising from a trigonal prism are shown below.

  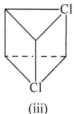

(i)   (ii)   (iii)

The fact that the trigonal prismatic structure does not afford the correct number of isomers is a clear indication that the ion actually adopts some other structural form (i.e., the theoretical model is contradicted by the experimental result). We know now of course, that this ion has an octahedral structure and as a result, it can exist only in *cis* and *trans* configurations.

(b) All attempts to produce optical isomers of $[Co(en)_3]^{3+}$ based upon a trigonal prismatic structure are shown below. The ethylenediamine ligand appears as an arc in diagrams below:

(i)   (ii)   (iii)

Only structure (iii), which has an ethylenediamine ligand connecting the diagonal corners of a face can give rise to optical isomers. Structure (iii) is highly unlikely, however, because the ethylenediamine ligand is simply too short to effectively span the diagonal distance across the face of the prism. Thus, barring any unusual stretching of the ethylenediamine ligand, a trigonal prismatic structure cannot account for the optical isomerism that was observed for $[Co(en)_3]^{3+}$.

65. (D) Assuming that each hydroxide ligand bears its normal −1 charge, and that each ammonia ligand is neutral, the total contribution of negative charge from the ligands is −6. Since the net charge on the complex ions is +6, the average oxidation state for each Co atom must be +3 (i.e., each Co in the complex can be viewed as a Co^{3+} $3d^6$ ion surrounded by six ligands.) The five $3d$ orbitals on each Co are split by the octahedrally arranged ligands into three lower energy orbitals, called t_{2g} orbitals, and two higher energy orbitals, called e_g orbitals. We are told in the question that the complex is *low spin*. This is simply another way of saying that all six $3d$ electrons on each Co are paired up in the t_{2g} set as a result of the e_g and t_{2g} orbitals being separated by a relatively large energy gap (see below). Hence, there should be no unpaired electrons in the hexacation (i.e., the cation is expected to be diamagnetic).

Low Spin Co^{3+}
(Octahedral Environment):

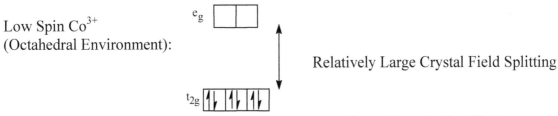

Relatively Large Crystal Field Splitting

The Lewis structures for the two optical isomers (enantiomers) are depicted below:

Non-superimposable mirror images of one another

66. **(D)** The data used to construct a plot of hydration energy as a function of metal ion atomic number is collected in the table below. The graph of hydration energy (kJ mol^{-1}) versus metal ion atomic number is located beneath the table.

Metal ion	Atomic number	Hydration energy
Ca^{2+}	20	−2468 kJ mol^{-1}
Sc^{2+}	21	−2673 kJ mol^{-1}
Ti^{2+}	22	−2750 kJ mol^{-1}
V^{2+}	23	−2814 kJ mol^{-1}
Cr^{2+}	24	−2799 kJ mol^{-1}
Mn^{2+}	25	−2743 kJ mol^{-1}
Fe^{2+}	26	−2843 kJ mol^{-1}
Co^{2+}	27	−2904 kJ mol^{-1}
Ni^{2+}	28	−2986 kJ mol^{-1}
Cu^{2+}	29	−2989 kJ mol^{-1}
Zn^{2+}	30	−2936 kJ mol^{-1}

(b) When a metal ion is placed in an octahedral field of ligands, the five d-orbitals are split into e_g and t_{2g} subsets, as shown in the diagram below:

(octahedral field)

Since water is a weak field ligand, the magnitude of the splitting is relatively small. As a consequence, high-spin configurations result for all of the hexaaqua complexes. The electron configurations for the metal ions in the high-spin hexaaqua complexes and their associated crystal field stabilization energies (CFSE) are provided in the table below

Metal Ion	Configuration	t_{2g}	e_g	number of unpaired e^-	CFSE(Δ_o)
Ca^{2+}	$3d^0$	0	0	0	0
Sc^{2+}	$3d^1$	1	0	1	$-^2/_5$
Ti^{2+}	$3d^2$	2	0	2	$-^4/_5$
V^{2+}	$3d^3$	3	0	3	$-^6/_5$
Cr^{2+}	$3d^4$	3	1	4	$-^3/_5$
Mn^{2+}	$3d^5$	3	2	5	0
Fe^{2+}	$3d^6$	4	2	4	$-^2/_5$
Co^{2+}	$3d^7$	5	2	3	$-^4/_5$
Ni^{2+}	$3d^8$	6	2	2	$-^6/_5$
Cu^{2+}	$3d^9$	6	3	1	$-^3/_5$
Zn^{2+}	$3d^{10}$	6	4	0	0

Thus, the crystal field stabilization energy is zero for Ca^{2+}. Mn^{2+} and Zn^{2+}.

(c) The lines drawn between those ions that have a CFSE = 0 show the trend for the enthalpy of hydration after the contribution from the crystal field stabilization energy has been subtracted from the experimental values. The Ca to Mn and Mn to Zn lines are quite similar. Both line have slopes that are negative and are of comparable magnitude. This trend shows that as one proceeds from left to right across the periodic table, the energy of hydration for dications becomes increasingly more negative. The hexaaqua complexes become progressively more stable because the Z_{eff} experienced by the bonding electrons in the valence shell of the metal ion steadily increases as we move further and further to the right. Put another way, the Z_{eff} climbs steadily as we move from left to right and this leads to the positive charge density on the metal becoming larger and larger, which results in the water ligands steadily being pulled closer and closer to the nucleus. Of course, the closer the approach of the water ligands to the metal, the greater is the energy released upon successful coordination of the ligand.

(d) Those ions that exhibit crystal field stabilization energies greater than zero have heats of hydration that are more negative (i.e. more energy released) than the hypothetical heat of hydration for the ion with CFSE subtracted out. The heat of hydration without CFSE for a given ion falls on the line drawn between the two flanking ions with CFSE = 0 at a position directly above the point for the experimental hydration energy. The energy difference between the observed heat of hydration for the ion and the heat of hydration without CFSE is, of course, approximately equal to the CFSE for the ion.

(e) As was mentioned in the answer to part (c), the straight line drawn between manganese and zinc (both ions with CFSE = 0) on the previous plot, describes the enthalpy trend after the ligand field stabilization energy has been subtracted from the experimental values for the hydration enthalpy. Thus, Δ_o for Fe^{2+} in $[Fe(H_2O)_6]^{2+}$ is approximately equal to $^5/_2$ of the energy difference (in kJ/mol) between the observed hydration energy for $Fe^{2+}(g)$ and the point for Fe^{2+} on the line connecting Mn^{2+} and Zn^{2+}, which is the expected enthalpy of hydration after the CFSE has been subtracted out. Remember that the crystal field stabilization energy for Fe^{2+} that is obtained from the graph is not Δ_o, but rather $^2/_5\Delta_o$, since the CFSE for a $3d^6$ ion in an octahedral field is just $^2/_5$ of Δ_o. Consequently, to obtain Δ_o, we must multiply the enthalpy difference by $^5/_2$. According to the graph, the high-spin CFSE for Fe^{2+} is -2843 kJ $mol^{-1} - (-2782$ kJ $mol^{-1})$ or -61 kJ/mol. Consequently, $\Delta_o = ^5/_2(-61$ kJ $mol^{-1}) = -153$ kJ mol^{-1}, or 1.5×10^2 kJ mol^{-1} is the energy difference between the e_g and t_{2g} orbital sets.

(f) The color of an octahedral complex is the result of the promotion of an electron on the metal from a t_{2g} orbital $\rightarrow e_g$ orbital. The energy difference between the e_g and t_{2g} orbital sets is Δ_o. As the metal-ligand bonding becomes stronger, the separation between the t_{2g} and e_g orbitals becomes larger. If the e_g set is not full, then the metal complex will exhibit an absorption band corresponding to a $t_{2g} \rightarrow e_g$ transition. Thus, the $[Fe(H_2O)_6]^{2+}$ complex ion should absorb electromagnetic radiation that has $E_{photon} = \Delta_o$. Since $\Delta_o \approx 150$ kJ mol^{-1} (calculated in part (e) of this question) for a mole of $[Fe(H_2O)_6]^{2+}(aq)$,

$$E_{photon} = \frac{1.5\times10^2\,kJ}{1\,mol\,[Fe(H_2O)_6]^{2+}} \times \frac{1\,mol\,[Fe(H_2O)_6]^{2+}}{6.022\times10^{23}\,[Fe(H_2O)_6]^{2+}} \times \frac{1000\,J}{1\,kJ}$$
$$= 2.5 \times 10^{-19}\ J\ per\ ion$$
$$\nu = \frac{E}{h} = \frac{2.5\times10^{-19}\,J}{6.626\times10^{-34}\,J\,s} = 3.8 \times 10^{14}\ s^{-1}$$
$$\lambda = \frac{c}{h} = \frac{2.998\times10^8\,m\,s^{-1}}{3.8\times10^{14}\,s^{-1}} = 7.8 \times 10^{-7}\ m\ (780\ nm)$$

So, the $[Fe(H_2O)_6]^{2+}$ ion will absorb radiation with a wavelength of 780 nm, which is red light in the visible part of the electromagnetic spectrum.

SELF-ASSESSMENT EXERCISES

67. **(E)**
    (a) Coordination number is the number of ligands coordinated to a transition metal complex.
    (b) Δ_0 is the crystal field splitting parameter which depends on the coordination geometry of a transition metal complex.
    (c) Ammine complex is the complex that contains NH_3 ligands.
    (d) An enantiomer is one of two stereoisomers that are mirror images of each other that are "non-superposable" (not identical).

68. **(E)**
    (a) A spectrochemical series is a list of ligands ordered on ligand strength and a list of metal ions based on oxidation number, group and identity.
    (b) Crystal field theory (CFT) is a model that describes the electronic structure of transition metal compounds, all of which can be considered coordination complexes.
    (c) Optical isomers are two compounds which contain the same number and kinds of atoms, and bonds (i.e., the connectivity between atoms is the same), and different spatial arrangements of the atoms, but which have non-superimposable mirror images.
    (d) Constitutional (structural) isomerism in accordance with IUPAC, is a form of isomerism in which molecules with the same molecular formula have atoms bonded together in different orders.

69. **(E)**
    (a) Coordination number is the number of ligands coordinated to a transition metal complex. Oxidation number of a central atom in a coordination compound is the charge that it would have if all the ligands were removed along with the electron pairs that were shared with the central atom.
    (b) A monodentate ligand has one point at which it can attach to the central atom. Polydentate ligand has many points at which it can coordinate to a transition metal.
    (c) Cis isomer has identical groups on the same side. In trans isomer, on the other hand, identical groups are on the opposite side.
    (d) Dextrorotation and levorotation refer, respectively, to the properties of rotating plane polarized light clockwise (for dextrorotation) or counterclockwise (for levorotation). A compound with dextrorotation is called dextrorotary, while a compound with levorotation is called levorotary.
    (e) When metal is coordinated to ligands to form a complex, its "d" orbital splits into high and low energy groups of orbitals. Depending on the nature of the ligands, the energy difference separating these groups can be large or small. In the first case, electrons of the d orbital tend to pair in the low energy suborbitals, a configuration known as "low spin". If the energy difference is low, electrons tend to distribute unpaired, giving rise to a "high spin" configuration. High spin is associated with paramagnetism (the property of being attracted to magnetic fields), while low spin is associated to diamagnetism (inert or repelled by magnets).

<u>**70.**</u> **(E)** (d)

<u>**71.**</u> **(E)** (e)

72. **(E)** (b)

73. **(E)** (a)

74. **(E)** (d)

75. **(E)** (c)

76. **(E)** (b)

77. **(M)**
   (a) pentaamminebromidocobalt(III)sulfate, no isomerism.
   (b) hexaamminechromium(III)hexacyanidocobaltate(III), no isomerism.
   (c) sodiumhexanitrito-N-cobaltate(III), no isomerism
   (d) tris(ethylenediamine)cobalt(III)chloride, two optical isomers.

78. **(M)** **(a)** $[Ag(CN)_2]^-$; **(b)** $[Pt(NH_3)_3(NO_2)]^+$; **(c)** $[CoCl(en)_2(H_2O)]^{2+}$; **(d)** $K_4[Cr(CN)_6]$

79. **(M)**

80. **(M)**
   (a) one structure only (all positions are equivalent for the H_2O ligand; NH_3 ligands attach at the remaining five sites).

   (b) two structures, *cis* and *trans*, based on the placement of H_2O.

(c) two structures, *fac* and *mer*.

fac   mer

(d) two structures, *cis* and *trans*, based on the placement of NH_3.

trans   cis

81. **(M)**

(a) coordination isomerism, based on the interchange of ligands between the complex cation and complex anion.

(b) linkage isomerism, based on the mode of attachment of the SCN^- ligand (either $-SCN^-$ or $-NCS^-$).

(c) no isomerism

(d) geometric isomerism, based on whether Cl^- ligands are *cis* or *trans*.

(e) geometric isomerism, based on whether the NH_3 or OH^- ligands are *fac* or *mer*.

82. **(M)**

(a) geometric isomerism (*cis* and *trans*) and optical isomerism in the *cis* isomer.

(b) geometric isomerism (*cis* and *trans*), optical isomerism in the *cis* isomer, and linkage isomerism in the thiocyanate ligand.

(c) no isomers.

(d) no isomers for this square-planar complex.

(e) two geometric isomers, one with the tridentate ligand occupying meridional positions and the other with the tridentate ligand occupying facial positions.

83. **(M)** Because ethylenediamine (en) is a stronger field ligand than H_2O, more energy must be absorbed by $[Co(en)_3]^{3+}$ than by $[Co(H_2O)_6]^{3+}$ to simulate an electronic transition. This means that $[Co(en)_3]^{3+}$(aq) absorbs shorter wavelength light and transmits longer wavelength light than does $[Co(H_2O)_6]^{3+}$(aq). Thus $[Co(en)_3]^{3+}$(aq) is yellow and $[Co(H_2O)_6]^{3+}$(aq) is blue.

84. **(D)** When constructing a map, the following concepts should be incorporated: (a) crystal field theory with emphasis on octahedral and square planar complexes, (b) splitting diagrams and how is the energy dependent on strong and weak field ligands, (c) how can one predict a structure of a transition metal complex from its magnetic properties, (d) primary versus secondary colors, and (e) how can one calculate the splitting energy for a given transition metal complex based on the light absorbed and transmitted.

CHAPTER 25
NUCLEAR CHEMISTRY
PRACTICE EXAMPLES

1A   **(E)** A β^- has a mass number of zero and an "atomic number" of -1. Emission of this electron has the effect of transforming a neutron into a proton. $^{241}_{94}\text{Pu} \rightarrow ^{241}_{95}\text{Am} + ^{0}_{-1}\beta$

1B   **(E)** ^{58}Ni has a mass number of 58 and an atomic number of 28. A positron has a mass number of 0 and an effective atomic number of $+1$. Emission of a positron has the seeming effect of transforming a proton into a neutron. The parent nuclide must be copper-58.

$^{58}_{29}\text{Cu} \rightarrow ^{58}_{28}\text{Ni} + ^{0}_{+1}\beta$

2A   **(E)** The sum of the mass numbers $(139 + 12 = ? + 147)$ tells us that the other product species has $A = 4$. The atomic number of La is 57, that of C is 6, and that of Eu is 63. The atomic number sum $(57 + 6 = ? + 63)$ indicates that the atomic number of this product species is zero. Therefore, four neutrons must have been emitted. $^{139}_{57}\text{La} + ^{12}_{6}\text{C} \rightarrow ^{147}_{63}\text{Eu} + 4^{0}_{1}n$

2B   **(E)** An alpha particle is $^{4}_{2}\text{He}$ and a positron is $^{0}_{+1}\beta$. We note that the total mass number in the first equation is 125; the mass number of the additional product is 1.
The total atomic number is 53; the atomic number of the additional product is 0; it is a neutron. $^{121}_{51}\text{Sb} + ^{4}_{2}\text{He} \rightarrow ^{124}_{53}\text{I} + ^{1}_{0}\text{n}$

In the second equation, the positron has a mass number of 0, meaning that the mass number of the product is 124. Because the atomic number of the positron is $+1$, that of the product is 52; it is $^{124}_{52}\text{Te}$.

$^{124}_{53}\text{I} \rightarrow ^{0}_{+1}\beta + ^{124}_{52}\text{Te}$

3A   **(M) (a)**   The decay constant is found from the 8.040-day half-life.

$$\lambda = \frac{0.693}{8.040 \text{ d}} = 0.0862 \text{ d}^{-1} \times \frac{1 \text{ d}}{24 \text{ h}} \times \frac{1 \text{ h}}{60 \text{ min}} \times \frac{1 \text{ min}}{60 \text{ s}} = 9.98 \times 10^{-7} \text{ s}^{-1}$$

     (b)   The number of ^{131}I atoms is used to find the activity.

$$\text{no.}^{131}\text{I atoms} = 2.05 \text{ mg} \times \frac{1 \text{ g}}{1000 \text{ mg}} \times \frac{1 \text{ mol}^{131}\text{ I}}{131 \text{ g}^{131}\text{ I}} \times \frac{6.022 \times 10^{23} \text{ atoms}}{1 \text{ mol}^{131}\text{ I}}$$

$$= 9.42 \times 10^{18} \text{ atoms}^{131}\text{I}$$

$$\text{activity} = \lambda N = 9.98 \times 10^{-7} \text{ s}^{-1} \times 9.42 \times 10^{18} \text{ atoms} = 9.40 \times 10^{12} \text{ disintegrations / second}$$

(c) We now determine the number of atoms remaining after 16 days. Because two half-lives elapse in 16 days, the number of atoms has been halved twice, to one-fourth (25%) the original number of atoms.

$$N_t = 0.25 \times N_0 = 0.25 \times 9.42 \times 10^{18} \text{ atoms} = 2.36 \times 10^{18} \text{ atoms}$$

(d) The rate after 14 days is determined by the number of atoms present on day 14.

$$\text{rate} = \lambda N_t = 9.98 \times 10^{-7} \text{ s}^{-1} \times 2.36 \times 10^{18} \text{ atoms} = 2.36 \times 10^{12} \text{ dis/s}$$

3B **(M)** First we determine the value of λ: $\quad \lambda = \dfrac{0.693}{t_{1/2}} = \dfrac{0.693}{11.43 \text{ d}} = 0.0606 \text{ d}^{-1}$

Then we set $N_t = 1\% N_0 = 0.010 N_0$ in equation (25.12).

$$\ln \frac{N_t}{N_0} = -\lambda t = \ln \frac{0.010 N_0}{N_0} = \ln (0.010) = -4.61 = -\left(0.0608 \text{ d}^{-1}\right) t$$

$$t = \frac{-4.61}{-0.0608 \text{ d}^{-1}} = 75.8 \text{ d}$$

4A **(M)** The half-life of ^{14}C is 5730 a and $\lambda = 1.21 \times 10^{-4} \text{ a}^{-1}$. The activity of ^{14}C when the object supposedly stopped growing was 15 dis/min per g C. We use equation (25.12) with activities (λN) in place of numbers of atoms (N).

$$\ln \frac{A_t}{A_0} = -\lambda t = \ln \frac{8.5 \text{ dis / min}}{15 \text{ dis / min}} = -\left(1.21 \times 10^{-4} \text{ a}^{-1}\right) t = -0.56_8 \; ; t = \frac{0.57}{1.21 \times 10^{-4} \text{ a}^{-1}} = 4.7 \times 10^3 \text{ a}$$

4B **(M)** The half-life of ^{14}C is 5730 a and $\lambda = 1.21 \times 10^{-4} \text{ a}^{-1}$. The activity of ^{14}C when the object supposedly stopped growing was 15 dis/min per g C. We use equation (25.12) with activities (λN) in place of numbers of atoms (N).

$$\ln \frac{A_t}{A_0} = -\lambda t = \ln \frac{A_t}{15 \text{ dis / min}} = -\left(1.21 \times 10^{-4} \text{ a}^{-1}\right)(1100 \text{ a}) = -0.13$$

$$\frac{A_t}{15 \text{ dis/min}} = e^{-0.13} = 0.88 \, , A_t = 0.88 \times 15 \text{ dis/min} = 13 \text{ dis/min (per gram of C)}$$

5A **(M)** mass defect. $= 145.913053 \text{ u} \left(^{146} \text{Sm}\right) - 141.907719 \text{ u} \left(^{142} \text{Nd}\right) - 4.002603 \text{ u} \left(^4 \text{He}\right) = 0.002731 \text{ u}$

Then, from the text, we have 931.5 MeV $= 1$ u $E = 0.002731 \text{ u} \times \dfrac{931.5 \text{ MeV}}{1 \text{ u}} = 2.544 \text{ MeV}$

5B **(M)** Unfortunately, we cannot use the result of Example 25–5 ($0.0045 \text{ u} = 4.2 \text{ MeV}$) because it is expressed to only two significant figures, and here we begin with four significant figures. But, we essentially work backwards through that calculation. The last conversion factor is from Table 2-1.

$$E = 5.590 \text{ MeV} \times \frac{1.602 \times 10^{-13} \text{ J}}{1 \text{ MeV}} = 8.955 \times 10^{-13} \text{ J} = mc^2 = m\left(2.9979 \times 10^8 \text{ m/s}\right)^2$$

$$m = \frac{8.955 \times 10^{-13} \text{ J}}{\left(2.9979 \times 10^8 \text{ m/s}\right)^2} \times \frac{1000 \text{ g}}{1 \text{ kg}} \times \frac{1.0073 \text{ u}}{1.673 \times 10^{-24} \text{ g}} = 0.005999 \text{ u}$$

Or we could use $m = 5.590 \text{ MeV} \times \dfrac{1 \text{ u}}{931.5 \text{ MeV}} = 0.006001 \text{ u}$

6A **(E) (a)** ^{88}Sr has an even atomic number (38) and an even neutron number (50); its mass number (88) is not too far from the average mass (87.6) of Sr. It should be stable.

(b) ^{118}Cs has an odd atomic number (55) and a mass number (118) that is pretty far from the average mass of Cs (132.9). It should be radioactive.

(c) ^{30}S has an even atomic number (16) and an even neutron number (14); but its mass number (30) is too far from the average mass of S (32.1). It should be radioactive.

6B **(M)** We know that ^{19}F is stable, with approximately the same number of neutrons and protons: 9 protons, and 10 neutrons. Thus, nuclides of light elements with approximately the same number of neutrons and protons should be stable. In Practice Example 25–1 we saw that positron emission has the effect of transforming a proton into a neutron. β^- emission has the opposite effect, namely, the transformation of a neutron into a proton. The mass number does not change in either case. Now let us analyze our two nuclides.

^{17}F has 9 protons and 8 neutrons. Replacing a proton with a neutron would produce a more stable nuclide. Thus, we predict positron emission by ^{17}F to produce ^{17}O.

^{22}F has 9 protons and 13 neutrons. Replacing a neutron with a proton would produce a more stable nuclide. Thus, we predict β^- emission by ^{22}F to produce ^{22}Ne.

INTEGRATIVE EXAMPLE

A. **(M)** $\lambda = \dfrac{0.693}{1.26 \times 10^9 \text{ a}} = 5.50 \times 10^{-10} \text{ a}^{-1}$ Calculate the fraction of ^{40}K that remains after 1.5×10^9 a.

$$\ln \frac{N_t}{N_0} = -\lambda t = -5.50 \times 10^{-10} \text{ a}^{-1} \times 1.5 \times 10^9 \text{ a} = -0.83 \qquad \frac{N_t}{N_0} = 0.44$$

Thus, the fraction of ^{40}K that has decayed is $1.000 - 0.44 = 0.56$.

The fraction of the ^{40}K that has decayed into ^{40}Ar is $0.110 \times 0.56 = 0.062$.

This fraction is proportional to the mass of ^{40}Ar. Then the ratio of masses is determined.

$$\frac{\text{mass } ^{40}Ar}{\text{mass } ^{40}K} = \frac{0.062}{0.44} = 0.14$$

B. **(M) (a)** $Zr(s) + 6H_2O(l) \rightarrow ZrO_2(s) + 4 H_3O^+(aq) + 4 e^-$ 1.43 V

         $4 H_2O(l) + 4 e^- \rightarrow 2 H_2(g) + 4 OH^-(aq)$ -0.828 V

         $Zr(s) + 2 H_2O(l) \rightarrow ZrO_2(s) + 2 H_2(g)$ 0.602 V (spont)

     Yes, Zr can reduce water under standard conditions.

(b) $E° = \frac{0.0592}{z} \ln K_{eq}$ $0.602 \text{ V} = \frac{0.0592}{4} \ln K_{eq}$ $K_{eq} = 4.67 \times 10^{40}$

(c) $pH = 7$ Therefore, $[OH^-] = [H_3O^+] = 1.0 \times 10^{-7}$

     $E_{ox} = E°_{ox} - \frac{0.0257}{z} \ln Q = 1.43 \text{ V} - \frac{0.0257}{4} \ln (1.0 \times 10^{-7})^4 = 1.84 \text{ V}$

     $E_{red} = E°_{red} - \frac{0.0257}{z} \ln Q = -0.828 \text{ V} - \frac{0.0257}{4} \ln (1 \times 10^{-7})^4 = -0.414 \text{ V}$

     $E_{cell} = E_{ox} + E_{red} = 1.84 + (-0.414) = 1.43 \text{ V}$ (spontaneous)

(d)   Zr may be the culprit responsible for the $H_2(g)$ formation. In the Chernobyl accident, the reaction of carbon with superheated steam played a major role.
     Reaction: $H_2O(g) + C(s) \rightarrow CO_{(g)} + H_2(g)$

EXERCISES

Radioactive Processes

1.   **(E) (a)** $^{55}_{26}Fe \rightarrow ^{55}_{27}Co + ^{0}_{-1}e$

    (b) $^{238}_{92}U \rightarrow ^{234}_{90}Th + ^{4}_{2}He$

    (c) $^{222}_{86}Rn \rightarrow ^{218}_{84}Po + ^{4}_{2}He$; $^{218}_{84}Po \rightarrow ^{214}_{82}Pb + ^{4}_{2}He$

    (d) $^{64}_{29}Cu \rightarrow ^{64}_{30}Zn + ^{0}_{-1}e$; $^{64}_{30}Zn \rightarrow ^{64}_{31}Ga + ^{0}_{-1}e$

2.   **(E) (a)** $^{214}_{82}Pb \rightarrow ^{214}_{83}Bi + ^{0}_{-1}e$; $^{214}_{83}Bi \rightarrow ^{214}_{84}Po + ^{0}_{-1}e$

    (b) $^{226}_{88}Ra \rightarrow ^{222}_{86}Rn + ^{4}_{2}He$; $^{222}_{86}Rn \rightarrow ^{218}_{84}Po + ^{4}_{2}He$; $^{218}_{84}Po \rightarrow ^{214}_{82}Pb + ^{4}_{2}He$

    (c) $^{69}_{33}As \rightarrow ^{69}_{32}Ge + ^{0}_{+1}e$

3. **(E)** We would expect a neutron:proton ratio that is closer to 1:1 than that of ^{14}C. This would be achieved if the product were ^{14}N, which is the result of β^- decay: $^{14}_{6}C \rightarrow {}^{14}_{7}N + {}^{0}_{-1}e$.

4. **(E)** A nuclide with a closer to 1:1 neutron:proton ratio (than that of tritium) is helium-3, arrived at by beta emission: $^{3}_{1}H \rightarrow {}^{3}_{2}He + {}^{0}_{-1}e$. Another possible product is deuterium, which is arrived at by neutron emission: $^{3}_{1}H \rightarrow {}^{2}_{1}H + {}^{1}_{0}n$

Radioactive Decay Series

5. **(M)** We first write conventional nuclear reactions for each step in the decay series.

$$^{232}_{90}Th \rightarrow {}^{228}_{88}Ra + {}^{4}_{2}He \qquad {}^{228}_{88}Ra \rightarrow {}^{228}_{89}Ac + {}^{0}_{-1}e \qquad {}^{228}_{89}Ac \rightarrow {}^{228}_{90}Th + {}^{0}_{-1}e$$

$$^{228}_{90}Th \rightarrow {}^{224}_{88}Ra + {}^{4}_{2}He \qquad {}^{224}_{88}Ra \rightarrow {}^{220}_{86}Rn + {}^{4}_{2}He \qquad {}^{220}_{86}Rn \rightarrow {}^{216}_{84}Po + {}^{4}_{2}He$$

Now for a branch in the series:

these two $\qquad {}^{216}_{84}Po \rightarrow {}^{212}_{82}Pb + {}^{4}_{2}He \qquad {}^{212}_{82}Pb \rightarrow {}^{212}_{83}Bi + {}^{0}_{-1}e$

or these two $\qquad {}^{216}_{84}Po \rightarrow {}^{216}_{85}At + {}^{0}_{-1}e \qquad {}^{216}_{85}At \rightarrow {}^{212}_{83}Bi + {}^{4}_{2}He$

And now a second branch:

these two $\qquad {}^{212}_{83}Bi \rightarrow {}^{208}_{81}Tl + {}^{4}_{2}He \qquad {}^{208}_{81}Tl \rightarrow {}^{208}_{82}Pb + {}^{0}_{-1}e$

or these two $\qquad {}^{212}_{83}Bi \rightarrow {}^{212}_{84}Po + {}^{0}_{-1}e \qquad {}^{212}_{84}Po \rightarrow {}^{208}_{82}Pb + {}^{4}_{2}He$

Both branches end at the isotope $^{208}_{82}Pb$. The graph, similar to Figure 25-2, is drawn below.

6. **(M)** The series begins with uranium-235, and ends with lead-207.

$$^{235}_{92}U \rightarrow \,^{231}_{90}Th + \,^4_2He \qquad\qquad ^{231}_{90}Th \rightarrow \,^{231}_{91}Pa + \,^0_{-1}e \qquad\qquad ^{231}_{91}Pa \rightarrow \,^{227}_{89}Ac + \,^4_2He$$

Now the series branches:

these two $\qquad\qquad ^{227}_{89}Ac \rightarrow \,^{223}_{87}Fr + \,^4_2He \qquad\qquad ^{223}_{87}Fr \rightarrow \,^{223}_{88}Ra + \,^0_{-1}e$

or these two $\qquad ^{227}_{89}Ac \rightarrow \,^{227}_{90}Th + \,^0_{-1}e \qquad\qquad ^{227}_{90}Th \rightarrow \,^{223}_{88}Ra + \,^4_2He$

then $^{223}_{88}Ra \rightarrow \,^{219}_{86}Rn + \,^4_2He \qquad\qquad ^{219}_{86}Rn \rightarrow \,^{215}_{84}Po + \,^4_2He \qquad\qquad ^{215}_{84}Po \rightarrow \,^{211}_{82}Pb + \,^4_2He$

$$^{211}_{82}Pb \rightarrow \,^{211}_{83}Bi + \,^0_{-1}e$$

The series branches again:

these two $\qquad\qquad ^{211}_{83}Bi \rightarrow \,^{207}_{81}Tl + \,^4_2He \qquad\qquad ^{207}_{81}Tl \rightarrow \,^{207}_{82}Pb + \,^0_{-1}e$

or these two $\qquad\quad ^{211}_{83}Bi \rightarrow \,^{211}_{84}Po + \,^0_{-1}e \qquad\qquad ^{211}_{84}Po \rightarrow \,^{207}_{82}Pb + \,^4_2He$

The plot of atomic mass versus atomic number for these decay series is shown below.

7. **(E)** In Figure 25–2, only the following mass numbers are represented: 206, 210, 214, 218, 222, 226, 230, 234, and 238. We see that these mass numbers are separated from each other by 4 units. The first of them, 206, equals $(4 \times 51) + 2$, that is $4n + 2$, where $n = 51$.

8. **(M)** The series to which each nuclide belongs is determined by dividing its mass number by 4 and obtaining the remainder.

  (a) The mass number of $^{214}_{83}Bi$ is 214, and the remainder following its division by 4 is 2. This nuclide is a member of the $4n + 2$ series.

  (b) The mass number of $^{216}_{84}Po$ is 216, and the remainder following its division by 4 is 0. This nuclide is a member of the $4n$ series.

(c) The mass number of $^{215}_{85}\text{At}$ is 215, and the remainder following its division by 4 is 3. This nuclide is a member of the $4n+3$ series.

(d) The mass number of $^{235}_{92}\text{U}$ is 235, and the remainder following its division by 4 is 3. This nuclide is a member of the $4n+3$ series.

Nuclear Reactions

9. **(E)** **(a)** $^{160}_{74}\text{W} \rightarrow {}^{156}_{72}\text{Hf} + {}^{4}_{2}\text{He}$ **(b)** $^{38}_{17}\text{Cl} \rightarrow {}^{38}_{18}\text{Ar} + {}^{0}_{-1}\beta$

     (c) $^{214}_{83}\text{Bi} \rightarrow {}^{214}_{84}\text{Po} + {}^{0}_{-1}\beta$ **(d)** $^{32}_{17}\text{Cl} \rightarrow {}^{32}_{16}\text{S} + {}^{0}_{+1}\beta$

10. **(E)** **(a)** $^{27}_{13}\text{Al} + {}^{4}_{2}\text{He} \rightarrow {}^{30}_{15}\text{P} + {}^{1}_{0}\text{n}$ **(b)** $^{63}_{29}\text{Cu} + {}^{2}_{1}\text{H} \rightarrow {}^{63}_{30}\text{Zn} + 2{}^{1}_{0}\text{n}$

     (c) $^{236}_{92}\text{U} + {}^{1}_{0}\text{n} \rightarrow {}^{95}_{42}\text{Mo} + {}^{140}_{50}\text{Sn} + 2{}^{1}_{0}\text{n}$ **(d)** $^{31}_{15}\text{P} + {}^{1}_{1}\text{H} \rightarrow {}^{28}_{14}\text{Si} + {}^{4}_{2}\text{He}$

     (e) $^{11}_{5}\text{B} + {}^{4}_{2}\text{He} \rightarrow {}^{14}_{7}\text{N} + {}^{1}_{0}\text{n}$

11. **(E)** **(a)** $^{7}_{3}\text{Li} + {}^{1}_{1}\text{H} \rightarrow {}^{8}_{4}\text{Be} + \gamma$ **(b)** $^{9}_{4}\text{Be} + {}^{2}_{1}\text{H} \rightarrow {}^{10}_{5}\text{B} + {}^{1}_{0}\text{n}$

     (c) $^{14}_{7}\text{N} + {}^{1}_{0}\text{n} \rightarrow {}^{14}_{6}\text{C} + {}^{1}_{1}\text{H}$

12. **(E)** **(a)** $^{238}_{92}\text{U} + {}^{4}_{2}\text{He} \rightarrow {}^{239}_{94}\text{Pu} + 3{}^{1}_{0}\text{n}$ **(b)** $^{3}_{1}\text{H} + {}^{2}_{1}\text{H} \rightarrow {}^{4}_{2}\text{He} + {}^{1}_{0}\text{n}$

     (c) $^{33}_{16}\text{S} + {}^{1}_{0}\text{n} \rightarrow {}^{33}_{15}\text{P} + {}^{1}_{1}\text{H}$

13. **(E)** $^{238}_{92}\text{U} + {}^{2}_{1}\text{H} \rightarrow {}^{238}_{93}\text{Np} + 2{}^{1}_{0}\text{n}$; $^{238}_{93}\text{Np} \rightarrow 5{}^{4}_{2}\text{He} + {}^{218}_{83}\text{Bi}$

14. **(E)** $^{208}_{82}\text{Pb} + {}^{86}_{36}\text{Kr} \rightarrow {}^{293}_{118}\text{E} + {}^{1}_{0}\text{n}$; $^{293}_{118}\text{E} \rightarrow 6{}^{4}_{2}\text{He} + {}^{269}_{106}\text{Sg}$

15. **(M)** $^{48}_{20}\text{Ca} + {}^{249}_{98}\text{Cf} \rightarrow {}^{249}_{118}\text{Unk} + {}^{1}_{0}n + {}^{1}_{0}n + {}^{1}_{0}n$

16. **(M)** $^{293}_{118}\text{Lv} \rightarrow {}^{289}_{116}\text{Lv} + {}^{4}\text{He}$

17. **(M)** $^{58}_{26}\text{Fe} + {}^{244}_{94}\text{Pu} \rightarrow {}^{302}_{120}\text{Unk}$

18. **(M)** $^{238}_{92}\text{U} + {}^{64}_{28}\text{Ni} \rightarrow {}^{302}_{120}\text{Unk}$

Rate of Radioactive Decay

19. **(M)**

     (a) related Since the decay constant is inversely to the half-life, the nuclide with the smallest half-life also has the largest value of its decay constant. This is the nuclide $^{214}_{84}\text{Po}$, with a half-life of 1.64×10^{-4} s.

     (b) The nuclide that displays a 75% reduction in its radioactivity has passed through two half-lives in a period of one month. Thus, this is the nuclide with a half-life of approximately two weeks. This is the nuclide $^{32}_{15}\text{P}$, with a half-life of 14.3 days.

(c) If more than 99% of the radioactivity is lost, less than 1% remains. Thus $(\frac{1}{2})^n < 0.010$. Now, when $n = 7$, $(\frac{1}{2})^n = 0.0078$. Thus, seven half-lives have elapsed in one month, and each half-life approximates 4.3 days. The longest lived nuclide that fits this description is $^{222}_{86}Rn$, which has a half-life of 3.823 days. Of course, all other nuclides with shorter half-lives also meet this criterion, specifically the following nuclides: $^{13}_{8}O\left(8.7\times10^{-3} \text{ s}\right)$, $^{28}_{12}Mg\left(21 \text{ h}\right)$, $^{80}_{35}Br\left(17.6\text{min}\right)$ and $^{214}_{84}Po\left(1.64\times10^{-4} \text{ s}\right)$.

20. **(M)** Since $16 = 2^4$, four half-lives have elapsed in 18.0 h, and each half-life equals 4.50 h. The half-life of isotope B thus is $2.5 \times 4.50 \text{ h} = 11.25 \text{ h}$. Now, since $32 = 2^5$, five half-lives must elapse before the decay rate of isotope B falls to $\frac{1}{32}$ of its original value. Thus, the time elapsed for this amount of decay is:

$$\text{time elapsed} = 5 \text{ half-lives} \times \frac{11.25}{1 \text{ half-life}} = 56.3 \text{ h}$$

21. **(M)** We use equation (25.13) to determine λ and then equation (25.11) to determine the number of atoms.

$$t_{1/2} = \frac{0.693}{\lambda} \Rightarrow \lambda = \frac{0.693}{t_{1/2}} = \frac{0.693}{3.30 \text{ year}} \times \frac{1 \text{ year}}{365 \text{ days}} \times \frac{1 \text{ day}}{24 \text{ h}} = 2.40 \times 10^{-5} \text{ h}^{-1}$$

$$N = \frac{\text{rate of decay}}{\lambda} = \frac{4560 \text{ atoms h}^{-1}}{2.40 \times 10^{-5} \text{ h}^{-1}} = 1.90 \times 10^8 \text{atoms of } {}^{101}_{45}Rh$$

22. **(M)** This follows first-order kinetics (as do all radioactive decay processes) with a rate of decay directly proportional to the number of atoms. We therefore use equation (25.12), with rates substituted for numbers of atoms.

$$4560 \frac{\text{dis}}{\text{hr}} \times \frac{1\text{hr}}{60\text{min}} = 76 \frac{\text{dis}}{\text{min}}$$

$$\ln\frac{R_t}{R_o} = -\lambda t = \ln\frac{74 \text{ dis/min}}{76 \text{ dis/min}} = -2.40 \times 10^{-5}\text{hr}^{-1}t = -0.0267$$

$$t = \frac{0.0267}{2.40 \times 10^{-5}\text{hr}^{-1}} = 1.11 \times 10^3 \text{h} \times \frac{1 \text{ d}}{24 \text{ h}} \times \frac{1 \text{ y}}{365.25 \text{ d}} = 0.127 \text{ y}$$

23. **(M)** Let us use the first and the last values to determine the decay constant.

$$\ln\frac{R_t}{R_o} = -\lambda t = \ln\frac{138 \text{ cpm}}{1000 \text{ cpm}} = -\lambda 250 \text{ h} = -1.981 \qquad \lambda = \frac{1.981}{250 \text{ h}} = 0.00792 \text{ h}^{-1}$$

$$t_{1/2} = \frac{0.693}{\lambda} = \frac{0.693}{0.00792 \text{ h}^{-1}} = 87.5 \text{ h}$$

A slightly different value of $t_{1/2}$ may result from other combinations of R_o and R_t.

24. **(M)** First we calculate the decay constant.

$$\lambda = \frac{0.693}{1.7 \times 10^7 \text{ a}} \times \frac{1 \text{ a}}{365.25 \text{ d}} \times \frac{1 \text{ d}}{24 \text{ h}} \times \frac{1 \text{ h}}{3600 \text{ s}} = 1.3 \times 10^{-15} \text{ s}^{-1}$$

$$N = 1.00 \text{ mg } {}^{129}\text{I} \times \frac{1 \text{ g}}{1000 \text{ mg}} \times \frac{1 \text{ mol } {}^{129}\text{I}}{129 \text{ g}} \times \frac{6.022 \times 10^{23} \text{ atoms}}{1 \text{ mol } {}^{129}\text{I}} = 4.67 \times 10^{18} \text{ } {}^{129}\text{I atoms}$$

decay rate $= \lambda N = 1.3 \times 10^{-15} \text{ s}^{-1} \times 4.67 \times 10^{18} \text{ atoms} = 6.1 \times 10^3 \text{ dis/s}$

25. **(M)** ${}_{15}^{32}\text{P}$ half-life = 14.3 d. We need to determine the time necessary to get to the detectable

limit, $\frac{1}{1000}$ of the initial value. Use $\lambda = \frac{0.693}{t_{1/2}} = \frac{0.693}{14.3 \text{ d}} = 0.0485 \text{ d}^{-1}$

$$\ln\left(\frac{1}{1000}\right) = -0.0485 \text{ d}^{-1}(t) \qquad t = 142 \text{ days}$$

26. **(M)** $1.00 \text{ mCi} = 1.00 \times 10^{-3} (3.70 \times 10^{10} \text{ dis s}^{-1}) = 3.70 \times 10^7 \text{ dis s}^{-1}$

$$\lambda = \frac{0.693}{t_{1/2}} = \frac{0.693}{5730 \text{ a}} = 1.21 \times 10^{-4} \text{ a}^{-1} \quad (1 \text{ a} = 365.25 \text{ d} = 3.15\underline{6} \times 10^7 \text{ s})$$

$$\lambda = \frac{1.21 \times 10^{-4}}{\text{a}} \times \frac{1 \text{ y}}{3.15_6 \times 10^7 \text{ s}} = 3.83 \times 10^{-12} \text{ s}^{-1}$$

$1.00 \text{ mCi} = 3.70 \times 10^7 \text{ dis s}^{-1} = \lambda N = 3.83 \times 10^{-12} \text{ s}^{-1}(N)$

$N = 9.66 \times 10^{18}$ atoms of ${}^{14}\text{C}$ or $1.60\underline{4} \times 10^{-5} \text{ mol } {}^{14}\text{C}$

mass of ${}^{14}\text{C} = 1.60\underline{4} \times 10^{-5} \text{ mol } {}^{14}\text{C} \times \frac{14.00 \text{ g } {}^{14}\text{C}}{1 \text{ mol } {}^{14}\text{C}} = 2.25 \times 10^{-4} \text{ g } {}^{14}\text{C}$

Age Determinations with Radioisotopes

27. **(E)** Again we use equations (25.12) and (25.13) to determine the time elapsed. The initial rate of decay is about 15 dis/min. First we compute the decay constant.

$$\lambda = \frac{0.693}{5730 \text{ a}} = 1.21 \times 10^{-4} \text{ a}^{-1}$$

$$\ln\frac{10 \text{ dis / min}}{15 \text{ dis / min}} = -0.40_5 = -\lambda t; \qquad t = \frac{0.40_5}{1.21 \times 10^{-4} \text{ a}^{-1}} = 3.4 \times 10^3 \text{ a}$$

The object is a bit more than 3000 years old, and thus is probably not from the pyramid era, which occurred about 3000 B.C.

28. **(E)** We use the value of λ from the previous exercise.

$$\ln \frac{R_t}{R_o} = -\lambda t = -\left(1.21\times10^{-4}\ a^{-1}\right)t = \ln\frac{0.03\ \text{dis}\,\text{min}^{-1}\,\text{g}^{-1}}{15\ \text{dis}\,\text{min}^{-1}\,\text{g}^{-1}} = -6.2$$

$$t = \frac{6.2}{1.21\times10^{-4}\ a^{-1}} = 5.1\times10^{4}\ a$$

29. <u>**(M)**</u> First we determine the decay constant. $\lambda = \dfrac{0.693}{1.40\times10^{10}\ a} = 4.99\times10^{-11}\ a^{-1}$

Then we can determine the ratio of (N_t), the number of thorium atoms after 2.7×10^{9} a, to (N_0), the initial number of thorium atoms:

$$\ln\frac{N_t}{N_0} = -kt = -\left(4.99\times10^{-11}\ a^{-1}\right)\left(2.7\times10^{9}\ a\right) = -0.13 \qquad \frac{N_t}{N_0} = 0.88$$

Thus, for every mole of ^{232}Th present initially, after 2.7×10^{9} a there are

0.88 mol ^{232}Th and 0.12 mol ^{208}Pb. From this information, we can compute the mass ratio.

$$\frac{0.12\ \text{mol}\ ^{208}\text{Pb}}{0.88\ \text{mol}\ ^{232}\text{Th}} \times \frac{1\ \text{mol}\ ^{232}\text{Th}}{232\ \text{g}\ ^{232}\text{Th}} \times \frac{208\ \text{g}\ ^{208}\text{Pb}}{1\ \text{mol}\ ^{208}\text{Pb}} = \frac{0.12\ \text{g}\ ^{208}\text{Pb}}{1\ \text{g}\ ^{232}\text{Th}}$$

30. **(M)** First we determine the decay constant. $\lambda = \dfrac{0.693}{1.39\times10^{10}\ a} = 4.99\times10^{-11}\ a^{-1}$

The rock currently contains 1.00 g ^{232}Th and 0.25 g ^{208}Pb. We can calculate the mass of ^{232}Th that must have been present to produce this 0.25 g ^{208}Pb, and from that find the original mass of ^{232}Th.

$$\text{original mass } ^{232}\text{Th} = 1.00\ \text{g}\ ^{232}\text{Th now} + \left(0.25\ \text{g}\ ^{208}\text{Pb}\times\frac{232\ \text{g}\ ^{232}\text{Th}}{208\ \text{g}\ ^{208}\text{Pb}}\right)$$

$$= (1.00+0.28)\ \text{g} = 1.28\ \text{g}$$

$$\ln\frac{N_t}{N_0} = -\lambda t = \ln\frac{1.00\ \text{g}\ ^{232}\text{Th now}}{1.28\ \text{g originally}} = -0.247 = -4.99\times10^{-11}\ a^{-1}t;$$

$$t = \frac{0.247}{4.99\times10^{-11}\ a^{-1}} = 4.95\times10^{9}\ a$$

31. <u>**(M)**</u> First convert argon-40 to the number of atoms/g in the sample. Next, convert % potassium to atoms/g in the sample. Finally, use equation (25.21) to determine the final answer 3.03×10^{9} a.

32. **(M)** To find the age of a piece of volcanic rock, we use equations (25.13) and (25.18):

$$\lambda_{\beta\text{-decay}} = \frac{0.693}{1.26\times10^{9}\,\text{year}} = 5.50\times10^{-10}\,\text{year}^{-1} \text{ and } \lambda_{\text{electron capt.}} = \frac{0.693}{1.4\times10^{9}\,\text{y}} = 4.95\times10^{-10}\,\text{year}^{-1}$$

$$t = \frac{1}{\lambda_{\varepsilon}+\lambda_{\beta}}\ln\left[\frac{^{40}Ar}{^{40}K}\left(\frac{\lambda_{\varepsilon}+\lambda_{\beta}}{\lambda_{\varepsilon}}+1\right)\right]$$

$$t = \frac{1}{(5.50\times10^{-10}+4.95\times10^{-10})\,\text{year}^{-1}}\ln\left[1.9\times\left(\frac{5.50\times10^{-10}+4.95\times10^{-10}}{4.95\times10^{-10}}+1\right)\right] = 1.7\times10^{9}\,\text{years}$$

Energetics of Nuclear Reactions

33. **(M)** The principal equation that we shall employ is $E = mc^2$, along with conversion factors.

(a) $E = 6.02\times10^{-23}\ \text{g}\times\dfrac{1\ \text{kg}}{1000\ \text{g}}\times\left(3.00\times10^{8}\ \text{m/s}\right)^2 = 5.42\times10^{-9}\ \text{kg m}^2\ \text{s}^{-2} = 5.42\times10^{-9}\ \text{J}$

(b) $E = 4.0015\ \text{u}\times\dfrac{931.5\ \text{MeV}}{1\ \text{u}} = 3727\ \text{MeV}$

34. **(M)** mass of individual particles $= \left(47\ \text{p}\times\dfrac{1.0073\ \text{u}}{1\ \text{p}}\right) + \left(60\ \text{n}\times\dfrac{1.0087\ \text{u}}{1\ \text{n}}\right)$

$$= 47.3431\ \text{u} + 60.5220\ \text{u} = 107.8651\ \text{u}$$

$$\frac{\text{binding energy}}{\text{nucleon}} = \frac{107.8651\ \text{u} - 106.879289\ \text{u}}{107\ \text{nucleons}}\times\frac{931.5\ \text{MeV}}{1\ \text{u}} = 8.58\ \text{MeV / nucleon}$$

35. **(E)** The mass defect is the difference between the mass of the nuclide and the sum of the masses of its constituent particles. The binding energy is this mass defect expressed as an energy.

particle mass $\quad = 9\,p + 10\,n + 9\,e = 9\left(p+n+e\right)+n$

$$= 9\left(1.0073 + 1.0087 + 0.0005486\right)\ \text{u} + 1.0087\ \text{u} = 19.1576\ \text{u}$$

mass defect $= 19.1576\ \text{u} - 18.998403\ \text{u} = 0.1592\ \text{u}$

binding energy per nucleon $= \dfrac{0.1592\ \text{u}\times\dfrac{931.5\,\text{MeV}}{1\text{u}}}{19\ \text{nucleons}} = 7.805\ \text{MeV/nucleon}$

36. **(E)** The mass defect is the difference between the mass of the nuclide and the sum of the masses of its constituent particles. The binding energy is this mass defect expressed as an energy.

particle mass $\quad = 26\,p + 30\,n + 26\,e = 26\left(p+n+e\right)+4n$

$$= 26\left(1.0073 + 1.0087 + 0.0005486\right)\ \text{u} + 4\times1.0087\ \text{u} = 56.4651\ \text{u}$$

mass defect $= 56.4651 \text{ u} - 55.934939 \text{ u} = 0.5302 \text{ u}$

$$\text{binding energy per nucleon } = \frac{0.5302 \,\text{u} \times \dfrac{931.5 \,\text{MeV}}{1\text{u}}}{56 \,\text{nucleons}} = 8.819 \text{ MeV/nucleon}$$

37. **(E)** mass defect $= (10.01294 \text{ u} + 4.00260 \text{ u}) - (13.00335 \text{ u} + 1.00783 \text{ u}) = 0.00436 \text{ u}$

energy $= 0.00436 \text{ u} \times \dfrac{931.5 \text{ MeV}}{1 \text{ u}} = 4.06 \text{ MeV}$

38. **(E)** mass defect $= (6.01513 \text{ u} + 1.008665 \text{ u}) - (4.00260 \text{ u} + 3.01604 \text{ u}) = 0.00516 \text{ u}$

energy $= 0.00516 \text{ u} \times \dfrac{931.5 \text{ MeV}}{1 \text{ u}} = 4.81 \text{ MeV}$

39. **(E)** 1 neutron $\approx$ 1 amu $= 1.66 \times 10^{-27}$ kg

$E = mc^2 = 1.66 \times 10^{-27} \text{ kg}(2.998 \times 10^8 \text{ m s}^{-1})^2 = 1.49 \times 10^{-10}$ J (1 neutron)

1 eV $= 1.602 \times 10^{-19}$ J,

Hence, 1 neutron $= 1.49 \times 10^{-10}$ J $\times \dfrac{1 \text{ eV}}{1.602 \times 10^{-19} \text{ J}} = 9.30 \times 10^8$ eV or 930. MeV

6.75×10^6 MeV $\times \dfrac{1 \text{ neutron}}{930 \text{ MeV}} = 7.26 \times 10^3$ neutrons

40. **(M)** $\beta^+ + \beta^-$ collide $\rightarrow$ produce two γ-rays.

Basically the mass of $\beta^+ = \beta^- =$ mass of an electron (9.11×10^{-31} kg)
Each γ-ray has the same energy as the complete conversion of one electron into pure energy.
$E = mc^2 = (9.11 \times 10^{-31}$ kg$) (2.998 \times 10^8$ m s$^{-1})^2 = 8.19 \times 10^{-14}$ J
In electron volts: 8.19×10^{-14} J $\times \dfrac{1 \text{ eV}}{1.602 \times 10^{-19} \text{ J}} = 5.11 \times 10^5$ eV or 0.511 MeV
Each γ-ray has an energy of 0.511 MeV

Nuclear Stability

41. **(E) (a)** We expect ^{20}Ne to be more stable than ^{22}Ne. A neutron-to-proton ratio of 1-to-1 is associated with stability for elements of low atomic number (with $Z \leq 20$).

(b) We expect ^{18}O to be more stable than ^{17}O. An even number of protons and an even number of neutrons are associated with a stable isotope.

(c) We expect ^{7}Li to be more stable than ^{6}Li. Both isotopes have an odd number of protons, but only ^{7}Li has an even number of neutrons.

42. **(E) (a)** We expect ^{40}Ca to be more stable than ^{42}Ca. A neutron-to-proton ratio of 1-to-1 is associated with stability for elements of low atomic number (with $Z \le 20$).

(b) We expect ^{31}P to be more stable than ^{32}P. Both isotopes have an odd number of protons, but only ^{31}P has an even number of neutrons.

(c) We expect ^{64}Zn to be more stable than ^{63}Zn. An even number of protons and an even number of neutrons are associated with a stable isotope.

43. **(M)** β^- emission has the effect of "converting" a neutron to a proton. β^+ emission, on the other hand, has the effect of "converting" a proton to a neutron.

(a) The most stable isotope of phosphorus is ^{31}P, with a neutron-to-proton ratio of close to 1-to-1 and an even number of neutrons. Thus, ^{29}P has "too few" neutrons, or too many protons. It should decay by β^+ emission. In contrast, ^{33}P has "too many" neutrons, or "too few" protons. Therefore, ^{33}P should decay by β^- emission.

(b) Based on the atomic mass of I (126.90447), we expect the isotopes of iodine to have mass numbers close to 127. This means that ^{120}I has "too few" neutrons and therefore should decay by β^+ emission, whereas ^{134}I has "too many" neutrons (or "too few" protons) and therefore should decay by β^- emission.

44. **(M)** β^- emission has the effect of converting a neutron to a proton, while β^+ emission has the effect of converting a proton to a neutron.

(a) Based on the fact that elements of low atomic number have about the same number of protons as neutrons, $^{28}_{15}$P—with 15 protons and 13 neutrons—has too few neutrons. Therefore, it should decay by β^+ emission.

(b) Once again, elements of low atomic number have about the same number of protons as neutrons. $^{45}_{19}$K with 19 protons and 26 neutrons—has too many neutrons. Therefore, it should decay by β^- emission.

(c) Based on the atomic mass of zinc (65.39) we expect most of its isotopes to have about 36 neutrons. There are 42 neutrons in $^{72}_{30}$Zn, more than we expect. Thus we expect this nuclide to decay by β^- emission.

45. **(M)** A "doubly magic" nuclide is one in which the atomic number is a magic number (2, 8, 20, 28, 50, 82, 114) and the number of neutrons also is a magic number (2, 8, 20, 28, 50, 82, 126, 184). Nuclides that fit this description are given below.

Nuclide	^{4}He	^{16}O	^{40}Ca	^{56}Ni	^{208}Pb
No. of protons	2	8	20	28	82
No. of neutrons	2	8	20	28	126

46. **(M)** For isotopes of high atomic number, stable nuclides are characterized by a neutron-to-proton ratio greater than 1, which increases with increasing atomic number. Naturally occurring isotopes of high atomic number decrease their atomic number by losing an alpha particle, which has a neutron-to-proton ratio of 1. This leaves the neutron-to-proton ratio for the daughter that is higher than that of the parent, when it should be slightly lower. In order to redress this, the number of neutrons needs to be decreased and the number of protons increased. Beta emission accomplishes this. In contrast, artificially produced isotopes have no definite neutron-to-proton ratio. Thus, sometimes, the number of neutrons needs to be decreased, which is accomplished by beta emission, while at other times the number of protons needs to be decreased, which is accomplished by positron emission.

Fission and Fusion

47. **(E)** We use the conversion factor between number of curies and mass of ^{131}I which was developed in the Integrative Example.

$$\text{no. g } ^{131}I = 170 \text{ curies} \times \frac{18.8 \text{ g } ^{131}I}{2.33 \times 10^6 \text{ curie}} = 1.37 \times 10^{-3} \text{ g} = 1.37 \text{ mg}$$

48. **(M)** Nuclear fission is the process by which a heavy nucleus disintegrates into neutrons and stable nuclei with smaller mass numbers. For instance, uranium-238 undergoes fission according to the equation

$$^{238}_{92}U \rightarrow ^{234}_{90}Th + ^{4}_{2}He$$

The nuclear binding energy for uranium-238 is less than the sum of the binding energies for thorium-234 and helium-4. Consequently, when a uranium-238 nucleus splits apart, energy is released. Nuclear fusion, by contrast, involves the amalgamation of light nuclei into heavier, more stable nuclei. For instance, part of the energy released by our Sun is believed to come from the fusion of hydrogen to form deuterium:

$$^{1}_{1}H + ^{1}_{1}H \rightarrow ^{2}_{1}H + ^{0}_{-1}e$$

Although both fusion and fission release vast amounts of energy, fusion releases far more energy on a per nucleon basis. To understand why this is so, we need to refer to Figure 25-6, which is a plot of average binding energy per nucleon as a function of atomic number. The graph clearly shows that the increase in binding energy observed for the formation of the lightest nuclides (e.g., deuterium, tritium, helium-3) is much more dramatic than the decrease in binding energy that is seen for the fragmentation of heavier nuclei such as uranium-235. Thus, the plot indicates that more energy should be released by the combination of light nuclei (nuclear fusion) than by the disintegration of heavy nuclei (nuclear fission).

Effect of Radiation on Matter

49. **(E)** The term "rem" is an acronym for "radiation equivalent-man," and takes into account the quantity of biological damage done by a given dosage of radiation. On the other hand, the rad is the dosage that places 0.010 J of energy into each kilogram of irradiated matter. Thus, for living tissue, the rem provides a good idea of how much tissue damage a certain kind and quantity of radiation damage will do. But for nonliving materials, the rad is usually preferred, and indeed is often the only unit of utility.

50. **(M)** Low-level radiation is very close in its dosage to background radiation and one problem is to separate out the effects of the two sources (low-level and background). The other problem is that low-level radiation does not produce severe damage in a short period of time. Thus the effects of low-level radiation will only be observed over a long time period. Of course other effects, such as chemical and biological toxins, will also be observed over these time periods, and we have to try to separate these two types of effects. (There also is the genetic heritage of the organism to consider, of course.)

51. **(M)** One reason why ^{90}Sr is hazardous is because strontium is in the same family of the periodic table as calcium, and hence often reacts in a similar fashion to calcium. The most likely place for calcium to be incorporated into the body is in bones, where it resides for a long time. Strontium is expected to behave in a similar fashion. Thus, it will be retained in the body for a long time. Bone is an especially dangerous place for a radioisotope to be present—even if it has low penetrating power, as do β^- rays—because blood cells are produced in bone marrow.

52. **(M)** It is not particularly hazardous to be near a flask of ^{222}Rn, because it is unlikely that the alpha particles can get through the walls of the flask. (Note that since radon is a gas, the flask must be sealed.) The decay products of ^{222}Rn may produce other forms of radiation that are more penetrating, such as β^- particles and γ rays, so being near the flask may still pose a risk. ^{222}Rn can be potentially hazardous if one breathes the gas.

Applications of Radioisotopes

53. **(M)** Mix a small amount of tritium with the $H_2(g)$ and detect where the radioactivity appears with a Geiger counter.

54. **(M)** In neutron activation analysis, the sample is bombarded with neutrons. Radioisotopes are produced by this process. These radioisotopes can be easily detected even in very small quantities, much smaller, in fact, than the quantities that can be detected by conventional means of quantitative analysis. These radioisotopes are produced in quantities that are proportional to the quantity of each element originally present in the sample. And each radioisotope is characteristic of the element from which it was produced by neutron bombardment. Even microscopic samples can be analyzed by this technique. Finally, neutron activation analysis is a nondestructive technique, while the conventional techniques of precipitation or titration require that all of the sample, or at least part of it, be destroyed.

55. **(M)** The recovered sample will be radioactive. When NaCl(s) and $NaNO_3(s)$ are dissolved in solution, the ions (Na^+, Cl^-, and NO_3^-) are free to move throughout the solution. A given anion does not remain associated with a particular cation. Thus, all the anions and cations are shuffled and some of the radioactive ^{24}Na will end up in the crystallized $NaNO_3$.

56. (M) We would expect the tritium label to appear in both the $NH_3(g)$ and $H_2O(l)$. When $NH_4^+(aq)$ is formed, one of the four chemically and spatially equivalent H atoms is occasionally a tritium atom. In the subsequent reaction between the marked NH_4Cl and NaOH to form $NH_3(g)$ and $H_2O(l)$, there are three chances in four that a tritium atom will remain attached to N in NH_3, and one chance in four that a tritium ion will react with a hydroxide ion to form $H_2O(l)$.

INTEGRATIVE AND ADVANCED EXERCISES

57. (M) In the cases where rounding off the atomic mass produces the mass number of the most stable isotope, there often is but one stable isotope. This frequently is the case when the atomic number of the element is an odd number. For instance, think of situation with ^{39}K ($Z = 19$) and ^{85}Rb ($Z = 37$), but not ^{88}Sr ($Z = 38$). In the cases where this technique of rounding does not work, there are two or more stable isotopes of significant abundance. Note that the rounding off does not work in situations where it predicts a nuclide with an odd number of neutrons and an odd number of protons (such as ^{64}Cu with 29 protons and 35 neutrons), whereas the rounding off technique works when the predicted nuclide has an even number of protons, an even number of neutrons, or both.

58. (M) Each α particle contains two protons and has a mass number of 4. Thus each α particle emission reduces the mass number by 4 and the atomic number by 2. The emission of 8 α particles would reduce the mass number by 32 and the atomic number by 16. Thus the overall reaction would be as follows: $^{238}_{92}U \longrightarrow 8\,^{4}_{2}He + ^{206}_{76}Os$ (76 protons and 130 neutrons). In Figure 25-7, a nuclide with 76 protons and 130 neutrons lies above, to the left of the belt of stability; it is radioactive.

59. (M) We use $\Delta H_f^\circ[CO_2(g)] = -393.51$ kJ/mol as the heat of combustion of 1 mole of carbon. In the text, the energy produced by the fission of 1.00 g ^{235}U is determined as 8.20×10^7 kJ.

metric tons of coal required $= 1.00$ kg $^{235}U \times \dfrac{1000\ g}{1\ kg} \times \dfrac{8.20 \times 10^7\ kJ}{1.00\ g\ ^{235}U} \times \dfrac{1\ mol\ C}{393.5\ kJ} \times \dfrac{12.01\ g\ C}{1\ mol\ C}$

$\times \dfrac{1.00\ g\ coal}{0.85\ gC} \times \dfrac{1\ kg}{1000g} \times \dfrac{1\ metric\ ton}{1000\ kg} = 2.9 \times 10^3\ metric\ tons$

60. (M) Since the two nuclides have the same mass number, the ratio of their masses is the same as the ratio of the number of atoms of each type. We use equation (25.12) to determine the time required for the Rb to decrease from 1.004 to 1.00. First we compute the decay constant.

$\lambda = \dfrac{0.693}{4.88 \times 10^{10}\ a} = 1.42 \times 10^{-11}\ a^{-1}$

$\ln \dfrac{1.00}{1.004} = -4.0 \times 10^{-3} = -\lambda t = -1.42 \times 10^{-11}\ a^{-1}\ t$ $\qquad t = \dfrac{-4.0 \times 10^{-3}}{-1.42 \times 10^{-11}\ a^{-1}} = 2.8 \times 10^8\ a$

61. (M) $\lambda = \dfrac{0.693}{7.9 \times 10^3 \text{ a}} \times \dfrac{1 \text{ a}}{365.25 \text{ d}} \times \dfrac{1 \text{ d}}{24 \text{ h}} \times \dfrac{1 \text{ h}}{3600 \text{ s}} = 2.78 \times 10^{-12} \text{ s}^{-1}$

$N = 5.10 \text{ mg} \times \dfrac{1 \text{g}}{1000 \text{ mg}} \times \dfrac{1 \text{ mol }^{229}\text{Th}}{229 \text{ g }^{229}\text{Th}} \times \dfrac{6.022 \times 10^{23} \ ^{229}\text{Th atoms}}{1 \text{ mol }^{229}\text{Th}} = 1.34 \times 10^{19} \ ^{229}\text{Th atoms}$

decay rate in disintegrations/s $= \lambda N = 2.78 \times 10^{-12} \text{ s}^{-1} \times 1.34 \times 10^{19} \text{ atoms } \times \dfrac{1 \text{ Ci}}{3.7 \times 10^{10} \text{ dis/s}}$

$\times \dfrac{1000 \text{ mCi}}{1 \text{ Ci}} = 1.0 \text{ mCi}$

62. (D) First we find the decay constant. The activity (λN) is the product of the decay constant and the number of atoms.

$\lambda = \dfrac{0.693}{29.1 \text{ a}} \times \dfrac{1 \text{ a}}{365.25 \text{ d}} \times \dfrac{1 \text{ d}}{24 \text{ h}} \times \dfrac{1 \text{ h}}{3600 \text{ s}} = 7.55 \times 10^{-10} \text{ s}^{-1}$

radioactivity $= 1.00 \text{ mCi} \times \dfrac{1 \text{ Ci}}{1000 \text{ mCi}} \times \dfrac{3.7 \times 10^{10} \text{ dis/s}}{1 \text{ Ci}} = 3.7 \times 10^7 \text{ dis/s}$

$N = \dfrac{\text{activity}}{\lambda} = \dfrac{3.7 \times 10^7 \text{ dis/s}}{7.55 \times 10^{-10} \text{ s}^{-1}} = 4.9 \times 10^{16} \ ^{90}\text{Sr atoms} \times \dfrac{1 \text{ mol }^{90}\text{Sr}}{6.022 \times 10^{23} \text{ atoms}} \times \dfrac{90 \text{ g }^{90}\text{Sr}}{1 \text{ mol }^{90}\text{Sr}}$

$= 7.3 \times 10^{-6} \text{ g }^{90}\text{Sr} = 7.3 \ \mu\text{g }^{90}\text{Sr}$

63. (D) decay rate $= 89.8 \text{ mCi} \times \dfrac{1 \text{ Ci}}{1000 \text{ mCi}} \times \dfrac{3.7 \times 10^{10} \text{ dis/s}}{1 \text{ Ci}} = 3.3_2 \times 10^9 \text{ dis/s}$

$N = 1.00 \text{ mg} \times \dfrac{1 \text{ g}}{1000 \text{ mg}} \times \dfrac{1 \text{ mol }^{137}\text{Cs}}{137 \text{ g }^{137}\text{Cs}} \times \dfrac{6.022 \times 10^{23} \text{ atoms}}{1 \text{ mol}} = 4.40 \times 10^{18} \ ^{137}\text{Cs atoms}$

decay rate $= \lambda N \qquad \lambda = \dfrac{\text{decay rate}}{N} = \dfrac{3.3_2 \times 10^9 \text{ dis/s}}{4.40 \times 10^{18} \text{ atoms}} = 7.5_5 \times 10^{-10} \text{ s}^{-1}$

$t_{1/2} = \dfrac{0.693}{\lambda} = \dfrac{0.693}{7.5_5 \times 10^{-10} \text{ s}^{-1}} \times \dfrac{1 \text{ h}}{3600 \text{ s}} \times \dfrac{1 \text{ d}}{24 \text{ h}} \times \dfrac{1 \text{ a}}{365.25 \text{ d}} = 29 \text{ a}$

64. (D) $\lambda = \dfrac{0.693}{1.26 \times 10^9 \text{ a}} \times \dfrac{1 \text{ a}}{365.25 \text{ d}} \times \dfrac{1 \text{ d}}{24 \text{ h}} \times \dfrac{1 \text{ h}}{3600 \text{ s}} = 1.74 \times 10^{-17} \text{ s}^{-1}$

$N = 1.00 \text{ g KAlSi}_3\text{O}_8 \times \dfrac{1 \text{ mol KAlSi}_3\text{O}_8}{278.3 \text{ g KAlSi}_3\text{O}_8} \times \dfrac{1 \text{ mol K}}{1 \text{ mol KAlSi}_3\text{O}_8} \times \dfrac{0.000117 \text{ mol }^{40}\text{K}}{1 \text{ mol K}}$

$\times \dfrac{6.022 \times 10^{23} \ ^{40}\text{K atoms}}{1 \text{ mol }^{40}\text{K}} = 2.53 \times 10^{17} \ ^{40}\text{K atoms}$

rate $= 0.89\lambda N = 0.89 \times 1.74 \times 10^{-17} \text{ s}^{-1} \times 2.53 \times 10^{17} \text{ atoms} = 3.9 \text{ dis/s}$

65. (D) ^{14}C is produced from ^{14}N by neutron bombardment. Since ^{14}N is a common element, constituting 78% of the atmosphere, any activity that increases the emission of neutrons will increase the production of ^{14}C. A major source used to be thermonuclear explosions, particularly atmospheric detonations. But most tests now take place underground. Nonetheless, the extensive thermonuclear testing that took place during the 1950s and 1960s could have produced sufficient ^{14}C to invalidate the radiocarbon dating of materials that were alive during that period. Nuclear power plants are a very minor source of ^{14}C, as is bringing to the surface neutron-emitting isotopes by mining activities.

Although we might suspect ozone depletion of playing a role in increasing the quantity of ^{14}C, such is not the case. Ozone absorbs ultraviolet radiation, not neutrons. And, in any case, there is about the same proportion of ^{14}N in the upper atmosphere as there is further down, in layers that recently have become exposed to ultraviolet radiation because of the depletion of ozone.

66. (D) product masses = $^{17}O + {}^1H = 16.99913\ u + 1.00783\ u = 18.00696\ u$

reactant masses = $^4He + {}^{14}N = 4.00260\ u + 14.00307\ u = 18.00567\ u$

The products have more mass than the reactants. The difference must be supplied as energy from the reactants. This difference in energy ends up entirely to the $E_{kinetic}$ of the α particle. Compute this energy in MeV.

$$\text{energy} = (18.00696\ u - 18.00567\ u) \times \frac{931.5\ \text{MeV}}{1\ u} = 1.20\ \text{MeV}$$

67. (D) Assume we have in our possession 100 g of the hydrogen/tritium mixture. This sample will afford us 95 g hydrogen and 5 g tritium.

$$\text{mol hydrogen} = \frac{95.00\ gH}{1.008\ g/mol} = 94.246\ \text{mol hydrogen}$$

$$\text{mol tritium} = \frac{5.00\ gH}{3.02\ g/mol} = 1.656\ \text{mol tritium}$$

$$\text{mole fraction tritium} = \frac{1.656\ \text{mol tritium}}{1.656\ \text{mol tritium} + 94.246\ \text{mol hydrogen}} = 1.72_7 \times 10^{-2}$$

$$\text{total moles of gas in mixture} = \frac{PV}{RT} = \frac{(1.05\ \text{atm})(4.65\ \text{L})}{0.0821 \dfrac{\text{L atm}}{\text{mol K}}(298.15\ \text{K})} = 0.199_5\ \text{mol}$$

mols of tritium = $(0.1995\ \text{mol})(1.727 \times 10^{-2}\ \text{mol tritium / mol mixture}) = 3.445 \times 10^{-3}\ \text{mol tritium}$

\# of tritium atoms (N) = $(2 \times 3.445 \times 10^{-3}\ \text{mol tritium})(6.022 \times 10^{23}\ \text{tritium atoms/mol}) = 4.15 \times 10^{21}\ \text{tritium atoms}$

$$\text{rate} = \frac{0.693}{t_{1/2}} N = \frac{0.693}{12.3\ a \times \dfrac{365\ d}{1\ a} \times \dfrac{24\ h}{1\ d} \times \dfrac{60\ \text{min}}{1\ h} \times \dfrac{60\ s}{1\ \text{min}}} \times 4.15 \times 10^{21} = 7.42 \times 10^{12}\ \text{disintegrations/s}$$

7

$$\text{activity in curies} = \frac{7.42 \times 10^{12}\ \text{disintegrations/s}}{3.7 \times 10^{10}\ \dfrac{\text{disintegrations/s}}{Ci}} = 2.0 \times 10^2\ Ci$$

68. (D) $\text{energy} = 1.00 \times 10^3 \text{ cm}^3 \times \dfrac{2.5 \text{ g}}{1 \text{ cm}^3} \times \dfrac{0.006 \text{ g U}}{100.000 \text{ g shale}} \times \dfrac{1 \text{ mol U}}{238 \text{ g U}}$

$\times \dfrac{6.022 \times 10^{23} \text{ U atoms}}{1 \text{ mol U}} \times \dfrac{3.20 \times 10^{-11} \text{ J}}{1 \text{ U atom}} \times \dfrac{1 \text{ kJ}}{1000 \text{ J}} = 1.2 \times 10^7 \text{ kJ}$

69. (D)

$$\underset{\text{O}}{\overset{\overset{\displaystyle O}{\|}}{\text{R}-\text{C}}}\boxed{-\text{O}-\text{H H}}-\text{O}^{18}-\text{R} \qquad \text{versus} \qquad \text{R}-\overset{\overset{\displaystyle O}{\|}}{\text{C}}-\text{O}\boxed{-\text{H H}-\text{O}^{18}}-\text{R}'$$

$$\downarrow$$

$$\text{H}-\text{O}-\text{H}$$
$$+$$
$$\underset{}{\overset{\overset{\displaystyle O}{\|}}{\text{R}-\text{C}}}-\text{O}^{18}-\text{R}'$$

It is evident that the $\text{O}^{18}-\text{R}'$ bond does not break like an OH bond ($\text{Na}^+ = \text{R}'$). From this labeling experiment, we see that it must be the C-O bond in the organic acid that breaks.

70. (D) $6 \text{ CO}_2(g) + 6 \text{ H}_2\text{O}^{18}(l) - \text{light} \rightarrow \text{C}_6\text{H}_{12}\text{O}_6(s) + 6 \text{ O}_2^{18}(g)$

$6 \text{ CO}_2^{18}(g) + 6 \text{ H}_2\text{O}(l) - \text{light} \rightarrow \text{C}_6\text{H}_{12}\text{O}_6(s) + 6 \text{ O}_2(g)$

Basically, the results shows that the O_2 arises from the oxidation of H_2O and that the CO_2 involved in this reaction remains intact. Simplistically, this can be explained by using two half-reactions:

$$12 \text{ H}_2\text{O}^{18}(l) \rightarrow 6 \text{ O}_2^{18}(g) + 24 \text{ H}^+ + 24 \text{ e}^-$$

$$\underline{24 \text{ e}^- + 24 \text{ H}^+ + 6 \text{ CO}_2(g) \rightarrow \text{C}_6\text{H}_{12}\text{O}_6(s) + 6 \text{ H}_2\text{O}}$$

$$6 \text{ CO}_2(g) + 6 \text{ H}_2\text{O}^{18}(l) \rightarrow \text{C}_6\text{H}_{12}\text{O}_6(s) + 6 \text{ O}_2^{18}(g)$$

In reality, the reaction is not this simple, however. What this labeling study shows is that the O_2 is evolved from the oxidation of water (the only time $\text{O}_2^{18}(g)$ forms is when H_2O^{18} is used).

71. (D) Initially $\dfrac{\text{U}^{238}}{\text{U}^{235}} = 1$ $\quad$ $\text{U}^{238} \ t_{1/2} = 4.5 \times 10^9 \text{ years}$ $\quad$ $\text{U}^{235} \ t_{1/2} = 7.1 \times 10^8 \text{ years}$

Currently $\dfrac{\text{U}^{238}}{\text{U}^{235}} = \dfrac{0.9928}{0.0072} = 138$

Remember $t_{1/2} = \dfrac{0.693}{\lambda}$ $\quad$ Hence $\lambda = \dfrac{0.693}{t_{1/2}}$ $\quad$ $\lambda_{\text{U}^{238}} = 1.5\underline{4} \times 10^{-10}$ $\quad$ $\lambda_{\text{U}^{235}} = 9.7\underline{6} \times 10^{-10}$

For any radioactive isotope, the amount remaining is $e^{-\lambda t}$.

Currently, $\dfrac{e^{-\lambda t}(U^{238})}{e^{-\lambda t}(U^{235})} = 138 = \dfrac{e^{-1.54 \times 10^{-10}t}(U^{238})}{e^{-9.76 \times 10^{-10}t}(U^{235})} = e^{8.22 \times 10^{-10}t} = 138$ (take ln of both sides)

$8.2\underline{2} \times 10^{-10}t = \ln 138 = 4.9\underline{27}$ $\quad$ $t = \dfrac{4.9\underline{27}}{8.2\underline{2} \times 10^{-10}} = 6.0 \times 10^9 \text{ years}$

FEATURE PROBLEMS

72. **(D)** First tabulate the isotope symbols, the mass of the isotope and its associated packing fraction.

Isotope Symbol	Mass of Isotope (u)	Packing Fraction
^{1}H	1.007825	0.007825
^{4}He	4.002603	0.000651
^{9}Be	9.012186	0.001354
^{12}C	12	0
^{16}O	15.994915	−0.000318
^{20}Ne	19.992440	−0.000378
^{24}Mg	23.985042	−0.000623
^{32}S	31.972074	−0.000873
^{40}Ar	39.962384	−0.000940
^{40}Ca	39.962589	−0.000935
^{48}Ti	47.947960	−0.001084
^{52}Cr	51.940513	−0.001144
^{56}Fe	55.934936	−0.001162
^{58}Ni	57.935342	−0.001115
^{64}Zn	63.929146	−0.001107
^{80}Se	79.916527	−0.001043
^{84}Kr	83.911503	−0.001054
^{90}Zr	89.904700	−0.001059
^{102}Ru	101.904348	−0.000938
^{114}Cd	113.903360	−0.000848
^{130}Te	129.906238	−0.000721
^{138}Ba	137.905000	−0.000688
^{142}Nd	141.907663	−0.000650
^{158}Gd	157.924178	−0.000480
^{166}Er	165.932060	−0.000409

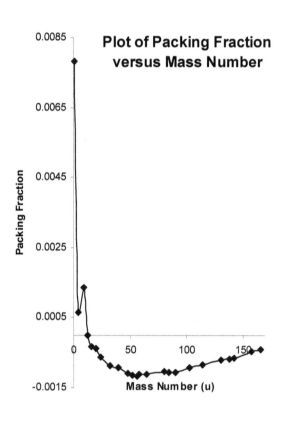

This graph and Fig. 25-6 are almost exactly the inverse of one another, with the maxima of one being the minima of the other. Actual nuclidic mass is often a number slightly less than the number of nucleons (mass number). This difference divided by the number of nucleons (packing fraction) is proportional to the negative of the mass defect per nucleon.

73. **(D)**

(a) The rate of decay depends on both the half-life and the number of radioactive atoms present. In the early stages of the decay chain, the larger number of radium-226, atoms multiplied by the very small decay constant is still larger than the product of the very small number of radon-222 atoms and its much larger decay constant. Only after some time has elapsed, does the rate of decay of radon-222 approach the rate at which it is formed from radium-226 and the amount of radon-222 reaches a maximum. Beyond this point, the rate of decay of radon-222 exceeds its rate of formation.

(b) $\dfrac{dD}{dt} = \lambda_p P - \lambda_d D = \lambda_p N_o e^{-\lambda_p t} - \lambda_d D$

(c) The number of radon-222 atoms at the proposed times are: 2.90×10^{15} atoms after 1 day; 1.26×10^{16} after 1 week; 1.75×10^{16} after 1 year; 1.68×10^{16} after one century; and 1.13×10^{16} after 1 millennium. The actual maximum comes after about 2 months, but the amount after 1 year is only slightly smaller.

74. (D) (a) Average atomic mass of Sr in the rock

$\dfrac{^{87}Sr}{^{86}Sr} = 2.25 \qquad \dfrac{^{86}Sr}{^{88}Sr} = 0.119 \qquad \dfrac{^{84}Sr}{^{88}Sr} = 0.007 \qquad$ Given: 15.5 ppm Sr

Let $x = {}^{86}Sr$, $y = {}^{88}Sr$, $z = {}^{87}Sr$, $w = {}^{84}Sr \quad x + y + z + w = 15.5$ ppm

$\dfrac{z}{x} = 2.25$, $\dfrac{x}{y} = 0.119$, $\dfrac{w}{y} = 0.007$

Set $x = {}^{86}Sr = 1$ and find the relative atom ratio of the other

Hence, $z = 2.25x = 2.25 \times 1 = 2.25$

$y = \dfrac{x}{0.119} = \dfrac{1}{0.119} = 8.40\underline{3}$

$w = 0.007y = 0.007 \times 8.40\underline{3} = 0.05\underline{88}$

$x + y + z + w = 1 + 2.25 + 8.40\underline{3} + 0.05\underline{88} = 11.7\underline{12}$

As a percent abundance, we find the following for the Sr in the sample.

$\%^{86}Sr = 1/11.7\underline{12} \times 100\ \% = 8.53\underline{8}\ \%$

$\%^{88}Sr = 8.40\underline{3}/11.7\underline{12} \times 100\ \% = 71.7\underline{5}\ \%$

$\%^{87}Sr = 2.25/11.7\underline{12} \times 100\ \% = 19.2\underline{1}\ \%$

$\%^{84}Sr = 0.05\underline{88}/11.7\underline{12} \times 100\ \% = 0.5\ \%$

av. mass Sr = mass^{86}Sr (% ^{86}Sr) + mass^{88}Sr (% ^{88}Sr) + mass^{87}Sr (% ^{87}Sr) + mass^{84}Sr (% ^{84}Sr)

av. mass Sr = $8.53\underline{8}\ \%$ (85.909 u) + $71.7\underline{5}\ \%$ (87.906 u) + $19.2\underline{1}\ \%$ (86.909 u) + $0.5\%(83.913\ u)$

average atomic mass Sr = $7.33\underline{5}$ u + $63.0\underline{7}$ u + $16.6\underline{95}$ u + $0.4\underline{2}$ u = 87.5 u

current atom ratio is $\dfrac{^{87}Rb}{^{85}Rb} = 0.330$

Set 1000 atoms for ^{85}Rb and 330 atoms ^{87}Rb or a total of 1330 atoms of Rb

Percent abundance of each isotope: ^{85}Rb = (1000/1330)×100% = 75.2 % ^{85}Rb

^{87}Rb = (1000/1330)×100% = 24.8 % ^{87}Rb

av. mass Rb = mass^{85}Rb (% ^{85}Rb) + mass^{87}Rb (% ^{87}Rb)

av. mass Rb = 75.2 % (84.912 u) + 24.8 % (86.909 u)

average atomic mass Rb = $63.8\underline{5}$ u + $21.5\underline{5}$ u = 85.4 u

(b) Original Rb in rock?

Need to convert atom ratio → isotope concentration in ppm.

^{85}Rb concentration in ppm

$$= \frac{1000 \text{ atoms } ^{85}\text{Rb}}{1330 \text{ atoms Rb}} \times \frac{1 \text{ atom Rb}}{85.4 \text{ u Rb}} \times \frac{84.912 \text{ u } ^{85}\text{Rb}}{1 \text{ atom } ^{85}\text{Rb}} \times 265.4 \text{ ppm Rb} = 198.4 \text{ ppm } ^{85}\text{Rb}$$

^{87}Rb concentration in ppm

$$= \frac{330 \text{ atoms } ^{87}\text{Rb}}{1330 \text{ atoms Rb}} \times \frac{1 \text{ atom Rb}}{85.4 \text{ u Rb}} \times \frac{86.909 \text{ u } ^{87}\text{Rb}}{1 \text{ atom } ^{87}\text{Rb}} \times 265.4 \text{ ppm Rb} = 67.0 \text{ ppm } ^{87}\text{Rb}$$

Currently 265.4 ppm (198.4 ppm ^{85}Rb + 67.0 ppm ^{87}Rb)

Recall earlier calculations showed: $\%^{86}\text{Sr} = 8.53\underline{8}$ %; $\%^{88}\text{Sr} = 71.7\underline{5}$ %;
$\%^{87}\text{Sr} = 19.2\underline{1}$ %; $\%^{84}\text{Sr} = 0.5$ %

Consider 100,000 atoms of Sr. Calculate the concentration (in ppm) of ^{86}Sr and ^{87}Sr.
^{86}Sr concentration in ppm

$$= \frac{8538 \text{ atoms } ^{86}\text{Sr}}{100,000 \text{ atoms Sr}} \times \frac{1 \text{ atom Sr}}{87.5 \text{ u Sr}} \times \frac{85.909 \text{ u } ^{86}\text{Sr}}{1 \text{ atom } ^{86}\text{Sr}} \times 15.5 \text{ ppm Sr} = 1.299 \text{ ppm } ^{86}\text{Sr}$$

^{87}Sr concentration in ppm

$$= \frac{19,210 \text{ atoms } ^{87}\text{Sr}}{100,000 \text{ atoms Sr}} \times \frac{1 \text{ atom Sr}}{87.5 \text{ u Sr}} \times \frac{86.909 \text{ u } ^{87}\text{Sr}}{1 \text{ atom } ^{87}\text{Sr}} \times 15.5 \text{ ppm Sr} = 2.957 \text{ ppm } ^{87}\text{Sr}$$

Currently: $\dfrac{^{87}\text{Sr}}{^{86}\text{Sr}} = 2.25 = \dfrac{19,210 \text{ atoms } ^{87}\text{Sr}}{8,538 \text{ atoms } ^{86}\text{Sr}}$

Originally: $\dfrac{^{87}\text{Sr}}{^{86}\text{Sr}} = 0.700$ or $^{87}\text{Sr} = {}^{86}\text{Sr} \times 0.700 = 8,538 \times 0.700 = 5,977 \text{ atoms } ^{87}\text{Sr}$

Change in ^{87}Sr = 192$\underline{10}$ – 59$\underline{77}$ = 132$\underline{33}$ atoms ^{87}Sr (per 100,000 Sr atoms)
Currently, 19210 per 100,000 atoms is ^{87}Sr which represents 2.957 ppm.
A change of 13233 atoms represents (13233/19210)×2.957 ppm = 2.037 ppm ^{87}Sr

The source of ^{87}Sr is radioactive decay from ^{87}Rb (a 1:1 relation).

Change in the ^{87}Rb (through radioactive decay) = change in ^{87}Sr = 2.037 ppm

Isotope:	^{87}Rb	^{85}Rb	Total Rb
Current concentration	67.0 ppm	198.4 ppm	265.4 ppm
Change concentration	+2.037 ppm	—	+2.037 ppm
Original concentration	69.04 ppm	198.4 ppm	267.44 ppm

(c) % ^{87}Rb decayed $= \left(\dfrac{2.037 \text{ ppm}}{69.04 \text{ ppm}} \right) \times 100\% = 2.95 \%$ (% ^{87}Rb remaining $= 97.05\%$)

(d) $\ln(0.9705) = -\lambda t$ $\left(\lambda = \dfrac{0.693}{t_{1/2}} = \dfrac{0.693}{4.88 \times 10^{10} \text{ a}} = 1.420 \times 10^{-11} \text{ a}^{-1} \right)$

$\ln(0.9705) = -1.444 \times 10^{-11} \text{ a}^{-1} t;$ $t = 2.11 \times 10^9$ years

SELF-ASSESSMENT EXERCISES

75. (E)

(a) Alpha particles are the nuclei of helium-4 atoms, $_2^4\text{He}^{2+}$, ejected spontaneously from the nuclei of certain radioactive atoms.

(b) β^- particles are electrons, but they are electrons that originate from the nuclei of atoms in nuclear decay processes.

(c) β^+ particle, also called a positron, has properties similar to the β^- particle, except that it carries a positive charge.

(d) Gamma (γ) rays are highly penetrating form of radiation that are undeflected by electric and magnetic fields.

(e) $t_{1/2}$ is the half-life of a reaction, i.e. a time required for the reaction to go to 50% completion.

76. (E)

(a) All naturally occurring radioactive nuclides of high atomic number are members of a radioactive decay series that originates with a long-lived isotope of high atomic number and terminates with a stable isotope.

(b) A charged particle accelerator is a device that uses electric fields to propel charged particles to high speeds and to contain them in well-defined beams.

(c) The stable nuclides of low atomic numbers have a neutron-to-proton ratio of one, or nearly so. At higher atomic numbers, the neutron-to-proton ratios increase to about 1.5.

(d) The energy change accompanying a nuclear reaction can be described by using the mass–energy relationship derived by Albert Einstein: $E=mc^2$.

(e) All life exists against a background of naturally occurring ionizing radiation-cosmic rays, ultraviolet light, and emanations from radioactive elements, such as uranium in rocks. The level of this radiation varies from point to point on Earth, being greater, for instance, at higher elevations.

77. **(E)**

   (a) Electrons are negatively charged species, whereas positrons are positive.

   (b) Half-life is the time taken for the activity of a given amount of a radioactive substance to decay to half of its initial value. Decay constant (λ) is the inverse of the mean lifetime.

   (c) The difference between the unbound system calculated mass and experimentally measured mass of nucleus is called mass defect. It is denoted by Δm. The amount of energy required to break the nucleus of an atom into its isolated nucleons is called nuclear binding energy.

   (d) In nuclear chemistry, nuclear fission is a nuclear reaction in which the nucleus of an atom splits into smaller parts, often producing free neutrons and lighter nuclei. Nuclear fusion, on the other hand, is the process by which multiple atomic nuclei join together to form a single heavier nucleus. It is accompanied by the release or absorption of energy.

   (e) The ionized electrons produced directly by the collisions of particles of radiation with atoms are called primary electrons. These electrons may themselves possess sufficient energies to cause secondary ionizations.

78. **(E)** (c)

79. **(E)** (b)

80. **(E)** (d)

81. **(E)** (c)

82. **(E)** (c)

83. **(E)** (d)

84. **(E)** (d)

85. **(M)**

   (a) $^{214}_{88}\text{Ra} \rightarrow {}^{210}_{86}\text{Rn} + {}^{4}_{2}\text{He}$

   (b) $^{205}_{85}\text{At} \rightarrow {}^{205}_{84}\text{Po} + {}^{0}_{+1}\text{b}$

   (c) $^{212}_{87}\text{Fr} + e^{-} \rightarrow {}^{212}_{86}\text{Rn}$

   (d) $^{2}_{1}\text{H} + {}^{2}_{1}\text{H} \rightarrow {}^{3}_{2}\text{He} + {}^{1}_{0}\text{n}$

   (e) $^{241}_{95}\text{Am} + {}^{4}_{2}\text{He} \rightarrow {}^{243}_{97}\text{Bk} + 2\,{}^{1}_{0}\text{n}$

   (f) $^{232}_{90}\text{Th} + {}^{4}_{2}\text{He} \rightarrow {}^{232}_{92}\text{U} + 4\,{}^{1}_{0}\text{n}$

86. **(M)** First use the equation $t_{1/2} = \dfrac{0.693}{\lambda}$ to determine λ from $t_{1/2}$:

$$\lambda = \frac{0.693}{t_{1/2}} = \frac{0.693}{11.43\,d} = 0.0606\ d^{-1}$$

Then use the equation $\ln\left(\dfrac{N_t}{N_0}\right) = -\lambda t$ with $\dfrac{N_t}{N_0} = 0.01$ and solve for t:

$$\ln(0.01) = -0.0606t \Rightarrow t = \frac{-4.605}{-0.0606} = 76\ \text{days}$$

87. **(M)** First use the equation $t_{1/2} = \dfrac{0.693}{\lambda}$ to determine λ from $t_{1/2}$:

$$\lambda = \frac{0.693}{t_{1/2}} = \frac{0.693}{87.9\,d} = 7.88 \times 10^{-3}\,d^{-1}$$

Then use the equation $\ln\left(\dfrac{N_t}{N_0}\right) = -\lambda t$ with $\dfrac{N_t}{N_0} = \dfrac{253}{1000}, \dfrac{104}{1000},$ and $\dfrac{52}{1000}$ and solve for t:

$$t_a = \frac{\ln\dfrac{253}{1000}}{7.88 \times 10^{-3}} = 174\ \text{days}$$

$$t_b = \frac{\ln\dfrac{104}{1000}}{7.88 \times 10^{-3}} = 287\ \text{days}$$

$$t_c = \frac{\ln\dfrac{52}{1000}}{7.88 \times 10^{-3}} = 375\ \text{days}$$

88. **(M)** (b)

89. **(M)** (d)

90. **(M)** (c)

91. **(M)** (a)

92. **(M)** (b)

93. **(M)** Radioactivity is not temperature dependent because it occurs by tunneling. The rate of tunneling does not depend on temperature.

CHAPTER 26
STRUCTURES OF ORGANIC COMPOUNDS
PRACTICE EXAMPLES

1A **(E)** We have shown only the C atoms and the bonds between them. Remember that there are four bonds to each C atom; the remaining bonds not shown are to H atoms. First we realize there is only one isomer with all six C atoms in one line. Then we draw the isomers with one 1-C branch. The isomers with two 1-C branches can have them both on the same atom or on different atoms. This accounts for all five isomers.

C—C—C—C—C—C

$CH_3CH_2CH_2CH_2CH_2CH_3$

C—C—C—C—C (with C branch)

$(CH_3)_2CHCH_2CH_2CH_3$

C—C—C—C—C (with C branch)

$CH_3CH_2CH(CH_3)CH_2CH_3$

C—C—C—C (with two C branches on adjacent atoms)

$(CH_3)_2CHCH(CH_3)_2$

C—C—C—C (with two C branches on same atom)

$(CH_3)_3CCH_2CH_3$

1B **(E)** We have shown only the C atoms and the bonds between them. Remember that there are four bonds to each C atom; the remaining bonds not shown are to H atoms.

C—C—C—C—C—C—C

$CH_3CH_2CH_2CH_2CH_2CH_2CH_3$

C—C—C—C—C—C (with C branch)

$(CH_3)_2CHCH_2CH_2CH_2CH_3$

C—C—C—C—C—C (with C branch)

$CH_3CH_2CH(CH_3)CH_2CH_2CH_3$

C—C—C—C—C (with two C branches)

$(CH_3)_2CHCH_2CHC(CH_3)_2$

C—C—C—C—C (with two C branches)

$(CH_3)_2CHCH(CH_3)CH_2CH_3$

C—C—C—C—C (with C branches)

$(CH_3)_3CCH_2CH_2CH_3$

C—C—C—C—C (with C branches)

$CH_3CH_2C(CH_3)_2CH_2CH_3$

C—C—C—C (with C branches)

$(CH_3)_3CCH(CH_3)_2$

C—C—C—C—C (with C—C branch)

$CH(CH_2CH_3)_3$

2A **(M)**

3,3,6-trimethyloctane

Numbering starts from the right and goes left so that the substituents appear with the lowest numbers possible. This is 3,6,6-trimethyloctane.

2B **(M)**

This is a symmetrical molecule. Therefore it does not matter whether numbering starts from left or right. The compound's name is 3,6-dimethyloctane.

3A **(M)**

3-ethyl-2,6-dimethylheptane

3B **(M)**

3-ethyl-2,4-dimethylpentane

4A   **(M)** The structural diagram for 2-methylpentane is given below:

$$CH_3$$
$$CH_2 \qquad CH$$
$$CH_3 \qquad CH_2 \qquad CH_3$$

2-methylpentane

When the molecule is viewed along C1-C2 bond there are several possible staggered conformations:

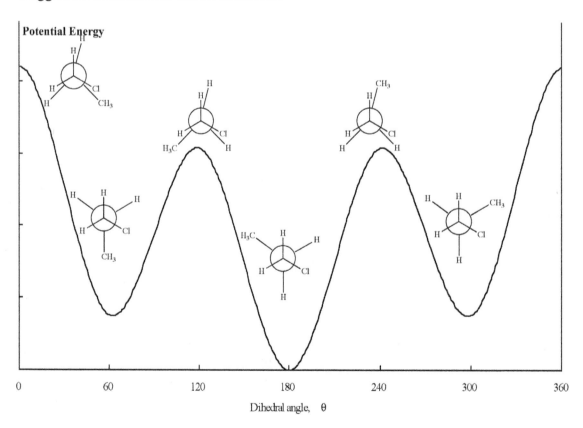

There are no gauche interactions in this molecule. Therefore, conformations (a), (b) and (c) all have the same energy.

4B   **(D)** When 1-chloropropane molecule is viewed along the C1-C2 bond, several eclipsed and staggered conformations can be identified:

5A **(M)** We are dealing with a trans isomer, and so both methyl groups are adjacent to opposite face of the ring. The conformation of the lowest energy will be the one that has the methyl groups in the equatorial positions.

5B **(M)** For this molecule, it is more favorable to place tert-butyl group in the equatorial position.

6A. **(M)**

(a)

All three carbon atoms in this molecule are attached to at least two groups of the same type; thus, the molecule is achiral

(b)

This molecule contains a carbon atom that is bonded to four different groups; consequently, the molecule is chiral.

(c)

This molecule contains a carbon atom that is attached to four different groups; consequently, the molecule is chiral.

6B. **(M)**

(a)

None of the three carbon atoms in this alcohol are bonded to four different groups; consequently the molecule is achiral

(b)

This molecule contains a carbon atom that is bonded to four different groups; consequently, the molecule is chiral.

(c)

This molecule contains a carbon atom that is bonded to four different groups; consequently, the molecule is chiral. The molecule is also unstable and eliminates HCl to form propanal CH_3CH_2CHO.

7A **(M)** Chiral carbon atoms (*) are indicated below:

7B **(M)** The molecular structure of 1,1,3-trimethylcyclohexane is shown below and chiral carbon atoms indicated by "*":

8A **(D)**

8B **(D)**

(a)

     Thus, the structures are enantiomers.

(b)

   Thus, the structures are enantiomers.

9A **(M)** **(a)** This is the (E) stereoisomer

$$H_3CH_2C \quad\quad H$$
$$\backslash\quad\quad /$$
$$C = C$$
$$/\quad\quad \backslash$$
$$H \quad\quad CH_2CH_3$$

(b) This is the (Z) stereoisomer

$$H_3C \quad\quad CH_2Br$$
$$\backslash\quad /$$
$$=$$
$$/\quad \backslash$$
$$H \quad\quad CH_3$$

(c) This is the (Z) stereoisomer

$$ClH_2CH_2C \quad\quad F$$
$$\backslash\quad\quad /$$
$$C = C$$
$$/\quad\quad \backslash$$
$$H_3CH_2C \quad\quad H$$

9B **(M)** **(a)**

(Z) stereoisomer

$$H_3CH_2C \quad\quad CH_3$$
$$\backslash\quad\quad /$$
$$C = C$$
$$/\quad\quad \backslash$$
$$H \quad\quad H$$

(E) stereoisomer

$$H_3CH_2C \quad\quad H$$
$$\backslash\quad\quad /$$
$$C = C$$
$$/\quad\quad \backslash$$
$$H \quad\quad CH_3$$

(b)

(Z) stereoisomer

$$Cl \quad\quad CH_2CH_3$$
$$\backslash\quad\quad /$$
$$C = C$$
$$/\quad\quad \backslash$$
$$H_3CH_2C \quad\quad H$$

(E) stereoisomer

$$Cl \quad\quad H$$
$$\backslash\quad\quad /$$
$$C = C$$
$$/\quad\quad \backslash$$
$$H_3CH_2C \quad\quad CH_2CH_3$$

(c)

(Z) stereoisomer

$$H_3CH_2C \quad\quad CH_3$$
$$\backslash\quad\quad /$$
$$C = C$$
$$/\quad\quad \backslash$$
$$H_3C \quad\quad H$$

(E) stereoisomer

$$H_3CH_2C \quad\quad H$$
$$\backslash\quad\quad /$$
$$C = C$$
$$/\quad\quad \backslash$$
$$H_3C \quad\quad CH_3$$

10A **(M)** We need to establish the degree of unsaturation in the molecule and then construct one example of each type of molecule that can be formed. The maximum number of hydrogen atoms is $5 \times 2 + 2 = 12$. The molecular formula has only 11 hydrogen atoms, so we know the degree of unsaturation is one. Several possibilities are possible:

10B. (D) We need to establish the degree of unsaturation in the molecule and then construct one example of each type of molecule that can be formed. The maximum number of hydrogen atoms is $5 \times 2 + 2 = 12$. The molecular formula has only 10 hydrogen atoms, so we know the degree of unsaturation is one. Several possibilities are possible and some of them are shown below:

INTEGRATIVE EXAMPLE

11A. (M) Compound A has a formula C_3H_8O and it is coordinatively saturated. It reacts with sodium metal to produce gas and also is further oxidized by the treatment with chromic acid. Compound A must therefore be a primary alcohol, $CH_3\text{-}CH_2\text{-}CH_2\text{-}OH$. On treatment with chromic acid, $CH_3\text{-}CH_2\text{-}CH_2\text{-}OH$ is completely oxidized to carboxylic acid, $CH_3\text{-}CH_2\text{-}CH_2\text{-}COOH$ (compound B). $CH_3\text{-}CH_2\text{-}CH_2\text{-}COOH$ further reacts with base Na_2CO_3 to yield $CH_3\text{-}CH_2\text{-}CH_2\text{-}COO^-Na^+$. It also reacts with ethanol to produce ester $CH_3\text{-}CH_2\text{-}CH_2\text{-}COO\text{-}CH_2CH_3$ (compound C).

11B. (M) Compounds (a) and (b) are both ethers. Ethers are relatively unreactive and the ether linkage is stable in the presence of most oxidizing and reducing agents, as well as dilute acids and alkalis. Compound (c) is unsaturated secondary alcohol. It will decolorize a Br_2/CCl_4 solution. Compound (d), on the other hand is an aldehyde. On treatment with chromic acid it will be oxidized to carboxylic acid. The same reaction would not happen with compound (c). Although the principal oxidation product of the unsaturated secondary alcohols with chromic acid will be a ketone, the reaction of chromic acid with the aldehyde will appear identical to that of the secondary alcohol (i.e., the chromic acid will change from a red solution to a green solution). A subsequent $NaHCO_3$ treatment would be needed to test for the presence of carboxylic acid (evolution of CO_2).

EXERCISES

Organic Structures

1. **(E)** In the following structural formulas, the hydrogen atoms are omitted for clarity. Remember that there are four bonds to each carbon atom. The missing bonds are C—H bonds.

(a)
```
        C    Br   Cl
        |    |    |
  C—C—C—C—C—C—C
             |
             Br
```

(b)
```
                  C
                  |
  C=C—C—C—C—C
            |
            Br
```

(c)
```
            C
            |
  C—C—C—C—C
            |
            C
```

(d)
```
        C
        |
  C—C—C=C—C—C
        |     |
        C     C
```

2. **(E)** In the structural formulas drawn below, we omit the hydrogen atoms. Remember that there are four bonds to each C atom. The bonds that are not shown are C—H bonds.

(a) 3-isopropyloctane
```
        C—C—C          C
             |          |
  C—C—C—C—C—C—C
```
The preferred IUPAC name is 3-ethyl-2-methyloctane.

(b) 2-chloro-3-methylpentane
```
        Cl  C
        |   |
  C—C—C—C—C
```

(c) 2-pentene

C–C=C–C–C

The preferred IUPAC name is pent-2-ene.

(d) dipropyl ether

C–C–C–O–C–C–C

The preferred IUPAC name is 1-propoxypropane.

3. **(E) (a)**

(b)

(c)

4. **(E)** In the following structural formulas, the hydrogen atoms are omitted for simplicity. Remember that there are four bonds to each carbon atom. The missing bonds are C—H bonds.

(a) $(CH_3)_3CCH_2CH(CH_3)CH_2CH_2CH_3$
```
        C       C
        |       |
  C—C—C—C—C—C—C
        |
        C
```

(b) $(CH_3)_2CHCH_2C(CH_3)_2CH_2Br$
```
          C       C
          |       |
  C—C—C—C—C—Br
                  |
                  C
```

(c) $Cl_3CCH_2CH(CH_3)CH_2Cl$

```
        Cl      CH₂Cl
        |        |
Cl—C—C—C—C
        |
        Cl
```

5. **(M)**

(a)
```
    H  :Br: H   H
    |   |   |   |
H—C—C—C—C—H
    |   |   |   |
    H  :Br: H   H
```

(b)
```
         H  H  H
         |  |  |
H—Ö—C—C—C—H
         |  H  H
    H—C—H
         |
         H
```

(c)
```
    :F:      Ö:
    |        ‖
:F—C—C
    |        \
    :F:      O—H
```

(d)
```
    H  :O:  H   H
    |   ‖   |   |
H—C—C—C—C—H
    |        |   |
    :Br:     H   H
```

6. **(M)** **(a)**
```
    H  H  :O:
    |  |   ‖
H—C—C—C—Ö—H
    |  |
    H  H
```

(b)
```
    H
    |
H—C—C≡N:
    |
    H
```

(c)
```
    H  H  H
    |  |  |
H—C—C—N—H
    |  |
    H  H
```

7. **(M)**

(a) Each carbon atom is sp^3 hybridized. All of the C–H bonds in the structure (drawn below) are sigma bonds, between the $1s$ orbital of H and the sp^3 orbital of C. The C–C bond is between sp^3 orbitals on each C atom.

(b) Both carbon atoms are sp^2 hybridized. All of the C–H bonds in the structure (below) are sigma bonds between the $1s$ orbital of H and the sp^2 orbital of C. The C–Cl bond is between the sp^2 orbital on C and the $3p$ orbital on Cl. The C=C double bond is composed of a sigma bond between the sp^2 orbitals on each C atom and a pi bond between the $2p_z$ orbitals on the two C atoms.

(c) The left-most C atom (in the structure drawn below) is sp^3 hybridized, and the C–H bonds to that C atom are between the sp^3 orbitals on C and the $1s$ orbital on H. The other two C atoms are sp hybridized. The right-hand C–H bond is between the sp orbital on C and the $1s$ orbital on H. The C ≡ C triple bond is composed of one sigma bond formed by overlap of sp orbitals, one from each C atom, and two pi bonds, each formed by the overlap of two $2p$ orbitals, one from each C atom (that is a $2p_y$—$2p_y$ overlap and a $2p_z$—$2p_z$ overlap).

(a)
```
    H  H  H  H
    |  |  |  |
H—C—C—C—C—H
    |  |  |  |
    H  H  H  H
```

(b)
```
H—C=C—Cl
    |  |
    H  H
```

(c)
```
         H
         |
H—C—C≡C—H
         |
         H
```

1234

8. **(M)**

(a) The left- and right-most C atoms in the structure (drawn below) are sp^3 hybridized. All C−H bonds are sigma bonds formed by the overlap of an sp^3 orbital on C with a 1s orbital on H. The central C atom is sp^2 hybridized; both C−C bonds are sigma bonds, formed by the overlap between the sp^3 orbital on the terminal C atom and an sp^2 orbital on the central C atom. The C=O double bond is composed of a σ bond between the sp^2 orbital on the central C atom and either an sp^2 or a $2p_y$ orbital on the O atom (depending on whether or not we choose to invoke hybridization for the O atom), and a π bond between the $2p_z$ orbital on the central C atom and the $2p_z$ orbital on the O atom.

(b) The left C atom in the structure (drawn below) is sp^3 hybridized. All C−H bonds are sigma bonds formed by the overlap of an sp^3 orbital on C with a 1s orbital on H. The central C atom is sp^2 hybridized; the C−C bond is a sigma bond, formed by the overlap between the sp^3 orbital on the terminal C atom and an sp^2 orbital on the central C atom. The C=O double bond is composed of a σ bond between the sp^2 orbital on the central C atom and an sp^2 or a $2p_y$ orbital on the O atom (depending on whether we choose to invoke hybridization for the O atom), and a π bond between the $2p_z$ orbital on the central C atom and the $2p_z$ orbital on the O atom. The right O atom is sp^3 hybridized; the C−O sigma bond forms by the overlap of $C\left(sp^2\right)$ with $O(sp^3)$ and the O−H bond forms by overlap of the $O\left(sp^3\right)$ with the H(1s).

(c) The two end C's are sp^2 hybridized; all C−H bonds form by the overlap of $C(sp^2)$ with H(1s). The central C is sp hybridized. Both C=C bonds consist of a σ bond formed by $C_{central}(sp)$ with $C_{end}(sp^2)$ overlap and a π bond formed by $C_{central}\left(2p\right)$ with $C_{end}(2p)$ overlap. Note: The $2p$ orbitals that make up each pi bond are mutually perpendicular relative the left or right side of the molecule.

(a)

```
    H   O   H
    |   ||  |
H―C―C―C―H
    |       |
    H       H
```

(b)

```
    H   O
    |   ||
H―C―C―O―H
    |
    H
```

(c)

```
H―C=C=C―H
    |       |
    H       H
```

Isomers

9. **(E)** Constitutional isomers have different bond connectivities, and thus different skeletal structures. Stereoisomers have the same connectivities, but a different arrangement of the atoms in space.

(a) The structures are identical.

(b) The two compounds are constitutional isomers.

(c) The two compounds have no relationship. They have different molecular formulas.

(d) The two compounds are constitutional isomers.

(e) The two compounds are stereoisomers.

10. (M)

(a) The two compounds are identical.

(b) The two compounds are constitutional isomers.

(c) The two compounds are stereoisomers, specifically enantiomers.

(d) The two compounds are constitutional isomers.

(e) The two compounds are constitutional isomers. They differ in the mode of attachment of bromine atoms. In the first one, bromine atoms are attached to the same carbon, whereas in the second one they are attached to two adjacent carbon atoms.

11. **(D)** We show only the carbon skeleton in each case. Remember that there are four bonds to carbon. The bonds that are not included in the following structures represent C—H bonds. There are a total of seven isomers of pentanol.

12. **(D)** In each case, we draw only the carbon skeleton. It is understood that there are four bonds to each carbon atom. The bonds that are not shown are C – H bonds.

(a)

$$C-C-C-C-C-C$$
n-hexane

2-methylpentane

3-methylpentane

2,3-dimethylbutane

2,2-dimethylbutane

(b)

$$C=C-C-C \quad C-C=C-C$$
but-2-ene

cyclobutane

methylcyclopropane

2-methylprop-1-ene

(c)

C=C—C—C	C—C≡C—C	cyclobutene	C=C—C=C	C=C=C—C
but-1-yne	but-2-yne		buta-1,3-diene	buta-1,2-diene

13. (M)

(a)

Carbon 2 is chiral.

(b)

There are no chiral carbon atoms.

(c)

Carbon 2 is chiral.

14. (M)

(a) There are no chiral carbon atoms in compound (a)

(b)

*indicates chiral carbon atom

(c) There are no chiral carbon atoms in compound (c)

15. (M) Chiral carbon atoms are indicated by *. Compound (b) does not contain any chiral carbon atoms.

(a) HO ... OH

(b) ... NH₂

no chiral atoms

(c) Br ...

HOOCCH₂ ... COOH   OH

CH₃ ... CH(CH₃)₂   H

16. (M)

(a)

*indicates chiral carbon atom

(b)

(c) There is no chiral carbon atoms in compound (c).

Functional Groups

17. (E)

(a)

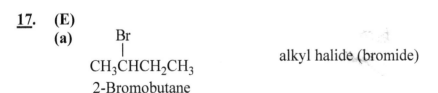

Br
|
CH₃CHCH₂CH₃
2-Bromobutane

alkyl halide (bromide)

(b)

phenylacetaldehyde

aldehyde

(c)

butan-2-one

ketone

(d)

2, 3 or 4-hydroxyphenol
(only 4-hydroxyphenol shown)

alcohol, specifically a hydroxyphenol

18. **(E)**

(a) $CH_3CH_2CH_2CHCH_3$ alcohol
    $|$
    OH

(b) CH_3
    $|$
    CH_3CCH_2COOH carboxylic acid
    $|$
    CH_3

(c) O
    $||$
    $CH_3CHCOCH_2CH_3$ ester
    $|$
    CH_3

(d) CH_3
    $|$
    CH_3CNH_2 amine
    $|$
    CH_3

(e) $CH_3CH_2CH_2CHO$ aldehyde

19. **(M)**

(a) A carbonyl group is $>C=O$, whereas a carboxyl group is $-C(O)-OH$

The essential difference between them is the hydroxyl group, — OH.

(b) An aldehyde has a carbonyl group with a hydrogen and a carbon group attached.

$$O$$
$$||$$
$$R-C-H$$

In a ketone, the carbonyl group is attached to two carbons.

$$O$$
$$||$$
$$R-C-R'$$

(c) Acetic acid is
$$O$$
$$||$$
$$H_3C-C-OH,$$
while an acetyl group is
$$O$$
$$||$$
$$H_3C-C-$$

The essential difference is the presence of the — OH group in acetic acid.

20. **(M)**

(a) aromatic nitro compound, $C_6H_5NO_2$, nitrobenzene

(b) aliphatic amine, $C_2H_5NH_2$, ethanamine

(c) chlorophenol, $p\text{-}ClC_6H_4OH$, para-chlorophenol (drawn below)

(d) aliphatic diol, $HOCH_2CH_2OH$, ethane-1,2-diol

(e) unsaturated aliphatic alcohol, $CH_2{=}CHCH_2CH_2OH$, but-3-en-ol

(f) alicyclic ketone, $C_6H_{10}O$, cyclohexanone (drawn below)

(g) halogenated alkane, $CH_3CHICH_2CH_3$, 2-iodobutane

(h) aromatic dicarboxylic acid, $o\text{-}C_6H_4(COOH)_2$, phthalic acid (drawn below)

(c)   **(f)**   **(h)**

21. **(M)** **(a)**

carboxylic acid group   disubstituted aromatic ring   hydroxyl group

(b)

ester group

(c)

ketone group   carboxylic acid group

(d)

CHO } aldehyde group

— disubstituted aromatic ring

OH } hydroxyl group

22. **(M)** **(a)**

ketone group   ketone group

(b)

amide group

(c)

hydroxyl group

hydroxyl group

OH H

HO —◯— $CH-CH_2-N-CH_3$

ether group

amine group

H_3C-O trisubstituted aromatic ring

(d)

$$H_2C-\overset{\displaystyle O}{\underset{\displaystyle \|}{C}}-OH$$

$$HO-C-\overset{\displaystyle O}{\underset{\displaystyle \|}{C}}-OH$$

hydroxyl group

$$H_2C-\overset{\displaystyle O}{\underset{\displaystyle \|}{C}}-OH$$

carboxylic acid groups

23.

IUPAC name:	ethoxyethane	1-methoxypropane	2-methoxypropane
common name:	diethyl ether	methyl propyl ether	isopropyl methyl ether

24. (M)

25. (M)

26. (M)

27. (M)

28. (M)

29. (M)

30. (D) There are numerous isomers; here are a few of them

Nomenclature and Formulas

31. **(M)**

(a) The longest chain is eight carbons, and the three methyl groups are attached to carbon atoms at positions 2, 4, and 6. The name of the structure is 2,4,6-trimethyloctane.

$$\begin{array}{c} \quad CH_3 \qquad\quad CH_3 \\ \text{1 } \text{2| } \text{3 } \text{ 4 } \text{ 5 } \text{6| } \text{ 7 } \text{ 8} \\ CH_3CHCH_2CHCH_2CHCH_2CH_3 \\ \quad\quad\quad\quad | \\ \quad\quad\quad\quad CH_3 \end{array}$$

2,4,6-trimethyloctane

(b) The longest chain is seven carbons, the methyl group is attached to the carbon atom at position 2, and the ethyl group at position 4. The name of the structure is 4-ethyl-2-methylheptane.

$$\begin{array}{c} \quad\quad\quad CH_3 \\ \quad\quad\quad | \quad\quad 1 \\ \quad\quad\quad CH_2 \quad\ CH_3 \\ \text{7 } \text{ 6 } \text{ 5 } \text{4| } \text{ 3 } \text{2|} \\ CH_3CH_2CH_2CHCH_2CH \\ \quad\quad\quad\quad\quad | \\ \quad\quad\quad\quad\quad CH_3 \end{array}$$

4-ethyl-2-methylheptane

(c) The longest carbon chain is 3 carbons. There is one chloro group attached to the carbon atom at position 2 and one methyl group attached to the carbon atom at position 2. The name of the structure is 2-chloro-2-methylpropane.

$$\begin{array}{c} \quad\quad 1\,CH_3 \\ \text{3 } \quad 2| \\ CH_3 - C - Cl \\ \quad\quad | \\ \quad\quad CH_3 \end{array}$$

2-chloro-2-methylpropane

(d) The longest carbon chain is 9 carbons. There is one chloro group attached to the carbon atom at position 3, one methyl group attached to the carbon atom at position 4, and one ethyl group attached to the carbon atom at position 7. The name of the structure is 3-chloro-7-ethyl-4methylnonane.

$$\begin{array}{c} \quad\quad\quad\quad\quad CH_3 \\ \text{9 } \text{ 8 } \text{ 7 } \text{ 6 } \text{ 5 } \text{4| } \text{ 3 } \text{ 2 } \text{ 1} \\ CH_3CH_2CHCH_2CH_2CHCHCH_2CH_3 \\ \quad\quad\quad | \quad\quad\quad\quad | \\ \quad\quad\quad CH_2 \quad\quad\quad Cl \\ \quad\quad\quad | \\ \quad\quad\quad CH_3 \end{array}$$

3-chloro-7-ethyl-4-methylnonane

32. **(E)**

(a) There are 2 chloro groups at the 1 and 3 positions on a benzene ring. This is 1,3-dichlorobenzene or meta-dichlorobenzene.

(b) There is a methyl group at position 1 on a benzene ring, and a nitro group at position 3. This is 3-nitrotoluene or meta-nitrotoluene.

(c) There is a — COOH group at position 1 on the benzene ring, and a — NH_2 group at position 4, or para to the — COOH group. This is 4-aminobenzoic acid or *p*-aminobenzoic acid.

33. **(M)**

(a) The longest carbon chain has four carbon atoms and there are 2 methyl groups attached to carbon 2. This is 2,2-dimethylbutane.

(b) The longest chain is three carbons long, there is a double bond between carbons 1 and 2, and a methyl group attached to carbon 2. This is 2-methylpropene.

(c) Two methyl groups are attached to a three-carbon ring. This is 1,2-dimethylcyclopropane.

(d) The longest chain is 5 carbons long, there is a triple bond between carbons 2 and 3 and a methyl group attached to carbon 4. This is 4-methylpent-2-yne.

(e) The longest chain is 6 carbons long. This compound is 3,4-dimethylhexane

(f) The longest carbon chain containing the double bond is 5 carbons long. The double bond is between carbons 1 and 2. There is a propyl group on carbon 2, and carbons 3 and 4 each have one methyl group. This is 3,4-dimethyl-2-propylpent-1-ene.

34. **(M)** Again we do not show the hydrogen atoms in the structures below. But we realize that there are four bonds to each C atom and the missing bonds are $C-H$ bonds.

(a) methylbutane

(b) cyclohexene

(c) 2-methylhex-3-yne

(d) butan-2-ol

$$
\begin{array}{c}
\text{OH} \\
| \\
\text{C}-\text{C}-\text{C}-\text{C}
\end{array}
$$

(e) ethyl isopropyl ether

(f) Propanal

$$
\begin{array}{c}
\text{O} \\
\| \\
\text{C}-\text{C}-\text{C}-\text{H}
\end{array}
$$

35. **(M)**

(a) The name pentene is insufficient. pent-1-ene is $CH_2=CHCH_2CH_2CH_3$ and pent-2-ene is $CH_3CH=CHCH_2CH_3$.

(b) The name butanone is sufficient. There is only one four-carbon ketone.

(c) The name butyl alcohol is insufficient. There are numerous butanols. butan-1-ol is $HOCH_2CH_2CH_2CH_3$, butan-2-ol is $CH_3CH(OH)CH_2CH_3$, isobutyl alcohol is $HOCH_2CH(CH_3)_2$, and t-butyl alcohol is $(CH_3)_3COH$.

(d) The name methylaniline is insufficient. It specifies $CH_3-C_6H_4-NH_2$, with no relative locations for the $-NH_2$ and $-CH_3$ substituents.

(e) The name methylcyclopentane is sufficiently precise. It does not matter where on a five-carbon ring with only $C-C$ single bonds a methyl group is placed.

(f) Dibromobenzene is insufficient. It specifies $Br-C_6H_4-Br$, with no indication of the relative locations of the two bromo groups on the ring.

36. **(M)**

    (a) pent-3-ene specifies $CH_3CH_2CH{=}CHCH_3$. The proper name for this compound is pent-2-ene. The number for the functional group should be as small as possible.

    (b) Pentadiene is insufficient. Possible pentadienes are penta-1,2-diene $CH_2{=}C{=}CHCH_2CH_3$, penta-1,3-diene, $CH_2{=}CHCH{=}CHCH_3$, and penta-2,3-diene, $CH_3CH{=}C{=}CHCH_3$.

    (c) Propan-1-one is incorrect. There cannot be a ketone on the first carbon of a chain. The compound specified is either propionaldehyde, CH_3CH_2CHO, or propanone (propan-2-one).

    (d) Bromopropane is insufficient. It could be either 1-bromopropane, $BrCH_2CH_2CH_3$, or 2-bromopropane, $CH_3CHBrCH_3$.

    (e) Although 2,6-dichlorobenzene conveys enough information, the proper name for the compound is meta-dichlorobenzene, or 1,3-dichlorobenzene. Substituent numbers should be as small as possible.

    (f) 2-methyl-pent-3-yne is $(CH_3)_2CHC{\equiv}CCH_3$. The proper name for this compound is 4-methyl-pent-2-yne. The number of the triple bond should be as small as possible.

37. **(M)**

    (a) 2,4,6-trinitrotoluene   **(b)** methyl salicylate

    (c) 2-hydroxy-1,2,3-propanetricarboxylic acid: $HOOCCH_2C(OH)(COOH)CH_2COOH$

38. **(M)**

    (a) o-t-butylphenol   **(b)** 1-phenyl-2-aminopropane   **(c)** 2-methylheptadecane

$(CH_3)_2CH(CH_2)_{14}CH_3$

39. **(M)**

    (a) $HN(CH_2CH_3)_2$

         diethylamine

    (b)

p-nitroaniline

(c)

⬠—NH—CH$_2$—CH$_3$

N-ethylcyclopentanamine

(d) CH$_3$CH$_2$N(CH$_3$)CH$_2$CH$_3$

N-ethyl-*N*-methylethanamine

40. **(M)**

(a) ethanamine

CH$_3$CH$_2$NH$_2$

(b) 3-chloroaniline:

H$_2$N—◯—Cl

(c) dicyclopropylamine

△   △
    N
    H

(d) 2-chloroethan-1-amine

ClCH$_2$CH$_2$NH$_2$

Alkanes and Cycloalkanes

41. **(M)**

2-methylbutane   2,2-dimethylpropane

42. **(M)**

2,4-dimethylpentane   ethylcyclobutane

43. **(M)** Conformation (d) is lowest in energy. Conformation (a) is highest in energy.

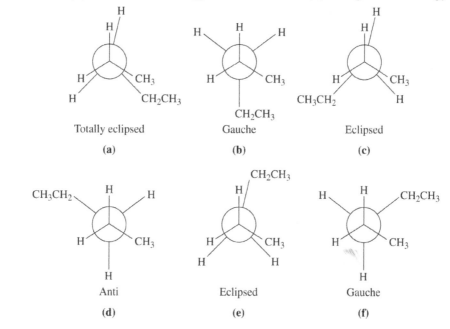

44. **(M)** Conformations (b) and (d) are lowest in energy.

Totally eclipsed
(a)

Gauche
(b)

Eclipsed
(c)

Anti
(d)

Eclipsed
(e)

Gauche
(f)

45. **(E)** The most stable conformation is:

46. **(E)** The most stable conformation is:

47. **(M)**

(a) The more stable conformation involves placing OH group in the equatorial position:

more stable

(b) The more stable configuration involves placing OH group in the axial position:

more stable

48. (M)

(a) The more stable conformation involves placing the isopropyl group in the equatorial position:

more stable

(b) The more stable conformation involves placing tert-butyl group in the equatorial position:

more stable

Alkenes

49. **(E)** In the case of ethene there are only two carbon atoms between which there can be a double bond. Thus, specifying the compound as ethene is unnecessary. In the case of propene, there can be a double bond only between the central carbon atom and a terminal carbon atom. Thus here also, specifying the compound as prop-1-ene is unnecessary. The case of butene is different, however, since but-1-ene, $CH_2 = CHCH_2CH_3$, is distinct from but-2-ene, $CH_3CH = CHCH_3$.

50. **(E)** In an alkene there is a $C = C$ double bond. On the other hand, in an cyclic alkane there are no double bonds, but rather a chain of carbon atoms joined at the ends into a ring.

51. **(M)** The E, Z system is used to name highly substituted alkenes. The stereochemistry about the double bond is assigned Z if the two groups of higher priority at each end of the double bond are on the same side of the molecule. If the two groups of higher priority are on the opposite sides of the double bond, the configuration is denoted by E.

(a) *E* isomer

highest priority
on carbon 2

highest priority
on carbon 1

(b) *E* isomer

highest priority
on carbon 2

highest priority
on carbon 1

(c) *Z* isomer

highest priority
on carbon 1

highest priority
on carbon 2

(d) *E* isomer

highest priority
on carbon 2

highest priority
on carbon 1

(e) *Z* isomer

highest priority
on carbon 1

highest priority
on carbon 2

52 **(M)**

(a)   (b)   (c)

53. **(M)**

(a) 2-chlorobut-2-ene   (b) 3-methylpent-2-ene

54. **(M)**

(a) 3-methylhex-3-ene   (b) 3-fluoro-2-methylhex-3-ene

Aromatic Compounds

55. **(E)**

(a) phenylacetylene

(b) meta-dichlorobenzene

(c) 1,3,5-trihydroxybenzene

56. **(E)**

(a) *p*-phenylphenol

(b)

2-isopropyl-5-methylphenol
or
3-hydroxy-4-isopropyltoluene

(c) meta-dinitrobenzene

Organic Stereochemistry

57. **(E)** The four structural isomers are 1,2-dichloropropane, 1,3-dichloropropane, 2,2-dichloropropane and 1,1-dichloropropane.

1,2-dichloropropane   1,3-dichloropropane   2,2-dichloropropane   1,1-dichloropropane

58. **(M)**

(a) The molecules are not constitutional isomers. The first compound is alkane and the second one is alkene.

(b) The two compounds are constitutional isomers, they have the same chemical formula but different structure.

(c) The two compounds are not constitutional isomers. They have different chemical formulas.

(d) The same compound.

(e) The same compound.

(f) The two compounds are constitutional isomers. In the first one, the NO_2 group is ortho to OH group. In the second one, the NO_2 group is para to OH group.

59. **(M)**

60. **(M)**

61. **(M)**

(a) (*S*)-3-bromo-2-methylpentane

$$CH_3—CH(CH_3)—\overset{Br}{\underset{CH_2CH_3}{\overset{(S)}{C}}}—H$$

(b) (*S*)-1,2-dibromopentane

$$CH_3CH_2CH_2—\overset{CH_2Br}{\underset{Br}{\overset{(S)}{C}}}—H$$

(c) (*R*)-3-(bromomethyl)-1-chloropentan-3-ol

$$CH_3CH_2—\overset{CH_2Br}{\underset{OH}{\overset{(R)}{C}}}—CH_2CH_2Cl$$

(d) (*S*)-1-bromopropan-2-ol

$$H—\overset{CH_2Br}{\underset{CH_3}{\overset{(S)}{C}}}—OH$$

62. **(M)**

(a)

$$CH_3CH_2CH_2—\overset{OH}{\underset{H}{\overset{(R)}{C}}}—CH_3$$

(*R*)-pentan-2-ol

(b)

$$CH_3(CH_3)CH—\overset{NH_2}{\underset{CH_3}{\overset{(S)}{C}}}—H$$

(*S*)-3-methylbutan-2-amine

(c)

$$CH_3—\overset{CH_2Br}{\underset{CH_2CH_3}{\overset{(S)}{C}}}—Cl$$

(*S*)-1-bromo-2-chloro-2-methylbutane

(d)

$$H—\overset{OH}{\underset{CH_2OH}{\overset{(S)}{C}}}—CH_2CH_2CH_3$$

(*S*)-pentane-1,2-diol

63. **(M)**

(a)

(*Z*)-pent-2-ene

(b)

(*E*)-1-chloro-2-methylbut-1-ene

(c)

(*E*)-4-(chloromethyl)-3,7-dimethyloct-3-ene

(d)

(*Z*)-5-bromo-3-(bromomethyl)-2-methylpent-2-enal

1251

Chapter 26: Structures of Organic Compounds

64. (M)

(a)

(*E*)-1,4-dichloro-2,3-dimethylbut-2-ene

(b)

(*E*)-2-(chloromethyl)-3-methylpent-2-en-1-ol

(c)

(*Z*)-6-chloro-3-ethynyl-4-(hydroxymethyl)hept-3-en-2-one

(d)

2-ethyl-3-methylbut-2-en-1-ol

65. (M)

(a)

(*Z*)-1,3,5-tribromopent-2-ene

(b)

(*E*)-1,2-dibromo-3-methylhex-2-ene

(c)

(*S*)-1-bromo-1-chlorobutane

(d)

(*R*)-1,3-dibromohexane

(e)

(*S*)-1-chloropropan-2-ol

66. (M)

(a)

(*R*)-1-bromo-1-chloroethane

(b)

(*E*)-2-bromopent-2-ene

(c)

(*Z*)-1-chloro-3-ethylhept-3-ene

(d)

(*R*)-2-hydroxypropanoic acid

(e)

(*S*)-2-aminopropanoate anion

1252

Structures and Properties of Organic Compounds

67. **(E)**
  (a) $C_4H_{11}N$ has zero elements of unsaturation.
  (b) C_4H_6O has two elements of unsaturation.
  (c) $C_9H_{15}ClO$ has two elements of unsaturation.

68. **(E)**
  (a) C_5H_9NO has two elements of unsaturation.
  (b) $C_5H_8O_3$ has two elements of unsaturation.
  (c) C_5H_9ClO has one element of unsaturation.

69. **(M)** There are two elements of unsaturation in the molecule (one π bond and one ring structure). The molecular formula is $C_8H_{15}NO$.

70. **(M)** There are five elements of unsaturation in the molecule (two π bonds, one ring structure and additional triple bond for CN which counts as two). The molecular formula is C_6H_4BrN.

71. **(M)** Compound 1 contains carbon-carbon double bond and ether linkage. It will decolorize bromine water according to the following chemical reaction:

Compound 2 is a primary alcohol and is easily oxidized. Primary alcohols readily react with sodium metal to liberate hydrogen gas according to the following chemical reaction:

Compound 3 is a carboxylic acid. It reacts with $Na_2CO_3(aq)$ to generate $CO_2(g)$:

72. **(M)** Compound 1 absorbs hydrogen in the presence of a metal catalyst:

Compound 2 forms an ether when heated strongly with concentrated sulfuric acid:

Compound 3 neutralizes dilute NaOH and forms an ester with ethanol:

73. **(M)** Cyclic ethers do not contain OH groups. Possible structures for the compound with molecular formula C_4H_6O (two elements of unsaturation) are:

74. **(M)** Possible structures for aldehydes and ketones having the formula $C_5H_{10}O$ are:

INTEGRATIVE AND ADVANCED EXERCISES

75. **(E)**

(a) cycloocta-1,5-diene

(b) 3,7,11-trimethyldodeca-2,6,10-trien-1-ol

$HOCH_2CH = C(CH_3)CH_2CH_2CH = C(CH_3)CH_2CH_2CH = C(CH_3)_2$

(c) 2,6-dimethylhept-5-enal

$$OHCCH(CH_3)CH_2CH_2CH = C(CH_3)_2$$

76. **(M)** We have show only the carbon atom skeleton in each case. Remember that there are four bonds to carbon. The bonds that are not indicated in these structures are C—H bonds. Boiling points are given in parentheses after the name of each compound.

Butane C_4H_{10} (−0.5 °C)   Hexane C_6H_{14} (68.7 °C)

```
C−C−C−C                        C−C−C−C−C−C
```

2-methylpropane   (−11.7 °C)   3-methylpentane   (63.3 °C)

```
      C                              C
      |                              |
    C−C−C                        C−C−C−C−C
```

Pentane C_5H_{12} (36.1 °C)   2-methylpentane   (58.0 °C)

```
C−C−C−C−C                          C
                                   |
                               C−C−C−C−C−C
```

2-methylbutane   (27.9 °C)   2,3-dimethylbutane   (58.0 °C)

```
    C                            C   C
    |                            |   |
  C−C−C−C                      C−C−C−C
```

2,2-dimethylpropane   (9.5 °C)   2,2-dimethylbutane   (49.7 °C)

```
    C                              C
    |                              |
  C−C−C                          C−C−C−C
    |                              |
    C                              C
```

As we proceed down each list of isomeric alkanes, the structures become more compact, and the boiling points decrease.

77. **(D)** In the structures below we have omitted the hydrogen atoms. Remember that there are four bonds to each C atom. The bonds that are missing are C—H bonds.

```
                              Cl                            Cl
                              |                             |
C−C−C−C−C−C−Cl        C−C−C−C−C−C              C−C−C−C−C−C
    C                     C                        C    Cl
    |                     |                        |    |
Cl−C−C−C−C−C          C−C−C−C−C−Cl              C−C−C−C−C
  C  Cl                   C                        C
  |  |                    |                        |
C−C−C−C−C              C−C−C−C−C              C−C−C−C−C−Cl
                          |
                          Cl
```

```
                          Cl
  Cl C                    C                    C                C  C
  |  |                    |                    |                |  |
C−C−C−C−C          C−C−C−C−C          C−C−C−C−C        Cl−C−C−C−C
                                                 |
                                                 Cl
```

```
    C  C                  C                    C                Cl C
    |  |                  |                    |                |  |
  C−C−C−C          Cl−C−C−C−C          C−C−C−C−Cl        C−C−C−C
    |                     |                    |                |
    Cl                    C                    C                C
```

78. **(M)** In one regard, benzene and cyclohexa-1,3,5-triene are the same substance; whenever there are alternating single and double bonds around a six-membered ring of carbon atoms, an aromatic ring forms. In another sense, these two compounds are different, thus, the name cyclohexa-1,3,5-triene implies that the three alternating double bonds in a six-membered carbon ring do not interact with each other, but they clearly do and the compound should be called benzene.

<u>**79.**</u> **(D)**

(a) Oxdn : $\{Fe \longrightarrow Fe^{3+} + 3\,e^-\}$ $\times 2$

Redn : $\underline{C_6H_5NO_2 + 7\,H^+ + 6\,e^- \longrightarrow C_6H_5NH_3^+ + 2\,H_2O}$

$C_6H_5NO_2 + 7\,H^+ + 2\,Fe \longrightarrow C_6H_5NH_3^+ + 2\,H_2O + 2\,Fe^{3+}$

(b) Oxdn : $\{C_6H_5CH_2OH + H_2O \longrightarrow C_6H_5COOH + 4\,H^+ + 4\,e^-\} \times 3$

Redn : $\underline{\{Cr_2O_7^{2-} + 14\,H^+ + 6\,e^- \longrightarrow 2\,Cr^{3+} + 7\,H_2O\} \quad \times 2}$

$3\,C_6H_5CH_2OH + 2\,Cr_2O_7^{2-} + 16\,H^+ \longrightarrow 3\,C_6H_5COOH + 4\,Cr^{3+} + 11\,H_2O$

(c) Oxdn: $\{CH_3CH{=}CH_2 + 2\ OH^- \longrightarrow CH_3CHOHCH_2OH + 2\,e^-\} \times 3$

Redn : $\underline{\{MnO_4^- + 2\,H_2O + 3\,e^- \longrightarrow MnO_2 + 4\,OH^-\} \quad \times 2}$

$3\,CH_3CH{=}\ CH_2 + 2\,MnO_4^- + 4\,H_2O \longrightarrow 3\,CH_3CHOHCH_2OH + 2\,MnO_2 + 2\,OH^-$

80. **(D)** We first write the equation for the reaction that occurs. Note that each mole of benzaldehyde yields one mole of benzoic acid. We are given the mass of each reagent; we need to determine which reagent is limiting.

$$3\,C_6H_5CHO + 2\,KMnO_4 + KOH \longrightarrow 3\,C_6H_5COO^-K^+ + 2\,MnO_2 + 2\,H_2O$$

$$3\,C_6H_5COO^-K^+ + 3\,H^+ \longrightarrow 3\,C_6H_5COOH + 3\,K^+$$

$$mass_{C_6H_5COOH} = 10.6\ g\ C_6H_5CHO \times \frac{1\ mol\ C_6H_5CHO}{106.1\ g\ C_6H_5CHO} \times \frac{1\ mol\ C_6H_5COOH}{1\ mol\ C_6H_5CHO} \times \frac{122.1\ g\ C_6H_5COOH}{1\ mol\ C_6H_5COOH}$$

$$= 12.2\ g\ C_6H_5COOH$$

$$mass_{C_6H_5COOH} = 5.9\ g\ KMnO_4 \times \frac{1\ mol\ KMnO_4}{158.0\ g\ KMnO_4} \times \frac{3\ mol\ C_6H_5COOH}{2\ mol\ KMnO_4} \times \frac{122.1\ g\ C_6H_5COOH}{1\ mol\ C_6H_5COOH}$$

$$= 6.8\ g\ C_6H_5COOH$$

From these two calculations, we conclude that $KMnO_4$ is the limiting reactant and 6.8 g C_6H_5COOH is expected.

$$\%\ yield = \frac{6.1\ g\ C_6H_5COOH\ produced}{6.8\ g\ \ C_6H_5COOH\ calculated} \times 100\% = 90.\%\ yield$$

81. **(D)** We suspect the compound contains C, H, N, and O. The %N by mass in the compound can be found using the ideal gas law:

$$\text{amount N}_2 = \frac{PV}{RT} = \frac{(735-9)\text{ mmHg} \times \dfrac{1\,\text{atm}}{760\text{ mmHg}} \times 0.0402\text{ L}}{0.08206\text{ L atm mol}^{-1}\text{ K}^{-1} \times 298\text{ K}} = 1.57 \times 10^{-3}\text{ mol N}_2$$

$$\%\ N = \frac{1.57 \times 10^{-3}\text{ mol N}_2 \times \dfrac{28.01\text{ g N}_2}{1\text{ mol N}_2}}{0.1825\text{ g sample}} \times 100\% = 24.1\%\ N$$

Now we determine the amounts of C, H, N, and O in the first sample.

$$\text{amount C} = 0.2895\text{ g CO}_2 \times \frac{1\text{ mol CO}_2}{44.010\text{ g CO}_2} \times \frac{1\text{ mol C}}{1\text{ mol CO}_2} = 0.006578\text{ mol C}$$

$$\text{mass C} = 0.006578\text{ mol C} \times \frac{12.011\text{ g C}}{1\text{ mol C}} = 0.07901\text{ g C}$$

$$\text{amount H} = 0.1192\text{ g H}_2\text{O} \times \frac{1\text{ mol H}_2\text{O}}{18.015\text{ g H}_2\text{O}} \times \frac{2\text{ mol H}}{1\text{ mol H}_2\text{O}} = 0.01323\text{ mol H}$$

$$\text{mass H} = 0.01323\text{ mol H} \times \frac{1.0079\text{ g H}}{1\text{ mol H}} = 0.01334\text{ g H}$$

$$\text{amount N} = 0.1908\text{ g} \times \frac{24.1\ \text{g N}}{100.0\text{ g sample}} = 0.0460\ \text{g N} \times \frac{1\ \text{mol N}}{14.007\text{ g N}} = 0.00328\text{ mol N}$$

$$\text{amount O} = (0.1908\text{ g} - 0.0460\text{ g N} - 0.07901\text{ g C} - 0.01334\text{ g H}) \times \frac{1\text{ mol O}}{15.999\text{ g O}} = 0.00328\text{ mol O}$$

From this information we determine the empirical formula of the compound.

0.006578 mol C ÷0.00328 ⟶ 2.01 mol C		0.01323 mol H ÷0.00328 ⟶ 4.03 mol H	
0.00328 mol N ÷0.00328 ⟶ 1.00 mol N		0.00328 mol O ÷0.00328 ⟶ 1.00 mol O	

The compound has an empirical formula of C_2H_4NO, which has a molar mass of 58.1 g/mol. We use the freezing point depression data to determine the number of moles of compound dissolved, and then its molar mass. First, the molality of the

$$\text{solution: } m = \frac{\Delta T_f}{K_f} = \frac{3.66\,^\circ\text{C} - 5.50\,^\circ\text{C}}{-5.12\,^\circ\text{C}/m} = 0.359\ m$$

$$\text{amount solute} = 0.02600\text{ kg benzene} \times \frac{0.359\text{ mol solute}}{1\text{ kg benzene}} = 0.00933\text{ mol solute}$$

$$M = \frac{1.082\text{ g}}{0.00933\text{ mol}} = 116\text{ g/mol}$$ This molar mass is twice the empirical molar mass.

Thus, the molecular formula is twice the empirical formula. Namely, the molecular formula = $C_4H_8N_2O_2$

82. (M)

(a)

1,2-dimethylbenzene   1,3-dimethylbenzene

ethyl benzene

1,4-dimethylbenzene

(b)

1,2,3-trimethylbenzene

1,2,4-trimethylbenzene

1,3,5-trimethylbenzene

1-ethyl-2-methylbenzene   1-ethyl-3-methylbenzene

1-ethyl-4-methylbenzene

propylbenzene

isopropylbenzene

83. (M) There are four different monochloro derivatives of 2-methylbutane:

1-chloro-2-methylbutane

2-chloro-3-methylbutane

1-chloro-3-methylbutane

2-chloro-2-methylbutane

84. (D)

(1) The molar masses of the five compounds are the same to one significant figure:

butan-1-ol	diethyl ether	methyl propyl ether	butyraldehyde	propionic acid
74.12 g/mol	74.12 g/mol	74.12 g/mol	72.11 g/mol	74.08 g/mol

Since the freezing point depression is known to only one significant figure, the molar mass of the unknown can only be determined to one significant figure. Thus, the cited freezing point depression data are insufficiently precise to differentiate between the compounds.

(2) Propionic acid would produce an aqueous solution that would turn blue litmus red. The unknown compound cannot be propionic acid.

(3) Both alcohols and aldehydes are oxidized to carboxylic acids by aqueous $KMnO_4$. Ethers are not oxidized by $KMnO_4$. Thus, the unknown must be butan-1-ol or butyraldehyde.

The identity of the unknown can be established by treatment with a carboxylic acid. If the unknown is an alcohol, it will form a pleasant smelling ester upon heating with a carboxylic acid such as acetic acid. If the compound is an aldehyde, it will not react with the carboxylic acid under these conditions.

85. (M)

2,4-dimethylpenta-1,4-diene   2,3-dimethylpentane   1,2,4-tribromobenzene

methyl acetate   butan-2-one

86. (M)

(a) 2-chloro-4-methyloctane **(b)** 2-amino-3-chloropentanoic acid

(c) Ethyl methyl ether **(d)** 3-chloropropan-1-amine

(e) (Z)-1,3-dichloro-2-methylbut-2-ene

87. (D)

4-chlorobut-1-ene

3-chlorobut-1-ene

Cl

(R and S)

2-chlorobut-1-ene

Cl

(Z)-1-chlorobut-1-ene

Cl

(E)-1-chlorobut-1-ene

Cl

1-chloro-2-methylprop-1-ene

Cl

3-chloro-2-methylprop-1-ene

Cl

(E)-1-chlorobut-2-ene

Cl

(Z)-1-chlorobut-2-ene

Cl

(Z)-2-chlorobut-2-ene

Cl

(E)-2-chlorobut-2-ene

Cl

1-chloro-2-methylcyclopropane

Cl Cl
cis- trans-

1-chloro-1-methylcyclopropane

Cl

(chloromethyl)cyclopropane

Cl

chlorocyclobutane

Cl

88. (D) From the formula $C_5H_{12}O$ we can see that this is a saturated alcohol. This question involves chiral alcohols, hence the possibilities are:

pentan-2-ol

OH OH
(R) (S)

CrO₃/pyridine

pentan-2-one

O

(achiral)

3-methylbutan-2-ol

(R) (S)
OH OH

CrO₃/pyridine

3-methylbutan-2-one

O

(achiral)

2-methylbutan-1-ol

OH OH
(R) (S)

CrO₃/pyridine

2-methylbutanal

O O
(R) (S)

Thus, compound **A** must be either (S)-2-methylbutan-1-ol or (R)-2-methylbutan-1-ol
Compound **B** must be either (S)-2-methylbutanal or (R)-2-methylbutanal.

89. **(M)**

  (a) ester, amine(tertiary), arene

  (b) $C_1 = sp^2$, $C_2 = sp^3$, $C_3 = sp^3$, $C_4 = sp^3$, $N = sp^3$

  (c) Carbons 2 and 4 are chiral.

90. **(M)**

  (a) alcohol, secondary amide, sulfone, arene, alkyl halide

  (b) $C_1 = sp^3$, $C_2 = sp^2$, $C_3 = sp^3$, $C_4 = sp^3$, $C_5 = sp^2$, $N = sp^3$

  (c) Carbons 3 and 4 are chiral.

91. **(M)**

  (a) alcohol, amine(secondary), arene

  (b) $C_1 = sp^2$, $C_2 = sp^3$, $C_3 = sp^3$, $C_4 = sp^3$, $N = sp^3$

  (c) Carbons 2 and 3 are chiral.

  (d) $C_{10}H_{15}NO$ has a molar mass of 165.24 g/mol.

Assume no volume change and
1 g water = 1 mL water, hence, 1g in 200 g of water represents 0.030 M.
Since the pH = 10.8, it is a base (symbolized as A⁻). Set up I.C.E. table.

Reaction	A⁻(aq)	+	H₂O(l)	⇔	HA(aq)	+	OH⁻(aq)
Initial	0.030 M		—		0 M		≈ 0 M
Change	-x		—		+x		+x
Equilibrium	0.030-x		—		x		x

pH = 10.8 hence pOH = 3.2 and [OH⁻] = 0.00063 M = x
$K_b = x^2/(0.30-x) = (0.00063)^2/(0.030-0.00063) = 1.35 \times 10^{-5}$, $pK_b = 4.87$

92. **(M)**

  (a)   **(b)**

  (c)

93. **(M)**

(a) (b)

94. **(D)**

(a) (b) (c)

95. **(D)** Cholesterol has eight chiral centers. The configuration of the carbon atom bonded to the OH group is S and the configuration of the double bond is Z.

96. (D)

(1)

more stable conformation

No chiral senters are present due to a plane of symmetry passing through C1 and C4

(2)

more stable configuration
two bromine atoms in equatorial positions

FEATURE PROBLEM

97. (D)

(a) The corresponding values are tabulated below:

Type of bond	Wavenumber (cm^{-1})	Wavelength (nm)	Frequency (Hz)
Single bonds			
-C-H	2850-3300	3030-3509	8.5×10^{13}-9.9×10^{13}
=C-H	3000-3100	3226-3333	9.0×10^{13}-9.3×10^{13}
≡C-H	3300	3030	9.9×10^{13}
N-H	3300-3500	2857-3030	9.9×10^{13}-1.1×10^{14}
O-H	3200-3600	2778-3125	9.6×10^{13}-1.1×10^{14}

(b) The two compounds of interest are acetone and propan-1-ol, both of which are colorless liquids.

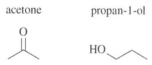

acetone   propan-1-ol

Absorption labeled A clearly corresponds to O-H stretch. Absorptions labeled B and C correspond to C-H stretches. Lastly, absorption labeled D indicates the presence of a carbonyl group C=O. Therefore, the spectrum with C and D labeled peaks corresponds to acetone.

(c) The characteristic IR absorption at 1645 cm^{-1} corresponds to C=C, which is further confirmed by the fact that the compound decolorizes Br$_2$. Strong absorption band from 2860-3600 cm^{-1} is indicative of an alcohol. Alcohols react with sodium metal to liberate hydrogen gas. Based on the information provided, the isomer of acetone is most likely prop-2-en-1-ol.

prop-2-en-1-ol

SELF-ASSESSMENT EXERCISES

98. **(E)**

(a) In organic chemistry, tert group is a four carbon group with the general formula C$_4$H$_9$, derived from the isomer of butane. Structure of tert butyl group is:

(b) R group is commonly used in organic chemistry to indicate different substituents, such as methyl, ethyl, isopropyl, etc.

(c) Compound shown is benzene with the molecular formula C$_6$H$_6$.

(d) Carbonyl group is a functional group composed of a carbon atom double-bonded to an oxygen atom, C=O.

(e) Amines are organic compounds that contain basic nitrogen atom with a lone pair. Primary amines arise when one of the three hydrogen atoms in ammonia is replaced by a carbon group such as alkyl or aryl.

99. **(E)**

(a) Alkanes are saturated compounds with the general formula C$_n$H$_{2n+2}$. Alkenes, on the other hand, are unsaturated compounds containing C=C double bonds. General formula of alkenes is C$_n$H$_{2n}$.

(b) In organic chemistry, compounds composed of carbon and hydrogen are divided into two classes: aromatic compounds, which contain benzene rings or similar rings of atoms, and aliphatic compounds, which do not contain aromatic rings.

(c) Phenols are aromatic compounds that contain -OH group bonded to a benzene ring. Alcohols are compounds that contain –OH groups bonded to sp^3 carbon atoms.

(d) Ether is a class of organic compounds that contain an oxygen atom connected to two alkyl or aryl groups, of general formula R–O–R. Esters are chemical compounds derived by reacting an oxoacid (one containing an oxo group, X=O) with a hydroxyl compound such as an alcohol or phenol. Ester functionality is C(O)O-R.

(e) Amines are ammonia derivatives with one, two or three hydrogens replaced by an alkyl or aryl groups.

100. (E)

(a) Structural isomerism, or constitutional isomerism, is a form of isomerism in which molecules with the same molecular formula have atoms bonded together in different orders, as opposed to stereoisomerism.

(b) Stereoisomers are isomeric molecules that have the same molecular formula and sequence of bonded atoms (constitution), but which differ only in the three-dimensional orientations of their atoms in space.

(c) When the substituent groups are oriented in the same direction, the diastereomer is referred to as cis, whereas, when the substituents are oriented in opposing directions, the diastereomer is referred to as trans.

(d) Ortho position refers to 1,2-disubstituted benzene.

101. (M) The main carbon-carbon chain in isoheptane contains six carbon atoms. Furthermore, isoheptane contains isopropyl group, $CH(CH_3)_2$. The correct structure is structure (c).

102. (M) The molecular formula of cyclobutane is C_4H_8. The correct answer is (b).

103. (M) Hydrocarbons with four of more carbon atoms form isomers. The correct answer is (e). The three isomers of the compound with molecular formula C_5H_{12} are:

pentane   2-methylbutane   2,2-dimethylpropane

104. (M)

(a)

2-bromo-4-chloro-2,6-dimethylheptane

(b)

isopropylcyclohexane

(c)

5,5-dibromo-2-chloro-3,3-difluoroheptane

105. (M)

(1)   **(2)**   **(3)**

(4)   **(5)**

(a) (2) and (3) are identical.
(b) (1) and (2) are constitutional isomers.
(c) (1) and (5) are diastereomers.
(d) (3) and (4) are enatiomers.

106. (M)

(a) Constitutional isomers

(b) Constitutional isomers

(c) Constitutional isomers

(d) Stereoisomers

107. (M)

2-methylhexane

lowest energy (only 1 gauche interaction)

108. (M) The correct answer is (c).

(a) propan-2-ol

(b) butan-1-ol

(c) butan-2-ol

(d) tert-butyl alcohol
or
2-methylpropan-2-ol

oxidation

ethyl methyl ketone
or
butan-2-one

109. (M) C_4H_{10} has only two isomers (n-butane and 2-methylpropane), whereas C_4H_8 has six (but-1-ene, (*E*)-but-2-ene, (*Z*)-but-2-ene, 2-merthylpropene, cyclobutane, and methylcyclopropane.).

110. (M)

(a) C_6H_{12} is expected to have higher boiling point than C_2H_4.

(b) C_3H_7OH is expected to have higher solubility in water because of smaller hydrocarbon chain.

(c) Benzoic acid (C_6H_5COOH) has greater acidity than benzaldehyde.

111. (M)

(*E*)-3-benzyl-2,5-dichloro-4-methylhex-3-ene

1-nitro-4-vinylbenzene

trans-1-(4-bromophenyl)-2-methylcyclohexane

CHAPTER 27
REACTIONS OF ORGANIC COMPOUNDS
PRACTICE EXAMPLES

1A **(M)**

   (a) Because hydrogen atom in benzene is replaced by a bromine atom, this reaction is a substitution reaction.

   (b) This reaction involves only a change in the skeletal structure (constitution), and so the reaction is a rearrangement reaction.

   (c) In this reaction, there is a reduction of C=O bond, i.e. the alcohol is adding across a ketone group. This is an example of an addition reaction.

1B **(M)**

   (a) This in an example of an elimination reaction. HBr is being eliminated from bromobutane to yield but-1-ene.

   (b) This is an example of a substitution reaction in which Cl group is replaced by $N(CH_2CH_3)_3$ group.

   (c) This is an example of a substitution reaction in which bromine is being replaced by a butynyl group.

2A **(M)**

   (a)

$$H-\overset{..}{\underset{..}{O}}{:}^{\ominus} \; + \; CH_3-I \longrightarrow CH_3-\overset{..}{O}H \; + \; :\overset{..}{\underset{..}{I}}{:}^{\ominus}$$

nucleophile   electrophile   leaving group

   (b)

$$H-\overset{..}{\underset{..}{O}}{:}^{\ominus} \; + \; \underset{H-\overset{..}{\underset{..}{O}}{}}{\overset{\overset{..}{O}}{C}}-CH_2-CH_2-CH_3 \longrightarrow H_2O \; + \; {}^{\ominus}\underset{:\overset{..}{O}:}{\overset{\overset{..}{O}}{C}}-CH_2-CH_2-CH_3$$

base   acid

2B **(M)**

   (a)

$$H_2\overset{..}{N}{:}^{\ominus} \; + \; H-\overset{..}{\underset{..}{O}}-CH_2-CH_3 \longrightarrow \overset{..}{N}H_3 \; + \; {}^{\ominus}{:}\overset{..}{\underset{..}{O}}-CH_2-CH_3$$

base   acid

   (b)

$$CH_3-\overset{..}{\underset{..}{S}}{:}^{\ominus} \; + \; :\overset{..}{\underset{..}{Br}}-CH_2-CH_2-CH\overset{CH_3}{\underset{CH_3}{}} \longrightarrow H_3C-\overset{..}{\underset{..}{S}}-CH_2-CH_2-CH\overset{CH_3}{\underset{CH_3}{}} \; + \; :\overset{..}{\underset{..}{Br}}{:}^{\ominus}$$

nucleophile   electrophile   leaving group

3A **(M)**

(a) $CH_3C\equiv C^- + CH_3Br \xrightarrow{\;S_N2\;} CH_3C\equiv CCH_3 + Br^-$

(b) $Cl^- + CH_3CH_2CN \rightarrow$ NO REACTION

The nucleophile in this reaction is Cl^- whereas the leaving group is the CN^-. The CN^- ion is a much stronger nucleophile than Cl^-, so the equilibrium will strongly favor the reactants. In other words, no reaction is expected.

(c) $CH_3NH_2 + (CH_3)_3CCl \xrightarrow{\;S_N1\;} CH_3 + NH_2C(CH_3)_3 + Cl^-$

3B **(M)**

(a)

(R)-2-chlorobutane   (S)-2-cyanobutane

Because the configuration at the stereogenic carbon has undergone an inversion, we can conclude that the reaction has occurred via an S_N2 mechanism.

(b)

start with pure   50:50 mixture of
(R) or (S)   (R) and (S)

Clearly, since a racemic mixture forms, the reaction must occur via an S_N1 mechanism.

topside attack
OR
bottomside attack

50:50 mixture of
(R) and (S)

4A **(M)** SCH$_3^-$ is a nucleophile and haloalkane is the electrophile. The nucleophile is charged and is therefore a strong nucleophile. The substitution reaction should occur via S$_N$2 mechanism.

(R)-2-bromo-4-methylpentane   (S)-2-methyl-4-(methylthio)pentane

4B **(M)** Water is a weak nucleophile. The reaction should proceed via S$_N$1 mechanism to give a mixture of products (R and S). Because the haloalkane is symmetrical only one compound will form.

single compound
no chiral carbon atoms present

pentan-3-ol (symmetrical molecule)

5A **(M)** This is an S_N2 reaction leading to the alkyl sulfide product.

$$CH_3-\underset{\underset{H}{|}}{\overset{\overset{H}{|}}{C}}-CH_2-Br \ + \ CH_3S^\ominus \ \longrightarrow \ CH_3-\underset{\underset{H}{|}}{\overset{\overset{H}{|}}{C}}-CH_2-SCH_3 \ + \ Br^\ominus$$

5B **(M)** Electrophile is a secondary haloalkane. The nucleophile is $(CH_3)_2CHO^-$, a relatively hindered strong base. Therefore, the reaction may proceed by $S_N1/E1$, although it may also proceed to a significant degree by S_N2 and E2.

S_N1 (major product)

+

$$CH_3-CH=CH-CH_3$$

E1 (minor product)

6A **(M)**

(a) This reaction employs a strong oxidizing agent. The secondary alcohol will be oxidized to a ketone.

(R)-butan-2-ol   butan-2-one

$$\overset{Na_2Cr_2O_7}{\underset{H_2SO_4}{\longrightarrow}}$$

(b) Propan-1-ol is a primary alcohol and for the conditions specified, a dehydration reaction will occur. The product is prop-1-ene and it is formed by a concerted E2 reaction following protonation of the alcohol. The reaction mechanism is shown below:

$$CH_3-CH_2-CH_2-\ddot{O}-H \ + \ H-\overset{\oplus}{\underset{\underset{H}{|}}{\ddot{O}}}-H \ \rightleftharpoons \ CH_3-CH_2-CH_2-\overset{\overset{H}{|}{\oplus}}{\underset{..}{O}}-H \ + \ H_2O$$

prop-1-ene

6B **(M)**

(a) Primary alcohols are readily converted to alkyl halides. The reactions proceeds via a S_N2 mechanism.

3-methylbutan-1-ol   1-iodo-3-methylbutane

$$\overset{HI}{\longrightarrow}$$

(b) In this reaction, an alcohol reacts with a sodium metal to produce sodium tert-butoxide and hydrogen gas.

2-methylpropan-2-ol

OH $\xrightarrow{\text{Na}}$ ONa + 1/2H$_2$

7A **(D)** In this reaction, three products are possible, the major one being 3-nitro-benzaldehyde.

3-nitrobenzaldehyde   2-nitrobenzaldehyde   4-nitrobenzaldehyde

meta (major)   ortho (minor)   para (minor)

7B **(M)** Chlorine group is ortho and para directing. Several products are possible:

major   minor

INTEGRATIVE EXAMPLE

A. **(D)** Alkanes are relatively unreactive. However, they will undergo bromination reaction in the presence of light. Such reaction will generate bromo-cyclohexane in the first step. In the presence of a base, elimination will occur resulting in the formation of cyclohexene. Subsequent repetition of these two steps will genererate the desired product, 1,3-cyclohexadiene. Typically, in the second step, selective allylic bromination is achieved utilizing brominating agent, N-bromosuccinimide (NBS).

$\xrightarrow[\text{light}]{\text{Br}_2}$ Br $\xrightarrow{\text{Base}}$

$\xrightarrow[\text{light}]{\text{Bromination}}$ Br $\xrightarrow{\text{Base}}$

Brominating agent:

N-bromosuccinimide

Br

B. **(M)** SO_3H and NO_2 groups are meta directing, whereas bromine group is ortho and para directing. The given compound could therefore be synthesized using the following sequence of reactions:

EXERCISES

Types of Organic Reactions

1. **(E)**

(a) Nucleophilic substitution is a fundamental class of substitution reaction in which an "electron rich" nucleophile selectively bonds with or attacks the positive or partially positive charge of an atom attached to a group or atom called the leaving group; the positive or partially positive atom is referred to as an electrophile.

$$R\text{-}Br + OH^- \rightarrow R - OH + Br^-$$

(b) Electrophilic substitution reactions are chemical reactions in which an electrophile displaces another group, typically but not always hydrogen. Electrophilic substitution is characteristic of aromatic compounds. Electrophilic aromatic substitution is an important way of introducing functional groups onto benzene rings.

(c) Generally, in an addition reaction, a molecule adds across a double or triple bond in another molecule.

(d) In an elimination reaction, atoms or groups that are bonded to adjacent atoms are eliminated as a small molecule.

(e) When an organic compound undergoes a rearrangement reaction, the carbon skeleton of a molecule is rearranged.

minor product (*S* and *R*)   major product (*S* and *R*)

chiral carbon atom indicated by*

2. **(E)**

(a) Dehydration reaction typically corresponds to elimination of water from an alcohol to yield an alkene.

(b) Hydrolysis is a chemical reaction during which molecules of water (H_2O) are split into hydrogen (H) and hydroxide anions (OH^-) in the process of a chemical mechanism. One example is the hydrolysis of an amide into a carboxylic acid and an amine or ammonia, the carboxylic acid has a hydroxyl group derived from a water molecule and the amine (or ammonia) gains the hydrogen ion.

(c) Solvolysis reaction is a reaction in which a solvent molecule acts as a nucleophile.

(d) Hydration of an alkene is the addition of water to an alkene to generate an alcohol.

alkene   water   alcohol

3. **(E) (a)** substitution reaction.   **(b)** addition reaction.   **(c)** substitution reaction.

4. **(E) (a)** substitution.   **(b)** oxidation.   **(c)** addition.   **(d)** elimination.

5. **(M)**

(a) This is an addition reaction.

(b) This is an elimination reaction.

(c) This is a substitution reaction.

6. (M)

(a) This is a rearrangement reaction.

3,3-dimethylbut-1-ene   2,3-dimethylbut-2-ene

(b) This is a substitution reaction.

1-iodo-2,2-dimethylpropane   2,2-dimethylpropan-1-ol

(c) This is an elimination reaction.

2-chloro-2-methylpropane   2-methylprop-1-ene

Substitution and Elimination Reactions

7. (E)

8. (E)

2. (M)

(a) rate = k[CH₃CH₂CH₂CH₂Br][NaOH]

(b)

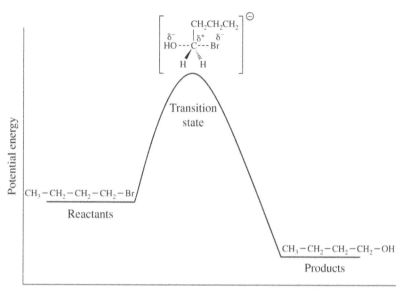

(c) Doubling the concentration of n-butyl bromide will also double the rate.

(d) Decreasing the concentration of NaOH by a factor of two will decrease the rate by a factor of 2.

10. (M)

(a) Rate = k[2-bromo-2-methylpentane]

(b)

(c) The rate will double.

(d) The rate will not change because it is independent on the concentration of ethanol.

11. **(M)**

(a) Rate = k[CH$_3$CH$_2$CH$_2$Br][OH$^-$]

(b)

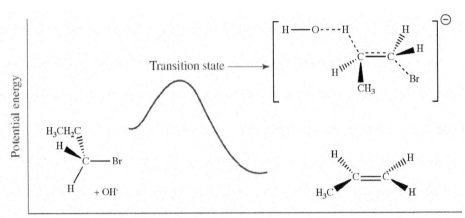

(c) The rate will double.

(d) The rate will decrease by a factor of 2.

12. **(M)**

(a) Rate = k[CH$_3$CH$_2$C(CH$_3$)$_2$Br]

(b)

(c) The rate will double.

(d) The rate will remain the same.

13. **(M)** Equilibrium favors the formation of products if the leaving group is a weaker base than the nucleophile.

(a) The leaving group, I$^-$, is a weaker base than the nucleophile, CH$_3$CH$_2$O$^-$. Therefore, equilibrium favors the formation of products.

$$CH_3CH_2O^- + CH_3CH_2CH_2I \rightleftharpoons CH_3CH_2CH_2OCH_2CH_3 + NaI$$

nucleophile   electrophile   leaving group

(b) Since the leaving group, NH_3, is a stronger base than the nucleophile, I^-, the forward reaction is not favored. Equilibrium favors the formation of reactants.

$$CH_3CH_2NH_3^+ \quad + \; KI^- \quad \rightleftharpoons \quad NH_3 \quad + \quad CH_3CH_2I \; + \; K^+$$
electrophile   nucleophile   leaving group

14. **(M)** Equilibrium favors the formation of products if the leaving group is a weaker base than the nucleophile.
    (a) The leaving group, I^-, is a weaker base than the nucleophile, N_3^-, so equilibrium favors the formation of products.

electrophile   nucleophile   leaving group

    (b) The leaving group, NH_2^-, is a stronger base than the nucleophile, Br^-, so the formation of products is not favored. Equilibrium favors the formation of reactants.

electrophile   nucleophile   leaving group
               weak base   strong base

15. **(M)** Molecule (a) reacts faster in the S_N2 reaction than does molecule (b) because there is less steric hindrance. In molecule (b), the steric hindrance is associated with a methyl group being positioned in the axial position.

16. **(M)** 1,3-Diaxial steric interactions in the cis diastereomer would enhance the departure of the leaving group (Br^-).

17. **(M)** The reaction most likely proceeded via S_N1 mechanism resulting in racemization of the product (equal amounts of S and R isomers).

(*S* and *R*)

18. (M) The resulting product is optically active S isomer. The reaction proceeded via S_N2 mechanism.

19. (M) The resulting product is an equimolar mixture of S and R isomers. The reaction proceeded via S_N1 mechanism.

(*S* and *R*)

20. (M) The resulting product is optically active S isomer. The reaction proceeded via S_N2 mechanism.

(*R*)-2-iodobutane   (*S*)-2-methylbutanenitrile

21. (M)

(a) In this reaction we are dealing with a primary alkyl halide and a strong but bulky base. The reaction is going to proceed via an E_2 mechanism. The product of the reaction is methylenecyclopentane.

(b) In this reaction we are dealing with a secondary alkyl halide and a weak base which is also a good nucleophile. The reaction is most likely going to proceed via S_N2 mechanism.

(c) A 2° substrate, a weak nucleophile, and a polar protic solvent favor substitution by S_N1. Substitution by S_N1 involves the formation of a carbocation in the rate-determining step, followed by nucleophilic attack. The major substitution products will be (*R*) and (*S*) $(CH_3)_3CCH(OCH_2CH_3)CH_3$. S_N1 is always accompanied by $E1$, so there will also be some elimination product, $CH_2 = CHC(CH_3)_3$. A methide shift could also occur leading to $(CH_3)_2C = C(CH_3)_2$.

S_N1

(S) $\overset{\text{H}}{\underset{\text{OCH}_2\text{CH}_3}{}}$ +   (R) $\overset{\text{OCH}_2\text{CH}_3}{\underset{\text{H}}{}}$

(S) $\overset{\text{H}}{\underset{\text{Br}}{}}$ + CH₃CH₂OH

(*R* and *S*)-3-ethoxy-2,2-dimethylbutane
major products

E1

3,3-dimethylbut-1-ene   +   2,3-dimethylbut-2-ene
minor product   **minor product**

22. **(M)**

(a) In this case we are dealing with a secondary alkyl halide and a strong base. The reaction is most likely going to proceed via elimination by E2 mechanism.

(b) In this reaction we are reacting primary alkyl halide with a sterically not hindered base. However, the base is a good nucleophile. The reaction is most likely going to proceed via a S$_N$2 mechanism.

OCH₂CH₃   + some E2 products

(c) In this reaction we are reacting secondary alkyl halide with a weak base that is also an excellent nucleophile. The reaction is going to proceed via S$_N$2 mechanism.

SH

(S)

Alcohols and Alkenes

<u>**23.**</u> **(E)**

(a) $(CH_3)_2CHCH_2OH + HBr \longrightarrow (CH_3)_2CHCH_2Br + H_2O$

(b) $(CH_3)_3COH + K \longrightarrow (CH_3)_3CO^-K^+ + \frac{1}{2}H_2(g)$

(c) $(CH_3)_2CHOH \xrightarrow{[O]} (CH_3)_2CO$

(d) There is no reaction.

24. **(M)**

(a) $(CH_3)_2CHCH_2OH \xrightarrow{[O]} (CH_3)_2CHC\overset{\text{O}}{\underset{\text{OH}}{\diagup}}$

(b) $CH_3CH_2OH + (CH_3)_2CHCOOH \longrightarrow (CH_3)_2CHC\overset{\text{O}}{\underset{\text{OCH}_2CH_3}{\diagup}}$

(c)

only product if S$_N$2

If S$_N$1, the products will be:

major   minor

(d) $CH_3CH_2CH_2OH \xrightarrow[\Delta]{H_2SO_4} CH_3CH=CH_2 + H_2O$

25.   **(M)** We are converting alcohol to alkyl halide.

26.   **(M)** A simple way to carry out the required conversion is to heat 3-methylbutan-1-ol in the presence of H_2SO_4. Primary alcohols dehydrate mainly through the E2 mechanism.

3-methylbut-1-ene

27.   **(M)** If no rearrangement occurs the expected product would be 4,4-dimethyl-pent-2-ene

Since the main product is 2,3-dimethyl-2-pentene, the rearrangement of carbocation via 1.2-methyl shift occurred to afford more substituted alkene.

28. **(D)** In this case rearrangement of carbocation occurred

2-methyl-1-butene   2-methyl-2-butene

29. **(M)**

(a) $CH_3 - CH = CH_2 \xrightarrow[Pt]{H_2} CH_3 - CH_2 - CH_3$

(b)

30. **(M)**

(a)

(b) HCN does not add to alkenes.

(c)

31. **(M)**

(a)

(b)

(Z)-but-2-ene   (R)-2-iodobutane   (S)-2-iodobutane

(c)

32. (M)

(a)

(b)

$$CH_3-CH_2-CH=\overset{\overset{\textstyle CH_3}{|}}{C}-CH_3 \ + \ H_2O \ \xrightarrow{H_2SO_4} \ CH_3-CH_2-CH_2-\overset{\overset{\textstyle CH_3}{|}}{\underset{\underset{\textstyle OH}{|}}{C}}-CH_3$$

(c)

33. (M)

(a)

(b)

(c)

(d)

34. (M)

(a)

(b)

(c)

(d)

Electrophilic Aromatic Substitution

35. (M)

36. (M)

37. (M)

$(CH_3)_2CHCl + AlCl_3 \rightleftharpoons (CH_3)_2\overset{\oplus}{C}H + AlCl_4^{\ominus}$

38. (D)

39. **(M)**

(a)

(b) NO$_2$ group is meta directing

(c) NO$_2$ group is meta directing and CH$_3$ group is both ortho and para directing.

40. **(M)**

(a) COOH group is meta directing

(b) OH group is ortho and para directing

(c) NO$_2$ group is meta directing and CHO group is meta directing

major

Reactions of Alkanes

41. **(M)**

2,2,3-trimethylpentane   (R)-3-bromo-2,2,3-trimethylpentane   (S)-3-bromo-2,2,3-trimethylpentane

42. **(M)** Free radical bromination is generally much more selective than chlorination. The product selectivity is mostly governed by the radical stability of the carbon atom after the hydrogen atom abstraction by a bromine radical, with the 3° radical being more stable than the 2° or 1° radical. Methylcyclohexane contains one tertiary carbon atom. Therefore, the expected major product is 1-bromo-1-methylcyclohexane.

Free radical chlorination is generally much less selective. Products of monochlorination of methylcyclohexane are shown below.

43. **(M)**

(a)

Initiation

$$F-F \xrightarrow[\text{light}]{\text{heat or}} F^{\bullet} + F^{\bullet}$$

Propagation

1-fluoro-2,3-dimethylbutane

Termination

$$F^{\bullet} + F^{\bullet} \longrightarrow F-F$$

(b) Statistically, there is a higher probability of abstracting an H atom from 12 CH_3 protons to yield 1-fluoro-2,3-dimethybutane than of abstracting an H atom from 2 CH protons to yield 2-fluoro-2,3-dimethylbutane.

44. **(M)**

Initiation: $Br-Br \xrightarrow[\text{light}]{\text{heat}} Br^{\bullet} + Br^{\bullet}$

Propagation:

Termination: $Br^{\bullet} + Br^{\bullet} \longrightarrow Br_2$

Polymerization Reactions

45. **(M)** The reason lies in the statistics. During polymerization reaction, polymers of different chain-lengths are formed. As a result, we can only speak of average molecular weight.

46. **(M)** Dacron is the polymer formed in the condensation of a carboxylic acid and alcohol. It is called a polyester because it contains ester linkages along polymer chains. To calculate the percent of oxygen by mass, we consider the smallest repeating unit in Dacron.

$$\% \, 0 = \frac{2 \times 2 \times 16.00}{10 \times 12.00 + 4 \times 16.00 + 8 \times 1.008} \times 100\% = \frac{64}{192.064} \times 100\% = 33.3\%$$

47. **(M)**

48. **(M)** No polymer formation is expected because ethyl alcohol does not contain two functional groups capable of undergoing a condensation reaction. With an —OH group on each of its three carbons, glycerol is capable of polymerizing with terephthalic acid.

Synthesis of Organic Compounds

49. **(D)**

50. **(M)**

51. (D)

$$H-C\equiv C-H \xrightarrow[CH_3CH_2Br]{NaNH_2} H-C\equiv C-CH_2-CH_3 \xrightarrow[CH_3-CH_2CH_2Br]{NaNH_2}$$

(structure: $CH_2-CH_2-C\equiv C-CH_2$ with CH_3 groups)

$$CH_3-CH_2-CH_2-C\equiv C-CH_2-CH_3 \xrightarrow[\substack{Lindlar's \\ catalyst}]{H_2}$$

cis isomer

$$CH_3-CH_2-CH_2-C\equiv C-CH_2-CH_3 \xrightarrow[NH_3]{Na}$$

trans isomer

52. (M)

(structure of (S)-2-iodobutane) + $NH_3 \longrightarrow$ (structure of (R)-butan-2-amine) + HI

(S)-2-iodobutane

(R)-butan-2-amine

53. (D)

$$CH_3-CH_2-CH_2Cl + NaN_3 \longrightarrow CH_3-CH_2-CH_2N_3 + NaCl$$

$$CH_3-CH_2-CH_2N_3 \xrightarrow{reduction} CH_3-CH_2-CH_2-NH_2 + N_2$$

54. (M)

$$CH_3-CH_2-Cl + CN^{\ominus} \longrightarrow CH_3-CH_2-CN \xrightarrow{H_2} CH_3-CH_2-CH_2-NH_2$$

INTEGRATIVE AND ADVANCED EXERCISES

55. **(M)**

(a) $CH_3-CH_2-CH_2-CH_2-CH_2-OH \xrightarrow[H^+]{Cr_2O_7^{2-}} CH_3-CH_2-CH_2-CH_2-C\overset{\displaystyle O}{\underset{\displaystyle OH}{\big\langle}}$

(b) $CH_3-CH_2-CH_2-C\overset{\displaystyle O}{\underset{\displaystyle OH}{\big\langle}} + CH_3-CH_2-OH \xrightarrow{H^+} CH_3-CH_2-CH_2-C\overset{\displaystyle O}{\underset{\displaystyle O-CH_2-CH_3}{\big\langle}} + H_2O$

(c) $CH_2{=}\overset{\displaystyle CH_3}{\underset{\displaystyle}{C}}{-}CH_2{-}CH_3 + HBr \longrightarrow CH_3-\overset{\displaystyle CH_3}{\underset{\displaystyle Br}{C}}-CH_2-CH_3 + H_2O$

56. **(M)**

(a) Nitro group is meta directing

(b) NH$_2$ group is ortho and para directing

(c) –OCH$_3$ and Br are both ortho and para directing

57. **(M)**

58. **(M)**

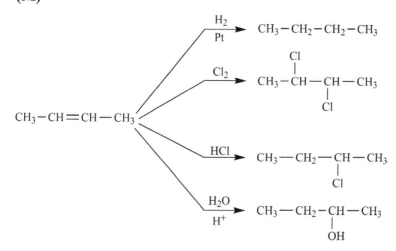

59. **(M)**

(a) Esters are prone to hydrolysis under basic conditions

$$CH_3-CH_2-\overset{\overset{\displaystyle O}{\|}}{C}-O-CH_3 \xrightarrow{\ OH^-\ } CH_3-CH_2-\overset{\overset{\displaystyle O}{\|}}{C}-O^{\ominus}$$

(b) Carboxylic acids react with dilute NaOH

$$CH_3-CH_2-\overset{O}{\underset{O-H}{C}} \quad + \quad NaOH \longrightarrow CH_3-CH_2-\overset{O}{\underset{O^{\ominus}\overset{\oplus}{Na}}{C}} \quad + \quad H_2O$$

(c) Anion is basic and it will react with dilute HCl

$$CH_3-\overset{O}{\underset{O^{\ominus}}{C}} \quad + \quad HCl \longrightarrow CH_3-\overset{O}{\underset{OH}{C}} \quad + \quad Cl^{\ominus}$$

60. (M)

(a) Amides are prone to hydrolysis

$$CH_3-CH_2-C\underset{NH_2}{\overset{O}{\diagup}} \longrightarrow CH_3-CH_2-C\underset{OH}{\overset{O}{\diagup}}$$

(b) Amines are basic. They will neutralize dilute HCl

$$CH_3-CH_2-NH_2 \xrightarrow{\text{HCl}} CH_3-CH_2-\overset{\oplus}{N}H_3\overset{\ominus}{Cl}$$

(c) Ammonium salts are slightly acidic. They will neutralize dilute NaOH

$$CH_3-CH_2-CH_2-\overset{\oplus}{N}H_3\overset{\ominus}{Cl} \xrightarrow{\text{NaOH}} CH_3-CH_2-CH_2-NH_2 + NaCl + H_2O$$

61. (M)

(a) $CH_3CH_2NH_2 + HCl \longrightarrow CH_3CH_2\overset{\oplus}{N}H_3\overset{\ominus}{Cl}$

(b) $(CH_3)_3\overset{\oplus}{N}H\ \overset{\ominus}{Br}$

(c) no reaction

(d) $CH_3CH_2\overset{\oplus}{N}H_3 + OH^{\ominus} \longrightarrow CH_3CH_2NH_2 + H_2O$

62. (M)

(a) no reaction

(b)

$$\underset{}{\bigcirc}NH + HCl \longrightarrow \underset{}{\bigcirc}\overset{\oplus}{N}\underset{H}{\overset{H}{\diagup}} + Cl^{\ominus}$$

(c) no reaction

(d) $(CH_3)_3\overset{\oplus}{N}H + OH^{\ominus} \longrightarrow (CH_3)_3N + H_2O$

63. (M)

To prepare butan-2-one, one should oxidize secondary alcohol butan-2-ol.

$$CH_3-\underset{\overset{|}{OH}}{CH}-CH_2-CH_3 \xrightarrow{[O]} CH_3-\underset{\underset{\text{butan-2-one}}{}}{\overset{O}{\overset{||}{C}}}-CH_2-CH_3$$

64. (M)

(a) $CH_3CH_2CH{=}CH_2 \xrightarrow[\text{H}_2\text{SO}_4]{\text{H}_2\text{O}} CH_3-CH_2-\overset{*}{C}H-CH_3$ (racemic product)
$\underset{\overset{|}{OH}}{}$

(b) CH_3—CH_2—CH_3 $\xrightarrow[\text{light}]{Cl_2}$ CH_3—CH_2—CH_2Cl + CH_3—$\underset{\underset{Cl}{|}}{CH}$—$CH_3$ +

mixtures of dihalogenated, trihalogenated
and multihalogenated products

(c) $\underset{CH_3}{\overset{CH_3}{{>}}}CH$—$OH$ + [benzene ring with COOH] ⟶ [benzene ring with C=O, O—CH bearing two CH₃]

(d) CH_3—CH_2—$\underset{\underset{OH}{|}}{\overset{\overset{CH_3}{|}}{C}}$—$H$ $\xrightarrow[\text{H}_2\text{SO}_4]{\text{Cr}_2\text{O}_7^{2-}}$ CH_3—CH_2—$C\overset{\overset{O}{\diagup}}{\underset{CH_3}{\diagdown}}$

---

65. **(M)**

(a) Generally, primary alcohols can be easily oxidized to either aldehydes or carboxylic acids depending on the reaction conditions. Aldehydes are similarly oxidized to carboxylic acids. The oxidizing agent typically used for the reaction is a solution of sodium or potassium dichromate(VI) acidified with dilute sulfuric acid.

[Structure: propanol → propionaldehyde → propionic acid sequence]

propan-1-ol → propionaldehyde → propionic acid

[Structure: butyraldehyde → butyric acid]

butyraldehyde → butyric acid

(b) Propionic acid is a weak monoprotic acid that will react with NaOH. The products of the neutralization reaction are the corresponding sodium salt and water.

[Structure] + NaOH ⟶ [Structure with O^-Na^+] + H_2O

(c) Propionic acid reacts with ethanol to form the ester ethyl propionate. This reaction is called esterification. The additional product is H_2O.

[Structure] + CH_3CH_2OH $\xrightarrow{H^+}$ [Structure] + H_2O

ethyl propionate

(d) Alcohols and aldehydes can be oxidized to carboxylic acids. The products are propionic and butyric acids, respectively (see part a).

(e) Carboxylic acids and aldehydes can be reduced to primary alcohols. Typically, strong reducing agents, such as lithium tetrahydridoaluminate LiAlH$_4$ (carboxylic acids and aldehydes) or sodium tetrahydridoborate NaBH$_4$ (aldehydes), are used.

66. (M)

(1) Compound (1) neutralizes HCl(aq) (a), forms an amide with ethanoic acid (c)

(2) Compound (2) reacts with ammonia and CN$^-$ (d) and (e)

(3) Ethers are typically inert. Hydrogen halides such as HI, HBr, and HCl protonate ethers. Typically, only HI and HBr can cleave ethers.

67. (M)

68. (M) Cl—Cl $\longrightarrow$ 2Cl

CH$_4$ + Cl$^\bullet$ $\longrightarrow$ CH$_3^\bullet$ + HCl

CH$_3^\bullet$ + Cl—Cl $\longrightarrow$ CH$_3$Cl + Cl$^\bullet$

CH$_3$Cl + Cl$^\bullet$ $\longrightarrow$ CH$_2$Cl$^\bullet$ + HCl

CH$_2$Cl$^\bullet$ + CH$_3^\bullet$ $\longrightarrow$ CH$_3$CH$_2$Cl

Product is formed as a result of radical termination reaction

69. **(D)** Halogen group is ortho and para directing

(I)

(II)

(III)

70. **(D)**
(a) The compound could be *m*-xylene or ethylbenzene.

m-xylene

Identical compounds

minor product

ethylbenzene

minor product

(b)

(c)

71. (D)

2-methylbutane contains nine primary hydrogens, two secondary hydrogens and one tertiary hydrogen. The possible products of monochlorination are:

Chlorination at A
1-chloro-2-methylbutane

Chlorination at B
1-chloro-3-methylbutane

Chlorination at C
2-chloro-3-methylbutane

Chlorination at D
2-chloro-2-methylbutane

To calculate the yield of each product, find the number of hydrogens in the starting alkane that give rise to the product under consideration and multiply by the relative reactivity corresponding to the type of hydrogen

Product	Relative yield	Absolute yield
1-chloro-2-methylbutane	$6 \times 1 = 6$	$6/19.3 = 0.31 = 31\%$
1-chloro-3-methylbutane	$3 \times 1 = 3$	$3/19.3 = 0.16 = 16\%$
2-chloro-3-methylbutane	$2 \times 3 = 6$	$6/19.3 = 0.31 = 31\%$
2-chloro-2-methylbutane	$1 \times 4.3 = 4.3$	$4/19.3 = 0.21 = 21\%$
	Total = 19.3	

72. **(M)**

Sodium butanoate can be converted to butanoic acid by treatment with hydrochloric acid.

73. **(M)**

$$CH_3CH_2OH + HI \xrightarrow{\Delta} CH_3CH_2I + H_2O$$

In the presence of strong acid (HI), the oxygen atom of the — OH group is protonated, forming $CH_3CH_2-\overset{\oplus}{O}H_2$. H_2O is a weaker base than OH^- and is therefore a good leaving group. Reaction occurs via S_N2 mechanism with the inversion of configuration.

74. **(D)**

(a) N-methylpropanamide can be synthesized by reacting carboxylic acid with a primary amine.

(b) Ethyl ethanoate can be synthesized by reacting ethanol with ethanoic acid (esterification)

(c) $CH_3Cl \xrightarrow{NaN_3} CH_3-N_3 \xrightarrow{red} CH_3-NH_2$

$CH_3-NH_2 + CH_3CH_2Cl \longrightarrow CH_3-NH-CH_2CH_3$

(d) $CH_3Cl \xrightarrow{NaN_3} CH_3-N_3 \xrightarrow{red} CH_3-NH_2$

75. **(D)** The reaction of interest is the acid-catalyzed hydration:

3-methylbutan-2-ol
minor product

Carbocation rearrangement occurs by 1,2-hydride shift to give a more stable tertiary carbocation which undergoes attack by water, followed by deprotonation, to give the major product.

2-methylbutan-2-ol
major product

76. **(D)** The reaction is likely to occur via elimination

77. **(D)** The desired product can be synthesized using the following sequences of chemical reactions:

$$CH_4 + Cl_2 \xrightarrow{h\nu} CH_3Cl + Cl_2 \xrightarrow{h\nu} CH_2Cl_2$$

$$CH_4 + Cl_2 \xrightarrow{h\nu} CH_3Cl \xrightarrow{OH^-} CH_3OH$$

FEATURE PROBLEM

78. (D)

(a)

1-pentanol

(b)

2-hexanol

(c)

2-methyl-2-hexanol

(d)

This product can alternatively be prepared from aromatic ketone and methyl magnesium chloride

(e)

(f)

$$\underset{\substack{\parallel \\ O}}{H-C-H} \;+\; CH_3CH_2CH_2CH_2C\equiv CMgBr \;\longrightarrow\; BrMgO-\underset{\substack{| \\ H}}{\overset{\substack{H \\ |}}{C}}-C\equiv C-CH_2CH_2CH_2CH_3$$

$$BrMgO-\underset{\substack{| \\ H}}{\overset{\substack{H \\ |}}{C}}-C\equiv C\text{-}CH_2CH_2CH_2CH_3 \;\xrightarrow[H^+]{H_2O}\; HO-\underset{\substack{| \\ H}}{\overset{\substack{H \\ |}}{C}}-C\equiv C-CH_2CH_2CH_2CH_3$$

SELF-ASSESSMENT EXERCISES

79. **(E)**

(a) Nucleophilic substitution corresponds to a substitution (either S_N1 or S_N2) for aliphatic compounds.

Electrophilic aromatic substitution is typical for aromatic compounds (an atom is replaced by an electrophile)

(b) An addition reaction is the opposite of an elimination reaction. In an addition reaction, two or more atoms (molecules) combine to form a larger one.

(c) S_N1 reaction involves the formation of carbocation. S_N2 reaction, on the other hand, is a one-step process in which bond breaking and bond making occur simultaneously at a carbon atom with a suitable leaving group.

(d) E1 reactions are unimolecular elimination reactions that proceed via carbocation intermediates. E2 reactions are bimolecular, one-step reactions that require an antiperiplanar conformation at the time of π-bond formation and β-bond breaking and do not involve carbocations.

80. **(E)**

(a) Basicity is a measure of the tendency of an electron pair donor to react with a proton. Nucleophilicity is a measure of how readily (and fast) a nucleophile attacks an electrophilic carbon atom.

(b) α-carbon typically corresponds to the first atom in the molecule, or the first atom next to a functional group of interest. β-atom (carbon) is the second atom in the molecule.

(c) Polar protic solvent is a polar solvent that contains protons attached to oxygen or nitrogen. Aprotic polar solvent, on the other hand, does not contain protons attached to oxygen or nitrogen.

(d) Carbocations are positively charged species. Radicals are neutral. Both are reactive because they lack an octet of electrons around the charged or odd-electron atoms.

$$R-\underset{\substack{| \\ R}}{\overset{\oplus}{C}}-R \qquad R-\underset{\substack{| \\ R}}{\overset{\bullet}{C}}-R$$

carbocation   radical

81. **(M)**

  (a) CN⁻ is a better nucleophile than Cl⁻ and it will therefore react faster

  (b) Although both substrates are primary alkyl halides, the uncrowded CH_3I reacts faster than the more crowded 1-iodo-2-methyl-butane in an S_N2 reaction.

82. **(M)** Substrate (e) CH_3S^- is the strongest nucleophile.

83. **(M)** Ether formation proceeds via an S_N2 mechanism. The combination of $(CH_3)_2CHONa$ and CH_3I will be better for S_N2 (backside attack) because there is less crowding of the α carbon atom in CH_3I than in $(CH_3)_2CHI$ and no chance of forming an alkene by elimination. The first reaction will favor E-2.

84. **(M)** Since $(CH_3CH_2)_3CO^-$ is a large base (sterically hindered), it will preferentially attack the more exposed H atoms, yielding the least substituted alkene.

  (a)

  (b)

85. **(M)**

  (a)

  (b)

  (c)

  (d)

  (e)

86. (D)

major

minor

CHAPTER 28
CHEMISTRY OF THE LIVING STATE
PRACTICE EXAMPLES

1A **(E)**

$$H_2N-CH-\overset{\overset{\displaystyle O}{\|}}{C}-NH-CH-\overset{\overset{\displaystyle O}{\|}}{C}-NH-CH-\overset{\overset{\displaystyle O}{\|}}{C}-OH$$

with side chains: CHOH–CH₃, CHOH–CH₃, (CH₂)₂–S–CH₃

The amino acids are threonine, threonine, and methionine. This tripeptide is dithreonylmethionine.

1B **(E)** The amino acids are serine, glycine, and valine. The N terminus is first.

$$H_2N-CH-\overset{\overset{\displaystyle O}{\|}}{C}-NH-CH-\overset{\overset{\displaystyle O}{\|}}{C}-NH-CH-\overset{\overset{\displaystyle O}{\|}}{C}-OH$$

with side chains: CH₂–OH, H, H₃C–CH–CH₃

2A **(M)** Because it is a pentapeptide and five amino acids have been identified, no amino acid is repeated. The sequences fall into place, as follows.

	Gly	Cys			second fragment
		Cys	Val	Phe	third fragment
			Val	Phe	first fragment
				Phe Tyr	fourth fragment
pentapeptide sequence	Gly	Cys	Val	Phe	Tyr

2B **(M)** Because it is a hexapeptide and there are five distinct amino acids, one amino acid must appear twice. The fragmentation pattern indicates that the doubled amino acid is glycine. The sequences fall into place if we begin with the N-terminal end.

	Ser	Gly	Gly			third fragment
		Gly	Gly	Ala		second fragment
			Ala	Val	Trp	fourth fragment
				Val	Trp	first fragment
hexapeptide sequence	Ser	Gly	Gly	Ala	Val	Trp

INTEGRATIVE EXAMPLE

A. **(M)**

$\Pi = MRT$

$$\text{mol MyG} = 0.500 \text{ g MyG} \times \frac{1 \text{ mol MyG}}{16900 \text{ g MyG}} = 2.985 \times 10^{-5} \text{ mol MyG}$$

$$M = \frac{2.985 \times 10^{-5} \text{ mol MyG}}{0.025 \text{ L}} = 0.0011834 \text{ M}$$

$$\Pi = (0.0011834 \text{ M})(0.08206 \text{ L} \cdot \text{atm} \cdot \text{K}^{-1})(298 \text{ K}) = 0.02894 \text{ atm}$$

$$\Pi(\text{Pa}) = 0.02894 \text{ atm} \times \frac{101325 \text{ Pa}}{1 \text{ atm}} = 2932 \text{ Pa}$$

To determine the height of the water column, several things should be kept in mind:

1) The pressure unit, 1 Pascal (Pa) is defined as 1 N/m^2 (1 Newton of force per m^2)

2) Force (F) in Newtons is given by F = mg. Since m is in units of kg and g in units of m/s^2, Newtons can be expressed in units of kg · m/s^2.

With the above points in mind,

$$P = \frac{F}{A} = \frac{m \cdot g}{A}$$

Since mass (m) = density (D) × volume (V), we can make the following substitutions:

$$P = \frac{m \cdot g}{A} = \frac{D \times V \times g}{A} = \frac{D \times (w \times l \times h) \times g}{w \times l} = D \times h \times g$$

$$2932 \frac{N}{m^2} = 1000 \frac{kg}{m^3} \times h \times 9.8 \frac{m}{s^2}$$

$$h = 0.300 \text{ m}$$

B. **(D)**
(a)

(b)

Given Data	
Rate (M/s), V	[CO2] (M), S
9.02E – 05	1.25E – 03
1.67E – 04	2.50E – 03
2.90E – 04	5.00E – 03
6.47E – 04	2.00E – 02

→

Lineweaver-Burk Eq.	
1/V	1/S
1.11E + 04	8.00E + 02
5.99E + 03	4.00E + 02
3.45E + 03	2.00E + 02
1.55E + 03	5.00E + 01

$y = 12.72281x + 905.07396$
$R^2 = 1.00000$

The Lineweaver-Burk equation is

$$\frac{1}{V} = \frac{1}{V_{max}} + \frac{K_M}{V_{max}} \cdot \frac{1}{[S]}$$

From the graph and the linear regression, we can see that the slope of the line m (K_M/V_{max}) = 12.7228 s, and the y-intercept b ($1/V_{max}$) = 905.074 $(M/s)^{-1}$. Therefore,

$$V_{max} = 1/905.074 = 0.001105 \text{ M/s}$$

$$\frac{K_M}{V_{max}} = \frac{K_M}{0.001105 \text{ M/s}} = 12.723 \text{ s}$$

$$K_M = 0.01406 \text{ M} = 14.1 \text{ mM}$$

From the problem, we note that $V_{max} = k_2 [E]_0$. The value for k_2, therefore, is:

$$k_2 = \frac{V_{max}}{[E]_0} = \frac{0.001105 \text{ M/s}}{2.3 \times 10^{-9} \text{ M}} = 4.8 \times 10^5 \text{ s}^{-1}$$

EXERCISES

Structure and Composition of the Cell

1. **(M)** The volume of a cylinder is given by $V = \pi r^2 h = \pi d^2 h / 4$.

$$V = \left[3.14159 \left(1 \times 10^{-6} \text{ m}\right)^2 \left(2 \times 10^{-6} \text{ m}\right) \div 4 \right] \times \frac{1000 \text{ L}}{1 \text{ m}^3} = 1.6 \times 10^{-15} \text{ L}$$

The volume of the solution in the cell is $V_{soln} = 0.80 \times 1.6 \times 10^{-15} \text{ L} = 1.3 \times 10^{-15} \text{ L}$.

(a) $\left[H^+ \right] = 10^{-6.4} = 4 \times 10^{-7} \text{ M}$

$$\text{no. } H_3O^+ \text{ ions} = 1.3 \times 10^{-15} \text{ L} \times \frac{4 \times 10^{-7} \text{ mol } H^+ \text{ ions}}{1 \text{ L soln}} \times \frac{6.022 \times 10^{23} \text{ ions}}{1 \text{ mol ions}}$$

$$= 3 \times 10^2 \text{ } H_3O^+ \text{ ions}$$

(b) $\text{no. } K^+ \text{ ions} = 1.3 \times 10^{-15} \text{ L} \times \frac{1.5 \times 10^{-4} \text{ mol } K^+ \text{ ions}}{1 \text{ L soln}} \times \frac{6.022 \times 10^{23} \text{ ions}}{1 \text{ mol ions}}$

$$\text{no. } K^+ \text{ ions} = 1.2 \times 10^5 \text{ } K^+ \text{ ions}$$

2. **(E)** Mass of all lipid molecules $= 0.02 \times 2 \times 10^{-12} \text{ g} = 4 \times 10^{-14} \text{ g}$.

$$\text{lipid molecules} = 4 \times 10^{-14} \text{ g} \times \frac{1 \text{ u}}{1.66 \times 10^{-24} \text{ g}} \times \frac{1 \text{ lipid molecule}}{700 \text{ u}} = 3 \times 10^7 \text{ lipid molecules}$$

3. **(E)** mass of protein in cytoplasm $= 0.15 \times 0.90 \times 2 \times 10^{-12}$ g $= 2.7 \times 10^{-13}$ g.

no. of protein molecules $= 2.7 \times 10^{-13}$ g $\times \dfrac{1 \text{ mol protein}}{3 \times 10^{4} \text{ g}} \times \dfrac{6.022 \times 10^{23} \text{ molecules}}{1 \text{ mol protein}}$

$= 5 \times 10^{6}$ protein molecules

4. **(M)**

DNA length $= 4.5 \times 10^{6}$ mononucleotides $\times \dfrac{450 \text{ pm}}{1 \text{ mononucleotide}} \times \dfrac{10^{-12} \text{ m}}{1 \text{ pm}} = 2 \times 10^{-3}$ m $= 2$ mm

2 mm $= 2 \times 10^{3} \mu$ m. Thus the length of the stretched out DNA is one thousand times the length of the cell, which is $2 \ \mu$m. Consequently, the DNA must be wrapped up, or coiled, within the cell.

Lipids

5. **(M)**

(a) $C_{15}H_{31}COOH$ is palmitic acid. $C_{17}H_{29}COOH$ is linolenic acid or eleosteric acid. $C_{11}H_{23}COOH$ is lauric acid. Thus, the given compound is glyceryl palmitolinolenolaurate or glyceryl palmitoeleosterolaurate.

(b) $C_{17}H_{33}COOH$ is oleic acid. Thus, the compound is glyceryl trioleate or triolein.

(c) $C_{13}H_{27}COOH$ is myristic acid. Thus, the compound is sodium myristate.

6. **(E)**

(a) glyceryl palmitolauroeleosterate

$$CH_2O-\overset{\overset{\displaystyle O}{\|}}{C}-(CH_2)_{14}CH_3$$

$$CHO-\overset{\overset{\displaystyle O}{\|}}{C}-(CH_2)_{10}CH_3$$

$$CH_2O-\overset{\overset{\displaystyle O}{\|}}{C}-(CH_2)_7-CH{=}CH-CH{=}CH-CH{=}CH(CH_2)_3CH_3$$

(b) tripalmitin

$$CH_2O-\overset{\overset{\displaystyle O}{\|}}{C}-(CH_2)_{14}CH_3$$

$$CHO-\overset{\overset{\displaystyle O}{\|}}{C}-(CH_2)_{14}CH_3$$

$$CH_2O-\overset{\overset{\displaystyle O}{\|}}{C}-(CH_2)_{14}CH_3$$

(c) potassium myristate

$$CH_3(CH_2)_{12}-\overset{\overset{\displaystyle O}{||}}{C}-O^-K^+$$

(d) butyl oleate

$$CH_3(CH_2)_3-O-\overset{\overset{\displaystyle O}{||}}{C}-(CH_2)_7-CH=CH-(CH_2)_7-CH_3$$

7. **(M)**
(a)

Trilaurin	**Trilinolein**

$$CH_2-O-\overset{\overset{\displaystyle O}{||}}{C}-C_{11}H_{23}$$
$$|$$
$$CH-O-\overset{\overset{\displaystyle O}{||}}{C}-C_{11}H_{23}$$
$$|$$
$$CH_2-O-\overset{\overset{\displaystyle O}{||}}{C}-C_{11}H_{23}$$

A triglyceride or glycerol ester

Saturated triglyceride
-made using saturated acid

A fat (usually solid at room
temperature)

$$CH_2-O-\overset{\overset{\displaystyle O}{||}}{C}-C_{17}H_{31}$$
$$|$$
$$CH-O-\overset{\overset{\displaystyle O}{||}}{C}-C_{17}H_{31}$$
$$|$$
$$CH_2-O-\overset{\overset{\displaystyle O}{||}}{C}-C_{17}H_{31}$$

A triglyceride or glycerol ester

Unsaturated triglyceride
-made using unsaturated acid

An oil (usually liquid at room
temperature)

(b) Soaps: salts of fatty acids (from saponification of triglycerides)

Phospholipids: derived from glycerols, fatty acids, phosphoric acid, and a nitrogen containing base (both soaps and phospholipids have hydrophilic heads and hydrophobic tails.)

8.   (M)

Monoglyceride   Diglyceride

9.   **(E)** Polyunsaturated fatty acids are characterized by a large number of $C = C$ double bonds in their hydrocarbon chain. Stearic acid has no $C = C$ double bonds and therefore is not unsaturated, let alone polyunsaturated. But eleostearic acid has three $C = C$ double bonds and thus is polyunsaturated. Polyunsaturated fatty acids are recommended in dietary programs since saturated fats are linked to a high incidence of heart disease. Of the lipids listed in Table 28-2, safflower oil has the highest percentage of unsaturated fatty acids, predominately linoleic acid, which is an unsaturated fatty acid with two C=C bonds.

10.   **(E)** Safflower oil contains a larger percentage of the unsaturated fatty acid, linoleic acid (two C=C bonds) (75 – 80%), than does corn oil (34 – 62%). It also contains a smaller percentage of saturated fatty acids, particularly palmitic acid (6 – 7%) than does corn oil (8 – 12%). And the two oils contain about the same proportion of the unsaturated fatty acid, oleic acid (one C=C bond). Consequently, safflower oil should require the greater amount of $H_2(g)$ for its complete hydrogenation to a solid fat.

11. **(E)**

tripalmitin

saponification products of tripalmitin:
sodium palmitate and glycerol

$$CH_2OOC(CH_2)_{14}CH_3$$
$$CHOOC(CH_2)_{14}CH_3$$
$$CH_2OOC(CH_2)_{14}CH_3$$

$$CH_2OHCHOHCH_2OH$$
$$NaOOC(CH_2)_{14}CH_3$$

12. **(E)** First we write the equation for the saponification reaction.

$$CH_2OOCC_{13}H_{27}$$
$$CHOOCC_{13}H_{27} + 3\ NaOH \rightarrow CH_2OHCHOHCH_2OH + 3\ NaOOCC_{13}H_{27}$$
$$CH_2OOCC_{13}H_{27}$$

$$\text{mass of soap} = 105\ \text{g triglyceride} \times \frac{1\ \text{mol triglyceride}}{723.2\ \text{g triglyceride}} \times \frac{3\ \text{mol soap}}{1\ \text{mol triglyceride}} \times \frac{250.4\ \text{g soap}}{1\ \text{mol soap}}$$

$$= 109\ \text{g soap}$$

Carbohydrates

13. **(M)**

L-Glucose
Aldohexose

D-Erythrulose
Ketotetrose

14. **(M)**

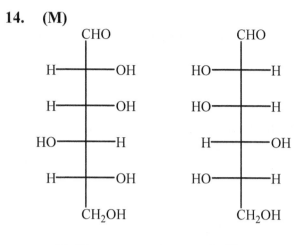

D-Glucose   L-Glucose   ⟵——— These molecules are enantiomers

The designation "L" in L-Glucose simply arises from nomenclature and does not convey either a dextrorotatory or levorotatory designation. The structure of a "chiral" molecule will determine whether it is dextrorotatory or levorotatory. Put another way, the D- and L- designation arises from the rules of nomenclature, whereas the dextrorotatory or levorotatory designation must be experimentally determined.

15. **(M)**

(a)   D-(−)-arabinose is the optical isomer of L-(+)-arabinose. Its structure is shown below.

(b)   A diastereomer of L-(+)-arabinose is a molecule that is its optical isomer, but not its mirror image. There are several such diastereomers, some of which are shown below.

(a)   **(b)**

16. **(M)**

(a) β has OH equatorial at C_1 **(b)**   **(c)**

All three molecules are optically active

cyclized/open-chain forms

17. **(M)**

(a) A dextrorotatory compound rotates the plane of polarized light to the right, namely clockwise.

(b) A levorotatory compound is one that rotates the plane of polarized light to the left, namely counterclockwise.

(c) A racemic mixture has equal amounts of an optically active compound and its enantiomer. Since these two compounds rotate polarized light by the same amount but in opposite directions, such a mixture does not exhibit a net rotation of the plane of polarized light.

(d) (*R*) In organic nomenclature, this designation is given to a chiral carbon atom. First, we must assign priorities to the four substituents on the chiral carbon atom. With the lowest priority group pointing directly away from the viewer, we say that the stereogenic center has an *R*-configuration if a curved arrow from the group of highest priority through to the one of lowest priority is drawn in a clockwise direction.

18. **(E)**

(a) Two compounds that are optical isomers of each other—they have different locations of the substituent groups around their chiral carbons—but are not mirror images of each other are diastereomers.

(b) Two isomers that are nonsuperimposable mirror images of one other are called enantiomers.

(c) (−) is another way of designating a levorotatory compound.

(d) D indicates that, in the Fisher projection of the compound, the — OH group on the penultimate carbon atom is to the right and the — H group is to the left.

19. **(E)**

A reducing sugar has a sufficient amount of the straight-chain form present in equilibrium with its cyclic form such that the sugar will reduce $Cu^{2+}(aq)$ to insoluble, red $Cu_2O(s)$. Only free aldehyde groups are able to reduce the copper(II) ion down to copper (I).

Next, we need to calculate the mass of Cu_2O expected when 0.500 g of glucose is oxidized in the reducing sugar test:

$$\text{mass } Cu_2O \text{ (g)} = \frac{1 \text{ mol glucose}}{180.2 \text{ g glucose}} \times \frac{2 \text{ mol } Cu^{2+}}{1 \text{ mol glucose}} \times \frac{1 \text{ mol } Cu_2O}{2 \text{ mol } Cu^{2+}} \times \frac{143.1 \text{ g } Cu_2O}{1 \text{ mol } Cu_2O} = 0.397 \text{g } Cu_2O$$

20. **(D)** The eight aldopentoses are drawn below as Fischer structures.
Note: There are 4 pairs of enantiomers and each structure has 6 diasteromers.

21. **(E)** Enantiomers are alike in all respects, including in the degree to which they rotate polarized light. They differ only in the direction in which this rotation occurs. Since α-glucose and β-glucose rotate the plane of polarized light by different degrees, and in the same direction, they are not enantiomers, but rather diastereomers.

22. **(M)** We let x represent the fraction of α-D-glucose. Then $1-x$ is the fraction of β-D-glucose.

$$+52.7° = x(112°) + (1-x)(18.7°) = 112°x + 18.7° - 18.7°x = 93°x + 18.7°$$

$$x = \frac{52.7° - 18.7°}{93°} = 0.37$$ The solution is 37% α-D-glucose; and thus 63% β-D-glucose.

Fischer Projections and *R, S* Nomenclature

23. **(E)**
  (a) Enantiomers: *S*-configuration (leftmost structure), *R*-config. (rightmost structure)
  (b) Different molecules: different formulas
  (c) Diasteriomers: *S,R* configuration (leftmost structure–top to bottom), *S,S*-configuration. (rightmost structure)
  (d) Diasteriomers: *R,R*-configuration (leftmost structure–top to bottom), *R, S*-configuation (rightmost structure–top to bottom)

24. **(E)**
  (a) Same molecule: both *R*-configuration
  (b) Same molecule: both *R*-configuration
  (c) Enantiomers: *S, S*-configuation (leftmost structure), *R, R*-config. (rightmost structure)
  (d) Diasteriomers: *S, R*-configuration (leftmost structure–top to bottom), *R, R*-configuration (rightmost structure)

25. **(M)**

(a)   (b)   (c)   (d)

26. **(M)**

(a)   (b)   (c)   (d)   (e)

Amino Acids, Polypeptides, and Proteins

27. **(E)**

(a) An α-amino acid has an amine group ($-NH_2$) bonded to the same carbon as the carboxyl group ($-COOH$). For example: glycine (H_2NCH_2COOH) is the simplest α-amino acid.

(b) A zwitterion is a form of an amino acid in which the amine group is protonated $(-NH_3^+)$ and the carboxyl group is deprotonated $(-COO^-)$. For instance, the zwitterion form of glycine is $^+H_3NCH_2COO^-$.

(c) The pH at which the zwitterion form of an amino acid predominates in solution is known as the isoelectric point. The isoelectric point of glycine is $pI = 6.03$.

(d) The peptide bond is the bond that forms between the carbonyl group of one amino acid and the amine group of another, with the elimination of a water molecule between them. The peptide bond between two glycine molecules is shown as a bold dash (▬▬) in the structure below.

$$H_2N-CH_2-\overset{\overset{\displaystyle O}{\|}}{C} ▬▬ NH-CH_2-\overset{\overset{\displaystyle O}{\|}}{C}-OH$$

(e) Tertiary structure describes how a coiled protein chain further interacts with itself to wrap into a cluster through a combination of salt linkages, hydrogen bonding, and disulfide linkages, to name a few.

28. **(E)**

(a) A polypeptide is a long chain of amino acids, joined together by peptide bonds.

(b) A protein is another name for a polypeptide, but a distinction is often made. Proteins are longer chains than polypeptides, and proteins are biologically active.

(c) The N-terminal amino acid in a polypeptide is the one at the end of the polypeptide chain that possesses a free NH_2. The N-terminal amino acid is at the left end of the structure of diglycine in the answer to the previous exercise.

(d) An α helix is a natural secondary structure adopted by many proteins. It is rather like a spiral rising upward to the right (that is, clockwise as viewed from the bottom). This is a right-handed screw. The alpha helix is shown in Figure 28–12.

(e) Denaturation is that process in which at least some of the structure of a protein is disrupted, either thermally (with heat), mechanically, or by changing the pH or the ionic strength of the medium in which the protein is enveloped. Denaturation is accompanied by a decrease in the biological activity. Denaturation can be temporary or permanent.

29. **(M)** The pI of phenylalanine is 5.74. Thus, phenylalanine is in the form of a cation in 1.0 M HCl (pH = 0.0), an anion in 1.0 M NaOH (pH = 14.0), and a zwitterion at pH = 5.7. These three structures follow.

(a)
$$\text{C}_6\text{H}_5-\text{CH}_2-\overset{\overset{\textstyle NH_3^+\ Cl^-}{|}}{\text{CH}}\ \text{COOH}$$

(b)
$$\text{C}_6\text{H}_5-\text{CH}_2-\overset{\overset{\textstyle NH_2}{|}}{\text{CH}}\ \text{COO}^-\text{Na}^+$$

(c)
$$\text{C}_6\text{H}_5-\text{CH}_2-\overset{\overset{\textstyle NH_3^+}{|}}{\text{CH}}\ \text{COO}^-$$

30. **(M)** The pI of histidine is 7.6. Thus, histidine is in the form of a cation at pH = 3.0), an anion at pH = 12.0), and a zwitterion at pH = 7.6. These three structures follow.

(a) pH = 3.0

$CH_2CH(NH_3^+)CO_2H$

(b) pH = 7.6

$CH_2CH(NH_3^+)CO_2^-$

(c) pH = 12.0

$CH_2CH(NH_2)CO_2^-$

31. **(E)**

(a) alanylcysteine

$$\underset{\underset{CH_3}{|}}{H_2N-CH}-\overset{\overset{O}{||}}{C}-NH-\underset{\underset{\underset{SH}{|}}{CH_2}}{CH}-\overset{\overset{O}{||}}{C}-OH$$

(b) threonylvalylglycine

$$\underset{\underset{\underset{CH_3}{|}}{CHOH}}{H_2N-CH}-\overset{\overset{O}{||}}{C}-NH-\underset{\underset{\underset{CH_3}{|}}{H_3C-CH}}{CH}-\overset{\overset{O}{||}}{C}-NH-\underset{\underset{H}{|}}{CH}-\overset{\overset{O}{||}}{C}-OH$$

32. **(E)**

(a)

$$\underset{\underset{\underset{S-CH_3}{|}}{(CH_2)_2}}{H_2N-CH}-\overset{\overset{O}{||}}{C}-NH-\underset{\underset{\underset{CH_3}{|}}{H_3C-CH}}{CH}-\overset{\overset{O}{||}}{C}-NH-\underset{\underset{\underset{CH_3}{|}}{CHOH}}{CH}-\overset{\overset{O}{||}}{C}-NH-\underset{\underset{\underset{SH}{|}}{CH_2}}{CH}-\overset{\overset{O}{||}}{C}-OH$$

(b) methionylvalylthreonylcysteine

33. **(M)** pH = 6.3 is near the isoelectric point of proline (6.21). Thus proline will not migrate very effectively under these conditions. But pH = 6.3 is considerably more acidic than the isoelectric point of lysine ($pI = 9.74$). Thus, lysine is positively charged in this solution and consequently will migrate toward the negatively charged cathode. Furthermore, pH = 6.3 is much less acidic than the isoelectric point of aspartic acid ($pI = 2.96$). Aspartic acid, therefore, is negatively charged in this solution and consequently will migrate toward the positively charged anode.

34. **(M)** pI = 5.74 is the isoelectric point of phenylalanine. Thus phenylalanine will not migrate. But pH = 5.7 is more acidic than the isoelectric point of histidine ($pI = 7.58$). Thus, histidine is positively charged in this solution and will migrate toward the negatively charged cathode. And pH = 5.7 is less acidic than the isoelectric point of glutamic acid ($pI = 3.22$). Glutamic acid is negatively charged in this solution; it will migrate to the positively charged anode.

35. **(M)**

    (a) in strongly acidic solution   **(b)** at the isoelectric point

          $^+H_3NCH(CHOHCH_3)COOH$ $^+H_3NCH(CHOHCH_3)COO^-$

    (c) in strongly basic solution $H_2NCH(CHOHCH_3)COO^-$

36. **(M)**

    (a) aspartic acid   **(b)** lysine   **(c)** alanine

    $H_2NCH(CH_2COO^-)COO^-$ $^+H_3NCH((CH_2)_4NH_3^+)COO^-$ $^+H_3NCH(CH_3)COO^-$

37. **(D)**

    (a) The structures of the six tripeptides that contain one alanine, one serine, and one lysine are drawn below (in no particular order).

    Lys-Ser-Ala (1 of 6)

Lys-Ala-Ser (2 of 6)

$$NH_2-CH-\overset{\displaystyle O}{\overset{\|}{C}}-NH-CH-\overset{\displaystyle O}{\overset{\|}{C}}-NH-CH-\overset{\displaystyle O}{\overset{\|}{C}}-OH$$

with side chains: $(CH_2)_4-NH_2$; CH_3 ; CH_2OH

Ser-Lys-Ala (3 of 6)

$$NH_2-CH-\overset{\displaystyle O}{\overset{\|}{C}}-NH-CH-\overset{\displaystyle O}{\overset{\|}{C}}-NH-CH-\overset{\displaystyle O}{\overset{\|}{C}}-OH$$

with side chains: CH_2OH ; $(CH_2)_4-NH_2$; CH_3

Ser-Ala-Lys (4 of 6)

$$NH_2-CH-\overset{\displaystyle O}{\overset{\|}{C}}-NH-CH-\overset{\displaystyle O}{\overset{\|}{C}}-NH-CH-\overset{\displaystyle O}{\overset{\|}{C}}-OH$$

with side chains: CH_2OH ; CH_3 ; $(CH_2)_4-NH_2$

Ala-Ser-Lys (5 of 6)

$$NH_2-CH-\overset{\displaystyle O}{\overset{\|}{C}}-NH-CH-\overset{\displaystyle O}{\overset{\|}{C}}-NH-CH-\overset{\displaystyle O}{\overset{\|}{C}}-OH$$

with side chains: CH_3 ; CH_2OH ; $(CH_2)_4-NH_2$

Ala-Lys-Ser (6 of 6)

$$NH_2-CH-\overset{\displaystyle O}{\overset{\|}{C}}-NH-CH-\overset{\displaystyle O}{\overset{\|}{C}}-NH-CH-\overset{\displaystyle O}{\overset{\|}{C}}-OH$$

with side chains: CH_3 ; $(CH_2)_4-NH_2$; CH_2OH

(b) The structures of the six tetrapeptides that contain two serine and two alanine amino acids each follow (in no particular order).

Ala-Ser-Ala-Ser (1 of 6)

$$NH_2-CH-\overset{\overset{\displaystyle O}{\|}}{C}-NH-CH-\overset{\overset{\displaystyle O}{\|}}{C}-NH-CH-\overset{\overset{\displaystyle O}{\|}}{C}-NH-CH-\overset{\overset{\displaystyle O}{\|}}{C}-OH$$

with side chains: CH_3, CH_2OH, CH_3, CH_2OH

Ala-Ala-Ser-Ser (2 of 6)

$$NH_2-CH-\overset{\overset{\displaystyle O}{\|}}{C}-NH-CH-\overset{\overset{\displaystyle O}{\|}}{C}-NH-CH-\overset{\overset{\displaystyle O}{\|}}{C}-NH-CH-\overset{\overset{\displaystyle O}{\|}}{C}-OH$$

with side chains: CH_3, CH_3, CH_2OH, CH_2OH

Ala-Ser-Ser-Ala (3 of 6)

$$NH_2-CH-\overset{\overset{\displaystyle O}{\|}}{C}-NH-CH-\overset{\overset{\displaystyle O}{\|}}{C}-NH-CH-\overset{\overset{\displaystyle O}{\|}}{C}-NH-CH-\overset{\overset{\displaystyle O}{\|}}{C}-OH$$

with side chains: CH_3, CH_2OH, CH_2OH, CH_3

Ser-Ser-Ala-Ala (4 of 6)

$$NH_2-CH-\overset{\overset{\displaystyle O}{\|}}{C}-NH-CH-\overset{\overset{\displaystyle O}{\|}}{C}-NH-CH-\overset{\overset{\displaystyle O}{\|}}{C}-NH-CH-\overset{\overset{\displaystyle O}{\|}}{C}-OH$$

with side chains: CH_2OH, CH_2OH, CH_3, CH_3

Ser-Ala-Ser-Ala (5 of 6)

$$NH_2-CH-\overset{\overset{\displaystyle O}{\|}}{C}-NH-CH-\overset{\overset{\displaystyle O}{\|}}{C}-NH-CH-\overset{\overset{\displaystyle O}{\|}}{C}-NH-CH-\overset{\overset{\displaystyle O}{\|}}{C}-OH$$

with side chains: CH_2OH, CH_3, CH_2OH, CH_3

Ser-Ala-Ala-Ser (6 of 6)

$$NH_2-CH-\overset{\overset{\displaystyle O}{\|}}{C}-NH-CH-\overset{\overset{\displaystyle O}{\|}}{C}-NH-CH-\overset{\overset{\displaystyle O}{\|}}{C}-NH-CH-\overset{\overset{\displaystyle O}{\|}}{C}-OH$$

with side chains: CH_2OH, CH_3, CH_3, CH_2OH

38. **(M)** There are *twenty four* possible combinations. They are listed below.

Ala-Lys-Ser-Phe	Lys-Ala-Ser-Phe	Ser-Ala-Phe-Lys	Phe-Ala-Ser-Lys
Ala-Lys-Phe-Ser	Lys-Ala-Phe-Ser	Ser-Ala-Lys-Phe	Phe-Ala-Lys-Ser
Ala-Ser-Lys-Phe	Lys-Ser-Phe-Ala	Ser-Lys-Phe-Ala	Phe-Lys-Ser-Ala
Ala-Ser-Phe-Lys	Lys-Ser-Ala-Phe	Ser-Lys-Ala-Phe	Phe-Lys-Ala-Ser
Ala-Phe-Ser-Lys	Lys-Phe-Ser-Ala	Ser-Phe-Ala-Lys	Phe-Ser-Ala-Lys
Ala-Phe-Lys-Ser	Lys-Phe-Ala-Ser	Ser-Phe-Lys-Ala	Phe-Ser-Lys-Ala

39. **(M)**

(a) We put the fragments together as follows, starting from the Ala end, and then placing them in a matching pattern. We do not assume that the fragments are given with the N-terminal end first.

Fragments:	Ala	Ser					3rd fragment
		Ser	Gly	Val			1st fragment
			Gly	Val	Thr		5th fragment
				Val	Thr		2nd fragment, reversed
				Val	Thr	Leu	4th fragment, reversed
Result:	Ala	Ser	Gly	Val	Thr	Leu	

(b) alanyl-seryl-glycyl-valyl-threonyl-leucine, or alanylserylglycylvalylthreonylleucine

40. **(M)**

(a) We put the fragments together as follows, starting from the Ala end, and then simply aligning them in a matching pattern. We do not assume that the fragments are given with the N-terminal end first.

Fragments:	Ala	Lys	Ser				1st fragment
		Lys	Ser	Gly			5th fragment
			Ser	Gly			3rd fragment
				Gly	Phe		4th fragment
				Gly	Phe	Gly	2nd fragment
Result:	Ala	Lys	Ser	Gly	Phe	Gly	

(b) alanyl-lysyl-seryl-glycyl-phenylalanyl-glycine, or alanyllysylserylglycylphenylalanylglycine

41. **(E)**

The *primary* structure of an amino acid is the sequence of amino acids in the chain of the polypeptide. The *secondary* structure describes how the protein chain is folded, coiled, or convoluted. Possible structures include α-helices and β-pleated sheets. These secondary structures are held together principally by hydrogen bonds. The *tertiary* structure of a protein refers to how different parts of the molecules, often quite distant from each other, interact with each other to maintain the overall shape of the protein macromolecule. Although hydrogen bonding is involved here as well, disulfide linkages, hydrophobic interactions, and hydrophilic interactions (salt bridges) are responsible as well for tertiary structure. Finally, quaternary structure refers to how two or more protein molecules pack together into a larger protein complex. Not all proteins have a *quaternary* structure since many proteins have only one polypeptide chain.

42. **(E)** The difference between sickle cell hemoglobin and normal hemoglobin is due solely to the substitution of one amino acid for another (valine for glutamic acid) at one position in the entire protein. This changes the quaternary structure of the hemoglobin. The sickle cell defect arises from the mistaken incorporation of one molecule for another during protein synthesis. This is why the name "molecular disease" is apt.

<u>43.</u> **(M)**

$$CH_3$$
$$H_2N-\textcircled{R}-H \quad \textit{R-alanine}$$
$$CO_2H$$

<u>44.</u> **(M)**

$$CH_2OH$$
$$H_2N-\textcircled{R}-H \quad \textit{R-serine}$$
$$CO_2H$$

<u>45.</u> **(D)**

S-alanine   S-alanine   S-phenylalanine   S-phenylalanine

46. **(D)**

R-proline   R-proline   S-valine   S-valine

Nucleic Acids

47. **(E)** Two major types of nucleic acids are DNA (deoxyribonucleic acid), and RNA (ribonucleic acid). Both of them contain phosphate groups. These phosphate groups alternate with sugars to form the backbone of the molecule. The sugars are deoxyribose in the case of DNA and ribose in the case of RNA. Attached to each sugar is a purine or a pyrimidine base. The purine bases are adenine and guanine. One pyrimidine base is cytosine. In the case of RNA the other pyrimidine base is uracil, while for DNA the other pyrimidine base is thymine.

48. **(E)** The "thread of life" is an apt name for DNA, being both a literal and a figurative description. It is literal in that it is thread-like, long and narrow, in shape and is an essential molecule for life. It is figurative in that DNA is essential for the continuance of life and runs like a thread through all stages in the life of the organism, from origin through growth and reproduction to final death.

49. **(D)** The complementary sequence to AGC is TCG. One polynucleotide chain is completely shown, as is the hydrogen bonding to the bases in the other polynucleotide chain. Because of the distortions that result from depicting a 3-D structure in two dimensions, the H- bonds themselves are distorted (they are all of approximately equal length) and the second sugar phosphate chain has been omitted.

50. **(D)** The complementary sequence to TCT is AGA. One polynucleotide chain is completely shown, as is the hydrogen bonding to the bases in the other polynucleotide chain. Because of the distortions that result from depicting a three-dimensional structure in two dimensions, the hydrogen bonds themselves are distorted (they are all of approximately equal length) in the diagram.

INTEGRATIVE AND ADVANCED EXERCISES

51. **(E)** $M = \dfrac{100.00 \text{ g hemoglobin}}{0.34 \text{ g Fe}} \times \dfrac{55.85 \text{ g Fe}}{1 \text{ mol Fe}} \times \dfrac{4 \text{ mol Fe}}{1 \text{ mol hemoglobin}} = 6.6 \times 10^4 \text{ g/mol hemoglobin.}$

52. **(E)** If we assume that there is only one active site per enzyme and that a silver ion is necessary to deactivate each active site, we obtain the molar mass of the protein as follows.

$\text{molar mass} = \dfrac{1.00 \text{ mg}}{0.346 \text{ }\mu\text{mol Ag}^+} \times \dfrac{1 \text{ }\mu\text{mol}}{10^{-6} \text{ mol}} \times \dfrac{1 \text{ mol Ag}^+}{1 \text{ mol protein}} \times \dfrac{1 \text{ g}}{1000 \text{ mg}} = 2.9 \times 10^3 \text{ g/mol}$

This is a minimum value because we have assumed that 1 Ag^+ ion is all that is necessary to denature each protein molecule. If more than one silver ion were required, the next to last factor in the calculation above would be larger than 1 mol Ag^+/1 mol protein, and the molar mass would increase correspondingly.

53. (M) Triolein → tristearin

Triolein (901.44 g/mol)
$C_{57}H_{104}O_7$

↓ 3 $H_2(g)$

Tristearin (907.49 g/mol
$C_{57}H_{110}O_7$

$$n_{H_2} = 15.5\,\text{kg triolein} \times \frac{1\,\text{mol triolein}}{0.90144\,\text{kg triolein}} \times \frac{3\,\text{mol H}_2}{1\,\text{mol triolein}} = 51.6\,\text{mol H}_2$$

$$CH_4(g) + H_2O(g) \rightarrow CO(g) + 3\,H_2(g) \qquad 92.0\,\%$$
$$C_2H_6(g) + 2\,H_2O(g) \rightarrow 2\,CO(g) + 5\,H_2(g) \qquad 8.0\,\%$$

Consider 1.00 L → Determine the moles of H_2 formed.

1.00 L of natural gas contains 0.920 L CH_4 and 0.080 L C_2H_6

$$n_{CH_4} = \frac{\left(756\,\text{mmHg} \times \dfrac{1\,\text{atm}}{760\,\text{mmHg}}\right)(0.920\,\text{L})}{(0.08206\,\text{L atm K}^{-1}\text{mol}^{-1})(25.5 + 275.15\,\text{K})} = 0.03734\,\text{mol CH}_4$$

$$n_{C_2H_6} = \frac{\left(756\,\text{mmHg} \times \dfrac{1\,\text{atm}}{760\,\text{mmHg}}\right)(0.080\,\text{L})}{(0.08206\,\text{L atm K}^{-1}\text{mol}^{-1})(25.5 + 275.15\,\text{K})} = 0.00325\,\text{mol C}_2\text{H}_6$$

$$n_{H_2}(CH_4) = n_{CH_4} \times 3 = 0.112\,\text{mol H}_2 \qquad n_{H_2}(C_2H_6) = n_{C_2H_6} \times 5 = 0.016\,\text{mol H}_2$$

$$n_{H_2}(\text{total}) = n_{H_2}(CH_4) + n_{H_2}(C_2H_6) = 0.112\,\text{mol H}_2 + 0.016\,\text{mol H}_2 = 0.128\,\text{mol H}_2$$

Hence, 1.00 L of natural gas gives 0.128 moles of H_2

$$V_{\text{natural gas}} = 51.6\,\text{mol H}_2 \times \frac{1.00\,\text{L natural gas}}{0.128\,\text{mol H}_2} = 403\,\text{L natural gas}$$

54. (D) Structures of the 16 aldohexoses – identification of enantiomers

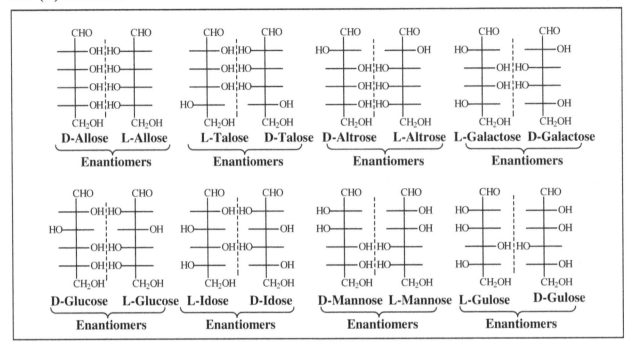

55. (M) As alluded to by the problem, there are eight possible aldopentoses, or more precisely, the L- and D- isomers of four aldopentoses: Ribose, Arabinose, Xylose, and Lyxose.

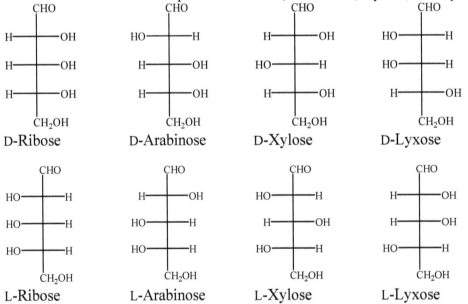

The sets of epimers are:

D-Ribose	D-Arabinose	D-Xylose	D-Lyxose
D-Arabinose	L-Xylose	D-Lyxose	L-Ribose
D-Xylose	D-Lyxose	L-Arabinose	
L-Lyxose			

Of course, using the L- isomers of the above aldopentoses yields the complementary result.

56. (M) The pI value is the pH at the second equivalence point, much like the pH of HPO_4^{2-} is $pI = \frac{1}{2}(pK_{a_2} + pK_{a_3})$.

$pK_I = \frac{1}{2}(pK_{a_2} + pK_{a_3}) = \frac{1}{2}(8.65 + 10.76) = 9.71$

highly acidic form $^+H_3NCH_2CH_2CH(NH_3^+)COOH$

acidic form $^+H_3NCH_2CH_2CH(NH_3^+)COO^-$

zwitterion $H_2NCH_2CH_2CH(NH_3^+)COO^-$

$pK_{a_1} = 1.94$ $pK_{a_2} = 8.65$ $pK_{a_3} = 10.76$

57. (D) We represent the division and replication of DNA in the following diagram.

parents: $^{15}N \parallel {}^{15}N$

1st $^{15}N \parallel {}^{14}N$ $^{14}N \parallel {}^{15}N$

Subsequent division then occurs as follows. Note that each double strand in the first generation contains one strand (of the two) that is nitrogen-15 labeled.

1st (fraction ^{15}N: 0.5): $^{15}N \parallel {}^{14}N$

2nd (fraction ^{15}N: 0.25): $^{15}N \parallel {}^{14}N$ $^{14}N \parallel {}^{14}N$

3rd (fraction ^{15}N: 0.125): $^{15}N \parallel {}^{14}N$ $^{14}N \parallel {}^{14}N$ $^{14}N \parallel {}^{14}N$ $^{14}N \parallel {}^{14}N$

4th (fraction ^{15}N: 0.0625):

   $^{15}N \parallel {}^{14}N \;\; {}^{14}N \parallel {}^{14}N \;\; {}^{14}N \parallel {}^{14}N \;\; {}^{14}N \parallel {}^{14}N \;\; {}^{14}N \parallel {}^{14}N \;\; {}^{14}N \parallel {}^{14}N \;\; {}^{14}N \parallel {}^{14}N \;\; {}^{14}N \parallel {}^{14}N$

We see that, out of the eight double strands of DNA produced in the third generation, only one of them incorporates ^{15}N. Thus, one eighth of the DNA incorporates ^{15}N.

58. (D) Assume all the fragments are given with the N-terminal end listed first. Since there is Arg at the N-terminal end (and only two Arg amino acids), we begin with the fragment that starts with an Arg residue and build the chain from there, making sure to end with an Arg fragment.

Fragments:	Arg	Pro	Pro						
		Pro	Pro	Gly					
			Pro	Gly	Phe				
				Gly	Phe	Ser	Pro		
						Ser	Pro	Phe	
							Pro	Phe	Arg
								Phe	Arg
Nonapeptide:	Arg	Pro	Pro	Gly	Phe	Ser	Pro	Phe	Arg

59. (D)

Amino Acid	Messenger RNA	DNA
serine	UCU	AGA
	UCC	AGG
	UCA	AGT
	UCG	AGC
glycine	GGU	CCA
	GGC	CCG
	GGA	CCT
	GGG	CCC
valine	GUU	CAA
	GUC	CAG
	GUA	CAT
	GUG	CAC
alanine	GCU	CGA
	GCC	CGG
	GCA	CGT
	GCG	CGC

One example for the required sequence would be AGA CCA CAA CGA. The redundancy enables the organism to produce a given amino acid in several ways in case of transcription error. For example, CG and any third DNA nucleotide will yield alanine in the polypeptide chain.

60. (D) Sketch of the titration curve for threonine in 1 M HCl

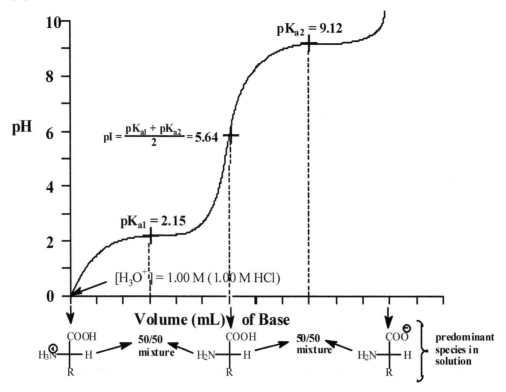

61. (D)

(a) Consider successive 90° rotations in a Fischer projection of the chiral molecule R(+) Glyceraldehyde

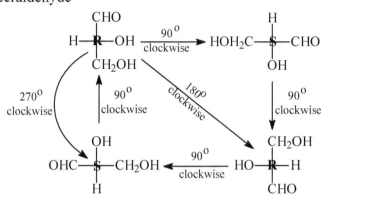

Each 90° rotation about the chiral carbon atom results in an inversion of the stereochemistry at the chiral carbon atom.

(b) Consider interchange of two groups on chiral carbon atom in the molecule R(+) Glyceraldehyde

Each interchange of two groups on the chiral carbon atom results in an inversion of the stereochemistry at the chiral carbon atom. The effect of two such interchanges results in the regeneration of the same molecule (enantiomer). The trivial case of interchanging the same two groups twice shows that two interchanges result in the same molecule being represented.

62. (M) Reaction of the pentapeptide with DFNB indicates that Met is the N-terminal end. The remaining information provides the following possible sequences of fragments.

(1) Met   Met Gly *or*   Met Gly Met

(2) Met   Met

(3) Ser   Met

(4) Met   Met Ser *or*   Met Ser Met

The fact that no fragment contains both Ser and Gly is strong evidence that these two amino acids are not adjacent in the chain. In fact, there must be a Met between them. Experiment (2) indicates that two Met residues are adjacent. Experiments (1) and (4), in combination with the fact that Met is the N-terminal end, mean that a Gly-Met-Ser or a Ser-Met-Gly sequence cannot end the chain. Hence,

Met   Gly Met Met Ser   or   Met Ser Met Met Gly

Experiment (3) confirms that the right-hand order above must be correct, for there is no way that a dipeptide with Ser as the N-terminal end can be obtained from the left-hand order above.

63. (M)

Most amino acids have the COOH as priority 2 and the "R" group as priority 3. In cysteine, the "R" group has priority 2 and the COOH group has priority 3. Effectively, this is an interchange of the two groups on a chiral carbon, resulting in an inversion in the stereochemistry of the chiral carbon.

64. (M) Threonine (2S, 3R)-2-amino-3-hydroxybutanoic acid has four stereoisomers—all are shown below.

65. (D)

(a) $\Delta_r G^{\circ\prime} = -RT\ln K$

$$\ln K = \frac{-\Delta_r G^{\circ\prime}}{RT} = \frac{-23000 \text{ J}}{(8.31 \text{ J/K} \cdot \text{mol})(298.15 \text{ K})} = -9.3 \quad K = e^{-9.3} = 9.3 \times 10^{-5}$$

(b) $\ln K = \frac{-\Delta_r G^{\circ\prime}}{RT} = \frac{-(-30000 \text{ J})}{(8.31 \text{ J/K} \cdot \text{mol})(298.15 \text{ K})} = 12.1 \quad K = e^{12.1} = 1.8 \times 10^5$

(c) $A + ADP + Pi \longrightarrow B + ATP$ so...

$$\frac{[B]}{[A]} = \frac{[ADP][K][Pi]}{[ATP]} = \frac{1}{400}(1.8 \times 10^5)(0.005) = 2.25 \quad \frac{\text{coupled}}{\text{uncoupled}} = \frac{2.25}{9.3 \times 10^{-5}}$$

$$= 2.4 \times 10^4$$

FEATURE PROBLEMS

66. **(D)**

Glyceryl Tristearate   **Glyceryl Trioleate**

Molar Mass = 891.5 g mol^{-1} Molar Mass = 885.45 g mol^{-1}

(a) Saponification value of glyceryl tristearate: mass of KOH

$$= 1.00 \text{ g glyceryl tristearate} \times \frac{1 \text{ mol glyceryl tristearate}}{891.5 \text{ g glyceryl tristearate}} \times \frac{3 \text{ mol KOH}}{1 \text{ mol glyceryl tristearate}}$$

$$\times \frac{56.1056 \text{ g KOH}}{1 \text{ mol KOH}} = 0.189 \text{ g KOH or 189 mg KOH} \quad \text{Saponification value} = 189$$

Iodine number for glyceryl trioleate: mass of I$_2$

$$= 100 \text{ g glyceryl trioleate} \times \frac{1 \text{ mol glyceryl trioleate}}{885.45 \text{ g glyceryl trioleate}} \times \frac{3 \text{ mol I}_2}{1 \text{ mol glyceryl trioleate}}$$

$$\times \frac{253.81 \text{ g I}_2}{1 \text{ mol I}_2} = 86.0 \text{ g I}_2 \quad \text{Iodine number} = 86.0$$

(b) As we do not know the types of substances present in castor oil and their percentages, we will assume that castor oil is the only glyceryl triricnoleate.

$$CH_2-O-\overset{\overset{O}{\|}}{C}-(CH_2)_7CH=CHCH_2CHOH(CH_2)_5CH_3$$
$$CH-O-\overset{\overset{O}{\|}}{C}-(CH_2)_7CH=CHCH_2CHOH(CH_2)_5CH_3$$
$$CH_2-O-\overset{\overset{O}{\|}}{C}-(CH_2)_7CH=CHCH_2CHOH(CH_2)_5CH_3$$

Glyceryl Triricnoleate
Molar Mass = 933.4 g mol^{-1}

Iodine number for glyceryl triricnoleate: mass of I$_2$

$$= 100 \text{ g glyceryl triricnoleate}$$

$$\times \frac{1 \text{ mol glyceryl triricnoleate}}{933.4 \text{ g glyceryl triricnoleate}} \times \frac{3 \text{ mol I}_2}{1 \text{ mol glyceryl triricnoleate}} \times \frac{253.81 \text{ g I}_2}{1 \text{ mol I}_2}$$

$$= 81.6 \text{ g I}_2 \quad \text{Iodine number} = 81.6$$

Saponification value of glyceryl triricnoleate: mass of KOH = 1.00 g glyceryl triricnoleate

$$\times \frac{1 \text{ mol glyceryl triricnoleate}}{933.4 \text{ g glyceryl triricnoleate}} \times \frac{3 \text{ mol KOH}}{1 \text{ mol glyceryl triricnoleate}} \times \frac{56.1056 \text{ g KOH}}{1 \text{ mol KOH}}$$

= 0.180 g KOH or 180. mg KOH   Saponification value = 180.

If castor oil and the other components have similar saponification values, then we would expect an overall saponification value of 180. However, if the remaining substances have a saponification value of zero, the overall saponification value is expected to be ~160 (90/100 × 180).

(c) Safflower oil: Consider each component

Palmitic acid: Molar mass: $C_3H_5(C_{15}H_{31}CO_2)_3 = 807.34 \text{ g mol}^{-1}$

Iodine number = 0 (saturated)

Saponification value of palmitic acid: mass of KOH

= 1.00 g palmitic acid

$$\times \frac{1 \text{ mol palmitic acid}}{807.33 \text{ g palmitic acid}} \times \frac{3 \text{ mol KOH}}{1 \text{ mol palmitic acid}} \times \frac{56.1056 \text{ g KOH}}{1 \text{ mol KOH}}$$

= 0.208 g KOH or 208 mg KOH   Saponification value = 208

Stearic acid: Molar mass: $C_3H_5(C_{17}H_{35}CO_2)_3 = 891.49 \text{ g mol}^{-1}$

Iodine number = 0 (saturated)

Saponification value of stearic acid: mass of KOH

$$= 1.00 \text{ g stearic acid} \times \frac{1 \text{ mol stearic acid}}{891.49 \text{ g stearic acid}} \times \frac{3 \text{ mol KOH}}{1 \text{ mol stearic acid}} \times \frac{56.1056 \text{ g KOH}}{1 \text{ mol KOH}}$$

= 0.189 g KOH or 189 mg KOH   Saponification value = 189

Oleic acid: Molar mass: $C_3H_5(C_{17}H_{33}CO_2)_3 = 885.45 \text{ g mol}^{-1}$

Iodine number for oleic acid: mass of I_2

$$= 100 \text{ g oleic acid} \times \frac{1 \text{ mol oleic acid}}{885.45 \text{ g oleic acid}} \times \frac{3 \text{ mol } I_2}{1 \text{ mol oleic acid}} \times \frac{253.81 \text{ g } I_2}{1 \text{ mol } I_2} = 86.0 \text{ g } I_2$$

Iodine number = 86.0

Saponification value of oleic acid: mass of KOH

$$= 1.00 \text{ g oleic acid} \times \frac{1 \text{ mol oleic acid}}{885.45 \text{ g oleic acid}} \times \frac{3 \text{ mol KOH}}{1 \text{ mol oleic acid}} \times \frac{56.1056 \text{ g KOH}}{1 \text{ mol KOH}}$$

= 0.190 g KOH or 190. mg KOH   Saponification value = 190.

Linoleic acid: Molar mass: $C_3H_5(C_{17}H_{31}CO_2)_3 = 879.402$ g mol^{-1}

Iodine number for linoleic acid: mass of I_2

$$= 100 \text{ g linoleic acid} \times \frac{1 \text{ mol linoleic acid}}{879.402 \text{ g linoleic acid}} \times \frac{6 \text{ mol } I_2}{1 \text{ mol linoleic acid}} \times \frac{253.81 \text{ g } I_2}{1 \text{ mol } I_2}$$

$= 173$ g I_2 Iodine number $= 173$

Saponification value of linoleic acid: mass of KOH

$$= 1.00 \text{ g linoleic acid} \times \frac{1 \text{ mol linoleic acid}}{879.402 \text{ g linoleic acid}} \times \frac{3 \text{ mol KOH}}{1 \text{ mol linoleic acid}} \times \frac{56.1056 \text{ g KOH}}{1 \text{ mol KOH}}$$

$= 0.191$ g KOH or 191 mg KOH   Saponification value $= 191$

Linolenic acid: Molar mass: $C_3H_5(C_{17}H_{29}CO_2)_3 = 873.348$ g mol^{-1}

Iodine number for linolenic acid: mass of I_2

$$= 100 \text{ g linolenic acid} \times \frac{1 \text{ mol linolenic acid}}{873.354 \text{ g linolenic acid}} \times \frac{9 \text{ mol } I_2}{1 \text{ mol linolenic acid}} \times \frac{253.81 \text{ g } I_2}{1 \text{ mol } I_2}$$

$= 261.\underline{6}$ g I_2 Iodine number $= 261.\underline{6} \approx 262$

Saponification value of linolenic acid: mass of KOH

$$= 1.00 \text{ g linolenic acid} \times \frac{1 \text{ mol linolenic acid}}{873.354 \text{ g linolenic acid}} \times \frac{3 \text{ mol KOH}}{1 \text{ mol linolenic acid}} \times \frac{56.1056 \text{ g KOH}}{1 \text{ mol KOH}}$$

$= 0.193$ g KOH or 193 mg KOH   Saponification value $= 193$

Summary:

Acid	I_2#	Sap#	%	High I_2 # %	Low I_2 # %	High Sap# %	Low Sap# %
Palmitic	0	208	6–7	6	7	7	6
Stearic	0	189	2–3	2	3	2	3
Oleic	86	190	12–14	12	14	12	14
Linoleic	173	191	75–80	78.5	75.5	87.5	76.5
Linolenic	262	193	0.5–1.5	1.5	0.5	1.5	0.5

Hence: The iodine number for safflower oil may range between 150 to 144.
The saponification value for safflower oil may range between 211 and 179.
(Note:the high iodine number contribution for each acid in the mixture is calculated by multiplying its percentage by its iodine number. The sum of all of the high iodine number contributions for all of the components in the mixture equals the high iodine number for safflower oil. Similar calculations were used to obtain the low iodine number, along with the high/low saponification numbers.

67. (D)

(a)

D-Glucose $\xrightarrow[\text{Ca(OH)}_2]{\text{Br}_2, \text{H}_2\text{O}}$ (calcium salt) $\xrightarrow[\text{Fe}^{3+}]{\text{H}_2\text{O}_2}$ D-Arabinose $\xleftarrow[\text{Fe}^{3+}]{\text{H}_2\text{O}_2}$ (calcium salt) $\xleftarrow[\text{Ca(OH)}_2]{\text{Br}_2, \text{H}_2\text{O}}$ D-Manose

$+ \text{CO}_2(g)$

(b)

D-Erythrose $\xrightarrow[\text{Ca(OH)}_2]{\text{Br}_2, \text{H}_2\text{O}}$ (calcium salt) $\xrightarrow[\text{Fe}^{3+}]{\text{H}_2\text{O}_2}$ D-Glyceraldehyde $\xleftarrow[\text{Fe}^{3+}]{\text{H}_2\text{O}_2}$ (calcium salt) $\xleftarrow[\text{Ca(OH)}_2]{\text{Br}_2, \text{H}_2\text{O}}$ D-Threose

$+ \text{CO}_2(g)$

68. (a-c)
(M)

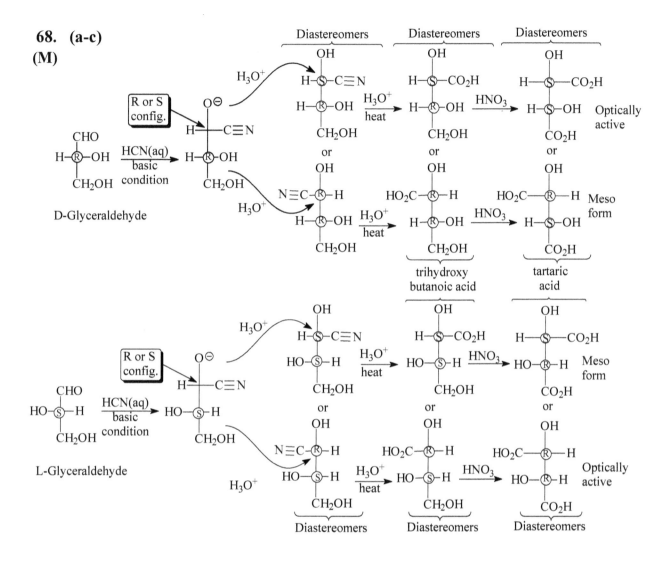

(d) Meso form of Tartaric acid

Meso form is not optically active because one end of the molecule rotates polarized light by +x degrees, while the other end of the molecule rotates it by −x degrees. The net result is that polarized light is unaffected by this type of compound, even though it has two chiral carbons. Meso forms must have a mirror plane running through them; for every chiral carbon, there must exist its mirror image on the other side of the molecule.

SELF-ASSESSMENT EXERCISES

69. **(E)**

  (a) (+): Notation to indicate that a compound rotates the plane of polarized light in a dextrorotatory (right-handed) direction.

  (b) (L): The Fischer notation to indicate side of the horizontal line has the main substituent, L is for left.

  (c) Sugar: A mono- or oligosaccharide. Saccharides are cyclic hydroxyketone or hydroxyaldehyde

  (d) α-amino acid: An amino acid is a compound that has both a carboxylic acid (-COOH) and an amino (-NH$_2$) group. An α-amino acid is one that has the amino group on the α-carbon, which is the carbon adjacent to the carboxylic group.

  (e) Isoelectric point: The pH at which an ionic molecule has no net electric charge.

70. **(E)**

  (a) Saponification: The process of turning a triglyceride into a soap by hydrolyzing it to glycerol and fatty acid salt.

  (b) Chiral carbon atom: A carbon atom in a molecule which is *sp³* hybridized and is bonded to four different constituents.

  (c) Racemic mixture: A mixture of a chiral species and its enantiomer in equal amounts. This mixture does not rotate a plane of polarized light.

  (d) Denaturation of protein: A mechanical/chemical process by which a protein loses its tertiary (overall shape and folding) and possibly its secondary (local structure like α-helix or β-sheet) structure.

71. **(E)**

  (a) Fat vs. oil: Both are triglycerides. However, fats are glyceryl esters in which saturated fatty acid components predominate, making them solid at room temperature. In oils, unsaturated fatty acids predominate, making them liquids at room temperature.

  (b) Enantiomer vs. diasteriomer: An enantiomer is a compound with chirality. Diastereomer are stereoisomers that are not enantiomers (these compounds have two or more stereocenters).

  (c) Primary vs. secondary structure of protein: The primary structure of a protein involves the amino acid sequence that comprises the protein. The secondary structure refers to the shape of segments of protein and is determined by the amino acids comprising a segment and the polarity of the solvent.

  (d) DNA vs. RNA: Simply from a chemical standpoint, DNA is deoxyribonucleic acid; it is made of pentose sugar 2-deoxyribose, and bases adenine, guanine, thymine, and cytosine. RNA is ribonucleic acid; it is made of ribose, and the base uracil instead of thymine.

  (e) ADP vs. ATP: ATP is adenosine triphosphate. It is made up of the nucleoside adenosine, and three phosphate groups in series. It undergoes oxidative phosphorylation to release energy, lose a phosphate, and convert to ADP, which is adenosine diphosphate. Adenosine diphosphate converts to ATP using the energy provided by oxidation of food.

72. **(E)** The answer is (b), oil. Glyceryl trilinoleate is a triglyceride containing three linolic acid substituents. Linolic acid is unsaturated, making it likely that it is a liquid at room temperature and therefore an oil.

73. **(E)** The answer is (d), neither to the left nor the right. DL-erythrose describes a racemic mixture: one which rotates a plane of polarized light in a dextrorotatory, and the other in a levorotatotory fashion. The two substances cancel each other out in their effect in rotating a plane of polarized light.

74. **(E)** The answer is (a), β-galactose.

75. **(E)** The answer is (d), denaturation of protein. Heating the egg white causes the protein tertiary and secondary structure to change and makes the protein molecules coagulate.

76. **(E)** The answer is (e), ATP.

77. **(E)** The answer is (c). Glycerol is part of the triglycerides.

78. **(E)** The answer is (b), double helix.

79. **(M)** Below is the structure of glyceryltripalmitate:

Based on the molecular structure, its MW = 224 (MW of palmitate) × 3 + 42.06 (MW of C_3H_6, glyceride) = 714.06 g/mol.

$$125 \text{ g Gly-tripalmitate(GTP)} \times \frac{\text{mol GTP}}{714.06 \text{ g GTP}} \times \frac{3 \text{ mol palmitate}}{1 \text{ mol GTP}} \times \frac{1 \text{ mol Na(palm.)}}{1 \text{ mol palm.}}$$

$$\times \frac{247 \text{ g Na(palm)}}{1 \text{ mol Na(palm.)}} = 129 \text{ g sodium palmitate soap}$$

80. **(M)** There are two major things to look for to determine if the chain is DNA or RNA: the ribose/deoxyribose sugar and presence of uracil or thymine. Looking at the structure, it is seen that the bases attached to the sugars down the right side of the structure are adenine (purine), uracil (pyrimidine), guanine (purine), and cytosine (pyrimidine). Furthermore, the sugar is ribose, making this an RNA chain.

81. **(M)** The answer is (e), none of these. Consulting Table 28.3, it is seen that the residue does not match that of any amino acid given.

82. **(M)** The answer is (b), 1,4-dichlorobutane. See structure below:

83. **(E)** The answer is (a), glycine. It is the only non-chiral amino acid, because the –R group is just –H.

84. **(E)** The answer is (d), they always rotate plane-polarized light.

85. **(E)** The answer is (c), $-CH(CH_3)_2$.

86. **(E)** The answer is (d), condensation. The carboxylic terminus from one amino acid reacts with the amino terminus from another one to form a peptide bond and eliminate water.

87. **(E)** The answer is (b.), Oleic acid.

88. **(D)** Following the method in Example 28-2, the sequence is Gly-Cys-Val-Phe-Tyr.

89. **(M)** In this chapter, the only overarching concept is biomolecules, which are molecules needed for sustaining life. They either provide structure to the body, are metabolized by the body, or are involved in information transfer. The main concepts falling under the overarching concept of biomolecules are proteins, lipids, carbohydrates, and nucleic acids. Proteins could further be described in terms of their primary, secondary, and tertiary structures. The primary structure can be described in terms of the individual amino acids. Secondary structure involves beta sheets or alpha helices. In this case of lipids, we can further describe them in terms of triglycerides, both saturated and unsaturated. For nucleic acids, we can further break them down in the terms of the major bases, ribose sugar, and phosphate. Carbohydrates encompass many simpler concepts. Take a look at the subsection headings and problems for more refining of the general and specific concepts.